pg 88 true/false

Discovering Geometry

An Investigative Approach

Third Edition

Michael Serra

Project Editor
Joan Lewis

Project Administrator
Erin Gray

Consulting Editors
Christian Aviles-Scott, Heather Dever, Ladie Malek

Editorial Assistant
Shannon Miller

Mathematics Consultant and Writer
Larry Copes

Teacher Consultants
Judy Hicks, James Rahn

Accuracy Checker
Dudley Brooks

Editorial Production Manager
Deborah Cogan

Production Editor
Kristin Ferraioli

Copyeditor
Mary Roybal

Production Director
Diana Jean Parks

Production Coordinator
Ann Rothenbuhler

Cover Designer
Jill Kongabel

Art Editor
Jason Luz

Art and Design Coordinator
Caroline Ayres

Technical Artist
Precision Graphics

Text Designer
Jenny Somerville

Photo Editor
Margee Robinson

Compositor and Prepress
TSI Graphics

Printing
Von Hoffman Press

Executive Editor
Casey FitzSimons

Publisher
Steven Rasmussen

Key Curriculum Press
1150 65th Street
Emeryville, CA 94608
510-595-7000
editorial@keypress.com
http://www.keypress.com

Printed in the United States of America

10 9 8 7 6 5 06 05

ISBN 1-55953-460-5

Discovering Geometry Acknowledgments

Reviewers and Contributors, Third Edition

Michael de Villiers, Ph.D., University of Durban, Westville, Pinetown, South Africa

Cavan Fang, Saint Paul, Minnesota

David Hoppe, New York, New York

David Keiser, Montclair State University, Upper Montclair, New Jersey

Stacey Miceli, Chicago, Illinois

Swapna Mukhopadhyay, Ph.D., San Diego State University, San Diego, California

David Rasmussen, Nova Scotia, Canada

Davia Schmidt, San Francisco, California

Advisors and Contributors, Second Edition

Dean Azule, Confederated Tribes of the Grand Ronde Community, Grand Ronde, Oregon

Sheldon Berman, Simon Gratz High School, Philadelphia, Pennsylvania

Dudley Brooks, San Francisco, California

Donald Collins, Ph.D., Western Kentucky University, College of Education, Bowling Green, Kentucky

Bob Garvey, Louisville Collegiate School, Louisville, Kentucky

Joyla Gregory, Chula Vista, California

Regina Heinicke, San Francisco, California

José López, Lawrence Berkeley Laboratory, Berkeley, California

Beatrice Lumpkin, Chicago, Illinois

M. Mamikon, Davis, California

Charlene Morrow, Mount Holyoke College, South Hadley, Massachusetts

Beth Porter, George School, Newtown, Pennsylvania

Doris Schattschneider, Ph.D., Moravian College, Bethlehem, Pennsylvania

Mal Singer, University High School, San Francisco, California

Kimlynne Lee Slagel, Kamehameha Secondary School, Honolulu, Hawaii

Sue Yabuki, Northwest Equals, Portland State University, Portland, Oregon

Teacher Consultants and Field Testers, Second Edition

Archie Benton, North Buncombe High School, Weaverville, North Carolina

Ralph Bothe, Edward C. Reed High School, Reno, Nevada

Larry Chiucarello, Nonnewaug High School, Woodbury, Connecticut

Dave Damcke, Jefferson High School, Portland, Oregon

John Dumanske, Philip and Sala Burton Academic High School, San Francisco, California

Genie Dunn, Miami Killian Senior High School, Miami, Florida

Sharon Grand, Baton Rouge High School, Baton Rouge, Louisiana

Rodger Gray, Lincoln High School, Stockton, California

Judy Hicks, Ralston Valley High School, Arvada, Colorado

Carol Miller, Tascosa High School, Amarillo, Texas

Oran Pyle, Tennyson High School, Hayward, California

Jorge Rivera, Saint John's School, San Juan, Puerto Rico

Carolyn Sessions, Louisiana State University Laboratory School, Baton Rouge, Louisiana

Wendy Struhl, Oakland Technical High School, Oakland, California

Tom Swartz, George Washington High School, San Francisco, California

Dixie Trollinger, Mainland High School, Daytona Beach, Florida

Advisors, Contributors, and Field Testers, First Edition

Dianne Borchardt, Sandie Gilliam, and Dennis Olson, San Lorenzo Valley High School, Felton, California

Sam Butscher, Ph.D., Theresa Hernandez-Heinz, Robert Knapp, Jeff Salisbury, Tom Swartz, Edward Van Pelt, and Li Oi Yu, San Francisco Unified School District, San Francisco, California

Connie Callos, Evergreen High School, Vancouver, Washington

Dave Damcke and John P. Oppedisano, Jefferson High School, Portland, Oregon

Bob Eckland and Katie Makar, Catlin Gabel School, Portland, Oregon

Debbie Lindow and Charlene Trachsel, Reynolds High School, Troutdale, Oregon

Katie Makar, Catlin Gabel School, Portland, Oregon

John Olive, Ph.D., University of Georgia, Athens, Georgia

David Rasmussen, Cabot High School, Nova Scotia, Canada

J. Michael Shaughnessy, Ph.D., Portland State University, Portland, Oregon

Tom Swartz, George Washington High School, San Francisco, California

Richard Wertheimer, School District of Pittsburgh, Pittsburgh, Pennsylvania

A Note from the Publisher

When Key Curriculum Press first published *Discovering Geometry* in 1989, it was unique among high school geometry books because of its discovery approach. *Discovering Geometry* still presents concepts visually, and students explore ideas analytically, then inductively, and finally deductively—developing insight, confidence, and increasingly sophisticated mathematical understanding. As J. Michael Shaughnessy, mathematics professor at Portland State University, said, "This is a book for 'doers.' Students constantly *do* things in this book, both alone and in groups. If you want your students to become actively involved in the process of learning and creating geometry, then this is the book for you."

The mathematics we learn and teach in school changes over time, driven by new scientific discoveries, new research in education, changing societal needs, and by the use of new technology in work and in education. The effectiveness of *Discovering Geometry*'s investigative approach has been substantiated in many thousands of classrooms and is reflected in the *Principles and Standards for School Mathematics*, the guiding document of the National Council of Teachers of Mathematics (NCTM). In this, the third edition, you will find many of the text's original and hallmark features—plus a host of improvements. The layout is easier to follow, and the additional examples from art and science will be a motivating complement to your curriculum. We have carefully analyzed the exercises for optimal practice and real-world interest. There are more opportunities to review algebra and more ways to use technology, especially The Geometer's Sketchpad® software, in the projects and homework assignments. These changes will give you—the student, parent, or teacher—greater flexibility in attaining your educational goals. They will enable more students to succeed in high school geometry and achieve continued success in future mathematics courses, other areas of education, and eventual careers.

Experience as well as sound educational research on how geometry thinking develops during adolescence tells us that, regardless of the subject or level, students learn mathematics best when they understand the concepts. The positive feedback we have received over the years for *Discovering Geometry* has inspired us to create an entire series. Key Curriculum Press now offers the *Discovering Mathematics* series, a complete program of algebra, geometry, and advanced algebra. Through the investigations that are the heart of the series, students discover many important mathematical principles. In the process, they come to believe in their ability to succeed at mathematics, they understand the course content more deeply, and they realize that they can re-create their discoveries if they need to.

If you are a student, we hope that as you work through this course you gain knowledge for a lifetime. If you are a parent, we hope you enjoy watching your student develop mathematical power. If you are a teacher, we hope you find that *Discovering Geometry* makes a significant positive impact in your classroom. Whether you are learning, guiding, or teaching, please share your trials and successes with the professional team at Key Curriculum Press.

Steven Rasmussen, President
Key Curriculum Press

Contents

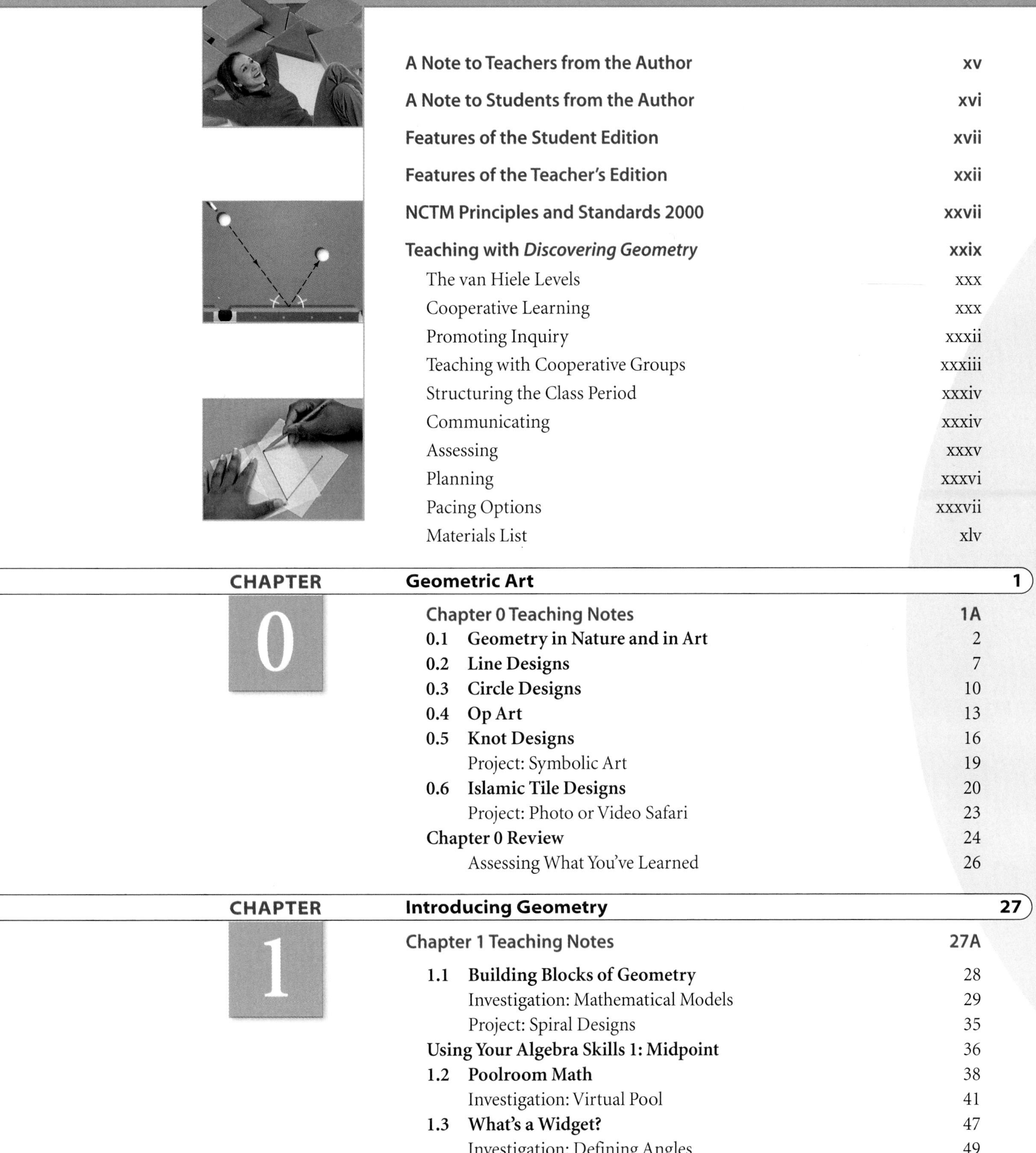

CHAPTER 9 **The Pythagorean Theorem** 461

A Note to Teachers from the Author

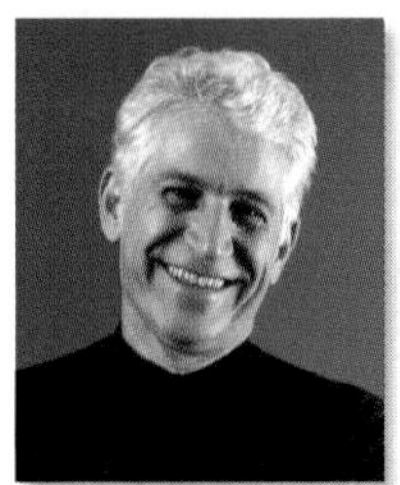

Michael Serra

Discovering Geometry began in my classroom. During my first decade of teaching I did not use a textbook, but created my own daily lessons. At National Council of Teachers of Mathematics (NCTM) and California Mathematics Council conferences the experts in geometry pedagogy all seemed to be saying the same thing: the concrete should precede the abstract; students learn with greater depth of understanding and retention when they are actively engaged in the process of discovering concepts for themselves; and we should delay the introduction of proof and of geometry as a mathematical system until students are ready. Yet no textbook was doing that! All the available textbooks assumed that classrooms were teacher-centered and instruction was lecture-driven: "Here is the rule, the proof, and the example; now practice with 25 homework problems." These textbooks each began by establishing postulates and proving theorems.

I was also involved in a Research in Industry Grant where I repeatedly heard that the skills valued by industries were the ability to express ideas verbally and in writing and the ability to work as part of a team. I knew I wanted my students to be engaged daily in doing mathematics and talking about it in cooperative small groups.

After over a decade of using my *Inductive Geometry* worksheets, I published the first edition of *Discovering Geometry* with Key Curriculum Press. We were delighted to find so many teachers around the country eager to turn from their file cabinet of supplementary materials to my book. We were pleased to discover that much of what we were advocating in *Discovering Geometry* was to be found in the then soon-to-be-released NCTM *Standards. Discovering Geometry* has changed the way geometry textbooks are written. We have seen many other publishers attempt to copy us. But more than other authors and publishers, we are guided by the research of Pierre and Dina van Hiele, by strong belief in the cooperative classroom, by discovery learning, by the new NCTM *Principles and Standards,* and by the work of Michael de Villiers on the purposes of proof.

All of us at Key Curriculum Press believe that when students are given the opportunity to be actively involved in their own discovery of mathematics, they become better problem solvers and develop a deeper understanding of the concepts. Because *Discovering Geometry* concepts are connected to a story that explains how and why these geometry properties came to be, students have a greater retention of the material.

During the 14 years the two editions of *Discovering Geometry* have been in print, new hands-on techniques, curriculum research, and technologies have added to the vision of what we want to see happening in a geometry class. This third edition uses these advances. Those of you familiar with previous editions of *Discovering Geometry* will be pleased to see the changes. Perhaps the most significant change is this Teacher's Edition, which helps teachers create a discovery classroom. There are also many additions and refinements to the student edition and the teaching resources package.

This edition was advanced and inspired by teachers using the previous editions. Likewise, I encourage you to contribute your feedback to the next edition with the sincere assurance that the evolution of *Discovering Geometry* is guided by the needs of your students and your efforts toward their success.

Michael Serra

A Note to Students from the Author

What Makes *Discovering Geometry* Different?

Discovering Geometry was designed so that you can be actively engaged as you learn geometry. In this book you "learn by doing." You will learn to use the tools of geometry and to perform geometry **investigations** with them. Many of the geometry investigations are carried out in small **cooperative groups** in which you jointly plan and find solutions with other students. Your investigations will lead you to the discovery of geometry properties. In addition, you will gradually learn about proof, a form of reasoning that will help explain why your discoveries are true.

Discovering Geometry was designed so that you and your teacher can have fun while learning geometry. It has a lot of "extras." Each lesson begins with a **quote** that I hope you will find funny or thought provoking. I think you'll enjoy the extra challenges in the **Improving Your . . . Skills** puzzles at the end of most lessons. To solve each puzzle, you'll need clever visual thinking skills or sharp reasoning skills or both. I hope you will find some of the **illustrated word problems** humorous. I created them in the hope of reducing any anxiety you might have about word problems. In the **explorations** you will learn about geometric probability, build geometric solids, find the height of your school building, and discover why elephants have big ears. In the **projects** you will draw the impossible, make kaleidoscopes, design a racetrack, and create a mural. There are also several **graphing calculator projects, Fathom Dynamic Statistics™ projects, The Geometer's Sketchpad explorations,** and **web links** that will allow you to practice and improve your skills with the latest educational technology.

You can do the projects, the puzzles, and the calculator and computer activities independently, whether or not your class tackles them as a group. Read through them as you proceed through the book.

Suggestions for Success

It is important to be organized. Keep a notebook with a section for definitions, a section for your geometry investigations, a section for discoveries, and a section for daily notes and exercises. Develop the habit of writing a summary page when you have completed each chapter. Study your notebook regularly.

You will need four tools for the investigations: a compass, a protractor, a straightedge, and a ruler. Some investigations use waxed "patty paper" that can be used as a unique geometry tool. Keep a graphing calculator handy, too.

You will find hints for some exercises in the back of the book. Those exercises are marked with an ⓗ. Try to solve the problems on your own first. Refer to the hints to check your method or as a last resort if you can't solve a problem.

Discovering Geometry will ask you to work cooperatively with your classmates. When you are working cooperatively, always be willing to listen to each other, to participate actively, to ask each other questions, and to help each other when asked. You can accomplish much more cooperatively than you can individually. And, best of all, you'll experience less frustration and have much more fun.

Michael Serra

Features of the Student Edition

Investigations promote responsibility for learning and lead to important insights. You can opt to have student groups work through each investigation or on different investigations, pooling their results during class discussion.

Opening text orients students in the content sequence and often relates the lesson topic to real-world experience.

A thought-provoking **quotation** introduces each lesson.

You will need lists help students organize the materials and tools they need for the investigation.

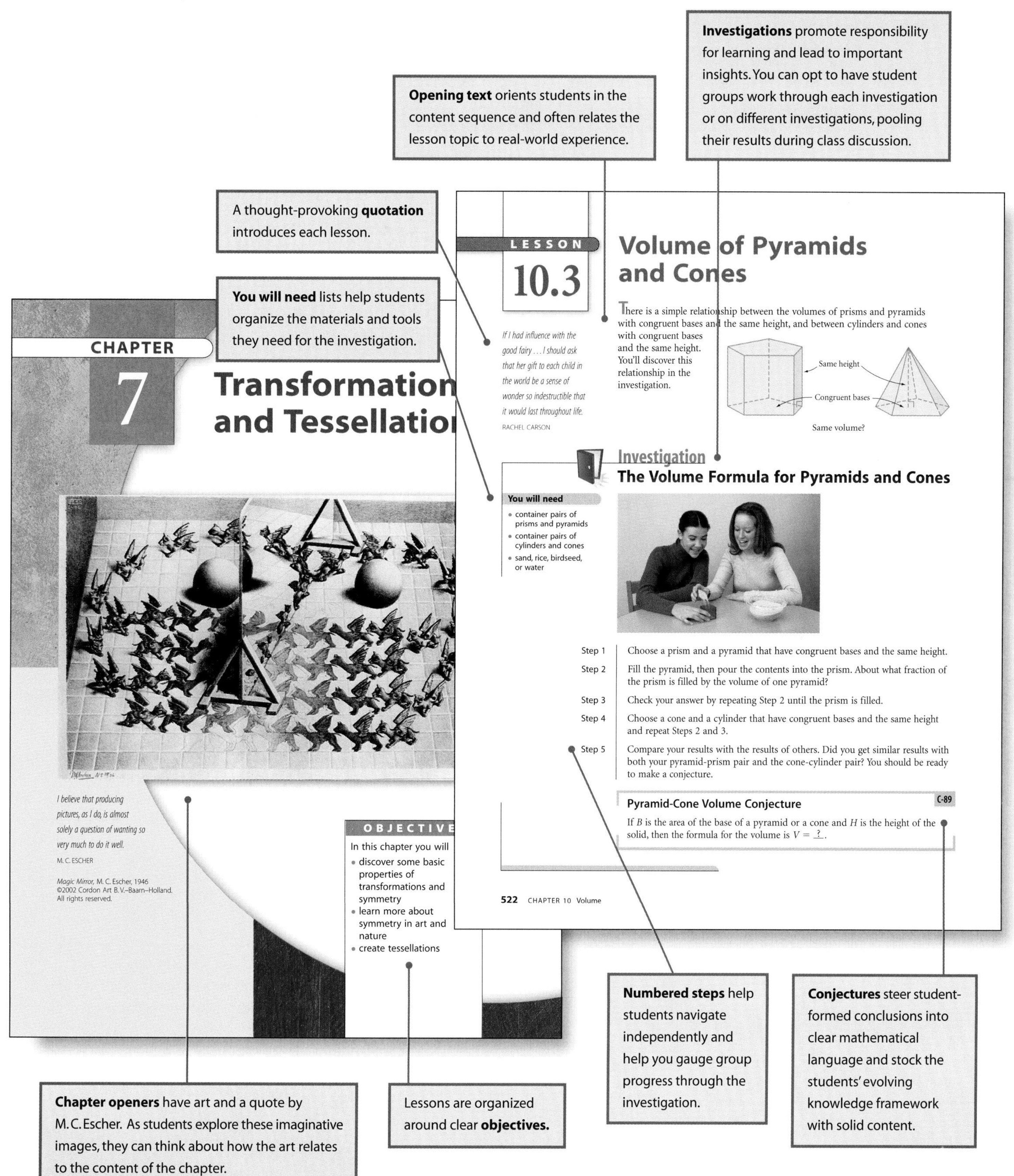

CHAPTER
7
Transformations
and Tessellations
I believe that producing pictures, as I do, is almost solely a question of wanting so very much to do it well.
M. C. ESCHER
Magic Mirror, M. C. Escher, 1946
©2002 Cordon Art B.V.–Baarn–Holland. All rights reserved.
OBJECTIVES
In this chapter you will
• discover some basic properties of transformations and symmetry
• learn more about symmetry in art and nature
• create tessellations
LESSON
10.3
Volume of Pyramids and Cones
If I had influence with the good fairy . . . I should ask that her gift to each child in the world be a sense of wonder so indestructible that it would last throughout life.
RACHEL CARSON
There is a simple relationship between the volumes of prisms and pyramids with congruent bases and the same height, and between cylinders and cones with congruent bases and the same height. You'll discover this relationship in the investigation.
Same height
Congruent bases
Same volume?
Investigation
The Volume Formula for Pyramids and Cones
You will need
• container pairs of prisms and pyramids
• container pairs of cylinders and cones
• sand, rice, birdseed, or water
Step 1 Choose a prism and a pyramid that have congruent bases and the same height.
Step 2 Fill the pyramid, then pour the contents into the prism. About what fraction of the prism is filled by the volume of one pyramid?
Step 3 Check your answer by repeating Step 2 until the prism is filled.
Step 4 Choose a cone and a cylinder that have congruent bases and the same height and repeat Steps 2 and 3.
Step 5 Compare your results with the results of others. Did you get similar results with both your pyramid-prism pair and the cone-cylinder pair? You should be ready to make a conjecture.
Pyramid-Cone Volume Conjecture C-89
If B is the area of the base of a pyramid or a cone and H is the height of the solid, then the formula for the volume is V = ?.
522 CHAPTER 10 Volume

Numbered steps help students navigate independently and help you gauge group progress through the investigation.

Conjectures steer student-formed conclusions into clear mathematical language and stock the students' evolving knowledge framework with solid content.

Chapter openers have art and a quote by M. C. Escher. As students explore these imaginative images, they can think about how the art relates to the content of the chapter.

Lessons are organized around clear **objectives.**

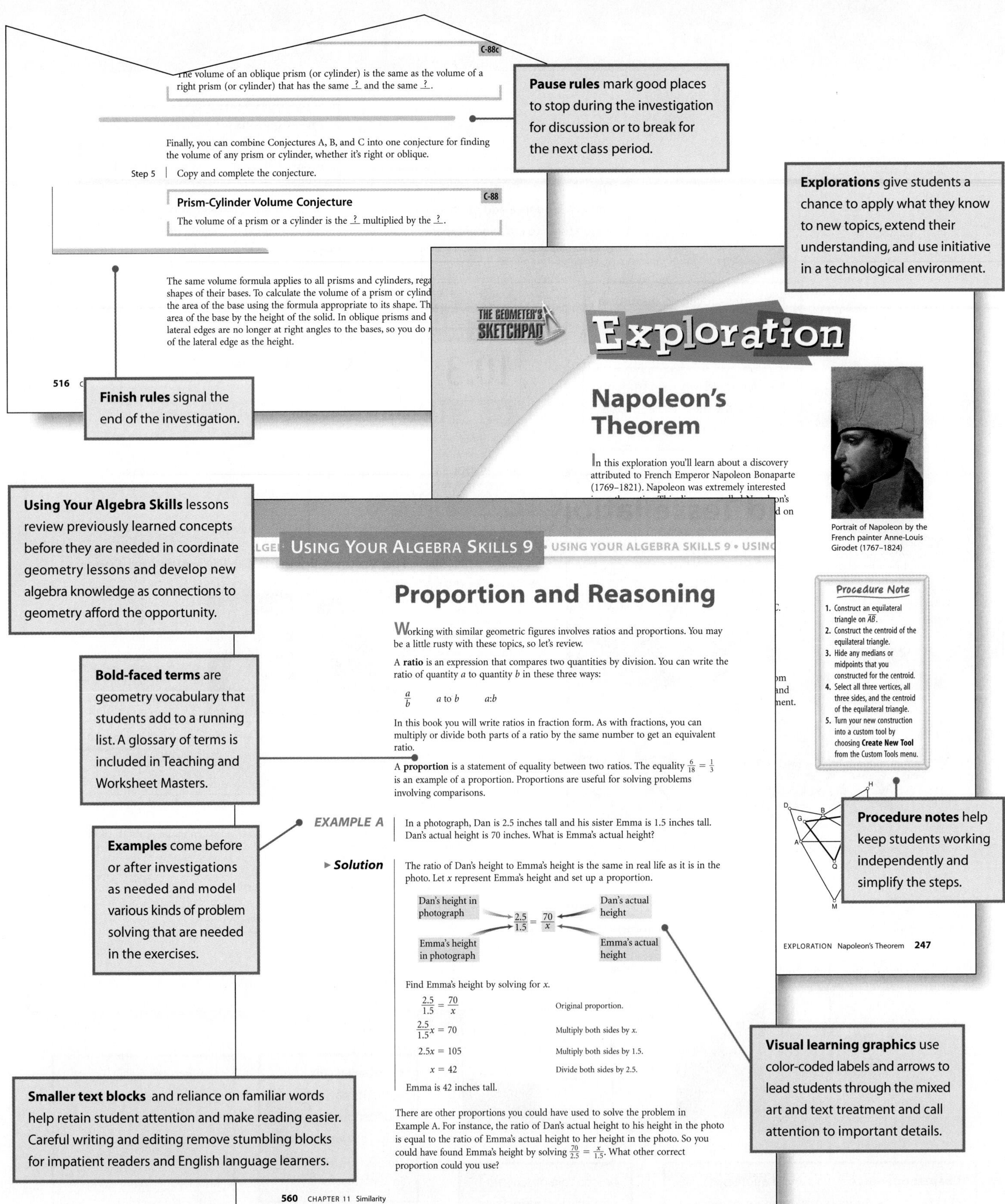
C-88c
The volume of an oblique prism (or cylinder) is the same as the volume of a right prism (or cylinder) that has the same ? and the same ?.
Pause rules mark good places to stop during the investigation for discussion or to break for the next class period.
Finally, you can combine Conjectures A, B, and C into one conjecture for finding the volume of any prism or cylinder, whether it's right or oblique.
Step 5 Copy and complete the conjecture.
Prism-Cylinder Volume Conjecture C-88
The volume of a prism or a cylinder is the ? multiplied by the ?.
Explorations give students a chance to apply what they know to new topics, extend their understanding, and use initiative in a technological environment.
516
Finish rules signal the end of the investigation.
THE GEOMETER'S SKETCHPAD
Exploration
Napoleon's Theorem
In this exploration you'll learn about a discovery attributed to French Emperor Napoleon Bonaparte (1769–1821). Napoleon was extremely interested
Portrait of Napoleon by the French painter Anne-Louis Girodet (1767–1824)
Procedure Note
1. Construct an equilateral triangle on $\overline{AB}$.
2. Construct the centroid of the equilateral triangle.
3. Hide any medians or midpoints that you constructed for the centroid.
4. Select all three vertices, all three sides, and the centroid of the equilateral triangle.
5. Turn your new construction into a custom tool by choosing Create New Tool from the Custom Tools menu.
Procedure notes help keep students working independently and simplify the steps.
EXPLORATION Napoleon's Theorem 247
Using Your Algebra Skills lessons review previously learned concepts before they are needed in coordinate geometry lessons and develop new algebra knowledge as connections to geometry afford the opportunity.
USING YOUR ALGEBRA SKILLS 9
Proportion and Reasoning
Working with similar geometric figures involves ratios and proportions. You may be a little rusty with these topics, so let's review.
A ratio is an expression that compares two quantities by division. You can write the ratio of quantity a to quantity b in these three ways:
$\frac{a}{b}$ a to b a:b
In this book you will write ratios in fraction form. As with fractions, you can multiply or divide both parts of a ratio by the same number to get an equivalent ratio.
A proportion is a statement of equality between two ratios. The equality $\frac{6}{18} = \frac{1}{3}$ is an example of a proportion. Proportions are useful for solving problems involving comparisons.
Bold-faced terms are geometry vocabulary that students add to a running list. A glossary of terms is included in Teaching and Worksheet Masters.
EXAMPLE A
In a photograph, Dan is 2.5 inches tall and his sister Emma is 1.5 inches tall. Dan's actual height is 70 inches. What is Emma's actual height?
Examples come before or after investigations as needed and model various kinds of problem solving that are needed in the exercises.
Solution
The ratio of Dan's height to Emma's height is the same in real life as it is in the photo. Let x represent Emma's height and set up a proportion.
Dan's height in photograph
Dan's actual height
$\frac{2.5}{1.5} = \frac{70}{x}$
Emma's height in photograph
Emma's actual height
Find Emma's height by solving for x.
$\frac{2.5}{1.5} = \frac{70}{x}$ Original proportion.
$\frac{2.5}{1.5}x = 70$ Multiply both sides by x.
$2.5x = 105$ Multiply both sides by 1.5.
$x = 42$ Divide both sides by 2.5.
Emma is 42 inches tall.
Visual learning graphics use color-coded labels and arrows to lead students through the mixed art and text treatment and call attention to important details.
Smaller text blocks and reliance on familiar words help retain student attention and make reading easier. Careful writing and editing remove stumbling blocks for impatient readers and English language learners.
There are other proportions you could have used to solve the problem in Example A. For instance, the ratio of Dan's actual height to his height in the photo is equal to the ratio of Emma's actual height to her height in the photo. So you could have found Emma's height by solving $\frac{70}{2.5} = \frac{x}{1.5}$. What other correct proportion could you use?
560 CHAPTER 11 Similarity

Paragraph proofs are introduced early in the course to model the process of justifying conclusions. More than explanations, paragraph proofs give logical steps along with reasons in narrative form.

EXAMPLE A

In the figure at right, $\overline{EC} \cong \overline{AC}$ and $\overline{ER} \cong \overline{AR}$. Is $\angle A \cong \angle E$? If so, give a logical argument to explain why they are congruent.

▸ Solution

First mark the given information on the figure. Then consider whether $\angle A$ is congruent to $\angle E$, and why.

Paragraph Proof: Show that $\angle A \cong \angle E$.

$\overline{EC} \cong \overline{AC}$ and $\overline{ER} \cong \overline{AR}$ because that information is given. $\overline{RC} \cong \overline{RC}$ because it is the same segment, and any segment is congruent to itself. So, $\triangle CRE \cong \triangle CRA$ by the SSS Congruence Conjecture. If $\triangle CRE \cong \triangle CRA$, then $\angle A \cong \angle E$ by CPCTC. ■

Career CONNECTION

If section-num-In = section-num-comp
No: Write major-tot-line
Yes: Write minor-tot-line
Add 2 To

Were you able to follow the logical steps in Exam... argument or a proof is long and complex, and a... clearest way to present all the steps. In Chapter 1... visualize the relationships among different kinds... concept map that shows all the steps in a compli... Arrows connect the boxes to show how facts lea...

Flowcharts make your logic visible so that others...

Flowchart proofs appeal to visual learners and impatient readers. They graphically develop logical argument, revealing the structure of a proof, and are especially helpful when several conditions lead to a single conclusion.

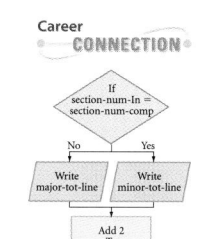

▸ Solution

First, restate the given information c... on the figure. Then state what you a...

Given: $\overline{AR} \cong \overline{ER}$
$\overline{EC} \cong \overline{AC}$

Show: $\angle E \cong \angle A$

Flowchart Proof

1. $\overline{AR} \cong \overline{ER}$ — Given
2. $\overline{EC} \cong \overline{AC}$ — Given
3. $\overline{RC} \cong \overline{RC}$ — Same segment
4. $\triangle RCE \cong \triangle RCA$ — SSS Congruence Conjecture
5. $\angle E \cong \angle A$ — CPCTC

Two-column Proof

Statement	Reason
1. $ABCD$ is a parallelogram	**1.** Given
2. $\overline{AB} \parallel \overline{DC}$ and $\overline{AD} \parallel \overline{BC}$	**2.** Definition of parallelogram
3. $\angle CAB \cong \angle ACD$ and $\angle BCA \cong \angle DAC$	**3.** AIA Theorem
4. $\overline{AC} \cong \overline{AC}$	**4.** Identity property of congruence
5. $\triangle ABC \cong \triangle CDA$	**5.** ASA Congruence Postulate

We'll call the lemma proved in the example the Parallelogram Diagonal Lemma. You can now use it to prove other parallelogram conjectures in the investigation.

Two-column proofs are introduced once the proper logical foundations are in place.

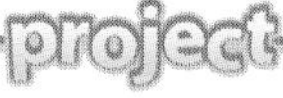

POLYA'S PROBLEM

George Polya (1887–1985) was a mathematician who specialized in problem-solving methods. He taught mathematics and problem solving at Stanford University for many years, and wrote the book *How to Solve It.*

He posed this problem to his students: Into how many parts will five random planes divide space?

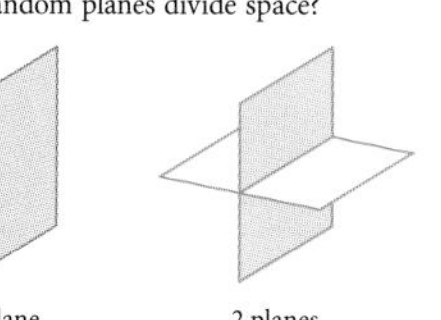

1 plane 2 planes 3 planes

It is difficult to visualize five random planes intersecting in space. What strategies would you use to find the answer?

Your project is to solve this problem, and to show how you know your answer is correct. Here are some of Polya's problem-solving strategies to help you.

- Understand the problem. Draw a figure or build a model. Can you restate the problem in your own words?
- Break down the problem. Have you done any simpler problems that are like this one?

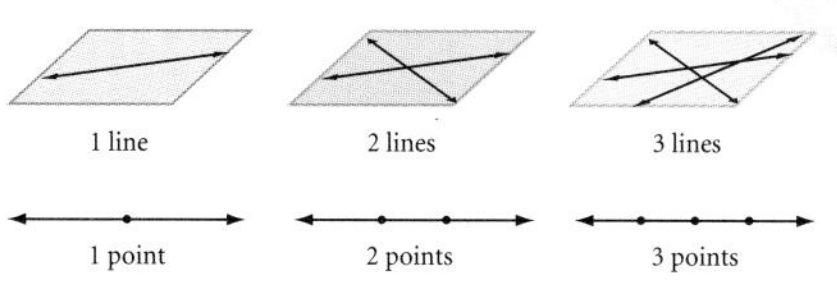

1 line 2 lines 3 lines

1 point 2 points 3 points

- Check your answer. Can you find the answer in a different way to show that it is correct? (The answer, by the way, is not 32!)

Your method is as important as your answer. Keep track of all the different things you try. Write down your strategies, your results, and your thinking, as well as your answer.

234 CHAPTER 4 Discovering and Proving Triangle Properties

Projects are practical, cultural, and mathematical extensions that engage individuals and groups in research, construction, and presentation activities. Some have special technology opportunities.

Exercise sets are designed for optimal topic coverage and practice of recently acquired skills.

Applications help students practice newly acquired skills in a real-world context. Some of the exercises are **mini-investigations** that will lead students to make discoveries on their own.

Optional technology exercises allow students to explore geometry properties and make discoveries quickly, using any available geometry software.

Review keeps previous learning current.

In the exercises you will learn how to use area in buying rolls of wallpaper, gallons of paint, bundles of shingles, square yards of carpet, and square feet of tile. Keep in mind that you can't buy $12\frac{11}{16}$ gallons of paint! You must buy 13 gallons. If your calculations tell you that you need 5.25 bundles of shingles, you have to buy 6 bundles. In this type of rounding, you must always round upward.

EXERCISES

1. **APPLICATION** Tammy is estimating how much she should charge for painting 148 rooms in a new motel with one coat of base paint and one coat of finishing paint. The four walls and the ceiling of each room must be painted. Each room measures 14 ft by 16 ft by 10 ft high.
   a. Calculate the total area of all the surfaces to be painted with each coat. Ignore doors and windows.
   b. One gallon of base paint covers 500 square feet. One gallon of finishing paint covers 250 square feet. How many gallons of each will Tammy need for the job?
2. **APPLICATION** Rashad wants to wallpaper the four walls of his bedroom. The room is rectangular and measures 11 feet by 13 feet. The ceiling is 10 feet high. A roll of wallpaper at the store is 2.5 feet wide and 50 feet long. How many rolls should he buy? (Wallpaper is hung from ceiling to floor. Ignore the doors and windows.)
3. **APPLICATION** It takes 65,000 solar cells, each 1.25 in. by 2.75 in., to power the Helios Prototype, shown below. How much surface area, in square feet, must be covered with the cells? The cells on Helios are 18% efficient. Suppose they were only 12% efficient, like solar cells used in homes. How much more surface area would need to be covered to deliver the same amount of power?

Technology CONNECTION

In August 2001, the Helios Prototype, a remotely controlled, nonpolluting solar-powered aircraft, reached 96,500 feet—a record for nonrocket aircraft. Soon, the Helios will likely sustain flight long enough to enable weather monitoring and other satellite functions. For news and updates, go to www.keymath.com/DG.

16. What would be a good approximation for the area of a regular 100-gon inscribed in a circle with radius r? Explain your reasoning.

Review

17. $A = \underline{?}$

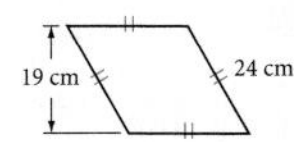
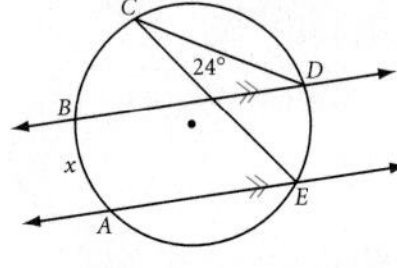

18. $A = \underline{?}$

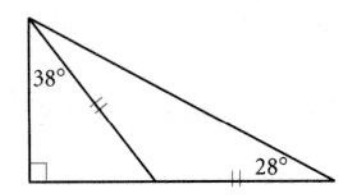

19. *Technology* Construct a parallelogram and a point in its interior. Construct segments from this point to each vertex, forming four triangles. Measure the area of each triangle. Move the point to find a location where all four triangles have equal area. Is there more than one such location? Explain your findings.

20. Explain why x must be 48°.

21. What's wrong with this picture?

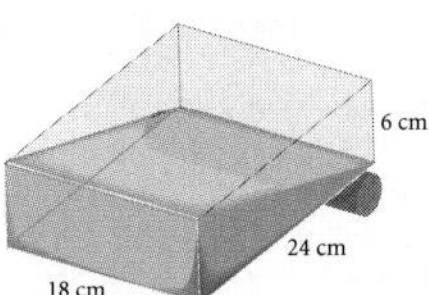

22. The 6-by-18-by-24 cm clear plastic sealed container is resting on a cylinder. It is partially filled with liquid, as shown. Sketch the container resting on its smallest face. Show the liquid level in this position.

IMPROVING YOUR VISUAL THINKING SKILLS

Random Points

What is the probability of randomly selecting from the 3-by-3 grid at right three points that form the vertices of an isosceles triangle?

Connections are a rich source of cultural and career information.

Improving Your Skills features are puzzles that reward students at the end of a lesson and approach critical thinking from different points of view.

Web markers to www.keymath.com/DG lead students to more resources.

The **Chapter Review** begins with a summary of the new mathematical ideas. The exercises are similar to those in the lessons and those that will appear on the chapter test. A more extensive **Mixed Review** is provided every four chapters.

• CHAPTER 2 REVIEW • CHAPTER 2 REVIEW • CHA

CHAPTER 2 REVIEW

This chapter introduced you to inductive reasoning. You used inductive reasoning to observe patterns and make conjectures. You learned to disprove a conjecture with a counterexample and to explain why a conjecture is true with deductive reasoning. You learned how to predict number sequences with rules and how to use these rules to model application problems. Then you discovered special relationships about angle pairs and made your first geometry conjectures. Finally you explored the properties of corresponding, alternate interior, and alternate exterior angles formed by a transversal across parallel lines. As you review the chapter, be sure you understand all the important terms. Go back to the lesson to review any terms you're unsure of.

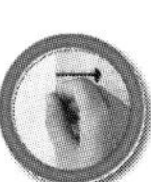

EXERCISES

1. "My dad is in the navy, and he says that food is great on submarines," said Diana. "My mom is a pilot," added Jill, "and she says that airline food is notoriously bad." "My mom is an astronaut trainee," said Julio, "and she says that astronauts' food is the worst imaginable." "You know," concluded Diana, "I bet no life exists beyond Earth! As you move farther and farther from the surface of Earth, food tastes worse and worse. At extreme altitudes, food must taste so bad that no creature could stand to eat. Therefore, no life exists out there." What do you think of Diana's reasoning? Is it inductive or deductive?

2. Think of a situation you observed outside of school in which inductive reasoning was used incorrectly. Write a paragraph or two describing what happened and explaining why you think it was poor inductive reasoning.

3. Think of a situation you observed outside of school in which deductive reasoning was used incorrectly. Write a paragraph or two describing what happened and explaining why you think it was poor deductive reasoning.

For Exercises 4–7, find the next two terms in the sequence.

4. 7, 21, 35, 49, 63, 77, ?, ?

5. Z, 1, Y, 2, X, 4, W, 8, ?, ? ⓗ

6. 7, 2, 5, −3, 8, −11, ?, ?

7. A, 4, D, 9, H, 16, M,

For Exercises 8 and 9, generate the first six terms in the sequence for each funct

8. $f(n) = n^2 + 1$

9. $f(n) = 2^{n-1}$ ⓗ

For Exercises 10 and 11, draw the next shape in the pattern.

10.

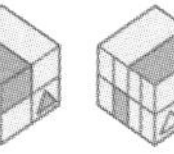

11. ⓗ

138 CHAPTER 2 Reasoning in Geometry

Hints found in the back of the book help students get started on some exercises.

Take Another Look gives students a chance to approach concepts from a different angle by giving a visual slant or calling out connections between mathematical ideas.

TAKE ANOTHER LOOK

1. Use geometry software to demonstrate the Pythagorean Theorem. Does your demonstration still work if you use a shape other than a square—for example, an equilateral triangle or a semicircle?

2. Find Elisha Scott Loomis's *Pythagorean Proposition* and demonstrate one of the proofs of the Pythagorean Theorem from the book.

EVIEW 501

shown. Continue ... of the previous triangle at least five ... length of each hypotenuse and leave them in ...

Assessing What You've Learned

UPDATE YOUR PORTFOLIO Choose a challenging project, Take Another Lo... activity, or exercise you did in this chapter and add it to your portfolio. Ex... the strategies you used.

ORGANIZE YOUR NOTEBOOK Review your notebook and your conjecture li... sure they are complete. Write a one-page chapter summary.

WRITE IN YOUR JOURNAL Why do you think the Pythagorean Theorem is considered one of the most important theorems in mathematics?

WRITE TEST ITEMS Work with group members to write test items for this ... Try to demonstrate more than one way to solve each problem.

GIVE A PRESENTATION Create a visual aid and give a presentation about th... Pythagorean Theorem.

502 CHAPTER 9 The Pythagorean Theorem

Assessing What You've Learned helps students capture their learning experiences and identify gaps in their understanding. It introduces students to the use of portfolios, journals, notebooks, presentations, and performance assessment as ways to assume responsibility for their own learning. Students will find chapter-specific suggestions to help them recognize their strengths and stay on top of their weaknesses.

Features of the Teacher's Edition

An **overview** of the chapter contents appears as the first item in the interleaf pages that open each chapter of the Teacher's Edition.

CHAPTER

4

Discovering and Proving Triangle Properties

Overview

In Chapter 4, students explore properties of triangles, including the conditions that guarantee that two triangles are congruent. In **Lessons 4.1 to 4.3,** students explore and make conjectures about the sum of the measures of interior angles and exterior angles of triangles, properties of isosceles triangles, and inequality relationships among the sides and angles of triangles. **Using Your Algebra Skills 4** reviews linear equations. In **Lesson 4.4,** students use compass and straightedge to discover that SSS and SAS are shortcuts for determining congruence of triangles but SSA is not. They discover in **Lesson 4.5** that ASA and SAA are both congruence shortcuts but AAA is not. Students use corresponding parts of congruent triangles in paragraph proofs in **Lesson 4.6** and in flowchart proofs in **Lesson 4.7.** Isosceles triangles are reexamined in **Lesson 4.8,** and students discover that for isosceles triangles the angle bisector of the vertex angle and the median and altitude from that angle are the same line. The **Exploration Napoleon's Theorem** investigates the centroids of equilateral triangles constructed on the sides of a triangle.

The Mathematics

The study of triangles in this chapter lays the groundwork for much of the rest of the course. Not only are the conjectures important in themselves, but some of the underlying processes are essential to good geometric thinking.

The conjectures focus on triangle congruence and on the special case of isosceles triangles, with additional study of sums of the measures of interior angles of a triangle. The standard triangle congruence theorems, abbreviated SSS, SAS, ASA, and SAA, are viewed as shortcuts to proving that two triangles are congruent. In Chapter 1, the congruence of two polygons was defined to mean that all sides and angles of one are congruent to corresponding sides and angles of the other. The triangle congruence shortcuts allow us to conclude that two triangles are congruent after we have shown the congruence of only three of the six pairs of corresponding parts.

Considering triangles in this larger context opens the way to studying other polygons in Chapter 5. The triangle conjectures of this chapter will also be important in later chapters about right triangles, in the context of the Pythagorean Theorem (Chapter 9) and trigonometry (Chapter 12). Chapter 11 on similarity also emphasizes triangles.

Beyond the conjectures, triangles are important because the rigidity of triangular structures helps students understand what parts determine a unique triangle and, from this, what information determines the congruence of two triangles. The logic is somewhat subtle. Suppose we assume that three segments determine a unique triangle, as in Lesson 3.6. Then, if we know that three sides of one triangle are congruent, respectively, to three sides of another triangle, we can conclude that those triangles are congruent; otherwise, we would have two different triangles determined by the same three segments. Thus physical determination is tied to logical determination, or implication, which is essential to all deductive reasoning.

Reasoning about triangles offers some of the easiest deduction for students, so this chapter includes deductive proofs of many of the conjectures made. (It omits proofs of the congruence shortcuts because one must be an axiom, and proving the others involves somewhat subtle indirect proofs.) Proofs are still playing the role of explanations. Most students at van Hiele level 2 do not yet understand the importance of other functions of proof, such as justification, organization, or communication. The strategy of a flowchart proof is introduced as a way to make the steps of a proof easier to understand, an important factor in proof as communication.

CHAPTER 4 INTERLEAF 19

The Mathematics gives a survey of the chapter content that places the mathematics in context and discusses topics in greater depth or at a higher level than is presented in the student book.

Using This Chapter tells you which lessons to emphasize and which ones may be optional for your geometry curriculum.

The **materials** needed for the chapter are summarized in a list.

Using This Chapter

If you must shorten the time you spend on this chapter, you might use Lesson 4.8 as a project for students who finish the chapter review quickly. Have them present their work on isosceles triangles to the class, because all students should be familiar with these properties.

Cooperative Learning Using Pair Share

Many of the investigations in this chapter can be done with the pair-share cooperative learning model. One person in each pair might be the reader and the other the investigator. (The pairs and roles change from one activity to another.) Each reader reads the instructions and makes sure the paired investigator follows them. Each pair makes a conjecture, and then the two pairs compare conjectures and reach consensus. In the investigation in Lesson 4.2, students working in groups of four can pair off. One pair will construct isosceles triangles with acute vertex angles, and the other pair will construct isosceles triangles with obtuse vertex angles. After each pair has finished, have the pairs share their ideas.

The think-aloud pair-share (TAPS) adaptation is appropriate when a group is facing a problem rather than a task. The investigator thinks aloud while trying to solve the problem, and the reader (now more appropriately called the listener) asks questions to clarify the investigator's thoughts.

Resources

Discovering Geometry Resources

Teaching and Worksheet Masters
Lessons 4.1, 4.2, 4.4–4.8, and Chapter 4 Review

Sketchpad Demonstration
Lesson 4.1

Discovering Geometry with The Geometer's Sketchpad
Lessons 4.1–4.5, 4.8
Using Your Algebra Skills 4

Assessment Resources A and B
Quiz 1 (Lessons 4.1–4.3)
Quiz 2 (Lessons 4.4, 4.5)
Quiz 3 (Lessons 4.6–4.8)
Chapter 4 Test
Chapter 4 Constructive Assessment Options

Practice Your Skills for Chapter 4

Condensed Lessons for Chapter 4

Other Resources

www.keypress.com/DG

Materials

- construction tools (compass, straightedge, and patty paper)
- protractors
- scissors
- uncooked spaghetti, *optional*
- The Geometer's Sketchpad, *optional*

Pacing Guide

	day 1	day 2	day 3	day 4	day 5	day 6	day 7	day 8	day 9	day 10
standard	4.1	4.2	algebra	4.3	quiz, 4.4	4.4, 4.5	4.5	4.6	quiz, 4.7	4.8
enriched	4.1	4.2	algebra	4.3	quiz, 4.4	4.5	4.6	project, quiz	4.7	4.8
block	4.1, 4.2	algebra, 4.3	quiz, 4.4, 4.5	4.6, 4.7	quiz, 4.8	Exploration, review	assessment, TAL			

	day 11	day 12	day 13	day 14	day 15	day 16	day 17	day 18	day 19	day 20
standard	review, project	review	assessment							
enriched	Exploration	review, project	assessment, TAL							

197B CHAPTER 4 INTERLEAF Discovering and Proving Triangle Properties

The **Pacing Guide** lets you see at a glance which lessons may require two days and when you might use a quiz or enrich your curriculum with a project.

The publisher **web site** offers you links to more resources that you can use in your classroom.

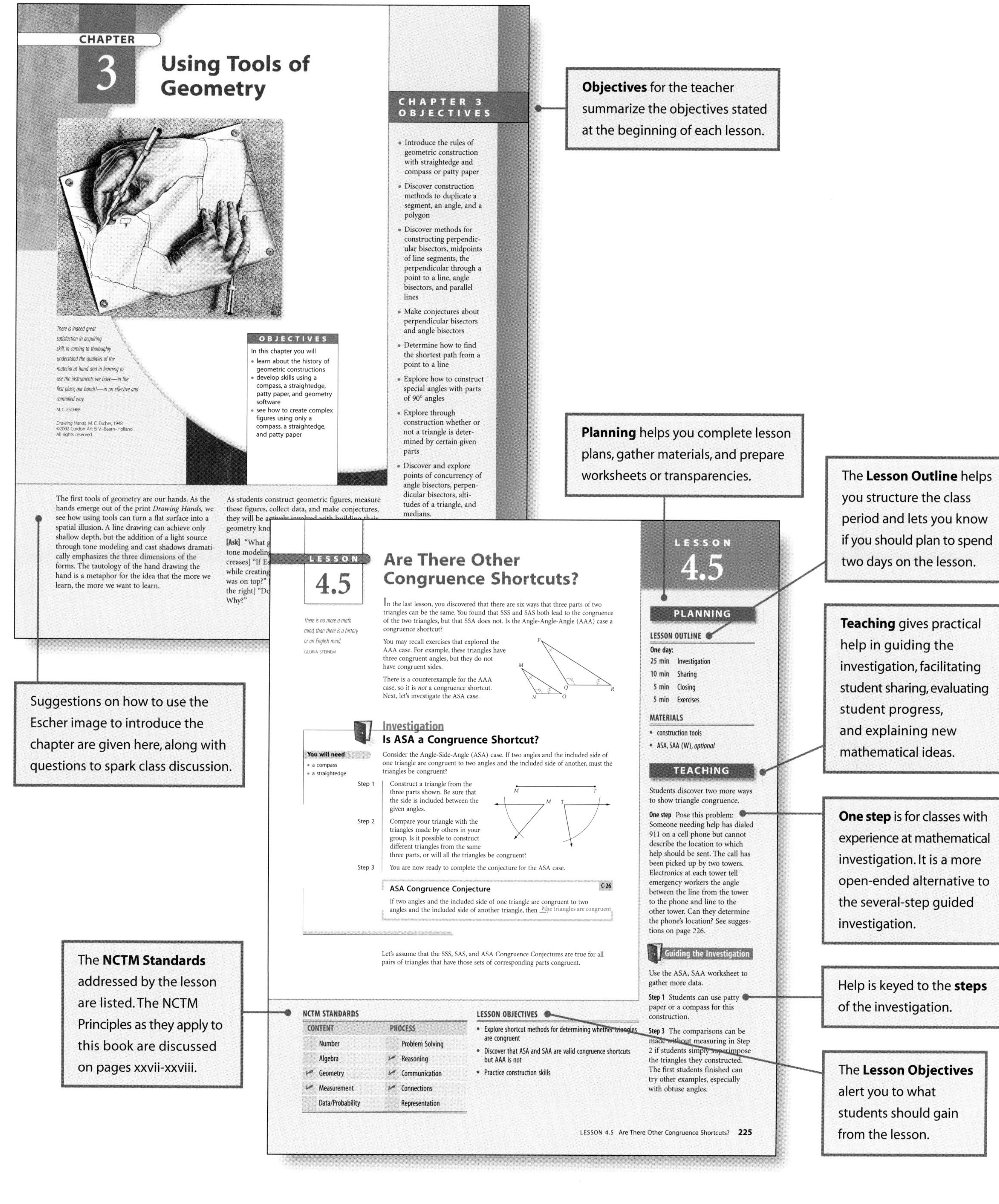

CHAPTER 3
Using Tools of Geometry
There is indeed great satisfaction in acquiring skill, in coming to thoroughly understand the qualities of the material at hand and in learning to use the instruments we have—in the first place, our hands!—in an effective and controlled way.
M. C. ESCHER
Drawing Hands, M. C. Escher, 1948 ©2002 Cordon Art B. V.–Baarn–Holland. All rights reserved.
OBJECTIVES
In this chapter you will
• learn about the history of geometric constructions
• develop skills using a compass, a straightedge, patty paper, and geometry software
• see how to create complex figures using only a compass, a straightedge, and patty paper
CHAPTER 3 OBJECTIVES
• Introduce the rules of geometric construction with straightedge and compass or patty paper
• Discover construction methods to duplicate a segment, an angle, and a polygon
• Discover methods for constructing perpendicular bisectors, midpoints of line segments, the perpendicular through a point to a line, angle bisectors, and parallel lines
• Make conjectures about perpendicular bisectors and angle bisectors
• Determine how to find the shortest path from a point to a line
• Explore how to construct special angles with parts of 90° angles
• Explore through construction whether or not a triangle is determined by certain given parts
• Discover and explore points of concurrency of angle bisectors, perpendicular bisectors, altitudes of a triangle, and medians.
The first tools of geometry are our hands. As the hands emerge out of the print Drawing Hands, we see how using tools can turn a flat surface into a spatial illusion. A line drawing can achieve only shallow depth, but the addition of a light source through tone modeling and cast shadows dramatically emphasizes the three dimensions of the forms. The tautology of the hand drawing the hand is a metaphor for the idea that the more we learn, the more we want to learn.
Objectives for the teacher summarize the objectives stated at the beginning of each lesson.
Planning helps you complete lesson plans, gather materials, and prepare worksheets or transparencies.
The Lesson Outline helps you structure the class period and lets you know if you should plan to spend two days on the lesson.
Teaching gives practical help in guiding the investigation, facilitating student sharing, evaluating student progress, and explaining new mathematical ideas.
One step is for classes with experience at mathematical investigation. It is a more open-ended alternative to the several-step guided investigation.
Help is keyed to the steps of the investigation.
The Lesson Objectives alert you to what students should gain from the lesson.
Suggestions on how to use the Escher image to introduce the chapter are given here, along with questions to spark class discussion.
The NCTM Standards addressed by the lesson are listed. The NCTM Principles as they apply to this book are discussed on pages xxvii–xxviii.
LESSON 4.5
Are There Other Congruence Shortcuts?
In the last lesson, you discovered that there are six ways that three parts of two triangles can be the same. You found that SSS and SAS both lead to the congruence of the two triangles, but that SSA does not. Is the Angle-Angle-Angle (AAA) case a congruence shortcut?
You may recall exercises that explored the AAA case. For example, these triangles have three congruent angles, but they do not have congruent sides.
There is a counterexample for the AAA case, so it is not a congruence shortcut. Next, let's investigate the ASA case.
Investigation
Is ASA a Congruence Shortcut?
Consider the Angle-Side-Angle (ASA) case. If two angles and the included side of one triangle are congruent to two angles and the included side of another, must the triangles be congruent?
You will need
• a compass
• a straightedge
Step 1 Construct a triangle from the three parts shown. Be sure that the side is included between the given angles.
Step 2 Compare your triangle with the triangles made by others in your group. Is it possible to construct different triangles from the same three parts, or will all the triangles be congruent?
Step 3 You are now ready to complete the conjecture for the ASA case.
ASA Congruence Conjecture C-26
If two angles and the included side of one triangle are congruent to two angles and the included side of another triangle, then ? the triangles are congruent
Let's assume that the SSS, SAS, and ASA Congruence Conjectures are true for all pairs of triangles that have those sets of corresponding parts congruent.
PLANNING
LESSON OUTLINE
One day:
25 min Investigation
10 min Sharing
5 min Closing
5 min Exercises
MATERIALS
• construction tools
• ASA, SAA (W), optional
TEACHING
Students discover two more ways to show triangle congruence.
One step Pose this problem: Someone needing help has dialed 911 on a cell phone but cannot describe the location to which help should be sent. The call has been picked up by two towers. Electronics at each tower tell emergency workers the angle between the line from the tower to the phone and line to the other tower. Can they determine the phone's location? See suggestions on page 226.
Guiding the Investigation
Use the ASA, SAA worksheet to gather more data.
Step 1 Students can use patty paper or a compass for this construction.
Step 3 The comparisons can be made without measuring in Step 2 if students simply superimpose the triangles they constructed. The first students finished can try other examples, especially with obtuse angles.
NCTM STANDARDS
CONTENT: Number, Algebra, Geometry, Measurement, Data/Probability
PROCESS: Problem Solving, Reasoning, Communication, Connections, Representation
LESSON OBJECTIVES
• Explore shortcut methods for determining whether triangles are congruent
• Discover that ASA and SAA are valid congruence shortcuts but AAA is not
• Practice construction skills
LESSON 4.5 Are There Other Congruence Shortcuts? 225

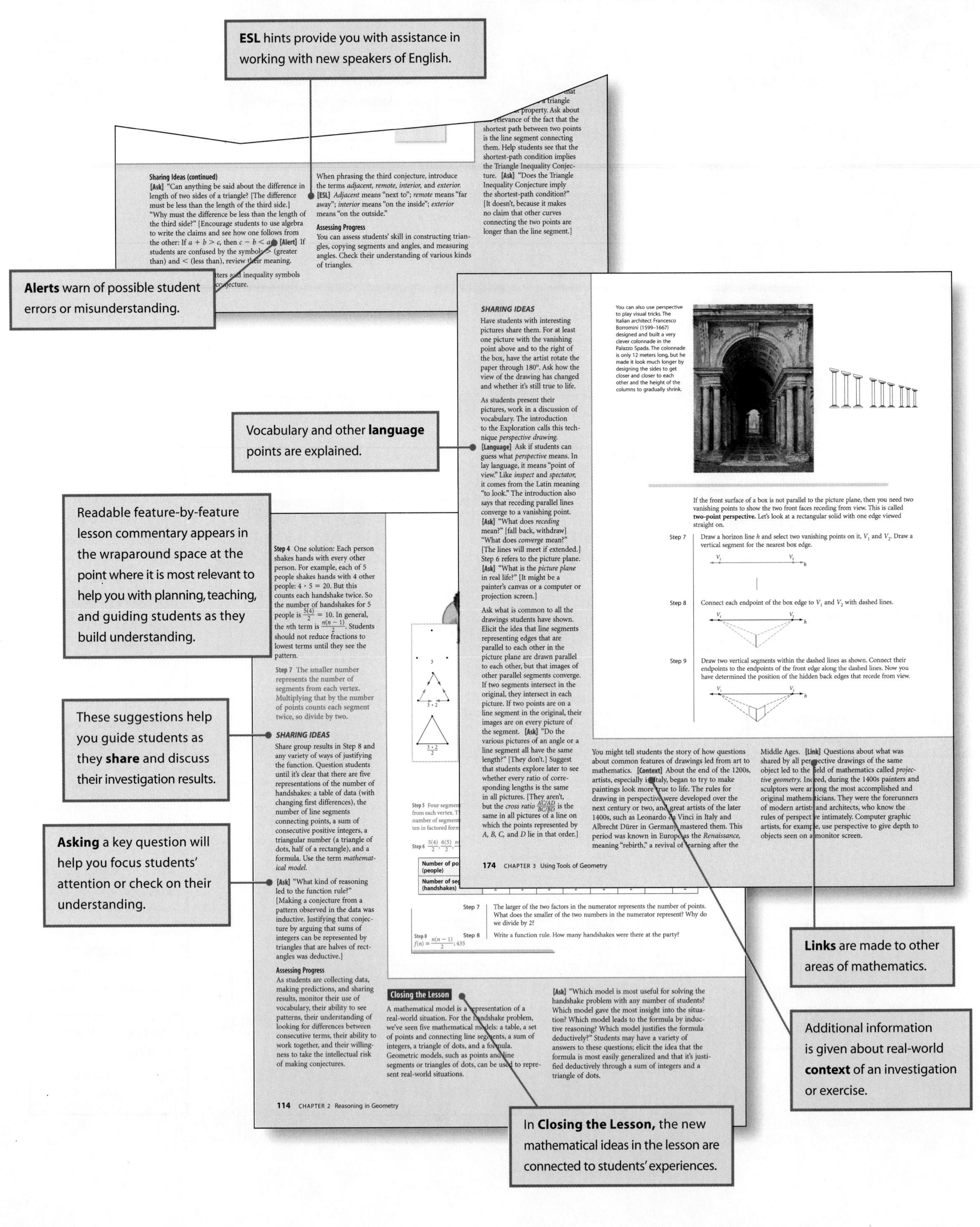
ESL hints provide you with assistance in working with new speakers of English.
Alerts warn of possible student errors or misunderstanding.
Vocabulary and other **language** points are explained.
Readable feature-by-feature lesson commentary appears in the wraparound space at the point where it is most relevant to help you with planning, teaching, and guiding students as they build understanding.
These suggestions help you guide students as they **share** and discuss their investigation results.
Asking a key question will help you focus students' attention or check on their understanding.
Links are made to other areas of mathematics.
Additional information is given about real-world **context** of an investigation or exercise.
In **Closing the Lesson,** the new mathematical ideas in the lesson are connected to students' experiences.

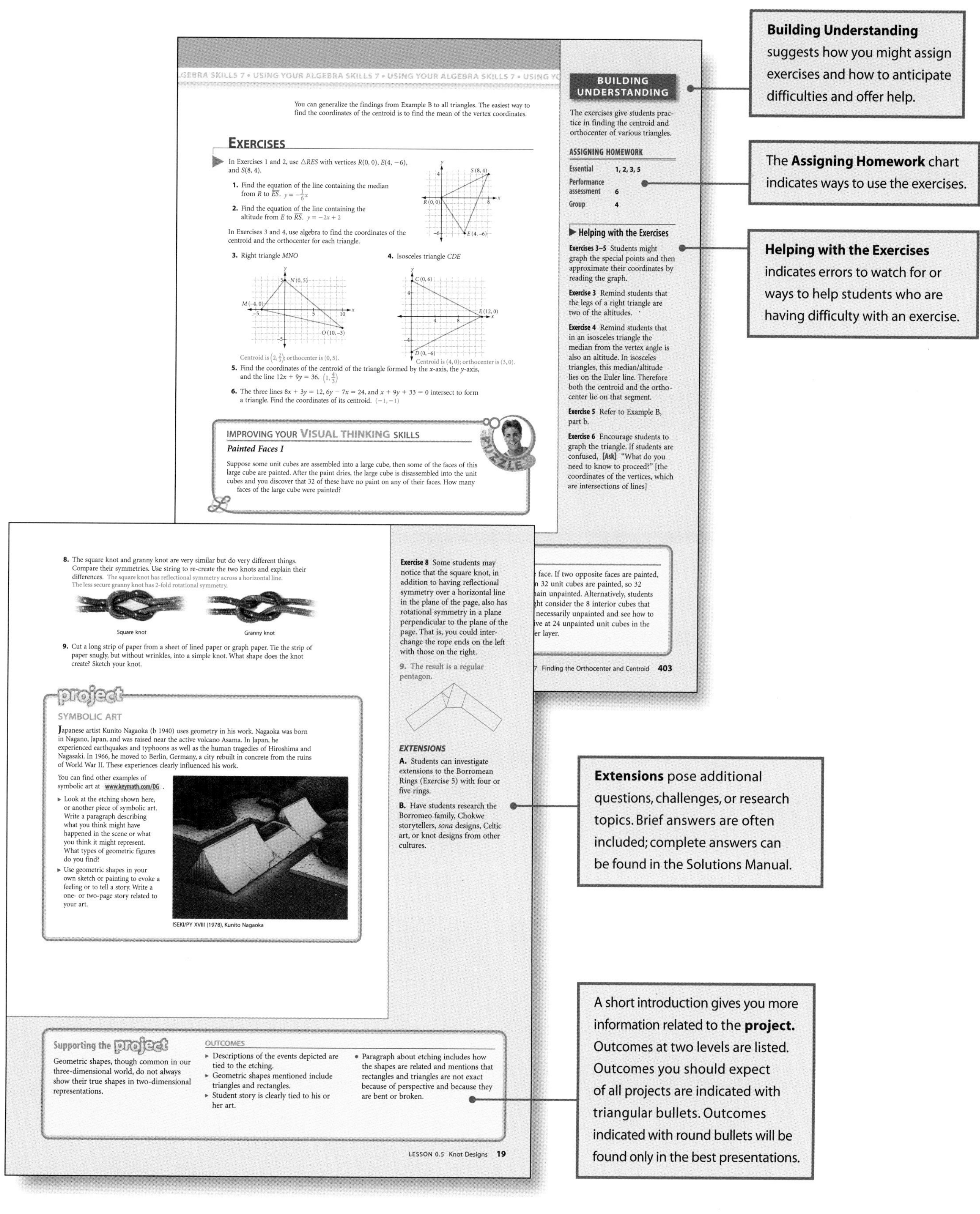

Building Understanding suggests how you might assign exercises and how to anticipate difficulties and offer help.

The **Assigning Homework** chart indicates ways to use the exercises.

Helping with the Exercises indicates errors to watch for or ways to help students who are having difficulty with an exercise.

Extensions pose additional questions, challenges, or research topics. Brief answers are often included; complete answers can be found in the Solutions Manual.

A short introduction gives you more information related to the **project.** Outcomes at two levels are listed. Outcomes you should expect of all projects are indicated with triangular bullets. Outcomes indicated with round bullets will be found only in the best presentations.

Annotations that appear in magenta on the student page, in wraparound text, or in the back of the book give answers or suggestions for possible answers.

The numbers in blue listed before the review exercises tell you which lesson or Using Your Algebra Skills (UYAS) is being reviewed.

Approaches and answers to each **Improving Your Skills** enrichment puzzle are given.

Answers are included for each **Take Another Look** activity.

15. Use the Triangle Sum Conjecture and the figures at right to write a paragraph proof explaining why the Third Angle Conjecture is true. ⓗ

16. Write a paragraph proof, or use algebra, to explain why each angle of an equiangular triangle measures 60°.

For any triangle, the sum of the angle measures is 180°, by the Triangle Sum Conjecture. Since the triangle is equiangular, each angle has the same measure, say x. So $x + x + x = 180°$, and $x = 60°$.

Review

In Exercises 17–21, tell whether the statement is true or false. For each false statement, explain why it is false or sketch a counterexample.

3.6 **17.** If two sides in one triangle are congruent to two sides in another triangle, then the two triangles are congruent. false

3.6 **18.** If two angles in one triangle are congruent to two angles in another triangle, then the two triangles are congruent. false

3.6 **19.** If a side and an angle in one triangle are congruent to a side and an angle in another triangle, then the two triangles are congruent. false

3.6 **20.** If three angles in one triangle are congruent to three angles in another triangle, then the two triangles are congruent. false

3.6 **21.** If three sides in one triangle are congruent to three sides in another triangle, then the two triangles are congruent. true

2.3 **22.** What is the number of stories in the tallest house you can build with two 52-card decks? eight How many cards would it take? 100

One story (2 cards) Two stories (7 cards) Three stories (15 cards)

IMPROVING YOUR VISUAL THINKING SKILLS

Dissecting a Hexagon I

Trace this regular hexagon twice.

1. Divide one hexagon into four congruent trapezoids.
2. Divide the other hexagon into eight congruent parts. What shape is each part?

15. You know from the Triangle Sum Conjecture that $m\angle A + m\angle B + m\angle C = 180°$, and $m\angle D + m\angle E + m\angle F = 180°$. By the transitive property, $m\angle A + m\angle B + m\angle C = m\angle D + m\angle E + m\angle F$. You also know that $m\angle A = m\angle D$, and $m\angle B = m\angle E$. You can substitute for $m\angle D$ and $m\angle E$ in the longer equation to get $m\angle A + m\angle B + m\angle C = m\angle A + m\angle B + m\angle F$. Subtracting equal terms from both sides, you are left with $m\angle C = m\angle F$.

Exercises 17–21 These exercises are very important preparation for the lessons on congruence shortcuts. You might want to start some of them in class by asking for and demonstrating counterexamples. Then complete the discussion of these exercises at the start of the next class period.

17.

18.

19.

20.

EXTENSION

Use Take Another Look activity 1 on page 253.

IMPROVING VISUAL THINKING SKILLS

1. If students are having difficulty, ask if they can divide the hexagon into two congruent parts.

Each part is a right trapezoid.

2\.

CHAPTER 8 REVIEW • CHAPTER 8 REVIEW • CHAPTER 8 REVIEW • CHAPTER 8 REVIEW • CHAPTER

45. The measurements of a chemical storage container are shown in meters. Find the cost of painting the exterior of nine of these large cylindrical containers with sealant. The sealant costs $32 per gallon. Each gallon covers 18 square meters. Do not paint the bottom faces. $4160

46. The measurements of a copper cone are shown in inches. Find the cost of spraying an oxidizer on 100 of these copper cones. The oxidizer costs $26 per pint. Each pint covers approximately 5000 square inches. Spray only the lateral surface. $2002

47. Hector is a very cost-conscious produce buyer. He usually buys asparagus in large bundles, each 44 cm in circumference. But today there are only small bundles that are 22 cm in circumference. Two 22 cm bundles are the same price as one 44 cm bundle. Is this a good deal or a bad deal? Why? It's a bad deal. $2\pi r_1 = 44$ cm. $2\pi r_2 = 22$ cm, which implies $4\pi r_2 = 44$ cm. Therefore $r_1 = 2r_2$. The area of the large bundle is $4\pi(r_2)^2$ cm². The combined area of two small bundles is $2\pi(r_2)^2$ cm². Thus he is getting half as much for the same price.

TAKE ANOTHER LOOK

1. Use geometry software to construct these shapes.
   a. A triangle whose perimeter can vary, but whose area stays constant
   b. A parallelogram whose perimeter can vary, but whose area stays constant
2. True or false? The area of a triangle is equal to half the perimeter of the triangle times the radius of the inscribed circle. Support your conclusion with a convincing argument.
3. Does the area formula for a kite hold for a dart (a concave kite)? Support your conclusion with a convincing argument.
4. How can you use the Regular Polygon Area Conjecture to arrive at a formula for the area of a circle? Use a series of diagrams to help explain your reasoning.
5. Use algebra to show that the total surface area of a prism with a regular polygon base is given by the formula $SA = P(h + a)$, where h is height of the prism, a is the apothem of the base, and P is the perimeter of the base.
6. Use algebra to show that the total surface area of a cylinder is given by the formula $SA = C(h + r)$, where h is the height of the cylinder, r is the radius of the base, and C is the circumference of the base.
7. Here is a different formula for the area of a trapezoid: $A = mh$, where m is the length of the midsegment and h is the height. Does the formula work? Use algebra or a diagram to explain why or why not. Does it work for a triangle?

Exercise 46 The oxidizer creates a green patina on the cones.

Exercise 47 Students might not recognize that they need to compare only the areas of two circles. This exercise foreshadows work with proportions in Lesson 11.5. A bundle with $\frac{1}{2}$ the linear dimensions will have $\left(\frac{1}{2}\right)^2$ the area; it should be $\frac{1}{4}$ the price.

Take Another Look

1. A possible approach for the triangle: To make a base of constant length, construct line j between points A and B. Mark vector AB. Construct point C on line j. Translate point C to C' by the marked vector. Then CC' will be constant. To create a constant altitude, construct point D not on line j. Construct line k through point D parallel to line j. Construct point E on line k. Construct segments to form $\triangle CC'E$ of constant base and height. Then hide points A, B, and D and lines j and k.

2. True. Given $\triangle ABC$ with inscribed circle O as shown:

The triangle is composed of three pairs of congruent right triangles. Its area is therefore

$\frac{1}{2}r(a + b + b + c + c + a) = \frac{1}{2}Pr$

3. yes; area of kite $= \frac{1}{2} \cdot d_1 \cdot d_2 = \frac{1}{2} \cdot x \cdot 2y = xy$

area of two triangles $= 2 \cdot \frac{1}{2} \cdot x \cdot y = xy$

4. See Lesson 8.5, Exercise 16. As $n \to \infty$, $a \to r$. Therefore $A = \frac{1}{2}aP \to A = \frac{1}{2}r \cdot 2\pi r = \pi r^2$.

5. area of two bases $= 2 \cdot \frac{1}{2} \cdot a \cdot P = aP$

area of n rectangular sides $= n \cdot$ side length of polygon $\cdot h = P \cdot h$

total surface area $= Ph + aP = P(h + a)$

6. Students may point out that as the number of sides of the base gets larger, the prism approaches a cylinder and a becomes r. Or they might repeat the argument in activity 5, except with C and r:

area of two bases $= 2 \cdot \pi r^2$

area of side $= C \cdot h$

$$\text{total surface area} = C \cdot h + 2\pi r^2 = C \cdot h + 2\pi r \cdot r = C \cdot h + C \cdot r = C(h + r)$$

CHAPTER 8 REVIEW 459

NCTM Principles and Standards 2000

As part of the Key Curriculum Press *Discovering Mathematics* series, *Discovering Geometry: An Investigative Approach* exemplifies the *Principles and Standards for School Mathematics* set forth by the National Council of Teachers of Mathematics (NCTM) in 2000.

The Equity Principle

Excellence in mathematics education requires equity—high expectations and strong support for all students. (*Principles and Standards for School Mathematics.* Reston, Virginia: National Council of Teachers of Mathematics, 2000, page 12.)

Discovering Geometry grew out of the belief that all students—not just a select few—are capable of learning mathematics. Research shows that most learning takes place while students are actively engaged. That's why *Discovering Geometry* is structured around investigations and activities. Through these experiences, students who may have difficulty memorizing proofs or doing calculations come to understand geometry concepts, see relationships, make conjectures, explain these conjectures, and reason clearly.

Different students, however, need a variety of experiences. Some need extra skills practice; *Discovering Geometry* provides that. Others learn from puzzles and different perspectives; the *Discovering Geometry* sections Improving Your Reasoning Skills or Improving Your Visual Thinking Skills and Take Another Look provide such challenges. Other students face learning disabilities or language barriers, while some students may learn faster than others learn and need more challenges. The *Discovering Geometry Teacher's Edition* provides advice for accommodating such differences through **[Alert]**, **[Language]**, and **[ESL]** prompts, through **[Ask]** prompts that can help clarify or challenge, and through extensions. An enriched class, or individuals who like challenges, can follow the extensions that explore geometry on a sphere using the Lénárt Sphere™.

The Curriculum Principle

A curriculum is more than a collection of activities: it must be coherent, focused on important mathematics, and well articulated across the grades. (NCTM *Principles and Standards,* page 14.)

The investigations and activities in *Discovering Geometry* are coherently organized and carefully crafted. They promote an intuitive understanding of geometry concepts and objects. Only after students come to understand a concept through experience are they introduced to the appropriate symbols and given opportunities to practice mechanics and problem solving.

Moreover, the investigations help students focus on a major mathematical idea in each lesson. The central idea is summarized in each lesson's closing in the *Discovering Geometry Teacher's Edition.*

This geometry course does not stand alone. *Discovering Geometry* is part of the Key Curriculum Press *Discovering Mathematics* series, which articulates a three-year high school curriculum that includes the most important ideas of algebra and geometry.

As part of this series, *Discovering Geometry* ties geometry to other mathematical topics. It provides practice in algebra skills, both independently and in applications to geometric figures; it enhances proportional reasoning in the context of similarity; it provides explorations of topics from trigonometry and probability; it visits properties of arithmetic as postulates in a deductive system; and it strengthens inductive and deductive reasoning skills.

The *Principles* state (page 15), "... teachers also need to be able to adjust [the curriculum] and take advantage of opportunities to move lessons in unanticipated directions." To help you maintain this flexibility, the *Discovering Geometry Teacher's Edition* includes ideas of the form "If students ask . . . , then you might . . . ."

The Teaching Principle

Effective mathematics teaching requires understanding what students know and need to learn and then challenging and supporting them to learn it well. (NCTM *Principles and Standards,* page 16.)

The *Discovering Geometry Teacher's Edition* assumes that you are a creative professional and don't just follow a script. It supports the four primary aspects of professional teaching outlined in the *Principles*:

Your mathematical understanding is supported by the essay titled The Mathematics in each chapter interleaf of the *Discovering Geometry Teacher's Edition.* Each essay summarizes the mathematics in the chapter, places it in historical context, and relates new material to what your students already know.

The *Discovering Geometry Teacher's Edition* helps you create an effective learning environment by offering advice throughout. Later in this introduction—and in the interleaves of the first few chapters—you'll find tested ideas about how to promote inquiry through cooperative learning.

While interacting with students, you might encounter confusion or questions that hint at a misunderstanding. The commentary in the *Discovering Geometry Teacher's Edition* alerts you to and articulates comprehension issues, suggests reasons why they arise, and proposes questions (with an **[Ask]** prompt) and alternative representations that you might use to alleviate them.

Occasional advice about analysis and reflection with regard to your teaching helps save you time in engaging in these important activities.

The Learning Principle

Students must learn mathematics with understanding, actively building new knowledge from experience and prior knowledge. (NCTM *Principles and Standards,* page 20.)

We want our students to gain in factual knowledge, become proficient at procedures, improve at learning on their own, and become better at applying their learning in this changing, technological world. Research shows that these four outcomes comprise one underlying goal: conceptual understanding. If you emphasize conceptual understanding, you can reach a large part of that diverse group of students who are not motivated to learn facts and procedures without understanding.

Conceptual understanding comes from interacting with ideas—encountering them independent of their names or formulas and connecting them to individual past experience. Contextually based investigations in *Discovering Geometry* lead students to experiment with concepts before related terminology and formulas are introduced. They facilitate a cooperative classroom climate that encourages students to make connections as they work with their peers.

In pursuit of the specific goal of helping students become accomplished at applying their learning, *Discovering Geometry* takes students beyond learning geometry. They also learn to be open to new ideas as they solve problems, examine alternatives, think critically, and use initiative. Moreover, the investigations empower students to communicate by asking them to record their reactions, make conjectures (perhaps with the help of technology), and prove or disprove their hypotheses.

The Technology Principle

Technology is essential in teaching and learning mathematics; it influences the mathematics that is taught and enhances students' learning. (NCTM *Principles and Standards,* page 24.)

Technology is no substitute for conceptual understanding, but it is useful for deepening that understanding. Technological tools allow students to get beyond algorithmic barriers and focus on concepts. *Discovering Geometry* is technology-friendly; it lends itself to presentations with software, graphing calculators, the Lénárt Sphere, and the Internet. Though none of these technologies are required, their use will speed up and enhance students' conceptual understanding.

Discovering Geometry includes projects, exercises, and extensions that can be done with graphing calculators, the Lénárt Sphere, Fathom Dynamic Statistics software, or Dynamic Geometry software, such as The Geometer's Sketchpad. The teaching resources include Sketchpad demonstrations that can help students visualize concepts and changing relationships. *Discovering Geometry with The Geometer's Sketchpad* contains alternative lessons that guide students in investigating relationships dynamically. Take Another Look activities comparing geometry on a plane to geometry on a sphere can be explored on the Lénárt Sphere. These tools for exploration and investigation encourage students to ask "What if . . ." questions because pursuing them is easy. The tools allow students to focus on decision making, reflection, reasoning, and problem solving, and they erase artificial lines separating algebra, geometry, and calculus.

To help students make connections, *Discovering Geometry* includes numerous exercises from situations all over the world. Links at www.keymath.com/DG lead students to web pages related to those situations.

The Assessment Principle

Assessment should support the learning of important mathematics and furnish useful information to both teachers and students. (NCTM *Principles and Standards,* page 22.)

Often the focus of teaching is on final assessment: quizzes and tests with right or wrong answers. But also important is ongoing assessment of how students are thinking, so that they can see how well they're learning and you can modify your teaching to accommodate each individual. *Discovering Geometry* supports both kinds of assessment.

In this *Discovering Geometry Teacher's Edition,* each lesson includes a section that lists what you can assess as you observe students while they work or present ideas. The list includes concepts and skills from earlier lessons, as well as visualization, problem solving, and group work. Later in this introduction you can find detailed advice on assessing group work.

Students can learn from self-assessment as well. Ideas for self-assessment appear at the end of each chapter of the student book. Ancillaries for the course include many resources: quizzes and tests (with answers) for skill assessment, and constructive assessments (with rubrics) to assess conceptual understanding.

The Content and Process Standards

Each lesson addresses many of the NCTM content and process standards. At the beginning of each lesson, the *Discovering Geometry Teacher's Edition* lists the relevant standards.

Teaching with *Discovering Geometry*

Since the publication of the first edition in 1989, *Discovering Geometry* has gained a reputation as a leading text to help students learn through doing. This third edition continues the tradition. It is designed to engage students in learning through cooperative group activities that help students make sense of geometry ideas as they improve their reasoning skills.

One very important ingredient of traditional geometry courses has been deductive proof. But you may have observed that many students don't see any reason to prove deductively what appears obvious. Moreover, students have often been asked to prove statements about concepts they understand incompletely. In *Discovering Geometry,* formal proofs within an axiom system are postponed until the end of the book. Activities throughout the book concentrate on preparing students for systematic proof by helping them understand the geometry ideas, developing their appreciation for the need for justification of relationships, and improving their reasoning skills.

You and your students will benefit if you know something about the learning theory that supports this approach. The van Hiele model, more fully set out on the next page, describes the levels through which students progress as they develop readiness for proving theorems within a deductive system. Only at higher levels in the development of their geometric thinking can students begin to reason deductively. Students must pass through the lower levels before reaching higher levels. The impossibility of skipping levels explains why so many students aren't ready for proof when it arises in traditional geometry courses. *Discovering Geometry* is designed to help students move through the first three levels on their way to understanding proof.

Students gain experience with both inductive and deductive reasoning. They use inductive reasoning when they perform investigations and make conjectures, and begin deductive reasoning informally with exercises that ask them to "explain why." Examples of algebraic, paragraph, and flowchart proofs are modeled early. By Chapter 4, students are asked to follow the reasoning in paragraph proofs and to complete simple flowchart proofs. A series of three logic explorations eases students' transition from explaining why to more formal deductive reasoning. Finally students develop geometry as a mathematical system. After establishing definitions, properties of algebra and properties of congruence, as well as the postulates of geometry, students begin to use these premises to establish theorems and to see the connections between groups of theorems.

This third edition has been revised in response to feedback from many teachers who have used *Discovering Geometry.* Some students are advanced enough in the van Hiele scheme to justify earlier introduction of deductive reasoning in this edition. Other revisions take recent learning theories into account. For students who need more help with exploration, investigations have been broken down into steps. This *Teacher's Edition* contains one-step investigations you can use as alternatives when students require less structure and will profit from a more open approach. Extensions to the geometry on a sphere using the Lénárt Sphere and explorations using geometry software can stretch creative students, leading them to ask their own questions and seek answers.

As in previous editions, you'll find many connections to other areas of mathematics. Links through the www.keymath.com/DG site can help students pursue connections and extensions more fully.

The investigations and extensions your students pursue will decrease the amount of time they spend on rote memorization while increasing their understanding of geometry. Teaching with *Discovering Geometry* changes the rules for what is expected of students and what they should expect of their teachers. Their success depends on your enthusiasm.

The van Hiele Levels

In 1957, Dutch educators Dina van Hiele-Geldof and Pierre van Hiele proposed that the development of a student's understanding of reasoning and proof progresses through five distinct levels.

Level 0: Visual. Students at the first van Hiele level identify and reason about shapes and other geometric configurations based on shapes as visual wholes rather than on geometry properties. For instance, they might identify a rectangle as a "door shape." They would identify two shapes as congruent because they look the same, not because of shared properties.

Level 1: Descriptive/Analytic. At the second van Hiele level, students recognize and characterize shapes by their properties. For example, they can identify a rectangle as a shape with opposite sides parallel and four right angles. Students at this level still do not see relationships between classes of shapes (e.g., all rectangles are parallelograms), and they tend to name all properties they know to describe a class, instead of a sufficient set.

Level 2: Abstract/Relational. At the third van Hiele level, students are able to form abstract definitions and distinguish between necessary and sufficient sets of conditions for a class of shapes, recognizing that some properties imply others. At this level students also first establish a network of logical properties and begin to engage in deductive reasoning, though more for organizing than for proving theorems.

Level 3: Formal Deduction and Proof. Students who have reached the fourth van Hiele level are able to prove theorems formally within a deductive system. They are able to understand the roles of postulates, definitions, and proofs in geometry, and they can make conjectures and try to verify them deductively.

Level 4: Rigor. Mathematicians operate at this highest level. It is generally not relevant to high school geometry.

Most students begin high school geometry at level 0. They find moving into level 1 challenging, particularly if they are second language learners grappling with a lot of new terminology. *Discovering Geometry* pays special attention to this development, even as it includes some deductive reasoning for more sophisticated reasoners. The goal is to help all students move up to level 3 by the end of the course. As you watch individual students investigate and present their ideas, you can monitor their van Hiele levels; you can do more formal assessments as students complete Assessing What You've Learned at the end of each chapter.

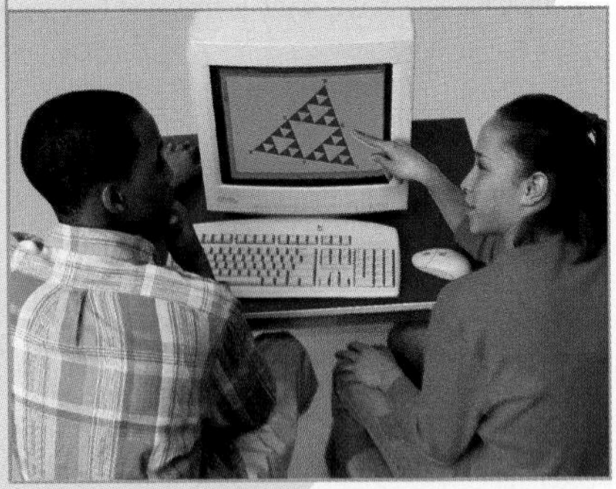

Cooperative Learning

Students with a wide range of backgrounds flourish in a course that catches their interest. *Discovering Geometry*'s investigations can begin to generate that interest. Using technology engages students even more. The most dramatic way to engage students, however, is to have them work in cooperative groups.

If you haven't already experienced the power of teaching with cooperative groups, you might have several questions: Why use groups? How big should groups be? How do I decide group membership? How often do they change? Do they require working at tables? How do I teach group cooperation skills? How can I structure the class period? What do I do as a teacher?

Why use groups? Cooperative learning has many benefits:

- Students learn and practice the essential life skill of working with others. In a cooperative learning environment, the groups' cooperative skills are an integral part of the curriculum.
- Students are exposed to more ideas for solving problems. In solving challenging problems, "two heads are better than one."
- Students who are good in social situations can gain confidence in their mathematical abilities, even if they have previously been unsuccessful in mathematics.

- Students understand an idea more deeply if they have to articulate it for someone else.
- Students learn to solve more complex problems than they could if they didn't have other members of a group to contribute different areas of expertise.
- Groups working in a supportive atmosphere can provide quicker feedback on ideas than a single teacher could offer.
- Some students will be more willing to contribute to a small group than to a full class, thus practicing oral communication skills.

How big should groups be? Groups of no more than four are usually best.

What about membership and change in groups? At first, assign students to groups randomly. As you get to know the students, think about who works well with whom. Mixing abilities is best, but putting the strongest and weakest students together can frustrate both. Keep student groups together long enough for the members to get to know one another, but change group assignment every four to six weeks for variety and for a healthy dynamic.

Do groups need to work at tables? Tables are best for giving students plenty of work space. But desks are okay, too, and have the one advantage of flexibility on exam days. If you use desks, bring the desktops together to form an area as close to a single surface as possible—and to have students facing each other.

How can you teach cooperative skills? One way is to make clear to the class your reasons for preferring group work. Try to counter some students' ideas that learning is competitive, that a course is about delivering information that only the teacher knows, or that stronger students will be graded lower because they are working with weaker students.

Develop with your students some specific guidelines to follow for productive work. These might include: be considerate, listen without interrupting, ask questions when needed, help others in the group, and make sure everyone in the group understands the ideas well enough to present them to the class. A poster listing the skills is helpful.

Hold each group fully accountable. End most group sessions with presentations to the class. You won't have time for all groups to present each time, but each student should be prepared.

Hold individuals responsible for group participation. As you move around the room, sometimes carry a copy of the roll and record points or a plus or minus sign for individual contributions to the group. Make these marks part of each student's participation grade. As the course progresses, you might extend your observation sheet to include items such as contributing ideas, asking questions, giving directions, actively listening, expressing support, encouraging members to participate, summarizing, talking through problems, and justifying viewpoints. Let your students know when you are looking for specific contribution skills so that they can learn from the assessment.

Most important, trust the group process. Allow plenty of time for the group to correct mistakes. If a student asks you a question, turn it back to the group. If some students are causing behavior problems, try to facilitate a group solution by reviewing the guidelines with the group or helping students clarify their roles. In some cases you will need to call a student aside for a discussion of poor group behavior. When you do so, also talk with the other group members individually about your expectations. Sometimes it helps to point out that the groups will change and that students will have a chance to work with a different set of classmates soon.

Promoting Inquiry

The investigations in *Discovering Geometry* encourage students to inquire about relevant ideas and issues beyond the bounds of the course. Students have legitimate opportunities to experiment, hypothesize, measure, analyze, test, talk, write, explain, and justify their ideas. In short, they engage in real mathematics.

Inquiry-based classes go beyond engaging students in activities—they place students in the role of researchers. The quality of students' investigations is linked to the quality of their own inquiries. The motivation for pursuing answers to their own questions is very strong. In fact, it conforms to the old educational maxim "Don't answer questions that students haven't asked." Being flexible challenges you and the students in several ways. An inquiry-based classroom requires several things from both you and your students.

- First, it challenges everyone to develop skills for problem posing as well as problem solving. Encourage the posing of new problems during Sharing and Closing. You can foster problem posing by using question openers such as those listed in the box.
- Second, develop a list of inquiry questions that includes some specific to the lesson you're ready to do next. Use the questions suggested in this *Teacher's Edition* for that lesson as well as the questions based on interlesson connections summarized in the section The Mathematics in the *Teacher's Edition* chapter introductions. What questions does each lesson answer? Where did these questions arise in previous lessons?
- Third, students must take responsibility for their own learning and recognize that learning is an active, not a passive, process. *Discovering Geometry*'s cooperative investigations are chosen for their value as vehicles to promote activity and help students construct their own knowledge. The interaction, discussion, questions, suggestions, and ideas that students offer while working in their groups can benefit all group members. Some students will want more from you than to help them help themselves. It is not the way they have played the learning game, but it is the way a work environment runs. Their grades in the course, like their evaluations in the workplace, take into account how well they're learning to do research in a team, not just the results of that research.
- Fourth, you have to play the role of an experienced coresearcher rather than of someone with all the answers. Don't give too many hints. Give encouragement for good thinking, not just for right answers. Treat right answers as discussion topics until the class—the research team—agrees on them. As soon as you acknowledge a right answer, you often shut off thinking about that problem, even if students don't understand the answer. You will find that if you provide answers and explanations too quickly students may continue to expect and depend on your answers.
- Fifth, students must not conceive of mathematics as a collection of facts and procedures. Many mathematical investigations, such as those in *Discovering Geometry,* don't have just one answer, and rarely is there only one valid approach to a solution. Justifying ideas and problem solving become more important than the actual solutions. The goal is for students to experience mathematics as a process of finding and connecting ideas. Let students know that the thinking and problem-solving skills they develop can serve them in all aspects of their lives. They are learning more than geometry.
- Sixth, as you plan, be flexible in responding to students' ideas. Spend planning time thinking of how students might address the problem under investigation. This *Teacher's Edition* can help you anticipate places where students might need help and suggest good questions that you can ask to keep students thinking.

Inquiry Question Openers

What happens if . . . ?	What's the largest/smallest . . . ?
What if not . . . ?	What are the properties of . . . ?
Why . . . ?	What other . . . ?
How many . . . ?	How do you know . . . ?
In general, . . . ?	Is it always true that . . . ?
What do we mean by . . . ?	Is it possible . . . ?
Is there a relationship . . . ?	How can you . . . ?
Under what conditions . . . ?	Is there a similarity between . . . ?

Teaching with Cooperative Groups

If you are new to the investigative approach, the change of your role may be the most difficult part of learning to create an inquiry-based classroom. You might be comfortable with situations in which you are the center of attention and follow a standard script. Now's your chance to become a leader in problem solving. You will constantly be making professional judgments in response to student contributions.

One basis for those judgments is in how you see your role shifting from telling students mathematical ideas to helping investigation teams function well. Well-functioning groups working on well-planned investigations such as those in *Discovering Geometry* will gain conceptual understanding without your having to give explanations.

How does this work in practice? After you give groups a few minutes to settle down and get started (a good time to take attendance), move among groups, observing carefully, encouraging as necessary, but trying not to turn attention toward yourself. Sit down if there's an empty seat nearby. If students ask you a mathematical question, reflect it back to the group. Don't be too quick to jump in and correct errors. If the students in the group don't catch a common error, make a note to have someone from that group present that error later so that the entire class can learn from its correction.

Take special notice of any groups that don't seem to be on task. If your joining them doesn't refocus them, ask about their progress. If they think they've finished the task, look at their work, ask questions, and challenge them to extend it, perhaps by taking another approach. If they say they're stuck, ask one group member to describe what they've done, and ask other members for their ideas about it. If they're not cooperating, remind them of the group process guidelines. Praise good group work and good thinking, even if the group is not yet on the right track.

As you listen to functioning groups, plan the Sharing time. Who should present what, and in what order? What questions should be asked and what points raised? Consider an example: The group that actually constructed the next stage of a fractal design and counted areas should be chosen to show its picture first. Group members should come forward together, because two of them haven't presented recently. If no student asks if there's an easier way, you might. Then Chris, who is quite articulate and used the area formula for triangles, could describe that formula. Someone will raise a question about patterns. Finally Mario and Robin could show the pattern they found. They don't have good calculation skills, but their creativity in problem solving can be an inspiration. You also want to praise the teamwork of another group, even though there's no reason to have them present today.

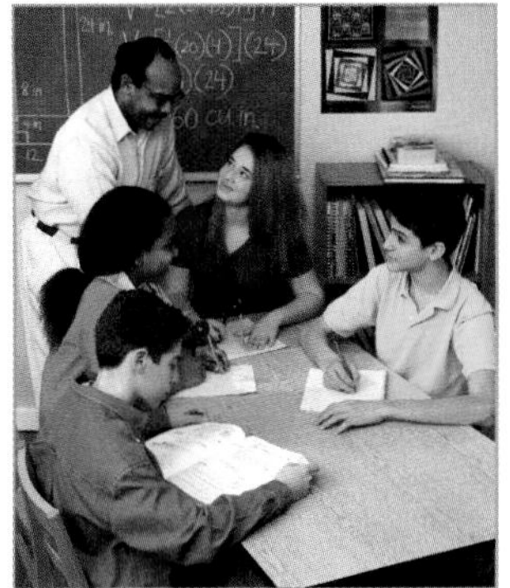

During student presentations to the class, sit down and watch. Keep in mind that if you take the stage or answer a question, many students will stop thinking about that question. You can ask questions to help clarify points, and you might wonder aloud about possible relationships and extensions (following suggestions in this *Teacher's Edition*)—but wait for students to do so first.

One warning: It's tempting to assume that an emphasis on process over product means that "anything goes." But sloppy thinking is no more acceptable now than before; indeed, you want students to be convinced that everything in mathematics can be justified logically and that conflicts between intuition and logic can be resolved by logic. On the other hand, in an open atmosphere, small groups and the class will be largely self-correcting. Even if they don't catch errors, students will learn the lessons of reasoning and cooperation better if you ask for clarification than if you simply say "That's wrong."

Structuring the Class Period

The order of events in a class period will vary with the lesson, with your class's growing experience in independent learning, with the need for variety, and with how students are responding. If they're lethargic, have them act out the investigation. If they're overly excited, channel the energy into their inquiry.

Here's a suggested schedule to use as a starting point:

Introduction (5–10 minutes). After you have responded to homework questions, set the context for the investigation. Pose the problem and be sure the terms are clear. Resist the temptation to tell students how to do the investigation; they will learn in part from making mistakes. Sometimes you'll want to go over an example of a concept before students begin the investigation. Though an introduction is not usually mentioned in the Pacing Guide, it is assumed that you will spend some time every class period preparing students for the investigations.

Investigation (15–50 minutes). Students work in groups while you observe, encourage, and craft plans for the rest of the class period. (The longer time applies to those lessons for which the Pacing Guide recommends spending two days. The section Using This Chapter in the interleaf pages that begin each chapter of the *Teacher's Edition* will help you decide which lessons you can skip, depending on the requirements of your curriculum, in order to give more time to other lessons.)

Sharing (10–20 minutes). Selected students report to the class. As needed, you help the class reach consensus about how to phrase conjectures and also introduce terminology and notation. Ask questions that help clarify or lead to further thought about the ideas that have arisen. Praise good teamwork. As appropriate, facilitate the study of examples in the text that can deepen understanding of the main concepts of the lesson.

Closing (5 minutes). Remind students of the main mathematical ideas and where they arose in the lesson. If cooperative learning is new to your students, you might lead a short discussion on how the groups are functioning, what areas they can improve in, and what they are doing well. Or ask students to write briefly about what they learned or what they're confused about.

Exercises (5–10 minutes). Assign and begin work on the exercises.

For most lessons, the *Discovering Geometry Teacher's Edition* includes a section called **One step,** which offers an alternative to the several-step investigation(s) and frequently to some examples. You can use the one-step approach for classes that are experienced at investigation. Even if your class needs more guidance at the beginning of the course, read through these alternatives to keep in view your goal of helping your students become more independent investigators. This practice will help you become better at finding "teachable moments" as you interact with your students.

Communicating

Over the last decade, teachers and researchers have become aware that the ability to read mathematics and other technical material and to communicate ideas orally and in writing not only enhances students' understanding of the concepts but also improves their other language abilities.

The author and editors have taken care to make *Discovering Geometry* readable. Students will read the steps of an investigation, the contexts of the applications, and other parts of the student book. Ideally you won't tell them what they can read in the book, and you'll point out that they can use the book as a resource.

As you embark on teaching the course, be sensitive to students' inexperience with reading mathematics and, perhaps, English. You can take steps to help them. Ask a student to read a brief passage or instruction aloud. If one student in the class or a group reads an instruction or problem aloud, the others (especially auditory learners) might benefit from hearing it. But don't ask students to read aloud anything that they haven't first read silently. You might, for example, ask all students to read through some instructions silently and then ask a student in each group to read them aloud. You might suggest that a group rotate readers to be sure everyone gets a chance to read aloud.

It is also helpful to ask students to paraphrase. After one student reads aloud, ask another student to restate the instruction or problem in different words. After they have read a passage, help struggling students by emphasizing main ideas and relating the ideas to what students have learned.

(continued)

Assessing

Assessment is your way of getting feedback about how well your students are learning. Students want to know how well they are doing, too. The materials accompanying *Discovering Geometry* support a variety of methods for assessing both processes and results.

As you circulate among groups or watch students' presentations, engage in informal assessment of students' previous learning. Assessing Progress sections in the *Discovering Geometry Teacher's Edition* provide ideas for what to look for. Also, during class, note how effectively the lesson is proceeding so you can make adjustments as you go. Throughout the *Teacher's Edition* you can find ideas for what to look for. You can also assess group process skills as described in the Cooperative Learning section in these teaching notes. And because *Discovering Geometry* emphasizes conceptual understanding, journal entries describing how individual students are making sense of the ideas can be especially useful for assessment.

You will also use more intentionally focused activities to evaluate students' learning. *Discovering Geometry Assessment Resources A* and *B* include two versions of quizzes, tests, and Constructive Assessment Options for each chapter, as well as unit tests and a final exam. If you feel that in-class examinations don't allow you to assess the depth of students' understanding, you can use the projects in *Discovering Geometry* for assessment. Or you might have students prepare portfolios of their best work. This *Teacher's Edition* lists exercises that you might assign for inclusion in a portfolio. At the end of each chapter of the student book, the section Assessing What You've Learned contains suggestions for student self-assessment that will give both you and your students additional feedback on their learning.

You can find more details about assessment in the front matter for *Assessment Resources A* and *Assessment Resources B.*

(Communicating—continued)

The real-life context of the material will help motivate student reading and enhance critical thinking skills as students solve problems that they can relate to familiar situations. If students are having difficulty understanding an exercise they read, refer them back to the mathematical concepts involved in solving the problems. It is crucial that students recognize the underlying mathematical concepts and how they apply to specific situations.

Students can often deepen their comprehension of a chapter through writing—outlining the chapter and listing the objectives and main ideas in their notebooks. Students need to record definitions and conjectures as these are agreed upon in class, because they don't appear in the student book and will be needed for future reference.

Writing is also an important tool for clarifying ideas. As the saying goes, "Writing is nature's way of telling us what we don't understand." The same holds true for careful speaking. Cultivate in your students the habit of reflecting on what they are saying and writing. Encourage them not to turn in their scratch paper for a homework assignment but to write up a careful presentation of their answer and its justification. When you grade homework or critique a presentation, ask for clarification of vague expressions or murky logic.

Encourage students to use graphics in communicating, both orally and in writing. They can create overhead transparencies, use computer graphics programs, or employ geometry software to incorporate graphical illustrations into oral presentations and written reports.

Planning

The *Discovering Geometry Teacher's Edition* includes many ideas for planning. For each chapter and lesson it lists objectives and materials and also outlines how to spend class time. The commentary on the lesson includes alerts, based on teachers' experience, about difficulties students might have (but not be able to articulate) and suggestions on how you might respond to them. But every class is different. Don't limit your planning to reading through these comments. Think about each chapter and lesson with your own students and schedule in mind.

Planning a Course

Use the curriculum guidelines for your school, the Pacing Guides, and the interleaf sections Using this Chapter to outline your year. Think about what topics students must learn and what explorations or projects you want them to experience. Leave blank days in your schedule for the unexpected, and plan for some extra days where you will concentrate on homework questions or catch up on investigations and Sharing.

Planning a Chapter

To allow flexibility to meet your class's needs, each chapter of *Discovering Geometry* contains more material than most classes will have time to cover. While all the investigations are valuable, you probably won't be able to do all of them in equal depth. Complete those you choose to do in class and have students share their findings. You might choose to work through an investigation as a whole class, assign groups to different investigations, or even omit an investigation because of time constraints. Ask yourself, "What do my own students need at this time?" The section Using This Chapter on the interleaf page before each student chapter can help you decide what you might skip.

Part of planning involves deepening your own understanding of the mathematics. Some might think that because students are to figure out the mathematics themselves, you yourself don't need to know the mathematics very well. Such a belief doesn't take into account the intellectual level of an investigation-based classroom. Students working collaboratively in groups will find themselves on many paths that you haven't explored before. Students using geometry software or graphing calculators may raise "What if . . ." questions that astound you. Even though your role is no longer to provide answers, you need to keep encouraging and challenging students. To do so, you need a deep understanding of the mathematical ideas. Reading the section The Mathematics in the chapter interleaves will help you.

Planning a Lesson

You need to think about your students' strengths and weaknesses in planning individual lessons as well. Work through the investigation; ask yourself how your students will respond to it and how you can facilitate. If you have time, ask friends and colleagues to think out loud about how they would do the investigation.

While planning lessons, keep in mind that the approach of this course is different from what you might be used to. Instead of telling students everything they need to know before they embark on an investigation (and then retelling them as they work), you should aim to have students encounter the mathematical ideas during the investigation. Later those ideas can be formalized with a name and a definition. Remember that your role is to help students discover mathematics, in both the processes and the content of the journey.

Planning Assignments

In planning homework assignments, be aware that *Discovering Geometry* contains many more exercises than most classes will have time to work on. Select those you think can generate interest among your own students and satisfy your curriculum goals. At times you might want to assign different exercises to different groups or individuals and follow with classroom presentations. The Assigning Homework chart offers guidance about the appropriateness of the exercises for particular goals. When hardworking students return to class with questions, consider asking them to continue working on the assignment and turn it in the following day.

Although careful planning is necessary, don't let it get in the way of your teaching. Planning should not mean preparing a script you have to follow. What students do with technology-enhanced investigations can be different from what you anticipated. Each day you'll need to adjust your plans for the next few days. The farther you can see ahead, the better you'll be able to decide how to balance allowing students to explore and answer their own questions with getting the class through the course.

The Lesson Outline suggests pacing for each lesson over one or two class periods. These outlines are only guidelines. You may want to add time to answer homework questions. You should also prepare to move faster or more slowly according to how well your class is learning.

The Pacing Options chart indicates the days per lesson for several schedules:

- a block schedule, in which there are fewer, longer class periods each week
- a standard one-year geometry course, covering all the essential lessons
- an enriched course, in which students cover all the topics and the projects

If you are teaching a two-year geometry course, you can spend one day on the investigation and a second day on the exercises for each lesson.

Pacing Options

Pacing Guide for Standard Schedules

Chapter	day 1	day 2	day 3	day 4	day 5	day 6	day 7	day 8	day 9	day 10
0	0.1	0.2	0.3	0.4, 0.5, or 0.6	0.4, 0.5, or 0.6	sharing	review	assessment		
1	1.1	Algebra 1	1.2	1.3	quiz, 1.4	1.5	quiz, 1.6	1.7	1.8	review
	day 11									
	assessment									
2	2.1	2.2	2.3	quiz, 2.4	2.5	2.5	2.6	quiz, Algebra 2	review	assessment
3	3.1	3.2	3.3	quiz, 3.4	3.4, 3.5	3.5, Algebra 3	3.6	quiz, Exploration	3.7	3.8
	day 11	day 12	day 13	day 14						
	Exploration	review	review	assessment						
4	4.1	4.2	Algebra 4	4.3	quiz, 4.4	4.4, 4.5	4.5	4.6	quiz, 4.7	4.8
	day 11	day 12	day 13							
	review, project	review	assessment							
5	5.1	5.2	quiz, 5.3	5.4	5.5	quiz, Algebra 5	5.6	5.7	quiz, review	review
	day 11									
	assessment									

Pacing Guide for Standard Schedules (continued)

Chapter										
6	**day 1**	**day 2**	**day 3**	**day 4**	**day 5**	**day 6**	**day 7**	**day 8**	**day 9**	**day 10**
	6.1	6.2	6.3	6.3	6.4	Algebra 6	6.5	6.6	6.7	review
	day 11	**day 12**	**day 13**							
	assessment	review	assessment							
7	**day 1**	**day 2**	**day 3**	**day 4**	**day 5**	**day 6**	**day 7**	**day 8**	**day 9**	**day 10**
	7.1	7.2	7.3, quiz	7.4	quiz	7.5	7.6, quiz	7.7	7.8	Algebra 7
	day 11	**day 12**								
	review	assessment								
8	**day 1**	**day 2**	**day 3**	**day 4**	**day 5**	**day 6**	**day 7**	**day 8**	**day 9**	**day 10**
	8.1	8.2	quiz, 8.3	8.4	Exploration	8.5	quiz, 8.6	Exploration	8.7	Exploration
	day 11	**day 12**	**day 13**	**day 14**						
	quiz, IYVTS	review	review	assessment						
9	**day 1**	**day 2**	**day 3**	**day 4**	**day 5**	**day 6**	**day 7**	**day 8**	**day 9**	**day 10**
	9.1	9.2	Algebra 8	9.3	Exploration	quiz, Exploration	9.4	9.5	Exploration	9.6
	day 11	**day 12**	**day 13**	**day 14**	**day 15**					
	quiz, review	review	assessment	mixed review	unit test					

Pacing Guide for Standard Schedules (continued)

Chapter	day 1	day 2	day 3	day 4	day 5	day 6	day 7	day 8	day 9	day 10
10	10.1	Exploration	10.2	10.3	quiz, Exploration	10.4	10.5	quiz, Exploration	10.6	10.7
	day 11	day 12	day 13	day 14						
	quiz, Exploration	review	review	assessment						
	day 1	day 2	day 3	day 4	day 5	day 6	day 7	day 8	day 9	day 10
11	Algebra 9	11.1	11.1	11.2	project or Exploration	11.3	quiz, 11.4	11.5	Exploration	11.6
	day 11	day 12	day 13	day 14						
	Exploration	review	review	assessment						
	day 1	day 2	day 3	day 4	day 5	day 6	day 7	day 8	day 9	day 10
12	12.1	12.2	quiz, Exploration	12.3	12.4	12.5	quiz, project	Exploration	Exploration	review
	day 11	day 12								
	review	assessment								
	day 1	day 2	day 3	day 4	day 5	day 6	day 7	day 8	day 9	day 10
13	13.1	13.2	13.3	quiz, 13.4	13.5	13.6	13.7	Exploration	quiz, review	review
	day 11	day 12	day 13	day 14						
	assessment	review	review	assessment						

Pacing Options

Pacing Guide for an Enriched Class

Chapter										
0	day 1	day 2	day 3	day 4	day 5	day 6	day 7	day 8	day 9	
	0.1	0.2	0.3	0.4	0.5	0.6	projects	review	assessment	
1	day 1	day 2	day 3	day 4	day 5	day 6	day 7	day 8	day 9	day 10
	1.1	Algebra 1, 1.2	1.3	quiz, 1.4	1.5	quiz, 1.6	1.7	1.8	Exploration	review, TAL
	day 11									
	assessment									
2	day 1	day 2	day 3	day 4	day 5	day 6	day 7	day 8	day 9	day 10
	2.1	2.2	2.2	quiz, 2.4	2.5	2.5, Exploration	2.6	quiz, Algebra 2	review, Exploration	assessment
3	day 1	day 2	day 3	day 4	day 5	day 6	day 7	day 8	day 9	day 10
	3.1	3.2	3.2	quiz, 3.4	3.5	Algebra 3, 3.6	quiz	Exploration	3.7	3.8
	day 11	day 12	day 13	day 14						
	Exploration	review, project	review	assessment						
4	day 1	day 2	day 3	day 4	day 5	day 6	day 7	day 8	day 9	day 10
	4.1	4.2	Algebra 4	4.3	quiz, 4.4	4.5	4.6	project, quiz	4.7	4.8
	day 11	day 12	day 13							
	Exploration	review, project	assessment, TAL							
5	day 1	day 2	day 3	day 4	day 5	day 6	day 7	day 8	day 9	day 10
	5.1, extension	5.2	quiz, Exploration	5.3	5.4	5.5	quiz, project, Algebra 5	5.6	5.7	quiz, review
	day 11	day 12								
	project, review	assessment, TAL								

Pacing Guide for an Enriched Class (continued)

Chapter	day 1	day 2	day 3	day 4	day 5	day 6	day 7	day 8	day 9	day 10
6	6.1	6.2	6.3	6.3	6.4	Algebra 6, TAL	6.5	6.6	6.7, project	review, Exploration
	day 11	day 12	day 13							
	assessment, TAL	review, TAL	assessment, TAL							
	day 1	day 2	day 3	day 4	day 5	day 6	day 7	day 8	day 9	day 10
7	7.1	7.2	7.3, project	quiz, 7.4	7.5	quiz, project	7.6, quiz	7.7	7.8	Algebra 7
	day 11	day 12								
	review	assessment								
	day 1	day 2	day 3	day 4	day 5	day 6	day 7	day 8	day 9	day 10
8	8.1	8.2, project	quiz, 8.3	8.4	Exploration	8.5	quiz, 8.6	project, Exploration	8.7	Exploration, quiz
	day 11	day 12	day 13	day 14						
	IYVTS, Exploration	review, TAL	review, TAL	assessment						
	day 1	day 2	day 3	day 4	day 5	day 6	day 7	day 8	day 9	day 10
9	9.1, project	9.2	Algebra 8	9.3	Exploration	quiz, Exploration	9.4	9.5	Exploration	9.6
	day 11	day 12	day 13	day 14	day 15					
	quiz, review, TAL	review, TAL	assessment	mixed review	unit test					
	day 1	day 2	day 3	day 4	day 5	day 6	day 7	day 8	day 9	day 10
10	10.1	Exploration	10.2, project	10.3, project	quiz, Exploration	10.4	10.5, project	quiz, Exploration	10.6	10.7
	day 11	day 12	day 13	day 14						
	quiz, Exploration	review	review	assessment						

Pacing Guide for an Enriched Class (continued)

Chapter										
11	**day 1**	**day 2**	**day 3**	**day 4**	**day 5**	**day 6**	**day 7**	**day 8**	**day 9**	**day 10**
	Algebra 9, 11.1	11.1	11.1, project	project	11.2	Exploration	11.3	quiz, 11.4	11.5	project
	day 11	**day 12**	**day 13**	**day 14**	**day 15**					
	Exploration	11.6	Exploration	review, TAL	assessment, TAL					
12	**day 1**	**day 2**	**day 3**	**day 4**	**day 5**	**day 6**	**day 7**	**day 8**	**day 9**	**day 10**
	12.2	12.2, project	quiz, Exploration	12.3	12.4	12.5	quiz, Exploration	Exploration	project	Exploration
	day 11	**day 12**	**day 13**							
	review	review, TAL	assessment, TAL							
13	**day 1**	**day 2**	**day 3**	**day 4**	**day 5**	**day 6**	**day 7**	**day 8**	**day 9**	**day 10**
	13.1	13.2	13.3	quiz, 13.4	Exploration	13.5	13.6	13.7, project	quiz, Exploration	review
	day 11	**day 12**	**day 13**	**day 14**						
	assessment	review	review	assessment						

Pacing Guide for Block Schedules

Chapter	day 1	day 2	day 3	day 4	day 5	day 6	day 7	day 8	day 9
0	0.1, 0.2	0.2, 0.3	0.4, 0.5, or 0.6	sharing, projects	review, assessment				
1	1.1, 1.2	1.3, 1.4	quiz, 1.5	1.6, 1.7	quiz, 1.8	Exploration, review	TAL, assessment		
2	2.1, 2.2	2.3, 2.4	quiz, 2.5	2.6, Algebra 2	Exploration, review	assessment			
3	3.1, 3.2	3.3, 3.4	quiz, 3.5	Algebra 3, 3.6	Exploration, 3.7	3.8, review	Exploration, review	assessment, review	
4	4.1, 4.2	Algebra 4, 4.3	quiz, 4.4, 4.5	4.6, 4.7	quiz, 4.8	Exploration, review	assessment, TAL		
5	5.1, 5.2	quiz, 5.3, Exploration	5.4, project	quiz, 5.5	Algebra 5, 5.6	5.7	quiz, review, project	assessment	
6	6.1, 6.2	6.3	6.4, Algebra 6	6.5, 6.6	6.7, review	assessment	review, TAL	assessment	
7	7.1, 7.2	7.3, quiz, project	7.4, 7.5	project, 7.6	7.7, 7.8	review	assessment		
8	8.1, 8.2	8.3, 8.4	Exploration, 8.5	8.6, Exploration	8.7	Exploration, IYVTS	review, TAL	TAL, assessment	
9	9.1, 9.2	Algebra 8, 9.3	quiz, 9.4, Exploration	9.5, Exploration	9.6, quiz, review	review, TAL	assessment, TAL	mixed review	unit test

Pacing Guide for Block Schedules (continued)

Chapter	day 1	day 2	day 3	day 4	day 5	day 6	day 7	day 8	day 9
10	10.1, Exploration	10.2, 10.3	quiz, Exploration	10.4, 10.5	quiz, Exploration	10.6, 10.7	quiz, Exploration	review, TAL	assessment
	day 1	day 2	day 3	day 4	day 5	day 6	day 7	day 8	day 9
11	Algebra 9, 11.1	11.1, 11.2	Exploration, 11.3	11.4	11.5, project	Exploration	11.6, Exploration	quiz, review, TAL	review, TAL assessment,
	day 1	day 2	day 3	day 4	day 5	day 6	day 7	day 8	day 9
12	12.1, 12.2	quiz, Exploration	12.3, 12.4	12.5, Exploration	Exploration, quiz, project	Exploration	review, TAL	assessment	TAL
	day 1	day 2	day 3	day 4	day 5	day 6	day 7	day 8	day 9
13	13.1, 13.2	13.3, 13.4	quiz, 13.5, Exploration	13.6, 13.7	project, quiz, Exploration	review	assessment	review	assessment

Material	Quantity
calculators, scientific or graphing	1 per student
cardboard boxes or plastic dishpans	1 per group
cardboard cut-outs of geometric shapes taped to stiff wire	1 set per class
circle of latex with the edges stretched out, *optional*	1 per class
circular objects, *optional*	several per group
colored pens or pencils	
compasses	1 per student
computer drawing program, *optional*	
dominoes, *optional*	
drinking straws	1 per student
Dynamic Geometry software, *optional*	
Dynamic Statistics software, *optional*	
geoboards, *optional*	2 per group
geometric patterns from art, architecture, and nature	
glue sticks	2 per group
graph paper	
hollow pairs of cylinders and cones	2 per group
hollow pairs of hemispheres and cones or cylinders	2 per group
hollow pairs of prisms and pyramids	2 per group
interlocking cubes	1000
large paper, *optional*	
large rubber bands, *optional*	10 per class
Lénárt Spheres that can be drawn on, *optional*	1 per class or group

Materials List

Material	Quantity
masking tape	
mat board, cardboard, or manila folders	
measuring tapes, *optional*	1 per group
metersticks	3 per group
mirrors	2 per group
modeling clay	$\frac{1}{4}$ cup per group
paper clips	6 per group
pattern blocks	1 set per group
patty paper	
physical objects to represent geometry concepts	
plumb weights (such as washers)	1 per student
protractors	1 per student
ream of paper or stack of cards	
rulers	1 per student
sand, rice, birdseed, or water	3 to 4 cups per group
science reference books, *optional*	
scissors	2 per group
stack of disks such as coins or chemistry filters	1 per class
straightedges	1 per student
string	
tape	
toothpicks	250 per group
tracing paper	
uncooked spaghetti, *optional*	1 package per class
wooden or sugar cubes	12 per group

CHAPTER

0

Geometric Art

Overview

In Chapter 0, students see that geometry is a way of thinking about and seeing the world. They become aware of geometry in nature, and they discover that geometry is alive in cultures and art forms around the world. **Lesson 0.1** looks at symmetry in nature and in art. Then students gain experience with construction tools—the straightedge as they construct line designs in **Lesson 0.2,** and the compass as they construct circle designs in **Lesson 0.3.** In **Lesson 0.4,** students use both these tools together to explore visual effects that can be achieved with geometric patterns. Ties to the art of different cultures are explored in the next lessons as students study knot designs in **Lesson 0.5** and tile designs in **Lesson 0.6.**

The Mathematics

Symmetry

Students are introduced to the most common geometric characteristics found in both art and nature: reflectional and rotational symmetry. Students will be familiar with these terms from earlier math courses. Don't expect rigorous knowledge of symmetry at this point; students will return to symmetry in review exercises and in Chapter 7, through transformations generating tessellations (repeated shapes that fill the plane without gaps or overlaps). Symmetry can also be used to help students understand properties of quadrilaterals in Chapter 5. In Chapter 0, reflectional symmetry and rotational symmetry are described as properties of objects.

A figure has *reflectional symmetry* if there is at least one line (a *line of reflection*) such that a mirror reflection over it results in the same figure. A special kind of reflectional symmetry is *bilateral symmetry,* in which there is only one line of reflection.

A figure has *n-fold rotational symmetry* about a given point if a rotation of the figure through an angle that measures $\frac{360}{n}$ degrees results in the same figure. Having 2-fold rotational symmetry, through an angle that measures 180° (sometimes called *point symmetry*), is equivalent to having reflectional symmetry over two perpendicular lines.

Constructions

Many Classical Greeks believed that the most perfect geometric shapes were the straight line and the circle, so geometric constructions should be done with a straightedge (with no marks) and a compass. The tradition of using these two classical tools remains useful in helping students acquire hands-on understanding of geometric ideas. For example, this chapter has students make regular hexagons by marking the radius of a circle six times along the circumference. For one hexagon-based design, students use the midpoints of the sides. Students will need a ruler for that task until they learn in Chapter 3 to bisect line segments using a compass. The term **construction tools** in the materials list means compass (or patty paper) and straightedge.

Three Dimensions into Two

When drawing simple three-dimensional figures such as knots, as in Lesson 0.5, eliminating hidden lines is sufficient to make the picture look true to life. Sometimes shaping contour lines, as in some op art designs from Lesson 0.4, can give the impression of depth. To make realistic pictures of figures with more depth, however, artists usually employ some kind of optical perspective. Students interested in perspective drawing can do the exploration on page 178.

Van Hiele Learning Model

The assumption for this chapter and the next is that students are at level 0 of the van Hiele model and moving into level 1. That is, they recognize figures as total entities but are being challenged—primarily through discussion—to analyze component parts of figures and characteristics, such as symmetry. Students may not yet be able to explain interrelationships between figures and these properties. See page xxx for more on the van Hiele model.

Using This Chapter

Even without covering Chapter 0, students are likely to have enough previous experience with and intuitive grasp of symmetry to answer the relevant review questions. However, this chapter will help set up a positive, nonthreatening, "I can do it" atmosphere. One of the chapter's goals is to hook students who may be turned off to mathematics by showing its creative side. Create a wall display of geometric art, adding student work from each lesson.

To help students become familiar with some of the tools of geometry, you might do at least the first three lessons. Then each student in a cooperative group might do a different lesson from among the next three and share what he or she has learned with the others in the group. (This is known as the jigsaw model for cooperative learning.) Or you might use the remaining lessons from the chapter as change-of-pace lessons between later chapters.

Compass constructions will be used throughout the course, so give students time to gain skill at drawing circles. They should always use a compass with a stack of paper under their work. Tell frustrated students that the three main geometry tools are a compass, a straightedge, and patience. Coach them to keep pressure on the center point so it doesn't move, let the lead touch the paper enough to make a mark, and rotate the compass.

Cooperative Learning

If you are new to cooperative groups, read pages xxx–xxxii. More information on cooperative groups can be found at www.keypress.com/DG. Talk with students about and list the norms for cooperative behavior. Each student has the responsibility to

- listen carefully and with respect to the others in the group
- contribute to the group task
- ask for help from the group when needed
- help others in the group when asked
- change his or her mind only when logically persuaded (Ideally, the group reaches consensus, not majority rule.)

Resources

Discovering Geometry Resources

Teaching and Worksheet Masters
Lessons 0.1, 0.2, 0.5, and 0.6

Discovering Geometry with The Geometer's Sketchpad
Lessons 0.2–0.4, and 0.6

Other Resources

Optical Illusions by Bruno Ernst.

Geometry in Our World slide collection by The National Council of Teachers of Mathematics.

Introduction to Line Designs by Dale Seymour.

For complete references on these and other sources see www.keypress.com/DG.

Materials

- construction tools (straightedge and compass)
- protractors
- rulers
- small mirrors, *optional*
- graph paper
- isometric and square dot paper
- unlined paper
- patty paper
- tracing paper, *optional*
- a computer with a drawing program, *optional*
- examples of geometric patterns in art, architecture, and nature
- examples of Islamic art
- colored pens or pencils
- three metersticks or yardsticks, *optional*

Pacing Guide

	day 1	day 2	day 3	day 4	day 5	day 6	day 7	day 8	day 9	day 10
standard	0.1	0.2	0.3	0.4, 0.5, or 0.6	0.4, 0.5, or 0.6	sharing	review	assessment		
enriched	0.1	0.2	0.3	0.4	0.5	0.6	projects	review	assessment	
block	0.1, 0.2	0.2, 0.3	0.4, 0.5, or 0.6	sharing, projects	review, assessment					

CHAPTER

0 Geometric Art

A work by Dutch graphic artist M. C. Escher (1898–1972) opens each chapter in this book. Escher used geometry in creative ways to make his interesting and unusual works of art. As you come to each new chapter, see if you can connect the Escher work to the content of the chapter.

My subjects are often playful. . . . It is, for example, a pleasure to deliberately mix together objects of two and of three dimensions, surface and spatial relationships, and to make fun of gravity.

M. C. ESCHER

Print Gallery, M. C. Escher, 1956

OBJECTIVES

In this chapter you will

- see examples of geometry in nature
- study geometric art forms of cultures around the world
- study the symmetry in flowers, crystals, and animals
- see geometry as a way of thinking and of looking at the world
- practice using a compass and straightedge

CHAPTER 0 OBJECTIVES

- Set the tone with a positive, unthreatening start of the course
- Discover geometry in nature, art, and world cultures
- Discover the characteristics of reflectional and rotational symmetry
- Develop observational and visual thinking skills
- Create a variety of designs with straightedge and compass
- Construct regular hexagons with compass and straightedge
- Encounter tessellations

In *Print Gallery*, Escher has used artistic techniques for representing physical space, and brought two spaces together in a print of a print in a print gallery.

[Ask] "What makes Escher's *Print Gallery* interesting to you? What quality of the picture causes your eye to explore the picture in more depth? What artistic techniques are used to show depth? How do you think Escher used mathematics in making *Print Gallery*? What does the cityscape look like from the viewpoint of the person in the picture? Why has Escher signed and dated the print in the center?"

LESSON

0.1

PLANNING

LESSON OUTLINE

One day:

20 min Investigation

10 min Sharing

5 min Closing

10 min Exercises

MATERIALS

- rulers
- protractors
- examples of geometry in art and nature
- small mirrors, *optional*
- Pretty Pictures (W) for One step

TEACHING

This lesson gives an overview of the other lessons in the chapter and introduces symmetry. Most students will enjoy the change from the symbolic representation of algebra that the study of geometry, specifically symmetry, affords. Begin by showing or describing examples of geometry in art and nature; perhaps wear clothing exhibiting geometric patterns. Use your examples to demonstrate reflectional and rotational symmetry.

LESSON 0.1

Geometry in Nature and in Art

There is one art,
no more no less,
To do all things
with artlessness.
PIET HEIN

Nature displays a seemingly infinite variety of geometric shapes, from tiny atoms to great galaxies. Crystals, honeycombs, snowflakes, spiral shells, spiderwebs, and seed arrangements on sunflowers and pinecones are just a few of nature's geometric masterpieces.

Circle

Hexagon

Pentagon

Geometry includes the study of the properties of shapes such as circles, hexagons, and pentagons. Outlines of the sun, the moon, and the planets appear as circles. Snowflakes, honeycombs, and many crystals are hexagonal (6-sided). Many living things, such as flowers and starfish, are pentagonal (5-sided).

People observe geometric patterns in nature and use them in a variety of art forms. Basket weavers, woodworkers, and other artisans often use geometric designs to make their works more interesting and beautiful. You will learn some of their techniques in this chapter.

In the Celtic knot design above, the curves seem to weave together.

This Islamic design from Egypt uses 4-sided and 6-sided shapes, as well as 5-pointed and 12-pointed stars.

INTRODUCTION

[Language] You might discuss the etymology of *geometry*: *geo* means "earth" and *metres* means "measure." **[Context]** Geometry began as the study of earth measure; the ancient Egyptians used geometry for reestablishing land boundaries after the yearly flooding of the Nile. **[Ask]** "What other words have *geo* as a root?" [geography, geodesic, geology, geode, geocentric]

[Ask] "What words have *metry* or *metric* as a suffix?" [symmetry (measurement of similarity), chronometry (measurement of time), photometry (measurement of the intensity of light), gravimetry (measurement of the specific gravity of a solid or liquid), the metric system]

Riddle: "What did the acorn say after it grew up?" Answer: "Gee, I'm a tree." (geometry)

LESSON OBJECTIVES

- Discover geometry in nature, art, and world cultures
- Discover the characteristics of reflectional and rotational symmetry
- Set the tone with a positive, unthreatening start of the course
- Develop observational and visual thinking skills

Artists rely on geometry to show perspective and proportion, and to produce certain optical effects. Using their understanding of lines, artists can give depth to their drawings. Or they can use lines and curves to create designs that seem to pop out of the page. You will create your own optical designs in Lesson 0.4.

Hungarian artist Victor Vasarely (1908–1997) had a strong interest in geometry, which was reflected in his work. In this series, he used curved lines to produce the illusion of three spheres.

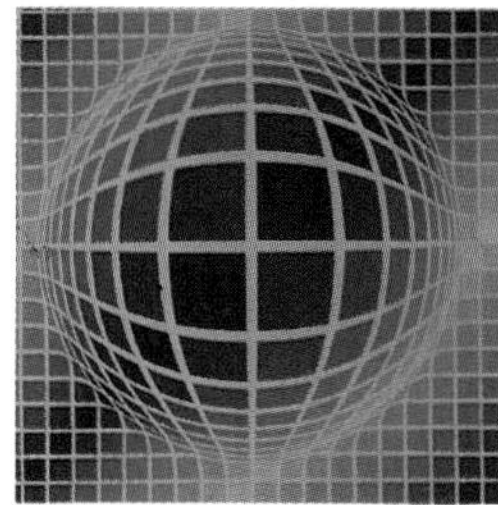

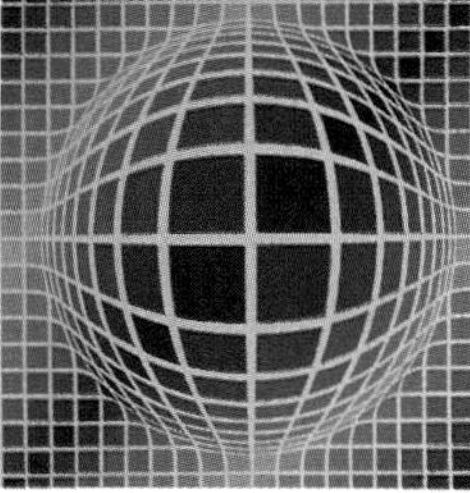

Tsiga I, II, III (1991), Victor Vasarely, courtesy of the artist.

Symmetry is a geometric characteristic of both nature and art. You may already know the two basic types of symmetry, reflectional symmetry and rotational symmetry. A design has **reflectional symmetry** if you can fold it along a **line of symmetry** so that all the points on one side of the line exactly coincide with (or match) all the points on the other side of the line.

This leaf has reflectional symmetry.

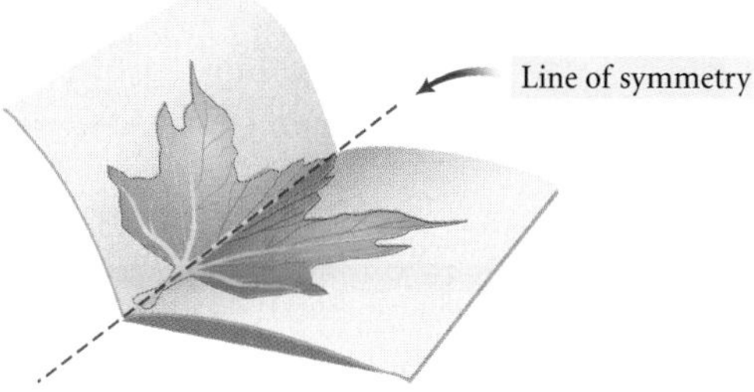

You can place a mirror on the line of symmetry so that half the figure and its mirror image re-create the original figure. So, reflectional symmetry is also called *line symmetry* or *mirror symmetry.*

An object with reflectional symmetry looks balanced. And an object with just one line of symmetry, like the human body or a butterfly, has **bilateral symmetry.**

A butterfly has one line of reflectional symmetry.

A design has **rotational symmetry** if it looks the same after you turn it around a point by less than a full circle. The number of times that the design looks the same as you turn it through a complete 360° circle determines the type of rotational symmetry. The Apache basket has 3-fold rotational symmetry because it looks the same after you rotate it 120° (a third of a circle), 240° (two-thirds of a circle), and 360° (one full circle).

This Apache basket has 3-fold rotational symmetry.

One step One-step investigations allow your students to construct mathematical knowledge in the context of a single rich problem while you play the role of consultant. For this lesson, you might hand out the Pretty Pictures worksheet and ask "What characteristics do these figures have that make them pretty, nice, balanced, regular?" (Or you might make up your own transparency of familiar organizational logos or the happy face. Include examples of reflectional symmetry that is not bilateral, of bilateral symmetry, and of rotational symmetry.) You might have available some small mirrors, rulers, and protractors for students to use as they wish. As students (in groups or as a class) try to articulate the ideas in their own words, be encouraging, praising all attempts, but resist telling. Challenge students to try a variety of ideas. When appropriate (perhaps after some time), begin attaching mathematical terms to the ideas: *reflectional (mirror) symmetry, bilateral symmetry, rotational symmetry.*

Ask students, in groups or individually, to look at the pictures and test the symmetries of the various example figures. Students can use small mirrors to test the reflectional symmetries of the butterfly on page 3 and the flag on page 4. As you circulate, look for interesting ideas to be reported during Sharing.

[Language] *Optical* means "relating to the eye."

NCTM STANDARDS

CONTENT		PROCESS	
	Number		Problem Solving
	Algebra		Reasoning
✓	Geometry	✓	Communication
✓	Measurement	✓	Connections
	Data/Probability	✓	Representation

SHARING IDEAS

As students talk about the symmetry they find, ask them to specify the kind of rotational symmetry each figure has. **[Alert]** Students may need reminding that angles are measured in degrees and that there are 360° in a full circle. **[Alert]** We often say an object has "3-fold rotational symmetry." However, students are likely to think of *fold* literally. Folding an object and finding it symmetric actually indicates reflectional symmetry. Be sure students are clear on the use of *fold* in *3-fold* as meaning to rotate an object one-third of a complete rotation and see that the image looks exactly as the object looked in the original position. You might also use the phrase "symmetry under a rotation by 120°."

[Language] *Bilateral* means "two sides."

If you plan to assign Exercise 1, be sure the terms *hexagon* and *pentagon* come up during class discussion.

You might ask what *artlessness* means in the quotation that opens the lesson. In this word, *art* means "deceit" as in *artificial.* Ask students in what sense all art is deceptive and whether *truth* is the same as *factual.*

Assessing Progress

Through your observations of students' artwork, you can begin to assess their progress in understanding the various types of symmetry. Notice students who have weak motor skills; they will need more help. Also watch for students' ability to work with groups.

A starfish has 5-fold symmetry. It looks the same after you rotate it 72°, 144°, 216°, 288°, or 360°.

The square fabric has 4-fold rotational symmetry and a starfish has 5-fold rotational symmetry. What type of rotational symmetry does a circular plate have?

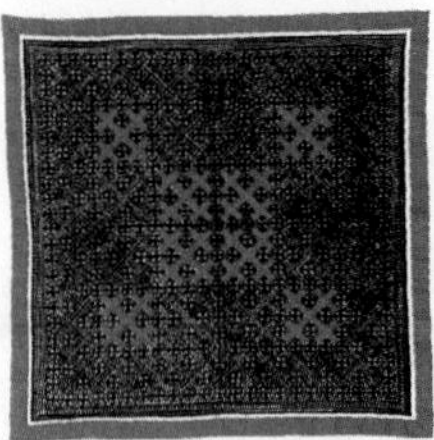

Countries throughout the world use symmetry in their national flags. Notice that the Jamaican flag has rotational symmetry in addition to two lines of reflectional symmetry. You can rotate the flag 180° without changing its appearance. The origami boxes, however, have rotational symmetry, but not reflectional symmetry. (The Apache basket on page 3 *almost* has reflectional symmetry. Can you see why it doesn't?)

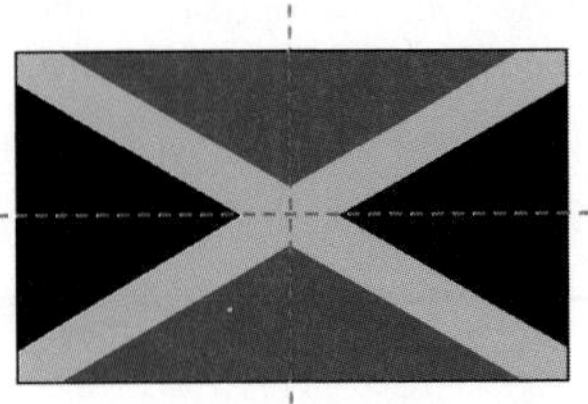

The Jamaican flag has two lines of reflectional symmetry.

If you ignore colors, the Japanese origami box on the left has 3-fold rotational symmetry. What type of symmetry does the other box have?

Consumer CONNECTION

Many products have eye-catching labels, logos, and designs. Have you ever paid more attention to a product because the geometric design of its logo was familiar or attractive to you?

EXERCISES

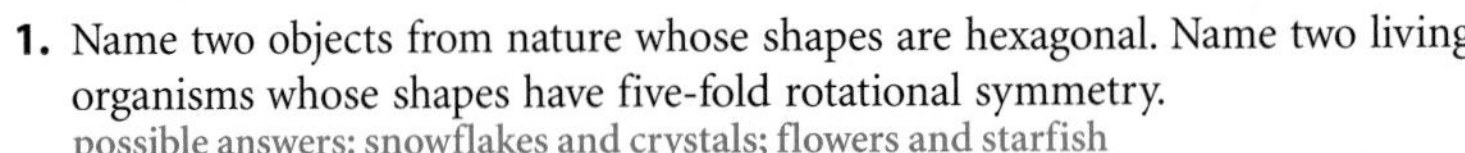

1. Name two objects from nature whose shapes are hexagonal. Name two living organisms whose shapes have five-fold rotational symmetry.
possible answers: snowflakes and crystals; flowers and starfish
2. Describe some ways that artists use geometry.
Answers might include shapes and patterns, perspective, proportions, or optical illusions.
3. Name some objects with only one line of symmetry. What is the name for this type of symmetry? Answers will vary. Bilateral symmetry.

Closing the Lesson

Quickly summarize the two major kinds of symmetry: reflectional (or mirror) symmetry, in which the figure can be folded along a line (a line of symmetry) so that each point on one side of the line matches up exactly with a point on the other side; and rotational symmetry, in which the figure looks the same after being rotated about a point in less than a full circle. Also note that a special case of reflectional symmetry is bilateral symmetry, in which the figure has only one line of symmetry. There are many kinds of rotational symmetry, through various angles.

4. Which of these objects have reflectional symmetry (or approximate reflectional symmetry)? A, B, C, and F

A.

B.

C.

D.

E.

F.

5. Which of the objects in Exercise 4 have rotational symmetry (or approximate rotational symmetry)? A, B, D, and E

6. Which of these playing cards have rotational symmetry? Which ones have reflectional symmetry? 4 of diamonds; none

7. British artist Andy Goldsworthy (b 1956) uses materials from nature to create beautiful outdoor sculptures. The artful arrangement of sticks below might appear to have rotational symmetry, but instead it has one line of reflectional symmetry. Can you find the line of symmetry? ⓗ The line of reflection is a line along the surface of the lake.

If an exercise has an ⓗ at the end, you can find a hint to help you in Hints for Selected Exercises at the back of the book.

For the title of this outdoor sculpture by Andy Goldsworthy, see the hint to Exercise 7 in the Hints section.

Courtesy of the artist and Galerie Lelong, New York.

BUILDING UNDERSTANDING

The exercises focus on applying knowledge of reflectional, bilateral, and rotational symmetry. Exercises 10 and 11 encourage students to begin looking at their environment in a new way.

ASSIGNING HOMEWORK

Essential	1, 3, 4, 5, 10, 11
Portfolio	8, 9
Journal	2
Group	6, 7

▶ Helping with the Exercises

Exercise 4 Students may not notice that some of the rounded corners on the triangular sections in D are more rounded than others; they may therefore say D has reflectional symmetry.

8. One line of symmetry is a vertical line through the middle of the Taj Mahal, and the other is a horizontal line between the Taj Mahal and the reflecting pool. The pool reflects the building, giving the scene more reflectional symmetry than the building itself has.

Exercise 9 If you have some pattern blocks, students might find them useful for this exercise.

9. Designs will vary, but all should have 2-fold rotational symmetry.

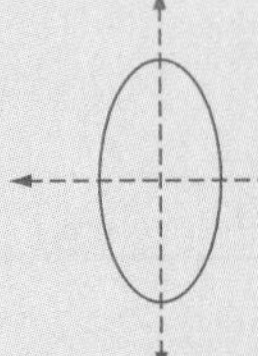

2 lines of reflectional symmetry

It is impossible to have 2 lines of reflectional symmetry without rotational symmetry.

Exercises 10, 11 Students could vote on the most creative geometric objects or the most interesting clothing that displays geometric art.

EXTENSIONS

A. Pose this problem: Look at cross sections of various fruits and vegetables. Categorize them by shape, symmetry, or some other attribute.

B. Ask students to discuss how human bilateral symmetry facilitates motion and other activities.

C. Show the collection of slides from NCTM's *Geometry in Our World.*

D. Origami can be used to help students understand many geometry concepts. You might choose an extension activity from *Unfolding Mathematics with Unit Origami* by Betsy Franco.

8. Shah Jahan, Mughal emperor of India from 1628 to 1658, had the beautiful Taj Mahal built in memory of his wife, Mumtaz Mahal. Its architect, Ustad Ahmad Lahori, designed it with perfect symmetry. Describe two lines of symmetry in this photo. How does the design of the building's grounds give this view of the Taj Mahal even more symmetry than the building itself has?

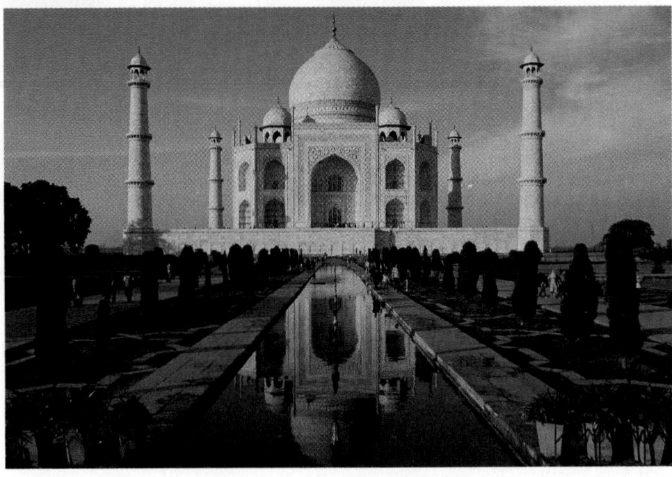

The Taj Mahal in Agra, India, was described by the poet Rabindranath Tagore as "rising above the banks of the river like a solitary tear suspended on the cheek of time."

9. Create a simple design that has two lines of reflectional symmetry. Does it have rotational symmetry? Next, try to create another design with two lines of reflectional symmetry, but without rotational symmetry. Any luck?

10. Bring to class an object from nature that shows geometry. Describe the geometry that you find in the object as well as any symmetry the object has. Answers will vary.

11. Bring an object to school or wear something that displays a form of handmade or manufactured geometric art. Describe any symmetry the object has. Answers will vary.

IMPROVING YOUR VISUAL THINKING SKILLS

Pickup Sticks

Pickup sticks is a good game for developing motor skills, but you can turn it into a challenging visual puzzle. In what order should you pick up the sticks so that you are always removing the top stick?

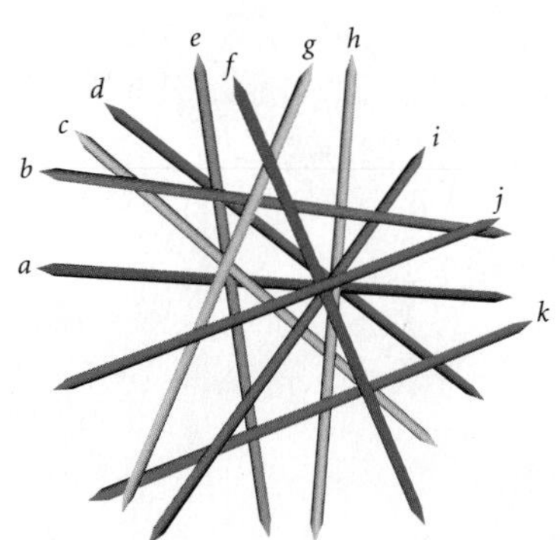

IMPROVING VISUAL THINKING SKILLS

Encourage students to look first only at the top stick, mentally remove it, and visualize what stick can be removed next, continuing as long as they can. When they get stuck, you might challenge them to build the drawing with toothpicks, keeping notes on how the pile was built. Then you could have them write a narrative explaining how they built it and how they should dismantle it.

The order of removal is *j, f, g, b, i, k, h, c, e, a, d.*

LESSON 0.2

Line Designs

The symmetry and patterns in geometric designs make them very appealing. You can make many designs using the basic tools of geometry—**compass** and **straightedge.**

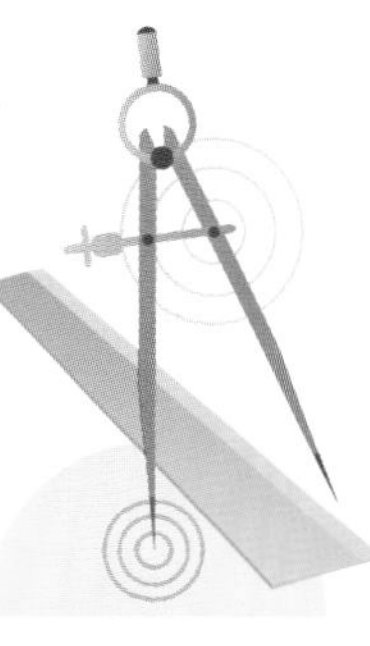

You'll use a straightedge to construct straight lines and a compass to construct circles and to mark off equal distances. A straightedge is like a ruler but it has no marks. You can use the edge of a ruler as a straightedge. The straightedge and the compass are the classical construction tools used by the ancient Greeks, who laid the foundations of the geometry that you are studying.

We especially need imagination in science. It is not all mathematics, nor all logic, but it is somewhat beauty and poetry.

MARIA MITCHELL

Japanese design is known for its simple, clean lines.

The complementary line designs on the arched ceiling and tile floor make this building lobby look grandiose.

Notice how the patterns of these Guatemalan rugs are a non-uniform and dynamic arrangement of lines.

Some of the lines in this mosaic appear to be tied in knots!

NCTM STANDARDS

CONTENT		PROCESS	
	Number	✓	Problem Solving
	Algebra	✓	Reasoning
✓	Geometry		Communication
✓	Measurement	✓	Connections
	Data/Probability	✓	Representation

LESSON OBJECTIVES

- Create line designs with straightedges
- Give students an appreciation for geometry

LESSON 0.2

PLANNING

LESSON OUTLINE

One day:

20 min Investigation

10 min Sharing

5 min Closing

10 min Exercises

MATERIALS

- construction tools
- protractors
- graph paper
- colored pens or pencils
- Curves by Lines (W) for One step
- Astrid and 8-pointed Star (W), *optional*

TEACHING

In this lesson, students learn that the straightedge tool is different from a ruler and that curves can be simulated by a set of straight lines. Students "measure" by comparing segments, not by using a standard unit system.

INTRODUCTION

Give students a chance to "show and tell" some of the objects they brought in as part of the assignment from Lesson 0.1. Depending on how group work went in the previous lesson, you might want to talk about norms and expectations for teamwork, such as: Should groups discuss every question? Should they agree on an answer before writing it down? Does each student write down the answers in his or her notebook? See Teaching with Cooperative Groups (page xxxii) for more details.

One step Hand out a copy of the Curves by Lines worksheet to each group and ask each student to try drawing the Astrid using only a straightedge and a pencil. They may discuss their work with their groups, but each student should produce a separate figure. As you circulate, note interesting approaches for later presentations. Resist talking except to encourage diverse approaches. Watch to see who, if anyone, actually uses the terms *reflectional symmetry* and *rotational symmetry,* and be aware of students' different levels of understanding. If a group finishes early, ask the group members to try to construct the 8-pointed star, again using only a straightedge, or to make their own design.

For more structure, demonstrate to the class how to construct a line design. Then have students follow the steps to create the Astrid and the 8-pointed star while you circulate to check on their progress. **[Alert]** Some students may have difficulty connecting the final product with the steps needed to draw it. Ask questions that will help students understand a good place to start. A transparency of Astrid and 8-pointed Star can be used during Sharing.

SHARING IDEAS

Select some students to share their approaches or samples of line designs. Ask how to make curves from straight lines. If some students planned their work in stages, ask how they determined what their final drawing would look like. Ask what kinds of symmetry the various figures have. You might also lead a discussion of whether or not the curves appearing in these figures are really curves. **[Language]** In mathematics the category *curve* includes a line (a straight line is a special case of a curve). On the other hand, in art the word *line* includes curves.

You can create many types of designs using only straight lines. Here are two line designs and the steps for creating each one.

The Astrid **The 8-pointed Star**

The Astrid

Step 1 Step 2 Step 3 Step 4

The 8-pointed Star

Step 1 Step 2 Step 3 Step 4

EXERCISES

1. What are the classical construction tools of geometry? compass and straightedge
2. Create a line design from this lesson. Color your design.
   Answer will be the Astrid or 8-pointed star, possibly with variations.
3. Each of these line designs uses straight lines only. Select one design and re-create it on a sheet of paper. ⓗ Answers will be a design from among the three choices.

4. Describe the symmetries of the three designs in Exercise 3. For the third design, does color matter?

The lines that seem to form a curve are related. Foreshadow the notion of a geometric transformation. **[Ask]** "How might one line be changed repeatedly to make the others?" [It is rotated and stretched.]

You might also mention that designs made primarily with lines can be found in many cultures around the world. You can point out examples in the student book, or bring in some of your own.

Assessing Progress

As you observe groups and individuals at work and presenting, look for ability in identifying the kinds of symmetry discussed in Lesson 0.1. Watch for skill at working with groups and taking the initiative in investigations.

Closing the Lesson

Remind students of the two central ideas of this lesson: that a **straightedge** is different from a ruler and that straight lines can appear to make curves.

5. Many quilt designers create beautiful geometric patterns with reflectional symmetry. One-fourth of a 4-by-4 quilt pattern and its reflection are shown at right. Copy the designs onto graph paper, and complete the 4-by-4 pattern so that it has two lines of reflectional symmetry. Color your quilt.

6. Geometric patterns seem to be in motion in a quilt design with rotational symmetry. Copy the 4-by-4 quilt piece shown in Exercise 5 onto graph paper, and complete the quilt pattern so that it has 4-fold rotational symmetry. Color your quilt.

0.1 7. Organic molecules have geometric shapes. How many different lines of reflectional symmetry does this benzene molecule have? How about rotational symmetry? Sketch your answers.

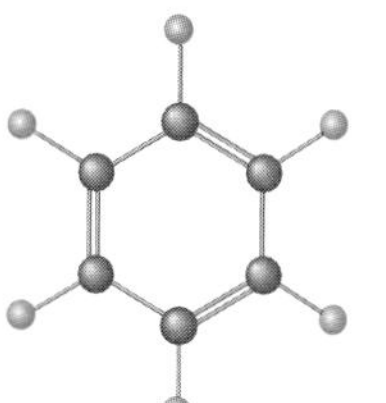

Benzene molecule

Architecture CONNECTION

Frank Lloyd Wright (1867–1959) is often called America's favorite architect. He built homes in 36 states—sometimes in unusual settings. *Fallingwater,* located in Pennsylvania, is a building designed by Wright that displays his obvious love of geometry. Can you describe the geometry you see? Find more information on Frank Lloyd Wright at www.keymath.com/DG .

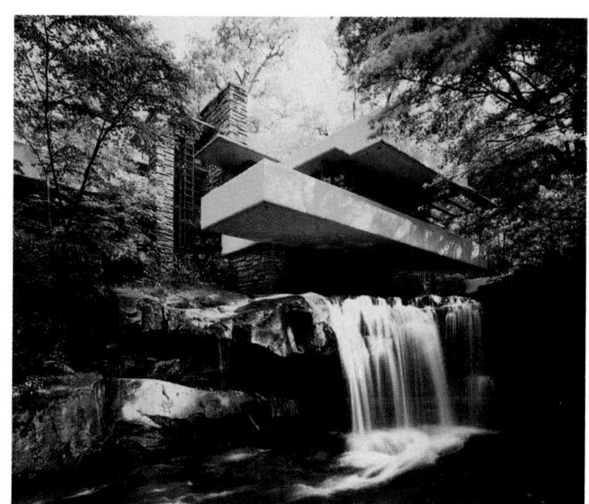

IMPROVING YOUR ALGEBRA SKILLS

Pyramid Puzzle I

Place four different numbers in the bubbles at the vertices of the pyramid so that the two numbers at the ends of each edge or diagonal add up to the number on that edge.

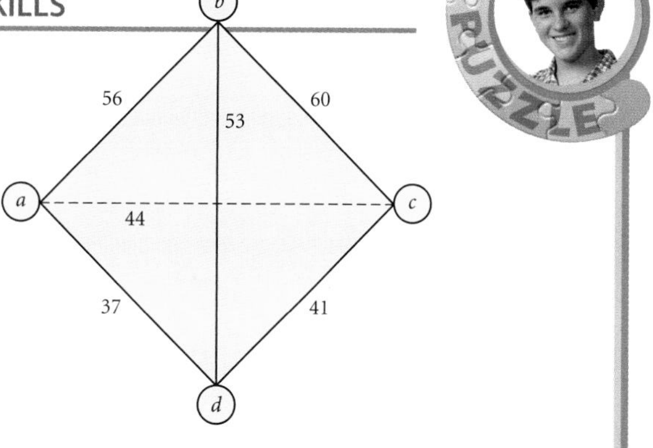

IMPROVING ALGEBRA SKILLS

Students who don't remember how to work with systems of equations may find this puzzle especially challenging. You might challenge them to use the given information to find a difference, such as $b - c = 12$, and then see if they can put the difference together with the sum of the same two variables to get the value of one variable.

The values are $a = 20$, $b = 36$, $c = 24$, $d = 17$.

BUILDING UNDERSTANDING

Besides giving practice using the straightedge, these exercises review the ideas of symmetry.

ASSIGNING HOMEWORK

Essential	1, 3, 4, 6
Performance assessment	2
Portfolio	5
Review	7

Helping with the Exercises

Exercise 2 Alternatively, students may use a line design they find from another source.

4. The first design has 4-fold symmetry and four lines of reflectional symmetry. The triangle has 3-fold rotational symmetry and three lines of reflectional symmetry. The third design has 6-fold rotational symmetry if you ignore color and 2-fold rotational symmetry if you don't.

Exercise 7 [Alert] The model appears at first to have 6-fold symmetry, but the three double bonds give it only 3-fold symmetry.

EXTENSIONS

A. Challenge students to create line designs by stringing thread systematically on nails equally spaced in a circle, an ellipse, a square, or any other shape on a piece of plywood, tagboard, or cardboard.

B. Have students create line designs using geometry software on the computer or on the calculator. **[Link]** Some of these designs can lead to a discussion of conic sections, studied in more advanced mathematics classes.

See page 767 for answers to Exercises 5–7.

LESSON

0.3

PLANNING

LESSON OUTLINE

One day:

25 min Investigation

5 min Sharing

5 min Closing

10 min Exercises

MATERIALS

- construction tools
- colored pens or pencils

TEACHING

Circle designs consist primarily of circles. **[Language]** *Circular* is an adjective used to describe something that is round or moves in a circle. When *circle* is used as an adjective as in "circle designs," it means that the noun it modifies contains circles.

One step Ask each student to draw his or her own version of the circle design on page 11 created by Schuyler Smith. Students may use only a compass and straightedge. They may consult with their groups but should produce their own copy. As you circulate, begin to use the word *radius.* You may need to suggest that students mark one point on the larger circle and then repeatedly mark off a radius around the circle beginning at that point. You may also need to offer tips on using the compass. (See page 1B.) Otherwise, don't say much. Watch for and encourage the independent use of the notions of symmetry. Anyone finishing early can start on the 12-petal daisy and the field of daisies. (For these designs they may use a ruler to find midpoints.)

LESSON 0.3

Circle Designs

It's where we go, and what we do when we get there, that tells us who we are.
JOYCE CAROL OATES

People have always been fascinated by circles. Circles are used in the design of mosaics, baskets, and ceramics, as well as in the architectural design of buildings.

Chinese pottery

Palestinian cloth

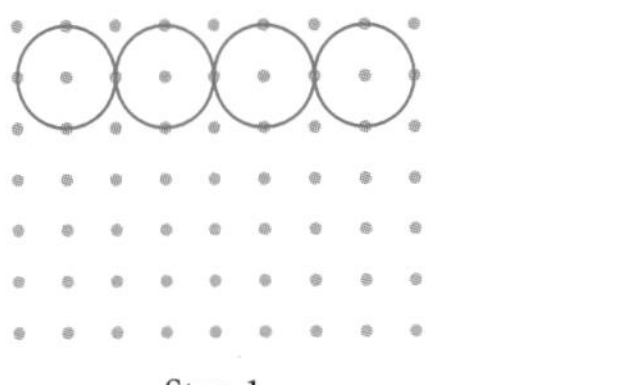

Circular window

You can make circle designs with a compass as your primary tool. For example, here is a design you can make on a square dot grid.

Begin with a 7-by-9 square dot grid. Construct three rows of four circles.

Step 1

Step 2

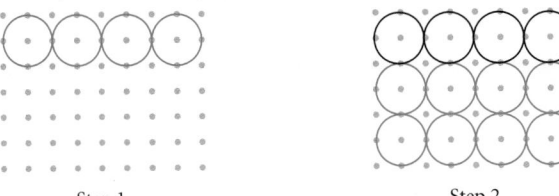

Construct two rows of three circles using the points between the first set of circles as centers. The result is a set of six circles overlapping the original 12 circles. Decorate your design.

Step 3

Step 4

LESSON OBJECTIVES

- Create circle designs with a compass
- Construct regular hexagons with a compass and straightedge
- Practice using construction tools

NCTM STANDARDS

CONTENT		PROCESS	
✓	Number		Problem Solving
	Algebra	✓	Reasoning
✓	Geometry		Communication
✓	Measurement	✓	Connections
	Data/Probability	✓	Representation

Here is another design that you can make using only a compass. Start by constructing a circle, then select any point on it. Without changing your compass setting, swing an arc centered at the selected point. Swing an arc with each of the two new points as centers, and so on.

The Daisy

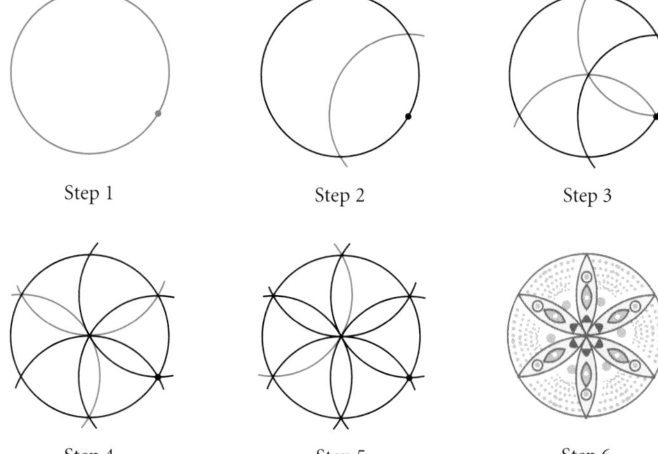

Step 1 Step 2 Step 3

Step 4 Step 5 Step 6

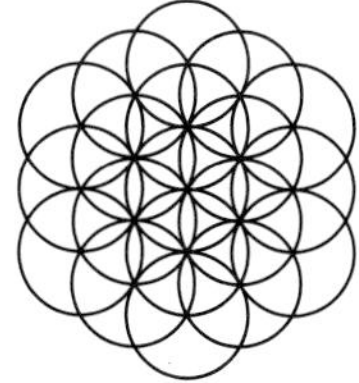

Instead of stopping at the perimeter of the first circle, you can continue to swing full circles. Then you get a "field of daisies," as shown above.

Notice the shape you get by connecting the six petal tips of the daisy. This is a **regular hexagon,** a 6-sided figure whose sides are the same length and whose angles are all the same size.

You can do many variations on a daisy design.

12-petal daisy

Field of daisies

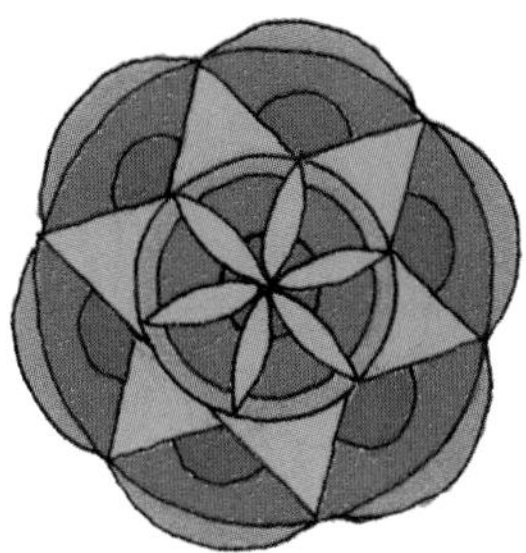

Combination line and circle design (Can you see how it was made?)

Schuyler Smith, geometry student

For more structure, you may demonstrate how to draw a daisy design. Then ask students to create one of the designs on page 11.

[Alert] Be aware that incorporating more than one type of symmetry can be difficult for many students.

SHARING IDEAS

Try to select students who haven't presented before to show their work. If they don't mention it, ask about the kinds of symmetry their designs have. Most will have rotational symmetry; ask how many fold it is. **[Ask]** "Can the design be changed to make rotational symmetry of a different kind?" As needed, point out that coloring can change the symmetry, perhaps removing reflectional symmetry while keeping rotational symmetry.

Elicit the observation that connecting consecutive tips of the daisies with line segments forms a regular hexagon. Remind students that a hexagon has six sides. To preview Chapter 1, you might say that this hexagon is *regular* because it has equal sides and equal angles. **[Ask]** "What design would be formed if alternate corners were connected?" [equilateral triangle] "What shape would be formed if both sets of alternate corners were connected?" [6-pointed star] Point out the regular hexagon in the middle of the 6-pointed star; it is rotated from the original. If time permits, explore together starting with more points on the circle and skipping other numbers of points in making the connections. Look at the patterns formed when odd numbers of points are skipped and when even numbers of points are skipped.

You might also tie this lesson to the previous one by asking if the apparent curves formed by the lines in the Curves by Lines worksheet are arcs of circles and, if so, what their radius is.

Students can also use the dynamic geometry exploration at www.keymath.com/DG to explore how to use a compass or geometry software to construct daisy designs.

Assessing Progress

Watch for familiarity with the kinds of symmetry, ability to use tools precisely, ability to work with a group, and responsibility in working on an investigation.

Closing the Lesson

As needed, remind students that the **radius** of a circle is the distance from the center to the circumference. Formalize the fact that if a radius is marked off consecutively around the circle's circumference the sixth mark will coincide with the beginning mark. Connecting the marks makes a **regular hexagon**—a 6-sided figure whose sides are the same length and whose angles have the same measure. Coloring can affect the symmetry of a figure.

BUILDING UNDERSTANDING

The exercises focus on making designs with a compass and finding regular hexagons in those designs.

ASSIGNING HOMEWORK

Essential	1, 2, 4, 5
Performance assessment	3

MATERIALS

- isometric and square dot paper

▶Helping with the Exercises

1. Design with reflectional symmetry is drawn on this background.

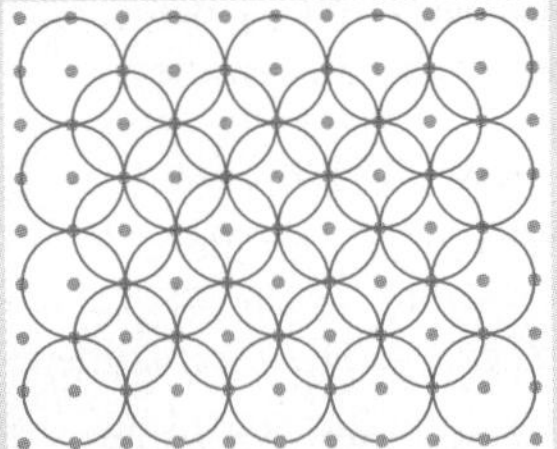

Exercise 2 You may need to hand out isometric dot paper or at least explain that it has dots on a triangular grid. **[Language]** *Isometric* means "same measure." In isometric dot paper the distance between adjacent dots is always the same. Using isometric dot grids early helps students develop skills that will be needed in later visual thinking activities.

2. Design should have rotational symmetry. Possible answer:

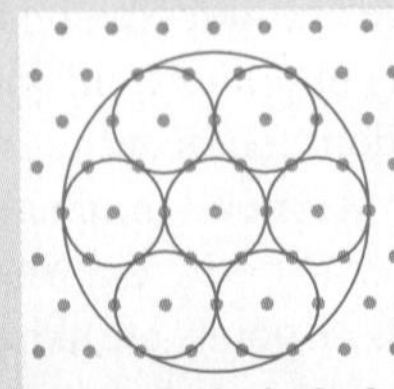

Exercise 5 This exercise previews the tessellations of Lesson 0.6.

See page 767 for answer to Exercise 4.

EXERCISES

You will need

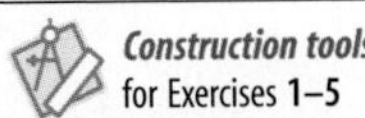
Construction tools
for Exercises 1–5

▶ For Exercises 1–5, use your construction tools.

1. Use square dot paper to create a 4-by-5 grid of 20 circles, and 12 circles overlapping them. Color or shade the design so that it has reflectional symmetry.

2. Use your compass to create a set of seven identical circles that touch but do not overlap. Draw a larger circle that encloses the seven circles. Color or shade your design so that it has rotational symmetry. ⓗ

This rose window at the National Cathedral in Washington, D.C. has a central design of seven circles enclosed in a larger circle.

3. Create a 6-petal daisy design and color or shade it so that it has rotational symmetry, but not reflectional symmetry.

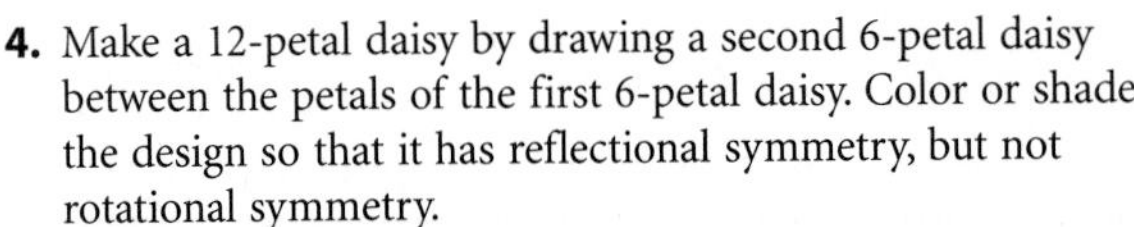

4. Make a 12-petal daisy by drawing a second 6-petal daisy between the petals of the first 6-petal daisy. Color or shade the design so that it has reflectional symmetry, but not rotational symmetry.

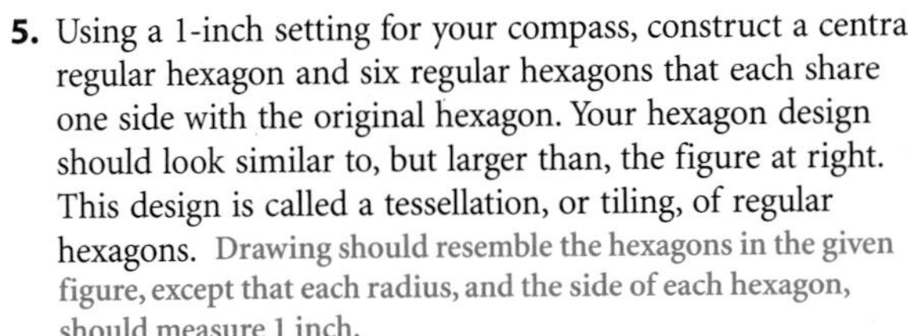

5. Using a 1-inch setting for your compass, construct a central regular hexagon and six regular hexagons that each share one side with the original hexagon. Your hexagon design should look similar to, but larger than, the figure at right. This design is called a tessellation, or tiling, of regular hexagons. Drawing should resemble the hexagons in the given figure, except that each radius, and the side of each hexagon, should measure 1 inch.

IMPROVING YOUR ALGEGRA SKILLS

PUZZLE

Algebraic Magic Squares I

A magic square is an arrangement of numbers in a square grid. The numbers in every row, column, or diagonal add up to the same number. For example, in the magic square on the left, the sum of each row, column, and diagonal is 18.

Complete the 5-by-5 magic square on the right. Use only the numbers in this list: 6, 7, 9, 13, 17, 21, 23, 24, 27, and 28.

5	10	3
4	6	8
9	2	7

20			8	14
	19	25	26	
	12	18		30
29	10	11		
22			15	16

3. possible answer:

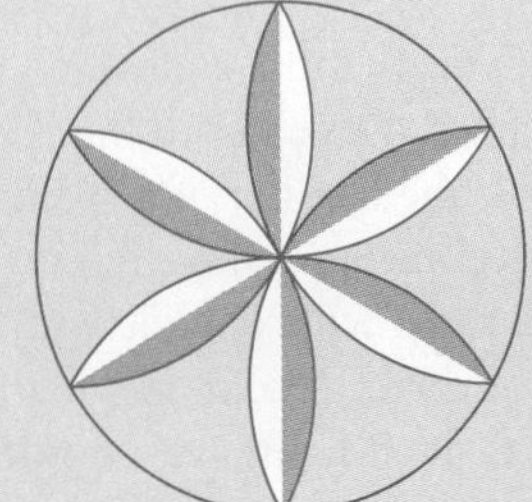

IMPROVING ALGEBRA SKILLS

To help struggling students, **[Ask]** "What will be the sum of each row?" [90 because one diagonal sums to 90]

20	21	27	8	14
13	19	25	26	7
6	12	18	24	30
29	10	11	17	23
22	28	9	15	16

LESSON 0.4

Op Art

Everything is an illusion, including this notion.

STANISLAW J. LEC

Op art, or optical art, is a form of abstract art that uses lines or geometric patterns to create a special visual effect. The contrasting dark and light regions sometimes appear to be in motion or to represent a change in surface, direction, and dimension. Victor Vasarely was one artist who transformed grids so that spheres seem to bulge from them. Recall the series *Tsiga I, II,* and *III* that appears in Lesson 0.1. *Harlequin,* shown at right, is a rare Vasarely work that includes a human form. Still, you can see Vasarely's trademark sphere in the clown's bulging belly.

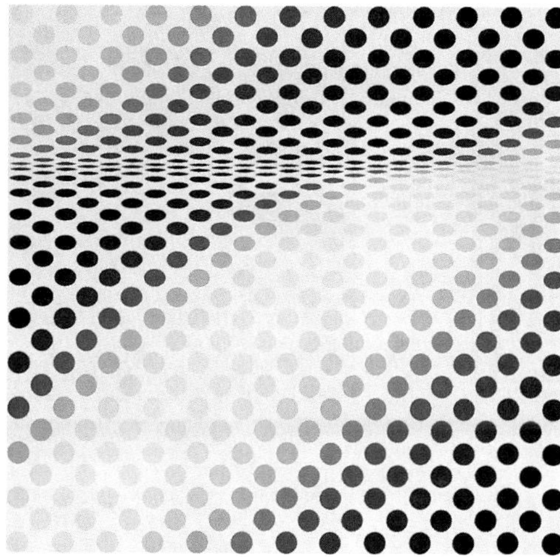

In *Hesitate,* by contemporary op artist Bridget Riley (b 1931), what effect do the changing dots produce?

Harlequin, Victor Vasarely, courtesy of the artist.

In *Harlequin,* Victor Vasarely used curved lines and shading to create the form of a clown in motion.

Op art is fun and easy to create. To create one kind of op art design, first make a design in outline. Next, draw horizontal or vertical lines, gradually varying the space between the lines to create an illusion of hills and valleys. Finally, color in alternating spaces.

The Wavy Letter

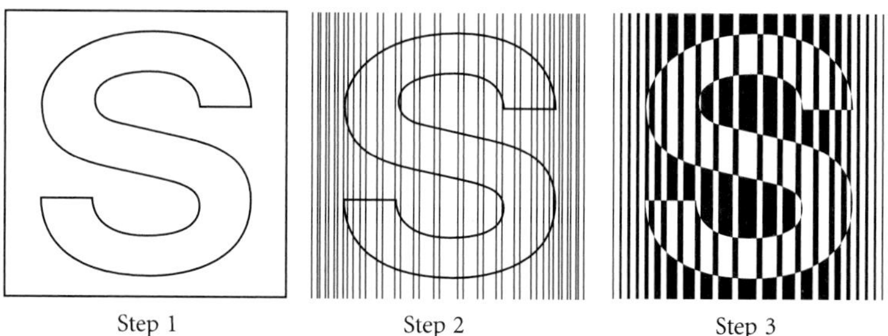

NCTM STANDARDS

CONTENT		PROCESS	
✓	Number		Problem Solving
	Algebra	✓	Reasoning
✓	Geometry		Communication
	Measurement	✓	Connections
	Data/Probability	✓	Representation

LESSON OBJECTIVES

- Create optical art using geometry tools
- Introduce students to examples of optical art
- Use the straightedge and compass together

LESSON 0.4

PLANNING

LESSON OUTLINE

One day:

25 min	Investigation
10 min	Sharing
5 min	Closing
5 min	Exercises

MATERIALS

- construction tools
- colored pens or pencils
- examples of optical art, *optional*

TEACHING

Making optical art (op art) allows students to use construction tools while reviewing ideas of symmetry. Encourage creativity—this will help students improve visual thinking skills and the stepwise problem solving needed for deduction.

INTRODUCTION

Discuss the changing dots of *Hesitate.* Use this and other pieces of art to help students recognize clues in two-dimensional drawings that contribute three-dimensional illusions.

[Ask] "Does the *Harlequin* painting suggest any illusion?" **[Language]** The *op* in op art is short for *optical,* meaning "of the eye." Op art tricks the part of the brain that interprets signals from the eye. The brain might keep changing how it interprets a pattern, or it may tell you there is motion or non-existent dots or depth.

One step Pose this problem: "Discuss with your group what the illusion is in each example on pages 13 and 14 and what contributes to that illusion. Then plan an op art picture of your own—a design that has at least one kind of symmetry—and make it if there is time. The more planning you do, the better your final product will be."

For students who need more structure, lead a class discussion about the optical illusions in the examples and the symmetry in each. Then have students follow the steps to make one or both pictures in the student book.

SHARING IDEAS

Select for presentation a few student works that incorporate various types of symmetry, and be sure the symmetry is discussed. You might ask what op art techniques convey depth.

You might ask for students' opinions about the quotation that opens the lesson. The statement is an example of "self-reference," a powerful tool in twentieth-century mathematics and art. Do students think it's funny? If not, you might try "An optical illusion isn't really an illusion; it just looks like one."

Assessing Progress
Check for students' skill at using a straightedge and a compass and for their familiarity with kinds of symmetry. Also watch for group participation and investigation skills.

Closing the Lesson

The primary idea of this lesson is that you can use various kinds of symmetry in op art to suggest depth and other illusions.

To create the next design, first locate a point on each of the four sides of a square. Each point should be the same distance from a corner, as shown. Your compass is a good tool for measuring equal lengths. Connect these four points to create another square within the first. Repeat the process until the squares appear to converge on the center. Be careful that you don't fall in!

The Square Spiral

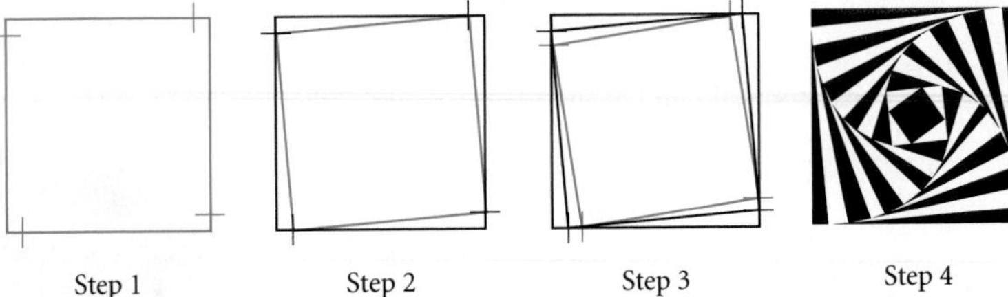

Here are some other examples of op art.

Square tunnel or top of pyramid?

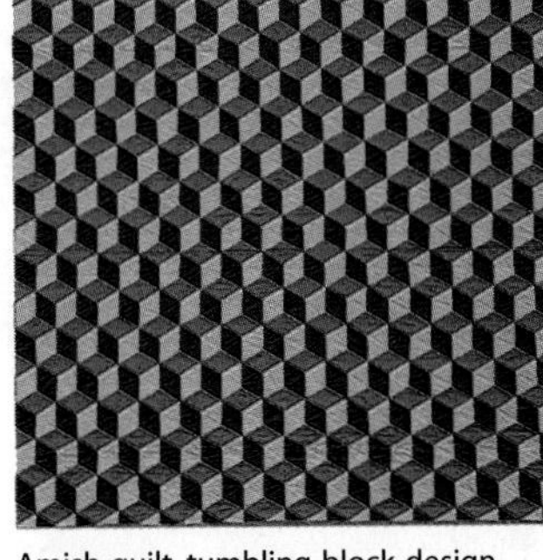

Amish quilt, tumbling block design

Japanese Op Art, Hajime Juchi, Dover Publications

Op art by Carmen Apodaca, geometry student

You can create any of the designs on this page using just a compass and straightedge (and doing some careful coloring). Can you figure out how each of these op art designs was created?

Solving Bagels
Many students have difficulty with Bagels because they fail to recognize the value of negative information. They tend to think that "wrong" is the same as "bad." For example, Clue 1 (bagels) narrows the possibilities considerably by eliminating any use of the digits 1, 2, and 3 in Game 1 and the digits 9, 0, and 8 in Game 2.

Some students may also have trouble thinking of what possibilities remain. For example, the next two clues in Game 1 say that only two of the remaining digits are used; the fact that no digit is repeated means that the digit 0 is definitely included.

Students must also remember to keep looking back and reinterpreting previous information as more is learned. Clue 3 in Game 2 says that 3 and 7 are both in the solution because Clue 1 already eliminated 8. Because 7 is not in the correct place in Clue 5, it must be the *pico,* not the *fermi,* in Clue 3.

EXERCISES

1. What is the optical effect in each piece of art in this lesson?

2. Nature creates its own optical art. At first the black and white stripes of a zebra appear to work against it, standing out against the golden brown grasses of the African plain. However, the stripes do provide the zebras with very effective protection from predators. When and how?

3. Select one type of op art design from this lesson and create your own version of it. Designs will vary.

4. Create an op art design that has reflectional symmetry, but not rotational symmetry. Designs will vary.

5. Antoni Gaudí (1852–1926) designed the Bishop's Palace in Astorga, Spain. List as many geometric shapes as you can recognize on the palace (flat, two-dimensional shapes such as rectangles as well as solid, three-dimensional shapes such as cylinders). What type of symmetry do you see on the palace?

Bishop's Palace, Astorga, Spain

IMPROVING YOUR REASONING SKILLS

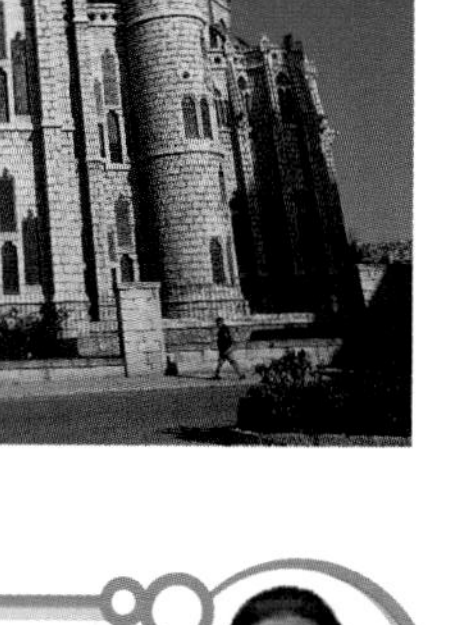

Bagels

In the original computer game of bagels, a player determines a three-digit number (no digit repeated) by making educated guesses. After each guess, the computer gives a clue about the guess. Here are the clues.

bagels: no digit is correct

pico: one digit is correct but in the wrong position

fermi: one digit is correct and in the correct position

In each of the games below, a number of guesses have been made, with the clue for each guess shown to its right. From the given set of guesses and clues, determine the three-digit number. If there is more than one solution, find them all.

Game 1:			Game 2:		
	1 2 3	*bagels*		9 0 8	*bagels*
	4 5 6	*pico*		1 3 4	*pico*
	7 8 9	*pico*		3 8 7	*pico fermi*
	0 7 5	*pico fermi*		2 5 6	*fermi*
	0 8 7	*pico*		2 3 7	*pico pico*
	? ? ?			? ? ?	

BUILDING UNDERSTANDING

The exercises reinforce the idea of symmetry in op art.

ASSIGNING HOMEWORK

Essential	1, 2
Performance assessment	3
Portfolio	4
Group	5

Helping with the Exercises

Exercises 3, 4 If you assign both of these exercises, you might stipulate that only one of the two need be a "finished" work of art.

Exercise 5 [Context] The style of nineteenth-century European art and architecture was changing at the turn of the twentieth century, making the climate right for Gaudí's unique and often outlandish style. The palace has neo-Gothic (medieval) elements as well as elements of the emerging art nouveau style, but it is still very "Gaudí." Some of Gaudí's designs would be great for student projects.

5. Possible answers: 2-D: rectangle, triangle, trapezoid; 3-D: cylinder, cone, prism. The palace facade has one line of reflectional symmetry (bilateral symmetry).

See page 767 for answers to Exercises 1 and 2.

IMPROVING REASONING SKILLS

Continuing the solution for Game 1 from the information in Solving Bagels on page 14, you see that Clue 4 says that one—but not both—of the other digits must be 7 or 5. Because 0 is definitely included, 0 is the digit referred to by the next clue, so 7 and 8 are eliminated. By previous clues, Clue 2 eliminates 4 and 6, and Clue 3 verifies that the third digit is 9. The three digits, then, are 0, 5, and 9. All clues can be reexamined to determine where the digits are. By the last given clue, 0 is not in the first place. So *fermi* in the previous clue must be referring to 5. (This is verified by the second clue.) Hence 0 is in the middle and 9 is at the beginning. That is, the unique solution is 905.

For Game 2, the unique solution is 376.

LESSON

0.5

PLANNING

LESSON OUTLINE

One day:

25 min Investigation

10 min Sharing

5 min Closing

5 min Exercises

MATERIALS

- construction tools
- graph paper
- a drawing template, *optional*
- colored pens or pencils
- books or slides of knot designs
- Nigerian Knot (T) for One step

TEACHING

Lines and circles are the components of designs that resemble abstract ropes or rings woven together. The three-dimensional illusion of the designs comes in part from erasing lines that represent hidden edges.

One step Show the Nigerian Knot transparency and ask students to draw it for themselves using a straightedge and compass. (Alternatively, they might create their own design that requires both tools.) Do not insist that the inside corners of the square be curved, but help students as needed to find an appropriate radius for the outside corners. (You might wonder aloud how to find the center of a square, but you needn't explain about diagonals.) Don't push too hard at this point to have the lines hidden appropriately, but note several different results for later presentation. If someone notes that tiny gaps in lines indicate

LESSON 0.5

Knot Designs

In the old days, a love-sick sailor might send his sweetheart a length of fishline loosely tied in a love knot. If the knot was returned pulled tight it meant the passion was strong. But if the knot was returned untied—ah, matey, time to ship out.

OLD SAILOR'S TALE

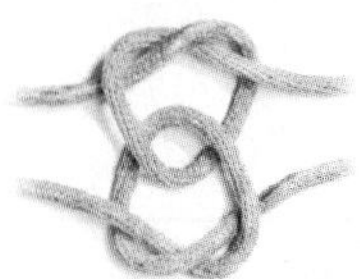

Knot designs are geometric designs that appear to weave or to interlace like a knot. Some of the earliest known designs are found in Celtic art from the northern regions of England and Scotland. In their carved stone designs, the artists imitated the rich geometric patterns of three-dimensional crafts such as weaving and basketry. The *Book of Kells* (8th and 9th centuries) is the most famous collection of Celtic knot designs.

Celtic knot design

Carved knot pattern from Nigeria

Today a very familiar knot design is the set of interconnected rings (shown at right) used as the logo for the Olympic Games.

Here are the steps for creating two examples of knot designs. Look them over before you begin the exercises.

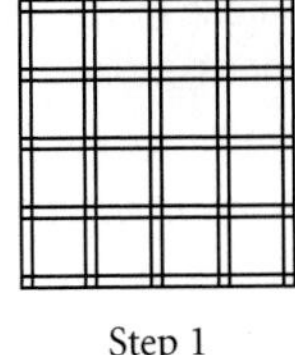

Step 1

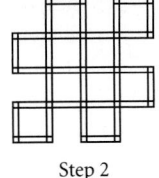

Step 2

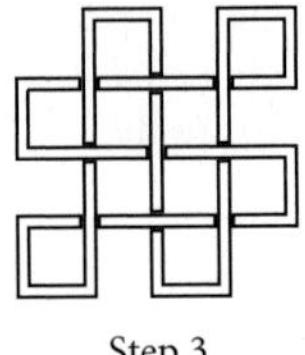

Step 3

Step 4

You can use a similar approach to create a knot design with rings.

Step 1

Step 2

Step 3

Step 4

that they're passing under other lines, have them present their observation during Sharing. (This kind of overlapping, called *occlusion,* is used by artists to create depth on a flat surface.)

LESSON OBJECTIVES

- Explore geometric patterns in knot designs
- Demonstrate cultural ties to geometric art
- Visualize three dimensions on a flat surface
- Represent three dimensions on a flat surface
- Practice using geometry tools
- Use dashed or hidden lines to represent edges of three-dimensional objects

Here are some more examples of knot designs.

Knot design by Scott Shanks, geometry student

Tiger Tail, Diane Cassell, parent of geometry student

Medieval Russian knot design

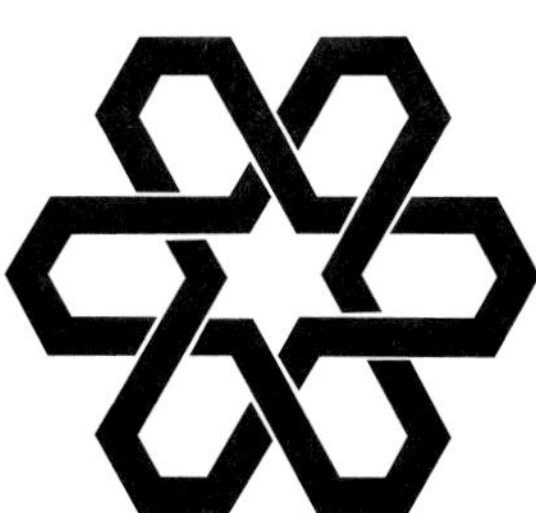

Japanese knot design

The last woodcut made by M. C. Escher is a knot design called *Snakes.* The rings and the snakes interlace, and the design has 3-fold rotational symmetry.

Snakes, M. C. Escher, 1969/

For more structure, you might first demonstrate how to create simple knot designs, giving special attention to erasing lines that represent hidden edges. Then have students follow the steps to construct the designs in the student book. If necessary, you might prepare a template for some students to follow.

SHARING IDEAS

Again, try to choose students who haven't presented before but who show a range of approaches. Ask how they decided what lines not to draw or what lines to erase. You might have other students add their work to the class art gallery. Encourage creativity even when not well executed, but remark on how precision contributes to illusion and general visual appearance.

Ask about the symmetry of various knot designs. Students may suggest reflectional symmetry that exists only if the crossings are ignored. Rotational symmetry is probably more common among knot designs. Challenge students to produce designs with reflectional symmetry.

Assessing Progress

As you circulate and observe presentations, note ability to visualize depth, facility with straightedge and compass, familiarity with kinds of symmetry, and ability to work in groups and contribute to investigations.

NCTM STANDARDS

CONTENT		PROCESS	
	Number		Problem Solving
✓	Algebra		Reasoning
✓	Geometry	✓	Communication
	Measurement	✓	Connections
	Data/Probability	✓	Representation

Closing the Lesson

Quickly summarize the major ideas of this lesson: Knot designs resemble abstract ropes or rings woven together. The straightedge and compass can be useful for making them. The three-dimensional appearance of the designs comes from hiding some lines. You might mention that the question of hidden lines and being able to imagine three-dimensional forms is very important to mathematicians in geometry and in occupations that rely on geometry, such as architecture, building trades, and product design.

BUILDING UNDERSTANDING

The exercises involve knot designs, their connectedness, and their symmetries.

ASSIGNING HOMEWORK

Essential	1, 2, 3
Performance assessment	4
Portfolio	5
Journal	7, 8
Group	6, 8, 9
Review	3

MATERIALS

- Exercise 5 (T), *optional*

▶ Helping with the Exercises

2. possible answer:

3. possible answer:

4. possible answer:

Cut the middle ring.

EXERCISES

You will need

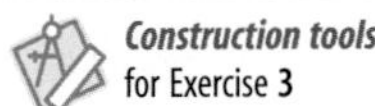

1. Name a culture or country whose art uses knot designs. possible answers: Scotland, Nigeria

2. Create a knot design of your own, using only straight lines on graph paper.

3. Create a knot design of your own with rotational symmetry, using a compass or a circle template.

4. Sketch five rings linked together so that you could separate all five by cutting open one ring.

5. The coat of arms of the Borromeo family, who lived during the Italian Renaissance (ca. 15th century), showed a very interesting knot design known as the Borromean Rings. In it, three rings are linked together so that if any one ring is removed the remaining two rings are no longer connected. Got that? Good. Sketch the Borromean Rings.

6. The Chokwe storytellers of northeastern Angola are called *Akwa kuta sona* ("those who know how to draw"). When they sit down to draw and to tell their stories, they clear the ground and set up a grid of points in the sand with their fingertips, as shown below left. Then they begin to tell a story and, at the same time, trace a finger through the sand to create a *lusona* design with one smooth, continuous motion. Try your hand at creating *sona* (plural of *lusona*). Begin with the correct number of dots. Then, in one motion, re-create one of the *sona* below. The initial dot grid is shown for the rat. Answers will be a *lusona* from among the three choices.

Initial dot grid | Rat | Mbemba bird | Scorpion

7. In Greek mythology, the Gordian knot was such a complicated knot that no one could undo it. Oracles claimed that whoever could undo the knot would become the ruler of Gordium. When Alexander the Great (356–323 B.C.E.) came upon the knot, he simply cut it with his sword and claimed he had fulfilled the prophecy, so the throne was his. The expression "cutting the Gordian knot" is still used today. What do you think it means? It means to solve a problem boldly and decisively or in a creative way not considered by others.

Science CONNECTION

Mathematician DeWitt Sumners at Florida State University and biophysicist Sylvia Spenger at the University of California, Berkeley, have discovered that when a virus attacks DNA, it creates a knot on the DNA.

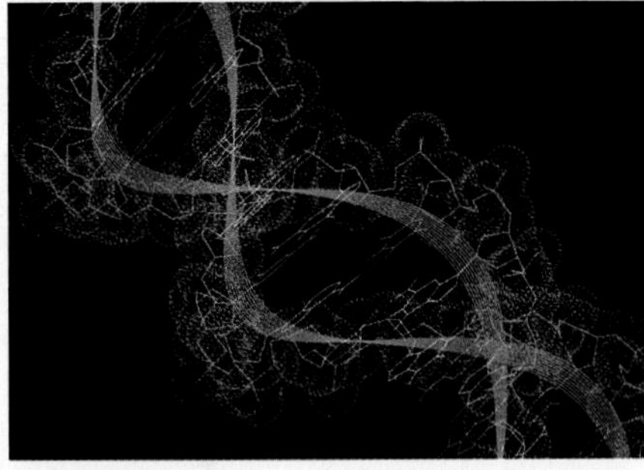

Exercise 5 [Context] The Italian Renaissance was a period of increased learning starting after the Middle Ages (eleventh century) and continuing until the Age of Enlightenment (eighteenth century). It was at its height during the life of Leonardo da Vinci (1452–1519). You might use the transparency Borromean Rings as you discuss the answer.

Exercise 6 [Context] Angola is a country on the eastern coast of Africa below the equator.

5.

8. The square knot and granny knot are very similar but do very different things. Compare their symmetries. Use string to re-create the two knots and explain their differences. The square knot has reflectional symmetry across a horizontal line. The less secure granny knot has 2-fold rotational symmetry.

Square knot

Granny knot

9. Cut a long strip of paper from a sheet of lined paper or graph paper. Tie the strip of paper snugly, but without wrinkles, into a simple knot. What shape does the knot create? Sketch your knot.

project

SYMBOLIC ART

Japanese artist Kunito Nagaoka (b 1940) uses geometry in his work. Nagaoka was born in Nagano, Japan, and was raised near the active volcano Asama. In Japan, he experienced earthquakes and typhoons as well as the human tragedies of Hiroshima and Nagasaki. In 1966, he moved to Berlin, Germany, a city rebuilt in concrete from the ruins of World War II. These experiences clearly influenced his work.

You can find other examples of symbolic art at www.keymath.com/DG .

- Look at the etching shown here, or another piece of symbolic art. Write a paragraph describing what you think might have happened in the scene or what you think it might represent. What types of geometric figures do you find?
- Use geometric shapes in your own sketch or painting to evoke a feeling or to tell a story. Write a one- or two-page story related to your art.

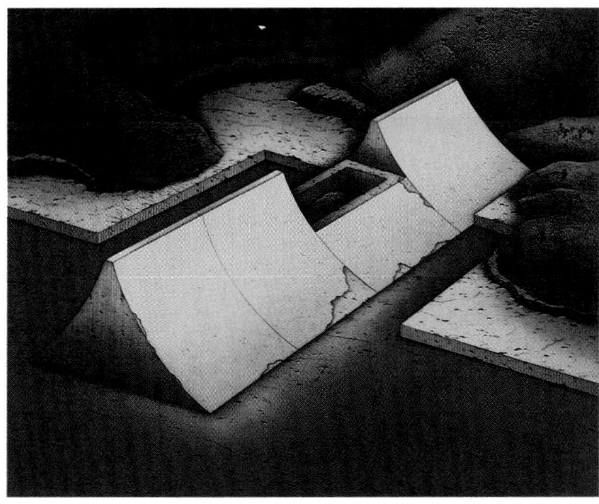
ISEKI/PY XVIII (1978), Kunito Nagaoka

Exercise 8 Some students may notice that the square knot, in addition to having reflectional symmetry over a horizontal line in the plane of the page, also has rotational symmetry in a plane perpendicular to the plane of the page. That is, you could interchange the rope ends on the left with those on the right.

9. The result is a regular pentagon.

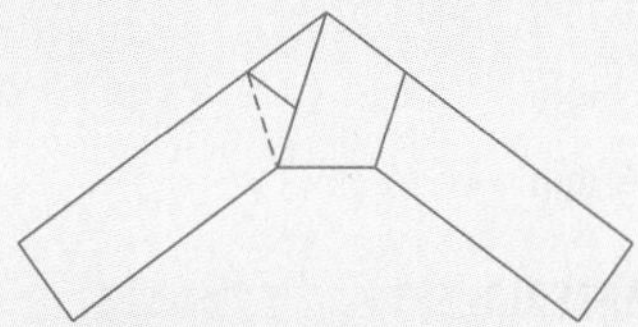

EXTENSIONS

A. Students can investigate extensions to the Borromean Rings (Exercise 5) with four or five rings.

B. Have students research the Borromeo family, Chokwe storytellers, *sona* designs, Celtic art, or knot designs from other cultures.

Supporting the project

Geometric shapes, though common in our three-dimensional world, do not always show their true shapes in two-dimensional representations.

OUTCOMES

- Descriptions of the events depicted are tied to the etching.
- Geometric shapes mentioned include triangles and rectangles.
- Student story is clearly tied to his or her art.

- Paragraph about etching includes how the shapes are related and mentions that rectangles and triangles are not exact because of perspective and because they are bent or broken.

LESSON

0.6

PLANNING

LESSON OUTLINE

One day:

25 min Investigation

10 min Sharing

5 min Closing

5 min Exercises

MATERIALS

- construction tools
- tracing paper, *optional*
- a computer with a drawing program, *optional*
- colored pens or pencils
- examples of Islamic art, *optional*
- One Piece (T) for One step

TEACHING

A straightedge and compass can be used to make tessellations. Emphasize that the plane continues infinitely.

One step Show the One Piece transparency and ask students to work in their groups to construct it with straightedge, compass, and ruler. Specify that they should begin by making a hexagon in a circle of radius $1\frac{1}{2}$ inches and then use the midpoints of the edges of that hexagon and the 6-pointed star within the original hexagon. They'll need to use a ruler to find midpoints. As needed, remind students of how to mark off radii along the edge of a circle to find the corners of a hexagon and how to join those marks to make a 6-pointed star. Have each group copy its result onto a blank overhead transparency. During Sharing, ask groups to overlay their transparencies to see how the pattern makes a tessellation, as in the Hexagon Tile Design of the student book. If there's time, work on making the 8-pointed Star as a class. (Students might begin with a template of a square or a piece of graph paper to create this design.)

LESSON

0.6

Islamic Tile Designs

Islamic art is rich in geometric forms. Early Islamic, or Muslim, artists became familiar with geometry through the works of Euclid, Pythagoras, and other mathematicians of antiquity, and they used geometric patterns extensively in their art and architecture.

Patience with small details makes perfect a large work, like the universe.

JALALUDDIN RUMI

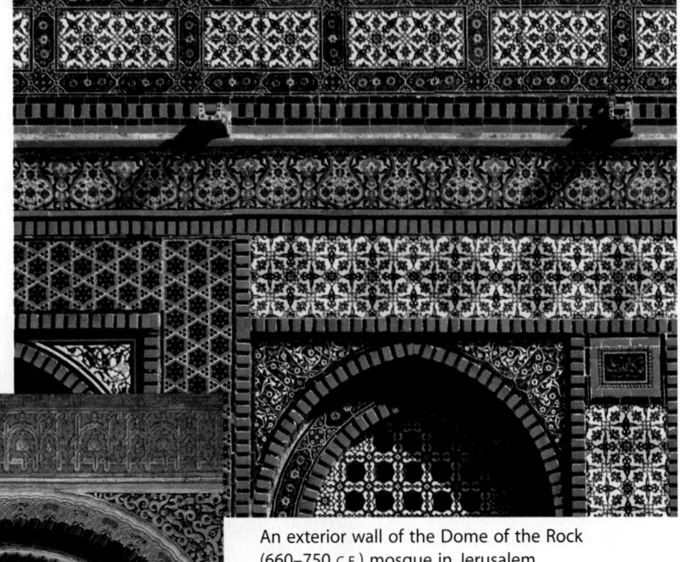

An exterior wall of the Dome of the Rock (660–750 C.E.) mosque in Jerusalem

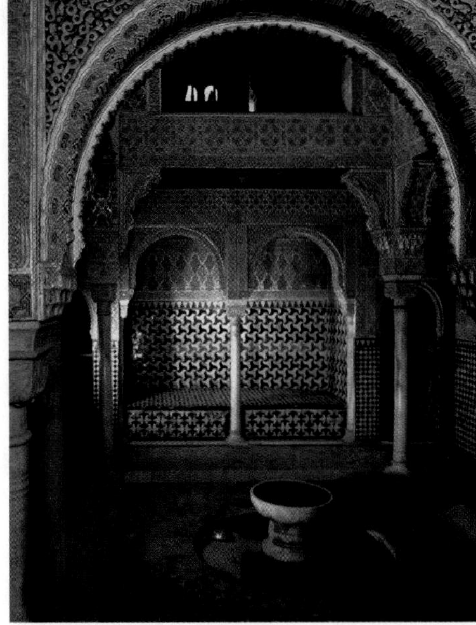

Alcove in the Hall of Ambassadors, the Alhambra, a Moorish palace in Granada, Spain

Islam forbids the representation of humans or animals in religious art. So, instead, the artists use intricate geometric patterns.

One of the most striking examples of Islamic architecture is the Alhambra Palace, in Granada, Spain. Built over 600 years ago by Moors and Spaniards, the Alhambra is filled from floor to ceiling with marvelous geometric patterns. The designs you see on this page are but a few of the hundreds of intricate geometric patterns found in the tile work and the inlaid wood ceilings of buildings like the Alhambra and the Dome of the Rock.

Carpets and hand-tooled bronze plates from the Islamic world also show geometric designs. The patterns often elaborate on basic grids of regular hexagons, equilateral triangles, or squares. These complex Islamic patterns were constructed with no more than a compass and a straightedge. Repeating patterns like these are called **tessellations.** You'll learn more about tessellations in Chapter 7.

LESSON OBJECTIVES

- Explore geometry in Islamic art
- Practice using geometry tools
- Encounter tessellations

The two examples below show how to create one tile in a square-based and a hexagon-based design. The hexagon-based pattern is also a knot design.

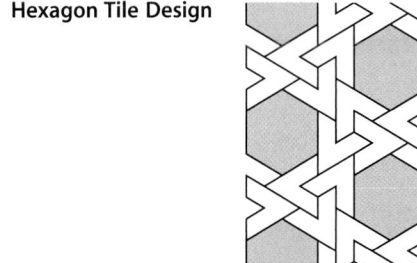

8-pointed Star

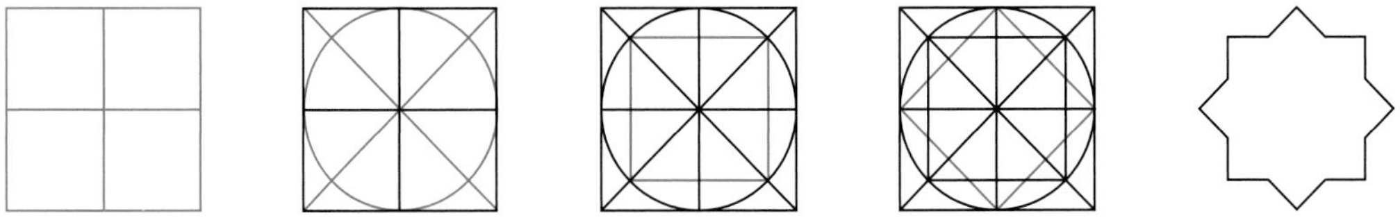

Step 1 Step 2 Step 3 Step 4 Step 5

Hexagon Tile Design

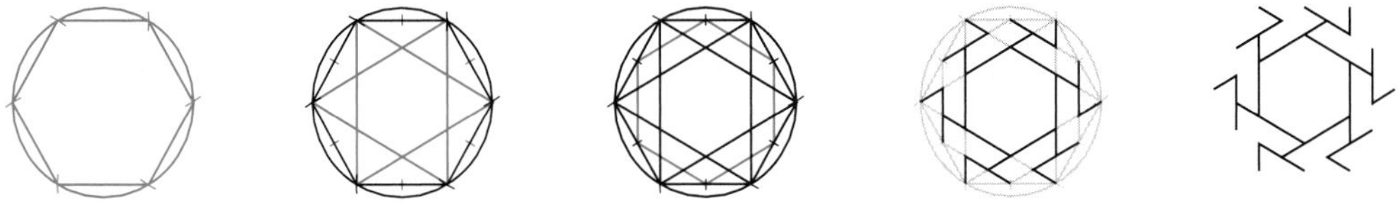

Step 1 Step 2 Step 3 Step 4 Step 5

For more structure, demonstrate how to make the 8-pointed Star in the student book and then ask students to walk through the steps to make Hexagon Tile Design themselves.

SHARING IDEAS

Have students who used different approaches talk about their methods. Begin to use the word *tessellation* for repeated shapes that fill the infinite plane with no gaps or overlaps. **[Language]** *Tessellation* comes from the word *tessera* meaning "a small square stone." Talk about the pictured examples of tessellations, and perhaps show your own examples. Students should be able to visualize the repeating unit in a tessellation in various ways.

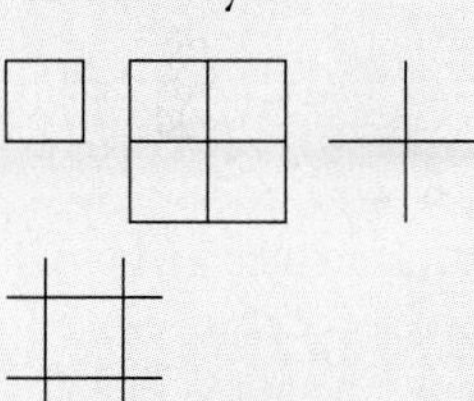

Students will use the 8-pointed Star to make tessellations in their homework. Work on Hexagon Tile Design will give students practice with the important geometry tool the compass.

If there's time to lay some groundwork for Chapter 7, you might have students speculate on how to design a shape that will be part of a tessellation. You might also wonder aloud if there's a way to bisect a line segment without using a ruler. This question helps motivate Chapter 3.

Assessing Progress

Check students' use of construction tools (especially the compass), students' group skills, and students' ability to visualize shapes and repeating units.

NCTM STANDARDS

	CONTENT		PROCESS
	Number	✓	Problem Solving
	Algebra		Reasoning
✓	Geometry		Communication
✓	Measurement	✓	Connections
	Data/Probability		Representation

Closing the Lesson

The major idea of this lesson is that a **tessellation** is a pattern of repeated shapes that fill the plane with no gaps or overlaps. More than 600 years ago, Islamic artists used straightedges and compasses to create complex designs that form the basis of tessellations.

BUILDING UNDERSTANDING

The exercises focus on tessellations of patterns constructed with straightedge and compass.

ASSIGNING HOMEWORK

Essential	3, 4, 6, 7, 8
Performance assessment	6, 7, 8
Portfolio	5
Group	1, 2

▶ Helping with the Exercises

Exercise 3 Students may think that the figure in Step 5 of the 8-pointed Star is to be repeated to make the tessellation. Point out that the cross-shaped regions between the stars are part of the tessellation as well, because a tessellation has no gaps. The full region between the stars can be included with one adjacent star or can be broken up into parts to be included with each surrounding star. The resulting shapes must be identical. **[Language]** Students might also be confused by the words *translate* and *translation.* To translate a figure means to shift it to another spot on the plane without changing its shape or size. A tessellation consists of repeated translations of a single figure.

In Morocco, *zillij,* the art of using glazed tiles to form geometric patterns, is the most common practice for making mosaics. *Zillij* artists cut stars, octagons, and other shapes from clay tiles and place them upside down into the lines of their design. When the tiling is complete, artists pour concrete over the tiles to form a slab. When the concrete dries, they lift the whole mosaic, displaying the colors and connected shapes, and mount it against a fountain, palace, or other building.

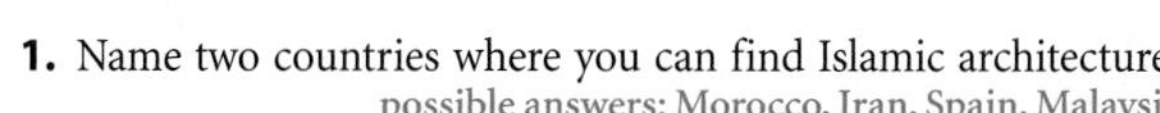

EXERCISES

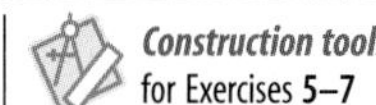

You will need

Construction tools for Exercises 5–7

1. Name two countries where you can find Islamic architecture. possible answers: Morocco, Iran, Spain, Malaysia
2. What is the name of the famous palace in Granada, Spain, where you can find beautiful examples of tile patterns? Alhambra
3. Using tracing paper or transparency film, trace a few tiles from the 8-pointed star design. Notice that you can slide, or translate, the tracing in a straight line horizontally, vertically, and even diagonally to other positions so that the tracing will fit exactly onto the tiles again. What is the shortest translation distance you can find, in centimeters? 2.1 cm
4. Notice that when you rotate your tracing from Exercise 3 about certain points in the tessellation, the tracing fits exactly onto the tiles again. Find two different points of rotation. (Put your pencil on the point and try rotating the tracing paper or transparency.) How many times in one rotation can you make the tiles match up again?

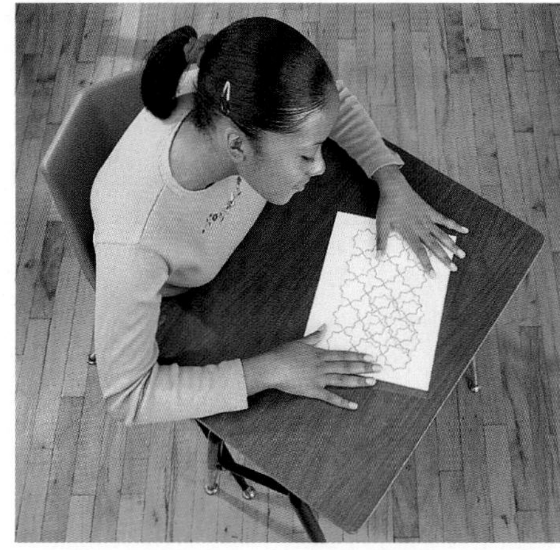

Exercise 4 Students should place the tracing on top of the original picture in the student book and rotate it about a point. The rotated tracing might very well extend past the edge of the picture. Encourage students to think of the original picture as just part of a tessellation that covers the entire plane extending beyond the plane of the page.

4. in terms of the original square tile: 4-fold in the center (center of orange) or corner (center of white); 2-fold in the midpoint of the edge of the tile (where two orange shapes meet)

Architecture CONNECTION

After studying buildings in other Muslim countries, the architect of the Petronas Twin Towers, Cesar Pelli (b 1926), decided that geometric tiling patterns would be key to the design. For the floor plan, his team used a very traditional tile design, the 8-pointed star—two intersecting squares. To add space and connect the design to the traditional "arabesques," the design team added arcs of circles between the eight points.

5. Currently the tallest buildings in the world are the Petronas Twin Towers in Kuala Lumpur, Malaysia. Notice that the floor plans of the towers have the shape of Islamic designs. Use your compass and straightedge to re-create the design of the base of the Petronas Twin Towers, shown at right. ⓗ

6. Use your protractor and ruler to draw a square tile. Use your compass, straightedge, and eraser to modify and decorate it. See the example in this lesson for ideas, but yours can be different. Be creative! Designs will vary.

7. Construct a regular hexagon tile and modify and decorate it. See the example in this lesson for ideas, but yours can be different. Designs will vary, but should contain a regular hexagon.

8. Create a tessellation with one of the designs you made in Exercises 6 and 7. Trace or photocopy several copies and paste them together in a tile pattern. (You can also create your tessellation using geometry software and print out a copy.) Add finishing touches to your tessellation by adding, erasing, or whiting out lines as desired. If you want, see if you can interweave a knot design within your tessellation. Color your tessellation. Tessellations will vary.

PHOTO OR VIDEO SAFARI

In Lesson 0.1, you saw a few examples of geometry and symmetry in nature and art. Now go out with your group and document examples of geometry in nature and art. Use a camera or video camera to take pictures of as many examples of geometry in nature and art as you can. Look for many different types of symmetry, and try to photograph art and crafts from many different cultures. Consider visiting museums and art galleries, but make sure it's okay to take pictures when you visit. You might find examples in your home or in the homes of friends and neighbors.

If you take photographs, write captions for them that describe the geometry and the types of symmetries you find. If you record video, record your commentary on the soundtrack.

Architecture Connection
An *arabesque* is a sinuous, spiraling, undulating, or serpentine line motif. Here the word *line* is used in the art sense of a line, curved or straight.

Exercises 6–8 To complete Exercise 8, students must have worked on at least one of the two previous exercises.

EXTENSION

Have students do library research on the tilings of the Alhambra or look for tessellations in the art of other cultures.

Supporting the project

The goal is for students to see examples of geometry in nature and art. Their understanding of the geometry around them has grown since Lesson 0.1.

OUTCOMES

- Students present photographs with captions or a videotape with commentary.
- The captions or the commentary mentions geometry terms from this chapter.
- The use of terms is accurate.

PLANNING

LESSON OUTLINE

10 min Reviewing

25 min Exercises

10 min Student self-assessment

REVIEWING

Display student art around the room, perhaps including some from past years. Choose at least one piece from each lesson of the chapter and ask students what mathematics they see in it. Elicit the ideas of different types of symmetry, how to construct regular hexagons, the use of hidden lines to assist visualization of three dimensions, and tessellations. Praise accurate use of new terms.

ASSIGNING HOMEWORK

Ask students to work alone on Exercises 4, 5, 8, 9, and 12 (or 7, 10, and 11 instead of 12). Exercises 1, 2, 3, 6, and 13 can be discussed in groups or as a class.

► Helping with the Exercises

2. Sometimes the large hexagons appear as blocks with a corner removed, and sometimes they appear as corners with small cubes nestled in them.

3. Compass: A geometry tool used to construct circles.

Straightedge: A geometry tool used to construct straight lines.

CHAPTER 0 REVIEW

In this chapter, you described the geometric shapes and symmetries you see in nature, in everyday objects, in art, and in architecture. You learned that geometry appears in many types of art—ancient and modern, from every culture—and you learned specific ways in which some cultures use geometry in their art. You also used a compass and straightedge to create your own works of geometric art.

The end of a chapter is a good time to review and organize your work. Each chapter in this book will end with a review lesson.

EXERCISES

You will need

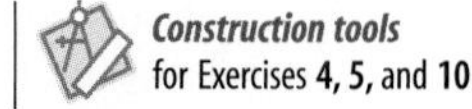

Construction tools for Exercises **4**, **5**, and **10**

1. List three cultures that use geometry in their art. possible answer: Islamic, Hindu, Celtic
2. What is the optical effect of the op art design at right?
3. Name the basic tools of geometry you used in this chapter and describe their uses.
4. With a compass, draw a 12-petal daisy.
5. *Construction* With a compass and straightedge, construct a regular hexagon.
6. List three things in nature that have geometric shapes. Name their shapes. possible answers: hexagon: honeycomb, snowflake; pentagon: starfish, flower
7. Draw an original knot design. Answers will vary. Should be some form of an interweaving design.
8. Which of the wheels below have reflectional symmetry? How many lines of symmetry does each have?

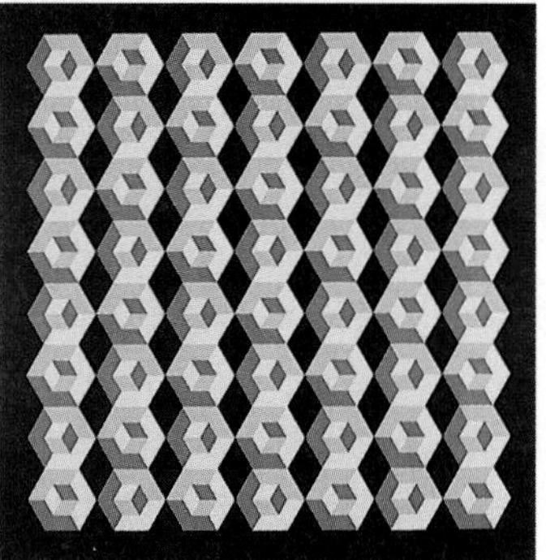

Hot Blocks (1966–67), Edna Andrade

Wheel A

Wheel B

Wheel C

Wheel D

9. Which of the wheels in Exercise 8 have *only* rotational symmetry? What kind of rotational symmetry does each have? Wheels B and D have only rotational symmetry. Wheels A and B have 4-fold, Wheel C has 5-fold, and Wheel D has 3-fold rotational symmetry.

Exercise 4 If students want to be sure the daisy has 12-fold symmetry, they'll also need a ruler to bisect a line segment.

4. possible answer:

5.

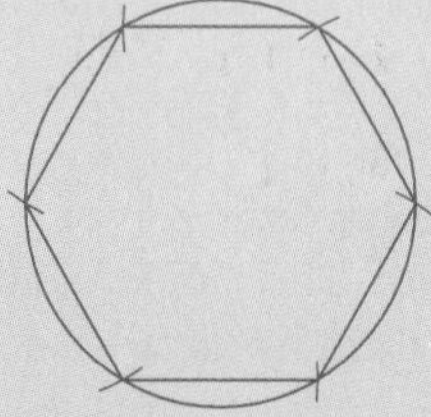

8. Wheel A has four lines of reflectional symmetry; Wheel C has five lines of reflectional symmetry. Wheels B and D do not have reflectional symmetry.

10. A *mandala* is a circular design arranged in rings that radiate from the center. (See the Cultural Connection below.) Use your compass and straightedge to create a mandala. Draw several circles using the same point as the center. Create a geometric design in the center circle, and decorate each ring with a symmetric geometric design. Color or decorate your mandala. Two examples are shown below.

The first mandala uses daisy designs. The second mandala is a combination knot and Islamic design by Scott Shanks, geometry student.

10, 11. Drawing should contain concentric circles and symmetry in some of the rings.

11. Create your own personal mandala. You might include your name, cultural symbols, photos of friends and relatives, and symbols that have personal meaning for you. Color it.

12. Create one mandala that uses techniques from Islamic art, is a knot design, and also has optical effects. The mandala should contain all the required elements.

Cultural CONNECTION

The word *mandala* comes from Sanskrit, the classical language of India, and means "circle" or "center." Hindus use mandala designs for meditation. The Aztec calendar stone below left is an example of a mandala. In the center is the mask of the sun god. Notice the symbols are arranged symmetrically within each circle. The rose windows in many gothic cathedrals, like the one below right from the Chartres Cathedral in France, are also mandalas. Notice all the circles within circles, each one filled with a design or picture.

Exercise 10 [Language] The word *radiate* comes from *radius*; *radiating* means "moving out from a central point." You can use the word *concentric* to talk about circles that share the same center.

Exercise 13a Usually when people say a figure is "symmetric" they mean it has reflectional symmetry. Here the term refers to reflectional or rotational symmetry.

13c. possible answers: Japan

Nigeria

ASSESSING

There is no test for this chapter, but you might want to grade student portfolios or a single piece of artwork from each student. Consider precision in use of tools, creativity, number of geometric properties incorporated, and complexity of the effort.

13. Did you know that "flags" is the most widely read topic of the *World Book Encyclopedia*? Research answers to these questions. More information about flags is available at www.keymath.com/DG .

a. Is the flag of Puerto Rico symmetric? Explain.

b. Does the flag of Kenya have rotational symmetry? Explain.

c. Name a country whose flag has both rotational and reflectional symmetry. Sketch the flag.

13a. The flag of Puerto Rico is not symmetric because of the star and the colors.

13b. The flag of Kenya does not have rotational symmetry because of the spearheads.

Assessing What You've Learned

This section suggests how you might review, organize, and communicate to others what you've learned. Whether you follow these suggestions or directions from your teacher, or use study strategies of your own, be sure to reflect on all you've learned.

KEEPING A PORTFOLIO

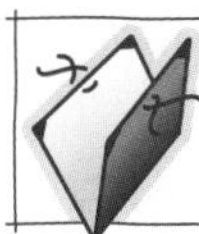

An essential part of learning is being able to show yourself and others how much you know and what you can do. Assessment isn't limited to tests and quizzes. Assessment isn't even limited to what your teacher sees or what makes up your grade. Every piece of art you make, and every project or exercise you complete, gives you a chance to demonstrate to somebody—yourself, at least—what you're capable of.

BEGIN A PORTFOLIO This chapter is primarily about art, so you might organize your work the way a professional artist does—in a portfolio. A portfolio is different from a notebook, both for an artist and for a geometry student. An artist's notebook might contain everything from scratch work to practice sketches to random ideas jotted down. A portfolio is reserved for an artist's most significant or *best* work. It's his or her portfolio that an artist presents to the world to demonstrate what he or she is capable of doing. The portfolio can also show how an artist's work has changed over time.

Review all the work you've done so far and choose one or more examples of your best art projects to include in your portfolio. Write a paragraph or two about each piece, addressing these questions:

- What is the piece an example of?
- Does this piece represent your best work? Why else did you choose it?
- What mathematics did you learn or apply in this piece?
- How would you improve the piece if you redid or revised it?

Portfolios are an ongoing and ever-changing display of your work and growth. As you finish each chapter, update your portfolio by adding new work.

FACILITATING SELF-ASSESSMENT

Portfolios are an assessment idea borrowed from the art world, so if you plan to have your students keep portfolios it is appropriate that the first portfolio piece be a work of student art. The criteria for the portfolio can be either suggested by you or developed in conversation with students. If the school publishes a fine arts magazine, suggest that students submit artwork for publication.

The exercises designated in the lessons as appropriate for portfolios are Lesson 0.1, Exercises 8 and 9; Lesson 0.2, Exercise 5; Lesson 0.4, Exercise 4; Lesson 0.5, Exercise 5; and Lesson 0.6, Exercise 5.

CHAPTER

1

Introducing Geometry

Overview

This chapter introduces students to geometry terms and gives them experience defining and using those terms. **Lesson 1.1** introduces the basic geometry terms: *point, line, plane, segment, ray,* and *collinear* and *coplanar points.* In **Lesson 1.2,** students practice using these terms and *angle,* practice using a protractor, and learn how to mark diagrams. **Using Your Algebra Skills 1** between the first two lessons explores the coordinates of a midpoint. In **Lessons 1.3** to **1.6,** students work in cooperative groups studying examples and non-examples of terms so that the students themselves come up with many of the definitions they will be using in this course. In **Lessons 1.7** and **1.8,** students practice translating geometry word problems into diagrams and work with space geometry.

The Mathematics

Deductive Systems

One characteristic of mathematics is that for a result to be considered valid it must fit into a system. The system includes a list of results, or *theorems.* Each theorem can be proved deductively from theorems earlier in the list, or from a few assumptions that are taken without proof, called *postulates* or *axioms.* Because the entire list depends on these assumptions, it is called an *axiom system* or, since this book doesn't use the term *axiom* it is called a *deductive system.* The linear nature of the list ensures against circular reasoning.

Another feature of a deductive system is intended to keep the meanings of technical terms clear. Interspersed among the theorems are definitions of terms. Before any theorem appears, all of its technical terms must be defined. And the only technical terms being used in a definition must have been defined earlier in the list. To start the list of definitions, a few terms must be taken explicitly as undefined.

Traditionally, geometry courses have been structured around a deductive system. They begin with undefined terms and axioms and then give theorems and their proofs. However, educators no longer place so much emphasis on the deductive system in a geometry course, for several reasons:

- For most students, understanding of mathematical ideas comes through hands-on investigation of the figures rather than through a study of their logical relationships.
- Few students will appreciate the value of a deductive system when they're first learning the big ideas of the field.
- In mathematical research, making conjectures through creativity and intuition is as important as deductive proof. An emphasis on rigorous proof can give the false impression that all of mathematical thinking is deductive.
- Most mathematical research undertaken to discover and prove new theorems occurs at a point in the system that's far from its logical foundations.

Although students will spend a lot of time in this chapter creating and writing careful definitions of terms, the focus is actually on giving students experiences that will help them understand the concepts behind those terms. To develop that understanding, students need to draw pictures, use physical models, consider the etymology of the terms—and certainly use terms that haven't previously been defined. Most students are at levels 0 and 1 of the van Hiele model; not until level 3 will they have made enough sense of the ideas to be ready to work within a deductive system.

Defining *Line Segment*

Perhaps the most familiar attempt to define *line segment* is as "the shortest distance between two points." There are two drawbacks to this definition: First, a distance is a number, and a segment isn't. Even if "distance" is replaced by "path," the second drawback remains: The suggested definition uses a term (*distance* or *path*) that would have to be defined earlier in the deductive system, and the most reasonable definitions of that term use the term *line segment.* Attempts to use the word *straight* or *symmetric* lead to similar circularity. Most rigorous accounts explicitly take the terms *point, line,* and *between* as undefined, and define *line segment* using those terms.

Synthetic Versus Analytic Approach

These comments about defining line segments relate to a *synthetic* deductive system for geometry. In contrast is an *analytical* deductive system, using coordinates. In analytic geometry, you can define a *point* as an ordered pair of real numbers, and you can define *line* as a set of ordered pairs (x, y) that satisfy an equation such as $y = a + bx$ for some real numbers a and b. For a rigorous coordinate approach, you must first define ideas about real numbers and their arithmetic or take them among the undefined terms and postulates. *Discovering Geometry* integrates the two approaches, building gradually from informal to more logically rigorous as students' mathematical abilities develop.

Using This Chapter

To help students learn and remember the many new terms and symbols, you might use overhead transparencies for visual recognition drills or create games that allow students to practice their new vocabulary. At the conclusion of Chapter 1, you might want to give your students a copy of the terms in Chapter 1. A glossary by chapter can be found at www.keypress.com/DG.

Cooperative Learning

The social skills for cooperative learning include using 2-foot voices, staying on task, asking for help, being supportive, asking for reasons, criticizing ideas not people, relating present learning to past learning, and a sense of humor.

Resources

Discovering Geometry Resources

Teaching and Worksheet Masters
  Lessons 1.1, 1.2, 1.4, 1.6–1.8, and Chapter 1 Review

Sketchpad Demonstrations
  Lesson 1.5

Discovering Geometry with The Geometer's Sketchpad
  Using Your Algebra Skills 1
  Lessons 1.5 and 1.6

Assessment Resources A and B
  Quiz 1 (Lessons 1.1–1.3)
  Quiz 2 (Lessons 1.4 and 1.5)
  Quiz 3 (Lessons 1.6–1.8)
  Chapter 1 Test
  Chapter 1 Constructive Assessment Options

Practice Your Skills for Chapter 1

Condensed Lessons for Chapter 1

Other Resources

Visual Thinking: A Strategy Manual for Problem Solving by Robert McKim.

For complete references on this and other sources see www.keypress.com/DG.

Materials

- construction tools (straightedge, compass, patty paper)
- a ruler
- a protractor
- a glue stick
- graph paper
- isometric dot paper
- two-volume set of books, *optional*
- physical objects to represent geometry concepts (such as a tack for *point,* uncooked spaghetti or string for *line,* cardboard for *plane*)
- cardboard cutouts of a rectangle, semicircle, and right triangle, each taped to a pencil or stiff wire to use as models
- stiff wire
- modeling clay

Pacing Guide

	day 1	day 2	day 3	day 4	day 5	day 6	day 7	day 8	day 9	day 10
standard	1.1	Algebra 1	1.2	1.3	quiz, 1.4	1.5	quiz, 1.6	1.7	1.8	review
enriched	1.1	Algebra 1, 1.2	1.3	quiz, 1.4	1.5	quiz, 1.6	1.7	1.8	Exploration	review, TAL
block	1.1, Algebra 1	1.2, 1.3	1.4	quiz, 1.5	1.6, 1.7	quiz, 1.8	Exploration, review	TAL, assessment		
	day 11	**day 12**	**day 13**	**day 14**	**day 15**	**day 16**	**day 17**	**day 18**	**day 19**	**day 20**
standard	assessment									
enriched	assessment									

CHAPTER

1 Introducing Geometry

Although I am absolutely without training or knowledge in the exact sciences, I often seem to have more in common with mathematicians than with my fellow artists.

M. C. ESCHER

Three Worlds, M. C. Escher, 1955

OBJECTIVES

In this chapter you will

- write your own definitions of many geometry terms and geometric figures
- start a notebook with a list of all the terms and their definitions
- develop very useful visual thinking skills

M. C. Escher had difficulty with arithmetic and algebra, but geometry gave him a chance to use his imagination and express his fascination with order. *Three Worlds* shows how the graphic artist perceived space and how he used the leaves, trees, and fish to set up planes and show depth. The three worlds in this work overlap in a definite order. **[Ask]** "What are the three worlds pictured?" [possible answers: below the water, the surface of the lake, and the world from the viewpoint of the observer above the surface, which is illustrated in the reflection; or the animal world (fish), the vegetable world (leaves), and the mineral world (water); or the animate world (fish), the inanimate (water, air), and both (tree as living branches and dead leaves)]

CHAPTER 1 OBJECTIVES

- Learn the terminology and notation associated with geometric objects, such as *point, segment, line, ray, plane, angle, polygon* (*triangle, quadrilateral, pentagon, hexagon*), *circle, sphere, cylinder,* and *cone*
- Become familiar with the objects that have special characteristics: acute and obtuse angles and triangles; scalene triangles; collinear points; coplanar figures; congruent figures; equilateral, equiangular, and regular polygons
- Begin defining parts of geometric objects: center, radius, chord, and diameter of a circle; cross section of a three-dimensional solid
- Translate descriptions into diagrams, and vice versa
- Develop the skills of measuring angles and line segments, marking figures, and writing and recording definitions
- Encounter some real-world applications of geometry
- Develop critical thinking
- Develop visual thinking skills
- Review or develop construction skills
- Practice cooperative behavior

LESSON 1.1

PLANNING

LESSON OUTLINE

One day:

20 min Investigation

15 min Sharing

10 min Exercises

MATERIALS

- rulers
- Example of a Definition List (T), *optional*

TEACHING

Students encounter some of the most basic undefined terms and definitions of geometry and practice recording definitions in their notebooks.

INTRODUCTION

[Language] If you didn't start the course with Chapter 0, you might discuss the etymology of *geometry*: *geo* means "earth," and *metry* means "measure." See page 2.

If this is the first time your students have worked in groups in this course, you might want to go over norms, social skills, and expectations for teamwork.

LESSON 1.1

Building Blocks of Geometry

Nature's Great Book is written in mathematical symbols.

GALILEO GALILEI

Three building blocks of geometry are points, lines, and planes. A **point** is the most basic building block of geometry. It has no size. It has only location. You represent a point with a dot, and you name it with a capital letter. The point shown below is called P.

P

Mathematical model of a point

A tiny seed is a physical model of a point.

A **line** is a straight, continuous arrangement of infinitely many points. It has infinite length but no thickness. It extends forever in two directions. You name a line by giving the letter names of any two points on the line and by placing the line symbol above the letters, for example, $\overleftrightarrow{AB}$ or $\overleftrightarrow{BA}$.

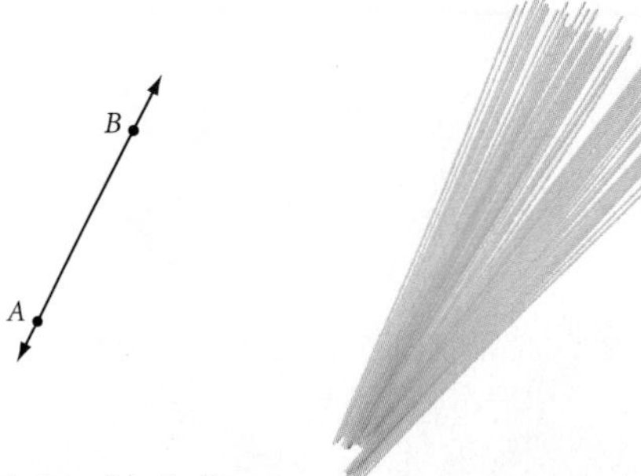

Mathematical model of a line

A piece of spaghetti is a physical model of a line. A line, however, is longer, straighter, and thinner than any piece of spaghetti ever made.

A **plane** has length and width but no thickness. It is like a flat surface that extends infinitely along its length and width. You represent a plane with a four-sided figure, like a tilted piece of paper, drawn in perspective. Of course, this actually illustrates only part of a plane. You name a plane with a script capital letter, such as $\mathcal{P}$.

A Plane
landing on a Plane

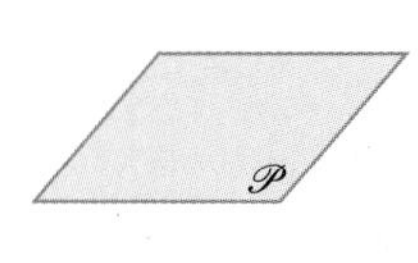

Mathematical model of a plane

A flat piece of rolled-out dough is a model of a plane, but a plane is broader, wider, and thinner than any piece of dough you could roll.

LESSON OBJECTIVES

- Learn the terminology and notation of points, segments, lines, rays, planes, angles, and collinear and coplanar points
- Learn the idea of congruence of line segments
- Begin keeping a notebook of definitions
- Practice cooperative behavior

NCTM STANDARDS

	CONTENT		PROCESS
	Number		Problem Solving
✓	Algebra	✓	Reasoning
✓	Geometry	✓	Communication
✓	Measurement	✓	Connections
	Data/Probability	✓	Representation

Investigation
Mathematical Models

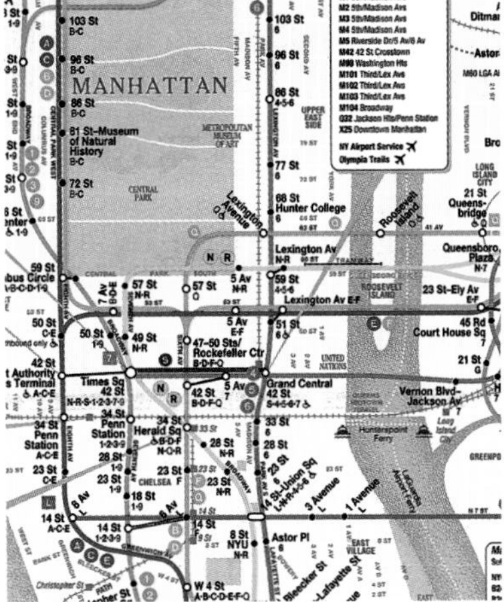

Step 1 | Identify examples of points, lines, and planes in these pictures.

Step 2 | Explain in your own words what point, line, and plane mean.

It can be difficult to explain what points, lines, and planes are. Yet, you probably recognized several models of each in the investigation. Early mathematicians tried to define these terms.

Guiding the Investigation

One step One-step investigations allow the students to construct mathematical knowledge in the context of a single problem, with the teacher playing the role of consultant. For this lesson, you might pose this problem: "A mathematical definition of a term gives its meaning using only previously defined mathematical terms and common words like *the* and *any.* Try to arrange the terms *point, line, line segment, midpoint*, and *plane* in an appropriate order and write mathematical definitions for them." As you circulate among groups, note interesting responses for later sharing with the class. You need not say much except to encourage thinking and debate.

If you or your students need more structure, explain what a mathematical definition is and have students work in groups on the investigation, identifying models and discussing definitions of *point, line,* and *plane.*

Step 1 points: where structure lines of the building cross, intersections, interchanges, dots that provide shading on the river; lines: window frames, roads, parts of letters; planes: sides of the building, surface of the map

Step 2 Let students struggle with this step for a while before having them share their ideas.

SHARING IDEAS

Ask selected students to share the definitions their groups propose, and have the class critique them. Lead the class to the notion that some terms must come first and therefore can't be defined using only predefined terms. Normally geometers take three terms as undefined elements: *point, line,* and *plane.* Ask students for their own physical examples of these ideas to be sure they understand them even if they are not defined. Brainstorm common meanings of these three terms, and discuss how these meanings relate to the geometry meanings. **[Language]** *Plane* means "flat" or "level surface"; it is also used as a shortened form of airplane. (The homonym *plain* means "clear" or "without decorations.") In geometry, points have no dimension, and lines and planes have no thickness.

Now see how students' definitions of *line segment* and *midpoint* (not *symmetry* yet) can be phrased using the undefined terms. A line segment is often called simply a *segment.* Don't expect mathematically perfect definitions from students operating at van Hiele level 0 or 1, a common level among beginning geometry students.

It is time-consuming to write out phrases such as "line *AB*" or "line segment *PQ*." **[Ask]** "How might we label lines and line segments?" Suggest that students look in their book for its conventions. While they're looking at the book, point out the descriptions given of *line, plane,* and *point.* Ask students what they think *continuous* means. [no breaks]

The ancient Greeks said, "A point is that which has no part. A line is breadthless length." The Mohist philosophers of ancient China said, "The line is divided into parts, and that part which has no remaining part is a point." Those definitions don't help much, do they?

A **definition** is a statement that clarifies or explains the meaning of a word or a phrase. However, it is impossible to define point, line, and plane without using words or phrases that themselves need definition. So these terms remain undefined. Yet, they are the basis for all of geometry.

Using the undefined terms *point, line,* and *plane,* you can define all other geometry terms and geometric figures. Many are defined in this book, and others will be defined by you and your classmates.

Keep a definition list in your notebook, and each time you encounter new geometry vocabulary, add the term to your list. Illustrate each definition with a simple sketch.

Here are your first definitions. Begin your list and draw sketches for all definitions.

Collinear means on the same line.

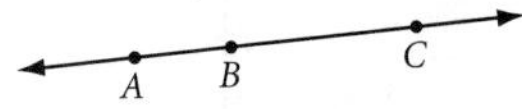

Points *A, B,* and *C* are collinear.

Coplanar means on the same plane.

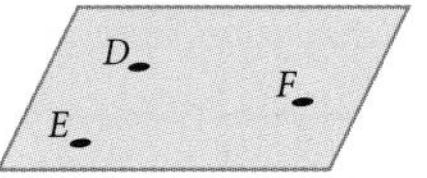

Points *D, E,* and *F* are coplanar.

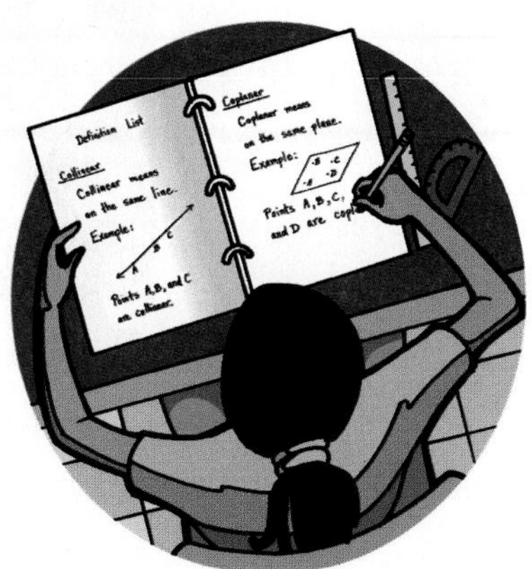

Name three balls that are collinear. Name three balls that are coplanar but not collinear. Name four balls that are not coplanar.

collinear points: *B, D,* and *G,* or *E, F,* and *G*
coplanar but noncollinear points: any other set of three points.

noncoplanar points: any set of four points that includes *A* (in his pocket) and/or *C*

[Language] Ask what they think *breadthless* means. [no width] **[Ask]** "What might the ancient Greeks and Chinese have meant by *part*?" [Perhaps a part was something that could be measured.] Ask students how they would define *infinite.* Give students an appreciation for what mathematicians struggle with when they try to understand basic concepts. **[Ask]** "How can a line have an infinite length when it's made up of points that have no size?" Discuss the meanings of *intuitive, analogy, common language,* and *physical model.*

DEFINITIONS

Ask students to study the definitions given in the student book and compare them with their own. Encourage criticism of all definitions, with suggestions for improvement. Be sure students note the definition of *ray* after the example.

Demonstrate how students should organize the definition list in their notebooks, including sketches, and help them get started with these new terms. You might use the Example of a Definition List transparency.

A **line segment** consists of two points called the **endpoints** of the segment and all the points between them that are collinear with the two points.

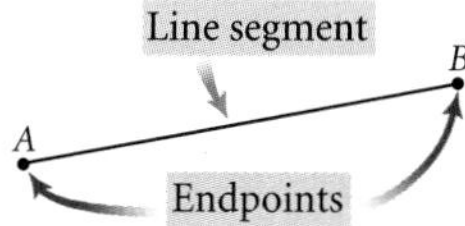

You can write line segment AB, using a segment symbol, as $\overline{AB}$ or $\overline{BA}$. There are two ways to write the length of a segment. You can write $AB = 2$ in., meaning the distance from A to B is 2 inches. You can also use an m for "measure" in front of the segment name, and write the distance as $m\overline{AB} = 2$ in. If no measurement units are used for the length of a segment, it is understood that the choice of units is not important, or is based on the length of the smallest square in the grid.

Figure A

A 2 B

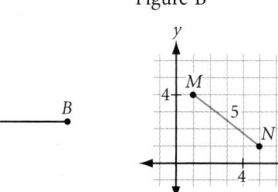

$AB = 2$ in., or $m\overline{AB} = 2$ in.

Figure B

y M 4 5 N x 4

$m\overline{MN} = 5$ units

Two segments are **congruent segments** if and only if they have the same measure or length. The symbol for congruence is $\cong$, and you say it as "is congruent to." You use the equals symbol, $=$, between equal numbers and the congruence symbol, $\cong$, between congruent figures.

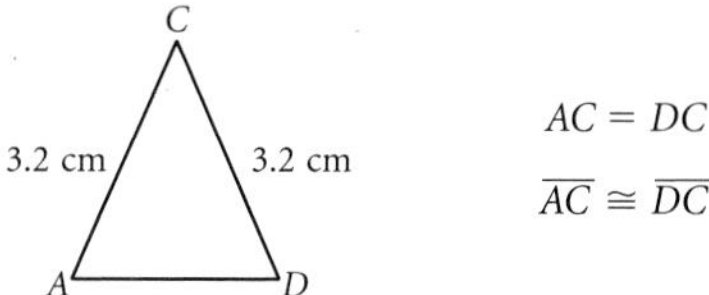

$AC = DC$

$\overline{AC} \cong \overline{DC}$

When drawing figures, you show congruent segments by making identical markings.

These single marks mean these two segments are congruent to each other.

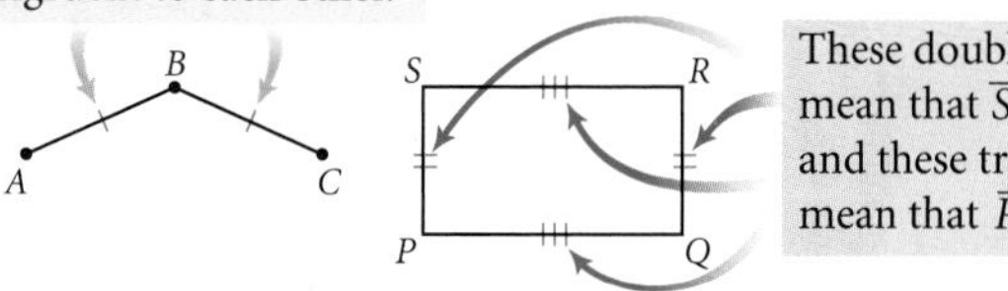

These double marks mean that $\overline{SP} \cong \overline{RQ}$, and these triple marks mean that $\overline{PQ} \cong \overline{SR}$.

The **midpoint** of a segment is the point on the segment that is the same distance from both endpoints. The midpoint **bisects** the segment, or divides the segment into two congruent segments.

If you studied symmetry in Chapter 0, have students share and critique definitions of *symmetry*, but keep open the challenge of writing a good definition, as motivation for Chapter 7. **[Ask]** "Which figures or terms in this lesson are symmetric?" [A point has reflectional symmetry over any line containing it and rotational symmetry of any-fold about itself. A line has reflectional symmetry over itself and over any line perpendicular to itself, and it has 2-fold rotational symmetry about any point on it. A line segment has reflectional symmetry over the line containing it and over any perpendicular line through its midpoint, and it has 2-fold rotational symmetry about its midpoint. A ray has reflectional symmetry over the line containing it. A plane has reflectional symmetry over any line in it or perpendicular to it and rotational symmetry of any fold about any point in it.]

Ask the class to answer the questions in the tennis action photo. Balls B, D, and G or E, F, and G are collinear. Any other set of three balls is coplanar but not collinear. That may be obvious for balls that lie in the plane of the court but students may need persuading that balls A, B, and C, for example, are coplanar.

[Ask] "What other words begin with *co*?" [*coworker, coincide, cooperate, coexist*]

[Alert] Students may not realize that points can be collinear whether or not a line has been drawn connecting them.

Dimensions

If you like, you can mention that planes are two-dimensional, because they have length and width but no height. Lines are one-dimensional, because they have only length. Points are zero-dimensional, because they have no measure in any direction. Space, which will be studied in Lesson 1.8, is three-dimensional, because it has length, width, and height.

Coordinate Geometry

To help students prepare for Exercises 7, 12, and 29–33, you might take a minute to review coordinate geometry, especially the conventions for plotting points on a coordinate plane. You can simply draw the two axes and ask students how to plot several points, including some points in each quadrant.

▶ EXAMPLE

The example illustrates the important point that we can't make assumptions about a picture. Points F and N look like the midpoints of $\overline{EG}$ and $\overline{MP}$, but we can't assume they are unless the picture contains some marks that say so.

Assessing Progress

As you observe group work and presentations, watch for skill in working with groups and staying on task. If your class did Chapter 0, also assess students' understanding of symmetry.

Closing the Lesson

Because this is an initial lesson on definitions, symbols, and drawings, be sure to emphasize some of the good techniques being used by students so that others will be encouraged to use these methods. Point out the good cooperative behavior demonstrated by some of the groups.

The key mathematical content of this lesson includes mathematical definitions and the need for undefined terms (**point, line, plane**). Most terms defined were of zero- or one-dimensional objects (**collinear points, segment** or **line segment, endpoints, midpoint, ray**), but also included were **plane** and **coplanar.** The lesson visited notation for lines and line segments and the **length** of a line segment and for **congruence** of line segments.

EXAMPLE

Study the diagrams below.

a. Name each midpoint and the segment it bisects.

b. Name all the congruent segments. Use the congruence symbol to write your answers.

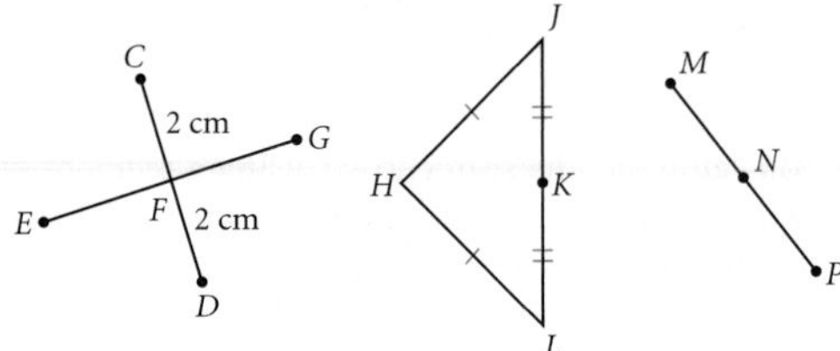

▶ Solution

Look carefully at the markings and apply the midpoint definition.

a. $CF \cong FD$, so F is the midpoint of $\overline{CD}$; $\overline{JK} \cong \overline{KL}$, so K is the midpoint of $\overline{JL}$.

b. $\overline{CF} \cong \overline{FD}$, $\overline{HJ} \cong \overline{HL}$, and $\overline{JK} \cong \overline{KL}$.

Even though $\overline{EF}$ and $\overline{FG}$ appear to have the same length, you cannot assume they are congruent without the markings. The same is true for $\overline{MN}$ and $\overline{NP}$.

Ray AB is the part of $\overleftrightarrow{AB}$ that contains point A and all the points on $\overleftrightarrow{AB}$ that are on the same side of point A as point B. Imagine cutting off all the points to the left of point A.

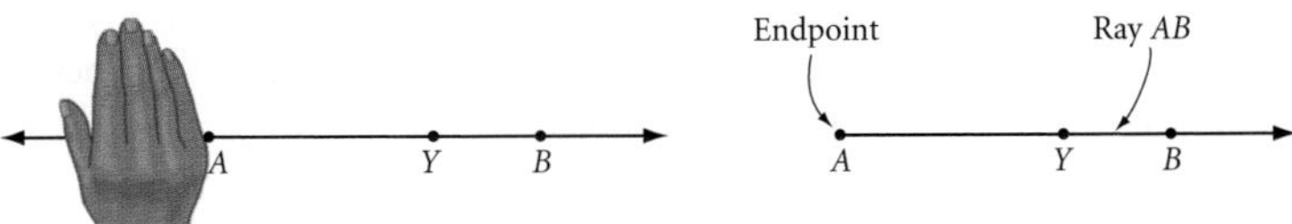

In the figure above, $\overrightarrow{AY}$ and $\overrightarrow{AB}$ are two ways to name the same ray. Note that $\overrightarrow{AB}$ is not the same as $\overrightarrow{BA}$!

A ray begins at a point and extends infinitely in one direction. You need two letters to name a ray. The first letter is the endpoint of the ray, and the second letter is any other point that the ray passes through.

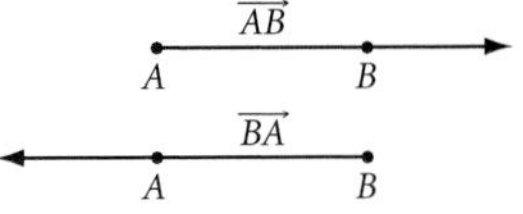

Physical model of a ray: beams of light

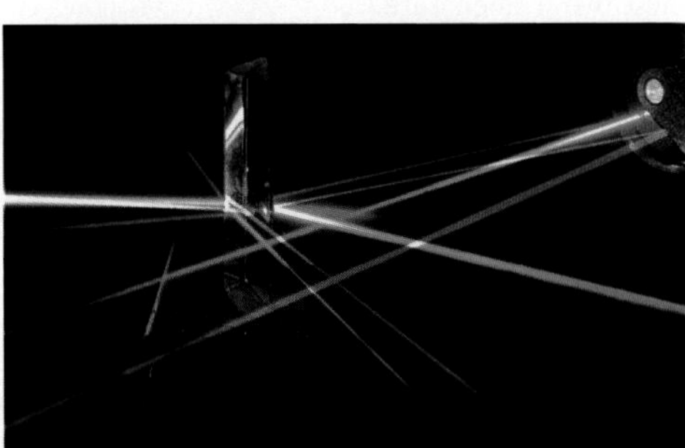

EXERCISES

1. Identify the models in the photos below for point, segment, plane, collinear points, and coplanar points.

For Exercises 2–4, name each line in two different ways.

2. 

$\overleftrightarrow{PT}$, $\overleftrightarrow{TP}$

3. ⓗ 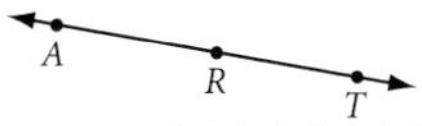

any two of the following: $\overleftrightarrow{AR}$, $\overleftrightarrow{RA}$, $\overleftrightarrow{AT}$, $\overleftrightarrow{TA}$, $\overleftrightarrow{RT}$, $\overleftrightarrow{TR}$

4. 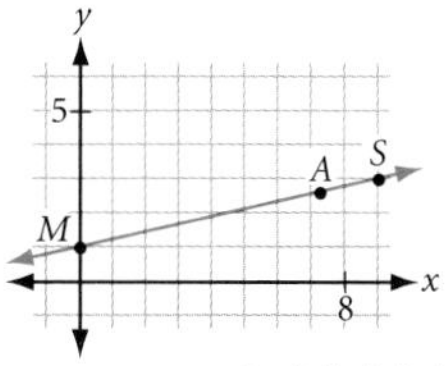

any two of the following: $\overleftrightarrow{MA}$, $\overleftrightarrow{MS}$, $\overleftrightarrow{AS}$, $\overleftrightarrow{AM}$, $\overleftrightarrow{SA}$, $\overleftrightarrow{SM}$

For Exercises 5–7, draw two points and label them. Then use a ruler to draw each line. Don't forget to use arrowheads to show that it extends indefinitely.

5. $\overleftrightarrow{AB}$

6. $\overleftrightarrow{KL}$

7. $\overleftrightarrow{DE}$ with $D(-3, 0)$ and $E(0, -3)$

For Exercises 8–10, name each line segment.

8. 

$\overline{AC}$ or $\overline{CA}$

9. 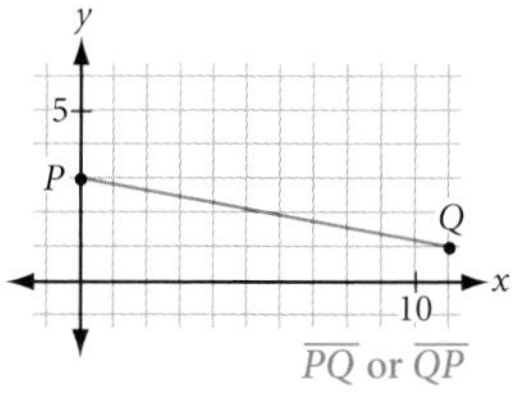

$\overline{PQ}$ or $\overline{QP}$

10. 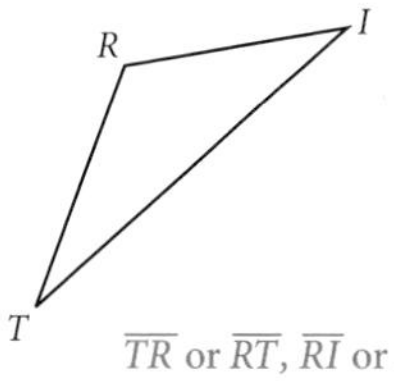

$\overline{TR}$ or $\overline{RT}$, $\overline{RI}$ or $\overline{IR}$, and $\overline{TI}$ or $\overline{IT}$

For Exercises 11 and 12, draw and label each line segment.

11. $\overline{AB}$

12. $\overline{RS}$ with $R(0, 3)$ and $S(-2, 11)$

For Exercises 13 and 14, use your ruler to find the length of each line segment to the nearest tenth of a centimeter. Write your answer in the form $m\overline{AB} = \underline{?}$.

13. 

$m\overline{AB} = 14.3$ cm

14. 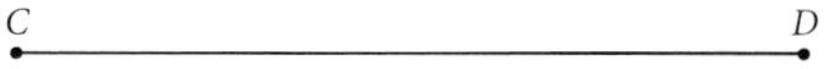

$m\overline{CD} = 6.7$ cm

For Exercises 15–17, use your ruler to draw each segment as accurately as you can. Label each segment. Check each length to see if it is correct. Refer to text for measurements.

15. $AB = 4.5$ cm

16. $CD = 3$ in.

17. $EF = 24.8$ cm

5. 

6. 

7. 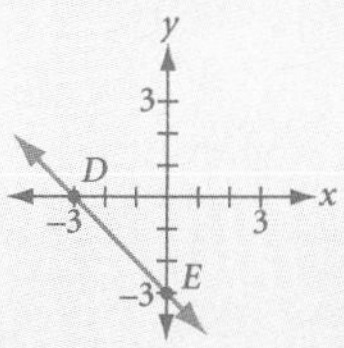

11. 

12. 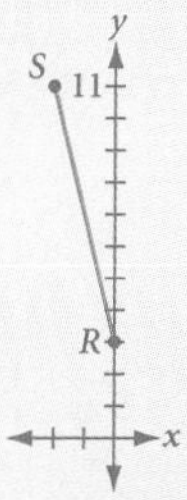

BUILDING UNDERSTANDING

This is a long exercise set, but it should go quickly. You might assign all the exercises or let students work on the even-numbered exercises in groups and the odd-numbered exercises as homework.

ASSIGNING HOMEWORK

Essential	odds
Performance assessment	20
Portfolio	27
Journal	32
Group	evens

▶ Helping with the Exercises

Exercise 1 This is a good place to be sure students see the difference among objects, terms for objects, symbols for objects, and drawings of objects. A mathematical *model* is a mathematical object, such as a line segment or an equation, that represents a real-world object or situation. In this exercise the word *model* refers to a physical model for the mathematical object.

1. sample answers: point: balls, where lines cross; segment: lines of the parachute, court markings; collinear: points along a line of the court structure; coplanar: each boy's hand, navel, and kneecap, points along two strings

Exercises 2–4 [Alert] If a line has more than two points labeled, students sometimes mistakenly use more than two letters to name the line.

Exercises 5–7 Some students may ask "Where do I put points *A*, *B*, *K*, *L*, *D*, and *E*?" Point out that the instructions say that they are to draw and label two points for each exercise.

Exercises 19, 20 [Ask] "If we see only the final picture, how do we know we have a midpoint?" [from markings]

19. possible answers:

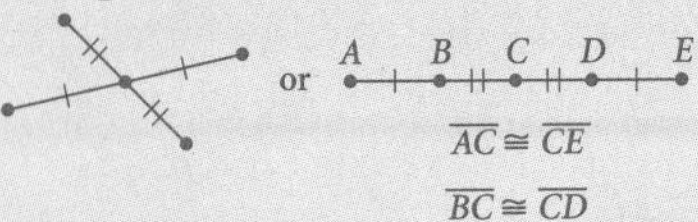

20.

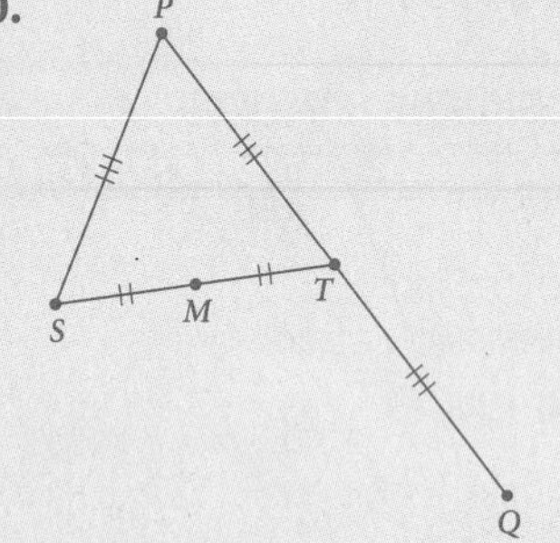

Exercises 21–26 [Alert] Some students have difficulty with the symbol for rays and don't realize that the first letter always indicates the endpoint. Some students don't realize that the ray symbol always points to the right even though the ray may point in a different direction in the drawing. **[Alert]** Students often draw rays that almost appear to be segments. Encourage them to extend the ray past the second point. For Exercises 21–23, students may correctly mention $\overrightarrow{BC}$, $\overrightarrow{NM}$, and $\overrightarrow{YZ}$.

24.

25.

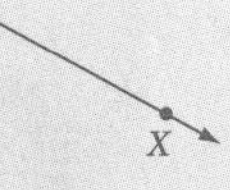

26. M N

27.

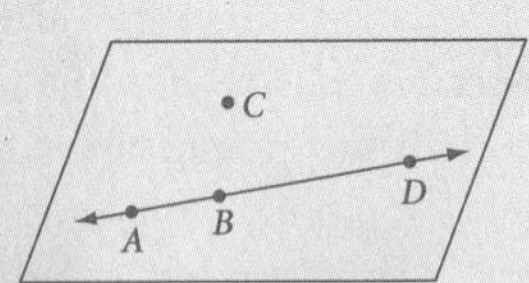

Exercise 28 The number of segments is the same if the points are not collinear.

Exercises 29–33 [Alert] Students may need reminders of how to plot points in the coordinate plane.

18. Name each midpoint and the segment it bisects.

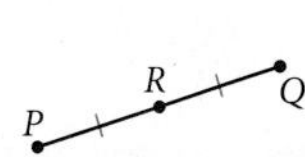

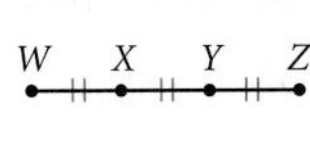

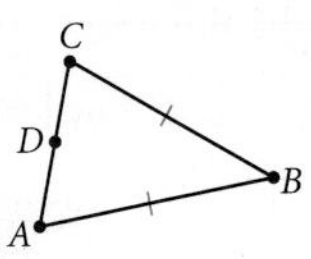

R is the midpoint of $\overline{PQ}$. *X* is the midpoint of $\overline{WY}$. *Y* is the midpoint of $\overline{XZ}$. No midpoints are shown in $\triangle ABC$.

19. Draw two segments that have the same midpoint. Mark your drawing to show congruent segments.

20. Draw and mark a figure in which *M* is the midpoint of $\overline{ST}$, $SP = PT$, and *T* is the midpoint of $\overline{PQ}$.

For Exercises 21–23, name the ray in two different ways.

21. ⓗ A B C — $\overrightarrow{AB}$, $\overrightarrow{AC}$

22. M N P — $\overrightarrow{PM}$, $\overrightarrow{PN}$

23. Z Y X — $\overrightarrow{XY}$, $\overrightarrow{XZ}$

For Exercises 24–26, draw and label each ray.

24. $\overrightarrow{AB}$ **25.** $\overrightarrow{YX}$ **26.** $\overrightarrow{MN}$

27. Draw a plane containing four coplanar points *A*, *B*, *C*, and *D*, with exactly three collinear points *A*, *B*, and *D*.

28. Given two points *A* and *B*, there is only one segment that you can name: $\overline{AB}$. With three collinear points *A*, *B*, and *C*, there are three different segments that you can name: $\overline{AB}$, $\overline{AC}$, and $\overline{BC}$. With five collinear points *A*, *B*, *C*, *D*, and *E*, how many different segments can you name? 10

For Exercises 29–31, draw axes onto graph paper and locate point *A*(4, 0) as shown.

29. Draw $\overline{AB}$, where point *B* has coordinates $(2, -6)$.

30. Draw $\overrightarrow{OM}$ with endpoint (0, 0) that goes through point *M*(2, 2).

31. Draw $\overleftrightarrow{CD}$ through points $C(-2, 1)$ and $D(-2, -3)$.

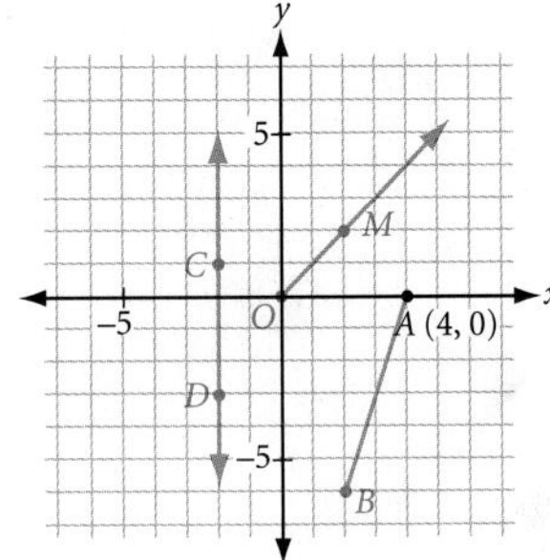

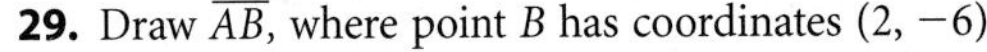

Career CONNECTION

Woodworkers use a tool called a plane to shave a rough wooden surface to create a perfectly smooth planar surface. The smooth board can then be made into a tabletop, a door, or a cabinet.

Woodworking is a very precise process. Producing high-quality pieces requires an understanding of lines, planes, and angles as well as careful measurements.

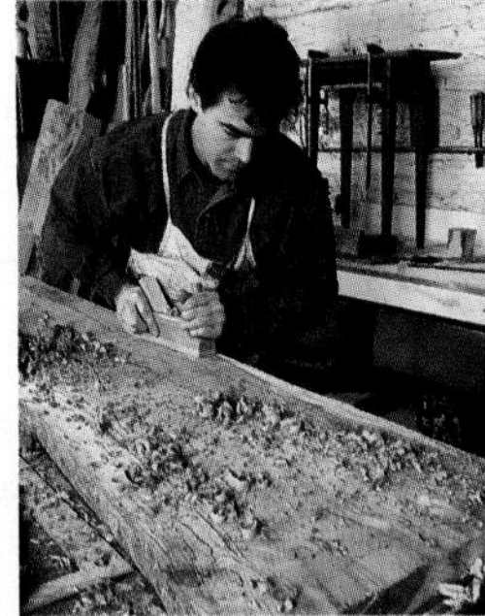

32. If the signs of the coordinates of collinear points $P(-6, -2)$, $Q(-5, 2)$, and $R(-4, 6)$ are reversed, are the three new points still collinear? Draw a picture and explain why. Yes, $P'(6, 2)$, $Q'(5, -2)$, $R'(4, -6)$; the slope between any two of the points is $\frac{4}{1}$.

33. Draw a segment with midpoint $N(-3, 2)$. Label it $\overline{PQ}$.

34. Copy triangle TRY shown at right. Use your ruler to find the midpoint A of side $\overline{TR}$ and the midpoint G of side $\overline{TY}$. Draw $\overline{AG}$.

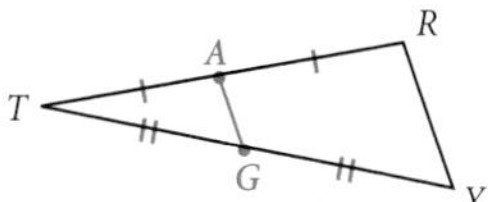

SPIRAL DESIGNS

The circle design shown below is used in a variety of cultures to create mosaic decorations. The spiral design may have been inspired by patterns in nature. Notice that the seeds on the sunflower also spiral out from the center.

Here are the steps to make the spirals.

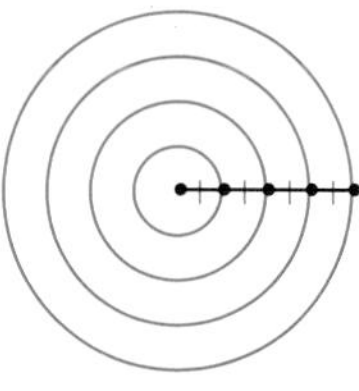
Step 1

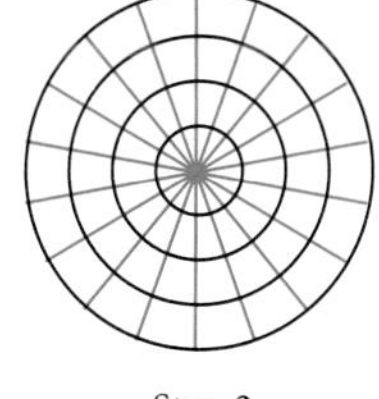
Step 2

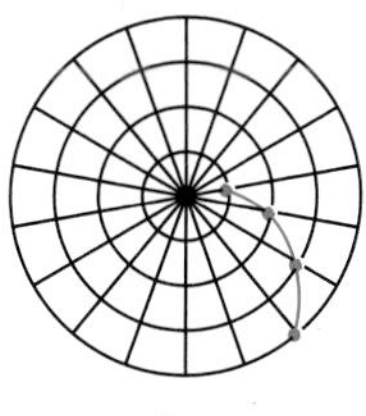
Step 3

Step 4

The more circles and radii you draw, the more detailed your design will be. Create and decorate your own spiral design.

32.

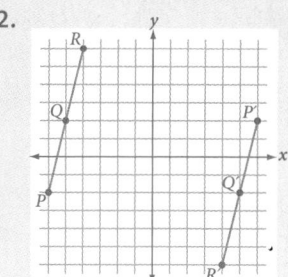

33. possible answer:

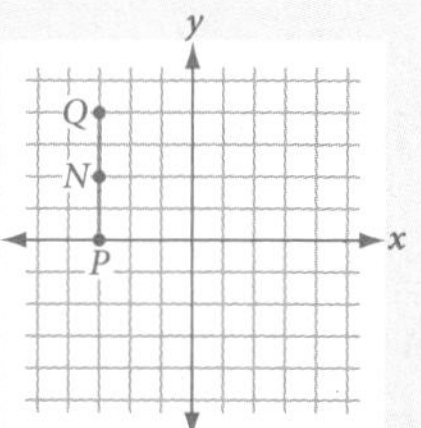

Exercise 34 [Ask] "Name a different way to find a midpoint." [measurement]

Supporting the project

When spirals occur in nature, the number of spirals is usually a Fibonacci number: a number in the sequence 1, 1, 2, 3, 5, 8, 13, 21, 34, 55, 89, ... The sunflower, for example, has 89 clockwise spirals and 34 counterclockwise spirals. The sample pattern has 18 spirals.

Students can use the dynamic geometry exploration at www.keymath.com/DG to better understand how to use compass and straightedge or geometry software to complete this project.

OUTCOMES

- Student uses concentric circles whose radii increase by a constant amount and segments divide the circle into equal sectors.
- The decoration of the design emphasizes the spirals.
- Student creates clockwise and counterclockwise spirals in one design.

Using Your Algebra Skills 1

PLANNING

LESSON OUTLINE

One day:

10 min Example

20 min Exercises

MATERIALS

- graph paper, *optional*

TEACHING

One step Present a problem like this one: A treasure is buried in a field halfway between a large rock and the tip of a pond. The tip of the pond is 250 feet east and 325 feet north of the rock. At what point should you dig for the treasure? [125 feet east and 162.5 feet north of the rock]

[Language] The coordinates are often referred to as *rectangular coordinates* because the axes are perpendicular, but the scales on the two axes may be different.

Midpoint

A midpoint is the point on a line segment that is the same distance from both endpoints.

You can think of a midpoint as being halfway between two locations. You know how to mark a midpoint. But when the position and location matter, such as in navigation and geography, you can use a coordinate grid and some algebra to find the exact location of the midpoint. You can calculate the coordinates of the midpoint of a segment on a coordinate grid using a formula.

Coordinate Midpoint Property

If (x_1, y_1) and (x_2, y_2) are the coordinates of the endpoints of a segment, then the coordinates of the midpoint are

$$\left(\frac{x_1 + x_2}{2}, \frac{y_1 + y_2}{2}\right)$$

History CONNECTION

Surveyors and mapmakers of ancient Egypt, China, Greece, and Rome used various coordinate systems to locate points. Egyptians made extensive use of square grids and used the first known rectangular coordinates at Saqqara around 2650 B.C.E. By the seventeenth century, the age of European exploration, the need for accurate maps and the development of easy-to-use algebraic symbols gave rise to modern coordinate geometry. Notice the lines of latitude and longitude in this seventeenth-century map.

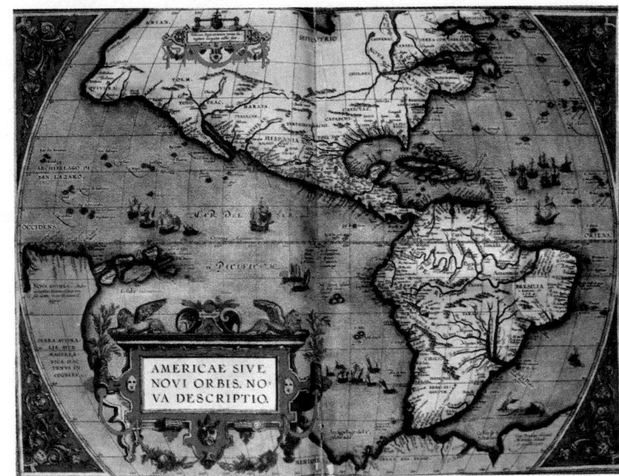

LESSON OBJECTIVES

- Review coordinate midpoint property

NCTM STANDARDS

	CONTENT		PROCESS
	Number		Problem Solving
✓	Algebra	✓	Reasoning
✓	Geometry		Communication
✓	Measurement	✓	Connections
	Data/Probability	✓	Representation

EXAMPLE Segment AB has endpoints $(-8, 5)$ and $(3, -6)$. Find the coordinates of the midpoint of $\overline{AB}$.

▶ Solution The midpoint is not on a grid intersection point, so we can use the coordinate midpoint property.

$$x = \frac{x_1 + x_2}{2} = \frac{(-8 + 3)}{2} = -2.5$$

$$y = \frac{y_1 + y_2}{2} = \frac{(5 + -6)}{2} = -0.5$$

The midpoint of $\overline{AB}$ is $(-2.5, -0.5)$.

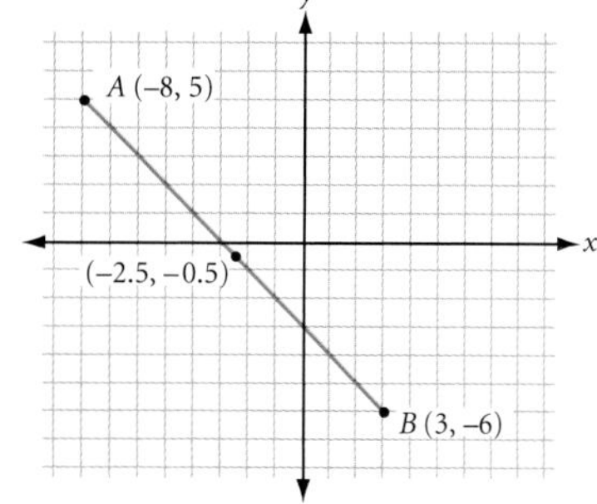

EXERCISES

For Exercises 1–3, find the coordinates of the midpoint of the segment with each pair of endpoints.

1. $(12, -7)$ and $(-6, 15)$ (3, 4)
2. $(-17, -8)$ and $(-1, 11)$ (−9, 1.5)
3. $(14, -7)$ and $(-3, 18)$ (5.5, 5.5)
4. One endpoint of a segment is $(12, -8)$. The midpoint is $(3, 18)$. Find the coordinates of the other endpoint. (−6, 44)
5. A classmate tells you, "Finding the coordinates of a midpoint is easy. You just find the averages." Is there any truth to it? Explain what you think your classmate means.
6. Find the two points on $\overline{AB}$ that divide the segment into three congruent parts. Point A has coordinates $(0, 0)$ and point B has coordinates $(9, 6)$. Explain your method.
7. Describe a way to find points that divide a segment into fourths. Find the midpoint, then find the midpoint of each half.
8. In each figure below, imagine drawing the diagonals $\overline{AC}$ and $\overline{BD}$.
   a. Find the midpoint of $\overline{AC}$ and the midpoint of $\overline{BD}$ in each figure.
   b. What do you notice about the midpoints?

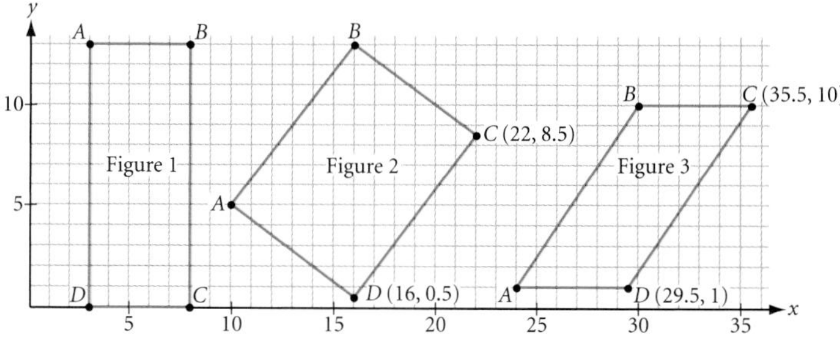

▶ EXAMPLE

Remind students as needed that the number halfway between two numbers is the average, or arithmetic mean. Each coordinate of a midpoint is the mean of the corresponding coordinates of the endpoints.

BUILDING UNDERSTANDING

Students will be trying to find the midpoints of line segments.

ASSIGNING HOMEWORK

Essential	1–4
Performance assessment	4
Journal	5–8

▶ Helping with the Exercises

Exercises 1–4 Watch for difficulty adding with negative numbers.

5. Yes. The coordinates of the midpoint of a segment with endpoints (a, b) and (c, d) are found by taking the average of the x-coordinates, $\frac{a+c}{2}$, and the average of the y-coordinates, $\frac{b+d}{2}$. Thus the midpoint is $\left(\frac{a+c}{2}, \frac{b+d}{2}\right)$.

Exercise 6 The extension made to the trisection is natural if students see the coordinates of the midpoint as means. **[Language]** A segment is *trisected* when it is divided into three congruent parts.

6. (3, 2) and (6, 4). To get the first point of trisection, sum the coordinates of points A and B to get (9, 6), then multiply those coordinates by $\frac{1}{3}$ to get (3, 2). To get the second point of trisection, sum the coordinates of points A and B to get (9, 6), then multiply those coordinates by $\frac{2}{3}$ to get (6, 4). This works because the coordinates of the first point are (0, 0).

Exercise 7 Another possible answer: Divide the sum of the x-coordinates by 4 and add the amount to the smaller x-coordinate three times to get the three x-coordinates of the three quarters. Do the same with the y-coordinates.

Exercise 8 Students will make a conjecture about the diagonals of a parallelogram in Lesson 5.5.

8a. Midpoints for Figure 1 are (5.5, 6.5), for Figure 2, (16, 6.75), and for Figure 3, (29.75, 5.5).

8b. For these figures the midpoints of the two diagonals are the same point.

LESSON

1.2

PLANNING

LESSON OUTLINE

One day:

10 min	Examples
15 min	Investigation
5 min	Sharing
15 min	Exercises

MATERIALS

- straightedges
- protractors
- Cool Pool (W) for One step

TEACHING

Angles can be defined, named, and measured. You can reinforce the concept of angle measure by using geometry software projected on a screen to show the measure of an angle changing as a ray is rotated. This is also a good way to begin introducing geometry software. There are many opportunities for you and your students to use geometry software for exploration and demonstration. As you do demonstrations, introduce students to the tools used to create the sketch.

You can start with the one-step investigation (page 39), or talk about the introductory material and work through the examples before starting students on the investigation in the student book.

LESSON

1.2

Poolroom Math

Inspiration is needed in geometry, just as much as in poetry.

ALEKSANDR PUSHKIN

People use angles every day. Plumbers measure the angle between connecting pipes to make a good fitting. Woodworkers adjust their saw blades to cut wood at just the correct angle. Air traffic controllers use angles to direct planes. And good pool players must know their angles to plan their shots.

Is the angle between the two hands of the wristwatch smaller than the angle between the hands of the large clock?

No. Angles are the same measure.

"Little Benji," the wristwatch

Big Ben at the Houses of Parliament in London, England

You can use the terms that you defined in Lesson 1.1 to write a precise definition of angle. An **angle** is formed by two rays that share a common endpoint, provided that the two rays are noncollinear. In other words, the rays cannot lie on the same line. The common endpoint of the two rays is the **vertex** of the angle. The two rays are the **sides** of the angle.

You can name the angle in the figure below angle *TAP* or angle *PAT*, or use the angle symbol and write $\angle TAP$ or $\angle PAT$. Notice that the vertex must be the middle letter, and the first and last letters each name a point on a different ray. Since there are no other angles with vertex *A*, you can also simply call this $\angle A$.

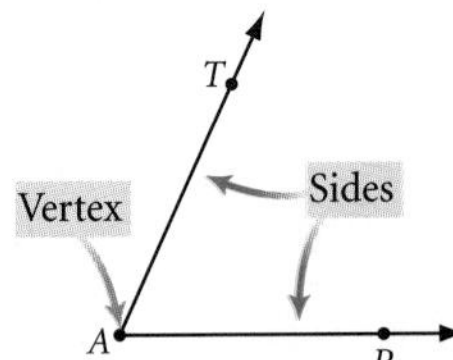

LESSON OBJECTIVES

- Learn how to show the measurement of angles and segments on figures
- Practice using the tools of measurement (protractor and ruler)
- Become familiar with the symbols for marking figures
- Learn the idea of congruence of angles
- Learn that in physical situations the incoming angle is equal in measure to the outgoing angle

NCTM STANDARDS

CONTENT		PROCESS	
	Number		Problem Solving
✓	Algebra	✓	Reasoning
✓	Geometry	✓	Communication
✓	Measurement		Connections
	Data/Probability	✓	Representation

Career
CONNECTION

In sports medicine, specialists may examine the healing rate of an injured joint by its angle of recovery. For example, a physician may assess how much physical therapy a patient needs by measuring the degree to which a patient can bend his or her ankle from the floor.

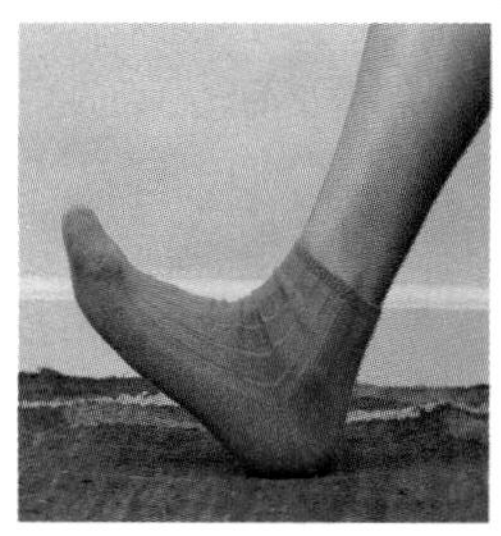

EXAMPLE A | Name all the angles in these drawings.

▶ Solution | The angles are ∠T, ∠V, ∠TUV, ∠1, ∠TUR, ∠XAY, ∠YAZ, and ∠XAZ. (Did you get them all?) Notice that ∠1 is a shorter way to name ∠RUV.

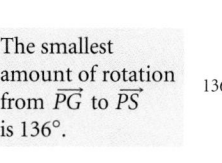

Which angles in Example A seem big to you? Which seem small? The **measure of an angle** is the smallest amount of rotation about the vertex from one ray to the other, measured in **degrees.** According to this definition, the measure of an angle can be any value between 0° and 180°.

The smallest amount of rotation from $\overrightarrow{PG}$ to $\overrightarrow{PS}$ is 136°.

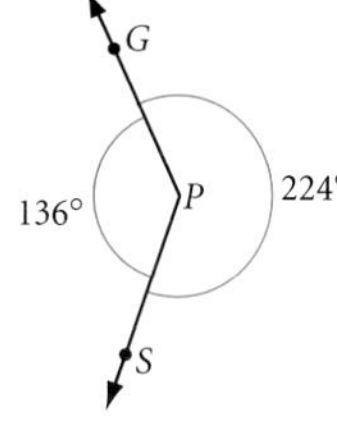

The geometry tool you use to measure an angle is a **protractor.** Here's how you use it.

Step 1: Place the center mark of the protractor on the vertex.

Step 2: Line up the 0-mark with one side of the angle.

Step 3: Read the measure on the protractor scale.

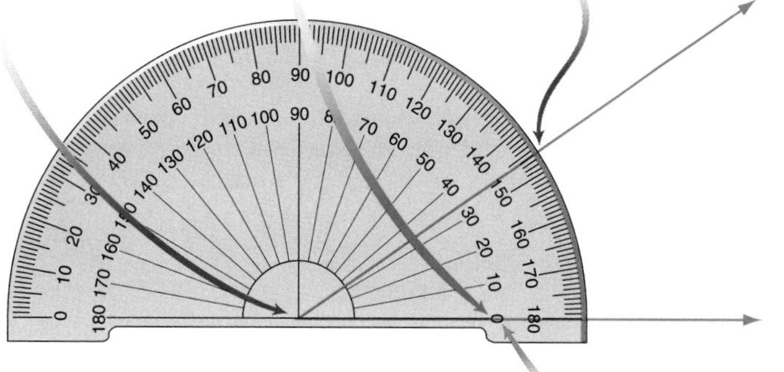

Step 4: Be sure you read the scale that has the 0-mark you are using! The angle in the diagram measures 34° and not 146°.

A television antenna is a physical model of an angle. Note that changing the length of the antenna doesn't change the angle.

One step Pass out the Cool Pool worksheet. **[Ask]** "At what angle would you hit the ball *Q* so that it would bounce off the cushions at least four times but not touch the line segment *CP*?" As you circulate, tell students that they should help each other rather than ask you for answers. If students have difficulty communicating with each other, suggest that they label the points at which the ball touches the cushions. Decide which students should present their results based on their using a variety of approaches; at least one approach should take into account that the incoming and outgoing angles have the same measure. During Sharing, allow the notions of angle measure, congruence, and bisector to arise from student work, and be sure that the class practices reading the angles in student presentations. Then go through the examples if needed. Also pose other problems from the investigation as time permits.

▶ EXAMPLE A

Ask students what the letters *TUV,* without the angle sign, might mean. Possible confusion with a triangle or an arc makes it important to include the word *angle* or the symbol ∠ before the letters *TUV.*

▶ EXAMPLE B

Demonstrate to the class how to use a protractor for measuring angles and how to label figures to reflect angle measures. You can do this by using a transparent protractor on the overhead projector or by using a large classroom protractor on the board.

Before using a protractor to measure an angle, students should decide whether the angle is acute or obtuse. This will help them when they use the two scales on most protractors.

[Alert] Students may need to be reminded that the scale lined up with zero on one ray of the angle determines the scale to use to read the angle measure. **[Alert]** The center mark can be different for different protractors, so lining up the angle with zero is very important. If you find that students are not as proficient as you would like, use the Practice Your Skills worksheet for Lesson 1.2.

▶ EXAMPLE C

The two smaller angles created when an angle is bisected have equal measure. Naming these angles requires three letters, because there is not just one angle at the vertex.

Some students may also deduce that $\angle YMO \cong \angle EMN$. They are not expected to conclude that until later in the course.

Guiding the Investigation

You can illustrate the concept of a billiard ball hitting the side of a pool table at the beginning of the investigation by rolling a ball along the floor and having it bounce off the wall. Use this illustration to bring out the terms *incoming* and *outgoing angles.* **[ESL]** Though *income* can mean "money earned" (money coming in), here *incoming* means "coming in" and *outgoing* means "going out."

To show the measure of an angle, use an *m* before the angle symbol. For example, $m\angle ZAP = 34°$ means the measure of $\angle ZAP$ is 34 degrees.

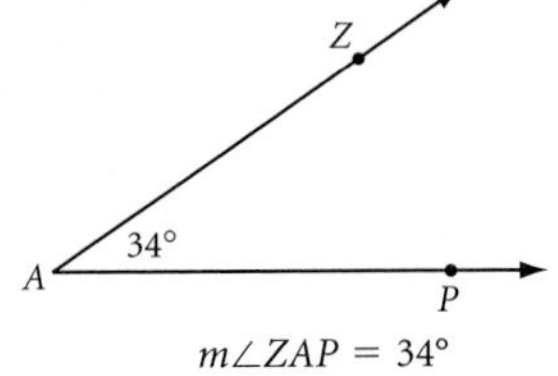

$m\angle ZAP = 34°$

EXAMPLE B Use your protractor to measure these angles as accurately as you can. Which ones measure more than 90°?

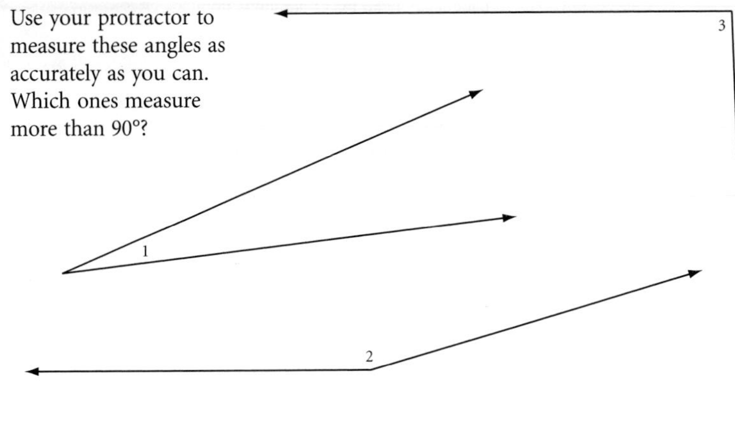

▶ Solution Measuring to the nearest degree, you should get these approximate answers. (The symbol ≈ means "is approximately equal to.")

$m\angle 1 \approx 16°$ $\quad$ $m\angle 3 \approx 92°$

$m\angle 2 \approx 164°$ $\quad$ $\angle 2$ and $\angle 3$ measure more than 90°.

Two angles are **congruent angles** if and only if they have the same measure. You use identical markings to show that two angles in a figure are congruent.

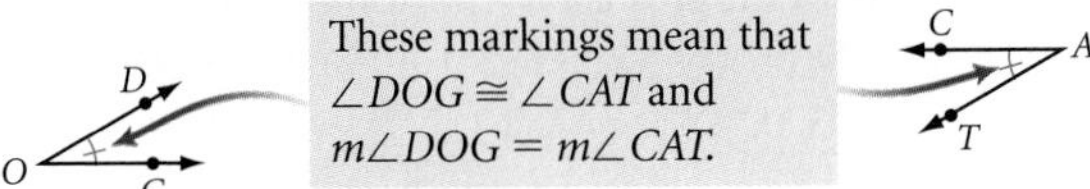

A ray is the **angle bisector** if it contains the vertex and divides the angle into two congruent angles. In the figure at right, $\overrightarrow{CD}$ bisects $\angle ACB$ so that $\angle ACD \cong \angle BCD$.

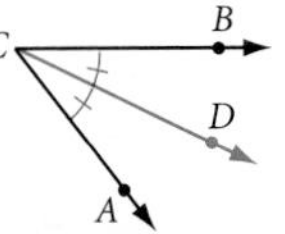

Science CONNECTION

Earth takes 365.25 days to travel a full 360° around the Sun. That means that each day, Earth travels a little less than 1° in its orbit around the Sun. Meanwhile, Earth also completes one full rotation each day, making the Sun appear to rise and set. By how many degrees does the Sun's position in the sky change every hour?

Some students may point out that a spinning ball (one with "English") will have a different outgoing angle. The student book assumes the ball has no spin.

Steps 4, 5 These steps are optional. *How* refers to where the ball will be aimed.

Step 5 You might challenge students to explore how much the aim can vary from hitting $\overline{AW}$ at a right angle and still have the ball hit cushions four times without hitting $\overline{CP}$. If the ball hits $\overline{AW}$ on the half of the cushion closer to *W,* the angle could be as small as about 65°. As long as the ball comes to a rest after at most seven bounces, it will not hit $\overline{CP}$. If the condition is that there are at least three bounces before it hits $\overline{CP}$, the angle could be smaller.

As you circulate while groups work on the investigation, look for students with differing approaches, and perhaps differing answers, to present. Save corrections and comments, other than encouragement, for Sharing. Encourage students to check the work of others in their group so that they can correct errors in using protractors.

EXAMPLE C

Look for angle bisectors and congruent angles in the figures below.

a. Name each angle bisector and the angle it bisects.

b. Name all the congruent angles in the figure. Use the congruence symbol and name the angles so there is no confusion about which angle you mean.

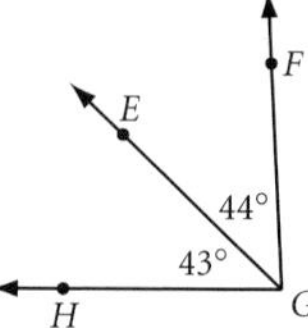

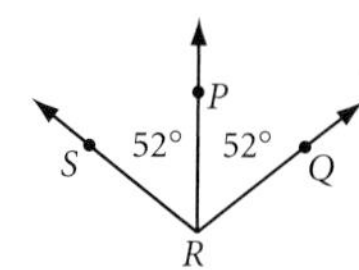

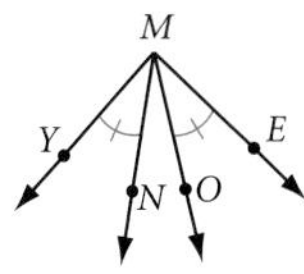

▸ ***Solution***

a. Use the angle bisector definition. $\angle SRP \cong \angle PRQ$, so $\overrightarrow{RP}$ bisects $\angle SRQ$.

b. $\angle SRP \cong \angle PRQ$ and $\angle YMN \cong \angle OME$.

Investigation
Virtual Pool

Outgoing angle

Cushion

Incoming angle

Pocket billiards, or pool, is a game of angles. When a ball bounces off the pool table's cushion, its path forms two angles with the edge of the cushion. The **incoming angle** is formed by the cushion and the path of the ball approaching the cushion.

The **outgoing angle** is formed by the cushion and the path of the ball leaving the cushion. As it turns out, the measure of the outgoing angle equals the measure of the incoming angle.

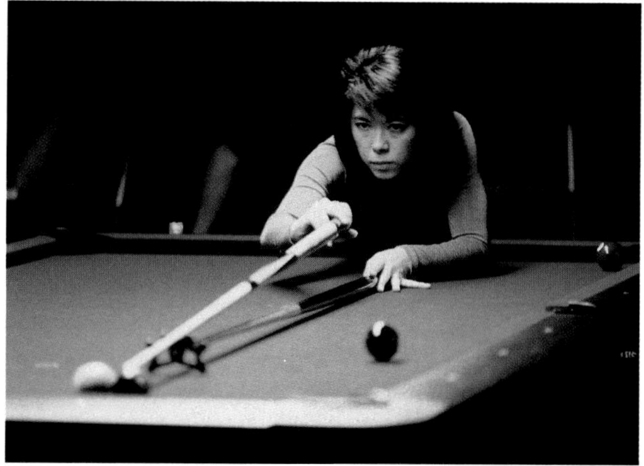

Computer scientist Nesli O'Hare is also a professional pool player.

SHARING IDEAS

Have each selected student present a solution to one problem in the investigation. Encourage discussion and critique of the approaches. If students reject an approach only because it differs from their own, try to encourage an open mind and rational critique. Watch carefully to be sure that students are naming angles correctly, especially when angles have a common vertex. If other students don't ask about an error, press for clarification to help students learn to think carefully and catch their own errors.

[Ask] "What is an angle, anyway? How might we define it?" Encourage ideas before pointing out the book's definition and asking for a critique. **[Ask]** "Does it make sense that the sides of angles are rays, that they are infinitely long? Are angles like lines in that the illustration shows only a part? Does the measure of the angle depend on how long the sides are drawn? Are angles still congruent if rays are drawn longer on one angle?" Note that the letter *m* is used for measure of an angle, as it was for length of a line segment. **[Ask]** "How will we be able to tell what kind of measure the letter *m* is referring to?"

[Ask] "What's *meant* by the measure of an angle?" Again consult the student book.
[Ask] "Why does the definition specify *smallest* amount of rotation?" [There needs to be just one measure for each angle, but you could also arrive at the same ray position by rotating in the opposite direction or by going a full rotation past the terminal ray.] You can postpone introducing the concept of the measure of a reflex angle (an angle with measure greater than 180°) until students explore properties of concave polygons.

Sharing Ideas (continued)

[Alert] Make sure students can distinguish between when a number inside an angle indicates its name and when it includes a degree symbol and thus indicates the measure of the angle.

[Link] In other math courses, such as trigonometry, angle measures can be 0°, 180°, greater than 180°, or even negative. In this book we won't use other angle-measure units, such as radians (which divide a circle into 2π units).

[Ask] "How accurate is your protractor?" This question might arise from student reports about pool angles such as $35\frac{1}{2}°$. Elicit the idea that any measurement is only an approximation. A board protractor scaled by 5° units would be less accurate than a protractor whose arc is divided by 1° units. With more precise tools, it is possible to measure angles to the nearest minute $\left(\frac{1}{60}\text{ of a degree}\right)$ or even second $\left(\frac{1}{60}\text{ of a minute}\right)$. The measure 46° 24′ 17″ is read "46 degrees 24 minutes 17 seconds."

Sharing Ideas (continued)

[Ask] "How does the book define congruent angles?"

[Language] *If and only if* means that the implication holds in both directions. Here: "If two angles have the same measure, they are congruent" and "If two angles are congruent, they have the same measure." Ask about the analogies between congruence of angles and congruence of line segments.

[Ask] "How do we mark congruent angles?"

[Ask] "Where besides pool tables are angles used?" [Navigation is one context. The angles that air-traffic controllers use to direct planes are measured from north; the term *bearing* is used to indicate the direction a plane is heading measured as an angle east or west of due north.]

Students might like to discuss more difficult pool shots.

Assessing Progress

Watch for voluntary use of terms from earlier lessons, such as *symmetry, rotation, straightedge, compass, ray, segment, plane.* Keep an eye on how well individuals are contributing to their group. Remind yourself that students don't "either understand it or not" but rather go through many different levels of understanding. Your goal is to assess the levels that students have attained so far.

Closing the Lesson

An **angle** consists of two rays and their common endpoint, the angle's **vertex.** The **measure** of an angle is the smallest amount of rotation about the vertex from one ray (**side**) to the other, measured in **degrees,** 360° to a complete rotation. Angles can be measured with **protractors.** Two angles that have the same measure are **congruent.** A ray is the **bisector** of an angle if its endpoint is the angle's vertex and it divides the angle into two congruent angles.

Use your protractor to study these shots.

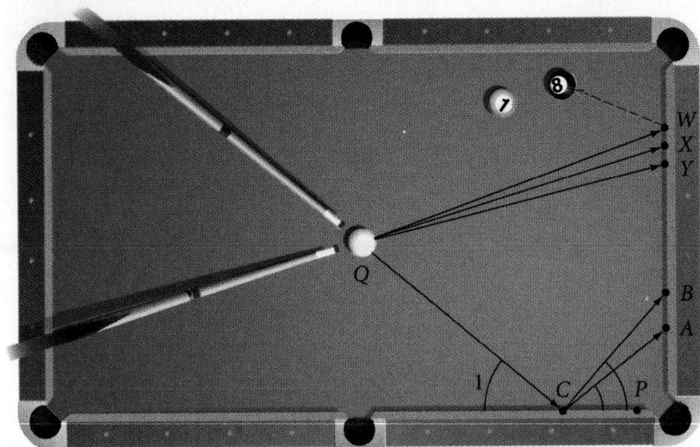

Step 4 You would hit it perpendicular to $\overleftrightarrow{AB}$. (Students have not studied the term yet, but they might say it should hit at a 90° angle.)

Step 5 You would hit it parallel to $\overline{CP}$ (or hit cushion $\overline{AW}$ at an angle greater than 80°).

Step 1 Use your protractor to find the measure of $\angle 1$. Which is the correct outgoing angle? Which point—*A* or *B*—will the ball hit? $m\angle 1 = 47°$; *B*

Step 2 Which point on the cushion—*W, X,* or *Y*—should the white ball hit so that the ray of the outgoing angle passes through the center of the 8-ball? *W*

Step 3 Compare your results with your group members' results. Does everyone agree?

Step 4 How would you hit the white ball against the cushion so that the ball passes over the same spot on the way back?

Step 5 How would you hit the ball so that it bounces off three different points on the cushions, without ever touching cushion $\overleftrightarrow{CP}$?

EXERCISES

1. Name each angle in three different ways. $\angle TEN$, $\angle NET$, $\angle E$; $\angle FOU$, $\angle UOF$, $\angle 1$; $\angle ROU$, $\angle UOR$, $\angle 2$

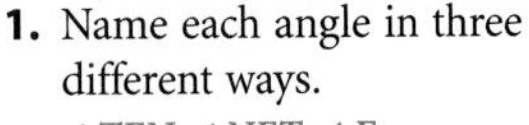

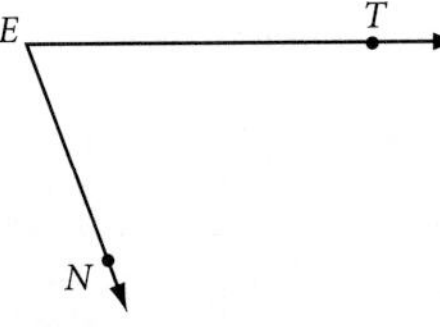

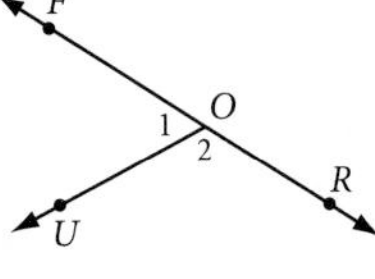

For Exercises 2–4, draw and label each angle.

2. $\angle TAN$
3. $\angle BIG$
4. $\angle SML$

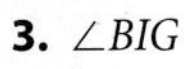

5. For each figure at right, list the angles that you can name using only the vertex letter. $\angle S$, $\angle P$, $\angle R$, $\angle Q$; none in the second figure

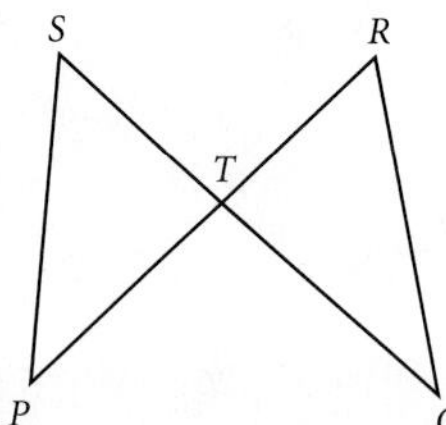

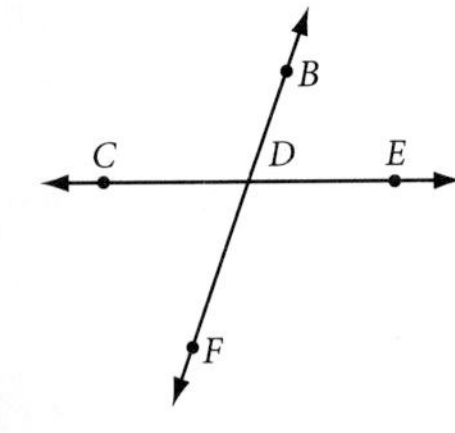

Exercise 1 Students might argue that $\angle FOR$ is an angle, but we are not including straight angles in the definition of *angle.*

2.

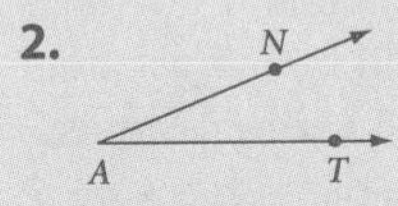

3.

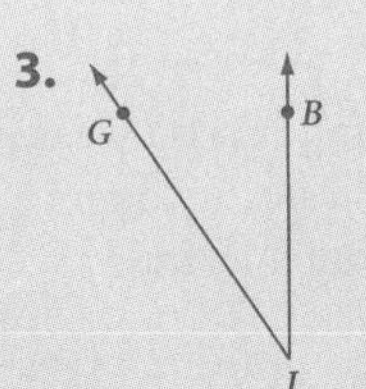

4.

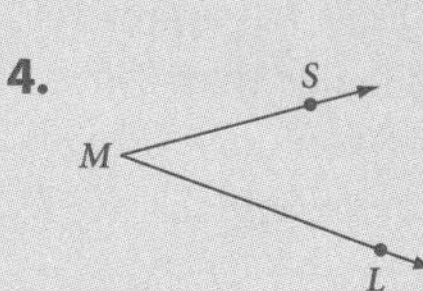

6. Draw a figure that contains at least three angles and requires three letters to name each angle. possible answer:

For Exercises 7–14, find the measure of each angle.

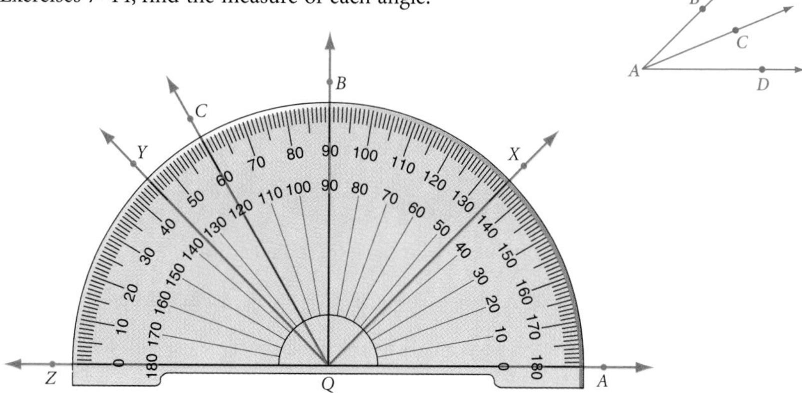

7. $m\angle AQB \approx$? 90° **8.** $m\angle AQC \approx$? 120° **9.** $m\angle XQA \approx$? 45° **10.** $m\angle AQY \approx$? 135°

11. $m\angle ZQY \approx$? 45° **12.** $m\angle ZQX \approx$? 135° **13.** $m\angle CQB \approx$? ⓗ 30° **14.** $m\angle XQY \approx$? 90°

For Exercises 15–19, use your protractor to find the measure of the angle to the nearest degree.

15. $m\angle MAC \approx$? 69°

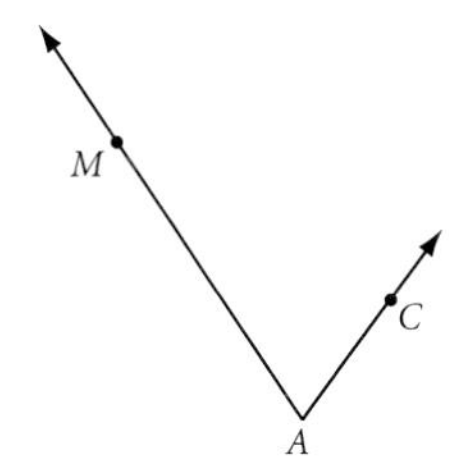
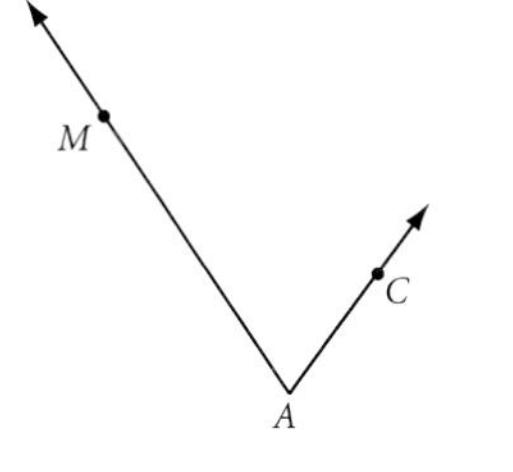

16. $m\angle IBM \approx$? 110°

17. $m\angle S \approx$? 40°

18. $m\angle SON \approx$? 125°

19. $m\angle NOR \approx$? 55°

20. Which angle below has the greater measure, $\angle SML$ or $\angle BIG$? Why?
$\angle SML$ has the greater measure because $m\angle SML \approx 30°$ and $m\angle BIG \approx 20°$.

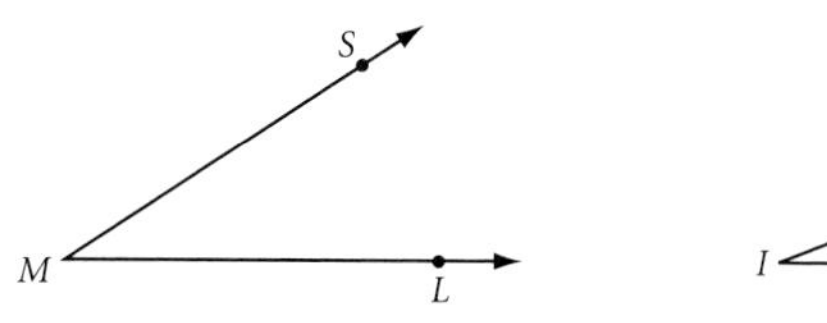

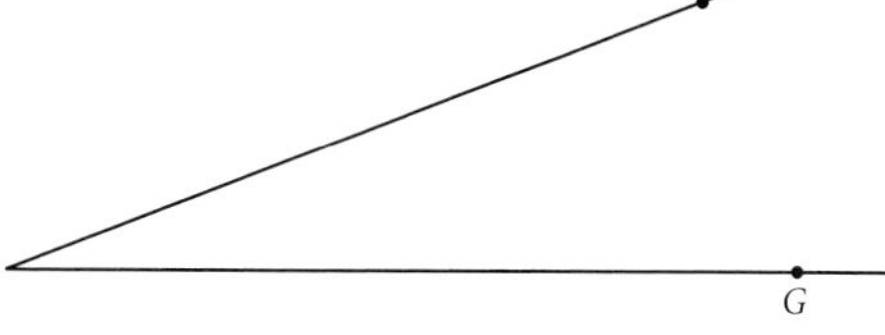

Exercise 20 The lengths of the drawn rays have nothing to do with the angle measure.

BUILDING UNDERSTANDING

Encourage students to enter their work in their notebooks. As needed, remind them to label their figures with appropriate markings. Emphasize the importance of good notation and accurate measuring in completing the exercises.

ASSIGNING HOMEWORK

Essential	2–40 evens
Performance assessment	27, 39
Portfolio	34, 41
Journal	44
Group	1–25 odds, 29–35 odds
Review	42–44

MATERIALS

- Exercises 7–14 (T), *optional*
- Exercises 39 and 40 (T), *optional*

▶ Helping with the Exercises

Exercises 2–4 If students ask questions like "Where do I put *T* and *A* and *N*?" say that they are to put the points anywhere convenient for drawing an angle.

Exercise 6 [Alert] Some students may have difficulty with drawings that have angles that must be named with three letters. Tracing the angle with their index finger may help them name the angle. Or they can use the middle letter and find the vertex first.

Exercises 7–14 Here the symbol ≈ is used instead of = because all measurements are approximate.

Exercises 13, 14 Encourage students to check their results using addition.

Exercises 15–25 If students are having trouble understanding how to use a protractor, you might refer them to the dynamic geometry exploration at www.keymath.com/DG.

21.

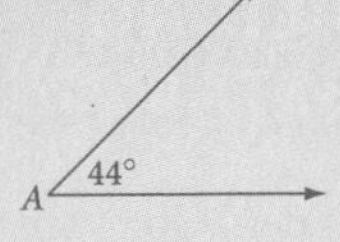

22.

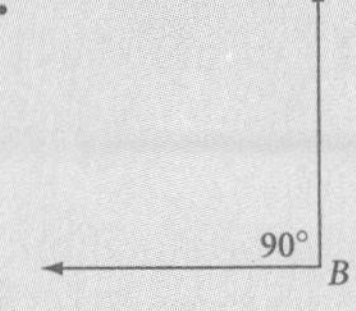

23.

C
135°
D E

24.

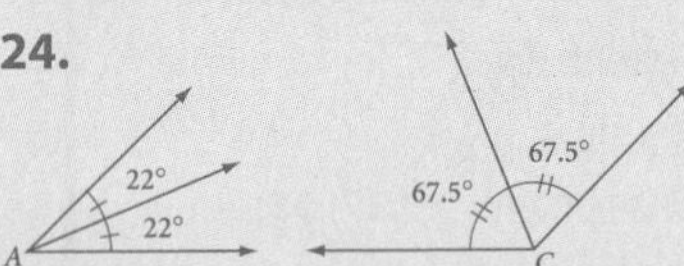

25. no

Exercises 26–29 Ask students to explain their reasoning. Students with digital watches may need to study an analog watch or clock. They should be careful to note the exact placement of the hour hand. For example, at 3:40 the minute hand has moved two-thirds of its complete rotation from 12 about the clock face, so the hour hand must have moved two-thirds of the way from 3 to 4.

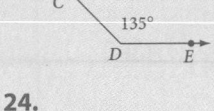

26.

27.

28.

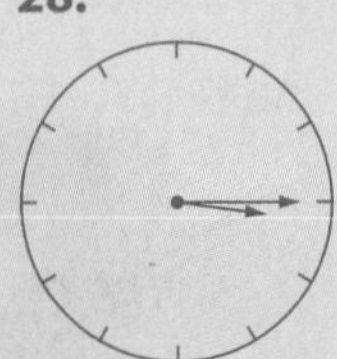

For Exercises 21–23, use your protractor to draw angles with these measures. Label them.

21. $m\angle A = 44°$ **22.** $m\angle B = 90°$ **23.** $m\angle CDE = 135°$

24. Use your protractor to draw the angle bisector of $\angle A$ in Exercise 21 and the angle bisector of $\angle D$ in Exercise 23. Use markings to show that the two halves are congruent.

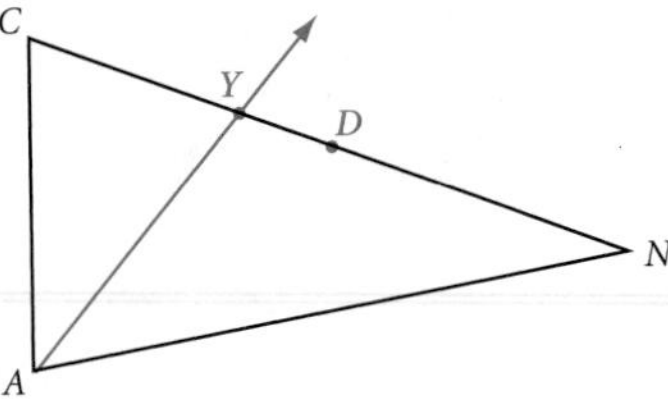

25. Copy triangle *CAN* shown at right. Use your protractor to find the angle bisector of $\angle A$. Label the point where it crosses $\overline{CN}$ point *Y*. Use your ruler to find the midpoint of $\overline{CN}$ and label it *D*. Are *D* and *Y* the same point?

For Exercises 26–28, draw a clock face with hands to show these times.

26. 3:30 Ⓗ **27.** 3:40 **28.** 3:15

29. Give an example of a time when the angle made by the hands of the clock will be greater than 90°. One possibility is 4:00.

For Exercises 30–33, copy each figure and mark it with all the given information.

30. $TH = 6$
$m\angle THO = 90°$
$OH = 8$

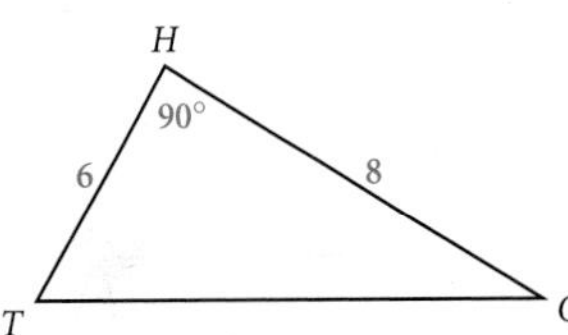

31. $RA = SA$
$m\angle T = m\angle H$
$RT = SH$

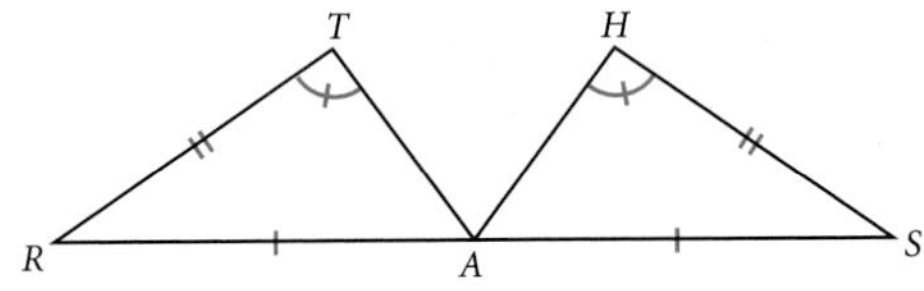

32. $AT = AG$ $\angle AGT \cong \angle ATG$
$AI = AN$ $GI = TN$

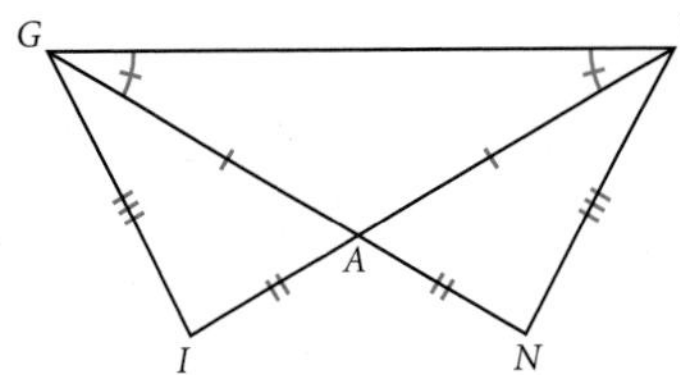

33. $\overline{BW} \cong \overline{TI}$ $\angle WBT \cong \angle ITB$
$\overline{WO} \cong \overline{IO}$ $\angle BWO \cong \angle TIO$

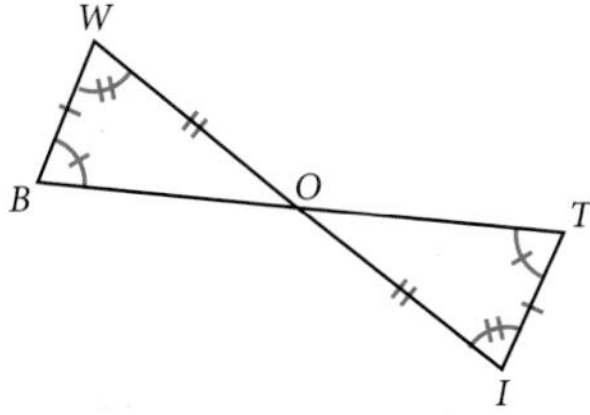

For Exercises 34 and 35, write down what you know from the markings. Do not use your protractor or your ruler.

34. $MI =$? MY
$IC =$? CK
$m\angle M =$? $m\angle I$

Y E
K C
M I

35. $\angle MEO \cong$? $\angle SEU$
$\angle SUE \cong$? $\angle EUO$
$OU =$? MO

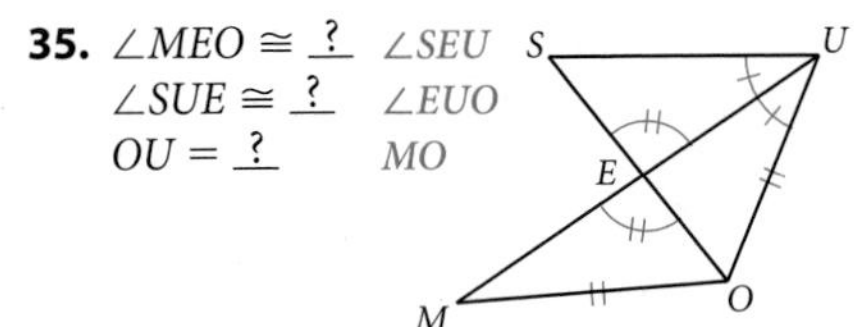

For Exercises 36–38, do not use a protractor. Recall from Chapter 0 that a complete rotation around a point is 360°. Find the angle measures represented by each letter.

36. ⓗ

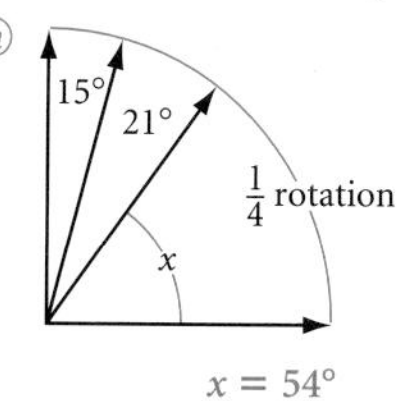

$x = 54°$

37.

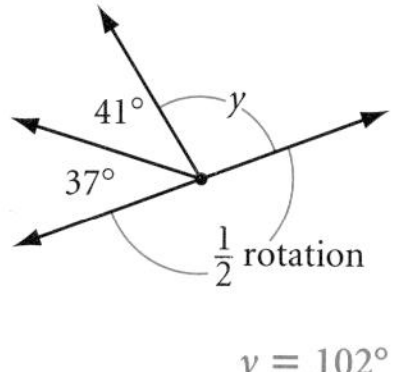

$y = 102°$

38.

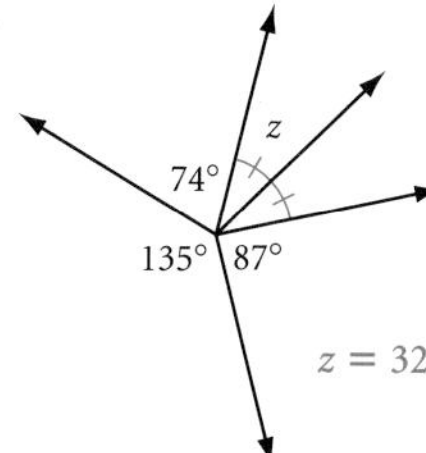

$z = 32°$

39. If the 4-ball is hit as shown, will it go into the corner pocket? Find the path of the ball using only your protractor and straightedge. no

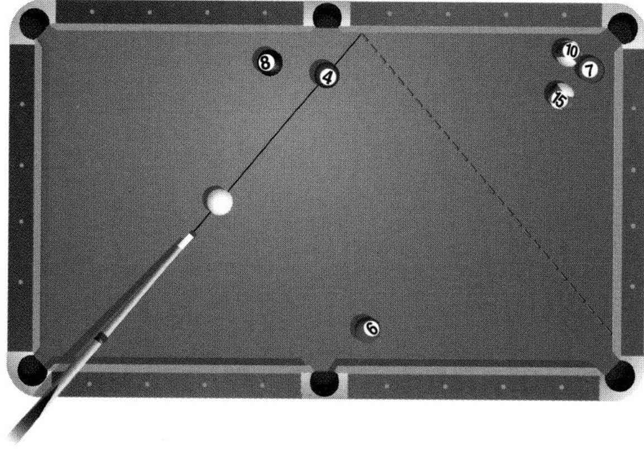

40. What is the measure of the incoming angle? Which point will the ball pass through? Use your protractor to find out. 73°, point *B*

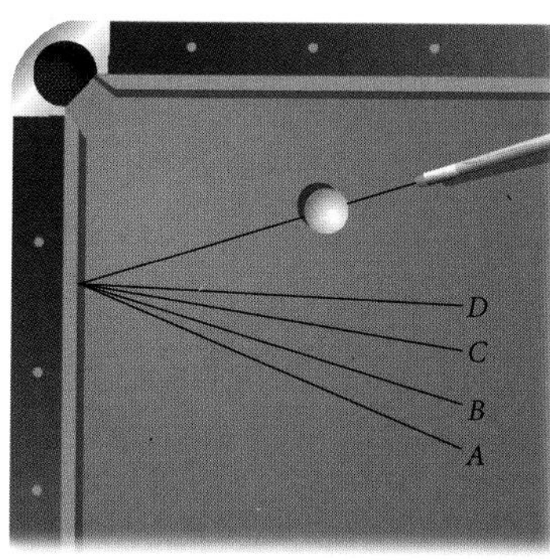

41. The principle you just learned for billiard balls is also true for a ray of light reflecting from a mirror. What you "see" in the mirror is actually light from an object bouncing off the mirror and traveling to your eye.

Will you be able to see your shoes in this mirror? Copy the illustration and draw rays to show the light traveling from your shoes to the mirror and back to your eye. yes

Exercises 36–41 Have students explain their reasoning.

42. 12 cm; 6 cm, 6 cm

44. $MS = DG$ means that the distance between M and S equals the distance between D and G. $MS \cong DG$ means that segment MS is congruent to segment DG. The first statement equates two numbers. The second statement concerns the congruence between two geometric figures. However, they convey the same information and are marked the same way on a diagram.

EXTENSION

Show the Walt Disney video *Donald in Mathemagic Land.* (Pool shots are part of the fun. The video is now out of print, but look for it on the Internet.)

Review

UYAS 1 **42.** Use your ruler to draw a segment with length 12 cm. Then use your ruler to locate the midpoint. Label and mark the figure.

UYAS 1 **43.** The balancing point of an object is called its *center of gravity*. Where is the center of gravity of a thin, rodlike piece of wire or tubing? Copy the thin wire shown below onto your paper. Mark the balance point or center of gravity.

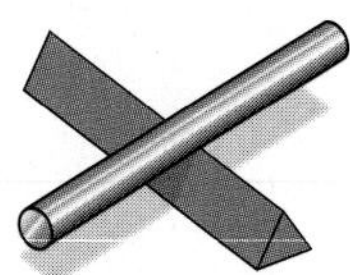

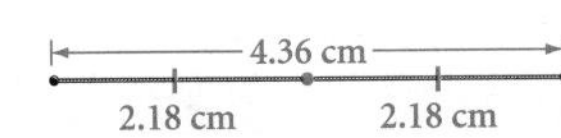

1.1 **44.** Explain the difference between $MS = DG$ and $\overline{MS} \cong \overline{DG}$.

IMPROVING YOUR VISUAL THINKING SKILLS

Coin Swap I and II

1. Arrange two dimes and two pennies on a grid of five squares, as shown. Your task is to switch the position of the two dimes and two pennies in exactly eight moves. A coin can slide into an empty square next to it, or it can jump over one coin into an empty space. Record your solution by drawing eight diagrams that show the moves.

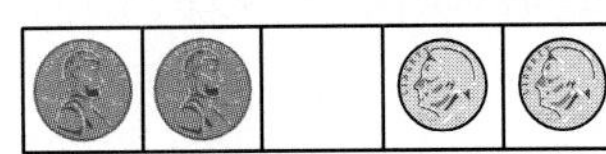

2. Arrange three dimes and three pennies on a grid of seven squares, as shown. Follow the same rules as above to switch the position of the three dimes and three pennies in exactly 15 moves. Record your solution by listing in order which coin is moved. For example, your list might begin PDP. . . .

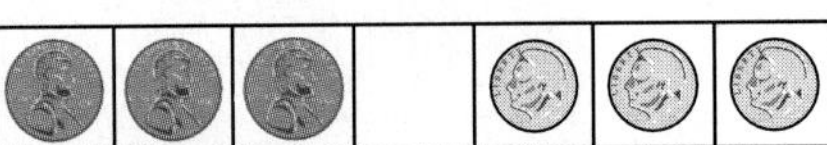

IMPROVING VISUAL THINKING SKILLS

1.

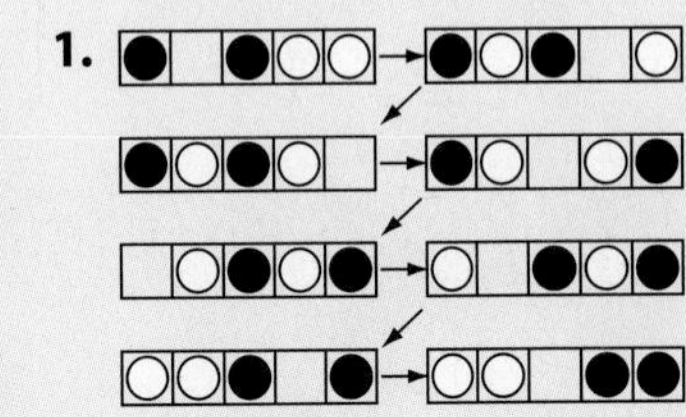

2. PDDPPPDDDPPPDDP

These are possible solutions. For example the first solution could be written PDDPPDDP, and DPPDDPPD is also a solution. You might ask students about the symmetry of these solutions.

LESSON

1.3

What's a Widget?

Good definitions are very important in geometry. In this lesson you will write your own geometry definitions.

Which creatures in the last group are Widgets?

"When I use a word," Humpty replied in a scornful tone, "it means just what I choose it to mean—neither more nor less." "The question is," said Alice, "whether you can make a word mean so many different things."
LEWIS CARROLL

Widgets

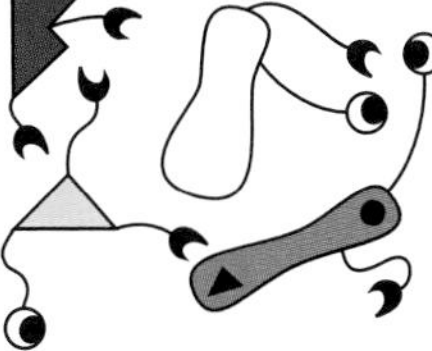

Not Widgets

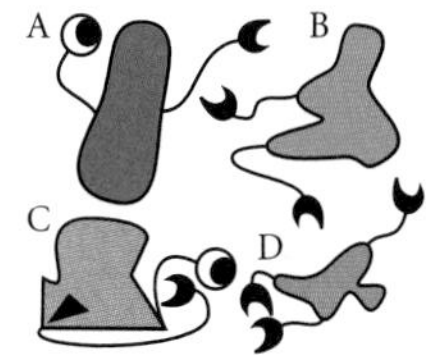

Who are Widgets? A

You might have asked yourself, "What things do all the Widgets have in common, and what things do Widgets have that others do not have?" In other words, what characteristics make a Widget a Widget? They all have colorful bodies with nothing else inside; two tails—one like a crescent moon, the other like an eyeball.

By observing what a Widget is and what a Widget isn't, you identified the characteristics that distinguish a Widget from a non-Widget. Based on these characteristics, you should have selected A as the only Widget in the last group. This same process can help you write good definitions of geometric figures.

This statement defines a protractor: "A protractor is a geometry tool used to measure angles." First, you classify what it is (a geometry tool), then you say how it differs from other geometry tools (it is the one you use to measure angles). What should go in the blanks to define a square?

A square is a ________ that ________.

Classify it. What is it? How does it differ from others?

Once you've written a definition, you should test it. To do this, you look for a **counterexample.** That is, try to create a figure that fits your definition but *isn't* what you're trying to define. If you can come up with a counterexample for your definition, you don't have a good definition.

EXAMPLE A

Everyone knows, "A square is a figure with four equal sides." What's wrong with this definition?

a. Sketch a counterexample. (You can probably find more than one!)

b. Write a better definition for a square.

NCTM STANDARDS

CONTENT		PROCESS	
	Number		Problem Solving
	Algebra		Reasoning
✓	Geometry	✓	Communication
✓	Measurement	✓	Connections
	Data/Probability	✓	Representation

LESSON OBJECTIVES

- Practice writing definitions
- Define special angle relationships
- Explore more vocabulary
- Develop critical thinking

LESSON

1.3

PLANNING

LESSON OUTLINE

One day:

20 min Investigation
5 min Sharing
5 min Closing
15 min Exercises

MATERIALS

- rulers
- protractors

TEACHING

Have individuals or groups think about the question of which figures are widgets and share their ideas about a definition of *widget.* If someone points out a nonwidget that satisfies a proposed definition, introduce the word *counterexample.*
[ESL] It will help students to pronounce out loud the new terms and any words in the book that may be new to them, such as *counterexample.*
[Language] *Widget* is used here as a nonsense word. The dictionary defines *widget* as "a small mechanical device whose name is not known."

You might begin the one-step investigation on page 48 or for more structure talk through the introductory material and examples and then engage students in the investigation.

▶ *EXAMPLE A*

This example helps students grasp the idea of a counter-example. Challenge students to answer the question before turning the page.

One step Direct the attention of the class to the examples of angles in the investigation. Ask each group to agree on a definition of each term, or divide the terms among the groups. As you circulate, concentrate on observing carefully and quietly and avoid telling. If you sit with a group, having the same eye level will help keep the group focused on itself rather than on you and students will be less likely to try to manipulate you into doing their thinking for them. During Sharing, have the class analyze the student book's definitions of *parallel* and *perpendicular* lines, and if needed read through Example A.

► *EXAMPLE B*

Some students may wonder "What if one line is in the plane and the other isn't?" If so, they're thinking of the plane as fixed, as if there is only one plane in the geometric space. When we say "lines in the same plane" we mean "there's a plane through the two lines."

You might also mention that segments are parallel if the lines containing them are parallel.

You could also say that the phrase "is perpendicular to" is represented by the symbol $\perp$. Ask the class to discuss the question. The definition of *parallel lines* must include "in the same plane" to exclude skew lines. For *perpendicular lines,* we do not need to say "in the same plane" because it's impossible for the lines to meet if they are not in the same plane.

► *Solution*

You probably noticed that "figure" is not specific enough to classify a square, and that "four equal sides" does not specify how it differs from the first counterexample shown below.

a. Three counterexamples are shown here, and you may have found others, too.

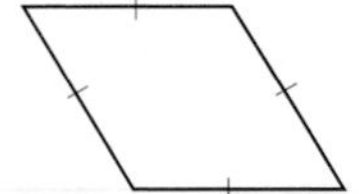
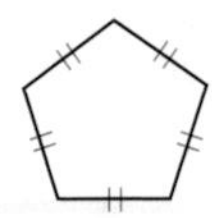
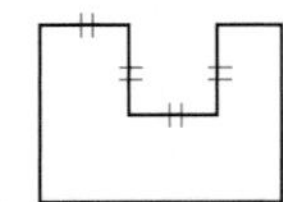

b. One better definition is "A square is a 4-sided figure that has all sides congruent and all angles measuring 90 degrees."

A restaurant counter example

Beginning Steps to Creating a Good Definition

1. **Classify** your term. What is it? ("A square is a 4-sided figure . . .")
2. **Differentiate** your term. How does it differ from others in that class? (". . . that has four congruent sides and four right angles.")
3. **Test** your definition by looking for a counterexample.

Ready to write a couple of definitions? First, here are two more types of markings that are very important in geometry.

The same number of arrow marks indicates that lines are parallel. The symbol $\parallel$ means "is parallel to." A small square in the corner of an angle indicates that it measures 90°. The symbol $\perp$ means "is perpendicular to."

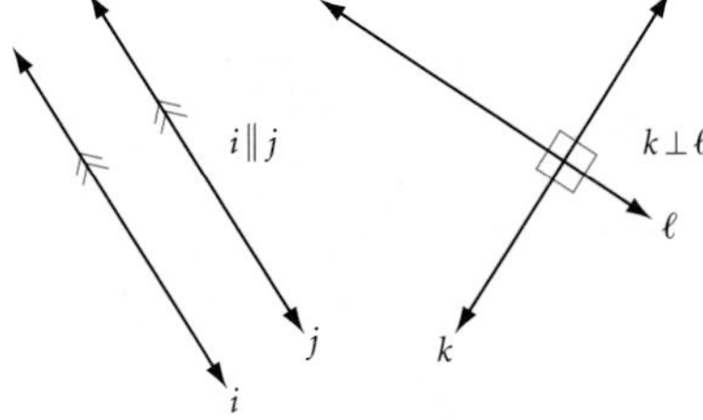

EXAMPLE B

Define these terms:

a. Parallel lines

b. Perpendicular lines

► *Solution*

Following these steps, classify and differentiate each term.

Classify. Differentiate.

a. Parallel lines are lines in the same plane that never meet.

b. Perpendicular lines are lines that meet at 90° angles.

Why do you need to say "in the same plane" for parallel lines but not for perpendicular lines? Sketch or demonstrate a counterexample to show the following definition is incomplete: "Parallel lines are lines that never meet." (Two lines that do not intersect and are noncoplanar are **skew** lines.)

[Link] You might mention that the field of projective geometry grew out of the study of properties shared by all two-dimensional pictures of the same three-dimensional scene. In projective geometry, there are no parallel lines. What we might think of as parallel lines are said to meet at "a point at infinity." The geometry we're studying in this course, called *Euclidean geometry,* is just one of many geometries. Several non-Euclidean geometries in addition to projective geometry were developed after about 1850.

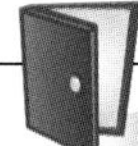

Investigation
Defining Angles

Here are some examples and non-examples of special types of angles.

Step 1 Write a definition for each boldfaced term. Make sure your definitions highlight important differences.

Step 2 Trade definitions and test each other's definitions by looking for counterexamples.

Step 3 If another group member finds a counterexample to one of your definitions, write a better definition. As a group, decide on the best definition for each term.

Step 4 As a class, agree on common definitions. Add these to your notebook. Draw and label a picture to illustrate each definition.

Right Angle A right angle is an angle that measures 90°.

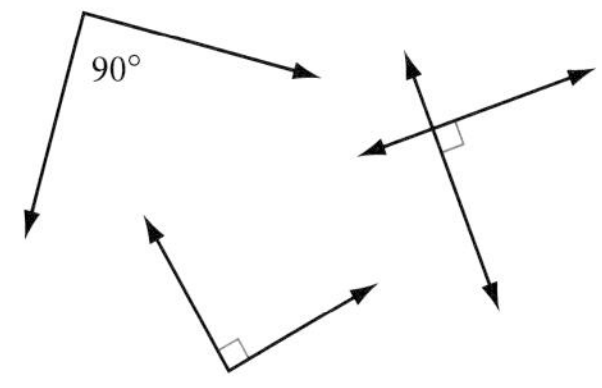

Right angles

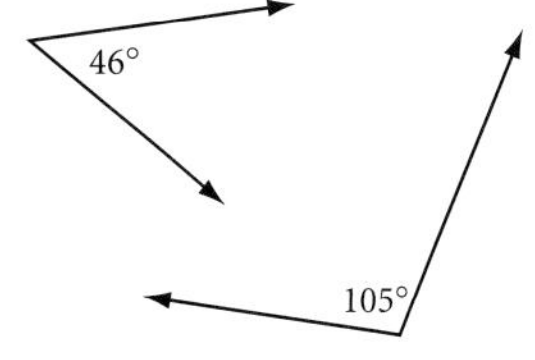

Not right angles

Acute Angle An acute angle measures less than 90°.

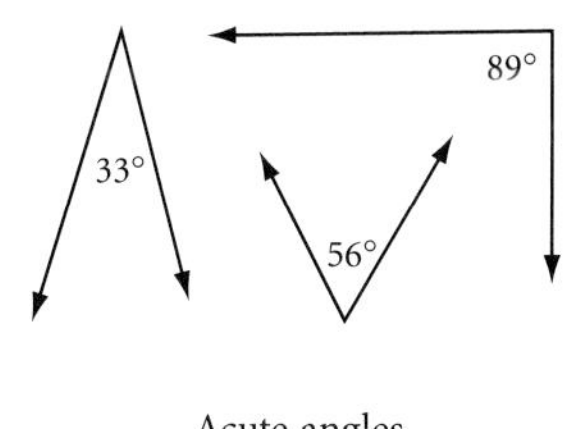

Acute angles

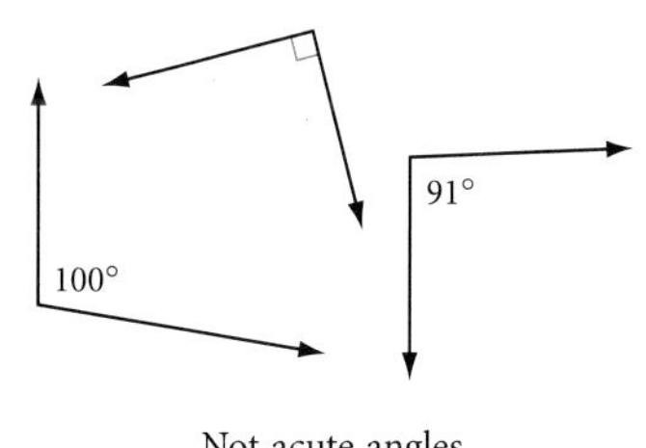

Not acute angles

Obtuse Angle An obtuse angle measures more than 90° but less than 180°.

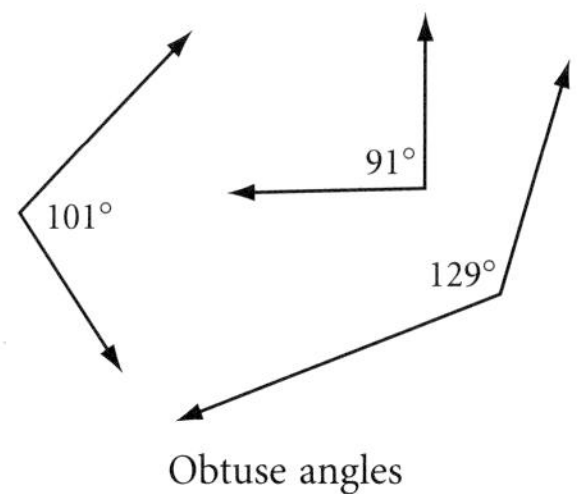

Obtuse angles

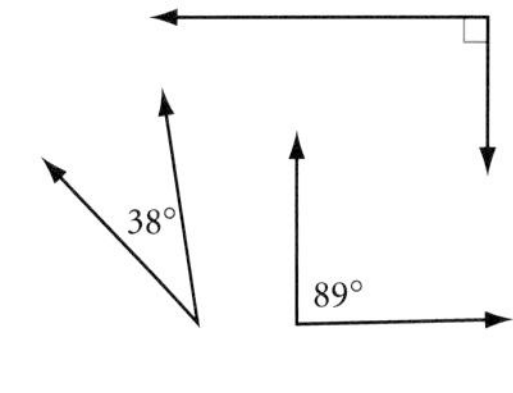

Not obtuse angles

Notice the many congruent angles in this Navajo transitional Wedgeweave blanket. Are they right, acute, or obtuse angles?

Guiding the Investigation

To get students started, you might have the class as a whole brainstorm possible definitions of *right angle.* Let students critique the proposals until they can agree on the one that seems most correct, precise, and concise. Then send students into their groups to write the other definitions. You could give each group one or two definitions to write or have each group member write one or two definitions and switch with a partner to check. You might make each group responsible for one definition to be shared with the rest of the class.

[Alert] Students defining *pair of vertical angles* and *linear pair of angles* may need a prompt, because these two definitions are the most challenging of this lesson. Suggest that students start with two lines and their point of intersection. If they need more help, start the definition: "If $\overleftrightarrow{AB}$ and $\overleftrightarrow{CD}$ intersect at point *P*, then $\angle APC$ and $\angle BPD$ are a pair of . . . ." Similarly, for *linear pair* suggest that students start their definition with "If *X, Y,* and *Z* are consecutive collinear points and *W* is a point not on $\overleftrightarrow{XZ}$, then $\angle XYW$ and . . . ."

[Language] Vertical angles don't have to be situated vertically. *Obtuse* used outside the context of mathematics means "not alert in perception or intellect; not sharp," and *acute* means "sharp." In everyday language, *supplementary* means "additional," and *complementary* means "completing." **[Ask]** "Do the everyday meanings of these words relate to their mathematical meanings?"

You might wish to have students use the dynamic geometry exploration at www.keymath.com/DG to explore the differences between right, acute, and obtuse angles, and to help them write definitions for these angles.

SHARING IDEAS

As students present, sit with the rest of the class (rather than standing) to act as a role model in asking questions and critiquing the proposed definitions. Encourage students to come up with counterexamples for any unsatisfactory definitions.

[Ask] "What makes a good definition?" [A good definition is precise, it uses no vague nonmathematical terms, and if it's defining an object it places the defined object in a well-defined category or class and differentiates or distinguishes it from other objects in that category.] Have students look at the form in the student book (A _?_ is a _?_ that _?_) and discuss the steps of classifying and differentiating. Help students rewrite their definitions in this form. (This form works best for defining shapes. For defining properties of shapes, a biconditional form, to be discussed later, is more appropriate.) Don't expect strict memorization (van Hiele level 3). At this stage students should be able to match given definitions with figures (van Hiele level 0).

Sharing Ideas (continued)
If students are expressing discomfort with the awkwardness or ambiguity of their definitions or difficulties in writing them, you might suggest that they write definitions that refer to named figures. For example, they can define a line segment by "Segment *AB* is a set consisting of points *A* and *B* and all points on $\overleftrightarrow{AB}$ that are between points *A* and *B*." Or they can define a ray by "Ray *AB* is a set consisting of $\overline{AB}$ and all other points *P* on $\overleftrightarrow{AB}$ such that point *B* is between points *A* and *P*." With this approach the definition is a description of how the figure is created. **[ESL]** The term *such that* means "under the condition that" or "so that."

[Ask] "What is the difference between a supplementary pair and a linear pair of angles?" Elicit the idea that a supplementary pair might not actually have two sides on the same line.

Make sure students add agreed-upon definitions to their definition lists. Remind them to include labeled sketches, especially if they name a segment or an angle in their definition. You might have the class use this technique to complete an alternative definition for a linear pair of angles. [If *X*, *Y*, and *Z* are consecutive collinear points and *W* . . . .]

Assessing Progress
Listen for the use of geometry terms, especially *point, line, line segment, plane, collinear,* and *angle measure.* Watch for careful use of protractors and for contributions to group work.

Closing the Lesson

Review the definitions agreed upon for **square, parallel lines, perpendicular lines, right angle, acute angle, obtuse angle, pair of vertical angles, linear pair of angles, pair of complementary angles,** and **pair of supplementary angles.**

What types of angles or angle pairs do you see in this magnified view of a computer chip?

Pair of Vertical Angles Vertical angles are angles formed by two intersecting lines; they share a common vertex but not a common side.

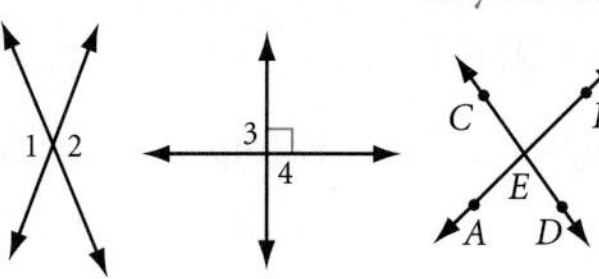

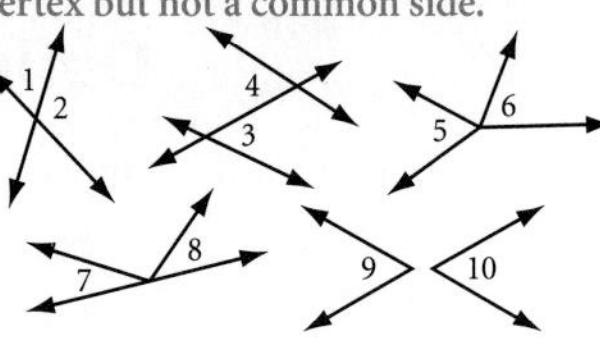

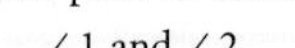

Pairs of vertical angles:

$\angle 1$ and $\angle 2$
$\angle 3$ and $\angle 4$
$\angle AED$ and $\angle BEC$
$\angle AEC$ and $\angle DEB$

Not pairs of vertical angles:

$\angle 1$ and $\angle 2$
$\angle 3$ and $\angle 4$
$\angle 5$ and $\angle 6$
$\angle 7$ and $\angle 8$
$\angle 9$ and $\angle 10$

Linear Pair of Angles Two angles are a linear pair if they share a vertex and a common side and their non-common sides form a line.

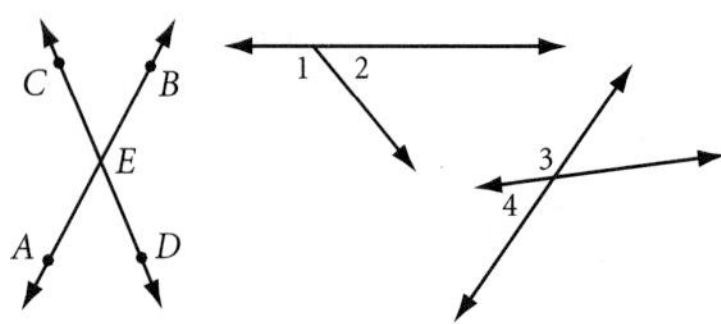

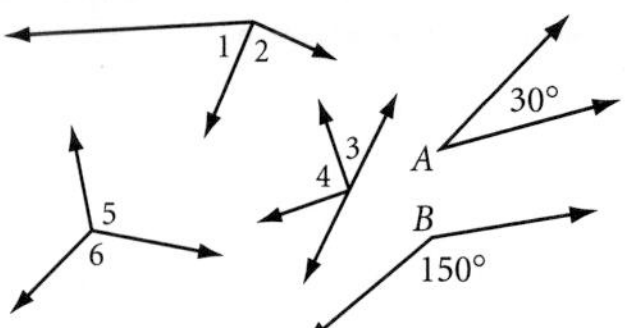

Linear pairs of angles:

$\angle 1$ and $\angle 2$
$\angle 3$ and $\angle 4$
$\angle AED$ and $\angle AEC$
$\angle BED$ and $\angle DEA$

Not linear pairs of angles:

$\angle 1$ and $\angle 2$
$\angle 3$ and $\angle 4$
$\angle 5$ and $\angle 6$
$\angle A$ and $\angle B$

Pair of Complementary Angles A pair of complementary angles has a sum of 90°.

$m\angle 1 + m\angle 2 = 90°$

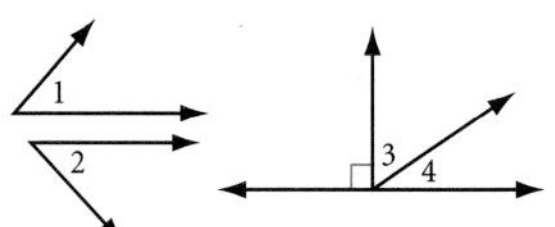

$m\angle 1 + m\angle 2 \neq 90°$

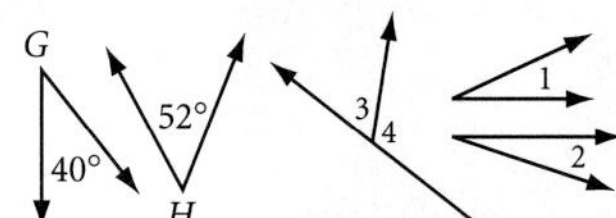

Pairs of complementary angles:

$\angle 1$ and $\angle 2$
$\angle 3$ and $\angle 4$

Not pairs of complementary angles:

$\angle G$ and $\angle H$ $\angle 1$ and $\angle 2$
$\angle 3$ and $\angle 4$

Pair of Supplementary Angles A pair of supplementary angles has a sum of 180°.

$m\angle 3 + m\angle 4 = 180°$

$m\angle 4 + m\angle 5 > 180°$

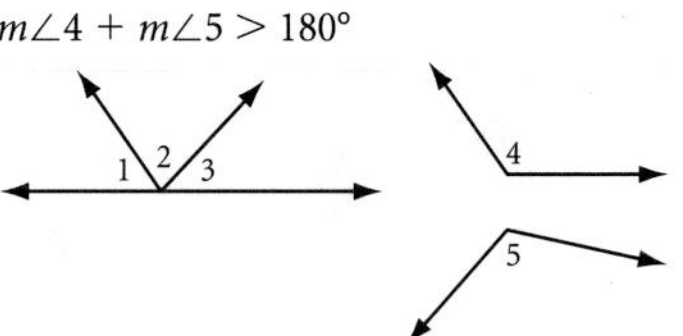

Pairs of supplementary angles:

$\angle 1$ and $\angle 2$
$\angle 3$ and $\angle 4$

Not pairs of supplementary angles:

$\angle 1$, $\angle 2$, and $\angle 3$
$\angle 4$ and $\angle 5$

How did you do? Did you notice the difference between a supplementary pair and a linear pair? Did you make it clear which is which in your definitions? The more you practice writing geometry definitions, the better you will get at it.

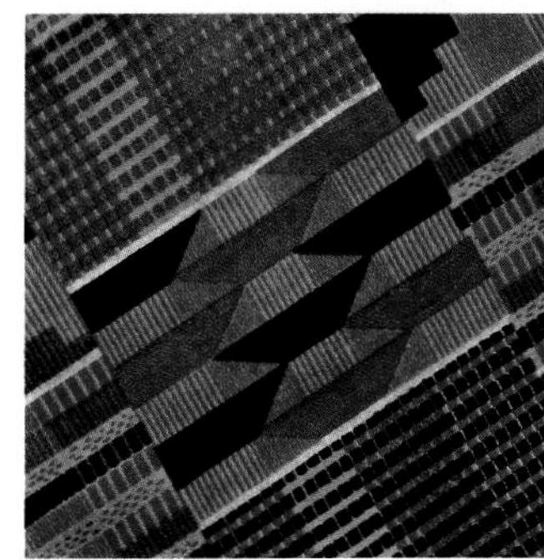

The design of this African Kente cloth contains examples of parallel and perpendicular lines, obtuse and acute angles, and complementary and supplementary angle pairs. To learn about the significance of Kente cloth designs, visit www.keymath.com/DG .

EXERCISES

For Exercises 1–8, draw and carefully label the figures. Use the appropriate marks to indicate right angles, parallel lines, congruent segments, and congruent angles. Use a protractor and a ruler when you need to.

1. Acute angle DOG with a measure of 45°

2. Right angle RTE

3. Obtuse angle BIG with angle bisector $\overrightarrow{IE}$

4. $\overline{DG} \parallel \overleftrightarrow{MS}$

5. $\overline{PE} \perp \overline{AR}$

6. Vertical angles ABC and DBE

7. Complementary angles $\angle A$ and $\angle B$ with $m\angle A = 40°$

8. Supplementary angles $\angle C$ and $\angle D$ with $m\angle D = 40°$

9. Which creatures in the last group below are Zoids? What makes a Zoid a Zoid?

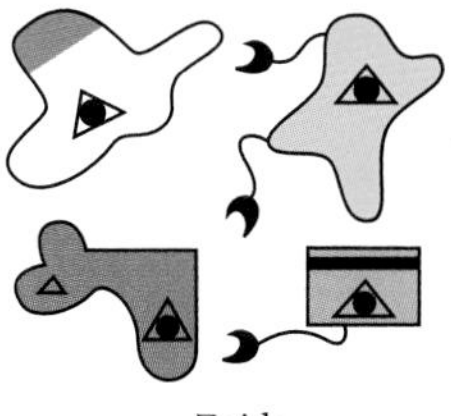
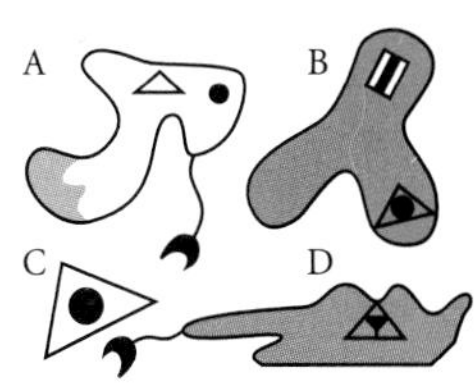

Zoids | Not Zoids | Who are Zoids?

10. What are the characteristics of a good definition? A good definition places an object in a class, and also differentiates it from other objects in that class. A good definition has no counterexamples.

For Exercises 11–20, four of the statements are true. Make a sketch or demonstrate each true statement. For each false statement, draw a counterexample.

11. For every line segment there is exactly one midpoint. true

12. For every angle there is exactly one angle bisector. true

13. If two different lines intersect, then they intersect at one and only one point. true

14. If two different circles intersect, then they intersect at one and only one point. false

Exercises 11–20 These are the most challenging exercises of the set. Encourage critical and creative thinking.

11.

12.

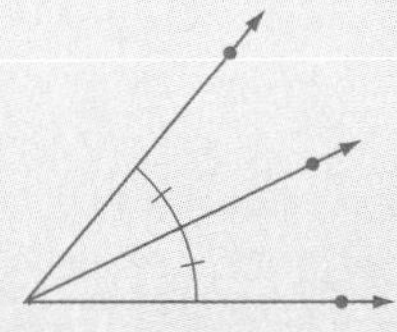

13.

14.

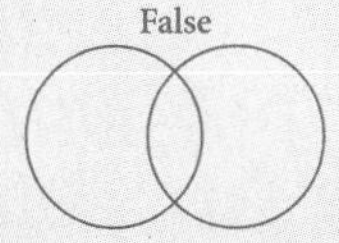

BUILDING UNDERSTANDING

The exercises give practice in using the newly defined terms.

ASSIGNING HOMEWORK

Essential	1–9, 11–20
Performance assessment	25
Portfolio	21
Journal	10
Group	23, 29, 30
Review	22–31

▶ Helping with the Exercises

1–3. possible answers:

1.

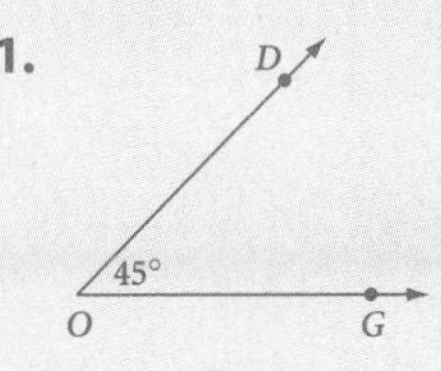

2.

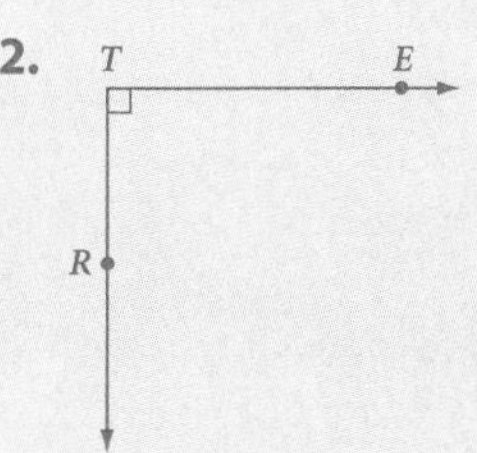

3.

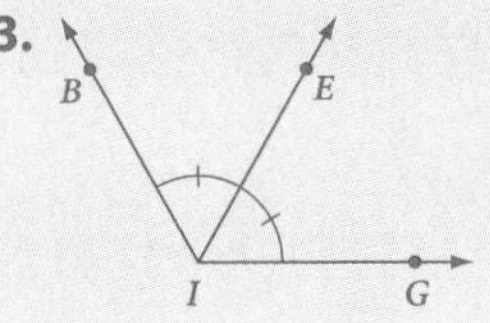

Exercise 4 A student might draw this figure and argue that it fits our definition (or implied definition if we didn't specify that the lines that contain the segments must be parallel).

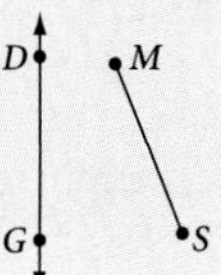

Praise this kind of critical thinking and ask how the definition might be clarified to rule out the counterexample.

See page 767 for answers to Exercises 4–9.

15.

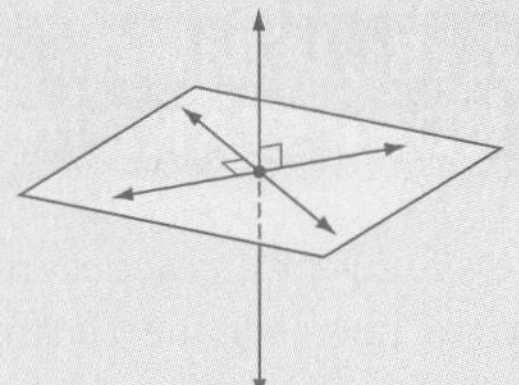

16.

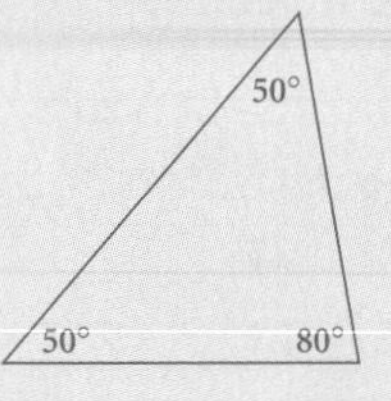

17.

Exercises 18, 20 As needed, encourage students to think "outside the box" (outside the line segment).

18. Though converse is true, a counterexample is

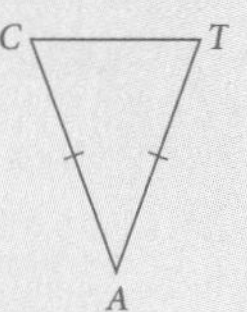

19.

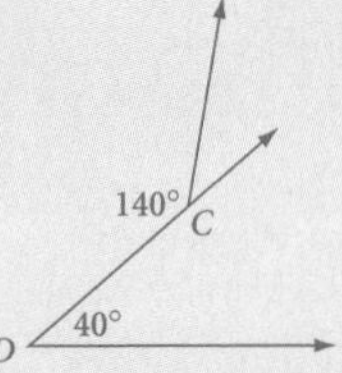

20.

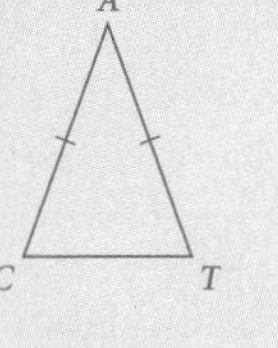

21.

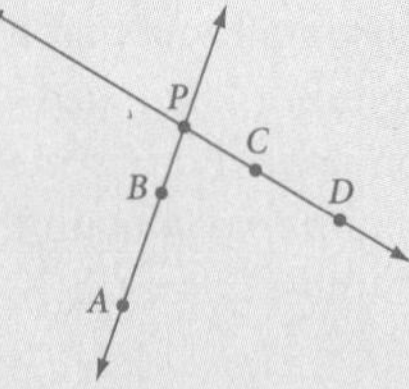

Exercises 22, 23 [Ask] "How many answers are there?" [infinitely many]

15. Through a given point on a line there is one and only one line perpendicular to the given line. ⓗ false

16. In every triangle there is exactly one right angle. false

17. Through a point not on a line, one and only one line can be constructed parallel to the given line. true

18. If $CA = AT$, then A is the midpoint of $\overline{CT}$. false

19. If $m\angle D = 40°$ and $m\angle C = 140°$, then angles C and D are a linear pair. false

20. If point A is not the midpoint of $\overline{CT}$, then $CA \neq AT$. false

21. There is something wrong with this definition for a pair of vertical angles: "If $\overleftrightarrow{AB}$ and $\overleftrightarrow{CD}$ intersect at point P, then $\angle APC$ and $\angle BPD$ are a pair of vertical angles." Sketch a counterexample to show why it is not correct. Can you add a phrase to correct it? If $\overleftrightarrow{AB}$ and $\overleftrightarrow{CD}$ intersect at point P so that P is between A and B and P is between C and D, then $\angle APC$ and $\angle BPD$ are a pair of vertical angles.

Review

For Exercises 22 and 23, refer to the graph at right.

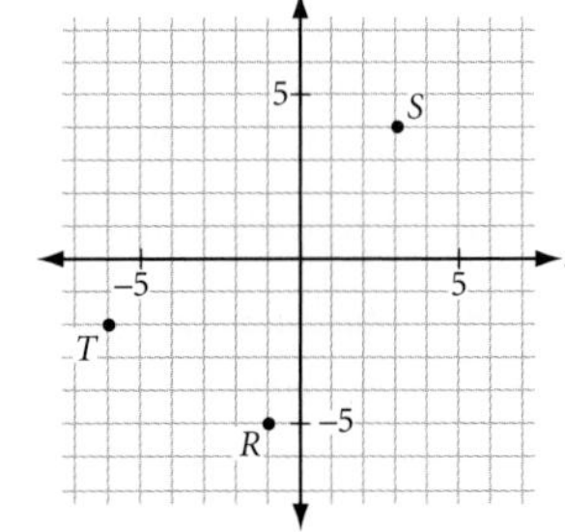

1.2 **22.** Find possible coordinates of a point P so that points P, T, and S are collinear. possible answers: $(-3, 0)$, $(0, 2)$, or $(6, 6)$.

1.1 **23.** Find possible coordinates of a point Q so that $\overleftrightarrow{QR} \parallel \overleftrightarrow{TS}$. possible answers: $(2, -3)$ or $(5, -1)$.

1.1 **24.** A *partial mirror* reflects some light and lets the rest of the light pass through. In the figure at right, half the light from point A passes through the partial mirror to point B. Copy the figure, then draw the outgoing angle for the light reflected from the mirror. What do you notice about the ray of reflected light and the ray of light that passes through? ⓗ The reflected ray and the ray that passes through (called the "refracted" ray) are mirror images of each other. Or they form congruent angles with the mirror.

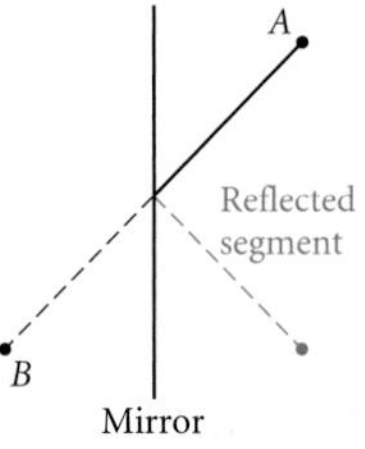

Science CONNECTION

Albert Abraham Michelson (1852–1931) designed the Michelson Interferometer to find the wavelength of light. A modern version of the experiment uses a partial mirror to split a laser beam so that it travels in two different directions, and mirrors to recombine the separated beams.

Partial mirror
Mirrors
Lens
Laser

EXTENSION

Try the Project The Daffynition Game in *Discovering Geometry More Projects and Explorations.*

1.2 **25.** Find possible coordinates of points A, B, and C so that $\angle BAC$ is a right angle, $\angle BAT$ is an acute angle, $\angle ABS$ is an obtuse angle, and the points C, T, and R are collinear. ⓗ One possible answer is $A(-8, 8)$, $B(-4.5, 6.5)$, $C(-11, 1)$.

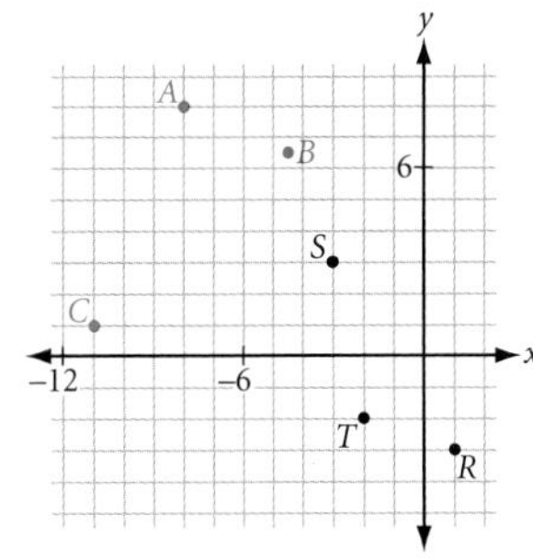

UYAS 1 **26.** If D is the midpoint of $\overline{AC}$ and C is the midpoint of $\overline{AB}$, and $AD = 3$ cm, what is the length of $\overline{AB}$? 12 cm

1.2 **27.** If $\overrightarrow{BD}$ is the angle bisector of $\angle ABC$, $\overrightarrow{BE}$ is the angle bisector of $\angle ABD$, and $m\angle DBC = 24°$, what is $m\angle EBC$? 36°

1.2 **28.** Draw and label a figure that has two congruent segments and three congruent angles. Mark the congruent angles and congruent segments.

1.1 **29.** Show how three lines in a plane can intersect in no points, exactly one point, exactly two points, or exactly three points.

1.1 **30.** Show how it is possible for two triangles to intersect in one point, two points, three points, four points, five points, or six points, but not seven points. Show how they can intersect in infinitely many points.

1.2 **31.** Each pizza is cut into slices from the center.

a. What fraction of the pizza is left?

$\frac{120°}{360°} = \frac{1}{3}, \frac{2}{3}$ left

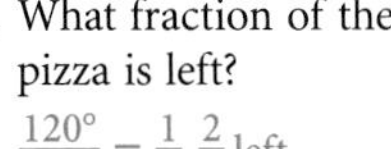

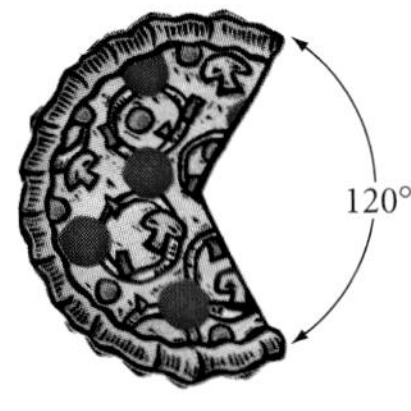

b. What fraction of the pizza is missing?

$\frac{60°}{360°} = \frac{1}{6}, \frac{1}{6}$ missing

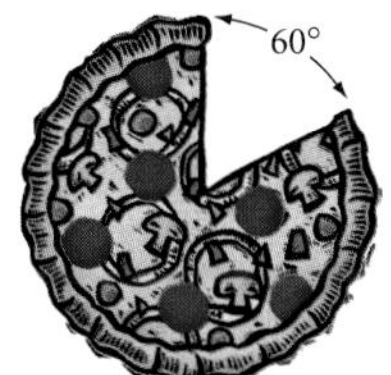

c. If the pizza is cut into nine equal slices, how many degrees is each angle at the center of the pizza?

$\frac{360°}{9} = 40°$

IMPROVING YOUR VISUAL THINKING SKILLS

Polyominoes

In 1953, United States mathematician Solomon Golomb introduced polyominoes at the Harvard Mathematics Club, and they have been played with and enjoyed throughout the world ever since. Polyominoes are shapes made by connecting congruent squares. The squares are joined together side to side. (A complete side must touch a complete side.) Some of the smaller polyominoes are shown below. There is only one monomino and only one domino, but there are two trominoes, as shown. There are five tetrominoes—one is shown. Sketch the other four.

Monomino

Domino

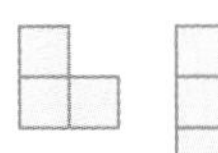
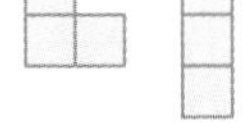

Trominoes

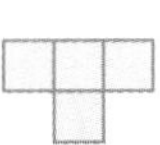
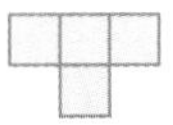

Tetromino

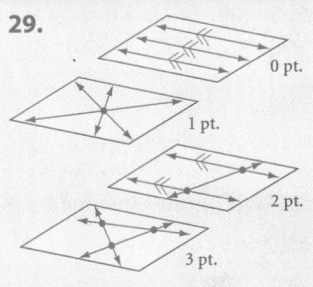

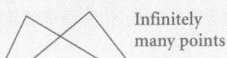

Exercise 25 For students who are struggling, give them point A at $(-8, 8)$.

Exercise 27 [Alert] Watch for the tendency to think of angle EBA instead of angle EBC.

Exercise 28 Students might rightfully point out that "has two congruent segments" does not rule out having three congruent segments, so an equilateral triangle is acceptable here.

28. possible answer:

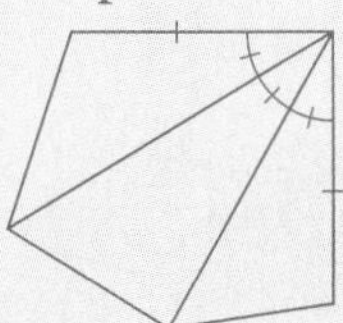

Exercises 29, 30 [Alert] Before assigning these exercises, you may want to use some physical objects to demonstrate properties of planes and/or triangles.

29.

0 pt.

1 pt.

2 pt.

3 pt.

30.

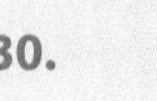

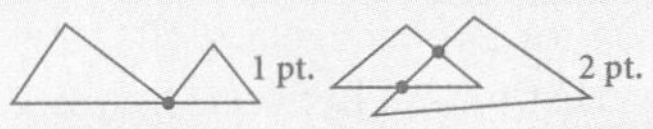

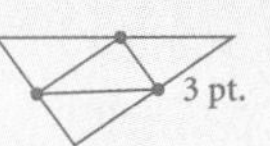

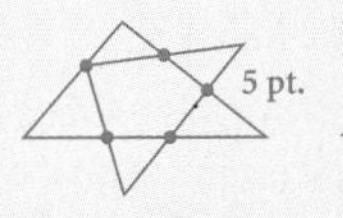

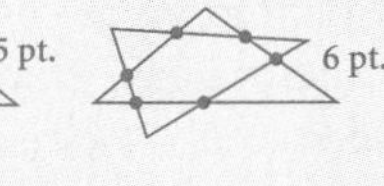

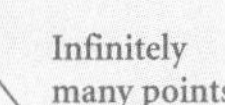

IMPROVING VISUAL THINKING SKILLS

Pronounce *polyominoes, monomino, trominoes,* and *tetrominoes.* You might point out that these prefixes are Greek, as opposed to the Latin prefixes in names of polygons. Ask if the student book is correct in saying that there are only five tetrominoes. It means tetrominoes that are not reflections (flips) or rotations of others. You might relate this idea to the idea of congruence: If tetrominoes are congruent, they represent the same tetromino. You can also tie this idea to the ideas of symmetry discussed in Chapter 0: The figure formed by merging a tetromino with one of its reflections or rotations has reflectional or rotational symmetry.

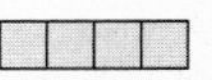

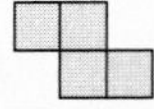

LESSON

1.4

PLANNING

LESSON OUTLINE

One day:

15 min Investigation

10 min Sharing

5 min Closing

15 min Exercises

MATERIALS

- straightedges
- protractors
- Convex and Concave (T) for One step

TEACHING

Polygons can be classified by the number of sides or by convexity. Two polygons are congruent if they have the same number of sides *and* if each side and angle of one are congruent to the corresponding side and angle of the other.

One step Show the Convex and Concave transparency. As a class, look for two categories, eliciting the distinction between (but not definitions of) convex and concave figures. Ask student groups to come up with names for the various kinds of polygons and definitions of *convex* and *concave.* Remind students as needed to use the classifying and differentiating method of writing a definition.

For more structure talk about the introductory material and the example using questions from Sharing. **[Language]** *Concave* polygons "cave in."

LESSON

1.4

Polygons

There are two kinds of people in this world: those who divide everything into two groups, and those who don't.

KENNETH BOULDING

A **polygon** is a closed figure in a plane, formed by connecting line segments endpoint to endpoint with each segment intersecting exactly two others. Each line segment is called a **side** of the polygon. Each endpoint where the sides meet is called a **vertex** of the polygon.

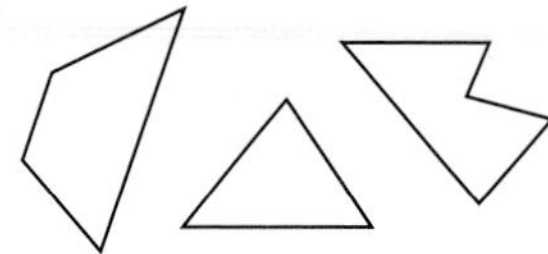

Polygons

Not polygons

You classify a polygon by the number of sides it has. Familiar polygons have specific names, listed in this table. The ones without specific names are called n-sided polygons, or n-gons. For instance, you call a 25-sided polygon a 25-gon.

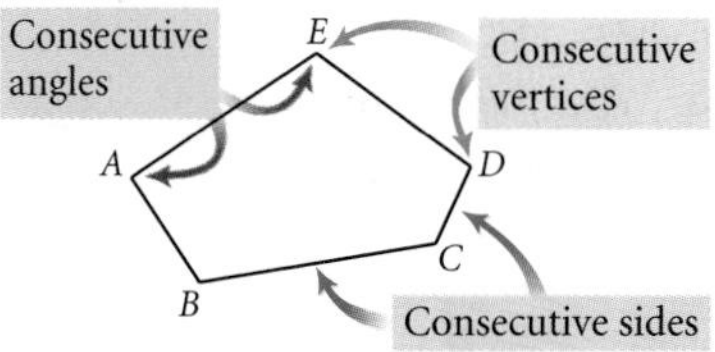

Sides	Name
3	Triangle
4	Quadrilateral
5	Pentagon
6	Hexagon
7	Heptagon
8	Octagon
9	Nonagon
10	Decagon
11	Undecagon
12	Dodecagon
n	n-gon

To name a polygon, list the vertices in consecutive order. You can name the pentagon above pentagon *ABCDE.* You can also call it *DCBAE,* but not *BCAED.* When the polygon is a triangle, you use the triangle symbol. For example, $\triangle ABC$ means triangle *ABC.*

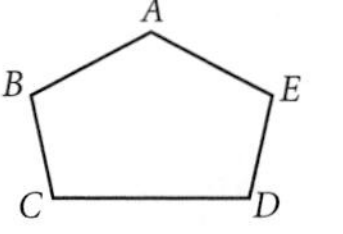

Pentagon *ABCDE*

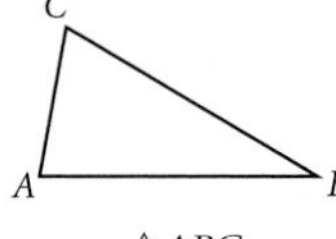

$\triangle ABC$

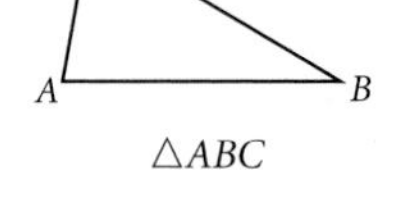

A **diagonal** of a polygon is a line segment that connects two nonconsecutive vertices.

A polygon is **convex** if no diagonal is outside the polygon. A polygon is **concave** if at least one diagonal is outside the polygon.

Convex polygons: All diagonals are inside

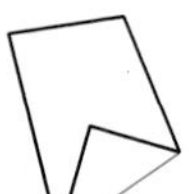

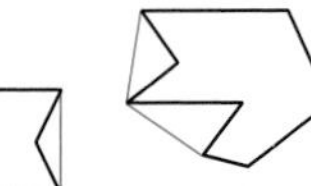

Concave polygons: One or more diagonals are outside

LESSON OBJECTIVES

- Define and classify polygons and related terms
- Practice writing definitions
- Learn even more vocabulary
- Develop critical thinking and cooperative behavior

NCTM STANDARDS

	CONTENT		PROCESS
	Number	✓	Problem Solving
✓	Algebra	✓	Reasoning
✓	Geometry	✓	Communication
✓	Measurement		Connections
	Data/Probability	✓	Representation

Recall that two segments or two angles are congruent if and only if they have the same measures. Two polygons are **congruent polygons** if and only if they are exactly the same size and shape. "If and only if" means that the statements work both ways.

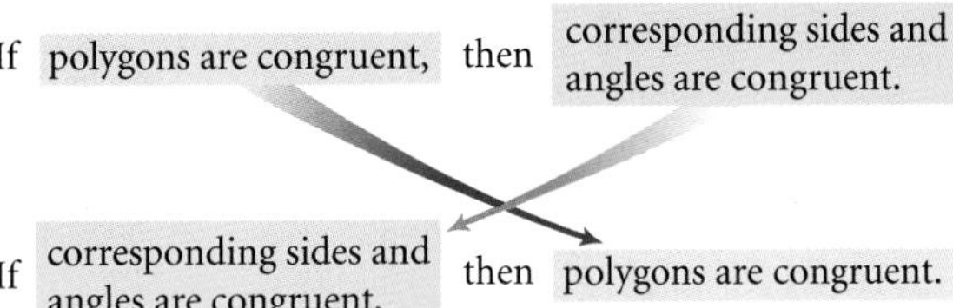

If polygons are congruent, then corresponding sides and angles are congruent.
If corresponding sides and angles are congruent, then polygons are congruent.

How does the shape of the framework of this Marc Chagall (1887–1985) stained glass window support the various shapes of the design?

For example, if quadrilateral *CAMP* is congruent to quadrilateral *SITE,* then their four pairs of corresponding angles and four pairs of corresponding sides are also congruent. When you write a statement of congruence, always write the letters of the corresponding vertices in an order that shows the correspondences.

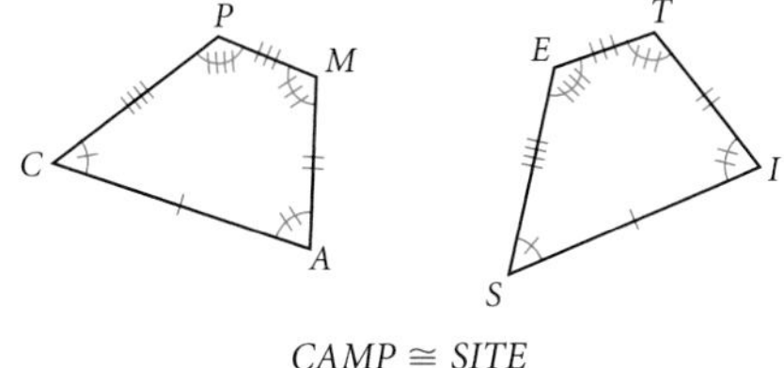

CAMP ≅ *SITE*

EXAMPLE

Which polygon is congruent to *ABCDE*?

ABCDE ≅ ?

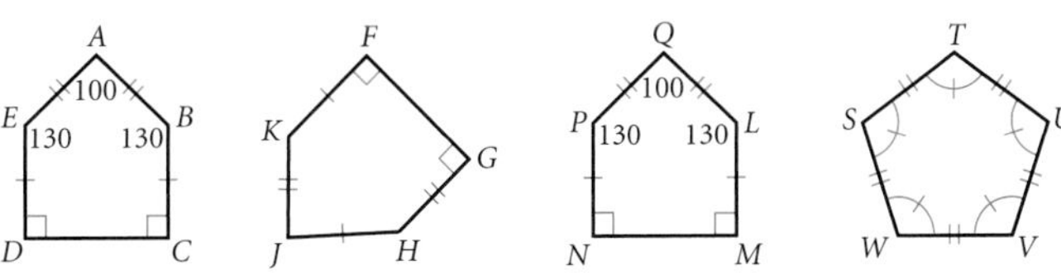

▶ Solution

All corresponding sides and angles must be congruent, so polygon *ABCDE* ≅ polygon *QLMNP.* You could also say *ABCDE* ≅ *QPNML,* because all the congruent parts would still match.

In an **equilateral polygon,** all the sides have equal length. In an **equiangular polygon,** all the angles have equal measure. A **regular polygon** is both equilateral and equiangular.

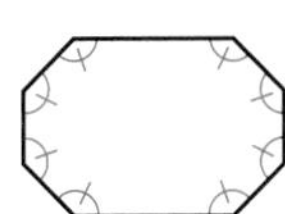

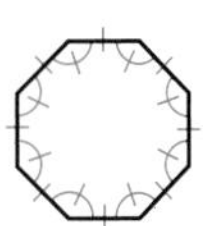

Equiangular octagon   Equilateral octagon   Regular octagon

▶ EXAMPLE

[Ask] "Are polygons with the same perimeter necessarily congruent?" (You may need to remind students that the perimeter of a polygon is the sum of the lengths of its sides.)

Assessing Progress

As students try to write definitions, watch for spontaneous use of vocabulary from earlier in the course: *symmetry, pentagon, hexagon, point, line, segment, plane, collinear, coplanar, congruent, angle, side* and *vertex of an angle, measure of an angle, triangle, parallel, perpendicular, right angle, acute angle, obtuse angle, vertical angle, complementary angles, supplementary angles, linear pair of angles.*

SHARING IDEAS

Students can present their names for the various kinds of polygons. Then have them present and critique their definitions of *convex* and *concave.* Introduce the term *diagonal* to help simplify the definitions. **[Alert]** A diagonal need not cut the polygon in half. Work as a class on defining *diagonal* and *polygon.* Ask if it makes sense to talk about *congruent polygons,* and try to form a class definition of that term.

Then have students compare the book's definitions with those of the class. **[Ask]** "Are all the parts of the definition really necessary?" [They are all necessary; as students try to shorten the definition, they will see why all the parts are needed.] **[Language]** *Vertices* is the plural of *vertex.*

Discuss the meaning of Greek and Latin prefixes and suffixes (*poly-, tri-, tetra-, penta-, hexa-, hepta-, octa-, nona-, deca-,* and *-gon*). Students might ask why a triangle isn't called a trigon, or a square a tetragon. *Tetragon* would be Greek; *quadrilateral* comes from the Latin, which also gives us *triangulum.* **[Ask]** "Why does the table omit polygons of zero, one, or two sides? What does *consecutive* mean?" Bring out the idea that vertices should be listed in the order in which they appear going around the polygon, not in consecutive order alphabetically. **[Language]** If vertices are *nonconsecutive,* they are not connected by a side. Discuss the meaning of *corresponding.*

Refer students to the tiling on page 22. **[Ask]** "Which tiles are concave? Which are equilateral, equiangular, or regular?"

Closing the Lesson

Summarize the main mathematical ideas of this lesson: **polygon** (and its sides, vertices, and diagonals); **convex** and **concave** polygons; **equilateral, equiangular,** and **regular** polygons; and **congruent** polygons. A **quadrilateral** is a 4-gon. You need not have students try to remember the names of n-gons for $n > 6$; rather, they can learn the terms as they use them while doing the exercises.

Have students add these new terms, with sketches, to their definition lists. To help them write good definitions, you might suggest that they make one column for the term, a second column for the classification, and a third column for the differentiation.

BUILDING UNDERSTANDING

The exercises give students practice in using the new terminology.

ASSIGNING HOMEWORK

Essential	**1–17, 19–21, 24, 25, 29, 30**
Examples	**18, 20, 23, 28**
Performance assessment	**31, 32, 38**
Portfolio	**36**
Group	**31–34**
Review	**35–38**

MATERIALS

- graph paper (Exercises 23–27)

▶ Helping with the Exercises

Exercises 1–8 If students are struggling, remind them that a polygon is classified by the number of sides it has. Refer them to the table on page 54.

Exercise 6 The polygon here is the hole in the coin.

EXERCISES

For Exercises 1–8, classify each polygon. Assume that the sides of the chips and crackers are straight.

1. octagon **2.** rectangle or square **3.** hexagon **4.** triangle

5. heptagon **6.** pentagon **7.** undecagon **8.** dodecagon

For Exercises 9–11, draw an example of each polygon.

9. Quadrilateral **10.** Dodecagon **11.** Octagon

For Exercises 12 and 13, give one possible name for each polygon. One possible answer for each is shown.

12.

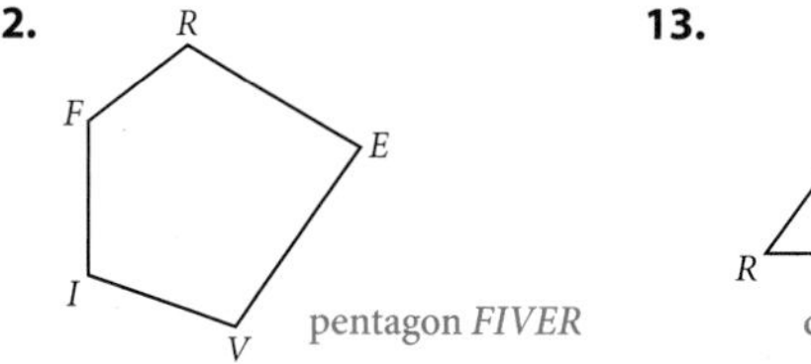

pentagon *FIVER*

13.

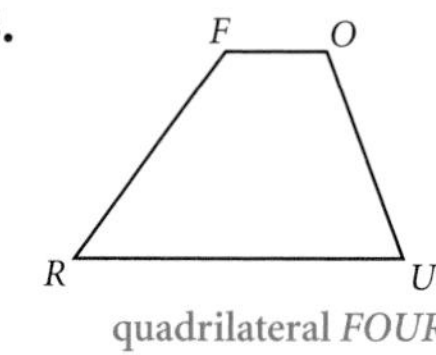

quadrilateral *FOUR*

14.

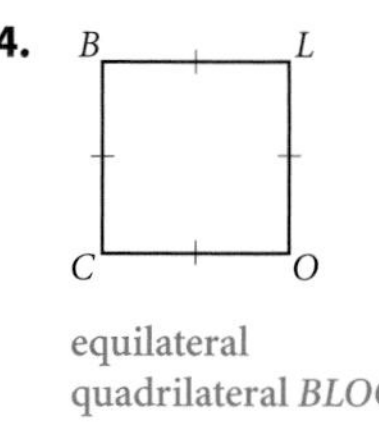

equilateral quadrilateral *BLOC*

15. Name a pair of consecutive angles and a pair of consecutive sides in the figure below. One possibility is $\angle C$ and $\angle Y$ are consecutive angles; $\overline{CY}$ and $\overline{YN}$ are consecutive sides.

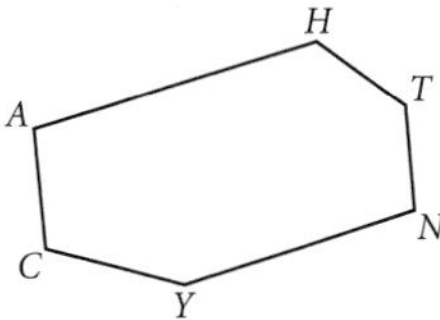

16. Draw a concave hexagon. How many diagonals does it have? nine

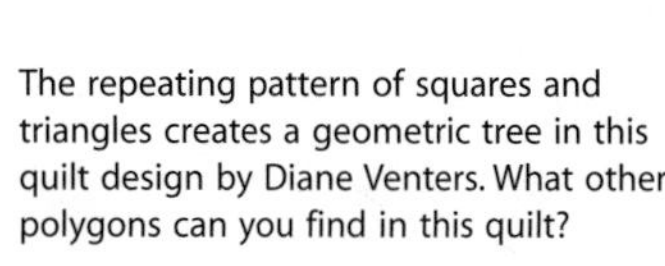

The repeating pattern of squares and triangles creates a geometric tree in this quilt design by Diane Venters. What other polygons can you find in this quilt?

Exercises 12–14 The polygon name can start with any letter as long as adjacent letters represent vertices with a side between them.

Exercise 16 Students may wonder if a concave hexagon can have fewer than nine diagonals, because some diagonals might lie on the same line and therefore not be distinguishable in a picture. The diagonals are different segments if they have different endpoints.

9–11, 16. possible answers:

9. **10.**

11.

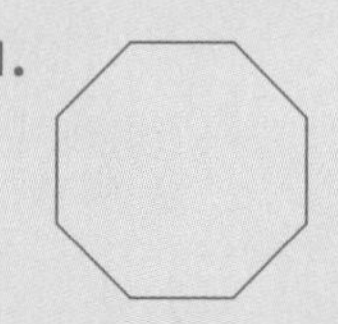

16.

17. Name the diagonals of pentagon $ABCDE$. $\overline{AC}, \overline{AD}, \overline{BD}, \overline{BE}, \overline{CE}$

For Exercises 18 and 19, use the information given to name the triangle that is congruent to the first one.

18. $\triangle EAR \cong \triangle$? ⓗ $\triangle TIN$

19. $\triangle OLD \cong \triangle$? $\triangle WEN$

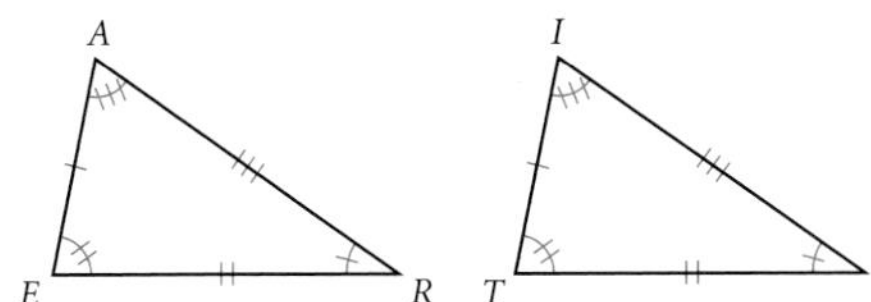

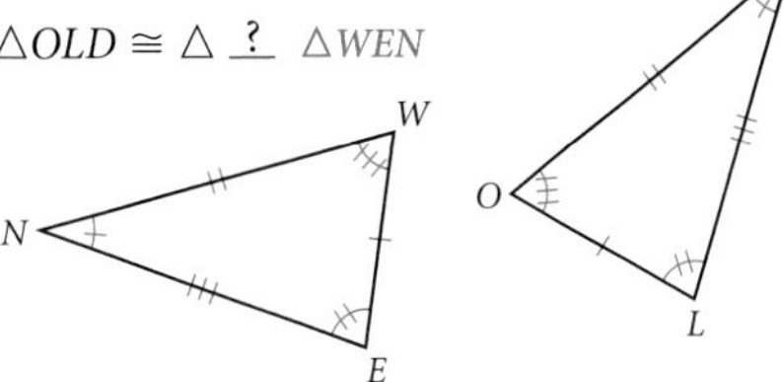

20. In the figure at right, $THINK \cong POWER$.

a. Find the missing measures.

b. If $m\angle P = 87°$ and $m\angle W = 165°$, which angles in $THINK$ do you know? Write their measures. $m\angle T = 87°$ and $m\angle I = 165°$

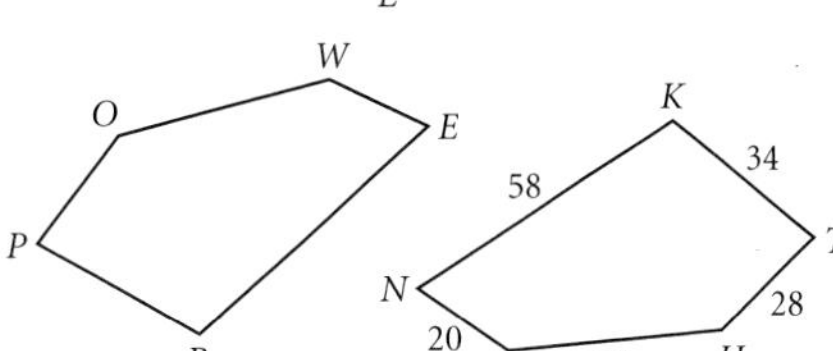

21. If pentagon $FIVER$ is congruent to pentagon $PANCH$, then which side in pentagon $FIVER$ is congruent to side $\overline{PA}$? Which angle in pentagon $PANCH$ is congruent to $\angle IVE$? $\overline{PA} \cong \overline{FI}$ and $\angle IVE \cong \angle ANC$

22. Draw an equilateral concave pentagon. Then draw an equiangular concave pentagon.

For Exercises 23–26, copy the given polygon and segment onto graph paper. Give the coordinates of the missing points.

23. $\triangle CAR \cong \triangle PET$ (5, 6)

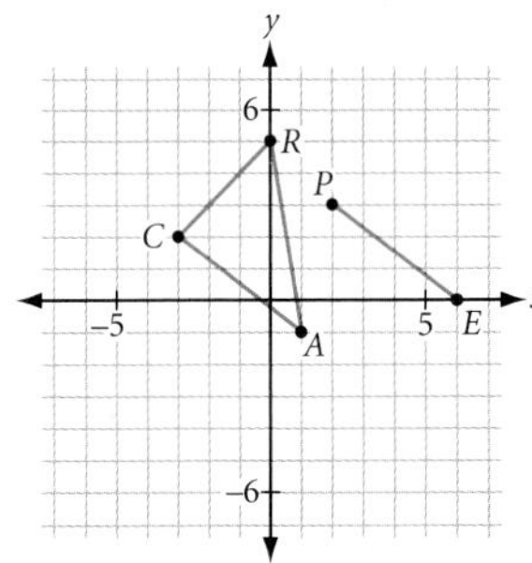

24. $TUNA \cong FISH$ $S(9, 0), I(4, -2)$

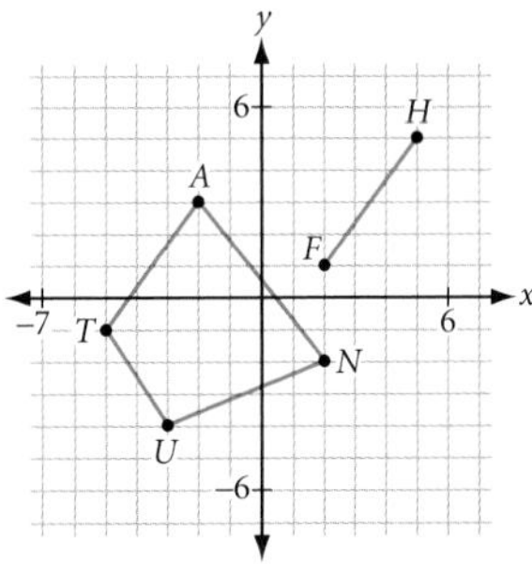

25. $BLUE \cong FISH$ $S(-3, 0), I(-1, -5)$

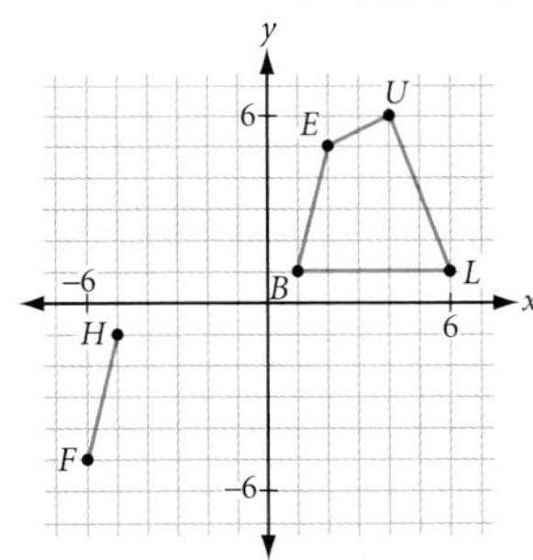

26. $RECT \cong ANGL$ $A(7, 6), N(5, 9)$ or $A(-5, -2), N(-7, 1)$

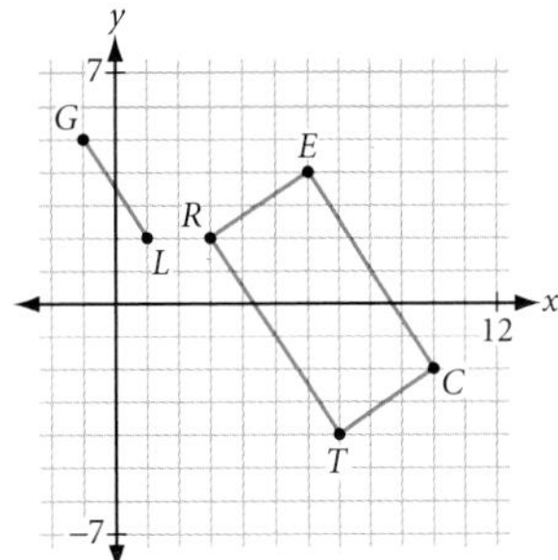

Exercises 16, 17 You might challenge students to find a general pattern: An n-gon has $\frac{n(n-1)}{2}$ pairs of vertices, so it has $\frac{n(n-1)}{2} - n$ diagonals.

20a. $PR = 34$, $EW = 20$, $PO = 28$, $RE = 58$, $WO = 44$

22.

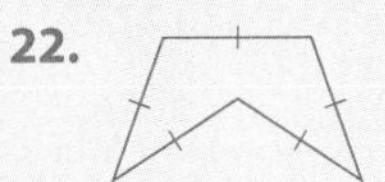

Equiangular concave is impossible.

Exercises 23–26 There are two answers to each exercise. One can be found from the other by reflecting the polygon over the given line. However, the second points are not integers except in Exercise 26, so students are unlikely to find them.

28.

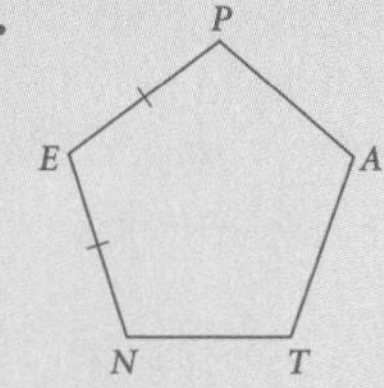

Exercises 28–32 If you did Chapter 0, you could ask students to discuss the symmetry of these figures. If you did not do Chapter 0, make sure students understand what reflectional symmetry is. Remind students to label their sketches completely. Answers are samples only.

30.

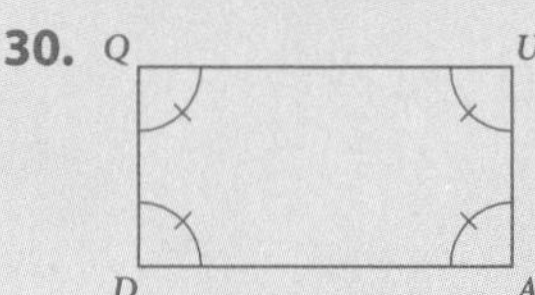

31.

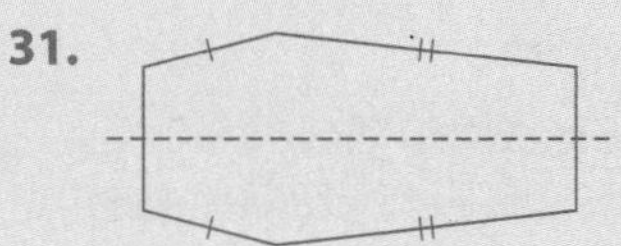

Exercise 32 One possible solution is to make one pentagon regular and the other pentagon only equilateral.

32.

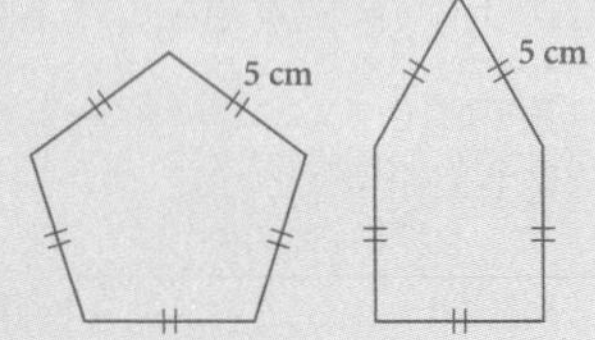

Exercise 37 **[Ask]** "How would you change the last five words of the statement to make it impossible to find a counterexample?" [a total of 25 meters]

37. possible answer:

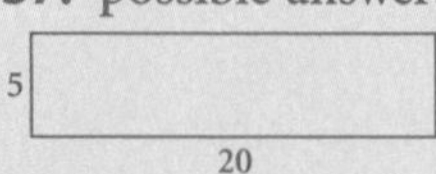

EXTENSION

Introduce polyhedra and discuss their classifications. (Students will see these again in Lesson 10.1.)

See pages 767–768 for answers to Exercises 29, 33, 36, and 38.

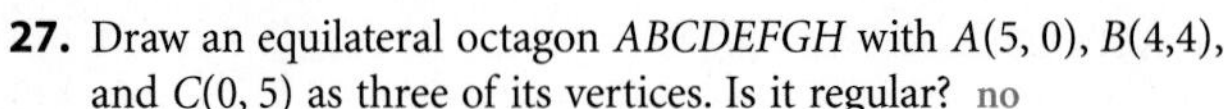

27. Draw an equilateral octagon *ABCDEFGH* with *A*(5, 0), *B*(4,4), and *C*(0, 5) as three of its vertices. Is it regular? no

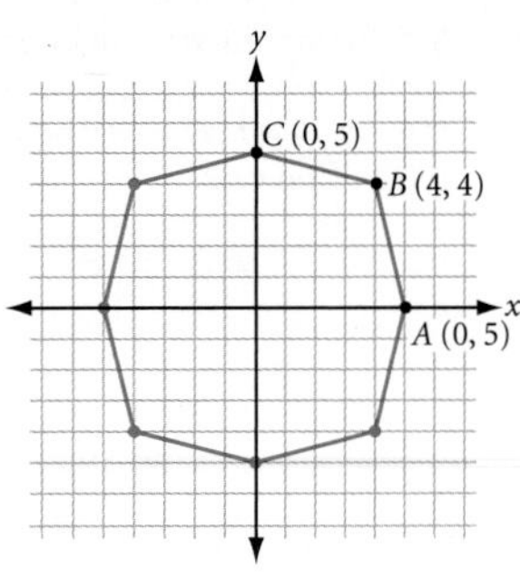

For Exercises 28–32, sketch and carefully label the figure. Mark the congruences.

28. Pentagon *PENTA* with $PE = EN$

29. Hexagon *NGAXEH* with $\angle HEX \cong \angle EXA$

30. Equiangular quadrilateral *QUAD* with $QU \neq QD$

31. A hexagon with exactly one line of reflectional symmetry ⓗ

32. Two different equilateral pentagons with perimeter 25 cm

33. Use your compass, protractor, and straightedge to draw a regular pentagon.

34. A rectangle with perimeter 198 cm is divided into five congruent rectangles as shown in the diagram at right. What is the perimeter of one of the five congruent rectangles? ⓗ 90 cm

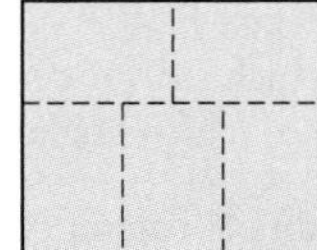

Review

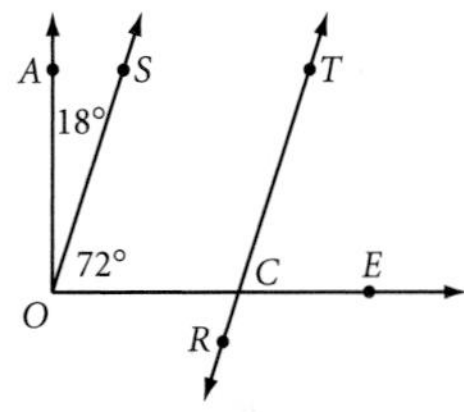

1.3 **35.** Name a pair of complementary angles and a pair of vertical angles in the figure at right. complementary angles: $\angle AOS$ and $\angle SOC$; vertical angles: $\angle OCT$ and $\angle ECR$ or $\angle TCE$ and $\angle RCO$

1.3 **36.** Draw $\overleftrightarrow{AB}$, $\overleftrightarrow{CD}$, and $\overleftrightarrow{EF}$ with $\overleftrightarrow{AB} \parallel \overleftrightarrow{CD}$ and $\overleftrightarrow{CD} \perp \overleftrightarrow{EF}$.

1.1 **37.** Draw a counterexample to show that this statement is false: "If a rectangle has perimeter 50 meters, then a pair of adjacent sides measures 10 meters and 15 meters."

1.1 **38.** Is it possible for four lines in a plane to intersect in exactly zero points? One point? Two points? Three points? Four points? Five points? Six points? Draw a figure to support each of your answers. ⓗ All are possible except two points.

IMPROVING YOUR VISUAL THINKING SKILLS

Pentominoes I

In Polyominoes I, you learned about shapes called polyominoes. Polyominoes with five squares are called pentominoes.

There are 12 pentominoes. Can you find them all? One is shown at right. Use graph paper or square dot paper to sketch all 12.

IMPROVING VISUAL THINKING SKILLS

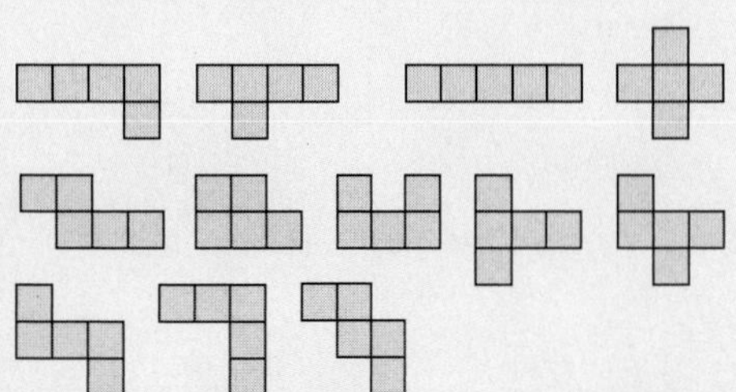

You might challenge students to make and cut out the 12 pentominoes and fit them together into a 5-by-12 rectangle or a 6-by-10 rectangle.

LESSON

1.5 Triangles and Special Quadrilaterals

The difference between the right word and the almost right word is the difference between lightning and the lightning bug.

MARK TWAIN

You have learned to be careful with geometry definitions. It turns out that you also have to be careful with diagrams.

When you look at a diagram, be careful not to assume too much from it. To **assume** something is to accept it as true without facts or proof.

Lightning

Not lightning

Things you can assume:

You may assume that lines are straight, and if two lines intersect, they intersect at one point.

You may assume that points on a line are collinear and that all points shown in a diagram are coplanar unless planes are drawn to show that they are noncoplanar.

Things you can't assume:

You may not assume that just because two lines or segments *look* parallel that they *are* parallel—they must be *marked* parallel!

You may not assume that two lines *are* perpendicular just because they *look* perpendicular—they must be *marked* perpendicular!

Pairs of angles, segments, or polygons are not necessarily congruent, unless they are *marked* with information that tells you they must be congruent!

EXAMPLE

In the diagrams below, which pairs of lines are perpendicular? Which pairs of lines are parallel? Which pair of triangles is congruent?

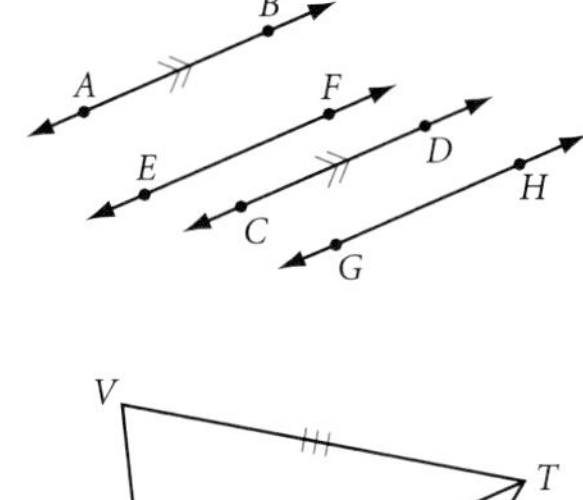

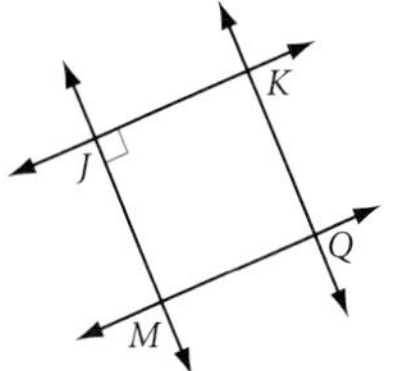

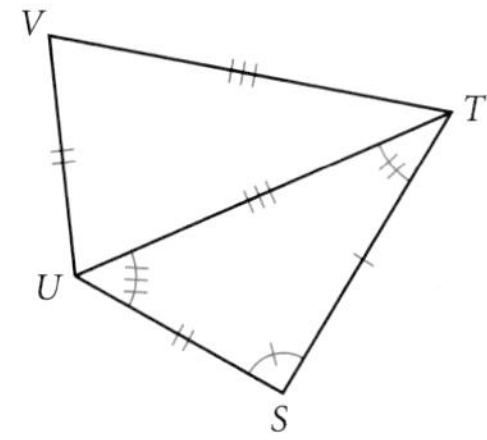

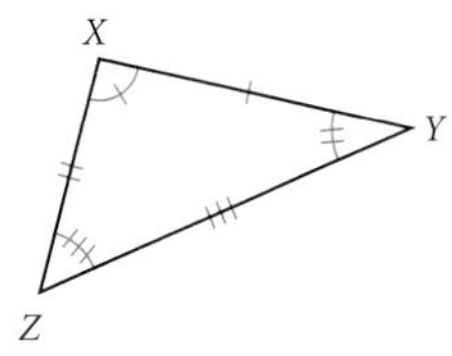

NCTM STANDARDS

CONTENT	PROCESS
Number	Problem Solving
✔ Algebra	✔ Reasoning
✔ Geometry	✔ Communication
✔ Measurement	✔ Connections
Data/Probability	✔ Representation

LESSON OBJECTIVES

- Define and classify triangles and quadrilaterals, along with their related parts
- Practice writing definitions
- Learn more vocabulary

LESSON 1.5

PLANNING

LESSON OUTLINE

One day:

25 min	Investigation
10 min	Sharing
5 min	Closing
5 min	Exercises

MATERIALS

- rulers
- protractors
- Sketchpad demonstration Classifying Parallelograms, *optional*

TEACHING

Students look at examples and non-examples to write definitions of common kinds of triangles and quadrilaterals. Start with the one-step investigation or use the example first.

One step Put student groups to work immediately on writing definitions of the terms in the investigation. Only if no students are noticing that others are making unwarranted assumptions should you point out assumptions to them. Generally save critiques for Sharing.

If students still need more structure, talk about the introduction and example and then start them working on the investigation in their groups.

▶ ***EXAMPLE***

This example is for students who might not yet have a clear grasp of parallel and perpendicular lines and congruent triangles.

▶ ***Solution*** By studying the markings, you can tell that $\overleftrightarrow{AB} \parallel \overleftrightarrow{CD}$, $\overleftrightarrow{JK} \perp \overleftrightarrow{JM}$, and $\triangle STU \cong \triangle XYZ$.

In this lesson you will write definitions that classify different kinds of triangles and special quadrilaterals, based on relationships among their sides and angles.

Investigation
Triangles and Special Quadrilaterals

Write a good definition of each boldfaced term. Discuss your definitions with others in your group. Agree on a common set of definitions for your class and add them to your definition list. In your notebook, draw and label a figure to illustrate each definition.

Right Triangle A right triangle has one right angle.

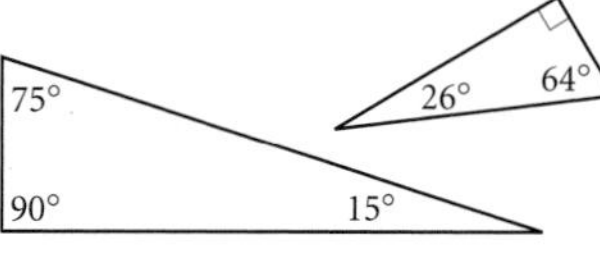

Right triangles

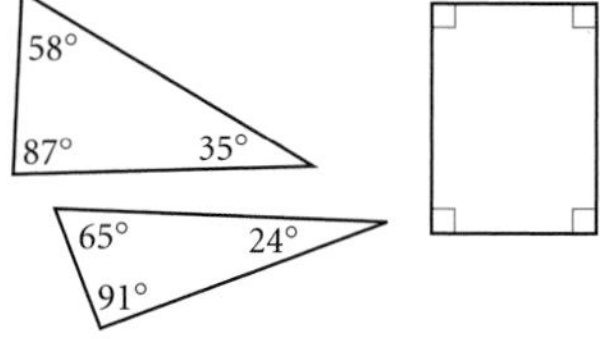

Not right triangles

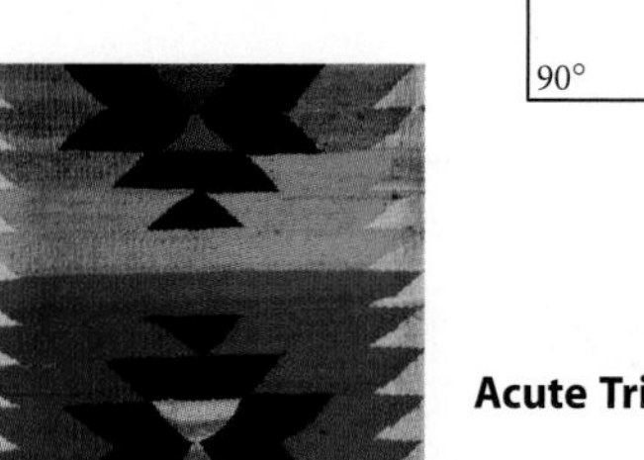

What shape is the basis for the design on this textile from Uzbekistan?

Acute Triangle An acute triangle has three acute angles.

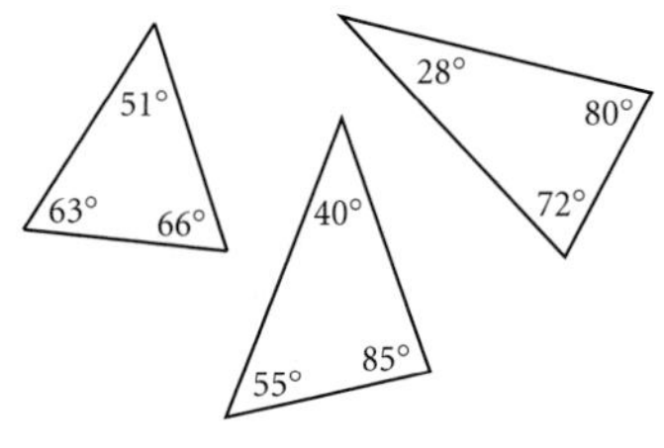

Acute triangles

50° 40° 27° 122° 31°

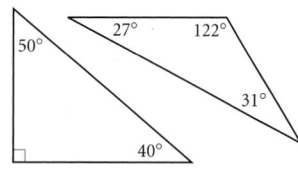

Not acute triangles

Obtuse Triangle An obtuse triangle has one obtuse angle.

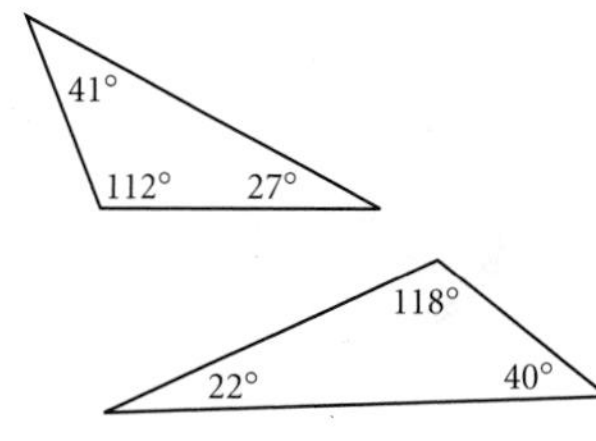

Obtuse triangles

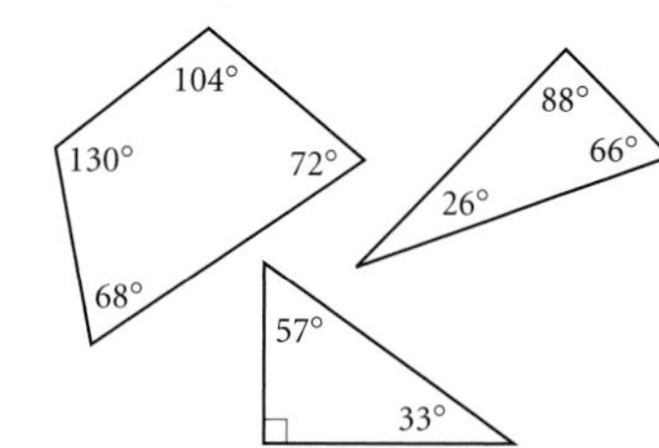

Not obtuse triangles

Guiding the Investigation

To save time you might have each group define two or three terms from the investigation. Make sure there is some overlap so that more than one group defines each term.

Discuss how student sketches should look when students illustrate their definitions, in light of assumptions.

[Alert] Some students may have trouble finding a clear definition for *kite.* Remind them about consecutive sides. It is appropriate to guide students as you talk with them about a definition while still giving them the feeling that they are coming up with the definition. The goal is to get them to the stage where they can carefully label a kite when asked; and, when given a diagram of a kite, they can identify it. They do not need to memorize a definition.

You might use The Geometer's Sketchpad demonstration Classifying Parallelograms.

The Sol LeWitt (b 1928, United States) design inside this art museum uses triangles and quadrilaterals to create a painting the size of an entire room.

Sol LeWitt, *Wall Drawing #652—On three walls, continuous forms with color ink washes superimposed, color in wash.* Collection: Indianapolis Museum of Art, Indianapolis, IN. September, 1990. Courtesy of the artist.

Scalene Triangle A scalene triangle is a triangle with no congruent sides.

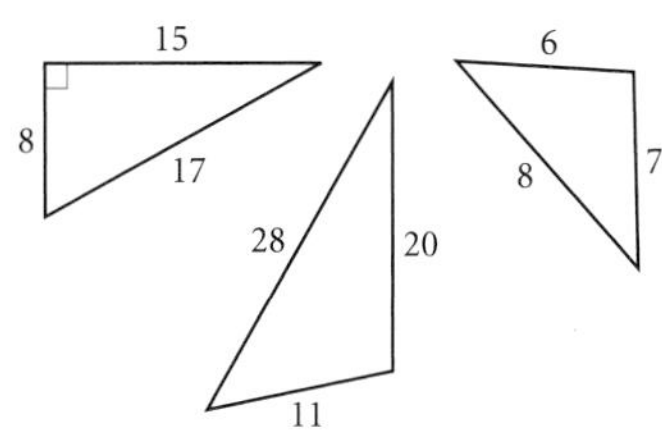

Scalene triangles

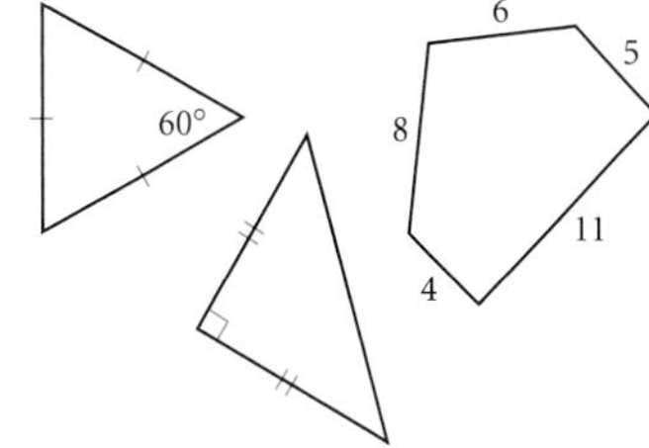

Not scalene triangles

Equilateral Triangle An equilateral triangle has three congruent sides.

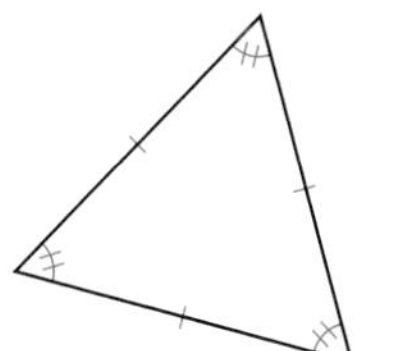

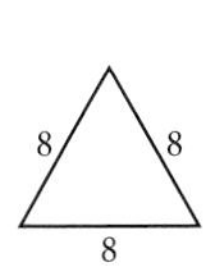

Equilateral triangles

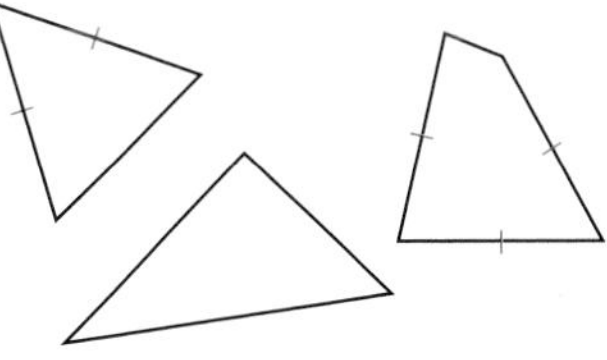

Not equilateral triangles

Isosceles Triangle An isosceles triangle has at least two congruent sides.

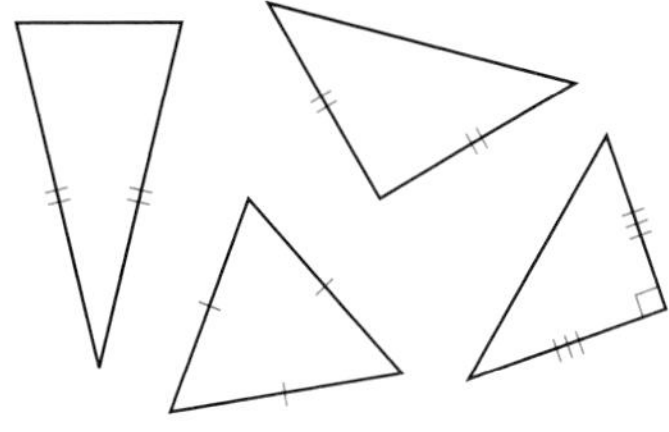

Isosceles triangles

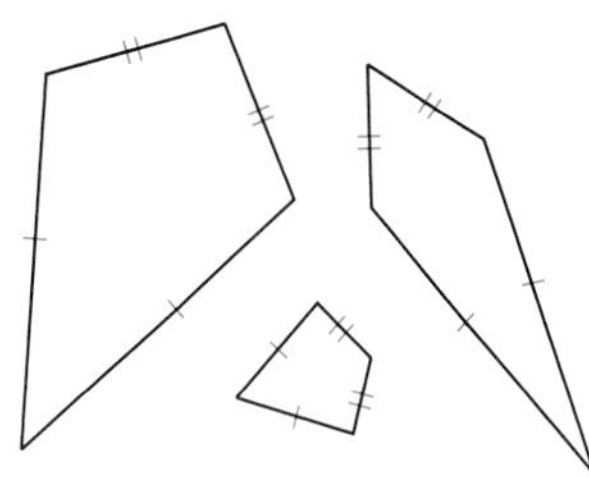

Not isosceles triangles

SHARING IDEAS

Select presenters, if possible including some students who are making unwarranted assumptions. **[Language]** Be sure students know how to pronounce *isosceles.* The prefix *iso* means "the same" or "equal." Have the class discuss the wording of each definition. You need not insist on complete uniformity of definitions, but try to agree on attributes.

Some students may want to define an equilateral triangle as having three congruent sides; others may want to say that the three angles are congruent. Because the word *equilateral* comes from *equi* meaning "equal" and *lateral* meaning "side," the former definition is better. There will be a conjecture in Lesson 4.8 about an equilateral triangle being equiangular and its converse. Students may make conjectures about whether one condition implies the other, but don't try to settle that question in this lesson.

Similarly, some students might want to say that a parallelogram has pairs of sides parallel; others may want to say that the pairs of alternating sides are congruent; still others may want to say that the pairs of alternating angles are congruent.

Encourage students to build on previous definitions; for example, rather than saying that a square has four congruent sides and four 90° angles, they might say that it's an equilateral equiangular rectangle; a regular quadrilateral; or even a rectangle with two adjacent sides congruent.

To define *trapezoid* and rule out the possibility of a parallelogram being included, the word *exactly* can be used.

To define *kite* and rule out the possibility of a rhombus being included, the word *distinct* can be used.

Sharing Ideas (continued)

You can motivate Chapter 3 by asking what would be needed to construct each kind of figure with a straightedge and compass. To construct a right triangle or a rectangle given two sides, you'd need to be able to construct perpendicular lines and copy the sides onto them. To construct a parallelogram, you'd need to be able to construct parallel lines. **[Ask]** "Which polygons must be symmetric?" [Kites, isosceles triangles, equilateral triangles, rhombuses, rectangles, and squares must have reflectional symmetry, and the last four of these plus parallelograms must have rotational symmetry.]

Assessing Progress

Watch for students' voluntary use of terminology, for their ability to classify and differentiate while writing definitions, and for their remembering to test proposed definitions for counterexamples.

In an isosceles triangle, the angle between the two sides of equal length is called the **vertex angle.** The side opposite the vertex angle is called the **base** of the isoceles triangle. The two angles opposite the two sides of equal length are called the **base angles** of the isoceles triangle.

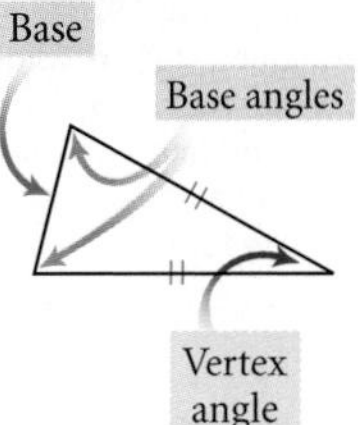

Now let's write definitions for quadrilaterals.

Trapezoid A trapezoid is a quadrilateral with exactly one pair of parallel sides.

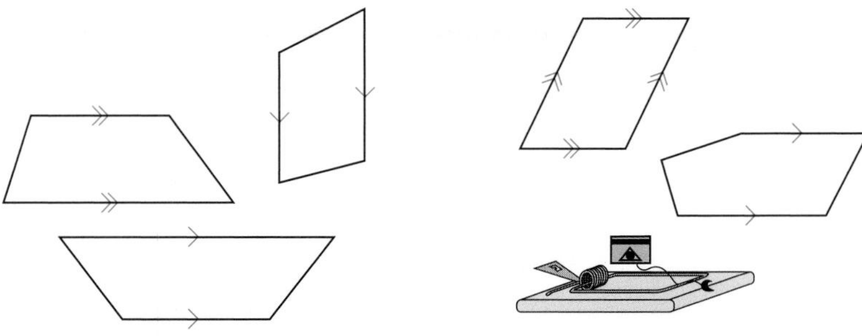

Trapezoids

Not trapezoids

How does this ancient pyramid in Mexico use shapes for practical purposes and also for its overall attractiveness?

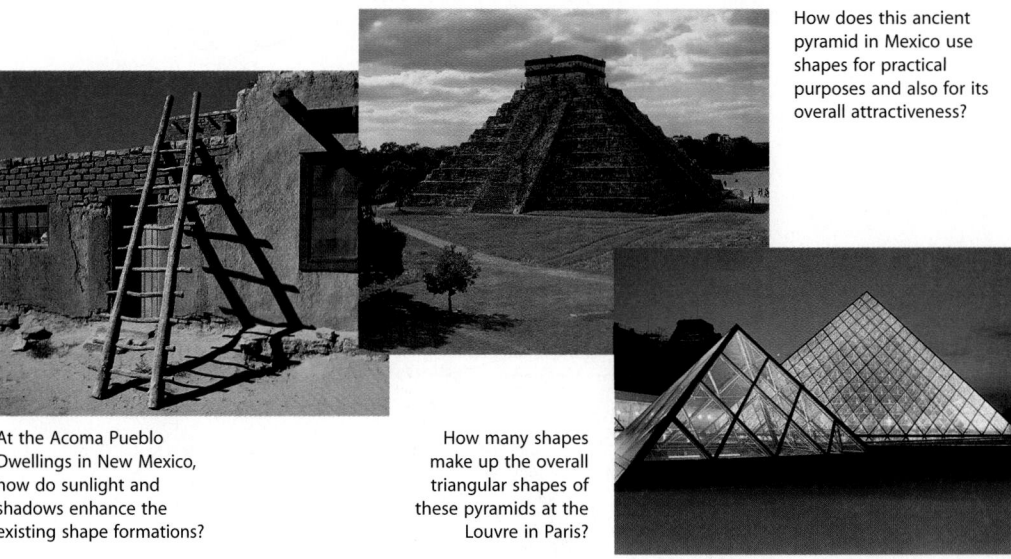

At the Acoma Pueblo Dwellings in New Mexico, how do sunlight and shadows enhance the existing shape formations?

How many shapes make up the overall triangular shapes of these pyramids at the Louvre in Paris?

Kite A kite is a quadrilateral with two distinct pairs of consecutive congruent sides.

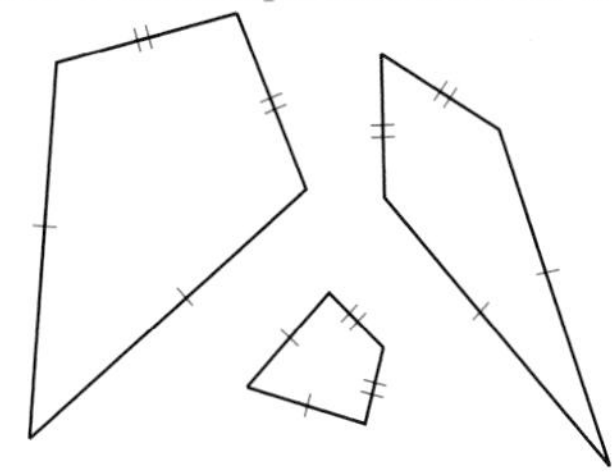

Kites

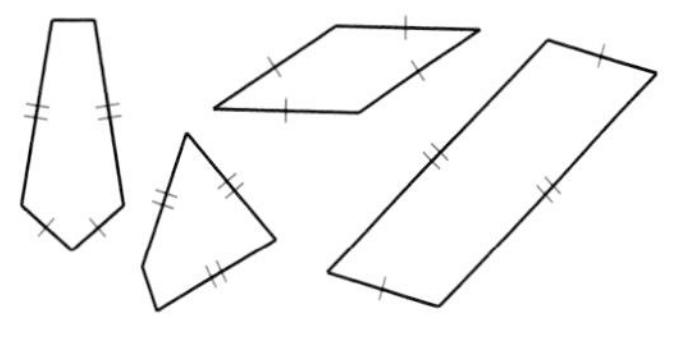

Not kites

Recreation CONNECTION

Today's kite designers use lightweight plastics, synthetic fabrics, and complex shapes to sustain kites in the air longer than earlier kites that were made of wood, cloth, and had the basic "kite" shape. Many countries even hold annual kite festivals where contestants fly flat kites, box kites, and fighter kites. The design will determine the fastest and most durable kite in the festival.

Parallelogram A parallelogram is a quadrilateral with two pairs of parallel sides.

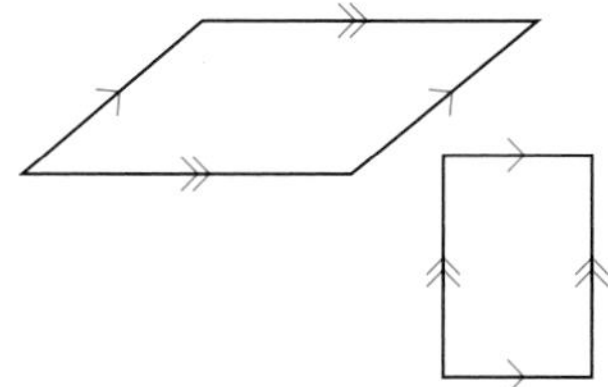

Parallelograms

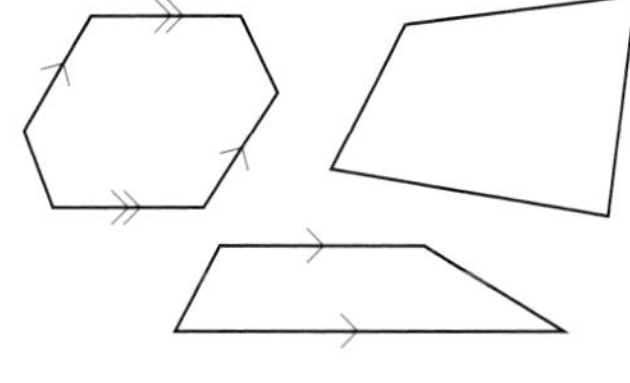

Not parallelograms

Rhombus A rhombus is an equilateral parallelogram.

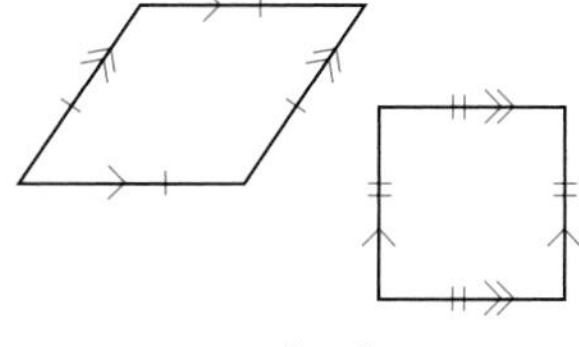

Rhombuses

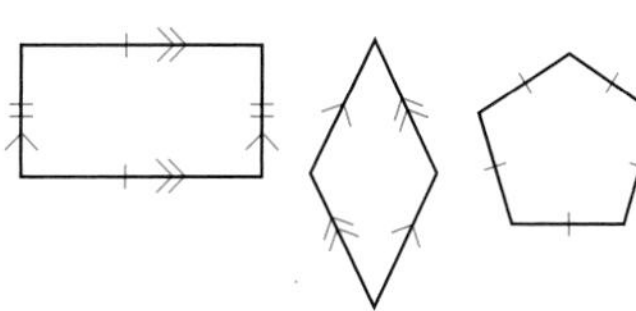

Not rhombuses

Rectangle A rectangle is a parallelogram with four congruent angles.

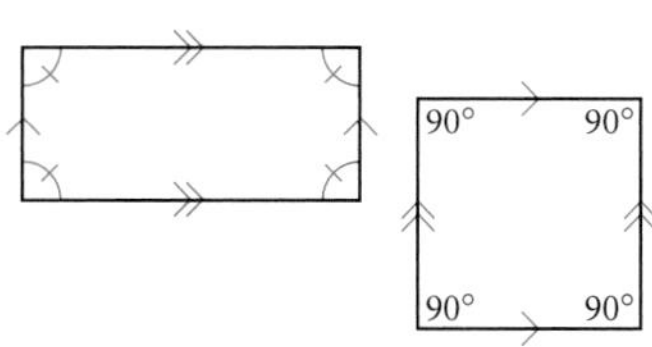

Rectangles

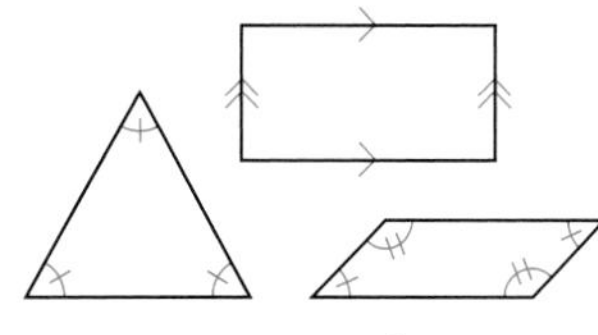

Not rectangles

Closing the Lesson

In this lesson, students have defined these terms: **right triangle, acute triangle, obtuse triangle, scalene triangle, isosceles triangle, equilateral triangle, trapezoid, kite, parallelogram, rhombus, rectangle,** and **square.** Have students add these new terms, with sketches, to their definition lists, again reminding them to label their sketches.

BUILDING UNDERSTANDING

If students complete these exercises in class, encourage them to try this set again at home on their own to be sure they feel confident making the diagrams themselves.

ASSIGNING HOMEWORK

Essential	1–16, 20–24
Performance assessment	30
Portfolio	17
Journal	31
Group	18, 19
Review	25–31

MATERIALS

- graph paper (Exercises 22–24)

▶Helping with the Exercises

1. first figure: quadrilateral with two congruent sides and one right angle; third figure: *IJKL* with two right angles

Exercises 10–18 The instructions are to *sketch* figures, meaning students can make a freehand drawing rather than using a ruler and protractor. (The distinctions among sketching, drawing, and constructing are made in Lesson 3.1.)

10.

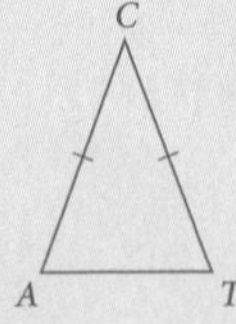

Square A square is an equilateral rectangle. A square is an equiangular rhombus. A square is a regular quadrilateral.

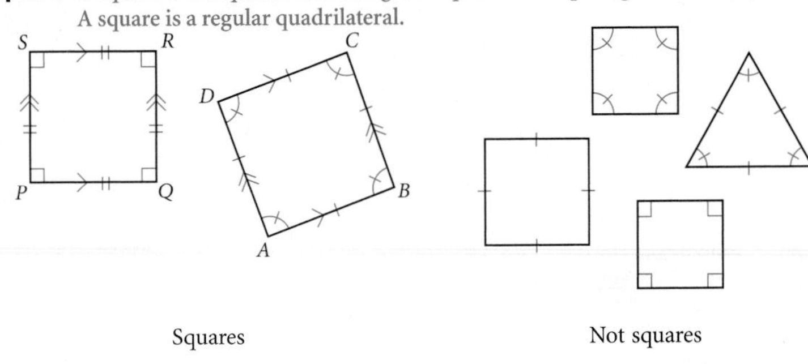

As you learned in the investigation, a square is not a square unless it has the proper markings. Keep this in mind as you work on the exercises.

EXERCISES

1. Based on the marks, what can you assume to be true in each figure?

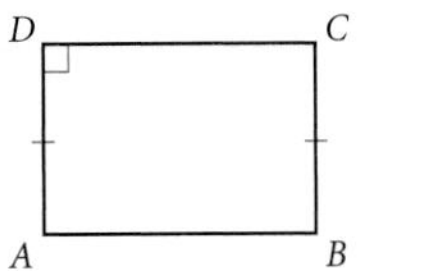

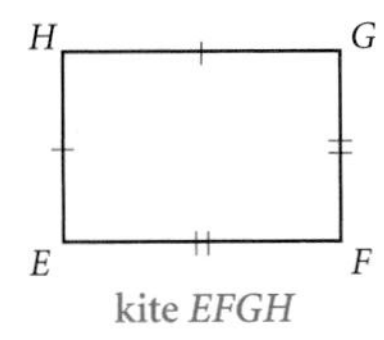

kite *EFGH*

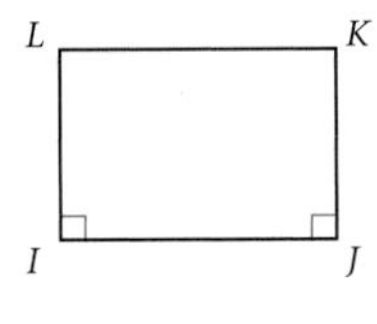

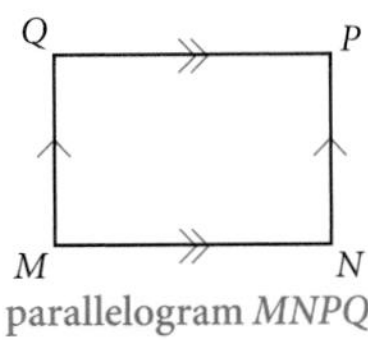

parallelogram *MNPQ*

For Exercises 2–9, match the term on the left with its figure on the right.

2. Scalene right triangle A

3. Isosceles right triangle E

4. Isosceles obtuse triangle D

5. Trapezoid B

6. Rhombus F

7. Rectangle I

8. Kite C

9. Parallelogram F, G, I

A. B. C. D.

E.

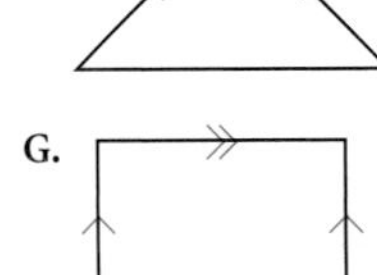

F.

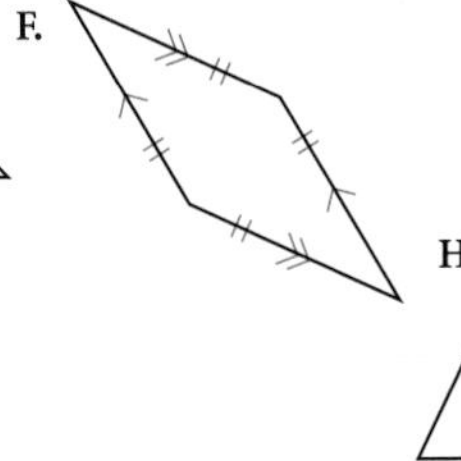

G. H. I.

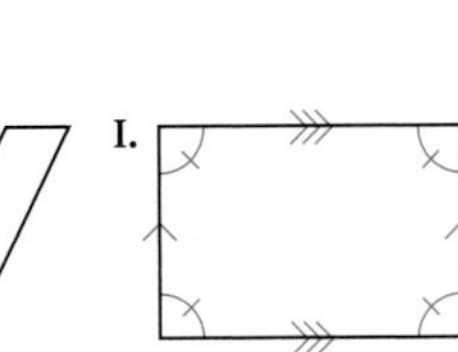

For Exercises 10–18, sketch and label the figure. Mark the figures.

10. Isosceles acute triangle *ACT* with $AC = CT$

11. Scalene triangle *SCL* with angle bisector $\overline{CM}$

12. Isosceles right triangle *CAR* with $m\angle CRA = 90°$

Exercise 11 An angle bisector is a ray, but it can be pictured as a segment.

11.

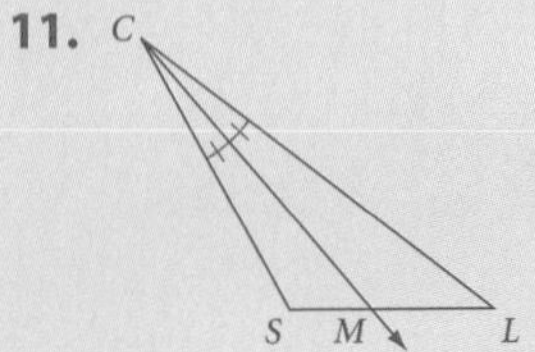

Exercise 12 If students need help, offer this hint: $\overline{CR} \cong \overline{AR}$.

12.

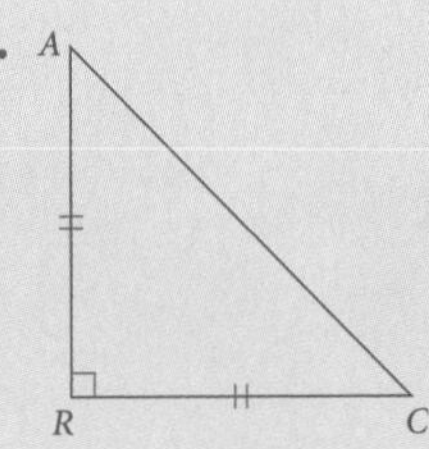

13. Trapezoid $ZOID$ with $\overline{ZO} \parallel \overline{ID}$

14. Kite $BENF$ with $BE = EN$

15. Rhombus $EQUL$ with diagonals $\overline{EU}$ and $\overline{QL}$ intersecting at A

16. Rectangle $RGHT$ with diagonals $\overline{RH}$ and $\overline{GT}$ intersecting at I

17. Two different isosceles triangles with perimeter $4a + b$

18. Two noncongruent triangles, each with side 6 cm and an angle measuring 40°

19. Draw a hexagon with exactly two outside diagonals.

20. Draw a regular quadrilateral. What is another name for this shape? square

21. Find the other two vertices of a square with one vertex (0, 0) and another vertex (4, 2). Can you find another answer? possible answers: $(2, 6), (-2, 4)$; $(6, -2), (2, -4)$; $(3, -1), (1, 3)$

Austrian architect and artist Friedensreich Hundertwasser (1928–2000) designed the apartment house Hundertwasser-House (1986) with a square spiral staircase in its center. What other shapes do you see?

For Exercises 22–24, use the graphs below. Can you find more than one answer?

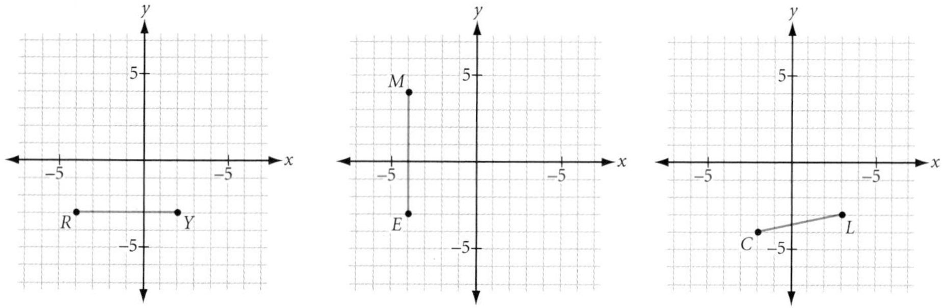

22. Locate a point L so that $\triangle LRY$ is an isosceles triangle. possible answers: $(-1, -1)$ or $(-1, 0)$

23. Locate a point O so that $\triangle MOE$ is an isosceles right triangle. possible answers: $(3, -3)$; $(3, 4)$; $(-11, 4)$; $(-11, -3)$; $(-0.5, 0.5)$; or $(-7.5, 0.5)$

24. Locate a point R so that $\triangle CRL$ is an isosceles right triangle. ⓗ possible answers: $(-3, 1)$; $(-1, -9)$; $(2, 2)$; $(4, -8)$; $(0, -1)$; or $(1, -6)$

Review

For Exercises 25–29, tell whether the statement is true or false. For each false statement, sketch a counterexample or explain why the statement is false.

1.3 **25.** An acute angle is an angle whose measure is less than 90°. true

1.3 **26.** If two lines intersect to form a right angle, then the lines are perpendicular. true

1.4 **27.** A diagonal is a line segment that connects any two vertices of a polygon. False, a diagonal connects nonconsecutive vertices.

Exercise 21 You might ask if students see a rule for finding the other vertices. If they remember slopes of lines, they may refer to that idea, or the pattern may preview slopes that they'll encounter later.

Exercises 22–24 Encourage students to label the congruent parts and right angles in their drawings.

13.
14.

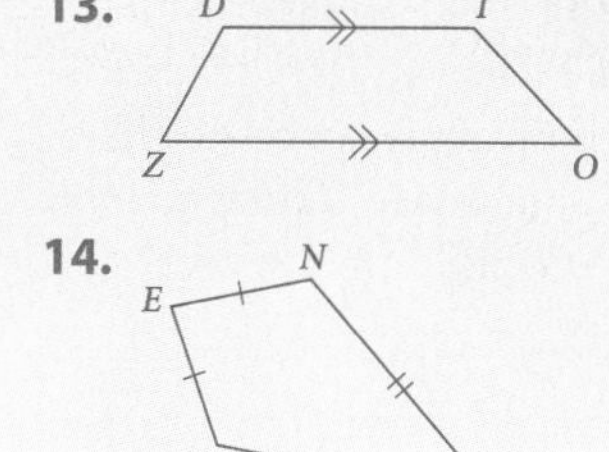

Exercises 15, 16 Encourage conjectures about diagonals and even testing of those conjectures on various quadrilaterals, but don't try to settle them here. When students do come up with their own conjectures, you might honor them by naming the conjecture after them, for example, the Roberto Conjecture. After the conjecture has been proved, it could be given a mathematical name.

15.

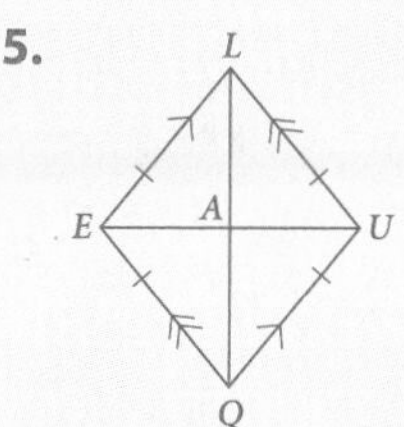

16.

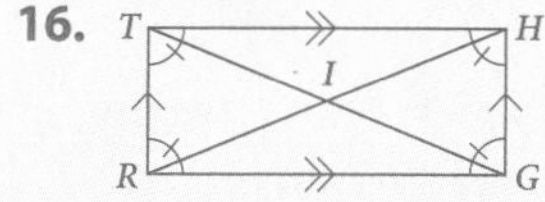

17. possible answer:

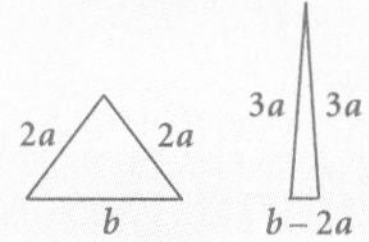

18. possible answer:

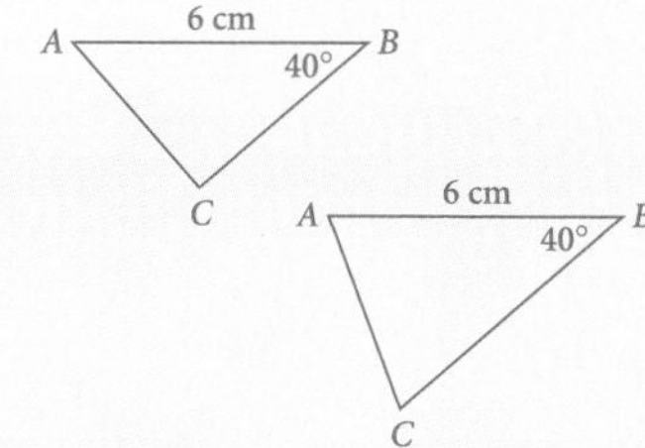

19.

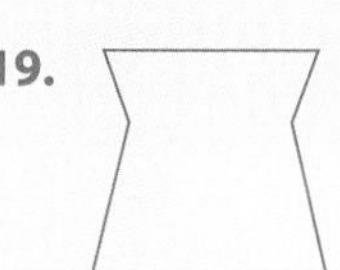

20.

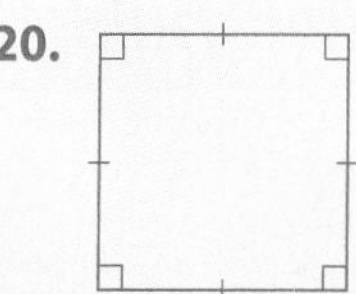

Exercise 30 [Ask] "This ordered pair rule tells you to move each vertex how many spaces to the right?" [one space] "How many spaces down?" [three spaces]

30. $(-4, 1) \rightarrow (-3, -2)$
$(1, 1) \rightarrow (2, -2)$
$(2, 4) \rightarrow (3, 1)$
$(-3, 5) \rightarrow (-2, 2)$
Yes, the quadrilaterals are congruent.

EXTENSION

Pose this problem: explore the properties of sets and subsets in more detail (including, if you're feeling ambitious, proper and improper subsets, the empty set, disjoint sets, union, and intersection). For example, every segment is a subset of some line.

1.2 **28.** A ray that divides the angle into two angles is the angle bisector.
False, an angle bisector divides an angle into two congruent angles.

1.3 **29.** An obtuse triangle has exactly one angle whose measure is greater than 90°. true

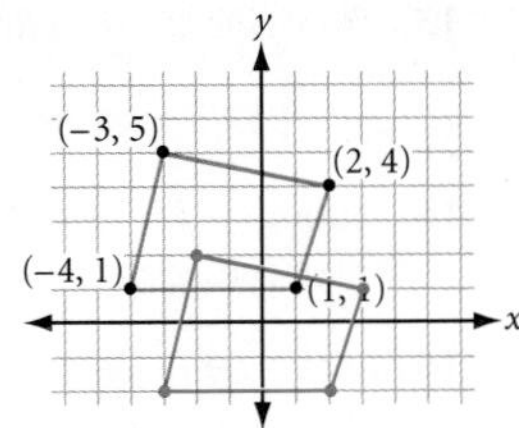

1.4 **30.** Use the ordered pair rule $(x, y) \rightarrow (x + 1, y - 3)$ to relocate the four vertices of the given quadrilateral. Connect the four new points to create a new quadrilateral. Do the two quadrilaterals appear congruent? Check your guess with tracing paper or patty paper.

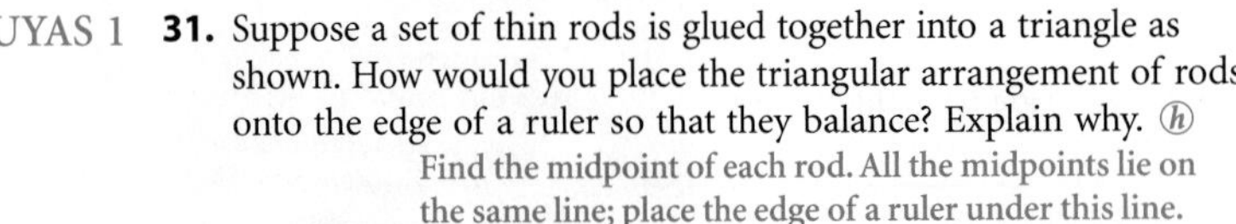

UYAS 1 **31.** Suppose a set of thin rods is glued together into a triangle as shown. How would you place the triangular arrangement of rods onto the edge of a ruler so that they balance? Explain why. ⓗ
Find the midpoint of each rod. All the midpoints lie on the same line; place the edge of a ruler under this line.

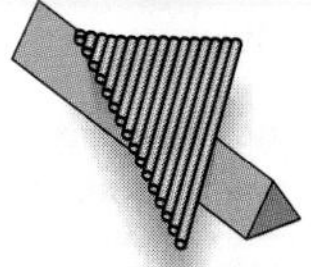

project

DRAWING THE IMPOSSIBLE

You experienced some optical illusions with op art in Chapter 0. Some optical illusions are tricks—they at first appear to be drawings of real objects, but actually they are impossible to make, except on paper. Reproduce the two impossible objects by drawing them on full sheets of paper.

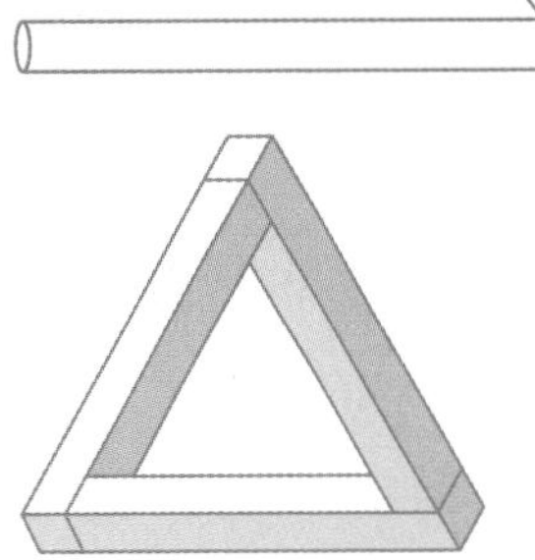

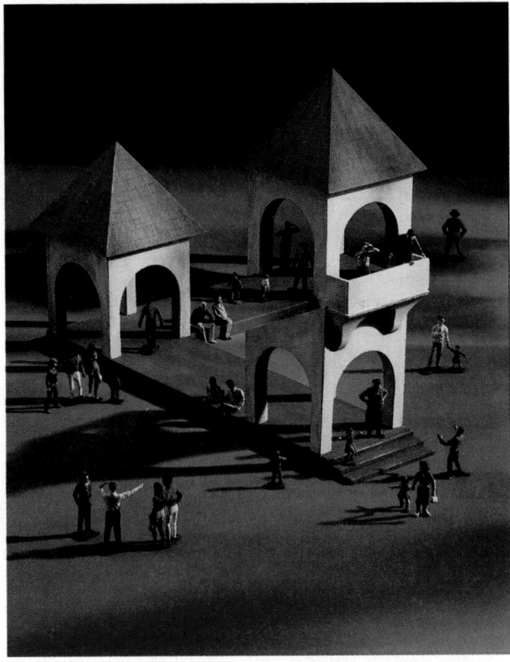

From WALTER WICK'S OPTICAL TRICKS. Published by Cartwheel Books, a division of Scholastic Inc. ©1998 by Walter Wick. Reprinted by permission.

Can you create an impossible object of your own? Try it.

Supporting the project

This activity helps students review the role of hidden lines in helping make a drawing appear realistic and increases visualization abilities. Show Escher's *Waterfall* (page 461) and *Belvedere* (page 619) and ask students to analyze how these artworks relate to the impossible figures pictured.

OUTCOMES

- ▸ The drawings will be based on one of the impossible figures in the book.
- ▸ Students should include attempts at drawing impossible objects.
- • Creative features accentuate the impossibility of the situations.
- • Students include analyses of the two Escher prints.

LESSON

1.6

I can never remember things I didn't understand in the first place.

AMY TAN

Circles

Unless you walked to school this morning, you arrived on a vehicle with circular wheels.

A **circle** is the set of all points in a plane at a given distance (radius) from a given point (center) in the plane. You name a circle by its center. The circle on the bicycle wheel, with center *O*, is called circle *O*. When you see a dot at the center of a circle, you can assume that it represents the center point.

A segment from the center to a point on the edge of the circle is called a **radius.** Its length is also called the radius.

The **diameter** is a line segment containing the center, with its endpoints on the circle. The length of this segment is also called the diameter.

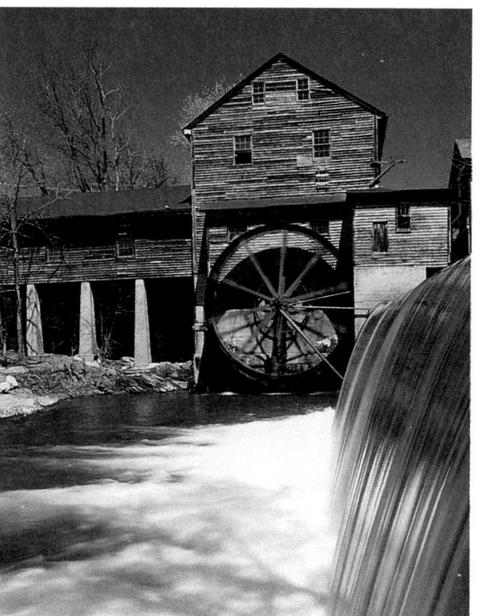

LESSON

1.6

PLANNING

LESSON OUTLINE

One day:

20 min	Investigation
5 min	Sharing
5 min	Closing
15 min	Exercises

MATERIALS

- construction tools
- protractors

TEACHING

Students define *circle* and various terms related to circles.

Use the one-step investigation, or start class by talking through the introductory material. Emphasize the meaning of the word *given,* which stands for the information given in the problem that can't be changed.

As you talk about vocabulary related to a circle, point out that *arc measure* does not refer to *arc length.* (Arc length will be discussed in Chapter 6.)

NCTM STANDARDS

CONTENT		PROCESS	
	Number	✓	Problem Solving
✓	Algebra		Reasoning
✓	Geometry	✓	Communication
✓	Measurement		Connections
	Data/Probability	✓	Representation

LESSON OBJECTIVES

- Define a circle and related figures
- Practice creating definitions
- Identify the parts of a circle
- Review construction skills
- Develop writing skills and cooperative behavior

Guiding the Investigation

One step Ask the class for a definition of *circle.* To classify, they'll need to use the idea of a set of points. To differentiate, they'll need to use a word like *given.* **[Language]** Students may have difficulty with the word *given.* If they introduce it rather than studying someone else's use, they are more likely to realize that it refers to information given in the problem, such as the radius and center of a circle, that cannot be changed for a particular problem. Given any particular radius and center, students can draw only one circle. Have students write definitions of the terms in the investigation.

As you circulate, emphasize as needed the process of classifying and differentiating. Encourage students to use the classification "set of points." Students' definitions of *circle* should lead to the idea that a point *inside* the circle is not *on* the circle.

SHARING IDEAS

For presenting definitions, try to select students who haven't presented before. Imperfect definitions lead to more discussion and insight than do high-quality definitions.

A common definition of *diameter* is "a set of points going all the way across the circle." If nobody else questions this definition, muse aloud about what "all the way across" means. Ask if the other newly defined term (*chord*) could be used to simplify the definition. If students propose "the longest chord of the circle," wonder aloud if it's possible to draw a chord that is longer than the diameter. [It is not.] "A chord through the circle's center" gives another definition. **[Ask]** "How do the radius and diameter relate?" (If needed, ask for an informal definition of *radius* here.) If students say that the

If two or more circles have the same radius, they are **congruent circles.** If two or more coplanar circles share the same center, they are **concentric circles.**

Congruent circles

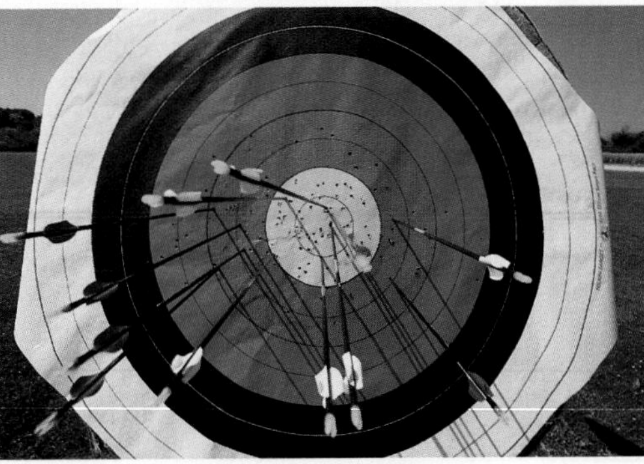
Concentric circles

An **arc of a circle** is two points on the circle and the continuous (unbroken) part of the circle between the two points. The two points are called the **endpoints** of the arc.

You write arc AB as $\overparen{AB}$ or $\overparen{BA}$. You classify arcs into three types: semicircles, minor arcs, and major arcs. A **semicircle** is an arc of a circle whose endpoints are the endpoints of a diameter. A **minor arc** is an arc of a circle that is smaller than a semicircle. A **major arc** is an arc of a circle that is larger than a semicircle. You can name minor arcs with the letters of the two endpoints. For semicircles and major arcs, you need three points to make clear which arc you mean—the first and last letters are the endpoints and the middle letter is any other point on the arc.

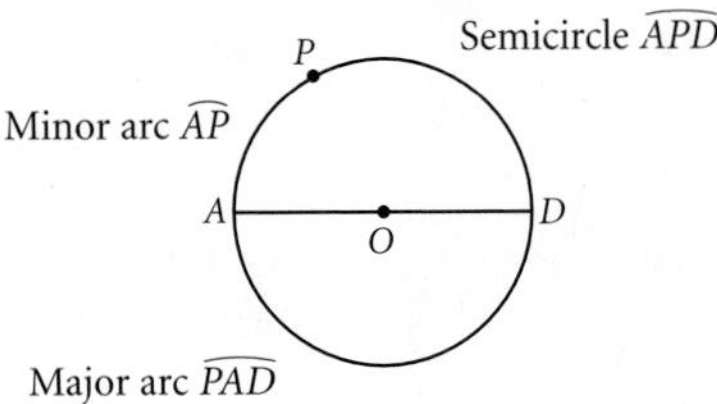

Arcs have a degree measure, just as angles do. A full circle has an arc measure of 360°, a semicircle has an arc measure of 180°, and so on. You find the **arc measure** by measuring the **central angle,** the angle with its vertex at the center of the circle, and sides passing through the endpoints of the arc.

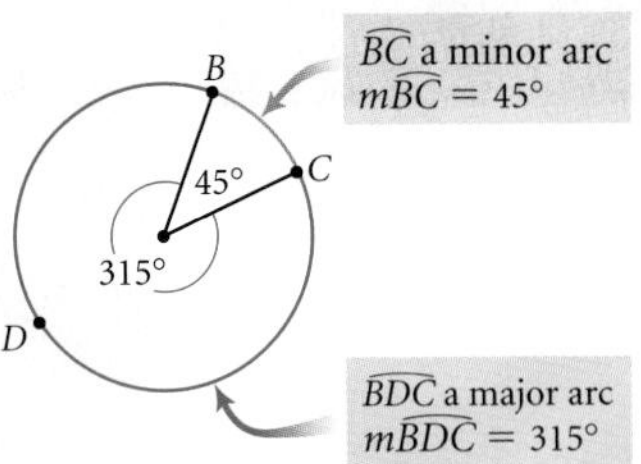

Investigation
Defining Circle Terms

Step 1 Write a good definition of each boldfaced term. Discuss your definitions with others in your group. Agree on a common set of definitions as a class and add them to your definition list. In your notebook, draw and label a figure to illustrate each definition.

Chord A chord is a line segment whose endpoints lie on the circle.

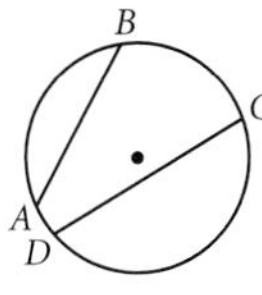

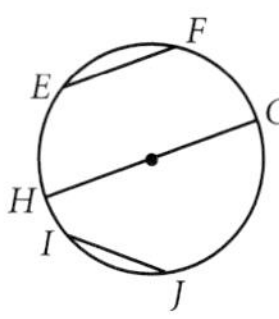

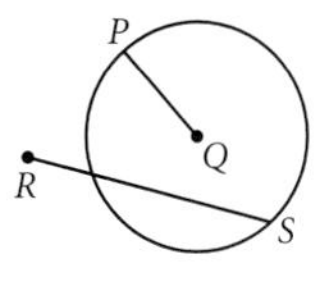

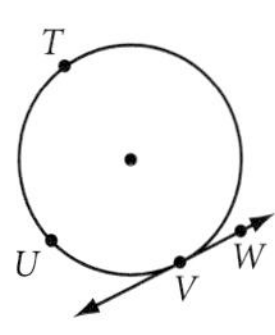

Chords:
$\overline{AB}$, $\overline{CD}$, $\overline{EF}$, $\overline{GH}$, and $\overline{IJ}$

Not chords:
$\overline{PQ}$, $\overline{RS}$, $\overrightarrow{TU}$, and $\overleftrightarrow{VW}$

Diameter A diameter is a chord that passes through the center. A diameter is the longest chord.

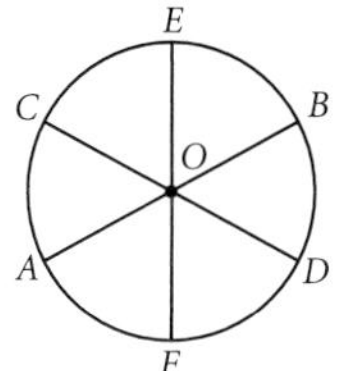

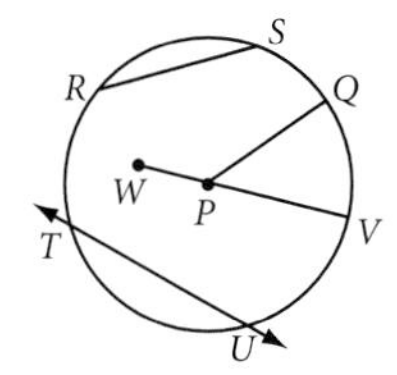

Diameters:
$\overline{AB}$, $\overline{CD}$, and $\overline{EF}$

Not diameters:
$\overline{PQ}$, $\overline{RS}$, $\overleftrightarrow{TU}$, and $\overline{VW}$

Tangent A tangent is a line that intersects the circle only once.

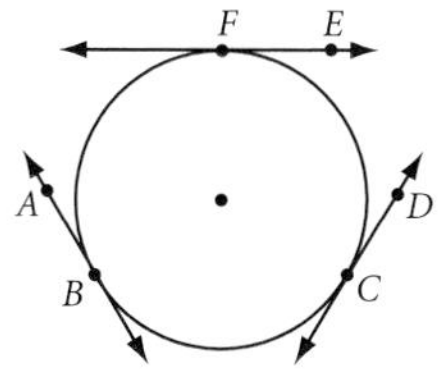

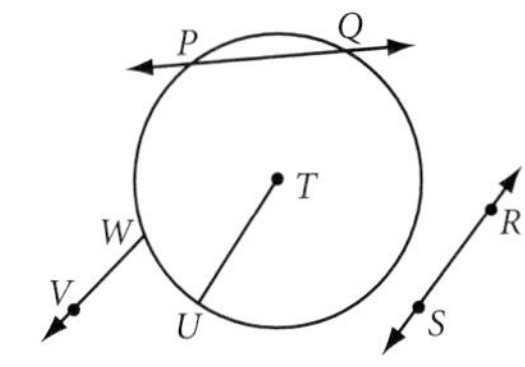

Tangents:
$\overleftrightarrow{AB}$, $\overleftrightarrow{CD}$, and $\overleftrightarrow{EF}$

Not tangents:
$\overleftrightarrow{PQ}$, $\overleftrightarrow{RS}$, $\overline{TU}$, and $\overline{VW}$

Note: You can say $\overleftrightarrow{AB}$ is a tangent, or you can say $\overleftrightarrow{AB}$ is tangent to circle O. The point where the tangent touches the circle is called the **point of tangency.**

Step 2 Can a chord of a circle also be a diameter of the circle? Can it be a tangent? Explain why or why not.

Step 3 Can two circles be tangent to the same line at the same point? Draw a sketch and explain.

Sharing Ideas (continued)
diameter is twice the radius, lead into a discussion of the two meanings of both terms: as segments and as lengths of those segments.

Ask students to give careful definitions of *radius* and *congruent circles,* and then have them analyze the definitions in the student book. Some students may challenge the sufficiency of the book's definition of *congruent circles*; does specifying a radius ensure that the circles are "the same size"? [yes] While they're examining the book, point out to students the definitions of *concentric circles, arc, semicircle, minor arc, major arc,* and *central angle.* Again, rather than just having students copy the book's definitions to be sketched and memorized, have them use their own words and even try to improve on the phrasing used in the student book. As they try to improve a definition, students will see how important each part is.

[Ask] "Can two circles be both concentric and congruent? What would they look like?" [They would be the same circle.]

[Alert] Many students confuse arc measure with arc length. **[Ask]** "Can two arcs have the same measure but different lengths?" [Yes. For example, they may be parts of two very different-size circles but each have an arc of 15°.]

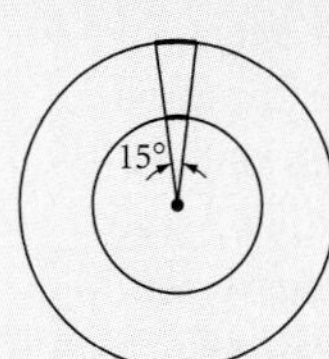

Assessing Progress
Check to see that students are continuing to label their sketches and to write definitions that classify and differentiate. Also watch for use of the terms from earlier lessons. Students should be picking up the idea that a good definition does not include statements about properties that derive from the critical attributes used to define the object.

Step 3 Student sketches can show tangent circles with a smaller circle inside a larger one or with neither circle inside the other.

Closing the Lesson

The major new ideas of this lesson are **circle, radius, center, diameter, congruent circles, concentric circles, chord, diameter, tangent, point of tangency, arc** (and its **endpoints**), **semicircle, arc measure, minor arc, major arc,** and **central angle.** You could have students review some of these ideas by doing the first eight exercises orally.

BUILDING UNDERSTANDING

In the exercises, students review definitions of terms related to a circle.

ASSIGNING HOMEWORK

Essential	1–10, 13–15, 17–19
Performance assessment	16
Portfolio	18, 19
Group	11, 12
Review	21–33

MATERIALS

- Exercises 1–8 (T), *optional*

Helping with the Exercises

4. five of the following: $\overset{\frown}{EF}$, $\overset{\frown}{AE}$, $\overset{\frown}{AB}$, $\overset{\frown}{BC}$, $\overset{\frown}{CD}$, $\overset{\frown}{DF}$, $\overset{\frown}{EB}$, $\overset{\frown}{ED}$, $\overset{\frown}{FC}$, $\overset{\frown}{AC}$, $\overset{\frown}{DB}$, $\overset{\frown}{AF}$, $\overset{\frown}{AD}$, $\overset{\frown}{BF}$

Exercise 9 [Context] Wheels are the basis of circular gears, developed at the beginning of the industrial revolution in the late eighteenth century. Some students might be interested in researching the advances of the industrial revolution that relied on mathematics. Or students might relate the mathematics of the circle to other important uses of the wheel, such as potters' wheels, clocks, and windmills.

In each photo, find examples of the terms introduced in this lesson.

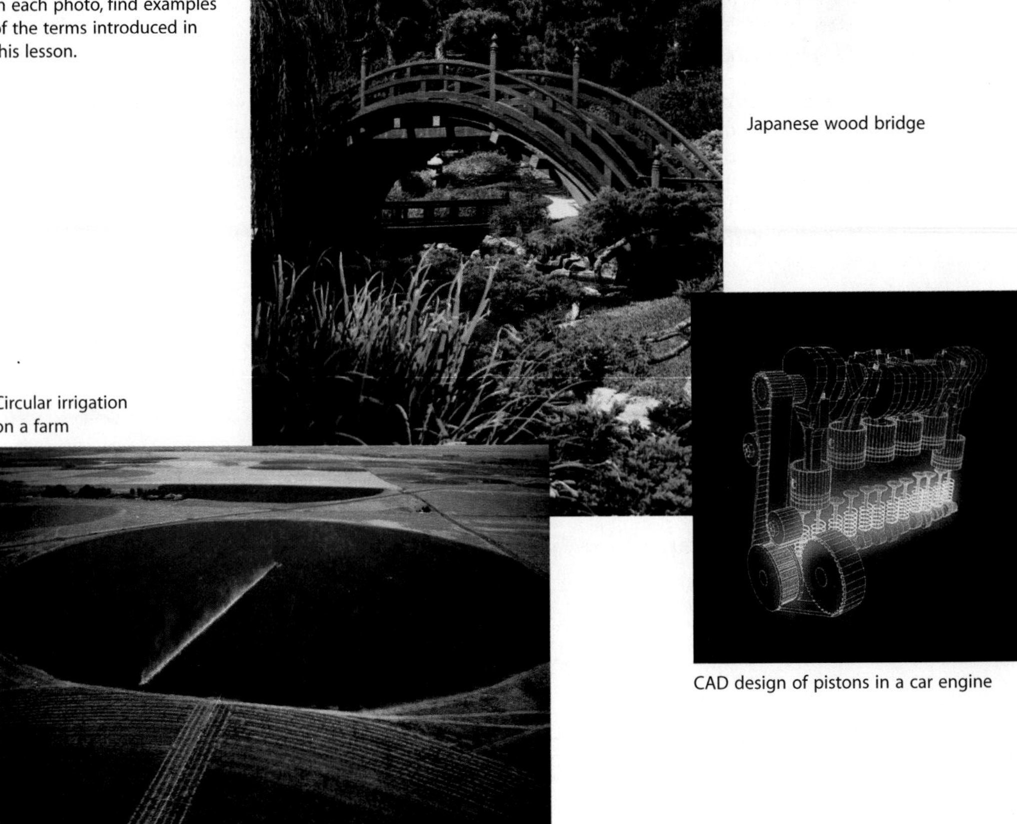

Japanese wood bridge

Circular irrigation on a farm

CAD design of pistons in a car engine

EXERCISES

For Exercises 1–8, use the diagram at right. Points E, P, and C are collinear.

H B C A P E D F G

1. Name three chords. three of the following: $\overline{AB}$, $\overline{BD}$, $\overline{EC}$, $\overline{EF}$
2. Name one diameter. $\overline{EC}$
3. Name five radii. $\overline{AP}$, $\overline{EP}$, $\overline{FP}$, $\overline{BP}$, $\overline{CP}$
4. Name five minor arcs.
5. Name two semicircles. $\overset{\frown}{EDC}$ or $\overset{\frown}{EFC}$, $\overset{\frown}{EBC}$ or $\overset{\frown}{EAC}$
6. Name two major arcs. two of the following: $\overset{\frown}{ECD}$, $\overset{\frown}{EDF}$, $\overset{\frown}{FEC}$, $\overset{\frown}{DEC}$, ...
7. Name two tangents. $\overleftrightarrow{FG}$, $\overleftrightarrow{HB}$
8. Name a point of tangency. either F or B
9. Name two types of vehicles that use wheels, two household appliances that use wheels, and two uses of the wheel in the world of entertainment.
10. In the figure at right, what is $m\overset{\frown}{PQ}$? $m\overset{\frown}{PRQ}$? $m\overset{\frown}{PQ} = 110°$; $m\overset{\frown}{PRQ} = 250°$

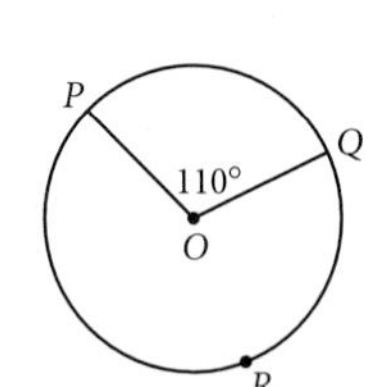

11. Use your compass and protractor to make an arc with measure 65°. Now make an arc with measure 215°. Label each arc with its measure.

9. possible answers: cars, trains, motorcycles; washing machines, dishwashers, vacuum cleaners; tape players, compact disc players, record players, car racing, Ferris wheel

Exercise 11 If you skipped Chapter 0, some students may need help in learning to use the compass carefully.

11.

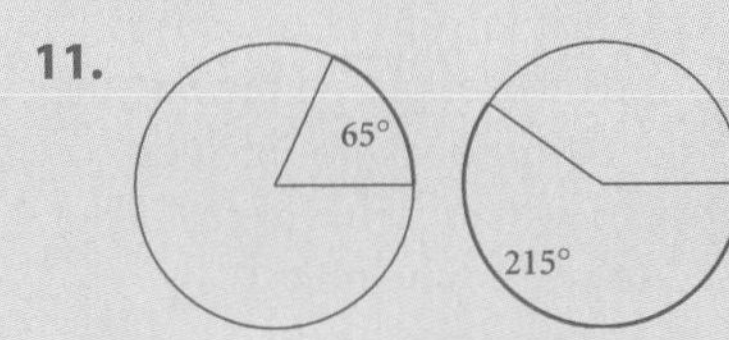

12. Name two places or objects where concentric circles appear. Bring an example of a set of concentric circles to class tomorrow. You might look in a magazine for a photo or make a copy of a photo from a book (but not this book!). possible answers: concentric rings on cross sections of trees (annual rings), bull's-eye or target, ripples from a rock falling into a pond.

13. Sketch two circles that appear to be concentric. Then use your compass to construct a pair of concentric circles.

14. Sketch circle *P*. Sketch a triangle inside circle *P* so that the three sides of the triangle are chords of the circle. This triangle is "inscribed" in the circle. Sketch another circle and label it *Q*. Sketch a triangle in the exterior of circle *Q* so that the three sides of the triangle are tangents of the circle. This triangle is "circumscribed" about the circle.

15. Use your compass to construct two circles with the same radius intersecting at two points. Label the centers *P* and *Q*. Label the points of intersection of the two circles *A* and *B*. Construct quadrilateral *PAQB*. What type of quadrilateral is it?

16. Do you remember the daisy construction from Chapter 0? Construct a circle with radius *s*. With the same compass setting, divide the circle into six congruent arcs. Construct the chords to form a regular hexagon inscribed in the circle. Construct radii to each of the six vertices. What type of triangles are formed? What is the ratio of the perimeter of the hexagon to the diameter of the circle? equilateral; 3 to 1

17. Sketch the path made by the midpoint of a radius of a circle if the radius is rotated about the center.

For Exercises 18–20, use the ordered pair rule shown to relocate the four points on the given circle. Can the four new points be connected to create a new circle? Does the new figure appear congruent to the original circle?

18. $(x, y) \rightarrow (x - 1, y + 2)$

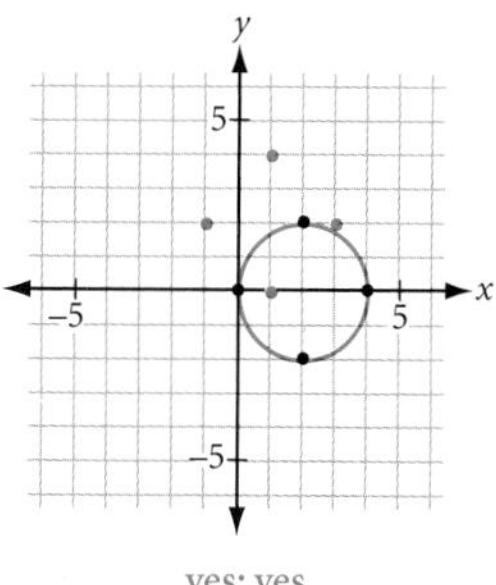

yes; yes

19. $(x, y) \rightarrow (2x, 2y)$ ⓗ

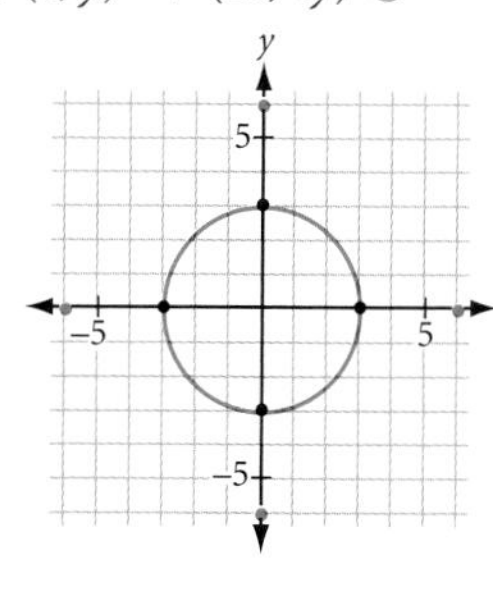

yes; no

20. $(x, y) \rightarrow (2x, y)$

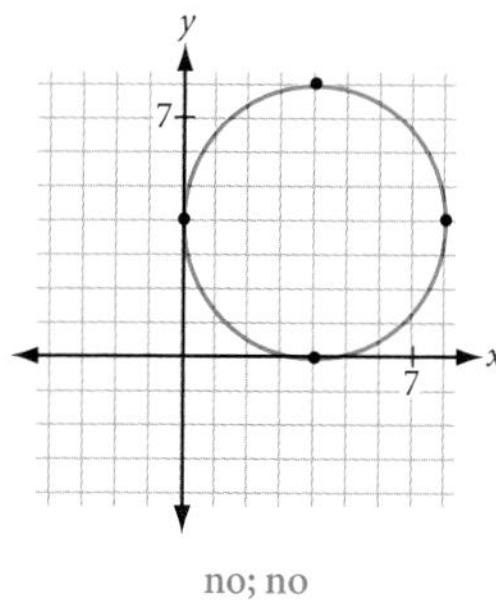

no; no

Review

For Exercises 21–24, draw each kind of triangle or write "not possible" and explain why. Use your geometry tools to make your drawings as accurate as possible.

1.5 **21.** Isosceles right triangle

1.5 **22.** Scalene isosceles triangle not possible

1.5 **23.** Scalene obtuse triangle

1.5 **24.** Isosceles obtuse triangle

Exercise 13 Sketching a circle is difficult, but students' initial (freehand) sketches will help them complete the final construction. Students with less manual dexterity can be guided to make larger circles with their wrists inside the arc.

13.

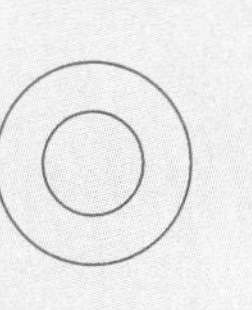

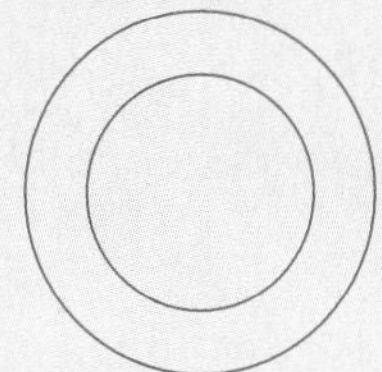

Exercise 14 The terms *inscribed* and *circumscribed* will be defined and used later.

14.

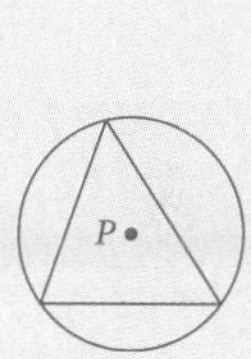

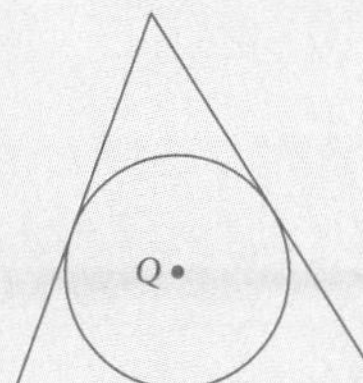

Exercises 15, 16 Students might need some help using a compass if you skipped Chapter 0.

15. rhombus (although technically until we've demonstrated some conjectures about the line joining the centers and the line of intersection, we can only say "equilateral quadrilateral")

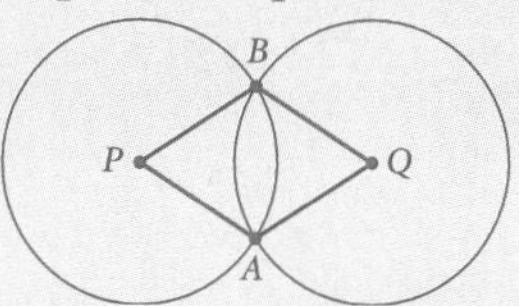

16.

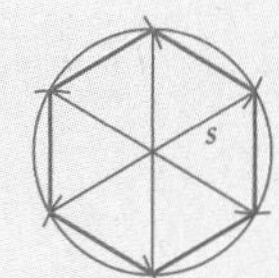

17.

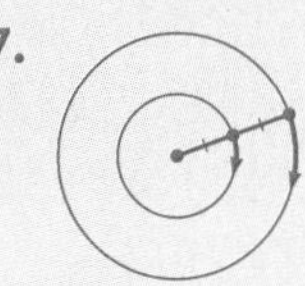

Exercise 17 After students have worked on this exercise, you might challenge them to use geometry software to create a demonstration of this path.

Exercises 18–20 If students are confused by the term *ordered pair rule*, describe it as a rule that states what should be done to each coordinate in the pair. The rule in Exercise 18 subtracts 1 from the *x*-coordinate (moves the point one space to the left) and adds 2 to the *y*-coordinate (moves the point up two spaces). These exercises help students connect their knowledge of algebra and geometry.

21.

Exercises 23–25 Complete labeling is important as students continue to review the definitions developed in this chapter. The labels show that students understand the characteristics that each figure must have and the specific location of those features.

23.

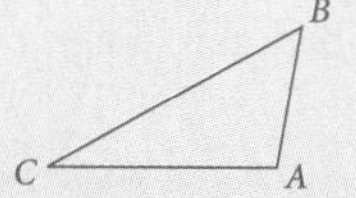

24.

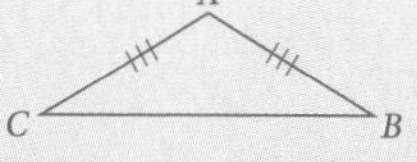

See page 768 for answer to Exercise 20.

25.

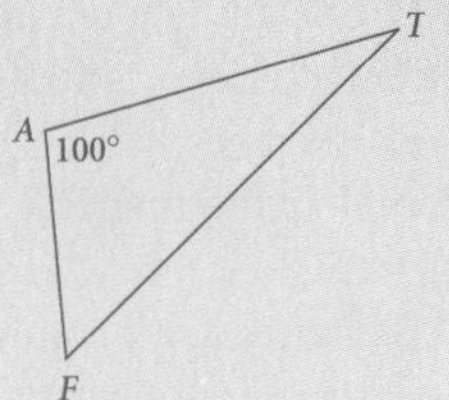

26.

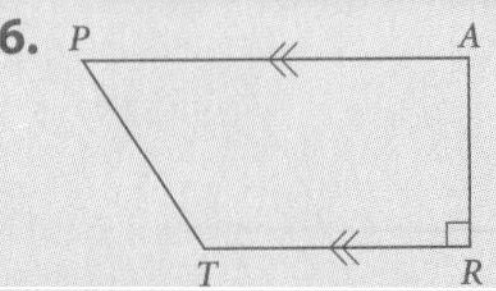

27.

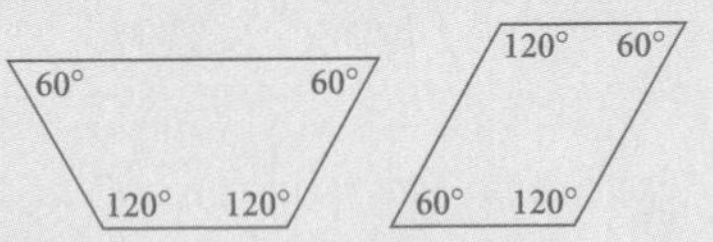

29.

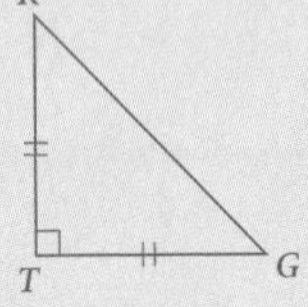

30.

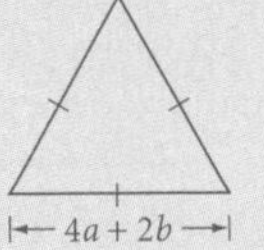

31.

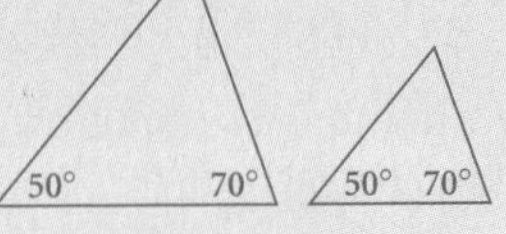

32.

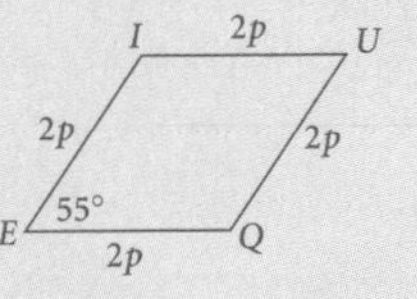

33.

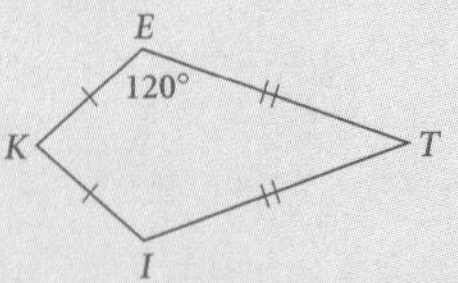

For Exercises 25–33, sketch, label, and mark the figure.

1.3 **25.** Obtuse scalene triangle FAT with $m\angle FAT = 100°$

1.4 **26.** Trapezoid $TRAP$ with $\overline{TR} \parallel \overline{AP}$ and $\angle TRA$ a right angle

1.4 **27.** Two different (noncongruent) quadrilaterals with angles of 60°, 60°, 120°, and 120°

1.3 **28.** Equilateral right triangle not possible

1.3 **29.** Right isosceles triangle RGT with $RT = GT$ and $m\angle RTG = 90°$

1.3 **30.** An equilateral triangle with perimeter $12a + 6b$

1.3 **31.** Two triangles that are not congruent, each with angles measuring 50° and 70°

1.4 **32.** Rhombus $EQUI$ with perimeter $8p$ and $m\angle IEQ = 55°$

1.4 **33.** Kite $KITE$ with $TE = 2EK$ and $m\angle TEK = 120°$

IMPROVING YOUR REASONING SKILLS

Checkerboard Puzzle

1. Four checkers—three red and one black—are arranged on the corner of a checkerboard, as shown at right. Any checker can jump any other checker. The checker that was jumped over is then removed. With exactly three horizontal or vertical jumps, remove all three red checkers, leaving the single black checker. Record your solution.

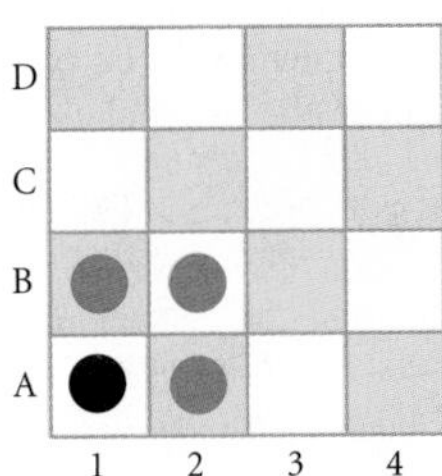

2. Now, with exactly seven horizontal or vertical jumps, remove all seven red checkers, leaving the single black checker. Record your solution.

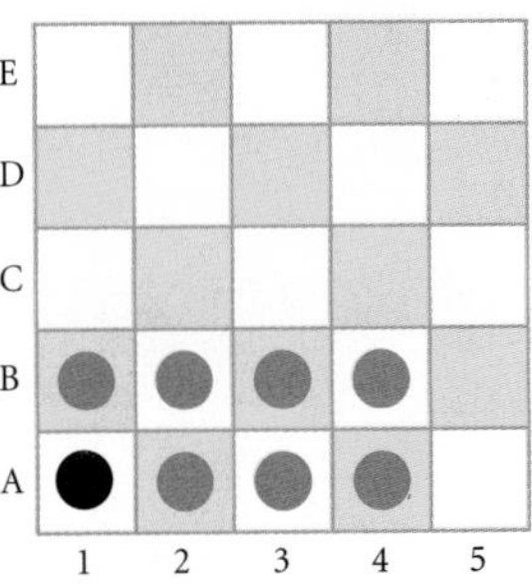

IMPROVING REASONING SKILLS

1. B1 to B3, A1 to A3, A3 to C3 or A2 to C2, A1 to C1, C1 to C3

2. A4 to C4, A3 to C3, C4 to C2, A1 to C1, C1 to C3, A2 to C2, C3 to C1

In either case the third step must be third, but the first two steps can be interchanged.

LESSON

1.7

A Picture Is Worth a Thousand Words

You can observe a lot just by watching.

YOGI BERRA

A picture is worth a thousand words! That expression certainly applies to geometry. A drawing of an object often conveys information more quickly than a long written description. People in many occupations use drawings and sketches to communicate ideas. Architects create blueprints. Composers create musical scores. Choreographers visualize and map out sequences of dance steps. Basketball coaches design plays. Interior designers—well, you get the picture.

Visualization skills are extremely important in geometry. So far, you have visualized geometric situations in every lesson. To visualize a plane, you pictured a flat surface extending infinitely. In another lesson, you visualized the number of different ways that four lines can intersect. Can you picture what the hands of a clock look like when it is 3:30?

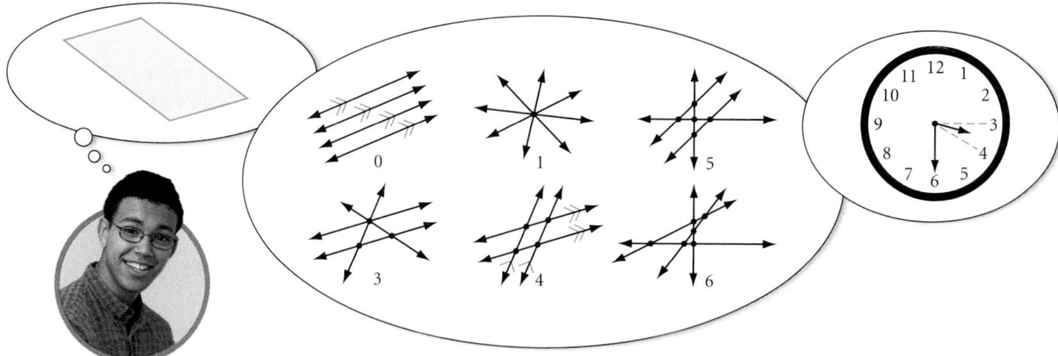

By drawing diagrams, you apply visual thinking to problem solving. Let's look at some examples that show how to use visual thinking to solve word problems.

EXAMPLE A

Volumes 1 and 2 of a two-volume set of math books sit next to each other on a shelf. They sit in their proper order: Volume 1 on the left and Volume 2 on the right. Each front and back cover is $\frac{1}{8}$ inch thick, and the pages portion of each book is 1 inch thick. If a bookworm starts at the first page of Volume 1 and burrows all the way through to the last page of Volume 2, how far will she travel?

Take a moment and try to solve the problem in your head.

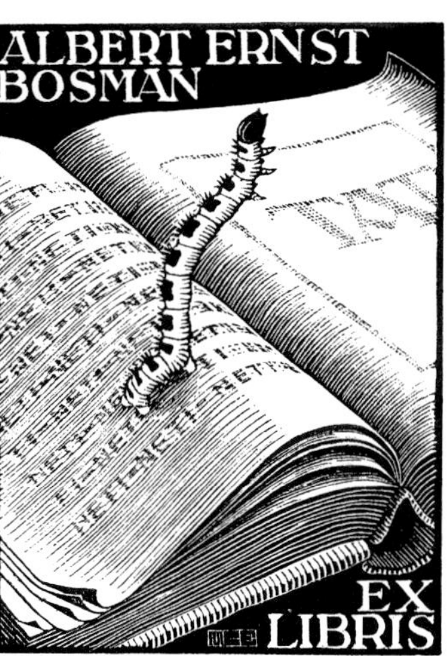

Bookplate for Albert Ernst Bosman, M. C. Escher, 1946

LESSON

1.7

PLANNING

LESSON OUTLINE

One day:

20 min Investigation

10 min Sharing

5 min Closing

10 min Exercises

MATERIALS

- a two-volume set of books, *optional*
- Visual Puzzles (W) for One step

TEACHING

Drawing diagrams can help students develop the visualization abilities. **[Language]** To *visualize* means "to form mental images or pictures." Use the one-step investigation on page 74 or talk through the examples.

▶ EXAMPLE A

Be sure students don't peek at the answer on the next page! If no students disagree with the claim that the worm crawls $2\frac{1}{4}$ inches, you might say that to help everyone understand you'd like a student to show the class the path the worm might take with two actual books. To make it very clear, suggest that the student remove one of the books. Mention how a careful drawing might have helped students visualize the situation better. As appropriate, use the term *length* of a line segment.

NCTM STANDARDS

CONTENT		PROCESS	
✓	Number	✓	Problem Solving
✓	Algebra	✓	Reasoning
✓	Geometry	✓	Communication
	Measurement	✓	Connections
	Data/Probability	✓	Representation

LESSON OBJECTIVES

- Translate descriptions into diagrams, and vice versa
- Solve word problems by first translating each into a labeled drawing
- Develop visual thinking skills

One step Hand out one copy of the Visual Puzzles worksheet to each group. Ask one person in the group to read the first problem silently and then to read it aloud to the group. Suggest that students first work alone to solve the problem in their heads and then discuss their solutions with their groups. After they agree on a solution, the process repeats with the next problem and a new reader.

SHARING IDEAS

For sharing, select students to represent a variety of approaches, including if possible some that demonstrate common errors. Encourage class critique, but moderate the discussion to keep comments from becoming personal. Keep requesting diagrams to help you and others understand the approach the presenter is taking. Encourage use of the terms *length* of a line segment, *perpendicular* and *parallel* lines, and *center* and *radius* of a circle.

For more structure, tell students about visualization and work through the examples. Then supervise their work on the exercises.

▶ EXAMPLE B

To emphasize the importance of diagrams, suggest that students first try solving the problem without looking at a sketch. As needed, remind students of the meaning of *perpendicular* and *parallel* lines.

Using the Quote
If you choose to refer to the quote at the beginning of the lesson, students may want to know that Yogi Berra (b 1925) was a professional baseball player for the New York Yankees in the 1940s, 1950s, and 1960s.

▶ Solution

Did you get $2\frac{1}{4}$ inches? It seems reasonable, doesn't it?

Guess what? That's not the answer. Let's get organized. Reread the problem to identify what information you are given and what you are trying to find.

You are given the thickness of each cover, the thickness of the page portion, and the position of the books on the shelf. You are trying to find how far it is from the first page of Volume 1 to the last page of Volume 2. Draw a picture and locate the position of the pages referred to in the problem.

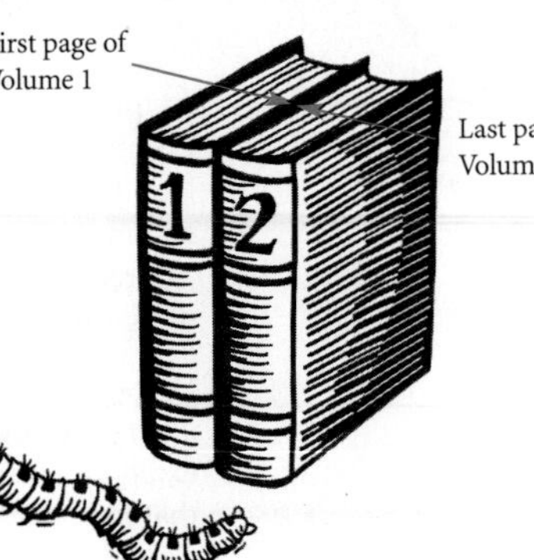

Now "look" how easy it is to solve the problem. She traveled only $\frac{1}{4}$ inch through the two covers!

EXAMPLE B

In Reasonville, many streets are named after famous mathematicians. Streets that end in an "s" run east-west. All other streets might run either way. Wiles Street runs perpendicular to Germain Street. Fermat Street runs parallel to Germain Street. Which direction does Fermat Street run?

Mathematics CONNECTION

The French mathematician Pierre de Fermat (1601–1665) developed analytic geometry. His algebraic approach is what made his influence on geometry so strong.

Sophie Germain (1776–1831), a French mathematician with no formal education, wrote a prize treatise, contributed to many theories, and worked extensively on Fermat's Last Theorem.

Andrew Wiles (b 1953), an English mathematician at Princeton University, began trying to prove Fermat's Last Theorem when he was just 10 years old. In 1993, after spending most of his career working on the theorem, sometimes in complete isolation, he announced a proof of the problem.

▶ Solution

Did you make a diagram? You can start your diagram with the first piece of information. Then you can add to the diagram as new information is added. Wiles Street ends in an "s," so it runs east-west. You are trying to find the direction of Fermat Street.

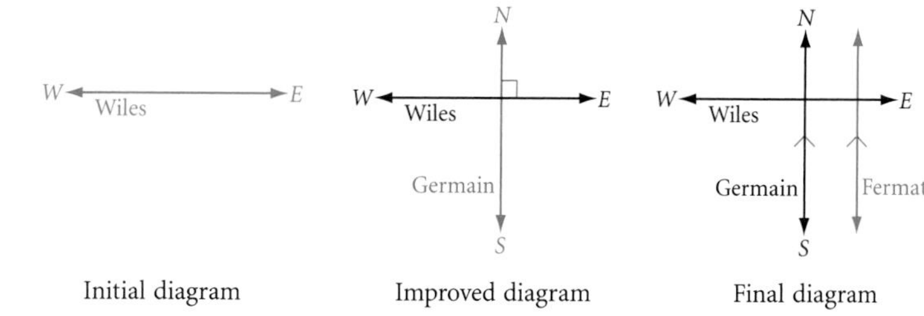

Initial diagram Improved diagram Final diagram

The final diagram reveals the answer. Fermat Street runs north–south.

Sometimes there is more than one point or even many points that satisfy a set of conditions. The set of points is called a **locus** of points. Let's look at an example showing how to solve a locus problem.

EXAMPLE C

Harold, Dina, and Linda are standing on a flat, dry field reading their treasure map. Harold is standing at one of the features marked on the map, a gnarled tree stump, and Dina is standing atop a large black boulder. The map shows that the treasure is buried 60 meters from the tree stump and 40 meters from the large black boulder. Harold and Dina are standing 80 meters apart. What is the locus of points where the treasure might be buried?

▶ *Solution*

Start by drawing a diagram based on the information given in the first two sentences, then add to the diagram as new information is added. Can you visualize all the points that are 60 meters from the tree stump? Mark them on your diagram. They should lie on a circle. The treasure is also 40 meters from the boulder. All the possible points lie in a circle around the boulder. The two possible spots where the treasure might be buried, or the locus of points, are the points where the two circles intersect.

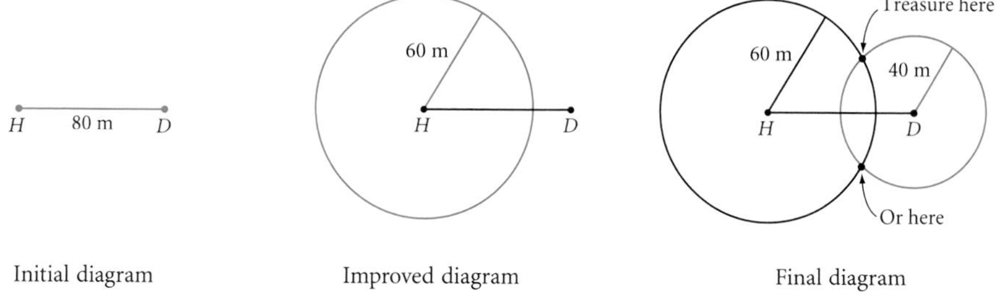

Initial diagram Improved diagram Final diagram

▶ *EXAMPLE C*

[Language] Many students will not be familiar with the term *locus of points.* Once students realize that this simply means the set, or locations, of all points that meet the given condition, it is easier for them to begin drawing a picture that describes the situation. If they need more help, **[Ask]** "What is the locus of points in a plane that are all the same distance from a given point?" [a circle] From the diagram, most students will be able to describe the points that meet the given condition(s). Help students form conjectures about when circles intersect at two points (using the terms *center* and *radius*), but reserve a discussion of those ideas for later.

Students can use the dynamic geometry exploration at www.keymath.com/DG to solve Example C, and to extend the scenario to explore different types of solutions that might come up for similar locus problems.

Assessing Progress

As students participate, try to assess the level of their understanding of terms used before in the course, especially *length* of a line segment, *perpendicular* and *parallel* lines, and *center* and *radius* of a circle.

Closing the Lesson

The main focus of this lesson was on drawing diagrams to help students develop visualization abilities and solve problems. While solving the puzzles, the class reviewed ideas about line segments, lines, and circles.

You might add as an assignment that students bring in examples of problems or games that emphasize visual thinking skills.

BUILDING UNDERSTANDING

Encourage labeling of figures in students' work.

ASSIGNING HOMEWORK

Essential	3–5, 13–18
Performance assessment	5, 6, 19–22
Portfolio	16, 17
Journal	1
Group	2, 6–12
Review	14, 17, 23–34

▶ Helping with the Exercises

Exercises 2–6, 10 If students are doing these exercises in class, they might benefit from working in pairs. Have one student be the reader and the other draw a figure that can be used to help them think through the problem. This way students move away from thinking of the exercises only as word problems. The figures help them build the needed connections. For more information on this pair-share method of cooperative learning, see *Discovering Mathematics* or www.keypress.com/DG.

Exercise 5 Suggest that students draw the diagram with the runners moving from left to right so the answer comes out *W-O-M-E-N*.

EXERCISES

You will need

Construction tools for Exercises **33** and **34**

1. Surgeons, engineers, carpenters, plumbers, electricians, and furniture movers all rely on trained experience with visual thinking. Describe how one of these tradespeople or someone in another occupation uses visual thinking in his or her work. Sample answer: Furniture movers might visualize how to rotate a couch to get it up a narrow staircase.

Now try your hand at some word problems. Read each problem carefully, determine what you are trying to find, and draw and label a diagram. Finally, solve the problem.

2. In the city of Rectangulus, all the streets running east–west are numbered and those streets running north–south are lettered. The even-numbered streets are one-way east and the odd-numbered streets are one-way west. All the vowel-lettered avenues are one-way north and the rest are two-way. Can a car traveling south on S Street make a legal left turn onto 14th Street? yes

3. Freddie the Frog is at the bottom of a 30-foot well. Each day he jumps up 3 feet, but then, during the night, he slides back down 2 feet. How many days will it take Freddie to get to the top and out? ⓗ 28 days

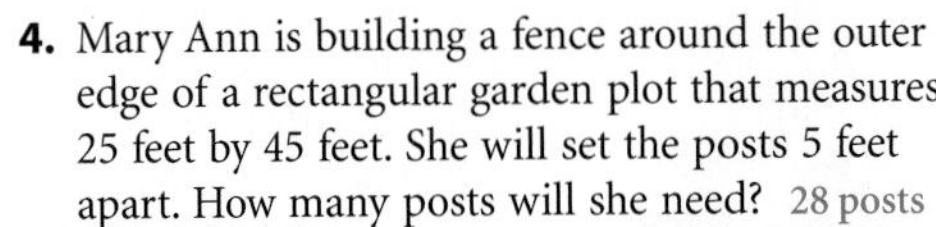

4. Mary Ann is building a fence around the outer edge of a rectangular garden plot that measures 25 feet by 45 feet. She will set the posts 5 feet apart. How many posts will she need? 28 posts

5. Midway through a 2000-meter race, a photo is taken of five runners. It shows Meg 20 meters behind Edith. Edith is 50 meters ahead of Wanda, who is 20 meters behind Olivia. Olivia is 40 meters behind Nadine. Who is ahead? In your diagram, use M for Meg, E for Edith, and so on. $\overrightarrow{W\,O\,M\,E\,N}$; Nadine is ahead.

6. Here is an exercise taken from Marilyn vos Savant's Ask Marilyn® column in *Parade* magazine. It is a good example of a difficult-sounding problem becoming clear once a diagram has been made. Try it. ⓗ

> A 30-foot cable is suspended between the tops of two 20-foot poles on level ground. The lowest point of the cable is 5 feet above the ground. What is the distance between the two poles? 0. (The poles must be touching!)

7. Points A and B lie in a plane. Sketch the locus of points in *the plane* that are equally distant from points A and B. Sketch the locus of points in *space* that are equally distant from points A and B. ⓗ

8. Draw an angle. Label it $\angle A$. Sketch the locus of points in the plane of angle A that are the same distance from the two sides of angle A.

9. Line AB lies in plane $\mathcal{P}$. Sketch the locus of points in plane $\mathcal{P}$ that are 3 cm from $\overleftrightarrow{AB}$. Sketch the locus of points in space that are 3 cm from $\overleftrightarrow{AB}$.

7.

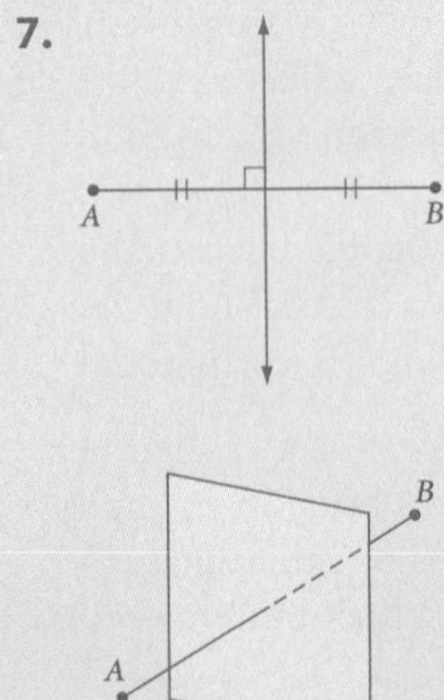

8.

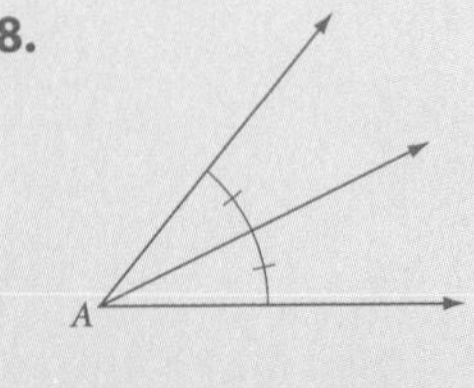

9.

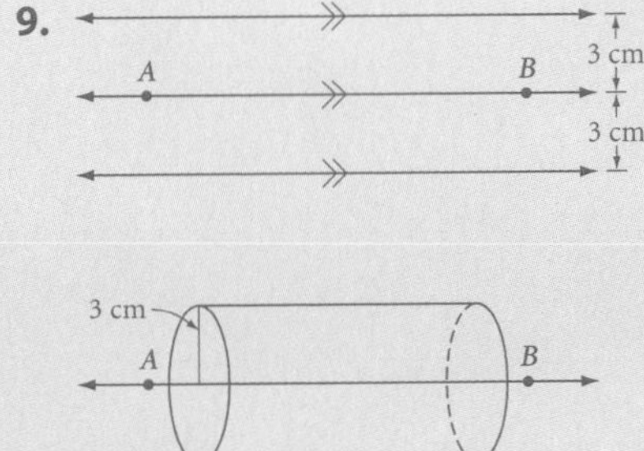

10. Beth Mack and her dog Trouble are exploring in the woods east of Birnam Woods Road, which runs north-south. They begin walking in a zigzag pattern: 1 km south, 1 km west, 1 km south, 2 km west, 1 km south, 3 km west, and so on. They walk at the rate of 4 km/h. If they started 15 km east of Birnam Woods Road at 3:00 P.M., and the sun sets at 7:30 P.M., will they reach Birnam Woods Road before sunset? no

In geometry you will use visual thinking all the time. In Exercises 11 and 12 you will be asked to locate and recognize congruent geometric figures even if they are in different positions due to translations (slides), rotations (turns), or reflections (flips).

11. If trapezoid $ABCD$ were rotated 90° counterclockwise about (0, 0), to what (x, y) location would points A, B, C, and D be relocated? ⓗ $C'(-2,3), A'(0,0), B'(0,5), D'(-2,1)$

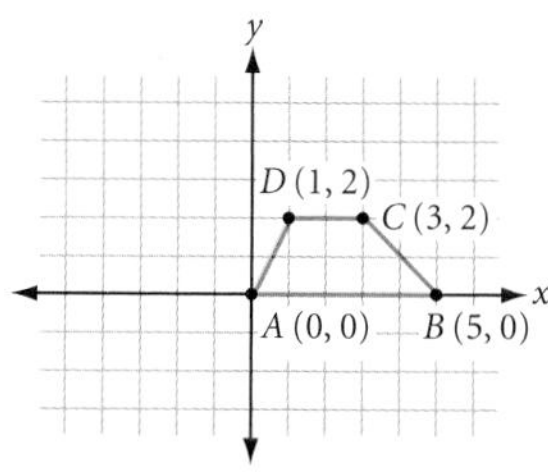

12. If $\triangle CYN$ were reflected over the y-axis, to what location would points C, N, and Y be relocated? $Y'(-4,1), C'(3,-1), N'(0,3)$

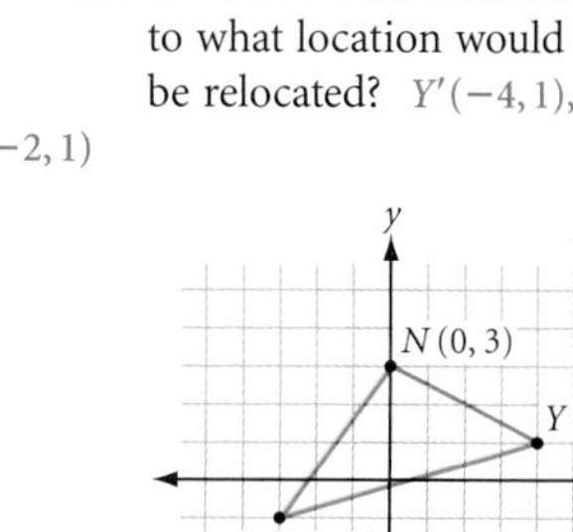

13. What was the ordered pair rule used to relocate the four vertices of $ABCD$ to $A'B'C'D'$? $(x, y) \rightarrow (x + 3, y + 2)$

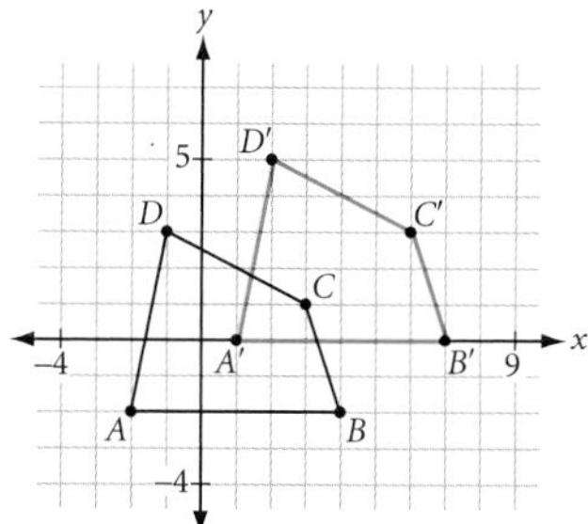

14. Which lines are perpendicular? Which lines are parallel?
$\overleftrightarrow{AB} \perp \overleftrightarrow{CP}, \overleftrightarrow{EF} \parallel \overleftrightarrow{GH}; i \perp k, j \perp k$

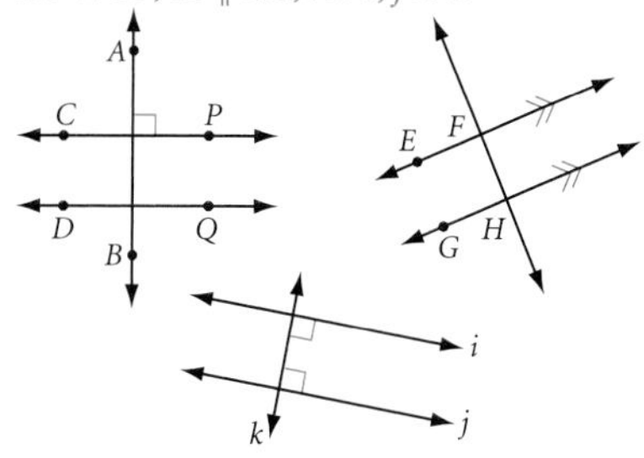

15. Sketch the next two figures in the pattern below. If this pattern were to continue, what would be the perimeter of the eighth figure in the pattern? (Assume the length of each segment is 1 cm.) ⓗ perimeter = 34 cm

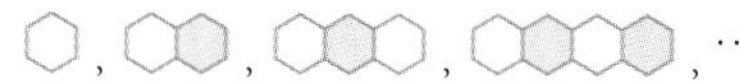

Exercise 10 The rate km/h means "kilometers per hour."

Exercises 11, 12 Here students think about performing transformations on geometric figures so that the figure is congruent but relocated. These exercises foreshadow Chapter 7.

Exercise 13 If students didn't do Exercises 18–20 in Lesson 1.6, they may need to be reminded what an "ordered pair rule" is. If needed, show the examples from Lesson 1.6. **[Ask]** "What was done to the x-coordinate of vertex A to get the x-coordinate of vertex A'? To the y-coordinate of vertex A to get that of vertex A'?"

Exercise 14 Some students may say something like "Line AB is perpendicular." Remind them that the terms *perpendicular* and *parallel* refer to more than one line. It can be deduced that $i \parallel j$, but students are not expected to know that.

Exercise 15 As needed, remind students that *perimeter* means "the sum of the lengths of the sides," sometimes imprecisely referred to as "the distance around." The algebraic expression for the perimeter of the nth term in the pattern is $4n + 2$.

15.

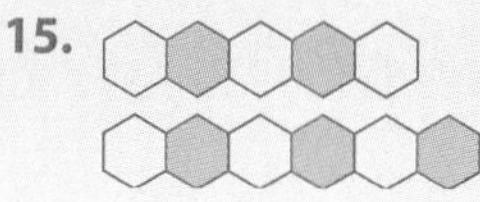

Exercise 16 A tree diagram of triangles could be organized by sides instead of by angles.

Exercises 16, 17 As an extension and a good review, you might suggest that students draw their own concept maps of all special triangles and quadrilaterals.

Exercises 18, 19 If students have difficulty with this visualization, encourage them to trace and cut out the nets and try folding them.

Exercise 22 **[Ask]** "What other pattern could be a net for a tetrahedron?"

16. Many of the geometric figures you have defined are closely related to one another. A diagram can help you see the relationships among them. At right is a concept map showing the relationships among members of the triangle family. This type of concept map is known as a **tree diagram** because the relationships are shown as branches of a tree. Copy and fill in the missing branches of the tree diagram for triangles.

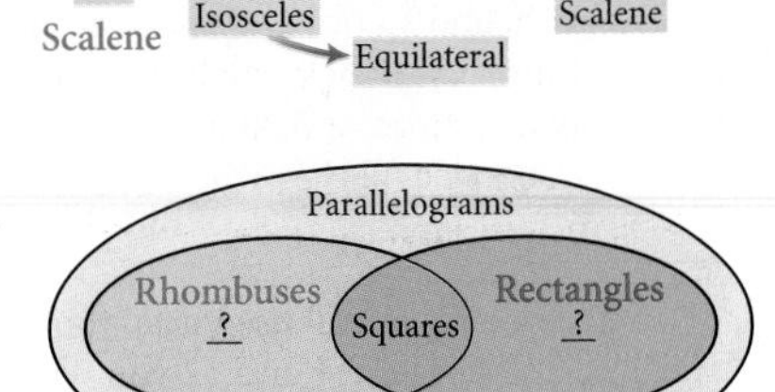

17. At right is a concept map showing the relationships among some members of the parallelogram family. This type of concept map is known as a **Venn diagram.** Fill in the missing names.

A **net** is a two-dimensional pattern that you can cut and fold to form a three-dimensional figure. Another visual thinking skill you will need is the ability to visualize nets being folded into solid objects and geometric solids being unfolded into nets. The net below left can be folded into a cube and the net below right can be folded into a pyramid.

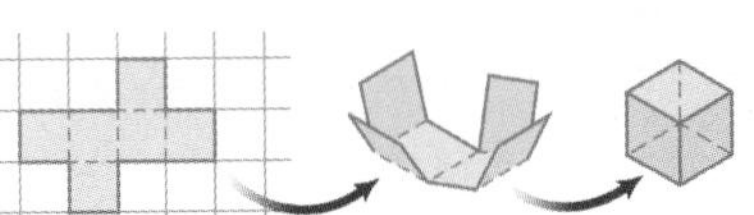

Net for a cube

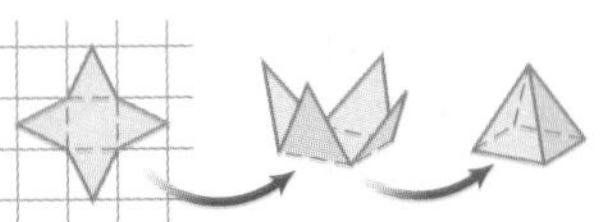

Net for a square-based pyramid

18. Which net(s) will fold to make a cube? B, D

A.
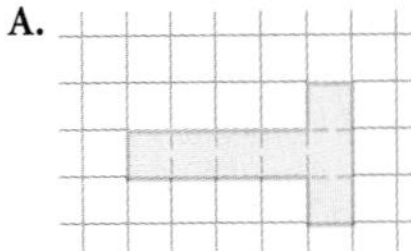

B.
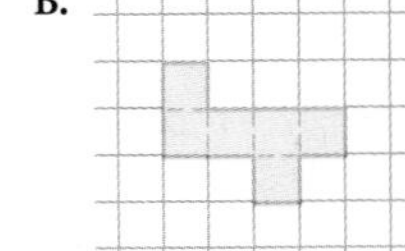

C.
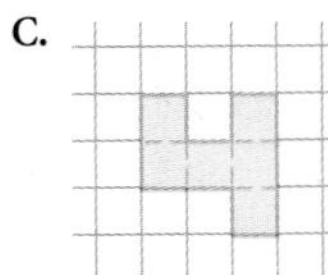

D.
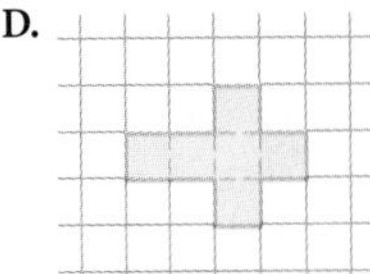

E.
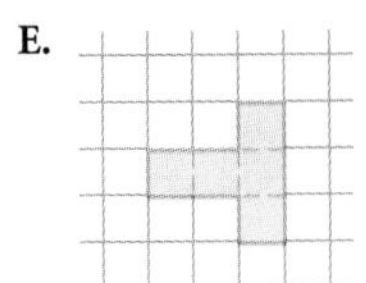

F.
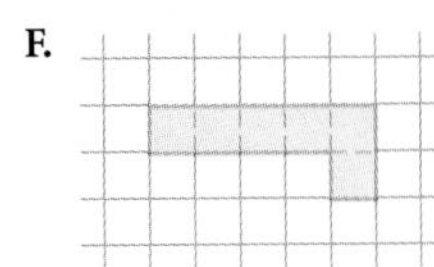

For Exercises 19–22, match the net with its geometric solid.

19. B
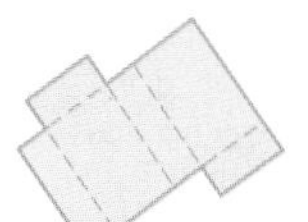

20. C
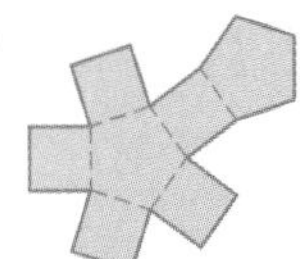

21. D
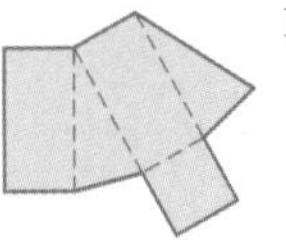

22. A
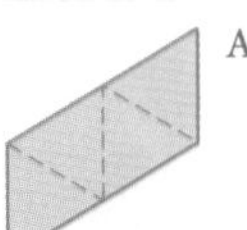

A.
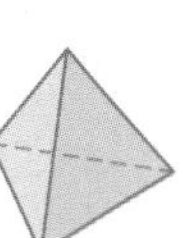

B.
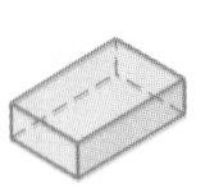

C.
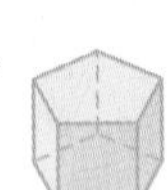

D.
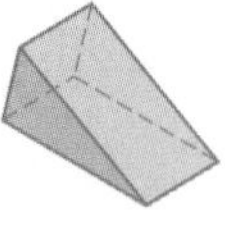

Review

For Exercises 23–32, write the words or the symbols that make the statement true.

1.1 **23.** The three undefined terms of geometry are _?_, _?_, and _?_. point, line, plane

1.1 **24.** "Line AB" may be written using a symbol as _?_. $\overleftrightarrow{AB}$

1.1 **25.** "Arc AB" may be written using a symbol as _?_. $\overset{\frown}{AB}$

1.2 **26.** The point where the two sides of an angle meet is the _?_ of the angle. vertex

1.1 **27.** "Ray AB" may be written using a symbol as _?_. $\overrightarrow{AB}$

1.3 **28.** "Line AB is parallel to segment CD" is written in symbolic form as _?_. $\overleftrightarrow{AB} \parallel \overline{CD}$

1.2 **29.** The geometry tool you use to measure an angle is a _?_. protractor

1.2 **30.** "Angle ABC" is written in symbolic form as _?_. $\angle ABC$

1.3 **31.** The sentence "Segment AB is perpendicular to line CD" is written in symbolic form as _?_. $\overline{AB} \perp \overleftrightarrow{CD}$

1.2 **32.** The angle formed by a light ray coming into a mirror is _?_ the angle formed by a light ray leaving the mirror. congruent to

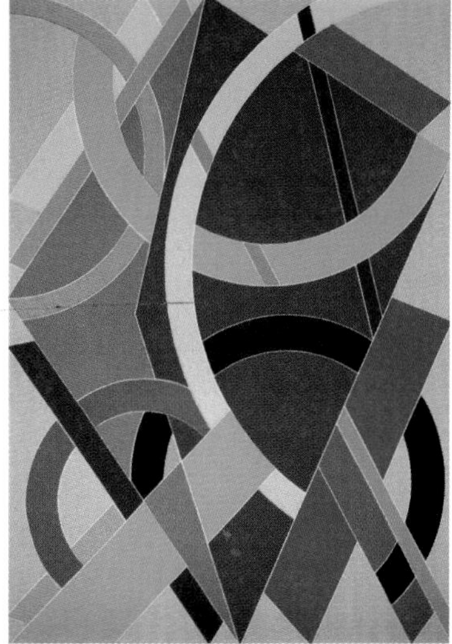

William Thomas Williams, DO YOU THINK A IS B, acrylic on canvas, 1975–77, Fisk University Galleries, Nashville, Tennessee.

1.6 **33.** Use your compass and straightedge to draw two congruent circles intersecting in exactly one point. How does the distance between the two centers compare with the radius? The distance is two times the radius.

1.6 **34.** Use your compass and straightedge to construct two congruent circles so that each circle passes through the center of the other circle. Label the centers P and Q. Construct $\overline{PQ}$ connecting the centers. Label the points of intersection of the two circles A and B. Construct chord $\overline{AB}$. What is the relationship between $\overline{AB}$ and $\overline{PQ}$? ⓗ They bisect each other and are perpendicular.

IMPROVING YOUR VISUAL THINKING SKILLS

Hexominoes

Polyominoes with six squares are called hexominoes. There are 35 different hexominoes. There is 1 with a longest string of six squares; there are 3 with a longest string of five squares, 13 with a longest string of four squares, 17 with a longest string of three squares; and there is 1 with a longest string of two squares. Use graph paper to sketch the 35 hexominoes. Which are nets for cubes? Here is one hexomino that does fold into a cube.

Exercises 33, 34 These exercises ask the students to make conjectures. Conjectures are not statements of fact, but educated guesses. They may be false. The idea of a conjecture is introduced in Chapter 2.

33.

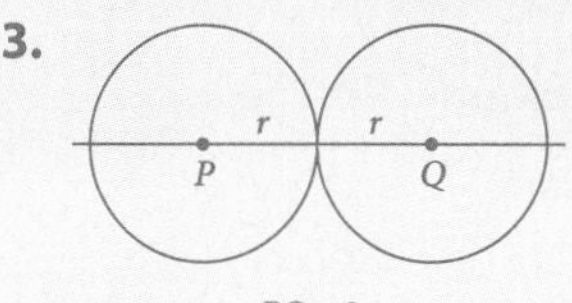

Exercise 34 [Alert] If students are confused, be sure they understand that the circles must be congruent.

34.

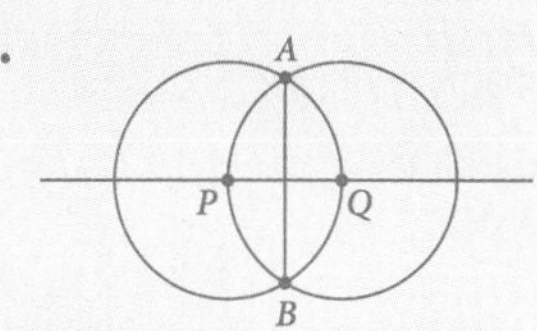

EXTENSIONS

Have each group pick an object in the room to describe in detail. Then challenge other groups to come up with a correct drawing of the object.

Have each student create some design (not too detailed) on a 3-by-5 card. (You can draw all of the designs in advance if you wish to maintain the same level of difficulty.) Then pair up the students, giving each a clean 3-by-5 card along with his or her design card. Each student will describe, in words only, how the partner can duplicate the design on the clean 3-by-5 card, including its relationship to a diagonal of the card. No fair peeking!

IMPROVING VISUAL THINKING SKILLS

The prefix *hex* in *hexomino* means "six," just as it does in *hexagon*.

The circled hexominoes are nets for cubes.

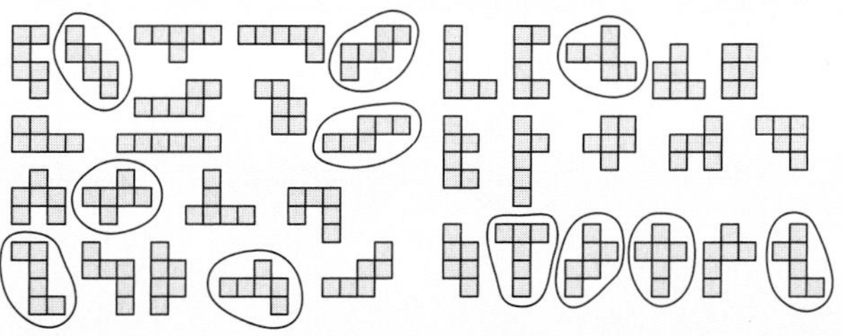

LESSON 1.8

PLANNING

LESSON OUTLINE

One day:

20 min Investigation

5 min Sharing

5 min Closing

15 min Exercises

MATERIALS

- isometric dot paper
- Three-Dimensional Figures (T) for One step

TEACHING

Learning to draw three-dimensional figures will help improve students' visualization abilities.

INTRODUCTION

If you assigned students to bring in examples that emphasize visual thinking skills, have them demonstrate.

One step Show the Three-Dimensional Figures transparency and ask students to draw the figures on their own paper. (You might have them divide up the figures among group members, or you might assign different figures to different groups.) As you circulate, be sure students use noncircular ellipses as the basis for the figures of the cone, cylinder, sphere, and hemisphere. As needed, suggest that students draw the prism and pyramid by first drawing a base. Then have groups start on the investigation.

LESSON 1.8

Space Geometry

When curiosity turns to serious matters, it's called research.

MARIE VON EBNER-ESCHENBACH

Lesson 1.1 introduced you to point, line, and plane. Throughout this chapter you have used these terms to define a wide range of other geometric figures, from rays to polygons. You did most of your work on a single flat surface, a single plane. Some problems, however, required you to step out of a single plane to visualize geometry in space. In this lesson you will learn more about space geometry, or solid geometry.

Space is the set of all points. Unlike lines and planes, space cannot be contained in a flat surface. Space is three-dimensional, or "3-D."

In an "edge view," you see the front edge of a building as a vertical line, and the other edges as diagonal lines. Isometric dot paper helps you draw these lines, as you can see in the steps below.

Let's practice the visual thinking skill of presenting three-dimensional (3-D) objects in two-dimensional (2-D) drawings.

The geometric solid you are probably most familiar with is a box, or rectangular prism. Below are steps for making a two-dimensional drawing of a rectangular prism. This type of drawing is called an **isometric drawing.** It shows three sides of an object in one view (an edge view). This method works best with isometric dot grid paper. After practicing, you will be able to draw the box without the aid of the dot grid.

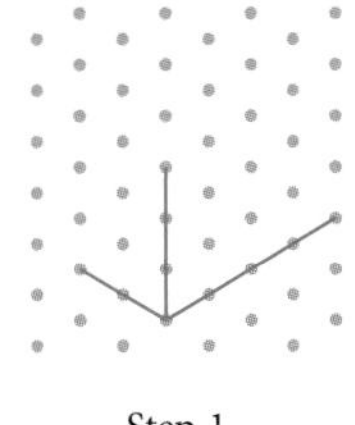

Step 1

Step 2

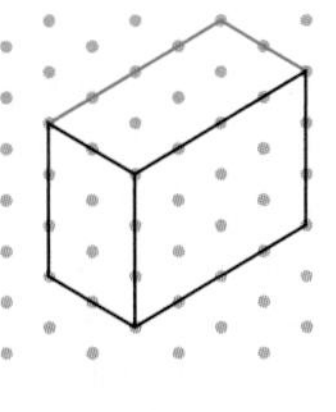

Step 3

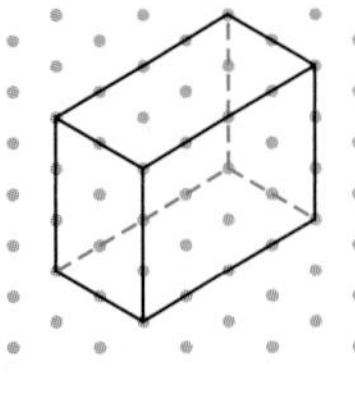

Step 4

Use dashed lines for edges that you couldn't see if the object were solid.

LESSON OBJECTIVES

- Visualize objects and relationships in two and three dimensions
- Practice drawing skills
- Introduce some of the geometric solids
- Discuss and visualize cross sections of solids

NCTM STANDARDS

CONTENT		PROCESS	
	Number		Problem Solving
	Algebra		Reasoning
✓	Geometry	✓	Communication
	Measurement	✓	Connections
	Data/Probability	✓	Representation

The three-dimensional objects you will study include the six types of geometric solids shown below.

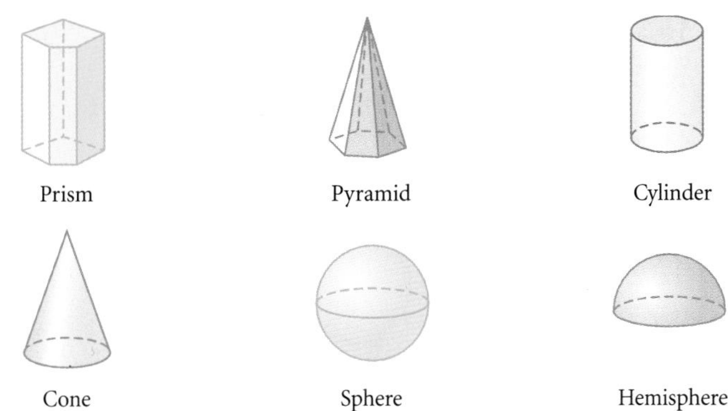

The shapes of these solids are probably already familiar to you even if you are not familiar with their proper names. The ability to draw these geometric solids is an important visual thinking skill. Here are some drawing tips. Remember to use dashes for the hidden lines.

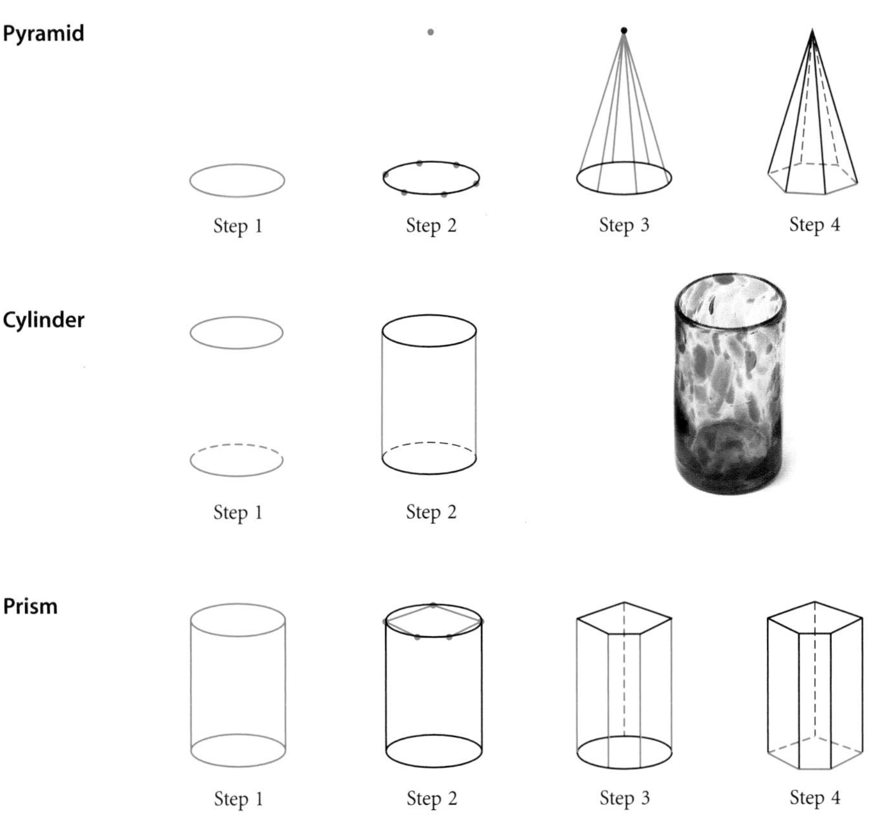

Drawing Solids

For more structure, demonstrate how to create an isometric drawing of a rectangular solid. Introduce the other six basic geometric solids that will be studied; then demonstrate how to draw a prism, cylinder, pyramid, and sphere. Give the students plenty of time to practice these as you circulate to answer questions.

Guiding the Investigation

Step 1 The tips of pencils or thumbtacks can represent points. Rulers, pencils, uncooked spaghetti, or stiff wires can represent lines. Sheets of heavy paper, cardboard, or desktops can represent planes.

SHARING IDEAS

Have students (groups) share their discoveries from the investigation.

The drawings are of three-dimensional figures. **[Ask]** "What does *dimension* mean?" **[Language]** The word *dimensions* can mean dimensions such as the three dimensions of length, width, and height; it can mean a measurement as in "The dimensions of the rectangle are 3 ft by 4 ft"; or it can mean the units attached to a measurement, for example, "feet."

[Ask] "How is an isometric drawing, such as the drawings in this lesson, different from a perspective drawing?" [Equal distances in real life appear equal in an isometric drawing, but they are not necessarily equal in a perspective drawing.] This comes up in the Exploration Orthographic Drawing in Chapter 10.

Assessing Progress
As you observe, watch for evidence that students can use the terminology of earlier lessons in this chapter, know how to label their figures, can work effectively in a group, and take initiative in investigating.

Closing the Lesson

Review the steps for drawing these common three-dimensional figures: **rectangular solid, cone, cylinder, sphere, hemisphere, prism,** and **pyramid.**

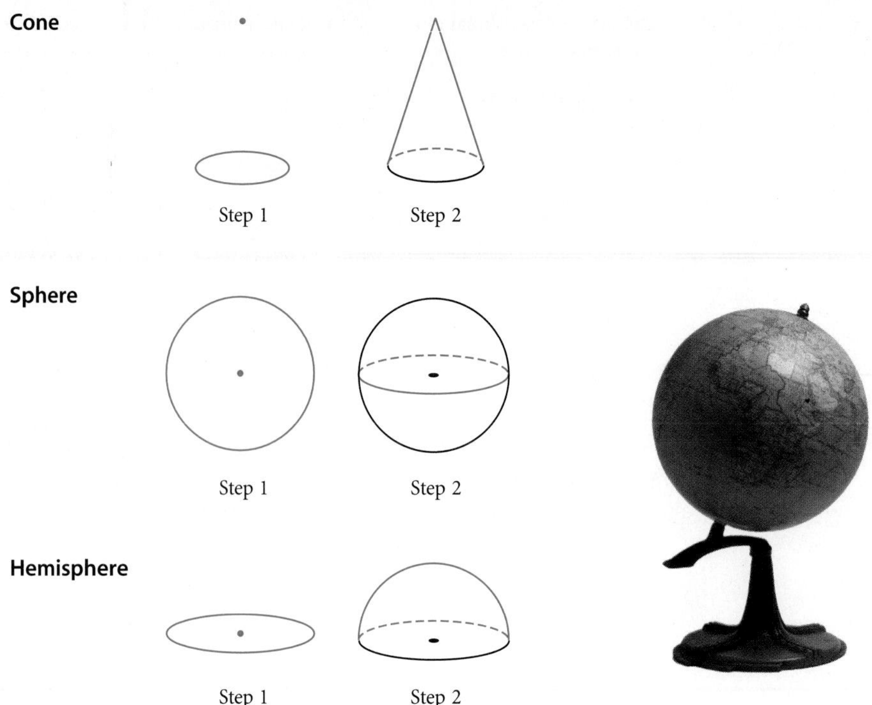

Solid geometry also involves visualizing points and lines in space. In the following investigation, you will have to visualize relationships between geometric figures in a plane and in space.

Investigation
Space Geometry

Step 1 Make a sketch or use physical objects to demonstrate each statement in the list below.

Step 2 Work with your group to determine whether each statement is true or false. If the statement is false, draw a picture and explain why it is false.

1. Only one line can be drawn through two different points.
2. Only one plane can pass through one line and a point that is not on the line.
3. If two coplanar lines are both perpendicular to a third line in the same plane, then the two lines are parallel.
4. If two planes do not intersect, then they are parallel.
5. If two lines do not intersect, then they must be parallel.
6. If a line is perpendicular to two lines in a plane, but the line is not contained in the plane, then the line is perpendicular to the plane.

Step 2 All the statements are true except the fifth one: If two lines do not meet, they might be skew, and not parallel.

BUILDING UNDERSTANDING

Students practice geometric drawing.

MATERIALS

- cardboard cutouts taped to stiff wire (Exercises 18, 19)
- stiff wire and clay (Exercises 20, 21)

ASSIGNING HOMEWORK

Essential	1–6, 8–16
Demonstration	20, 21
Performance assessment	22–29
Portfolio	1–7
Group	14, 17–28
Review	30–32

EXERCISES

For Exercises 1–6, draw each figure. Study the drawing tips provided on the previous page before you start.

A police station, or *koban,* in Tokyo, Japan

1. Cylinder
2. Cone
3. Prism with a hexagonal base
4. Sphere
5. Pyramid with a heptagonal base
6. Hemisphere
7. The photo at right shows a prism-shaped building with a pyramid roof and a cylindrical porch. Draw a cylindrical building with a cone roof and a prism-shaped porch.

For Exercises 8 and 9, make a drawing to scale of each figure. Use isometric dot grid paper. Label each figure. (For example, in Exercise 8, draw the solid so that the dimensions measure 2 units by 3 units by 4 units, then label the figure with meters.)

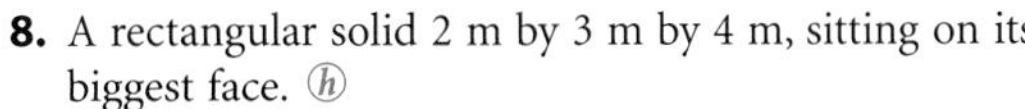

8. A rectangular solid 2 m by 3 m by 4 m, sitting on its biggest face. ⓗ
9. A rectangular solid 3 inches by 4 inches by 5 inches, resting on its smallest face. Draw lines on the three visible surfaces showing how you can divide the solid into cubic-inch boxes. How many such boxes will fit in the solid? ⓗ 60 boxes

For Exercises 10–12, use isometric dot grid paper to draw the figure shown.

10. 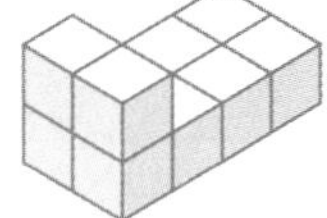

11. 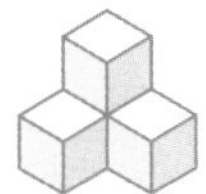

12. 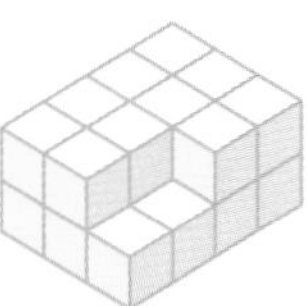

For Exercises 13–15, sketch the three-dimensional figure formed by folding each net into a solid. Name the solid.

13. 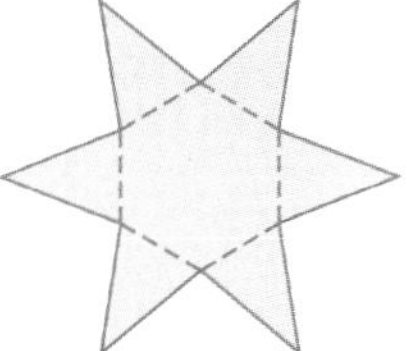

pyramid with hexagonal base

14. 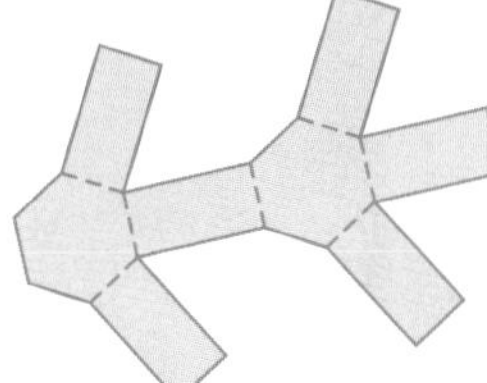

prism with hexagonal base

15. 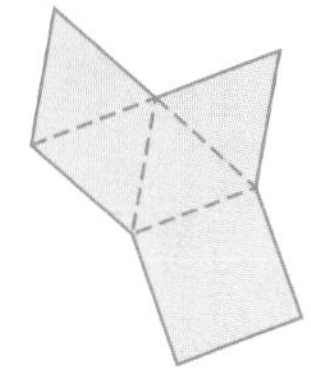

pyramid with square base

▶ Helping with the Exercises

Exercises 1–6 If students are still having difficulty, encourage them by saying that although sketching figures may be difficult and tedious at first, it is an essential skill for later in the course.

1. 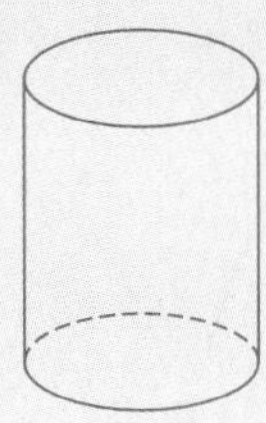

2. 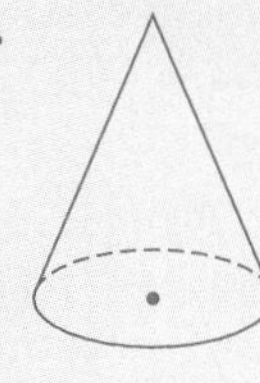

3. 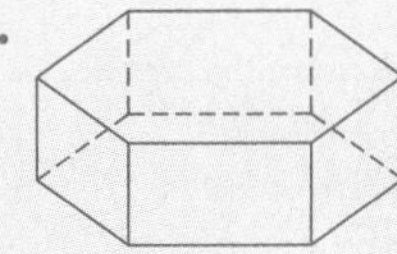

4. 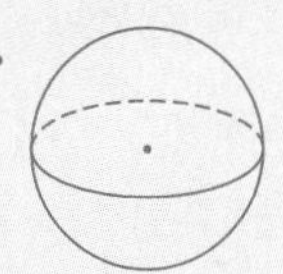

5. 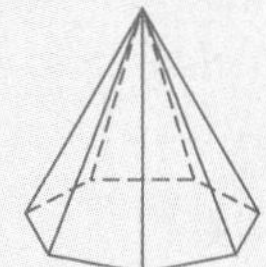

6. 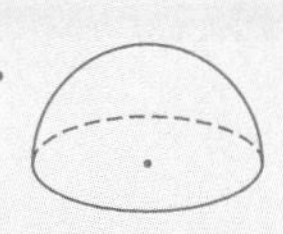

7. 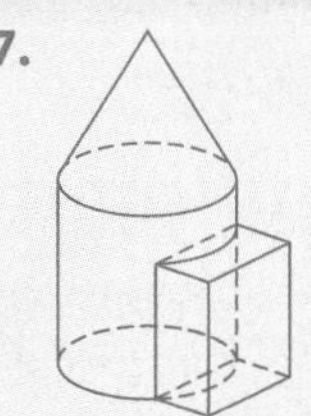

Exercises 8, 9 If students have difficulty, you might demonstrate how to draw the solid on the medium-size face and leave it for them to draw it on the biggest face in Exercise 8 and on the smallest face in Exercise 9.

Exercises 10–12 [Ask] "How many unit cubes are in each?" [10:10; 11:4; 12:22]

8. 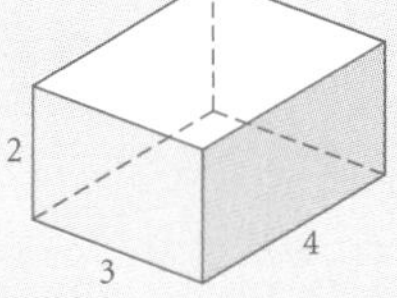

9. 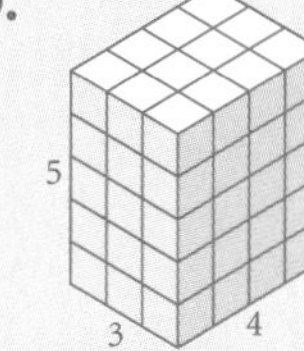

10. 

11. 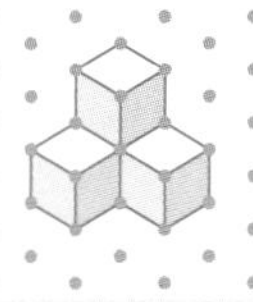

12. 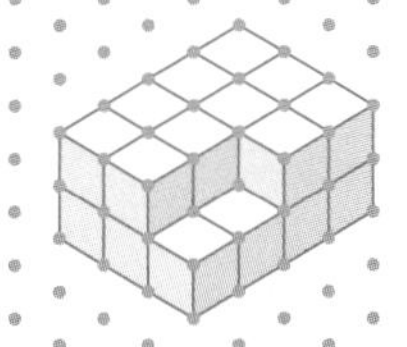

13. 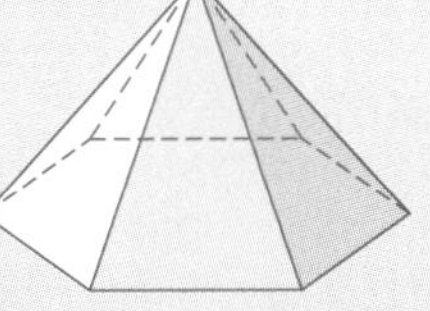

14. 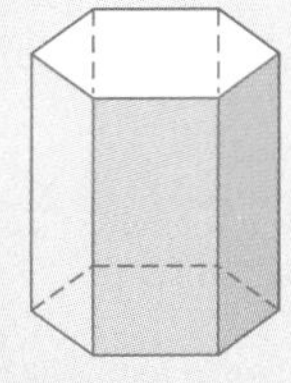

15. 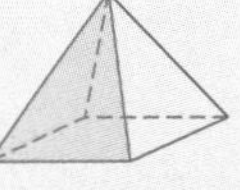

Exercises 18, 19 As needed, remind students that circles that are not parallel to the picture plane are represented as noncircular ellipses.

18.

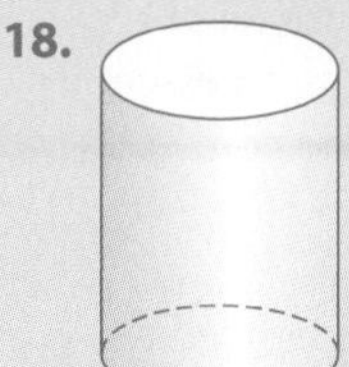

19.

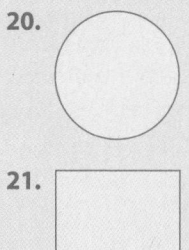

Exercises 20, 21 You can use either stiff wire and modeling clay or dental floss and homemade play dough for the models.

20.

21.

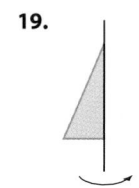

Exercises 22–29 Discuss these exercises in detail, using physical models where possible to demonstrate each situation. Some possibilities are pencils, thumbtacks, uncooked spaghetti, stiff wire, and heavy cardboard.

22.

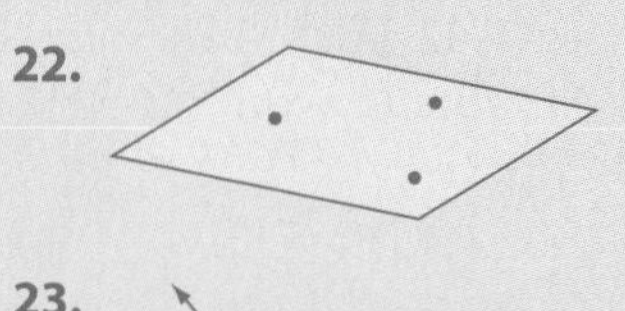

23.

24.

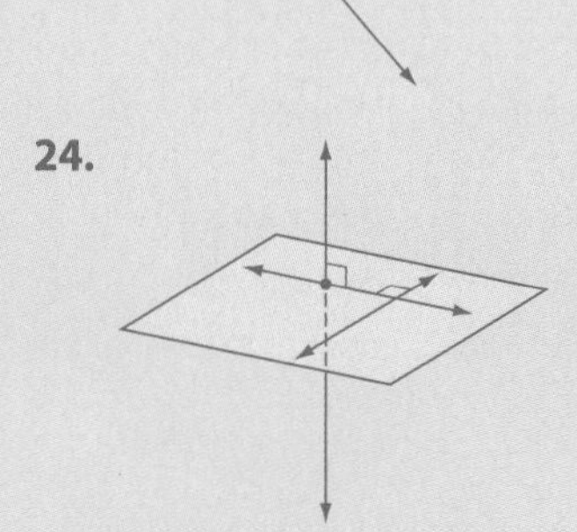

For Exercises 16 and 17, find the lengths x and y. (Every angle on each block is a right angle.)

16.

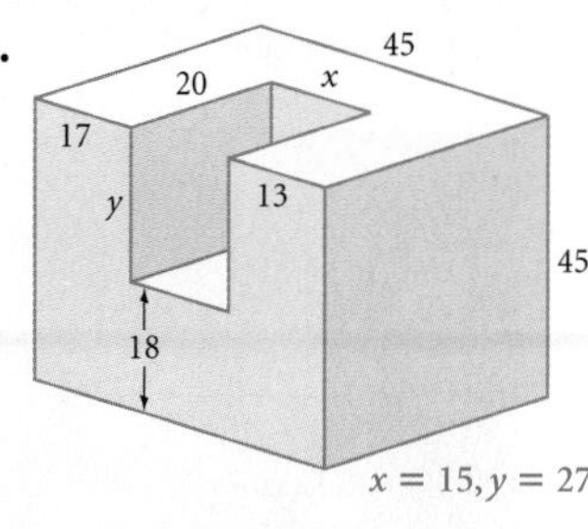

$x = 15, y = 27$

17.

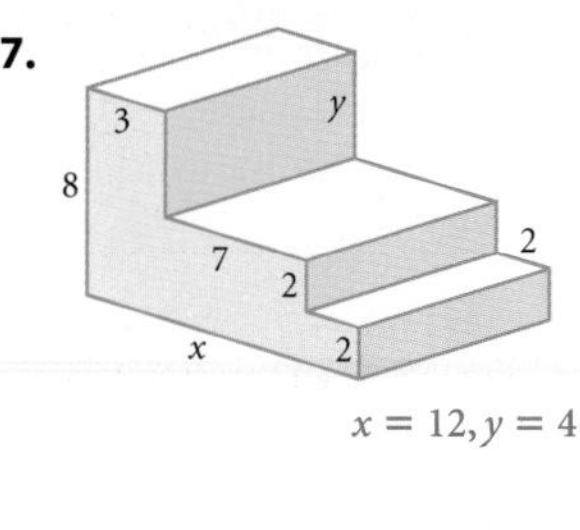

$x = 12, y = 4$

In Exercises 18 and 19, each figure represents a two-dimensional figure with a wire attached. The three-dimensional solid formed by spinning the figure on the wire between your fingers is called a **solid of revolution.** Sketch the solid of revolution formed by each two-dimensional figure.

18. ⓗ **19.**

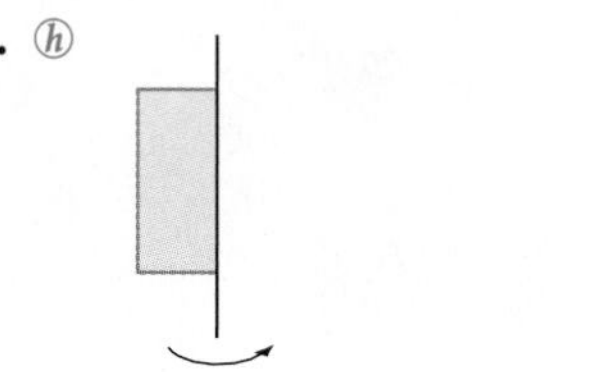

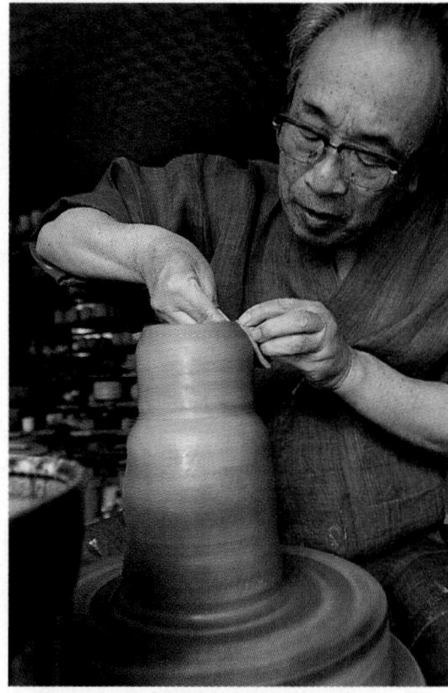

A real-life example of a "solid of revolution" is a clay pot on a potter's wheel.

When a solid is cut by a plane, the resulting two-dimensional figure is called a **section.** For Exercises 20 and 21, sketch the section formed when each solid is sliced by the plane, as shown.

20. ⓗ **21.**

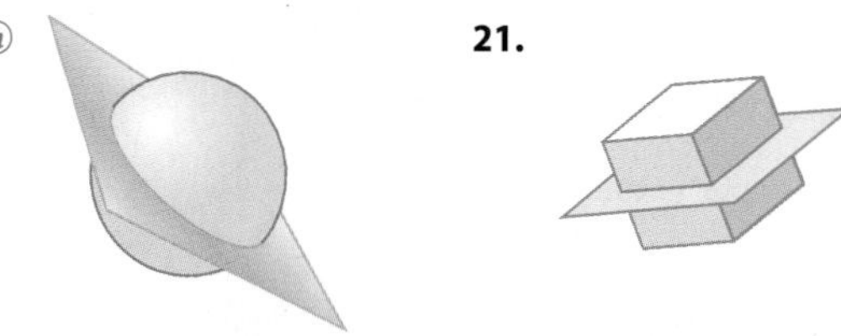

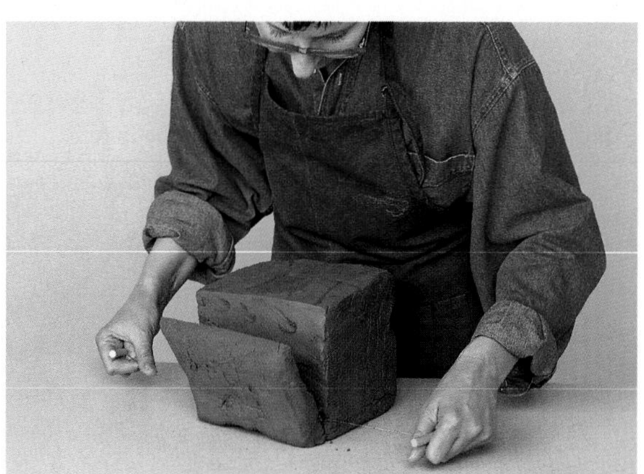

Slicing a block of clay reveals a section of the solid. Here, the section is a rectangle.

25.

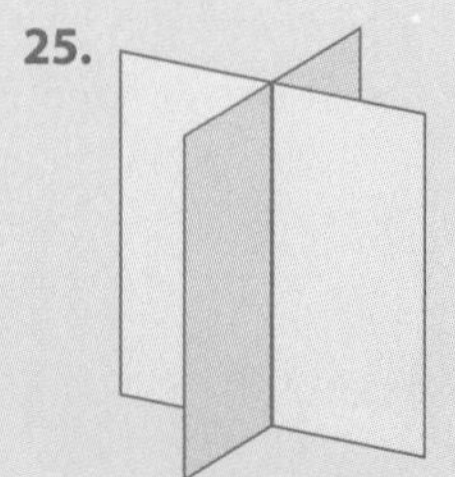

27.

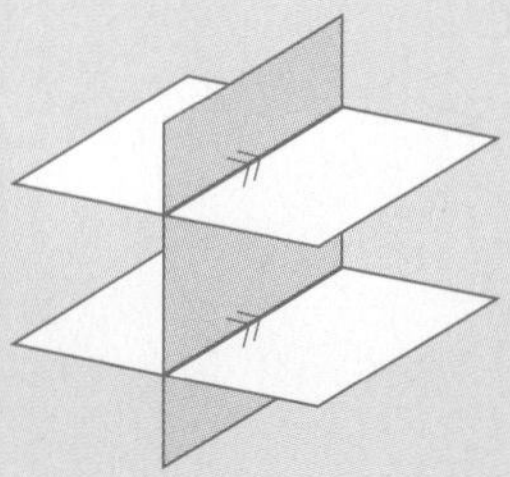

28.

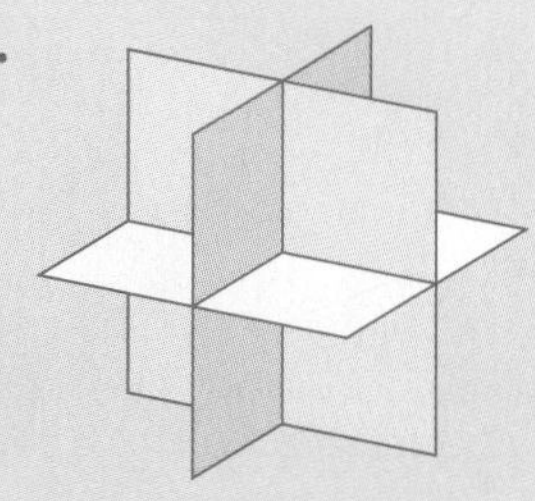

All of the statements in Exercises 22–29 are true except for two. Make a sketch to demonstrate each true statement. For each false statement, draw a sketch and explain why it is false.

Physical models can help you visualize the intersections of lines and planes in space. Can you see examples of intersecting lines in this photo? Parallel lines? Planes? Points?

22. Only one plane can pass through three noncollinear points. true

23. If a line intersects a plane that does not contain the line, then the intersection is exactly one point. true

24. If two lines are perpendicular to the same line, then they are parallel. ⓗ False. The two lines are not necessarily in the same plane, so they might be skew.

25. If two different planes intersect, then their intersection is a line. true

26. If a line and a plane have no points in common, then they are parallel. true

27. If a plane intersects two parallel planes, then the lines of intersection are parallel. true

28. If three random planes intersect (no two are parallel and all three do not share the same line), then they divide space into six parts. False. They divide space into eight parts.

29. If two lines are perpendicular to the same plane, then they are parallel to each other. true

Review

1.5 **30.** If the kite $DIAN$ were rotated 90° clockwise about the origin, to what location would point A be relocated? $(-3, 1)$

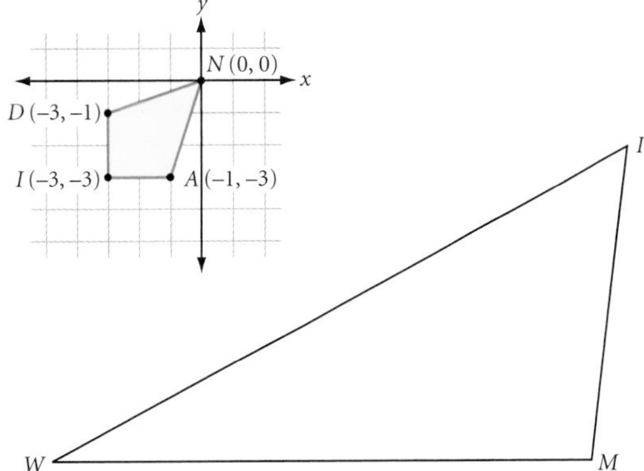

1.4 **31.** Use your ruler to measure the perimeter of $\triangle WIM$ (in centimeters) and your protractor to measure the largest angle. perimeter = 20.5 cm; m(largest angle) = 100°

1.4 **32.** Use your geometry tools to draw a triangle with two sides of length 8 cm and length 13 cm and the angle between them measuring 120°.

IMPROVING YOUR VISUAL THINKING SKILLS

Equal Distances

Here's a real challenge:

Show four points A, B, C, and D so that $AB = BC = AC = AD = BD = CD$.

IMPROVING VISUAL THINKING SKILLS

Points A, B, C, and D are the vertices of a tetrahedron.

32.

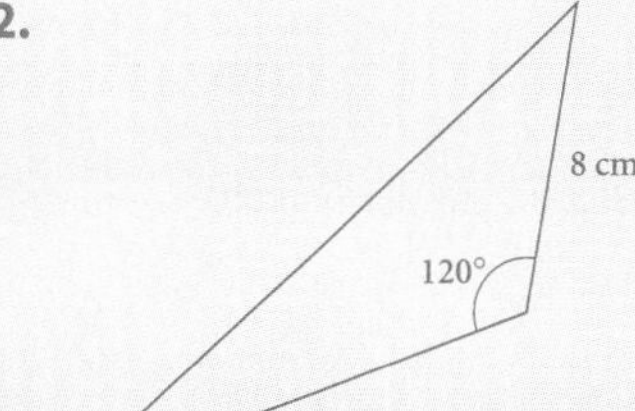

Exercise 26 If students point out that the notion of parallelism of a line and a plane hasn't yet been defined, ask them what they think the definition should be.

26.

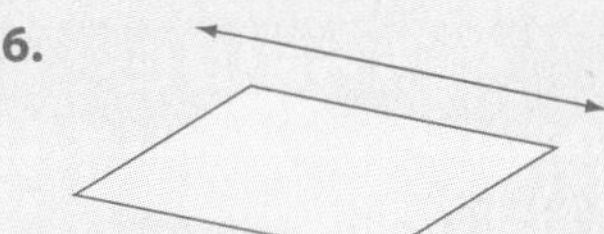

Exercise 29 To help students visualize this situation, suggest that they hold pencils at right angles to a piece of paper.

29.

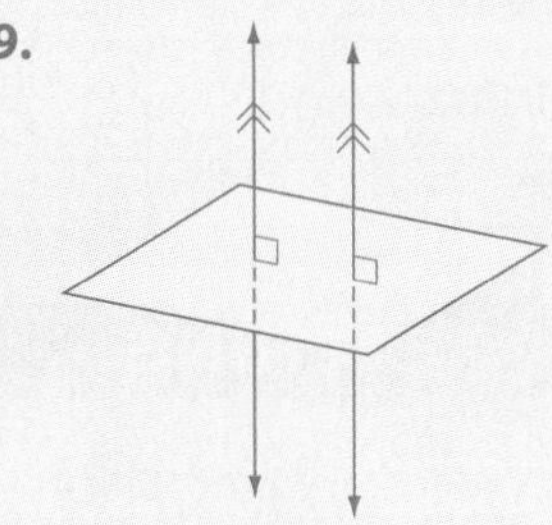

EXTENSIONS

A. Challenge students to divide the common solids into two groups based on a particular criterion. Let the class or other groups figure out what the criterion was.

B. Assign a few more difficult drawing problems. For example, draw solids with slices or corners removed. Discuss the names of some of these solids, for example, a truncated cube or a truncated tetrahedron.

C. Use straws held together with string or clay or make models from a Zome system, multi-link cubes, or Unifix cubes to help students visualize three-dimensional objects.

D. Ask students to bring in objects that have the basic shapes of different prisms, cylinders, pyramids, cones, and spheres and truncations of some of these shapes. This activity can be done as scavenger hunt competitions among groups.

EXPLORATION

PLANNING

LESSON OUTLINE

One day:

30 min Exploration

15 min Sharing

MATERIALS

- protractors
- rulers

TEACHING

The introductory probability example is based on counting total possible outcomes and desired outcomes. In subsequent examples geometric relationships are either part of the problem or part of the model used to solve the problem. Visual thinking is important, especially for The Bridge.

Guiding the Activity

The Spinner uses a spinner to model known probabilities. The Bridge requires students to analyze a situation visually and think about lengths and rotations. In The Bus Stop a geometric model is suggested, though the problem can be solved without it.

Step 1 A fair spinner is as likely to land in any one sector of a circle as it is to land in another.

[Ask] "What do you need to know to determine the probabilities?" [that the spinner is fair and spins around the center of the circle; the measure of each of the angles; the proportion that each angle measure is of the whole circle]

Exploration

Geometric Probability I

You probably know what probability means. The **probability,** or likelihood, of a particular outcome is the ratio of the number of successful outcomes to the number of possible outcomes. So the probability of rolling a 4 on a 6-sided die is $\frac{1}{6}$. Or, you can name an event that involves more than one outcome, like getting the total 4 on two 6-sided dice. Since each die can come up in six different ways, there are 6×6 or 36 combinations (count 'em!). You can get the total 4 with a 1 and a 3, a 3 and a 1, or a 2 and a 2. So the probability of getting the total 4 is $\frac{3}{36}$ or $\frac{1}{12}$. Anyway, that's the theory.

Activity
Chances Are

You will need

- a protractor
- a ruler

In this activity you'll see that you can apply probability theory to geometric figures.

The Spinner

After you've finished your homework and have eaten dinner, you play a game of chance using the spinner at right. Where the spinner lands determines how you'll spend the evening.

Sector A: Playing with your younger brother the whole evening

Sector B: Half the evening playing with your younger brother and half the evening watching TV

Sector C: Cleaning the birdcage, the hamster cage, and the aquarium the whole evening

Sector D: Playing in a band in a friend's garage the whole evening

LESSON OBJECTIVES

- Explore probability
- Use geometry to think about probability problems

NCTM STANDARDS

CONTENT		PROCESS	
✓	Number	✓	Problem Solving
	Algebra	✓	Reasoning
✓	Geometry	✓	Communication
	Measurement	✓	Connections
✓	Data/Probability	✓	Representation

Step 1 What is the probability of landing in each sector?

Step 2 What is the probability that you'll spend at least half the evening with your younger brother? What is the probability that you won't spend any time with him?

Step 2 $P(A) + P(B) = \frac{3}{4}$

The Bridge

A computer programmer who is trying to win money on a TV survival program builds a 120 ft rope bridge across a piranha-infested river 90 ft below.

Step 3 If the rope breaks where he is standing (a random point), but he is able to cling to one end of it, what is the probability that he'll avoid getting wet (or worse)?

Step 3 Depending on assumptions, P(doesn't get wet) can be 1 (if the short end could be grabbed), $\frac{3}{4}$ (if the probability of grabbing either end were equal), or something else.

Step 4 Suppose the probability that the rope breaks at all is $\frac{1}{2}$. Also suppose that, as long as he doesn't fall more than 30 ft, the probability that he can climb back up is $\frac{3}{4}$. What is the probability that he won't fall at all? What is the probability that if he does, he'll be able to climb back up?

Step 4 P(doesn't fall) = 1 − P(rope breaks) = $\frac{1}{2}$. P(he can climb out) is $\frac{1}{2}$ times $\frac{3}{4}$ times the probability he will grab the short end.

The Bus Stop

Noriko arrives at the bus stop at a random time between 3:00 and 4:30 P.M. each day. Her bus stops there every 20 minutes, including at 3:00 P.M.

Step 5 Number line with B at 3:00, 3:20, 3:40, 4:00, 4:20

Step 5 Draw a number line to show stopping times. (Don't worry about the length of time that the bus is actually stopped. Assume it is 0 minutes.)

Step 6 What is the probability that she will have to wait 5 minutes or more? 10 minutes or more? Hint: What line lengths represent possible waiting time?

Step 6 P(wait ≥ 5 minutes) = $\frac{3}{4}$ P(wait ≥ 10 minutes) = $\frac{1}{2}$

Step 7 If the bus stops for exactly 3 minutes, how do your answers to Step 6 change?

Step 7 The probability for a long waiting time decreases.

Step 8 List the geometric properties you needed in each of the three scenarios above and tell how your answers depended on them.

Step 9 How is geometric probability like the probability you've studied before? How is it different?

Step 10 Create your own geometric probability problem.

Step 9 Counting and number ratios are used for probability that can be solved using numeric or algebraic models. For those that could be solved with geometric models, angle measure or length ratios are used.

Step 8 A geometric model is used to find the probabilities for the spinner and for the bus. Knowledge of geometric shapes, their properties, and how lengths combine are used to solve the bridge problem.

Step 9 *Geometric probability* is usually defined as a probability that can be modeled using a geometric shape.

Step 10 One example: Determining the probability of hitting an area on a circular target with (random) darts requires knowledge of the areas of the rings and the bull's eye.

Step 1 Students can measure the angles of the sector and divide by 360 or think of area. $P(A) = \frac{1}{2}$, $P(B) = \frac{1}{4}$, $P(C) = \frac{1}{6}$, $P(D) = \frac{1}{12}$

Step 2 **[Ask]** "What assumption do you need to make to answer the second question?" **[Ask]** "What is the sum of your two probabilities?" [1] "Does that sum make sense?" [Yes, because there were no outcomes in which you could spend some time but not at least half the time with your brother.]

Step 3 **[Ask]** "What assumptions are you making?" [If students assume the contestant can always grab onto the shortest part, their answer will be 1. If students assume an equal chance of grabbing the longer or the shorter part, their answers will be close to $\frac{3}{4}$, varying according to other assumptions such as those made about the height of the contestant.]

Step 4 To answer the first question, no assumptions need to be made. But to answer the second question, students need to make assumptions. Ask them to list their assumptions and then give the probability based on those assumptions. Choose students who make different assumptions to present during Sharing.

Step 6 Noriko's arrival can be modeled as a random point chosen on one segment of a number line. The distance from that random point to the point representing the next bus arrival represents the waiting time. Three out of four times (15 out of 20), that distance will be at least 5 units long. Students again need to make assumptions.

CHAPTER REVIEW 1

PLANNING

LESSON OUTLINE

One day:

15 min Reviewing

25 min Exercises

5 min Self-Assessment

MATERIALS

- Two Solids (T)

REVIEWING

Show the Two Solids transparency (or hand around three-dimensional examples) and ask what geometric figures occur in each example. As students name figures, you might have them read careful definitions from their notebooks.

On the **square pyramid,** students can find examples of **points, line segments, endpoints of a line segment, angles** (with **vertices** and **sides,** including **right angles** on the base and **acute angles** on the other faces), and **convex polygons** (**equilateral triangles**—which are also **isosceles** and **acute**—and a **square** base—which, because opposite edges are **parallel** and adjacent edges **perpendicular,** making **right angles,** is also an example of a **rectangle,** a **rhombus,** a **parallelogram,** and a **quadrilateral**). The equilateral triangles are **congruent figures** and, because they're also **equiangular,** are **regular polygons.** The edges are **congruent line segments,** each angle is congruent to several others, and the lateral faces are congruent to each other. The **lengths** of the line segments can be measured by a **ruler,** and the angles can be measured in **degrees** using a **protractor.**

CHAPTER 1 REVIEW

It may seem that there's a lot to memorize in this chapter. But having defined terms yourself, you're more likely to remember and understand them. The key is to practice using these new terms and to be organized. Do the following exercises, then read Assessing What You've Learned for tips on staying organized.

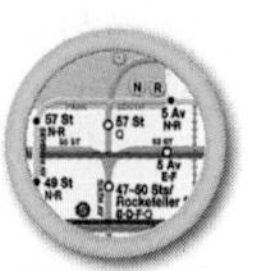

Whether you've been keeping a good list or not, go back now through each lesson in the chapter and double-check that you've completed each definition and that you understand it. For example, if someone mentions a geometry term to you, can you sketch it? If you are shown a geometric figure can you classify it? Compare your list of geometry terms with the lists of your group members.

EXERCISES

For Exercises 1–16, identify the statement as true or false. For each false statement, explain why it is false or sketch a counterexample.

1. The three basic building blocks of geometry are point, line, and plane. true
2. "The ray through point P from point Q" is written in symbolic form as $\overrightarrow{PQ}$. False; it is written as $\overrightarrow{QP}$.
3. "The length of segment PQ" can be written as PQ. true
4. The vertex of angle PDQ is point P. False; the vertex is point D.
5. The symbol for *perpendicular* is $\perp$. true
6. A scalene triangle is a triangle with no two sides the same length. true
7. An acute angle is an angle whose measure is more than 90°. False; its measure is less than 90°.
8. If $\overleftrightarrow{AB}$ intersects $\overleftrightarrow{CD}$ at point P, then $\angle APD$ and $\angle APC$ are a pair of vertical angles. false
9. A diagonal is a line segment in a polygon connecting any two nonconsecutive vertices. true
10. If two lines lie in the same plane and are perpendicular to the same line, then they are parallel. true
11. If the sum of the measures of two angles is 180°, then the two angles are complementary. False; they are supplementary.
12. A trapezoid is a quadrilateral having exactly one pair of parallel sides. true
13. A polygon with ten sides is a decagon. true

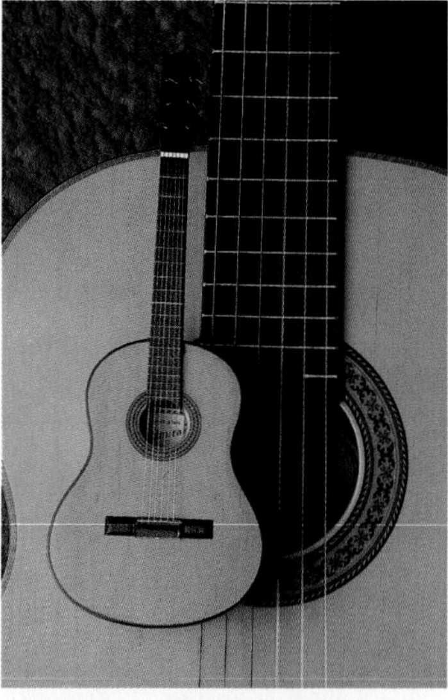

A knowledge of parallel lines, planes, arcs, circles, and symmetry is necessary to build durable guitars that sound pleasing.

There are no **lines, rays,** or **planes** in the figure, but the segments can be extended into lines or rays, and each face lies in a plane. Points on each line segment are **collinear,** and each segment has a **midpoint.**

8. two possible counterexamples:

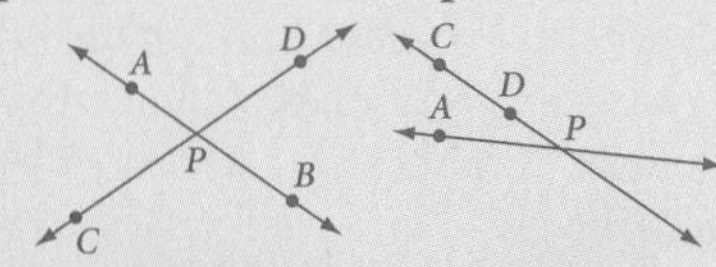

$\angle APD$ and $\angle APC$ are linear angles.

$\angle APD$ and $\angle APC$ are the same angle.

14. A square is a rectangle with all the sides equal in length. true

15. A pentagon has five sides and six diagonals. False; it has five diagonals.

16. The largest chord of a circle is a diameter of the circle. true

For Exercises 17–25, match each term with its figure below, or write "no match."

17. Isosceles acute triangle E

18. Isosceles right triangle G

19. Rhombus L

20. Trapezoid J

21. Pyramid C

22. Cylinder I

23. Concave polygon no match

24. Chord A

25. Minor arc no match

A.
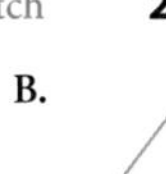
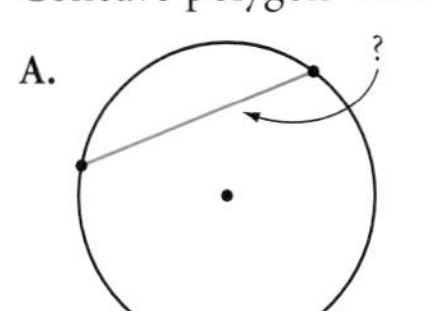

B.
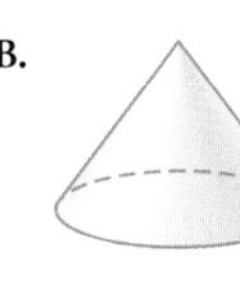

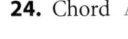

C.
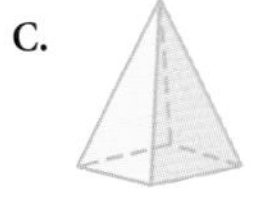

D.
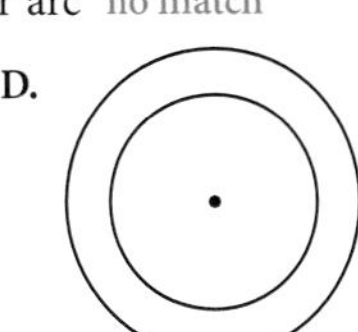

E.

F.

G.

H.
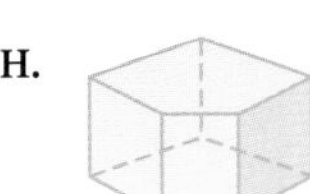

I.

J.
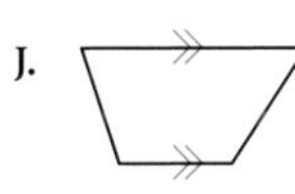

K.
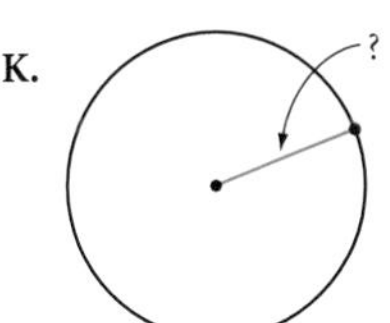

L.
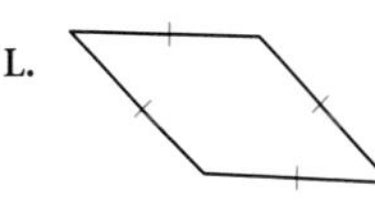

M.
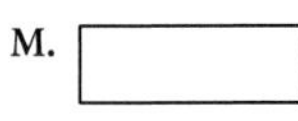

N.
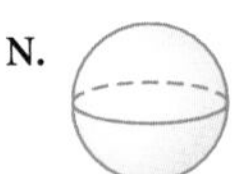

O.

For Exercises 26–33, sketch, label, and mark each figure.

26. Kite $KYTE$ with $\overline{KY} \cong \overline{YT}$

27. Scalene triangle PTS with $PS = 3$, $ST = 5$, $PT = 7$, and angle bisector $\overline{SO}$

28. Hexagon $REGINA$ with diagonal $\overline{AG}$ parallel to sides $\overline{RE}$ and $\overline{NI}$

29. Trapezoid $TRAP$ with $\overline{AR}$ and $\overline{PT}$ the nonparallel sides. Let E be the midpoint of $\overline{PT}$ and let Y be the midpoint of $\overline{AR}$. Draw $\overline{EY}$.

30. A triangle with exactly one line of reflectional symmetry

31. A circle with center at P, radii $\overline{PA}$ and $\overline{PT}$, and chord $\overline{TA}$ creating a minor arc $\overset{\frown}{TA}$

29.
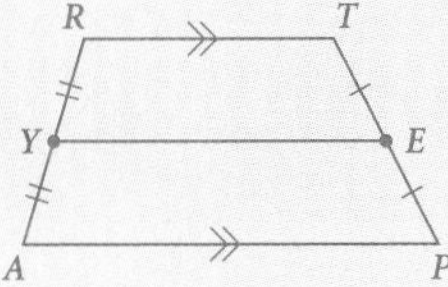

31.
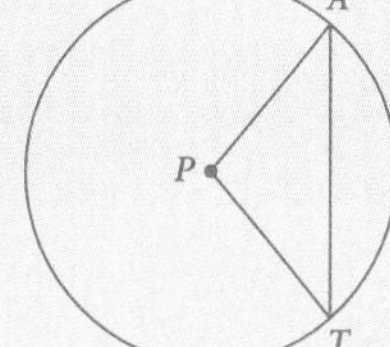

30.
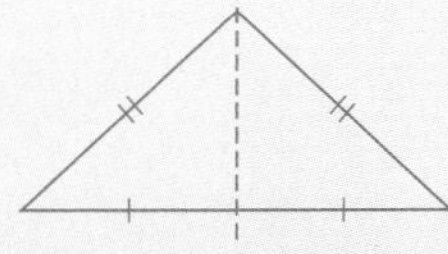

The **cylinder** inside another cylinder exhibits two **concentric circles,** each with a **center,** a **radius,** and **chords,** including **diameters.** The two ends of the cylinder are **congruent circles.** Vertical lines on the side of the cylinder are **tangent** to the circles. Each circle contains **arcs** and their **endpoints,** including **major arcs, minor arcs,** and **semicircles**—the **measure** of which can be determined by a protractor measuring a **central angle.**

The bases of the two figures are **coplanar,** and the figures reside in **space.**

Ask students how the figures could be modified to show **obtuse angles, concave polygons, right triangles, obtuse triangles, scalene triangles, trapezoids,** and **kites.** Or students might draw a **rectangular solid** or some other **prism** that contains these figures. Other terms to review are **cone, sphere, hemisphere,** and various pairs of angles: **vertical, linear, complementary,** and **supplementary.**

ASSIGNING HOMEWORK

You might also work through Exercises 1–16 orally.

26.
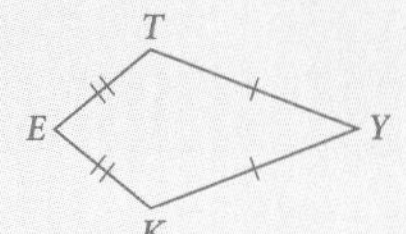

27.
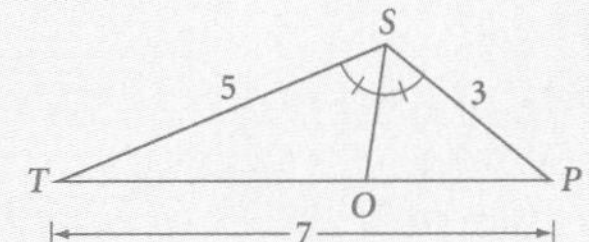

28.
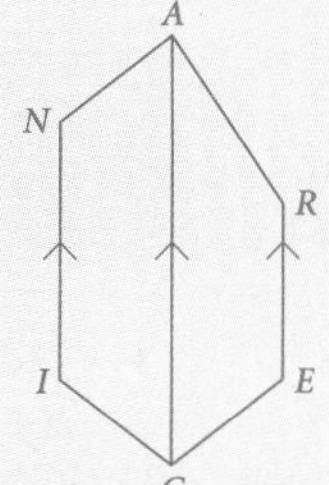

32. 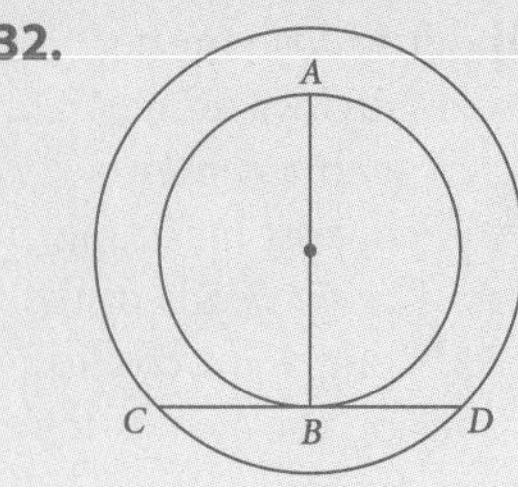

33. 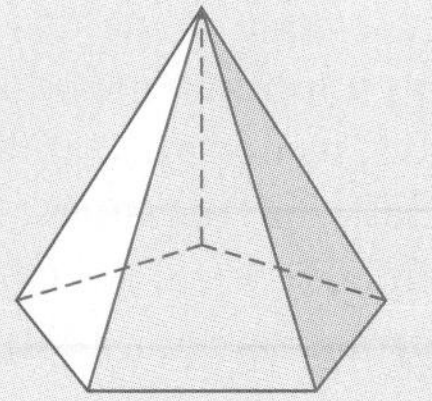

34. 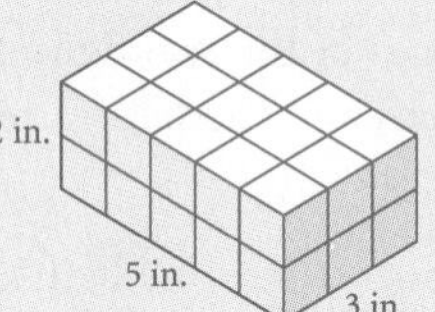

35. 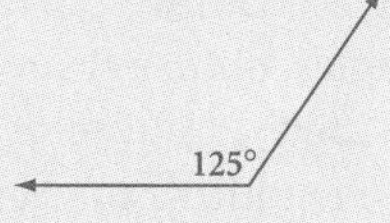

36. 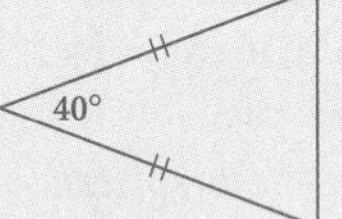

37. 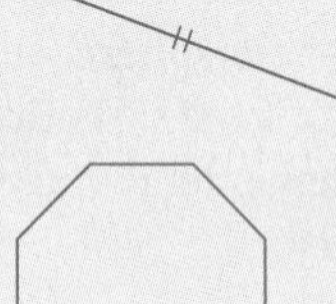

32. A pair of concentric circles with the diameter $\overline{AB}$ of the inner circle perpendicular at B to a chord $\overline{CD}$ of the larger circle

33. A pyramid with a pentagonal base

34. Draw a rectangular prism 2 inches by 3 inches by 5 inches, resting on its largest face. Draw lines on the three visible faces, showing how the solid can be divided into 30 smaller cubes.

35. Use your protractor to draw a 125° angle.

36. Use your protractor, ruler, and compass to draw an isosceles triangle with a vertex angle having a measure of 40°.

37. Use your geomety tools to draw a regular octagon. ⓗ

38. What is the measure of $\angle A$? Use your protractor. 114°

A

For Exercises 39–42, find the lengths x and y. (Every angle on each block is a right angle.)

39. 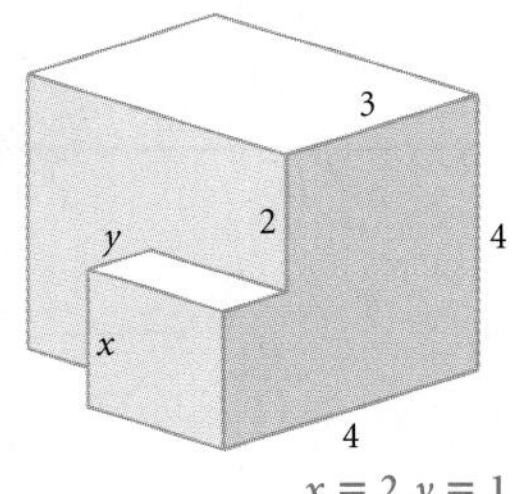

$x = 2, y = 1$

40. 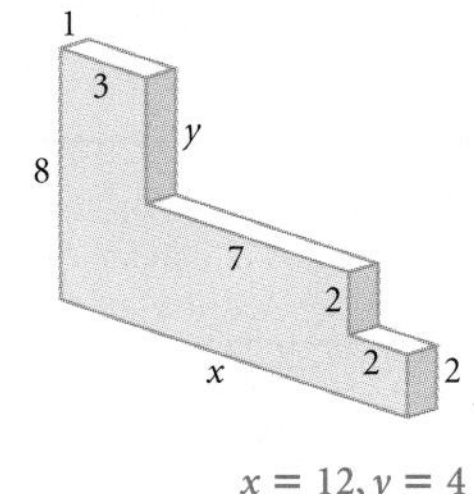

$x = 12, y = 4$

41. 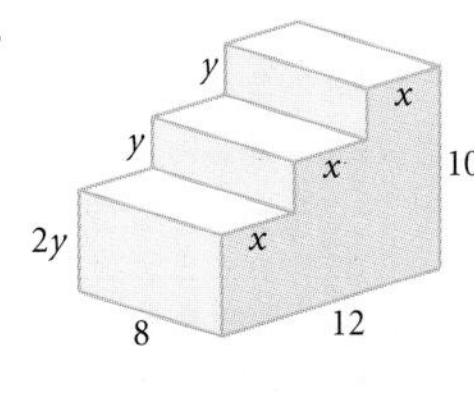

$x = 4, y = 2.5$

42. 18; 20; x; y; 12

$x = 10$
$y = 8$

43. If D is the midpoint of $\overline{AC}$, C is the midpoint of $\overline{AB}$, and $BD = 12$ cm, what is the length of $\overline{AB}$? $AB = 16$ cm

44. If $\overrightarrow{BD}$ is the angle bisector of $\angle ABC$ and $\overrightarrow{BE}$ is the angle bisector of $\angle DBC$, find $m\angle EBA$ if $m\angle DBE = 32°$? 96°

45. What is the measure of the angle formed by the hands of the clock at 2:30? ⓗ 105°

46. If the pizza is cut into 12 congruent pieces, how many degrees are in each central angle? 30°

47. Make a concept map (a tree diagram or a Venn diagram) to organize these quadrilaterals: rhombus, rectangle, square, trapezoid.

47. 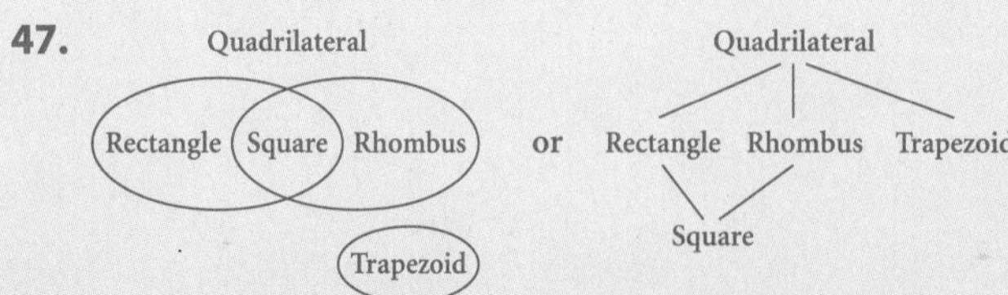

48. The box at right is wrapped with two strips of ribbon, as shown. What is the minimum length of ribbon needed to decorate the box? 66 inches

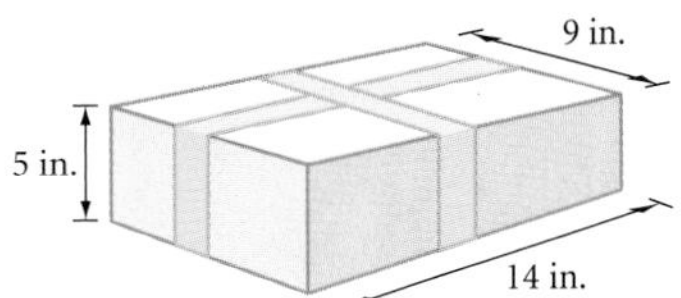

49. At one point in a race, Rico was 15 ft behind Paul and 18 ft ahead of Joe. Joe was trailing George by 30 ft. Paul was ahead of George by how many ft? 3 feet

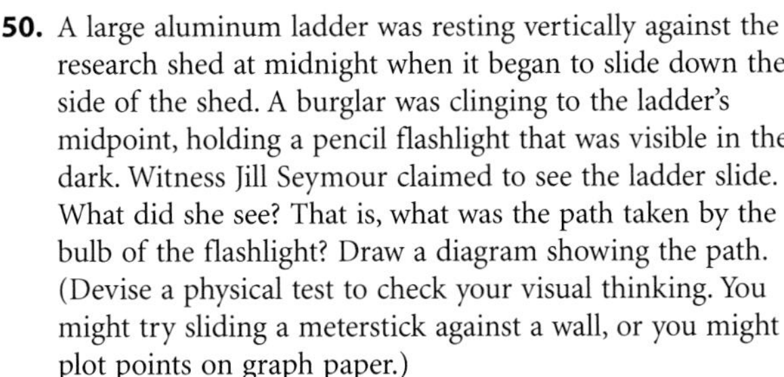

50. A large aluminum ladder was resting vertically against the research shed at midnight when it began to slide down the side of the shed. A burglar was clinging to the ladder's midpoint, holding a pencil flashlight that was visible in the dark. Witness Jill Seymour claimed to see the ladder slide. What did she see? That is, what was the path taken by the bulb of the flashlight? Draw a diagram showing the path. (Devise a physical test to check your visual thinking. You might try sliding a meterstick against a wall, or you might plot points on graph paper.)

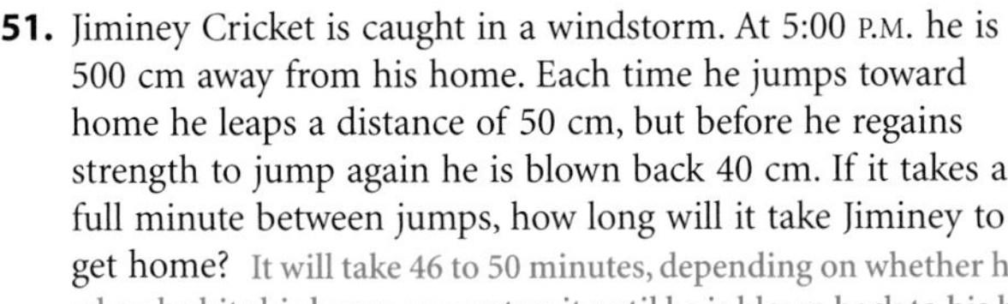

51. Jiminey Cricket is caught in a windstorm. At 5:00 P.M. he is 500 cm away from his home. Each time he jumps toward home he leaps a distance of 50 cm, but before he regains strength to jump again he is blown back 40 cm. If it takes a full minute between jumps, how long will it take Jiminey to get home? It will take 46 to 50 minutes, depending on whether he can stop when he hits his house or must wait until he is blown back to his house.

52. If the right triangle BAR were rotated 90° clockwise about point B, to what location would point A be relocated? (2, 3)

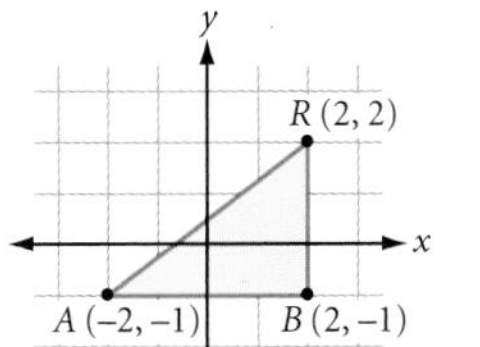

53. Sketch the three-dimensional figure formed by folding the net below into a solid.

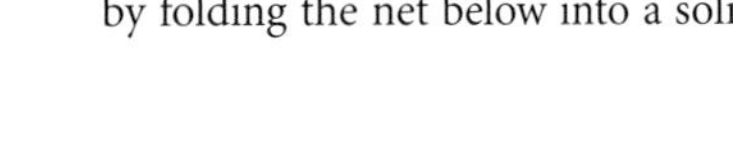

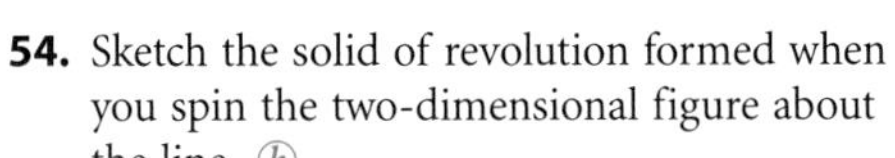

54. Sketch the solid of revolution formed when you spin the two-dimensional figure about the line. ⓗ

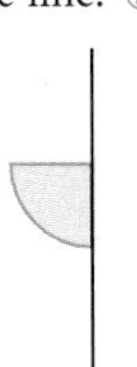

55. Sketch the section formed when the solid is sliced by the plane, as shown.

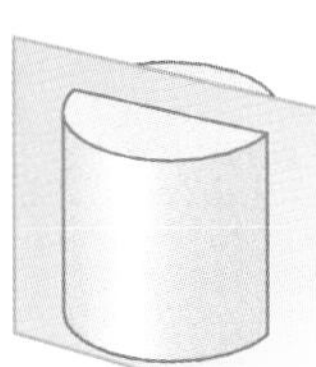

Exercise 50 This is the most challenging exercise.

50. The path taken by the midpoint of the ladder is an arc of a circle or a quarter-circle if the ladder slides all the way from the vertical to the horizontal.

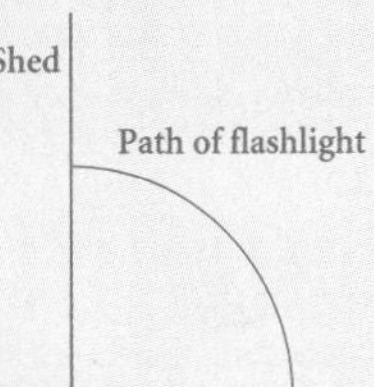

53.

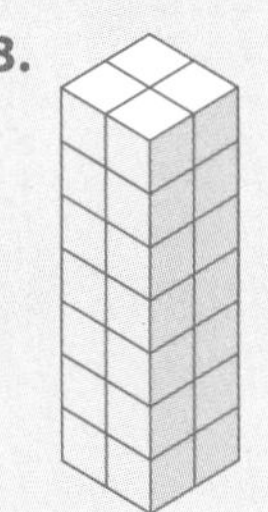

54.

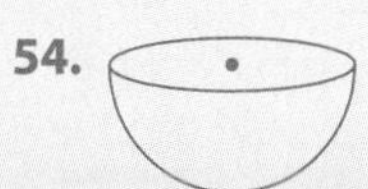

55.

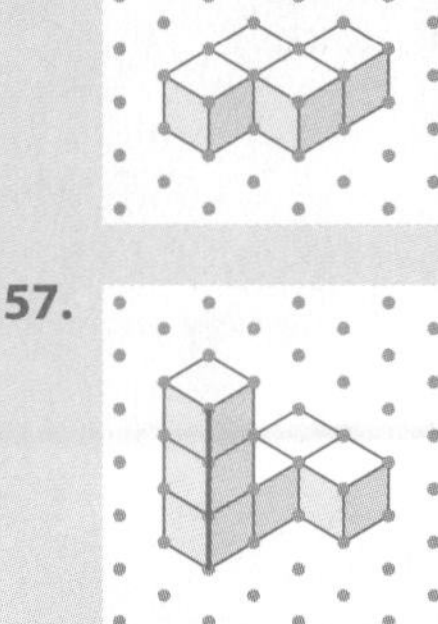

ASSESSING

If students have reviewed the new terms and symbols often, they should do well on the chapter test. In addition to the quizzes and test, you can assess students' definition lists. At this point all students should be able to cite classifying and differentiating as steps in writing a definition and should be able to draw and label required diagrams (in two dimensions). They should be able to say why some terms are undefined and to distinguish between a definition and a conclusion.

FACILITATING SELF-ASSESSMENT

To motivate students to organize their notebooks, you might allow them to use them on tests. To be sure students are learning the vocabulary and not relying only on their written definitions, you might require them to pass a matching quiz on the terms before they are allowed to use their notebooks on tests.

The exercises designated in the lessons as appropriate for portfolios are
Lesson 1.1, Exercise 27;
Lesson 1.2, Exercises 34 and 41;
Lesson 1.3, Exercise 21;
Lesson 1.4, Exercise 36;
Lesson 1.5, Exercise 17;
Lesson 1.6, Exercises 18 and 19;
Lesson 1.7, Exercises 16 and 17;
and Lesson 1.8, Exercises 1–7.

56. Use an isometric dot grid to sketch the figure shown below.

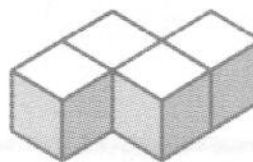

57. Sketch the figure shown with the red edge vertical and facing the viewer. ⓗ

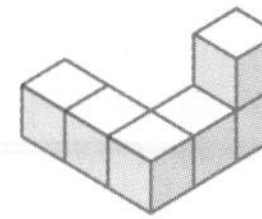

Assessing What You've Learned

ORGANIZE YOUR NOTEBOOK

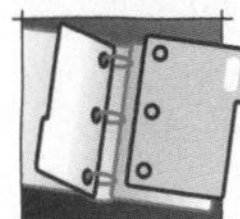

Is this textbook filling up with folded-up papers stuffed between pages? If so, that's a bad sign! But it's not too late to get organized. Keeping a well-organized notebook is one of the best habits you can develop to improve and assess your learning. You should have sections for your classwork, definition list, and homework exercises. There should be room to make corrections and to summarize what you learned and write down questions you still have.

Many books include a definition list (sometimes called a glossary) in the back. This book makes you responsible for your own glossary, so it's essential that, in addition to taking good notes, you keep a complete definition list that you can refer to. You started a definition list in Lesson 1.1. Get help from classmates or your teacher on any definition you don't understand.

As you progress through the course, your notebook will become more and more important. A good way to review a chapter is to read through the chapter and your notes and write a one-page summary of the chapter. And if you create a one-page summary for each chapter, the summaries will be very helpful to you when it comes time for midterms and final exams. You'll find no better learning and study aid than a summary page for each chapter, and your definition list, kept in an organized notebook.

UPDATE YOUR PORTFOLIO

- If you did the project in this chapter, document your work and add it to your portfolio.
- Choose one homework assignment that demonstrates your best work in terms of completeness, correctness, and neatness. Add it (or a copy of it) to your portfolio.

CHAPTER

2

Reasoning in Geometry

Overview

Though some of Chapter 2 doesn't look like traditional geometry, the inductive reasoning and deductive reasoning introduced here are fundamental to all that follow. In **Lesson 2.1,** students learn about inductive reasoning and practice finding the next term of numerical and picture sequences. Deductive reasoning is introduced and contrasted with inductive reasoning in **Lesson 2.2.** In **Lesson 2.3,** students learn how to find formulas for the *n*th term of linear sequences typically found in geometry problems. Then in **Lesson 2.4,** they formulate mathematical models and discover that these geometric models can represent, and model, physical situations. The **exploration** gives students a chance to look for pattens in traveling networks. Students use inductive reasoning to make conjectures about linear pairs and vertical angles in **Lesson 2.5** and about angles formed when a transversal crosses parallel lines in **Lesson 2.6.** Students see informal arguments (proofs) of some of these conjectures. **Using Your Algebra Skills 2** reviews slope and the final **exploration** looks at patterns in fractals.

The Mathematics

Most of us recall our geometry courses as constructing or memorizing proofs. We remember putting statements in one column, reasons in another. A few of us loved this; many of us didn't.

Proof is important to geometry, and to the rest of mathematics as well. Thales ['thā-lēz] one of the earliest Greek mathematicians and philosophers (ca. 625–547 B.C.E.), set the precedent of insisting on logical proof as the way to truth because he found that results derived from experience were sometimes false. Logical proof has been a central feature of mathematical process ever since.

The verification role of proof is now seen as only one of several purposes it serves. Students at van Hiele levels 1 and 2 don't usually appreciate the need for verification. Instead, they're more likely to see a need for proof as a means of answering the question "Why?" This chapter and the next few chapters of *Discovering Geometry* focus on the explanation role of proof in order to help prepare students to deal with other purposes of proof they will encounter later in the course.

Most mathematical investigation does not begin with proof. Instead, it begins with *inductive reasoning,* which starts with data and leads through patterns to a conjecture. Then the investigator asks "But *why* should that conjecture be true?" Enter *deductive reasoning*—looking for a reason, for a proof that applies to all cases.

As an example, suppose you measure a lot of angles formed by a line intersecting a pair of parallel lines and apply inductive reasoning to your data to make the Corresponding Angles Conjecture: If two parallel lines are cut by a transversal, then corresponding angles are congruent. Then you ask "But *why*?" To answer this question, you draw a diagram and label some points.

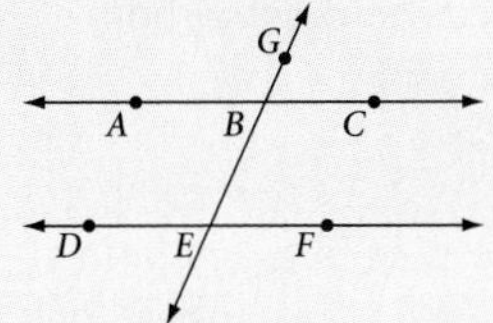

You decide that you want to explain why corresponding angles $\angle GBC$ and $\angle GEF$ are congruent. You might realize "Ah! $\angle GEF \cong \angle ABE$, by the Alternate Interior Angles Conjecture, and $\angle ABE \cong \angle GBC$, because they're vertical angles. Therefore, if we substitute, we see that $\angle GEF \cong \angle GBC$."

Note two features of this explanatory proof. First, it depends on assumptions about vertical angles and alternate interior angles. Are these assumptions valid? Can they too be proved? A proof of the Alternate Interior Angles Conjecture appears in the student book, and it assumes the Corresponding Angles Conjecture. Second, the given proof is only one of many possible proofs. As an alternative explanation, perhaps you would say, "Ah! $\angle GEF$ is just a shift of $\angle GBC$, so of course they're congruent." This alternative proof depends on the meaning of "a shift."

Proofs as explanations are usually written in paragraph form. Early in the course, paragraph proofs are preferable to two-column proofs not only because formality is intimidating, but also because providing a reason for each statement in a two-column proof requires more attention to detail than students at van Hiele level 1 or 2 can appreciate. For example, if we break down our explanatory proof of the Corresponding Angles Conjecture, we must cite a reason why substitution is allowed. At this point, most students see no need to document what they consider to be an obvious justification. Moreover, in reporting mathematical research, mathematicians write paragraph proofs, not two-column proofs. Justifying every step can detract from the explanation.

Using This Chapter

You should cover all the lessons in this chapter. You might combine lessons. The last two lessons develop special angle relationships. It is possible to combine these lessons, using cooperative groups to complete separate parts of the investigations and then share results with the class. You will want to give all students an opportunity to practice both inductive and deductive reasoning.

Cooperative Learning

Teaching with cooperative learning puts you in the role of a manager of investigative teams. Instead of being the source of answers, you are the creator of an environment in which students work well enough together to achieve good results. You might keep in mind five principles of management.

- Set clear objectives.
- Monitor the working groups carefully, listening in on groups and helping them to answer each other's questions without giving answers yourself.
- Intervene only when necessary.
- Limit behavioral difficulties.
- Evaluate progress students make in understanding, as well as social skills and group participation.

Resources

Discovering Geometry Resources

Teaching and Worksheet Masters
Lessons 2.1–2.3, 2.5, 2.6, and Chapter 2 Review

Sketchpad Demonstrations
Lessons 2.2, 2.3, and 2.5

Discovering Geometry with The Geometer's Sketchpad
Lessons 2.5 and 2.6
Using Your Algebra Skills 2

Assessment Resources A and B
Quiz 1 (Lessons 2.1 and 2.2)
Quiz 2 (Lessons 2.3 and 2.4)
Quiz 3 (Lessons 2.5 and 2.6)
Chapter 2 Test
Chapter 2 Constructive Assessment Options

Practice Your Skills for Chapter 2

Condensed Lessons for Chapter 2

Other Resources

An Introduction to the History of Mathematics by Howard Eves.

For complete references on this and other resources see www.keypress.com/DG.

Materials

- construction tools (straightedge, compass, patty paper)
- protractors
- geometry software, *optional*

Pacing Guide

	day 1	day 2	day 3	day 4	day 5	day 6	day 7	day 8	day 9	day 10
standard	2.1	2.2	2.3	quiz, 2.4	2.5	2.5	2.6	quiz, Algebra 2	review	assessment
enriched	2.1	2.2	2.2	quiz, 2.4	2.5	2.5 Exploration	2.6	quiz, Algebra 2	review, Exploration	assessment
block	2.1, 2.2	2.3, 2.4	quiz, 2.5	2.6, Algebra 2	Exploration, review	assessment				

CHAPTER 2 Reasoning in Geometry

That which an artist makes is a mirror image of what he sees around him.

M. C. ESCHER

Hand with Reflecting Sphere (Self-Portrait in Spherical Mirror), M. C. Escher

OBJECTIVES

In this chapter you will

- perform geometry investigations and make many discoveries by observing common features or patterns
- use your discoveries to solve problems through a process called inductive reasoning
- use inductive reasoning to discover patterns
- learn to use deductive reasoning
- learn about vertical angles and linear pairs
- make conjectures

Escher has captured himself and his room in this print of a spherical mirror. The plate for the print was made from a drawing Escher had made while holding such a sphere.

[Ask] "What parts of the room do you see?" [floor, ceiling, four walls] "Which parts of the room are least distorted? Most distorted? Why? What is the center of the circle that represents the sphere?" [the point right between the artist's eyes]

[Ask] "If Escher drew a sketch for this print while holding the sphere and then made an etching of the drawing on a plate to print, is he right handed or left handed? How do you know?" [He drew it holding the sphere in his right hand and drawing with his left. When printed, the right hand was reflected to look like a left hand.] "What else can you learn about the artist from this self-portrait?" [Possible answer: He liked books and conversation, and kept his space free of clutter.] "What are the clues?"

CHAPTER 2 OBJECTIVES

- Introduce and familiarize students with inductive reasoning
- Introduce and familiarize students with deductive reasoning and how it relates to inductive reasoning
- Use inductive reasoning to find the next term in a number or picture pattern
- Generalize basic number patterns to find the nth term in a number sequence
- Discover relationships between special pairs of angles
- Explore relationships of the angles formed by a transversal cutting parallel lines
- Apply mathematical models to problem solving
- Practice performing investigations and writing conjectures
- Develop visualization skills and cooperative behavior
- Practice measurement and construction skills

LESSON

2.1

PLANNING

LESSON OUTLINE

One day:

10 min Examples

20 min Investigation

5 min Sharing

5 min Closing

5 min Exercises

MATERIALS

- Shape Shifters (W) for One step

TEACHING

Most learning occurs through inductive reasoning, making generalizations from observed patterns in data.

You can use the one-step investigation after discussing the connection. Or you can discuss the examples and then start student groups on the steps of the investigation.

One step Give a copy of the Shape Shifters worksheet to each group. Ask students to draw the 25th shape in the sequence and write a description of the 30th shape. As you circulate, give the hint to look at alternate terms only if students are on the verge of abandoning their work out of frustration; they will enjoy finding the pattern themselves if they can. If some students still ask you how to solve the problem, try looking at the student next to them as if the questioner were addressing that person. If the questioner persists in involving you, ask "What do the rest of you think about that?" During Sharing, mention that what students have done is called *inductive reasoning,* and use the examples as needed.

LESSON 2.1

Inductive Reasoning

We have to reinvent the wheel every once in a while, not because we need a lot of wheels; but because we need a lot of inventors.

BRUCE JOYCE

As a child you learned by experimenting with the natural world around you. You learned how to walk, to talk, and to ride your first bicycle, all by trial and error. From experience you learned to turn a water faucet on with a counterclockwise motion and to turn it off with a clockwise motion. You achieved most of your learning by a process called **inductive reasoning.** It is the process of observing data, recognizing patterns, and making generalizations about those patterns.

Geometry is rooted in inductive reasoning. In ancient Egypt and Babylonia, geometry began when people developed procedures for measurement after much experience and observation. Assessors and surveyors used these procedures to calculate land areas and to reestablish the boundaries of agricultural fields after floods. Engineers used the procedures to build canals, reservoirs, and the Great Pyramids. Throughout this course you will use inductive reasoning. You will perform investigations, observe similarities and patterns, and make many discoveries that you can use to solve problems.

Language CONNECTION

The word "geometry" means "measure of the earth" and was originally inspired by the ancient Egyptians. The ancient Egyptians devised a complex system of land surveying in order to reestablish land boundaries that were erased each spring by the annual flooding of the Nile River.

Inductive reasoning guides scientists, investors, and business managers. All of these professionals use past experience to assess what is likely to happen in the future.

When you use inductive reasoning to make a generalization, the generalization is called a **conjecture.** Consider the following example from science.

MAKING THE CONNECTION

Ancient Egyptians recorded their history on stone or on carefully preserved papyrus. Babylonians used clay tablets. Because these materials are so durable, we know a great deal about the early geometry of these cultures. Bamboo and bark, materials that decay more quickly, were the writing materials of ancient India and China. Thus, unfortunately, we know very little about the early geometry of these countries. However, it seems reasonable that the inductive reasoning process preceded any formal deductive arguments in India and China as well as in Egypt. In *An Introduction to the History of Mathematics,* Howard Eves asserts that ancient Indian geometry was primarily empirical, that is, based on procedures for measurement. The ancient *Sulvasutras* demonstrate that Hindus used empirical geometry to build altars, among other things.

EXAMPLE A

A scientist dips a platinum wire into a solution containing salt (sodium chloride), passes the wire over a flame, and observes that it produces an orange-yellow flame.

She does this with many other solutions that contain salt, finding that they all produce an orange-yellow flame. Make a conjecture based on her findings.

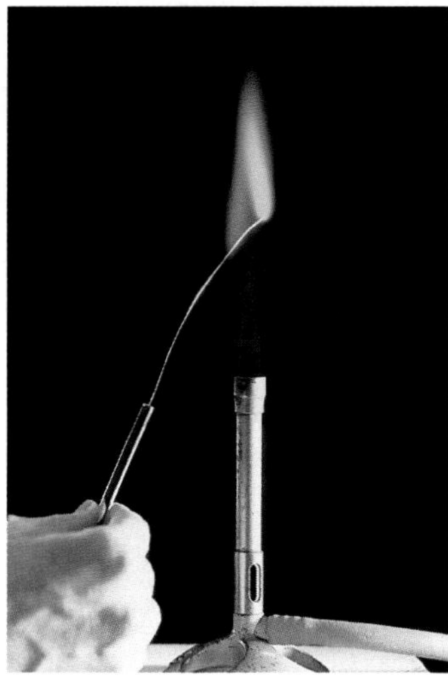

Platinum wire flame test

▸ Solution

The scientist tested many other solutions containing salt, and found no counterexamples. You should conjecture: "If a solution contains sodium chloride, then in a flame test it produces an orange-yellow flame."

Like scientists, mathematicians often use inductive reasoning to make discoveries. For example, a mathematician might use inductive reasoning to find patterns in a number sequence. Once he knows the pattern, he can find the next term.

EXAMPLE B

Consider the sequence

2, 4, 7, 11, . . .

Make a conjecture about the rule for generating the sequence. Then find the next three terms.

▸ Solution

Look at the numbers you add to get each term. The 1st term in the sequence is 2. You add 2 to find the 2nd term. Then you add 3 to find the 3rd term, and so on.

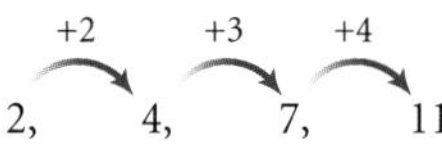

You can conjecture that if the pattern continues, you always add the next counting number to get the next term. The next three terms in the sequence will be 16, 22, and 29.

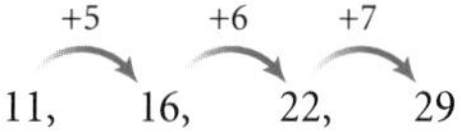

In the following investigation you will use inductive reasoning to recognize a pattern in a series of drawings and use it to find a term much farther out in a sequence.

▸ EXAMPLE A

This is an example of inductive reasoning closely related to academic work. If students are concerned that it seems unrelated to geometry, point out that the kinds of reasoning they learn in geometry can be used in other fields. Inductive reasoning is the main kind of reasoning used by all of us but especially by scientists, who observe data, recognize patterns, and make generalizations.

▸ EXAMPLE B

In this example students see a mathematical instance of inductive reasoning. **[Ask]** "What does the word *sequence* mean?" Get students' ideas. **[Language]** The prefix *seq-* comes from Latin meaning "to follow." Although students are not yet being asked to write an *n*th term for this sequence, it is a good time to get students thinking about how they might write an expression that could represent any term in the sequence. They will do this in Lesson 2.3.

LESSON OBJECTIVES

- Introduce and familiarize students with inductive reasoning
- Use inductive reasoning to find the next term in a number or picture pattern
- Develop cooperative behavior

NCTM STANDARDS

	CONTENT		PROCESS
✓	Number	✓	Problem Solving
	Algebra	✓	Reasoning
✓	Geometry	✓	Communication
✓	Measurement	✓	Connections
✓	Data/Probability		Representation

Guiding the Investigation

Steps 1, 2 Some students may find it helpful to copy shapes 1, 3, and 5 in one row and shapes 2, 4, and 6 in another row. Or suggest that they put their fingers over drawings that aren't being considered in Steps 1 and 2.

Steps 4, 5 Some students will have trouble imagining how to get to the 25th and 30th shapes. **[Ask]** "Is shape 25 a circle or a polygon?" [Elicit the idea that 1, 3, and 5 are odd and 25 is odd.] "How soon will you see shape 1 again?" "And then when again after that?" For the 30th shape, ask similar questions. Students should see that shape 2 has 2 + 1 sides and that shape 4 has 4 + 1 sides. **[Ask]** "So how many sides does shape 30 have?"

Step 5 Students may have difficulty articulating what they see. At this point it's more important to concentrate on encouragement than on precision of language.

SHARING IDEAS

Use and encourage the use of terminology from previous chapters. Students may not yet be comfortable with that terminology; revisiting ideas in different contexts means that students aren't expected to achieve mastery of an idea the first time they encounter it.

[Ask] "How did your group use the given data to describe the 25th and 30th shapes?" "What constant pattern did you observe while investigating the sequences?" "What numerical patterns did you observe while investigating the sequences?" Stress that the kind of reasoning they are doing here—making conjectures by generalizing from patterns in data—is called *inductive reasoning.*

[Ask] "Are all conjectures that arise from inductive reasoning true?" Point out the discussion that follows the investigation in the student book. Some students may not recall that a *prime number* is a number that has exactly two distinct factors, itself and 1. Ask how we might be sure of the truth of our conjectures. Leave the answer until Lesson 2.2.

Assessing Progress

Watch for students' use of terms from earlier chapters, especially references to kinds of geometric figures and their parts and symmetry. Also assess how students are contributing to their working groups and how comfortable they are with multiple ways of thinking about problems and ideas.

Investigation
Shape Shifters

Step 1 The odd-numbered shapes are all half-shaded circles. Each circle is rotated a quarter turn counterclockwise from the previous circle.

Step 2 The even-numbered shapes are polygons with consecutive odd numbers of sides. There are three small circles in each; the two on the bottom are hollow and the centered one at the top is solid.

Look at the sequence of shapes below. Pay close attention to the patterns that occur in every other shape.

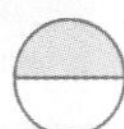 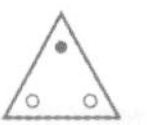  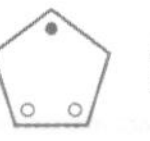 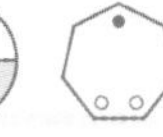

Step 1 What patterns do you notice in the 1st, 3rd, and 5th shapes?

Step 2 What patterns do you notice in the 2nd, 4th, and 6th shapes?

Step 3 Draw the next two shapes in the sequence.

Step 4 Use the patterns you discovered to draw the 25th shape.

Step 5 Describe the 30th shape in the sequence. You do not have to draw it!
The 30th shape is a 31-sided polygon containing the triangular pattern of dots.

Step 3
7th shape: 8th shape:

Step 4

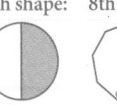

Sometimes a conjecture is difficult to find because the data collected are unorganized or the observer is mistaking coincidence with cause and effect. Good use of inductive reasoning depends on the quantity and quality of data. Sometimes not enough information or data have been collected to make a proper conjecture. For example, if you are asked to find the next term in the pattern 3, 5, 7, you might conjecture that the next term is 9—the next odd number. Someone else might notice that the pattern is the consecutive odd primes and say that the next term is 11. If the pattern was 3, 5, 7, 11, 13, what would you be more likely to conjecture?

EXERCISES

1. On his way to the local Hunting and Gathering Convention, caveperson Stony Grok picks up a rock, drops it into a lake, and notices that it sinks. He picks up a second rock, drops it into the lake, and notices that it also sinks. He does this five more times. Each time, the rock sinks straight to the bottom of the lake. Stony conjectures: "Ura nok seblu," which translates to _?_. What counterexample would Stony Grok need to find to disprove, or at least to refine, his conjecture? ⓗ
"All rocks sink." Stony needs to find one rock that will not sink.

Closing the Lesson

The main idea of this lesson is that inductive reasoning involves making conjectures that generalize from observed patterns in data. Most learning, as well as most research in mathematics and science, begins with inductive reasoning. In mathematics a conjecture is not considered to be true until it is verified by deductive reasoning.

If students need more examples of inductive reasoning, you might want to work with them on Exercise 1 or one of Exercises 3–10.

2. Sean draws these geometric figures on paper. His sister Courtney measures each angle with a protractor. They add the measures of each pair of angles to form a conjecture. Write their conjecture. If two angles are formed by drawing a ray from a line, then their measures add up to 180°.

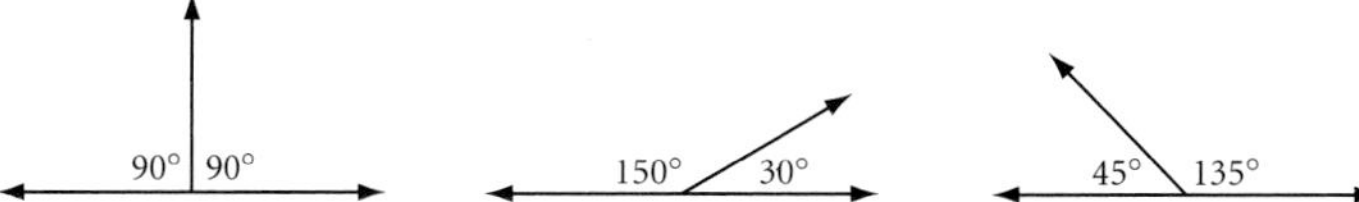

For Exercises 3–10, use inductive reasoning to find the next two terms in each sequence.

3. 1, 10, 100, 1000, ?, ?

4. $\frac{1}{6}, \frac{1}{3}, \frac{1}{2}, \frac{2}{3}$, ?, ? ⓗ

5. 7, 3, −1, −5, −9, −13, ?, ? −17, −21

6. 1, 3, 6, 10, 15, 21, ?, ? 28, 36

7. 1, 1, 2, 3, 5, 8, 13, ?, ? ⓗ 21, 34

8. 1, 4, 9, 16, 25, 36, ?, ? ⓗ 49, 64

9. 32, 30, 26, 20, 12, 2, ?, ? −10, −24

10. 1, 2, 4, 8, 16, 32, ?, ? 64, 128

For Exercises 11–16, use inductive reasoning to draw the next shape in each picture pattern.

11.

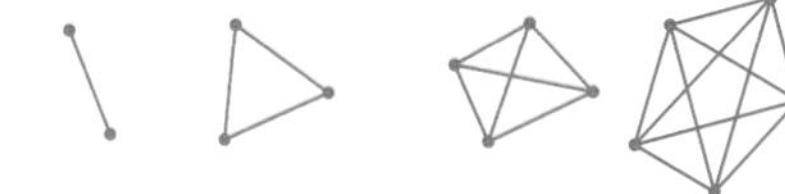

12.

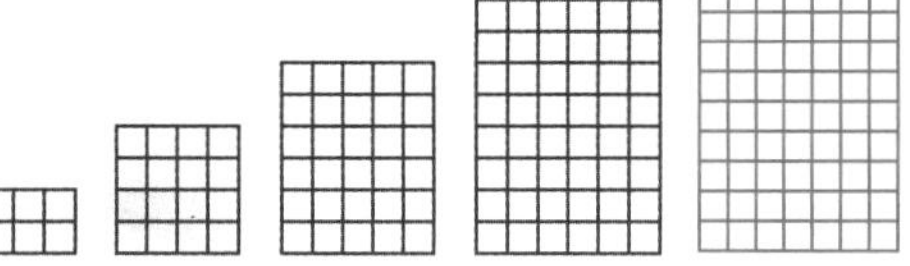

13. ⓗ

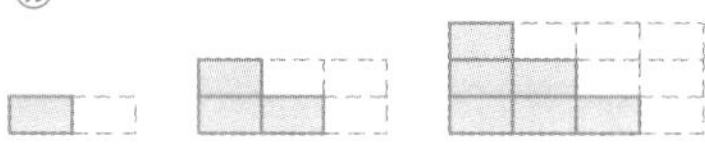

14. ⓗ

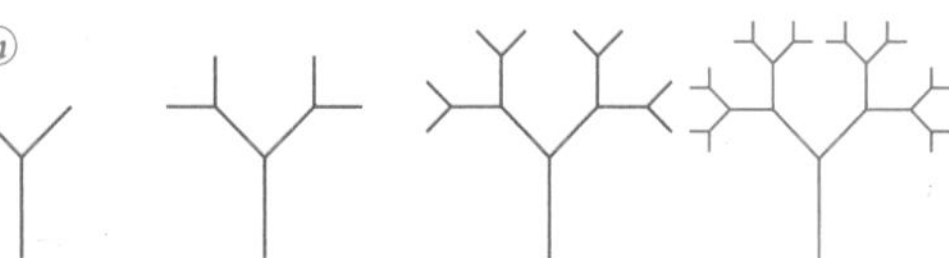

15. ⓗ

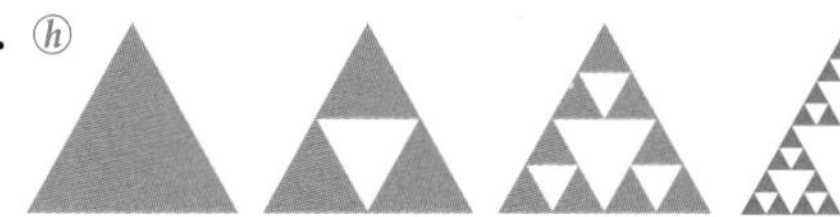

16.

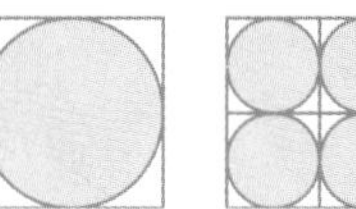

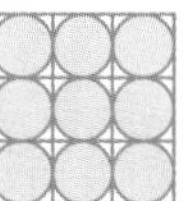

Use the rule provided to generate the first five terms of the sequence in Exercise 17 and the next five terms of the sequence in Exercise 18.

17. $3n - 2$ ⓗ 1, 4, 7, 10, 13

18. 1, 3, 6, 10, . . . , $\frac{n(n+1)}{2}$, . . . 15, 21, 28, 36, 45

19. Now it's your turn. Generate the first five terms of a sequence. Give the sequence to a member of your family or to a friend and ask him or her to find the next two terms in the sequence. Can he or she find your pattern? Answers will vary.

20. Write the first five terms of two different sequences in which 12 is the 3rd term. Sample answers: 3, 6, 12, 24, 48, . . . and 4, 8, 12, 16, 20, . . .

21. Think of a situation in which you have used inductive reasoning. Write a paragraph describing what happened and explaining why you think it was inductive reasoning. ⓗ Answers will vary.

Exercises 11–16 Those with less developed visual skills may find it helpful to express each term numerically, counting sides, blocks, triangles, or circles.

13.

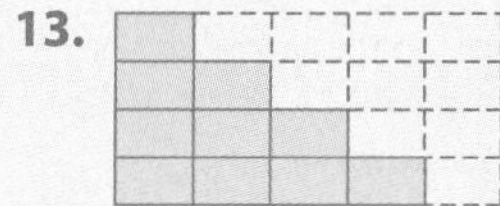

Exercise 18 [Alert] Students may perform the order of operations incorrectly. Remind them to do the operation within the parentheses before multiplying.

Exercise 19 Encourage serious thinking about this exercise. You might use it for class discussion, thus allowing more practice of group skills. Encourage students to be creative with their sequence. They need not be able to write a rule for generating its *n*th term. As an extension, students could come up with a sequence in which the first few terms are missing and challenge classmates to work backward to fill them in.

BUILDING UNDERSTANDING

Assign some of the review exercises as homework, but leave others as class starters earning participation points or as quiz questions. If students know that the exercises will be class starters or quiz questions, they will be more likely to work the problems at home.

ASSIGNING HOMEWORK

Essential	**1–15 odds, 22**
Performance assessment	**20**
Portfolio	**18, 22**
Journal	**21**
Group	**2–16 evens, 17–19**
Review	**23–41**

▶ Helping with the Exercises

Exercise 2 This exercise foreshadows the Linear Pair Conjecture in Lesson 2.5. **[Language]** As needed, use the term *adjacent angles* to describe a pair of nonoverlapping angles with the same vertex that share a side.

Exercises 3–10 [Ask] "What is being done to each term to get the next?" Have students pair each term with its number in the sequence. Then relate each term to its number in the sequence rather than to the previous term. You might challenge some students at this point to find a rule for generating the *n*th term of the sequence.

3. 10000, 100000, ... Each term is 10 times the previous term.

4. $\frac{5}{6}$, 1, ... (Written with the common denominator of 6, the pattern becomes $\frac{1}{6}, \frac{2}{6}, \frac{3}{6}, \frac{4}{6}, \frac{5}{6}, \frac{6}{6}, \ldots$)

23. 

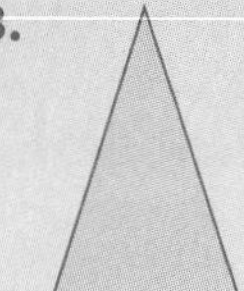

24. 

25. 

26. 

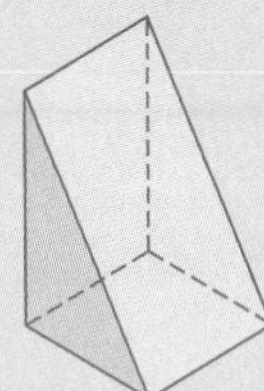

27. possible answers:

28. sample answer:

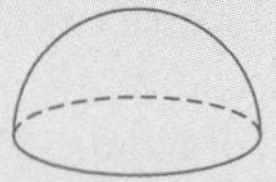

Exercises 31–34, 36 **[ESL]** The *a(n)* means "a or an."

QUALITY OF DATA

Some students will have trouble understanding how the organization of data affects conjectures they might make from the data. If numerical data are not presented in an orderly sequence, a trend in differences between adjacent values will not emerge. In Lesson 2.4, for example, the difference between terms will be much easier to spot if students don't reduce fractions but instead leave expressions in factored form. This is another kind of organization.

22. Look at the pattern in these pairs of equations. Decide if the conjecture is true. If it is not true, find a counterexample.

$12^2 = 144$ and $21^2 = 441$

$13^2 = 169$ and $31^2 = 961$

$103^2 = 10609$ and $301^2 = 90601$

$112^2 = 12544$ and $211^2 = 44521$

Conjecture: If two numbers have the same digits in reverse order, then the squares of those numbers will have identical digits but in reverse order.

Conjecture is false; $14^2 = 196$ but $41^2 = 1681$.

Review

1.8 **23.** Sketch the section formed when the cone is sliced by the plane, as shown.

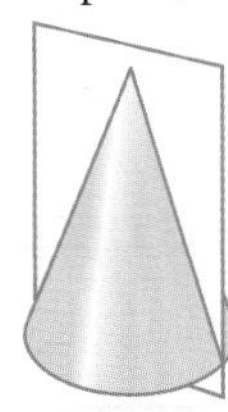

1.8 **24.**

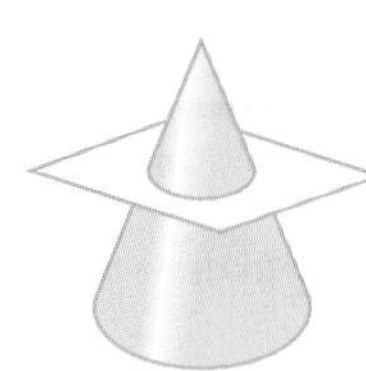

1.8 **25.**

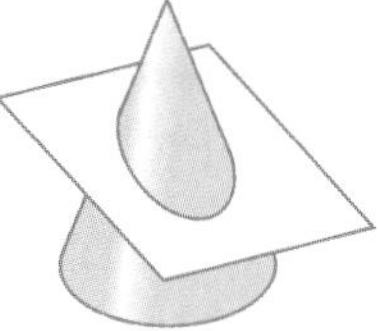

1.7 **26.** Sketch the three-dimensional figure formed by folding the net below into a solid. ⓗ

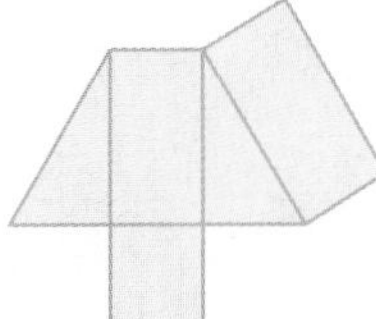

1.8 **27.** Sketch the figure shown below but with the red edge vertical and facing you. ⓗ

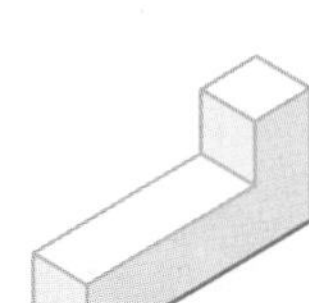

1.8 **28.** Sketch the solid of revolution formed when the two-dimensional figure is rotated about the line. ⓗ

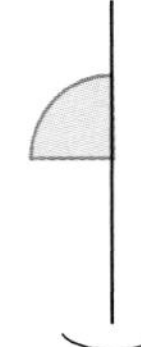

For Exercises 29–38, write the word that makes the statement true.

1.1 **29.** Points are _?_ if they lie on the same line. collinear

1.5 **30.** A triangle with two congruent sides is _?_. isosceles

1.2 **31.** The geometry tool used to measure the size of an angle in degrees is called a(n) _?_. protractor

1.6 **32.** A(n) _?_ of a circle connects its center to a point on the circle. radius

1.4 **33.** A segment connecting any two non-adjacent vertices in a polygon is called a(n) _?_. diagonal

1.4 **34.** A polygon with 12 sides is called a(n) _?_. dodecagon

1.5 **35.** A trapezoid has exactly one pair of _?_ sides. parallel

[Alert] Some students will have trouble understanding the issue of linking data that are not related by cause and effect. Give this example: Suppose one classmate wore a plaid shirt on the first rainy day in October, two wore plaid when it rained again, three wore plaid the third time it rained, and this pattern kept up through six rainy days. Is it reasonable to conjecture that on the tenth rainy day ten people will be wearing plaid? Of course not. This is only a coincidence, so it isn't possible to find a conjecture that holds up even given more data.

[Link] The problem of causation and how it affects the correlation of data is a big issue in the study of statistics and has important applications in medicine and social science.

1.4 **36.** A(n) $\underline{\ ?\ }$ polygon is both equiangular and equilateral. regular

1.3 **37.** If angles are complementary, then their measures add to $\underline{\ ?\ }$. 90°

1.3 **38.** If two lines intersect to form a right angle, then they are $\underline{\ ?\ }$. perpendicular

For Exercises 39–42, sketch and label the figure.

1.4 **39.** Pentagon *GIANT* with diagonal $\overline{AG}$ parallel to side $\overline{NT}$

Chapter 0 **40.** A quadrilateral that has reflectional symmetry but not rotational symmetry

1.8 **41.** A prism with a hexagonal base

1.5 **42.** A counterexample to show that the following statement is false: The diagonals of a kite bisect the angles. ⓗ

IMPROVING YOUR REASONING SKILLS

Puzzling Patterns

These patterns are "different." Your task is to find the next term.

1. 18, 46, 94, 63, 52, 61, $\underline{\ ?\ }$
2. O, T, T, F, F, S, S, E, N, $\underline{\ ?\ }$
3. 1, 4, 3, 16, 5, 36, 7, $\underline{\ ?\ }$
4. 4, 8, 61, 221, 244, 884, $\underline{\ ?\ }$
5. 6, 8, 5, 10, 3, 14, 1, $\underline{\ ?\ }$
6. **B, 0, C, 2, D, 0, E, 3, F, 3, G,** $\underline{\ ?\ }$
7. 2, 3, 6, 1, 8, 6, 8, 4, 8, 4, 8, 3, 2, 3, 2, 3, $\underline{\ ?\ }$
8. A E F H I K L M N T V W
   B C D G J O P Q R S U
   Where do the X, Y, and Z go?

39. sample answer:

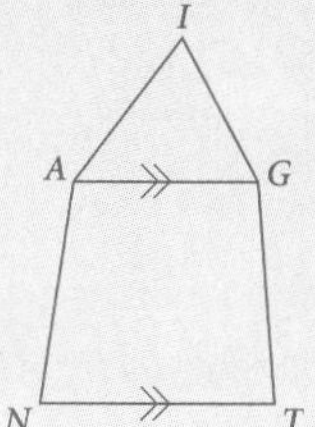

Exercise 40 If you skipped Chapter 0, use this exercise to review rotational and reflectional symmetry.

40. sample answer:

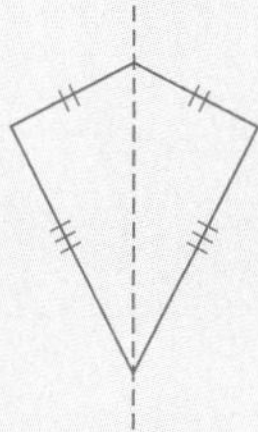

41. sample answer:

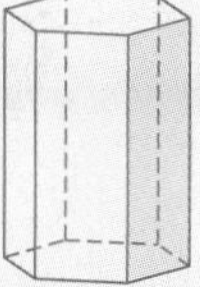

42. possible answer:

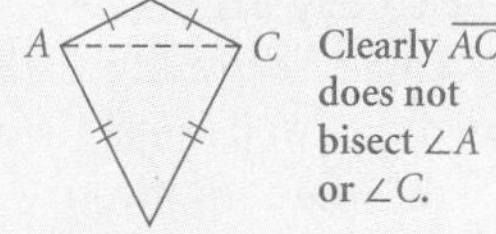

EXTENSION

Hold a discussion about problems that could arise through faulty inductive reasoning, such as prejudices and stereotypes.

IMPROVING REASONING SKILLS

If students are having trouble, suggest that they revisit these sequences several times and consult with friends.

1. 9 (perfect squares written backward)
2. T (as in *Ten*)
3. 64 (1, 2 squared, 3, 4 squared, 5, 6 squared, 7, 8 squared, . . .)
4. 8671 (2 · 884 = 1768; 1768 backward is 8671)
5. 18 (The differences are primes, alternating adding and subtracting.)
6. 2 (the number of end points on the preceding letter)
7. 2 (Multiply two terms and write the product's digits at the end. Then multiply the next pair of digits and write the product's digits at the end of the sequence. The 2 at the end comes from 32, the product of the third 8 and the second 4.)
8. in the top row, with the other letters that have only straight lines

LESSON

2.2

PLANNING

LESSON OUTLINE

One day:

10 min Examples

15 min Investigation

5 min Sharing

5 min Closing

10 min Exercises

MATERIALS

- construction tools
- protractors
- Overlapping Segments (T) for One step
- Sketchpad demonstration Overlapping Segments, *optional*

TEACHING

Deductive reasoning involves logical and orderly reasoning from accepted truths. Groups can start on the one-step investigation, or the class can discuss the examples and then work through the steps of the investigation in groups.

▸ EXAMPLE A

This example illustrates deductive reasoning.

[Alert] Some students may have difficulty remembering the properties of equality used to support the algebraic steps. As needed, remind them of the names or be more flexible about what reasons you accept. For example, "subtraction property of equality" might be stated as "subtracting the same quantity from both sides of the equation." The important idea is not the exact expression but that students know what they are doing to both sides of the equation.

LESSON 2.2

Deductive Reasoning

That's the way things come clear. All of a sudden. And then you realize how obvious they've been all along.

MADELEINE L'ENGLE

Have you ever noticed that the days are longer in the summer? Or that mosquitoes appear after a summer rain? Over the years you have made conjectures, using inductive reasoning, based on patterns you have observed. When you make a conjecture, the process of discovery may not always help explain *why* the conjecture works. You need another kind of reasoning to help answer this question.

Deductive reasoning is the process of showing that certain statements follow logically from agreed-upon assumptions and proven facts. When you use deductive reasoning, you try to reason in an orderly way to convince yourself or someone else that your conclusion is valid. If your initial statements are true, and you give a logical argument, then you have shown that your conclusion is true. For example, in a trial, lawyers use deductive arguments to show how the evidence that they present proves their case. A lawyer might make a very good argument. But first, the court must believe the evidence and accept it as true.

The success of an attorney's case depends on the jury accepting the evidence as true and following the steps in her deductive reasoning.

You use deductive reasoning in algebra. When you provide a reason for each step in the process of solving an equation, you are using deductive reasoning. Here is an example.

EXAMPLE A

Solve the equation for x. Give a reason for each step in the process.

$$3(2x + 1) + 2(2x + 1) + 7 = 42 - 5x$$

▸ Solution

$3(2x + 1) + 2(2x + 1) + 7 = 42 - 5x$	The original equation.
$5(2x + 1) + 7 = 42 - 5x$	Combining like terms.
$5(2x + 1) = 35 - 5x$	Subtraction property of equality.
$10x + 5 = 35 - 5x$	Distributive property.
$10x = 30 - 5x$	Subtraction property of equality.
$15x = 30$	Addition property of equality.
$x = 2$	Division property of equality.

[Ask] "Is there another approach to solving this equation?" Many students will want to distribute first. Encourage a variety of approaches to problem solving in order to help students avoid getting stuck by trying to remember "the right way."

LESSON OBJECTIVES

- Introduce and familiarize students with the deductive reasoning process
- Learn the relationship between inductive and deductive reasoning

The next example shows how to use both kinds of reasoning: inductive reasoning to discover the property and deductive reasoning to explain why it works.

EXAMPLE B

In each diagram, $\overrightarrow{AC}$ bisects obtuse angle BAD. Classify $\angle BAD$, $\angle DAC$, and $\angle CAB$ as *acute, right,* or *obtuse.* Then complete the conjecture.

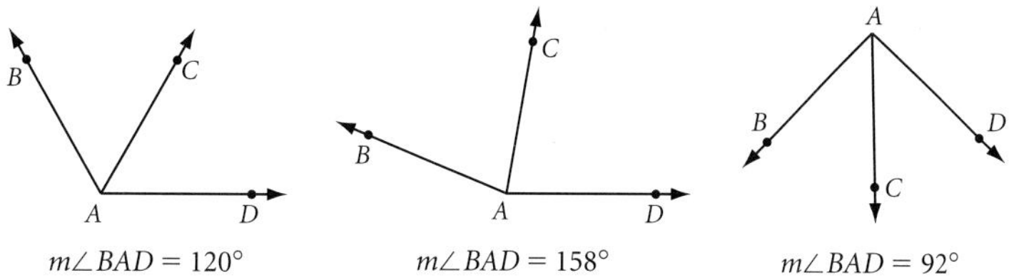

$m\angle BAD = 120°$ $m\angle BAD = 158°$ $m\angle BAD = 92°$

Conjecture: If an obtuse angle is bisected, then the two newly formed congruent angles are _?_.

Justify your answers with a deductive argument.

▶ Solution

In each diagram, $\angle BAD$ is obtuse because $m\angle BAD$ is greater than 90°. In each diagram, the angles formed by the bisector are acute because their measures—60°, 79°, and 46°—are less than 90°. So one possible conjecture is

Conjecture: If an obtuse angle is bisected, then the two newly formed congruent angles are *acute.*

Why? According to our definition of an angle, every angle measure is less than 180°. So, using algebra, if m is the measure of an obtuse angle, then $m < 180°$. When you bisect an angle, the two newly formed angles each measure half of the original angle, or $\frac{1}{2}m$. If $m < 180°$, then $\frac{1}{2}m < \frac{1}{2}(180)$, so $\frac{1}{2}m < 90°$. The two angles are each less than 90°, so they are acute.

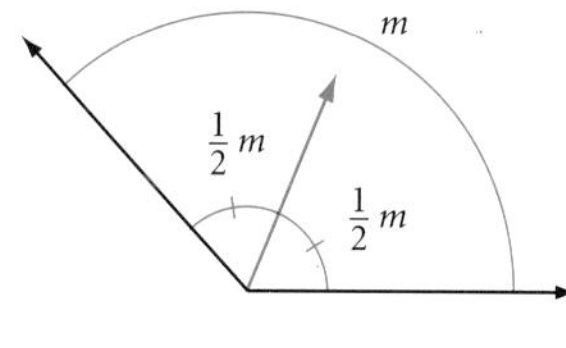

Science CONNECTION

Here is an example of inductive reasoning, supported by deductive reasoning. El Niño is the warming of water in the tropical Pacific Ocean, which produces unusual weather conditions and storms worldwide. For centuries, farmers living in the Andes Mountains of South America have observed the stars in the Pleiades constellation to predict El Niño conditions. If the Pleiades look dim in June, they predict an El Niño year. What is the connection? Scientists have recently found that in an El Niño year, increased evaporation from the ocean produces high-altitude clouds that are invisible to the eye, but create a haze that makes stars more difficult to see. Therefore, the pattern that the Andean farmers knew about for centuries is now supported by a scientific explanation. To find out more about this story, go to www.keymath.com/DG

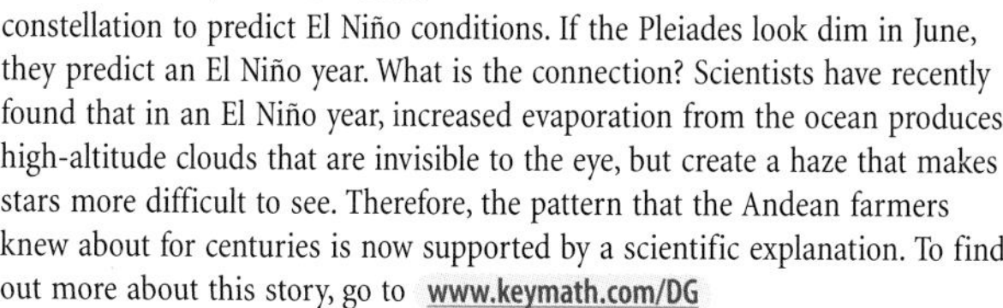

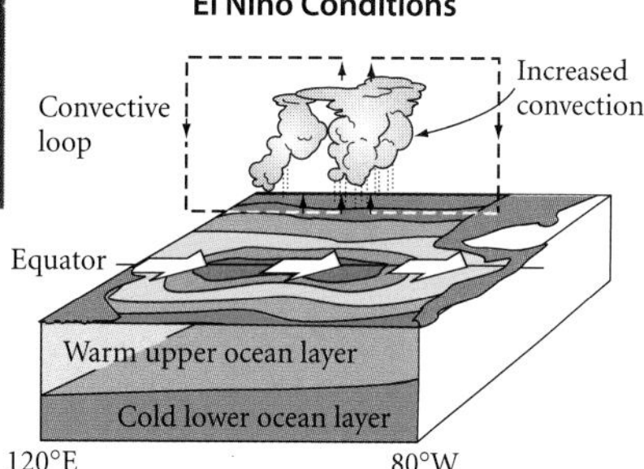

▶ EXAMPLE B

This example compares deductive and inductive reasoning. **[Alert]** Some students will say that this example is intuitively obvious. Stress that what seems intuitively obvious may not be true. Also, students are learning how to play a new game—deductive reasoning. Help them see that it is very easy to write "If an angle with measure m is obtuse, then $m < 180°$" and then algebraically manipulate the expression until they get the statement $\frac{1}{2}m < 90°$.

NCTM STANDARDS

CONTENT		PROCESS	
✓	Number		Problem Solving
✓	Algebra	✓	Reasoning
✓	Geometry	✓	Communication
✓	Measurement	✓	Connections
	Data/Probability	✓	Representation

Guiding the Investigation

One step Show the Overlapping Segments transparency and ask each student to copy it, making sure that lengths *AB* and *CD* are equal. Have students exchange copies within their groups and see what they can tell about lengths *AC* and *BD*. Ask them to write their conjectures carefully and then try to justify them. During Sharing, consider a range of statements of and justifications for the conjecture, encouraging critique of each.

See the Sketchpad demonstration Overlapping Segments for a dynamic alternative for this investigation.

Step 2 If students reverse the order of points *B* and *C* on their segment, they should still notice that $AC = BD$. Their deductive argument in Step 5 would then involve subtraction instead of addition.

Step 5 Encourage different proofs. One proof might use measurement: If *AB* and *CD* are both 0.25 cm, and *BC* is 0.4 cm, then both *AC* and *BD* are 0.65 cm and equal to each other. Another proof might avoid measurement but still involve addition: $AB = CD$, so $AB + BC = CD + BC$, making $AC = BD$. $\overline{AB} \cong \overline{CD}$, and you're adding the same length, the measure of $\overline{BC}$, to both. Or some students may use subtraction of equal lengths from *AD*: $AC = AD - CD = AD - AB = BD$.

Inductive reasoning allows you to discover new ideas based on observed patterns. Deductive reasoning can help explain why your conjectures are true.

Inductive and deductive reasoning work very well together. In this investigation you will use inductive reasoning to form a conjecture and deductive reasoning to explain why it's true.

Investigation
Overlapping Segments

In each segment, $\overline{AB} \cong \overline{CD}$.

25 cm, 75 cm, 25 cm: A B C D
36 cm, 80 cm, 36 cm: A B C D

Step 1 $AC = 100$, $BD = 100$; $AC = 116$, $BD = 116$; $\overline{AC} \cong \overline{BD}$

Step 1 From the markings on each diagram, determine the lengths of $\overline{AC}$ and $\overline{BD}$. What do you discover about these segments?

Step 2 Draw a new segment. Label it $\overline{AD}$. Place your own points *B* and *C* on $\overline{AD}$ so that $\overline{AB} \cong \overline{CD}$.

A BC D

Step 3 $AC = BD$

Step 3 Measure $\overline{AC}$ and $\overline{BD}$. How do these lengths compare?

Step 4 Complete the conclusion of this conjecture:

If $\overline{AD}$ has points *A, B, C,* and *D* in that order with $\overline{AB} \cong \overline{CD}$, then __?__.
the overlapping segments *AC* and *BD* are congruent

Step 5 Sample answers: If *AB* and *CD* are both 0.25 cm, and *BC* is 0.4 cm, then both *AC* and *BD* are 0.65 cm, and equal to each other. Or, $\overline{AB} \cong \overline{CD}$, and you're adding the same segment, $\overline{BC}$, to both.

Now you will use deductive reasoning and algebra to explain why the conjecture from Step 4 is true.

Step 5 Use deductive reasoning to convince your group that *AC* will always equal *BD*. Take turns explaining to each other. Write your argument algebraically.

In the investigation you used both inductive and deductive reasoning to convince yourself of the overlapping segments property. You will use a similar process in the next lesson to discover and prove the overlapping angles property in Exercise 17.

Good use of deductive reasoning depends on the quality of the argument. Just like the saying, "A chain is only as strong as its weakest link," a deductive argument is only as good (or as true) as the statements used in the argument. A conclusion in a deductive argument is true only if *all* the statements in the argument are true. Also, the statements in your argument must clearly follow from each other. Did you use clear arguments in explaining the investigation steps? Did you point out that $\overline{BC}$ is part of both $\overline{AC}$ and $\overline{BD}$? Did you point out that if you add the same amount to things that are equal the resulting sum must be equal?

SHARING IDEAS

Ask selected students or groups to present their conjectures and proofs, aiming to include variety. Lead the critique of each presentation, keeping the tone low-key. Don't expect students to write either perfect statements or infallible proofs at this point. For each proof, concentrate on having students understand the flow of the argument; don't worry about steps or justifications. Elicit the difference between inductive reasoning, which led to the conjecture, and deductive reasoning, which leads to the proof.

Assessing Progress
Note how individual students use terms from earlier chapters and refer to inductive reasoning.

Closing the Lesson

Remind students that inductive reasoning can be used to discover a conjecture and deductive reasoning can be used to explain why that conjecture is true. Inductive reasoning occasionally leads to conjectures that are not true. Doing mathematics involves the interaction between inductive and deductive reasoning.

EXERCISES

1. When you use _?_ reasoning you are generalizing from careful observation that something is probably true. When you use _?_ reasoning you are establishing that, if a set of properties is accepted as true, something else must be true. inductive; deductive

2. $\angle A$ and $\angle B$ are complementary. $m\angle A = 25°$. What is $m\angle B$? What type of reasoning do you use, inductive or deductive reasoning, when solving this problem? $m\angle B = 65°$; deductive or inductive

3. If the pattern continues, what are the next two terms?

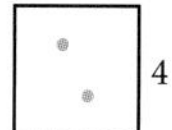

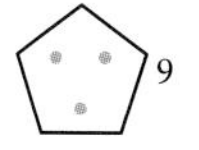

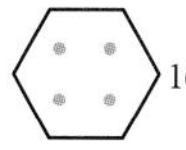

What type of reasoning do you use, inductive or deductive reasoning, when solving this problem? inductive

4. $\triangle DGT$ is isosceles with $TD = DG$. If the perimeter of $\triangle DGT$ is 756 cm and $GT = 240$ cm, then $DG =$ _?_. What type of reasoning do you use, inductive or deductive reasoning, when solving this problem? $DG = 258$ cm; deductive

5. ***Mini-Investigation*** The sum of the measures of the five marked angles in stars A through C is shown below each star. Use your protractor to carefully measure the five marked angles in star D.

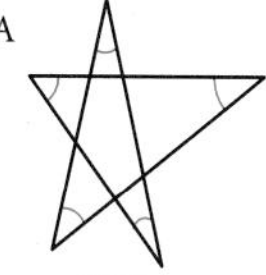

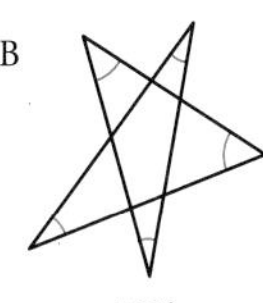

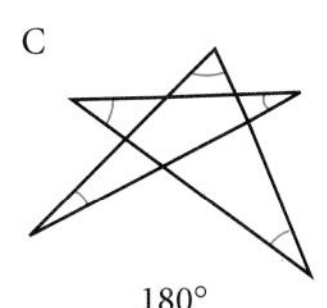

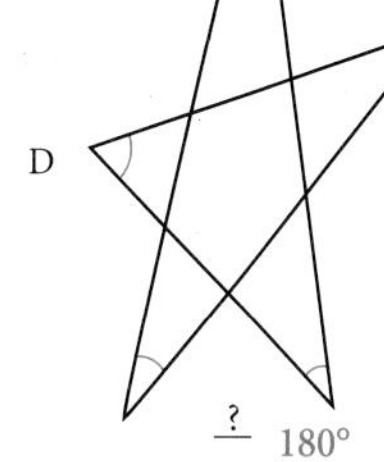

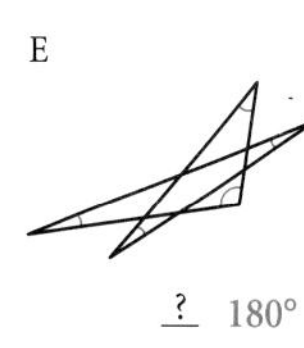

If this pattern continues, without measuring, what would be the sum of the measures of the marked angles in star E? What type of reasoning do you use, inductive or deductive reasoning, when solving this problem? sum of the five angles is 180°; inductive

6. The definition of a parallelogram says, "If both pairs of opposite sides of a quadrilateral are parallel, then the quadrilateral is a parallelogram." Quadrilateral *LNDA* has both pairs of opposite sides parallel. What conclusion can you make? What type of reasoning did you use? *LNDA* is a parallelogram; deductive

7. Use the overlapping segments property to complete each statement.

A B C D

a. If $AB = 3$, then $CD =$ _?_. 3

b. If $AC = 10$, then $BD =$ _?_. 10

c. If $BC = 4$ and $CD = 3$, then $AC =$ _?_. 7

8. In Example B of this lesson you discovered through inductive reasoning that if an obtuse angle is bisected, then the two newly formed congruent angles are acute. You then used deductive reasoning to explain why they were acute. Go back to the example and look at the sizes of the acute angles formed. What is the smallest possible size for the two congruent acute angles formed by the bisector? Can you use deductive reasoning to explain why? ⓗ just over 45°; if $m > 90°$, then $\frac{1}{2}m > 45°$

BUILDING UNDERSTANDING

ASSIGNING HOMEWORK

Essential	1–9
Performance assessment	7, 9
Portfolio	5
Journal	8, 10, 11
Group	6, 8
Review	11–33

Helping with the Exercises

Exercise 2 This question can be answered inductively (by measuring) or deductively (by subtracting 25 from 90).

3.

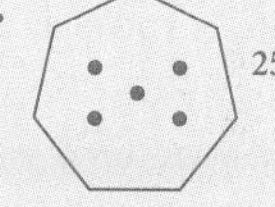

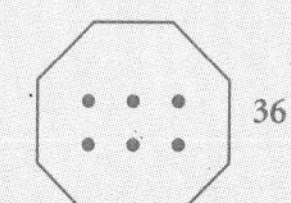

Exercise 9 You might mention that something that has the same letters or numbers whether written backward or forward is called a *palindrome.* Give examples of word palindromes, such as "Otto," "racecar," or "A Man, A Plan, A Canal, Panama." If students have covered Chapter 0: **[Ask]** "What kind of symmetry does a palindrome have?" [It doesn't have visual symmetry except in very special cases, but the order of letters, though not the letters themselves, is reflected over a line of reflection.]

Exercise 10 Students might find it very difficult to think of a real-life example of deductive reasoning. Simple examples include reasoning such as this: If I have enough money, I'll buy the CD. I have enough money. Therefore I'll buy the CD."

11. The pattern cannot be generalized because once the river is straight, it cannot get any shorter.

15.

16.

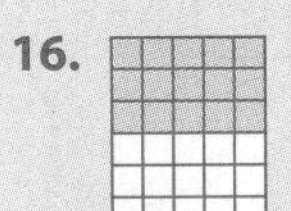

17.

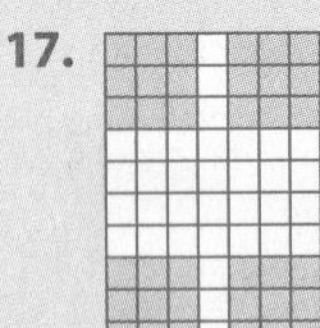

18.

9. Study the pattern and make a conjecture by completing the fifth line. What would be the conjecture for the sixth line? The tenth line? ⓗ

$1 \cdot 1 = 1$

$11 \cdot 11 = 121$

$111 \cdot 111 = 12{,}321$

$1{,}111 \cdot 1{,}111 = 1{,}234{,}321$

$11{,}111 \cdot 11{,}111 = \underline{\ ?\ }$

If 11,111 is multiplied by itself, then the product will be 123,454,321. But when 1,111,111,111 is multiplied by itself, the digits can't go up to 10. So 1,111,111,111 · 1,111,111,111 = 1,234,567,900,987,654,321.

10. Think of a situation you observed outside of school in which deductive reasoning was used correctly. Write a paragraph or two describing what happened and explaining why you think it was deductive reasoning. Answers will vary.

Review

2.1 **11.** Mark Twain once observed that the lower Mississippi River is very crooked and that over the years, as the bends and the turns straighten out, the river gets shorter and shorter. Using numerical data about the length of the lower part of the river, he noticed that in the year 1700 the river was more than 1200 miles long, yet by the year 1875 it was only 973 miles long. Twain concluded that any person "can see that 742 years from now the lower Mississippi will be only a mile and three-quarters long." What is wrong with this inductive reasoning?

Aerial photo of the Mississippi River

For Exercises 12–14, use inductive reasoning to find the next two terms of the sequence.

2.1 **12.** 180, 360, 540, 720, _?_, _?_ ⓗ 900, 1080

2.1 **13.** 0, 10, 21, 33, 46, 60, _?_, _?_ 75, 91

2.1 **14.** $\frac{1}{2}$, 9, $\frac{2}{3}$, 10, $\frac{3}{4}$, 11, _?_, _?_ $\frac{4}{5}$, 12

For Exercises 15–18, draw the next shape in each picture pattern.

2.1 **15.**

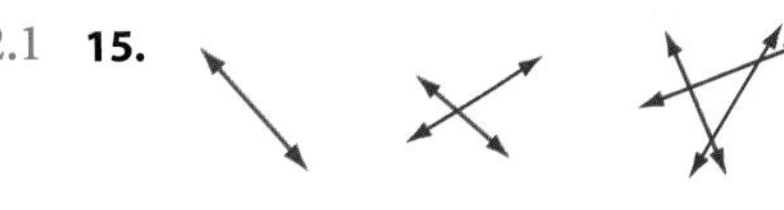

2.1 **16.** ⓗ

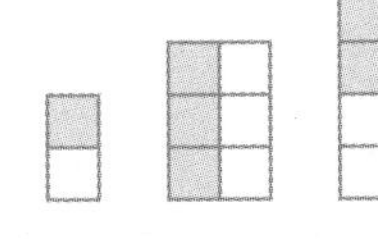

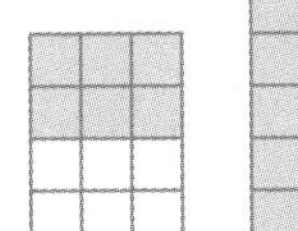

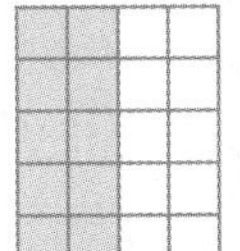

2.1 **17.** ⓗ

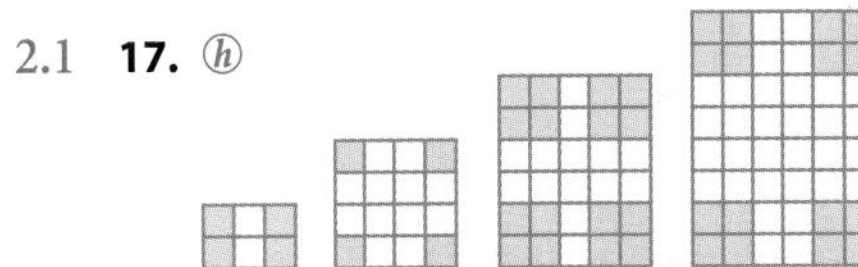

2.1 **18.**

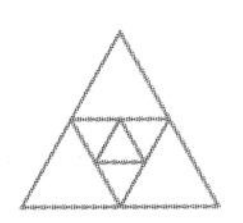

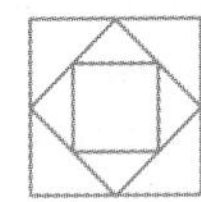

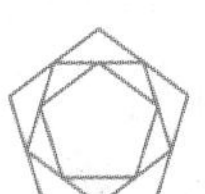

2.1 **19.** Think of a situation you have observed in which inductive reasoning was used incorrectly. Write a paragraph or two describing what happened and explaining why you think it was an incorrect use of inductive reasoning.

19. Sample answer: There were three sunny days in a row, so I assumed it would be sunny the fourth day, but it rained.

Match each term in Exercises 20–29 with one of the figures A–O.

1.5 **20.** Kite L

1.4 **21.** Consecutive angles in a polygon M

1.4 **22.** Trapezoid A

1.5 **23.** Diagonal in a polygon B

1.3 **24.** Pair of complementary angles E

1.6 **25.** Radius C

1.3 **26.** Pair of vertical angles G

1.6 **27.** Chord D

1.3 **28.** Acute angle H

1.2 **29.** Angle bisector in a triangle I

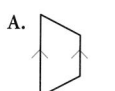

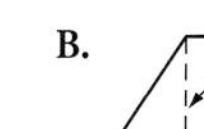
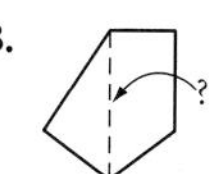
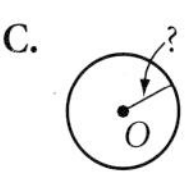
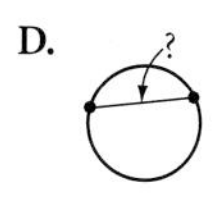
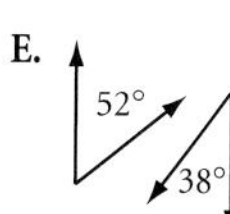

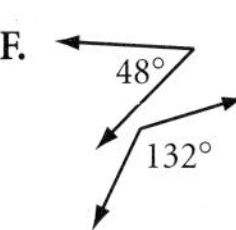
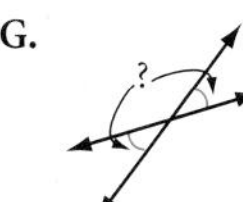
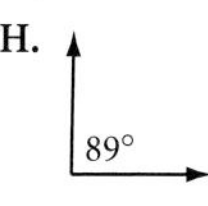
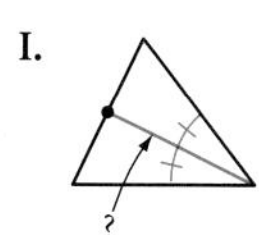
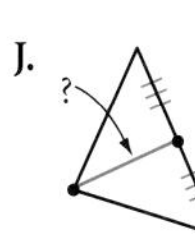

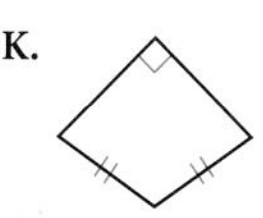
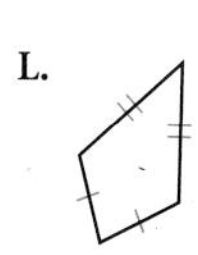
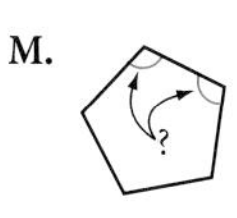
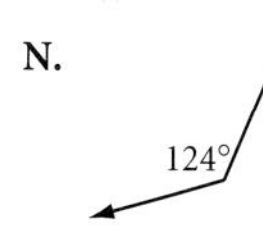
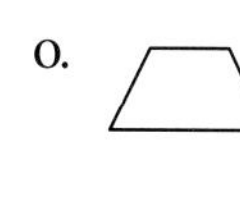

For Exercises 30–33, sketch and carefully label the figure.

1.4 **30.** Pentagon *WILDE* with $\angle ILD \cong \angle LDE$ and $\overline{LD} \cong \overline{DE}$

1.5 **31.** Isosceles obtuse triangle *OBG* with $m\angle BGO = 140°$

1.6 **32.** Circle *O* with a chord $\overline{CD}$ perpendicular to radius $\overline{OT}$

1.6 **33.** Circle *K* with angle *DIN* where *D, I,* and *N* are points on circle *K*

IMPROVING YOUR VISUAL THINKING SKILLS

Rotating Gears

In what direction will gear E rotate if gear A rotates in a counterclockwise direction?

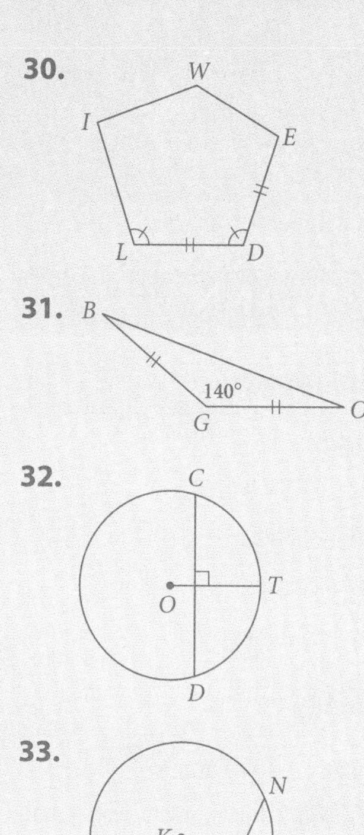

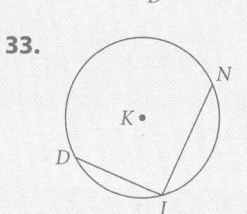

EXTENSION

In mathematics we are usually confident of the truth of our premises, but in the real world truth can be difficult to establish. Discuss how we attempt to determine the truth. In courts of law, we have judges and juries and do not rely solely on the statements of the witnesses or advocates. Students may or may not realize the difference in the burden of proof in civil trials (a preponderance of evidence, or 51%) and that in criminal trials (beyond a reasonable doubt, or 99%).

IMPROVING VISUAL THINKING SKILLS

Gear E will rotate counterclockwise.

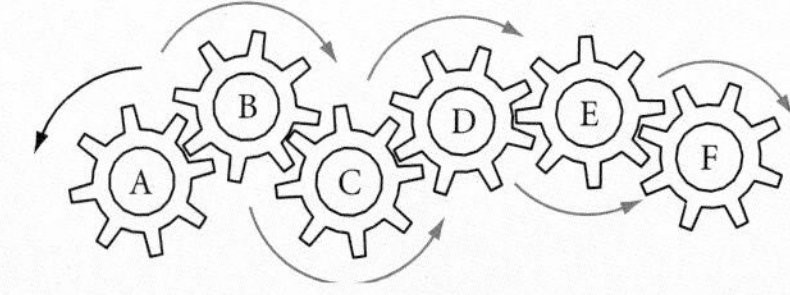

LESSON
2.3

PLANNING

LESSON OUTLINE

One day:

25 min Investigation

10 min Sharing

5 min Closing

5 min Exercises

MATERIALS

- Sequence (T) for One step
- Sketchpad demonstration Overlapping Angles, *optional*

TEACHING

This lesson concerns finding a rule for the *n*th step in a linear numerical sequence. For many students, it may be the most difficult lesson in the book, so be patient and supportive, and have lots of examples ready!

[Context] The cartoon refers to a cheer often heard at sporting events: "Two, four, six, eight, who do we appreciate?"

Guiding the Investigation

One step Show the Sequence transparency. Ask what the next two terms are, and then ask what the 200th term will be. As you circulate, encourage groups to draw graphs and guess and check. If a group finds a successful rule, push its members to generate other sequences with constant differences and see if their method for finding a rule applies to those sequences as well.

Step 1 You might go through the first table with the whole class before sending the students into their groups. Urge students to check their calculations as they fill in the charts.

LESSON 2.3

Finding the *n*th Term

If you do something once, people call it an accident. If you do it twice, they call it a coincidence. But do it a third time and you've just proven a natural law.

GRACE MURRAY HOPPER

What would you do to get the next term in the sequence 20, 27, 34, 41, 48, 55, . . . ? A good strategy would be to find a pattern, using inductive reasoning. Then you would look at the differences between consecutive terms and predict what comes next. In this case there is a constant difference of +7. That is, you add 7 each time.

The next term is 55 + 7, or 62. What if you needed to know the value of the 200th term of the sequence? You certainly don't want to generate the next 193 terms just to get one answer. If you knew a rule for calculating *any* term in a sequence, without having to know the previous term, you could apply it to directly calculate the 200th term. The rule that gives the *n*th term for a sequence is called the **function rule.**

Let's see how the constant difference can help you find the function rule for some sequences.

DRABBLE reprinted by permission of United Feature Syndicate, Inc.

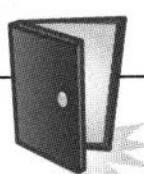

Investigation
Finding the Rule

Step 1 Copy and complete each table. Find the differences between consecutive values.

a.

n	1	2	3	4	5	6	7	8
$n - 5$	−4	−3	−2	−1	0	1	2	3

differences: +1

b.

n	1	2	3	4	5	6	7	8
$4n - 3$	1	5	9	13	17	21	25	29

+4

c.

n	1	2	3	4	5	6	7	8
$-2n + 5$	3	1	−1	−3	−5	−7	−9	−11

−2

d.

n	1	2	3	4	5	6	7	8
$3n - 2$	1	4	7	10	13	16	19	22

+3

e.

n	1	2	3	4	5	6	7	8
$-5n + 7$	2	−3	−8	−13	−18	−23	−28	−33

−5

Using the Quotation

Grace Murray Hopper has been called the Mother of Computing because she helped develop the first commercial computer language and was one of the first mathematicians to study the science of computing. **[Ask]** "In the quotation, is the word *proven* used in a mathematical sense?" [She's reflecting on inductive reasoning rather than deductive reasoning, and she was probably joking about needing only three instances in order to draw a conclusion.]

LESSON OBJECTIVES

- Generalize basic number patterns to a method for finding the *n*th term in a linear number sequence
- Learn new vocabulary
- Practice inductive reasoning and cooperative behavior

Step 2 | Did you spot the pattern? If a sequence has a constant difference of 4, then the number in front of the n (the coefficient of n) is ? . In general, if the difference between the values of consecutive terms of a sequence is always the same, say m (a constant), then the coefficient of n in the formula is ? .

4

m

Let's return to the sequence at the beginning of the lesson.

Term	1	2	3	4	5	6	7	...	n
Value	20	27	34	41	48	55	62	...	

+7 +7

The constant difference is 7, so you know part of the rule is $7n$. How do you find the rest of the rule?

Step 3 By adding 13, because $7 + 13 = 20$. So the rule should be $7n + 13$.

Step 3 | The first term ($n = 1$) of the sequence is 20, but if you apply the part of the rule you have so far using $n = 1$, you get $7n = 7(1) = 7$, not 20. So how should you fix the rule? How can you get from 7 to 20? What is the rule for this sequence?

Step 4 | Check your rule by trying the rule with other terms in the sequence.

Let's look at an example of how to find a function rule, for the nth term in a number pattern.

EXAMPLE A

Find the rule for the sequence 7, 2, −3, −8, −13, −18, . . .

▶ Solution

Placing the terms and values in a table we get

Term	1	2	3	4	5	6	...	n
Value	7	2	−3	−8	−13	−18	...	

The difference between the terms is always −5. So the rule is

$-5n +$ "something"

Let's use c to stand for the unknown "something." So the rule is

$5n + c$

To find c, replace the n in the rule with a term number. Try $n = 1$ and set the expression equal to 7.

$-5(1) + c = 7$

$c = 12$

The rule is $-5n + 12$.

You can find the value of any term in the sequence by substituting the term number for n in the function rule. Let's look at an example of how to find the 200th term in a geometric pattern.

Step 4

4	5
$7(4) + 13$	$7(5) + 13$
41	48

SHARING IDEAS

Have students demonstrate a variety of approaches.
[Ask] "Where else have you seen a constant rate of change?" Many students are familiar with visualizing a set of values by graphing them. Elicit the idea of linear growth from algebra, where the slope of a straight line gives the constant amount of rise for each unit of horizontal run. Students may then conclude that "the graph of a sequence with a constant difference is a set of points that lie on a straight line with that slope." They might also notice that the y-intercept for the graph tells how to adjust an expression to fit the data. If students are familiar with the idea of a "function machine," mention it as well.

[Ask] "Are you using inductive or deductive reasoning to find the nth term of a sequence?" [some may think that, because the rule is not recursive, the reasoning is deductive. Getting from the data (constant differences) to a rule is inductive reasoning; no deductive proof of the rule is possible without knowing the infinitely many values of the system.]

NCTM STANDARDS

CONTENT	PROCESS
✓ Number	✓ Problem Solving
✓ Algebra	✓ Reasoning
✓ Geometry	✓ Communication
✓ Measurement	Connections
✓ Data/Probability	✓ Representation

▶ EXAMPLE A

Use this example to illustrate a negative coefficient for a decreasing sequence.

You may want to have a graph of this sequence ready to show to students so they can make the connection between the −5 for the coefficient of the nth term and the slope of the line they are viewing. Students will also be able to see that the "something" is not so mysterious. It is the y-intercept of the linear graph. By graphing the data, students will also be able to see why the functions are linear.

▶ EXAMPLE B

This example combines generating data and finding a rule for the nth term.

As needed, explain that the number of points dividing the line is n and we are trying to predict the number of non-overlapping rays and segments using n. Some students may miss the "non-overlapping" condition and think that, for example, three points generate three segments or six rays. **[ESL]** The term *distinct* means "not the same." It is used here as a synonym for *non-overlapping.*

[Alert] If students are confused over the different placement of n in the two examples, explain that n can be any number in the sequence, not just the last number. In Example B, it is placed before the last term because students will find the formula for n before they find the value of the last term.

Assessing Progress

Monitor students' use of geometric terms from earlier chapters, as well as their familiarity with inductive and deductive reasoning.

EXAMPLE B If you place 200 points on a line, into how many non-overlapping rays and segments does it divide the line?

▶ Solution Wait! don't start placing 200 points on a line. You need to find a rule that relates the number of points placed on a line to the number of parts created by those points. Then you can use your rule to answer the problem.

Start by creating a table.

Points dividing the line	1	2	3	4	5	6	...	n	...	200
Non-overlapping rays							...		...	
Non-overlapping segments							...		...	
Total							...		...	

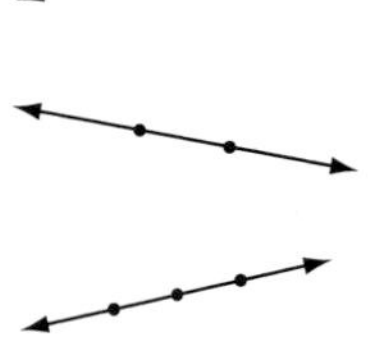

Sketch one point dividing a line. One point gives you just two rays. Enter that into the table.

Next, sketch two points dividing a line. This gives one segment and the two end rays. Enter the value into your table.

Next, sketch three points dividing a line, then four, then five, and so on. The table completed for one to three points is

Points dividing the line	1	2	3	4	5	6	...	n	...	200
Non-overlapping rays	2	2	2	2	2	2	...	2	...	2
Non-overlapping segments	0	1	2	3	4	5	...	$n - 1$	...	199
Total	2	3	4	5	6	7	...	$n + 1$	...	201

Once you have found values for 1, 2, 3, 4, 5, and 6 points on a line you next try to find the rule for each sequence. There are always two non-overlapping rays so for 200 points there will be two rays. The rule, or nth term, for the number of non-overlapping segments is $n - 1$. For 200 points there will be 199 segments. The rule, or nth term, for the total number of distinct rays and segments of the line is $n + 1$. For 200 points there will be 201 distinct parts of the line.

This process of looking at patterns and generalizing a rule, or nth term, is inductive reasoning. To understand why the rule is what it is, you can turn to deductive reasoning. Notice that adding another point on a line divides a segment into two segments. So each new point adds one more segment to the pattern.

Rules that generate a sequence with a constant difference are **linear functions.** To see why they're called linear, you can graph the term number and the value for the sequence as ordered pairs of the form (*term number, value*) on the coordinate plane. At left is the graph of the sequence from Example A.

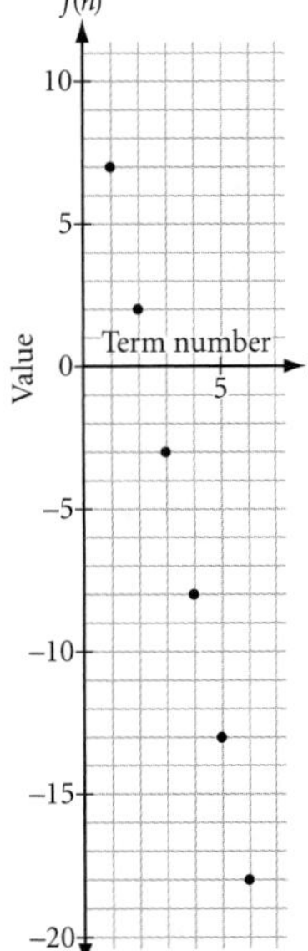

Term number n	1	2	3	4	5	6	...	n
Value $f(n)$	7	2	-3	-8	-13	-18	...	$-5n + 12$

Closing the Lesson

Summarize students' findings: To determine a rule for the nth term of a sequence in which consecutive pairs of terms differ by the same constant, use that constant as a coefficient of the variable n and adjust the rule as needed to fit the data.

EXERCISES

For Exercises 1–3, find the function rule $f(n)$ for each sequence. Then find the 20th term in the sequence.

1. ⓗ

n	1	2	3	4	5	6	...	n	...	20
$f(n)$	3	9	15	21	27	33	...		...	117

$6n - 3$

2.

n	1	2	3	4	5	6	...	n	...	20
$f(n)$	1	−2	−5	−8	−11	−14	...		...	−56

$-3n + 4$

3.

n	1	2	3	4	5	6	...	n	...	20
$f(n)$	−4	4	12	20	28	36	...		...	148

$8n - 12$

For Exercises 4–6, find the rule for the nth figure. Then find the number of colored tiles or matchsticks in the 200th figure.

4. ⓗ

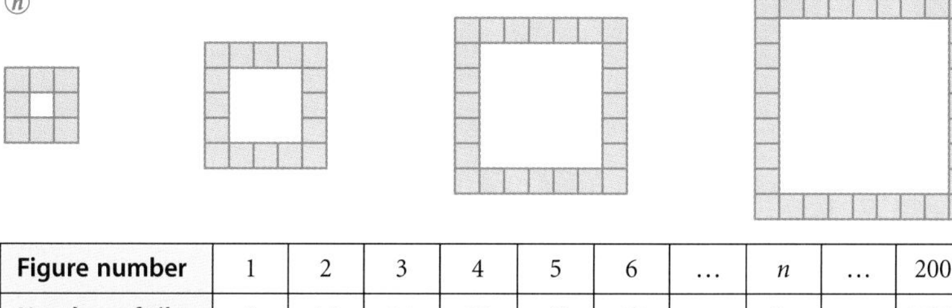

Figure number	1	2	3	4	5	6	...	n	...	200
Number of tiles	8	16	24	32	40	48	...	$8n$	...	1600

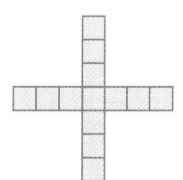

5.

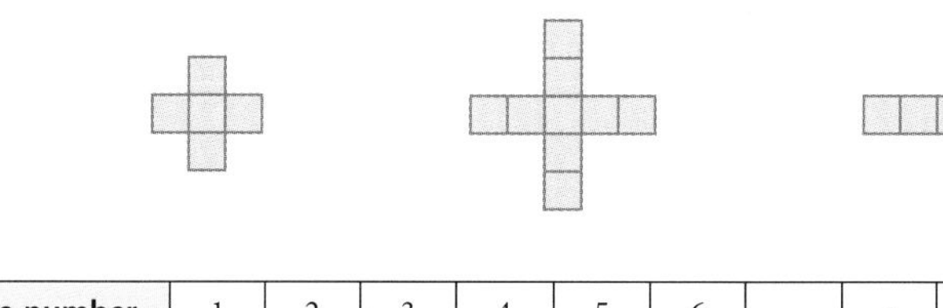

Figure number	1	2	3	4	5	6	...	n	...	200
Number of tiles	1	5	9	13	17	21	...		...	797

$4n - 3$

6.

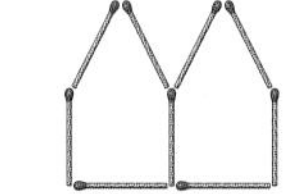

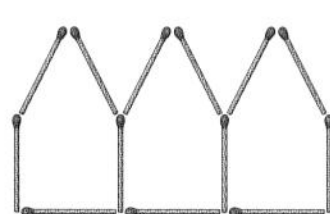

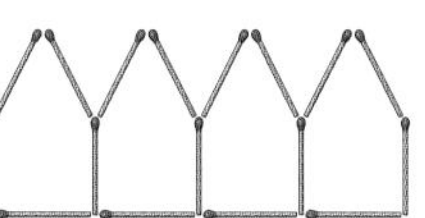

Figure number	1	2	3	4	5	6	...	n	...	200
Number of matchsticks	5	9	13	17	21	25	...	$4n + 1$	...	801
Number of matchsticks in perimeter of figure	5	8	11	14	17	20	...	$3n + 2$	...	602

BUILDING UNDERSTANDING

ASSIGNING HOMEWORK

Essential	1–8
Performance assessment	6
Portfolio	7
Journal	8
Group	9, 17
Review	10–16

▶ Helping with the Exercises

Exercises 1–3 Students have probably studied function rules in algebra. You may want to remind them of the input/output aspect of functions. In the notation used here, the input is the place in the sequence, and the output is the value of the sequence at that place. A graph might help some students with these exercises.

Exercises 1–7 Remind students that n can be any value—that is, n is not necessarily between 6 and 20 or 6 and 200. Students might use a calculator for these exercises.

Exercise 8 Students can graph manually or with a graphing calculator.

8.

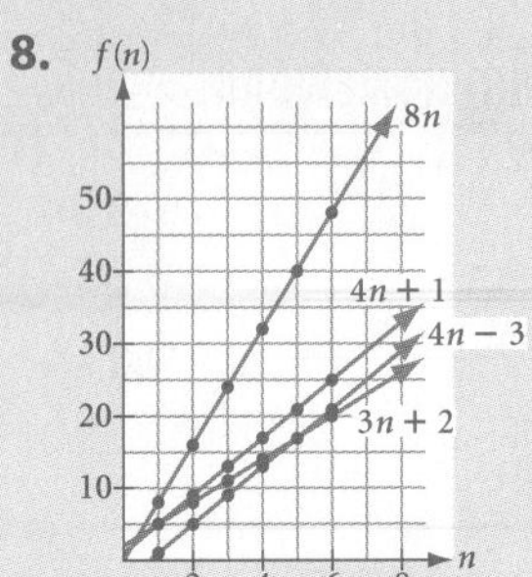

10.

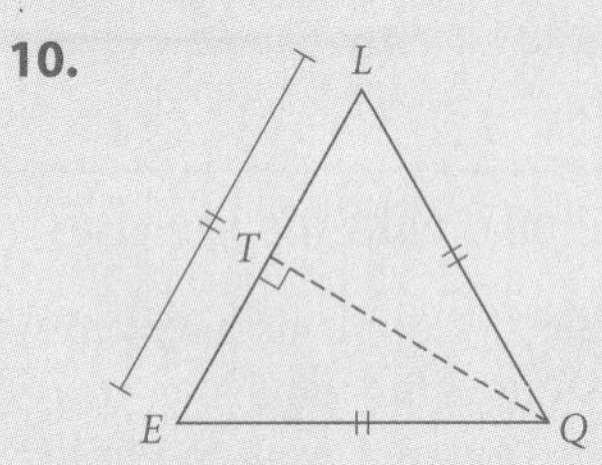

11. O M L Y

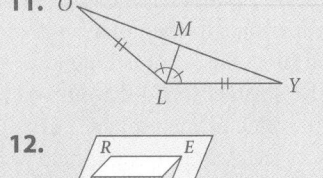

12. R E T C

13.

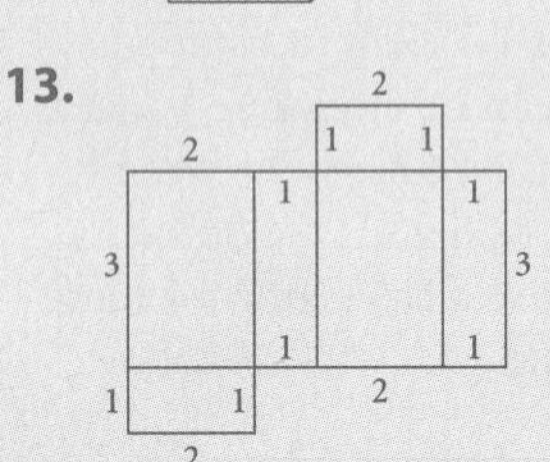

14. Márisol should respond by noticing that all the triangles José drew were isosceles, but it is possible to draw a triangle with no two sides congruent. In other words, she should show him a counterexample.

7. How many triangles are formed when you draw all the possible diagonals from just one vertex of a 35-gon? ⓗ

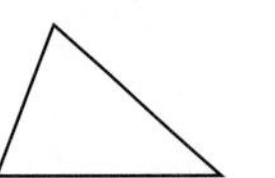 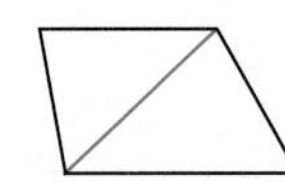 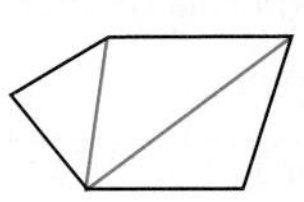 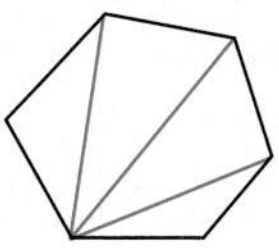

Number of sides	3	4	5	6	...	n	...	35
Number of triangles formed	1	2	3	4	...	$n-2$	...	33

8. Graph the values in your tables from Exercises 4–6. Which set of points lies on a steeper line? What number in the rule gives a measure of steepness? $8n$ is steeper; the coefficient of n

9. Find the rule for the set of points in the graph shown at right. Place the x-coordinate of each ordered pair in the top row of your table and the corresponding y-coordinate in the second row. What is the value of y in terms of x?
slope: $\frac{9-6}{4-2} = \frac{3}{2}$; y-intercept: $(0, 3)$; $y = \frac{3}{2}x + 3$

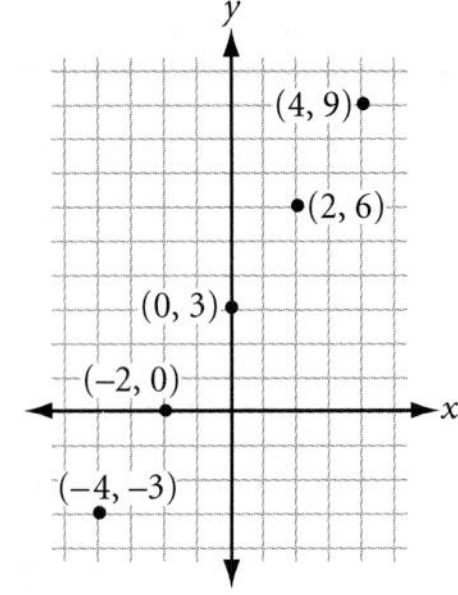

Review

For Exercises 10–13, sketch and carefully label the figure.

1.5 **10.** Equilateral triangle EQL with $\overline{QT}$ where T lies on $\overline{EL}$ and $\overline{QT} \perp \overline{EL}$

1.5 **11.** Isosceles obtuse triangle OLY with $\overline{OL} \cong \overline{YL}$ and angle bisector $\overline{LM}$

1.8 **12.** A cube with a plane passing through it; the cross section is rectangle $RECT$

1.7 **13.** A net for a rectangular solid with the dimensions 1 by 2 by 3 cm

2.1 **14.** Márisol's younger brother José was drawing triangles when he noticed that every triangle he drew turned out to have two sides congruent. José conjectures: "Look, Márisol, all triangles are isosceles." How should Márisol respond?

2.2 **15.** A midpoint divides a segment into two congruent segments. Point M divides segment $\overline{AY}$ into two congruent segments $\overline{AM}$ and $\overline{MY}$. What conclusion can you make? What type of reasoning did you use?
M is the midpoint of $\overline{AY}$; deductive

2.2 **16.** Tanya's favorite lunch is peanut butter and jelly on wheat bread with a glass of milk. Lately, she has been getting an allergic reaction after eating this lunch. She is wondering if she might be developing an allergy to peanut butter, wheat, or milk. What experiment could she do to find out which food it is? What type of reasoning would she be using? she could try eating one food at a time; inductive

2.2 **17.** ***Mini-Investigation*** Do the geometry investigation and make a conjecture.

Given $\angle APB$ with points C and D in its interior and $m\angle APC = m\angle DPB$,

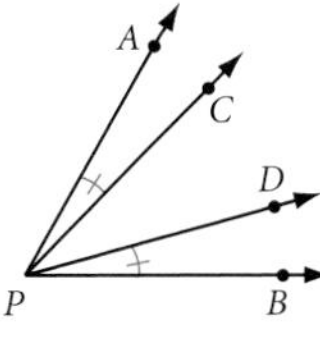

If $m\angle APD = 48°$, then $m\angle CPB = \underline{?}$ 48°

If $m\angle CPB = 17°$, then $m\angle APD = \underline{?}$ 17°

If $m\angle APD = 62°$, then $m\angle CPB = \underline{?}$ 62°

Conjecture: If points C and D lie in the interior of $\angle APB$, and $m\angle APC = m\angle DPB$ then $m\angle APD = \underline{?}$ (Overlapping angles property) $m\angle CPB$

Exercise 17 If students draw a picture and measure, their reasoning is inductive; encourage them to see the reasons behind the pattern, thus using deductive reasoning. See the Sketchpad demonstration Overlapping Angles for an alternative way to present this problem.

project

BEST-FIT LINES

The following table and graph show the mileage and lowest priced round-trip airfare between New York City and each destination city. Is there a relationship between the money you spend and how far you can travel?

Fathom

With Fathom Dynamic Statistics™ software, you can plot your data points and find the linear equation that best fits your data.

Lowest Round-trip Airfares from New York City on February 25, 2002

Destination City	Distance (miles)	Price ($)
Boston	215	$118
Chicago	784	$178
Atlanta	865	$158
Miami	1286	$170
Denver	1791	$238
Phoenix	2431	$338
Los Angeles	2763	$298

Source: http://www.Expedia.com

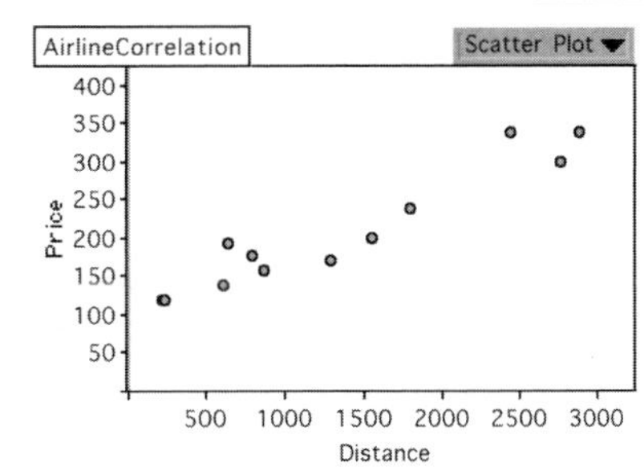

Even though the data are not linear, you can find a linear equation that *approximately* fits the data. The graph of this equation is called the **line of best fit.** How would you use the line of best fit to predict the cost of a round-trip ticket to Seattle (2814 miles)? How would you use it to determine how far you could travel (in miles) with $250? How accurate do you think the answer would be?

Choose a topic and a relationship to explore. You can use data from the census (such as age and income), or data you collect yourself (such as number of ice cubes in a glass and melting time). For more sources and ideas, go to www.keymath.com/DG .

Collect data points. Use Fathom to graph your points and to find the line of best fit. Write a summary of your results.

Supporting the project

If students are using Fathom, the Learning Guide included with the Fathom Student Edition can guide them in making data tables, creating graphs, and displaying the line of best fit.

OUTCOMES

- ▸ Topic, relationship, data, and source are clearly presented.
- ▸ Accurate graph shows a line of best fit.
- ▸ Writing shows an understanding of how good or bad the line of fit is and explains why.
- • Student chooses one relationship where it is expected the points will fall in a straight line and another where there is some scatter.
- • A geometric pattern is explored such as data on width and area of figures or number of figures in a sequence and figure perimeter.
- • A slider is used in Fathom to fit a curve to nonlinear data.

LESSON 2.4

PLANNING

LESSON OUTLINE

One day:

20 min Investigation

5 min Sharing

5 min Closing

15 min Exercises

MATERIALS

none

TEACHING

A mathematical model is a representation of a real-world situation. The model might consist of a table, graph, picture, expression, function, or equation. Several models of the same situation might be possible. Mathematical models are sometimes called *representations,* as in the NCTM *Principles and Standards.*

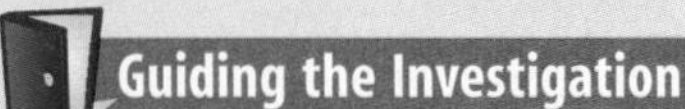

One step Pose the handshake problem at the beginning of the investigation using the number of students in your class, and ask the whole class how to solve the problem. Be open to all suggestions. If the class comes up with only one approach, ask if others are possible. Eventually the class will probably decide it's best to look for patterns in data with smaller numbers. Mention the term *inductive reasoning* and ask how the class might organize to collect the needed data. Add each piece of data to a list on the board. Then gather the students together to discuss the data and look for patterns. See if they think to look for constant differences between consecutive terms; some students may note that the

LESSON 2.4

Mathematical Modeling

It's amazing what one can do when one doesn't know what one can't do.

GARFIELD THE CAT

Physical models have many of the same features as the original object or activity they represent, but are often more convenient to study. For example, building a new airplane and testing it is difficult and expensive. But you can analyze a new airplane design by building a model and testing it in a wind tunnel.

In Chapter 1 you learned that geometry ideas such as points, lines, planes, triangles, polygons, and diagonals are **mathematical models** of physical objects.

When you draw graphs or pictures of situations, or when you write equations that describe a problem, you are creating mathematical models. A physical model of a complicated telecommunications network, for example, might not be practical, but you can draw a mathematical model of the network using points and lines.

This computer model tests the effectiveness of the car's design for minimizing wind resistance.

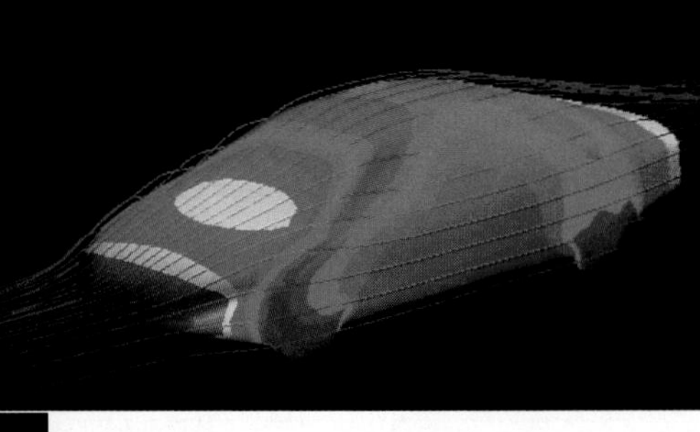

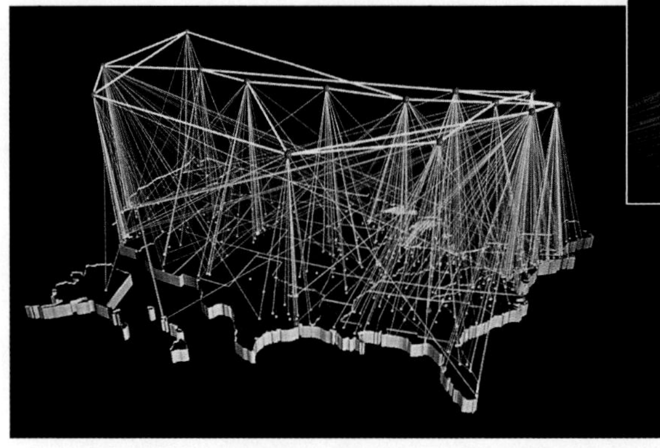

This computer-generated model uses points and line segments to show the volume of data traveling to different locations on the National Science Foundation Network.

In this investigation, you will attempt to solve a problem first by acting it out, then by creating a mathematical model.

Investigation
Party Handshakes

Each of the 30 people at a party shook hands with everyone else. How many handshakes were there altogether?

Step 1 Act out this problem with members of your group. Collect data for "parties" of one, two, three, and four people and record your results in a table.

People	1	2	3	4	...	30
Handshakes	0	1	3	6	...	435

LESSON OBJECTIVES

- Apply inductive reasoning to finding patterns
- Apply mathematical models to problem solving
- Develop visualization skills and cooperative behavior

NCTM STANDARDS

CONTENT		PROCESS	
✓	Number	✓	Problem Solving
✓	Algebra	✓	Reasoning
✓	Geometry	✓	Communication
	Measurement	✓	Connections
✓	Data/Probability	✓	Representation

Step 2 Adding all the preceding counting numbers gives the next term; it would take a lot of adding to find the 30th term.

Step 2 | Look for a pattern. Can you generalize from your pattern to find the 30th term?

Acting out a problem is a powerful problem-solving strategy that can give you important insight into a solution. Were you able to make a generalization from just four terms? If so, how confident are you of your generalization? To collect more data, you can ask more classmates to join your group. You can see, however, that acting out a problem sometimes has its practical limitations. That's where you can use mathematical models.

Step 3 | Model the problem by using points to represent people and line segments connecting the points to represent handshakes.

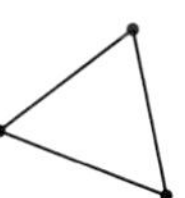

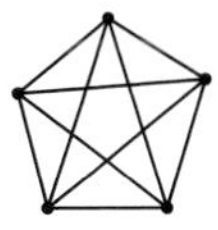
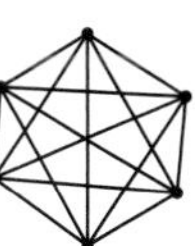

Record your results in a table like this one:

Number of points (people)	1	2	3	4	5	6	...	n	...	30
Number of segments (handshakes)	0	1	3	6	10	15	...		...	

Notice that the pattern does not have a constant difference. That is, the rule is not a linear function. So we need to look for a different kind of rule.

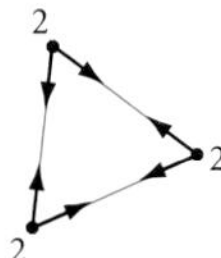

3 points
2 segments per vertex

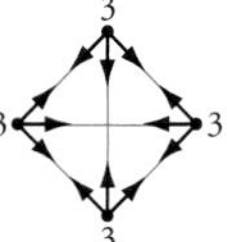

4 points
3 segments per vertex

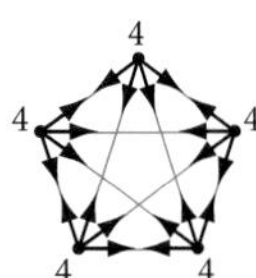

5 points
? segments per vertex
4

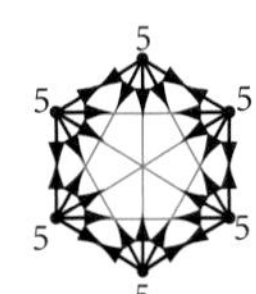

6 points
? segments per vertex
5

One step (continued)
differences of the differences are constant. Encourage all approaches, including graphing and vertex-edge graphs. By the time they solve the problem for the number of students in the class, students will probably have the insight needed to make the leap to the nth term. As needed, ask why the pattern makes sense, pushing for a deductive argument.

Step 3 Students may be drawing points rather randomly. **[Ask]** "How could you arrange the points to be sure that every pair is connected by a line segment?" [Using vertices of a convex polygon is a good arrangement.]

One way to organize the counting is to start out with one basic handshake (2 people, 1 handshake). Each person you add has to shake hands with the people who are already there. For example, the third person shakes 2 hands, the fourth person shakes 3 hands, and so forth, until all the guests are accounted for. This way of thinking of the situation leads to a mathematical model that is a sum of consecutive positive integers.

Step 4 One solution: Each person shakes hands with every other person. For example, each of 5 people shakes hands with 4 other people: $4 \cdot 5 = 20$. But this counts each handshake twice. So the number of handshakes for 5 people is $\frac{5(4)}{2} = 10$. In general, the nth term is $\frac{n(n-1)}{2}$. Students should not reduce fractions to lowest terms until they see the pattern.

Step 7 The smaller number represents the number of segments from each vertex. Multiplying that by the number of points counts each segment twice, so divide by two.

SHARING IDEAS

Share group results in Step 8 and any variety of ways of justifying the function. Question students until it's clear that there are five representations of the number of handshakes: a table of data (with changing first differences), the number of line segments connecting points, a sum of consecutive positive integers, a triangular number (a triangle of dots, half of a rectangle), and a formula. Use the term *mathematical model.*

[Ask] "What kind of reasoning led to the function rule?" [Making a conjecture from a pattern observed in the data was inductive. Justifying that conjecture by arguing that sums of integers can be represented by triangles that are halves of rectangles was deductive.]

Assessing Progress

As students are collecting data, making predictions, and sharing results, monitor their use of vocabulary, their ability to see patterns, their understanding of looking for differences between consecutive terms, their ability to work together, and their willingness to take the intellectual risk of making conjectures.

Step 4 Refer to the table you made for Step 3. The pattern of differences is increasing by one: 1, 2, 3, 4, 5, 6, 7. Read the dialogue between Erin and Stephanie as they attempt to combine inductive and deductive reasoning to find the rule.

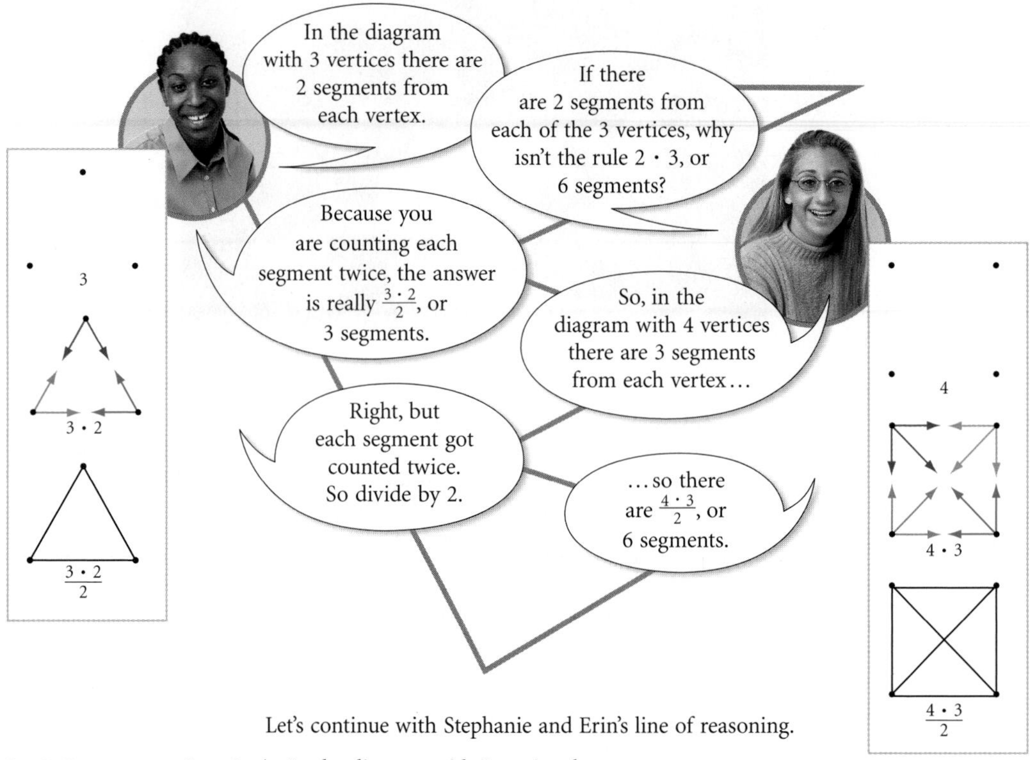

Let's continue with Stephanie and Erin's line of reasoning.

Step 5 Four segments from each vertex. The total number of segments written in factored form is $\frac{(5)(4)}{2}$.

Step 6 $\frac{5(4)}{2}, \frac{6(5)}{2}, \frac{n(n-1)}{2}$

Step 5 In the diagram with 5 vertices how many segments are there from each vertex? So the total number of segments written in factored form is $\frac{5 \cdot ?}{2}$.

Step 6 Complete the table below by expressing the total number of segments in factored form.

Number of points (people)	1	2	3	4	5	6	. . .	n
Number of segments (handshakes)	$\frac{(1)(0)}{2}$	$\frac{(2)(1)}{2}$	$\frac{(3)(2)}{2}$	$\frac{(4)(3)}{2}$	$\frac{(5)(?)}{2}$	$\frac{(6)(?)}{2}$	. . .	$\frac{(?)(?)}{2}$

Step 7 The larger of the two factors in the numerator represents the number of points. What does the smaller of the two numbers in the numerator represent? Why do we divide by 2?

Step 8 Write a function rule. How many handshakes were there at the party?

Step 8 $f(n) = \frac{n(n-1)}{2}$; 435

Closing the Lesson

A mathematical model is a representation of a real-world situation. For the handshake problem, we've seen five mathematical models: a table, a set of points and connecting line segments, a sum of integers, a triangle of dots, and a formula. Geometric models, such as points and line segments or triangles of dots, can be used to represent real-world situations.

[Ask] "Which model is most useful for solving the handshake problem with any number of students? Which model gave the most insight into the situation? Which model leads to the formula by inductive reasoning? Which model justifies the formula deductively?" Students may have a variety of answers to these questions; elicit the idea that the formula is most easily generalized and that it's justified deductively through a sum of integers and a triangle of dots.

Fifteen pool balls can be arranged in a triangle, so 15 is a triangular number.

The numbers in the pattern in the previous investigation are called the **triangular numbers** because you can arrange them into a triangular pattern of dots.

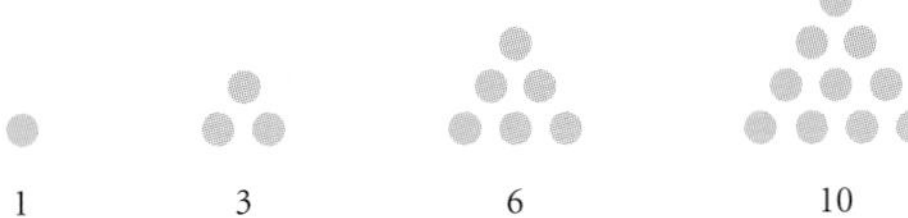

The triangular numbers appear in many geometric situations. You will see some of them in the exercises.

Here is a visual approach to arrive at the rule for this special pattern of numbers. If we arrange the triangular numbers in stacks,

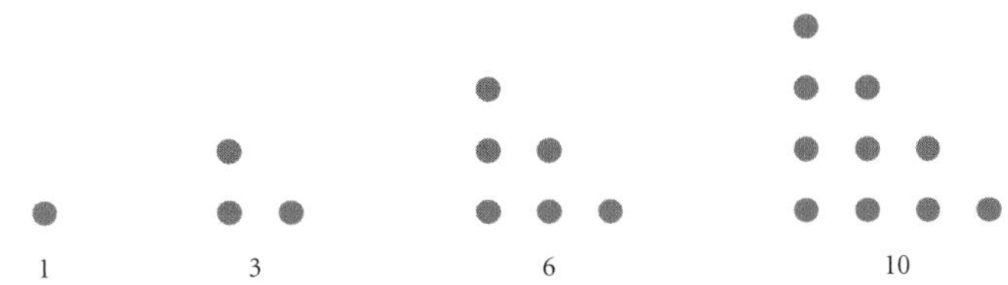

you can see that each is half of a **rectangular number.**

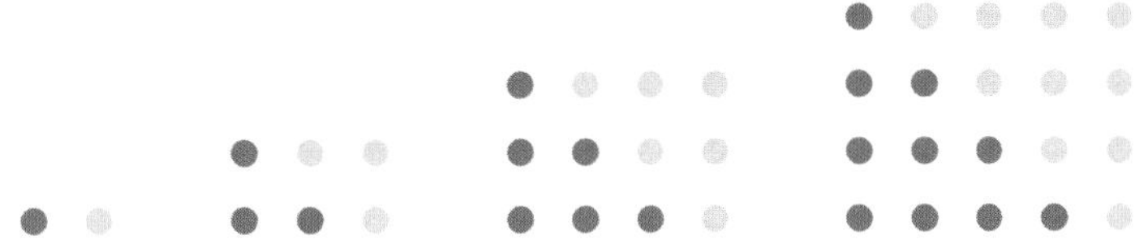

To get the total number of dots in a rectangular array, you multiply the number of rows by the number of dots in each row. In the case of this rectangular array, the nth rectangle has $n(n + 1)$ dots. So, the triangular array has $\frac{n(n+1)}{2}$ dots.

EXERCISES

For Exercises 1–6, draw the next figure. Complete a table and find the function rule. Then find the 35th term.

1. Lines passing through the same point are **concurrent.** Into how many regions do 35 concurrent lines divide the plane?

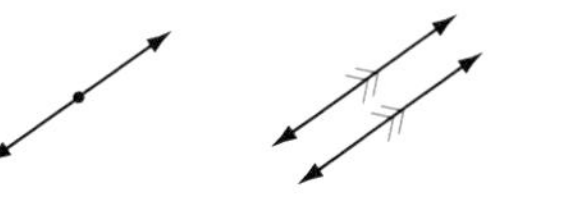

Lines	1	2	3	4	5	...	n	...	35
Regions	2	4	6	8	10	...	$2n$	...	70

2. Into how many regions do 35 parallel lines in a plane divide that plane? $n + 1$, 36

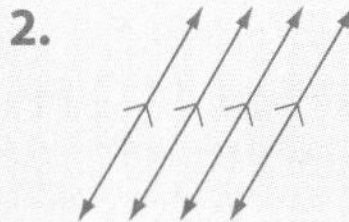

Triangular Numbers, Hand Shakes

The nth triangular number, $\frac{n(n+1)}{2}$, is the $n + 1$ number in the handshake rule $\frac{(n-1)n}{2}$.

BUILDING UNDERSTANDING

The exercises call for more inductive reasoning from geometric models to formulas and applications of the relationships of the lesson.

If students seem to need an application of the relationships investigated in this lesson, you might work together on Exercise 8.

ASSIGNING HOMEWORK

Essential	**1–4, 6, 8–14**
Performance assessment	**9**
Portfolio	**6, 10**
Journal	**7**
Group	**5, 10**
Review	**12–20**

Helping with the Exercises

Exercise 1 [Language] The word *concurrent* comes from Latin meaning "run (*current*) together (*con*)." Although line segments can also be concurrent, this exercise is definitely referring to lines, which extend indefinitely in both directions. Students may ask which plane is "the plane." In plane geometry, the term *the plane* means any plane.

Exercises 2–7 Encourage students to build a table of data where necessary, but point out that they can solve several of these problems by thinking about their results from previous exercises. **[Ask]** "The tables can be built by deciding two things: What will be represented by n, and what will $f(n)$ be?" Students will probably find pictures useful for collecting data for the tables.

2.

Exercise 4 This exercise can be done in at least three ways: as a pure number pattern, using constant second differences; as an extension of the investigation: $\frac{n(n-1)}{2} - n$; as an extension of Exercise 3: $\frac{\text{(diagonals from each vertex)(vertices)}}{2}$

Exercise 5 [Alert] This exercise can be very challenging if students don't see it as an extension of the investigation. As needed, help students begin to draw the first several lines. If they see the way they are drawing the lines enables the conditions in the exercise to be met, they will find it easier to draw the figure for 5, 6, and 7 points.

7. Answers will include relationships between points in Exercises 5 and 6 and vertices of a polygon. The total number of segments connecting n random points is the number of diagonals of the n-sided polygon, $\frac{n(n-3)}{2}$, plus the number of sides, n. Thus, the total number of segments connecting n random points is $\frac{n(n-3)}{2} + \frac{2n}{2} = \frac{n(n-3)+2n}{2} = \frac{n^2-3n+2n}{2} = \frac{n^2-n}{2} = \frac{n(n-1)}{2}$.

3. How many diagonals can you draw from one vertex in a polygon with 35 sides? $n - 3$, because you can draw a diagonal from one vertex to all the other vertices except three of them, the two adjacent vertices and the vertex itself; 32

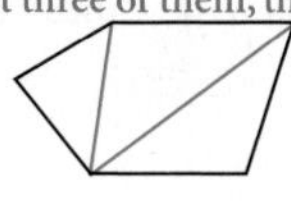

4. What's the total number of diagonals in a 35-sided polygon? ⓗ $\frac{n(n-3)}{2}$, 560

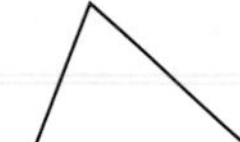

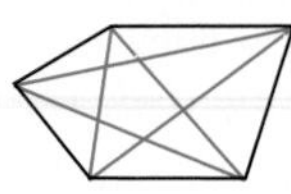

5. If you place 35 points on a piece of paper so that no three points are in a line, how many line segments are necessary to connect each point to all the others? ⓗ $\frac{n(n-1)}{2}$, 595

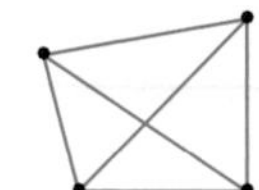

6. If you draw 35 lines on a piece of paper so that no two lines are parallel to each other and no three lines are concurrent, how many times will they intersect? ⓗ $\frac{n(n-1)}{2}$, 595

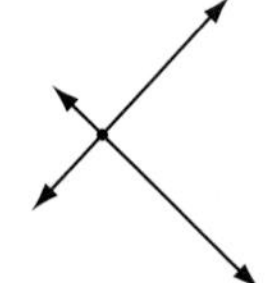
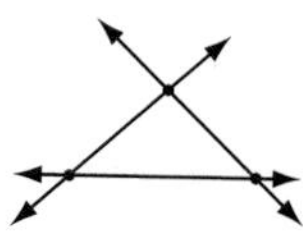
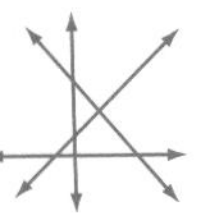

7. Look at the formulas you found in Exercises 4–6. Describe how the formulas are related. Then explain how the three problems are related geometrically. ⓗ

For Exercises 8–10, draw a diagram, find the appropriate geometric model, and solve.

8. If 40 houses in a community all need direct lines to one another in order to have telephone service, how many lines are necessary? Is that practical? Sketch and describe two models: first, model the situation in which direct lines connect every house to every other house and, second, model a more practical alternative.

9. If each team in a ten-team league plays each of the other teams four times in a season, how many league games are played during one season? What geometric figures can you use to model teams and games played? ⓗ

10. Each person at a party shook hands with everyone else exactly once. There were 66 handshakes. How many people were at the party? ⓗ If $\frac{n(n-1)}{2} = 66$, then $n(n-1) = 132$. What two consecutive numbers multiply to equal 132? 12 times 11. Thus, there were 12 people at the party.

Review

For Exercises 11–19, identify the statement as true or false. For each false statement, explain why it is false or sketch a counterexample.

1.6 **11.** The largest chord of a circle is a diameter of the circle. true

8. Use $\frac{n(n-1)}{2}$ to get 780 direct lines. Use a central hub with a line to each house to get 40 lines. The art shows the direct-line solution and the practical solution for six houses.

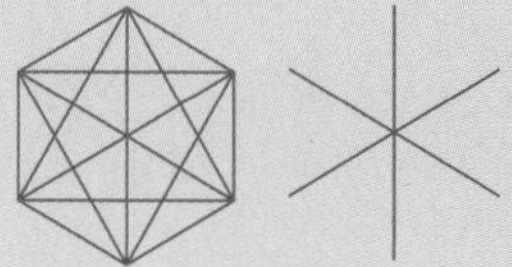

9. Use points for the 10 teams and segments connecting them to represent four games played between them. So, use $4 \cdot \frac{n(n-1)}{2}$ to get 180 games played.

Exercise 10 Students might use algebra to solve for the unknown, but if they don't remember solving quadratic equations they may think about the meaning of the expressions. For $n(n-1)$ to equal 132, we must find two numbers that differ by 1 and have the product 132.

1.3 **12.** The vertex of $\angle TOP$ is point O. true

1.5 **13.** An isosceles right triangle is a triangle with an angle measuring 90° and no two sides congruent. False; an isosceles right triangle has two sides congruent.

1.3 **14.** If $\overleftrightarrow{AB}$ intersects $\overleftrightarrow{CD}$ in point E, then $\angle AED$ and $\angle BED$ form a linear pair of angles. ⓗ

1.3 **15.** If two lines lie in the same plane and are perpendicular to the same line, they are perpendicular. False; they are parallel.

1.5 **16.** The opposite sides of a kite are never parallel. true

1.5 **17.** A rectangle is a parallelogram with all sides congruent. False; a rectangle is a parallelogram with all of its angles congruent.

1.4 **18.** A line segment that connects any two vertices in a polygon is called a diagonal. False; a diagonal is a segment in a polygon connecting any two nonconsecutive vertices.

1.3 **19.** To show that two lines are parallel, you mark them with the same number of arrowheads. true

2.3 **20.** Hydrocarbons are molecules that consist of carbon (C) and hydrogen (H). Hydrocarbons in which all the bonds between the carbon atoms are single bonds are called *alkanes*. The first four alkanes are modeled below.

Sketch the alkane with eight carbons in the chain. What is the general rule for alkanes $\left(C_nH_?\right)$? In other words, if there are n carbon atoms (C), how many hydrogen atoms (H) are in the alkane?

```
    H             H   H             H   H   H              H   H   H   H
    |             |   |             |   |   |              |   |   |   |
H - C - H     H - C - C - H     H - C - C - C - H      H - C - C - C - C - H
    |             |   |             |   |   |              |   |   |   |
    H             H   H             H   H   H              H   H   H   H
```

Methane $\left(CH_4\right)$ Ethane $\left(C_2H_6\right)$ Propane $\left(C_3H_8\right)$ Butane $\left(C_4H_{10}\right)$

Science CONNECTION

Organic chemistry is the study of carbon compounds and their reactions. Drugs, vitamins, synthetic fibers, and food all contain organic molecules. Organic chemists continue to improve our quality of life by the advances they make in medicine, nutrition, and manufacturing. To learn about new advances in organic chemistry, go to www.keymath.com/DG .

IMPROVING YOUR VISUAL THINKING SKILLS

Pentominoes II

In Pentominoes I, you found the 12 pentominoes. Which of the 12 pentominoes can you cut along the edges and fold into a box without a lid? Here is an example.

14. false

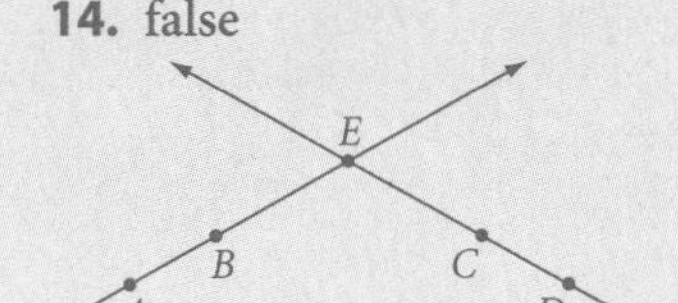

$\angle AED$ and $\angle BED$ are not a linear pair.

20. C_nH_{2n+2}

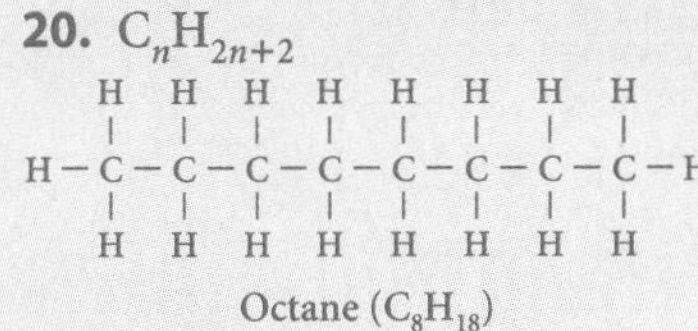

EXTENSION

Students might explore other second-degree (quadratic) functions to see if they also have a constant second difference and, if so, how that difference relates to the coefficient of the squared term in the function expression.

IMPROVING VISUAL THINKING SKILLS

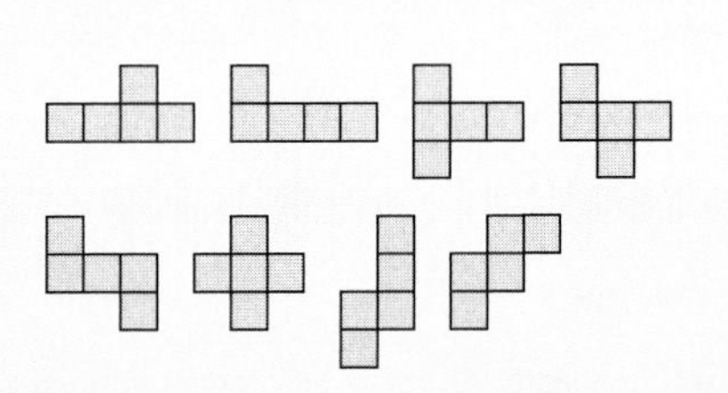

EXPLORATION

PLANNING

LESSON OUTLINE

One day:

30 min	Activity
10 min	Sharing
5 min	Closing

MATERIALS

none

TEACHING

In this lesson, students find a simple rule by which one can determine whether or not a network can be traversed using each edge exactly once. Historians often credit this problem as being the first in the field of topology, a study of connections between points in which distance and location are not so important as in the geometry we're studying.

Guiding the Activity

To convert the map to a network, the islands and mainland are points of intersection and the bridges are the paths.

Exploration

The Seven Bridges of Königsberg

Leonhard Euler

The River Pregel runs through the university town of Königsberg (now Kaliningrad in Russia). In the middle of the river are two islands connected to each other and to the rest of the city by seven bridges. Many years ago, a tradition developed among the townspeople of Königsberg. They challenged one another to make a round trip over all seven bridges, walking over each bridge once and only once before returning to the starting point.

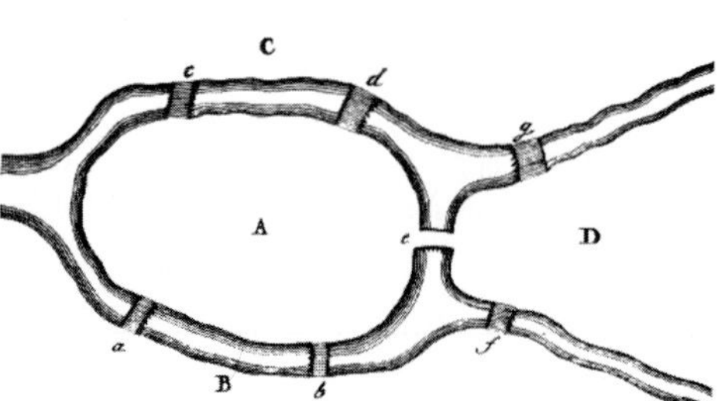

The seven bridges of Königsberg

For a long time no one was able to do it, and yet no one was able to show that it couldn't be done. In 1735, they finally wrote to Leonhard Euler (1707–1783), a Swiss mathematician, asking for his help on the problem. Euler (pronounced "oyler") reduced the problem to a network of paths connecting the two sides of the rivers C and B, and the two islands A and D, as shown in the network at right. Then Euler demonstrated that the task is impossible.

In this activity you will work with a variety of networks to see if you can come up with a rule to find out whether a network can or cannot be "traveled."

Activity
Traveling Networks

A collection of points connected by paths is called a **network.** When we say a network can be traveled, we mean that the network can be drawn with a pencil without lifting the pencil off the paper and without retracing any paths. (Points can be passed over more than once.)

LESSON OBJECTIVES

- Discover a rule for determining which networks can be traveled, using each edge exactly once
- Develop inductive reasoning

NCTM STANDARDS

CONTENT		PROCESS	
✓	Number	✓	Problem Solving
	Algebra	✓	Reasoning
✓	Geometry		Communication
	Measurement	✓	Connections
✓	Data/Probability	✓	Representation

Step 1 | Try these networks and see which ones can be traveled and which are impossible to travel.

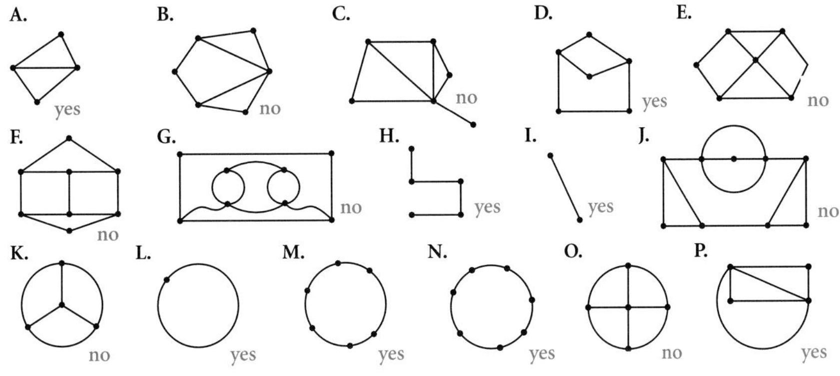

Which networks were impossible to travel? Are they impossible or just difficult? How can you be sure? As you do the next few steps, see if you can find the reason why some networks are impossible to travel.

Step 2 The new bridge must be between islands A and D.

Step 2 | Draw the River Pregel and the two islands shown on the first page of this exploration. Draw an eighth bridge so that you can travel over all the bridges exactly once if you start at point *C* and end at point *B*.

Step 3 | Draw the River Pregel and the two islands. Can you draw an eighth bridge so that you can travel over all the bridges exactly once, starting and finishing at the same point? How many solutions can you find? This is impossible.

Step 4 It is impossible for a network to have an odd number of odd points. Points must come in pairs, because one point in each pair must be the start of some path and the other point must be the end of it.

Step 4 | Euler realized that it is the points of intersection that determine whether a network can be traveled. Each point of intersection is either "odd" or "even."

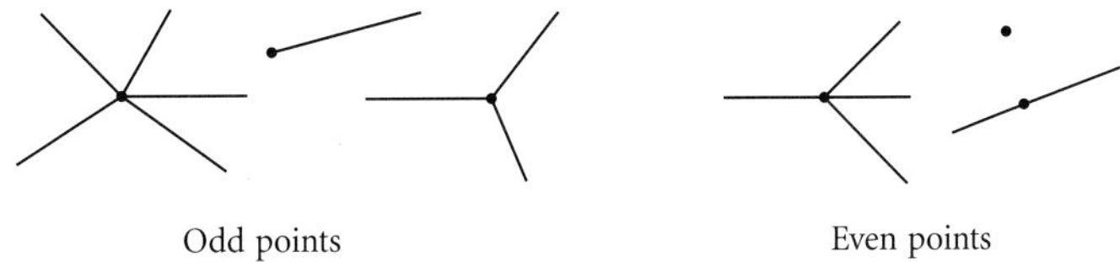

Did you find any networks that have only one odd point? Can you draw one? Try it. How about three odd points? Or five odd points? Can you create a network that has an odd number of odd points? Explain why or why not.

Step 5 | How does the number of even points and odd points affect whether a network can be traveled?

Conjecture

A network can be traveled if __?__. the number of odd points is zero or two

Step 2 [Alert] Some students may be satisfied with a path that touches every vertex exactly once but omits some edges.

Step 2

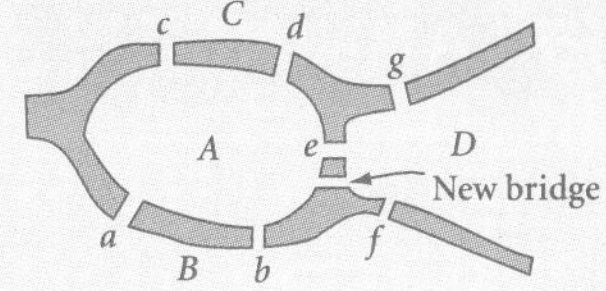

Step 3 Students may be confused by the question of how many when they can't find any. Remind them that zero is a good answer. The network would have to have zero odd points, but a single bridge changes, at most, two odd points to even points.

Step 5 [Link] In graph theory, a network is called a *graph,* a point of intersection is a *vertex,* and a line between points is called an *edge.* **[Ask]** "Why can't there be an odd number of odd points of intersection?" [If you add up the number of edges touching each point, you get twice the number—an even number. But the sum of an odd number of odd numbers is odd.]

SHARING IDEAS

[Ask] "Why do even and odd points make a difference?" [Not counting the first and last points, for each entry into a point, the path must exit, so the edges can be considered in pairs. The first and last points can be odd if the path doesn't make a complete circuit; if the path starts and ends at the same point, however, the first edge may be paired with the last, so this point too will be even.]

A network that can be traveled touching every edge once and only once is called *Eulerian.* This argument shows that if a graph is Eulerian, then every point must be even. It does not prove the converse, but the converse can indeed be proved.

See page 768 for answers to Step 5.

Closing the Lesson

Every network has an even number of odd points—points touched by an odd number of edges. A network can be traveled over each edge once and only once, if and only if it contains zero or two odd points. It can be traveled in this way with a return to the starting point, if and only if it contains no odd points.

Assessing Progress

Check how well students form and discern patterns and how articulately they express their ideas.

LESSON

2.5

PLANNING

LESSON OUTLINE

First day:

30 min Investigation 1

15 min Investigation 2

Second day:

15 min Investigation 2

15 min Sharing

5 min Closing

10 min Exercises

MATERIALS

- protractors
- patty paper or tracing paper
- Sketchpad demonstration Linear Pairs and Vertical Angles, *optional*

TEACHING

You can start with the one-step investigation below or begin by reviewing the definitions of *complementary, supplementary, vertical,* and *linear pairs of angles* before proceeding to the investigations. **[Alert]** Students may think that linear pairs of angles are always horizontally oriented. Use a variety of orientations when you illustrate geometry terms.

Guiding Investigation 1

You might use this investigation as a follow-along activity or use the Sketchpad demonstration Linear Pairs and Vertical Angles.

Step 1 Remind students that they can extend the rays to measure the angles. Conjectures may include that the angles are supplementary, that the sum of their measures is 180°, that the angles are adjacent, that they "make a line" or, as Euclid put it, "together form two right angles." Only one conjecture is intended but be open to all conjectures at this point.

One step Draw two intersecting lines, point out a pair of vertical angles and a linear pair of angles, and ask how their sizes are related. Accept all conjectures without judgment, and ask students to investigate in their groups by drawing pairs of intersecting lines and measuring the angles formed. As you circulate, ask groups to write conjectures beginning with "If two angles are vertical angles, then . . ."

LESSON

2.5

Angle Relationships

Discovery consists of looking at the same thing as everyone else and thinking something different.

ALBERT SZENT-GYÖRGYI

Now that you've had experience with inductive reasoning, let's use it to start discovering geometric relationships. This investigation is the first of many investigations you will do using your geometry tools.

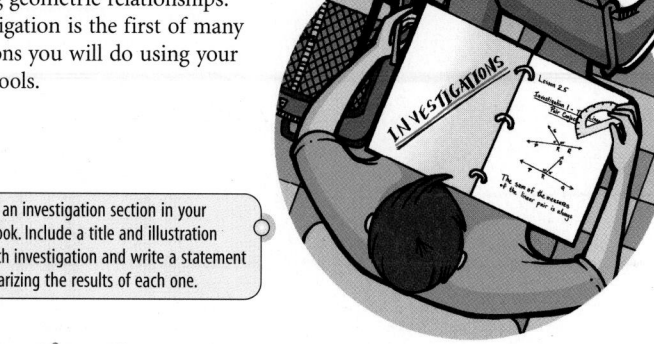

Create an investigation section in your notebook. Include a title and illustration for each investigation and write a statement summarizing the results of each one.

Investigation 1
The Linear Pair Conjecture

You will need

- a protractor

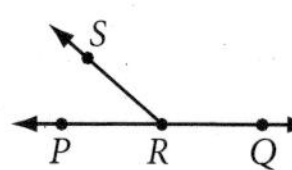

Step 1 180°

Step 1 On a sheet of paper, draw $\overleftrightarrow{PQ}$ and place a point R between P and Q. Choose another point S not on $\overleftrightarrow{PQ}$ and draw $\overrightarrow{RS}$. You have just created a linear pair of angles. Place the "zero edge" of your protractor along $\overleftrightarrow{PQ}$. What do you notice about the sum of the measures of the linear pair of angles?

Step 2 Compare your results with those of your group. Does everyone make the same observation? Complete the statement.

Linear Pair Conjecture C-1

If two angles form a linear pair, then __?__. (the measures of the angles add up to 180°)

The important conjectures have been given a name and a number. Start a list of them in your notebook. The Linear Pair Conjecture (C-1) and the Vertical Angles Conjecture (C-2) should be the first entries on your list. Make a sketch for each conjecture.

LESSON OBJECTIVES

- Discover relationships between special pairs of angles
- Practice performing investigations and writing conjectures
- Practice measurement skills
- Develop inductive reasoning and cooperative behavior

In the previous investigation you discovered the relationship between a linear pair of angles, such as ∠1 and ∠2 in the diagram at right.

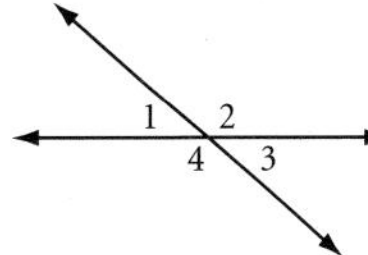

You will discover the relationship between vertical angles, such as ∠1 and ∠3, in the next investigation.

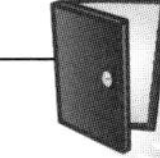

Investigation 2
Vertical Angles Conjecture

You will need

- a protractor
- patty paper

Step 1 ∠1 and ∠3; ∠2 and ∠4

Step 1 Draw two intersecting lines onto patty paper or tracing paper. Label the angles as shown. Which angles are vertical angles?

Step 2 They are equal.

Step 2 Fold the paper so that the vertical angles lie over each other. What do you notice about their measures?

Step 3 Repeat this investigation with another pair of intersecting lines.

Step 4 Compare your results with the results of others. Complete the statement.

Vertical Angles Conjecture C-2

If two angles are vertical angles, then __?__. *they have equal measures (are congruent)*

You used inductive reasoning to discover both the Linear Pair Conjecture and the Vertical Angles Conjecture. Are they related in any way? That is, if we accept the Linear Pair Conjecture as true, can we use deductive reasoning to show that the Vertical Angles Conjecture must be true?

EXAMPLE The Linear Pair Conjecture states that every linear pair adds up to 180°. Using this conjecture and the diagram, write a logical argument explaining why ∠1 must be congruent to ∠3.

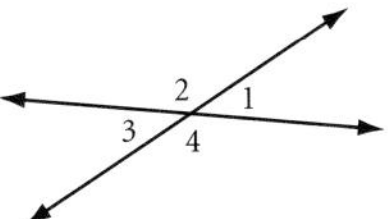

NCTM STANDARDS

CONTENT		PROCESS	
	Number		Problem Solving
	Algebra	✓	Reasoning
✓	Geometry	✓	Communication
✓	Measurement		Connections
	Data/Probability		Representation

Guiding Investigation 2

If students did the first investigation and time is short, you might do this investigation as a class, perhaps using the Sketchpad demonstration Linear Pairs and Vertical Angles.

Protractors aren't really needed, because folding is sufficient, but students might prefer to measure. Reasonable conjectures might be that vertical angles have the same measure, that they are congruent, or that they are symmetric about a line. Welcome all conjectures.

Ask students to attach (glue, tape, or staple) the patty paper to their reports in the investigation section of their notebooks. (Using a small amount of removable glue allows you to pull the patty paper off later to check how the investigation was done and then reattach it to the notebook.

► *EXAMPLE*

Students may have difficulty reading carefully enough to follow the reasoning in this proof. Encourage them to take one step at a time, but don't assume that if they follow each step then they understand the proof. Have them give the reasoning in their own words. They might say something like "Adding the same thing to these two angles gives the same result, 180°, so these two angles must be equal." Push for precision in the use of terms only if students are comfortable with the logic.

After working with the example, students might ask if deductive reasoning involves only numbers and equations. Point out that the proof is based on the Linear Pair Conjecture, which is certainly geometry. They may ask if the Linear Pair Conjecture needs to be proved also. Actually, it's a restatement of part of the definition of *linear pair,* which states that "a linear pair of angles is two adjacent angles whose sum is 180°."

SHARING IDEAS

Pick a variety of conjectures to be shared. As a class, discuss their mathematical value.

[Ask] "Do the conjectures capture any insight into the situation?" "Will they be useful?" Point out that in the future you'll be referring back to formal conjectures, so you need to agree on what is meant by each. If students want to have several competing conjectures be "official," you might give different names to them.

Allow disagreement. As students defend their ideas, they clarify their thinking. Some initial confusion can motivate deeper learning, but avoid allowing students to feel a debilitating degree of frustration.

[Ask] "What kind of reasoning led to the conjectures?" [Because the conjectures were based on patterns detected in several measurements, they were arrived at inductively.] In a mathematical sense, conjectures are not accepted as true until they have been proved deductively. Once a conjecture has been proved deductively, it is a theorem. In this course, conclusions arrived at inductively are assumed to be true. They will not be called *theorems* until they are proved within a mathematical system in Chapter 13. Ask students to verify either of the two conjectures by deductive reasoning. After they've tried, have them compare their attempts to the proof of the Vertical Angles Conjecture in the example.

Assessing Progress

As you observe students working and presenting their ideas, you can assess their ability to reason inductively, that is, to collect good data, look for patterns, and write a conjecture. In addition, you can check how well they use straightedges and protractors and assess their social skills during group work.

▸ ***Solution***

You can see that the measures of $\angle 1$ and $\angle 2$ add up to 180°, and that the measures of $\angle 3$ and $\angle 2$ also add up to 180°. Using algebra, we can write a logical argument to show that $\angle 1$ and $\angle 3$ must be congruent.

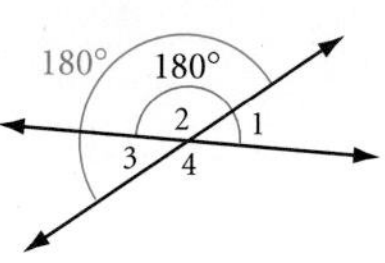

According to the Linear Pair Conjecture, $m\angle 1 + m\angle 2 = 180°$ and $m\angle 2 + m\angle 3 = 180°$. By substituting $m\angle 2 + m\angle 3$ for 180° in the first statement, you get $m\angle 1 + m\angle 2 = m\angle 2 + m\angle 3$. By the subtraction property of equality, you can subtract $m\angle 2$ from both sides of the equation to get $m\angle 1 = m\angle 3$. Therefore, vertical angles 1 and 3 have equal measures and are congruent.

Here are the algebraic steps:

$m\angle 2 + m\angle 3 = 180°$
$m\angle 1 + m\angle 2 = 180°$
$m\angle 1 + m\angle 2 = m\angle 2 + m\angle 3$
thus $m\angle 1 = m\angle 3$
therefore $\angle 1 \cong \angle 3$

This type of logical explanation, written as a paragraph, is called a **paragraph proof.**

Now consider another idea. You discovered the Vertical Angles Conjecture: If two angles are vertical angles, then they are congruent. Does that also mean that all congruent angles are vertical angles? The **converse** of an "if-then" statement switches the "if" and "then" parts. The converse of the Vertical Angles Conjecture may be stated: If two angles are congruent, then they are vertical angles. Is this converse statement true? Remember that if you can find even one counterexample, like the diagram below, then the statement is false.

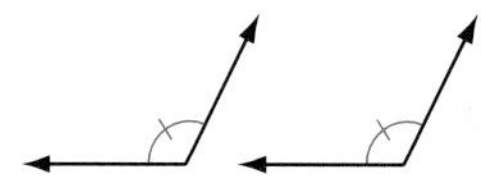

Therefore, the converse of the Vertical Angles Conjecture is false.

EXERCISES

You will need

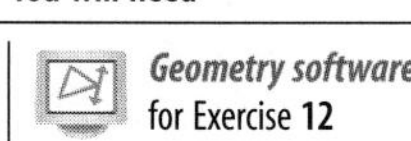

Geometry software for Exercise **12**

Without using a protractor, but with the aid of your two new conjectures, find the measure of each lettered angle in Exercises 1–5. Copy the diagrams so that you can write on them. List your answers in alphabetical order.

1.

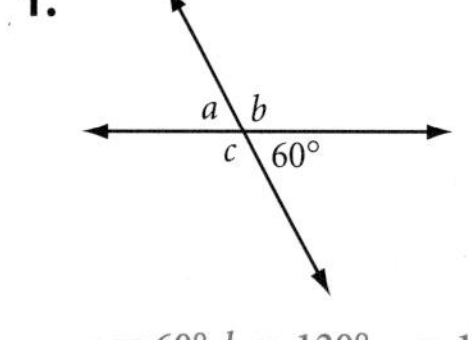

$a = 60°, b = 120°, c = 120°$

2.

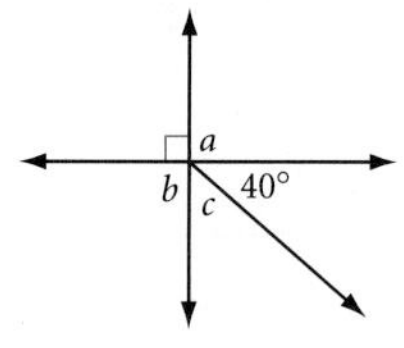

$a = 90°, b = 90°, c = 50°$

3.

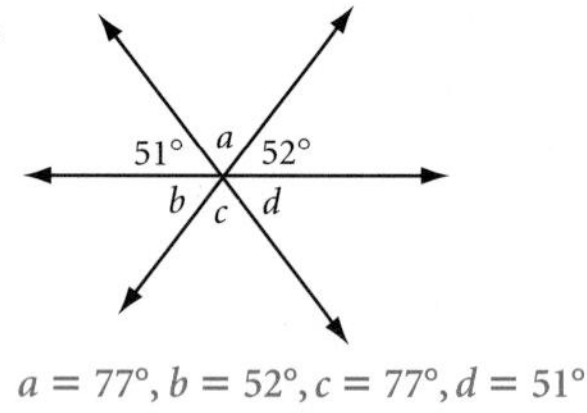

$a = 77°, b = 52°, c = 77°, d = 51°$

Converse

Insight into a theorem can often be gained by considering its converse. Besides considering the converse of the Vertical Angles Conjecture, as in the student book, you might ask about the converse of the Linear Pair Conjecture. The converse could be "If the sum of the measures of two angles is 180°, then the two angles form a linear pair."

Closing the Lesson

Remind students that inductive reasoning led to conjectures about linear pairs of angles and pairs of vertical angles. Restate the agreed-on Linear Pair Conjecture and Vertical Angles Conjecture and any other important conjectures that arose. The Vertical Angles Conjecture was proved deductively.

If students seem to be having difficulty with the conjectures, you might work one of the first five exercises together.

4. ⓗ

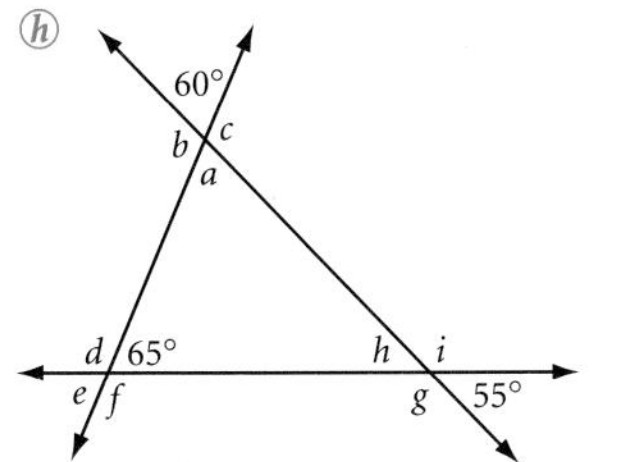

$a = 60°, b = c = 120°, d = f = 115°,$
$e = 65°, g = i = 125°, h = 55°$

5.

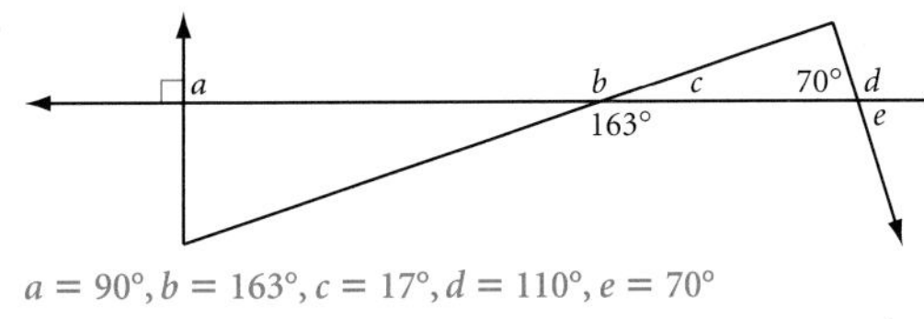

$a = 90°, b = 163°, c = 17°, d = 110°, e = 70°$

6. Points A, B, and C at right are collinear. What's wrong with this picture?
The measures of the linear pair of angles add up to 170°, not 180°.

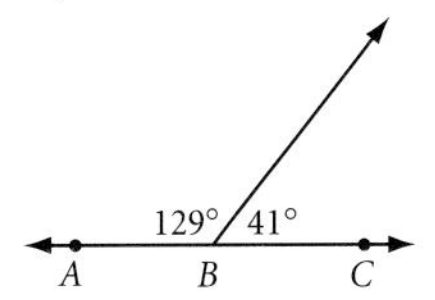

7. Yoshi is building a cold frame for his plants. He wants to cut two wood strips so that they'll fit together to make a right-angled corner. At what angle should he cut ends of the strips?
The best angles at which he should cut measure 45°.

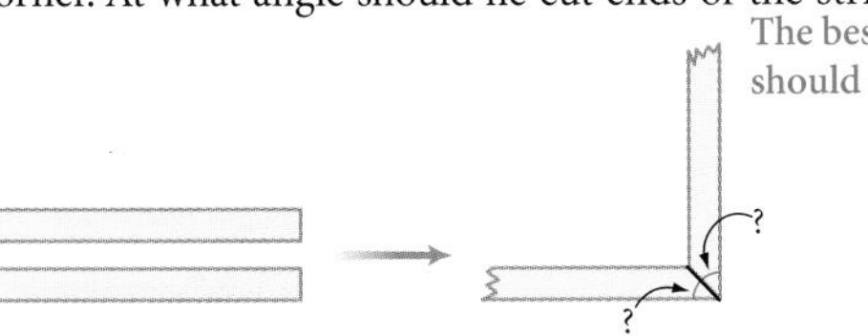

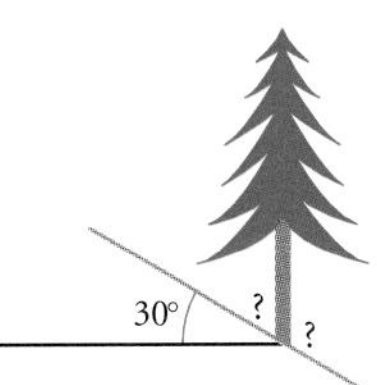

8. A tree on a 30° slope grows straight up. What are the measures of the greatest and smallest angles the tree makes with the hill? Explain.

9. You discovered that if a pair of angles is a linear pair then the angles are supplementary. Does that mean that all supplementary angles form a linear pair of angles? Is the converse true? If not, sketch a counterexample.
The converse is not true.

10. If two congruent angles are supplementary, what must be true of the two angles? Make a sketch, then complete the following conjecture: If two angles are both congruent and supplementary, then __?__. each must be a right angle

11. Using algebra, write a paragraph proof that explains why the conjecture from Exercise 10 is true. Let the measures of the congruent angles be x. They are supplementary, so $x + x = 180°$, $2x = 180°$, $x = 90°$. Thus each angle is a right angle.

12. ***Technology*** Use geometry software to construct two intersecting lines. Measure a pair of vertical angles. Use **calculate** to find the ratio of their measures. What is the ratio? Drag one of the lines. Does the ratio ever change? Does this demonstration convince you that the Vertical Angles Conjecture is true? Does it explain why it is true?
Ratio is 1. The ratio does not change as long as the lines don't coincide. Since the demonstration does not explain why, it is not a proof.

Review

For Exercises 13–17, sketch, label, and mark the figure.

1.5 **13.** Scalene obtuse triangle PAT with $PA = 3$ cm, $AT = 5$ cm, and $\angle A$ an obtuse angle

1.5 **14.** A quadrilateral that has rotational symmetry but not reflectional symmetry

1.6 **15.** A circle with center at O and radii $\overline{OA}$ and $\overline{OT}$ creating a minor arc $\widehat{AT}$

Exercise 10 This is the Congruent Supplements Conjecture; it will be a useful shortcut in some later proofs.

10.

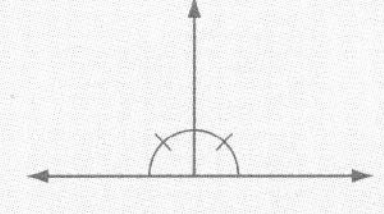

13.

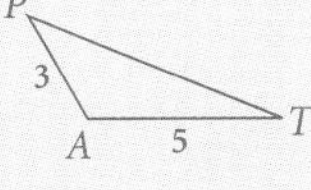

14.

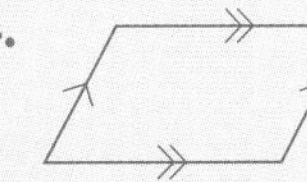

15.

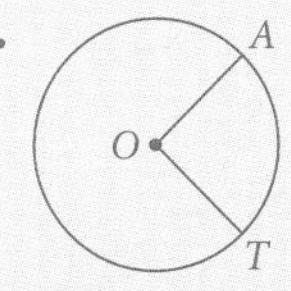

BUILDING UNDERSTANDING

The exercises provide applications of the two conjectures from the investigations.

ASSIGNING HOMEWORK

Essential	1–10
Performance assessment	9
Journal	8, 11, 12
Group	4, 5, 11
Review	13–27

MATERIALS

- Exercises 1–5 (T), *optional*

Helping with the Exercises

Exercise 6 You might want to model the kinds of answers students should be looking for in exercises such as this first of many instances of "What's wrong with this picture?"

8. Greatest: 120°. Smallest: 60°. One possible explanation: The tree is perpendicular to the horizontal. The angle of the hill measures 30°. The smaller angle and the angle between the hill and the horizontal form a pair of complementary angles, so the smaller angle equals $90° - 30° = 60°$. The smaller angle and larger angle form a linear pair, so the larger angle equals $180° - 60° = 120°$.

Exercise 9 To defend the opinion that the converse is false, students need to give a counterexample.

9. sample counterexample:

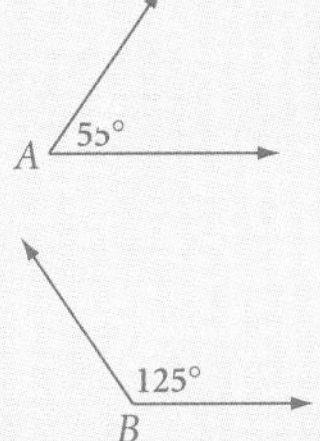

16.

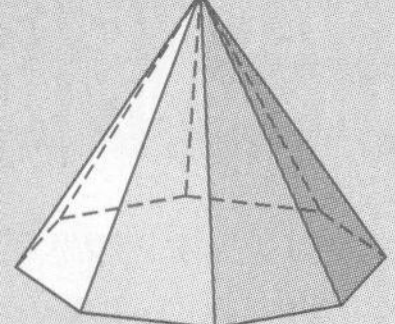

17.

18. Possible answer: All the cards look exactly as they did, so it must be the 4 of diamonds because it has rotational symmetry while the others do not.

20.

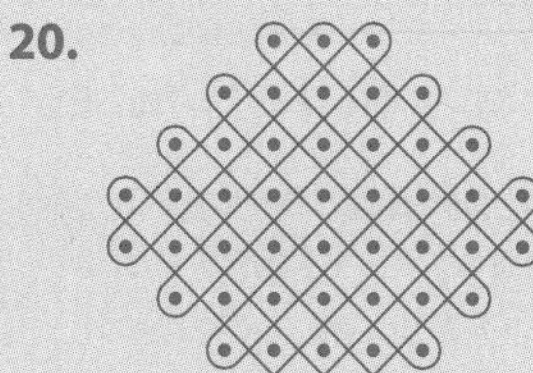

21. C_nH_{2n}

```
    H   H   H   H   H   H       H
    |   |   |   |   |   |       |
H - C - C - C - C - C - C - C = C
    |   |   |   |   |   |   |   |
    H   H   H   H   H   H   H   H
```

1.8 **16.** A pyramid with an octagonal base

1.8 **17.** A 3-by-4-by-6-inch rectangular solid rests on its smallest face. Draw lines on the three visible faces, showing how you can divide it into 72 identical smaller cubes.

Chapter 0 **18.** Miriam the Magnificent placed four cards face up (the first four cards shown below). Blindfolded, she asked someone from her audience to come up to the stage and turn one card 180°.

Before turn After turn

Miriam removed her blindfold and claimed she was able to determine which card was turned 180°. What is her trick? Can you figure out which card was turned? Explain.

1.6 **19.** If a pizza is cut into 16 congruent pieces, how many degrees are in each angle at the center of the pizza? 22.5°

2.3 **20.** Paulus Gerdes, a mathematician from Mozambique, uses traditional *lusona* patterns from Angola to practice inductive thinking. Shown below are three *sona* designs. Sketch the fourth *sona* design, assuming the pattern continues.

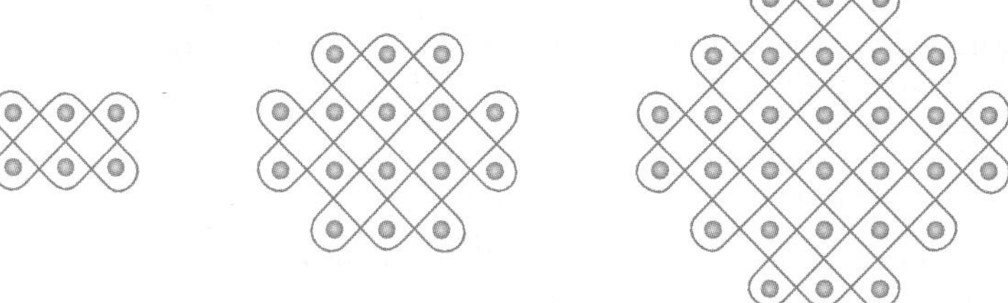

2.3 **21.** Hydrocarbon molecules in which all the bonds between the carbon atoms are single bonds except one double bond are called *alkenes*. The first three alkenes are modeled below.

```
        H             H     H              H   H       H
        |             |     |              |   |       |
    H - C = C     H - C - C = C        H - C - C - C = C
        |   |         |   |   |            |   |   |   |
        H   H         H   H   H            H   H   H   H
```

Ethene (C_2H_4) Propene (C_3H_6) Butene (C_4H_8)

Sketch the alkene with eight carbons in the chain. What is the general rule for alkenes ($C_nH_?$)? In other words, if there are *n* carbon atoms (C), how many hydrogen atoms (H) are in the alkene?

2.3 **22.** If the pattern of rectangles continues, what is the rule for the perimeter of the nth rectangle, and what is the perimeter of the 200th rectangle?

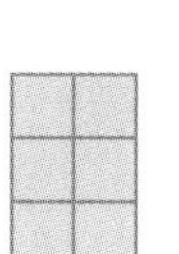
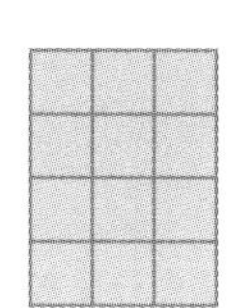
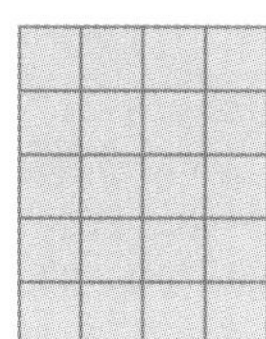

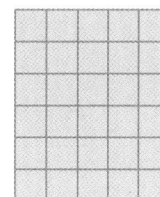

Perimeter in a rectangular pattern

Rectangle	1	2	3	4	5	6	...	n	...	200
Perimeter of rectangle	10	14	18	22	26	30	...		...	806

$4n + 6$

2.4 **23.** The twelfth grade class of 80 students is assembled in a large circle on the football field at halftime. Each student is connected by a string to each of the other class members. How many pieces of string are necessary to connect each student to all the others? ⓗ handshake problem: $\frac{n(n-1)}{2}$; $\frac{80(79)}{2} = 3160$ pieces of string

2.4 **24.** If you draw 80 lines on a piece of paper so that no 2 lines are parallel to each other and no 3 lines pass through the same point, how many intersections will there be? ⓗ 3160 intersections

2.4 **25.** If there are 20 couples at a party, how many different handshakes can there be between pairs of people? Assume that the two people in each couple do not shake hands with each other. ⓗ $\frac{n(n-2)}{2}$ yields 760 handshakes.

2.3 **26.** If a polygon has 24 sides, how many diagonals are there from each vertex? How many diagonals are there in all? 21; 252

2.4 **27.** If a polygon has a total of 560 diagonals, how many vertices does it have? ⓗ $\frac{n(n-3)}{2} = 560$; there are 35 vertices.

IMPROVING YOUR ALGEBRA SKILLS

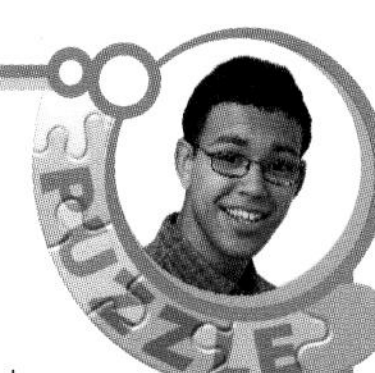

Number Line Diagrams

1. The two segments at right have the same length. Translate the number line diagram into an equation, then solve for the variable x.

$x-3$ | $x-3$ | $x-3$ | 20

$2x-23$ | $2x-23$ | 30

2. Translate this equation into a number line diagram.
$2(x + 3) + 14 = 3(x - 4) + 11$

Exercise 23 If students are struggling with this problem, remind them of the handshake problem.

IMPROVING ALGEBRA SKILLS

[Ask] "What do you notice about the two sets of line segments?" [The sets are equal in length, although they are broken into pieces of different lengths.] "How could knowing this information help you set up an equation that could be solved?"

Note that these problems provide both algebraic and geometric representations of the same quantities.

1. $3(x - 3) + 20 = 2(2x - 23) + 30$; $x = 27$

2.

$x+3$ | $x+3$ | 14

$x-4$ | $x-4$ | $x-4$ | 11

LESSON 2.6

PLANNING

LESSON OUTLINE

One day:

25 min Investigation
5 min Sharing
5 min Closing
10 min Exercises

MATERIALS

- protractors (or patty paper)
- straightedges (or lined paper)

TEACHING

Begin with the one-step investigation or introduce the definitions at the beginning of the lesson.

You might choose to use the lesson from *Discovering Geometry with The Geometer's Sketchpad.*

One step Draw two parallel line segments and a segment intersecting them, introducing the term *transversal.* **[Ask]** "How many angles are formed, and what relationships are there among those angles?" As students work, encourage them to state their observations as conjectures in if-then form. Conjectures won't be clearly stated unless students know names for the angles, but you need not show agreement or disagreement with any conjecture at this point. Challenge any group that comes up with a conjecture to consider its converse, reminding students as needed how to form the converse. During Sharing, introduce the terminology for angles when students see that their conjectures need clarifying.

LESSON 2.6 Special Angles on Parallel Lines

The greatest mistake you can make in life is to be continually fearing that you will make one.

ELLEN HUBBARD

A line intersecting two or more other lines in the plane is called a **transversal.** A transversal creates different types of angle pairs. Three types are listed below.

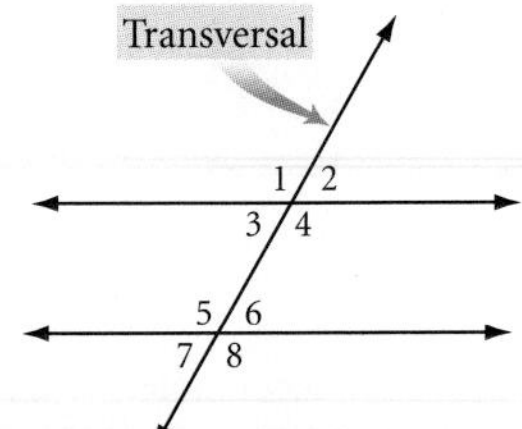

One pair of **corresponding angles** is $\angle 1$ and $\angle 5$. Can you find three more pairs of corresponding angles?

One pair of **alternate interior angles** is $\angle 3$ and $\angle 6$. Do you see another pair of alternate interior angles?

One pair of **alternate exterior angles** is $\angle 2$ and $\angle 7$. Do you see the other pair of alternate exterior angles?

When parallel lines are cut by a transversal, there is a special relationship among the angles. Let's investigate.

Investigation 1
Which Angles Are Congruent?

You will need

- lined paper or a straightedge
- patty paper
- a protractor

Using the lines on your paper as a guide, draw a pair of parallel lines. Or use both edges of your ruler or straightedge to create parallel lines. Label them k and ℓ. Now draw a transversal that intersects the parallel lines. Label the transversal m, and label the angles with numbers, as shown at right.

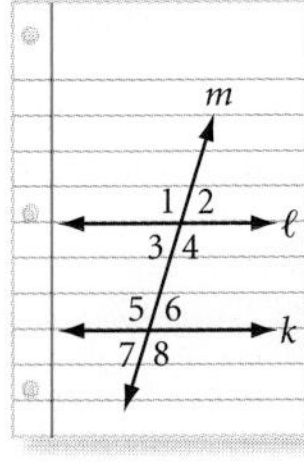

Step 1 Place a piece of patty paper over the set of angles 1, 2, 3, and 4. Copy the two intersecting lines m and ℓ and the four angles onto the patty paper.

Slide the patty paper down to the intersection of lines m and k, and compare angles 1 through 4 with each of the corresponding angles 5 through 8. What is the relationship between corresponding angles? Alternate interior angles? Alternate exterior angles?

congruent or equal in measure

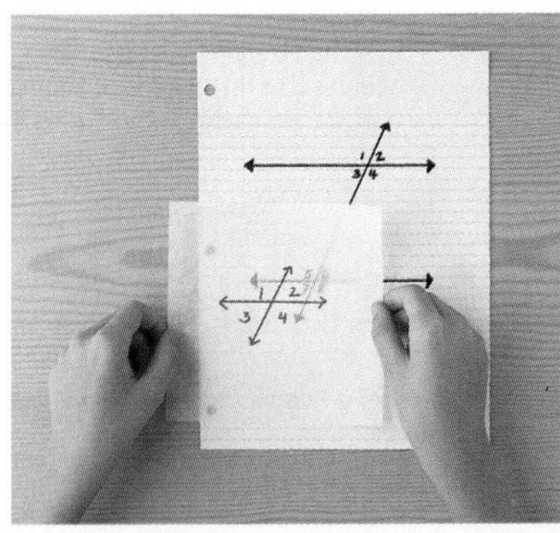

Guiding Investigation 1

Step 1 You may work through Step 1 as a follow-along activity. Students can use protractors to compare the angles if patty paper isn't available. Besides conjectures mentioning congruence, student conjectures might refer to angles as "shifts" of each other or even "flips" or "shifts and flips." Encourage a variety of ideas. (In fact, careful mathematical definitions of corresponding angles or alternate interior or exterior angles could be stated in terms of translations and reflections of the plane.) If students' conjectures refer to equal rather than congruent angles, save the critique for Sharing.

Compare your results with the results of others in your group and complete the three conjectures below.

Corresponding Angles Conjecture, or CA Conjecture

C-3a

If two parallel lines are cut by a transversal, then corresponding angles are _?_. congruent

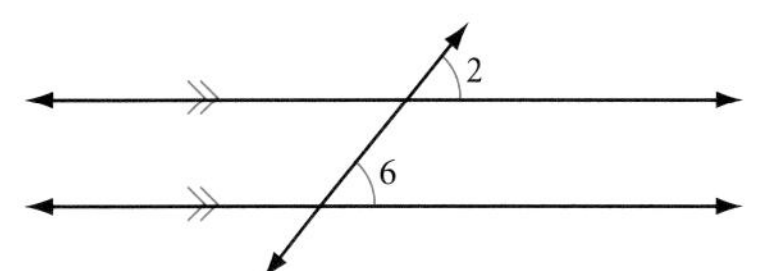

Alternate Interior Angles Conjecture, or AIA Conjecture

C-3b

If two parallel lines are cut by a transversal, then alternate interior angles are _?_. congruent

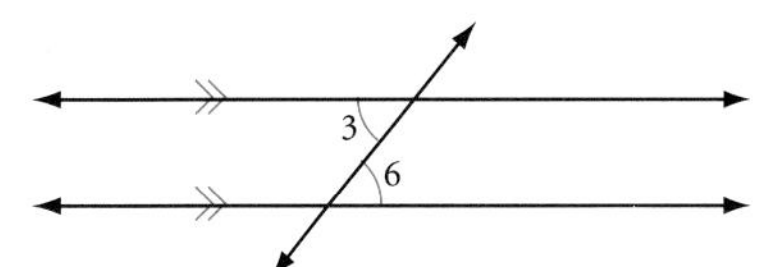

Alternate Exterior Angles Conjecture, or AEA Conjecture

C-3c

If two parallel lines are cut by a transversal, then alternate exterior angles are _?_. congruent

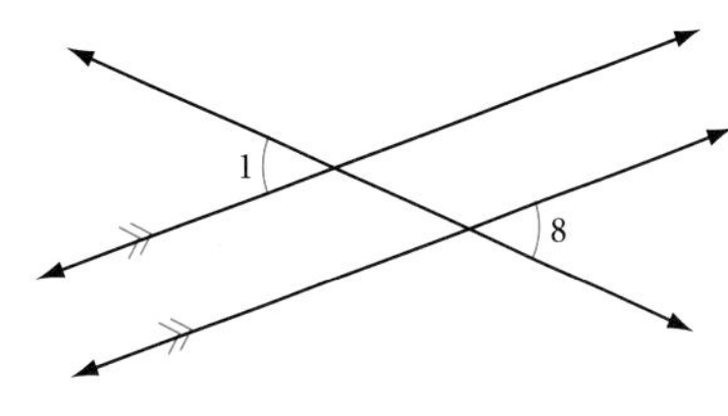

For an interactive version of this sketch, visit www.keymath.com/DG

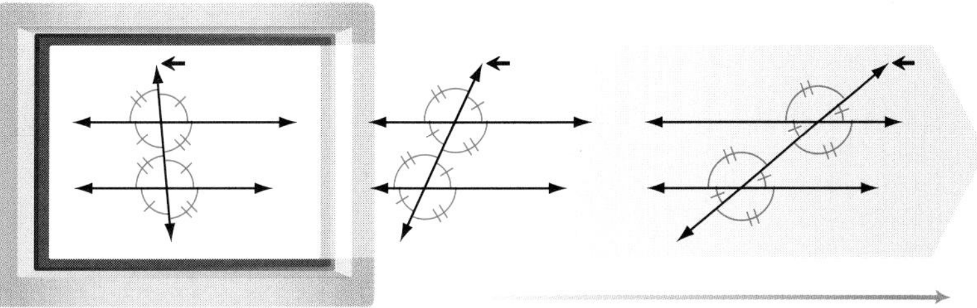

The three conjectures you wrote can all be combined to create a Parallel Lines Conjecture, which is really three conjectures in one.

Parallel Lines Conjecture

C-3

If two parallel lines are cut by a transversal, then corresponding angles are _?_, congruent alternate interior angles are _?_, congruent and alternate exterior angles are _?_. congruent

Students can use the dynamic geometry exploration at www.keymath.com/DG to investigate the parallel lines conjecture.

NCTM STANDARDS

CONTENT		PROCESS	
	Number		Problem Solving
	Algebra	✓	Reasoning
✓	Geometry	✓	Communication
✓	Measurement		Connections
✓	Data/Probability	✓	Representation

LESSON OBJECTIVES

- Explore relationships of the angles formed by a transversal cutting parallel lines
- Learn new vocabulary
- Practice construction skills
- Develop inductive reasoning abilities, problem-solving skills, and cooperative behavior

Guiding Investigation 2

Step 2 If students have difficulty following the instructions, urge them to read carefully and follow one instruction at a time. The pair-share format of cooperative learning can be helpful.

SHARING IDEAS

Choose students or groups to present a variety of conjectures. Lead a class discussion critiquing the conjectures until consensus is reached about which conjectures will get official names.

Be sure that any conjectures referring to "equal angles" are changed to contain the correct expression, "congruent angles" or "angles having equal measure."

[Alert] Some students have difficulty with the three terms used in this lesson. Help students develop ways to remember the terms. For example: **[Ask]** "Why are the angles called *alternate interior angles*? *Alternate exterior angles*? *Corresponding angles*?" [It is because of their relationship to the transversal and the parallel lines.]

Some students may have drawn the transversal perpendicular to the parallel lines. For Investigation 1, they may have conjectured that other angles were congruent or right angles. Encourage critique of this idea. For Investigation 2, they may have conjectured that the lines were parallel. Elicit the idea that the conjecture is an if-then statement; unless the special case is included in the "if" part, the conjecture is not complete even if the "then" part is true for the special case.

[Ask] "What kind of reasoning did you use to develop your conjectures?" [It was probably inductive.] If some students are at higher van Hiele levels, challenge them to prove their results deductively, assuming the Linear Pair and Vertical Angles Conjectures to be true. They won't be able to succeed unless they assume the truth of one of the three conjectures introduced in this lesson. If students are becoming too frustrated, direct them to the proof in the example. But remember that at this stage the book is modeling thinking at a higher van Hiele level. You should assess students based on their level of reasoning skills, not on skills they are not yet ready to use.

Close by discussing the importance of parallels in separating Euclidean geometry from non-Euclidean geometries.

Step 2 The conjecture is not true.

Step 2 What happens if the lines you start with are not parallel? Check whether your conjectures will work with nonparallel lines.

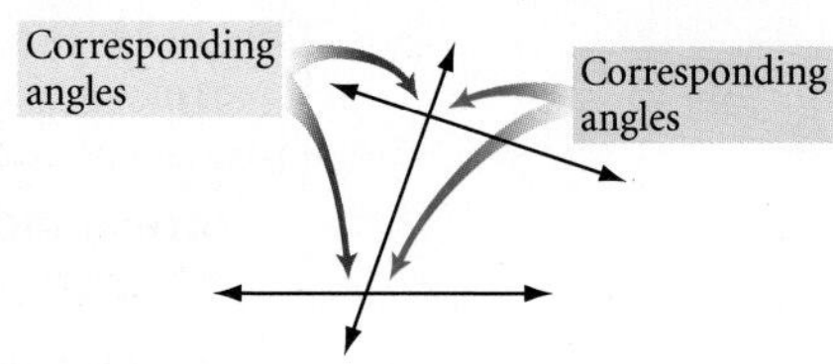

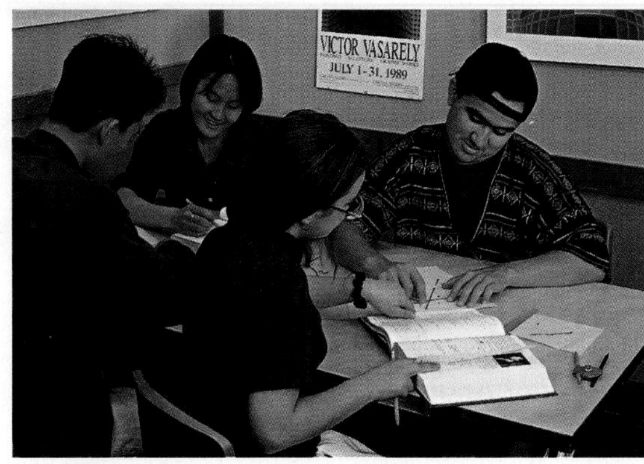

What about the converse of each of your conjectures? Suppose you know that a pair of corresponding angles, or alternate interior angles, is congruent. Will the lines be parallel? Is it possible for the angles to be congruent but for the lines not to be parallel?

Investigation 2
Is the Converse True?

You will need

- lined paper or a straightedge
- patty paper
- a protractor

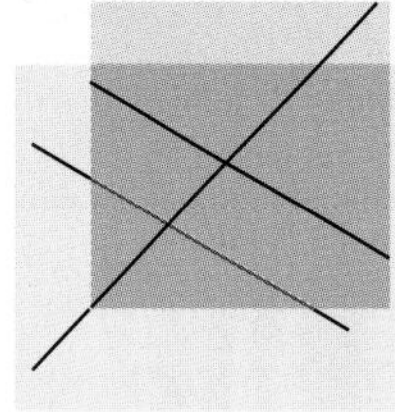

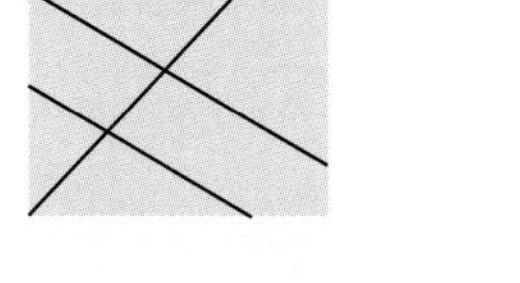

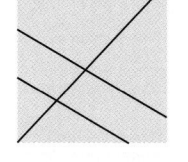

Step 1 Draw two intersecting lines on your paper. Copy these lines onto a piece of patty paper. Because you copied the angles, the two sets of angles are congruent.

Slide the top copy so that the transversal stays lined up.

Trace the lines and the angles from the bottom original onto the patty paper again. When you do this, you are constructing sets of congruent corresponding angles. Mark the congruent angles.

Step 1 yes

Are the two lines parallel? You can test to see if the distance between the two lines remains the same, which guarantees that they will never meet.

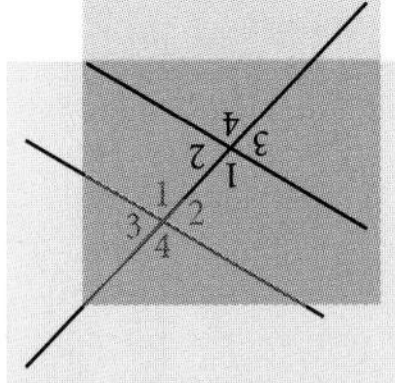

Step 2 alternate interior and alternate exterior angles; yes

Step 2 Repeat Step 1, but this time rotate your patty paper 180° so that the transversal lines up again. What kinds of congruent angles have you created? Trace the lines and angles and mark the congruent angles. Are the lines parallel? Check them.

Step 3 Compare your results with those of your group. If your results do not agree, discuss them until you have convinced each other. Complete the conjecture below and add it to your conjecture list.

Converse of the Parallel Lines Conjecture C-4

If two lines are cut by a transversal to form pairs of congruent corresponding angles, congruent alternate interior angles, or congruent alternate exterior angles, then the lines are _?_. parallel

You used inductive reasoning to discover all three parts of the Parallel Lines Conjecture. However, if you accept any one of them as true, you can use deductive reasoning to show that the others are true.

EXAMPLE Suppose we assume that the Vertical Angles Conjecture is true. Write a paragraph proof showing that if corresponding angles are congruent, then the Alternate Interior Angles Conjecture is true.

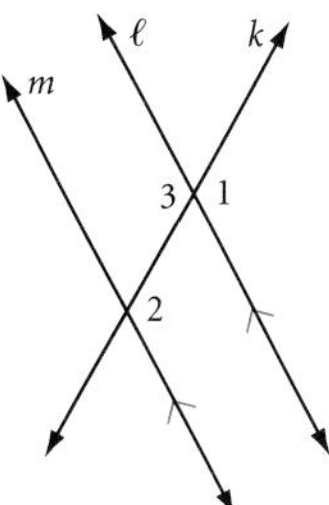

▶ ***Solution***

Paragraph Proof

Lines ℓ and m are parallel and intersected by transversal k. Pick any two alternate interior angles, such as $\angle 2$ and $\angle 3$. According to the Corresponding Angles Conjecture, $\angle 2 \cong \angle 1$. And, according to the Vertical Angles Conjecture, $\angle 1 \cong \angle 3$. Substitute $\angle 3$ for $\angle 1$ in the first statement to get $\angle 2 \cong \angle 3$. But $\angle 2$ and $\angle 3$ are alternate interior angles. Therefore, if the corresponding angles are congruent, then the alternate interior angles are congruent. ■

Here are the algebraic steps:

$\angle 2 \cong \angle 1$
$\angle 3 \cong \angle 1$
So $\angle 2 \cong \angle 3$

It helps to visualize each statement and to mark all congruences you know on your paper.

EXERCISES

Use your new conjectures in Exercises 1–6. A small letter in an angle represents the angle measure.

1. $r \parallel s$
$w =$ _?_ 63°

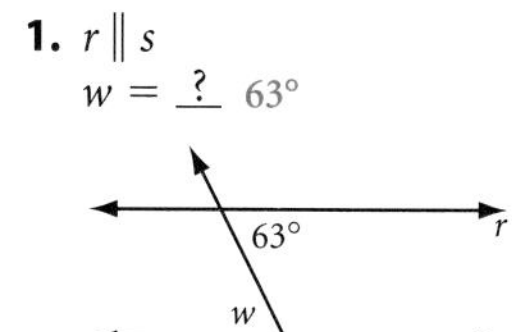

2. $p \parallel q$
$x =$ _?_ 90°

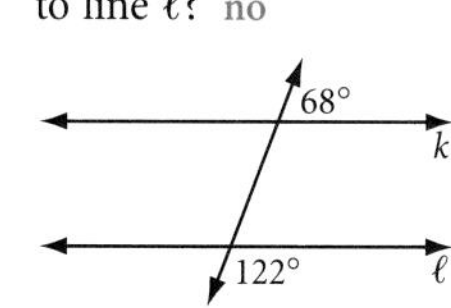

3. Is line k parallel to line ℓ? no

68°
k
122°
ℓ

ASSIGNING HOMEWORK

Essential	1–7
Performance assessment	9
Portfolio	11
Journal	8
Group	8, 10, 11
Review	12–21

MATERIALS

- Exercise 7 (T), *optional*

▶ ***EXAMPLE***

This example shows how to prove one angle relationship from another deductively. The justification for "substitution" is that angles congruent to the same angle are congruent to each other. This is a good example of how more detailed theorems would have to be developed in order to use a two-column proof, often distracting from the concepts. The orange bullet is used to indicate the end of a proof.

Assessing Progress

Assess students' abilities in collecting data, observing data, and making conjectures. Check their familiarity with parallel lines, angles, and vertical angles and their skill at using a protractor. Assess students' level of thinking. Those who easily understand a deductive proof when it is presented are at van Hiele level 2.

Closing the Lesson

Remind students of the important ideas: A transversal crossing two lines forms eight angles. Our conjectures say that if the lines are parallel, then the four pairs of corresponding angles are congruent, as are the two pairs of alternate interior angles and the two pairs of alternate exterior angles. Conversely, if one line crosses two others and if a pair of corresponding, alternate interior, or alternate exterior angles are congruent, we have conjectured that the two lines crossed are parallel. When we assumed one of the first three conjectures, we could prove the other two deductively.

BUILDING UNDERSTANDING

The exercises apply the conjectures about angle relationships when a transversal cuts two parallel lines. Students often must extend lines to see the pairs of angles.

▶Helping with the Exercises

Exercise 4 Students may guess that the measure of angle y is the only measure given in the diagram, but to get them to justify that conjecture you may need to suggest that they extend some of the sides so that they can see transversals cutting parallel lines.

Exercise 5 From Exercise 4, students may conjecture that if two lines are parallel, then consecutive interior angles are supplementary. That conjecture alone does not provide a justification for the claim that quadrilateral *FISH* is a parallelogram; only the converse of that conjecture could be used. On the other hand, if the sides of quadrilateral *FISH* are extended, then a justification can be provided using the Converse of the Parallel Lines Conjecture.

Exercise 6 Students can use alternate interior angles and linear pairs of angles.

Exercise 7 As students' conjecture lists grow, so does the number of conjectures needed to solve these angle-network exercises. Be sure students are aware that the angle measures need not be found in alphabetical order. If students get stuck, encourage them to find any angle measure they can, even if it's not labeled. These exercises, often called *angle-search exercises,* are great activities for pair share. Taking turns, one student finds an answer and explains why, then the other student finds an angle measure and explains why, continuing back and forth. After using pair share with a few of these angle-search exercises, you can introduce a variation. Taking turns, one student finds an answer and the second student explains why. Then the second student finds an angle measure and the first student explains why.

4. Quadrilateral *TUNA* is a parallelogram. $y = \underline{?}$ ⓗ 57°

5. Is quadrilateral *FISH* a parallelogram? yes

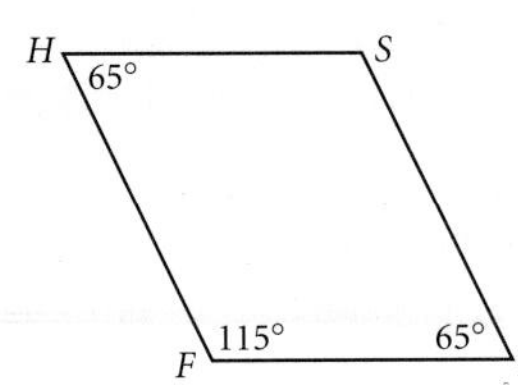

6. $m \parallel n$
$z = \underline{?}$ ⓗ 113°

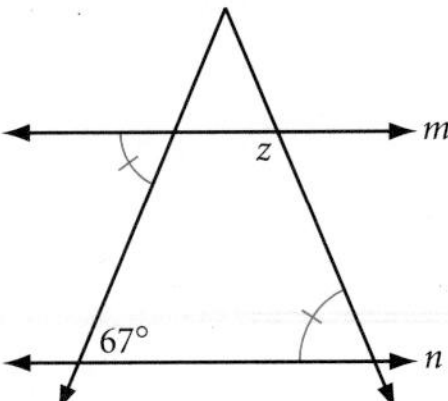

7. Trace the diagram below. Calculate each lettered angle measure. ⓗ

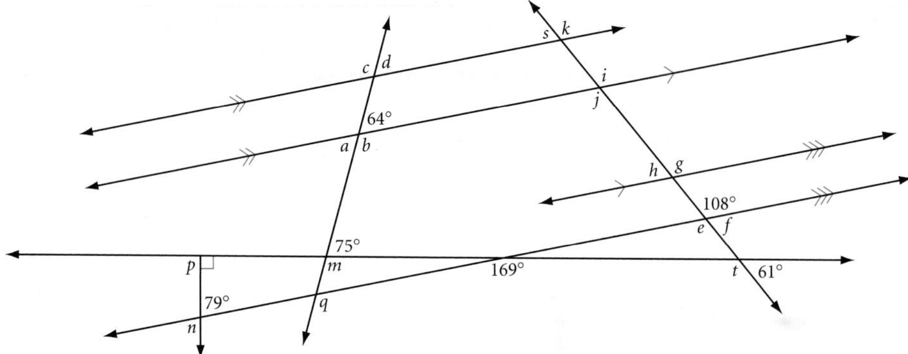

8. You've seen before how parallel lines appear to meet in the distance. Let's look at the converse of this effect: The top and the bottom of the Vietnam Veterans Memorial Wall appear to be parallel because they appear to meet so far in the distance. Consider the diagram of the corner of the memorial, shown below. You know that line ℓ_1 and line ℓ_2 eventually meet. Is the blue shaded portion of the wall a rectangle? Write a paragraph proof explaining why it is or is not a rectangle.

Possible answers might include $a + b < 180°$; they can't both be right angles, so the shaded portion is not rectangular. Students might also analyze height of people compared to the wall in the photo.

Sculptor Maya Lin designed the Vietnam Veterans Memorial Wall in Washington, D.C. Engraved in the granite wall are the names of United States armed forces service members who died in the Vietnam War or remain missing in action. To learn more about the Memorial Wall and Lin's other projects, visit www.keymath.com/DG

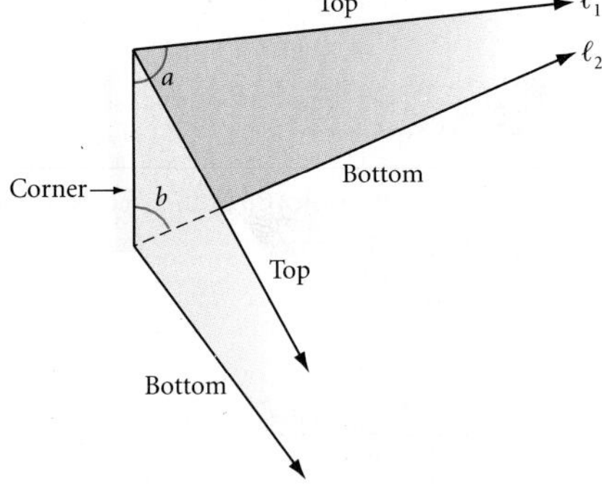

7. $a = d = 64°, b = c = 116°,$
$e = g = i = j = k = 108°, f = h = s = 72°,$
$m = 105°, n = 79°, p = 90°, q = 116°, t = 119°$

Exercise 8 Students could argue from the size of the people in the picture that the top and bottom of the wall are not parallel. Though they might mention that the angles do not measure 180°, that observation alone is not enough to prove anything about lines in a photograph or perspective drawings that do not lie in the plane of the picture.

9. What's wrong with this picture?

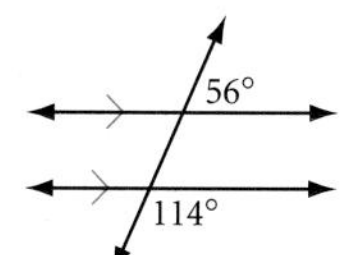

$56° + 114° = 170° \neq 180°$. Thus, the lines marked as parallel cannot really be parallel.

10. What's wrong with this picture?

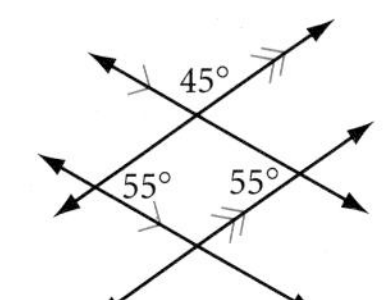

Alternate interior angles measure 55°, but $55° + 45° \neq 180°$.

11. A periscope permits a sailor on a submarine to see above the surface of the ocean. This periscope is designed so that the line of sight *a* is parallel to the light ray *b*. The middle tube is perpendicular to the top and bottom tubes. What are the measures of the incoming and outgoing angles formed by the light rays and the mirrors in this periscope? Are the surfaces of the mirrors parallel? How do you know?

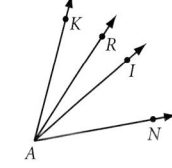

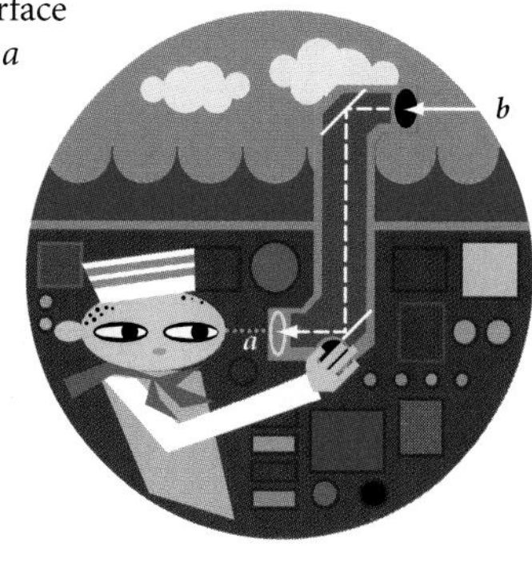

Review

1.5 **12.** What type (or types) of triangle has one or more lines of symmetry? isosceles triangle

1.5 **13.** What type (or types) of quadrilateral has only rotational symmetry? ⓗ

1.1 **14.** If *D* is the midpoint of $\overline{AC}$ and *C* is the midpoint of $\overline{BD}$, what is the length of $\overline{AB}$ if $BD = 12$ cm? 18 cm

2.2 **15.** If $\overrightarrow{AI}$ is the angle bisector of $\angle KAN$ and $\overrightarrow{AR}$ is the angle bisector of $\angle KAI$, what is $m\angle RAN$ if $m\angle RAK = 13°$? 39°

For Exercises 16–18, draw each polygon on graph paper. Relocate the vertices according to the rule. Connect the new points to form a new polygon. Describe what happened to the figure. Is the new polygon congruent to the original?

1.5 **16. Rule:** Subtract 1 from each *x*-coordinate. ⓗ

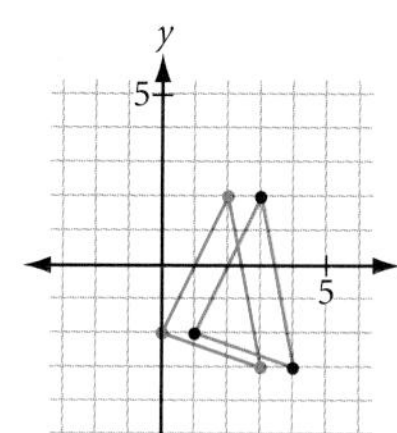

1.5 **17. Rule:** Reverse the sign of each *x*- and *y*-coordinate.

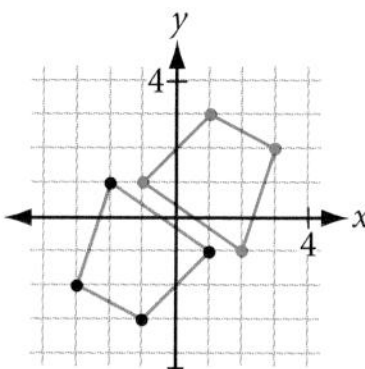

1.5 **18. Rule:** Switch the *x*- and *y*-coordinates. Pentagon *LEMON* with vertices:

$L(-4, 2)$
$E(-4, -3)$
$M(0, -5)$
$O(3, 1)$
$N(-1, 4)$

2.4 **19.** If everyone in the town of Skunk's Crossing (population 84) has a telephone, how many different lines are needed to connect all the phones to each other? 3486

20. How many squares of all sizes are in a 4-by-4 grid of squares? (There are more than 16!) ⓗ 30 squares (one 4-by-4, four 3-by-3, nine 2-by-2, and sixteen 1-by-1)

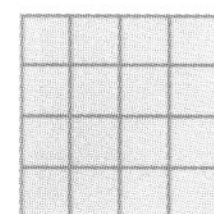

11. The incoming and outgoing angles measure 45°. Possible explanation: Yes, the alternate interior angles are congruent and thus, by the Converse of the Parallel Lines Conjecture, the mirrors are parallel.

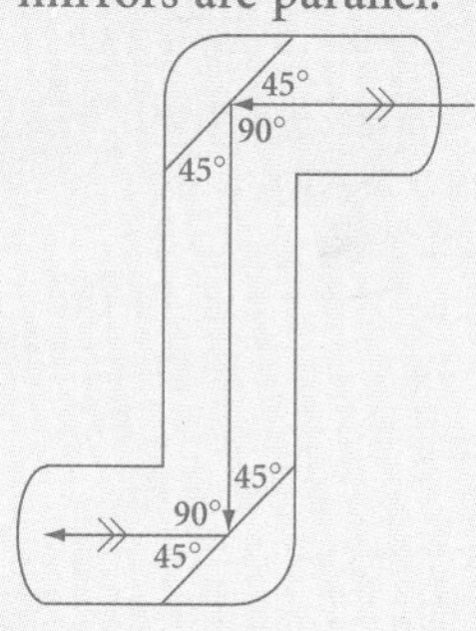

Exercises 12, 13 These exercises review Chapter 0. If you skipped Chapter 0, you can use them to assess what students know about symmetry.

13. a parallelogram that is not also a rectangle or a rhombus

16. The triangle moved to the left 1 unit. Yes, congruent to original.

17. The quadrilateral was reflected across both axis. Yes, congruent to original.

18. The pentagon was reflected across the line $x = y$. Yes, congruent to the original.

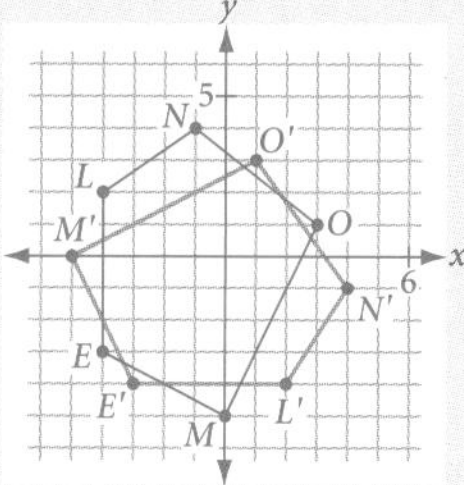

EXTENSIONS

A. Incorporate several sets of parallel lines within one drawing, and have students find missing angle measures.

B. Students could be challenged to think about "lines" on a cylinder. Lines are the shortest paths between points. [Some lines go "along" the cylinder, parallel to the center axis of the cylinder. Others are actually circles around the cylinder. Still others are helixes around the cylinder.] As on a plane, two of these "lines" are parallel if they don't intersect. Are the angle properties true for transversals crossing two parallel lines on a cylinder?

2.3 **21.** Assume the pattern of blue and yellow shaded **T**'s continues. Copy and complete the table for blue shaded and yellow shaded squares and for the total number of squares. ⓗ

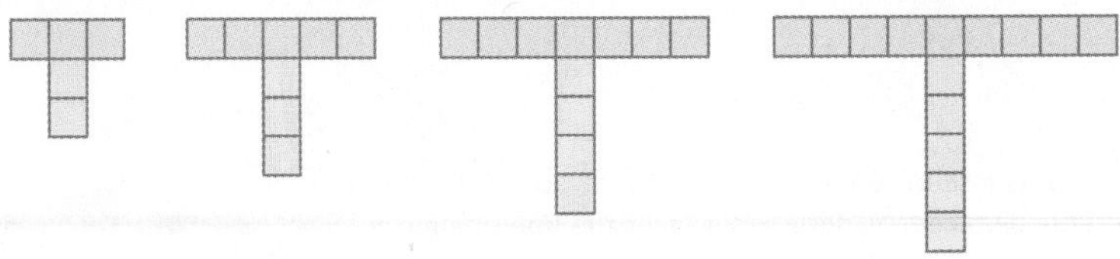

The T-formation

Figure number	1	2	3	4	5	6	...	n	...	35
Number of yellow squares	2	3	4	5	6	7	...	$n+1$	...	36
Number of blue squares	3	5	7	9	11	13	...	$2n+1$	...	71
Total number of squares	5	8	11	14	17	20	...	$3n+2$	...	107

project

LINE DESIGNS

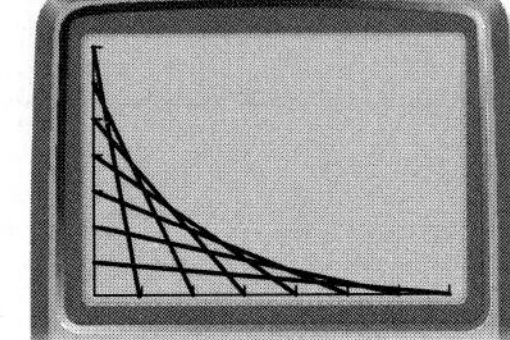

Can you use your graphing calculator to make the line design shown at right? You'll need to recall some algebra. Here are some hints.

1. The x- and y-ranges are set to minimums of 0 and maximums of 7.
2. The design consists of the graphs of seven lines.
3. The equation for one of the lines is $y = -\frac{1}{7}x + 1$.
4. There's a simple pattern in the slopes and y-intercepts of the lines.

You're on your own from here. Experiment! Then create a line design of your own and write the equations for it.

Supporting the project

In Chapter 0, some students created line designs by hand. Using this project as a starting point, they can create line designs on a graphing calculator.

OUTCOMES

- ▸ The equations for the lines are $y = -\frac{1}{7}x + 1$, $y = -\frac{2}{6}x + 2$, $y = -\frac{3}{5}x + 3$, $y = -\frac{4}{4}x + 4$, $y = -\frac{5}{3}x + 5$, $y = -\frac{6}{2}x + 6$, and $y = -7x + 7$.
- Student creates another line design and states equations that match the lines.

Slope

The slope of a line is a measure of its steepness. Measuring slope tells us the steepness of a hill, the pitch of a roof, or the incline of a ramp. On a graph, slope can tell us the rate of change, or speed.

To calculate slope, you find the ratio of the vertical distance to the horizontal distance traveled, sometimes referred to as "rise over run."

$$\text{slope} = \frac{\text{vertical change}}{\text{horizontal change}}$$

One way to find slope is to use a **slope triangle.** Then use the coordinates of its vertices in the formula.

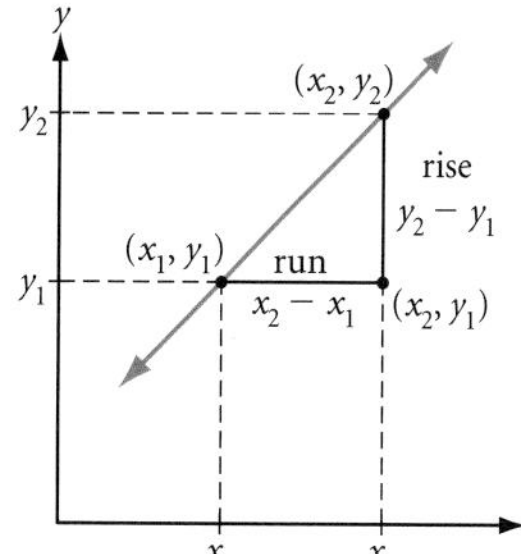

Slope Formula

The slope m of a line (or segment) through two points with coordinates (x_1, y_1) and (x_2, y_2) is

$$m = \frac{y_2 - y_1}{x_2 - x_1}$$

where $x_2 - x_1 \neq 0$.

EXAMPLE

Draw the slope triangle and find the slope for $\overline{AB}$.

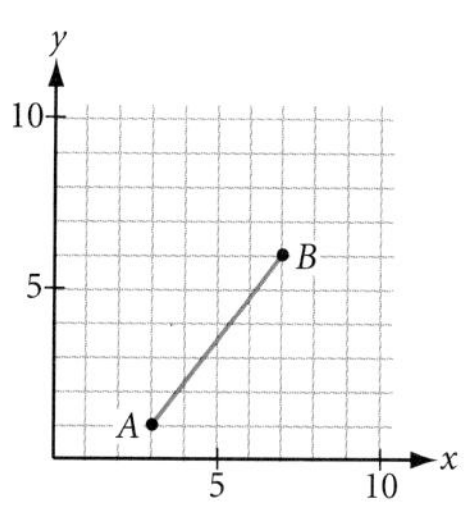

▶ Solution

Draw the horizontal and vertical sides of the slope triangle below the line. Use them to calculate the side lengths.

$$m = \frac{y_2 - y_1}{x_2 - x_1} = \frac{6-1}{7-3} = \frac{5}{4}$$

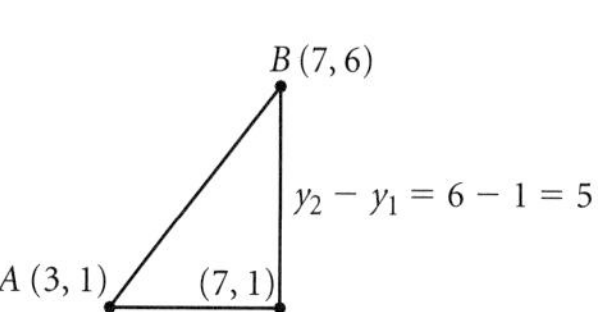

Note that if the slope triangle is *above* the line, you subtract the numbers in reverse order, but still get the same result.

$$m = \frac{1-6}{3-7} = \frac{-5}{-4} = \frac{5}{4}$$

USING YOUR ALGEBRA SKILLS 2

PLANNING

LESSON OUTLINE

One day:

10 min Examples

35 min Exercises

MATERIALS

none

TEACHING

One measure of steepness is slope. For many students, a simpler way to measure steepness is to measure the angle of the line with the horizontal or the vertical. (Thinking about a ratio requires keeping in mind two numbers, whereas the measure of an angle is only one number.) **[Link]** In trigonometric terms, the slope is the tangent of this angle. Another ratio that might be used is the sine of the angle; in fact, in measuring the steepness of a given object, it's often easier to measure the diagonal than to measure the horizontal change.

▶ EXAMPLE

The slope of any horizontal line is zero. For vertical lines, the slope is undefined.

NCTM STANDARDS

CONTENT		PROCESS	
	Number		Problem Solving
✓	Algebra		Reasoning
✓	Geometry	✓	Communication
	Measurement	✓	Connections
	Data/Probability	✓	Representation

LESSON OBJECTIVE

- Review slope as a measure of steepness and how to use slope triangles to calculate the slope of a graphed line

BUILDING UNDERSTANDING

The exercises ask students to calculate the slopes of lines through points whose coordinates are given, to relate slope to speed, and to apply slope to road grades and roofs.

ASSIGNING HOMEWORK

Essential	1–8
Performance assessment	8
Journal	6, 10
Group	9

▶ Helping with the Exercises

Exercises 1–3 [Alert] You may need to remind students that they must subtract the coordinates in the same order.

8. At 6 m/sec Skater 1 is 4 m/sec faster than Skater 2 at 2 m/sec.

Exercise 9 [Ask] "What road that you know has the steepest grade? What do you think the grade is?" Road grades rarely exceed 15%.

9. A 100% grade has a slope of 1. It has an inclination of 45°, so you probably could not drive up it. You might be able to walk up it. Grades higher than 100% are possible, but the angle of inclination would be greater than 45°.

Exercise 10 A shallow roof whose pitch is "2 in 12" is quite easy to walk on. A steep roof, which would be difficult to walk on, might have a slope of "6 in 12," or $\frac{1}{2}$. The roof pictured ("24 to 12") is too steep to walk on. To repair it, a roofer might use a ladder.

10. The slope of the adobe house flat roof is approximately 0. The Connecticut roof is steeper with a slope of about 2 and will shed the snow.

The slope is positive when the line goes up from left to right. The slope is negative when the line goes down from left to right. When is the slope 0? What is the slope of a vertical line?

EXERCISES

In Exercises 1–3 find the slope of the line through the given points.

1. (16, 0) and (12, 8) -2

2. $(-3, -4)$ and $(-16, 8)$ $-\frac{12}{13}$

3. (5.3, 8.2) and $(0.7, -1.5)$ $\frac{97}{46} \approx 2.1$

4. A line through points $(-5, 2)$ and $(2, y)$ has a slope of 3. Find y. $y = 23$

5. A line through points $(x, 2)$ and $(7, 9)$ has a slope of $\frac{7}{3}$. Find x. $x = 4$

6. Find the coordinates of three more points that lie on the line passing through the points (0, 0) and $(3, -4)$. Explain your method. Any point of the form $(3p, -4p)$. Possible answer: $(6, -8)$, $(9, -12)$, and $(12, -16)$. To find another point go over 3 and down 4.

7. What is the speed, in miles per hour, represented by Graph A? ≈ 66.7 mi/hr

8. From Graph B, which in-line skater is faster? How much faster?

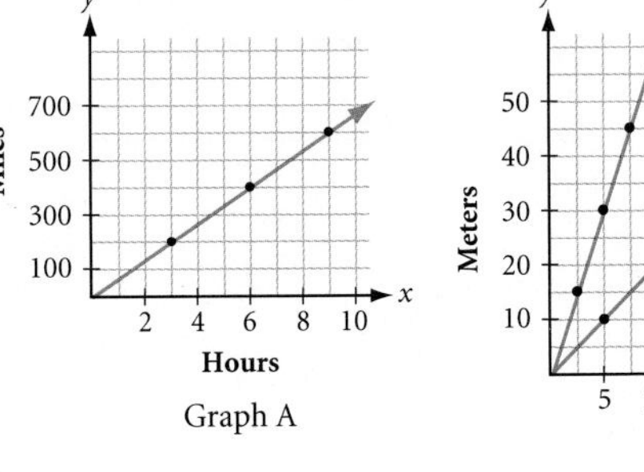

Graph A

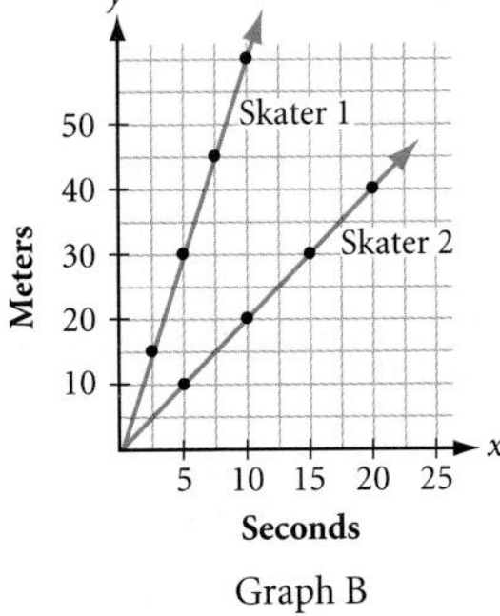

Graph B

9. The grade of a road is its slope, given as a percent. For example, a road with a 6% grade has slope $\frac{6}{100}$. It rises 6 feet for every 100 feet of horizontal run. Describe a 100% grade. Do you think you could drive up it? Could you walk up it? Is it possible for a grade to be greater than 100%?

10. What's the slope of the roof on the adobe house? Why might a roof in Connecticut be steeper than a roof in the desert?

Adobe house, New Mexico

Pitched-roof house, Connecticut

Exploration

Patterns in Fractals

In Lesson 2.1, you discovered patterns and used them to continue number sequences. In most cases, you found each term by applying a rule to the term before it. Such rules are called **recursive rules.** Some picture patterns are also generated by recursive rules. You find the next picture in the sequence by looking at the picture before it and comparing that to the picture before it, and so on.

The Geometer's Sketchpad® can repeat a recursive rule on a figure using a command called **Iterate.** Using **Iterate,** you can create the initial stages of fascinating geometric figures called **fractals.** Fractals have **self-similarity,** meaning that if you zoom in on a part of the figure, it looks like the whole. A true fractal would need infinitely many applications of the recursive rule. In this exploration, you'll use **Iterate** to create the first few stages of a fractal called the **Sierpiński triangle.**

In this procedure you will construct a triangle, its interior, and midpoints on its sides. Then you will use **Iterate** to repeat the process on three outer triangles formed by connecting the midpoints and vertices of the original triangle.

This fern frond illustrates self-similarity. Notice how each curled leaf resembles the shape of the entire curled frond.

EXPLORATION

PLANNING

LESSON OUTLINE

One day:

5 min Custom tool

40 min Exploration

MATERIALS

- The Geometer's Sketchpad

TEACHING

Students need to be experienced Sketchpad users to complete this exploration.

If your students are less adept with Sketchpad, or you don't have access to Sketchpad software, you might prefer to instead have students explore with the dynamic geometry exploration at www.keymath.com/DG.

[Language] The Sierpiński triangle is sometimes called the *Sierpiński gasket. Gasket* refers to a machine part with lots of holes used to make pieces fit tightly together.

[Language] Notice the phrase *infinitely many* in describing a true fractal. We haven't said "an infinite number of applications" since infinity is not a number. We cannot theoretically count high enough to ever reach infinity.

NCTM STANDARDS

CONTENT		PROCESS	
✓	Number		Problem Solving
	Algebra	✓	Reasoning
✓	Geometry		Communication
✓	Measurement	✓	Connections
	Data/Probability	✓	Representation

LESSON OBJECTIVES

- Explore a fractal design
- Look for patterns in the area and perimeter of a fractal

Guiding the Activity

The triangle shown at the beginning of the project is a Stage 4 triangle.

Procedure Note Step 5 [Language] *Iterate* means "to repeat a process" or "to apply a recursive rule."

Procedure Note Step 10 Students might be confused about what the hiding accomplishes. Hiding each layer of triangles is like removing the area of triangles in previous steps from the triangle. If the triangles at some layer are too small to select easily, suggest that students drag corners of their triangle to enlarge it.

Prodedure Note Step 11 If your computer has an extended keypad (with numeric keypad), students can use + or − on the numeric keypad instead of **Shift+plus** or **Shift+minus.**

Step 2 Using **Shift+minus,** students will not be able to decrease their construction to Stage 0. Remind them that Stage 0 is the original triangle ABC.

Steps 3, 4 One property of many fractals is that they have finite area but infinite perimeter.

Activity
The Sierpiński Triangle

Procedure Note

Sierpiński Triangle Iteration

1. Open a new Sketchpad™ sketch.
2. Use the **Segment** tool to draw triangle ABC.
3. Select the vertices, and construct the triangle interior.
4. Select $\overline{AB}$, $\overline{BC}$, and $\overline{CA}$, in that order, and construct the midpoints D, E, and F.
5. Select the vertices again, and choose **Iterate** from the Transform menu. An Iterate dialog box will open. Select points A, D, and F. This maps triangle ABC onto the smaller triangle ADF.
6. In the Iterate dialog box, choose **Add A New Map** from the Structure pop-up menu. Map triangle ABC onto triangle BED.
7. Repeat Step 6 to map triangle ABC onto triangle CFE.
8. In the Iterate dialog box, choose **Final Iteration Only** from the Display pop-up menu.
9. In the Iterate dialog box, click Iterate to complete your construction.
10. Click in the center of triangle ABC and hide the interior to see your fractal at Stage 3.
11. Use Shift+plus or Shift+minus to increase or decrease the stage of your fractal.

Step 1 The triangle is self-similar because any small triangle contained in it is a miniature copy of the entire triangle.

Step 1 Follow the Procedure Note to create the Stage 3 Sierpiński triangle. The original triangle ABC is a Stage 0 Sierpiński triangle. Practice the last step of the Procedure Note to see how the fractal grows in successive stages. Write a sentence or two explaining what the Sierpiński triangle shows you about self-similarity.

Notice that the fractal's property of self-similarity does not change as you drag the vertices. For an interactive version of this sketch, visit www.keymath.com/DG .

Step 2 What happens to the number of shaded triangles in successive stages of the Sierpiński triangle? Decrease your construction to Stage 1 and investigate. How many triangles would be shaded in a Stage n Sierpiński triangle? Use your construction and look for patterns to complete this table.

Stage number	0	1	2	3	…	n	…	50
Number of triangles	1	3	9	27	…	3^n	…	

$3^{50} \approx 7 \times 10^{23}$

What stage is the Sierpiński triangle shown on page 135? Stage 4

Step 3 The area would eventually become 0.

Step 3 Suppose you start with a Stage 0 triangle (just a plain old triangle) with an area of 1 unit. What would be the shaded area at Stage 1? What happens to the shaded area in successive stages of the Sierpiński triangle? Use your construction and look for patterns to complete this table.

Stage number	0	1	2	3	...	n	...	50
Shaded area	1	$\frac{3}{4}$	$\frac{9}{16}$	$\frac{27}{64}$	...	$\left(\frac{3}{4}\right)^n$	...	$\left(\frac{3}{4}\right)^{50} \approx 6 \times 10^{-7}$

What would happen to the shaded area if you could infinitely increase the stage number?

Step 4 The perimeter of the triangle would become infinite.

Step 4 Suppose you start with a Stage 0 triangle with a perimeter of 6 units. At Stage 1 the perimeter would be 9 units (the sum of the perimeters of the three triangles, each half the size of the original triangle). What happens to the perimeter in successive stages of the Sierpiński triangle? Complete this table.

Stage number	0	1	2	3	...	n	...	50
Perimeter	6	9	$\frac{27}{2}$	$\frac{81}{4}$	...	$6\left(\frac{3}{2}\right)^n$	...	$6\left(\frac{3}{2}\right)^{50} \approx 4 \times 10^9$

What would happen to the perimeter if you could infinitely increase the stage number?

Step 5 nine copies

Step 5 Increase your fractal to Stage 3 or 4. If you print three copies of your sketch, you can put the copies together to create a larger triangle one stage greater than your original. How many copies would you need to print in order to create a triangle two stages greater than your original? Print the copies you need and combine them into a poster or a bulletin board display.

Step 6 Answers will vary.

Step 6 Sketchpad comes with a sample file of interesting fractals. Explore these fractals and see if you can use **Iterate** to create them yourself. You can save any of your fractal constructions by selecting the entire construction and then choosing **Create New Tool** from the Custom Tools menu. When you use your custom tool in the future, the fractal will be created without having to use **Iterate.**

Step 4 It may help students in Step 4 to visualize the Stage 0 triangle as equilateral with each side measuring 2 units. Then the Stage 1 perimeter is the sum of three triangles with side lengths of 1 unit each: $3(3) = 9$.

Step 6 The directory for the sample file of fractals is **Sketchpad|Samples|Sketches|Fractals.gsp.** This is a multipage sketch, with each page containing a unique fractal. The sketch also contains defined custom tools for each fractal.

The word *fractal* was coined by Benoit Mandelbrot (b 1924), a pioneering researcher in this new field of mathematics. He was the first to use high-speed computers to create the figure below, called the Mandelbrot set.

Only the black area is part of the set itself. The rainbow colors represent properties of points near the Mandelbrot set. To learn more about different kinds of fractals, visit www.keymath.com/DG .

CHAPTER REVIEW 2

PLANNING

LESSON OUTLINE

One day:

10 min Reviewing

25 min Exercises and helping individuals

15 min Student self-assessment

MATERIALS

- Exercise 18 (T), *optional*

REVIEWING

Refer students to Example B in Lesson 2.1. Ask them to make a **conjecture** about a **recursive rule** and a **functional rule** for the **sequence.** This process is **inductive reasoning. [Ask]** "What might the corresponding **deductive reasoning** be?" [Checking to see that each term satisfies the proposed rule.] If the rule fails in one case, that case is called a **counterexample.**

[Ask] "What other ideas did you encounter in this chapter?" Students might mention **overlapping segments, overlapping angles, mathematical model, concurrent lines, linear pair, vertical angles, Parallel Lines Conjecture, Converse of the Parallel Lines Conjecture,** and **Sierpiński triangle.**

ASSIGNING HOMEWORK

Completing the even exercises individually and the odd exercises in groups will provide a good review.

Remember to avoid assigning exercises related to any sections of this chapter you de-emphasized.

CHAPTER 2 REVIEW

This chapter introduced you to inductive reasoning. You used inductive reasoning to observe patterns and make conjectures. You learned to disprove a conjecture with a counterexample and to explain why a conjecture is true with deductive reasoning. You learned how to predict number sequences with rules and how to use these rules to model application problems. Then you discovered special relationships about angle pairs and made your first geometry conjectures. Finally you explored the properties of corresponding, alternate interior, and alternate exterior angles formed by a transversal across parallel lines. As you review the chapter, be sure you understand all the important terms. Go back to the lesson to review any terms you're unsure of.

EXERCISES

1. "My dad is in the navy, and he says that food is great on submarines," said Diana. "My mom is a pilot," added Jill, "and she says that airline food is notoriously bad." "My mom is an astronaut trainee," said Julio, "and she says that astronauts' food is the worst imaginable." "You know," concluded Diana, "I bet no life exists beyond Earth! As you move farther and farther from the surface of Earth, food tastes worse and worse. At extreme altitudes, food must taste so bad that no creature could stand to eat. Therefore, no life exists out there." What do you think of Diana's reasoning? Is it inductive or deductive? poor inductive reasoning, but Diana was probably just being funny

2. Think of a situation you observed outside of school in which inductive reasoning was used incorrectly. Write a paragraph or two describing what happened and explaining why you think it was poor inductive reasoning. Answers will vary.

3. Think of a situation you observed outside of school in which deductive reasoning was used incorrectly. Write a paragraph or two describing what happened and explaining why you think it was poor deductive reasoning. Answers will vary.

For Exercises 4–7, find the next two terms in the sequence.

4. 7, 21, 35, 49, 63, 77, ?, ? 91, 105

5. Z, 1, Y, 2, X, 4, W, 8, ?, ? ⓗ V, 16

6. 7, 2, 5, −3, 8, −11, ?, ? 19, −30

7. A, 4, D, 9, H, 16, M, 25, ?, ? ⓗ S, 36

For Exercises 8 and 9, generate the first six terms in the sequence for each function rule.

8. $f(n) = n^2 + 1$ 2, 5, 10, 17, 26, 37

9. $f(n) = 2^{n-1}$ ⓗ 1, 2, 4, 8, 16, 32

For Exercises 10 and 11, draw the next shape in the pattern.

10. 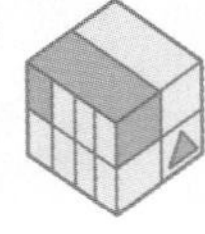 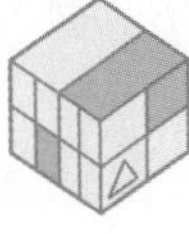 

11. ⓗ 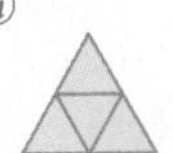   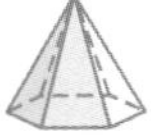

▶ Helping with the Exercises

Encourage any students having difficulty with an exercise to consult with their group or partner. The group might look through the chapter for a similar problem that could help them with the new exercise. If they still need your assistance, you might explicitly point them to an appropriate earlier exercise.

As needed, remind students that the process, not just the answer, is important. What students write about each exercise should demonstrate their understanding of inductive and deductive reasoning. The data they collect, the patterns they observe, and the conjectures they state are all part of the solution.

Exercises 8, 9 [Alert] Students may need to be reminded of the difference between 2^n and n^2.

10. 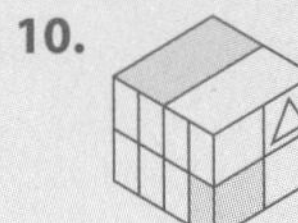

11.  

Exercises 20, 21 As needed, encourage students to make a table to see the relationship.

For Exercises 12–15, find the nth term and the 20th term in the sequence.

12.

n	1	2	3	4	5	6	...	n	...	20
$f(n)$	2	−1	−4	−7	−10	−13	...		...	−55

$-3n + 5$

13.

n	1	2	3	4	5	6	...	n	...	20
$f(n)$	1	4	9	16	25	36	...	n^2	...	400

14. ⓗ

n	1	2	3	4	5	6	...	n	...	20
$f(n)$	0	1	3	6	10	15	...	$\frac{n(n-1)}{2}$	...	190

15. ⓗ

n	1	2	3	4	5	6	...	n	...	20
$f(n)$	1	3	6	10	15	21	...	$\frac{n(n+1)}{2}$	...	210

For Exercises 16 and 17, find a relationship. Then complete the conjecture.

16. Conjecture: The sum of the first 30 positive odd whole numbers is _?_. $30^2 = 900$

17. Conjecture: The sum of the first 30 positive even whole numbers is _?_. ⓗ $(30)(31) = 930$

18. Viktoriya is a store window designer for Savant Toys. She plans to build a stack of blocks similar to the ones shown below but 30 blocks high. Make a conjecture for the value of the nth term and for the value of the 30th term. How many blocks will she need? ⓗ $n^2, 30^2 = 900$

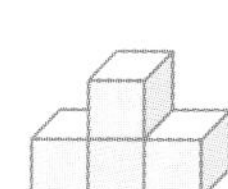
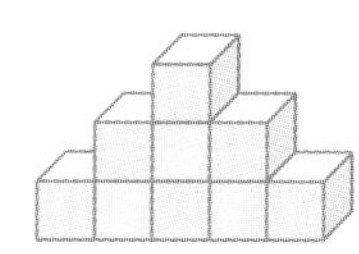
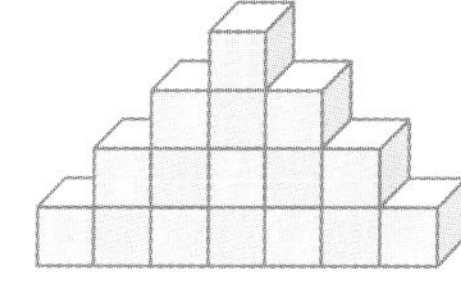

19. The stack of bricks at right is four bricks high. Find the total number of bricks for a stack that is 100 bricks high. $\frac{n(n+1)}{2}, \frac{100(101)}{2} = 5050$

20. For the 4-by-7 rectangular grid, the diagonal passes through 10 squares and 9 interior segments. In an 11-by-101 grid of squares, how many squares will the diagonal pass through? How many interior segments will it pass through? ⓗ It passes through $(10 + 101)$ squares, or 111 squares. It passes through $(10 + 100)$ segments, or 110 interior segments.

21. If at a party there are a total of 741 handshakes and each person shakes hands with everyone else at the party exactly once, how many people are at the party? $\frac{n(n-1)}{2} = 741$. Therefore, $n = 39$.

22. If 28 lines are drawn on a plane, what is the maximum number of points of intersection possible? $\frac{n(n-1)}{2}, \frac{28(27)}{2} = 378$

23. If a whole bunch of lines (no two parallel, no three concurrent) intersect in a plane 2926 times, how many lines are a whole bunch? ⓗ $\frac{n(n-1)}{2} = 2926$. Therefore, $n = 77$.

ASSESSING

Inductive reasoning should not be rushed. Therefore, you might first give a take-home test in which students can see new patterns and make new conjectures without time pressure. You can use the Chapter Review for this purpose. Let students confer with their groups after they've attempted the take-home test. Follow up the take-home test with a smaller, in-class test like those provided in *Assessment Resources.*

FACILITATING SELF-ASSESSMENT

For students whose notebooks are in order, it will be easy to pull out homework for a portfolio. To help students complete the portfolio described in Assessing What You've Learned, suggest that they consider for evaluation their work on Lesson 2.2, Exercise 5; Lesson 2.3, Exercise 7; Lesson 2.4, Exercise 6; and Lesson 2.6, Exercise 11.

24. If in a 54-sided polygon all possible diagonals are drawn from one vertex, they divide the interior of the polygon into how many regions? $n - 2, 54 - 2 = 52$

25. How many sides does the polygon have if all possible diagonals drawn from one vertex divide the interior of the polygon into 54 regions? $n - 2 = 54$. Therefore, $n = 56$.

26. Trace the diagram at right. Calculate each lettered angle measure. $a = 38°, b = 38°, c = 142°, d = 38°, e = 50°, f = 65°, g = 106°, h = 74°$

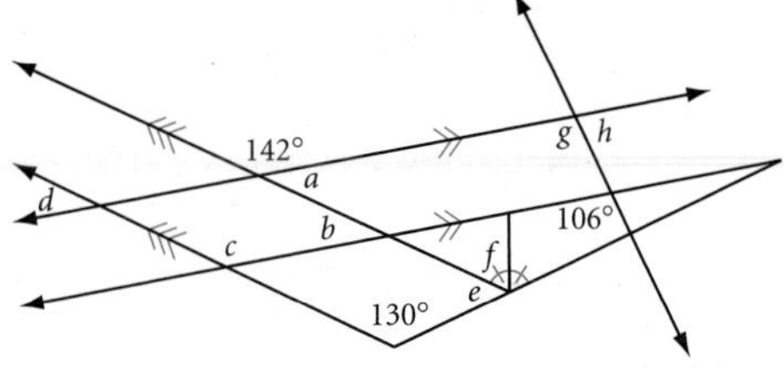

Assessing What You've Learned

WRITE IN YOUR JOURNAL

Many students find it useful to reflect on the mathematics they're learning by keeping a journal. Like a diary or a travel journal, a mathematics journal is a chance for you to reflect on what happens each day and your feelings about it. Unlike a diary, though, your mathematics journal isn't private—your teacher may ask to read it too, and may respond to you in writing. Reflecting on your learning experiences will help you assess your strengths and weaknesses, your preferences, and your learning style. Reading through your journal may help you see what obstacles you have overcome. Or it may help you realize when you need help.

- So far, you have written definitions, looked for patterns, and made conjectures. How does this way of doing mathematics compare to the way you have learned mathematics in the past?
- What are some of the most significant concepts or skills you've learned so far? Why are they significant to you?
- What are you looking forward to in your study of geometry? What are your goals for this class? What specific steps can you take to achieve your goals?
- What are you uncomfortable or concerned about? What are some things you or your teacher can do to help you overcome these obstacles?

KEEPING A NOTEBOOK You should now have four parts to your notebook: a section for homework and notes, an investigation section, a definition list, and now a conjecture list. Make sure these are up-to-date.

UPDATE YOUR PORTFOLIO Choose one or more pieces of your most significant work in this chapter to add to your portfolio. These could include an investigation, a project, or a complex homework exercise. Make sure your work is complete. Describe why you chose the piece and what you learned from it.

CHAPTER

3 Using Tools of Geometry

Overview

In Chapter 3, students perform investigations using geometric constructions and they make conjectures. In **Lesson 3.1,** they learn how to duplicate segments and angles. They learn how to construct perpendicular bisectors in **Lesson 3.2,** a perpendicular through a point to a line in **Lesson 3.3,** angle bisectors in **Lesson 3.4,** and parallel lines in **Lesson 3.5. Using Your Algebra Skills 3** reviews slope of perpendicular and parallel lines. In **Lesson 3.6,** students apply what they have learned about constructions to problems, some of which preview discoveries students will make later in the course. Special emphasis is given to the information needed to determine a triangle. Students practice perspective drawing in an **exploration.** In **Lessons 3.7** and **3.8,** students discover and use four points of concurrency in triangles: incenter, circumcenter, orthocenter, and centroid. The chapter ends with an **exploration** of the Euler line, a line containing the circumcenter, centroid, and orthocenter.

The Mathematics

Geometric Constructions

The Greek philosopher Plato articulated the rules for the ancient game of geometric constructions. The straightedge can be used only for drawing a line segment, not for measuring; and the compass can be used only for drawing a circle with a given center and a given radius measured from that center. Moreover, a Greek compass would collapse after drawing each circle.

Euclid showed how a line could be copied with a collapsing compass in the second proposition of his *Elements.* Therefore, it became allowable to transfer distances with a noncollapsing compass. In *Discovering Geometry* a main function of the compass is to copy a line segment or to transfer a distance from one place to another.

Patty paper (or waxed paper or tracing paper) can replace the compass in transferring distances. Patty paper can't replace a compass for drawing full circles, but students can trace a point or a line through translucent paper, perhaps after folding it.

Three major construction challenges held the attention of mathematicians for many centuries: trisecting any angle, constructing a square with the same area as a given circle (called *squaring the circle*), and constructing a cube with twice the volume of a given cube (called *doubling the cube*). Proofs that these constructions were impossible came only after mathematicians represented them algebraically. They determined the algebraic characteristics of constructible points when represented by coordinates and showed, for example, that to construct trisectors of some angles, they would have to construct points that were not constructible. Then certain points that are not constructible would have to be constructible.

Analytic Geometry and Parallel Lines

If you take a coordinate approach to a geometric postulate system, you can define a line as a set of ordered pairs (x, y) that satisfy an equation $ax + by = c$ for some real numbers a, b, and c. You can define the slope of the line to be $-\frac{c}{b}$, and parallel lines to be lines having the same slope. You can prove as theorems the properties that parallel lines don't intersect and that they are equidistant.

This chapter is based on the assumption that many students are still at van Hiele level 1 or 2 and thus most likely would not appreciate this kind of attention to alternative deductive systems.

Using This Chapter

Lessons 3.1 through 3.5 are fundamental constructions. The patty-paper constructions (pages 147, 153, and 157) are so obvious that you might have students do them with their books closed. The lessons on points of concurrency and the centroid and the two explorations could be treated using the jigsaw method of cooperative groups: groups do different parts and share results.

Many of the constructions in this chapter can be done using geometry software. The Geometer's Sketchpad is an excellent tool for Lessons 3.7 and 3.8.

Expect students to bring their geometry tools with them to class every day along with a notebook and a pencil. As you check student work be aware that answers for constructions based on given segments and angles have been reduced in the *Teacher's Edition.*

Student Assessment in a Cooperative Learning Situation

Make participation a part of each individual's grade, perhaps from 5 to 15 percent. A participation grade may include group participation as well as class participation (answering questions and posing good questions).

To help students and their parents understand the importance of group work, consider giving out a sheet mentioning the importance of teamwork skills and the fact that you base the group participation grade on your observations of group process and not on group results. You want to demonstrate that you believe in the value of cooperative group learning but understand that giving group grades based on results doesn't do this, because such grades tend to encourage students to relinquish their responsibilities to the highest-achieving member of their group.

Resources

Discovering Geometry Resources

Teaching and Worksheet Masters
- Lessons 3.1 and 3.8
- Exploration: Perspective Drawing

Sketchpad Demonstrations
- Lessons 3.7 and 3.8
- Exploration: The Euler Line

Discovering Geometry with The Geometer's Sketchpad
- Lessons 3.2–3.4, 3.7, and 3.8
- Using Your Algebra Skills 3
- Exploration: Perspective Drawing
- Exploration: The Euler Line

Assessment Resources A and B
- Quiz 1 (Lessons 3.1–3.3)
- Quiz 2 (Lessons 3.4–3.6)
- Quiz 3 (Lessons 3.7 and 3.8)
- Chapter 3 Test
- Chapter 3 Constructive Assessment Options
- Chapters 1–3 Exam

Practice Your Skills for Chapter 3

Condensed Lessons for Chapter 3

Other Resources

Geometry Revisited by H. S. M. Coxeter.

For the complete reference on this and other resources see www.keypress.com/DG.

Materials

- construction tools (straightedge, compass, patty paper)
- rulers
- protractors
- mat board, cardboard, or manila folders
- graph paper
- geometry software, *optional*

Pacing Guide

	day 1	day 2	day 3	day 4	day 5	day 6	day 7	day 8	day 9	day 10
standard	3.1	3.2	3.3	quiz, 3.4	3.4	3.5	Algebra 3	3.6	quiz, Exploration	3.7
enriched	3.1	3.2	3.3	quiz, 3.4	3.5	Algebra 3	3.6	quiz	Exploration	3.7
block	3.1, 3.2	3.3, 3.4	quiz, 3.5	Algebra 3, 3.6	Exploration, 3.7	3.8, review	Exploration	review	review, assessment	

	day 11	day 12	day 13	day 14	day 15	day 16	day 17	day 18	day 19	day 20
standard	3.8	Exploration	review	review	assessment					
enriched	3.8	Exploration	review, project	review	assessment					

CHAPTER

3 Using Tools of Geometry

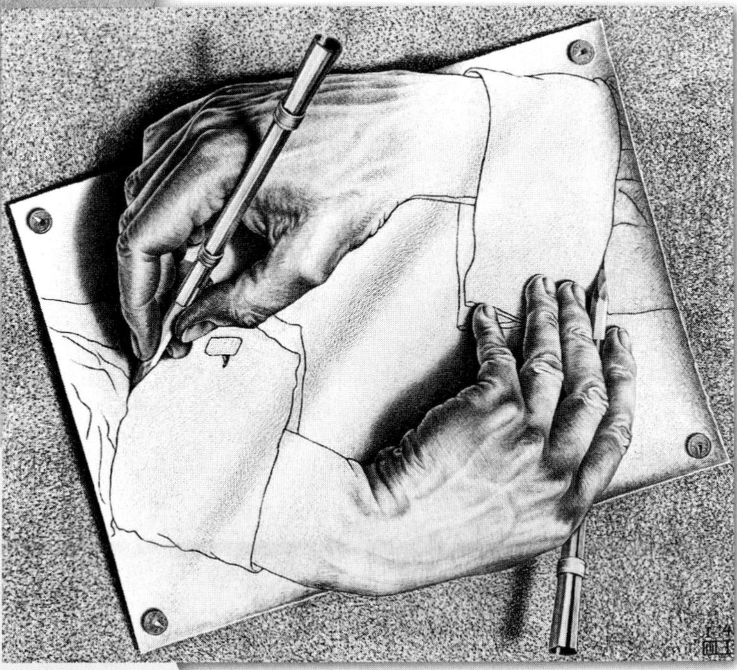

There is indeed great satisfaction in acquiring skill, in coming to thoroughly understand the qualities of the material at hand and in learning to use the instruments we have—in the first place, our hands!—in an effective and controlled way.

M. C. ESCHER

Drawing Hands, M. C. Escher, 1948

OBJECTIVES

In this chapter you will

- learn about the history of geometric constructions
- develop skills using a compass, a straightedge, patty paper, and geometry software
- see how to create complex figures using only a compass, a straightedge, and patty paper

The first tools of geometry are our hands. As the hands emerge out of the print *Drawing Hands,* we see how using tools can turn a flat surface into a spatial illusion. A line drawing can achieve only shallow depth, but the addition of a light source through tone modeling and cast shadows dramatically emphasizes the three dimensions of the forms. The tautology of the hand drawing the hand is a metaphor for the idea that the more we learn, the more we want to learn.

As students construct geometric figures, measure these figures, collect data, and make conjectures, they will be actively involved with building their geometry knowledge.

[Ask] "What gives depth to the hands?" [shadow, tone modeling of the skin to show veins and creases] "If Escher was using his hands as a model while creating the plate for this print, which hand was at the top of the drawing?" [left] "Do you think these are Escher's hands? Why?"

CHAPTER 3 OBJECTIVES

- Introduce the rules of geometric construction with straightedge and compass or patty paper
- Discover construction methods to duplicate a segment, an angle, and a polygon
- Discover methods for constructing perpendicular bisectors, midpoints of line segments, the perpendicular through a point to a line, angle bisectors, and parallel lines
- Make conjectures about perpendicular bisectors and angle bisectors
- Determine how to find the shortest path from a point to a line
- Explore how to construct special angles with parts of 90° angles
- Explore through construction whether or not a triangle is determined by certain given parts
- Discover and explore points of concurrency of angle bisectors, perpendicular bisectors, altitudes of a triangle, and medians.
- Solve application problems related to various constructions
- Distinguish constructions from sketches and drawings of geometric figures

LESSON

3.1

PLANNING

LESSON OUTLINE

One day:

20 min Investigation

5 min Sharing

5 min Closing

15 min Exercises

MATERIALS

- construction tools
- rulers
- protractors
- One Corner (W) for One step

TEACHING

Trying to draw figures with only a straightedge and compass is a game dating back to the classical Greeks. Constructions develop deductive reasoning while giving insight into geometry relationships. Two of the most common constructions are copying a line segment and copying an angle. Start with the one-step investigation (page 143), or use the introduction and then start groups on the steps of the investigations.

INTRODUCTION

The Greek philosopher Plato believed that all natural motion on earth was in a straight line, while all natural motion in the heavens was in circles. From this belief he concluded that the "best" geometric figures were straight lines and circles, and so the "best" geometry tools were the straightedge and compass. Ask whether students agree with his reasoning.

LESSON 3.1

Duplicating Segments and Angles

It is only the first step that is difficult.

MARIE DE VICHY-CHAMROD

The compass, like the straightedge, has been a useful geometry tool for thousands of years. The ancient Egyptians used the compass to mark off distances. During the Golden Age of Greece, Greek mathematicians made a game of geometric constructions. In his work *Elements,* Euclid (325–265 B.C.E.) established the basic rules for constructions using only a compass and a straightedge. In this course you will learn how to construct geometric figures using these tools as well as patty paper.

Constructions with patty paper are a variation on the ancient Greek game of geometric constructions. Almost all the figures that can be constructed with a compass and a straightedge can also be constructed using a straightedge and patty paper, waxed paper, or tracing paper. If you have access to a computer with a geometry software program, you can do constructions electronically.

In the previous chapters, you drew and sketched many figures. In this chapter, however, you'll construct geometric figures. The words *sketch, draw,* and *construct* have specific meanings in geometry.

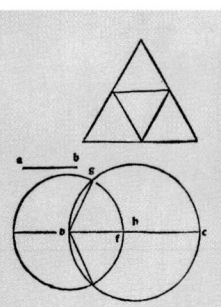

Mathematics CONNECTION

Euclidean geometry is the study of geometry based on the assumptions of Euclid (325–265 B.C.E.). Euclid established the basic rules for constructions using only a compass and a straightedge. In his work *Elements,* Euclid proposed definitions and constructions about points, lines, angles, surfaces, and solids. He also explained why the constructions were correct with deductive reasoning.

A page from a book on Euclid, above, shows some of his constructions and a translation of his explanations from Greek into Latin.

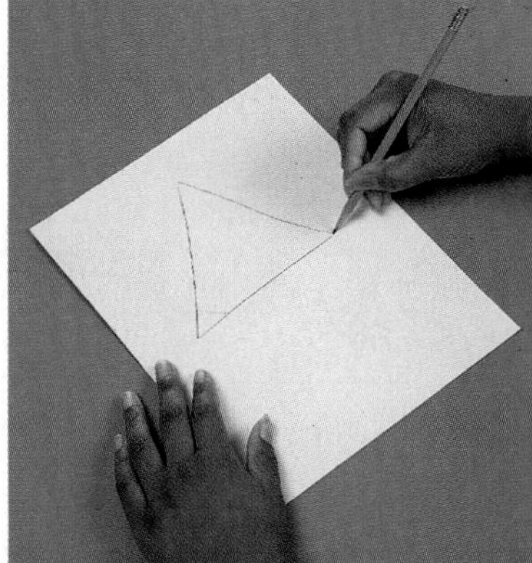

When you *sketch* an equilateral triangle, you may make a freehand sketch of a triangle that looks equilateral. You don't need to use any geometry tools.

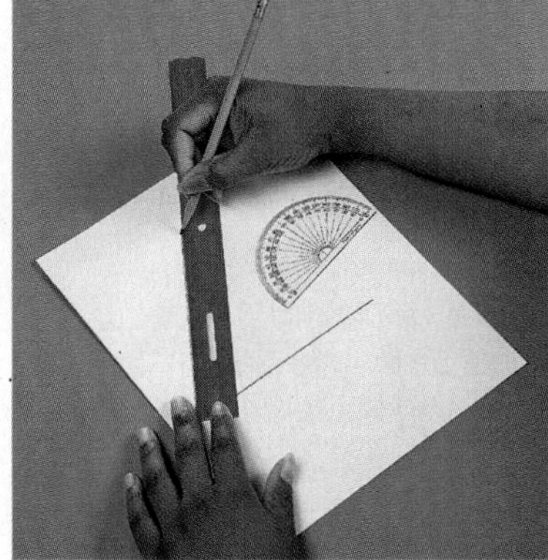

When you *draw* an equilateral triangle, you should draw it carefully and accurately, using your geometry tools. You may use a protractor to measure angles and a ruler to measure the sides to make sure they are equal in measure.

Making the Connection

For links to web sites about Euclid, some containing interactive construction, students can go to www.keymath.com/DG.

LESSON OBJECTIVES

- Introduce geometric construction with straightedge and compass, and with patty paper
- Distinguish among constructions, sketches, and drawings of geometric figures
- Discover construction methods to duplicate a segment, an angle, and a polygon
- Practice using construction tools

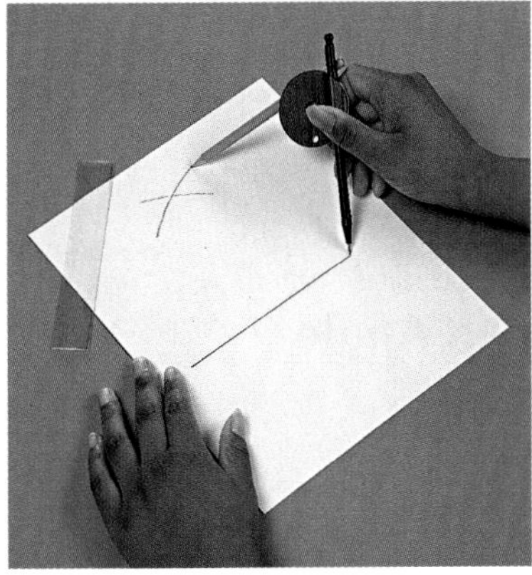

When you *construct* an equilateral triangle with a compass and straightedge, you don't rely on measurements from a protractor or ruler. You must use only a compass and a straightedge. This method of construction guarantees that your triangle is equilateral.

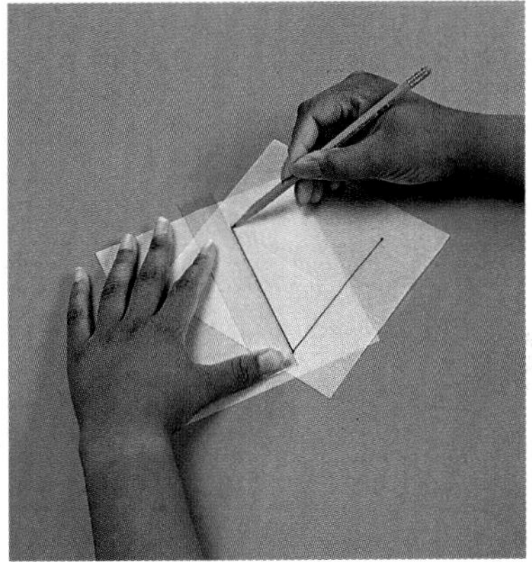

When you *construct* an equilateral triangle with patty paper and straightedge, you fold the paper and trace equal segments. You may use a straightedge to draw a segment, but you may not use a compass or any measuring tools.

When you sketch or draw, use the special marks that indicate right angles, parallel segments, and congruent segments and angles.

By tradition, neither a ruler nor a protractor is ever used to perform geometric constructions. Rulers and protractors are measuring tools, not construction tools. You may use a ruler as a straightedge in constructions, provided you do not use its marks for measuring. In the next two investigations you will discover how to duplicate a line segment using only your compass and straightedge, or using only patty paper.

Investigation 1
Copying a Segment

You will need

- a compass
- a straightedge
- a ruler
- patty paper

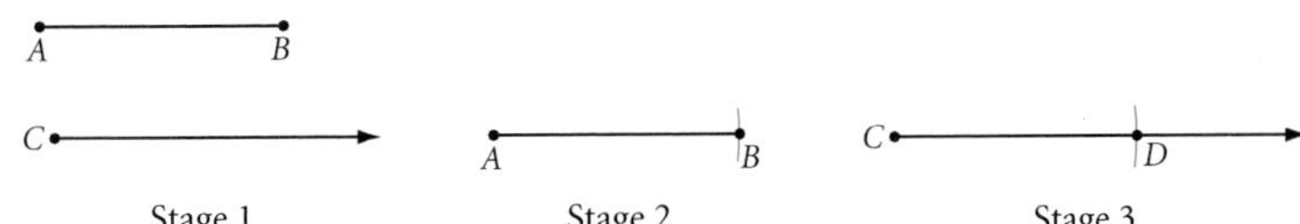

Step 1 The complete construction for copying a segment, $\overline{AB}$, is shown above. Describe each stage of the process.

Step 2 Use a ruler to measure $\overline{AB}$ and $\overline{CD}$. How do the two segments compare?

Step 3 Describe how to duplicate a segment using patty paper instead of a compass.

Step 2 $\overline{AB} \cong \overline{CD}$

Step 3 Trace the segment onto patty paper.

One step Give each group a copy of the One Corner worksheet. Announce that you have a puzzle for each group to solve. In the blank space on the worksheet, students should make as good a copy as possible of the figure shown, using only a straightedge and compass. In particular, they may not use a protractor or a ruler (or any marks on the straightedge). Have them share their various approaches and then have the class read through the introduction in the student book and compare their techniques with those used in the investigations.

Guiding Investigation 1

[Ask] "An arc is actually a part of what?" [a circle] Geometry software draws full circles rather than arcs.

Step 1 Sample answer: Construct a ray that extends longer than $\overline{AB}$. Label the endpoint C. Adjust the compass to match the length of AB. With the compass point on C, make an arc intersecting the ray. Label the point of intersection D so that $AB = CD$.

NCTM STANDARDS

CONTENT	PROCESS
Number	Problem Solving
Algebra	Reasoning
✓ Geometry	✓ Communication
✓ Measurement	✓ Connections
Data/Probability	Representation

Guiding Investigation 2

Suggest that students replicate the construction with compass and straightedge, and with patty paper. Encourage students to help each other with the constructions. Praise a group if all of its members can use the construction tools successfully.

SHARING IDEAS

As students present their constructions, ask them what use they are making of the compass. Elicit the idea that the compass is used not only for making arcs but also for transferring distances. This idea grows in importance throughout the chapter.

Point out the difference between the construction tools (straightedge and compass, or patty paper) and the measuring tools (protractor and ruler). Demonstrate tips and general guidelines for making constructions. (The Circle Master compass works well with overhead projector pens.)

Ask whether students prefer using patty paper or the compass. Although as a tool patty paper doesn't make circles, it can be used instead of a compass for transferring a distance.

Students may wonder why a tool they are using has the same name as a magnetic compass. **[Language]** *Compass* originally meant "measure." A magnetic compass is used to measure angles and indicate direction. This lesson shows how the construction tool can be used to measure distance.

Note that no conjectures are given for this lesson. Appropriate conjectures would have the form "Using only a straightedge and compass, it is possible to . . . ."

For more information about constructions, suggest that your students follow links at www.keymath.com/DG.

Using only a compass and a straightedge, how would you duplicate an angle? In other words, how would you construct an angle that is congruent to a given angle? You may not use your protractor, because a protractor is a measuring tool, not a construction tool.

Investigation 2
Copying an Angle

You will need

- a compass
- a straightedge

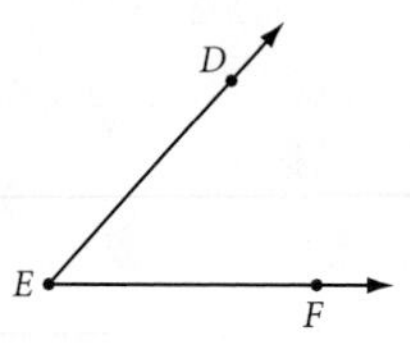

Step 1 Sample answer: Draw a ray. With compass point on E, make an arc intersecting both sides of $\angle DEF$. Make an identical arc with compass point on G so that the arc intersects the ray. Adjust the compass to match the length of the original arc. Mark this length on the second arc.

Step 1 The first two stages for copying $\angle DEF$ are shown below. Describe each stage of the process.

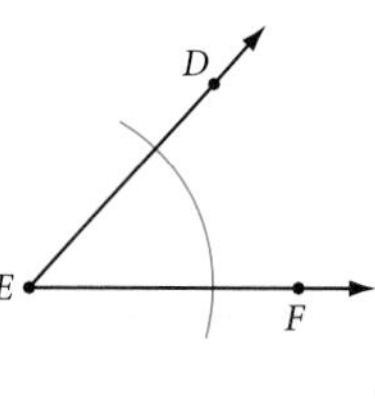

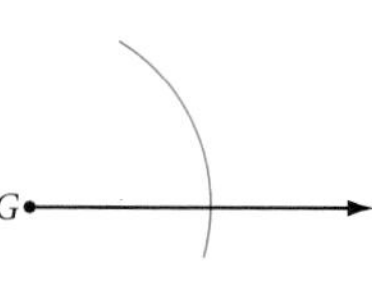

Stage 1

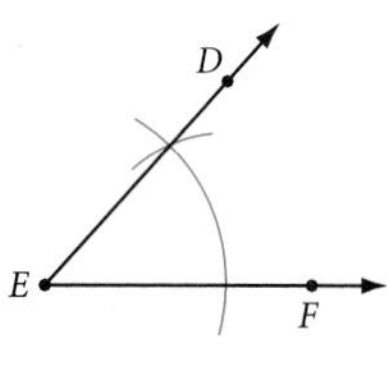

Stage 2

Step 2 What will be the final stage of the construction? Draw the ray as shown.

Step 3 Use a protractor to measure $\angle DEF$ and $\angle G$. What can you state about these angles?

Step 3 $m\angle DEF = m\angle G$, so $\angle DEF \cong \angle G$.

Step 4 Describe how to duplicate an angle using patty paper instead of a compass.

Step 4 Lay patty paper over the given angle, and trace it.

You've just discovered how to duplicate segments and angles using a straightedge and compass or patty paper. These are the basic constructions. You will use combinations of these to do many other constructions. You may be surprised that you can construct figures more precisely *without* using a ruler or protractor!

Called *vintas,* these canoes with brightly patterned sails are used for fishing in Zamboanga, Philippines. What angles and segments are duplicated in this photo?
angle of sail to horizontal, segments and angles in patterns of each sail

Assessing Progress

This lesson gives you opportunities to assess students' understanding of terms such as *segment, ray, line, line segment, length, acute, obtuse, measure of angles, acute triangle, equilateral triangle,* and *congruent quadrilaterals.* Watch also for mention of the ideas of inductive reasoning and conjectures.

Closing the Lesson

Remind students of the two constructions: copying a line segment and copying an angle.

EXERCISES

You will need

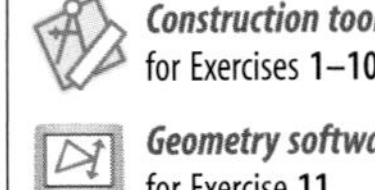

Construction tools for Exercises **1–10**

Geometry software for Exercise **11**

Construction Now that you can duplicate line segments and angles, do the constructions in Exercises 1–10. You will duplicate polygons in Exercises 7 and 10.

1. Using only a compass and a straightedge, duplicate the three line segments shown below. Label them as they're labeled in the figure.

A ———— B   C ———— D   E ———— F

2. Use the segments from Exercise 1 to construct a line segment with length $AB + CD$. ⓗ

3. Use the segments from Exercise 1 to construct a line segment with length $AB + 2EF - CD$.

4. Use a compass and a straightedge to duplicate each angle. There's an arc in each angle to help you.

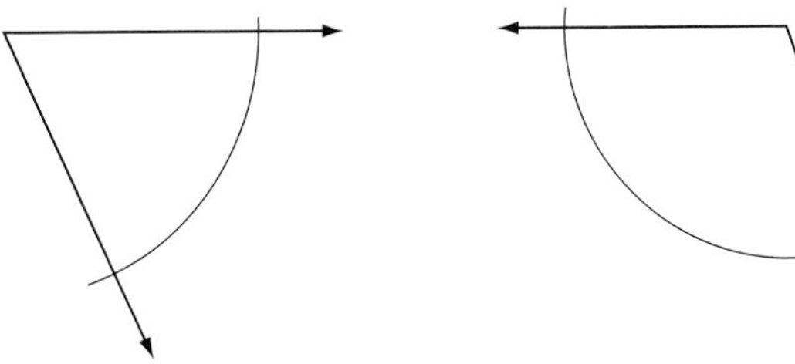

5. Draw an obtuse angle. Label it *LGE*, then duplicate it.

6. Draw two acute angles on your paper. Construct a third angle with a measure equal to the sum of the measures of the first two angles. Remember, you cannot use a protractor—use a compass and a straightedge only.

7. Draw a large acute triangle on the top half of your paper. Duplicate it on the bottom half, using your compass and straightedge. Do not erase your construction marks, so others can see your method.

8. Construct an equilateral triangle. Each side should be the length of this segment.

9. Repeat Exercises 7 and 8 using constructions with patty paper.

10. Draw quadrilateral *QUAD*. Duplicate it, using your compass and straightedge. Label the construction *COPY* so that $QUAD \cong COPY$. ⓗ

11. ***Technology*** Use geometry software to construct an equilateral triangle. Drag each vertex to make sure it remains equilateral.

Exercise 9 Duplicating segments and angles using patty paper is easy: Simply trace the figures. Constructing an equilateral triangle is a much more interesting patty-paper problem. As needed, suggest the use of several pieces of paper. For an extra challenge, suggest that students try to use patty paper to construct an equilateral triangle using its symmetry.

9. For Exercise 7, trace the triangle. For Exercise 8, trace the segment onto three separate pieces of patty paper. Lay them on top of each other, and slide them around until the segments join at the endpoints and form a triangle.

10. One method: Draw $\overline{DU}$. Copy $\angle Q$ and construct $\triangle COY \cong \triangle QUD$. Duplicate $\angle DUA$ at point *O*. Construct $\triangle OYP \cong \triangle UDA$.

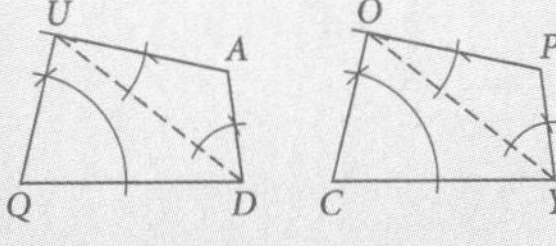

BUILDING UNDERSTANDING

The exercises focus on constructions with straightedge and compass. Remind students that the instruction to "construct" means to use only construction tools, not measurement tools.

ASSIGNING HOMEWORK

Essential	**1–8 (9 if using patty paper)**
Performance assessment	**10**
Portfolio	**3**
Journal	**14**
Review	**12–16**

▶ Helping with the Exercises

1.

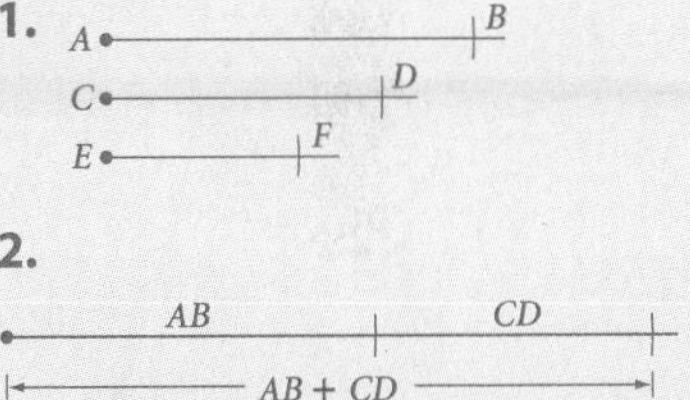

2.

AB   CD

AB + CD

Exercise 3 Students may wonder about how to multiply by 2 to get $2EF$. As needed, remind them that $2EF$ means $EF + EF$.

Exercise 4 Remind students not to write in their books.

Exercise 5 [Alert] Students may have more difficulty copying an obtuse angle than an acute angle. Make sure they can copy either kind of angle.

Exercises 8, 9 Students can make further discoveries about equilateral triangles. For example, they might discover that equilateral triangles are equiangular and vice versa, or they might discover symmetry properties. Encourage your students when they think beyond what is asked in the problem.

See page 768 for answers to Exercises 3–8, 11.

Exercise 13 As needed, remind students to draw a picture.

Exercise 14 This exercise reviews both the definition of an isosceles triangle and the concept of reflectional symmetry. If you did not do Chapter 0, use this problem to teach or review reflectional symmetry.

14. An isosceles triangle is a triangle that has at least one line of reflectional symmetry. Yes, all equilateral triangles are isosceles.

Exercise 15 For students stuck on this problem, suggest that they imagine that one corner of the triangle is pinned to the origin, A, and that points D and Y are rotated 90°.

15. new coordinates: $A'(0, 0)$, $Y'(5, 0)$, $D'(0, 2)$

16.

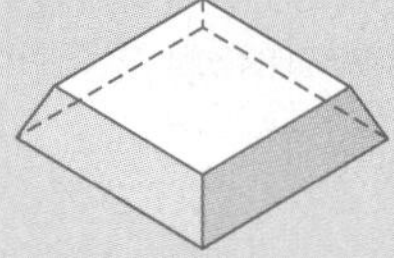

Review

2.6 **12.** Copy the diagram at right. Use the Vertical Angles Conjecture and the Parallel Lines Conjecture to calculate the measure of each angle.
$a = 50°, b = 130°, c = 50°, d = 130°, e = 50°,$
$f = 50°, g = 130°, h = 130°, k = 155°, l = 90°, m = 115°, n = 65°$

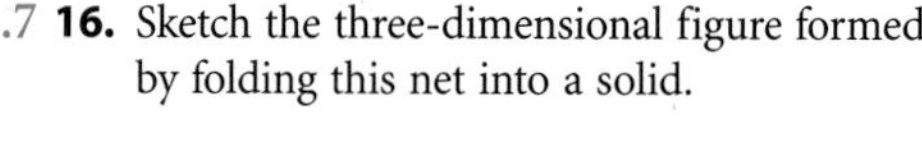

1.7 **13.** Hyacinth is standing on the curb waiting to cross 24th Street. A half block to her left is Avenue J, and Avenue K is a half block to her right. Numbered streets run parallel to one another and are all perpendicular to lettered avenues. If Avenue P is the northernmost avenue, which direction (N, S, E, or W) is she facing? west

1.5 **14.** Write a new definition for an isosceles triangle, based on the triangle's reflectional symmetry. Does your definition apply to equilateral triangles? Explain. ⓗ

1.7 **15.** Draw $\triangle DAY$ after it is rotated 90° clockwise about the origin. Label the coordinates of the vertices.

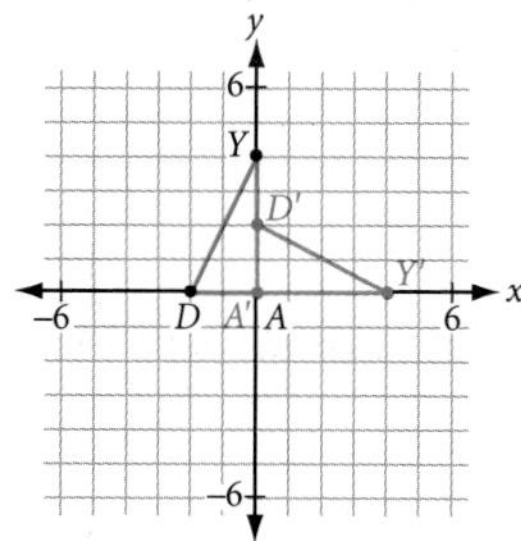

1.7 **16.** Sketch the three-dimensional figure formed by folding this net into a solid.

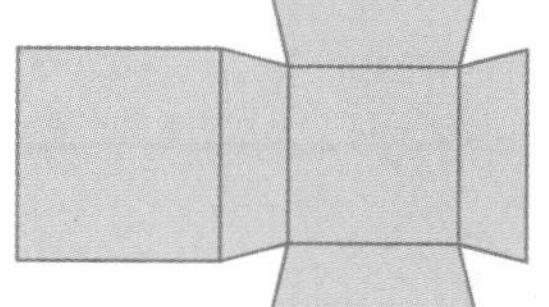

IMPROVING YOUR ALGEBRA SKILLS

Pyramid Puzzle II

Place four different numbers in the bubbles at the vertices of each pyramid so that the two numbers at the ends of each edge add to the number on that edge.

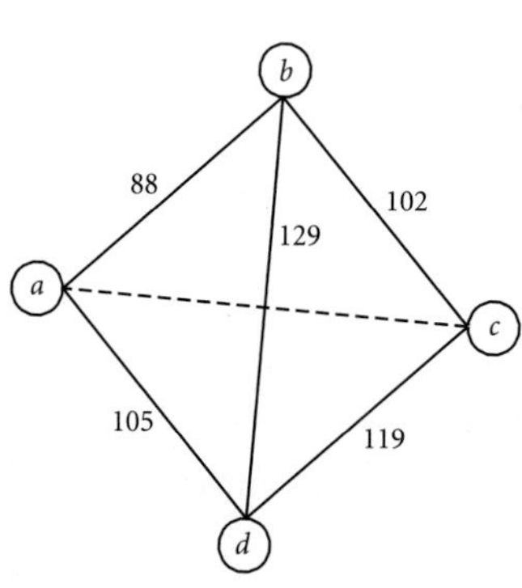

IMPROVING ALGEBRA SKILLS

If students want help getting started, **[Ask]** "What is the difference between d and c?" [Using the equations $b + d = 129$ and $b + c = 102$, students can find that $d - c = 27$.] Combining this equation with $d + c = 119$ gives $2d = 146$.

$a = 32, b = 56, c = 46, d = 73$

LESSON 3.2

Constructing Perpendicular Bisectors

To be successful, the first thing to do is to fall in love with your work.
SISTER MARY LAURETTA

Each segment has exactly one midpoint. A **segment bisector** is a line, ray, or segment in a plane that passes through the midpoint of a segment in a plane.

Segment $\overline{AB}$ has a midpoint O.

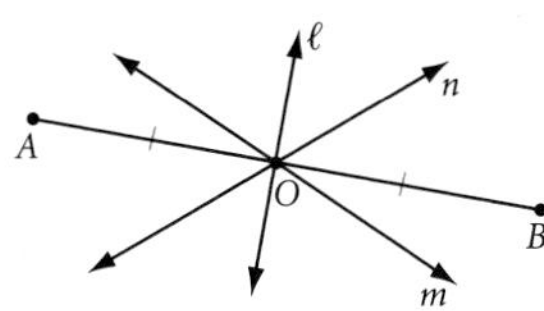

Lines ℓ, m, and n bisect $\overline{AB}$.

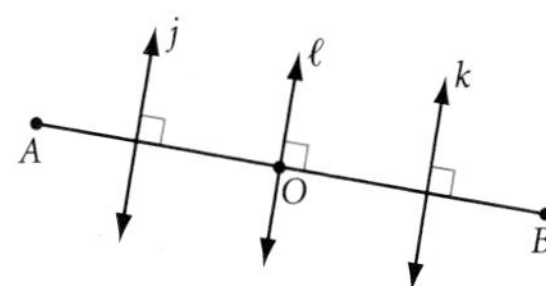

Lines j, k, and ℓ are perpendicular to $\overline{AB}$.

A segment has many perpendiculars and many bisectors, but each segment in a plane has only one bisector that is also perpendicular to the segment. This line is its **perpendicular bisector.**

Line ℓ is the perpendicular bisector of $\overline{AB}$.

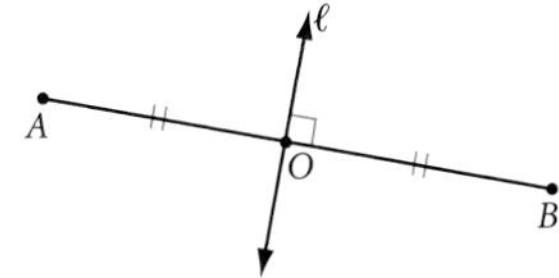

Investigation 1
Finding the Right Bisector

You will need
- patty paper

In this investigation you will discover how to construct the perpendicular bisector of a segment.

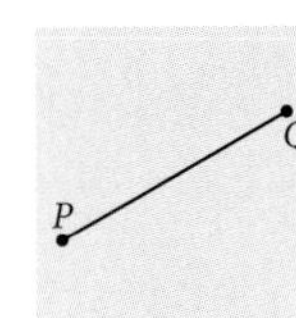

Step 1

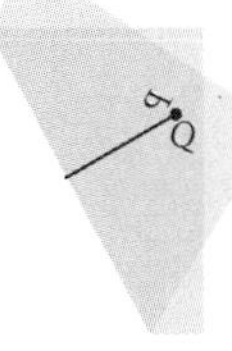

Step 2

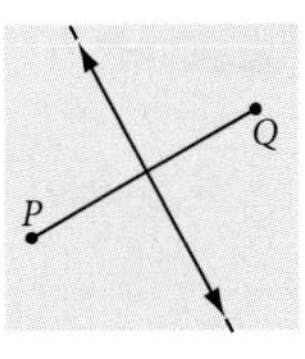

Step 3

Step 1 Draw a segment on patty paper. Label it $\overline{PQ}$.

Step 2 Fold your patty paper so that endpoints P and Q land exactly on top of each other, that is, they **coincide.** Crease your paper along the fold.

Step 3 Unfold your paper. Draw a line in the crease. What is the relationship of this line to $\overline{PQ}$? Check with others in your group. Use your ruler and protractor to verify your observations.

Step 3 It is perpendicular to $\overline{PQ}$ and bisects $\overline{PQ}$.

LESSON 3.2

PLANNING

LESSON OUTLINE

One day:

25 min Investigation
10 min Sharing
5 min Closing
5 min Exercises

MATERIALS

- construction tools
- rulers
- protractors

TEACHING

In this lesson students construct the perpendicular bisector of any given line segment, make a conjecture, and think about its converse. Start with the one-step investigation (page 148) or use the introduction and steps of the two investigations.

INTRODUCTION

To motivate the investigations, place a segment on your overhead or white board and then mark a series of arbitrary points (some equally distant to the endpoints). As you add each point, **[Ask]** "Which endpoint is this point closer to?" Review the definition of *midpoint of a line segment.* Ask students if it is obvious that a segment has many perpendiculars and many bisectors.

Guiding Investigation 1

This patty-paper construction is so obvious that you might pose the question with books closed. After students fold the perpendicular bisector they can open their books and answer the questions.

NCTM STANDARDS

CONTENT	PROCESS
✓ Number	✓ Problem Solving
Algebra	✓ Reasoning
✓ Geometry	✓ Communication
✓ Measurement	Connections
Data/Probability	✓ Representation

LESSON OBJECTIVES

- Discover a method of constructing perpendicular bisectors and midpoints
- Make conjectures about perpendicular bisectors
- Practice using geometry tools

Step 2 [ESL] *To crease* means "to make a hard line along a fold." (Some folds may not be creased but instead are pinched at a point.) *Crease* has nothing to do with *increase* or *decrease.*

Step 3 Students are using the protractor and ruler to verify their observations, not for construction.

Step 4 Here students use the compass to compare distances rather than for construction. Groups might fill in the conjecture with "halfway" or "the same distance." Let the class critique the wording during Sharing.

One step Ask what students think a perpendicular bisector of a line segment might be and, after a consensus has been reached, sketch a segment and its perpendicular bisector. Ask for ideas about how to construct the perpendicular bisector of a given segment, but don't expect great insights at first. Mention that to accomplish a construction it often helps to envision the result and conjecture about its properties. If students are not coming up with properties, suggest that distances between points are often good properties to look for. You might have groups draw perpendicular bisectors with protractors and measure distances with rulers, looking for properties that will allow for construction. As the idea emerges to try to find points equidistant from the endpoints, ask how many points are needed and how to make distances that are the same. Try to build on the understanding of the compass from the previous lesson. During Sharing, formalize the Perpendicular Bisector Conjecture and its converse.

Guiding Investigation 2

Step 2 [Alert] Students may not use a large enough compass opening; others may not swing long enough arcs. Intervene only if the groups don't self-correct.

How would you describe the relationship of the points on the perpendicular bisector to the endpoints of the bisected segment? There's one more step in your investigation.

Step 4 The distances from *P* and *Q* to each point are equal.

Step 4 Place three points on your perpendicular bisector. Label them *A, B,* and *C.* With your compass, compare the distances *PA* and *QA*. Compare the distances *PB* and *QB.* Compare the distances *PC* and *QC.* What do you notice about the two distances from each point on the perpendicular bisector to the endpoints of the segment? Compare your results with the results of others. Then copy and complete the conjecture.

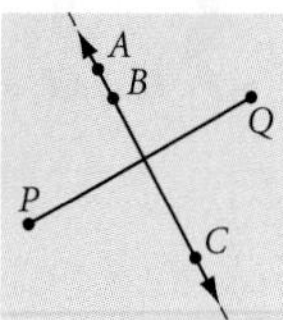

Remember to add each conjecture to your conjecture list and draw a figure for it.

Perpendicular Bisector Conjecture C-5

If a point is on the perpendicular bisector of a segment, then it is _?_ from the endpoints. equidistant

You've just completed the Perpendicular Bisector Conjecture. What about the converse of this statement?

Investigation 2
Right Down the Middle

You will need

- a compass
- a straightedge

If a point is **equidistant,** or the same distance, from two endpoints of a line segment in a plane, will it be on the segment's perpendicular bisector? If so, then locating two such points can help you construct the perpendicular bisector.

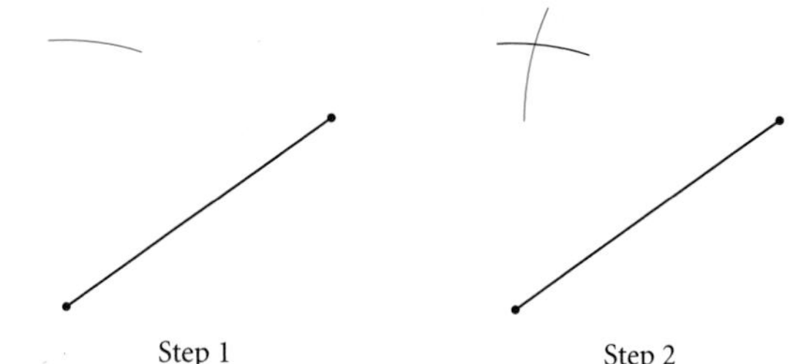

Step 1 Draw a line segment. Using one endpoint as center, swing an arc on one side of the segment.

Step 2 Using the same compass setting, but using the other endpoint as center, swing a second arc intersecting the first.

Step 3 yes

Step 3 The point where the two arcs intersect is equidistant from the endpoints of your segment. Use your compass to find another such point. Use these points to construct a line. Is this line the perpendicular bisector of the segment? Use the paper-folding technique of Investigation 1 to check.

Step 3 Students may not construct a second set of arcs as described. If they find they don't have two points to join with a line, you may need to suggest that they reread the instructions. The statement *the point where the two arcs intersect is equidistant from the endpoints* might not be obvious to students who don't realize that the compass is making lengths that are equal or to students who don't yet understand the meaning of *equidistant.*

Step 4 While students are writing conjectures in their notebooks, encourage them to add pictures as well.

SHARING IDEAS

As students present their results, encourage them to mark congruent segments formed by bisectors. Remind them of the meaning of *midpoint, perpendicular,* and *bisector* of a line segment, of what it means to bisect a segment and two points determine a plane. Review the symbol for *is perpendicular to.*

Step 4 | Complete the conjecture below, and write a summary of what you did in this investigation.

Converse of the Perpendicular Bisector Conjecture C-6

If a point is equidistant from the endpoints of a segment, then it is on the ? of the segment. perpendicular bisector

Notice that constructing the perpendicular bisector also locates the midpoint of a segment. Now that you know how to construct the perpendicular bisector and the midpoint, you can construct rectangles, squares, and right triangles. You can also construct two special segments in any triangle: medians and midsegments.

The segment connecting the vertex of a triangle to the midpoint of its opposite side is a **median.** There are three midpoints and three vertices in every triangle, so every triangle has three medians.

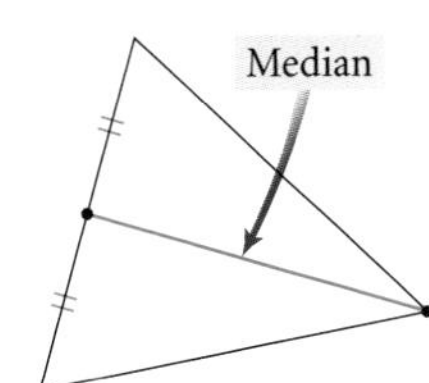

The segment that connects the midpoints of two sides of a triangle is a **midsegment.** A triangle has three sides, each with its own midpoint, so there are three midsegments in every triangle.

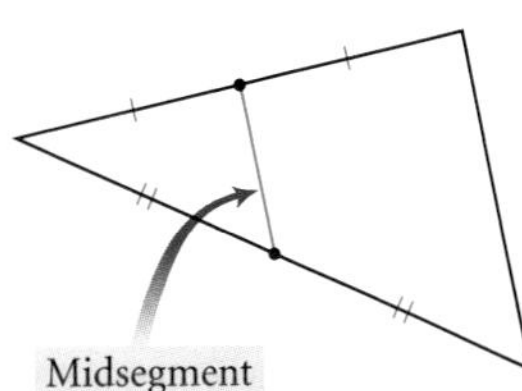

EXERCISES

You will need

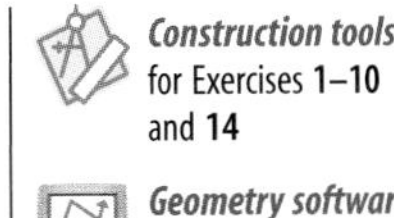

Construction tools for Exercises **1–10** and **14**

Geometry software for Exercise **13**

Construction For Exercises 1–5, construct the figures using only a compass and a straightedge.

1. Construct and label $\overline{AB}$. Construct the perpendicular bisector of $\overline{AB}$.
2. Construct and label $\overline{QD}$. Construct perpendicular bisectors to divide $\overline{QD}$ into four congruent segments. (h)
3. Construct a line segment so close to the edge of your paper that you can swing arcs on only one side of the segment. Then construct the perpendicular bisector of the segment. (h)
4. Using $\overline{AB}$ and $\overline{CD}$, construct a segment with length $2AB - \frac{1}{2}CD$. (h)

   A ——— B   C ——— D

5. Construct $\overline{MN}$ with length equal to the average length of $\overline{AB}$ and $\overline{CD}$ above. (h)

Sharing Ideas (continued)

Address any difficulties students are having in realizing that the compass is marking off lengths that are the same. **[Alert]** Watch to be sure that all confusion gets addressed. In particular, try hard not to react differently to "right answers" and "wrong answers" to your own questions but instead focus on making sure that everyone in the class agrees on the answers. (It's very tempting to move on as soon as you get an answer you like.)

Introduce the term *equidistant* as needed to help simplify statements of the conjectures.

Before directing students' attention to the discussion on medians and midsegments at the end of the lesson, **[Ask]** "If you needed to construct a midpoint of a segment, what modifications would you make in the construction you just performed?" [The intersection of a segment and a bisector is the midpoint of the segment.] Some students may want to use guess-and-check to locate the midpoint. This is not a valid approach to construction.

In discussing medians of a triangle, ask students if they've heard the word *median* in other contexts. A highway may have a median strip down the middle. In a mathematical context, the median of a sorted list of numbers is the "middle number," just as a median of a triangle is a "middle segment" between a vertex and the opposite side. You might ask students if this "middle segment" bisects the vertex angle; leave the question open for later investigation.

Assessing Progress

Through these investigations, presentations, and exercises, you can assess students' understanding of terms such as *line, line segment, midpoint, perpendicular, average, triangle,* and *rectangle.* Also look for understanding of the idea that a compass can be used to transfer a known distance, not just to draw circles. Watch how well students contribute to their groups and label constructions.

Closing the Lesson

This lesson concerns bisecting line segments by constructing their **perpendicular bisectors.** The **Perpendicular Bisector Conjecture** says that if a point is on the perpendicular bisector of a line segment then it is **equidistant** from the segment's endpoints. The **Converse of the Perpendicular Bisector Conjecture** is used to construct the perpendicular bisector of a segment, either with compass or with patty paper, which is folded to make the segment's endpoints **coincide.**

See pages 768–769 for answers to Exercises 1–5.

BUILDING UNDERSTANDING

Some exercises will require students to think critically and alter their construction techniques slightly to accomplish the task. Remind students that when they bisect a line segment they should label the two halves as congruent.

ASSIGNING HOMEWORK

Essential	1–10
Performance assessment	12
Portfolio	11
Review	13–23

Helping with the Exercises

Exercise 4 Some students may have difficulty realizing that they can construct half a length by finding the midpoint of the line segment.

Exercise 5 *Average* here means "mean." The mean of two lengths can be constructed by constructing the corresponding line segments on a line end-to-end and finding the midpoint of the new line segment.

7.

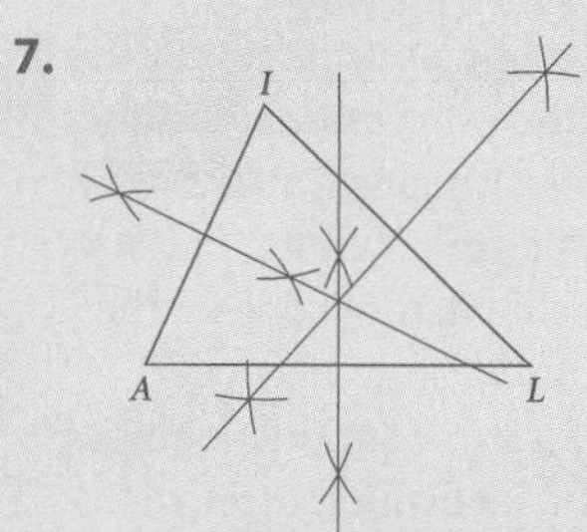

Exercise 8 [Ask] "What is the perimeter of $\triangle MNL$?" [half that of the original triangle] To preview the notion of similarity, you might also ask if the two triangles could be said to have the same shape. Some students may say that they do because they're both triangles. Don't insist on any particular answer now.

See page 769 for answer to Exercise 6.

6. ***Construction*** Do Exercises 1–5 using patty paper.

Construction For Exercises 7–10, you have your choice of construction tools. Use either a compass and a straightedge or patty paper and a straightedge. Do *not* use patty paper and compass together.

7. Construct $\triangle ALI$. Construct the perpendicular bisector of each side. What do you notice about the three bisectors? The perpendicular bisectors all intersect in one point.

8. Construct $\triangle ABC$. Construct medians $\overline{AM}$, $\overline{BN}$, and $\overline{CL}$. Notice anything special? ⓗ
The medians all intersect in one point.

9. Construct $\triangle DEF$. Construct midsegment $\overline{GH}$ where G is the midpoint of $\overline{DF}$ and H is the midpoint of $\overline{DE}$. What do you notice about the relationship between $\overline{EF}$ and $\overline{GH}$? $\overline{GH}$ appears to be parallel to $\overline{EF}$ and its length is half the length of $\overline{EF}$.

10. Copy rectangle $DSOE$ onto your paper. Construct the midpoint of each side. Label the midpoint of $\overline{DS}$ point I, the midpoint of $\overline{SO}$ point C, the midpoint of $\overline{OE}$ point V, and the midpoint of $\overline{ED}$ point R. Construct quadrilateral $RICV$. Describe $RICV$. The quadrilateral appears to be a rhombus.

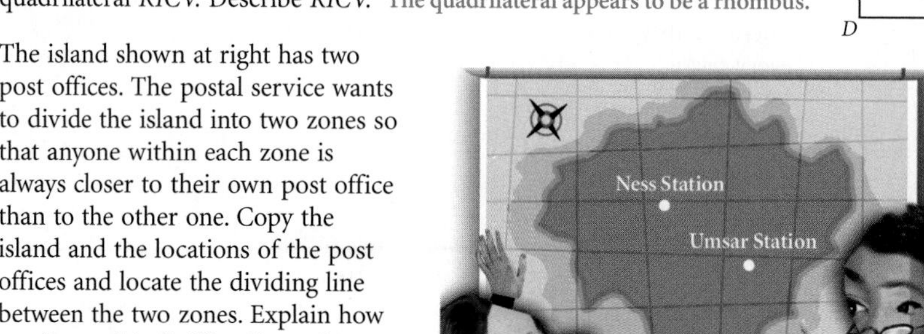

11. The island shown at right has two post offices. The postal service wants to divide the island into two zones so that anyone within each zone is always closer to their own post office than to the other one. Copy the island and the locations of the post offices and locate the dividing line between the two zones. Explain how you know this dividing line solves the problem. Or, pick several points in each zone and make sure they are closer to that zone's post office than they are to the other one.

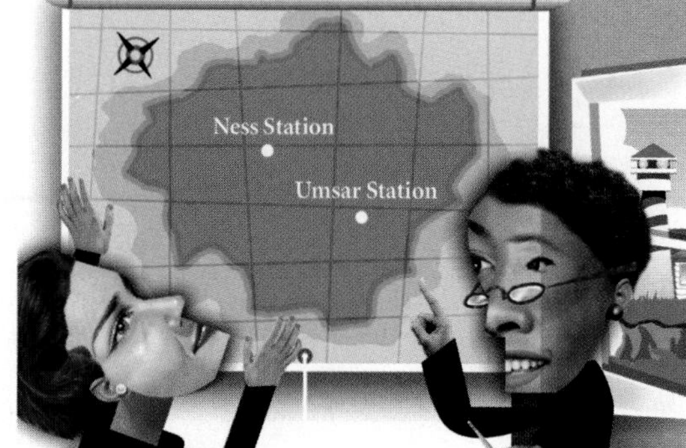

12. Copy parallelogram $FLAT$ onto your paper. Construct the perpendicular bisector of each side. What do you notice about the quadrilateral formed by the four lines? It is a parallelogram.

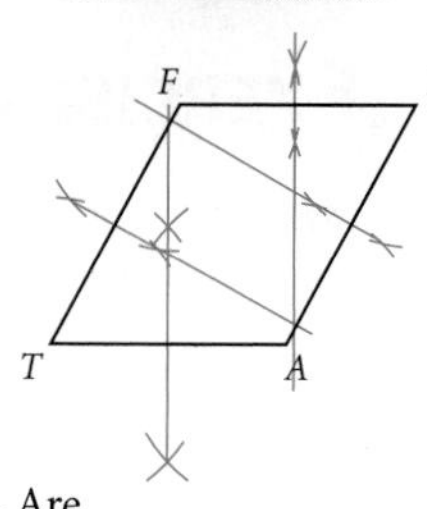

Review

13. ***Technology*** Use geometry software to construct a triangle. Construct a median. Are the two triangles created by the median congruent? Use an area measuring tool in your software program to find the areas of the two triangles. How do they compare? If you made the original triangle from heavy cardboard, and you wanted to balance that cardboard triangle on the edge of a ruler, what would you do?
The triangles are not necessarily congruent, but their areas are equal. A cardboard triangle would balance on its median.

14. ***Construction*** Construct a very large triangle on a piece of cardboard or mat board and construct its median. Cut out the triangle and see if you can balance it on the edge of a ruler. Sketch how you placed the triangle on the ruler. Cut the triangle into two pieces along the median and weigh the two pieces. Are they the same weight?
One way to balance it is along the median. The two halves weigh the same.

8.

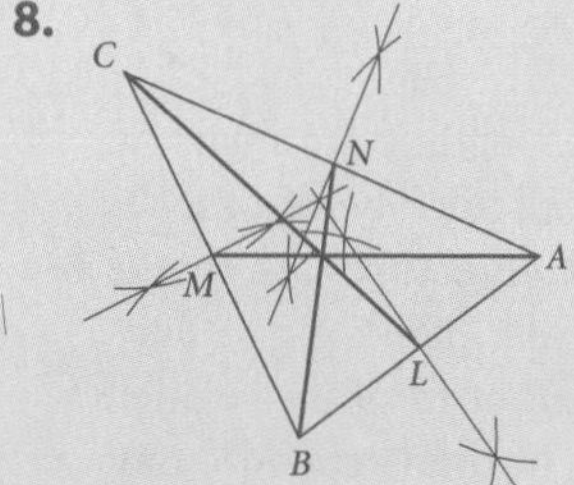

9.

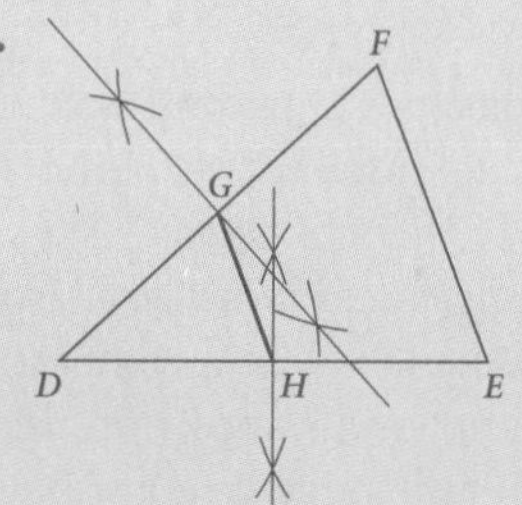

In Exercises 15–20, match the term with its figure below.

1.5 **15.** Scalene acute triangle F
1.5 **16.** Isosceles obtuse triangle E
1.5 **17.** Isosceles right triangle B
1.5 **18.** Isosceles acute triangle A
1.5 **19.** Scalene obtuse triangle D
1.5 **20.** Scalene right triangle C

A.
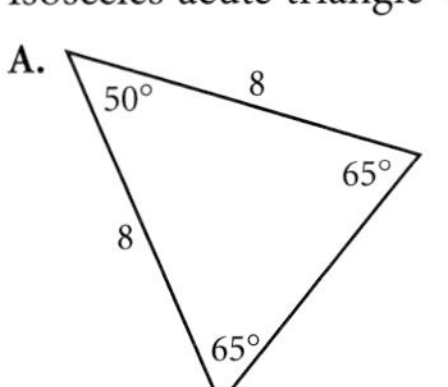

B.
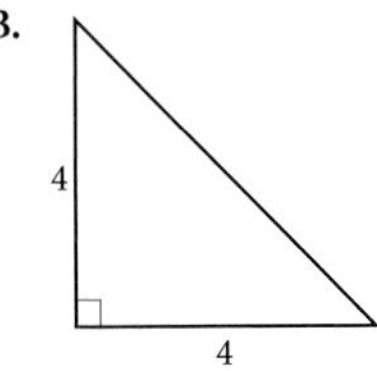

C.
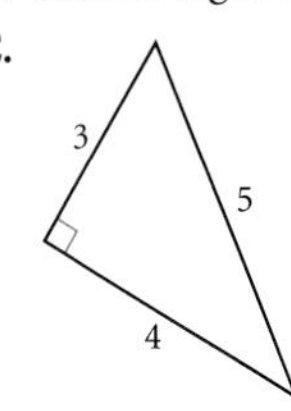

D.
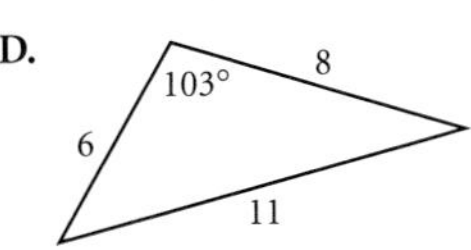

E.
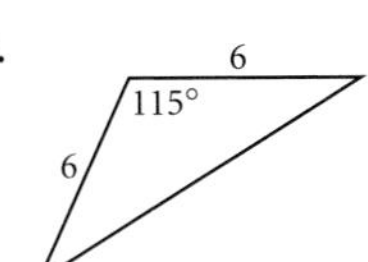

F.
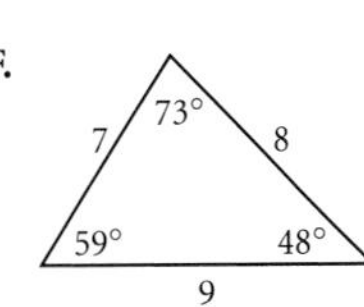

1.4 **21.** Sketch and label a polygon that has exactly three sides of equal length and exactly two angles of equal measure.

1.5 **22.** Sketch two triangles. Each should have one side measuring 5 cm and one side measuring 9 cm, but they should not be congruent.

0.1 **23.** List the letters from the alphabet below that have a horizontal line of symmetry.

A B C D E F G H I J K L M N O P Q R S T U V W X Y Z

C, D, E, H, I, O, X (B and K in some fonts, though not this one)

IMPROVING YOUR VISUAL THINKING SKILLS

Folding Cubes I

PUZZLE

In the problems below, the figure at the left represents the net for a cube. When the net is folded, which cube at the right will it become?

1.
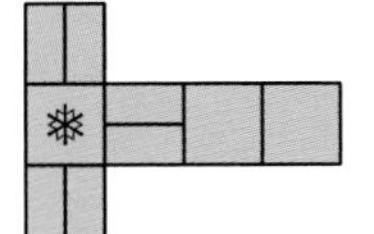
A.
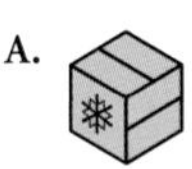
B.
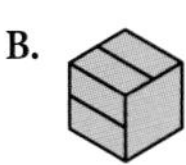
C.
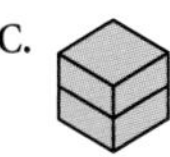

2.
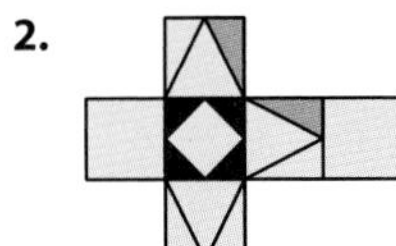
A.
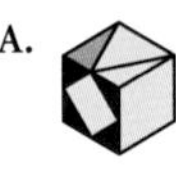
B.
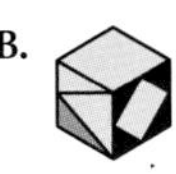
C.
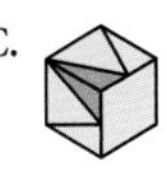

3.
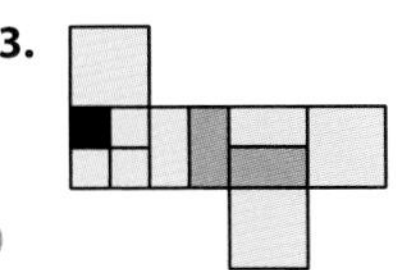
A.
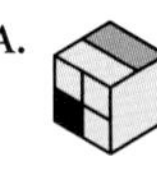
B.
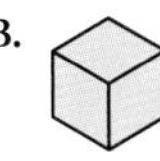
C.
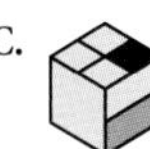

11.

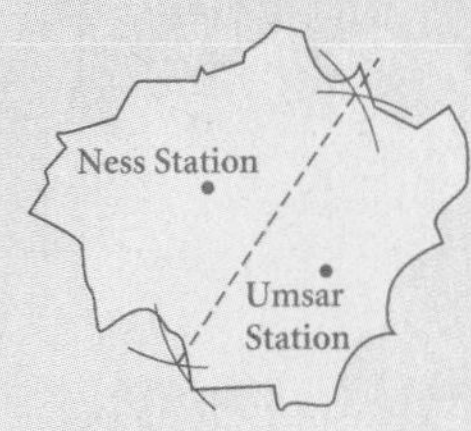

Any point on the perpendicular bisector of the segment connecting the two offices would be equidistant from the two post offices. Therefore, any point on one side of the perpendicular bisector would be closer to the post office on that side.

14. sample figure:

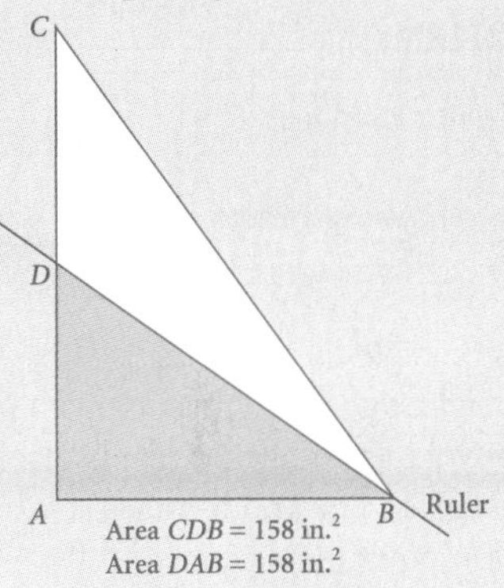

21. possible answer:

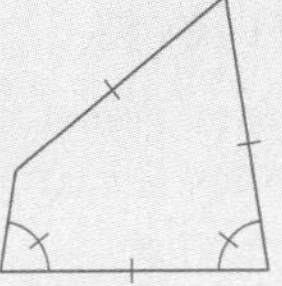

Exercise 22 Students may want help with this exercise. Suggest that they lay out one segment and then use the compass to see where endpoints of the second segment might lie.

22. possible answer:

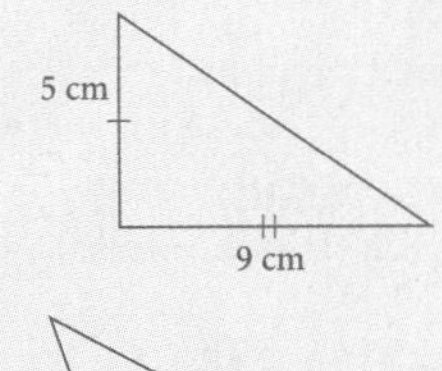

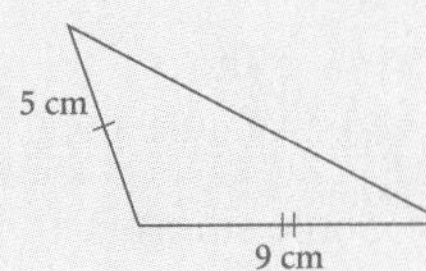

IMPROVING VISUAL THINKING SKILLS

1. B

2. C

3. A

LESSON

3.3

PLANNING

LESSON OUTLINE

One day:

25 min Investigation

5 min Sharing

5 min Closing

10 min Exercises

MATERIALS

- construction tools

TEACHING

It's possible to construct (with straightedge and either compass or patty paper) a line perpendicular to a given line and through a given point that is either on the given line or not on the line. The shortest path from the point to the line is along this perpendicular.

One step Draw a line and a point not on the line, and ask students to construct the shortest path from the point to the line. You might designate some groups to use compasses and other groups to use patty paper. As needed, ask students when they've constructed perpendicular lines before and point out that solving mathematics problems is often a matter of reducing them to problems that they have solved previously.

Guiding Investigation 1

Step 1 As needed, remind students that the first figure they draw is a line, not a segment.

Step 2 If students don't understand the reasons for what they're doing, **[Ask]** "When have you constructed perpendiculars before? On that line, can you make a segment whose perpendicular bisector goes through the

LESSON 3.3

Constructing Perpendiculars to a Line

Intelligence plus character—that is the goal of true education.

MARTIN LUTHER KING, JR.

If you are in a room, look over at one of the walls. What is the distance from where you are to that wall? How would you measure that distance? There are a lot of distances from where you are to the wall, but in geometry when we speak of a distance from a point to a line we mean a particular distance.

The construction of a perpendicular from a point to a line (with the point not on the line) is another of Euclid's constructions, and it has practical applications in many fields including agriculture and engineering. For example, think of a high-speed Internet cable as a line and a building as a point not on the line. Suppose you wanted to connect the building to the Internet cable using the shortest possible length of connecting wire. How can you find out how much wire you need, without buying too much?

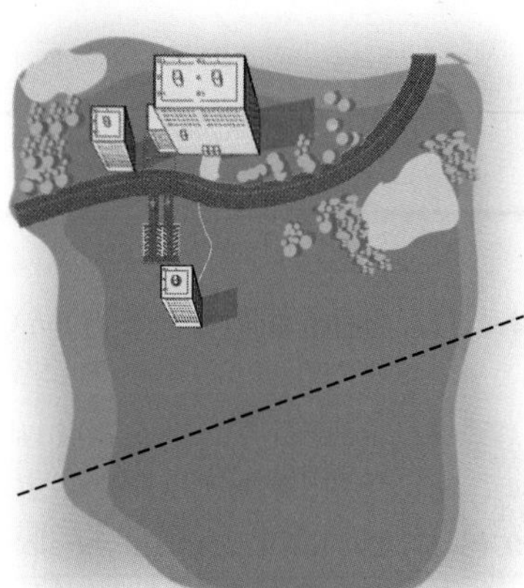

Investigation 1

Finding the Right Line

You will need

- a compass
- a straightedge

You already know how to construct perpendicular bisectors. You can't bisect a line because it is infinitely long, but you can use that know-how to construct a perpendicular from a point to a line.

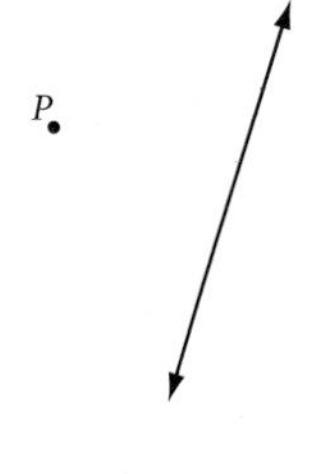

Stage 1

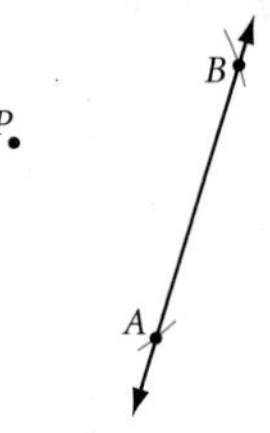

Stage 2

Step 1 Draw a line and a point labeled P not on the line, as shown above.

Step 2 Describe the construction steps you take at Stage 2.

Step 2 Swing equal arcs from P that intersect the line at A and B.

Step 3 How is PA related to PB? What does this answer tell you about where point P lies? Hint: See the Converse of the Perpendicular Bisector Conjecture.

Step 3 $PA = PB$; P is on the perpendicular bisector of $\overline{AB}$.

Step 4 Construct the perpendicular bisector of $\overline{AB}$. Label the midpoint M.

LESSON OBJECTIVES

- Discover methods of constructing a perpendicular to a line from a point not on the line and from a point on the line
- Determine a method of finding the shortest path from a point to a line
- Practice using geometry tools

NCTM STANDARDS

CONTENT		PROCESS	
	Number		Problem Solving
	Algebra	✓	Reasoning
✓	Geometry	✓	Communication
✓	Measurement	✓	Connections
	Data/Probability		Representation

You have now constructed a perpendicular through a point not on the line. This is useful for finding the distance to a line.

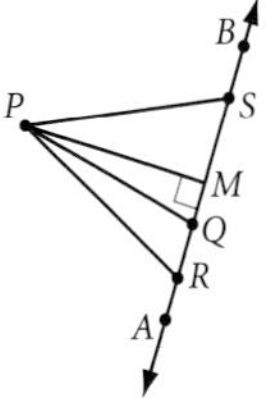

Step 5 PM is shortest.

Step 5 Label three randomly placed points on $\overleftrightarrow{AB}$ as Q, R, and S. Measure PQ, PR, PS, and PM. Which distance is shortest? Compare results with others in your group.

You are now ready to state your observations by completing the conjecture.

Shortest Distance Conjecture C-7

The shortest distance from a point to a line is measured along the _?_ from the point to the line. perpendicular segment

Let's take another look. How could you use patty paper to do this construction?

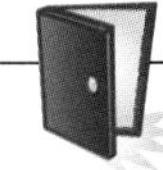

Investigation 2
Patty-Paper Perpendiculars

You will need
- patty paper
- a straightedge

In Investigation 1, you constructed a perpendicular from a point to a line. Now let's do the same construction using patty paper.

On a piece of patty paper, perform the steps below.

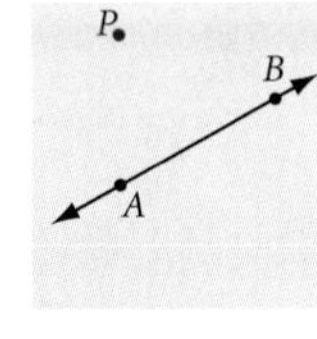

Step 1

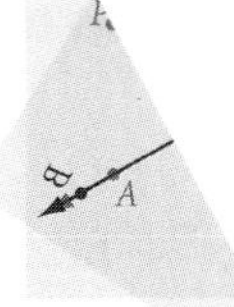

Step 2

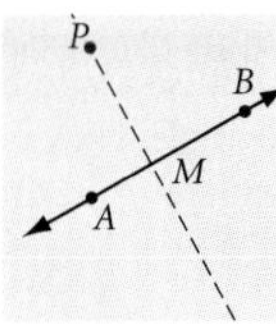

Step 3

Step 1 Draw and label $\overleftrightarrow{AB}$ and a point P not on $\overleftrightarrow{AB}$.

Step 2 yes

Step 2 Fold the line onto itself, and slide the layers of paper so that point P appears to be on the crease. Is the crease perpendicular to the line? Check it with the corner of a piece of patty paper.

Step 3 Yes, they are both right angles and they form a linear pair.

Step 3 Label the point of intersection M. Are $\angle AMP$ and $\angle BMP$ congruent? Supplementary? Why or why not?

In Investigation 2, is M the midpoint of $\overline{AB}$? Do you think it needs to be? Think about the techniques used in the two investigations. How do the techniques differ?

Guiding Investigation 1 (continued)
given point?" Remind students, as needed, that they aren't starting with two points on the line; points A and B are determined by the compass arcs.

Step 5 Here *measure* means "compare lengths." Challenge students to compare the lengths with their compasses instead of with their rulers.

Guiding Investigation 2

If some students finish before others, challenge them to find another way to fold paper to construct this perpendicular line. They might fold along the line and copy the point P to its reflection on the other side, then join the two points. The method in the student book is slightly better in that it can be used if point P is actually on the line. This other method should not be presented during Sharing unless students come up with it. If students are unsuccessful with meeting the challenge, wait until you are exploring reflections with patty paper. When they discover how to reflect a point over a line with patty paper, you will be able to ask "Is there anything special about the line connecting the point and its image point?"

SHARING IDEAS

As students present whatever variety of approaches they took, pose the question of the measure of the angle between two perpendicular lines. The fact that this measure is 90° is used in Lesson 3.4.

Students may have difficulty understanding that the perpendicular line from a point off the given line is the shortest path between the point and the line. Go over this idea several times if necessary. Note that the perpendicular line segment is a path, not a distance; the smallest distance is the length of this segment.

Sharing Ideas (continued)
Take some of the pictures displayed and add line segments to form a triangle, with the perpendicular line forming an altitude. Introduce the term *altitude* and ask how it might be defined. Compare the class definition to that in the book. **[Alert]** Students may have difficulty seeing that a triangle can have three different altitudes. Have various students draw in the other altitudes on the sample triangle. Then ask students to draw various kinds of triangles by placing point P in various positions relative to $\overline{AB}$ and to draw in all altitudes. Elicit the idea that at least one altitude of an obtuse triangle will lie outside the figure. Can students draw a triangle with more than one altitude that lies outside the triangle? This question foreshadows Exercise 3.

Using a patty-paper construction of the perpendicular, **[Ask]** "What can be said about the resulting angles?" [The fold creates two supplementary angles, and the fact that they match up means that they are congruent.]

The construction of a perpendicular from a point to a line lets you find the shortest distance from a point to a line. The geometry definition of distance from a point to a line is based on this construction, and it reads, "The **distance from a point to a line** is the length of the perpendicular segment from the point to the line."

You can also use this construction to find the altitude of a triangle. An **altitude** of a triangle is a perpendicular segment from a vertex to the opposite side or to a line containing the opposite side.

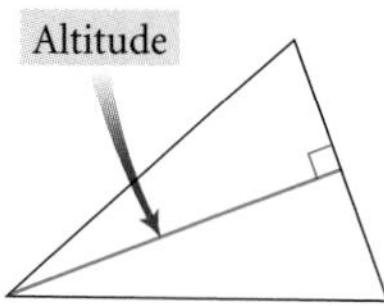

An altitude can be inside the triangle.

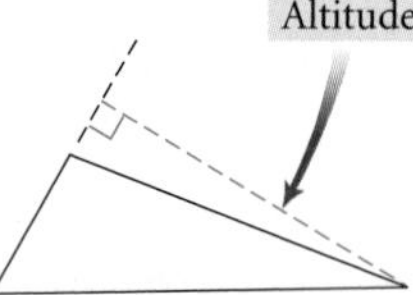

An altitude can be outside the triangle.

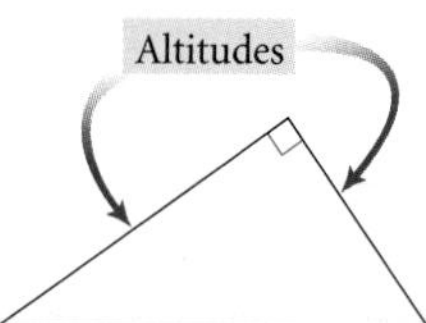

An altitude can be one of the sides of the triangle.

The length of the altitude is the height of the triangle. A triangle has three different altitudes, so it has three different heights.

EXERCISES

You will need

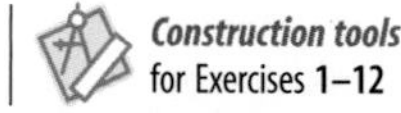
Construction tools for Exercises **1–12**

Construction Use your compass and straightedge and the definition of distance to do Exercises 1–5.

1. Draw an obtuse angle *BIG*. Place a point *P* inside the angle. Now construct perpendiculars from the point to both sides of the angle. Which side is closer to point *P*?

2. Draw an acute triangle. Label it *ABC*. Construct altitude $\overline{CD}$ with point *D* on $\overleftrightarrow{AB}$. (We didn't forget about point *D*. It's at the *foot* of the perpendicular. Your job is to locate it.)

In this futuristic painting, American artist Ralston Crawford (1906–1978) has constructed a set of converging lines and vertical lines to produce an illusion of distance.

3. Draw obtuse triangle *OBT* with obtuse angle *O*. Construct altitude $\overline{BU}$. In an obtuse triangle, an altitude can fall outside the triangle. To construct an altitude from point *B* of your triangle, extend side $\overline{OT}$. In an obtuse triangle, how many altitudes fall outside the triangle and how many fall inside the triangle? ⓗ

4. How can you construct a perpendicular to a line through a point that is on the line? Draw a line. Mark a point on your line. Now experiment. Devise a method to construct a perpendicular to your line at the point. ⓗ

5. Draw a line. Mark two points on the line and label them *Q* and *R*. Now construct a square *SQRE* with $\overline{QR}$ as a side. ⓗ

Assessing Progress

While students investigate and present, assess their understanding of perpendicular lines, supplementary angles, congruent angles, kinds of angles and triangles, and perpendicular bisector constructions. The exercises allow especially good opportunities to assess knowledge of acute and obtuse angles and triangles.

Closing the Lesson

Remind students of the ways to construct a perpendicular to a given line through a given point. If their understanding is still weak, you might do one of Exercises 1–3 as a class.

BUILDING UNDERSTANDING

Students may try to draw figures instead of constructing them. Ask students not to erase small arcs from compass constructions. You can look for arcs or, in patty-paper constructions, for folds.

ASSIGNING HOMEWORK

Essential	1–12
Performance assessment	6, 12
Portfolio	12
Group	7
Review	13–18

Helping with the Exercises

Exercises 1–9 Patty paper is a construction tool. If students ask for help, **[Ask]** "Are there any constructions that you have investigated before that can help you with this one?"

Exercise 3 **[Alert]** Constructing altitudes in obtuse triangles causes problems for some students later. Using patty paper will make it easier.

See pages 769–770 for answers to Exercises 1–5.

Exercise 4 If you get a chance, stress that students are constructing a 90° angle here. The ability to do this is mentioned in Lesson 3.4.

Exercise 5 Remind students that *construct* means "to use only straightedge and either compass or patty paper." They will be tempted to construct a right angle with a protractor. This is a good opportunity to encourage variety. Students might construct a perpendicular at each end of $\overline{QR}$, copy $\overline{QR}$ on each perpendicular, and join the other endpoints. Or they might construct a perpendicular at one endpoint, copy $\overline{QR}$ onto it, construct another perpendicular at the other endpoint of the first perpendicular, copy $\overline{QR}$ onto it, and join points. Or they might construct one perpendicular and then alternately copy segments and angles. If some students are finding the work easy, challenge them to think of other ways to do constructions such as this one.

Construction For Exercises 6–9, use patty paper. (Attach your patty-paper work to your problems.)

6. Draw a line across your patty paper with a straightedge. Place a point P not on the line, and fold the perpendicular to the line through the point P. How would you fold to construct a perpendicular through a point on a line? Place a point Q on the line. Fold a perpendicular to the line through point Q. What do you notice about the two folds? The two folds are parallel.

7. Draw a very large acute triangle on your patty paper. Place a point inside the triangle. Now construct perpendiculars from the point to all three sides of the triangle by folding. Mark your figure. How can you use your construction to decide which side of the triangle your point is closest to?

8. Construct an isosceles right triangle. Label its vertices A, B, and C, with point C the right angle. Fold to construct the altitude $\overline{CD}$. What do you notice about this line?

9. Draw obtuse triangle OBT with angle O obtuse. Fold to construct the altitude $\overline{BU}$. (Don't forget, you must extend the side $\overline{OT}$.)

Construction For Exercises 10–12, you may use either patty paper or a compass and a straightedge.

10. Construct a square $ABLE$ given $\overline{AL}$ as a diagonal.

A L

11. Construct a rectangle whose width is half its length.

12. Construct the complement of $\angle A$.

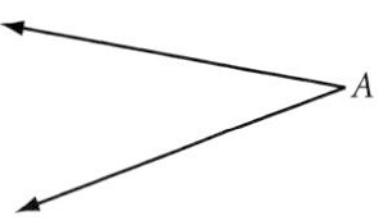

Review

2.3 **13.** Copy and complete the table. Make a conjecture for the value of the nth term and for the value of the 35th term. ⓗ

Rectangular pattern with triangles

Rectangle	1	2	3	4	5	6	...	n	...	35
Number of shaded triangles	2	9	20	35	54	77	...		...	2484

$(2n-1)(n+1)$

1.8 **14.** Sketch the solid of revolution formed when the two-dimensional figure at right is revolved about the line.

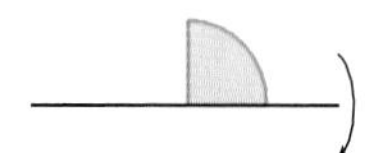

Exercise 6 The two lines (creases) might be parallel, or they might be the same line.

6.

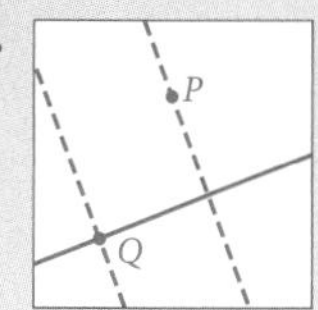

7. Fold the patty paper through the point so that two perpendiculars coincide to see the side closest to the point. Fold again using the perpendicular of the side closest to the point and the third perpendicular; compare those sides.

8. Draw a line. Mark two points on it, and label them A and C. Construct a perpendicular at C. Mark off $\overline{CB}$ congruent to $\overline{CA}$. The altitude $\overline{CD}$ is also the perpendicular bisector.

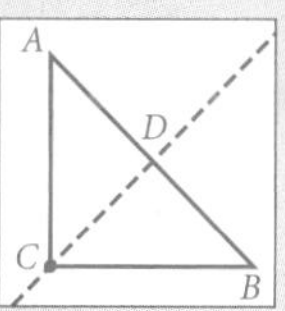

9.

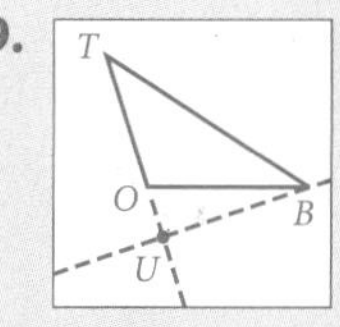

10.

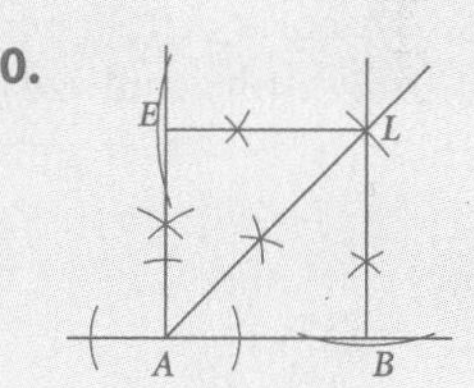

11.

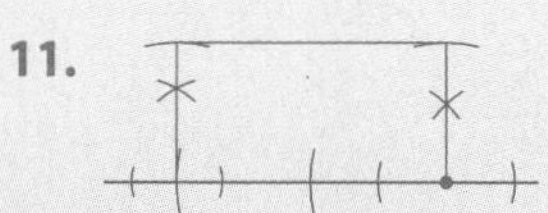

12.

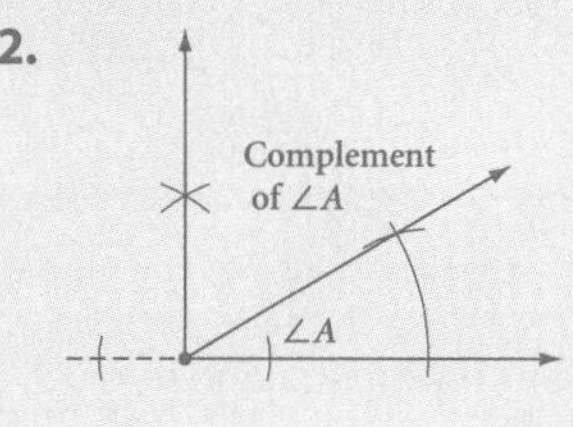

14.

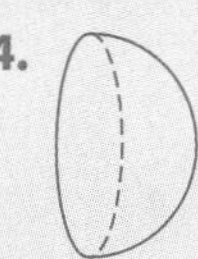

For Exercises 15–18, label the vertices with the appropriate letters. When you sketch or draw, use the special marks that indicate right angles, parallel segments, and congruent segments and angles.

3.2 **15.** Sketch obtuse triangle FIT with $m\angle I > 90°$ and median $\overline{IY}$.

1.3 **16.** Sketch $\overline{AB} \perp \overline{CD}$ and $\overline{EF} \perp \overline{CD}$.

1.4 **17.** Use your protractor to *draw* a regular pentagon. Draw all the diagonals. Use your compass to *construct* a regular hexagon. Draw three diagonals connecting alternating vertices. Do the same for the other three vertices. ⓗ

1.5 **18.** Draw a triangle with a 6 cm side and an 8 cm side and the angle between them measuring 40°. Draw a second triangle with a 6 cm side and an 8 cm side and exactly one 40° angle that is not between the two given sides. Are the two triangles congruent? not congruent

15.

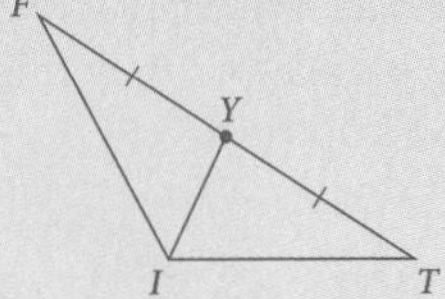

16.

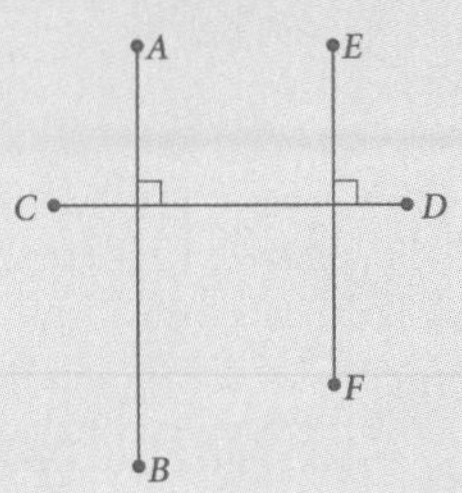

17.

18.

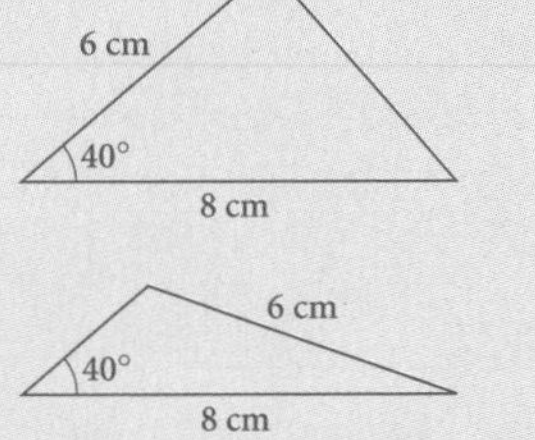

EXTENSION

Challenge students to construct a perpendicular bisector using only a straightedge with two parallel edges. [Put the straightedge on the line segment so that one end of the line segment touches one side of the straightedge and the other end touches the other side. Draw lines. Repeat with the sides touching opposite ends.]

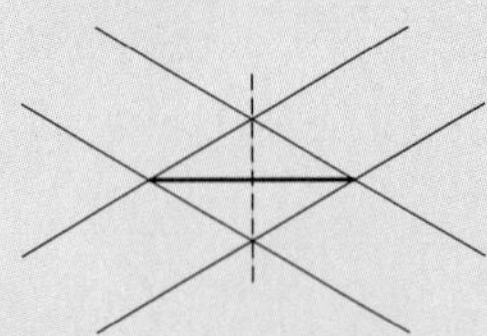

IMPROVING YOUR VISUAL THINKING SKILLS

Constructing an Islamic Design

PUZZLE

This Islamic design is based on two intersecting squares that form an 8-pointed star. Most Islamic designs of this kind can be constructed using only a compass and a straightedge. Try it. Use your compass and straightedge to re-create this design or to create a design of your own based on an 8-pointed star.

Here are two diagrams to get you started.

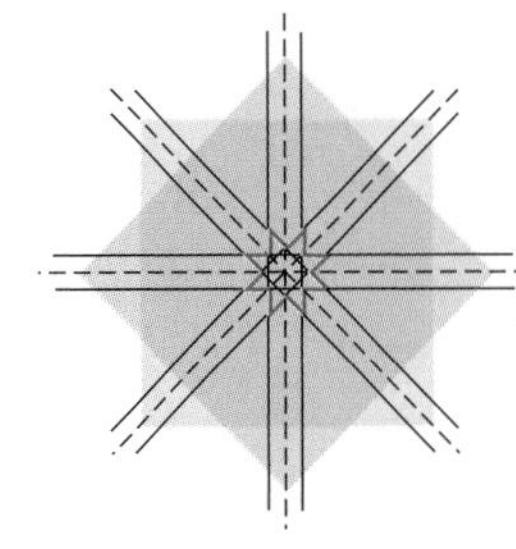

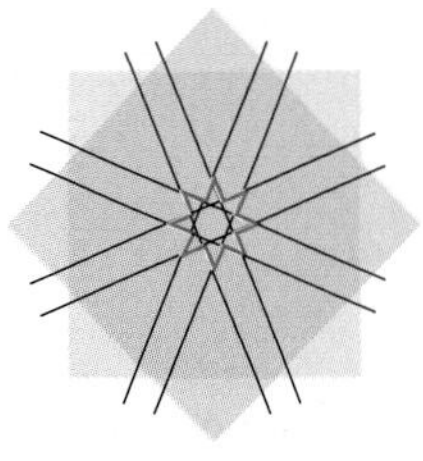

IMPROVING VISUAL THINKING SKILLS

Sample construction:

[Ask] "What geometric figures do you observe in the pictured construction?" [hexagons, kites, chevrons (concave hexagons), stars with 5, 8, and 16 points] "In your construction?" [octagon, triangle, 16-sided concave polygon (or 8-pointed star)] If students didn't study Chapter 0, use this problem to talk about rotational symmetry. **[Ask]** "What symmetries do you see in the construction in the book?" [4-fold rotational symmetry, four lines of reflectional symmetry] Describe the symmetries you placed in your construction. [for the sample construction: 8-fold rotational symmetry and eight lines of reflectional symmetry]

LESSON

3.4

Constructing Angle Bisectors

Challenges make you discover things about yourself that you never really knew.
CICELY TYSON

In Chapter 1, you learned that an **angle bisector** divides an angle into two congruent angles. While the definition states that the bisector of an angle is a ray, you may also refer to a segment as an angle bisector if the segment lies on the ray and passes through the vertex. For example, in this triangle the two angle bisectors are both segments.

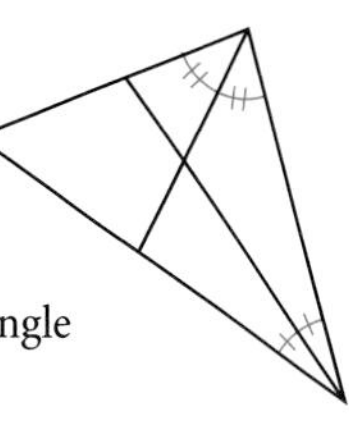

In Investigations 1 and 2, you will learn to construct the bisector of an angle.

Investigation 1
Angle Bisecting by Folding

You will need
- patty paper

Each person should draw his or her own acute angle for this investigation.

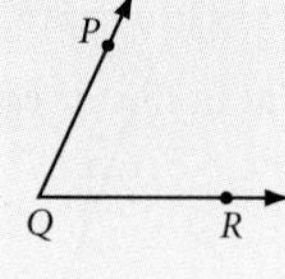

Step 1

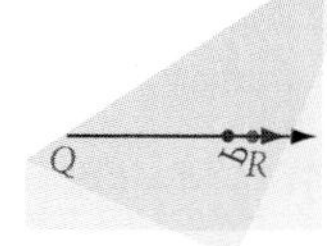

Step 2

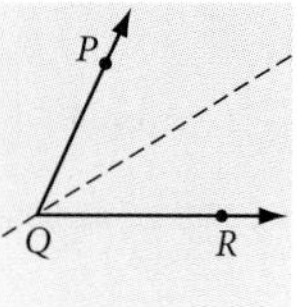

Step 3

Step 1 On patty paper, draw a large-scale angle. Label it *PQR*.

Step 2 Fold your patty paper so that $\overrightarrow{QP}$ and $\overrightarrow{QR}$ coincide. Crease the paper along the fold.

Step 3 Unfold your patty paper. Draw a ray with endpoint *Q* along the crease. Does the ray bisect $\angle PQR$? How can you tell?

Step 3 Yes, because the fold formed two angles that coincided.

Step 4 Repeat Steps 1–3 with an obtuse angle. Do you use different methods for finding the bisectors of different kinds of angles?

Step 4 No, use the same method.

Step 5 Place a point on your angle bisector. Label it *A*. Compare the distances from *A* to each of the two sides. Remember that "distance" means *shortest* distance! Try it with other points on the angle bisector. Compare your results with those of others. Copy and complete the conjecture.

Step 5 The distance from the two sides is equal.

Angle Bisector Conjecture C-8

If a point is on the bisector of an angle, then it is __?__ from the sides of the angle. equidistant

LESSON

3.4

PLANNING

LESSON OUTLINE

One day:

25 min	Investigation
10 min	Sharing
5 min	Closing
5 min	Exercises

MATERIALS
- construction tools
- protractors

TEACHING

Begin with the one-step investigation or use the steps of the two investigations.

Guiding Investigation 1

Step 3 Students can either use a protractor to verify that the angles are congruent, or they can observe that when the patty paper is folded two angles lie perfectly on top of each other.

You might skip Step 4 by assigning different groups (or different members within a group) to experiment with acute angles, obtuse angles, and right angles.

Step 5 Conjectures may include "the same distance," "equidistant," "in between," "halfway between," "not on," and so on. Praise variety and creativity, and save critique and consensus for Sharing.

One step Remind the class that they learned construction techniques for bisecting line segments. Ask them whether it's possible to bisect angles using only a straightedge and either patty paper or a compass. As they work, remind students as needed of the strategy of sketching the result and figuring

NCTM STANDARDS

CONTENT		PROCESS	
	Number	✓	Problem Solving
	Algebra	✓	Reasoning
✓	Geometry	✓	Communication
✓	Measurement	✓	Connections
	Data/Probability	✓	Representation

LESSON OBJECTIVES
- Discover methods of constructing an angle bisector
- Make a conjecture about angle bisectors
- Explore how to construct special angles by dividing and combining 60° and 90° angles
- Practice construction skills

One step (continued)
out what properties it might have; in this case the points on the angle's bisector are equidistant from its sides. As needed, **[Ask]** "What are the properties of the points on a line segment's perpendicular bisector?" Some students might remember that the shortest distance from a point to a line is along a perpendicular to the line and spend some time constructing perpendiculars. Be sure this idea is shared with the class, along with more efficient ways of finding "the same" (but not necessarily "the shortest") distance. Encourage groups to test their methods on different kinds of angles.

Guiding Investigation 2

Step 2 If students are having difficulty **[Ask]** "Would using a compass to transfer known distances help?" Wonder aloud if the construction from Investigation 1 might be useful. Using the hint, students may try to find a point for which the shortest paths (perpendiculars) to the sides go through those two points. Save any critique of methods for Sharing.

Step 4 Sample answer: Use the points of intersection of an arc and the angle's sides and find a point equidistant from those points. It is on the angle bisector.

SHARING IDEAS

If the idea of constructing perpendiculars doesn't arise in any group, you might suggest it yourself, perhaps saying that you'd seen the method proposed, and ask what they think of it. This strategy achieves several purposes: It gives students a review of constructing perpendiculars to lines; it allows a discussion of how the compass is used for transferring known distances and how equal distances are all you need here (not smallest distances); it reinforces the idea that you believe critical thinking and deep understanding are as important as remembering particular methods.

[Ask] "Can a segment be an angle bisector?" [The original definition of *angle bisector* defined it as a ray. Point out that the book extends the definition to include segments.] "What points can be endpoints of a segment that bisects an angle?" [One endpoint must be the angle's vertex.] "Does every angle have one or more bisectors?" [Every angle is bisected by one and only one ray, but infinitely many segments are bisectors.]

Remind students that they constructed 90° angles when they constructed perpendicular lines. **[Ask]** "What angles can you now construct?" Most will see that they can construct angles that measure, for example, 45°, 22.5°, or 11.25°. Elicit the idea that angles with the sums of these measures can also be constructed, such as a 135° angle.

You've found the bisector of an angle by folding patty paper. Now let's see how you can construct the angle bisector with a compass and a straightedge.

Investigation 2
Angle Bisecting with Compass

You will need
- a compass
- a straightedge

In this investigation, you will find a method for bisecting an angle using a compass and straightedge. Each person in your group should investigate a different angle.

Step 1 Draw an angle.

Step 2 Find a method for constructing the bisector of the angle. Experiment!

Hint: Start by drawing an arc centered at the vertex.

Step 3 Once you think you have constructed the angle bisector, fold your paper to see if the ray you constructed is actually the bisector. Share your method with other students in your group. Agree on a best method.

Step 4 Write a summary of what you did in this investigation.

In earlier lessons, you learned to construct a 90° angle. Now you know how to bisect an angle. What angles can you construct by combining these two skills?

EXERCISES

You will need
- ***Construction tools*** for Exercises **1–12**
- ***Geometry software*** for Exercise **17**

Construction For Exercises 1–5, match each geometric construction with its diagram.

1. Construction of an angle bisector D

2. Construction of a median F

3. Construction of a midsegment A

4. Construction of a perpendicular bisector C

5. Construction of an altitude E

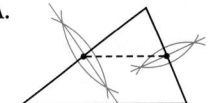

A.

B.

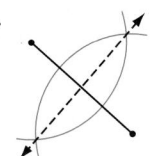

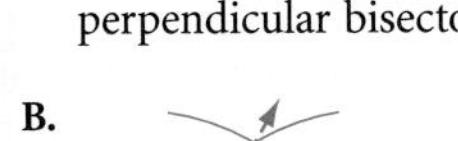

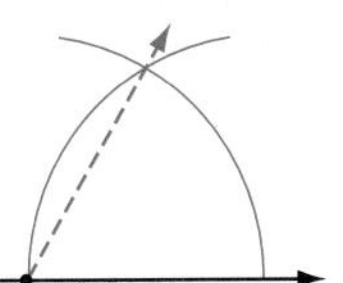

C.

D.

E.

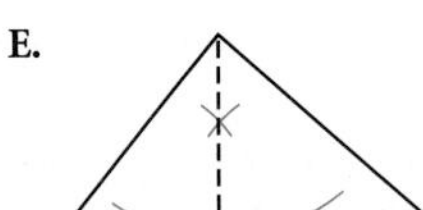

F.

Construction For Exercises 6–12, construct a figure with the given specifications.

6. Given:

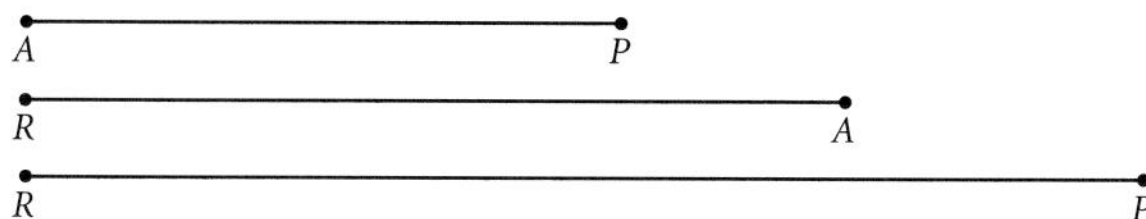

Construct: An isosceles right triangle with z as the length of each of the two congruent sides

7. Given:

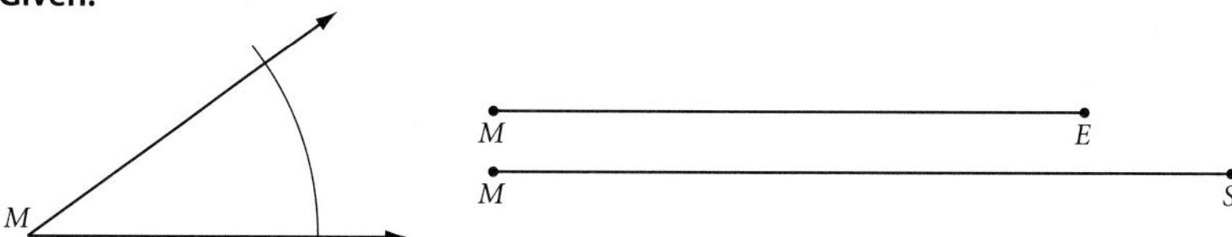

Construct: $\triangle RAP$ with median $\overline{PM}$ and angle bisector $\overline{RB}$

8. Given:

M

M E

M S

Construct: $\triangle MSE$ with $\overline{OU}$, where O is the midpoint of $\overline{MS}$ and U is the midpoint of $\overline{SE}$

9. Construct an angle with each given measure and label it. Remember, you may use only your compass and straightedge. No protractor!

a. 90° **b.** 45° **c.** 135°

10. Draw a large acute triangle. Bisect one vertex with a compass and a straightedge. Construct an altitude from the second vertex and a median from the third vertex.

11. Repeat Exercise 10 with patty paper. Which set of construction tools do you prefer? Why?

12. Use your straightedge to draw a linear pair of angles. Use your compass to bisect each angle of the linear pair. What do you notice about the two angle bisectors? Can you make a conjecture? Can you think of a way to explain why it is true?

13. In this lesson you discovered the Angle Bisector Conjecture. Write the converse of the Angle Bisector Conjecture. Do you think it's true? Why or why not?
If a point is equally distant from the sides of an angle, then it is on the bisector of an angle. This is true for points in the same plane as the angle.

Notice how this mosaic floor at Church of Pomposa in Italy (ca. 850 C.E.) uses many duplicated shapes. What constructions do you see in the square pattern? Are all the triangles in the isosceles triangle pattern identical? How can you tell?

Assessing Progress

Watch for students' understanding of the Perpendicular Bisector Conjecture and its converse. You can assess students' understanding of angles and their vertices and sides, of the definition of *angle bisector,* of the measure of an angle, and of the idea that a compass can be used to transfer known distances. You can note how skilled students are in using construction tools

Closing the Lesson

Review the big ideas of this lesson: how to construct an angle bisector with a straightedge and either patty paper or a compass, and the **Angle Bisector Conjecture.** If you think students need more help, you might do one of Exercises 6–9 with the class

BUILDING UNDERSTANDING

The exercises focus on deepening students' understanding of constructing angle bisectors.

ASSIGNING HOMEWORK

Essential	1–13
Performance assessment	12
Portfolio	9
Journal	16, 17
Group	14, 15
Review	14–17

▶ Helping with the Exercises

Exercises 1–5 You might work through these exercises as a class.

Exercise 12 Conjectures might include mention of congruent angles or linear pairs. Encourage students to draw several pictures. Be firm in insisting on deductive reasoning. Students should be able to support their conjectures with a few simple equations.

Mosaic answers: Square pattern constructions: perpendiculars, equal segments, and midpoints; The triangles are not congruent as the downward ones have longer bases.

Exercise 13 Encourage controversy here to generate review of the definition of sides of an angle (as rays) and to see that the distance from a point to a ray is not defined. If that distance is defined to be the same as the distance from the point to the line containing the ray, then points that are equidistant from an angle's sides will be on the line containing the angle bisector but not necessarily on the bisector itself. If the distance from a point to a ray is undefined, then there might be no perpendicular to the ray through

See page 770 for answers to Exercises 6–12.

Exercise 13 (continued)
the point, so the converse of the Angle Bisector Conjecture is true.

14.

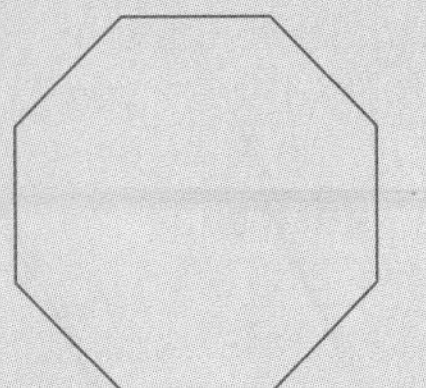

15.

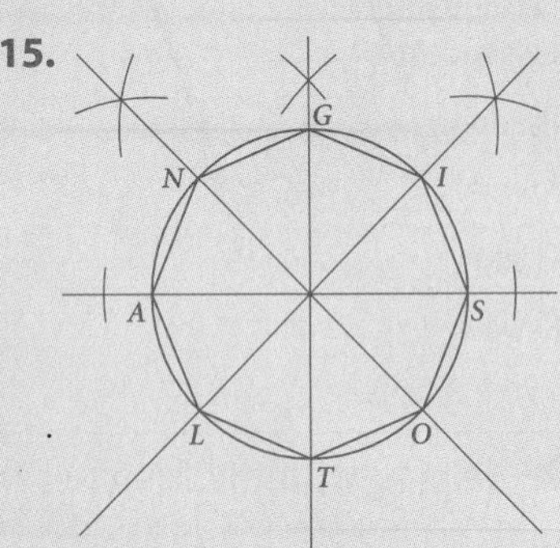

16.

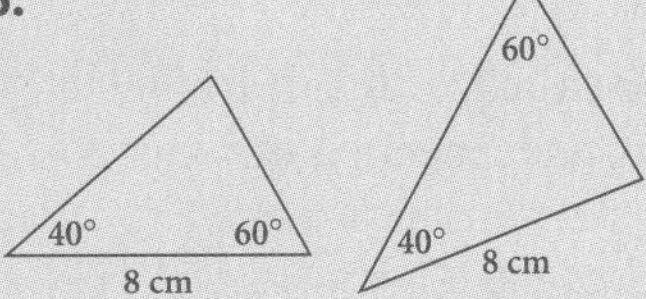

Review

Sketch, draw, or construct each figure in Exercises 14–17. Label the vertices with the appropriate letters.

1.4 **14.** Draw a regular octagon. What traffic sign comes to mind? ⓗ STOP

3.1 **15.** Construct regular octagon *ALTOSIGN*. ⓗ

1.5 **16.** Draw a triangle with a 40° angle, a 60° angle, and a side between the given angles measuring 8 cm. Draw a second triangle with a 40° angle and a 60° angle but with a side measuring 8 cm *opposite* the 60° angle. Are the triangles congruent? ⓗ No, the triangles don't look the same.

3.2 **17.** ***Technology*** Use geometry software to construct $\overline{AB}$ and $\overline{CD}$, with point C on $\overline{AB}$ and point D not on $\overleftrightarrow{AB}$. Construct the perpendicular bisector of $\overline{CD}$.

a. Trace this perpendicular bisector as you drag point C along $\overline{AB}$. Describe the shape formed by this locus of lines.

b. Erase the tracings from part a. Now trace the midpoint of $\overline{CD}$ as you drag C. Describe the locus of points. A line segment parallel to $\overline{AB}$ and half the length (the segment is actually the midsegment of $\triangle ABD$).

IMPROVING YOUR VISUAL THINKING SKILLS

Coin Swap III

Arrange four dimes and four pennies in a row of nine squares, as shown. Switch the position of the four dimes and four pennies in exactly 24 moves. A coin can slide into an empty square next to it or can jump over one coin into an empty space. Record your solution by listing, in order, which type of coin is moved. For example, your list might begin PDPDPPDD . . . .

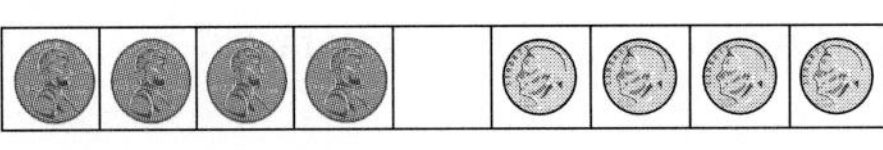

17a. A web of lines fill most of the plane, except a U-shaped region and a V-shaped region. (The U-shaped region is actually bounded by a section of a parabola and straight lines. If $\overline{AB}$ were extended to $\overleftrightarrow{AB}$, the U would be a complete parabola.)

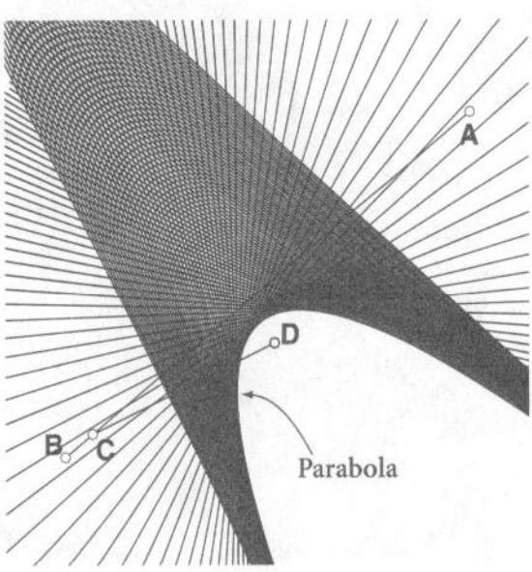

IMPROVING YOUR VISUAL THINKING SKILLS

PDDPPPDDDDPPPPDDDDPPPDDP

Exchanging Ps and Ds gives another answer.

EXTENSION

Challenge students to bisect an angle using only a straightedge with two parallel edges.

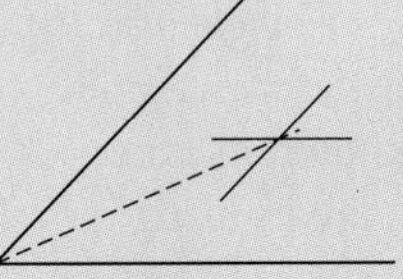

LESSON 3.5

Constructing Parallel Lines

When you stop to think, don't forget to start up again.

ANONYMOUS

Parallel lines are lines that lie in the same plane and do not intersect.

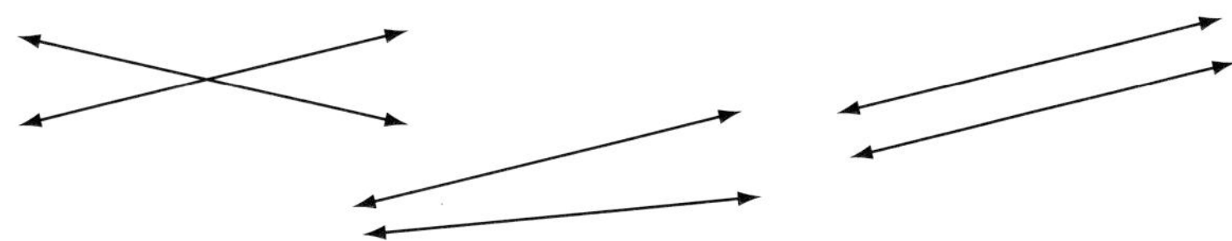

The lines in the first pair shown above intersect. They are clearly not parallel. The lines in the second pair do not meet as drawn. However, if they were extended, they would intersect. Therefore, they are not parallel. The lines in the third pair appear to be parallel, but if you extend them far enough in both directions, can you be sure they won't meet? There are many ways to be sure that the lines are parallel.

Investigation
Constructing Parallel Lines by Folding

You will need
- patty paper

How would you check whether two lines are parallel? One way is to draw a transversal and compare corresponding angles. You can also use this idea to *construct* a pair of parallel lines.

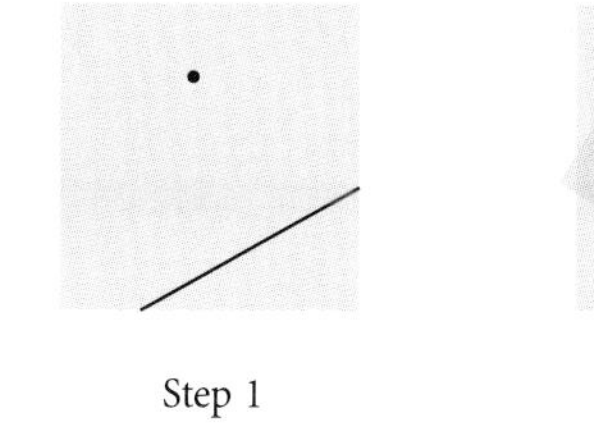

Step 1 Step 2

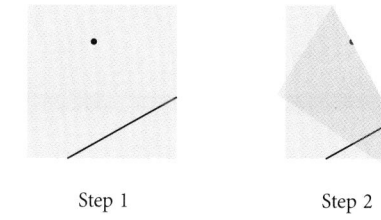

Step 1 Draw a line and a point on patty paper as shown.

Step 2 Fold the paper to construct a perpendicular so that the crease runs through the point as shown. Describe the four newly formed angles.

Step 2 Four congruent right angles are formed.

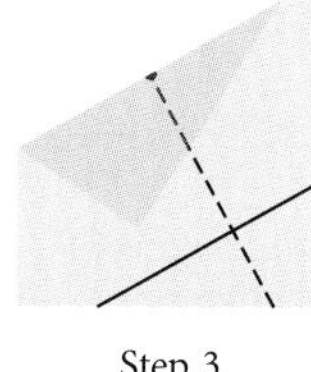

Step 3

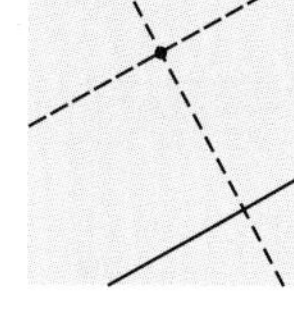

Step 4

Step 3 Through the point, make another fold that is perpendicular to the first crease.

Step 4 Match the pairs of corresponding angles created by the folds. Are they all congruent? Why? What conclusion can you make about the lines?

Step 4 Yes, because they're right angles; the lines are parallel.

NCTM STANDARDS

CONTENT		PROCESS	
	Number		Problem Solving
	Algebra	✓	Reasoning
✓	Geometry	✓	Communication
✓	Measurement	✓	Connections
	Data/Probability		Representation

LESSON OBJECTIVES
- Discover methods of constructing parallel lines
- Review vocabulary

LESSON 3.5

PLANNING

LESSON OUTLINE

One day:

20 min	Investigation
10 min	Sharing
5 min	Closing
10 min	Exercises

MATERIALS
- construction tools

TEACHING

Through a point not on a given line, a parallel line can be constructed in a variety of ways.

One step [Ask] "Given a line and a point not on the line, how many ways can you design to fold patty paper to construct a line parallel to the given line and through the given point?" As you circulate keep asking, as needed, "How do you know those lines are parallel?" **[Ask]** "Did we have some conjecture about when lines were parallel?" [the Converse of the Parallel Lines Conjecture in Lesson 2.6]

Guiding the Investigation

Step 2 [Alert] This is the same fold that was made in Investigation 2 (Patty-Paper Perpendiculars) in Lesson 3.3. The line must be folded on top of itself so that a perpendicular is formed.

Step 4 You can ask groups that finish early to look for other ways of constructing parallel lines.

SHARING IDEAS

Have groups share as many approaches as possible. Give labels to the methods, such as "perpendicular to a perpendicular, equidistant, corresponding angles, alternate interior angles." Keep asking students how they can justify their methods. As needed, point out the connections to the Converse of the Parallel Lines Conjecture. Also help students form some new conjectures: Two lines perpendicular to the same line are parallel, and parallel lines are everywhere equidistant. The equidistant method for constructing parallel lines is not presented in the book: To construct a parallel to line l, construct two perpendiculars to line l, mark equal distances from line l on both lines, and draw a line through those two marks.

Remind students in context that a line continues forever in both directions and is represented graphically by arrowheads on the ends of the part of the line that is pictured.

[Ask] "How many different lines are there parallel to a given line and through a given point?" [only one in a plane] "In space, is it possible for lines not to be parallel and not intersect?" [yes, skew lines] Tell students that non-Euclidean geometries includes the study of surfaces on which shortest paths don't satisfy this property; that is, through a point not on a line, there might be no lines parallel to the given line. Or there might be more than one line parallel to the given line. Challenge students to think about surfaces in which these properties hold to whet their interest in the Exploration Non-Euclidean Geometries in Chapter 13.

See pages 770–771 for answers to Exercises 1, 2, and 4–6.

There are many ways to construct parallel lines. You can construct parallel lines much more quickly with patty paper than with compass and straightedge. You can also use properties you discovered in the Parallel Lines Conjecture to construct parallel lines by duplicating corresponding angles, alternate interior angles, or alternate exterior angles. Or you can construct two perpendiculars to the same line. In the exercises you will practice all of these methods.

EXERCISES

You will need

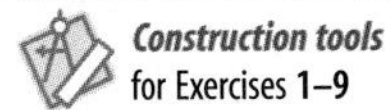

Construction tools for Exercises **1–9**

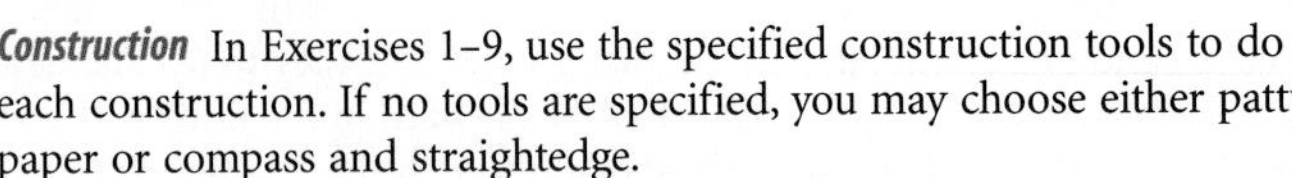

Construction In Exercises 1–9, use the specified construction tools to do each construction. If no tools are specified, you may choose either patty paper or compass and straightedge.

1. Use compass and straightedge. Draw a line and a point not on the line. Construct a second line through the point that is parallel to the first line, by duplicating alternate interior angles.

2. Use compass and straightedge. Draw a line and a point not on the line. Construct a second line through the point that is parallel to the first line, by duplicating corresponding angles.

3. Construct a square with perimeter z. ⓗ See below.

z

4. Construct a rhombus with x as the length of each side and $\angle A$ as one of the acute angles.

x

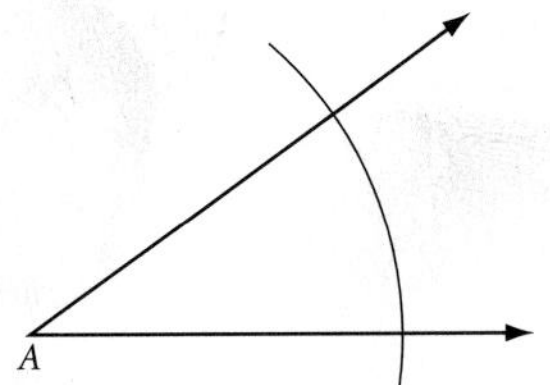

5. Construct trapezoid $TRAP$ with $\overline{TR}$ and $\overline{AP}$ as the two parallel sides and with AP as the distance between them. (There are many solutions!)

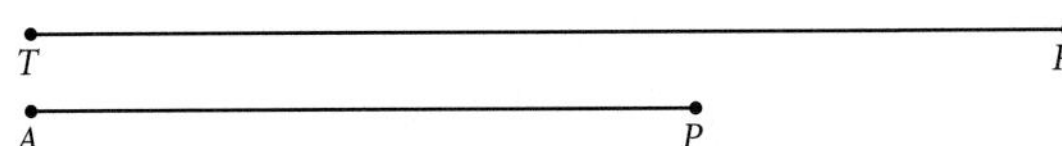

6. Using patty paper and straightedge, or a compass and straightedge, construct parallelogram $GRAM$ with $\overline{RG}$ and $\overline{RA}$ as two consecutive sides and ML as the distance between $\overline{RG}$ and $\overline{AM}$. (How many solutions can you find?) Draw a line and construct $\overline{ML}$ perpendicular to it. Swing an arc from point M to point G so that $MG = RA$. From point G, swing an arc to construct $\overline{RG}$. Finish the parallelogram by swinging an arc of length RA from R and swinging an arc of length GR from M. There is only one possible parallelogram.

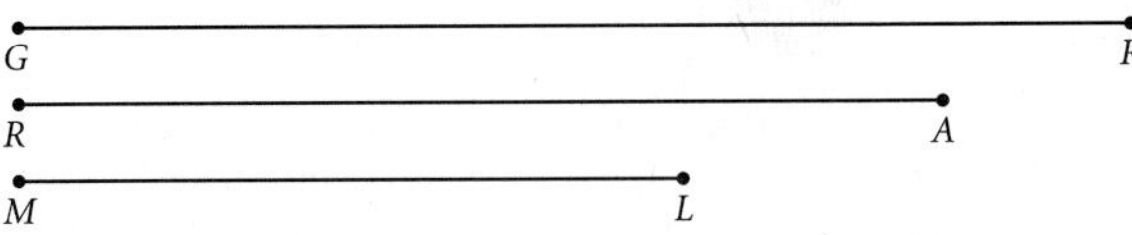

Assessing Progress

Assess students' understanding of the Converse of the Parallel Lines Conjecture. Can students name conditions that guarantee that two lines are parallel? Check also whether students are comfortable with folding perpendiculars on patty paper.

Closing the Lesson

Summarize the variety of methods for constructing a parallel line. Tie each to a conjecture justifying it.

3. Construct a segment with length z. Bisect the segment to get length $\frac{z}{2}$. Bisect again to get a segment with length $\frac{z}{4}$. Construct a square with each side of length $\frac{z}{4}$.

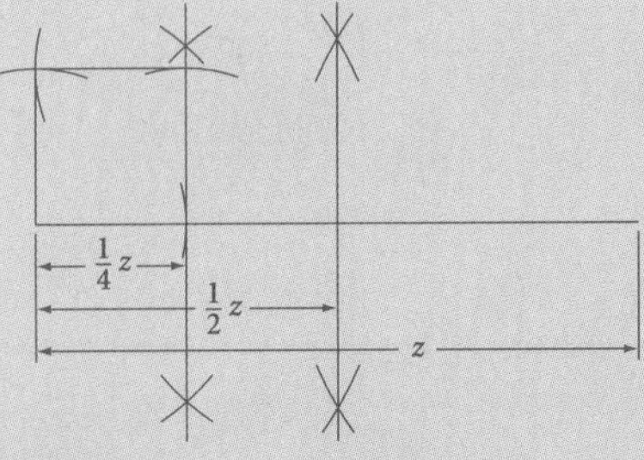

7. ***Mini-Investigation*** Construct a large scalene acute triangle and label it $\triangle SUM$. Through vertex M construct a line parallel to side $\overline{SU}$ as shown in the diagram. Use your protractor or a piece of patty paper to compare $\angle 1$ and $\angle 2$ with the other two angles of the triangle ($\angle S$ and $\angle U$). Notice anything special? Can you explain why? $\angle 1 \cong \angle S$, $\angle 2 \cong \angle U$; AIA

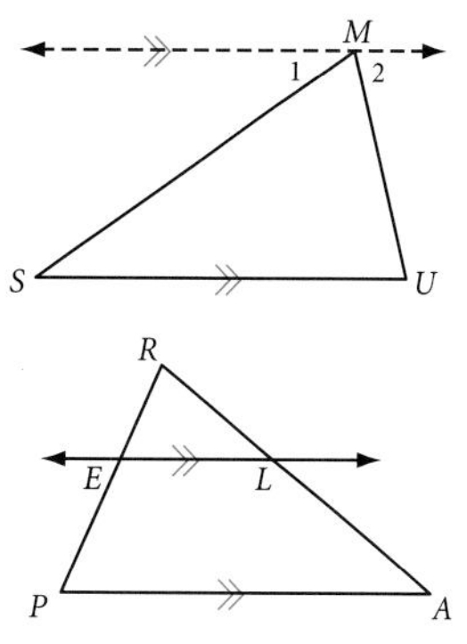

8. ***Mini-Investigation*** Construct a large scalene acute triangle and label it $\triangle PAR$. Place point E anywhere on side PR, and construct a line $\overleftrightarrow{EL}$ parallel to side $\overline{PA}$ as shown in the diagram. Use your ruler to measure the lengths of the four segments $\overline{AL}$, $\overline{LR}$, $\overline{RE}$, and $\overline{EP}$, and compare ratios $\frac{RL}{LA}$ and $\frac{RE}{EP}$. Notice anything special? (You may also do this problem using geometry software.) The ratios appear to be the same.

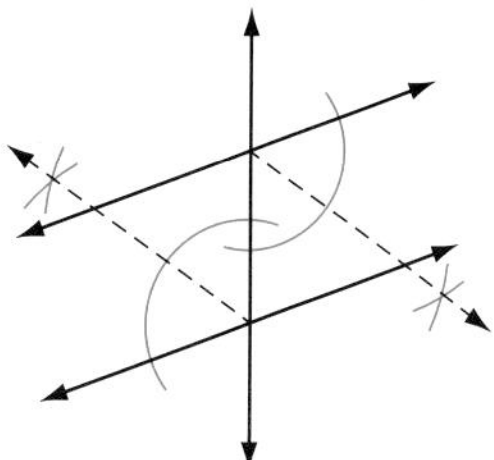

9. ***Mini-Investigation*** Draw a pair of parallel lines by tracing along both edges of your ruler. Draw a transversal. Use your compass to bisect each angle of a pair of alternate interior angles. What shape is formed? Can you explain why?

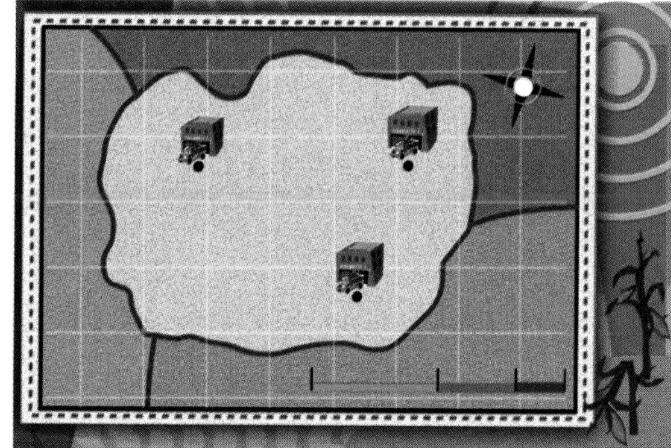

Review

3.2 **10.** There are three fire stations in the small county of Dry Lake. County planners need to divide the county into three zones so that fire alarms alert the closest station. Trace the county and the three fire stations onto patty paper, and locate the boundaries of the three zones. Explain how these boundaries solve the problem. ⓗ

2.6 **11.** Copy the diagram below. Use your conjectures to calculate the measure of each lettered angle.

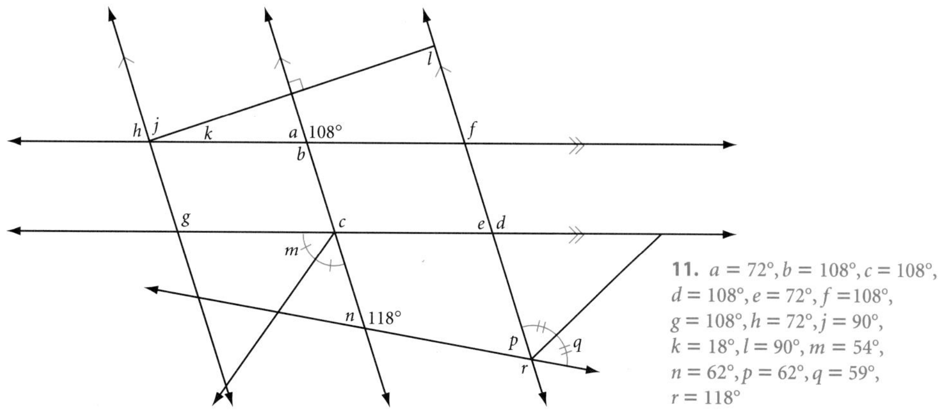

11. $a = 72°, b = 108°, c = 108°, d = 108°, e = 72°, f = 108°, g = 108°, h = 72°, j = 90°, k = 18°, l = 90°, m = 54°, n = 62°, p = 62°, q = 59°, r = 118°$

BUILDING UNDERSTANDING

You might do a sample from Exercises 5–11.

ASSIGNING HOMEWORK

Essential	1–9
Performance assessment	8
Portfolio	7
Journal	9, 10
Group	5
Review	10–14

Helping with the Exercises

Exercises 3–7 Keep asking students to support the method they're using to construct parallel lines.

Exercise 3 [Alert] Students may need help getting started with this exercise. Suggest that they talk with each other about the steps they might follow.

Exercise 6 Students may find this exercise difficult, so be prepared to offer encouragement. There's only one solution if reflections are considered to be the same.

Exercise 8 As needed, remind students of the meaning of *scalene triangle.* **[Ask]** "Do you notice anything about line EL and segment PA?"

Exercise 9 [Ask] "Can you support your belief deductively?"

9. A parallelogram. The angle bisectors are parallel: $\angle DAB \cong \angle ABC$, so $\overleftrightarrow{AD} \parallel \overleftrightarrow{BC}$.

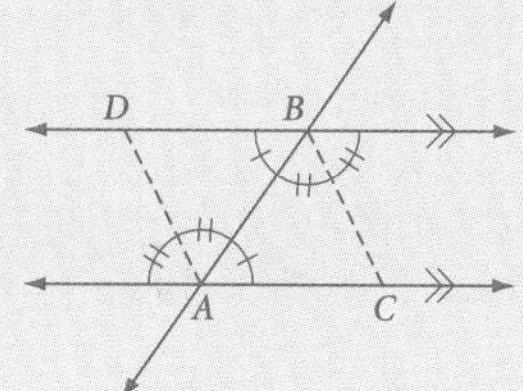

10. Construct the perpendicular bisector of each of the three segments connecting the fire stations.

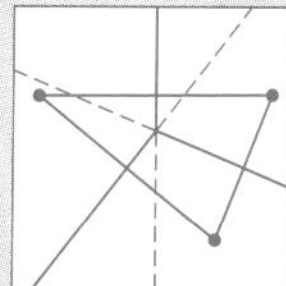

Eliminate the rays beyond where the bisectors intersect. A point within any region will be closest to the fire station in that region.

12. 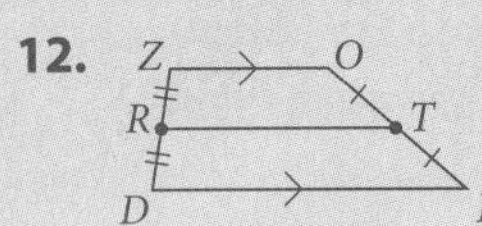

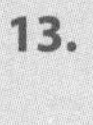

13. 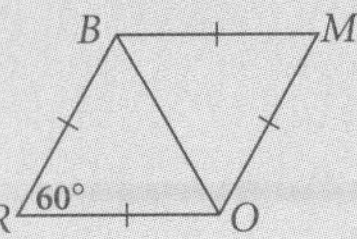

14. 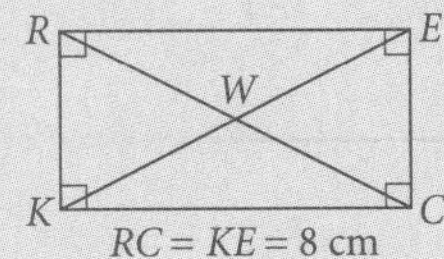

Sketch or draw each figure in Exercises 12–14. Label the vertices with the appropriate letters. Use the special marks that indicate right angles, parallel segments, and congruent segments and angles.

1.4 **12.** Sketch trapezoid *ZOID* with $\overline{ZO} \parallel \overline{ID}$, point *T* the midpoint of $\overline{OI}$, and *R* the midpoint of $\overline{ZD}$. Sketch segment *TR*.

1.4 **13.** Draw rhombus *ROMB* with $m\angle R = 60°$ and diagonal $\overline{OB}$.

1.4 **14.** Draw rectangle *RECK* with diagonals $\overline{RC}$ and $\overline{EK}$ both 8 cm long and intersecting at point *W*.

IMPROVING YOUR VISUAL THINKING SKILLS

PUZZLE

Visual Analogies

Which of the designs at right complete the statements at left? Explain.

1. [figure] is to [figure] as [figure] is to ? A. B. C. D.

2. [figure] is to [figure] as [figure] is to ? A. B. C. D.

3. [figure] is to [figure] as [figure] is to ? A. B. C. D.

IMPROVING VISUAL THINKING SKILLS

1. C

2. C

3. B

Slopes of Parallel and Perpendicular Lines

If two lines are parallel, how do their slopes compare? If two lines are perpendicular, how do *their* slopes compare? In this lesson you will review properties of the slopes of parallel and perpendicular lines.

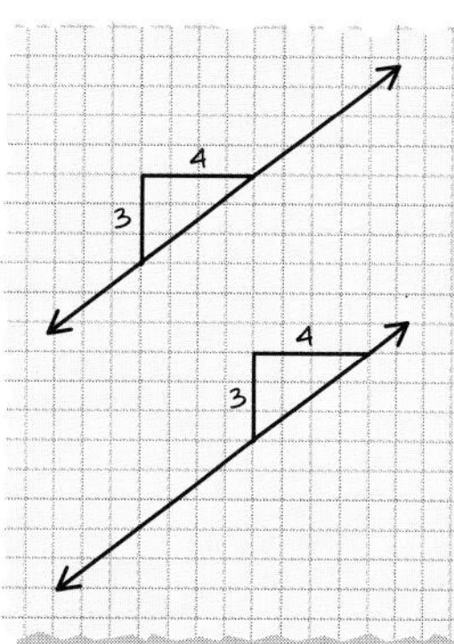

If the slopes of two or more distinct lines are equal, are the lines parallel? To find out, try drawing on graph paper two lines that have the same slope triangle.

Yes, the lines are parallel. In fact, in coordinate geometry, this is the definition of parallel lines. The converse of this is true as well: If two lines are parallel, their slopes must be equal.

Parallel Slope Property

In a coordinate plane, two distinct lines are parallel if and only if their slopes are equal.

If two lines are perpendicular, their slope triangles have a different relationship. Study the slopes of the two perpendicular lines at right.

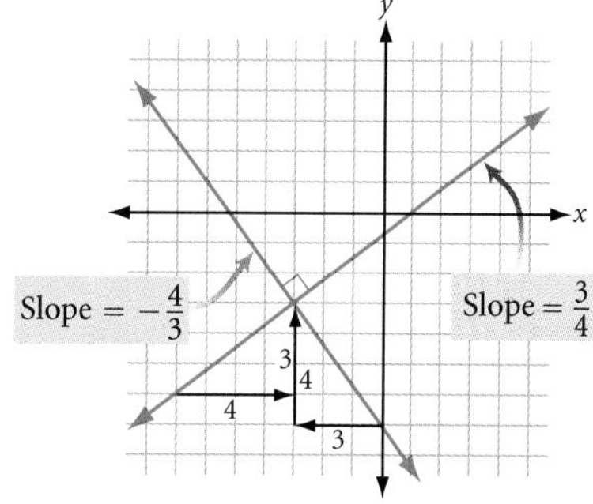

Perpendicular Slope Property

In a coordinate plane, two nonvertical lines are perpendicular if and only if their slopes are negative reciprocals of each other.

Can you explain why the slopes of perpendicular lines would have opposite signs? Can you explain why they would be reciprocals? Why do the lines need to be nonvertical?

Using Your Algebra Skills 3

PLANNING

LESSON OUTLINE

One day:

15 min Example A

10 min Example B

20 min Exercises

MATERIALS

- graph paper

TEACHING

Remind students of what a slope triangle is. The slope triangles drawn on the parallel lines have the same $\frac{\text{rise}}{\text{run}}$. One slope triangle is a 90° rotation of the other for perpendicular lines.

NCTM STANDARDS

CONTENT		PROCESS	
✓	Number	✓	Problem Solving
✓	Algebra		Reasoning
✓	Geometry		Communication
	Measurement	✓	Connections
	Data/Probability	✓	Representation

LESSON OBJECTIVES

- Investigate the relationship between the slopes of parallel lines
- Investigate the relationship between the slopes of perpendicular lines

▶ EXAMPLE A

Ask students to speculate about how to answer the given question based on graphs they draw. Then have them calculate the slopes (drawing in slope triangles may help) and ask how they are related.

[Alert] Students may think that the negative reciprocal of a number must be negative. **[ESL]** Here *negative* means "opposite in sign." The negative reciprocal of -5 is $+\frac{1}{5}$.

[Ask] "What is $\frac{2}{3} \cdot \frac{-3}{2}$?" $[-1]$ Another way to determine perpendicularity is to multiply the slopes and get -1.

▶ EXAMPLE B

Before they work through the solution, have students plot the three points on a coordinate grid to get a visual "feel" for the problem.

In the exercises, students will sometimes be asked to find more than one solution. **[Ask]** "How would you find another solution?" Let students suggest other solutions, and ask the class to confirm that the suggestions are indeed solutions.

Assessing Progress

You can assess how well students understand slope as "change in y per unit of change in x," as well as their arithmetic skill with negative numbers.

Closing the Lesson

The major ideas relate the perpendicular lines and parallel lines to their slopes: Perpendicular lines have slopes that are negative reciprocals, and parallel lines have the same slope.

EXAMPLE A Consider $A(-15, -6)$, $B(6, 8)$, $C(4, -2)$, and $D(-4, 10)$. Are $\overleftrightarrow{AB}$ and $\overleftrightarrow{CD}$ parallel, perpendicular, or neither?

▶ Solution Calculate the slope of each line.

$$\text{slope of } \overleftrightarrow{AB} = \frac{8-(-6)}{6-(-15)} = \frac{2}{3} \qquad \text{slope of } \overleftrightarrow{CD} = \frac{10-(-2)}{-4-4} = -\frac{3}{2}$$

The slopes, $\frac{2}{3}$ and $-\frac{3}{2}$, are negative reciprocals of each other, so $\overleftrightarrow{AB} \perp \overleftrightarrow{CD}$.

EXAMPLE B Given points $E(-3, 0)$, $F(5, -4)$, and $Q(4, 2)$, find the coordinates of a point P such that $\overleftrightarrow{PQ}$ is parallel to $\overleftrightarrow{EF}$.

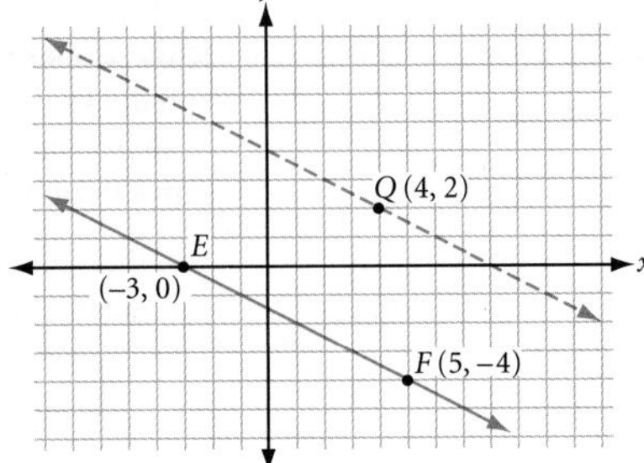

▶ Solution We know that if $\overleftrightarrow{PQ} \parallel \overleftrightarrow{EF}$, then the slope of $\overleftrightarrow{PQ}$ equals the slope of $\overleftrightarrow{EF}$. First find the slope of $\overleftrightarrow{EF}$.

$$\text{slope of } \overleftrightarrow{EF} = \frac{-4-0}{5-(-3)} = \frac{-4}{8} = -\frac{1}{2}$$

There are many possible ordered pairs (x, y) for P. Use (x, y) as the coordinates of P, and the given coordinates of Q, in the slope formula to get

$$\frac{2-y}{4-x} = -\frac{1}{2}$$

Now you can treat the denominators and numerators as separate equations.

$$\begin{aligned} 4 - x &= 2 \\ -x &= -2 \\ x &= 2 \end{aligned} \qquad \begin{aligned} 2 - y &= -1 \\ -y &= -3 \\ y &= 3 \end{aligned}$$

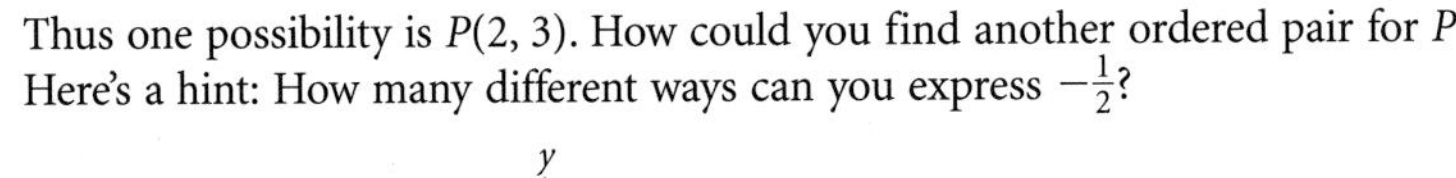

Thus one possibility is $P(2, 3)$. How could you find another ordered pair for P? Here's a hint: How many different ways can you express $-\frac{1}{2}$?

Language CONNECTION

Coordinate geometry is sometimes called "analytic geometry." This term implies that you can use algebra to further analyze what you see. For example, consider $\overleftrightarrow{AB}$ and $\overleftrightarrow{CD}$. They look parallel, but looks can be deceiving. Only by calculating the slopes will you see that the lines are not truly parallel.

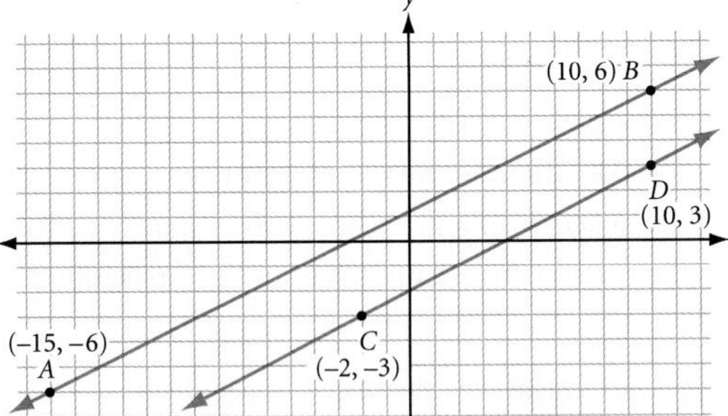

EXERCISES

For Exercises 1–4, determine whether each pair of lines through the points given below is parallel, perpendicular, or neither.

$A(1, 2)$ $B(3, 4)$ $C(5, 2)$ $D(8, 3)$ $E(3, 8)$ $F(-6, 5)$

1. $\overleftrightarrow{AB}$ and $\overleftrightarrow{BC}$ perpendicular **2.** $\overleftrightarrow{AB}$ and $\overleftrightarrow{CD}$ neither **3.** $\overleftrightarrow{AB}$ and $\overleftrightarrow{DE}$ perpendicular **4.** $\overleftrightarrow{CD}$ and $\overleftrightarrow{EF}$ parallel

5. Given $A(0, -3)$, $B(5, 3)$, and $Q(-3, -1)$, find two possible locations for a point P such that $\overleftrightarrow{PQ}$ is parallel to $\overleftrightarrow{AB}$. possible answer: (2, 5) and (7, 11)

6. Given $C(-2, -1)$, $D(5, -4)$, and $Q(4, 2)$, find two possible locations for a point P such that $\overleftrightarrow{PQ}$ is perpendicular to $\overleftrightarrow{CD}$. possible answer: (1, −5) and (−2, −12)

For Exercises 7–9, find the slope of each side, and then determine whether each figure is a trapezoid, a parallelogram, a rectangle, or just an ordinary quadrilateral. Explain how you know.

7.

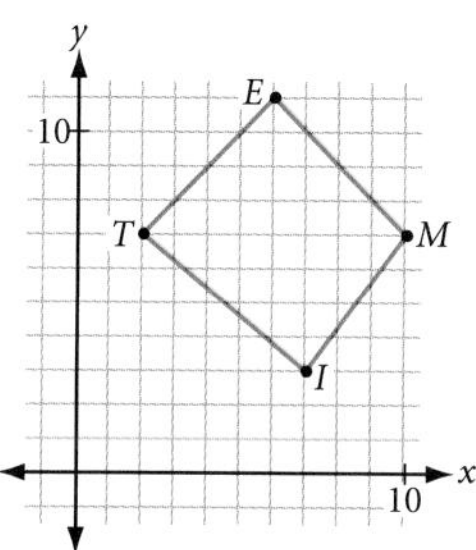

8.

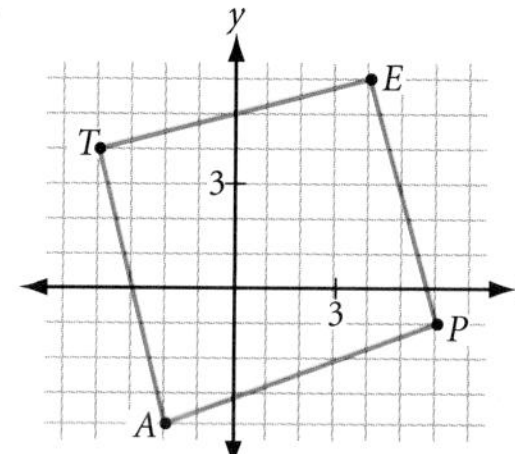

9.

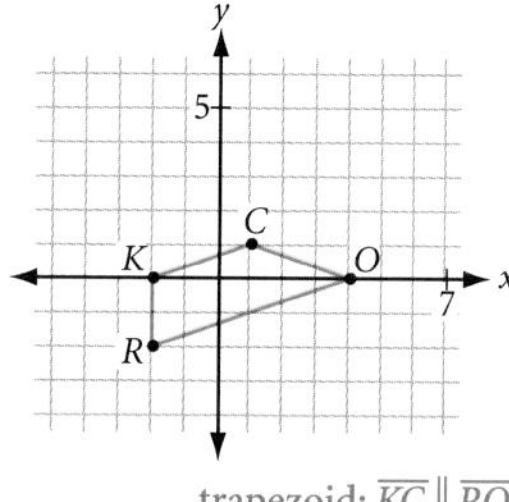

trapezoid: $\overline{KC} \parallel \overline{RO}$

10. Quadrilateral *HAND* has vertices $H(-5, -1)$, $A(7, 1)$, $N(6, 7)$, and $D(-6, 5)$.

a. Is quadrilateral *HAND* a parallelogram? A rectangle? Neither? Explain how you know.

b. Find the midpoint of each diagonal. What can you conjecture?

11. Quadrilateral *OVER* has vertices $O(-4, 2)$, $V(1, 1)$, $E(0, 6)$, and $R(-5, 7)$.

a. Are the diagonals perpendicular? Explain how you know.

b. Find the midpoint of each diagonal. What can you conjecture?

c. What type of quadrilateral does *OVER* appear to be? Explain how you know.

12. Consider the points $A(-5, -2)$, $B(1, 1)$, $C(-1, 0)$, and $D(3, 2)$.

a. Find the slopes of $\overline{AB}$ and $\overline{CD}$. Both slopes equal $\frac{1}{2}$.

b. Despite their slopes, $\overline{AB}$ and $\overline{CD}$ are not parallel. Why not? The segments are not parallel because they are coincident.

c. What word in the Parallel Slope Property addresses the problem in 12b? distinct

13. Given $A(-3, 2)$, $B(1, 5)$, and $C(7, -3)$, find point D such that quadrilateral *ABCD* is a rectangle. (3, −6)

10a. Slope $\overline{HA}$ = slope $\overline{ND} = \frac{1}{6}$; slope $\overline{HD}$ = slope $\overline{NA} = -6$. Quadrilateral *HAND* is a rectangle because opposite sides are parallel and adjacent sides are perpendicular.

10b. Midpoint $\overline{HN}$ = midpoint $\overline{AD} = \left(\frac{1}{2}, 3\right)$. The diagonals of a rectangle bisect each other.

11a. Yes, the diagonals are perpendicular. Slope $\overline{OE} = 1$; slope $\overline{VR} = -1$.

11b. Midpoint $\overline{VR}$ = midpoint $\overline{OE} = (-2, 4)$. The diagonals of *OVER* bisect each other.

11c. *OVER* appears to be a rhombus because the sides are parallel and appear to be the same length.

BUILDING UNDERSTANDING

The exercises give students an opportunity to work with the geometry concepts *parallel* and *perpendicular* as well as the algebraic concept of determining slope. While you are available for consultation, have students work through one problem from Exercises 1–4 and one from Exercises 11–13.

ASSIGNING HOMEWORK

Essential	1–10, 12, 13
Performance assessment	11

Helping with the Exercises

Exercises 1–4 Students can graph lines to help determine slopes and the relationship between the lines.

Exercises 5, 6 These exercises incorporate ideas of slope into recent constructions.

Exercises 7–13 If students are having difficulty getting started, suggest that they look up the relevant definitions. When they've answered each question, challenge them to support their answer by citing the slopes and the definitions.

7. Ordinary; no two slopes are the same, so no sides are parallel although $\overline{TE} \perp \overline{EM}$ because their slopes are negative reciprocals.

8. Ordinary, for the same reason as in Exercise 7—none of the sides are quite parallel.

LESSON

3.6

PLANNING

LESSON OUTLINE

One day:

10 min Examples

10 min Sharing

5 min Closing

20 min Exercises

MATERIALS

- construction tools
- geometry software, *optional*

TEACHING

You might let students do a one-step investigation to develop familiarity with the idea of determining a triangle. Or you can move quickly through the two examples as a class and have students spend most of the time working on the exercises. In the latter case, have students share ideas after working on the first few exercises. If you want to cover all the exercises in class, you may need a second day.

► *EXAMPLE A*

If you're demonstrating, have students vote to determine the order in which you use the segments, to illustrate that order doesn't matter.

Students might mistakenly think that a triangle can be constructed from any three segments. In Lesson 4.3, they will learn that the sum of the lengths of two sides must be greater than the length of the third (Triangle Inequality).

You can point out that $\triangle ABC$ could also be constructed on the other side of the initial segment, but that triangle would be congruent to the one in the solution.

LESSON 3.6

Construction Problems

People who are only good with hammers see every problem as a nail.

ABRAHAM MASLOW

Once you know the basic constructions, you can create more complex geometric figures.

You know how to duplicate segments and angles with a compass and straightedge. If given a triangle, you can use these two constructions to duplicate the triangle by copying each segment and angle. Can you construct a triangle if you are given the parts separately? Would you need all six parts—three segments and three angles—to construct a triangle?

Let's first consider a case in which only three segments are given.

EXAMPLE A

Construct $\triangle ABC$ using the three segments $\overline{AB}$, $\overline{BC}$, and $\overline{CA}$ shown below. How many different-size triangles can be drawn?

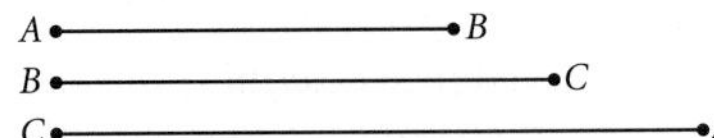

► *Solution*

You can begin by copying one segment, for example $\overline{AC}$. Then adjust your compass to match the length of another segment. Using this length as a radius, draw a circle centered at one endpoint of the first segment. Now use the third segment length as the radius for another circle, this one centered at the other endpoint. The third vertex of the triangle is where the circles intersect.

In the construction above, the segment lengths determine the sizes of the circles and where they intersect. Once the triangle "closes" at the intersection of the arcs, the angles are determined, too. So the lengths of the segments affect the size of the angles. There is only one size of triangle that can be drawn with the segments given, so the segments **determine** the triangle. Does having three angles also determine a triangle?

EXAMPLE B

Construct $\triangle ABC$ with patty paper by copying the three angles $\angle A$, $\angle B$, and $\angle C$ shown below. How many different size triangles can be drawn?

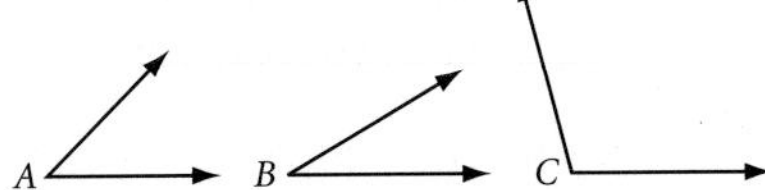

► *Solution*

In this patty-paper construction the angles do not determine the segment length. You can locate the endpoint of a segment anywhere along an angle's side without affecting the angle measures. Infinitely many different triangles can be drawn with the angles given. Here are just a few examples.

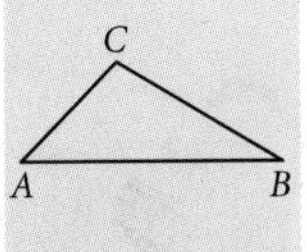

LESSON OBJECTIVES

- Explore through construction whether or not a triangle can be determined given certain parts
- Pull together a variety of construction techniques
- Develop problem-solving skills and cooperative behavior

NCTM STANDARDS

CONTENT		PROCESS	
	Number	✔	Problem Solving
✔	Algebra		Reasoning
✔	Geometry		Communication
✔	Measurement	✔	Connections
	Data/Probability		Representation

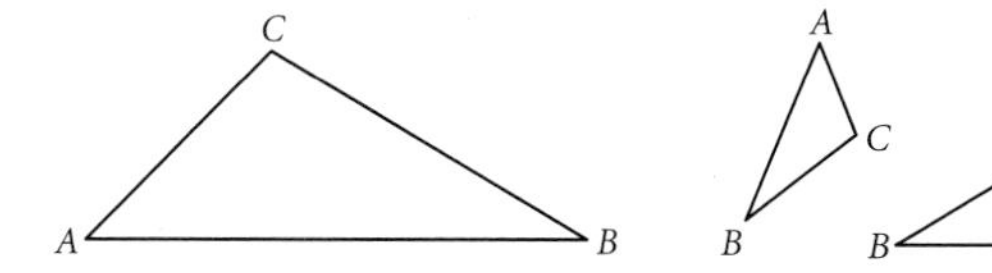

The angles do not determine a particular triangle.

Since a triangle has a total of six parts, there are several combinations of segments and angles that may or may not determine a triangle. Having one or two parts given is not enough to determine a triangle. Is having three parts enough? That answer depends on the combination. In the exercises you will construct triangles and quadrilaterals with various combinations of parts given.

EXERCISES

You will need

Construction tools for Exercises **1–10**

Geometry software for Exercise **11**

Construction In Exercises 1–10, first sketch and label the figure you are going to construct. Second, construct the figure, using either a compass and straightedge, or patty paper and straightedge. Third, describe the steps in your construction in a few sentences.

1. Given:

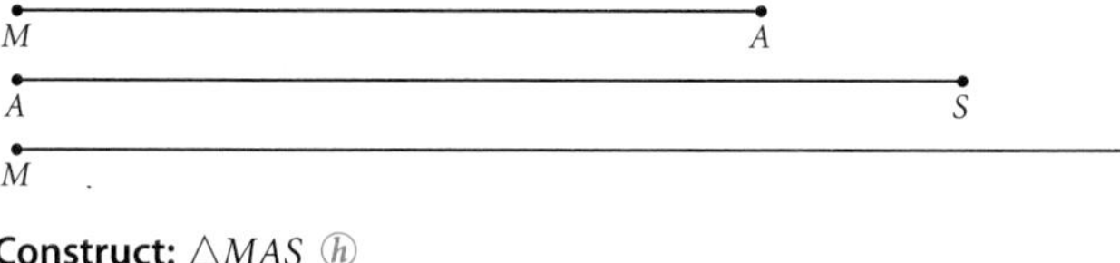

Construct: $\triangle MAS$ ⓗ

2. Given:

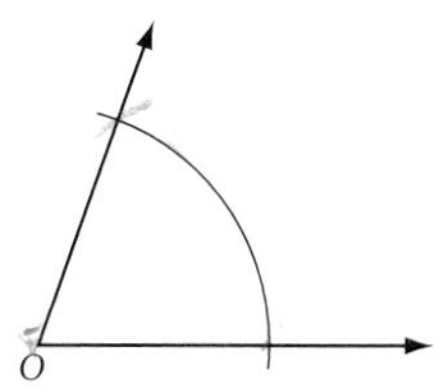

D — O

O — T

Construct: $\triangle DOT$

3. Given:

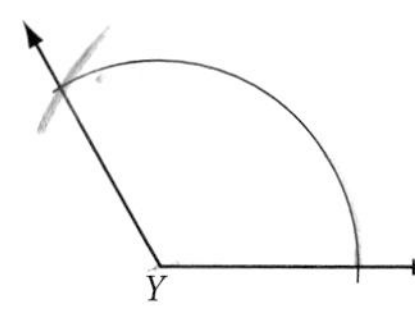

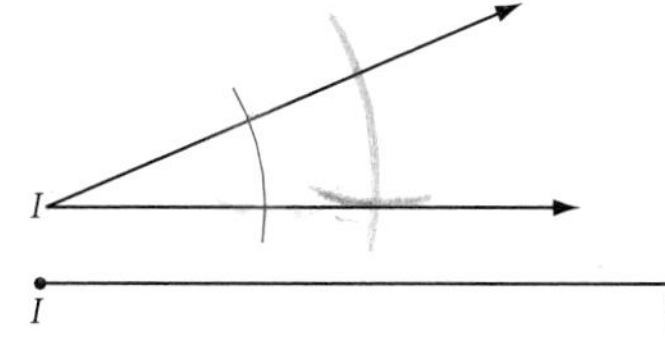

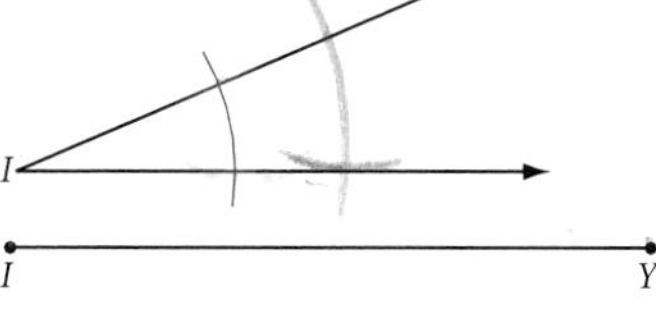

Construct: $\triangle IGY$

▸ EXAMPLE B

You might ask different groups to use different lengths of sides (but the same measures of angles) to dramatize the fact that triangles with the same angle measures need not be congruent.

Students at this stage might not know that the measures of the three angles must add up to 180° for the angles to form a triangle. For two angles to be part of a triangle, they must sum to less than 180°.

One step Point out that if students were given all six parts of a triangle, they could construct the triangle. But perhaps not all six parts are necessary. **[Ask]** "Can you construct the triangle from just one part, say, one side or one angle?" [They could construct lots of triangles, not just one.] "What if you had two parts?" [Again, they could construct many triangles.] The question for students to explore in their groups is, "Are three parts of a triangle (say, three sides or three angles) enough to allow a unique triangle to be constructed?" As you circulate, encourage students to justify their conjectures with deductive reasoning. If a group has answered the question for three sides and three angles to your satisfaction, suggest that they consider mixtures of sides and angles, still using three parts.

SHARING IDEAS

As students who completed the one-step investigation present ways of constructing a triangle from three sides, ask if *any* three sides can be formed into a triangle. You need not answer this question now.

Ask how the compass is being used. It's not being used just to transfer known distances but rather to draw significant parts of circles. Ask if students could accomplish the same construction with patty paper. [They could copy one segment onto each of three sheets, stack the sheets

Sharing Ideas (continued)

(adjusting so the segments form a triangle), and trace the lower two segments onto the top sheet.]

You can begin to refer to "determining" a triangle without defining the term. An assortment of sticks might help illustrate what determines a triangle.

As the class discussion turns to how many triangles can be constructed from three angles, ask if any two sides can fit into the three given angles to make a triangle. Recognize good thinking in students who observe that once they have drawn two angles and the side between them a triangle is determined.

At this point don't insist on mastery of the ideas of triangle congruence. These construction problems are laying the groundwork for the ideas presented in Chapter 4.

Wonder aloud whether triangles with the same three angles all have the same shape. Don't push for much understanding of similarity yet, but merely plant the idea.

Assessing Progress
Observations of group work and class participation can lead to assessing students' ability to copy segments and angles. From their work on the exercises, you can assess how well students can read the given information and solve problems using the construction techniques they have learned in this chapter. Some of the exercises require that students know the definitions of different types of triangles and of a kite.

Closing the Lesson

The major idea of this lesson is that three sides, but not three angles, **determine** a triangle. The rest of the congruence conditions appear in Lessons 4.4 and 4.5.

BUILDING UNDERSTANDING

The exercises integrate previously learned construction techniques with the idea of determining a figure. Using patty paper will make many of the constructions go more quickly.

ASSIGNING HOMEWORK

Essential	1–6
Performance assessment	5
Portfolio	10
Journal	11
Group	7–9, 11
Review	12–15

See page 771 for answers to Exercises 1–7.

4. Given the triangle shown at right, construct another triangle with angles congruent to the given angles but with sides *not* congruent to the given sides. Is there more than one triangle with the same three angles? Yes, students' constructions must be either larger or smaller than the triangle in the book.

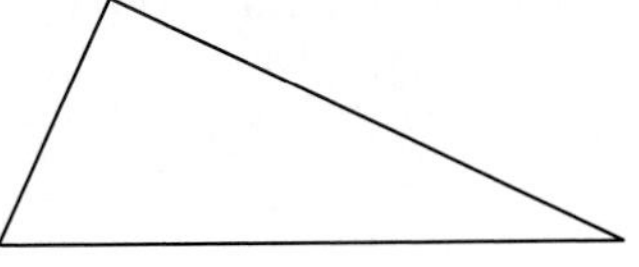

5. The two segments and the angle below do not determine a triangle.

Given:

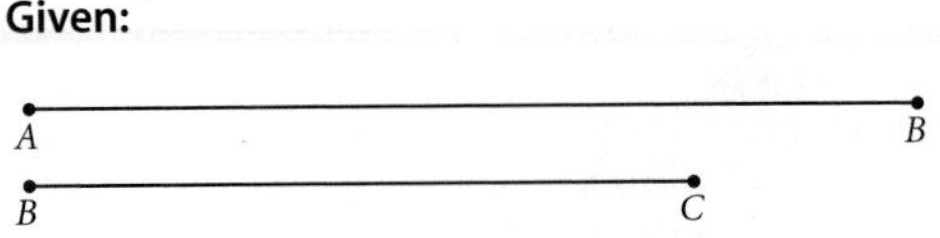

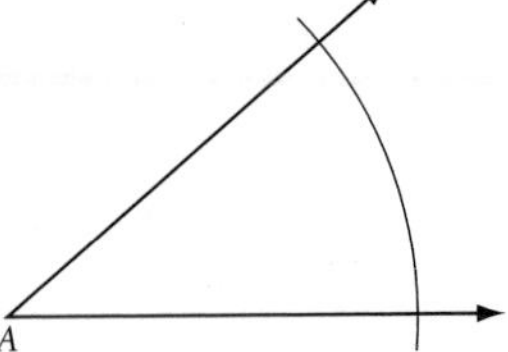

Construct: Two different (noncongruent) triangles named $\triangle ABC$ that have the three given parts ⓗ

6. Given:

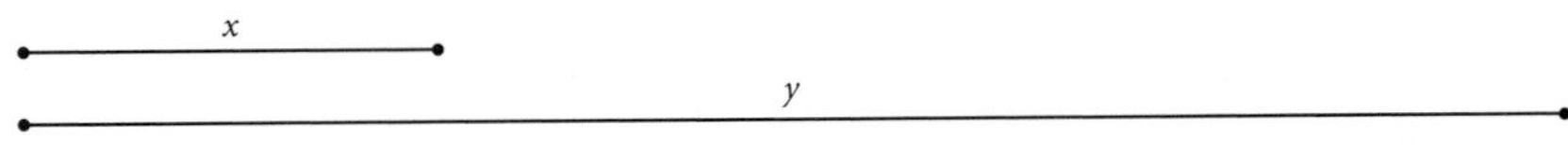

Construct: Isosceles triangle *CAT* with perimeter *y* and length of the base equal to *x* ⓗ

7. Construct a kite.

8. Construct a quadrilateral with two pairs of opposite sides of equal length.

9. Construct a quadrilateral with exactly three sides of equal length.

10. Construct a quadrilateral with all four sides of equal length.

11. ***Technology*** Using geometry software, draw a large scalene obtuse triangle *ABC* with $\angle B$ the obtuse angle. Construct the angle bisector $\overline{BR}$, the median $\overline{BM}$, and the altitude $\overline{BS}$. What is the order of the points on $\overline{AC}$? Drag *B*. Is the order of points always the same? Write a conjecture.

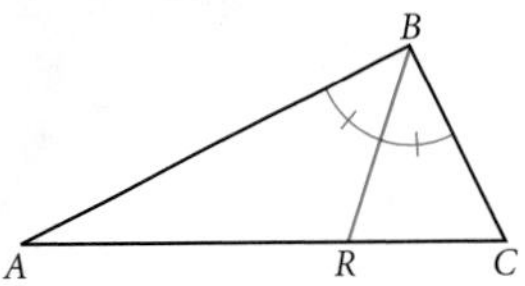

Answers will vary. The angle bisector lies between the median and the altitude. The order of the points is either *M, R, S* or *S, R, M*. One possible conjecture: In a scalene obtuse triangle the angle bisector is always between the median and the altitude.

Review

1.4 **12.** Draw each figure and decide how many reflectional and rotational symmetries it has. Copy and complete the table at right.

Figure	Reflectional symmetries	Rotational symmetries
Trapezoid	0	0
Kite	1	0
Parallelogram	0	2
Rhombus	2	2
Rectangle	2	2

Helping with the Exercises

Exercises 1–10 The instructions appear before Exercise 1.

Exercises 1–5 These exercises demonstrate that SSS, SAS, and ASA determine a triangle and that AAA and SSA do not. You might jigsaw these problems among groups during class and make time for students to share their results. For most classes introducing the shorthand at this point is premature.

Exercise 8 [Ask] What kind of a quadrilateral have you constructed?" [parallelogram]

8.

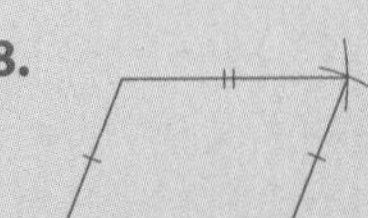

Sample description: Draw an angle and mark off unequal distances on the sides. Mark off a distance equal to the second length from the end of the first side and the first length from the end of the second side. Connect that mark to the corresponding marks on the first angle.

1.7 **13.** Draw the new position of $\triangle TEA$ if it is reflected over the dotted line. Label the coordinates of the vertices.

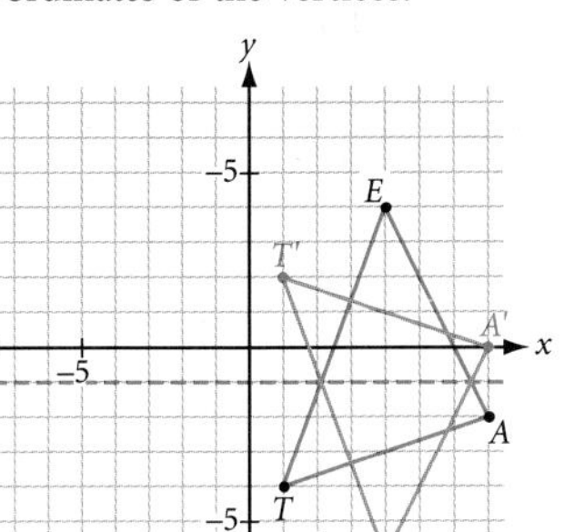

new coordinates: $E'(4, -6), A'(7, 0), T'(1, 2)$

1.7 **14.** Sketch the three-dimensional figure formed by folding the net below into a solid. half a cylinder

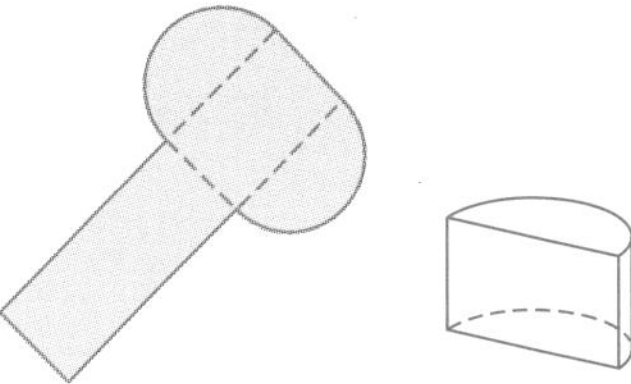

2.4 **15.** If a polygon has 500 diagonals from each vertex, how many sides does it have? 503

IMPROVING YOUR REASONING SKILLS

PUZZLE

Spelling Card Trick

This card trick uses one complete suit (hearts, clubs, spades, or diamonds) from a regular deck of playing cards. How must you arrange the cards so that you can successfully complete the trick? Here is what your audience should see and hear as you perform.

1. As you take the top card and place it at the bottom of the pile, say "A."
2. Then take the second card, place it at the bottom of the pile, and say "C."
3. Take the third card, place it at the bottom, and say "E."
4. You've just spelled *ace*. Now take the fourth card and turn it faceup on the table. The card should be an ace.
5. Continue in this fashion, saying "T," "W," and "O" for the next three cards. Then turn the next card faceup. It should be a 2.
6. Continue spelling *three, four, . . . , jack, queen, king*. Each time you spell a card, the next card turned faceup should be that card.

Exercise 9 [Ask] "Could you make a quadrilateral with exactly three sides congruent that is a special kind of quadrilateral?" [Yes, it could be an isosceles trapezoid.]

9.

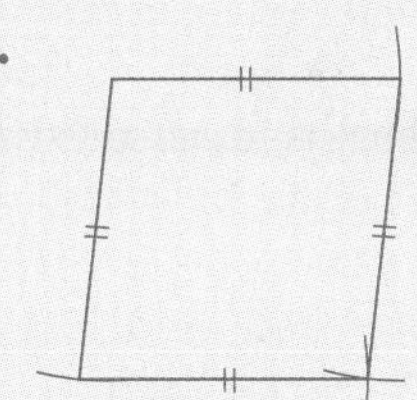

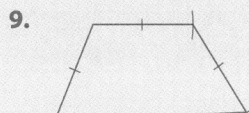

Sample description: Draw a segment and draw an angle at one end of the segment. Mark off a distance equal to that segment on the other side of the angle. Draw an angle at that point and mark off the same distance. Connect that point to the other end of the original segment.

Exercise 10 [Ask] "What kind of a quadrilateral have you constructed?" [rhombus]

10.

Sample description: Draw an angle and mark off equal lengths on the two sides. Use that length to determine another point that distance from the points on the sides. Connect that point with the two points on the side of the angle.

11.

$m\angle ABC = 111°$

B, A, S, R, M, C, Median, Altitude, Angle bisector

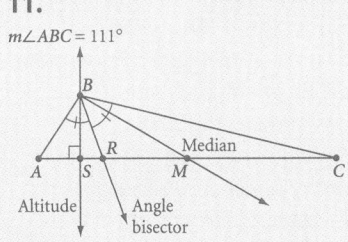

Exercise 12 A figure with 2-fold rotational symmetry has 2 rotational symmetries.

EXTENSION

Students can explore whether or not two angles and a side not between them (SAA) determine a triangle.

IMPROVING REASONING SKILLS

Be sure students realize that the faceup card is placed on the table and thus is removed from the deck. If students are having difficulty, ask if they can lay out the cards in a row to show you how the trick would work. They might begin with all cards upside down and then place one right-side up when its location is determined.

(top) 3, 8, 7, A, Q, 6, 4, 2, J, K, 10, 9, 5 (bottom)

EXPLORATION

PLANNING

LESSON OUTLINE

One day:

25 min Activity

15 min Sharing

5 min Closing

MATERIALS

- construction tools
- Box (T) for One step

TEACHING

Many students are highly motivated by this Exploration. The realism achieved in perspective drawing is persuasive evidence for students that geometry is relevant to the real world. On the other hand, some students have difficulty in getting beyond their knowledge of three-dimensional space to see how the two-dimensional figures are actually created. Having some real boxes around can help them. Being able to measure the boxes also helps students.

One step Display the Box transparency and ask students to draw their own copy. Tease them gently about how bad their copies are, and suggest that a pair of students from each group go to the screen and make some measurements with the meterstick or yardstick to see which lines are equal in length. Ask why they think parallel edges should have the same length and whether the two-dimensional figures displayed are actually parallelograms. As needed, wonder aloud what will happen if the students use metersticks to extend the lines of the drawing on the screen. As students get the idea that parallel lines extend to a

Exploration

Perspective Drawing

You know from experience that when you look down a long straight road, the parallel edges and the center line seem to meet at a point on the horizon. To show this effect in a drawing, artists use perspective, the technique of portraying solid objects and spatial relationships on a flat surface. Renaissance artists and architects in the fifteenth century developed **perspective,** turning to geometry to make art appear true-to-life.

In a perspective drawing, receding parallel lines (lines that run directly away from the viewer) converge at a **vanishing point** on the **horizon line.** Locate the horizon line, the vanishing point, and converging lines in the perspective study below by Jan Vredeman de Vries.

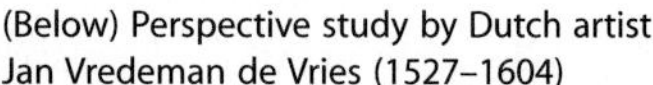

(Below) Perspective study by Dutch artist Jan Vredeman de Vries (1527–1604)

LESSON OBJECTIVES

- Construct realistic-looking boxes with the use of perspective
- Develop problem-solving skills and cooperative behavior

NCTM STANDARDS

CONTENT		PROCESS	
	Number	✓	Problem Solving
	Algebra		Reasoning
✓	Geometry		Communication
✓	Measurement	✓	Connections
	Data/Probability	✓	Representation

Activity
Boxes in Space

You will need

- a ruler

In this activity you'll learn to draw a box in perspective.

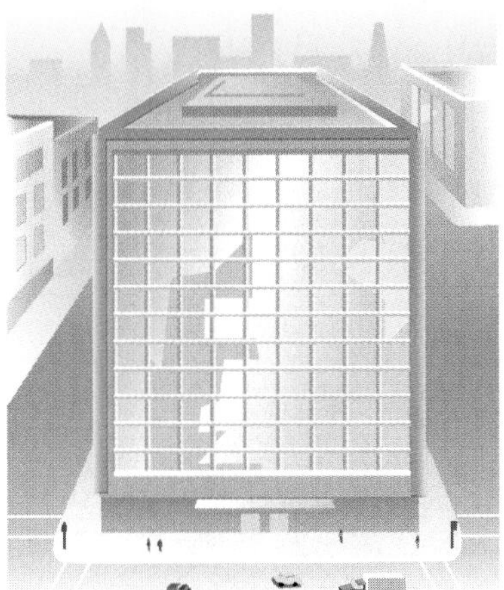

Perspective drawing is based on the relationships between many parallel and perpendicular lines. The lines that recede to the horizon make you visually think of parallel lines even though they actually intersect at a vanishing point.

First, you'll draw a rectangular solid, or box, in **one-point perspective.** Look at the diagrams below for each step.

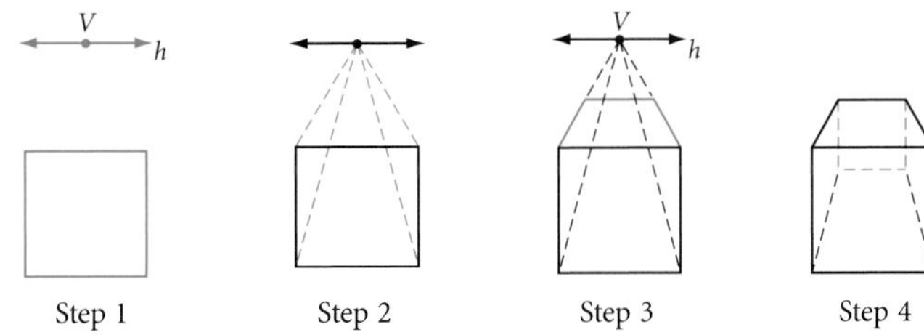

Step 1 Draw a horizon line *h* and a vanishing point *V*. Draw the front face of the box with its horizontal edges parallel to *h*.

Step 2 Connect the corners of the box face to *V* with dashed lines.

Step 3 Draw the upper rear box edge parallel to *h*. Its endpoints determine the vertical edges of the back face.

Step 4 Draw the hidden back vertical and horizontal edges with dashed lines. Erase unnecessary lines and dashed segments.

Step 5 Repeat Steps 1–4 several more times, each time placing the first box face in a different position with respect to *h* and *V*—above, below, or overlapping *h*; to the left or right of *V* or centered on *V*.

Step 6 Share your drawings in your group. Tell which faces of the box recede and which are parallel to the imaginary window or picture plane that you see through. What is the shape of a receding box face? Think of each drawing as a scene. Where do you seem to be standing to view each box? That is, how is the viewing position affected by placing *V* to the left or right of the box? Above or below the box?

One step (continued)

vanishing point, ask how they might draw a view of the box in which only the front and top of the box are visible.

Guiding the Activity

Students might jigsaw Step 5, with each group member using a different location for their box with respect to *V* and *h*.

Students might also jigsaw Step 11.

If students have difficulty, pull out some actual boxes and have students examine them from a variety of points of view.

SHARING IDEAS

Have students with interesting pictures share them. For at least one picture with the vanishing point above and to the right of the box, have the artist rotate the paper through 180°. Ask how the view of the drawing has changed and whether it's still true to life.

As students present their pictures, work in a discussion of vocabulary. The introduction to the Exploration calls this technique *perspective drawing.* **[Language]** Ask if students can guess what *perspective* means. In lay language, it means "point of view." Like *inspect* and *spectator,* it comes from the Latin word meaning "to look." The introduction also says that receding parallel lines converge to a vanishing point. **[Ask]** "What does *receding* mean?" [fall back, withdraw] "What does *converge* mean?" [The lines will meet if extended.] Step 6 refers to the picture plane. **[Ask]** "What is the *picture plane* in real life?" [It might be a painter's canvas or a computer or projection screen.]

Ask what is common to all the drawings students have shown. Elicit the idea that line segments representing edges that are parallel to each other in the picture plane are drawn parallel to each other, but that images of other parallel segments converge. If two segments intersect in the original, they intersect in each picture. If two points are on a line segment in the original, their images are on every picture of the segment. **[Ask]** "Do the various pictures of an angle or a line segment all have the same length?" [They don't.] Suggest that students explore later to see whether every ratio of corresponding lengths is the same in all pictures. [They aren't, but the *cross ratio* $\frac{AC/AD}{BC/BD}$ is the same in all pictures of a line on which the points represented by *A, B, C,* and *D* lie in that order.]

You can also use perspective to play visual tricks. The Italian architect Francesco Borromini (1599–1667) designed and built a very clever colonnade in the Palazzo Spada. The colonnade is only 12 meters long, but he made it look much longer by designing the sides to get closer and closer to each other and the height of the columns to gradually shrink.

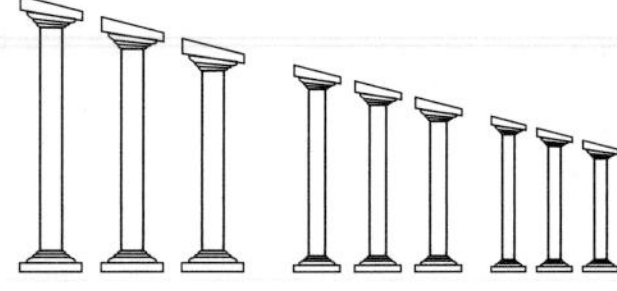

If the front surface of a box is not parallel to the picture plane, then you need two vanishing points to show the two front faces receding from view. This is called **two-point perspective.** Let's look at a rectangular solid with one edge viewed straight on.

Step 7 Draw a horizon line h and select two vanishing points on it, V_1 and V_2. Draw a vertical segment for the nearest box edge.

Step 8 Connect each endpoint of the box edge to V_1 and V_2 with dashed lines.

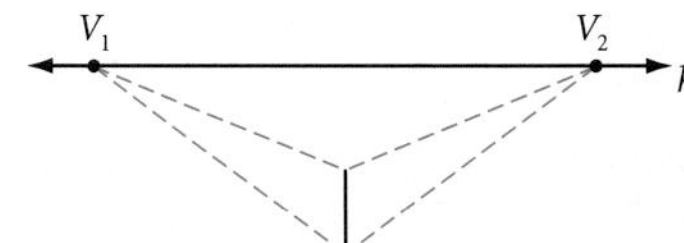

Step 9 Draw two vertical segments within the dashed lines as shown. Connect their endpoints to the endpoints of the front edge along the dashed lines. Now you have determined the position of the hidden back edges that recede from view.

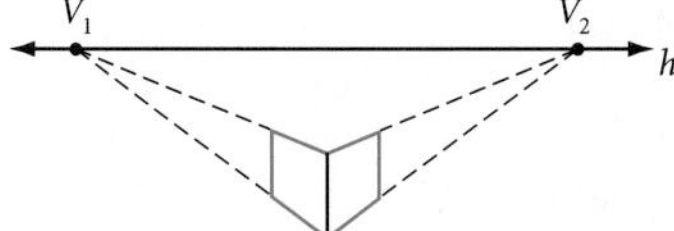

You might tell students the story of how questions about common features of drawings led from art to mathematics. **[Context]** About the end of the 1200s, artists, especially in Italy, began to try to make paintings look more true to life. The rules for drawing in perspective were developed over the next century or two, and great artists of the later 1400s, such as Leonardo da Vinci in Italy and Albrecht Dürer in Germany, mastered them. This period was known in Europe as the *Renaissance,* meaning "rebirth," a revival of learning after the Middle Ages. **[Link]** Questions about what was shared by all perspective drawings of the same object led to the field of mathematics called *projective geometry.* Indeed, during the 1400s painters and sculptors were among the most accomplished and original mathematicians. They were the forerunners of modern artists and architects, who know the rules of perspective intimately. Computer graphic artists, for example, use perspective to give depth to objects seen on a monitor screen.

Step 10 — Draw the remaining edges along vanishing lines, using dashed lines for hidden edges. Erase unnecessary dashed segments.

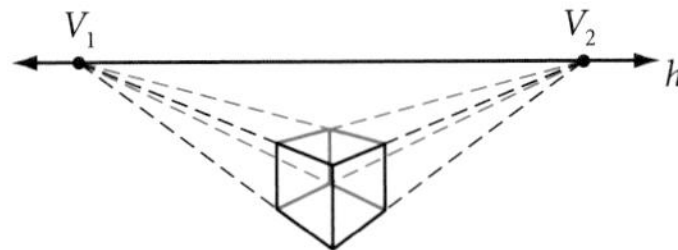

Step 11 — Repeat Steps 7–10 several times, each time placing the nearest box edge in a different position with respect to h, V_1, and V_2, and varying the distance between V_1, and V_2. You can also experiment with different-shaped boxes.

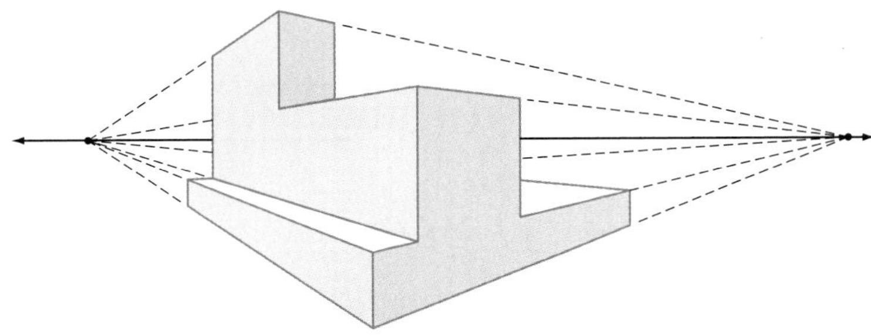

Step 12 — Share your drawings in your group. Are any faces of the box parallel to the picture plane? Does each box face have a pair of parallel sides?

Explain how the viewing position is affected by the distance between V_1 and V_2 relative to the size of the box. Must the box be between V_1 and V_2?

Perspective helps in designing the lettering painted on streets. From above, letters appear tall, but from a low angle they appear normal. Tilt the page up to your face. How do the letters look? They no longer appear too tall.

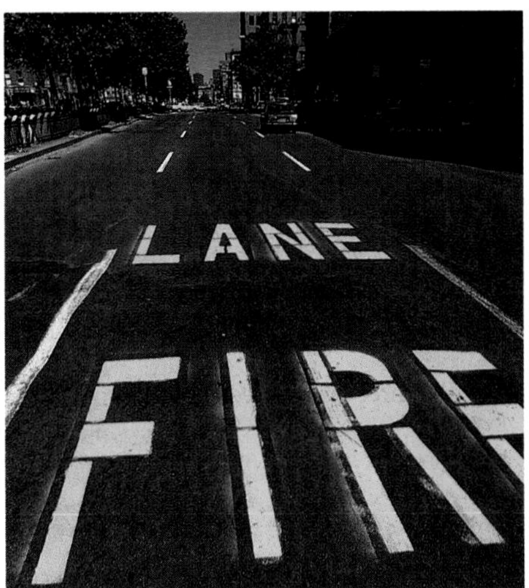

Sharing Ideas (continued)

If students are interested, you might add that the type of perspective being studied here is more specifically called *linear perspective.* It captures students' experience that objects closer to them appear larger than the same-size objects farther away. Another kind of perspective artists use is *aerial perspective,* in which more distant objects have dimmer colors and flatter forms due to atmospheric haze. Japanese woodcut artists and others sometimes use a *vertical perspective* that places more distant objects higher in the picture plane.

EXTENSIONS

A. Students can apply their new skills by drawing a building complete with doors and windows. Or they can create a template for on-street lettering of words like STOP or SLOW or three-dimensional lettering of their name.

B. Students can experiment with different vanishing points and with having the horizon line above or below the box.

LESSON 3.7

PLANNING

LESSON OUTLINE

One day:

25 min Investigation

10 min Sharing

5 min Closing

5 min Exercises

MATERIALS

- straightedges
- patty paper or compasses
- Sketchpad demonstration Points of Concurrency, *optional*
- geometry software, *optional*

TEACHING

In every triangle, the angle bisectors are concurrent (meet at a point), as are the altitudes and the perpendicular bisectors of the sides. (The concurrency of the medians is the focus of Lesson 3.8.) Using patty paper will take students less time than will using a compass.

One step Assign each group the construction of the angle bisectors, the perpendicular bisectors, or the altitudes of a variety of triangles and ask them to make conjectures. As you circulate, encourage students who have conjectured that the three segments always intersect in a single point to make conjectures about properties of that point. During Sharing, raise the question of whether or not the three points of concurrency are the same and give them names.

LESSON 3.7

Constructing Points of Concurrency

Nothing in life is to be feared, it is only to be understood.

MARIE CURIE

You now can perform a number of constructions in triangles, including angle bisectors, perpendicular bisectors of the sides, medians, and altitudes. In this lesson and the next lesson you will discover special properties of these lines and segments. When three or more lines have a point in common, they are **concurrent.** Segments, rays, and even planes are concurrent if they intersect in a single point.

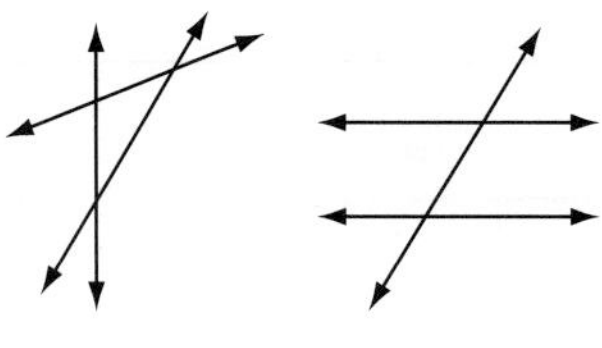

Not concurrent

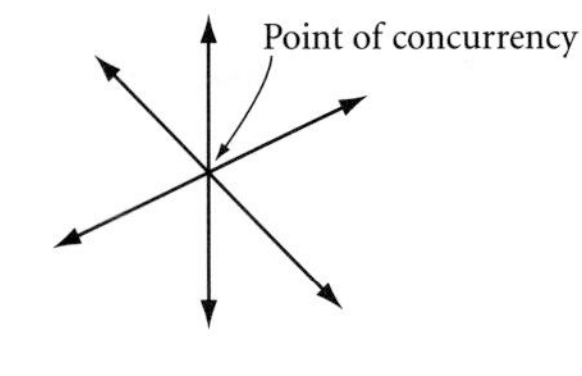

Concurrent

The point of intersection is the **point of concurrency.**

Investigation 1
Concurrence

You will need

- patty paper
- a compass
- a straightedge

In this investigation you will discover that some special lines in a triangle have points of concurrency.

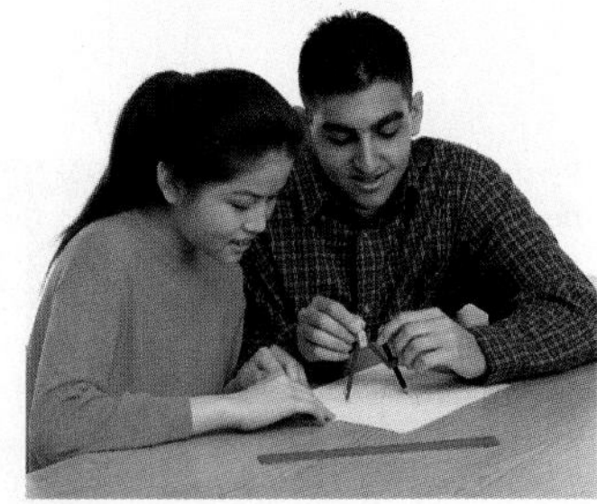

You should investigate each set of lines on an acute triangle, an obtuse triangle, and a right triangle to be sure your conjecture applies to all triangles.

Step 1 Draw a large acute triangle on one patty paper and an obtuse triangle on another. If you're using a compass and a straightedge, draw your triangles on the top and bottom halves of a piece of paper.

Step 2 Construct the three angle bisectors for each triangle. Are they concurrent?

Compare your results with the results of others. State your observations as a conjecture.

Angle Bisector Concurrency Conjecture C-9

The three angle bisectors of a triangle _?_. meet at a point (are concurrent)

Step 3 Construct the perpendicular bisector for each side of the triangle and complete the conjecture.

LESSON OBJECTIVES

- Discover points of concurrency of the angle bisectors, perpendicular bisectors, and altitudes of a triangle
- Explore the relationship between points of concurrency and inscribed and circumscribed circles
- Learn new terms
- Solve application problems related to points of concurrency
- Develop reading comprehension, problem-solving skills, and cooperative behavior

NCTM STANDARDS

	CONTENT		PROCESS
✓	Number	✓	Problem Solving
	Algebra	✓	Reasoning
✓	Geometry	✓	Communication
✓	Measurement	✓	Connections
	Data/Probability	✓	Representation

Perpendicular Bisector Concurrency Conjecture C-10

The three perpendicular bisectors of a triangle _?_. are concurrent

Step 4 Construct the lines containing the altitudes of your triangle and complete the conjecture.

Altitude Concurrency Conjecture C-11

The three altitudes (or the lines containing the altitudes) of a triangle _?_. are concurrent

Step 5 For what kind of triangle will the points of concurrency be the same point? equilateral triangle

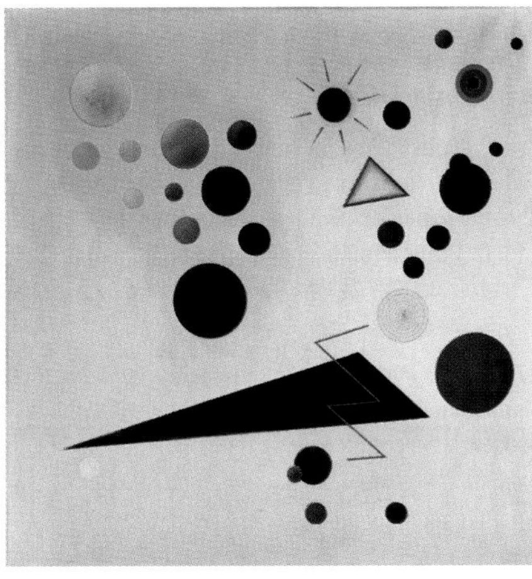

Rudolf Bauer (1889–1953) titled this painting *Rounds and Triangles.*

The point of concurrency for the three angle bisectors is the **incenter.** The point of concurrency for the perpendicular bisectors is the **circumcenter.** The point of concurrency for the three altitudes is called the **orthocenter.** You will investigate a triangle's medians in the next lesson.

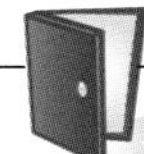

Investigation 2
Incenter and Circumcenter

You will need

- construction tools

In this investigation you will discover special properties of the incenter and the circumcenter.

Step 1 Measure and compare the distances from the circumcenter to each of the three vertices. Are they the same? Compare the distances from the circumcenter to each of the three sides. Are they the same? State your observations as your next conjecture.

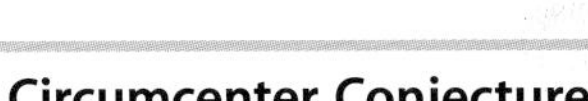

Circumcenter Conjecture C-12

The circumcenter of a triangle _?_. is equidistant from the vertices

Guiding Investigation 1

Start off by having one pair of students in each group draw large acute triangles and the other group members draw large obtuse triangles. If you are not using geometry software, divide the three conjectures among the groups for completion. If any students are working on more than one conjecture, suggest that each construction start with a new triangle.

Step 2 Proposed conjectures might include "are concurrent," "intersect at the same point," "are equidistant from all three sides," "bisect the opposite sides," and so on. Save critiques for Sharing.

Step 3 Conjectures might mention equidistance from the vertices or perhaps even meeting at the center of a circle that passes through all the vertices. Encourage variety.

Step 4 Besides concurrency, conjectures might include the idea that the lines are perpendicular to the sides or meet inside the triangle. Be prepared to have a variety of ideas presented for critique during Sharing.

Guiding Investigation 2

You might lead Investigation 2 as a follow-along activity and have each student draw a unique triangle and follow through the solution for that triangle. Bring out the use of the incenter and circumcenter of a triangle as a means of locating its inscribed and circumscribed circles.

Have students clearly label the incenter, circumcenter, and orthocenter and draw the inscribed and circumscribed circles for the triangles they drew in Investigation 1.

Step 2 The distances students measured in Step 1 were distances between points. Remind students that the distance from a point to a line is along a line segment perpendicular to that line. As needed, point out that the line may need to be constructed (by extending a segment) before the distance to it can be measured.

SHARING IDEAS

As students share, you might teach some of the skills of clear explanation by rephrasing what they say as "Are you saying that . . . ?" This approach allows you to maintain your role as manager of the investigation teams. Also keep suggesting that students use new vocabulary (here, *incenter, circumcenter,* and *orthocenter*) to express their ideas clearly. **[Language]** At some point you might mention the prefix *circum-*, meaning "to go about, to circle." Mention that Magellan *circum*navigated the globe and point out the *circum*ference of a circle. The *circum*center of a triangle is the center of the circle that *circum*scribes the triangle. The *in*center of a triangle is the center of the circle that is *in*scribed in the triangle. **[Language]** *Ortho-* comes from Greek meaning "straight, right, true." *Orthogonal* is another word for *perpendicular.* An orthodontist makes teeth straight.

Ask what *concurrent* means. **[Ask]** "Could we say that *two* lines are concurrent?" The student book's definition says "three or more lines," but two lines can have a point in common. We could say that two lines are concurrent if they aren't parallel or the same line.

Step 2 Measure and compare the distances from the incenter to each of the three sides. Are they the same? State your observations as your next conjecture.

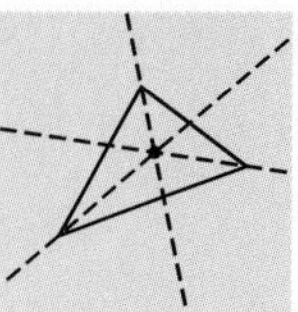

Incenter Conjecture C-13

The incenter of a triangle ?. is equidistant from the sides

You just discovered a very useful property of the circumcenter and a very useful property of the incenter. You will see some applications of these properties in the exercises. With earlier conjectures and logical reasoning, you can explain why your conjectures are true. Let's look at a paragraph proof of the Circumcenter Conjecture.

Paragraph Proof of the Circumcenter Conjecture

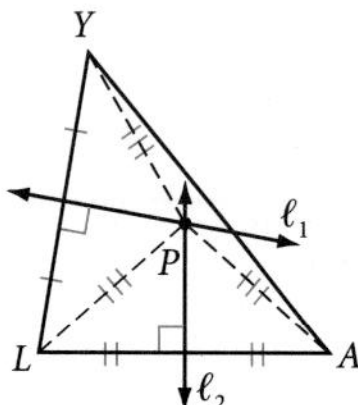

If the Perpendicular Bisector Conjecture is true, then you know that each point on a perpendicular bisector of a segment is equidistant from the endpoints of the segment. So, in the figure at left, since point P lies on the perpendicular bisector of $\overline{AL}$, it is equidistant from vertices A and L. Point P also lies on the perpendicular bisector of $\overline{LY}$, so it is also equidistant from vertices L and Y. Therefore P is equidistant from all three vertices. ■

In other words, the circumcenter of a triangle is on all three perpendicular bisectors, so it follows logically that it is equidistant from all three vertices of the triangle. Your investigation led you to believe the conjecture is true, and the logical argument helps to understand why it is true.

You can use your compass to construct a circle that passes through the three vertices of the triangle with the circumcenter as the center of the circle.

So, you can also think of the circumcenter as the center of a circle that passes through the three vertices of a triangle.

You can make a similar logical argument for the Incenter Conjecture.

Paragraph Proof of the Incenter Conjecture

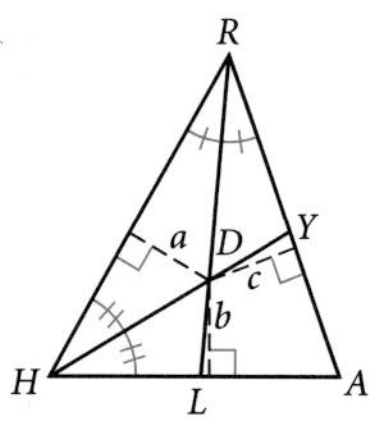

If the Angle Bisector Conjecture is true, then you know that each point on an angle bisector is equidistant from the sides of the angle. So, since point D lies on the angle bisector of $\angle RHA$, it is equidistant from $\overline{RH}$ and $\overline{HA}$. Point D also lies on RL, the angle bisector of $\angle HRA$, so it is also equidistant from $\overline{RH}$ and $\overline{RA}$. So point D is equidistant from all three sides. ■

In other words, the incenter of a triangle is on all three angle bisectors. It follows logically that the incenter is equidistant from all three sides. Again your investigation may have convinced you that this was true, but the logical argument explains why it is true.

[Ask] "Are the three points of concurrency the same?" [In general, they're not.] A good mathematical question to ask but not answer now is, "Are the points of concurrency the same in any triangle?" or "Is there a triangle in which the points of concurrency are the same?"

Ask students to talk through the paragraph proofs in their own words, explaining them to each other and to you. You might challenge them to write paragraph proofs of the other conjectures in this lesson.

Assessing Progress

You can assess students' ability to construct perpendicular bisectors, perpendiculars to a line through a point, and angle bisectors. Check their understanding of the distance between points and from points to lines. See how well they make conjectures, work in groups, and follow deductive proofs.

You can use your compass to construct a circle that is tangent to the three sides with the incenter as the center of a circle. To construct the circle you need the radius, the shortest distance from the incenter to each side. To get the radius, you construct the perpendicular from the incenter to one of the sides.

The incenter is the center of a circle that touches each side of the triangle. Here are a few vocabulary terms that help describe these geometric situations.

A circle is **circumscribed** about a polygon if and only if it passes through each vertex of the polygon. (The polygon is inscribed in the circle.)

A circle is **inscribed** in a polygon if and only if it touches each side of the polygon at exactly one point. (The polygon is circumscribed about the circle.)

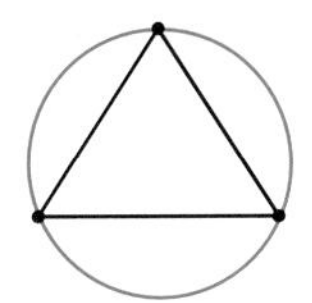

Circumscribed circle (inscribed triangle)

Inscribed circle (circumscribed triangle)

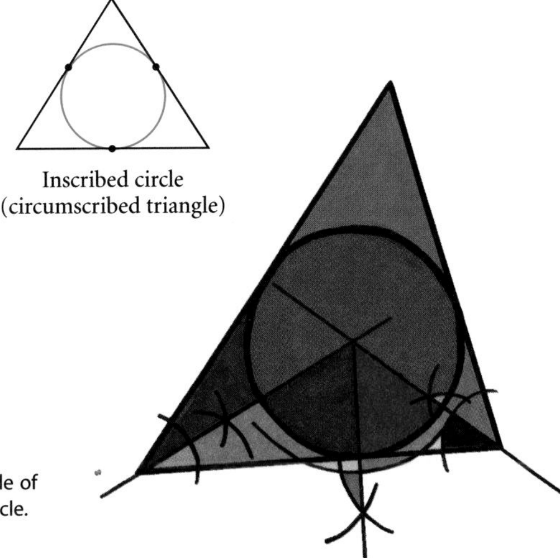

This geometric art by geometry student Ryan Garvin shows the construction of the incenter, its perpendicular distance to one side of the triangle, and the inscribed circle.

EXERCISES

You will need

Construction tools for Exercises **6, 7, 12–15,** and **17**

Geometry software for Exercises **10, 11,** and **18**

For Exercises 1–4, make a sketch and explain how to find the answer.

1. The first-aid center of Mt. Thermopolis State Park needs to be at a point that is equidistant from three bike paths that intersect to form a triangle. Locate this point so that in an emergency medical personnel will be able to get to any one of the paths by the shortest route possible. Which point of concurrency is it? incenter

2. Rosita wants to install a circular sink in her new triangular countertop. She wants to choose the largest sink that will fit. Which point of concurrency must she locate? Explain. incenter

3. Julian Chive wishes to center a butcher-block table at a location equidistant from the refrigerator, stove, and sink. Which point of concurrency does Julian need to locate? circumcenter

Closing the Lesson

Three major conjectures of this lesson concern **concurrency** of special lines in any triangle, specifically, of angle bisectors, perpendicular bisectors of the sides, and altitudes. The **point of concurrency** of the perpendicular bisectors is the center of a circle that **circumscribes** the triangle and thus is called the **circumcenter** of the triangle. The point of concurrency of the angle bisectors is the center of a circle that is **inscribed** in the triangle and thus is called the **incenter** of the triangle.

BUILDING UNDERSTANDING

The exercises focus on circles inscribed in and circumscribed about triangles and include some real-world applications.

ASSIGNING HOMEWORK

Essential	1–7
Portfolio	18
Journal	5, 8, 9
Group	10, 11, 20–24
Review	12–17, 19–24

MATERIALS

- graph paper (Exercises 10, 11)

1.

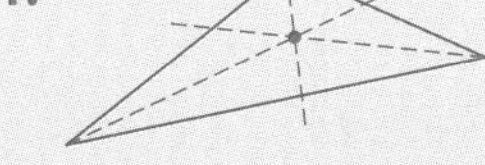

Since the station needs to be equidistant from the paths, it will need to be on each of the angle bisectors.

2.

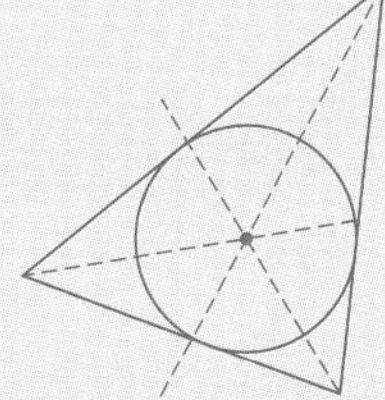

The center of the circular sink must be equidistant from the three counter edges, that is the incenter of the triangle.

3.

Stove

Fridge

Sink

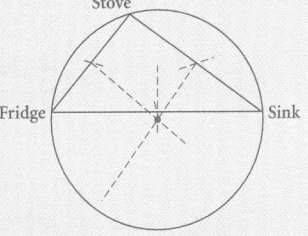

To find the point equidistant from three points, find the circumcenter of the triangle with those points as vertices.

▶Helping with the Exercises

5. Circumcenter. Find the perpendicular bisectors of two of the sides of the triangle formed by the classes. Locate the pie table where these two lines intersect.

Exercises 6, 7 Be sure students actually construct the circles as opposed to sketching them. If students are having difficulty, **[Ask]** "Which points need to be located in order to construct these two circles?"

6.

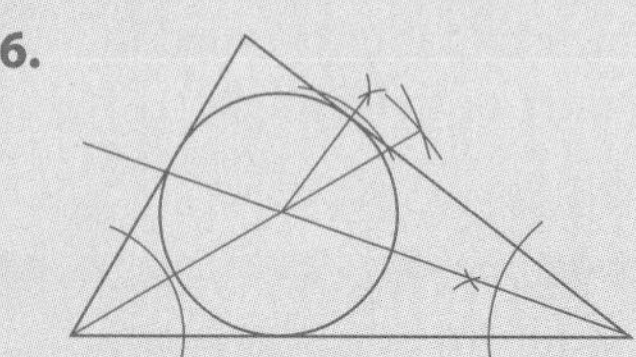

7.

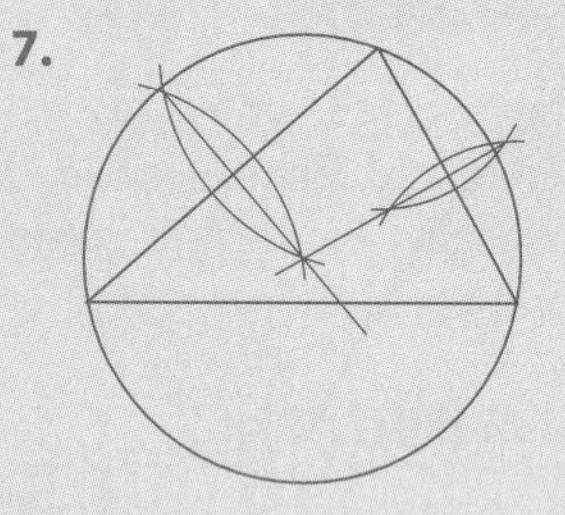

8. Yes, any circle with a larger radius would not fit within the triangle. To get a circle with a larger radius tangent to two of the sides would force the circle to pass through the third side twice.

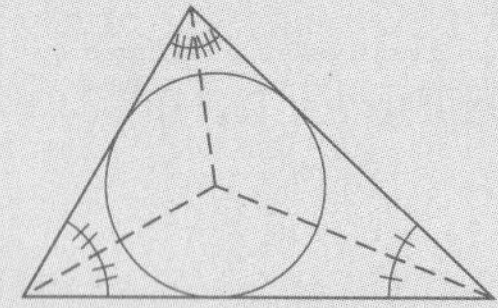

Art CONNECTION

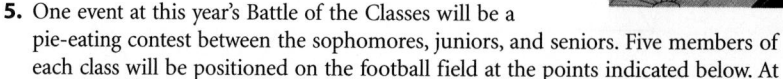

The designer of stained glass arranges pieces of painted glass to form the elaborate mosaics that you might see in Gothic cathedrals or on Tiffany lampshades. He first organizes the glass pieces by shape and color according to the design. He mounts these pieces into a metal framework that will hold the design. With precision, the designer cuts every glass piece so that it fits against the next one with a strip of cast lead. The result is a pleasing combination of colors and shapes that form a luminous design when viewed against light.

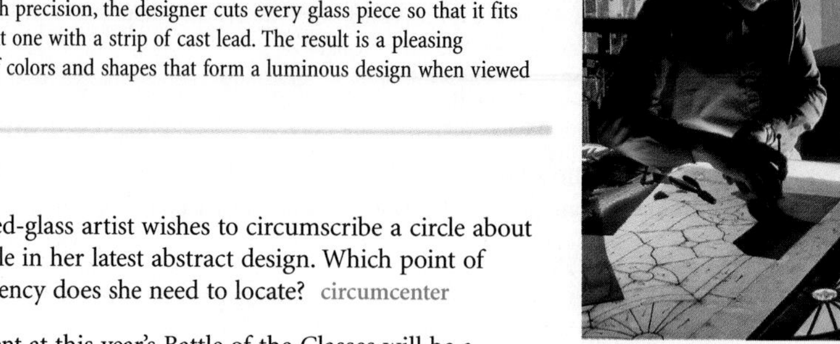

4. A stained-glass artist wishes to circumscribe a circle about a triangle in her latest abstract design. Which point of concurrency does she need to locate? circumcenter

5. One event at this year's Battle of the Classes will be a pie-eating contest between the sophomores, juniors, and seniors. Five members of each class will be positioned on the football field at the points indicated below. At the whistle, one student from each class will run to the pie table, eat exactly one pie, and run back to his or her group. The next student will then repeat the process. The first class to eat five pies and return to home base will be the winner of the pie-eating contest. Where should the pie table be located so that it will be a fair contest? Describe how the contest planners should find that point.

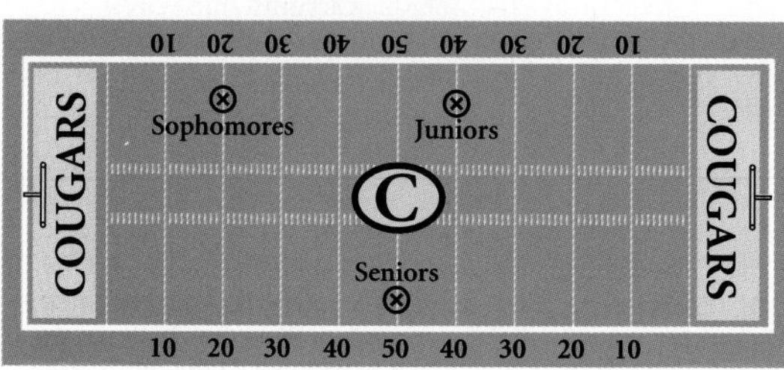

6. ***Construction*** Draw a large triangle. Construct a circle inscribed in the triangle. ⓗ

7. ***Construction*** Draw a triangle. Construct a circle circumscribed about the triangle. ⓗ

8. Is the inscribed circle the greatest circle to fit within a given triangle? Explain. If you think not, give a counterexample. ⓗ

9. Does the circumscribed circle create the smallest circular region that contains a given triangle? Explain. If you think not, give a counterexample. ⓗ

10. ***Technology*** Notice that the circumcenter is in the interior of acute triangles and on the exterior of obtuse triangles. Use geometry software to construct a right triangle. Where is the circumcenter of a right triangle? (This problem can also be done by drawing several right triangles on graph paper.) The circumcenter of a right triangle lies on the midpoint of the hypotenuse.

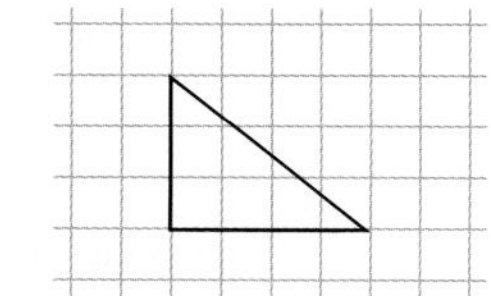

11. ***Technology*** Notice that the orthocenter is in the interior of acute triangles and on the exterior of obtuse triangles. Use geometry software to construct a right triangle. Where is the orthocenter of a right triangle? (This problem can also be done by drawing several right triangles on graph paper.) The orthocenter of a right triangle lies on the vertex of the right angle.

9. No, on an obtuse triangle the circle with the largest side of the triangle as the diameter of the circle creates the smallest circular region that contains the triangle. The circumscribed circle of an acute triangle does create the smallest circular region that contains the triangle.

Review

Construction Use the segments and angle at right to construct each figure in Exercises 12–15.

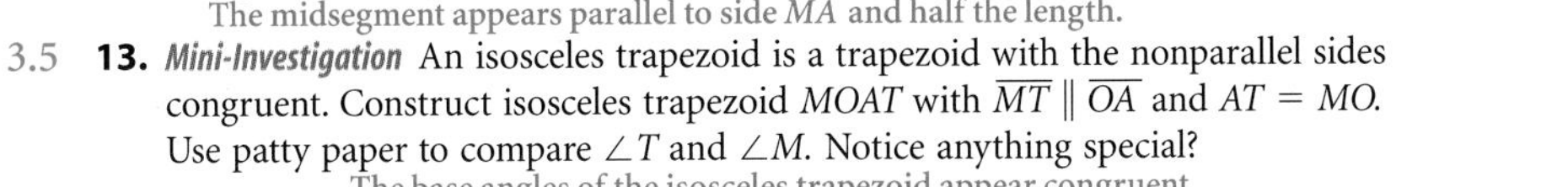

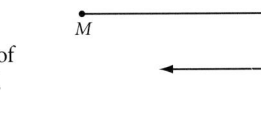

3.1 **12.** ***Mini-Investigation*** Construct $\triangle MAT$. Construct H the midpoint of $\overline{MT}$ and S the midpoint of $\overline{AT}$. Construct the midsegment $\overline{HS}$. Compare the lengths of $\overline{HS}$ and $\overline{MA}$. Notice anything special?
The midsegment appears parallel to side $\overline{MA}$ and half the length.

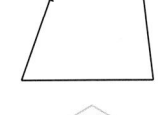

3.5 **13.** ***Mini-Investigation*** An isosceles trapezoid is a trapezoid with the nonparallel sides congruent. Construct isosceles trapezoid $MOAT$ with $\overline{MT} \parallel \overline{OA}$ and $AT = MO$. Use patty paper to compare $\angle T$ and $\angle M$. Notice anything special?
The base angles of the isosceles trapezoid appear congruent.

3.1 **14.** ***Mini-Investigation*** Construct a circle with diameter MT. Construct chord $\overline{TA}$. Construct chord $\overline{MA}$ to form $\triangle MTA$. What is the measure of $\angle A$? Notice anything special?
The measure of $\angle A$ is 90°. The angle inscribed in a semicircle appears to be a right angle.

3.1 **15.** ***Mini-Investigation*** Construct a rhombus with TA as the length of a side and $\angle T$ as one of the acute angles. Construct the two diagonals. Notice anything special?
The two diagonals appear to be perpendicular bisectors of each other.

1.7 **16.** Sketch the locus of points on the coordinate plane in which the sum of the x-coordinate and the y-coordinate is 9. ⓗ

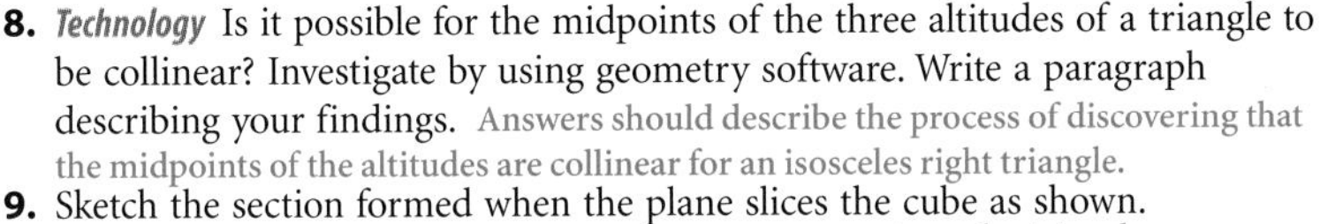

3.4 **17.** ***Construction*** Bisect the missing angle of this triangle. How can you do it without re-creating the third angle? ⓗ

18. ***Technology*** Is it possible for the midpoints of the three altitudes of a triangle to be collinear? Investigate by using geometry software. Write a paragraph describing your findings. Answers should describe the process of discovering that the midpoints of the altitudes are collinear for an isosceles right triangle.

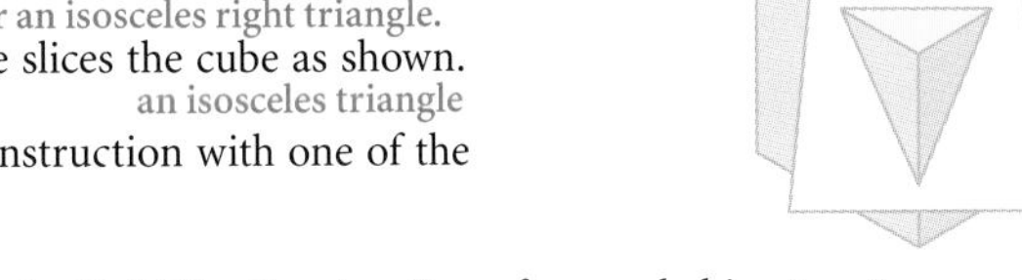

1.8 **19.** Sketch the section formed when the plane slices the cube as shown.
an isosceles triangle

For Exercises 20–24, match each geometric construction with one of the figures below.

3.2 **20.** Construction of a perpendicular bisector E

3.4 **21.** Construction of an angle bisector A

3.3 **22.** Construction of a perpendicular through a point on a line B

3.5 **23.** Construction of a line parallel to a given line through a given point not on the line C

3.1 **24.** Construction of an equilateral triangle D

A.

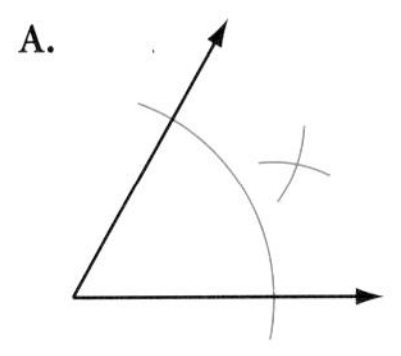

B.

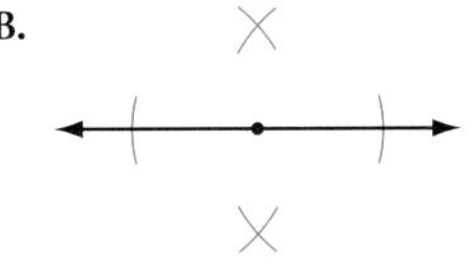

C.

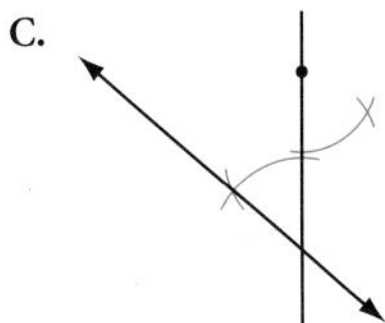

D.

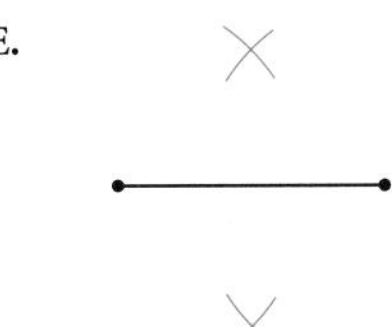

E.

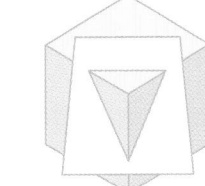

12.

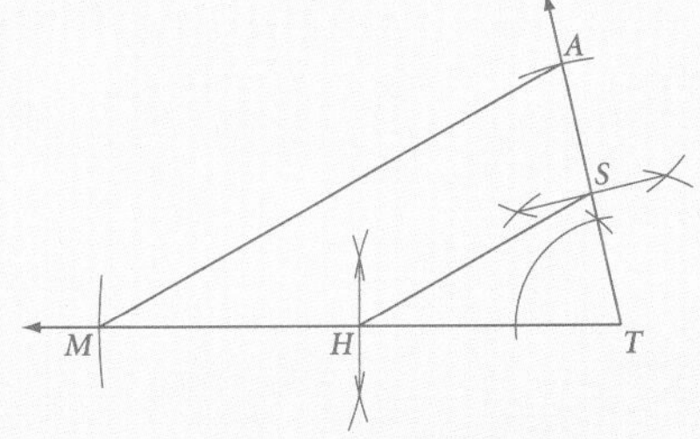

Exercises 12–15 These are mini-investigations leading to conjectures that are presented in later chapters.

12. See below.

13.

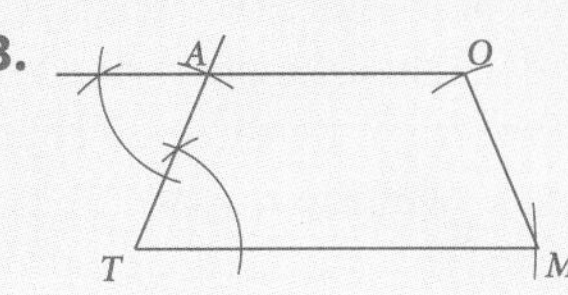

14.

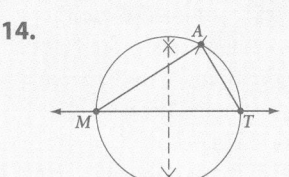

15.

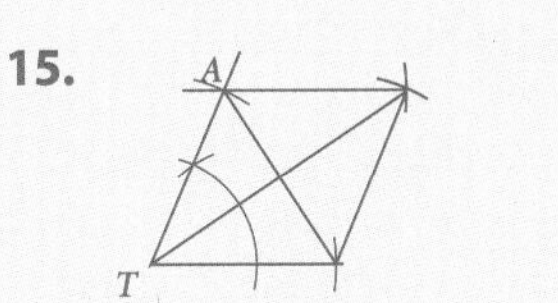

16.

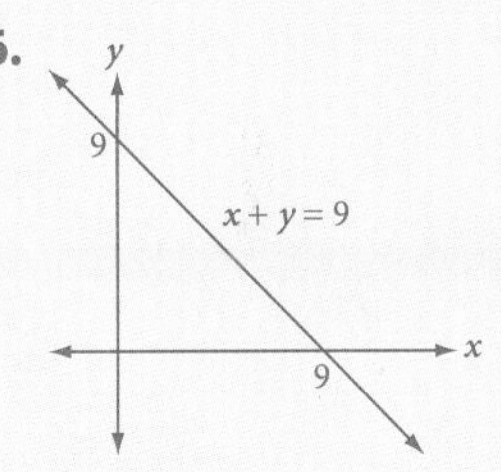

17. Construct the incenter by bisecting the two angles shown. Any other point on the angle bisector of the third angle must be equidistant from the two unfinished sides. Mark a point on each side of the triangle equidistant from the incenter. Use two congruent arcs to find another point that is equidistant from the two points you just constructed. The line that connects this point and the incenter is the angle bisector of the third angle.

Exercise 18 Students may need reminding that *collinear* means "on the same line."

EXTENSIONS

A. Pose this problem: Find the *excenters* of a triangle, the centers of the circles (called *excircles*) that are externally tangent to the extended sides of a triangle. How does the triangle formed by connecting the three excenters compare with the original triangle? The excenters can also lead to explorations of another point of concurrency, the Nagel Point (the point of concurrency for the segments between the point of tangency of each excircle and the opposite vertex). In addition, the segments connecting excenters to the opposite vertices are concurrent, and that point of concurrency is easily proved to be the incenter.

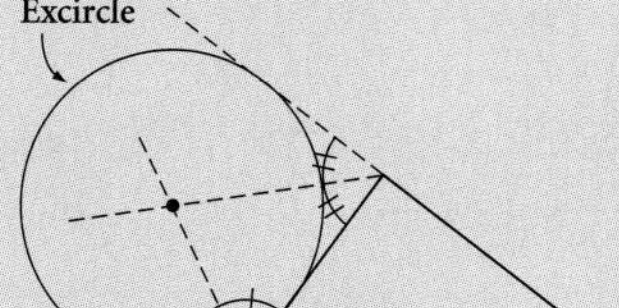

B. Challenge students to find more triangle points of concurrency. Many have been discovered.

IMPROVING YOUR VISUAL THINKING SKILLS

The Puzzle Lock

This mysterious pattern is a lock that must be solved like a puzzle. Here are the rules:

- You must make eight moves in the proper sequence.
- To make each move (except the last), you place a gold coin onto an empty circle, then slide it along a diagonal to another empty circle.
- You must place the first coin onto circle 1, then slide it to either circle 4 or circle 6.
- You must place the last coin onto circle 5.
- You do not slide the last coin.

Solve the puzzle. Copy and complete the table to show your solution.

Coin Movements

Coin	Placed on		Slid to
First	1	→	4
Second	2	→	7
Third	5	→	2
Fourth	6	→	1
Fifth	3	→	6
Sixth	8	→	3
Seventh	5	→	8
Eighth	5		

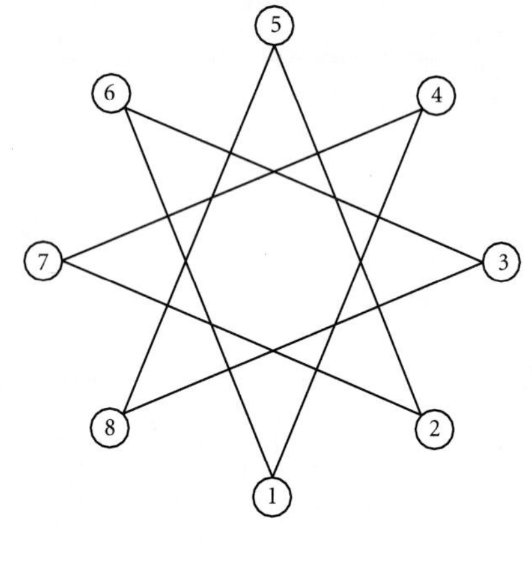

IMPROVING VISUAL THINKING SKILLS

One of several possible orders of moves is shown in the Coin Movements table above.

LESSON 3.8

The Centroid

The universe may be as great as they say, but it wouldn't be missed if it didn't exist.

PIET HEIN

In the previous lesson you discovered that the three angle bisectors are concurrent, the three perpendicular bisectors of the sides are concurrent, and the three altitudes in a triangle are concurrent. You also discovered the properties of the incenter and the circumcenter. In this lesson you will investigate the medians of a triangle.

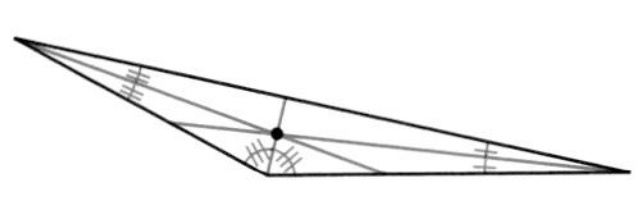

Three angle bisectors (incenter)

Three perpendicular bisectors (circumcenter)

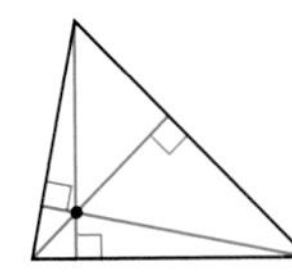

Three altitudes (orthocenter)

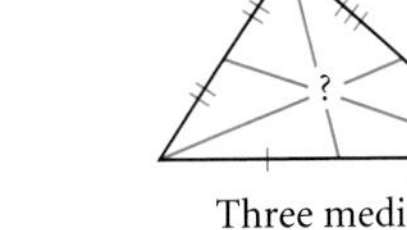

Three medians ?

Investigation 1
Are Medians Concurrent?

You will need

- patty paper
- a straightedge

Each person in your group should draw a different triangle for this investigation. Make sure you have at least one acute triangle, one obtuse triangle, and one right triangle in your group.

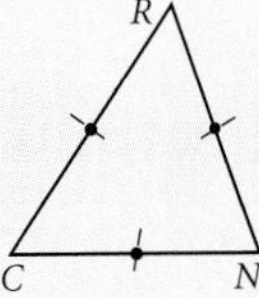

Step 1 On a sheet of patty paper, draw as large a scalene triangle as possible and label it *CNR*, as shown at right. Locate the midpoints of the three sides. Construct the medians and complete the conjecture.

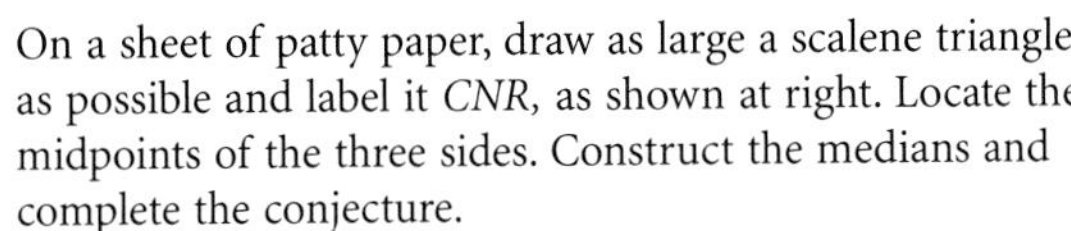

Median Concurrency Conjecture C-14

The three medians of a triangle ?. are concurrent

The point of concurrency of the three medians is the **centroid.**

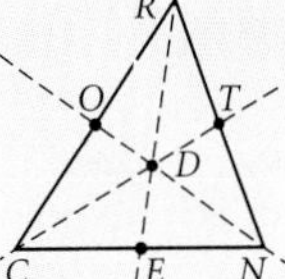

Step 2 Label the three medians $\overline{CT}$, $\overline{NO}$, and $\overline{RE}$. Label the centroid *D*.

Step 3 Use your compass or another sheet of patty paper to investigate whether there is anything special about the centroid. Is the centroid equidistant from the three vertices? From the three sides? Is the centroid the midpoint of each median?

NCTM STANDARDS

CONTENT		PROCESS	
✓	Number	✓	Problem Solving
✓	Algebra	✓	Reasoning
✓	Geometry	✓	Communication
✓	Measurement	✓	Connections
	Data/Probability		Representation

LESSON OBJECTIVES

- Discover the concurrence of the medians of a triangle (the centroid) and its applications
- Explore length relationships among the segments into which the centroid divides each median

LESSON 3.8

PLANNING

LESSON OUTLINE

One day:

20 min Investigation

10 min Sharing

5 min Closing

10 min Exercises

MATERIALS

- construction tools
- mat board, cardboard, or manila folders
- geometry software, *optional*

TEACHING

A triangle made of material whose mass is evenly distributed will balance on any of its medians. Thus the centroid is the center of mass, or balance point, of the triangle. You can use the one-step investigation in place of both Investigations 1 and 2, or you might do Investigation 1 and then the one-step investigation in place of Investigation 2.

You can also use the dynamic geometry exploration at www.keymath.com/DG as a replacement or extension of Investigation 1.

Guiding Investigation 1

Step 1 Be prepared to remind students as needed of what a scalene acute triangle is. Students might fill in the blank in the conjecture with "are concurrent," "pass through the same point," "divide the triangle in half," and so on.

Step 5 Conjectures might say that the distance to the vertex is bigger than the distance to the midpoint. Make sure students are referring to the midpoint of the triangle's side (rather than the midpoint of the median), and then save further critiques for Sharing.

One step Ask each group to draw a large scalene acute triangle on mat board, cardboard, or a manila folder and then cut it out and find the point where it balances on a pencil. **[Ask]** "Do you think this is one of the points of concurrency?" If students have no ideas after trying the points of concurrency they know, suggest that they try balancing the triangle on a line through that point. If students still have no ideas, ask them to draw a segment from each vertex through the balance point to the opposite side. During Sharing, bring out the idea of the centroid as a point of concurrency and complete the Investigation 1 conjectures.

Guiding Investigation 2

Although many students will assume that the balancing point is the centroid, encourage them to experiment with a variety of special points, using several different triangles.

You might assign this investigation to be completed out of class to allow more time in class for working on exercises.

SHARING IDEAS

After the students have presented a variety of conjectures and have agreed on wording for the Median Concurrency, Centroid, and Center of Gravity Conjectures, ask *why* the centroid is closer to the triangle's side than to its vertex. Although a deductive proof of this conjecture is beyond the capabilities of students at this time, they can still point out that more of the triangle's area, and hence more of its mass, is at the wider part.

Step 4 $\frac{\text{longer}}{\text{shorter}} = \frac{2}{1}$

Step 5 yes

Step 4 The centroid divides a median into two segments. Use your patty paper or compass to compare the length of the longer segment to the length of the shorter segment and find the ratio.

Step 5 Find the ratios of the lengths of the segment parts for the other two medians. Do you get the same ratio for each median?

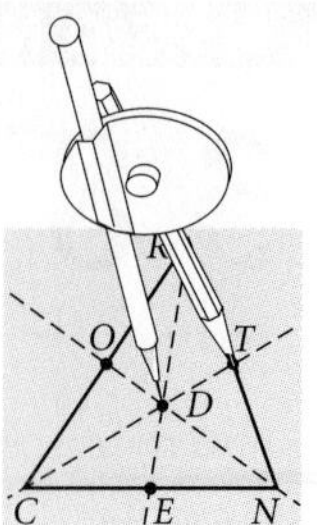

Compare your results with the results of others. State your discovery as a conjecture, and add it to your conjecture list.

Centroid Conjecture C-15

The centroid of a triangle divides each median into two parts so that the distance from the centroid to the vertex is __?__ the distance from the centroid to the midpoint of the opposite side. twice

In earlier lessons you discovered that the midpoint of a segment is the balance point or center of gravity. You also saw that when a set of segments is arranged into a triangle, the line through the midpoints of these segments can act as a line of balance for the triangle. Can you then balance a triangle on a median? Let's take a look.

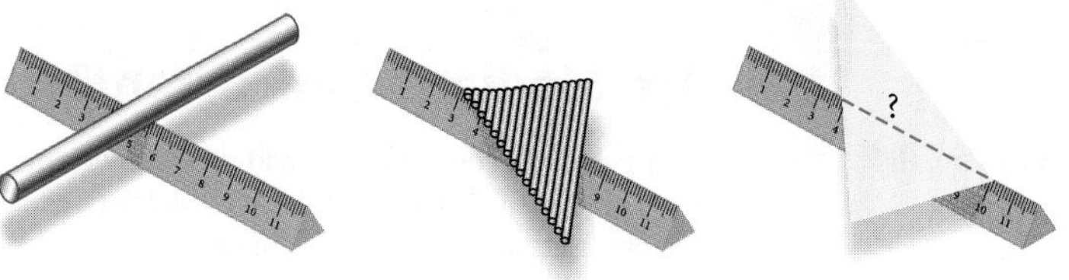

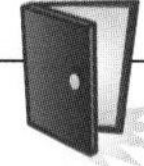

Investigation 2
Balancing Act

You will need
- cardboard

Use your patty paper from Investigation 1 for this investigation.

Step 1 Place your patty paper from the previous investigation on a piece of mat board or cardboard. With a sharp pencil tip or compass tip, mark the three vertices, the three midpoints, and the centroid on the board.

Step 2 Draw in the triangle and medians on the cardboard. Cut out the cardboard triangle.

Step 3 Try balancing the triangle on each of the three medians by placing the median on the edge of a ruler. If you are successful, what does that imply about the areas of the two triangles formed by one median?

Step 4 Is there a single point where you can balance the triangle?

Step 3 The two triangles formed by the median have the same area.

Step 4 yes, the centroid

If you have found the balancing point for the triangle, you have found its **center of gravity.** State your discovery as a conjecture, and add it to your conjecture list.

Center of Gravity Conjecture C-16

The _?_ of a triangle is the center of gravity of the triangular region.
centroid

The triangle balances on each median and the centroid is on each median, so the triangle balances on the centroid. As long as the weight of the cardboard is distributed evenly throughout the triangle, you can balance any triangle at its centroid. For this reason, the centroid is a very useful point of concurrency, especially in physics.

You have discovered special properties of three of the four points of concurrency—the incenter, the circumcenter, and the centroid. The incenter is the center of an inscribed circle, the circumcenter is the center of a circumscribed circle, and the centroid is the center of gravity.

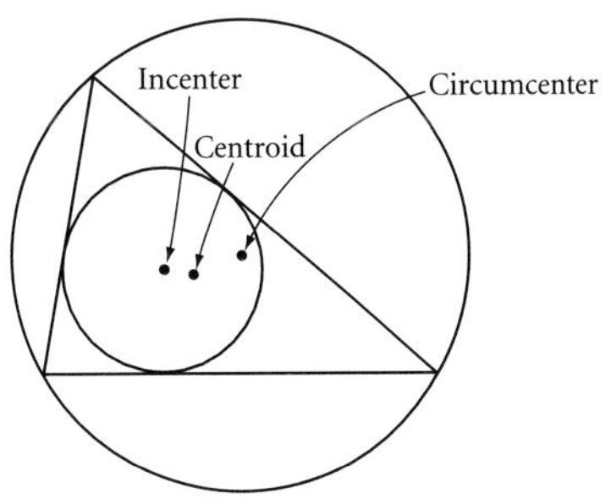

You can learn more about the orthocenter in the Project Is There More to the Orthocenter?

Science CONNECTION

In physics, the center of gravity of an object is an imaginary point where the total weight is concentrated. The center of gravity of a tennis ball, for example, would be in the hollow part, not in the actual material of the ball. The idea is useful in designing structures as complicated as bridges or as simple as furniture. Where is the center of gravity of the human body?

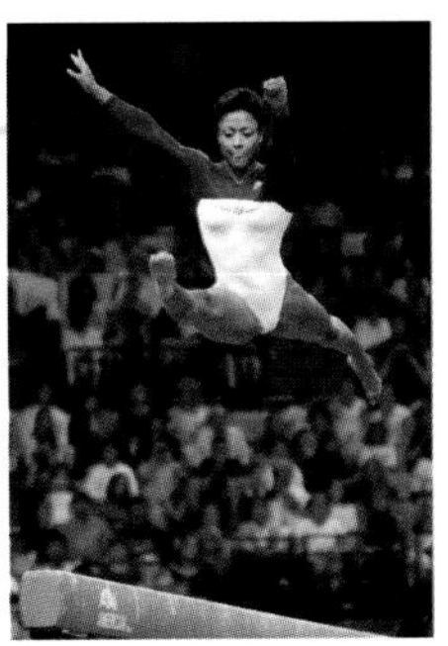

Sharing Ideas (continued)

Ask students to graph a triangle and find the mean of the x-coordinates and the mean of the y-coordinates of its three vertices. **[Ask]** "Is the point whose coordinates are those means an interesting point?" [It's the centroid.] "Why?" [The mean of a set of numbers is a balance point for that set.] This will be a warm-up to Using Your Algebra Skills 7.

You might also wonder aloud whether a median divides the area of the triangle in half. Some students might look at the two triangles formed as having equal bases and the same height and be able to answer this question. But don't worry about reaching agreement now. You will return to this topic in the chapter on area.

Ask students to experiment to see if other points of concurrency divide segments into a 2:1 ratio. Discovering that they don't may help students remember this special property of the centroid.

Assessing Progress

You can assess how well students know how to locate the midpoint of a segment. Also check their understanding of median, ratio, concurrent, and other points of concurrency.

Closing the Lesson

Review the big ideas of this lesson: The three medians of a triangle meet at a point called the **centroid;** the centroid divides each median into two segments, with the segment between the centroid and the vertex being twice as long as the other segment; the centroid is the **center of mass,** or balance point, of the whole triangle. If you think students are still having difficulty with the Centroid Conjecture, you might have the class work together on one of Exercises 2–4.

The exercises apply the Centroid Conjecture to finding distances, exploring the center of gravity of quadrilaterals, and comparing the centroid to other points of concurrency.

ASSIGNING HOMEWORK

Essential	1–6
Performance assessment	9
Portfolio	6
Journal	5
Group	7, 16
Review	9–16

MATERIALS

- Exercise 15 (T), *optional*

▶ Helping with the Exercises

5. The points of concurrency are the same point for equilateral triangles because the segments are the same.

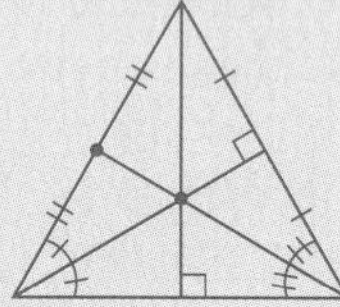

Exercise 6 This special case foreshadows the first part of the Exploration The Euler Line.

6.

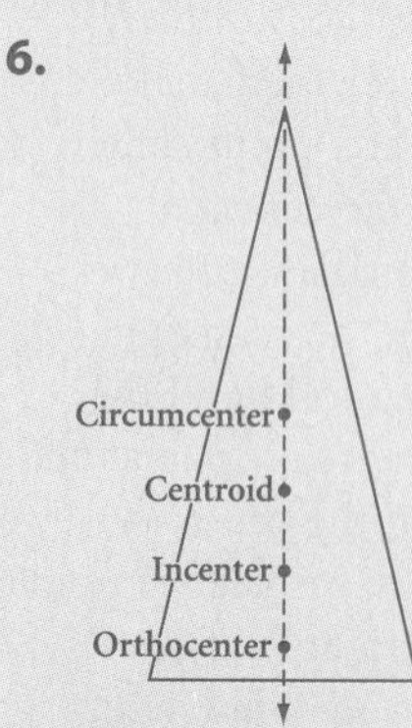

Exercise 7 At 90° the circumcenter and orthocenter are on the triangle; for obtuse angles they are outside.

EXERCISES

You will need

Construction tools for Exercises **5** and **6**

Geometry software for Exercise **7**

1. Birdy McFly is designing a large triangular hang glider. She needs to locate the center of gravity for her glider. Which point does she need to locate? Birdy wishes to decorate her glider with the largest possible circle within her large triangular hang glider. Which point of concurrency does she need to locate?

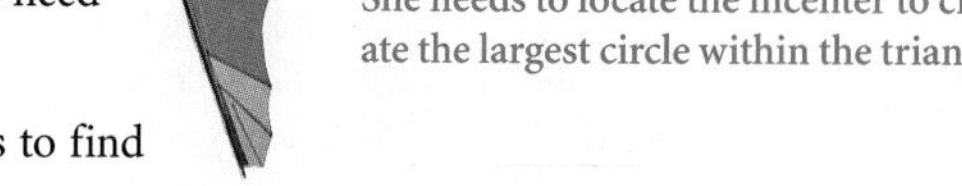

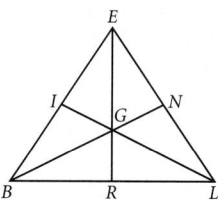

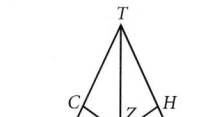

The center of gravity is the centroid. She needs to locate the incenter to create the largest circle within the triangle.

In Exercises 2–4, use your new conjectures to find each length.

2. Point M is the centroid. ⓗ

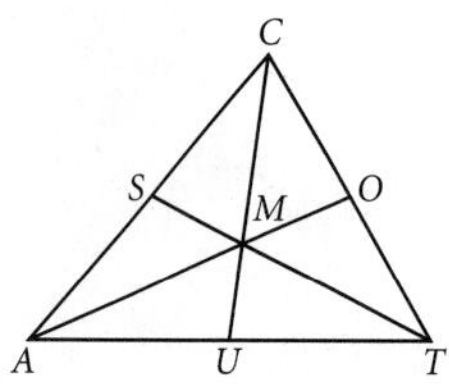

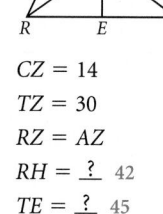

$CM = 16$
$MO = 10$
$TS = 21$
$AM = \underline{?}$ 20
$SM = \underline{?}$ 7
$TM = \underline{?}$ 14
$UM = \underline{?}$ 8

3. Point G is the centroid.

$GI = GR = GN$
$ER = 36$
$BG = \underline{?}$ 24
$IG = \underline{?}$ 12

4. Point Z is the centroid.

$CZ = 14$
$TZ = 30$
$RZ = AZ$
$RH = \underline{?}$ 42
$TE = \underline{?}$ 45

5. *Construction* Construct an equilateral triangle, then construct angle bisectors from two vertices, medians from two vertices, and altitudes from two vertices. What can you conclude?

6. *Construction* On patty paper, draw a large isosceles triangle with an acute vertex angle that measures less than 40°. Copy it onto three other pieces of patty paper. Construct the centroid on one patty paper, the incenter on a second, the circumcenter on a third, and the orthocenter on a fourth. Record the results of all four pieces of patty paper on one piece of patty paper. What do you notice about the four points of concurrency? What is the order of the four points of concurrency from the vertex to the opposite side in an acute isosceles triangle?

7. *Technology* Use geometry software to construct a large isosceles acute triangle. Construct the four points of concurrency. Hide all constructions except for the points of concurrency. Label them. Drag until it has an obtuse vertex angle. Now what is the order of the four points of concurrency from the vertex angle to the opposite side? When did the order change? Do the four points ever become one?

7. ortho-/in-/centroid/circum-; the order changes when the angle becomes larger than 60°. The points become one when the triangle is equilateral.

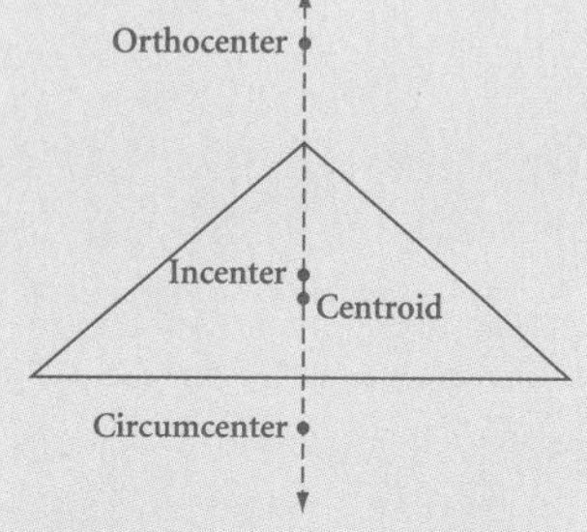

8. Where do you think the center of gravity is located on a square? A rectangle? A rhombus? In each case the center of gravity is not that difficult to find, but what about an ordinary quadrilateral? Experiment to discover a method for finding the center of gravity for a quadrilateral by geometric construction. Test your method on a large cardboard quadrilateral. ⓗ

Review

3.7 **9.** Sally Solar is the director of Lunar Planning for Galileo Station on the moon. She has been asked to locate the new food production facility so that it is equidistant from the three main lunar housing developments. Which point of concurrency does she need to locate? circumcenter

3.1 **10.** Construct circle O. Place an arbitrary point P within the circle. Construct the longest chord passing through P. Construct the shortest chord passing through P. How are they related?

1.2 **11.** A billiard ball is hit so that it travels a distance equal to AB but bounces off the cushion at point C. Copy the figure, and sketch where the ball will rest.

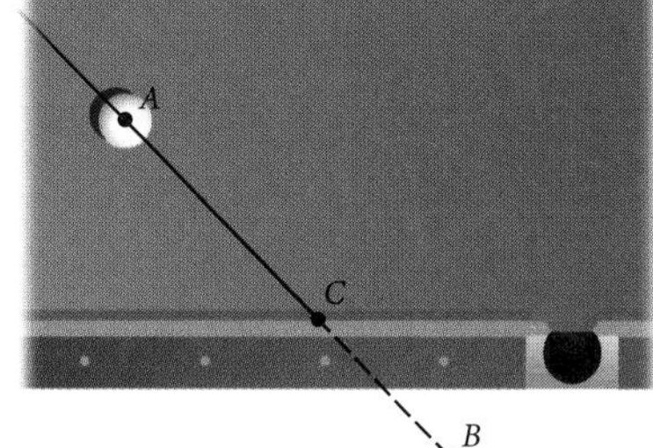

2.3 **12.** **APPLICATION** In alkyne molecules all the bonds are single bonds except one triple bond between two carbon atoms. The first three alkynes are modeled below. The dash (–) between letters represents single bonds. The triple dash (≡) between letters represents a triple bond.

```
                          H              H         H
                          |              |         |
H − C ≡ C − H   H − C ≡ C − C − H   H − C − C ≡ C − C − H
                          |              |         |
                          H              H         H
```

Ethyne (C_2H_2) Propyne (C_3H_4) Butyne (C_4H_6)

Sketch the alkyne with eight carbons in the chain. What is the general rule for alkynes ($C_nH_?$)? In other words, if there are n carbon atoms (C), how many hydrogen atoms (H) are in the alkyne? rule: $2n - 2$

8. Start by constructing a quadrilateral, then make a copy of it. Draw a diagonal in one, and draw a different diagonal in the second. Find the centroid of each of the four triangles. Construct a segment connecting the two centroids in each quadrilateral. Place the two quadrilaterals on top of each other matching the congruent segments and angles. Where the two segments connecting centroids intersect is the centroid of the quadrilateral.

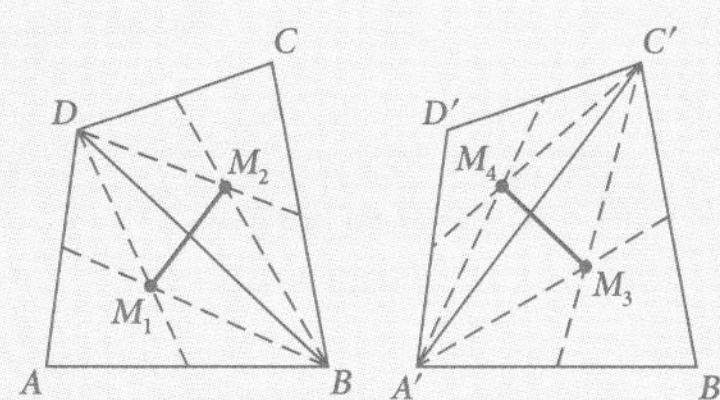

Exercise 8 This exercise is quite difficult. The initial guess might be the point of intersection of the diagonals. That approach works for any parallelogram or isosceles trapezoid. If students try this guess on a kite or a right trapezoid, they might be convinced that it's not a good general approach. Another thought might be to divide the trapezoid into two triangles, find their centroids, and take the midpoint of the segment connecting them. Again, a kite, with the diagonal separating a small part from a large part, might serve as an intuitive counterexample. Encourage students who have thought of this approach to extend it to using both diagonals.

10. The shortest chord through P is a segment perpendicular to the diameter through P, which is the longest chord through P. The longest chord is the diameter through P.

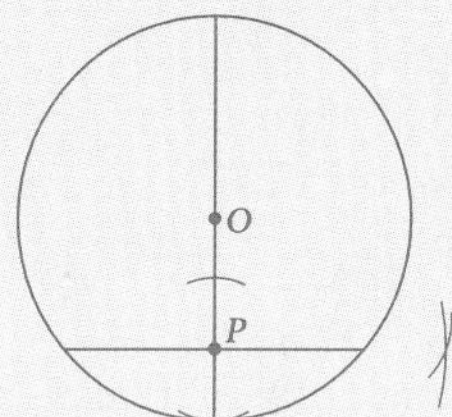

11.

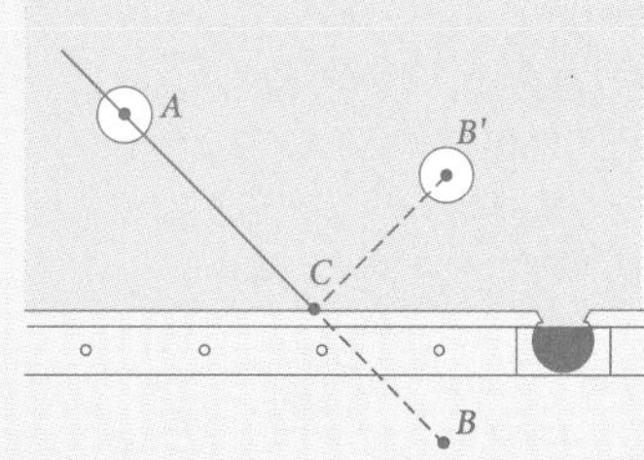

Exercise 12 Previously students have seen *alkanes* (Lesson 2.4, Exercise 20) and *alkenes* (Lesson 2.5, Exercise 21).

12. possible answer:

```
    H   H   H           H   H   H
    |   |   |           |   |   |
H − C − C − C − C ≡ C − C − C − C − H
    |   |   |           |   |   |
    H   H   H           H   H   H
```

13.

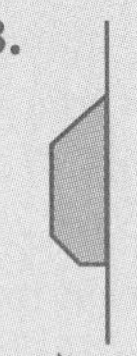

15. Construct altitudes from the two accessible vertices to construct the orthocenter. Through the orthocenter, construct a line perpendicular to the southern boundary of the property. This method will divide the property equally only if the southern boundary is the base of an isosceles triangle.

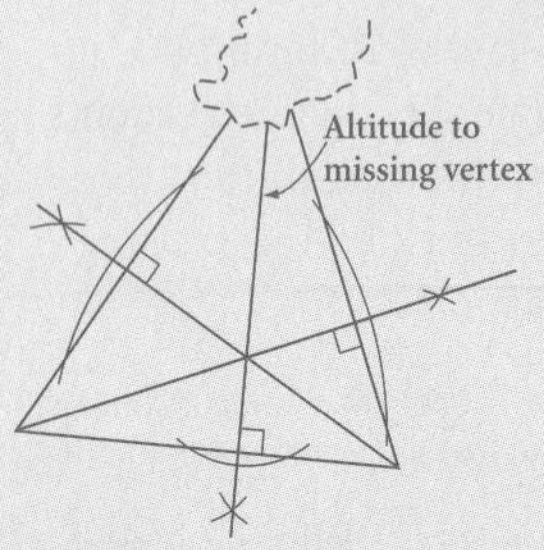

Exercise 16 [ESL] A *dorm,* or *dormitory,* is a school building in which students live. An *open house* is a social event to which nonresidents are invited.

EXTENSION

Research other interesting points in triangles, such as the Fermat Point and the Nagel Point. *Geometry Revisited,* by H. S. M. Coxeter, and *Episodes in Nineteenth and Twentieth Century Euclidean Geometry,* by Ross Honsberger, are good references for advanced problems.

1.8 **13.** When plane figure A is rotated about the line it produces the solid figure B. What is the plane figure that produces the solid figure D?

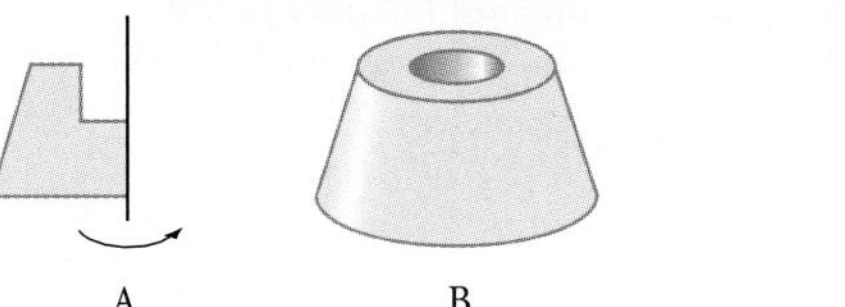
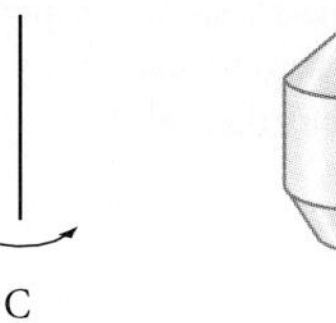
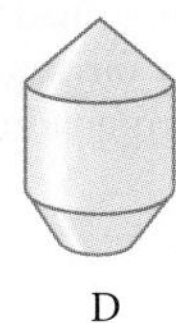

2.6 **14.** Copy the diagram below. Use your Vertical Angles Conjecture and Parallel Lines Conjecture to calculate each lettered angle measure.

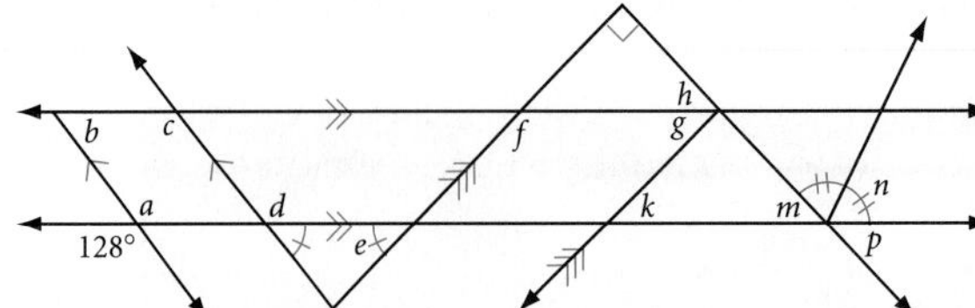

$a = 128°, b = 52°, c = 128°, d = 128°,$
$e = 52°, f = 128°, g = 52°, h = 38°,$
$k = 52°, m = 38°, n = 71°, p = 38°$

3.7 **15.** A brother and a sister have inherited a large triangular plot of land. The will states that the property is to be divided along the altitude from the northernmost point of the property. However, the property is covered with quicksand at the northern vertex. The will states that the heir who figures out how to draw the altitude without using the northern vertex point gets to choose his or her parcel first. How can the heirs construct the altitude? Is this a fair way to divide the land? Why or why not? ⓗ

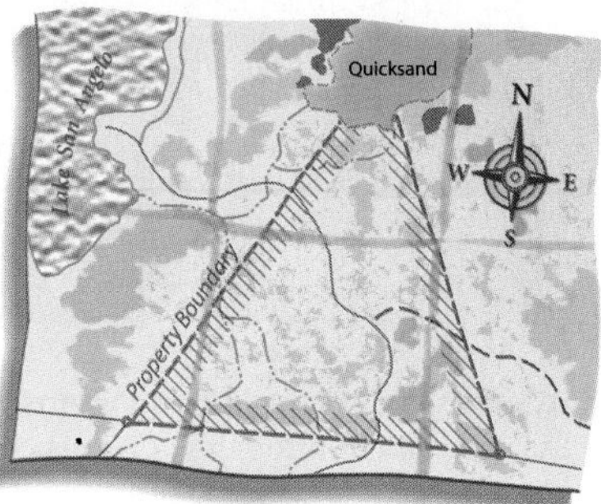

2.4 **16.** At the college dorm open house, each of the 20 dorm members brings two guests (usually their parents). How many greetings are possible if you do not count dorm members greeting their own guests? ⓗ 1710 greetings

IMPROVING YOUR REASONING SKILLS

The Dealer's Dilemma

In the game of bridge, the dealer deals 52 cards in a clockwise direction among four players. You are playing a game in which you are the dealer. You deal the cards, starting with the player on your left. However, in the middle of dealing you stop to answer the phone. When you return, no one can remember where the last card was dealt. (And, of course, no cards have been touched.) Without counting the number of cards in anyone's hand or the number of cards yet to be dealt, how can you rapidly finish dealing, giving each player exactly the same cards she or he would have received if you hadn't been interrupted?

IMPROVING REASONING SKILLS

Start dealing from the bottom of the deck in the opposite direction, starting with yourself, until all cards are dealt.

Exploration

The Euler Line

In the previous lessons you discovered the four points of concurrency: circumcenter, incenter, orthocenter, and centroid. In this activity you will discover how these points relate to a special line, the Euler line.

The Euler line is named after the Swiss mathematician Leonhard Euler (1707–1783), who proved that three points of concurrency are collinear.

Activity
Three Out of Four

You will need
- patty paper

You are going to look for a relationship among the points of concurrency.

Step 1 Draw a scalene triangle and have each person in your group trace the same triangle on a separate piece of patty paper.

Step 2 Have each group member construct with patty paper a different point of the four points of concurrency for the triangle.

Step 3 Record the group's results by tracing and labeling all four points of concurrency on one of the four pieces of patty paper. What do you notice? Compare your group results with the results of other groups near you. State your discovery as a conjecture.

Euler Line Conjecture

The _?_, _?_, and _?_ are the three points of concurrency that always lie on a line. circumcenter, centroid, orthocenter

The three special points that lie on the Euler line determine a segment called the **Euler segment.** The point of concurrency between the two endpoints of the Euler segment divides the segment into two smaller segments whose lengths have an exact ratio.

EXPLORATION

PLANNING

LESSON OUTLINE

One day:

35 min Investigation

5 min Sharing

5 min Closing

MATERIALS

- construction tools
- mat board, cardboard, or manila folders
- geometry software, *optional*
- Sketchpad demonstration The Euler Segment, *optional*

TEACHING

[Context] The mathematical output of Euler [ȯi-lər] was so tremendous that more than 40 volumes on his work have been published, and these contain only a small part of his work.

As an alternative to this Exploration, you might wish to have students work through the dynamic geometry exploration at www.keymath.com/DG.

Guiding the Activity

The activity works best in groups of four. Each person in a group of four can construct one of the four points of concurrency. The activity can also be done with geometry software.

NCTM STANDARDS

CONTENT		PROCESS	
	Number	✓	Problem Solving
✓	Algebra		Reasoning
✓	Geometry		Communication
✓	Measurement	✓	Connections
✓	Data/Probability		Representation

LESSON OBJECTIVES

- Look for a relationship among the centroid, incenter, circumcenter, and orthocenter
- Explore length relationships among the pieces into which the Euler segment is divided

SHARING IDEAS

After students have presented any variety of results, ask *why* these three points of concurrency lie on a straight line. You might suggest that students visualize what happens when every point of the triangle is moved along a straight line through the centroid to a point half as far away from the centroid as the original point but on the opposite side. The centroid itself is not moved; the vertices are moved to the midpoints, outlining the similar triangle formed by the midsegments (see Lesson 3.2); and the orthocenter is moved to the orthocenter of this smaller triangle. By the definition of *perpendicular bisector,* the orthocenter of the smaller triangle is the circumcenter of the original triangle, so this circumcenter is on the same line as the original orthocenter and centroid. You might refer students to www.keymath.com/DG for a link to an electronic demonstration of this reasoning.

Step 4 With a compass or patty paper, compare the lengths of the two parts of the Euler segment. What is the ratio? Compare your group's results with the results of other groups and state your conjecture.

Euler Segment Conjecture

The __?__ (centroid) divides the Euler segment into two parts so that the smaller part is __?__ (half) the larger part.

Step 5 Use your conjectures to solve this problem.

$\overline{AC}$ is an Euler segment. $AC = 24$ m.
$AB =$ __?__ (16) $BC =$ __?__ (8)

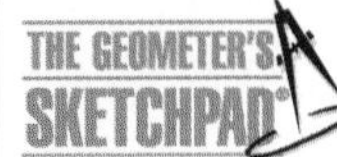

project

IS THERE MORE TO THE ORTHOCENTER?

At this point you may still wonder what's special about the orthocenter. It does lie on the Euler line. Is there anything else surprising or special about it?

Use geometry software to investigate the orthocenter. Draw a triangle *ABC* and construct its orthocenter *O*.

Drag a vertex of the triangle around, and observe the behavior of the orthocenter. Where does the orthocenter lie in an acute triangle? An obtuse triangle? A right triangle?

Drag the orthocenter. Describe how this affects the triangle.

Hide the altitudes. Draw segments from each vertex to the orthocenter, as shown, forming three triangles within the original triangle. Now find the orthocenter of each of the three triangles.

What happened? What does this mean?

Experiment dragging different points, and observe the relationships among the four orthocenters. Drag the orthocenter toward each vertex. What happens?

Write a paragraph about your findings, concluding with a conjecture about the orthocenter. Share your findings with your group members or classmates.

B
Orthocenter
A
C

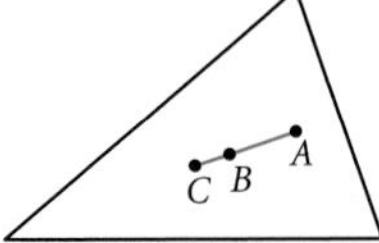

The Geometer's Sketchpad was used to create this diagram and to hide the unnecessary lines. Using Sketchpad, you can quickly construct triangles and their points of concurrency. Once you make a conjecture, you can drag to change the shape of the triangle to see whether your conjecture is true.

Supporting the project

This project could be done without technology, but dozens of drawings would be needed.

OUTCOMES

- The orthocenter of an acute triangle is inside the triangle, that of a right triangle is on the vertex of the right angle, and that of an obtuse triangle is outside the triangle.
- Given a triangle and its orthocenter, any triangle formed by the orthocenter and two vertices of the original triangle has as its orthocenter the third vertex of the original triangle.
- Conjecture: if in a given set of four points one of the points is the orthocenter of the other three, then each of the four points is the orthocenter of the other three.

CHAPTER 3 REVIEW

In Chapter 1, you defined many terms that help establish the building blocks of geometry. In Chapter 2, you learned and practiced inductive reasoning skills. With the construction skills you learned in this chapter, you performed investigations that lay the foundation for geometry.

The investigation section of your notebook should be a detailed report of the mathematics you've already done. Beginning in Chapter 1 and continuing in this chapter, you summarized your work in the definition list and the conjecture list. Before you begin the review exercises, make sure your conjecture list is complete. Do you understand each conjecture? Can you draw a clear diagram that demonstrates your understanding of each definition and conjecture? Can you explain them to others? Can you use them to solve geometry problems?

EXERCISES

You will need

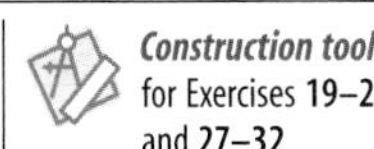

Construction tools for Exercises **19–24** and **27–32**

For Exercises 1–10, identify the statement as true or false. For each false statement, explain why it is false, or sketch a counterexample.

1. In a geometric construction, you use a protractor and a ruler. False; a geometric construction uses a straightedge and a compass.

2. A diagonal is a line segment in a polygon that connects any two vertices. False; a side connects two consecutive vertices.

3. A trapezoid is a quadrilateral with exactly one pair of parallel sides. true

4. A square is a rhombus with all angles congruent. true

5. If a point is equidistant from the endpoints of a segment, then it must be the midpoint of the segment.

6. The set of all the points in the plane that are a given distance from a line segment is a pair of lines parallel to the given segment.

7. It is not possible for a trapezoid to have three congruent sides.

8. The incenter of a triangle is the point of intersection of the three angle bisectors. true

9. The orthocenter of a triangle is the point of intersection of the three altitudes. true

10. The incenter, the centroid, and the orthocenter are always inside the triangle. False; the incenter does not always lie inside the triangle.

The Principles of Perspective, Italian, ca. 1780. Victoria and Albert Museum, London, Great Britain.

CHAPTER REVIEW 3

PLANNING

LESSON OUTLINE

One day:

30 min Exercises and helping individuals

15 min Student self-assessment

REVIEWING

Students can review most of the constructions and terms in this chapter by finding points of concurrency, for example, by working with the Exploration The Euler Line. Remind them also of how to construct parallel lines and of the fact that a triangle is determined by three sides but not by three angles.

ASSIGNING HOMEWORK

Students should be able to answer all of Exercises 1–18. Completing the even-numbered exercises from Exercises 19–31 individually and the odd-numbered in groups provides a good review.

Helping with the Exercises

5. false

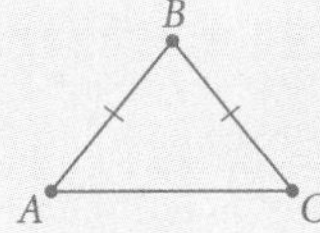

6. False; the lines can't be a given distance from a segment because the segment has finite length and the lines are infinite.

7. false

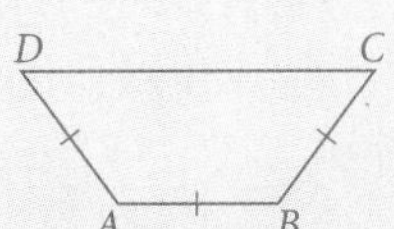

19.

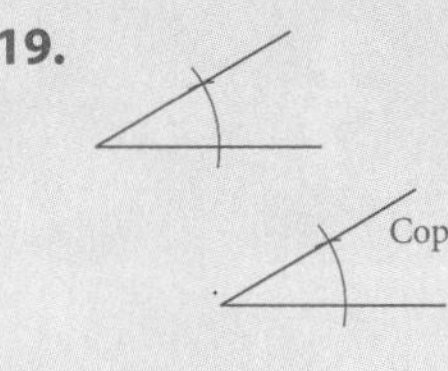

20.

21.

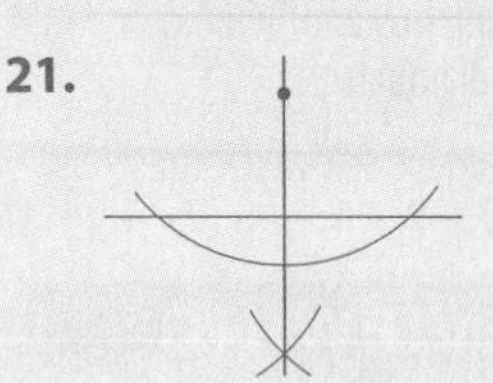

22.

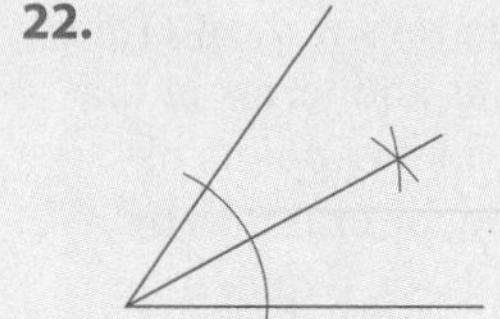

For Exercises 11–18, match each geometric construction with one of the figures below.

11. Construction of a midsegment A

12. Construction of an altitude B or K

13. Construction of a centroid in a triangle I

14. Construction of an incenter H

15. Construction of an orthocenter in a triangle G

16. Construction of a circumcenter D

17. Construction of an equilateral triangle J

18. Construction of an angle bisector C

A.

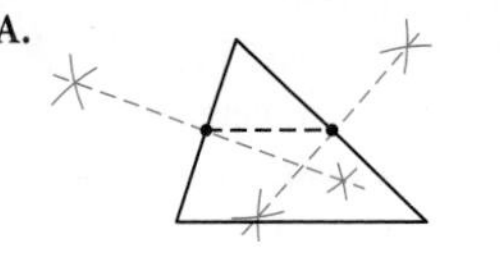

B.

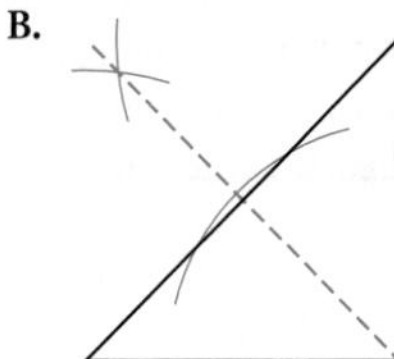

C.

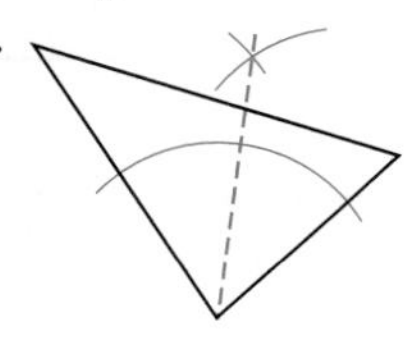

D.

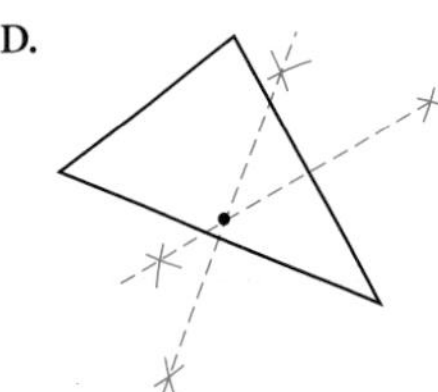

E.

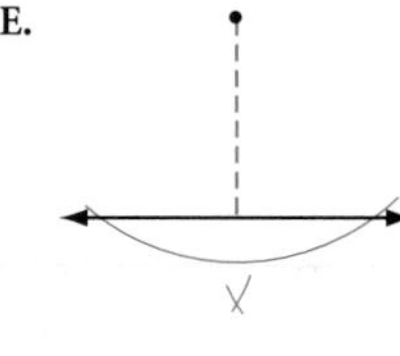

F.

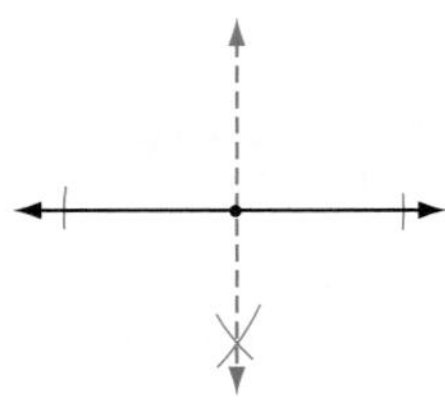

G.

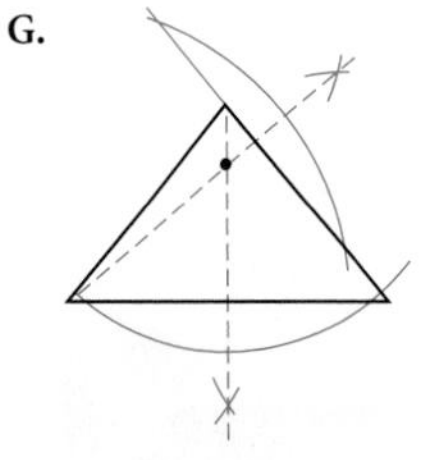

H.

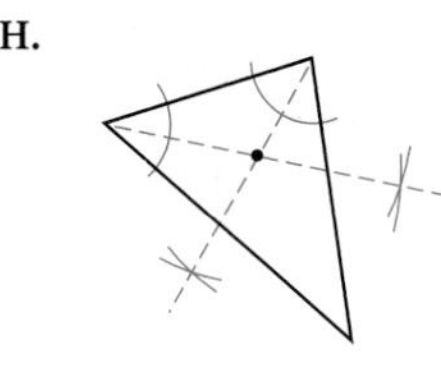

I.

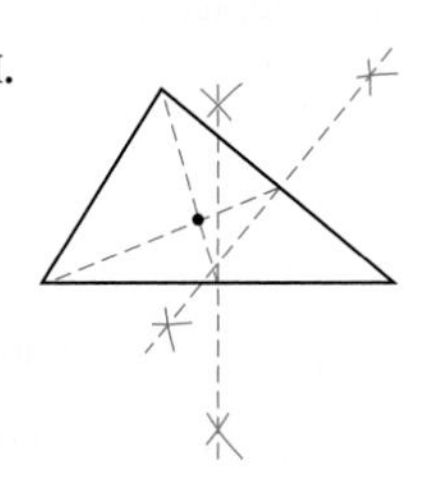

J.

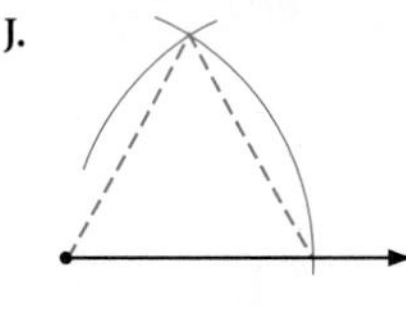

K.

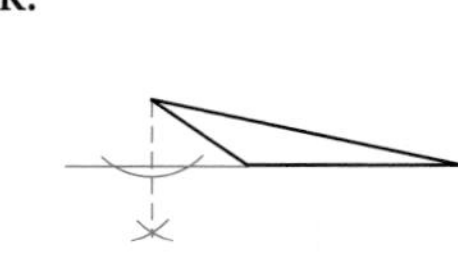

L.

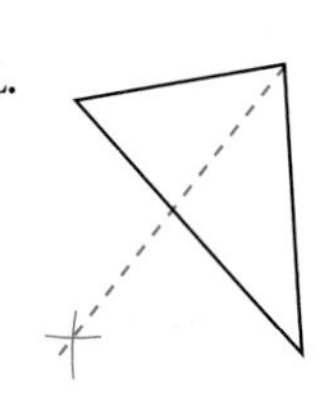

Construction For Exercises 19–24, perform a construction with compass and straightedge or with patty paper. Choose the method for each problem, but do not mix the tools in any one problem. In other words, play each construction game fairly.

19. Draw an angle and construct a duplicate of it.

20. Draw a line segment and construct its perpendicular bisector.

21. Draw a line and a point not on the line. Construct a perpendicular to the line through the point.

22. Draw an angle and bisect it.

23. Construct an angle that measures 22.5°. Construct a 90° angle and bisect it twice.

24. Draw a line and a point not on the line. Construct a second line so that it passes through the point and is parallel to the first line.

25. Brad and Janet are building a home for their pet hamsters, Riff and Raff, in the shape of a triangular prism. Which point of concurrency in the triangular base do they need to locate in order to construct the largest possible circular entrance? incenter

26. Adventurer Dakota Davis has a map that once showed the location of a large bag of gold. Unfortunately, the part of the map that showed the precise location of the gold has burned away. Dakota visits the area shown on the map anyway, hoping to find clues. To his surprise, he finds three headstones with geometric symbols on them.

The clues lead him to think that the treasure is buried at a point equidistant from the three stones. If Dakota's theory is correct, how should he go about locating the point where the bag of gold might be buried?

Construction For Exercises 27–32, use the given segments and angles to construct each figure. The lowercase letter above each segment represents the length of the segment.

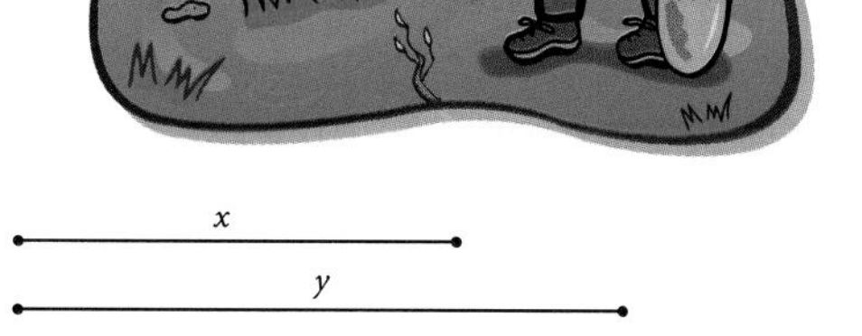

27. $\triangle ABC$ given $\angle A$, $\angle C$, and $AC = z$

28. A segment with length $2y + x - \frac{1}{2}z$ ⓗ

29. $\triangle PQR$ with $PQ = 3x$, $QR = 4x$, and $PR = 5x$

30. Isosceles triangle ABD given $\angle A$, and $AB = BD = 2y$

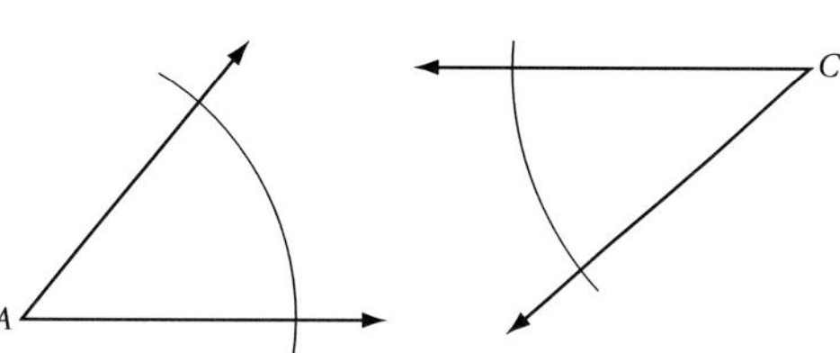

31. Quadrilateral $ABFD$ with $m\angle A = m\angle B$, $AD = BF = y$, and $AB = 4x$

32. Right triangle TRI with hypotenuse TI, $TR = x$, and $RI = y$ and a square on $\overline{TI}$, with $\overline{TI}$ as one side

24.

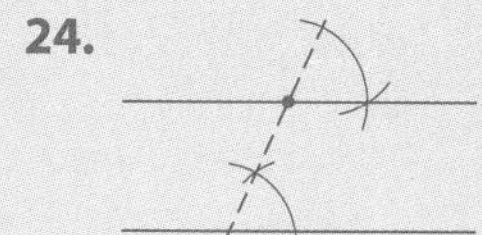

26. Dakota Davis should locate the circumcenter of the triangular region formed by the three stones, which is the location equidistant from the stones.

27.

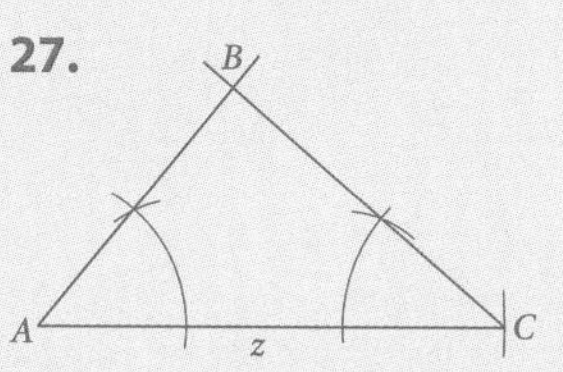

28. See below.

29.

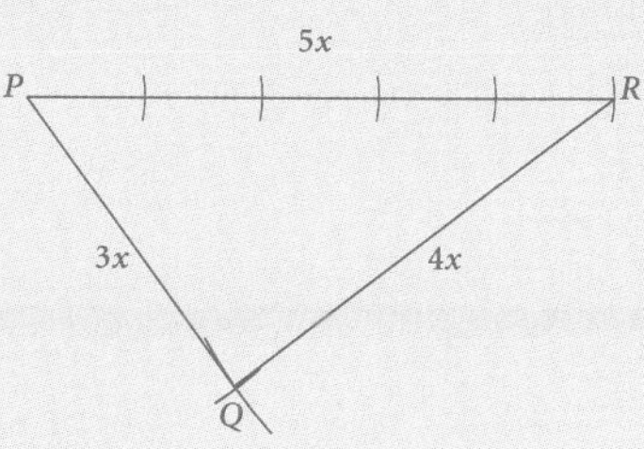

30. $m\angle A = m\angle D$.
You must first find $\angle B$.
$m\angle B = 180° - 2(m\angle A)$

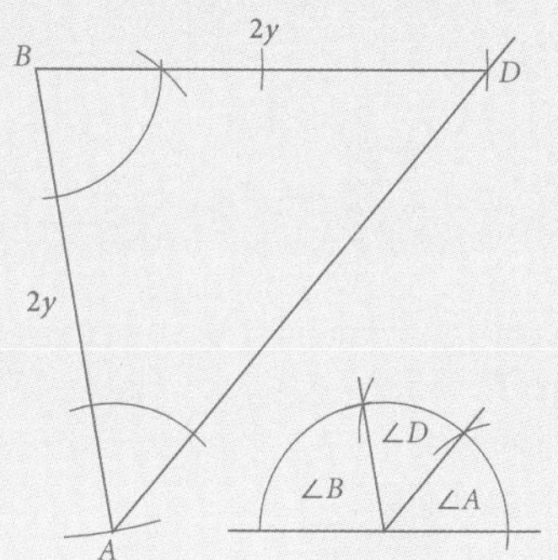

32.

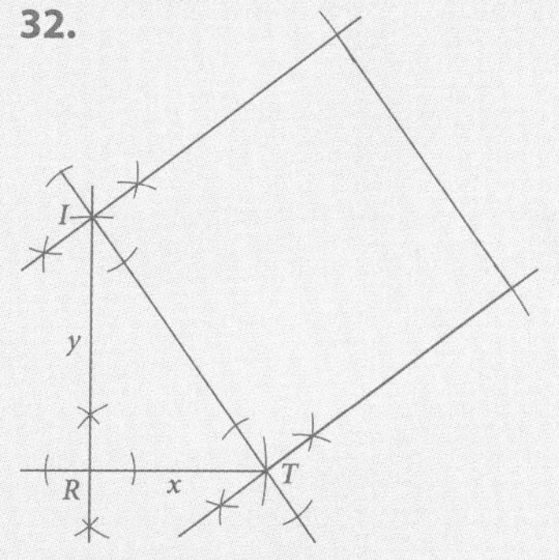

28.

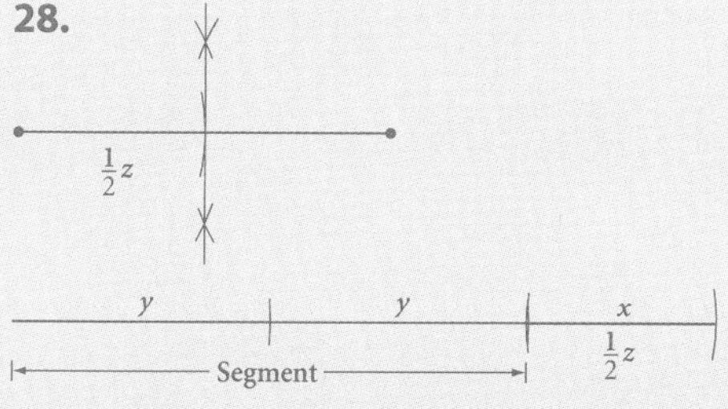

31.

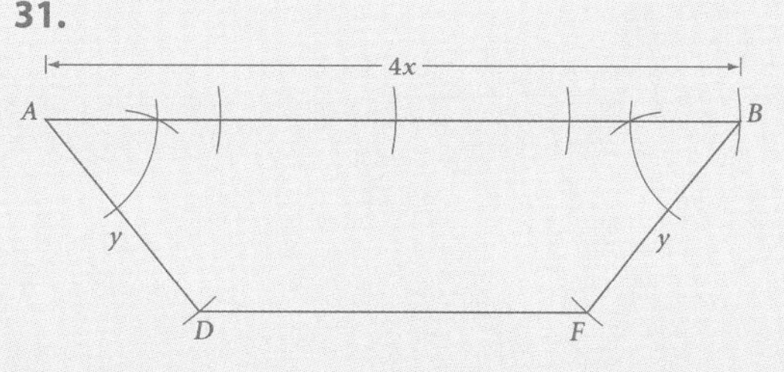

MIXED REVIEW

Tell whether each symbol in Exercises 33–36 has reflectional symmetry, rotational symmetry, neither, or both. (The symbols are used in meteorology to show weather conditions.)

0.1 **33.**  rotational symmetry

0.1 **34.**  neither

0.1 **35.**  both

0.1 **36.**  reflectional symmetry

For Exercises 37–40, match the term with its construction.

3.8 **37.** Centroid D

3.7 **38.** Circumcenter A

3.7 **39.** Incenter C

3.7 **40.** Orthocenter B

A. 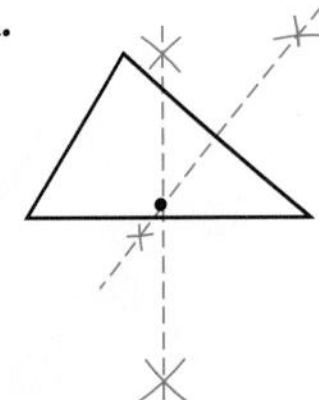

B. 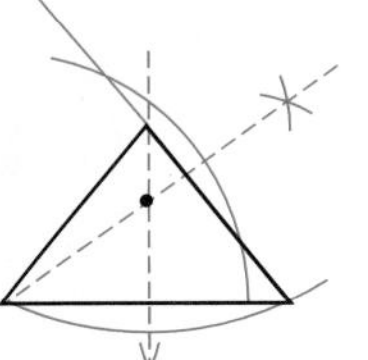

C. 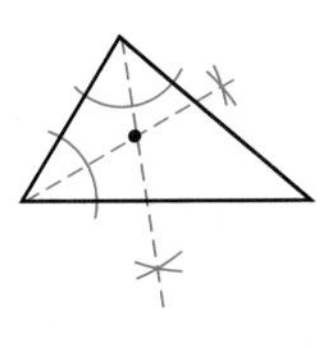

D. 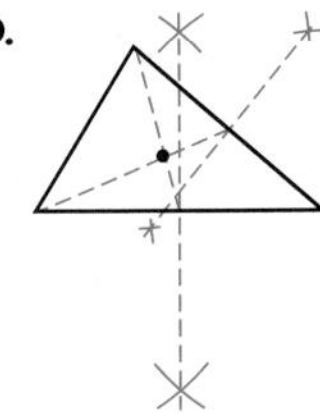

For Exercises 41–54, identify the statement as true or false. For each false statement, explain why it is false or sketch a counterexample.

1.5 **41.** An isosceles right triangle is a triangle with an angle measuring 90° and no two sides congruent.

2.6 **42.** If two parallel lines are cut by a transversal, then the alternate interior angles are congruent. true

3.3 **43.** An altitude of a triangle must be inside the triangle.

3.7 **44.** The orthocenter of a triangle is the point of intersection of the three perpendicular bisectors of the sides.

1.8 **45.** If two lines are parallel to the same line, then they are parallel to each other. true

2.5 **46.** If the sum of the measure of two angles is 180°, then the two angles are vertical angles.

1.5 **47.** Any two consecutive sides of a kite are congruent.

1.5 **48.** If a polygon has two pairs of parallel sides then it is a parallelogram.

1.6 **49.** The measure of an arc is equal to one half the measure of its central angle.

3.8 **50.** If $\overline{TR}$ is a median of $\triangle TIE$ and point D is the centroid, then $TD = 3DR$. false; $TD = 2DR$

1.6 **51.** The shortest chord of a circle is the radius of a circle. False; a radius is not a chord.

1.5 **52.** An obtuse triangle is a triangle that has one angle with measure greater than 90°. true

41. False; an isosceles triangle has two congruent sides.

43. False; any non-acute triangle is a counterexample.

44. False; possible explanation: The orthocenter is the point of intersection of the three altitudes.

46. False; any linear pair of angles is a counterexample.

47. False; each side is adjacent to one congruent side and one noncongruent side, so two consecutive sides may not be congruent.

48. false

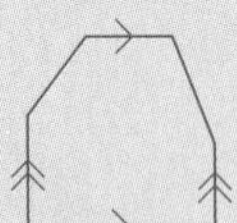

49. False; the measure of an arc is equal to the measure of its central angle.

2.1 **53.** Inductive reasoning is the process of showing that certain statements follow logically from accepted truths. False; inductive reasoning is the process of observing data, recognizing patterns, and making generalizations about those patterns.

54. There are exactly three true statements in Exercises 41–54. paradox

2.6 **55.** In the diagram, $p \parallel q$.

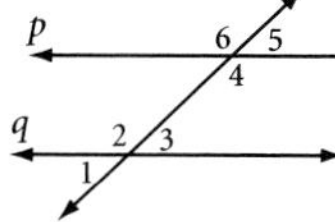

a. Name a pair of corresponding angles.

b. Name a pair of alternate exterior angles.

c. If $m\angle 3 = 42°$, what is $m\angle 6$? 138°

In Exercises 56 and 57, use inductive reasoning to find the next number or shape in the pattern.

2.1 **56.** 100, 97, 91, 82, 70 55

2.1 **57.**   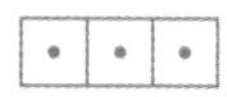 

2.5 **58.** Consider the statement "If the month is October, then the month has 31 days."

a. Is the statement true? yes

b. Write the converse of this statement.

c. Is the converse true? no

1.2 **59.** Find the point on the cushion at which a pool player should aim so that the white ball will hit the cushion and pass over point Q.

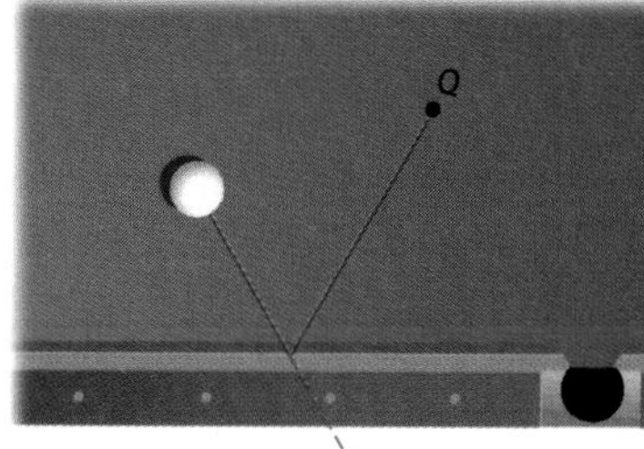

For Exercises 60 and 61, find the function rule for the sequence. Then find the 20th term.

2.3 **60.**

n	1	2	3	4	5	6	...	n	...	20
$f(n)$	−1	2	5	8	11	14	...		...	56

$f(n) = 3n - 4$

2.3 **61.**

n	1	2	3	4	5	6	...	n	...	20
$f(n)$	0	3	8	15	24	35	...		...	399

$f(n) = n^2 - 1$

2.6 **62.** Calculate each lettered angle measure.

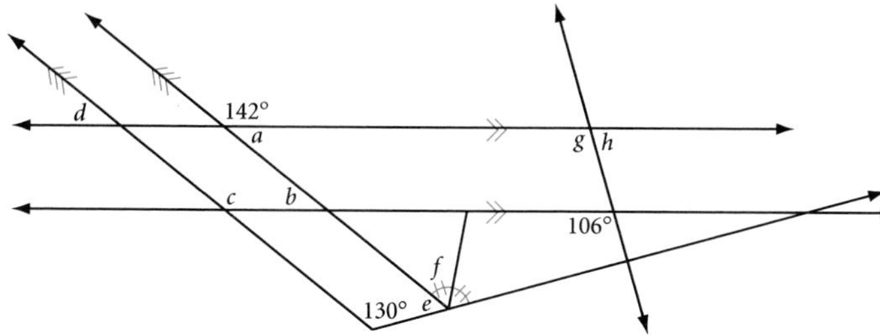

Exercise 54 This is a paradox. If students answer true because there are three true statements in Exercises 41–53, they make the statement false; if they answer false, then the statement is true.

55a. $\angle 2$ and $\angle 6$ or $\angle 3$ and $\angle 5$

55b. $\angle 1$ and $\angle 5$

57. possible answer:

58b. If the month has 31 days, then the month is October.

Exercise 61 If students are struggling, **[Ask]** "How does the function relate to n^2?" [$f(n)$ is one less than n^2.]

62. $a = 38°$, $b = 38°$, $c = 142°$, $d = 38°$, $e = 50°$, $f = 65°$, $g = 106°$, $h = 74°$

ASSESSING

You might use the performance assessment mentioned in Assessing What You've Learned for at least part of your chapter test.

FACILITATING SELF-ASSESSMENT

The Assessing What You've Learned section describes performance assessment. Students are encouraged to perform all the basic constructions and explain them to an observer. They might do this at home for a friend or family member as part of their review. Alternatively, if you give students a class period to review the chapter, you could record performance assessments while students are working in their groups. One way to streamline this process is to choose a group member randomly from each group to perform a randomly chosen construction. If the student does this and explains the construction satisfactorily, check off the entire group for this performance. If you use this method, inform students ahead of time so that they'll want to be sure all group members can do all the constructions. Give students/groups more than one chance to check off a performance. If you wish, you can make some number of performance checkoffs a grade requirement for the term.

To help students complete the portfolio described in Assessing What You've Learned, suggest that they consider for evaluation their work on
Lesson 3.1, Exercise 3;
Lesson 3.2, Exercise 11;
Lesson 3.3, Exercise 12;
Lesson 3.4, Exercise 9;
Lesson 3.5, Exercise 7;
Lesson 3.6, Exercise 10;
Lesson 3.7, Exercise 18; and
Lesson 3.8, Exercise 9.

3.7 **63.** Draw a scalene triangle *ABC*. Use a straightedge and compass to construct the incenter of $\triangle ABC$.
Triangles will vary. Check that the triangle is scalene and that at least two angle bisectors have been constructed.

2.6 **64.** What's wrong with this picture?

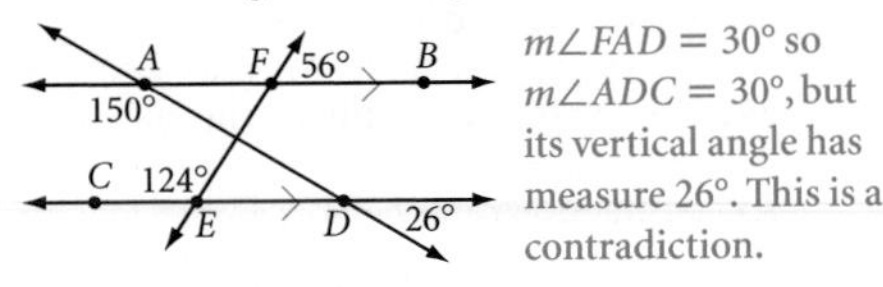

$m\angle FAD = 30°$ so $m\angle ADC = 30°$, but its vertical angle has measure 26°. This is a contradiction.

2.4 **65.** What is the minimum number of regions that are formed by 100 distinct lines in a plane? What is the maximum number of regions formed by 100 lines in the plane?
minimum: 101 regions by 100 parallel lines; maximum: 5051 regions by 100 intersecting, noncurrent lines

Assessing What You've Learned

PERFORMANCE ASSESSMENT

The subject of this chapter was the tools of geometry, so assessing what you've learned really means assessing what you can do with those tools. Can you do all the constructions you learned in this chapter? Can you show how you arrived at each conjecture? Demonstrating that you can do tasks like these is sometimes called **performance assessment.**

Look over the constructions in the Chapter Review. Practice doing any of the constructions that you're not absolutely sure of. Can you do each construction using either compass and straightedge or patty paper? Look over your conjecture list. Can you perform all the investigations that led to these conjectures?

Demonstrate at least one construction and at least one investigation for a classmate, a family member, or your teacher. Do every step from start to finish, and explain what you're doing.

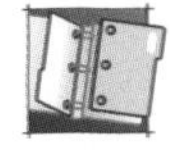

ORGANIZE YOUR NOTEBOOK

- Your notebook should have an investigation section, a definition list, and a conjecture list. Review the contents of these sections. Make sure they are complete, correct, and well organized.
- Write a one-page chapter summary from your notes.

WRITE IN YOUR JOURNAL How does the way you are learning geometry—doing constructions, looking for patterns, and making conjectures—compare to the way you've learned math in the past?

UPDATE YOUR PORTFOLIO Choose a construction problem from this chapter that you found particularly interesting and/or challenging. Describe each step, including how you figured out how to move on to the next step. Add this to your portfolio.

CHAPTER

4

Discovering and Proving Triangle Properties

Overview

In Chapter 4, students explore properties of triangles, including the conditions that guarantee that two triangles are congruent. In **Lessons 4.1** to **4.3,** students explore and make conjectures about the sum of the measures of interior angles and exterior angles of triangles, properties of isosceles triangles, and inequality relationships among the sides and angles of triangles. **Using Your Algebra Skills 4** reviews linear equations. In **Lesson 4.4,** students use compass and straightedge to discover that SSS and SAS are shortcuts for determining congruence of triangles but SSA is not. They discover in **Lesson 4.5** that ASA and SAA are both congruence shortcuts but AAA is not. Students use corresponding parts of congruent triangles in paragraph proofs in **Lesson 4.6** and in flowchart proofs in **Lesson 4.7.** Isosceles triangles are reexamined in **Lesson 4.8,** and students discover that for isosceles triangles the angle bisector of the vertex angle and the median and altitude from that angle are the same line. The **exploration** on Napoleon's Theorem investigates the centroids of equilateral triangles constructed on the sides of a triangle.

The Mathematics

The study of triangles in this chapter lays the groundwork for much of the rest of the course. Not only are the conjectures important in themselves, but some of the underlying processes are essential to good geometric thinking.

The conjectures focus on triangle congruence and on the special case of isosceles triangles, with additional study of sums of the measures of interior angles of a triangle. The standard triangle congruence theorems, abbreviated SSS, SAS, ASA, and SAA, are viewed as shortcuts to proving that two triangles are congruent. In Chapter 1, the congruence of two polygons was defined to mean that all sides and angles of one are congruent to corresponding sides and angles of the other. The triangle congruence shortcuts allow us to conclude that two triangles are congruent after we have shown the congruence of only three of the six pairs of corresponding parts.

Considering triangles in this larger context opens the way to studying other polygons in Chapter 5. The triangle conjectures of this chapter will also be important in later chapters about right triangles, in the context of the Pythagorean Theorem (Chapter 9) and trigonometry (Chapter 12). Chapter 11 on similarity also emphasizes triangles.

Beyond the conjectures, triangles are important because the rigidity of triangular structures helps students understand what parts determine a unique triangle and, from this, what information determines the congruence of two triangles. The logic is somewhat subtle. Suppose we assume that three segments determine a unique triangle, as in Lesson 3.6. Then, if we know that three sides of one triangle are congruent, respectively, to three sides of another triangle, we can conclude that those triangles are congruent; otherwise, we would have two different triangles determined by the same three segments. Thus physical determination is tied to logical determination, or implication, which is essential to all deductive reasoning.

Reasoning about triangles offers some of the easiest deduction for students, so this chapter includes deductive proofs of many of the conjectures made. (It omits proofs of the congruence shortcuts because one must be an axiom, and proving the others involves somewhat subtle indirect proofs.) Proofs are still playing the role of explanations. Most students at van Hiele level 2 do not yet understand the importance of other functions of proof, such as justification, organization, or communication. The strategy of a flowchart proof is introduced as a way to make the steps of a proof easier to understand, an important factor in proof as communication.

Using This Chapter

If you must shorten the time you spend on this chapter, you might use Lesson 4.8 as a project for students who finish the chapter review quickly. Have them present their work on isosceles triangles to the class, because all students should be familiar with these properties. When assessing student work, remember that constructions made from given parts have been reduced in the *Teacher's Edition.*

Cooperative Learning Using Pair Share

Many of the investigations in this chapter can be done with the pair-share cooperative learning model. One person in each pair might be the reader and the other the investigator. (The pairs and roles change from one activity to another.) Each reader reads the instructions and makes sure the paired investigator follows them. Each pair makes a conjecture, and then pairs compare conjectures and reach group consensus. In the investigation in Lesson 4.2, students working in groups of four can pair off. One pair will construct isosceles triangles with acute vertex angles, and the other pair will construct isosceles triangles with obtuse vertex angles. After each pair has finished, have the pairs share their ideas.

The think-aloud pair-share (TAPS) adaptation is appropriate when a group is facing a problem rather than a task. The investigator thinks aloud while trying to solve the problem, and the reader (now more appropriately called the listener) asks questions to clarify the investigator's thoughts.

Resources

Discovering Geometry Resources

Teaching and Worksheet Masters
Lessons 4.1, 4.2, 4.4–4.8, and Chapter 4 Review

Sketchpad Demonstration
Lesson 4.1
Using Your Algebra Skills 4

Discovering Geometry with The Geometer's Sketchpad
Lessons 4.1–4.5, 4.8
Using Your Algebra Skills 4

Assessment Resources A and B
Quiz 1 (Lessons 4.1–4.3)
Quiz 2 (Lessons 4.4 and 4.5)
Quiz 3 (Lessons 4.6–4.8)
Chapter 4 Test
Chapter 4 Constructive Assessment Options

Practice Your Skills for Chapter 4

Condensed Lessons for Chapter 4

Other Resources

www.keypress.com/DG

Materials

- construction tools
- protractors
- scissors
- uncooked spaghetti, *optional*
- The Geometer's Sketchpad, *optional*

Pacing Guide

	day 1	day 2	day 3	day 4	day 5	day 6	day 7	day 8	day 9	day 10
standard	4.1	4.2	Algebra 4	4.3	quiz, 4.4	4.4, 4.5	4.5	4.6	quiz, 4.7	4.7
enriched	4.1	4.2	Algebra 4	4.3	quiz, 4.4	4.5	4.6	project	quiz, 4.7	4.7
block	4.1, 4.2	Algebra 4, 4.3	quiz, 4.4, 4.5	4.6, 4.7	quiz, 4.8	Exploration, review	assessment, TAL			

	day 11	day 12	day 13	day 14	day 15	day 16	day 17	day 18	day 19	day 20
standard	4.8	review, project	review	assessment						
enriched	4.8	Exploration	review, project	assessment, TAL						

CHAPTER

4 Discovering and Proving Triangle Properties

Is it possible to make a representation of recognizable figures that has no background?

M. C. ESCHER

Symmetry Drawing E103, M. C. Escher, 1959

OBJECTIVES

In this chapter you will

- learn why triangles are so useful in structures
- discover relationships between the sides and angles of triangles
- learn about the conditions that guarantee that two triangles are congruent

Triangles can be put together to form other polygons. In this chapter students will discover properties of many kinds of triangles. In later chapters they will use their knowledge of these properties as they investigate other polygons. **[Ask]** "What symmetries do you notice in the drawing by Escher?" [reflectional and, ignoring color, 3-fold rotational symmetry] "Where do you see centers of 3-fold symmetry?" [where heads and tails meet and where fins meet] "What polygons can you locate in the drawing?" [equilateral triangles, rhombuses and other parallelograms, isosceles trapezoids, and hexagons]

CHAPTER 4 OBJECTIVES

- Discover and explain sums of the measures of two and three interior angles of a triangle
- Discover properties of the base angles and the vertex angle bisector in isosceles triangles
- Discover inequalities among sides and angles in triangles
- Investigate SSS, SAS, SSA, ASA, SAA, and AAA as potential shortcuts to proving triangle congruence
- Show that pairs of angles or pairs of sides are congruent by identifying related triangles and proving them congruent, then applying CPCTC
- Create flowchart proofs
- Review the algebra of linear equations and their graphs
- Develop logical and visual thinking skills
- Develop inductive reasoning, problem-solving skills, and cooperative behavior
- Practice using geometry tools

LESSON

4.1

PLANNING

LESSON OUTLINE

One day:

20 min Investigation

10 min Sharing

5 min Closing

10 min Exercises

MATERIALS

- construction tools
- protractors
- scissors
- Sketchpad demonstration The Triangle Sum, *optional*

TEACHING

Students think about the sum of the measures of the angles of a triangle, some explanations, and some consequences.

One step Pose this problem: "Draw a triangle on one patty paper. Create a second triangle on another patty paper by tracing two of the angles of the original triangle but making the side between the two angles longer. Guess how much larger the third angle of the new triangle is than the third angle of the original triangle. Justify your conjecture." Because the longer sides may make the angles on the second triangle look larger, students may be surprised to find that the angle measures are about the same. If students complain that the problem is misleading, remind them that real-world problems often make hidden assumptions, so students need to be skeptical. During class work and Sharing, keep asking questions to urge a full justification, namely, the Triangle Sum Conjecture and a proof of the Third Angle Conjecture via the argument that if equals are subtracted from equals, the differences are equal.

LESSON 4.1

Triangle Sum Conjecture

Teaching is the art of assisting discovery.

ALBERT VAN DOREN

Triangles have certain properties that make them useful in all kinds of structures, from bridges to high-rise buildings. One such property of triangles is their rigidity. If you build shelves like the first set shown at right, they will sway. But if you nail another board at the diagonal as in the second set, creating two triangles, you will have strong shelves. Rigid triangles such as these also give the bridge shown below its strength.

Steel truss bridge over the Columbia River Gorge in Oregon

Arranging congruent triangles can create parallel lines, as you can see from both the bridge and wood frame above. In this lesson you'll discover that this property is related to the sum of the angle measures in a triangle.

Architecture CONNECTION

American architect Julia Morgan (1872–1957) designed many noteworthy buildings, including Hearst Castle in central California. She often used triangular trusses made of redwood and exposed beams for strength and openness, as in this church in Berkeley, California. This building is now the Julia Morgan Center for the Arts.

MAKING THE CONNECTION

Julia Morgan was the first woman to earn an engineering degree at the University of California, Berkeley, and the first to earn an architecture degree from Beaux Arts in Paris.

LESSON OBJECTIVES

- Discover and explain the sum of the measures of the angles of a triangle
- Develop inductive and deductive reasoning
- Practice using geometry tools

Investigation
The Triangle Sum

You will need

- a protractor
- a straightedge
- scissors
- patty paper

There are an endless variety of triangles that you can draw, with different shapes and angle measures. Do their angle measures have anything in common? Start by drawing different kinds of triangles. Make sure your group has at least one acute and one obtuse triangle.

Step 1 Measure the three angles of each triangle as accurately as possible with your protractor.

Step 2 Find the sum of the measures of the three angles in each triangle. Compare results with others in your group. Does everyone get about the same result? What is it? 180°

Step 3 Check the sum another way. Write the letters *a*, *b*, and *c* in the interiors of the three angles of one of the triangles, and carefully cut out the triangle.

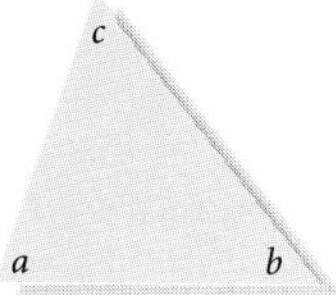

Step 4 Tear off the three angles.

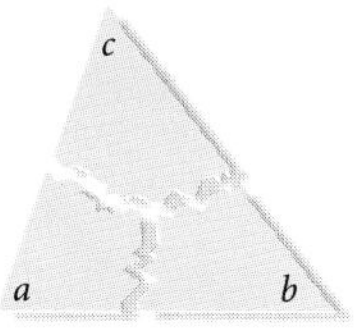

Step 5 Arrange the three angles so that their vertices meet at a point. How does this arrangement show the sum of the angle measures? Compare results with others in your group. State a conjecture.

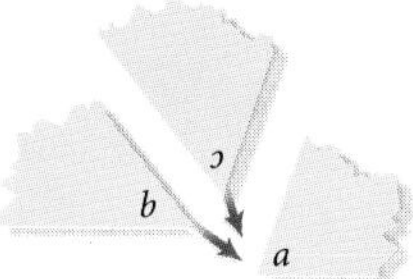

Triangle Sum Conjecture C-17

The sum of the measures of the angles in every triangle is __?__. 180°

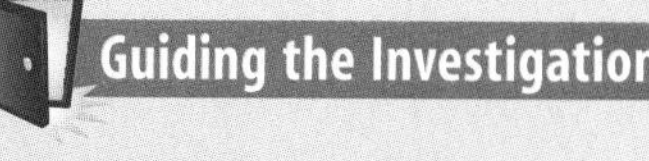

Guiding the Investigation

You might demonstrate the investigation as a follow-along activity by cutting out the triangles and displaying and measuring the pieces on an overhead projector.

Step 1 The triangles students measure should be large to reduce error. To save time, you might ask each group to explore a different triangle (obtuse, right, or acute). Each student measures the angles and the group averages the results. Then groups combine their findings. The technique of splitting up tasks and sharing results (cooperative group jigsaw method) is useful for saving time while gathering a lot of data.

Step 2 Some individuals, or even groups, may not get close enough to 180° to see a pattern. Don't press for that result at this stage.

Steps 3, 4 You might have students tear off two of the three angles from the triangle. Then they can glue the remaining part of the triangle onto a piece of paper and line up the two angles adjacent to the third angle to notice that the three angles form a straight line. This can also be done quickly with patty paper by tracing the triangle so you have three copies and lining up the three angles.

Step 5 One conjecture students might make is that the sum of the measures is larger than the measure of each angle. Another is that the sum of the measures is a straight line.

NCTM STANDARDS

	CONTENT		PROCESS
	Number		Problem Solving
✓	Algebra	✓	Reasoning
✓	Geometry	✓	Communication
✓	Measurement	✓	Connections
✓	Data/Probability	✓	Representation

Step 6 In Chapter 13, students will be given a postulate for adding angles. Here that postulate is assumed.

Step 7 Steps 7 and 8 can be used as a separate investigation. Students may find this step quite easy. **[Ask]** "What do you notice about two triangles that have matching angle measures?" [They are the same shape, in the sense that one is an enlargement of the other.]

Challenge students who finish early to find other proofs explaining the Triangle Sum Conjecture and to find a proof that explains the Third Angle Conjecture.

SHARING IDEAS

Have students share a variety of ideas about their conjectures and proofs of the first part of the lesson. Ask for critiques of the conjecture statements; for example, if one incomplete conjecture is that the sum of the measures is a straight line, elicit the point that a sum is a number and a straight line isn't.

[Ask] "What in Step 5 is also in the proof of Step 6?" [a line parallel to one side of the triangle]

For the Triangle Sum Conjecture, a student (or you) might offer an explanation that involves imagining walking clockwise around the triangle. If you start somewhere along one edge, you rotate clockwise at each vertex and end up back where you started, so the sum of the angle measures must be 360°. Encourage creative thinking such as this, which can give insight into other polygons later in the course. **[Ask]** "Why is the result not 180°?" As you ask for clarification, have the students draw in the angles through which the walker turns. (Or a student might go through the motions, following a triangle of masking tape fixed to the floor.) The turning angles won't be the angles of the triangle; instead, the turning angles provide an explanation of the Exterior Angle Sum Conjecture. However, if the walker turns through the interior angles, he or she will be walking backward along one side and along part of the side where the walk began. Ask students to model such a walk and explain the result in light of the Triangle Sum Conjecture. [When back at the starting point, the walker is facing in the opposite direction, having turned through 180°.]

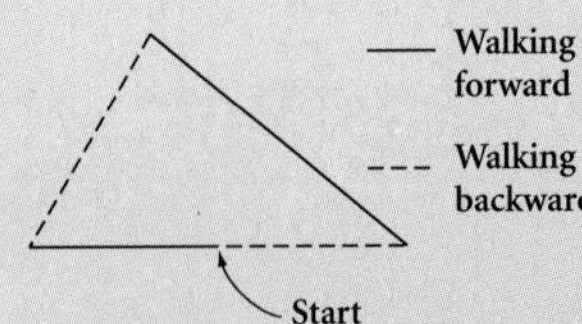

Steps 1 through 5 may have convinced you that the Triangle Sum Conjecture is true, but a proof will explain *why* it is true for every triangle.

Step 6 Copy and complete the paragraph proof below to explain the connection between the Parallel Lines Conjecture and the Triangle Sum Conjecture.

Paragraph Proof: The Triangle Sum Conjecture

To prove the Triangle Sum Conjecture, you need to show that the angle measures in a triangle add up to _?_ [180°]. Start by drawing any $\triangle ABC$, and $\overleftrightarrow{EC}$ parallel to side $\overline{AB}$.

$\overleftrightarrow{EC}$ is called an **auxiliary line,** because it is an extra line that helps with the proof.

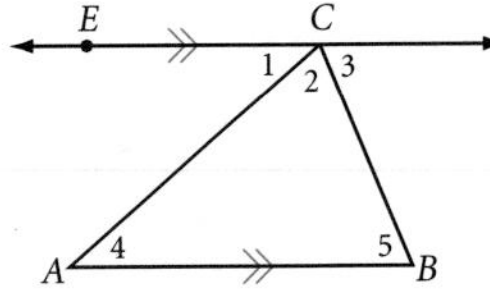

In the figure, $m\angle 1 + m\angle 2 + m\angle 3 = 180°$ if you consider $\angle 1 + \angle 2$ as one angle whose measure is $m\angle 1 + m\angle 2$, because _?_ [they are a linear pair]. You also know that $\overleftrightarrow{EC} \parallel \overline{AB}$, so $m\angle 1 = m\angle 4$ and $m\angle 3 = m\angle 5$, because _?_ [parallel lines cut by a transversal form congruent alternate interior angles.]. So, by substituting for $m\angle 1$ and $m\angle 3$ in the first equation, you get _?_ [$m\angle 4 + m\angle 2 + m\angle 5 = 180°$]. Therefore, the measures of the angles in a triangle add up to _?_ [180°]. ■

Step 7 Suppose two angles of one triangle have the same measures as two angles of another triangle. What can you conclude about the third pair of angles?

Step 7 Their measures are also equal.

You can investigate Step 7 with patty paper. Draw a triangle on your paper. Create a second triangle on patty paper by tracing two of the angles of your original triangle, but make the side between your new angles a different length from the side between the angles you copied in the first triangle. How do the third angles in the two triangles compare?

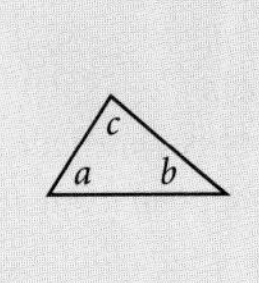

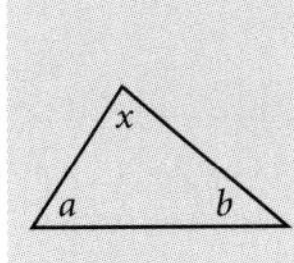

Step 8 Check your results with other students. You should be ready for your next conjecture.

Third Angle Conjecture C-18

If two angles of one triangle are equal in measure to two angles of another triangle, then the third angle in each triangle _?_ [is equal in measure to the third angle in the other triangle].

You can use the Triangle Sum Conjecture to show why the Third Angle Conjecture is true. You'll do this in Exercise 15.

EXAMPLE

In the figure at right, is $\angle C$ congruent to $\angle E$? Write a paragraph proof explaining why.

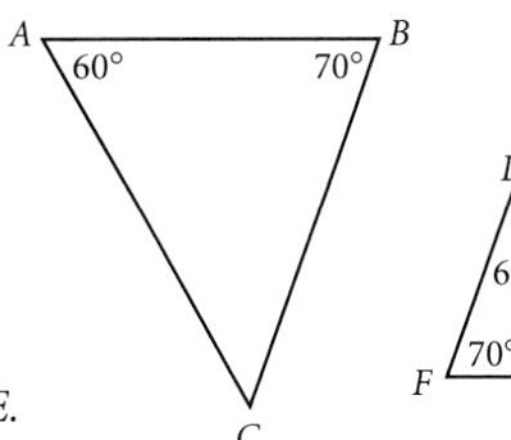

▶ Solution

Yes. By the Third Angle Conjecture, because $\angle A$ and $\angle B$ are congruent to $\angle D$ and $\angle F$, then $\angle C$ must be congruent to $\angle E$.

You could also use the Triangle Sum Conjecture to find that $\angle D$ and $\angle F$ both measure 50°. Since they have the same measure, they are congruent.

EXERCISES

You will need

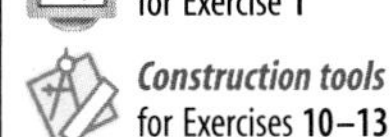

Geometry software for Exercise 1

Construction tools for Exercises 10–13

1. *Technology* Using geometry software, construct a triangle. Use the software to measure the three angles and calculate their sum.
   a. Drag the vertices and describe your observations. The angle measures change, but the sum remains 180°.
   b. Repeat the process for a right triangle. Measures of the acute angles change, but students may notice or deduce that their sum remains 90°.

Use the Triangle Sum Conjecture to determine each lettered angle measure in Exercises 2–5. You might find it helpful to copy the diagrams so you can write on them.

2. $x = \underline{?}$ 73°

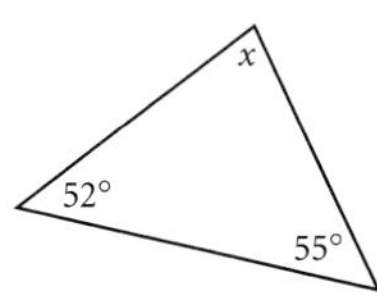

3. $v = \underline{?}$ 60°

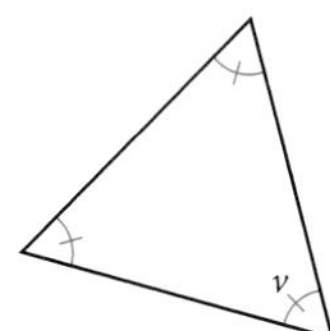

4. $z = \underline{?}$ ⓗ 110°

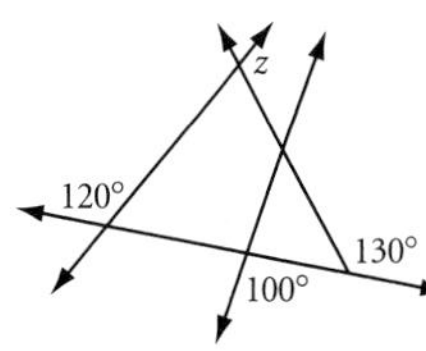

5. $w = \underline{?}$ 24°

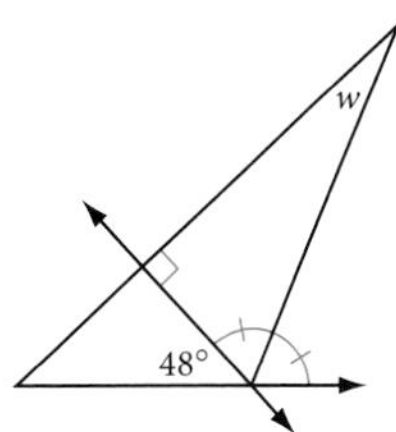

6. Find the sum of the measures of the marked angles. ⓗ $3 \cdot 360° - 180° = 900°$

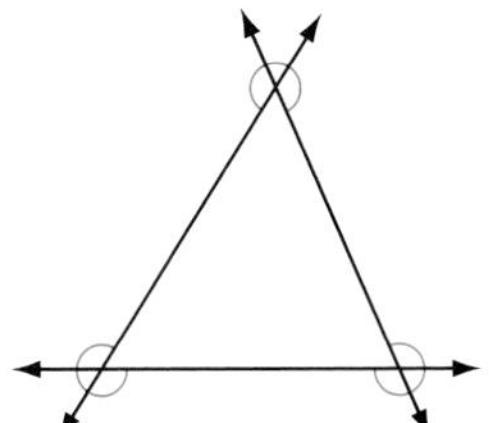

7. Find the sum of the measures of the marked angles. ⓗ $3 \cdot 180° - 180° = 360°$

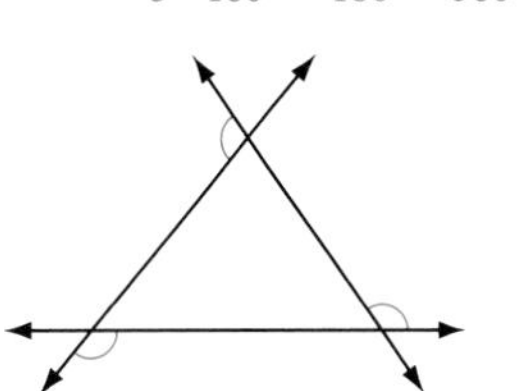

Assessing Progress

Observe how well students are collecting data and making conjectures from these data. Assess their skill at using a protractor, a straightedge, and patty paper and their understanding of *acute triangle, obtuse triangle, measure of an angle,* and the Alternate Interior Angles Conjecture.

▶ EXAMPLE

This example is good for students who need more help in understanding the two conjectures of the investigation.

Closing the Lesson

Remind students of the major points of this lesson: The Triangle Sum Conjecture says that the sum of the measures of the angles of any triangle is 180°. This conjecture can be proved in a number of ways. One consequence is the Third Angle Conjecture, which states that if two angles of one triangle are congruent to two angles of another triangle, then their third angles also have equal measure.

BUILDING UNDERSTANDING

The exercises focus on the Triangle Sum Conjecture.

ASSIGNING HOMEWORK

Essential	2–16 evens
Performance assessment	9
Portfolio	8
Journal	15
Group	1–13 odds
Review	17–22

MATERIALS

- Exercises 8 and 9 (T), *optional*

▶ Helping with the Exercises

Exercises 6, 7 If students are finding these exercises difficult, suggest that they think about subtraction or that they look at the hints.

Exercises 8, 9 These exercises may be a bit intimidating at first. You might do one in class, with students working in pairs explaining why we know each answer. This is another good opportunity for think aloud pair share where students take turns finding an answer and then explaining it. As needed, point out that some of the angles are in both a larger and a smaller triangle. Remind students that practice makes perfect and that it is much easier to practice in pencil than in pen.

8. $a =$? (h) 69°
$b =$? 47°
$c =$? 116°
$d =$? 93°
$e =$? 86°

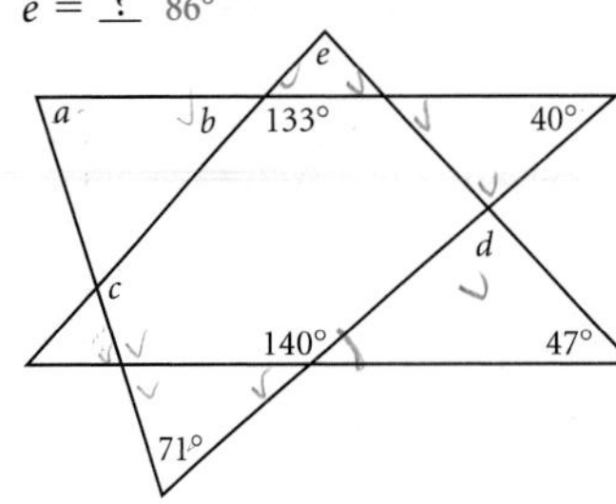

9. $m =$? 30°
$n =$? 50°
$p =$? 82°
$q =$? 28°
$r =$? 32°
$s =$? 78°
$t =$? 118°
$u =$? 50°

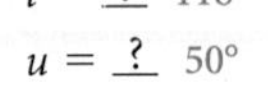

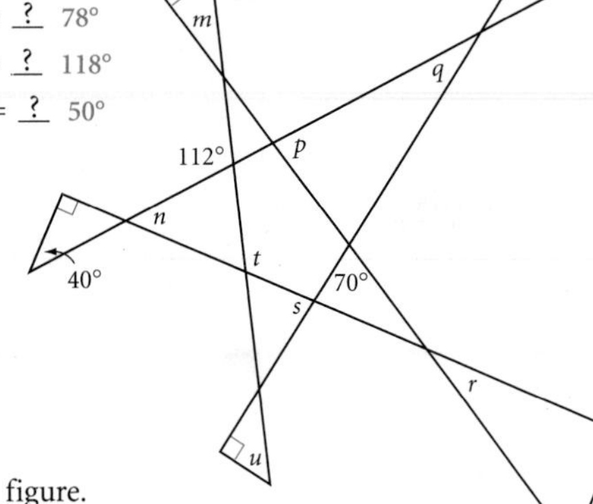

In Exercises 10–12, use what you know to construct each figure. Use only a compass and a straightedge.

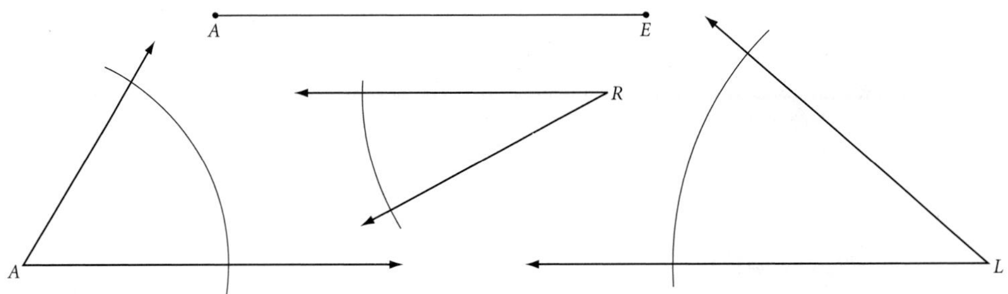

10. ***Construction*** Given $\angle A$ and $\angle R$ of $\triangle ARM$, construct $\angle M$.

11. ***Construction*** In $\triangle LEG$, $m\angle E = m\angle G$. Given $\angle L$, construct $\angle G$.

12. ***Construction*** Given $\angle A$, $\angle R$, and side $\overline{AE}$, construct $\triangle EAR$.

13. ***Construction*** Repeat Exercises 10–12 with patty-paper constructions.

14. In $\triangle MAS$ below, $\angle M$ is a right angle. Let's call the two acute angles, $\angle A$ and $\angle S$, "wrong angles." Write a paragraph proof or use algebra to show that "two wrongs make a right," at least for angles in a right triangle.

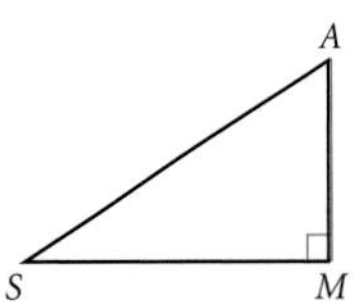

From the Triangle Sum Conjecture $m\angle A + m\angle S + m\angle M = 180°$. Because $\angle M$ is a right angle, $m\angle M = 90°$. By substitution, $m\angle A + m\angle S + 90° = 180°$. By subtraction, $m\angle A + m\angle S = 90°$. So two wrongs make a right!

THE FAR SIDE® By GARY LARSON

"Yes, yes, I *know* that, Sidney—*everybody* knows *that*! ... But look: Four wrongs *squared*, minus two wrongs to the fourth power, divided by this formula, *do* make a right."

Exercise 10 This construction could also be done by constructing the given angles on the ends of a line segment; then $\angle M$ is the third angle formed where the sides of the angles meet.

10.

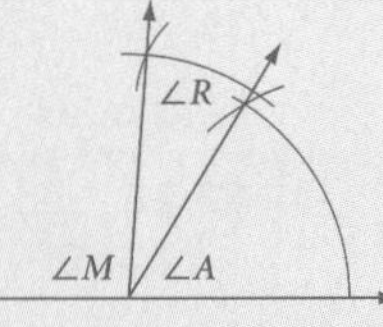

11.

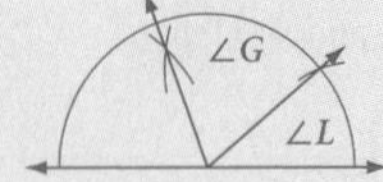

12. First construct $\angle E$, using the method used in Exercise 10.

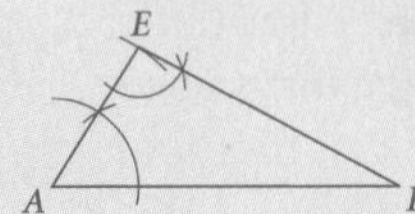

13.

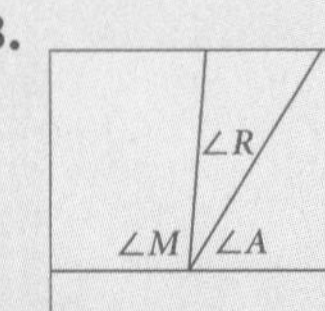

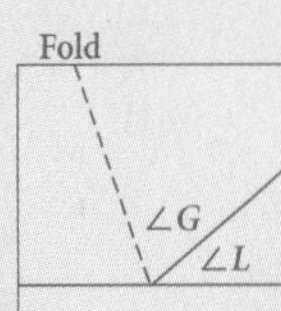

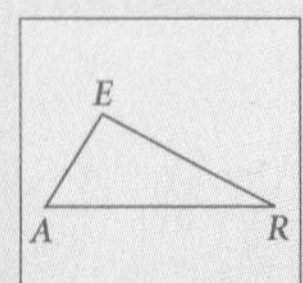

15. Use the Triangle Sum Conjecture and the figures at right to write a paragraph proof explaining why the Third Angle Conjecture is true. ⓗ

16. Write a paragraph proof, or use algebra, to explain why each angle of an equiangular triangle measures 60°.

For any triangle, the sum of the angle measures is 180°, by the Triangle Sum Conjecture. Since the triangle is equiangular, each angle has the same measure, say x. So $x + x + x = 180°$, and $x = 60°$.

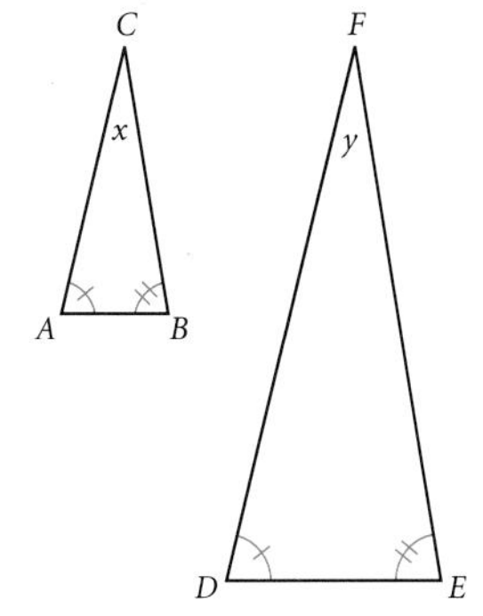

Review

In Exercises 17–21, tell whether the statement is true or false. For each false statement, explain why it is false or sketch a counterexample.

3.6 **17.** If two sides in one triangle are congruent to two sides in another triangle, then the two triangles are congruent. false

3.6 **18.** If two angles in one triangle are congruent to two angles in another triangle, then the two triangles are congruent. false

3.6 **19.** If a side and an angle in one triangle are congruent to a side and an angle in another triangle, then the two triangles are congruent. false

3.6 **20.** If three angles in one triangle are congruent to three angles in another triangle, then the two triangles are congruent. false

3.6 **21.** If three sides in one triangle are congruent to three sides in another triangle, then the two triangles are congruent. true

2.3 **22.** What is the number of stories in the tallest house you can build with two 52-card decks? eight How many cards would it take? 100

One story (2 cards)

Two stories (7 cards)

Three stories (15 cards)

IMPROVING YOUR VISUAL THINKING SKILLS

PUZZLE

Dissecting a Hexagon I

Trace this regular hexagon twice.

1. Divide one hexagon into four congruent trapezoids.
2. Divide the other hexagon into eight congruent parts. What shape is each part?

15. You know from the Triangle Sum Conjecture that $m\angle A + m\angle B + m\angle C = 180°$, and $m\angle D + m\angle E + m\angle F = 180°$. By the transitive property, $m\angle A + m\angle B + m\angle C = m\angle D + m\angle E + m\angle F$. You also know that $m\angle A = m\angle D$, and $m\angle B = m\angle E$. You can substitute for $m\angle D$ and $m\angle E$ in the longer equation to get $m\angle A + m\angle B + m\angle C = m\angle A + m\angle B + m\angle F$. Subtracting equal terms from both sides, you are left with $m\angle C = m\angle F$.

Exercises 17–21 These exercises are very important preparation for the lessons on congruence shortcuts. You might want to start some of them in class by asking for and demonstrating counterexamples. Then complete the discussion of these exercises at the start of the next class period.

17.

18.

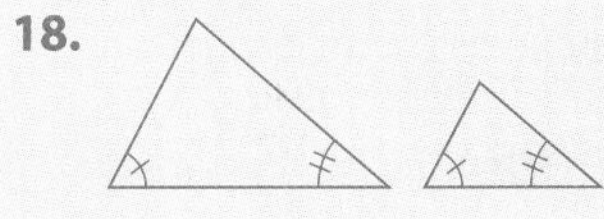

19.

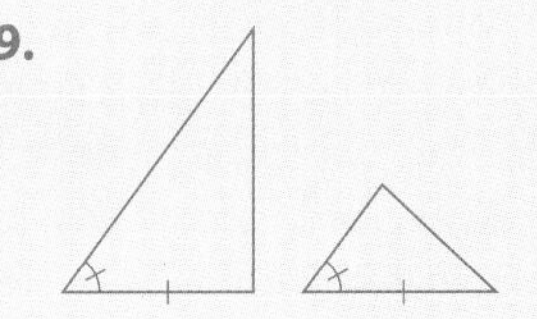

20.

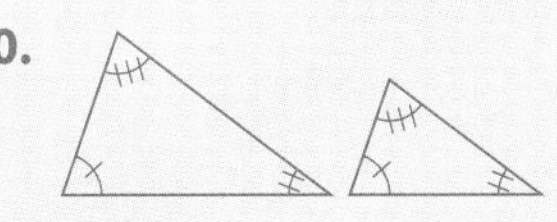

EXTENSION

Use Take Another Look activity 1 on page 253.

IMPROVING VISUAL THINKING SKILLS

1. If students are having difficulty, ask if they can divide the hexagon into two congruent parts.

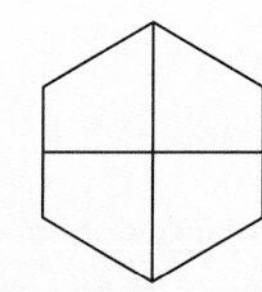

Each part is a right trapezoid.

2. Each part is a trapezoid with three congruent sides.

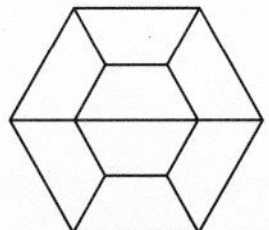

LESSON

4.2

PLANNING

LESSON OUTLINE

One day:

20 min Investigation

10 min Sharing

5 min Closing

10 min Exercises

MATERIALS

- tracing paper or patty paper
- protractors
- compasses

TEACHING

Students inductively conjecture that the base angles of an isosceles triangle are congruent, and the converse.

Start with the one-step investigation, or introduce the vocabulary before students begin to follow the steps of the investigations.

INTRODUCTION

[Ask] "What is the definition of an isosceles triangle?" [a triangle with at least two congruent sides] As needed, review vocabulary associated with an isosceles triangle: vertex angle and base angles.

LESSON 4.2

Properties of Special Triangles

Imagination is built upon knowledge.

ELIZABETH STUART PHELPS

Recall from Chapter 1 that an isosceles triangle is a triangle with at least two congruent sides. In an isosceles triangle, the angle between the two congruent sides is called the vertex angle, and the other two angles are called the base angles. The side between the two base angles is called the base of the isosceles triangle. The other two sides are called the **legs.**

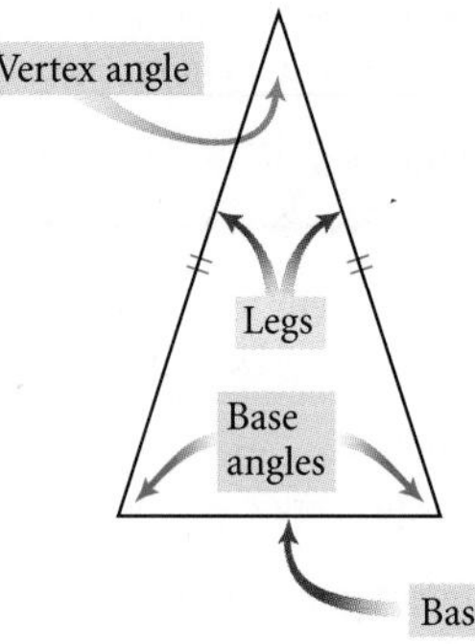

The famous Transamerica Building in San Francisco contains many isosceles triangles.

In this lesson you'll discover some properties of isosceles triangles.

The Rock and Roll Hall of Fame and Museum structure is a pyramid containing many triangles that are isosceles *and* equilateral.

Architecture CONNECTION

The Rock and Roll Hall of Fame and Museum in Cleveland, Ohio, is a dynamic structure. Its design reflects the innovative music that it honors. The front part of the museum is a large glass pyramid, divided into small triangular windows that resemble a Sierpiński tetrahedron, a three-dimensional Sierpiński triangle. The pyramid structure rests on a rectangular tower and a circular theater that looks like a performance drum. Architect I. M. Pei (b 1917) used geometric shapes to capture the resonance of rock and roll musical chords.

LESSON OBJECTIVES

- Discover a relationship between the base angles of an isosceles triangle
- Learn new vocabulary
- Develop problem-solving skills and inductive reasoning
- Practice using construction tools

NCTM STANDARDS

CONTENT		PROCESS	
	Number	✓	Problem Solving
	Algebra	✓	Reasoning
✓	Geometry	✓	Communication
✓	Measurement	✓	Connections
	Data/Probability		Representation

Investigation 1
Base Angles in an Isosceles Triangle

You will need

- patty paper
- a protractor

Let's examine the angles of an isosceles triangle. Each person in your group should draw a different angle for this investigation. Your group should have at least one acute angle and one obtuse angle.

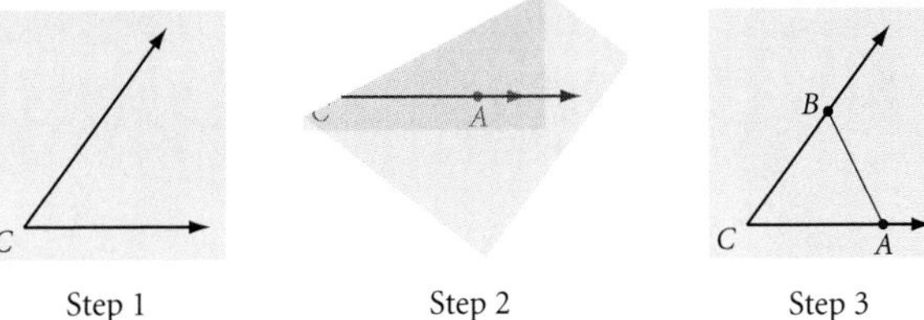

Step 1 Step 2 Step 3

Step 1 Draw an angle on patty paper. Label it $\angle C$. This angle will be the vertex angle of your isosceles triangle.

Step 2 Place a point A on one ray. Fold your patty paper so that the two rays match up. Trace point A onto the other ray.

Step 3 Label the point on the other ray point B. Draw $\overline{AB}$. You have constructed an isosceles triangle. Explain how you know it is isosceles. Name the base and the base angles.

Step 4 Use your protractor to compare the measures of the base angles. What relationship do you notice? How can you fold the paper to confirm your conclusion?

Step 5 Compare results in your group. Was the relationship you noticed the same for each isosceles triangle? State your observations as your next conjecture.

Isosceles Triangle Conjecture C-19

If a triangle is isosceles, then __?__. its base angles are congruent

Equilateral triangles have at least two congruent sides, so they fit the definition of isosceles triangles. That means any properties you discover for isosceles triangles will also apply to equilateral triangles. How does the Isosceles Triangle Conjecture apply to equilateral triangles?

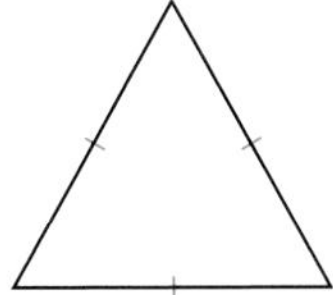

You can switch the "if" and "then" parts of the Isosceles Triangle Conjecture to obtain the converse of the conjecture. Is the converse of the Isosceles Triangle Conjecture true? Let's investigate.

One step Pose this problem: "Try to construct a triangle with both of these properties: The triangle has two equal sides (that is, it's isosceles), and the measures of all three angles are different." As you circulate among groups, encourage creative thinking. If students say that having two sides with equal length requires that two angles must be equal, ask them to state a conjecture describing which two angles must be equal. Respond similarly if they claim that equal angles imply equal sides. Challenge them to extend their conjectures to equilateral triangles, trapezoids, and other quadrilaterals. During Sharing, remind students of the meaning of an isosceles triangle, and introduce the terminology *base angles, vertex angle,* and *equiangular triangle.* Use the terms to elicit formal statements of the Isosceles Triangle Conjecture and its converse.

Guiding Investigation 1

Step 3 [Alert] Students may have difficulty if the vertex angle is lower on their paper than the base angles. You might suggest that they rotate their paper if this is the case.

Step 3 $\overline{CB} \cong \overline{CA}$ because they were drawn from the same point with the same distance. $\overline{AB}$, $\angle A$, $\angle B$

Step 4 Fold the paper so $\angle A$ and $\angle B$ coincide.

Guiding Investigation 2

Remind students of how to find a converse of a statement and that the converse of a true statement may be false.

Steps 1–4 If you used the pair-share cooperative group strategy for the first investigation, have students switch partners or roles for this investigation.

Students will prove these conjectures in Lesson 4.7, Exercises 4 and 5.

SHARING IDEAS

Have students share conjectures and come to a class consensus on their statements, to be entered into students' notebooks. As needed, discuss the converse of a conjecture. **[Ask]** "What is the converse of the converse?" [the original conjecture] A converse of a true conjecture need not be true, but if it is the two can be combined into a biconditional "if and only if" statement. **[Language]** *Bi* means "two," as in *biweekly* and *bicycle.* The word *biconditional* means "two conditions"; either part of the conjecture can be the condition, with the other part the conclusion.

[Alert] Some students have difficulty understanding that the Isosceles Triangle Conjecture and its converse are not the same thing. Restating the conjectures in exactly opposite forms may help: If a triangle has at least two congruent sides, then the angles opposite those sides are congruent. If a triangle has at least two congruent angles, then the sides opposite those angles are congruent. **[Ask]** "What are you beginning with in each conjecture? [The Isosceles Triangle Conjecture begins with (at least) two congruent sides, and the converse begins with two congruent angles.]

Investigation 2
Is the Converse True?

You will need
- a compass
- a straightedge

Suppose a triangle has two congruent angles. Must the triangle be isosceles?

Step 1

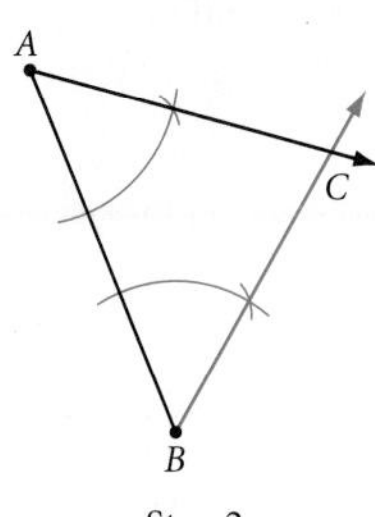

Step 2

Step 1 Draw a segment and label it $\overline{AB}$. Draw an acute angle at point A. This angle will be a base angle. (Why can't you draw an obtuse angle as a base angle?)

Step 1 The sum of the angles of the triangle would be more than 180°.

Step 2 Copy $\angle A$ at point B on the same side of $\overline{AB}$. Label the intersection of the two rays point C.

Step 3 Use your compass to compare the lengths of sides $\overline{AC}$ and $\overline{BC}$. What relationship do you notice? How can you use patty paper to confirm your conclusion?

Step 3 $AC = BC$. Fold the paper through point C so that $\angle A$ coincides with $\angle B$.

Step 4 Compare results in your group. State your observation as your next conjecture.

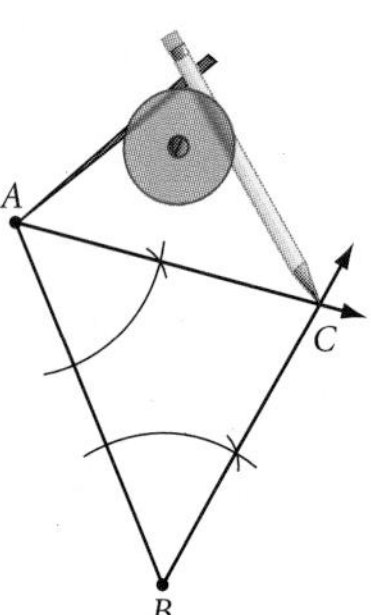

Converse of the Isosceles Triangle Conjecture  C-20

If a triangle has two congruent angles, then __?__. *it is an isosceles triangle*

EXERCISES

You will need

For Exercises 1–6, use your new conjectures to find the missing measures.

1. $m\angle H =$ __?__ ⓗ *79°*

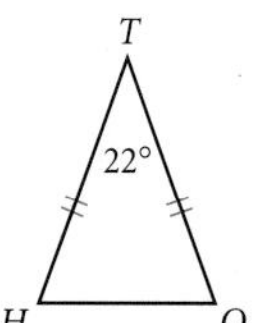

2. $m\angle G =$ __?__ *54°*

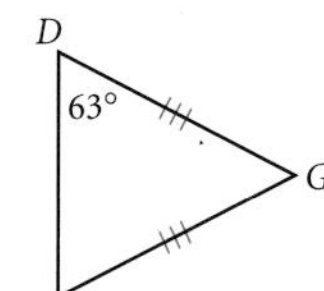

3. $m\angle OLE =$ __?__ *107.5°*

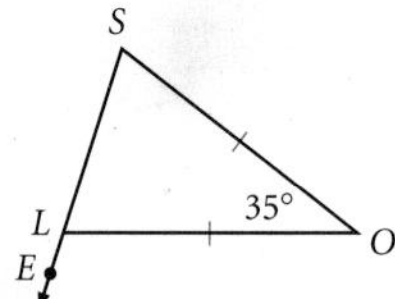

[Alert] Some students may phrase their conjectures as something like "Congruent angles make congruent sides" and vice versa. **[Ask]** "What does *make* mean?" "Do congruent angles make congruent sides in a quadrilateral?" [no]

Assessing Progress
Your observations of group work and presentations give you opportunities to assess students' understanding of isosceles triangle, vertex angle, base angle, ray, acute angle, obtuse angle, measure of an angle, congruent segments, congruent angles, and equilateral, equiangular, and regular polygons. Watch for their skill in using patty paper and a straightedge to copy segments and angles and in comparing lengths with a compass. Check how well they can write the converse of a given if-then statement.

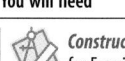

4. $m\angle R = \underline{?}$ 44°
$RM = \underline{?}$ 35 cm

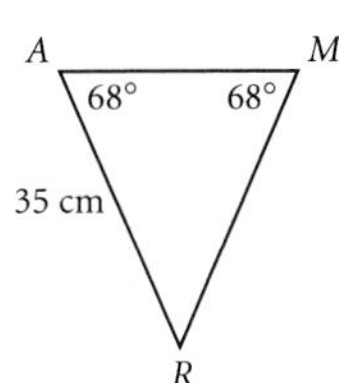

5. $m\angle Y = \underline{?}$ 76°
$RD = \underline{?}$ 3.5 cm

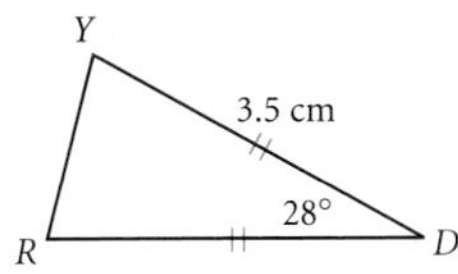

6. The perimeter of $\triangle MUD$ is 38 cm.
$m\angle D = \underline{?}$ 72°
$MD = \underline{?}$ 10 cm

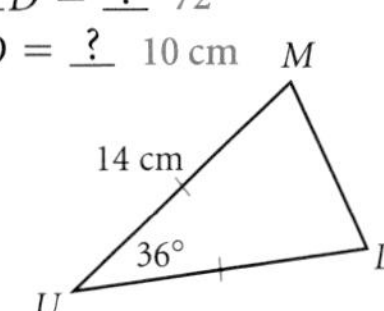

7. Copy the figure at right. Calculate the measure of each lettered angle. ⓗ $a = 124°, b = 56°, c = 56°, d = 38°, e = 38°, f = 76°, g = 66°, h = 104°, k = 76°, n = 86°, p = 38°$

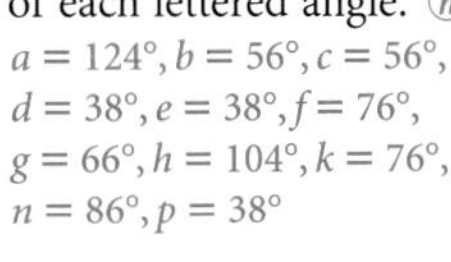

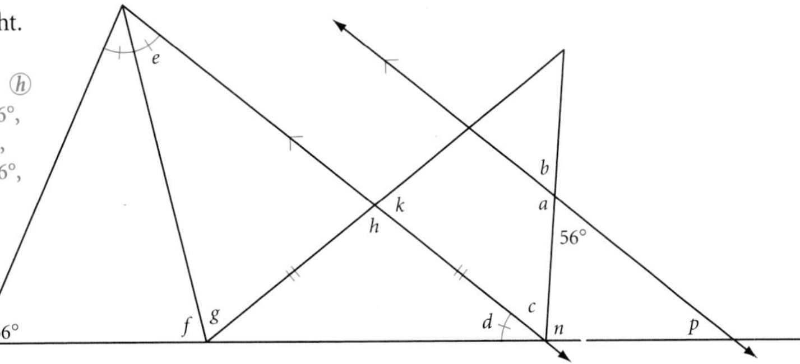

8. The Islamic design below right is based on the star decagon construction shown below left. The ten angles surrounding the center are all congruent. Find the lettered angle measures. How many triangles are not isosceles? ⓗ $a = 36°, b = 36°, c = 72°, d = 108°, e = 36°$; none

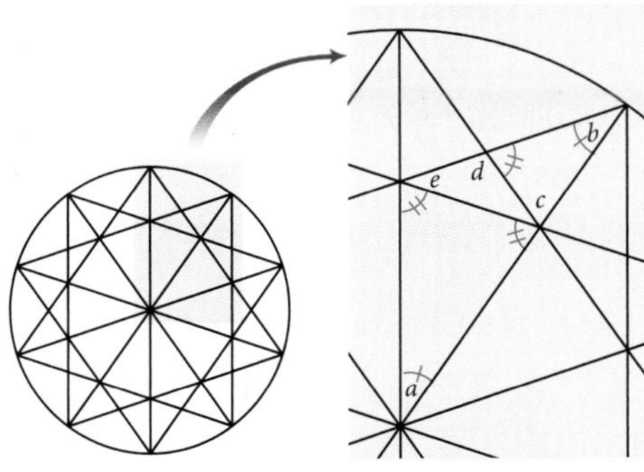

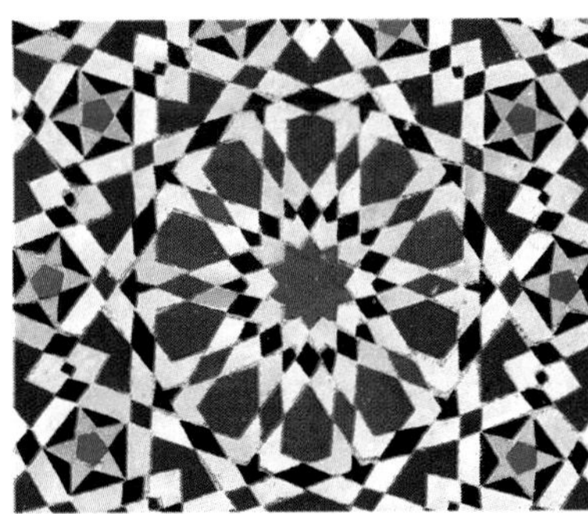

9. Study the triangles in the software constructions below. Each triangle has one vertex at the center of the circle, and two vertices on the circle. For an interactive version of this sketch, visit www.keymath.com/DG .

a. Are the triangles all isosceles? Write a paragraph proof explaining why or why not.

b. If the vertex at the center of the first circle has an angle measure of 60°, find the measures of the other two angles in that triangle. 60°

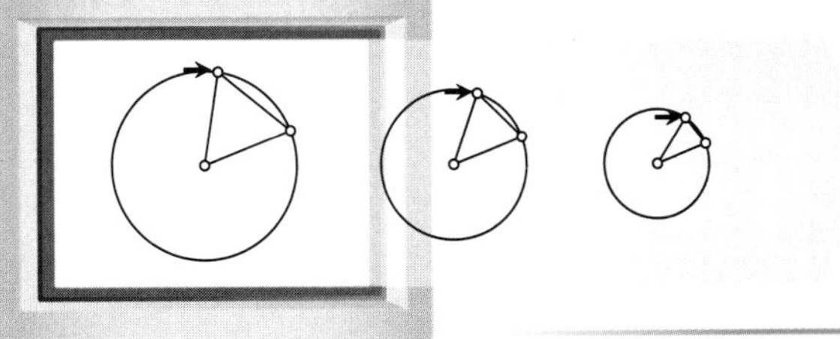

9a. Yes. Two sides are radii of a circle. Radii must be congruent, therefore each triangle must be isosceles.

Closing the Lesson

Remind students that the major conjectures of this lesson form a biconditional: Two sides of a triangle are congruent if and only if the angles opposite those sides are congruent. If needed, you might work one of Exercises 1–18.

BUILDING UNDERSTANDING

The exercises apply the Isosceles Triangle Conjecture and its converse.

ASSIGNING HOMEWORK

Essential	1–7
Performance assessment	8
Portfolio	6
Journal	9
Group	7
Review	10–22

MATERIALS

- Exercises 7 and 8 (T), *optional*
- Exercises 21 and 22 (T), *optional*

▶Helping with the Exercises

Exercise 7 If students are having difficulty getting started, suggest that they try working backward as well as forward: "What might I find out that would allow me to calculate this angle's measure?" It may be necessary to find measures of angles that aren't marked. Encourage students to look for larger triangles made up of smaller triangles. As needed, caution them not to assume that n is 90°; it's not marked as such.

Exercise 9 Students can use the dynamic geometry exploration at www.keymath.com/DG to investigate the properties of a triangle with one vertex at the center of a circle and the other two vertices on the circumference of the circle. This will help with solving Exercise 9.

Exercises 10, 11 Some students may not be able to easily make the jump from how three sides determine a triangle to the congruence of two triangles because of corresponding congruent sides. **[Ask]** "If you made one triangle with these three sides and then made another one, would the triangles be congruent?" [They would, because they're the same.] Solving these exercises requires none of the congruence shortcuts that are to come later in the chapter. Remind students that the vertices of congruent polygons should be labeled in corresponding order, as mentioned in Lesson 1.4.

12.

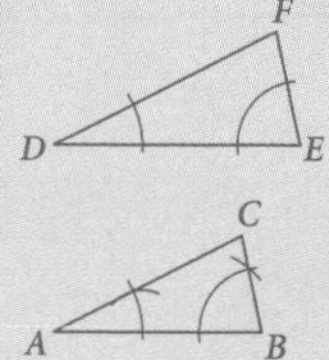

13.

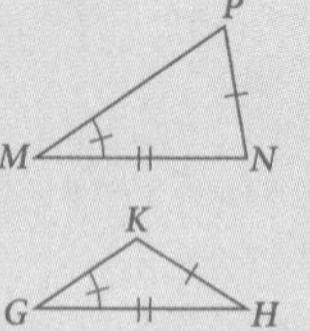

14. possible answer:

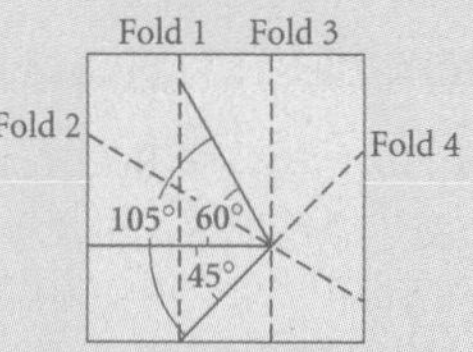

Exercise 19 Students may also notice it is a rectangle or even a square.

Exercise 20 Students need to extend the number line past 40.

Review

3.6 In Exercises 10 and 11, complete the statement of congruence from the information given. Remember to write the statement so that corresponding parts are in order.

10. $\triangle GEA \cong \triangle$ _?_ NCA

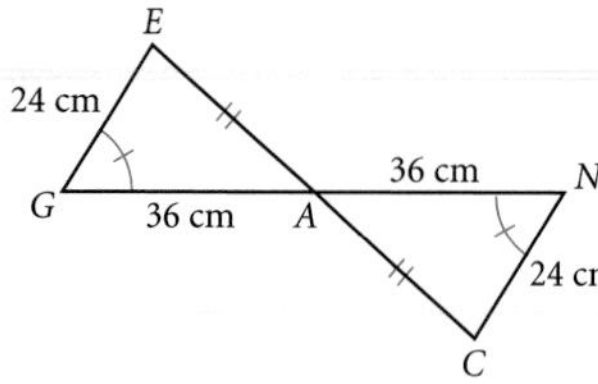

11. $\triangle JAN \cong \triangle$ _?_ IEC

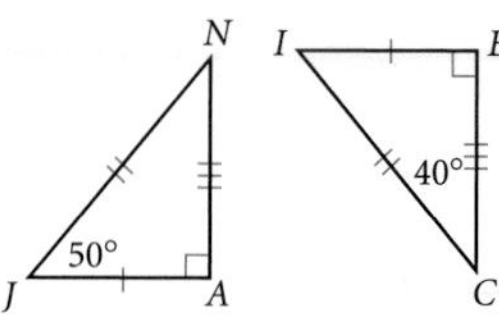

3.6 In Exercises 12 and 13, use compass and straightedge, or patty paper, to construct a triangle that is not congruent to the given triangle, but has the given parts congruent. The symbol $\ncong$ means "not congruent to."

12. ***Construction*** Construct $\triangle ABC \ncong \triangle DEF$ with $\angle A \cong \angle D$, $\angle B \cong \angle E$, and $\angle C \cong \angle F$. ⓗ

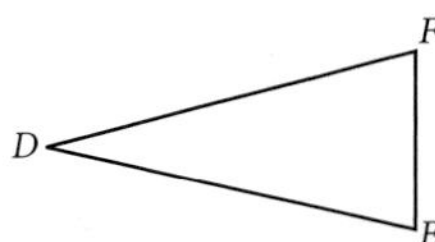

13. ***Construction*** Construct $\triangle GHK \ncong \triangle MNP$ with $\overline{HK} \cong \overline{NP}$, $\overline{GH} \cong \overline{MN}$, and $\angle G \cong \angle M$. ⓗ

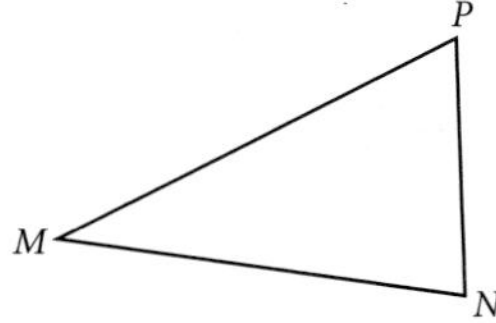

3.1 **14.** ***Construction*** With a straightedge and patty paper, construct an angle that measures 105°.

UYAS 3 In Exercises 15–18, determine whether each pair of lines through the points below is parallel, perpendicular, or neither.

$A(1, 3)$ $B(6, 0)$ $C(4, 3)$ $D(1, -2)$ $E(-3, 8)$ $F(-4, 1)$ $G(-1, 6)$ $H(4, -4)$

15. $\overleftrightarrow{AB}$ and $\overleftrightarrow{CD}$ ⓗ perpendicular

16. $\overleftrightarrow{FG}$ and $\overleftrightarrow{CD}$ parallel

17. $\overleftrightarrow{AD}$ and $\overleftrightarrow{CH}$ parallel

18. $\overleftrightarrow{DE}$ and $\overleftrightarrow{GH}$ neither

1.5 **19.** Using the coordinate points above, is $FGCD$ a trapezoid, a parallelogram, or neither? parallelogram

20. Picture the isosceles triangle below toppling side over side to the right along the line. Copy the triangle and line onto your paper, then construct the path of point P through two cycles. Where on the number line will the vertex point land? 40

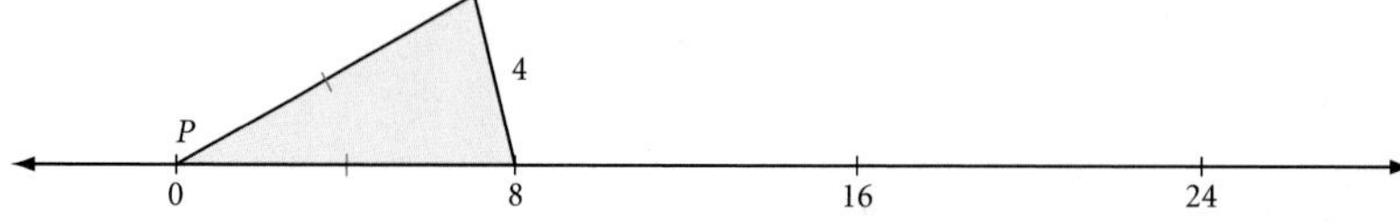

20.

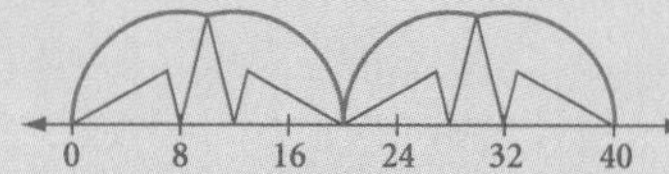

1.5 For Exercises 21 and 22, use the ordered pair rule shown to relocate each of the vertices of the given triangle. Connect the three new points to create a new triangle. Is the new triangle congruent to the original one? Describe how the new triangle has changed position from the original.

21. $(x, y) \rightarrow (x + 5, y - 3)$ ⓗ

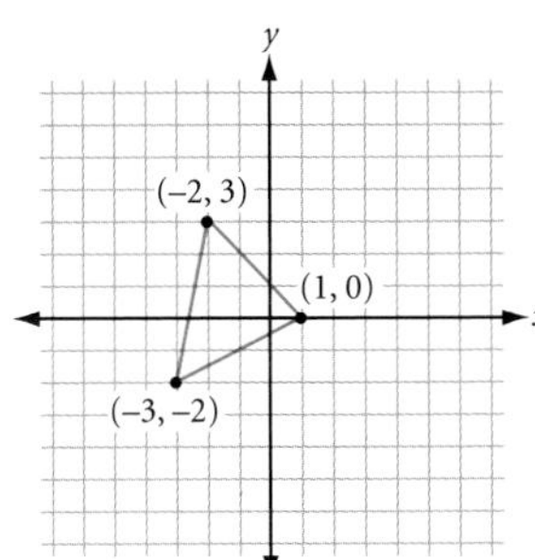

New: (6, −3), (2, −5), (3, 0). Triangles are congruent.

22. $(x, y) \rightarrow (x, -y)$

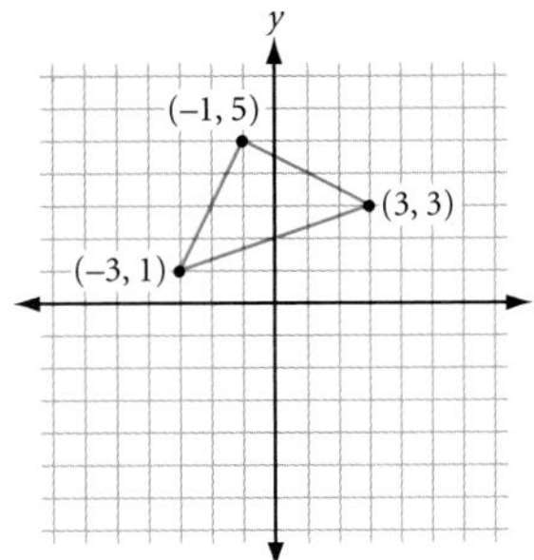

New: (3, −3), (−3, −1), (−1, −5). Triangles are congruent.

IMPROVING YOUR REASONING SKILLS

Hundreds Puzzle

Fill in the blanks of each equation below. All nine digits—1 through 9—must be used, in order! You may use any combination of signs for the four basic operations (+, −, ·, ÷), parentheses, decimal points, exponents, factorial signs, and square root symbols, and you may place the digits next to each other to create two-digit or three-digit numbers.

Example: $1 + 2(3 + 4.5) + 67 + 8 + 9 = 100$

1. $1 + 2 + 3 - 4 + 5 + 6 + \underline{?} + 9 = 100$

2. $1 + 2 + 3 + 4 + 5 + \underline{?} = 100$

3. $1 + 2 + [(3)(4)(5) \div 6] + \underline{?} = 100$

4. $[(-1 - \underline{?}) \div 5] + 6 + 7 + 89 = 100$

5. $1 + 23 - 4 + \underline{?} + 9 = 100$

Exercises 21, 22 [Ask] "If the triangles are indeed congruent after being repositioned, describe how each second triangle was created from the given triangle using the word *reflection, slide,* or *rotation.*" [21, slide right 5, down 3; 22, reflection across x-axis]

EXTENSIONS

A. Pose this problem: Someone claims that it is possible to divide any triangle into two isosceles triangles and a kite. Have students try this with geometry software or other tools. **[Ask]** "Do you agree?" If not, ask students to give a counterexample. If so, have them describe their method and explain their results.

B. Use Take Another Look activity 2 or 3 on page 253.

IMPROVING REASONING SKILLS

If students are having difficulty with any of these equations, ask which digits are used in the blank and what number the digits must equal when combined.

1. $1 + 2 + 3 - 4 + 5 + 6 + \mathbf{78} + 9$

2. $1 + 2 + 3 + 4 + 5 + \mathbf{6 + 7 + 8(9)}$

3. $1 + 2 + [(3)(4)(5) \div 6] + \mathbf{78 + 9}$

4. $[(-1 - \mathbf{2 - 3 - 4}) \div 5] + 6 + 7 + 89$

5. $1 + 23 - 4 + \mathbf{56 + 7 + 8} + 9$

Many other identities using all nine digits in order are possible, including $12 + 34 + (5)(6) + 7 + 8 + 9 = 100$, $123 - 4 - 5 - 6 - 7 + 8 - 9 = 100$, and $-1 + 2 + 3 + 4(5)(6) - 7 - 8 - 9 = 100$. You might suggest that students continue to search for other unique equations to add to a class list.

USING YOUR ALGEBRA SKILLS 4

PLANNING

LESSON OUTLINE

One day:

15 min Examples

30 min Exercises

MATERIALS

- Sketchpad demonstration Equations of Lines, *optional*

TEACHING

Students review equations of lines and applications to perpendicular lines and medians of triangles in coordinate geometry.

[Language] The term *y-intercept* is used for the *y*-coordinate of the point where the graph crosses the *y*-axis. Sometimes the term may also be used to refer to the point, $(0, y)$, where the line crosses the *y*-axis.

Assessing Progress
You can assess students' understanding of slope and *y*-intercept as students work through the exercises.

Writing Linear Equations

A linear equation is an equation whose graph is a straight line. Linear equations are useful in science, business, and many other areas. For example, the linear equation $f = 32 + \frac{9}{5}c$ gives the rule for converting a temperature from degrees Celsius, c, to degrees Fahrenheit, f. The numbers 32 and $\frac{9}{5}$ determine the graph of the equation.

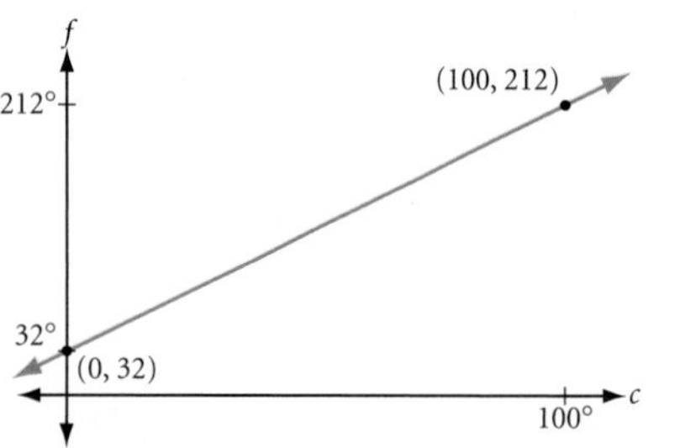

Understanding how the numbers in a linear equation determine the graph can help you write a linear equation based on information about a graph.

The *y*-coordinate at which a graph crosses the *y*-axis is called the *y*-intercept. The measure of steepness is called the slope. Below are the graphs of four equations. The table gives the equation, slope, and *y*-intercept for each graph. How do the numbers in each equation relate to the slope and *y*-intercept?

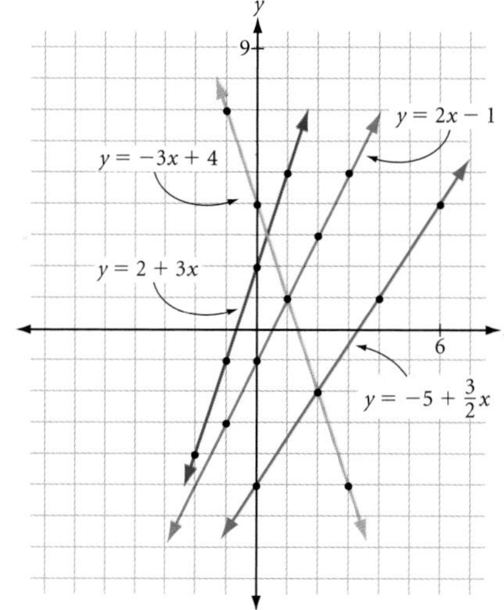

Equation	Slope	*y*-intercept
$y = 2 + 3x$	3	2
$y = 2x - 1$	2	-1
$y = -3x + 4$	-3	4
$y = -5 + \frac{3}{2}x$	$\frac{3}{2}$	-5

In each case, the slope of the line is the coefficient of x in the equation. The *y*-intercept is the constant that is added to, or subtracted from, the x term.

In your algebra class, you may have learned about one of these forms of a linear equation in slope-intercept form:

$y = a + bx$, where a is the *y*-intercept and b is the slope

$y = mx + b$, where m is the slope and b is the *y*-intercept

LESSON OBJECTIVES

- Review the relationship between the constant term in a linear equation of the form $y = a + bx$ (or $y = mx + b$) and the *y*-intercept of the equation's graph
- Review the relationship between the coefficient of x and the slope of the graph of a linear equation in intercept (or slope-intercept) form
- Write a linear equation from the graph of a line

NCTM STANDARDS

	CONTENT		PROCESS
	Number	✓	Problem Solving
✓	Algebra		Reasoning
✓	Geometry		Communication
	Measurement	✓	Connections
	Data/Probability	✓	Representation

The only difference between these two forms is the order of the x term and the constant term. For example, the equation of a line with slope -3 and y-intercept 1 can be written as $y = 1 - 3x$ or $y = -3x + 1$.

Let's look at a few examples that show how you can apply what you have learned about the relationship between a linear equation and its graph.

EXAMPLE A Find the equation of $\overleftrightarrow{AB}$ from its graph.

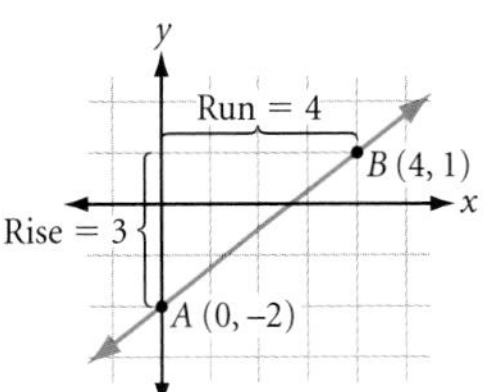

▶ Solution $\overleftrightarrow{AB}$ has y-intercept -2 and slope $\frac{3}{4}$, so the equation is

$$y = -2 + \frac{3}{4}x$$

EXAMPLE B Given points $C(4, 6)$ and $D(-2, 3)$, find the equation of $\overleftrightarrow{CD}$.

▶ Solution The slope of $\overleftrightarrow{CD}$ is $\frac{3-6}{-2-4}$, or $\frac{1}{2}$. The slope between any point (x, y) and one of the given points, say $(4, 6)$, must also be $\frac{1}{2}$.

$$\frac{y-6}{x-4} = \frac{1}{2}$$

$$y = \frac{1}{2}x + 4$$

EXAMPLE C Find the equation of the perpendicular bisector of the segment with endpoints $(2, 9)$ and $(-6, -7)$.

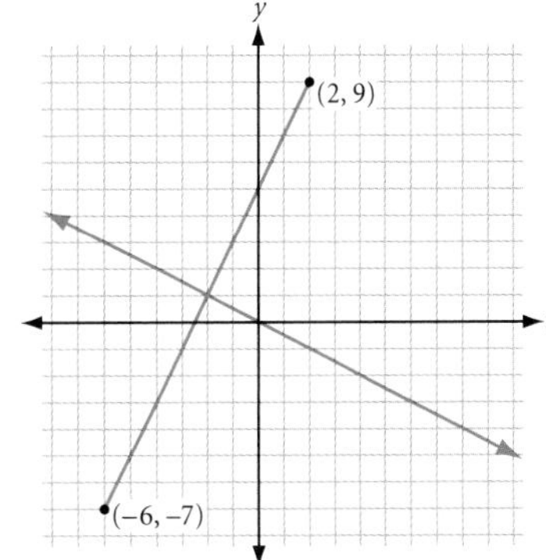

▶ Solution The perpendicular bisector passes through the midpoint. The midpoint of the segment is $\left(\frac{2+(-6)}{2}, \frac{9+(-7)}{2}\right)$, or $(-2, 1)$. The slope of the segment is $\frac{-7-9}{-6-2}$, or 2. So the slope of its perpendicular is $-\frac{1}{2}$. Write the equation of its perpendicular bisector and solve for y:

$$\frac{y-1}{x-(-2)} = -\frac{1}{2}$$

$$y = -\frac{1}{2}x$$

▶ EXAMPLE A

You might direct students to look first for the y-intercept and then for the slope of the line. **[Alert]** Many students reverse the definition of slope to be the change in x over the change in y. Remind them that larger positive slopes describe lines that are steeper, that is, lines that have more change vertically for the same horizontal change.

▶ EXAMPLE B

Another approach is to calculate the slope to be $\frac{1}{2}$, then pick one of the points, say $C(4, 6)$, and write $y = 6 + \frac{1}{2}(x - 4)$. Students will see that slope is rise over run and can be calculated as the change in y over the change in x: $\frac{y_2 - y_1}{x_2 - x_1}$. **[Alert]** Students may forget that the same point must be used first in the numerator and the denominator; the expression $\frac{y_1 - y_2}{x_1 - x_2}$ also gives the slope.

▶ EXAMPLE C

Make sure students know the relationship between the slope of a line and the slope of a perpendicular to the line: One slope is the negative (opposite) reciprocal of the other. **[Language]** To find a *reciprocal,* write the number as a fraction and interchange the numerator and the denominator. **[Language]** The *negative of* a number is the number with the opposite sign, often called the *opposite of* the number; the negative of a negative number is a positive number. **[Ask]** "What is the negative reciprocal of -5?" $\left[\frac{1}{5}\right]$

The graph shows that the perpendicular bisector passes through the origin. An alternative is to use the point-slope form, $y = y_1 + m(x - x_1)$, and substitute the point $(-2, 1)$:

$$y = 1 + \frac{1}{2}(m - 2)$$

$$y = 1 + \frac{1}{2}m - 1$$

$$y = \frac{1}{2}m$$

Closing the Lesson

Review the major points: Knowing how to find the equation of a line through two given points allows you to find an equation for each median of a triangle, given the coordinates of its vertices. You can use the point-slope form to find the equation of a perpendicular to a given line through a given point.

BUILDING UNDERSTANDING

The exercises have students move back and forth between graphs and equations of lines. Even if the focus of an exercise is on the equation, encourage students to draw a graph to help them detect any calculation errors they might have made.

ASSIGNING HOMEWORK

Essential	1–10
Performance assessment	11
Portfolio	7, 9
Group	12–14

▶ Helping with the Exercises

Exercises 12–14 Students may need to be reminded of the definitions of *median, perpendicular bisector,* and *altitude.* The coordinates of point O must be found before finding the equation in Exercise 12, but in Exercise 14 the coordinates of point T don't need to be determined.

EXERCISES

In Exercises 1–3, graph each linear equation.

1. $y = 1 - 2x$ **2.** $y = \frac{4}{3}x + 4$ **3.** $2y - 3x = 12$

Write an equation for each line in Exercises 4 and 5.

4.

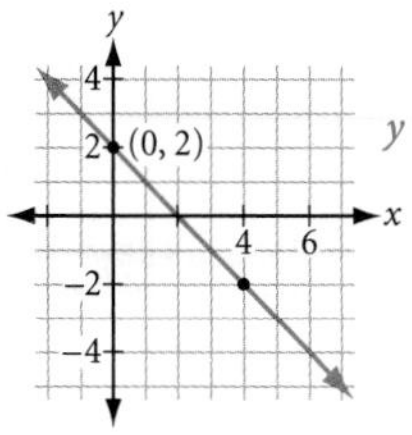

$y = -x + 2$

5.

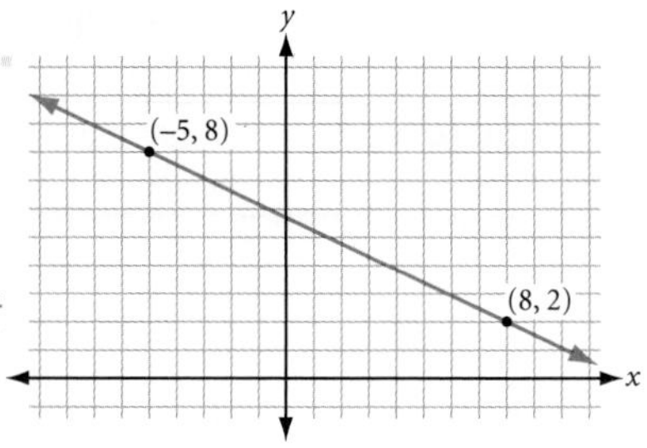

$y = -\frac{6}{13}x + \frac{74}{13}$

In Exercises 6–8, write an equation for the line through each pair of points.

6. (1, 2), (3, 4) $y = x + 1$ **7.** (1, 2), (3, −4) $y = -3x + 5$ **8.** (−1, −2), (−6, −4) $y = \frac{2}{5}x - \frac{8}{5}$

9. The math club is ordering printed T-shirts to sell for a fundraiser. The T-shirt company charges \$80 for the set-up fee and \$4 for each printed T-shirt. Using x for the number of shirts the club orders, write an equation for the total cost of the T-shirts. $y = 80 + 4x$

10. Write an equation for the line with slope −3 that passes through the midpoint of the segment with endpoints (3, 4) and (11, 6). $y = -3x + 26$

11. Write an equation for the line that is perpendicular to the line $y = 4x + 5$ and that passes through the point (0, −3). $y = -\frac{1}{4}x - 3$

For Exercises 12–14, the coordinates of the vertices of $\triangle WHY$ are $W(0, 0)$, $H(8, 3)$, and $Y(2, 9)$.

12. Find the equation of the line containing median $\overline{WO}$. $y = \frac{6}{5}x$

13. Find the equation of the perpendicular bisector of side $\overline{HY}$. $y = x + 1$

14. Find the equation of the line containing altitude $\overline{HT}$. $y = -\frac{2}{9}x + \frac{43}{9}$

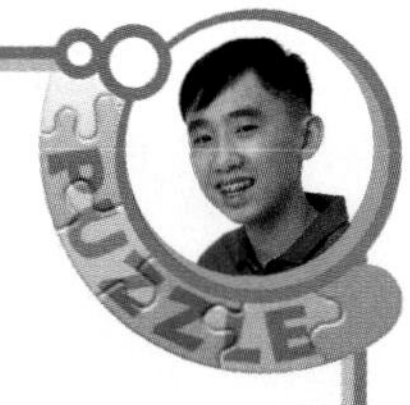

IMPROVING YOUR REASONING SKILLS

Container Problem I

You have an unmarked 9-liter container, an unmarked 4-liter container, and an unlimited supply of water. In table, symbol, or paragraph form, describe how you might end up with exactly 3 liters in one of the containers.

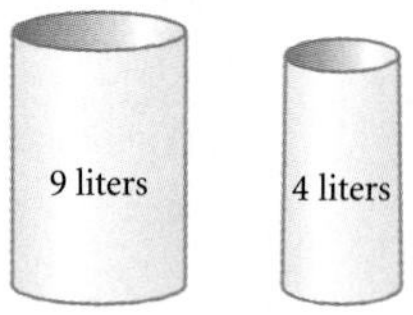

1.

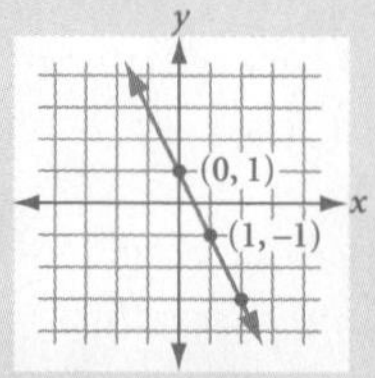

2.

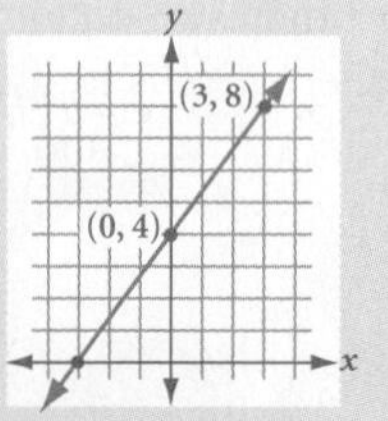

3.

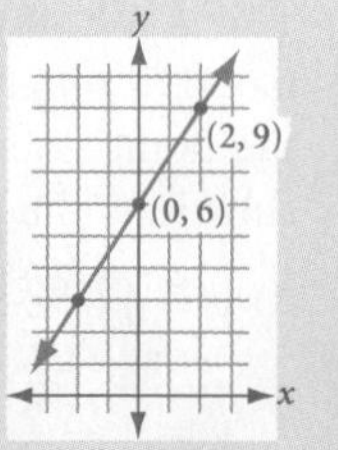

IMPROVING REASONING SKILLS

One of many possible solutions:
Fill the 4-liter container. Dump into the 9-liter container. Repeat. Then fill the 4-liter container and dump into the 9-liter container until the 9-liter container is full (1 liter). Three liters will be left in the 4-liter container.

LESSON

4.3

Triangle Inequalities

How long must each side of this drawbridge be so that the bridge spans the river when both sides come down?

Readers are plentiful, thinkers are rare.

HARRIET MARTINEAU

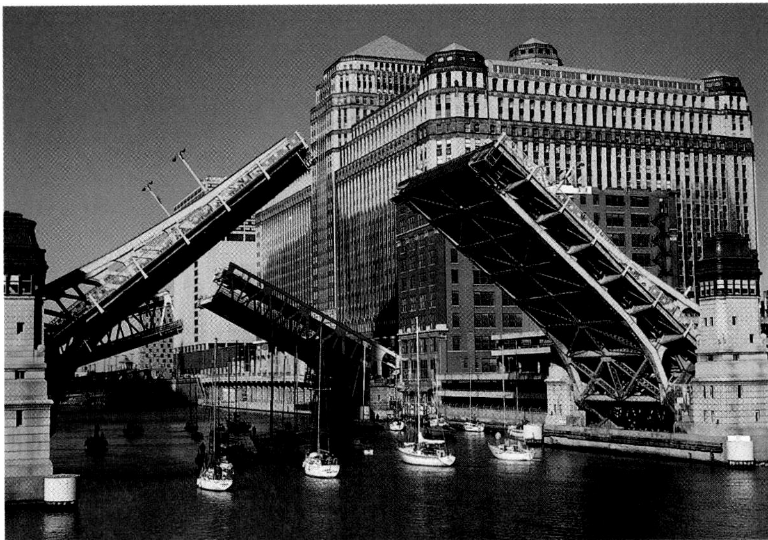

Drawbridges over the Chicago River in Chicago, Illinois

Triangles have similar requirements. In the triangles below, the blue segments are all congruent, and the red segments are all congruent. Yet, there are a variety of triangles. Notice how the length of the yellow segment changes. Notice also how the angle measures change.

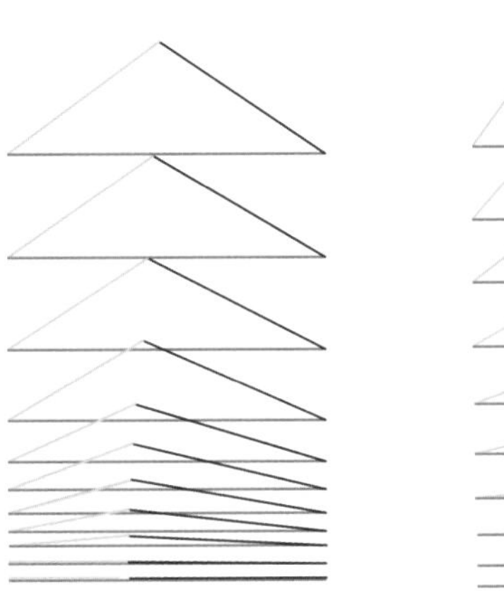

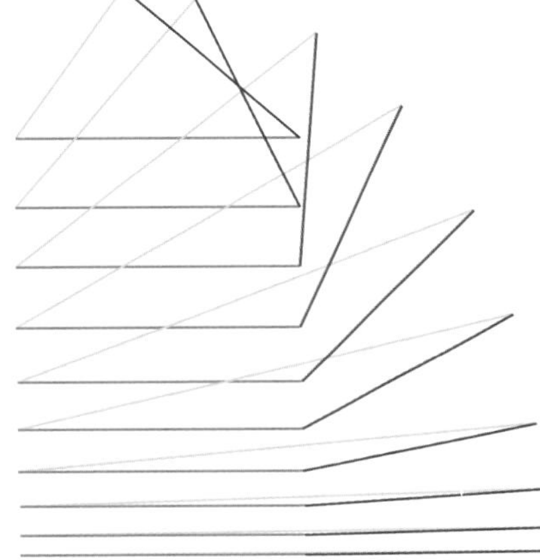

Can you form a triangle using sticks of any three lengths? How do the angle measures of a triangle relate to the lengths of its sides? In this lesson you will discover some geometric inequalities that answer these questions.

NCTM STANDARDS

CONTENT		PROCESS	
	Number		Problem Solving
✓	Algebra	✓	Reasoning
✓	Geometry	✓	Communication
✓	Measurement	✓	Connections
	Data/Probability		Representation

LESSON OBJECTIVES

- Investigate inequalities among sides and angles in triangles
- Discover the Exterior Angle Conjecture
- Practice construction skills
- Develop reasoning skills

LESSON

4.3

PLANNING

LESSON OUTLINE

One day:

25 min	Investigation
10 min	Sharing
5 min	Closing
5 min	Exercises

MATERIALS

- construction tools
- protractors
- scissors
- uncooked spaghetti, *optional*

TEACHING

This lesson concerns three properties of triangles: the triangle inequality, the side-angle inequality, and the exterior angle property.

One step To combine the three investigations, pose this problem: "Draw a horizontal line, which we'll call the base, and mark two points on it fairly close together. Make a triangle that has those two points as two of its vertices. Now, move one of the two selected points along the base, keeping both of the other sides of the triangle fixed in length. Stop the movement at various points and measure all angles and side lengths. Look for patterns and make conjectures." Students might use geometry software for their experimentation, or you might have some sticks or uncooked spaghetti available. While circulating, be sure some groups focus on exterior angles, some on relative side and angle measures, and some on what happens when the triangle disappears.

Guiding Investigation 1

Step 1 The construction can be done with either a compass or patty paper. You might want to have sticks or uncooked spaghetti available or encourage students to cut out paper strips to represent the line segments. **[Alert]** Students may have difficulty seeing what the constructions demonstrate about the lengths of the three sides. **[Ask]** "What would happen if the lengths of the two smaller sides added up to exactly the same length as the third side or added up to less than that of the third side?" Don't press students yet to understand in depth the connection to shortest paths; save that for Sharing.

Step 2 No. The two shorter sides are not long enough to form a triangle with the longest side.

Students can also use the dynamic geometry exploration at www.keymath.com/DG to help understand the triangle inequality conjecture.

Investigation 1
What Is the Shortest Path from *A* to *B*?

You will need

- a compass
- a straightedge

Each person in your group should do each construction. Compare results when you finish.

Step 1 Construct a triangle with each set of segments as sides.

Given:

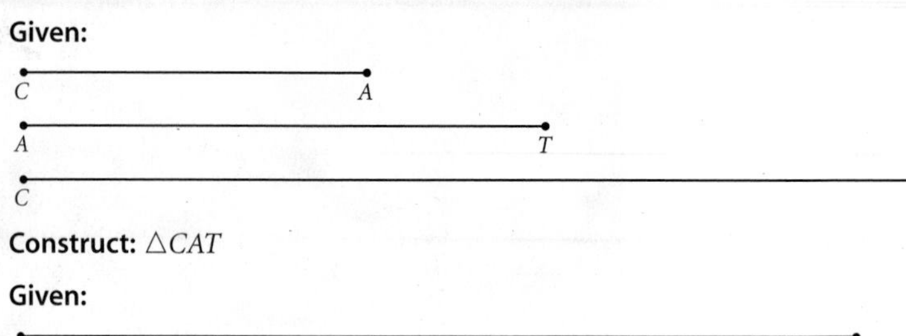

Construct: $\triangle CAT$

Given:

F S

S H

F H

Construct: $\triangle FSH$

Step 2 Were you able to construct $\triangle CAT$ and $\triangle FSH$? Why or why not? Discuss your results with others. State your observations as your next conjecture.

Triangle Inequality Conjecture C-21

The sum of the lengths of any two sides of a triangle is _?_ the length of the third side. greater than

The Triangle Inequality Conjecture relates the lengths of the three sides of a triangle. You can also think of it in another way: The shortest path between two points is along the segment connecting them. In other words, the path from *A* to *C* to *B* can't be shorter than the path from *A* to *B*.

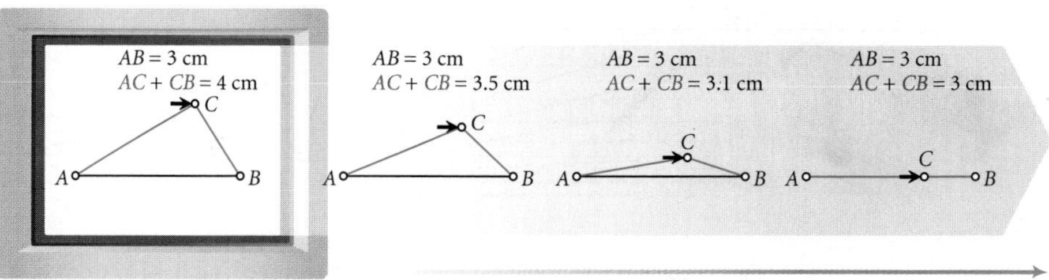

You can use geometry software to compare two different paths. See www.keymath.com/DG

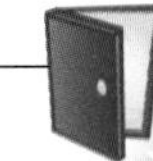

Investigation 2
Where Are the Largest and Smallest Angles?

You will need

- a ruler
- a protractor

Each person should draw a different scalene triangle for this investigation. Some group members should draw acute triangles, and some should draw obtuse triangles.

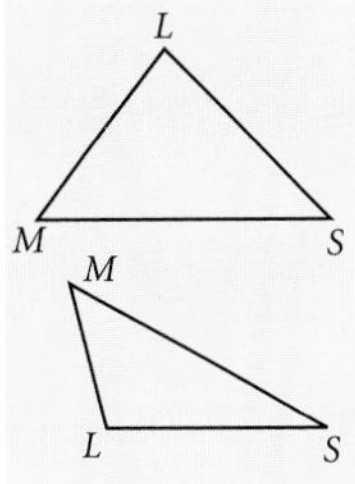

Step 1 Measure the angles in your triangle. Label the angle with greatest measure $\angle L$, the angle with second greatest measure $\angle M$, and the smallest angle $\angle S$.

Step 2 Measure the three sides. Label the longest side l, the second longest side m, and the shortest side s.

Step 3 Which side is opposite $\angle L$? $\angle M$? $\angle S$?

Step 3 The largest side will be opposite the largest angle, and so on.

Discuss your results with others. Write a conjecture that states where the largest and smallest angles are in a triangle, in relation to the longest and shortest sides.

Side-Angle Inequality Conjecture C-22

In a triangle, if one side is longer than another side, then the angle opposite the longer side is __?__. larger than the angle opposite the shorter side

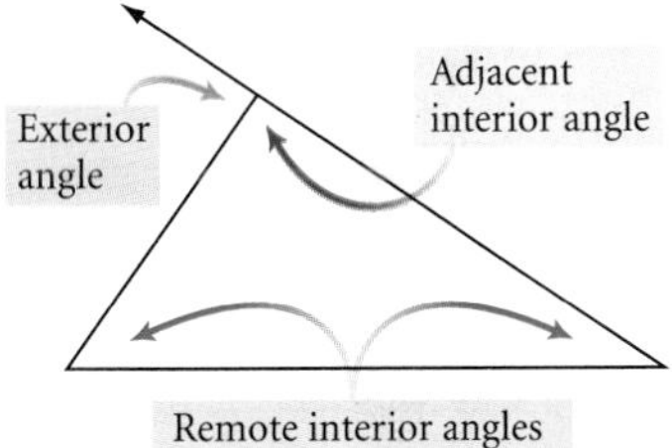

So far in this chapter, you have studied interior angles of triangles. Triangles also have exterior angles. If you extend one side of a triangle beyond its vertex, then you have constructed an **exterior angle** at that vertex.

Each exterior angle of a triangle has an **adjacent interior angle** and a pair of **remote interior angles.** The remote interior angles are the two angles in the triangle that do not share a vertex with the exterior angle.

Investigation 3
Exterior Angles of a Triangle

You will need

- a straightedge
- patty paper

Each person should draw a different scalene triangle for this investigation. Some group members should draw acute triangles, and some should draw obtuse triangles.

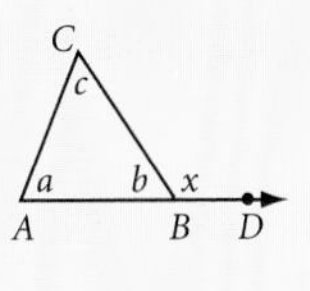

Step 1 On your paper, draw a scalene triangle, $\triangle ABC$. Extend $\overline{AB}$ beyond point B and label a point D outside the triangle on $\overrightarrow{AB}$. Label the angles as shown.

Guiding Investigation 2

The wording of this conjecture may show a lot of variation among the groups. Encourage variety and creativity. Groups may want to reword more than the end of the conjecture. For example: "In a triangle, the smallest angle is opposite the shortest side and the largest angle is opposite the longest side."

Guiding Investigation 3

This investigation may be done as a follow-along activity. **[Ask]** "How could you state a Triangle Exterior Angle Inequality Conjecture?" [The measure of the exterior angle of a triangle must be greater than the measure of either remote interior angle.]

SHARING IDEAS

Have students present a variety of statements of conjectures. Lead the class in critiquing them and in reaching consensus about which conjecture to use.

When you've reached consensus on the first conjecture, ask how to explain why the sum of the lengths of two sides of a triangle must be greater than the length of the third. Students will probably keep restating the fact that you just can't make a triangle without that property. Ask about the relevance of the fact that the shortest path between two points is the line segment connecting them. Help students see that the shortest-path condition implies the Triangle Inequality Conjecture. **[Ask]** "Does the Triangle Inequality Conjecture imply the shortest-path condition?" [It doesn't, because it makes no claim that other curves connecting the two points are longer than the line segment.]

Sharing Ideas (continued)

[Ask] "Can anything be said about the difference in length of two sides of a triangle? [The difference must be less than the length of the third side.] "Why must the difference be less than the length of the third side?" [Encourage students to use algebra to write the claims and see how one follows from the other: If $a + b > c$, then $c - b < a$.] **[Alert]** If students are confused by the symbols $>$ (greater than) and $<$ (less than), review their meaning.

You might also use letters and inequality symbols in stating the second conjecture: If $a > b$ then $m\angle A > m\angle B$. The same investigation could also lead to the converse: If $m\angle A > m\angle B$ then $a > b$.

When phrasing the third conjecture, introduce the terms *adjacent, remote, interior,* and *exterior.* **[ESL]** *Adjacent* means "next to"; *remote* means "far away"; *interior* means "on the inside"; *exterior* means "on the outside."

Assessing Progress
You can assess students' skill in constructing triangles, copying segments and angles, and measuring angles. Check their understanding of various kinds of triangles.

Closing the Lesson

Restate the three conjectures of this lesson: the Triangle Inequality Conjecture, the Side-Angle Inequality Conjecture, and the Triangle Exterior Angle Conjecture. If you plan to assign Exercise 11, also mention that the Triangle Inequality Conjecture implies that the difference in length of two sides of a triangle is less than the length of the third side; represent this inequality using letters and inequality symbols. If many students seem to be having difficulty, you may want to model sample problems, such as Exercise 5.

BUILDING UNDERSTANDING

The exercises apply the three conjectures of this lesson. Ask students which conjectures they are using to solve each exercise.

ASSIGNING HOMEWORK

Essential	2–18 evens
Performance assessment	15
Portfolio	14
Journal	17
Group	1–15 odds
Review	19–24

Helping with the Exercises

Exercises 1–4 If students are unsure, encourage them to make sketches.

Step 2 Copy the two remote interior angles, $\angle A$ and $\angle C$, onto patty paper to show their sum.

Step 3 How does the sum of a and c compare with x? Use your patty paper from Step 2 to compare.

Step 4 Discuss your results with your group. State your observations as a conjecture.

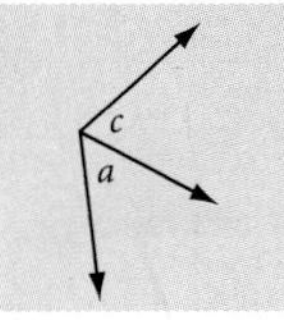

Triangle Exterior Angle Conjecture C-23

The measure of an exterior angle of a triangle _?_. is equal to the sum of the measures of the remote interior angles

You just discovered the Triangle Exterior Angle Conjecture by inductive reasoning. You can use the Triangle Sum Conjecture, some algebra, and deductive reasoning to show *why* the Triangle Exterior Angle Conjecture is true for all triangles.

You'll do the paragraph proof on your own in Exercise 17.

EXERCISES

In Exercises 1–4, determine whether it is possible to draw a triangle with sides of the given measures. If possible, write yes. If not possible, write no and make a sketch demonstrating why it is not possible.

1. 3 cm, 4 cm, 5 cm yes **2.** 4 m, 5 m, 9 m no **3.** 5 ft, 6 ft, 12 ft no **4.** 3.5 cm, 4.5 cm, 7 cm yes

In Exercises 5–10, use your new conjectures to arrange the unknown measures in order from greatest to least.

5. (h)

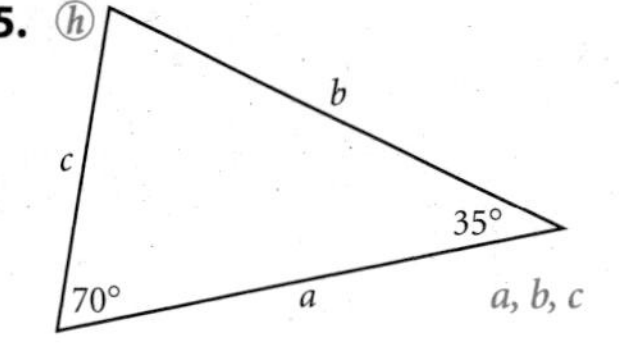

a, b, c

6. 55° b c 68° a

c, b, a

7.

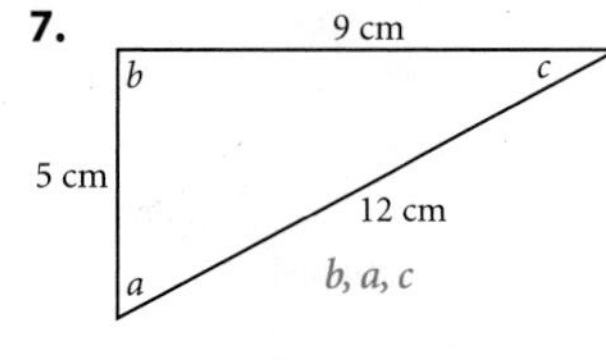

b, a, c

8.

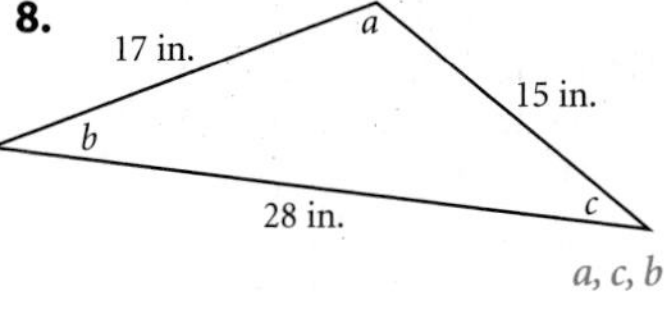

a, c, b

9. (h)

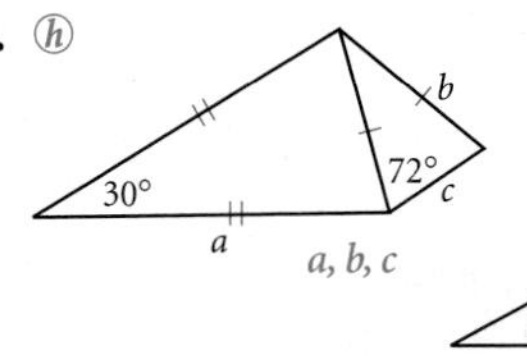

a, b, c

10.

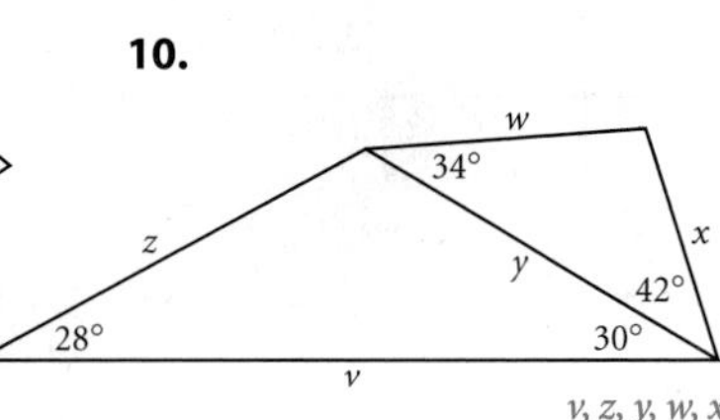

v, z, y, w, x

11. If 54 and 48 are the lengths of two sides of a triangle, what is the range of possible values for the length of the third side? (h) 6 < length < 102

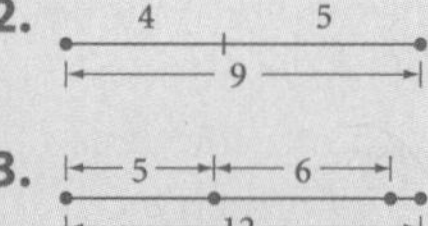

Exercise 11 As needed, remind students of the claims discussed in class: that the sum of the lengths of the two given sides is greater than the length of the third side, which is greater than the difference in the length of the two given sides.

12. What's wrong with this picture? Explain.

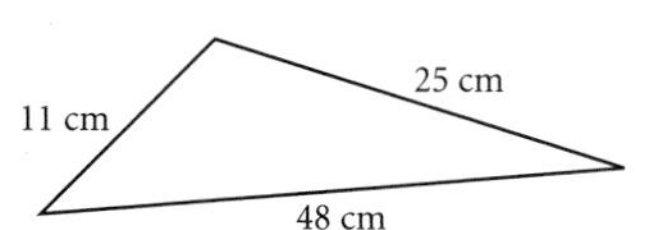

By the Triangle Inequality Conjecture, the sum of 11 cm and 25 cm should be greater than 48 cm.

13. What's wrong with this picture? Explain. ⓗ

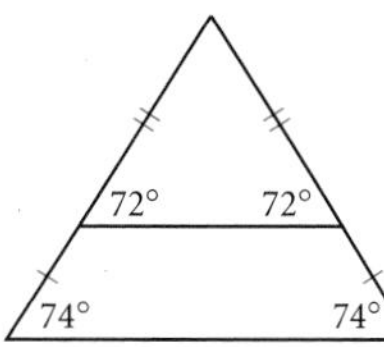

In Exercises 14–16, use one of your new conjectures to find the missing measures.

14. $t + p = \underline{?}$ ⓗ 135°

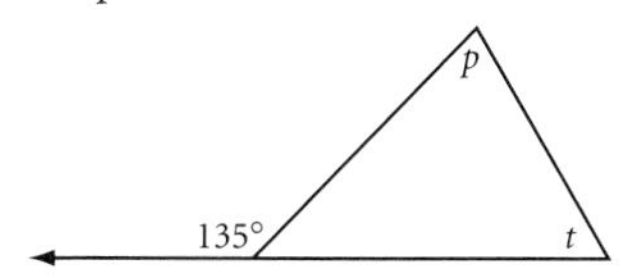

15. $r = \underline{?}$ 72°

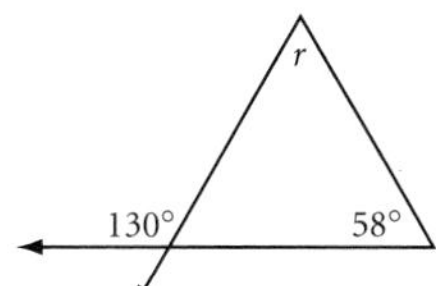

16. $x = \underline{?}$ 72°

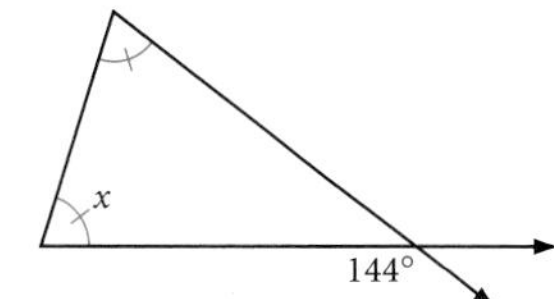

17. Use algebra and the Triangle Sum Conjecture to explain why the Triangle Exterior Angle Conjecture is true. Use the figure at right. ⓗ

18. Read the Recreation Connection below. If you want to know the perpendicular distance from a landmark to the path of your boat, what should be the measurement of your bow angle when you begin recording? 45°

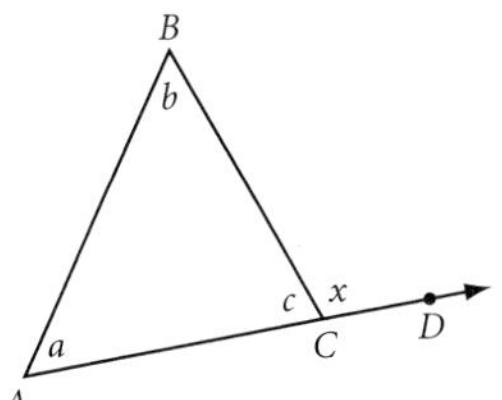

Recreation CONNECTION

Geometry is used quite often in sailing. For example, to find the distance between the boat and a landmark on shore, sailors use a rule called *doubling the angle on the bow.* The rule says, measure the angle on the bow (the angle formed by your path and your line of sight to the landmark) at point *A*. Check your bearing until, at point *B*, the bearing is double the reading at point *A*. The distance traveled from *A* to *B* is also the distance from the landmark to your new position.

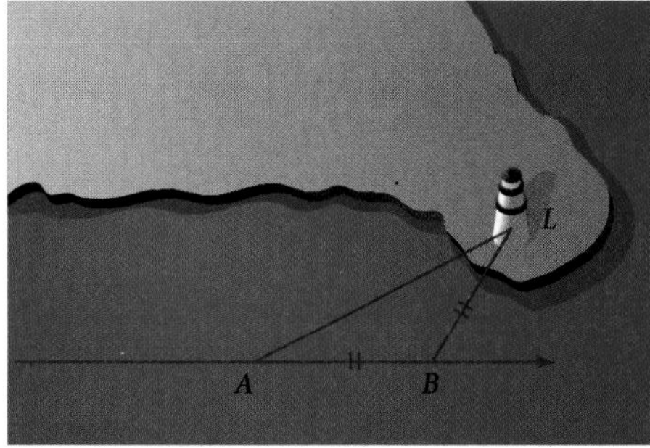

13. By the Triangle Sum Conjecture, the third angle must measure 36° in the small triangle, but it measures 32° in the large triangle. These are the same angle, so they can't have different measures.

17. $a + b + c = 180°$ and $x + c = 180°$. Subtract c from both sides of both equations to get $x = 180 - c$ and $a + b = 180 - c$. Substitute $a + b$ for $180 - c$ in the first equation to get $x = a + b$.

Exercises 24, 25 Check to be sure students go beyond visual estimation to calculate slopes and distances in identifying the special quadrilaterals.

EXTENSIONS

A. Ask students to use geometry software to explore congruence shortcuts. It's especially useful for the one-step investigation.

B. Use Take Another Look activity 4 on page 253.

Review

In Exercises 19 and 20, calculate each lettered angle measure.

19.

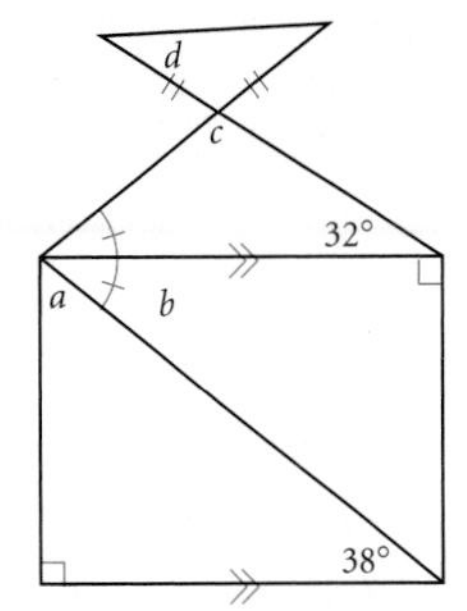

$a = 52°, b = 38°, c = 110°, d = 35°$

20.

$a = 90°$
$b = 68°$
$c = 112°$
$d = 112°$
$e = 68°$
$f = 56°$
$g = 124°$
$h = 124°$

In Exercises 21–23, complete the statement of congruence.

3.6 **21.** $\triangle BAR \cong \triangle$ _?_ ⓗ ABE

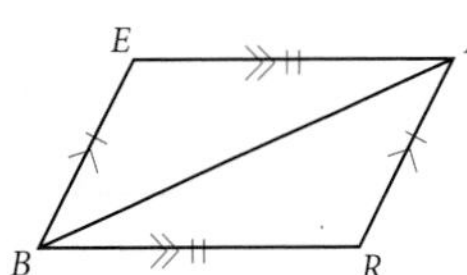

4.2 **22.** $\triangle FAR \cong \triangle$ _?_ FNK

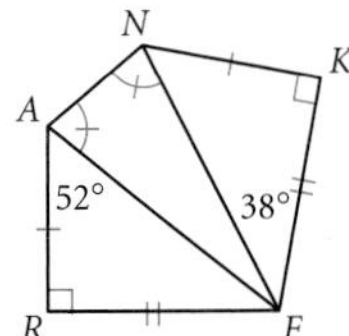

3.6 **23.** $\overline{HG} \cong \overline{HJ}$
$\triangle HEJ \cong \triangle$ _?_ cannot be determined

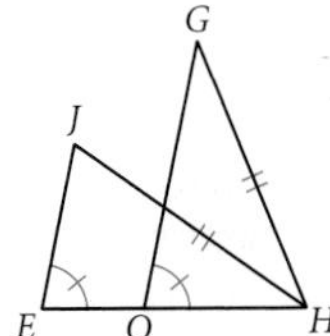

project

RANDOM TRIANGLES

Imagine you cut a 20 cm straw in two randomly selected places anywhere along its length. What is the probability that the three pieces will form a triangle? How do the locations of the cuts affect whether or not the pieces will form a triangle? Explore this situation by cutting a straw in different ways, or use geometry software to model different possibilities. Based on your informal exploration, predict the probability of the pieces forming a triangle.

Now generate a large number of randomly chosen lengths to simulate the cutting of the straw. Analyze the results and calculate the probability based on your data. How close was your prediction?

Your project should include

- Your prediction and an explanation of how you arrived at it.
- Your randomly generated data.
- An analysis of the results and your calculated probability.
- An explanation of how the location of the cuts affects the chances of a triangle being formed.

Fathom™

You can use Fathom to generate many sets of random numbers quickly. You can also set up tables to view your data, and enter formulas to calculate quantities based on your data.

Supporting the project

After students have worked on the project, discuss how collecting more and more data (or pooling data) gets you closer and closer to the theoretical probability. Go to www.keypress.com/DG for a Fathom demonstration. (To avoid wasting straws, ask students to randomly bend pipe cleaners.)

OUTCOMES

- Presentation of data is organized and clear.
- Explanations of predictions and descriptions of the results are consistent.
- If lengths are generated using a graphing calculator, Fathom, or another random-length generator, the experimental probability for large samples will be around 25%.
- A graph of the sample space uses shading to show cut combinations that do produce a triangle.

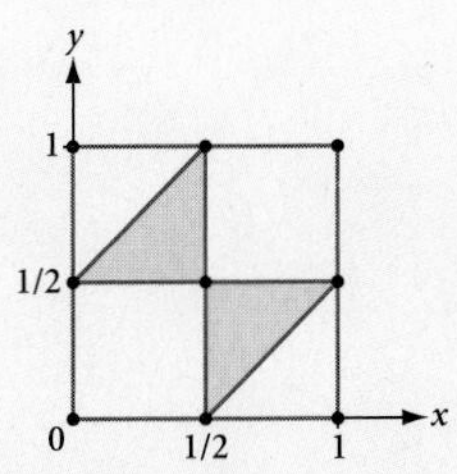

LESSON

4.4

Are There Congruence Shortcuts?

The person who knows how will always have a job; the person who knows why will always be that person's boss.
ANONYMOUS

A building contractor has just assembled two massive triangular trusses to support the roof of a recreation hall. Before the crane hoists them into place, the contractor needs to verify that the two triangular trusses are identical. Must the contractor measure and compare all six parts of both triangles?

You learned from the Third Angle Conjecture that if there is a pair of angles congruent in each of two triangles, then the third angles must be congruent. But will this guarantee that the trusses are the same size? You probably need to also know something about the sides in order to be sure that two triangles are congruent. Recall from earlier exercises that *fewer* than three parts of one triangle can be congruent to corresponding parts of another triangle, without the triangles being congruent.

So let's begin looking for congruence shortcuts by comparing three parts of each triangle.

There are six different ways that the same three parts of two triangles may be congruent. They are diagrammed below. An angle that is included between two sides of a triangle is called an **included angle.** A side that is included between two angles of a triangle is called an **included side.**

Side-Side-Side (SSS)

Three pairs of congruent sides

Side-Angle-Side (SAS)

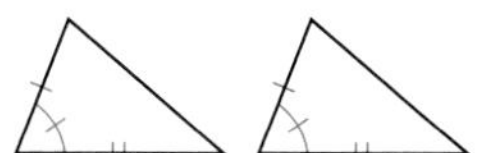

Two pairs of congruent sides and one pair of congruent angles (angles between the pairs of sides)

Angle-Side-Angle (ASA)

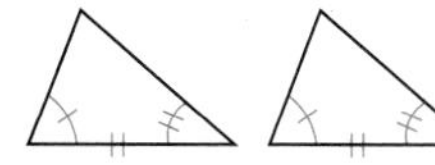

Two pairs of congruent angles and one pair of congruent sides (sides between the pairs of angles)

Side-Angle-Angle (SAA)

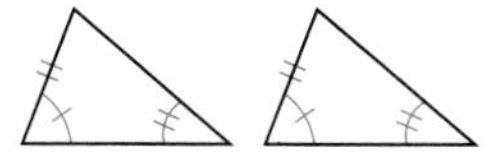

Two pairs of congruent angles and one pair of congruent sides (sides not between the pairs of angles)

Side-Side-Angle (SSA)

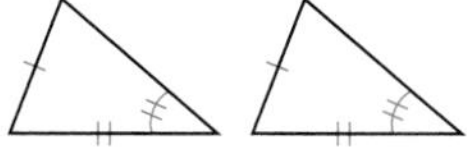

Two pairs of congruent sides and one pair of congruent angles (angles not between the pairs of sides)

Angle-Angle-Angle (AAA)

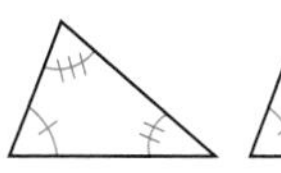

Three pairs of congruent angles

NCTM STANDARDS

CONTENT		PROCESS	
	Number		Problem Solving
	Algebra	✓	Reasoning
✓	Geometry	✓	Communication
✓	Measurement	✓	Connections
	Data/Probability		Representation

LESSON OBJECTIVES

- Explore shortcut methods for determining whether triangles are congruent
- Discover that SSS and SAS are valid congruence shortcuts but SSA is not
- Practice construction skills

LESSON

4.4

PLANNING

LESSON OUTLINE

One day:

20 min Investigation

10 min Sharing

5 min Closing

10 min Exercises

MATERIALS

- construction tools
- Exercise 17 (T) for One step
- SSS, SAS, SSA (W), *optional*

TEACHING

Two polygons are congruent if their corresponding sides and angles are congruent. In this lesson and the next, students look for ways to prove that two triangles are congruent by "shortcutting" the process of proving that all six pairs of sides and angles are congruent.

One step Display the Exercise 17 transparency and pose this problem: "NASA scientists want to use their lunar exploration vehicle, LEV, to find the distance across the deep crater shown. One of them has a plan: Start the LEV at point *A* and trace out the figure shown, with segments marked *a* having the same length, and the same for segments marked *b*. The scientist believes that the segments marked *x* will also have the same length. Do you agree? Why or why not?" Students may initially want to talk about the instructions the scientists will give the LEV to have it travel the designated route. Encourage this algorithmic thinking, but avoid its taking too long by assuring students that the LEV can mark a point at one

One step (continued)
time and head directly toward (and through) it later, and that the vehicle can keep track of how far it has traveled along any segment. The question comes down to whether or not two triangles are always congruent if they have two sides and the included angle congruent, so encourage students to experiment with lots of triangles, including obtuse and right triangles, and to make conjectures. Call their conjectures *shortcuts* to showing that each pair of angles and sides is congruent. Push the first students who finish this task to think about the case in which the angle is not between the sides.

INTRODUCTION

[ESL] Students may confuse *shortcut* (a quick way to reach a goal) with *abbreviation* (a short version to represent a longer word or phrase). As needed, review the definitions of congruent segments, angles, and polygons, and review how to set up a correspondence between points, sides, and angles of congruent polygons.

Ask if all six pairs of congruences must be shown in order to prove that two triangles are congruent or if there might be some shortcuts. **[Ask]** "What is the least amount of information needed?" Have students demonstrate with their own counterexamples that knowing just one side or one angle is insufficient to guarantee congruence of triangles. Also have them show why two sides, two angles, or one side and one angle are insufficient. (See Exercises 17–21 in Lesson 4.1.)

You will consider three of these cases in this lesson and three others in the next lesson. Let's begin by investigating SSS and SAS.

Investigation 1
Is SSS a Congruence Shortcut?

You will need

- a compass
- a straightedge

First you will investigate the Side-Side-Side (SSS) case. If the three sides of one triangle are congruent to the three sides of another, must the two triangles be congruent?

Step 1 Construct a triangle from the three parts shown. Be sure you match up the endpoints labeled with the same letter.

A ——— C
B ——— C
A ——— B

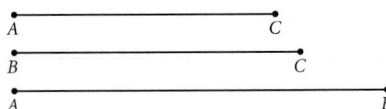

Step 2 Compare your triangle with the triangles made by others in your group. (One way to compare them is to place the triangles on top of each other and see if they coincide.) Is it possible to construct different triangles from the same three parts, or will all the triangles be congruent?

Step 3 You are now ready to complete the conjecture for the SSS case.

SSS Congruence Conjecture C-24

If the three sides of one triangle are congruent to the three sides of another triangle, then _?_. the triangles are congruent

Career CONNECTION

Congruence is very important in design and manufacturing. Modern assembly-line production relies on identical, or congruent, parts that are interchangeable. In the assembly of an automobile, for example, the same part needs to fit into each car coming down the assembly line.

[Ask] "Are three pieces of information sufficient?" "What are all the possible distinct ways you can have three pieces of information?" This lesson and the next lesson will be spent investigating, through constructions and counterexamples, which of these ways are valid shortcuts and which are not.

Investigation 2
Is SAS a Congruence Shortcut?

You will need

- a compass
- a straightedge

Next you will consider the Side-Angle-Side (SAS) case. If two sides and the included angle of one triangle are congruent to two sides and the included angle of another, must the triangles be congruent?

Step 1 Construct a triangle from the three parts shown. Be sure you match up the endpoints labeled with the same letter.

Step 2 Compare your triangle with the triangles made by others in your group. (One way to compare them is to place the triangles on top of each other and see if they coincide.) Is it possible to construct different triangles from the same three parts, or will all the triangles be congruent?

Step 3 You are now ready to complete the conjecture for the SAS case.

SAS Congruence Conjecture C-25

If two sides and the included angle of one triangle are congruent to two sides and the included angle of another triangle, then ?. the triangles are congruent

Next, let's look at the Side-Side-Angle (SSA) case.

EXAMPLE

If two sides and a non-included angle of one triangle are congruent to two corresponding sides and a non-included angle of another, must the triangles be congruent? In other words, can you construct only one triangle with the two sides and a non-included angle shown below?

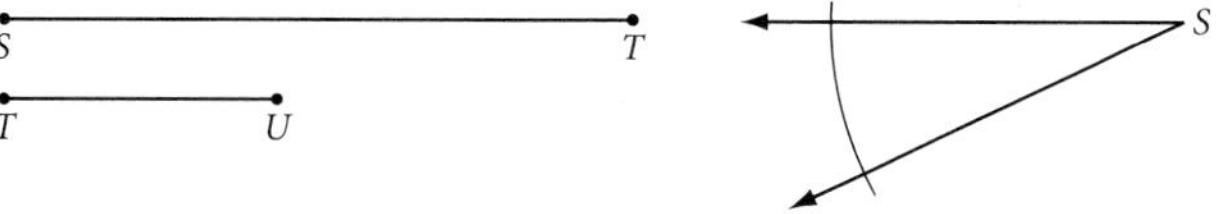

▶ ***Solution***

Once you construct $\overline{ST}$ on a side of $\angle S$, there are two possible locations for point U on the other side of the angle.

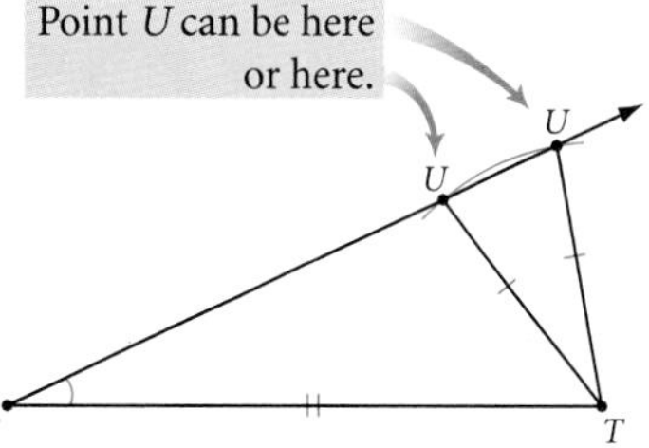

▶ ***EXAMPLE***

If groups explored SSA, be sure they have experienced why SSA is not sufficient to prove congruency. If they haven't yet investigated SSA, discuss the example.

You might do the example as a follow-along activity; actually having students construct these triangles might bring home the point that two sides and an angle not included often do not determine a triangle. For some combinations of two sides and an angle not included, a triangle is determined.

[Ask] "Under what conditions is SSA sufficient to prove congruency?" [The angle given is an obtuse angle, or the longer side is opposite the given angle.]

[Alert] Some students might not see the difference between SAS and SSA because both involve two sides and one angle. Point out that what matters is that the A in SSA is not between the two S's. Other students might not understand that you must find SAS in both triangles you are working with. You can't use SAS in one triangle and SSA in another triangle to show that the triangles are congruent.

Guiding the Investigations

You might divide the investigations (and perhaps the example) among the student groups so that each group performs only one of the investigations. Ask each group to explore many triangles, perhaps using the optional SSS, SAS, SSA worksheet; good inductive reasoning is based on many examples.

SHARING IDEAS

Have students present a variety of conjectures. Introduce the term *included* (angle or side) to help them improve the phrasing of their conjectures, and help the class reach consensus on the wording for their notebooks. Begin using the names SSS and SAS for these conjectures.

Students may believe that some triangles are not congruent when they are reflections of each other. This is good thinking that leads to a deeper understanding of congruence. Suggest that they pretend the triangles are made of wood, like the trusses described on page 219; turning them over would demonstrate their congruence more clearly. Also refer students back to the definition of *congruent polygons*: All corresponding pairs of sides and angles are congruent.

Remind students of what information they found to be necessary to construct a triangle in Lesson 3.6. They found (at least) that three sides determined a triangle and that three angles did not. Now ask if that result has anything to do with triangle congruence. Students may need time to think about this question, but they will probably conclude that, because three sides determine a triangle, all triangles with those sides are congruent to each other.

Assessing Progress
In this lesson you can assess students' understanding of congruent polygons (triangles in particular) and the fact that a compass transfers equal lengths. You can also assess their skill in using a straightedge and compass or patty paper.

Closing the Lesson

The main points of this lesson are that SSS and SAS can be used to establish the congruence of triangles but SSA cannot. Remind students of the reason why SSA fails. Ask students to list the other arrangements of three parts of a triangle (AAA, ASA, and SAA), and pose the problem of which of them might be a shortcut to congruence. This question is the topic of the next lesson.

BUILDING UNDERSTANDING

The exercises challenge students to think more deeply about the implications of the shortcuts investigated in this lesson.

ASSIGNING HOMEWORK

Essential	1–19 odds
Performance assessment	16
Portfolio	19
Journal	6, 17
Group	2–18 evens
Review	8, 20–24

MATERIALS

- Exercise 20 (T), *optional*

Helping with the Exercises

Exercise 3 $\triangle COT \cong \triangle NAP$ by SAS

6. SSS (and the Converse of the Isosceles Triangle Conjecture)

So two different triangles are possible in the SSA case, and the triangles are not necessarily congruent.

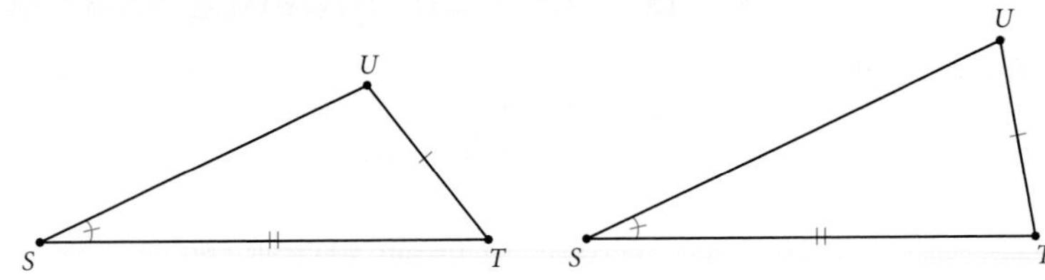

There is a counterexample for the SSA case, so it is *not* a congruence shortcut.

EXERCISES

You will need

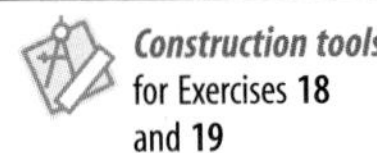

For Exercises 1–6, decide whether the triangles are congruent, and name the congruence shortcut you used. If the triangles cannot be shown to be congruent as labeled, write "cannot be determined."

1. Which conjecture tells you $\triangle LUZ \cong \triangle IDA$? ⓗ SAS

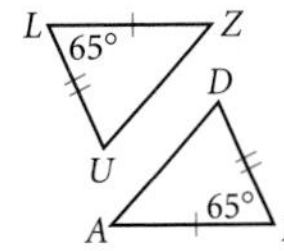

2. Which conjecture tells you $\triangle AFD \cong \triangle EFD$? ⓗ SSS

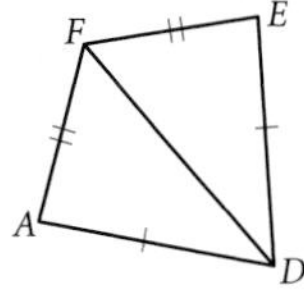

3. Which conjecture tells you $\triangle COT \cong \triangle NPA$?
cannot be determined

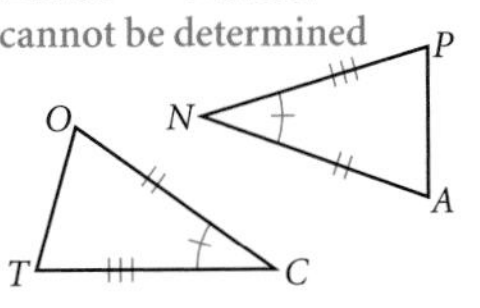

4. Which conjecture tells you $\triangle CAV \cong \triangle CEV$? SSS

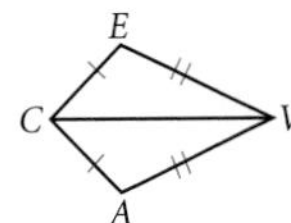

5. Which conjecture tells you $\triangle KAP \cong \triangle AKQ$? SAS

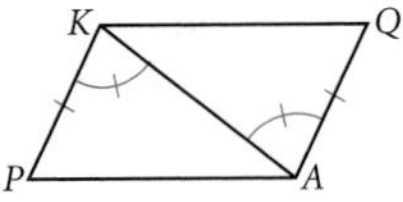

6. Y is a midpoint. Which conjecture tells you $\triangle AYB \cong \triangle RYN$?

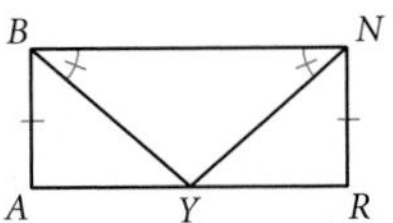

7. Explain why the boards that are nailed diagonally in the corners of this wooden gate make the gate stronger and prevent it from changing its shape under stress.
Possible answer: Boards nailed diagonally in the corners of the gate form triangles in those corners. Triangles are rigid, so the triangles in the gate's corners will increase the stability of those corners and keep them from changing shape.

8. What's wrong with this picture?

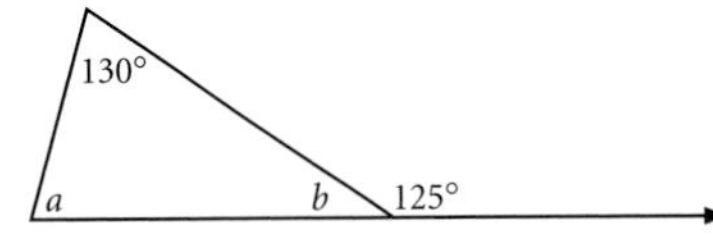

Exercise 7 An easier explanation might be one given in terms of Lesson 3.6, in which three sides *determine* a triangle. In terms of congruence, if the gate were to change shape, then there would be two noncongruent triangles with three congruent sides, a contradiction to SSS.

8. $b = 55°$, but $55° + 130° > 180°$, which is impossible by the Triangle Sum Conjecture.

In Exercises 9–14, name a triangle congruent to the given triangle and state the congruence conjecture. If you cannot show any triangles to be congruent from the information given, write "cannot be determined" and explain why.

9. $\triangle ANT \cong \triangle$ _?_ ⓗ *FLE* by SSS

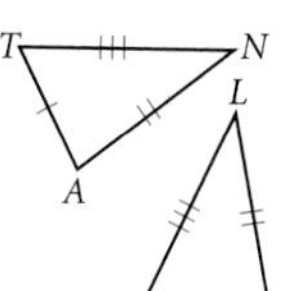

10. $\triangle RED \cong \triangle$ _?_

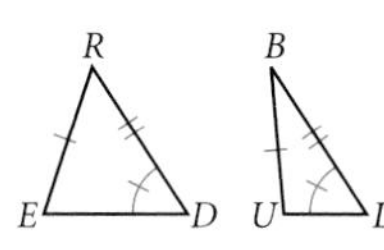

11. $\triangle WOM \cong \triangle$ _?_

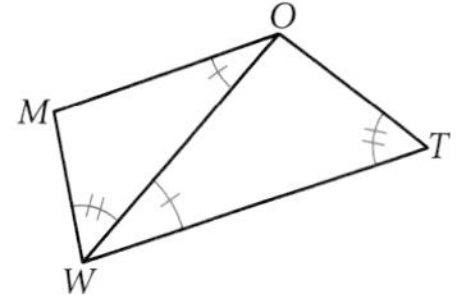

12. $\triangle MAN \cong \triangle$ _?_ ⓗ

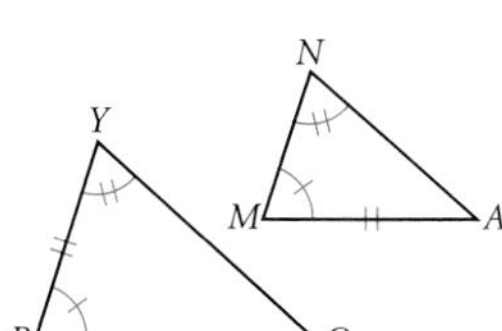

13. $\triangle SAT \cong \triangle$ _?_ *SAO* by SAS

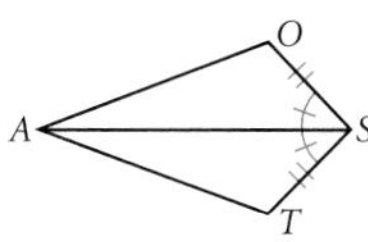

14. $\triangle GIT \cong \triangle$ _?_ *AIN* by SSS or SAS

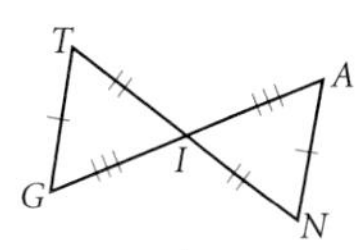

In Exercises 15 and 16, determine whether the segments or triangles in the coordinate plane are congruent and explain your reasoning.

15. $\triangle SUN \cong \triangle$ _?_ ⓗ *RAY* by SAS

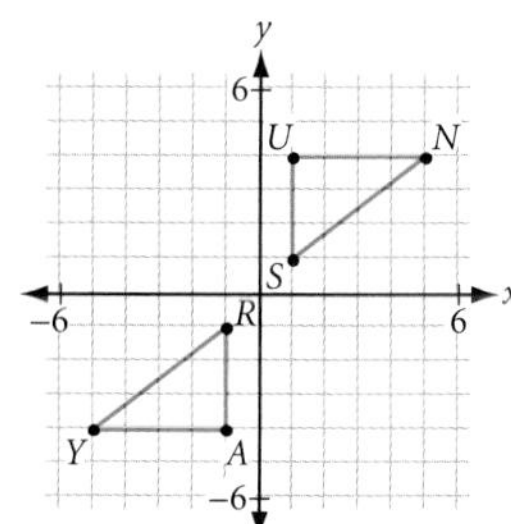

16. $\triangle DRO \cong \triangle$ _?_ The midpoint of $\overline{SD}$ and $\overline{PR}$ is (0, 0). Therefore, $\triangle DRO \cong \triangle SPO$ by SAS.

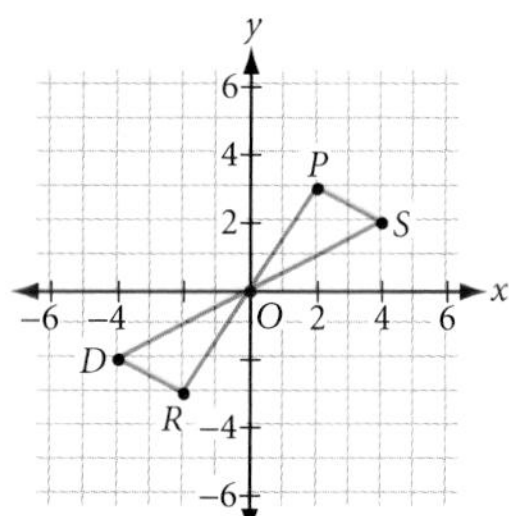

17. NASA scientists using a lunar exploration vehicle (LEV) wish to determine the distance across the deep crater shown at right. They have mapped out a path for the LEV as shown. How can the scientists use this set of measurements to calculate the approximate diameter of the crater?

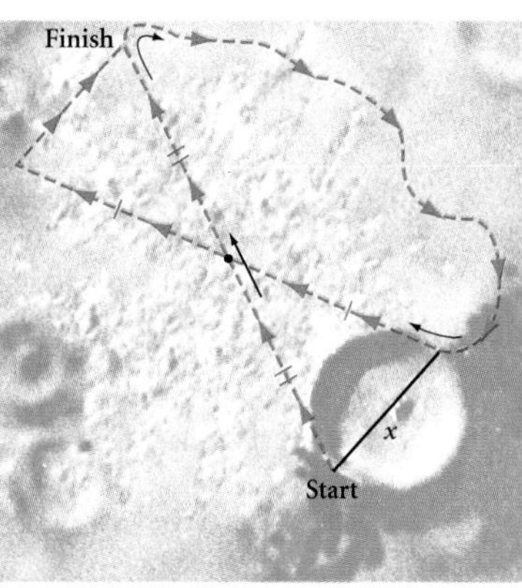

In Exercises 18 and 19, use a compass and straightedge, or patty paper, to perform these constructions.

18. ***Construction*** Draw a triangle. Use the SSS Congruence Conjecture to construct a second triangle congruent to the first.

19. ***Construction*** Draw a triangle. Use the SAS Congruence Conjecture to construct a second triangle congruent to the first.

Exercises 9–14 The main challenge of these exercises is not to determine which triangles are congruent, but to name the congruent triangles by listing their vertices in corresponding order.

10. Cannot be determined. SSA is not a congruence conjecture.

11. Cannot be determined. Parts do not correspond.

12. Cannot be determined. Parts do not correspond.

Exercise 17 This is the one-step investigation.

17. Since the LEV is marking out two triangles that are congruent by SAS, measuring the distance x will also approximate the diameter of the crater.

18.

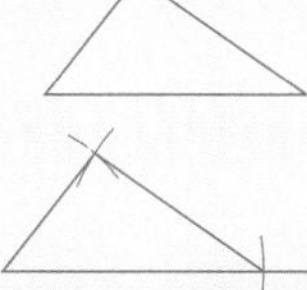

19.

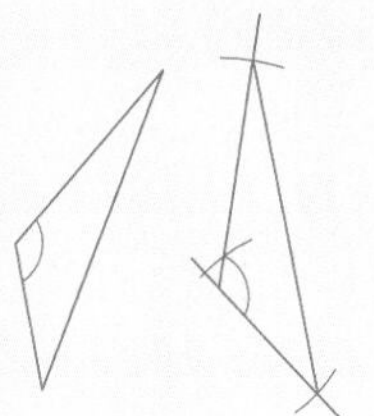

Exercise 23 This exercise reviews systems of linear equations.

EXTENSION

Pose this problem (Take Another Look activity 9): Is there a conjecture similar to the SSS Congruence Conjecture that you can make about congruence of quadrilaterals? For example, is SSSS a shortcut? Could a diagonal be used along with sides to determine a quadrilateral? [Neither SSSS nor SSSD guarantee congruence, but SSSDD does. Looking at the triangles formed can demonstrate that SSSDD does determine a quadrilateral.

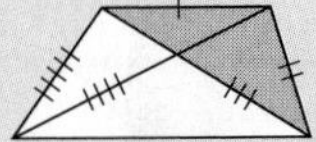

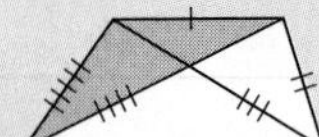

Encourage students to draw diagonals and consider triangle congruence. Four sides and an angle will guarantee congruence of quadrilaterals, and there are other possibilities.]

Review

20. Copy the figure. Calculate the measure of each lettered angle.

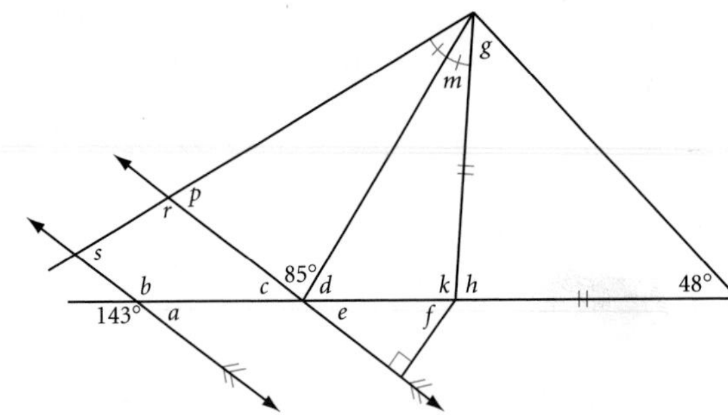

$a = 37°, b = 143°, c = 37°, d = 58°,$
$e = 37°, f = 53°, g = 48°, h = 84°, k = 96°,$
$m = 26°, p = 69°, r = 111°, s = 69°$

4.3 **21.** If two sides of a triangle measure 8 cm and 11 cm, what is the range of values for the length of the third side? 3 cm < third side < 19 cm

2.3 **22.** How many "elbow," "T," and "cross" pieces do you need to build a 20-by-20 grid? Start with the smaller grids shown below. Copy and complete the table.

Elbow: ┐
T: ┬
Cross: +

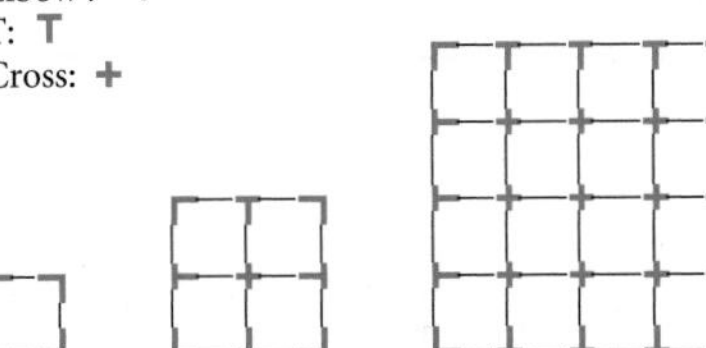

Side length	1	2	3	4	5	...	n	...	20
Elbows	4	4	4	4	4		4		4
T's	0	4	8	12	16		$4n - 4$		76
Crosses	0	1	4	9	16		$(n-1)^2$		361

UYAS 4 **23.** Find the point of intersection of the lines $y = \frac{2}{3}x - 1$ and $3x - 4y = 8$. (12, 7)

3.7 **24.** Isosceles right triangle ABC has vertices with coordinates $A(-8, 2)$, $B(-5, -3)$, and $C(0, 0)$. Find the coordinates of the orthocenter. $(-5, -3)$

IMPROVING YOUR REASONING SKILLS

Container Problem II

You have a small cylindrical measuring glass with a maximum capacity of 250 mL. All the marks have worn off except the 150 mL and 50 mL marks. You also have a large unmarked container. It is possible to fill the large container with exactly 350 mL. How? What is the fewest number of steps required to obtain 350 mL?

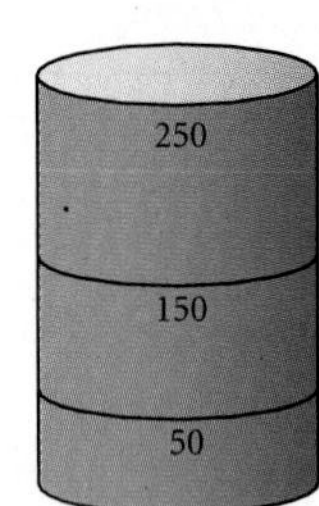

IMPROVING REASONING SKILLS

Fill the cylinder twice to the 150 mL mark and once to the 50 mL mark. Or fill the small container twice to the 250 mL mark, pouring the contents into the large container each time. Pour 150 mL from the large container back into the small container. It is not possible in fewer than three steps.

LESSON

4.5 Are There Other Congruence Shortcuts?

There is no more a math mind, than there is a history or an English mind.

GLORIA STEINEM

In the last lesson, you discovered that there are six ways that three parts of two triangles can be the same. You found that SSS and SAS both lead to the congruence of the two triangles, but that SSA does not. Is the Angle-Angle-Angle (AAA) case a congruence shortcut?

You may recall exercises that explored the AAA case. For example, these triangles have three congruent angles, but they do not have congruent sides.

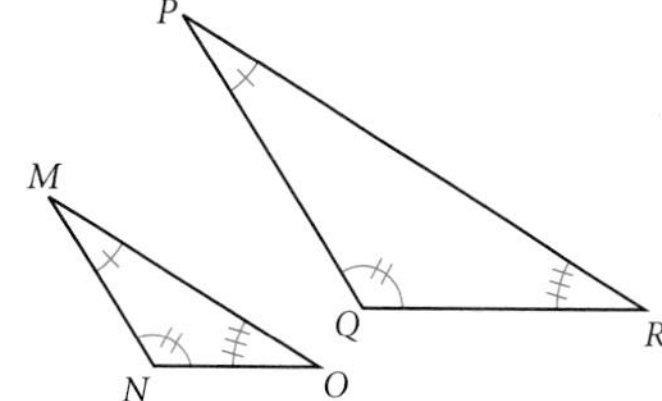

There is a counterexample for the AAA case, so it is *not* a congruence shortcut. Next, let's investigate the ASA case.

Investigation

Is ASA a Congruence Shortcut?

You will need

- a compass
- a straightedge

Consider the Angle-Side-Angle (ASA) case. If two angles and the included side of one triangle are congruent to two angles and the included side of another, must the triangles be congruent?

Step 1 Construct a triangle from the three parts shown. Be sure that the side is included between the given angles.

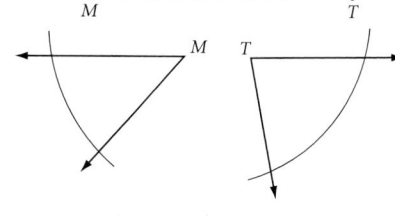

Step 2 Compare your triangle with the triangles made by others in your group. Is it possible to construct different triangles from the same three parts, or will all the triangles be congruent?

Step 3 You are now ready to complete the conjecture for the ASA case.

ASA Congruence Conjecture C-26

If two angles and the included side of one triangle are congruent to two angles and the included side of another triangle, then ? the triangles are congruent.

Let's assume that the SSS, SAS, and ASA Congruence Conjectures are true for all pairs of triangles that have those sets of corresponding parts congruent.

NCTM STANDARDS

CONTENT		PROCESS	
	Number	✓	Problem Solving
	Algebra	✓	Reasoning
✓	Geometry	✓	Communication
✓	Measurement	✓	Connections
	Data/Probability		Representation

LESSON OBJECTIVES

- Explore shortcut methods for determining whether triangles are congruent
- Discover that ASA and SAA are valid congruence shortcuts but AAA is not
- Practice construction skills

LESSON 4.5

PLANNING

LESSON OUTLINE

One day:

25 min Investigation

10 min Sharing

5 min Closing

5 min Exercises

MATERIALS

- construction tools
- ASA, SAA (W), *optional*

TEACHING

Students discover two more ways to show triangle congruence.

Guiding the Investigation

Use the ASA, SAA worksheet to gather more data.

Step 1 Students can use patty paper or a compass for this construction.

Step 3 The comparisons can be made without measuring in Step 2 if students simply superimpose the triangles they constructed. The first students finished can try other examples, especially with obtuse angles.

One step Pose this problem: "Someone needing help has dialed 911 on a cell phone but cannot describe the location to which help should be sent. The call has been picked up by two communication towers. Electronics at each tower tell emergency workers the angle between the line from the tower to the phone and line to the other tower. Can they determine the phone's location?"

One step (continued)

As you guide the one-step investigation, you will notice some students may start experimenting, not thinking of triangle congruence. Others may see that to determine the location precisely a triangle must be determined. Some may point out that knowing two parts of a triangle is not enough, and others may recall that even three angles don't determine a triangle. Ask if it would help if they knew the distance between the towers or the distance from the phone to one or both of the towers.

▸ EXAMPLE

Encourage students to verbalize which parts are congruent, and why, to help prepare them for a flowchart proof or paragraph proof later in the chapter. In particular, elicit the idea that ASA is being assumed as a valid shortcut to congruence. **[Alert]** Even though SAA follows from ASA, you must use just one of them in order to prove two triangles congruent. You can't use ASA in one triangle and SAA in another triangle to prove the two triangles congruent.

SHARING IDEAS

You might first deal with the AAA case, reaching class consensus that AAA is not a congruence shortcut. Address any lingering doubts about the relationship between "determining a triangle" and "being a congruence shortcut": If three parts of a triangle determine the triangle, they allow construction of just one triangle; therefore, any two triangles constructed with these parts will be congruent.

Have students present examples that led to conjectures about the ASA case. Encourage students who assert that one example is not enough for inductive reasoning.

Remind the class that although SAS is a congruence shortcut, SSA is not; wonder aloud whether a similar phenomenon occurs as we move from ASA to SAA. Try to elicit the idea that the third angle is determined by the construction, but don't discourage citations of the Triangle Sum Conjecture. Then have students critique the paragraph explanation in the example to encourage their critical thinking and bring about understanding.

[Ask] "Why is the word *corresponding* needed in the statement of the SAA shortcut but unnecessary in the statement of the ASA shortcut?" [There is only one way a side can be between two angles, but in SAA the side could be adjacent to either angle.]

Assessing Progress

You can assess students' ability to copy angles and segments, as well as their understanding of congruence and determination of triangles, AAA, and the importance of describing congruent triangles by listing their vertices in corresponding order.

The ASA case is closely related to another special case—the Side-Angle-Angle (SAA) case. You can investigate the SAA case with compass and straightedge, but you will have to use trial-and-error to accurately locate the second angle vertex because the side that is given is not the included side.

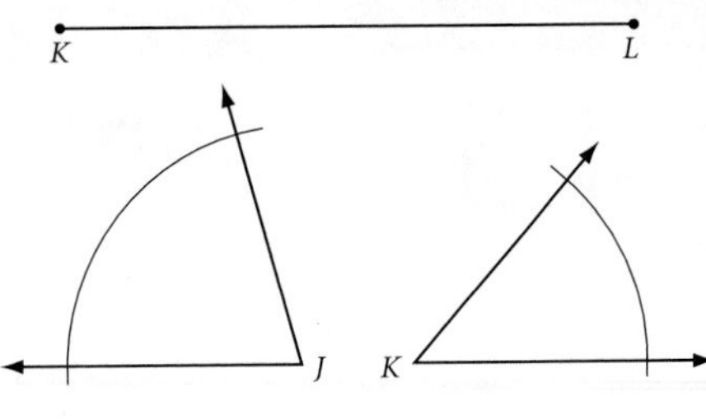

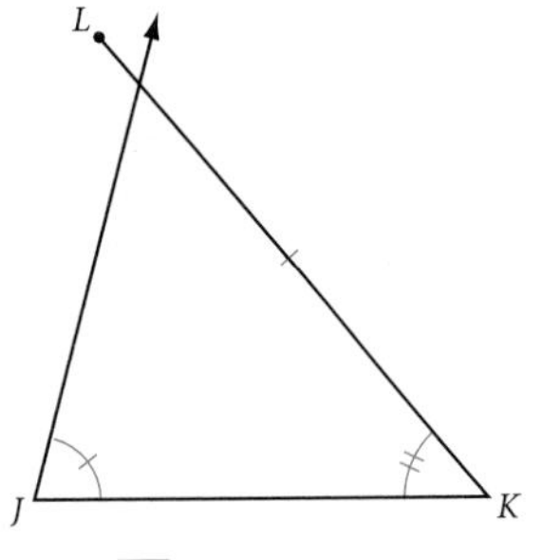

$\overline{JK}$ is too short.

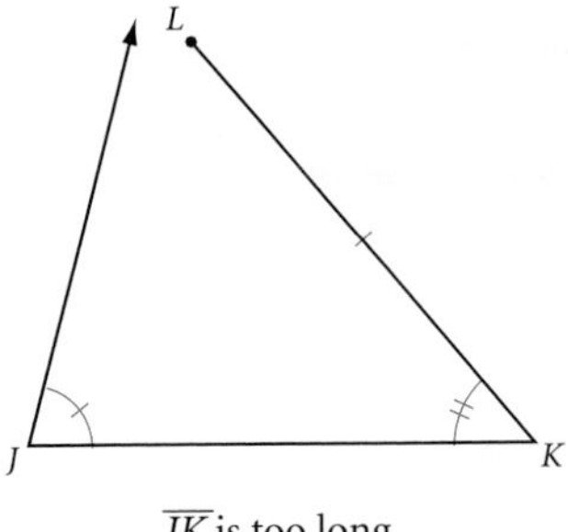

$\overline{JK}$ is too long.

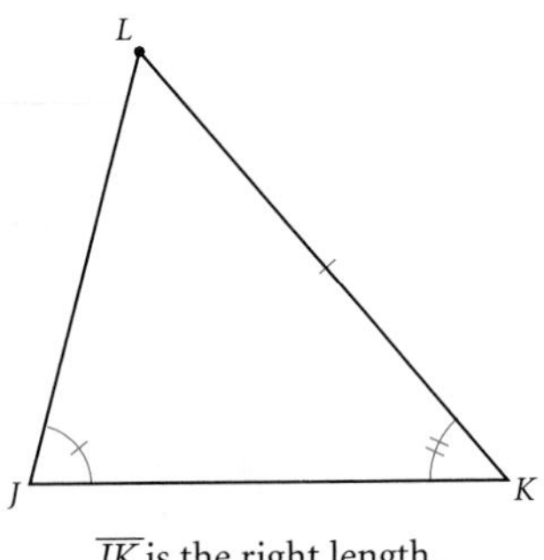

$\overline{JK}$ is the right length.

If two angles and a non-included side of one triangle are congruent to the corresponding two angles and non-included side of another, must the triangles be congruent? Let's look at it deductively.

EXAMPLE

In triangles ABC and XYZ, $\angle A \cong \angle X$, $\angle B \cong \angle Y$, and $\overline{BC} \cong \overline{YZ}$. Is $\triangle ABC \cong \triangle XYZ$? Explain your answer in a paragraph.

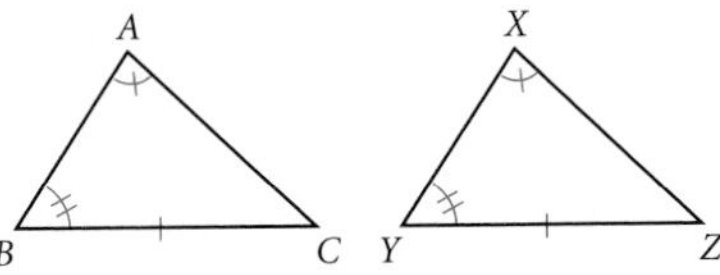

▸ Solution

Two angles in one triangle are congruent to two angles in another. The Third Angle Conjecture says that $\angle C \cong \angle Z$. The diagram now looks like this:

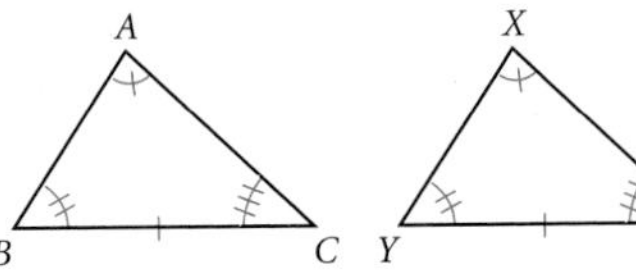

So you now have two angles and the *included* side of one triangle congruent to two angles and the included side of another. By the ASA Congruence Conjecture, $\triangle ABC \cong \triangle XYZ$.

So the SAA Congruence Conjecture follows easily from the ASA Congruence Conjecture. Complete the conjecture for the SAA case.

SAA Congruence Conjecture C-27

If two angles and a non-included side of one triangle are congruent to the corresponding angles and side of another triangle, then _?_. the triangles are congruent

Four of the six cases—SSS, SAS, ASA, and SAA—turned out to be congruence shortcuts. The diagram for each case is shown below.

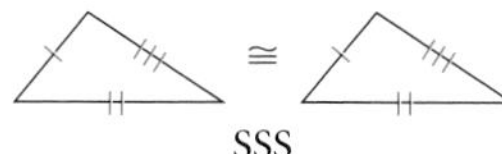

SSS

SAS

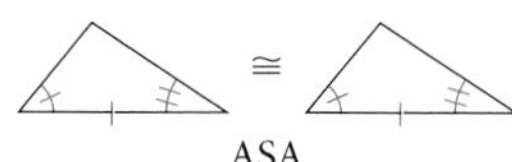

ASA

SAA

Add these diagrams, along with your congruence shortcut conjectures, to your conjecture list.

Many structures use congruent triangles for symmetry and strength. Can you tell which triangles in this toy structure are congruent?

Closing the Lesson

Remind students that a shortcut for showing triangle congruence allows us to avoid proving the congruence of all six pairs of corresponding parts. There are four shortcuts for proving triangle congruence. Students discovered SSS and SAS in the previous lesson. Now they have discovered ASA and SAA. SSA and AAA are not congruence shortcuts. Other arrangements of the letters, such as ASS (not a shortcut) and AAS (a shortcut), are included among these six.

Exercises

You will need

Construction tools for Exercises 17–19, 20, and 23

For Exercises 1–6, determine whether the triangles are congruent, and name the congruence shortcut. If the triangles cannot be shown to be congruent, write "cannot be determined."

1. $\triangle AMD \cong \triangle RMC$ ASA

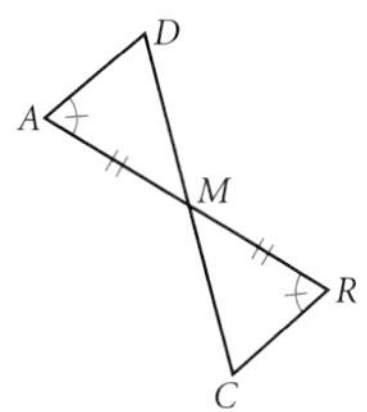

2. $\triangle BOX \cong \triangle CAR$ ASA

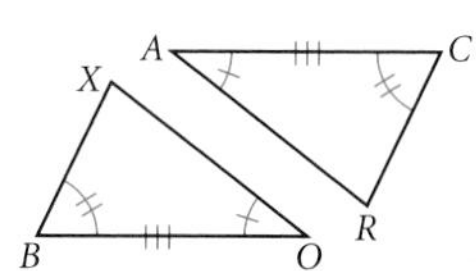

3. $\triangle GAS \cong \triangle IOL$ ⓗ SAA

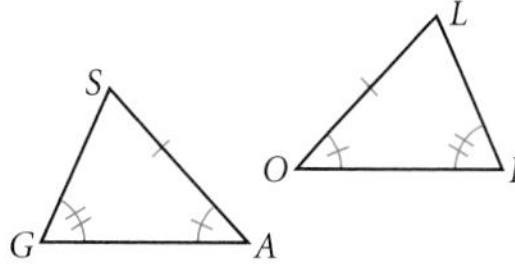

4. $\triangle HOW \cong \triangle FEW$

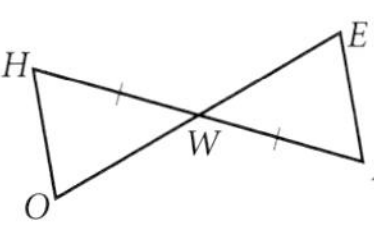

cannot be determined

5. $\triangle FSH \cong \triangle FSI$

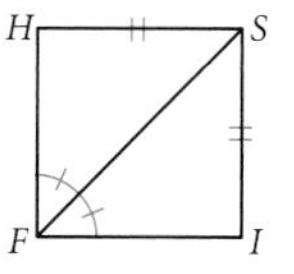

cannot be determined

6. $\triangle ALT \cong \triangle INT$

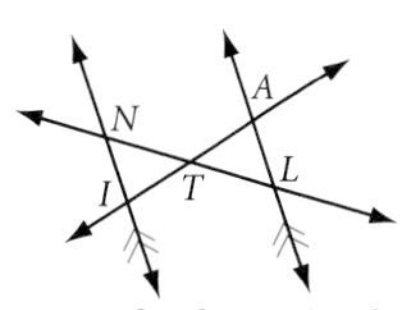

cannot be determined

BUILDING UNDERSTANDING

In these exercises students work with all the shortcuts for proving triangle congruence as well as the rejected shortcuts.

ASSIGNING HOMEWORK

Essential	2–18 evens
Performance assessment	15
Portfolio	17
Journal	15–18
Group	1–19
Review	20–25

Helping with the Exercises

Remind students that some of the triangles cannot be determined to be congruent.

Exercise 6 The triangles are similar.

Exercises 7–14 The main challenge of these exercises is not to determine which triangles are congruent, but to name the congruent triangles by listing their vertices in corresponding order.

16. Slope $\overline{AB}$ = slope $\overline{CD} = 3$ and slope $\overline{BC}$ = slope $\overline{DA} = -\frac{1}{3}$, so $\overline{AB} \perp \overline{BC}$. $\triangle ABC \cong \triangle CDA$ by SAA.

17.

18. The construction is the same as the construction using ASA once you find the third angle, which is given here.

19. Construction will show a similar but larger (or smaller) triangle constructed from a drawn triangle by duplicating two angles on either end of a new side that is not congruent to the corresponding side.

In Exercises 7–14, name a triangle congruent to the triangle given and state the congruence conjecture. If you cannot show any triangles to be congruent from the information given, write "cannot be determined" and explain why.

7. $\triangle FAD \cong \triangle$ _?_ *FED* by SSS

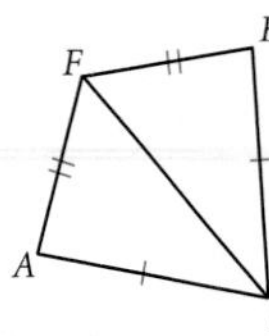

8. $\overline{OH} \parallel \overline{AT}$
$\triangle WHO \cong \triangle$ _?_ *WTA* by ASA or SAA

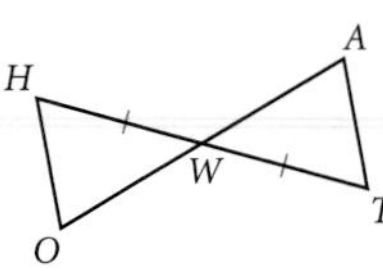

9. $\overline{AT}$ is an angle bisector.
$\triangle LAT \cong \triangle$ _?_ *SAT* by SAS

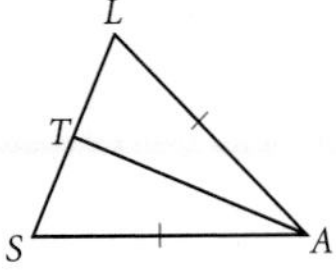

10. $PO = PR$
$\triangle POE \cong \triangle$ _?_ *PRN* by ASA or SAS
$\triangle SON \cong \triangle$ _?_ *SRE* by ASA

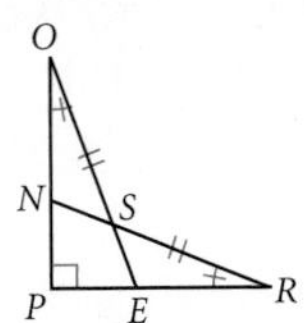

11. $\triangle$ _?_ $\cong \triangle$ _?_ Cannot be determined. Parts do not correspond.

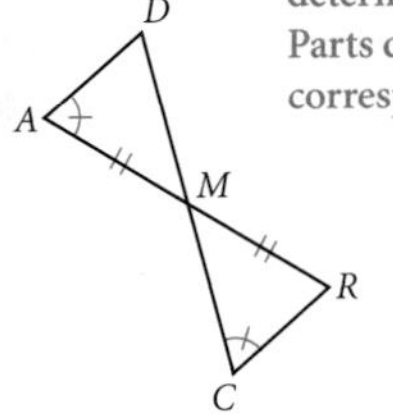

12. $\triangle RMF \cong \triangle$ _?_ *MRA* by SAS

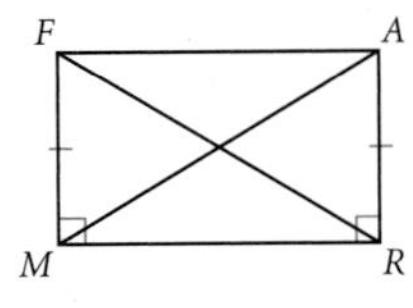

13. $\triangle BLA \cong \triangle$ _?_ Cannot be determined. AAA does not guarantee congruence.

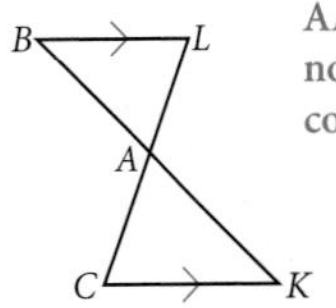

14. $\triangle LAW \cong \triangle$ _?_ *WKL* by ASA

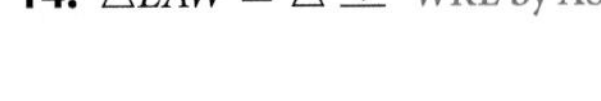

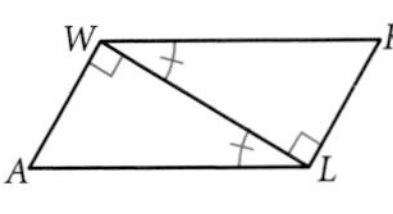

15. $\triangle SLN$ is equilateral.
Is $\triangle TIE$ equilateral? Explain. Yes, three exterior triangles are congruent by SAS.

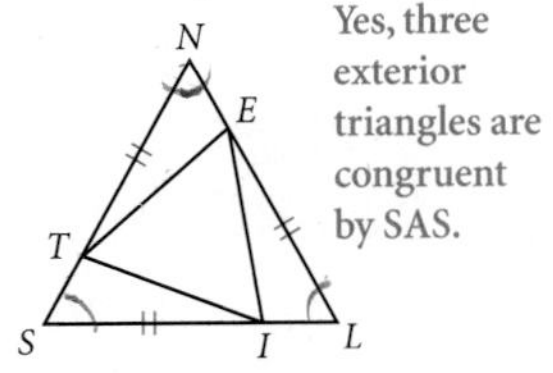

16. Use slope properties to show $\overline{AB} \perp \overline{BC}$, $\overline{CD} \perp \overline{DA}$, and $\overline{BC} \parallel \overline{DA}$. $\triangle ABC \cong \triangle$ _?_. Why?

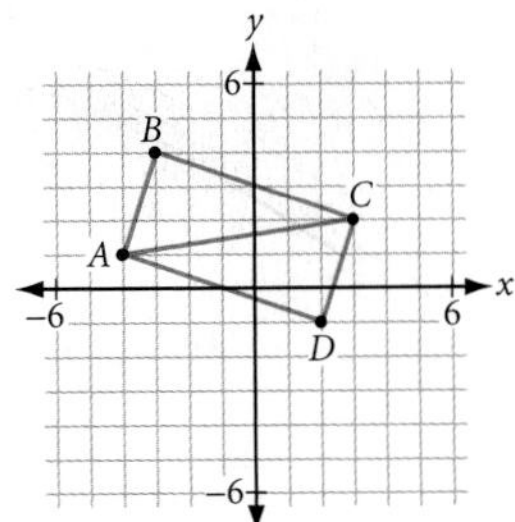

In Exercises 17–19, use a compass and a straightedge, or patty paper, to perform each construction.

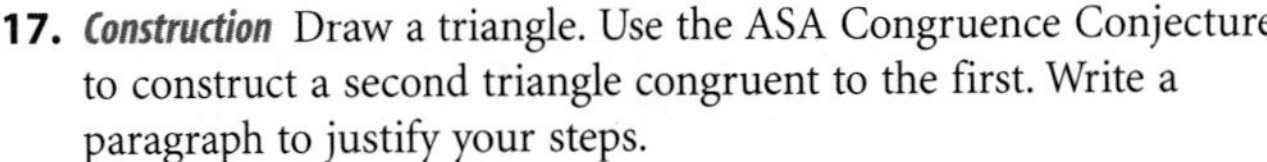

17. ***Construction*** Draw a triangle. Use the ASA Congruence Conjecture to construct a second triangle congruent to the first. Write a paragraph to justify your steps.

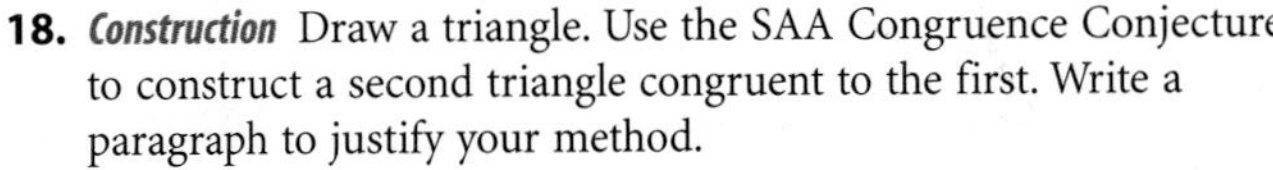

18. ***Construction*** Draw a triangle. Use the SAA Congruence Conjecture to construct a second triangle congruent to the first. Write a paragraph to justify your method.

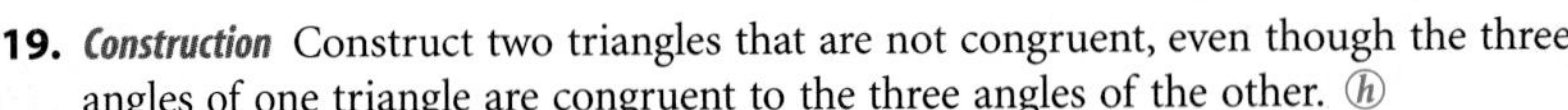

19. ***Construction*** Construct two triangles that are not congruent, even though the three angles of one triangle are congruent to the three angles of the other. ⓗ

Review

4.2 **20.** ***Construction*** Using only a compass and a straightedge, construct an isosceles triangle with a vertex angle that measures 135°. Draw a line segment. Construct a perpendicular. Bisect the right angle. Construct a triangle with two congruent sides and with a vertex that measures 135°.

2.4 **21.** If n concurrent lines divide the plane into 250 parts then $n = \underline{?}$. 125

1.5 **22.** "If the two diagonals of a quadrilateral are perpendicular, then the quadrilateral is a rhombus." Explain why this statement is true or sketch a counterexample. False. One possible counterexample is a kite.

4.4 **23.** ***Construction*** Construct an isosceles right triangle with $\overline{KM}$ as one of the legs. How many noncongruent triangles can you construct? Why?

K ———————— M

None. One triangle is determined by SAS.

2.4 **24.** Sketch five lines in a plane that intersect in exactly five points. Now do this in a different way.

3.7 **25.** APPLICATION Scientists use seismograms and a method called **triangulation** to pinpoint the epicenter of an earthquake.

a. Data recorded for one quake show that the epicenter is 480 km from Eureka, California; 720 km from Elko, Nevada; and 640 km from Las Vegas, Nevada. Trace the locations of these three towns and use the scale and your construction tools to find the location of the epicenter. about 100 km southeast of San Francisco

b. Is it necessary to have seismogram information from three towns? Would two towns suffice? Explain. Yes. No, two towns would narrow it down to two locations. The third circle narrows it down to one.

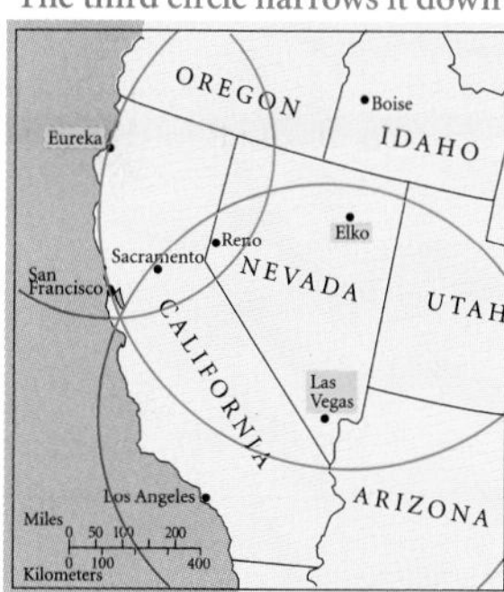

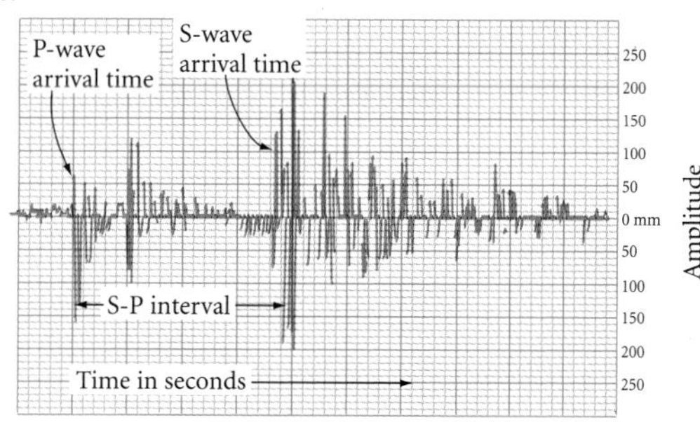

IMPROVING YOUR ALGEBRA SKILLS

Algebraic Sequences I

Find the next two terms of each algebraic sequence.

$x + 3y,\ 2x + y,\ 3x + 4y,\ 5x + 5y,\ 8x + 9y,\ 13x + 14y,\ \underline{?},\ \underline{?}$

$x + 7y,\ 2x + 2y,\ 4x - 3y,\ 8x - 8y,\ 16x - 13y,\ 32x - 18y,\ \underline{?},\ \underline{?}$

IMPROVING ALGEBRA SKILLS

The next terms in the sequences are $21x + 23y$, $34x + 37y$; and $64x - 23y$, $128x - 28y$.

C. Pose this problem: Is there a conjecture similar to SAS that will be a shortcut for proving the congruence of two quadrilaterals? Is SASA a shortcut? Is SASAS a shortcut? [SASA does not guarantee congruence, but SASAS does.]

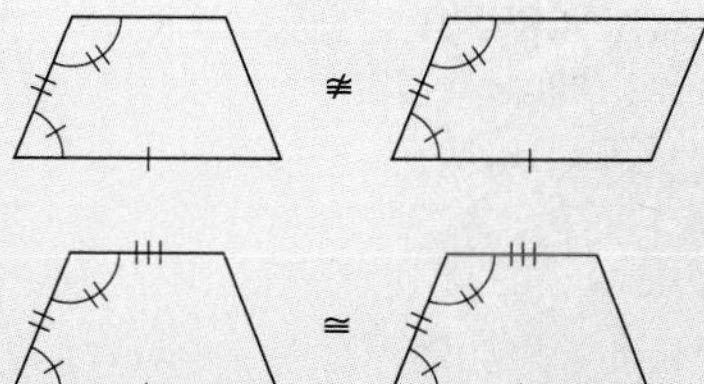

20.

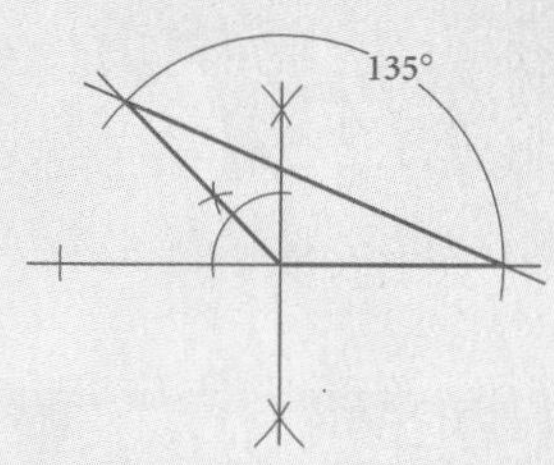

Exercise 23 Some students may try to put the right angle somewhere other than between the two congruent sides so that there might be two such triangles. **[Ask]** "Why must the right angle of an isosceles right triangle be included between the congruent sides?" [One reason: If one of the base angles were a right angle, then by the Isosceles Triangle Conjecture the other base angle would also be a right angle, so by the Triangle Sum Conjecture the vertex angle would have to measure 0°.]

23.

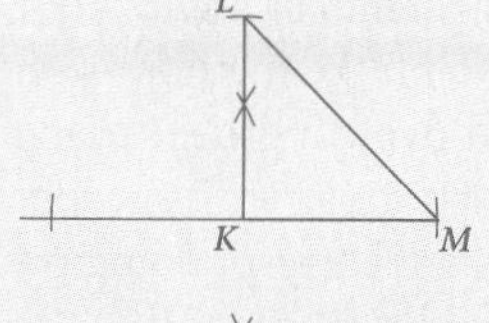

24.

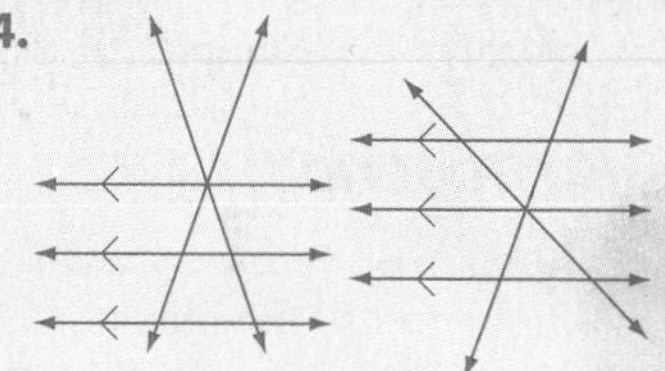

EXTENSIONS

A. Have students explain why the SAA Congruence Conjecture follows logically from the ASA Congruence Conjecture. [Given that any two corresponding angles of two triangles are congruent, the remaining corresponding angles are also congruent. Thus, ASA implies SAA, and SAA implies ASA.]

B. Use Take Another Look activities 5–8 on page 253.

LESSON

4.6

PLANNING

LESSON OUTLINE

One day:

15 min Examples

5 min Closing

25 min Exercises

MATERIALS

- construction tools
- Interlocking Triangles (T) for One step

TEACHING

When the goal is to show that two segments or angles are congruent, the method is often to find two congruent triangles in which those segments or angles are corresponding parts. You might choose to use the one-step investigation (page 231) in place of the examples.

INTRODUCTION

You may wish to have students continue to use the phrase "because corresponding parts of congruent triangles are congruent" instead of the abbreviation CPCTC until they understand the phrase.

Encourage students to draw pictures for each problem and to label all the given information. Then they can begin to label other angles or segments that they can conclude are congruent from various conjectures. Be sure students can cite conjectures to justify congruence rather than relying on the appearance of the drawings.

LESSON 4.6

Corresponding Parts of Congruent Triangles

The job of the younger generation is to find solutions to the solutions found by the older generation.

ANONYMOUS

In Lessons 4.4 and 4.5, you discovered four shortcuts for showing that two triangles are congruent—SSS, SAS, ASA, and SAA. The definition of congruent triangles states that if two triangles are congruent, then the ***corresponding parts of those congruent triangles are congruent***. We'll use the letters **CPCTC** to refer to the definition. Let's see how you can use congruent triangles and CPCTC.

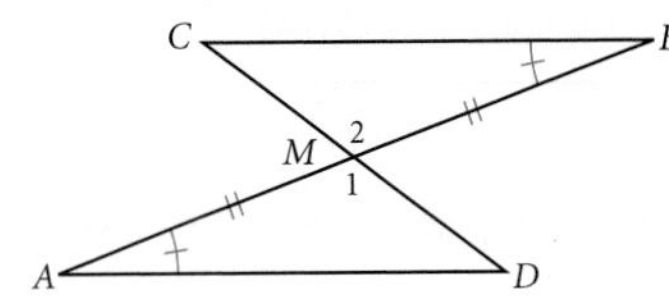

EXAMPLE A Is $\overline{AD} \cong \overline{BC}$ in the figure above? Use a deductive argument to explain why they must be congruent.

▶ ***Solution*** Here is one possible explanation: $\angle 1 \cong \angle 2$ because they are vertical angles. And it is given that $\overline{AM} \cong \overline{BM}$ and $\angle A \cong \angle B$. So, by ASA, $\triangle AMD \cong \triangle BMC$. Because the triangles are congruent, $\overline{AD} \cong \overline{BC}$ by CPCTC.

If you use a congruence shortcut to show that two triangles are congruent, then you can use CPCTC to show that any of their corresponding parts are congruent.

When you are trying to prove that triangles are congruent, it can be hard to keep track of what you know. Mark all the information on the figure. If the triangles are hard to see, use different colors or redraw them separately.

EXAMPLE B Is $\overline{AE} \cong \overline{BD}$? Write a paragraph proof explaining why.

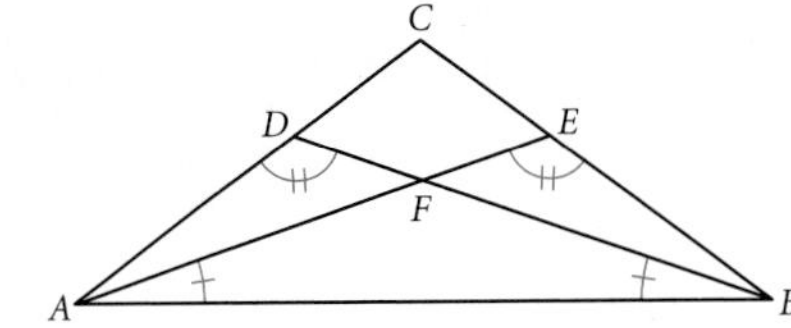

▶ ***Solution*** The triangles you can use to show congruence are $\triangle ABD$ and $\triangle BAE$. You can separate or color them to see them more clearly.

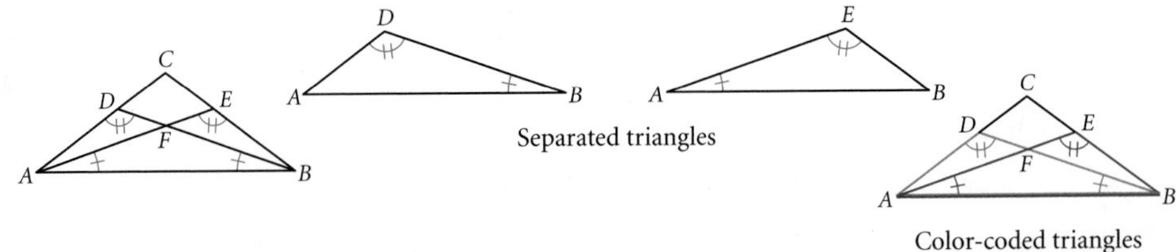

▶ *EXAMPLE A*

Students might ask if there's another possible explanation. A less elegant explanation might cite the Triangle Sum Conjecture (or the Parallel Lines Conjecture and its converse) to show that angles D and C are congruent, and then use SAA to prove triangle congruence.

▶ *EXAMPLE B*

You are trying to help students learn to put their reasoning into logical order by beginning with the given information and using the geometric relationships in the drawing to lead to the "show" statement. Having students write the proof in a paragraph format will help prepare them for the flowchart method introduced in the next lesson.

You can see that the two triangles have two pairs of congruent angles and they share a side.

Paragraph Proof: Show that $\overline{AE} \cong \overline{BD}$.

In $\triangle ABD$ and $\triangle BAE$, $\angle D \cong \angle E$ and $\angle B \cong \angle A$. Also, $\overline{AB} \cong \overline{BA}$ because they are the same segment. So $\triangle ABD \cong \triangle BAE$ by SAA. By CPCTC, $\overline{AE} \cong \overline{BD}$. ■

EXERCISES

You will need

Construction tools for Exercises **16** and **17**

For Exercises 1–9, copy the figures onto your paper and mark them with the given information. Answer the question about segment or angle congruence. If your answer is yes, write a paragraph proof explaining why. Remember to state which congruence shortcut you used. If there is not enough information to prove congruence, write "cannot be determined."

1. $\angle A \cong \angle C$, $\angle ABD \cong \angle CBD$
Is $\overline{AB} \cong \overline{CB}$? ⓗ yes

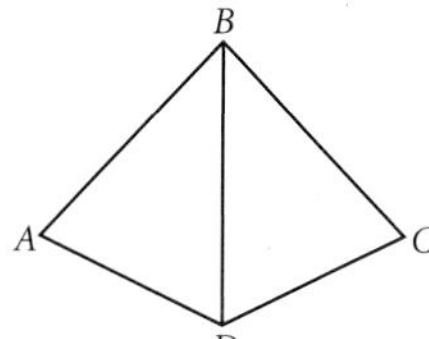

2. $\overline{CN} \cong \overline{WN}$, $\angle C \cong \angle W$
Is $\overline{RN} \cong \overline{ON}$? ⓗ yes

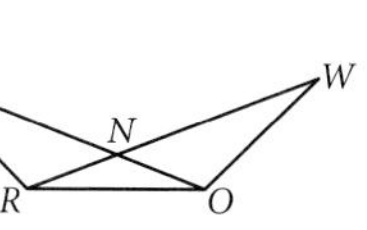

3. $\overline{CS} \cong \overline{HR}$, $\angle 1 \cong \angle 2$
Is $\overline{CR} \cong \overline{HS}$?
cannot be determined

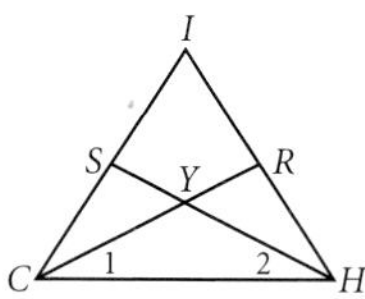

4. $\angle S \cong \angle I$, $\angle G \cong \angle A$
T is the midpoint of $\overline{SI}$.
Is $\overline{SG} \cong \overline{IA}$? ⓗ yes

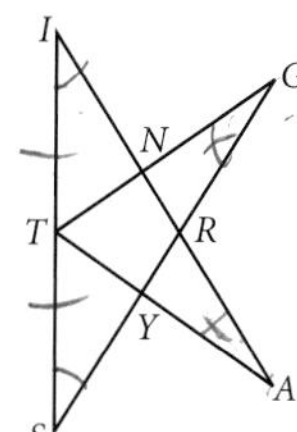

5. $\overline{FO} \cong \overline{FR}$, $\overline{UO} \cong \overline{UR}$
Is $\angle O \cong \angle R$? ⓗ yes

6. $\overline{MN} \cong \overline{MA}$, $\overline{ME} \cong \overline{MR}$
Is $\angle E \cong \angle R$? yes

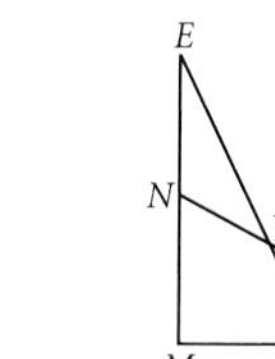

7. $\overline{BT} \cong \overline{EU}$, $\overline{BU} \cong \overline{ET}$
Is $\angle B \cong \angle E$? ⓗ yes

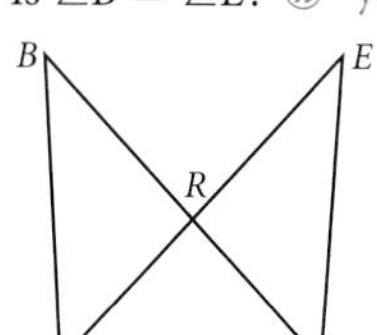

8. $HALF$ is a parallelogram.
Is $\overline{HA} \cong \overline{HF}$? cannot be determined

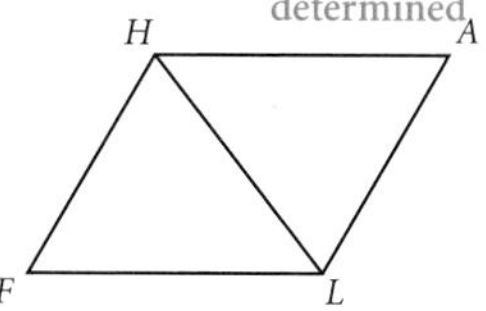

9. $\angle D \cong \angle C$, $\angle O \cong \angle A$, $\angle G \cong \angle T$. Is $\overline{TA} \cong \overline{GO}$?
cannot be determined

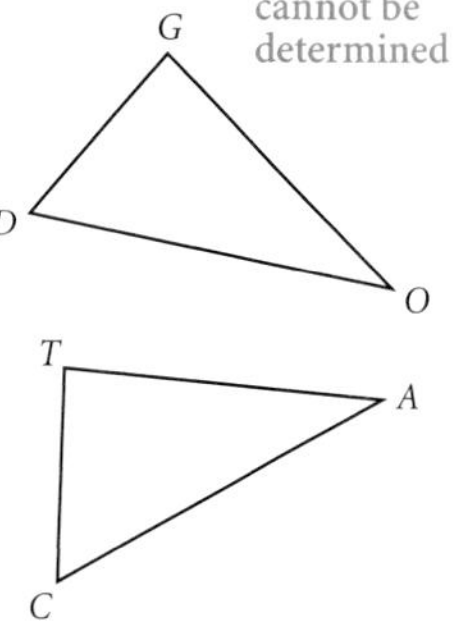

One step Show the Interlocking Triangles transparency and pose the challenge of Example B: "Is $\overline{AE}$ congruent to $\overline{BD}$?" As you circulate, if groups are stuck you can wonder aloud whether separating or coloring the triangles would help. If too many students are having difficulties, call them together and go through Example A. In Sharing, mention the abbreviation CPCTC.

Closing the Lesson

Remind students of the main point of this lesson: To show that two segments or angles (the targets) are congruent, they will often find two congruent triangles in which these segments or angles are corresponding parts. Sometimes it's fairly clear what triangles contain the corresponding parts, but often the parts are in several different triangles. Encourage students to begin with labeled pictures and look for other congruent parts of triangles containing the targets. They may draw auxiliary lines to make the needed triangles. Often they will work backward (Which triangles do I want to prove congruent?) as well as forward (Which triangles can I prove congruent from what I know?).

NCTM STANDARDS

CONTENT		PROCESS	
	Number		Problem Solving
	Algebra	✔	Reasoning
✔	Geometry	✔	Communication
	Measurement		Connections
	Data/Probability		Representation

LESSON OBJECTIVES

- Show that pairs of angles or pairs of sides are congruent by identifying related triangles and proving them congruent, then applying CPCTC
- Practice deductive reasoning

See page 772 for answers to Exercises 1–9.

BUILDING UNDERSTANDING

In the exercises students practice proving the congruence of angles or segments by seeing them as parts of congruent triangles.

ASSIGNING HOMEWORK

Essential	1–9
Performance assessment	6
Portfolio	2
Journal	12, 19
Group	21, 22
Review	13–23

MATERIALS

- Exercise 18 (T), *optional*

▶ Helping with the Exercises

Exercises 1–9 Be sure students don't answer yes only because the two parts appear to be congruent in the picture. The symbol ∴ meaning "therefore," used in the sample answers to save space, is not used in the student book until Chapter 13.

Exercise 3 Many students may find this exercise challenging. They may find several pairs of triangles satisfying SSA and may either conclude congruence or become frustrated. Help them focus on deciding whether or not triangles *CSH* and *HRC* are congruent and to work backward as well as forward. They may want to color differently or separate the two triangles under consideration. They don't have information that would allow them to decide that angles *SCH* and *RHC* are congruent, even though they appear to be congruent in the picture.

Exercise 4 Students may want to draw the triangles separately.

For Exercises 10 and 11, you can use the right angles and the lengths of horizontal and vertical segments shown on the grid. Answer the question about segment or angle congruence. If your answer is yes, explain why.

10. Is $\overline{FR} \cong \overline{GT}$? Why? ⓗ

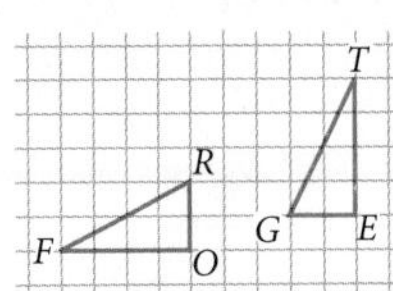

Yes. The triangles are congruent by SAS.

11. Is $\angle OND \cong \angle OCR$? Why?

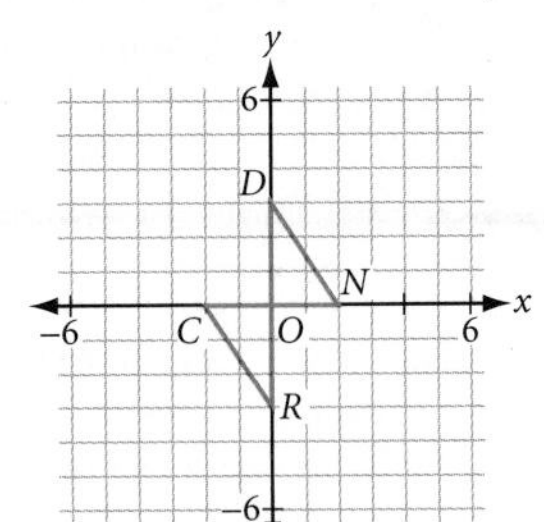

Yes. The triangles are congruent by SAS, and the angles are congruent by CPCTC.

12. In Chapter 3, you used inductive reasoning to discover how to duplicate an angle using a compass and straightedge. Now you have the skills to explain *why* the construction works using deductive reasoning. The construction is shown at right. Write a paragraph proof explaining why it works.

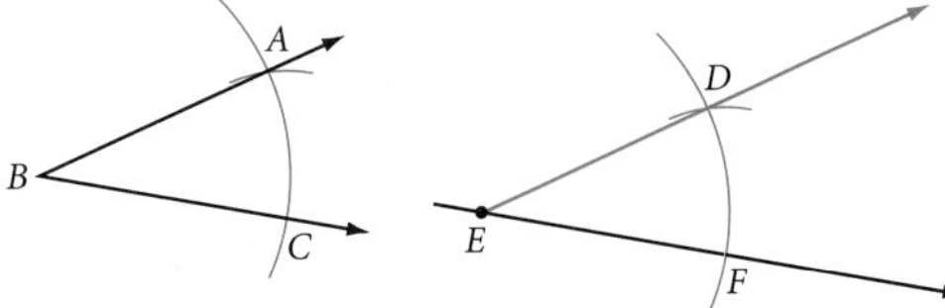

▶ Review

4.5 In Exercises 13–15, complete each statement. If the figure does not give you enough information to show that the triangles are congruent, write "cannot be determined."

13. $\overline{AM}$ is a median.
$\triangle CAM \cong \triangle$ _?_
cannot be determined

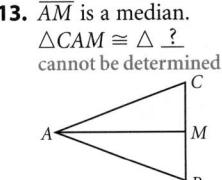

14. $\triangle HEI \cong \triangle$ _?_ *KEI* by ASA
Why?

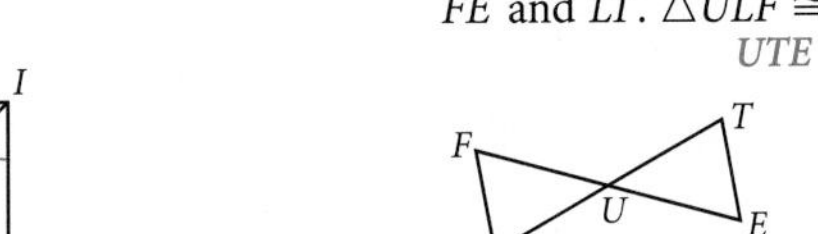

15. *U* is the midpoint of both $\overline{FE}$ and $\overline{LT}$. $\triangle ULF \cong \triangle$ _?_
UTE by SAS

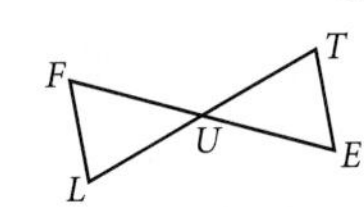

4.4 **16.** ***Construction*** Draw a triangle. Use the SAS Congruence Conjecture to construct a second triangle congruent to the first.

4.4 **17.** ***Construction*** Construct two triangles that are *not* congruent, even though two sides and a non-included angle of one triangle are congruent to two sides and a corresponding non-included angle of the other triangle. ⓗ

18. Copy the figure. Calculate the measure of each lettered angle. $a = 112°, b = 68°, c = 44°, d = 44°, e = 136°, f = 68°, g = 68°, h = 56°, k = 68°, l = 56°, m = 124°$

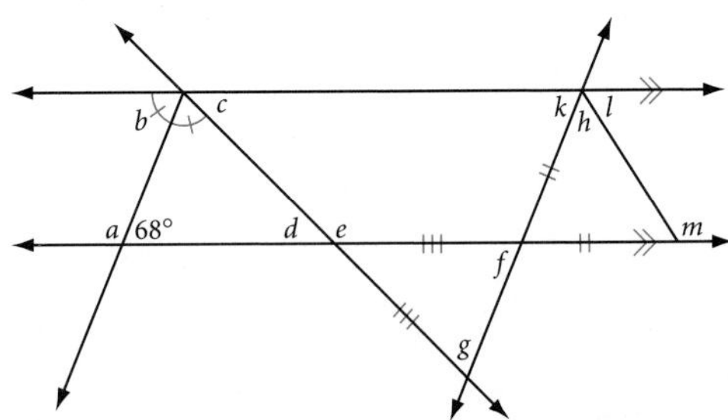

Exercise 5 A few students may need your suggestion to draw an auxiliary line. Ask if any work they've done recently might be relevant. If they say there are no triangles, **[Ask]** "How might you create some?"

Exercise 6 Students may want to claim that angle *M* is a right angle because it appears to be one. There's no evidence that it is, but what matters is that the angle is common to the two triangles in question.

Exercise 7 Students may claim that they don't have enough information to prove the given triangles congruent. **[Ask]** "Can you make any triangles that you could prove congruent from the given information?"

19. According to math legend, the Greek mathematician Thales (ca. 625–547 B.C.E.) could tell how far out to sea a ship was by using congruent triangles. First, he marked off a long segment in the sand. Then, from each endpoint of the segment, he drew the angle to the ship. He then remeasured the two angles on the other side of the segment away from the shore. The point where the rays of these two angles crossed located the ship. What congruence conjecture was Thales using? Explain. ASA. The "long segment in the sand" is a shared side of both triangles.

20. Isosceles right triangle ABC has vertices $A(-8, 2)$, $B(-5, -3)$, and $C(0, 0)$. Find the coordinates of the circumcenter. $(-4, 1)$

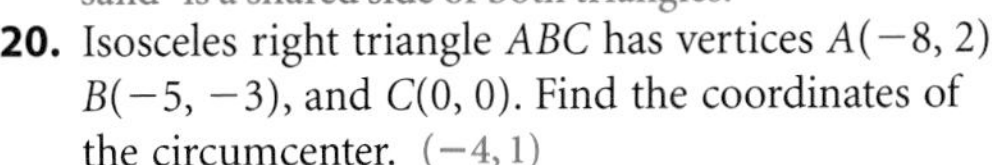

21. The SSS Congruence Conjecture explains why triangles are rigid structures though other polygons are not. By adding one "strut" (diagonal) to a quadrilateral you create a quadrilateral that consists of two triangles, and that makes it rigid. What is the minimum number of struts needed to make a pentagon rigid? A hexagon? A dodecagon? What is the minimum number of struts needed to make other polygons rigid? Complete the table and make your conjecture.

 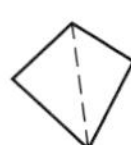 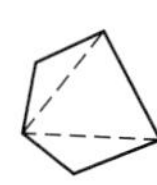 

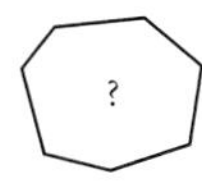

Number of sides	3	4	5	6	7	...	12	...	n
Number of struts needed to make polygon rigid	0	1	2	3	4	...	9	...	$n-3$

22. Line ℓ is parallel to $\overline{AB}$. If P moves to the right along ℓ, which of the following always decreases? Values c and d always decrease.

a. The distance PC

b. The distance from C to $\overline{AB}$

c. The ratio $\frac{AB}{AP}$

d. $AC - AP$

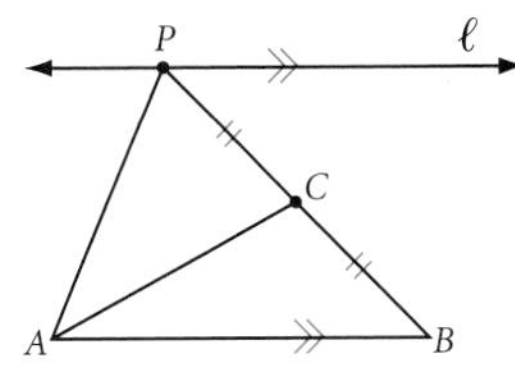

23. Find the lengths x and y. Each angle is a right angle. $x = 3, y = 10$

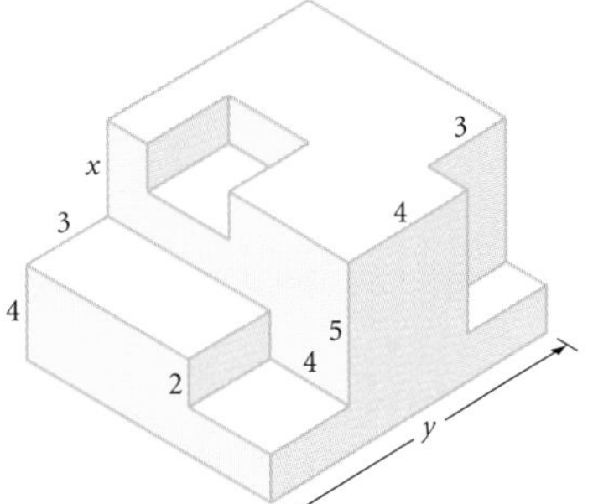

Exercise 12 If students are having difficulty, ask if any recent work they've done could be relevant. Encourage them to construct segments to make triangles.

12. Draw $\overline{AC}$ and $\overline{DF}$ to form $\triangle ABC$ and $\triangle DEF$. $\overline{AB} \cong \overline{CB} \cong \overline{DE} \cong \overline{FE}$ because all were drawn with the same radius. $\overline{AC} \cong \overline{DF}$ for the same reason. $\triangle ABC \cong \triangle DEF$ by SSS. Therefore, $\angle B \cong \angle E$ by CPCTC.

16.

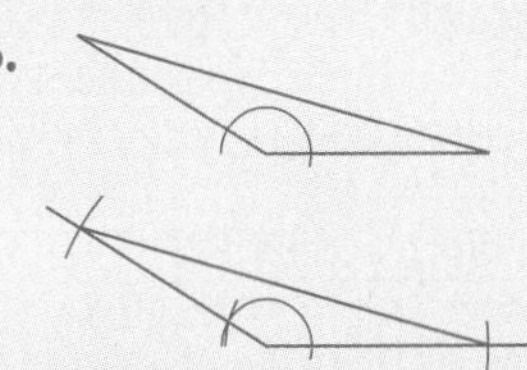

17.

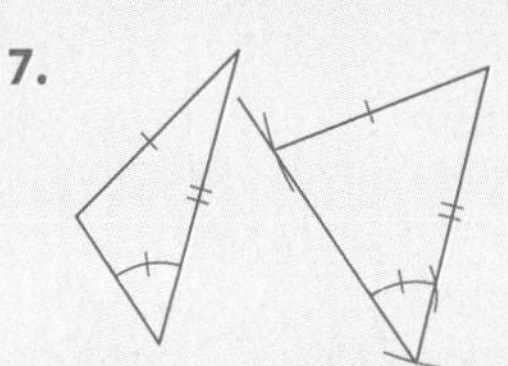

Exercise 19 This is the same Thales ['thā-lēz] who set the deductive reasoning precedent in mathematics.

Exercise 22 The distance from point P to point C decreases until $\overline{PB} \perp \ell$; then the distance begins to increase. The distance from C to $\overline{AB}$ remains constant; it is always halfway between the two parallel lines. Since AP is increasing and AB is not changing, the ratio $\frac{AB}{AP}$ is decreasing. Since AP is increasing faster than AC, the difference is always decreasing.

To help solve Exercise 22, students can use the dynamic geometry exploration at www.keymath.com/DG to investigate the properties of a triangle with a median as one vertex moves parallel to the base.

POLYA'S PROBLEM

While working on the project, students can learn to think about general cases. For example, in one special case all five planes pass through the same line, like a pinwheel; in another all five planes are parallel. Because the problem statement is about planes that are "random," no three planes share a line and no two are parallel. Special cases might lend insight into a problem, but none of them solves the problem.

One approach students might take is inductive reasoning. They note that one plane divides space into two parts, two planes divide space into four parts, and three planes divide space into eight parts. If they jump to a conjecture based on this pattern, suggest that they consider the case of lines dividing a plane. The same pattern holds initially, but three lines divide the plane into seven parts, not eight. The pattern breaks down even sooner with points dividing a line.

One way to understand the answer of 26 regions is to see that the number of points of space added at each step is the number of regions into which the new plane is divided by the lines that are its intersections with previously existing planes. For example, the fourth plane intersects the three existing planes in three lines, and three lines divide a plane into seven parts, so seven new regions are added by the third plane.

project

POLYA'S PROBLEM

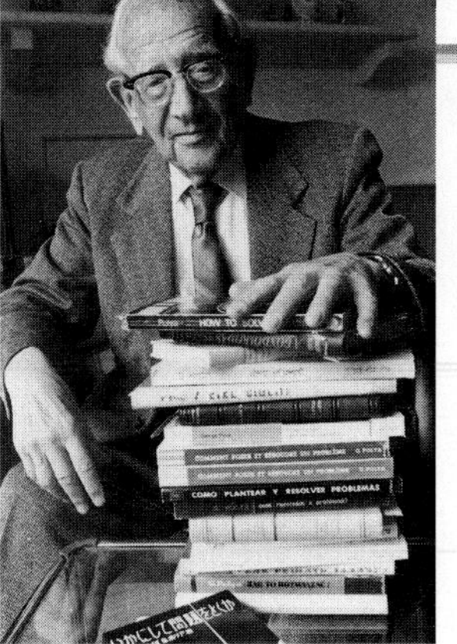

George Polya (1887–1985) was a mathematician who specialized in problem-solving methods. He taught mathematics and problem solving at Stanford University for many years, and wrote the book *How to Solve It.*

He posed this problem to his students: Into how many parts will five random planes divide space?

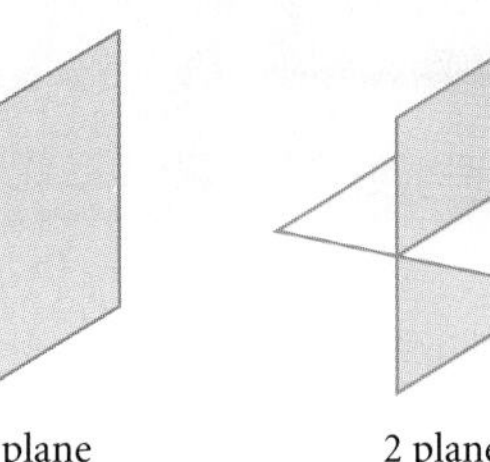

1 plane 2 planes 3 planes

It is difficult to visualize five random planes intersecting in space. What strategies would you use to find the answer?

Your project is to solve this problem, and to show how you know your answer is correct. Here are some of Polya's problem-solving strategies to help you.

- Understand the problem. Draw a figure or build a model. Can you restate the problem in your own words?
- Break down the problem. Have you done any simpler problems that are like this one?

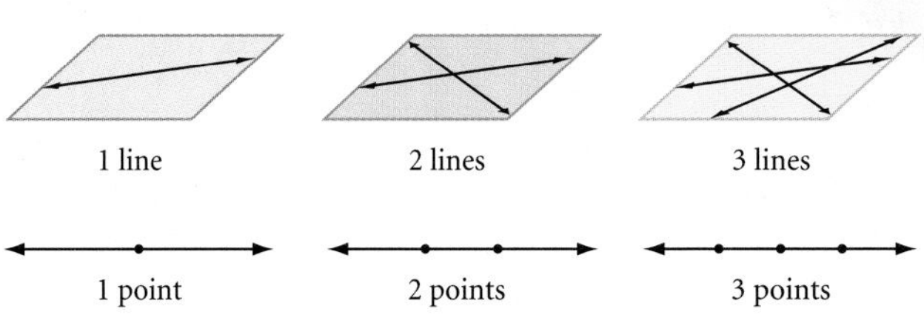

1 line 2 lines 3 lines

1 point 2 points 3 points

- Check your answer. Can you find the answer in a different way to show that it is correct? (The answer, by the way, is not 32!)

Your method is as important as your answer. Keep track of all the different things you try. Write down your strategies, your results, and your thinking, as well as your answer.

Supporting the project

This challenging problem makes a good long-term project. The goal is not the answer but the experience of working with smaller, analogous problems. You might challenge students to find the rules for points dividing a line $[n + 1]$ and lines dividing a plane $\left[\frac{1}{2}n^2 + \frac{1}{2}n + 1\right]$ and explain why they work.

OUTCOMES

- The answer is correct: 26 regions.
- The student has looked for analogies to the cases in other dimensions.
- Tables are used to look for patterns across dimensions.
- The problem is solved in more than one way.
- The student considered bounded and unbounded regions.
- The student used finite differences to find the cubic formula for the number of parts into which n random planes divide space: $f(n) = \frac{1}{6}n^3 + \frac{5}{6}n + 1$.

LESSON

4.7

Flowchart Thinking

If you can only find it, there is a reason for everything.

TRADITIONAL SAYING

You have been making many discoveries about triangles. As you try to explain why the new conjectures are true, you build upon definitions and conjectures you made before.

So far, you have written your explanations as paragraph proofs. First, we'll look at a diagram and explain why two angles must be congruent, by writing a paragraph proof, in Example A. Then we'll look at a different tool for writing proofs, and use that tool to write the same proof, in Example B.

EXAMPLE A

In the figure at right, $\overline{EC} \cong \overline{AC}$ and $\overline{ER} \cong \overline{AR}$. Is $\angle A \cong \angle E$? If so, give a logical argument to explain why they are congruent.

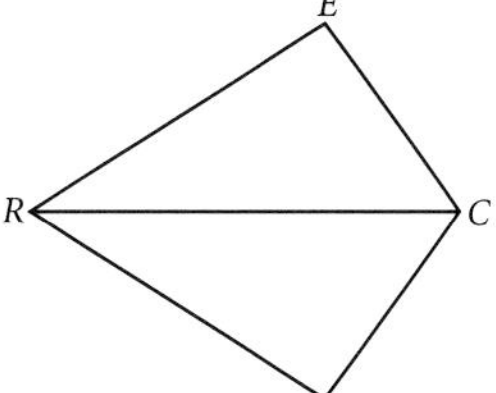

▶ Solution

First mark the given information on the figure. Then consider whether $\angle A$ is congruent to $\angle E$, and why.

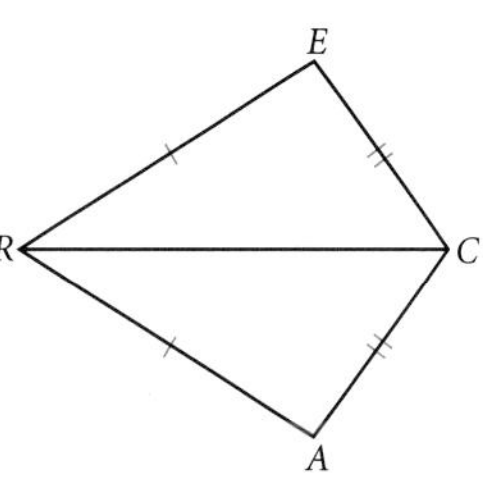

Paragraph Proof: Show that $\angle A \cong \angle E$.

$\overline{EC} \cong \overline{AC}$ and $\overline{ER} \cong \overline{AR}$ because that information is given. $\overline{RC} \cong \overline{RC}$ because it is the same segment, and any segment is congruent to itself. So, $\triangle CRE \cong \triangle CRA$ by the SSS Congruence Conjecture. If $\triangle CRE \cong \triangle CRA$, then $\angle A \cong \angle E$ by CPCTC. ■

Were you able to follow the logical steps in Example A? Sometimes a logical argument or a proof is long and complex, and a paragraph might not be the clearest way to present all the steps. In Chapter 1, you used concept maps to visualize the relationships among different kinds of polygons. A **flowchart** is a concept map that shows all the steps in a complicated procedure in proper order. Arrows connect the boxes to show how facts lead to conclusions.

Flowcharts make your logic visible so that others can follow your reasoning. To present your reasoning in flowchart form, create a **flowchart proof.** Place each statement in a box. Write the logical reason for each statement beneath its box. For example, you would write "$RC \cong RC$, because it is the same segment," as

$\overline{RC} \cong \overline{RC}$
Same segment

Career CONNECTION

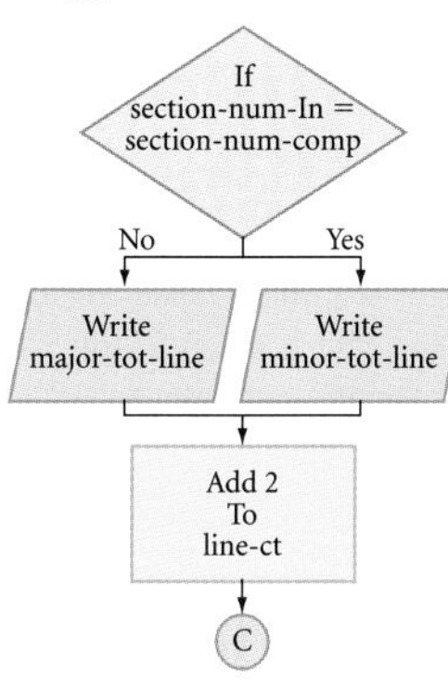

Computer programmers use programming language and detailed plans to design computer software. They often use flowcharts to plan the logic in programs.

NCTM STANDARDS

CONTENT		PROCESS	
	Number	✔	Problem Solving
✔	Algebra	✔	Reasoning
✔	Geometry	✔	Communication
✔	Measurement	✔	Connections
	Data/Probability	✔	Representation

LESSON OBJECTIVES

- Create flowchart proofs
- Develop problem-solving skills
- Develop logical and visual thinking skills

LESSON 4.7

PLANNING

LESSON OUTLINE

One day:

15 min Examples

5 min Closing

25 min Exercises

MATERIALS

- Big and Little (T) for One step

TEACHING

Sometimes proofs are so complicated that they're difficult to communicate in a paragraph's linear form. A flowchart can better demonstrate relationships among the ideas.

One step Show the Big and Little transparency and pose this problem: "If triangle *LAI* is isosceles with vertex angle *A*, write a paragraph proof explaining why segments *RD* and *ZD* are congruent." As students work, keep them focused on proving the congruence of either triangles *RDL* and *ZDI* or triangles *LZI* and *IRL*. Don't insist on excellent paragraph proofs; indeed, the point is that writing a clear paragraph proof is difficult. After sharing the groups' various proofs, lead the class in developing a flowchart that represents the logic of one of the simpler proofs, and then let the groups develop another flowchart proof.

▶ EXAMPLE A

If students have been following and writing paragraph proofs, they probably won't find this one too difficult. Tell them that they're learning a new proof format by starting with a simple proof.

▶ EXAMPLE B

Help students make the connection between the paragraph proof in Example A and the flowchart shown in this example. **[Alert]** Students may ask how many boxes are needed for each flowchart. Because the boxes are used simply to show the flow of the logic, the number of boxes will vary among proofs.

Draw a vertical version of the same flowchart to illustrate that flowcharts can move either from left to right or from top to bottom.

Closing the Lesson

Sometimes a flowchart can better demonstrate relationships among the ideas in a proof than can a paragraph. The flowchart can be horizontal (from left to right) or vertical (from top to bottom).

To make a flowchart proof, you can write down a box for the "Given" at the left or the top, and a box for the "Show" at the right or the bottom. Then fill in the other boxes, moving both forward and backward. By asking "What do I need to know in order to claim the conclusion is true? What must I show to prove that intermediate result?" you can plan a proof by reasoning backward.

Here is the same logical argument that you created in Example A in flowchart proof format.

EXAMPLE B

In the figure below, $\overline{EC} \cong \overline{AC}$ and $\overline{ER} \cong \overline{AR}$. Is $\angle E \cong \angle A$? If so, write a flowchart proof to explain why.

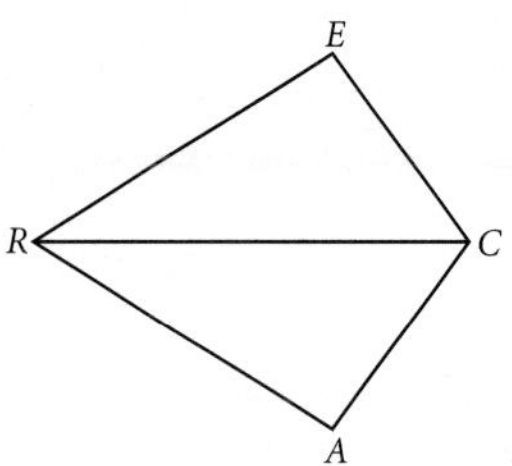

▶ Solution

First, restate the given information clearly. It helps to mark the given information on the figure. Then state what you are trying to show.

Given: $\overline{AR} \cong \overline{ER}$
$\overline{EC} \cong \overline{AC}$

Show: $\angle E \cong \angle A$

Flowchart Proof

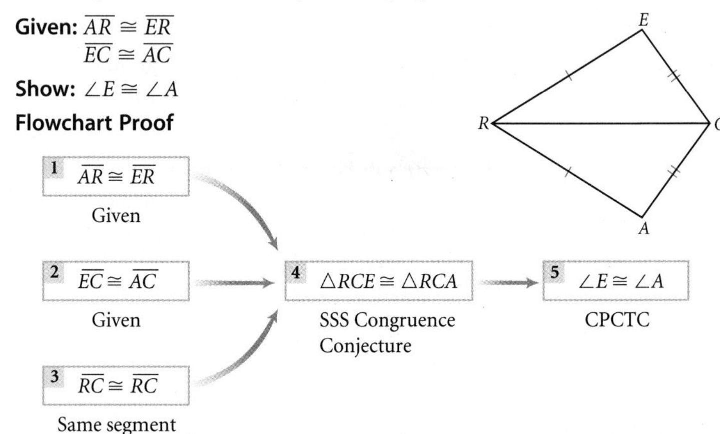

Is this contraption like a flowchart proof?

In a flowchart proof, the arrows show how the logical argument flows from the information that is given to the conclusion that you are trying to prove. Drawing an arrow is like saying "therefore." You can draw flowcharts top to bottom or left to right.

Compare the paragraph proof in Example A with the flowchart proof in Example B. What similarities and differences are there? What are the advantages of each format?

EXERCISES

1. Suppose you saw this step in a proof: Construct angle bisector CD to the midpoint of side AB in $\triangle ABC$. What's wrong with that step? Explain.

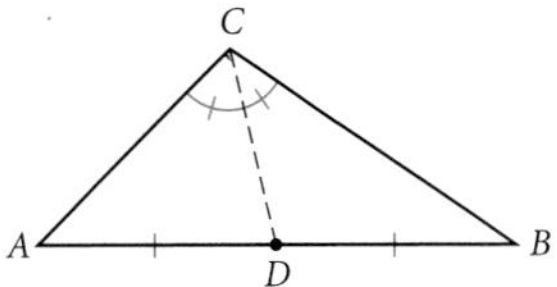

2. Copy the flowchart. Provide each missing reason or statement in the proof.

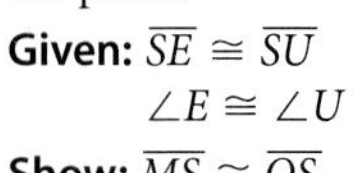

Given: $\overline{SE} \cong \overline{SU}$

$\angle E \cong \angle U$

Show: $\overline{MS} \cong \overline{OS}$

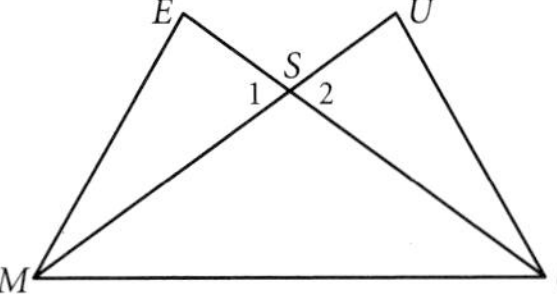

Flowchart Proof

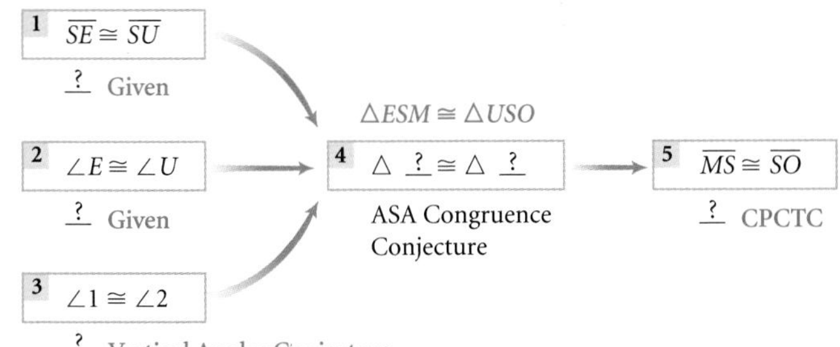

3. Copy the flowchart. Provide each missing reason or statement in the proof.

Given: I is the midpoint of $\overline{CM}$

I is the midpoint of $\overline{BL}$

Show: $\overline{CL} \cong \overline{MB}$

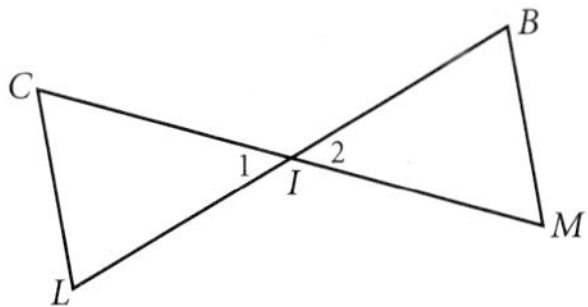

Flowchart Proof

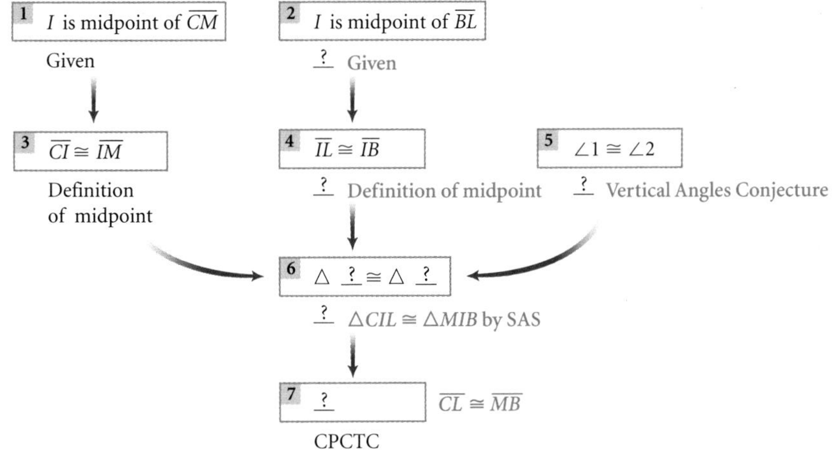

BUILDING UNDERSTANDING

In the exercises students begin by filling in missing parts of flowchart proofs and work up to creating the proofs themselves.

ASSIGNING HOMEWORK

Essential	**2–5, 7**
Performance assessment	**7**
Portfolio	**6**
Journal	**1**
Group	**6**
Review	**8–18**

MATERIALS

- Exercises 3 and 6 (T), *optional*
- Exercise 13 (T), *optional*

Helping with the Exercises

More than one proof can be written for many of the conjectures in these exercises, though only one proof is given for each. Some students may find vertical flowcharts both easier to construct and a more efficient use of their paper.

Exercise 1 Students might not understand what's wrong. Be sure that they are actually drawing a picture and that the triangle they draw is not a special kind, such as isosceles. This exercise helps motivate the ideas of Lesson 4.8.

1. The angle bisector does not go to the midpoint of the opposite side in any triangle, only in an isosceles triangle.

In Exercises 4–6, an auxiliary line segment has been added to the figure.

4. Complete this flowchart proof of the Isosceles Triangle Conjecture. Given that the triangle is isosceles, show that the base angles are congruent.

Given: $\triangle NEW$ is isosceles, with $\overline{WN} \cong \overline{EN}$ and median $\overline{NS}$

Show: $\angle W \cong \angle E$

Flowchart Proof

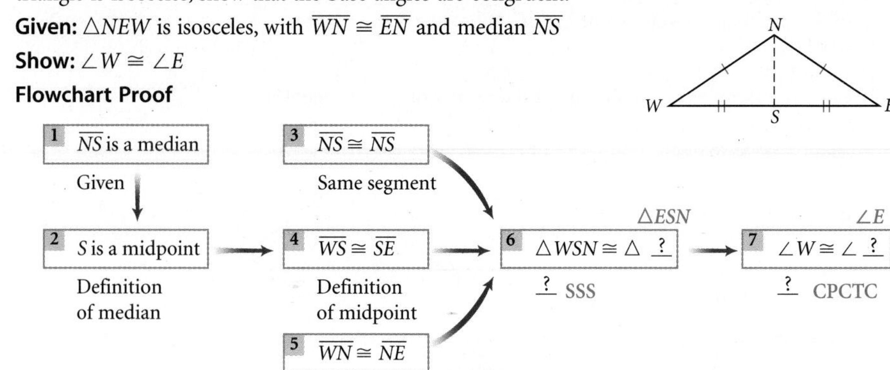

5. Complete this flowchart proof of the Converse of the Isosceles Triangle Conjecture.

Given: $\triangle NEW$ with $\angle W \cong \angle E$

$\overline{NS}$ is an angle bisector

Show: $\triangle NEW$ is an isosceles triangle

Flowchart Proof

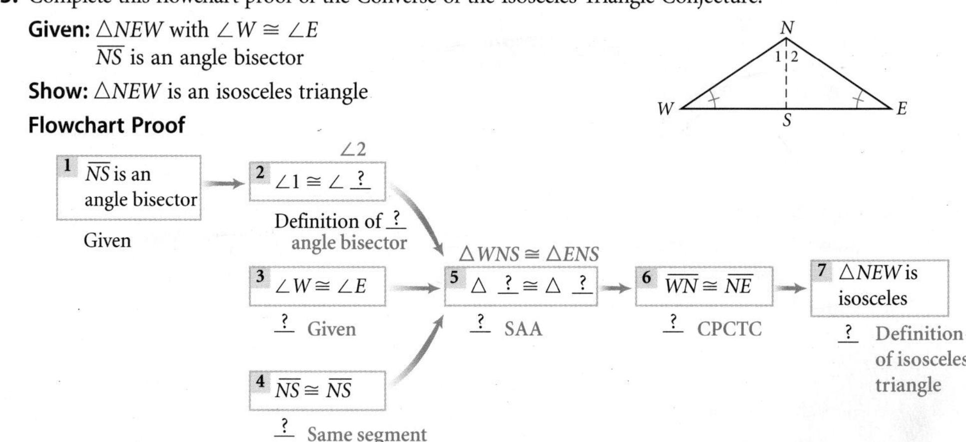

6. Complete the flowchart proof. What does this proof tell you about parallelograms?

Given: $\overline{SA} \parallel \overline{NE}$

$\overline{SE} \parallel \overline{NA}$

Show: $\overline{SA} \cong \overline{NE}$

Flowchart Proof

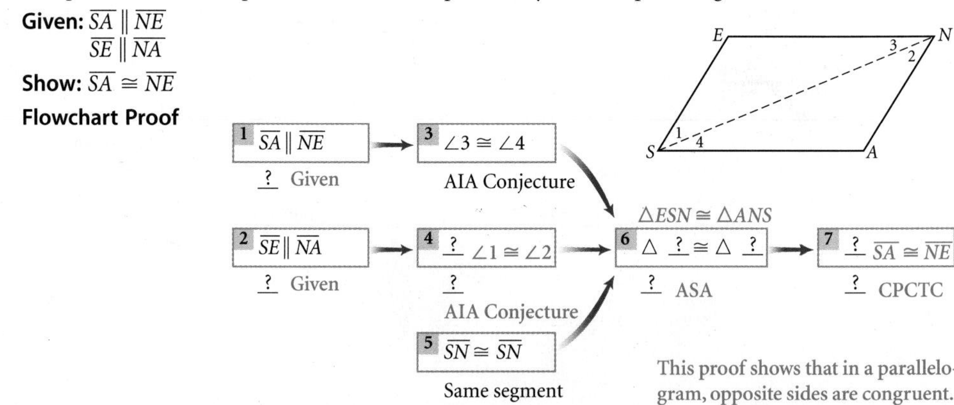

7. In Chapter 3, you learned how to construct the bisector of an angle. Now you have the skills to explain *why* the construction works, using deductive reasoning. Create a paragraph or flowchart proof to show that the construction method works. ⓗ

Given: $\angle ABC$ with $\overline{BA} \cong \overline{BC}$, $\overline{CD} \cong \overline{AD}$

Show: $\overrightarrow{BD}$ is the angle bisector of $\angle ABC$

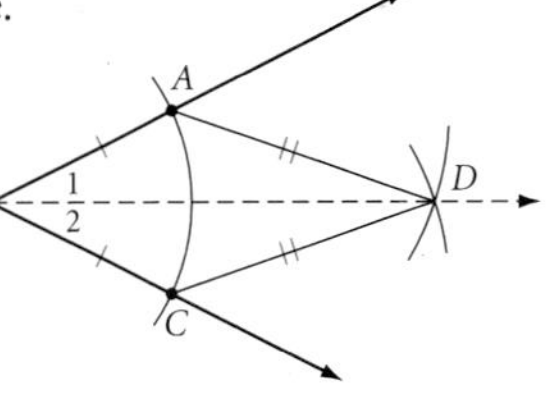

Exercise 7 The flowchart proof for this begins with three boxes.

7. We are given $\overline{AB} \cong \overline{BC}$ and $\overline{CD} \cong \overline{AD}$. We know that $\overline{BD} \cong \overline{BD}$ because they are the same segment, so by SSS we have $\triangle ABD \cong \triangle CBD$, and $\angle 1 \cong \angle 2$ by CPCTC. By the definition of angle bisector, $\overrightarrow{BD}$ bisects $\angle ABC$.

Review

4.3 **8.** Which segment is the shortest? Explain. ⓗ

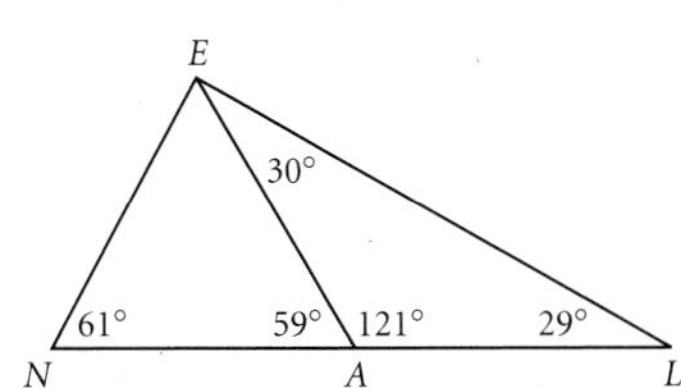

4.4 **9.** What's wrong with this picture? Explain.

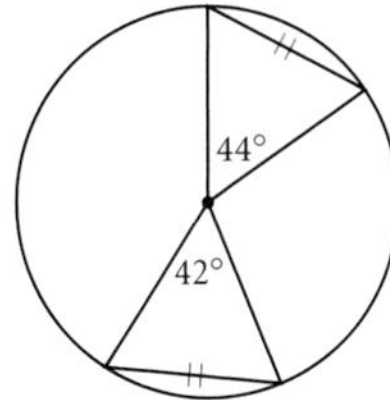

8. $\overline{NE}$, because it is across from the smallest angle in $\triangle NAE$. It is shorter than $\overline{AE}$, which is across from the smallest angle in $\triangle LAE$.

9. The triangles are congruent by SSS, so the two central angles cannot have different measures.

For Exercises 10–12, name the congruent triangles and explain why the triangles are congruent. If you cannot show that they are congruent, write "cannot be determined."

4.5 **10.** $\overline{PO} \cong \overline{PR}$

$\triangle POE \cong \triangle$? *PRN* by ASA

$\triangle SON \cong \triangle$? ⓗ *SRE* by ASA

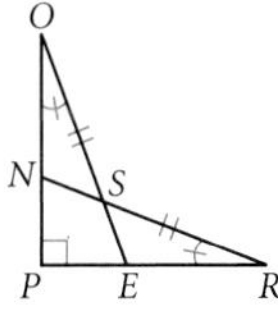

4.6 **11.** $\triangle$? $\cong \triangle$? ⓗ

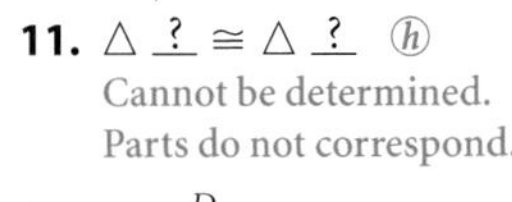
Cannot be determined.
Parts do not correspond.

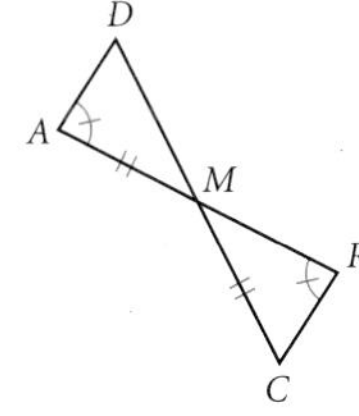

4.4 **12.** $\overline{AC} \cong \overline{CR}$, $\overline{CK}$ is a median of $\triangle ARC$. $\triangle RCK \cong \triangle$?

ACK by SSS

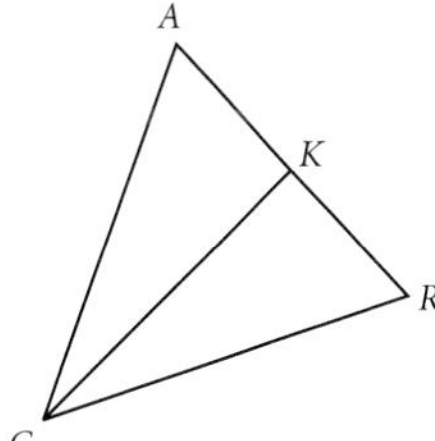

13. Copy the figure below. Calculate the measure of each lettered angle.

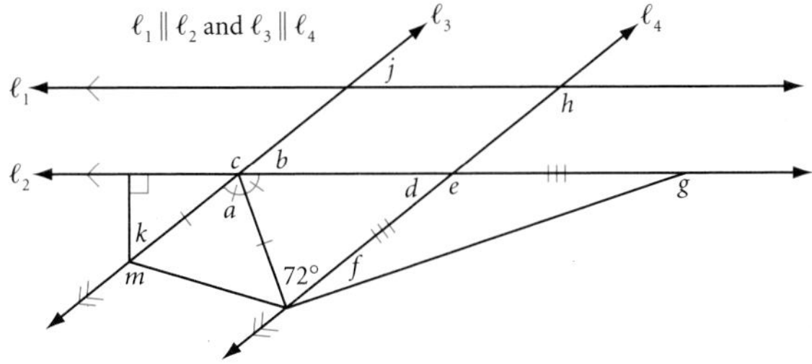

$a = 72°$, $b = 36°$, $c = 144°$, $d = 36°$, $e = 144°$, $f = 18°$, $g = 162°$, $h = 144°$, $j = 36°$, $k = 54°$, $m = 126°$

3.7 **14.** Which point of concurrency is equidistant from all three vertices? Explain why. Which point of concurrency is equidistant from all three sides? Explain why. ⓗ

14. The circumcenter is equidistant from all three vertices because it is on the perpendicular bisector of each side. The incenter is equidistant from all three sides because it is on the angle bisector of each angle.

15. ASA. The fishing pole forms the side. "Perpendicular to the ground" forms one angle. "Same angle on her line of sight" forms the other angle.

17.

4.5 **15.** Samantha is standing at the bank of a stream, wondering how wide the stream is. Remembering her geometry conjectures, she kneels down and holds her fishing pole perpendicular to the ground in front of her. She adjusts her hand on the pole so that she can see the opposite bank of the stream along her line of sight through her hand. She then turns, keeping a firm grip on the pole, and uses the same line of sight to spot a boulder on her side of the stream. She measures the distance to the boulder and concludes that this equals the distance across the stream. What triangle congruence shortcut is Samantha using? Explain.

1.4 **16.** What is the probability of randomly selecting one of the shortest diagonals from all the diagonals in a regular decagon? $\frac{2}{7}$

1.8 **17.** Sketch the solid shown with the red and green cubes removed. ⓗ

1.4 **18.** Sketch the new location of rectangle *BOXY* after it has been rotated 90° clockwise about the origin.

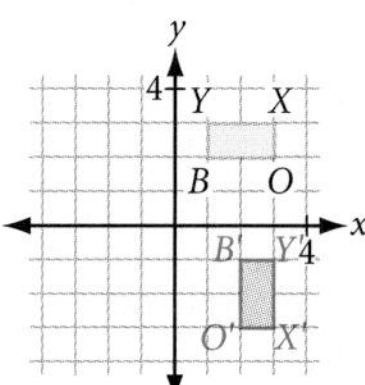

IMPROVING YOUR REASONING SKILLS

Pick a Card

Nine cards are arranged in a 3-by-3 array. Every jack borders on a king and on a queen. Every king borders on an ace. Every queen borders on a king and on an ace. (The cards border each other edge-to-edge, but not corner-to-corner.) There are at least two aces, two kings, two queens, and two jacks. Which card is in the center position of the 3-by-3 array?

IMPROVING REASONING SKILLS

In effect, the problem states that there is a unique solution, so finding any solution is sufficient. If students are stuck, suggest that they systematically try all possible locations of, say, two jacks. Point out as needed that they can use symmetry to diminish the number of possibilities; that is, for every placement of the jacks, they can rotate or reflect the entire square to account for other possibilities. (There are eight different placements of two identical cards in a 3-by-3 array.)

K	A	K
Q	A	Q
J	K	J

An ace is in the center.

LESSON

4.8

Proving Isosceles Triangle Conjectures

The right angle from which to approach any problem is the try angle.

ANONYMOUS

This boathouse is a remarkably symmetric structure with its isosceles triangle roof and the identical doors on each side. The rhombus-shaped attic window is centered on the line of symmetry of this face of the building. What might this building reveal about the special properties of the line of symmetry in an isosceles triangle?

In this lesson you will make a conjecture about a special segment in isosceles triangles. Then you will use logical reasoning to prove your conjecture is true for all isosceles triangles.

First, consider a scalene triangle. In $\triangle ARC$, $\overline{CD}$ is the altitude to the base $\overline{AR}$, $\overline{CE}$ is the angle bisector of $\angle ACR$, and $\overline{CF}$ is the median to the base $\overline{AR}$. From this example it is clear that the angle bisector, the altitude, and the median can all be different line segments. Is this true for all triangles? Can two of these ever be the same segment? Can they all be the same segment? Let's investigate.

For an interactive version of this sketch, visit www.keymath.com/DG .

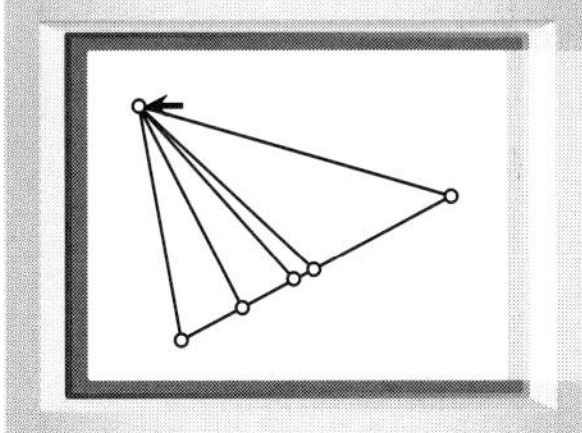

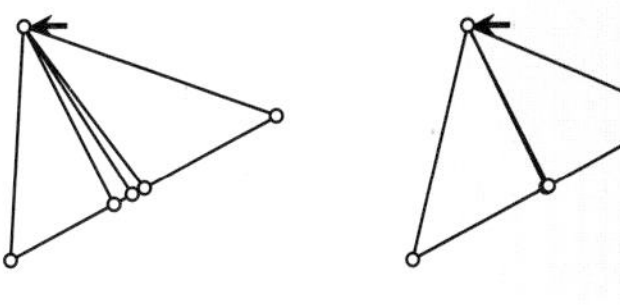

LESSON

4.8

PLANNING

LESSON OUTLINE

One day:

20 min	Investigation
15 min	Sharing
5 min	Closing
5 min	Exercises

MATERIALS

- construction tools
- protractors

TEACHING

In any isosceles triangle, the vertex angle bisector, the median, and the altitude are the same segment. This property also applies to the angle bisectors, medians, and altitudes of an equilateral triangle, since all equilateral triangles are isosceles. Students see a paragraph proof that equiangular triangles are equilateral.

One step Pose this problem: "Draw an angle—acute, obtuse, or right—and construct its bisector. Between the sides of the angle draw segments to make triangles that include the angle you started with. In which of those triangles is the angle's bisector a special line?" Students may have difficulty recognizing as isosceles a triangle whose vertex angle is not above the base angles. As they come up with ideas about triangles in which the angle bisectors are special, **[Ask]** "Are there other cases?" Request conjectures about bisectors of vertex angles in those triangles. When students seem satisfied with their conjectures, **[Ask]** "How might you explain the conjecture through deductive proof?"

LESSON OBJECTIVES

- Practice writing flowchart proofs
- Investigate vertex angle bisectors of isosceles triangles
- Develop logical and visual thinking skills

NCTM STANDARDS

	CONTENT		PROCESS
✓	Number		Problem Solving
	Algebra	✓	Reasoning
✓	Geometry	✓	Communication
✓	Measurement	✓	Connections
	Data/Probability		Representation

Step 1 To encourage good inductive reasoning, suggest that each group member investigate one of each different kind of triangle—acute, obtuse, and right.

Steps 3, 4 If students find that the segments or angles don't have exactly the same measure, let the group discuss the difficulty and perhaps bring it to the class during Sharing.

Step 5 Students might conclude "The angle bisector is also the perpendicular bisector of the base." Their conjecture is correct, though during Sharing the class might decide to state the conjecture in terms of the altitude.

Paragraph Proof

This proof of the Equilateral Triangle Conjecture, the converse of the Equiangular Triangle Conjecture, is a local proof that depends on the unproved Isosceles Triangle Conjecture; it is not a global proof.

[Ask] "Does *equilateral* imply *equiangular* for any polygons other than triangles?" [No, a rhombus is equilateral but not necessarily equiangular, and a rectangle is equiangular but not necessarily equilateral. These ideas will be developed in later chapters.] Ask if the word *regular* can be of use here. You might need to remind students that *regular* means "both equilateral and equiangular."

SHARING IDEAS

Have students share a variety of ideas. You might ask first that someone share results for the special case of an equilateral triangle.

A group may say that the segments or angles they measured did not have exactly the same measure. This observation can lead to a discussion of measurement errors and the need for deductive proof.

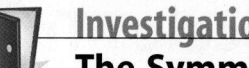

Investigation
The Symmetry Line in an Isosceles Triangle

You will need
- a compass
- a straightedge

Each person in your group should draw a different isosceles triangle for this investigation.

Step 1 Construct a large isosceles triangle on a sheet of unlined paper. Label it ARK, with K the vertex angle.

Step 2 Construct angle bisector $\overline{KD}$ with point D on $\overline{AR}$. Do $\triangle ADK$ and $\triangle RDK$ look congruent? yes

Step 3 With your compass, compare $\overline{AD}$ and $\overline{RD}$. Is D the midpoint of $\overline{AR}$? If D is the midpoint, then what type of special segment is $\overline{KD}$? yes; median

Step 4 Compare $\angle ADK$ and $\angle RDK$. Do they have equal measures? Are they supplementary? What conclusion can you make? yes; yes; $\overline{KD}$ is an altitude

Step 5 Compare your conjectures with the results of other students. Now combine the two conjectures from Steps 3 and 4 into one.

Vertex Angle Bisector Conjecture C-28

In an isosceles triangle, the bisector of the vertex angle is also __?__ and __?__. (the altitude; the median to the base)

The properties you just discovered for isosceles triangles also apply to equilateral triangles. Equilateral triangles are also isosceles, although isosceles triangles are not necessarily equilateral.

You have probably noticed the following property of equilateral triangles: When you construct an equilateral triangle, each angle measures 60°. If each angle measures 60°, then all three angles are congruent. So, if a triangle is equilateral, then it is equiangular. This is called the Equilateral Triangle Conjecture.

If we agree that the Isosceles Triangle Conjecture is true, we can write the paragraph proof below.

Paragraph Proof: The Equilateral Triangle Conjecture

We need to show that if $AB = AC = BC$, then $\triangle ABC$ is equiangular. By the Isosceles Triangle Conjecture,

If $AB = AC$, then $m\angle B = m\angle C$.

If $\triangle ABC$, then $\triangle ABC$.

As the class tries to reach consensus on how to phrase the conjecture, encourage thinking about the triangle, not just its parts. For example, "The bisector of the vertex angle is also the median and perpendicular bisector of the base" is at a higher van Hiele level than the conjecture "The bisector of the vertex angle is also the perpendicular bisector of the base," which refers to only a part of the triangle.

[Ask] "Why does the investigation title refer to the symmetry line?" [A figure has reflectional symmetry if you can fold it along a line so that all the points on one side of the line exactly coincide with corresponding points on the other side of the line. That line is called the *line of symmetry*.] "Why is the vertex angle bisector (or median or altitude) in an isosceles triangle a line of symmetry?" [Students can prove deductively that if any point on the triangle is folded across that line, it lies on another point of the triangle. Each point will follow the shortest path across the median, and the shortest path is perpendicular to the median.]

If $AB = BC$, then $m\angle A = m\angle C$.

If $_A\triangle^C_B$, then $_A\triangle^C_B$.

If $m\angle A = m\angle C$ and $m\angle B = m\angle C$, then $m\angle A = m\angle B = m\angle C$. So, $\triangle ABC$ is equiangular.

If $_A\triangle^C_B$ and $_A\triangle^C_B$, then $_A\triangle^C_B$. ■

The converse of the Equilateral Triangle Conjecture is called the Equiangular Triangle Conjecture, and it states: If a triangle is equiangular, then it is equilateral. Is this true? Yes, and the proof is almost identical to the proof above, except that you use the converse of the Isosceles Triangle Conjecture. So, if the Equilateral Triangle Conjecture and the Equiangular Triangle Conjecture are both true then we can combine them. Complete the conjecture below and add it to your conjecture list.

Equilateral/Equiangular Triangle Conjecture C-29

Every equilateral triangle is _?_, and, conversely, every equiangular triangle is _?_. equilateral equiangular

The Equilateral/Equiangular Triangle Conjecture is a **biconditional** conjecture: Both the statement and its converse are true. A triangle is equilateral *if and only if* it is equiangular. One condition cannot be true unless the other is also true.

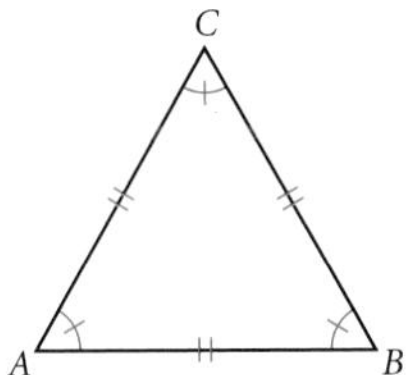

EXERCISES

You will need

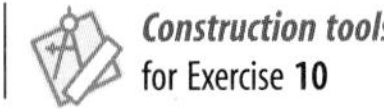

In Exercises 1–3, $\triangle ABC$ is isosceles with $\overline{AC} \cong \overline{BC}$.

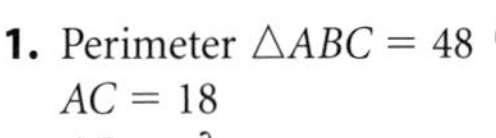

1. Perimeter $\triangle ABC = 48$ ⓗ
$AC = 18$
$AD =$ _?_ 6

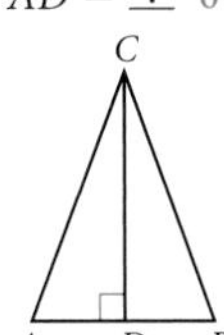

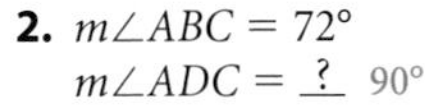

2. $m\angle ABC = 72°$
$m\angle ADC =$ _?_ 90°

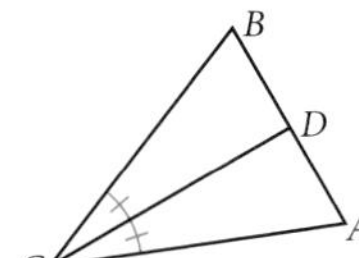

3. $m\angle CAB = 45°$
$m\angle ACD =$ _?_ 45°

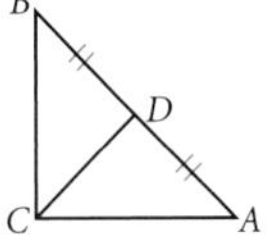

Sharing Ideas (continued)

[Ask] "Do the vertex angle bisector, median, and altitude coincide in any triangles other than isosceles?" [no, because isosceles includes equilateral]

Exercises 4 and 5 in the previous lesson involved proofs of the Isosceles Triangle Conjecture and its converse. Both proofs used the symmetry line, though it was not called that. **[Ask]** "What other proofs of these theorems might be possible using the Vertex Angle Bisector Conjecture?" It may confuse students that they no longer need to use the fact that the two sides of the original triangle are congruent; point out that this fact was used to prove the Vertex Angle Bisector Conjecture.

If you have time, say that someone once suggested this proof of the Isosceles Triangle Conjecture: "Think about triangle *ARK* in two ways, as triangle *ARK* and as triangle *AKR*. Because the triangle is isosceles, segment *AR* is congruent to segment *AK*, and vice versa. Moreover, $\overline{RK}$ is congruent to itself. Therefore, by SSS, $\triangle ARK \cong \triangle AKR$. So $\angle ARK \cong \angle AKR$, by CPCTC." **[Ask]** "Is this proof valid?" Encourage all critiques as students grapple with the logic. You might challenge them to prove the converse in a similar way.

Assessing Progress

While observing group work and the class discussion, you can assess students' understanding of isosceles triangle, vertex angle, base, acute triangle, obtuse triangle, right triangle, angle bisector, midpoint, supplementary angles, altitude, and median. You can also note students' ability to construct an isosceles triangle and an angle bisector, compare segment lengths with a compass, and measure angles with a protractor.

Closing the Lesson

Emphasize the point of this lesson: The vertex angle bisector, median, and altitude seem to be the same segment in any isosceles triangle. We have not yet explained the conjecture deductively, but the exercises include opportunities to do so. If you feel students need more help with these ideas, you might give an example by working through Exercise 4 as a class.

BUILDING UNDERSTANDING

The main focus of the exercises is proving the three parts of the Vertex Angle Bisector Conjecture.

ASSIGNING HOMEWORK

Essential	1–6
Performance assessment	7
Portfolio	6
Group	4, 5, 8, 9
Review	10–17

MATERIALS

- Exercises 4 and 5 (T), *optional*
- Exercise 11 (T), *optional*

▶ Helping with the Exercises

If students get stuck on a problem, they can move on and come back to it later.

Exercise 5 This proof illustrates how a previously proved conjecture can be used as the reason in another proof. It is not necessary to repeat the earlier proof.

In Exercises 4–6, copy the flowchart. Supply the missing statement and reasons in the proofs of Conjectures A, B, and C shown below. These three conjectures are all part of the Vertex Angle Bisector Conjecture.

4. Complete the flowchart proof for Conjecture A.

Conjecture A: The bisector of the vertex angle in an isosceles triangle divides the isosceles triangle into two congruent triangles.

Given: $\triangle ABC$ is isosceles
$\overline{AC} \cong \overline{BC}$, and $\overline{CD}$ is the bisector of $\angle C$

Show: $\triangle ADC \cong \triangle BDC$

Flowchart Proof

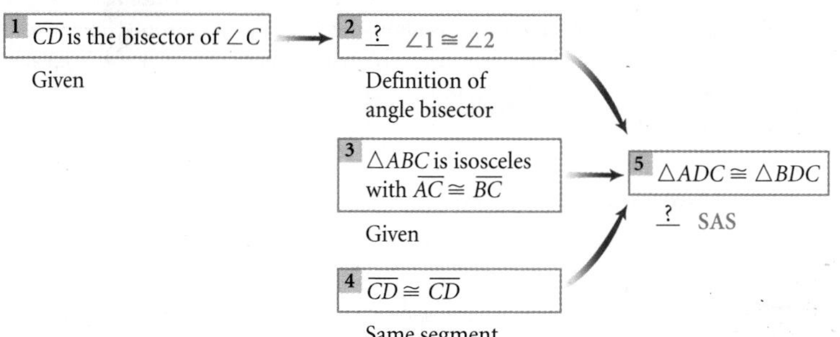

5. Complete the flowchart proof for Conjecture B.

Conjecture B: The bisector of the vertex angle in an isosceles triangle is also the altitude to the base.

Given: $\triangle ABC$ is isosceles
$\overline{AC} \cong \overline{BC}$, and $\overline{CD}$ bisects $\angle C$

Show: $\overline{CD}$ is an altitude

Flowchart Proof

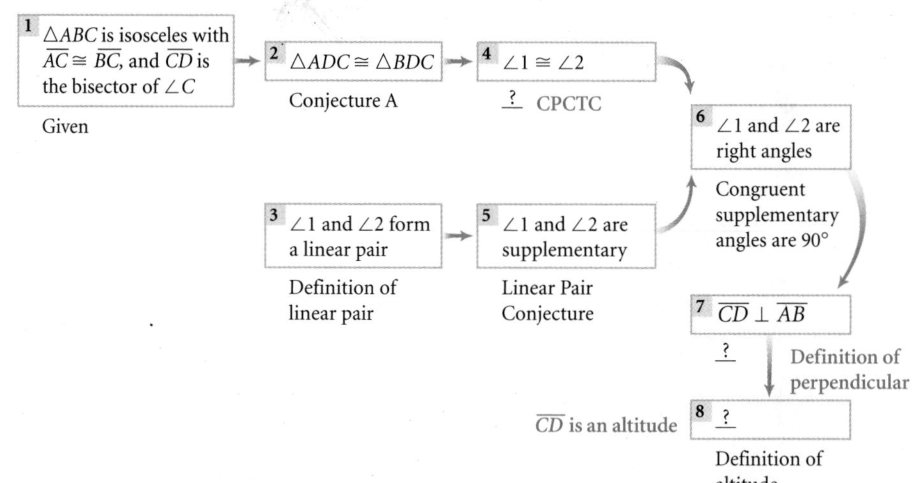

6. Create a flowchart proof for Conjecture C.

Conjecture C: The bisector of the vertex angle in an isosceles triangle is also the median to the base.

Given: $\triangle ABC$ is isosceles with $\overline{AC} \cong \overline{BC}$

$\overline{CD}$ is the bisector of $\angle C$

Show: $\overline{CD}$ is a median

7. In the figure at right, $\triangle ABC$, the plumb level is isosceles. A weight, called the plumb bob, hangs from a string attached at point C. If you place the level on a surface and the string is perpendicular to $\overline{AB}$ then the surface you are testing is level. To tell whether the string is perpendicular to $\overline{AB}$, check whether it passes through the midpoint of $\overline{AB}$. Create a flowchart proof to show that if D is the midpoint of $\overline{AB}$, then $\overline{CD}$ is perpendicular to $\overline{AB}$.

Given: $\triangle ABC$ is isosceles with $\overline{AC} \cong \overline{BC}$

D is the midpoint of $\overline{AB}$

Show: $\overline{CD} \perp \overline{AB}$

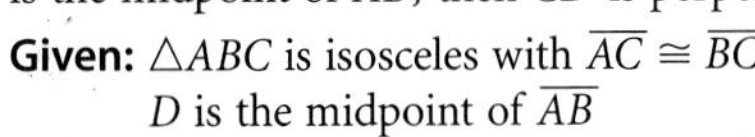

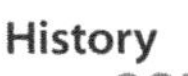

History CONNECTION

Builders in ancient Egypt used a tool called a *plumb level* in building the great pyramids. With a plumb level, you can use the basic properties of isosceles triangles to determine whether a surface is level.

8. Write a paragraph proof of the Isosceles Triangle Conjecture. ⓗ

9. Write a paragraph proof of the Equiangular Triangle Conjecture.

10. ***Construction*** Use compass and straightedge to construct a 30° angle.

Review

11. Trace the figure below. Calculate the measure of each lettered angle.

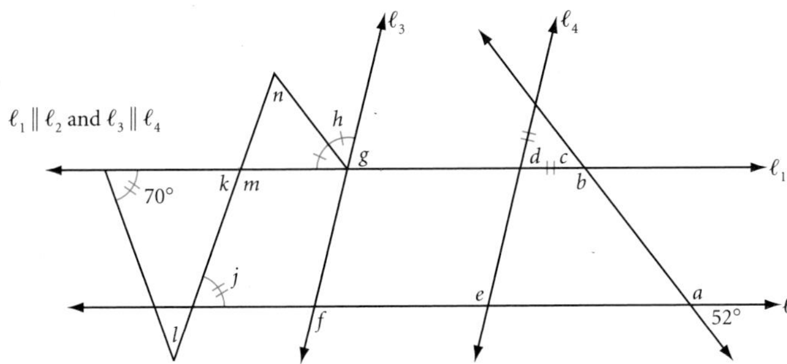

$a = 128°, b = 128°, c = 52°, d = 76°, e = 104°, f = 104°, g = 76°, h = 52°, j = 70°, k = 70°, l = 40°, m = 110°, n = 58°$

1.7 **12.** How many minutes after 3:00 will the hands of a clock overlap? ⓗ between 16 and 17 minutes

9. The proof is similar to the one on pages 242–243, but in reverse, and using the Converse of the Isosceles Triangle Conjecture.

10.

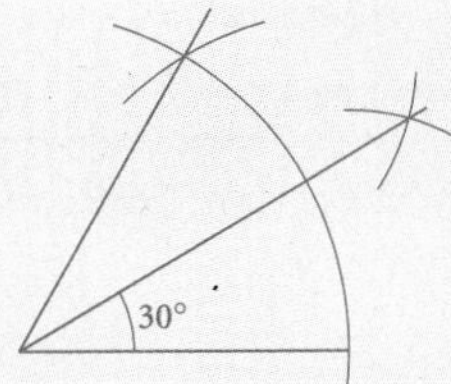

6.

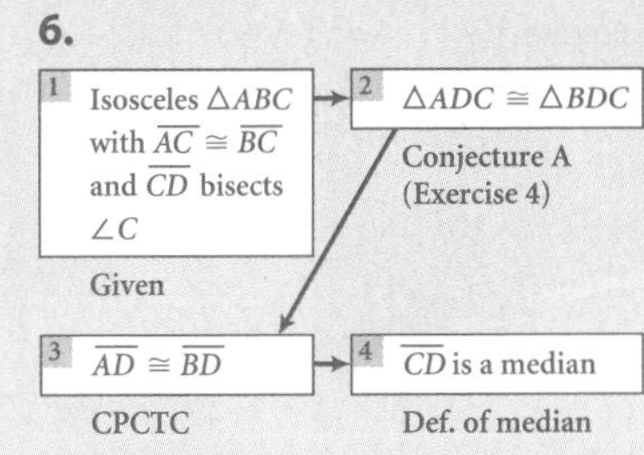

Exercise 7 Students might prove the triangles congruent (by SSS) and mimic part of the proof of Conjecture B (Exercise 5) to get to the perpendicular. Encourage them to use Conjecture B as a reason rather than restating some of its steps. They cannot yet justify a claim that the median is also an altitude, because the Vertex Angle Bisector Conjecture begins with the vertex angle bisector, not the median.

7.

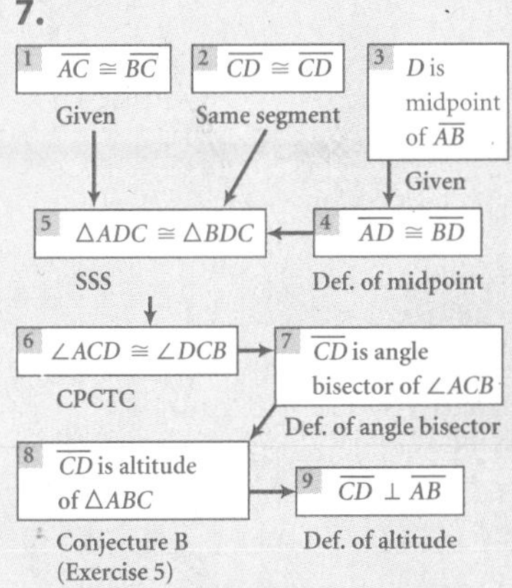

8.

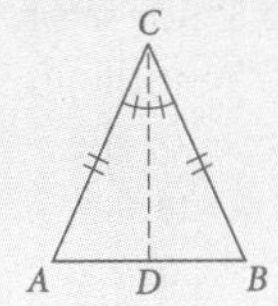

Drawing the vertex angle bisector as an auxiliary segment, we have two triangles. We can show them to be congruent by SAS, as we did in Exercise 4. Then, $\angle A \cong \angle B$, by CPCTC. Therefore, base angles of an isosceles triangle are congruent.

Exercise 15 Other answers include (4, 6) and (4, 0).

15. (4, 6) or (4, 0) or any point at which the x-coordinate is either 1 or 7 and the y-coordinate does not equal 3

16. Hugo and Duane can locate the site of the fireworks by creating a diagram using SSS.

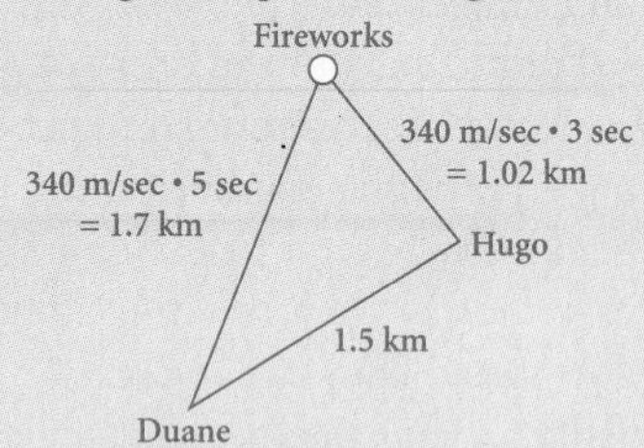

17. (C_nH_{2n})

EXTENSION

Challenge students to find out whether it is possible to construct a triangle in which exactly two of the three segments—angle bisector, median, and altitude—coincide. [If any two segments coincide, all three will. Proving this for the case in which the altitude is one of the segments is not difficult; proving it for the case of the angle bisector or the median is more challenging, because a quick proof would require SSA, which is not a valid congruence shortcut.]

UYAS 3 **13.** Find the equation of the line through point C that is parallel to side $\overline{AB}$ in $\triangle ABC$. The vertices are $A(1, 3)$, $B(4, -2)$, and $C(6, 6)$. Write your answer in slope-intercept form, $y = mx + b$. $y = -\frac{5}{3}x + 16$

2.4 **14.** Sixty concurrent lines in a plane divide the plane into how many regions? ⓗ 120

UYAS 3 **15.** If two vertices of a triangle have coordinates $A(1, 3)$ and $B(7, 3)$, find the coordinates of point C so that $\triangle ABC$ is a right triangle. Can you find any other points that would create a right triangle?

4.4 **16. APPLICATION** Hugo hears the sound of fireworks three seconds after he sees the flash. Duane hears the sound five seconds after he sees the flash. Hugo and Duane are 1.5 km apart. They know the flash was somewhere to the north. They also know that a flash can be seen almost instantly, but sound travels 340 m/sec. Do Hugo and Duane have enough information to locate the site of the fireworks? Make a sketch and label all the distances that they know or can calculate.

2.3 **17. APPLICATION** In an earlier exercise, you found the rule for the family of hydrocarbons called alkanes, or paraffins. These contain a straight chain of carbons. Alkanes can also form rings of carbon atoms. These molecules are called cycloparaffins. The first three cycloparaffins are shown below. Sketch the molecule cycloheptane. Write the general rule for cycloparaffins ($C_nH_?$). ⓗ

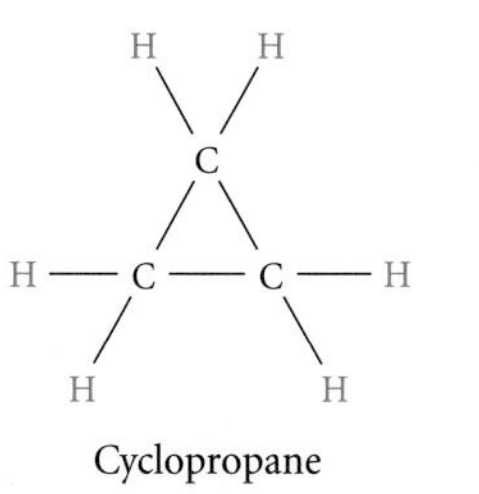
Cyclopropane

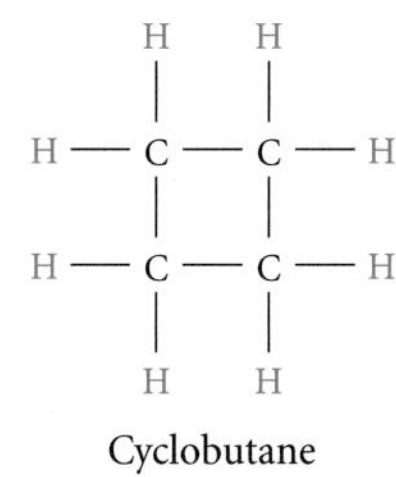
Cyclobutane

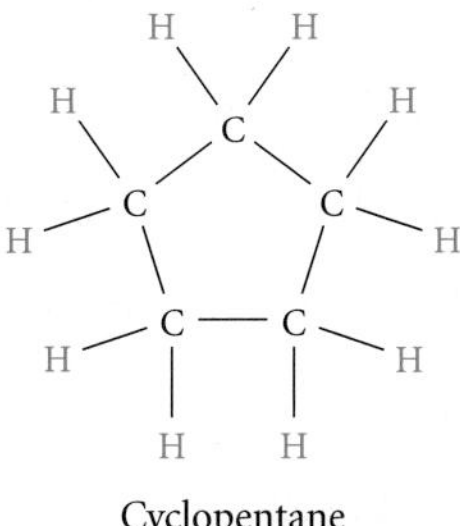
Cyclopentane

IMPROVING YOUR ALGEBRA SKILLS

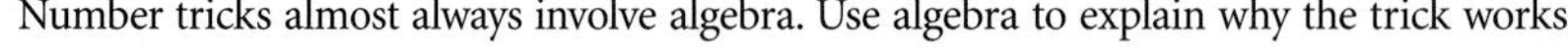

Number Tricks

Try this number trick.

Double the number of the month you were born. Subtract 16 from your answer. Multiply your result by 5, then add 100 to your answer. Subtract 20 from your result, then multiply by 10. Finally, add the day of the month you were born to your answer. The number you end up with shows the month and day you were born! For example, if you were born March 15th, your answer will be 315. If you were born December 7th, your answer will be 1207.

Number tricks almost always involve algebra. Use algebra to explain why the trick works.

IMPROVING ALGEBRA SKILLS

Let x represent the month you were born, and let y represent the day.

$2x$
$2x - 16$
$5(2x - 16) = 10x - 80$
$10x - 80 + 100 = 10x + 20$
$10x + 20 - 20 = 10x$
$10x \cdot 10 = 100x$
$100x + y$

Exploration

Napoleon's Theorem

Portrait of Napoleon by the French painter Anne-Louis Girodet (1767–1824)

In this exploration you'll learn about a discovery attributed to French Emperor Napoleon Bonaparte (1769–1821). Napoleon was extremely interested in mathematics. This discovery, called Napoleon's Theorem, uses equilateral triangles constructed on the sides of any triangle.

Activity

Napoleon Triangles

Step 1 Open a new Sketchpad sketch. Draw $\triangle ABC$.

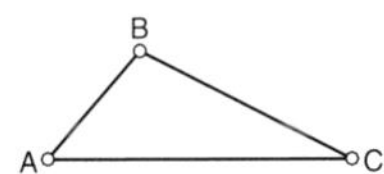

Step 2 Follow the Procedure Note to create a custom tool that constructs an equilateral triangle and its centroid given the endpoints of any segment.

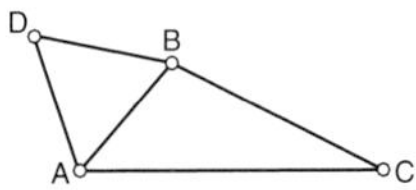

Procedure Note

1. Construct an equilateral triangle on $\overline{AB}$.
2. Construct the centroid of the equilateral triangle.
3. Hide any medians or midpoints that you constructed for the centroid.
4. Select all three vertices, all three sides, and the centroid of the equilateral triangle.
5. Turn your new construction into a custom tool by choosing **Create New Tool** from the Custom Tools menu.

Step 3 Use your custom tool on $\overline{BC}$ and $\overline{CA}$. If an equilateral triangle falls inside your triangle, undo and try again, selecting the two endpoints in reverse order.

Step 4 Connect the centroids of the equilateral triangles. Triangle *GQL* is called the *outer Napoleon triangle* of $\triangle ABC$.

Drag the vertices and the sides of $\triangle ABC$ and observe what happens.

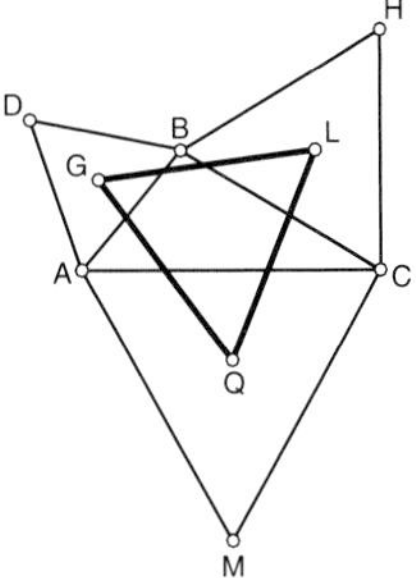

EXPLORATION

PLANNING

LESSON OUTLINE

One day:

15 min Activity

5 min Sharing

5 min Closing

MATERIALS

- The Geometer's Sketchpad

TEACHING

Students discover that there are equilateral triangles closely associated with any triangle.

Guiding the Activity

If your class doesn't have Napoleon's leisure for exploration, it's almost imperative that students use custom tools for constructing equilateral triangles and centroids.

[Link] An analogous theorem applied to rectangles is von Aubel's Theorem, which states that the centers of squares constructed on the sides of a quadrilateral form a quadrilateral with perpendicular diagonals.

[Link] Equilateral triangles constructed on the sides of a triangle can be used to locate the very useful *Fermat Point,* the sum of whose distances to the three vertices is minimal.

LESSON OBJECTIVE

- Explore a relationship between the centroids of equilateral triangles constructed on the sides of any triangle

NCTM STANDARDS

	CONTENT		PROCESS
	Number	✔	Problem Solving
	Algebra	✔	Reasoning
✔	Geometry	✔	Communication
	Measurement	✔	Connections
	Data/Probability		Representation

Step 5 The outer triangle is always equilateral.

Step 6 These three segments intersect at a single point and are equal in length.

Step 7 The area of the original triangle plus the area of the inner triangle equals the area of the outer triangle.

Closing the Lesson

You might mention that Napoleon pursued mathematics as a means of relaxation, as did other prominent leaders including U.S. President Abraham Lincoln and President James Garfield, who found an elegant algebraic proof of the Pythagorean Theorem.

Friendly Window for the Project
A friendly window is one in which the ratio of horizontal to vertical distances is the same as the ratio of the number of pixels horizontally and vertically on the screen. Therefore, in a friendly window there is not much distortion (for example, circles appear circular), and intersections of lines between rational points are more likely to occur at pixels. In the friendly window suggested, each unit encompasses ten pixels on a TI-82 or TI-83 calculator.

Step 5 | What can you say about the outer Napoleon triangle? Write what you think Napoleon discovered in his theorem.

Here are some extensions to this theorem for you to explore.

Step 6 | Construct segments connecting each vertex of your original triangle with the vertex of the equilateral triangle on the opposite side. What do you notice about these three segments? (This discovery was made by M. C. Escher.)

Step 7 | Construct the *inner Napoleon triangle* by reflecting each centroid across its corresponding side in the original triangle. Measure the areas of the original triangle and of the outer and inner Napoleon triangles. How do these areas compare?

LINES AND ISOSCELES TRIANGLES

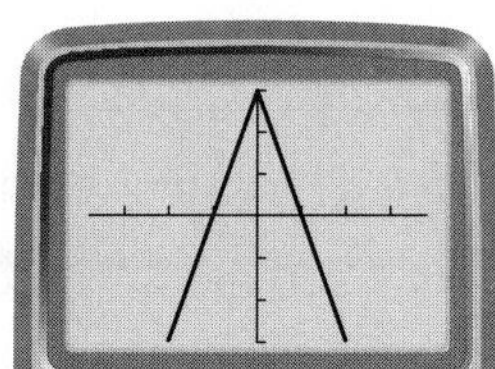

In this example, the lines $y = 3x + 3$ and $y = -3x + 3$ contain the sides of an isosceles triangle whose base is on the x-axis and whose line of symmetry is the y-axis. The window shown is $\{-4.7, 4.7, 1, -3.1, 3.1, 1\}$.

1. Find other pairs of lines that form isosceles triangles whose bases are on the x-axis and whose lines of symmetry are the y-axis.
2. Find pairs of lines that form isosceles triangles whose bases are on the y-axis and whose lines of symmetry are the x-axis.
3. A line $y = mx + b$ contains one side of an isosceles triangle whose base is on the x-axis and whose line of symmetry is the y-axis. What is the equation of the line containing the other side? Now suppose the line $y = mx + b$ contains one side of an isosceles triangle whose base is on the y-axis and whose line of symmetry is the x-axis. What is the equation of the line containing the other side?
4. Graph the lines $y = 2x - 2$, $y = \frac{1}{2}x + 1$, $y = x$, and $y = -x$. Describe the figure that the lines form. Find other sets of lines that form figures like this one.

Supporting the project

To get a good result, students need to know about friendly windows described above.

OUTCOMES

1. Any pair that has the same y-intercepts and slopes with the same value but opposite signs.
2. Any pair that has the same x-intercepts and slopes with the same value but opposite signs.
3. $y = -mx + b$; $y = -mx - b$
4. The lines form an isosceles triangle with the base on the line $y = -x$ and with line of symmetry the line $y = x$. Other such triangles are formed on the base $y = -x$ by lines with equations of the form $y = mx - m$ and $y = \left(\frac{1}{m}\right)x + 1$.

CHAPTER 4 REVIEW

In this chapter you made many conjectures about triangles. You discovered some basic properties of isosceles and equilateral triangles. You learned different ways to show that two triangles are congruent. Do you remember them all? Triangle congruence shortcuts are an important idea in geometry. You can use them to explain why your constructions work. In later chapters, you will use your triangle conjectures to investigate properties of other polygons.

You also practiced reading and writing flowchart proofs. Can you sketch a diagram illustrating each conjecture you made in this chapter?

Check your conjecture list to make sure it is up to date. Make sure you have a clear diagram illustrating each conjecture.

EXERCISES

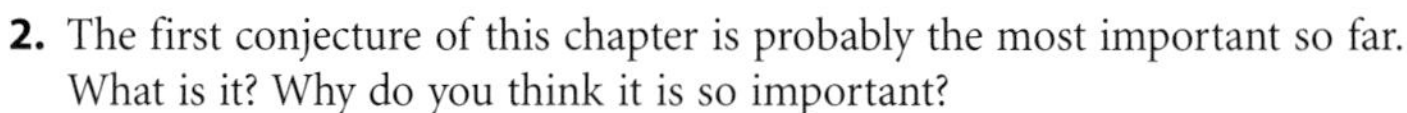

You will need

Construction tools for Exercises **33, 34,** and **37**

1. Why are triangles so useful in structures? Their rigidity gives strength.
2. The first conjecture of this chapter is probably the most important so far. What is it? Why do you think it is so important?
3. What special properties do isosceles triangles have? The angle bisector of the vertex angle is also the median and the altitude.
4. What does the statement "The shortest distance between two points is the straight line between them" have to do with the Triangle Inequality Conjecture?
5. What information do you need in order to determine that two triangles are congruent? That is, what are the four congruence shortcuts? SSS, SAS, ASA, or SAA
6. Explain why SSA is not a congruence shortcut.

High School geometry really paid off when, in planning his trip, Jake remembered that the shortest distance between two points is a straight line.

For Exercises 7–24, name the congruent triangles. State the conjecture or definition that supports the congruence statement. If you cannot show the triangles to be congruent from the information given, write "cannot be determined."

7. $\triangle PEA \cong \triangle$?

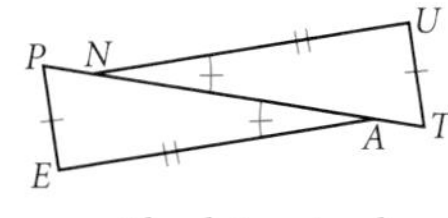

cannot be determined

8. $\triangle TOP \cong \triangle$? ZAP by SAA

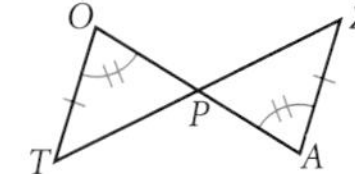

9. $\triangle MSE \cong \triangle$? OSU by SSS

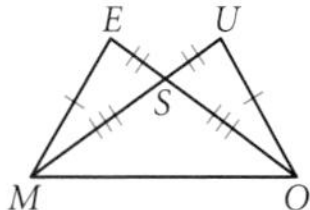

2. The Triangle Sum Conjecture states that the sum of the measures of the angles in every triangle is 180°. Possible answers: it applies to all triangles; many other conjectures rely on it.

4. The distance between A and B is along the segment connecting them. The distance from A to C to B can't be shorter than the distance from A to B. Therefore $AC + CB > AB$. Points A, B, and C form a triangle. Therefore the sum of the lengths of any two sides is greater than the length of the third side.

Exercise 6 [Ask] "If the angle in a triangle that has corresponding SSA congruent with another triangle is a specific kind of angle, the triangle is determined. What must the angle be?" [obtuse or known to be opposite the longer of the two given sides]

6. In some cases two different triangles can be constructed using the same two sides and non-included angle.

CHAPTER REVIEW 4

PLANNING

LESSON OUTLINE

30 min	Exercises and helping individuals
15 min	Student self-assessment

MATERIALS

- Exercise 27 (T), *optional*

REVIEWING

Pose this problem: "Suppose you have two isosceles triangles with congruent altitudes and a base angle of one congruent to a base angle of the other. Can you conclude that the two triangles are congruent?" Encourage students to find as many ways as they can to complete the proof, using flowcharts to show their proofs. Various proofs might cite the Triangle Sum Conjecture, the Third Angle Conjecture, the Isosceles Triangle Conjecture, the four congruence shortcuts, and the Vertex Angle Bisector Conjecture, thus reviewing the major topics of the chapter.

ASSIGNING HOMEWORK

You could ask groups to do pair share on the first six exercises and then complete the rest of the odd-numbered exercises in their groups. Students can do the remaining even-numbered exercises on their own.

Helping with the Exercises

Suggest that students refer to their assignments from throughout the chapter for help with the review exercises.

Exercise 12 The parts do not correspond.

10. $\triangle TIM \cong \triangle$ __?__

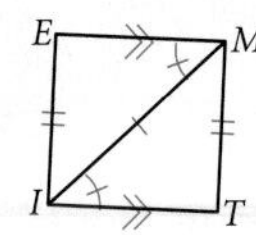

cannot be determined

11. $\triangle TRP \cong \triangle$ __?__ APR by SAS

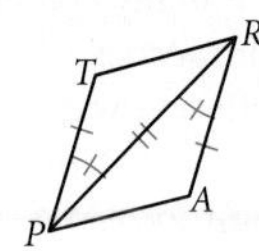

12. $\triangle CAT \cong \triangle$ __?__

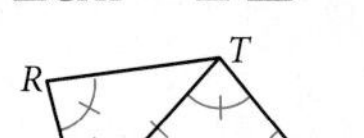

cannot be determined

13. $\triangle CGH \cong \triangle$ __?__ NGI by SAS

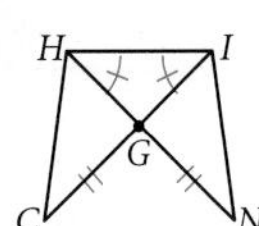

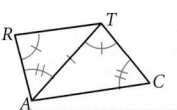

14. $\overleftrightarrow{AB} \parallel \overleftrightarrow{CD}$
$\triangle ABE \cong \triangle$ __?__ DCE by SAA or ASA

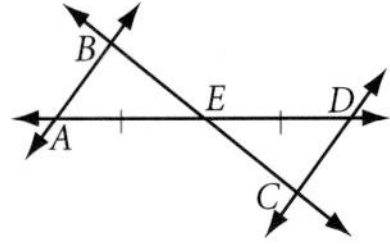

15. Polygon $CARBON$ is a regular hexagon.
$\triangle ACN \cong \triangle$ __?__ RBO or OBR by SAS

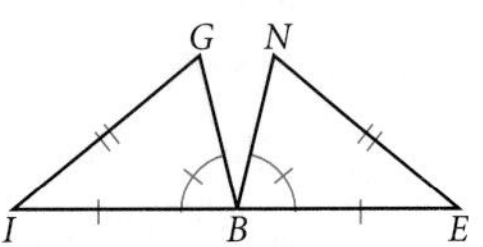

$\triangle AMD \cong \triangle UMT$ by SAS

16. $\triangle$ __?__ $\cong \triangle$ __?__, $\overline{AD} \cong$ __?__ $\overline{UT}$ by CPCTC

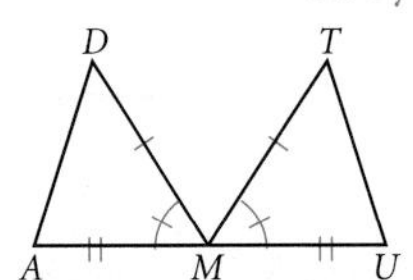

17. $\triangle$ __?__ $\cong \triangle$ __?__

cannot be determined

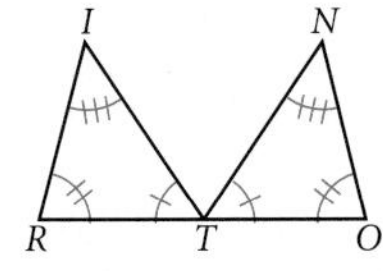

18. $\triangle$ __?__ $\cong \triangle$ __?__

cannot be determined

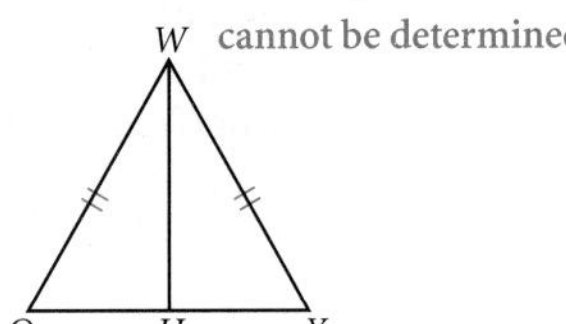

$\triangle TRI \cong \triangle ALS$ by SAA

19. $\triangle$ __?__ $\cong \triangle$ __?__, $\overline{TR} \cong$ __?__ ⓗ $\overline{AL}$ by CPCTC

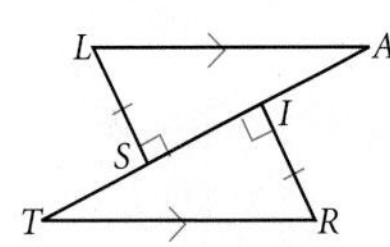

$\triangle SVE \cong \triangle NIK$ by SSS

20. $\triangle$ __?__ $\cong \triangle$ __?__, $\overline{EI} \cong$ __?__ $\overline{KV}$ by overlapping segments property

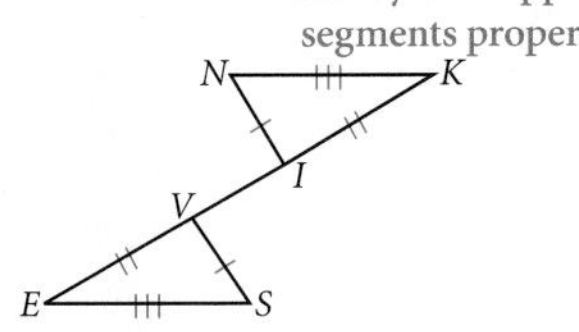

21. $\triangle$ __?__ $\cong \triangle$ __?__
Is $\overline{WH}$ a median? ⓗ cannot be determined

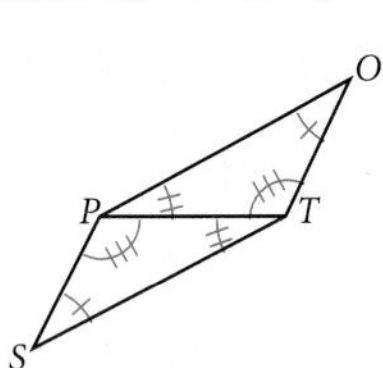

22. $\triangle$ __?__ $\cong \triangle$ __?__
Is $NCTM$ a parallelogram or a trapezoid?

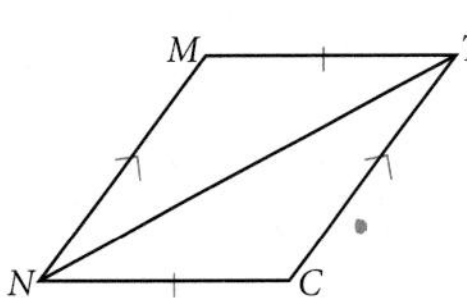

cannot be determined

23. $\triangle$ __?__ $\cong \triangle$ __?__
$\triangle LAI$ is isosceles with $\overline{IA} \cong \overline{LA}$. ⓗ

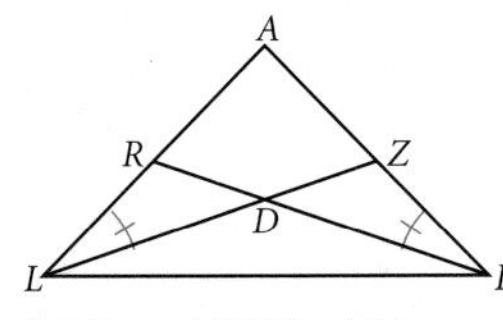

$\triangle LAZ \cong \triangle IAR$ by ASA, $\triangle LRI \cong \triangle IZL$ by ASA, and $\triangle LRD \cong \triangle IZD$ by ASA

$\triangle PTS \cong \triangle TPO$ by ASA or SAA

24. $\triangle$ __?__ $\cong \triangle$ __?__
Is $STOP$ a parallelogram? yes

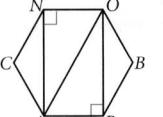

25. What's wrong with this picture? ⓗ

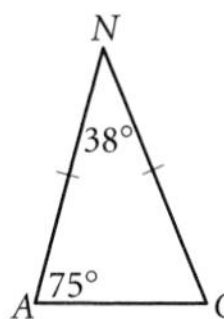

26. What's wrong with this picture?

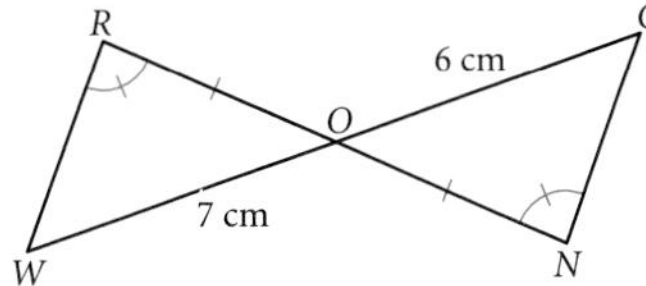

27. Quadrilateral *CAMP* has been divided into three triangles. Use the angle measures provided to determine the longest and shortest segments.

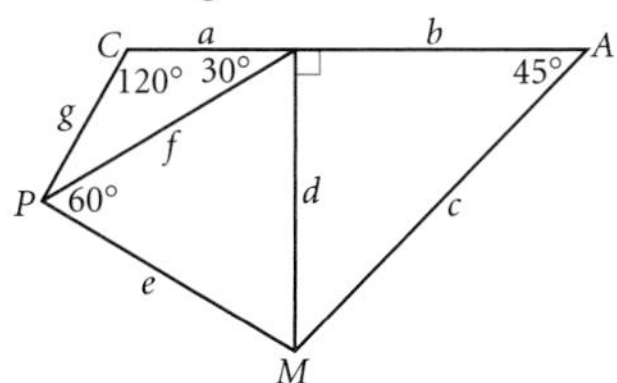

28. The measure of an angle formed by the bisectors of two angles in a triangle, as shown below, is 100°. What is angle measure x?

$x = 20°$

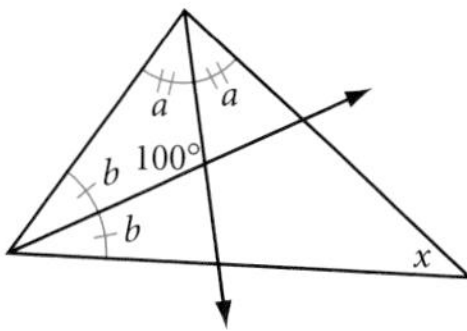

In Exercises 29 and 30, decide whether there is enough information to prove congruence. If there is, write a proof. If not, explain what is missing.

29. In the figure below, $\overline{RE} \cong \overline{AE}$, $\angle S \cong \angle T$, and $\angle ERL \cong \angle EAL$. Is $\overline{SA} \cong \overline{TR}$?

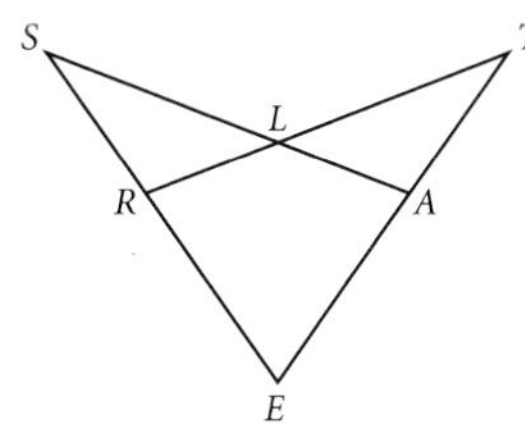

30. In the figure below, $\angle A \cong \angle M$, $\overline{AF} \perp \overline{FR}$, and $\overline{MR} \perp \overline{FR}$. Is $\triangle FRD$ isosceles?

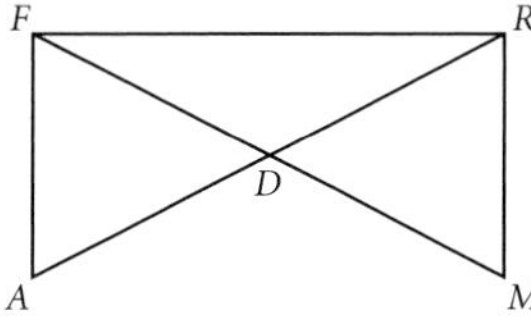

31. The measure of an angle formed by altitudes from two vertices of a triangle, as shown below, is 132°. What is angle measure x? $x = 48°$

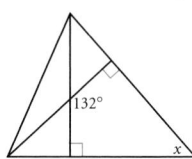

32. Connecting the legs of the chair at their midpoints as shown guarantees that the seat is parallel to the floor. Explain why. ⓗ

25. $\triangle ANG$ is isosceles, so $\angle A \cong \angle G$. However, the sum of $m\angle A + m\angle N + m\angle G = 188°$. The measures of the three angles of a triangle must sum to 180°.

26. $\triangle ROW \cong \triangle NOG$ by ASA, implying that $\overline{OW} \cong \overline{OG}$. However, the two segments shown are not equal in measure.

27. $a = g < e = d = b = f < c$. Thus, c is the longest segment and a and g are the shortest.

29. Yes. $\triangle TRE \cong \triangle SAE$ by SAA, so sides are congruent by CPCTC.

30. Yes. $\triangle FRM \cong \triangle RFA$ by SAA. $\angle RFM \cong \angle FRA$ by CPCTC. Since base angles are congruent, $\triangle FRD$ is isosceles.

32. The legs form two triangles that are congruent by SAS. Since alternate interior angles are congruent by CPCTC, the seat must be parallel to the floor.

For Exercises 33 and 34, use the segments and the angles below. Use either patty paper or a compass and a straightedge. The lowercase letter above each segment represents the length of the segment.

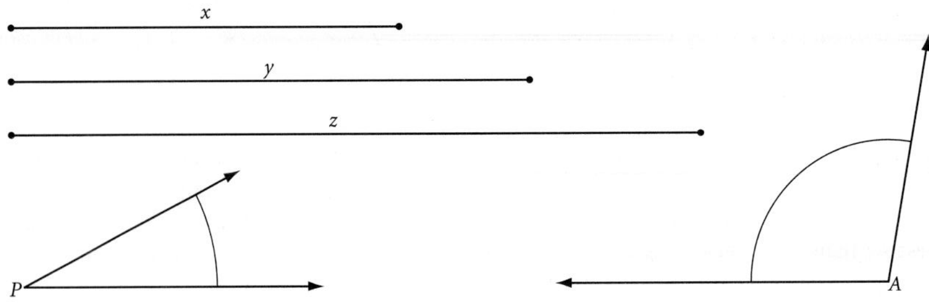

33. ***Construction*** Construct $\triangle PAL$ given $\angle P$, $\angle A$, and $AL = y$.

34. ***Construction*** Construct two triangles $\triangle PBS$ that are not congruent to each other given $\angle P$, $PB = z$, and $SB = x$.

35. In the figure at right, is $\overline{TI} \parallel \overline{RE}$? Complete the flowchart proof or explain why they are not parallel. ⓗ

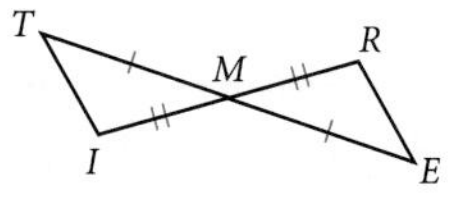

Given: M is the midpoint of both $\overline{TE}$ and $\overline{IR}$.

Show: $\overline{TI} \parallel \overline{RE}$

Flowchart Proof

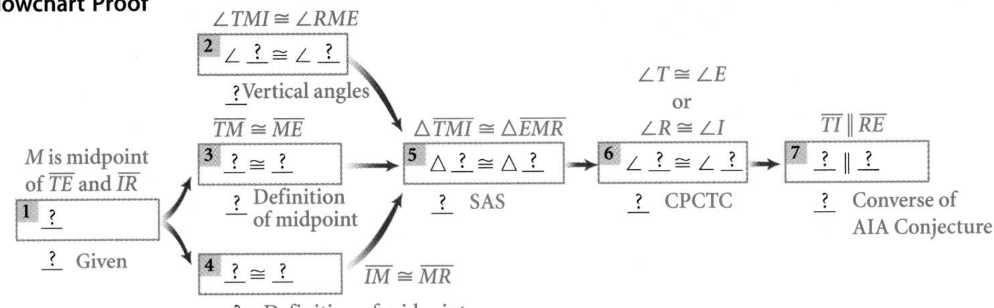

36. At the beginning of the chapter, you learned that triangles make structures more stable. Let's revisit the shelves from Lesson 4.1. Explain how the SSS congruence shortcut guarantees that the shelves on the right will retain their shape, and why the shelves on the left wobble.

37. ***Construction*** Use patty paper or compass and straightedge to construct a 75° angle. Explain your method.

33. Construct $\angle P$ and $\angle A$ to be adjacent. The angle that forms a linear pair with the conjunction of $\angle P$ and $\angle A$ is $\angle L$. Construct $\angle A$. Mark off the length AL on one ray. Construct $\angle L$. Extend the unconnected sides of the angles until they meet. Label the point of intersection P.

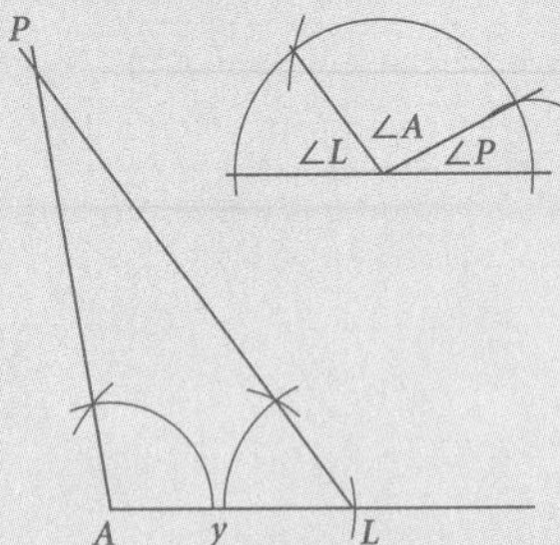

34. Construct $\angle P$. Mark off the length PB on one ray. From point B, mark off the two segments that intersect the other ray of $\angle P$ at distance x.

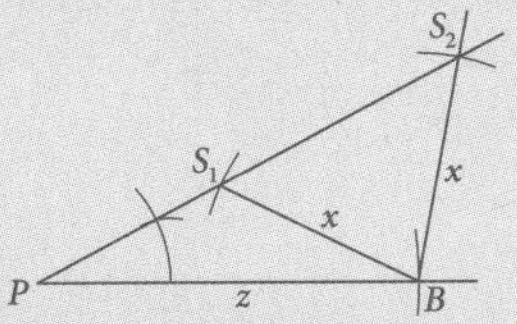

36. Given three sides, only one triangle is possible, therefore the shelves on the right hold their shape. The shelves on the left have no triangles and move freely as a parallelogram.

37. Possible method: Construct an equilateral triangle and bisect one angle to obtain 30°. Adjacent to that angle, construct a right angle and bisect it to obtain 45°.

▶ Take Another Look

1. On a sphere or a globe, angles are measured along tangent lines. It is indeed possible to draw a triangle with two or more obtuse angles, or three right angles.

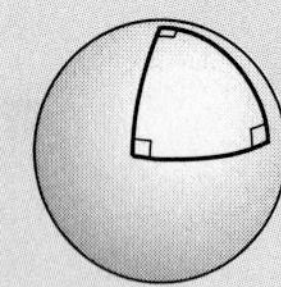

The sum of the interior angle measures of any triangle drawn on a sphere is always greater than 180°. The Lénárt Sphere pictured on page 253 is an excellent tool for studying spherical geometry. Students might keep a journal of their observations of geometry on a sphere and summarize those results when the class does the non-Euclidean geometry exploration at the end of the year.

2. Both conjectures are true on a sphere, but the angles in an equilateral triangle no longer measure 60°.

3. Be sure students are not still thinking about spheres. A triangle with the measure of one angle twice that of another can be divided into two isosceles triangles for certain only if the smallest angle measures less than 45°. When the angle with twice the measure is acute it works, but when this angle measures, for example, 100° it doesn't work.

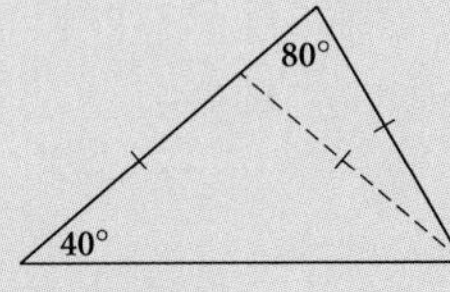

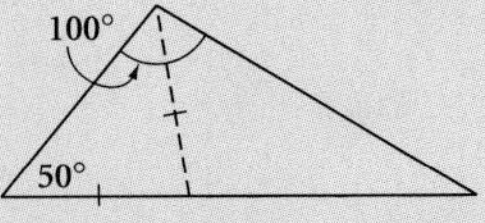

TAKE ANOTHER LOOK

The section that follows, Take Another Look, gives you a chance to extend, communicate, and assess your understanding of the work you did in the investigations in this chapter. Sometimes it will lead to new, related discoveries.

See page 252.

1. Explore the Triangle Sum Conjecture on a sphere or a globe. Can you draw a triangle that has two or more obtuse angles? Three right angles? Write an illustrated report of your findings.

See page 252.

2. Investigate the Isosceles Triangle Conjecture and the Equilateral/Equiangular Triangle Conjecture on a sphere. Write an illustrated report of your findings.

See page 252.

3. A friend claims that if the measure of one acute angle of a triangle is half the measure of another acute angle of the triangle, then the triangle can be divided into two isosceles triangles. Try this with a computer or other tools. Describe your method and explain why it works.

4. A friend claims that if one exterior angle has twice the measure of one of the remote interior angles, then the triangle is isosceles. Use a geometry software program or other tools to investigate this claim. Describe your findings.

5. Is there a conjecture (similar to the Triangle Exterior Angle Conjecture) that you can make about exterior and remote interior angles of a convex quadrilateral? Experiment. Write about your findings.

6. Is there a conjecture you can make about inequalities among the sums of the lengths of sides and/or diagonals of a quadrilateral? Experiment. Write about your findings.

7. In Chapter 3, you discovered how to construct the perpendicular bisector of a segment. Perform this construction. Now use what you've learned about congruence shortcuts to explain why this construction method works.

8. In Chapter 3, you discovered how to construct a perpendicular through a point on a line. Perform this construction. Use a congruence shortcut to explain why the construction works.

9. Is there a conjecture similar to the SSS Congruence Conjecture that you can make about congruence between quadrilaterals? For example, is SSSS a shortcut for quadrilateral congruence? Or, if three sides and a diagonal of one quadrilateral are congruent to the corresponding three sides and diagonal of another quadrilateral, must the two quadrilaterals be congruent (SSSD)? Investigate. Write a paragraph explaining how your conjectures follow from the triangle congruence conjectures you've learned.

4. The claim must always be true. Let a and b be the measures of interior angles A and B, respectively, and let x be the measure of the exterior angle to $\angle C$, with $x = 2a$. Then $2a = a + b$, so $a = b$.

5. The measure of an exterior angle of a convex quadrilateral is 180° less than the sum of the measures of the remote interior angles. (In a concave quadrilateral, with appropriate interpretation, the exterior angle at an angle with measure more than 180° is the supplement of the sum of the measures of the remote interior angles.)

6. Two possible answers: The sum of the lengths of any three sides of a quadrilateral is greater than the length of the remaining side. The sum of the lengths of any two consecutive sides of a quadrilateral is greater than the length of the diagonal joining their endpoints.

7. Use this construction to bisect $\overline{AB}$: From points A and B draw arcs that have the same radius and have length greater than $\frac{1}{2}AB$, intersecting at points C and D. $\overleftrightarrow{CD}$ is the perpendicular bisector, bisecting $\overline{AB}$ at point E. **[Hint]** If $\overline{AC} \cong \overline{BC} \cong \overline{AD} \cong \overline{BD}$, and $\overline{CD} \cong \overline{CD}$, then . . . .

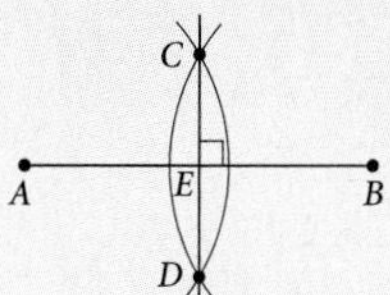

Proof: $\overline{AC} \cong \overline{BC} \cong \overline{AD} \cong \overline{BD}$ and $\overline{CD} \cong \overline{CD}$, so $\triangle ACD \cong \triangle BCD$ by SSS. Therefore $\angle ACE \cong \angle BCE$ and $\overline{CE} \cong \overline{CE}$. Therefore $\triangle ACE \cong \triangle BCE$ by SAS. $\overline{AE} \cong \overline{BE}$ by CPCTC, so $\overline{AB}$ is bisected by $\overleftrightarrow{CD}$, and $\angle AEC \cong \angle BEC$. $\angle AEC$ and $\angle BEC$ form a linear pair. Therefore $\angle AEC$ and $\angle BEC$ are right angles. Therefore $\overleftrightarrow{CD} \perp \overline{AB}$.

8. Use this construction of the perpendicular to a line through point P: With a compass, mark off points A and B on the line, equidistant from point P. Choose a longer radius for the compass and draw arcs with centers at points A and B and meeting at point Q. Draw $\overline{PQ}$. $\overline{PQ}$ is perpendicular to the line.

Proof: $\overline{AP} \cong \overline{BP}$, $\overline{AQ} \cong \overline{BQ}$, and $\overline{PQ} \cong \overline{PQ}$. So $\triangle APQ \cong \triangle BPQ$ by SSS. Therefore $\angle APQ \cong \angle BPQ$ and these angles form a linear pair, so they are right angles. Therefore $\overline{PQ} \perp \overline{AB}$.

9. See extensions on pages 224 and 229. **[Hint]** A square with sides measuring 5 cm and a (nonsquare) rhombus with sides measuring 5 cm are not congruent but have the SSS conditions. But when a diagonal is added, a rigid structure (two triangles) is created and there is a good case for finding congruence.

ASSESSING

Use one of the tests provided or use the Test Generator to combine some items on the Chapter Test with some Constructive Assessment items. You might choose to include some items written by students as part of their self-assessment.

FACILITATING SELF-ASSESSMENT

To help students complete the portfolio described in Assessing What You've Learned, suggest that they consider for evaluation their work on Lesson 4.1, Exercise 8; Lesson 4.2, Exercise 6; Lesson 4.3, Exercise 14; Lesson 4.5, Exercise 17; Lesson 4.6, Exercise 2; Lesson 4.7, Exercise 6; and Lesson 4.8, Exercise 6.

Assessing What You've Learned

WRITE TEST ITEMS

It's one thing to be able to do a math problem. It's another to be able to make one up. If you were writing a test for this chapter, what would it include?

Start by having a group discussion to identify the key ideas in each lesson of the chapter. Then divide the lessons among group members, and have each group member write a problem for each lesson assigned to them. Try to create a mix of problems in your group, from simple one-step exercises that require you to recall facts to more complex, multistep problems that require more thinking. An example of a simple problem might be finding a missing angle measure in a triangle. A more complex problem could be a flowchart for a logical argument, or a word problem that requires using geometry to model a real-world situation.

Share your problems with your group members and try out one another's problems. Then discuss the problems in your group: Were they representative of the content of the chapter? Were some too hard or too easy? Writing your own problems is an excellent way to assess and review what you've learned. Maybe you can even persuade your teacher to use one of your items on a real test!

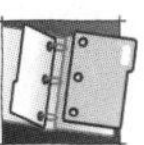

ORGANIZE YOUR NOTEBOOK Review your notebook to be sure it is complete and well organized. Write a one-page chapter summary based on your notes.

WRITE IN YOUR JOURNAL Write a paragraph or two about something you did in this class that gave you a great sense of accomplishment. What did you learn from it? What about the work makes you proud?

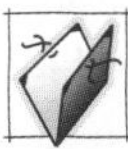

UPDATE YOUR PORTFOLIO Choose a piece of work from this chapter to add to your portfolio. Document the work, explaining what it is and why you chose it.

PERFORMANCE ASSESSMENT While a classmate, a friend, a family member, or your teacher observes, perform an investigation from this chapter. Explain each step, including how you arrived at the conjecture.

CHAPTER

5

Discovering and Proving Polygon Properties

Overview

In this chapter, students discover properties of polygons. In **Lessons 5.1** and **5.2,** they discover the sum of the angle measures in a polygon and the sum of the measures of a set of exterior angles of a polygon. The **exploration** looks at patterns in star polygons. Discovering kite and trapezoid properties in **Lesson 5.3** leads students to six conjectures about these quadrilaterals. In **Lesson 5.4,** students discover two properties of the midsegment of a triangle and two properties of the midsegment of a trapezoid. In **Lessons 5.5** and **5.6,** students investigate properties of parallelograms, rhombuses, rectangles, and squares. Between these lessons, **Using Your Algebra Skills 5** reviews solving linear equations. In **Lesson 5.7** students use paragraph and flowchart proofs to support those conjectures with deductive reasoning.

The Mathematics

This chapter moves down the hierarchy of polygons from the most general polygons and quadrilaterals to the most specific quadrilaterals, squares. It begins by extending the angle sum properties of triangles to polygons in general. Then it focuses on special kinds of quadrilaterals: trapezoids, kites, and parallelograms. It continues by examining two special kinds of parallelograms: rhombuses and rectangles (and squares, which are both). Underlying the progression through parallelograms is the theme that properties of one category are inherited by all subcategories. For example, the property of parallelograms that their diagonals bisect each other is true for all special kinds of parallelograms, such as rhombuses and rectangles.

All polygons of n sides share certain properties. The sum of the measures of their interior angles is $180(n - 2)$ degrees, and the sum of the measures of their exterior angles is 360°. Consequently, if a polygon is equiangular, each interior angle has measure $\frac{180(n-2)}{n}$ degrees, or $180 - \frac{360}{n}$ degrees.

Properties of the various quadrilaterals can be seen from their symmetry. A kite is symmetric about the diagonal through its vertex angles. From this fact it can be seen that this diagonal bisects the vertex angles and the other diagonal, that the two diagonals are perpendicular, and that the nonvertex angles are congruent.

An isosceles trapezoid also has reflectional symmetry, but over the line through the midpoints of the two parallel sides. This symmetry reveals that consecutive angles (on the bases) are congruent, as are the diagonals.

In contrast, a parallelogram has 2-fold rotational symmetry about the point at which its diagonals intersect. Because of the rotation, its properties mainly concern opposites: Opposite sides and angles are congruent. When the figure is rotated 180° about the intersection of the diagonals, each half of a diagonal is taken to the other half, so the diagonals bisect each other.

As students examine how polygons are related, you need to lead the way in modeling careful use of language. For example, it's easy to say "In a rectangle, adjacent sides are congruent." That's true in some rectangles. But the statement is false, because in mathematics *a* often means "any" or "every" or "all." Mathematical statements are understood to begin with one of the words *All* (equivalently, *Any* or *Every*), *Some* (equivalently, *At least one*), or *No.* When we say "A rectangle is a quadrilateral," we mean "All rectangles are quadrilaterals." Instead of saying "A rectangle is a square," we should say "Some rectangles are squares" or "At least one rectangle is a square." Also, instead of saying "All rectangles are not darts," which is ambiguous, we should say "No rectangle is a dart."

At this point in the course, many students are at van Hiele level 2. This chapter's consideration of inheritance of properties challenges them without asking them to move to a new level. If students propose different valid proofs of conjectures, you can begin to lay the groundwork for level 3 by legitimizing those proofs. You can also begin to ask students whether the reasons they're citing in flowchart proofs are conjectures or definitions, although it's too early to expect most students to appreciate the differences very deeply.

Using This Chapter

Lessons 5.1 and 5.2 are both quick, single-investigation lessons, but there are many follow-ups that you can do. Use the extensions and the Take Another Look activities if you have class time.

Cooperative Learning Using Jigsaw

Jigsaw methods of cooperative group learning involve assigning different problems, or pieces of a problem, to different groups. Later the groups report on their thoughts to the entire class or divide up so each group can share its thinking with one other group. Jigsaw work has the advantage of mimicking a workplace situation, in which teams don't replicate efforts. In addition students learn to learn from and teach each other. The jigsaw method is suggested for the investigations in Lessons 5.1 and 5.2 and the exercises in Lesson 5.7.

Resources

Discovering Geometry Resources

Teaching and Worksheet Masters
Lessons 5.1, 5.3–5.7

Sketchpad Demonstration
Lesson 5.2

Discovering Geometry with The Geometer's Sketchpad
Lessons 5.1–5.6

Assessment Resources A and B
Quiz 1 (Lessons 5.1 and 5.2)
Quiz 2 (Lessons 5.3 and 5.4)
Quiz 3 (Lessons 5.5–5.7)
Chapter 5 Test
Chapter 5 Constructive Assessment Options

Practice Your Skills for Chapter 5

Condensed Lessons for Chapter 5

Other Resources

www.keypress.com/DG

Materials

- construction tools
- protractors
- calculators
- scissors
- graph paper

Pacing Guide

	day 1	day 2	day 3	day 4	day 5	day 6	day 7	day 8	day 9	day 10
standard	5.1	5.2	quiz, 5.3	5.4	5.5	quiz, Algebra 5	5.6	5.7	quiz, review	review
enriched	5.1, extension	5.2,	quiz, Exploration	5.3	5.4	5.5	quiz, Algebra 5, project	5.6	5.7	quiz, review
block	5.1, 5.2	quiz, 5.3, Exploration	5.4, project	quiz, 5.5	Algebra 5, 5.6	5.7	quiz, review, project	assessment		

	day 11	day 12	day 13	day 14	day 15	day 16	day 17	day 18	day 19	day 20
standard	assessment									
enriched	project, review	assessment, TAL								

CHAPTER

5

Discovering and Proving Polygon Properties

The mathematicians may well nod their heads in a friendly and interested manner—I still am a tinkerer to them. And the "artistic" ones are primarily irritated. Still, maybe I'm on the right track if I experience more joy from my own little images than from the most beautiful camera in the world . . ."

Still Life and Street, M. C. Escher, 1967–1968

OBJECTIVES

In this chapter you will

- study properties of polygons
- discover relationships among their angles, sides, and diagonals
- learn about real-world applications of special polygons

The woodcut by M. C. Escher shows many different polygons and near-polygons, as well as polygons changing shape as they recede into the background. **[Ask]** "What polygons do you see?" [rectangles (books, windows), squares (windows), triangles (fence on the roof), parallelograms (tops of books seen in perspective), trapezoids (sides of buildings receding into background)]

CHAPTER 5 OBJECTIVES

- Discover the sum of both the interior and the exterior angle measures in a polygon
- Explore angle measures of equiangular and star polygons
- Discover properties of kites, trapezoids, and various kinds of parallelograms
- Define and discover properties of midsegments in triangles and trapezoids
- Practice writing flowchart and paragraph proofs
- Learn new vocabulary
- Practice construction skills
- Develop reasoning, problem-solving skills, and cooperative behavior

LESSON

5.1

PLANNING

LESSON OUTLINE

One day:

15 min Investigation

10 min Sharing

5 min Closing

15 min Exercises

MATERIALS

- construction tools
- protractors
- calculators
- Exercise 16 (T) for One step

TEACHING

Students find that all polygons with the same number of sides have the same angle measure sum. Conversely, knowing this sum allows students to find the number of sides.

Guiding the Investigation

One step Show the Exercise 16 transparency and pose this problem: "You need to build a window frame for an octagonal window like this one. To make the frame, you'll cut identical trapezoidal pieces. What are the measures of the angles of the trapezoids?" As you observe groups at work, encourage students to think about the sum of angle measures of octagons. As needed, suggest that they use inductive reasoning to make a conjecture about the angle sum of any polygon. You might encourage those who finish first to try to prove their conjectures.

Assign each group to explore a different kind of polygon (that is, a polygon with a different number of vertices). You need not assign a triangle, because students saw the Triangle Sum Conjecture in Chapter 4. Remind students that they are to look for patterns, as they did in Chapter 2.

Step 1 To get enough data, each student may need to draw several polygons. For advanced classes you might suggest that some of the polygons be concave.

Step 2 Don't worry too much if some groups aren't getting multiples of 180°; they'll see a pattern when results are shared.

Step 3 For this step, you'll need to have groups share with each other, either formally or by sending representatives to visit other groups. You might also have a table of interior angle sums on the board or overhead to be filled in by group representatives when each group has completed its investigation. You might keep the class together for the remaining steps. Emphasize that all students should copy the full table into their notebooks for future reference.

LESSON 5.1

Polygon Sum Conjecture

I find that the harder I work, the more luck I seem to have.

THOMAS JEFFERSON

There are many kinds of triangles, but in Chapter 4, you discovered that the sum of their angle measures is always 180°. In this lesson you'll investigate the sum of the angle measures in quadrilaterals, pentagons, and other polygons. Then you'll look for a pattern in the sum of the angle measures in *any* polygon.

Investigation
Is There a Polygon Sum Formula?

For this investigation each person in your group should draw a different version of the same polygon. For example, if your group is investigating hexagons, try to think of different ways you could draw a hexagon.

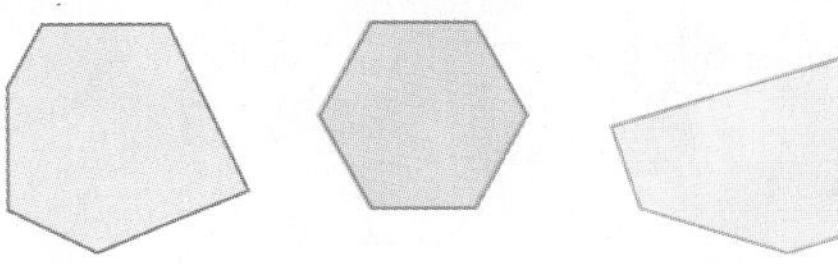

Step 1 Draw the polygon. Carefully measure all the interior angles, then find the sum.

Step 2 Share your results with your group. If you measured carefully, you should all have the same sum! If your answers aren't exactly the same, find the average.

Step 3 Copy the table below. Repeat Steps 1 and 2 with different polygons, or share results with other groups. Complete the table.

Number of sides of polygon	3	4	5	6	7	8	...	n
Sum of measures of angles	180°	360°	540°	720°	900°	1080°	...	

$180°(n-2)$

You can now make some conjectures.

Quadrilateral Sum Conjecture C-30

The sum of the measures of the four angles of any quadrilateral is __?__. 360°

Pentagon Sum Conjecture C-31

The sum of the measures of the five angles of any pentagon is __?__. 540°

If a polygon has n sides, it is called an ***n*-gon.**

Step 4 | Look for a pattern in the completed table. Write a general formula for the sum of the angle measures of a polygon in terms of the number of sides, n.

Polygon Sum Conjecture C-32

The sum of the measures of the n interior angles of an n-gon is _?_. $180°(n - 2)$

You used inductive reasoning to discover the formula. Now you can use deductive reasoning to see why the formula works.

Step 5 | Draw all the diagonals from *one* vertex of your polygon. How many triangles do the diagonals create? How does the number of triangles relate to the formula you found? How can you check that your formula is correct for a polygon with 12 sides?

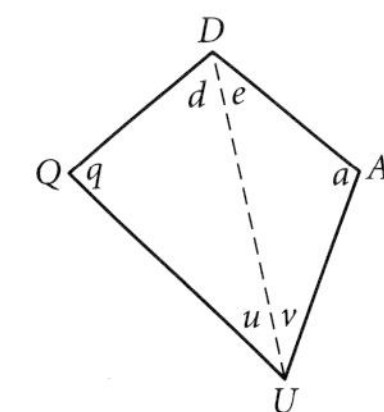

Step 6 | Write a short paragraph proof of the Quadrilateral Sum Conjecture. Use the diagram of quadrilateral *QUAD*. (Hint: Use the Triangle Sum Conjecture.)

Step 5 The number of triangles formed is $n - 2$.

Step 6 $q + d + u = 180°$ and $e + a + v = 180°$ by the Triangle Sum Conjecture. $q + d + e + a + v + u = 360°$ by addition property of equality. Therefore, the sum of the measures of the angles of a quadrilateral is 360°.

EXERCISES

You will need

Geometry software for Exercise **19**

1. Use the Polygon Sum Conjecture to complete the table.

Number of sides of polygon	7	8	9	10	11	20	55	100
Sum of measures of angles	900°	1080°	1260°	1440°	1620°	3240°	9540°	17640°

2. What is the measure of each angle of an equiangular pentagon? An equiangular hexagon? Complete the table. ⓗ

Number of sides of equiangular polygon	5	6	7	8	9	10	12	16	100
Measures of each angle of equiangular polygon	108°	120°	$128\frac{4}{7}°$	135°	140°	144°	150°	$157\frac{1}{2}°$	$176\frac{2}{5}°$

In Exercises 3–8, use your conjectures to calculate the measure of each lettered angle.

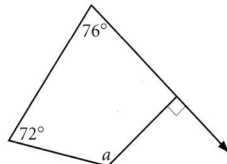

3. $a =$ _?_ 122°

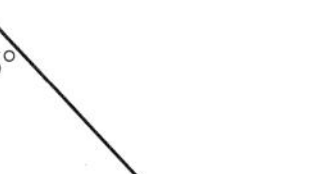

4. $b =$ _?_ 136°

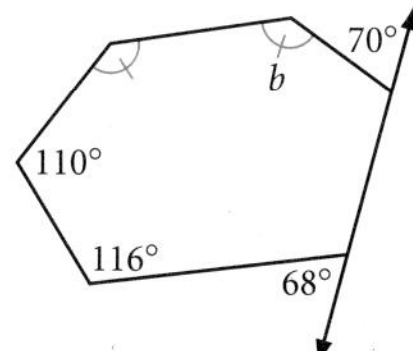

5. $e =$ _?_ 108°

$f =$ _?_ 36°

Step 5 [Alert] Students may have difficulty seeing that the number of triangles in an n-gon is $n - 2$. Suggest that they draw the line segments that form the triangles and describe what they are doing.

Step 6 Because d, e, u, and v are measures of angles, it's valid to write $d + e = m\angle D$ and $u + v = m\angle U$.

SHARING IDEAS

As a class, agree on the statements of the conjectures to be added to students' notebooks. In discussing the inductive reasoning process, **[Ask]** "What contributes to slight differences in answers?" [measurement error]

An alternative to drawing diagonals from one vertex is selecting a random point within the polygon and drawing segments to the vertices. Thus you always get n triangles, and the sum of the angle measures of the n triangles is $180n$ degrees. But you do not want the angle sum around the point, so you subtract 360°. Thus the formula is $180°n - 360°$, or $180°(n - 2)$.

You might ask whether students can explain why the sum is what it is by using techniques similar to those used for the Triangle Sum Conjecture. For example, they might tear off angles and form them around a point (see extensions). Or, if you imagined with your class the forward/backward walk around a triangle turning through the interior angles, students might imagine walking around the polygon.

Follow through with a question about equiangular polygons. For example, what's the measure of each angle of an equiangular polygon of 12 sides? Students need to realize that the number of angles equals the number of sides. Let students derive a formula for this measure if they wish, but don't insist that they do so.

NCTM STANDARDS

CONTENT		PROCESS	
	Number	✓	Problem Solving
✓	Algebra	✓	Reasoning
✓	Geometry	✓	Communication
✓	Measurement		Connections
✓	Data/Probability		Representation

LESSON OBJECTIVES

- Discover the sum of the angle measures in a polygon
- Practice construction skills
- Develop reasoning, problem-solving skills, and cooperative behavior

Closing the Lesson

The Polygon Sum Conjecture can be used to find the sum of angle measures for any polygon. Moreover, students can use it to find the number of sides given the total angle measure. If students seem uncomfortable with these ideas, you might do one of Exercises 3–8 before having the class begin on the other exercises.

BUILDING UNDERSTANDING

The exercises give practice in applying the Polygon Sum Conjecture.

ASSIGNING HOMEWORK

Essential	1–14
Performance assessment	15
Portfolio	12
Journal	16
Group	17
Review	18–22

MATERIALS

- Exercise 12 (T), *optional*

▶ Helping with the Exercises

Exercises 3–8 If students are having difficulty, suggest that they copy the diagrams and mark them with what they know.

9. The sum of the interior angle measures of the quadrilateral is 358°. It should be 360°.

10. The measures of the interior angles shown sum to 554°. However, the figure is a pentagon, so the measures of its interior angles should sum to 540°.

Exercise 11 This problem foreshadows Chapter 7 and tilings. You might ask what other combinations of polygons students can find that fit around a point.

6. $c = \underline{?}$ 108°
$d = \underline{?}$ ⓗ 106°

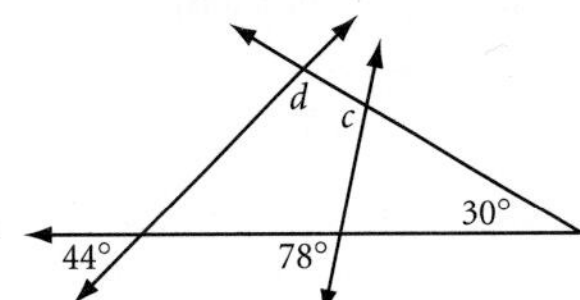

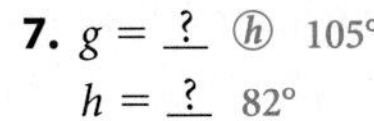

7. $g = \underline{?}$ ⓗ 105°
$h = \underline{?}$ 82°

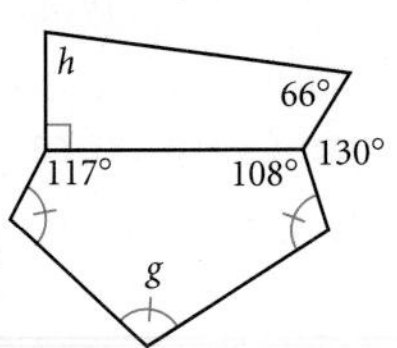
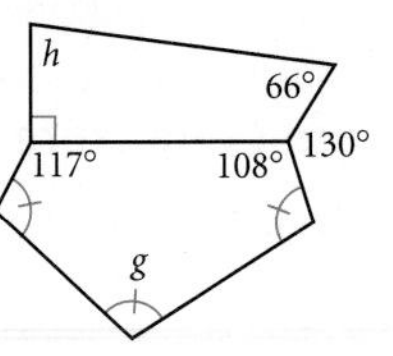

8. $j = \underline{?}$ 120°
$k = \underline{?}$ 38°

9. What's wrong with this picture?

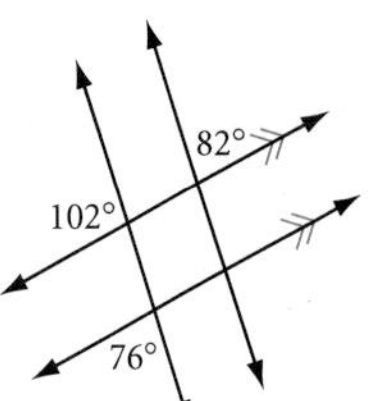

10. What's wrong with this picture?

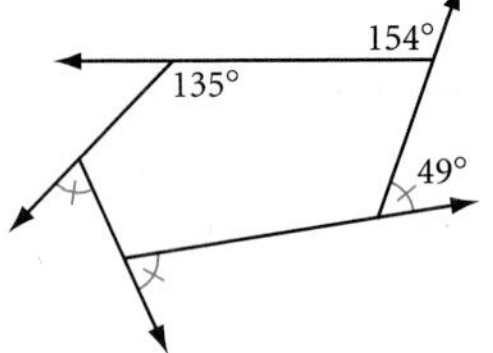

11. Three regular polygons meet at point *A*. How many sides does the largest polygon have? 18

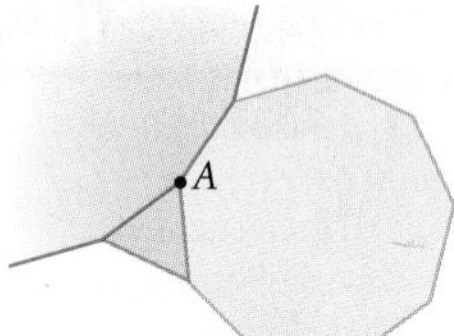

12. Trace the figure at right. Calculate each lettered angle measure. $a = 116°, b = 64°, c = 90°, d = 82°, e = 99°, f = 88°, g = 150°, h = 56°, j = 106°, k = 74°, m = 136°, n = 118°, p = 99°$

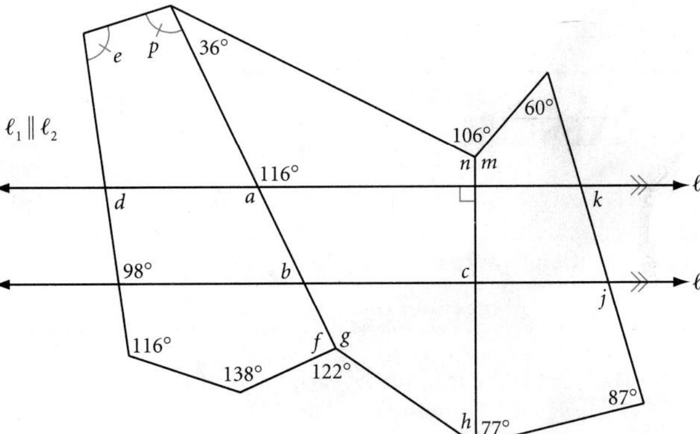

13. How many sides does a polygon have if the sum of its angle measures is 2700°? ⓗ 17

14. How many sides does an equiangular polygon have if each interior angle measures 156°? ⓗ 15

15. Archaeologist Ertha Diggs has uncovered a piece of a ceramic plate. She measures it and finds that each side has the same length and each angle has the same measure.

She conjectures that the original plate was the shape of a regular polygon. She knows that if the original plate was a regular 16-gon, it was probably a ceremonial dish from the third century. If it was a regular 18-gon, it was probably a palace dinner plate from the twelfth century.

If each angle measures 160°, from what century did the plate likely originate? the twelfth century

Exercise 12 Suggest that students use pair share on the angle-network exercises. One student finds an answer and explains why; then the partner agrees or disagrees, then finds another answer and explains why. Partners take turns back and forth as they progress through the network. There are variations on this method that you can use. For example, when student A finds an answer it is the task of student B to explain why; then student B finds the next answer and student A explains why.

Exercise 15 To extend this exercise, suggest that students bring in pieces of supposed "archaeological treasures" (fragments of regular polygons they make from paper, plastic, or other materials) and have other students determine the number of sides the unbroken "artifact" would have had.

16. **APPLICATION** You need to build a window frame for an octagonal window like this one. To make the frame, you'll cut identical trapezoidal pieces. What are the measures of the angles of the trapezoids? Explain how you found these measures.

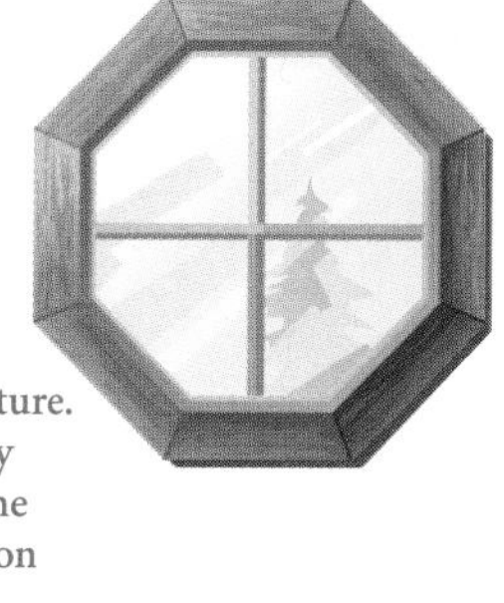

17. Use this diagram to prove the Pentagon Sum Conjecture. ⓗ

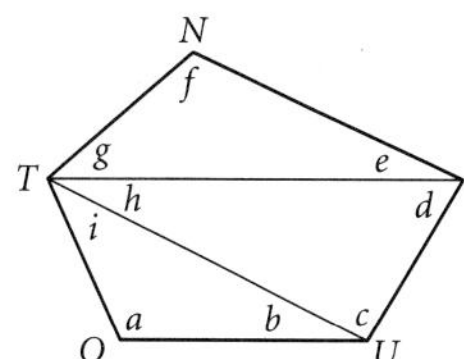

$a + b + i = 180°$, $c + d + h = 180°$, and $e + f + g = 180°$ by the Triangle Sum Conjecture. $a + b + c + d + e + f + g + h + i = 540°$ by the addition property of equality. Therefore the sum of the measures of the angles of a pentagon is 540°.

Review

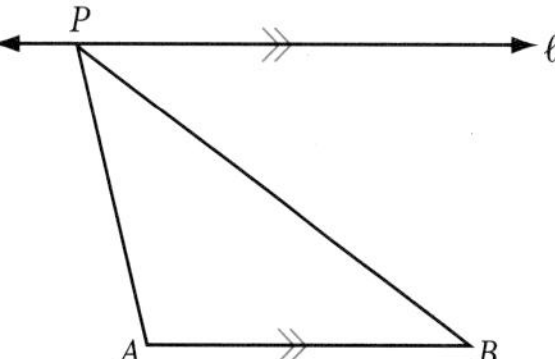

2.5 18. This figure is a detail of one vertex of the tiling at the beginning of this lesson. Find the missing angle measure x. $x = 120°$

19. *Technology* Use geometry software to construct a quadrilateral and locate the midpoints of its four sides. Construct segments connecting the midpoints of opposite sides. Construct the point of intersection of the two segments. Drag a vertex or a side so that the quadrilateral becomes concave. Observe these segments and make a conjecture. The segments joining the opposite midpoints of a quadrilateral always bisect each other.

UYAS 4 20. Write the equation of the perpendicular bisector of the segment with endpoints (−12, 15) and (4, −3). $y = \frac{8}{9}x + \frac{86}{9}$ or $8x - 9y = -86$

UYAS 4 21. $\triangle ABC$ has vertices $A(0, 0)$, $B(-4, -2)$, and $C(8, -8)$. What is the equation of the median to side $\overline{AB}$?

22. Line ℓ is parallel to $\overleftrightarrow{AB}$. As P moves to the right along ℓ, which of these measures will always increase? D

A. The distance PA

B. The measure of $\angle APB$

C. The perimeter of $\triangle ABP$

D. The measure of $\angle ABP$

IMPROVING YOUR VISUAL THINKING SKILLS

Net Puzzle

The clear cube shown has the letters *DOT* printed on one face. When a light is shined on that face, the image of *DOT* appears on the opposite face. The image of *DOT* on the opposite face is then painted. Copy the net of the cube and sketch the painted image of the word, *DOT*, on the correct square and in the correct position.

DOT

IMPROVING VISUAL THINKING SKILLS

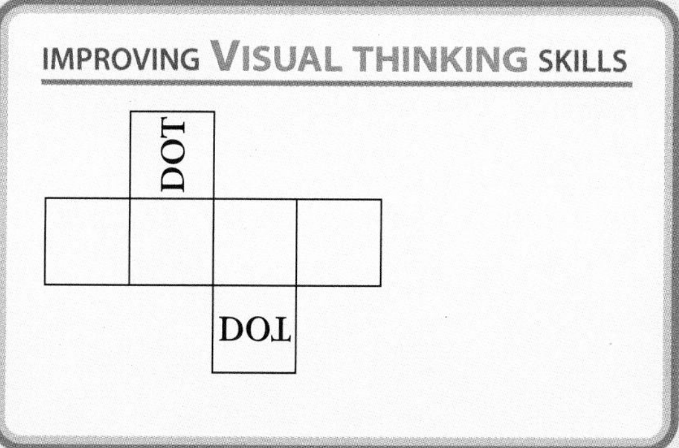

Exercise 16 This exercise is the one-step investigation.

16. The angles of the trapezoid measure 67.5° and 112.5°; 67.5° is half the value of each angle of a regular octagon, and 112.5° is half the value of 360° − 135°.

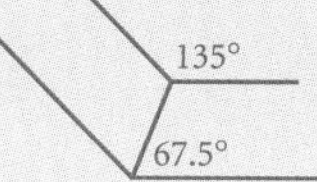

Exercise 17 [Language] *Prove* is used in this context to mean "explain why, or write an informal proof."

21. $y = -\frac{7}{10}x - \frac{12}{5}$ or $7x + 10y = -24$

Exercise 22 As vertex P moves from left to right: The distance PA decreases and then soon increases, the perimeter of the triangle decreases before it increases, and the measure of $\angle APB$ increases for a while but then decreases.

EXTENSIONS

A. Rather than measuring angles of a quadrilateral or pentagon, students can tear off the corners and arrange the angles of a polygon around a point, as they did when investigating triangle sums. [The angles of a quadrilateral completely surround a point, so the sum of their measures is 360°. The angles of a pentagon will begin to overlap and will surround a point $1\frac{1}{2}$ times (for a sum of 540°).]

B. Students could build window frames or picture frames based on different regular polygons.

C. Use Take Another Look activities 1 and 2 on page 303.

LESSON

5.2

PLANNING

LESSON OUTLINE

One day:

10 min Investigation

10 min Sharing

10 min Extensions

5 min Closing

10 min Exercises

MATERIALS

- construction tools
- protractors
- calculators
- Sketchpad demonstration Exterior Angles, *optional*

TEACHING

The sum of the exterior angles of any polygon is constant and is closely related to the sum of the interior angles.

Guiding the Investigation

One step Ask students to draw any polygon and imagine walking around it, always turning through an exterior angle and keeping track of the number of degrees they've turned. Encourage them to experiment with a variety of polygons, keeping track of the number of sides and the total measure of all the angles turned.

You might assign each group to investigate the same kind of polygon for which they found the sum of the interior angle measures in Lesson 5.1.

LESSON 5.2

Exterior Angles of a Polygon

If someone had told me I would be Pope someday, I would have studied harder.

POPE JOHN PAUL I

In Lesson 5.1, you discovered a formula for the sum of the measures of the *interior* angles of any polygon. In this lesson you will discover a formula for the sum of the measures of the *exterior* angles of a polygon.

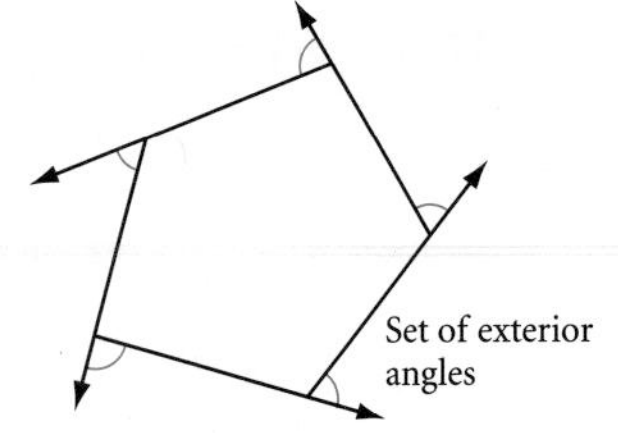

Best known for her participation in the Dada Movement, German artist Hannah Hoch (1889–1978) painted *Emerging Order* in the Cubist style. Do you see any examples of exterior angles in the painting?

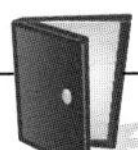

Investigation
Is There an Exterior Angle Sum?

You will need

- a straightedge
- a protractor

Let's use some inductive and deductive reasoning to find the exterior angle measures in a polygon.

Each person in your group should draw the same kind of polygon for Steps 1–5.

Step 1 Draw a large polygon. Extend its sides to form a set of exterior angles.

Step 2 Measure all the *interior* angles of the polygon except one. Use the Polygon Sum Conjecture to calculate the measure of the remaining interior angle. Check your answer using your protractor.

Step 3 Use the Linear Pair Conjecture to calculate the measure of each exterior angle.

Step 4 Calculate the sum of the measures of the exterior angles. Share your results with your group members.

Step 1 As needed, introduce the concept of an exterior angle of a polygon. Students should draw only one exterior angle at each vertex. You need not specify at this time which angle they should draw.

Step 4 Students can check their findings by measuring the exterior angles.

LESSON OBJECTIVES

- Discover the sum of the measures of the exterior angles of a polygon
- Practice construction skills
- Develop reasoning, problem-solving skills, and cooperative behavior

Step 5 Exterior angle measures add up to 360° for any polygon.

Step 5 Repeat Steps 1–4 with different kinds of polygons, or share results with other groups. Make a table to keep track of the number of sides and the sum of the exterior angle measures for each kind of polygon. Find a formula for the sum of the measures of a polygon's exterior angles.

Exterior Angle Sum Conjecture C-33

For any polygon, the sum of the measures of a set of exterior angles is _?_. 360°

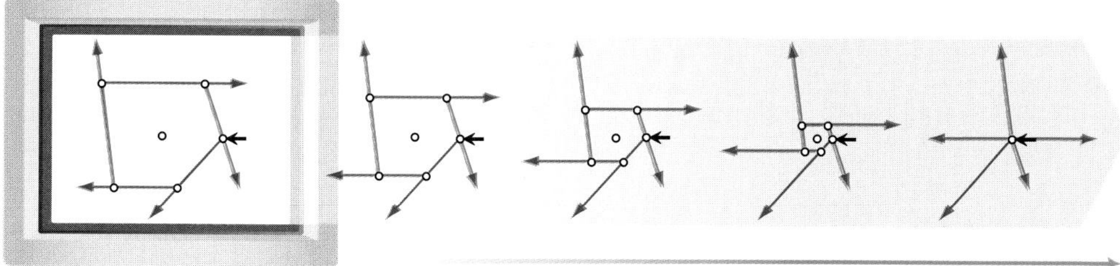

Step 6 The exterior angles slide into place as angles around a point, which always add up to 360°.

Step 7 $\frac{180°(n-2)}{n}$

Step 8 $\frac{360°}{n}$

Step 6 Study the software construction above. Explain how it demonstrates the Exterior Angle Sum Conjecture. For an interactive version of this sketch, visit www.keymath.com/DG .

Step 7 Using the Polygon Sum Conjecture, write a formula for the measure of each interior angle in an equiangular polygon.

Step 8 Using the Exterior Angle Sum Conjecture, write the formula for the measure of each exterior angle in an equiangular polygon.

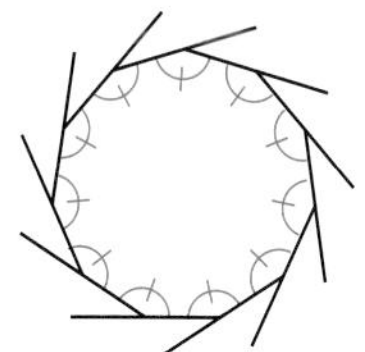

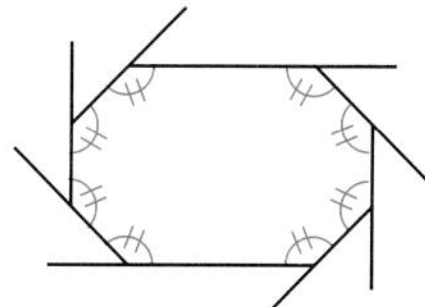

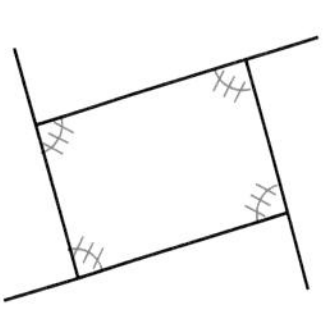

Step 9 Using your results from Step 8, you can write the formula for an interior angle a different way. How do you find the measure of an interior angle if you know the measure of its exterior angle? Complete the next conjecture.

Equiangular Polygon Conjecture C-34

You can find the measure of each interior angle of an equiangular n-gon by using either of these formulas: _?_ or _?_. $180° - \frac{360°}{n}$; $\frac{180°(n-2)}{n}$

NCTM STANDARDS

CONTENT		PROCESS	
	Number		Problem Solving
✓	Algebra	✓	Reasoning
✓	Geometry	✓	Communication
✓	Measurement		Connections
	Data/Probability		Representation

Step 5 The book tells students to "find a formula" for the sum of the exterior angle measures. This is intentionally somewhat misleading. They will find that the sum of the exterior angle measures is 360° for their polygon and may try to generalize this finding by writing a formula that includes n. For example, the pentagons group might write $180°(n - 3)$.

Step 6 Students can investigate Step 6 using the dynamic geometry exploration at www.keymath.com/DG.

Step 7 If students have trouble, remind them that the number of angles equals the number of sides, so n can be used for either.

Equiangular Polygon Conjecture
Ask why the two expressions are equivalent algebraically. After writing $\frac{180°(n-2)}{n}$, **[Ask]** "What does the order of operations tell us to do first?" [distribute] "The division symbol is a grouping symbol, so n should divide into what?" [$180n$ and 360] "To find the measure of an interior angle of an equiangular polygon, would it be easier to use the sum of exterior angles or the sum of interior angles?" [Exterior: *interior angle* $= 180° - \frac{360°}{n}$; interior: *interior angle* $= \frac{180°(n-2)}{n}$. Exterior is usually easier.]

SHARING IDEAS

Have students share a variety of formulas for the Exterior Angle Sum Conjecture. Let them discuss the discrepancies until they agree that the sum is always 360°. Many students learn best through discussion, so try not to limit it. Students may object that a constant isn't a formula. Say that constant functions or expressions are very important in mathematics. Remind students of the equation for a horizontal line, for example, $y = 4$. You might also make the point that it is important to consider a variety of examples before making a conjecture. Help students reach consensus on the phrasing to write in their notebooks.

Ask if it matters which exterior angle they chose at each vertex. Help them see that, where a polygon is convex, the two exterior angles are vertical angles and thus have the same measure.

If you did not do the one-step investigation, explore the conjecture as walking around the polygon and turning through the exterior angles. A walker will keep walking forward, turning a total of once around. The Polygon Sum Conjecture can be derived algebraically from the Exterior Angle Sum Conjecture: The total of the measures of the n interior plus n exterior angles is $180°n$, the interior angles add up to $180°n - 360°$, which factors to $180°(n - 2)$.

For the reverse situation, **[Ask]** "How could the Exterior Angle Sum Conjecture be derived algebraically from the Polygon Sum Conjecture?" [The sum of the exterior angle measures is $180°n - 180°(n - 2)$, which simplifies to 360°.]

Exterior Angles of a Concave Polygon
For advanced students who explored concave polygons, remind them that the exterior angle is the supplement of the interior angle. Define all exterior angles as having measure 180° minus the measure of the interior angle. If the interior angle's measure is more than 180°, the exterior angle has negative measure and is inside the figure. (It is an exterior angle only in a technical sense.) With that definition, the Exterior Angle Sum Conjecture is still true. This definition will make sense for the analogy of "walking around" the figure: If you are walking in a clockwise direction, you have to turn counterclockwise at a nonconvex vertex.

EXERCISES

1. Complete this flowchart proof of the Exterior Angle Sum Conjecture for a triangle.

Flowchart Proof

1. $a + b = 180°$ — Supplementary angles ?
2. $c + d = 180°$ — Supplementary angles ?
3. $e + f = 180°$ — Supplementary angles ?
4. $a + b + c + d + e + f =$? ° (540°) — Addition property of equality
5. $a + c + e =$? ° (180°) — ? Triangle Sum Conjecture
6. $b + d + f =$? ° (360°) — Subtraction property of equality

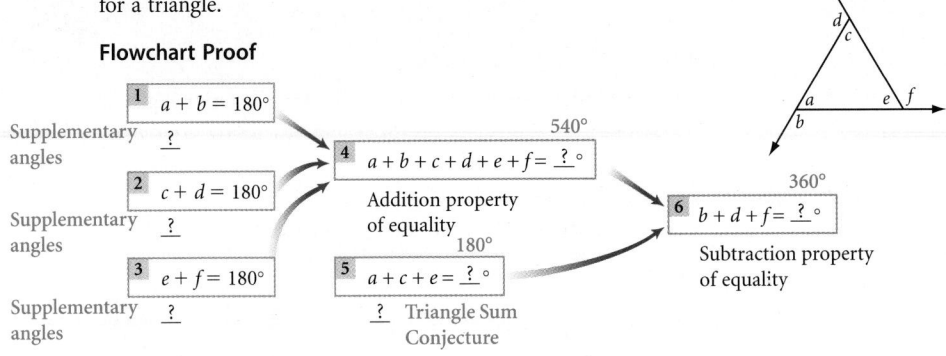

2. What is the sum of the measures of the exterior angles of a decagon? 360°

3. What is the measure of an exterior angle of an equiangular pentagon? An equiangular hexagon? 72°; 60°

In Exercises 4–9, use your new conjectures to calculate the measure of each lettered angle.

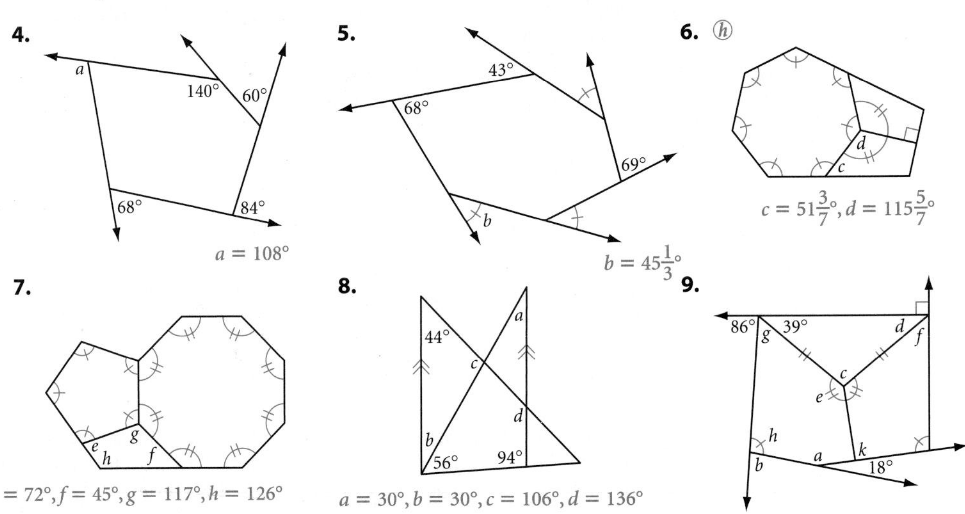

10. How many sides does a regular polygon have if each exterior angle measures 24°? ⓗ 15

11. How many sides does a polygon have if the sum of its interior angle measures is 7380°? 43

12. Is there a maximum number of obtuse exterior angles that any polygon can have? If so, what is the maximum? If not, why not? Is there a minimum number of acute interior angles that any polygon must have? If so, what is the minimum? If not, why not? ⓗ Yes. The maximum is three. The minimum is 0. A polygon might have no acute interior angles.

Assessing Progress
Check students' familiarity with the Polygon Sum Conjecture and the Linear Pair Conjecture, with various kinds of polygons and with interior and exterior angles.

Closing the Lesson

The fact that the sum of the measures of exterior angles of any polygon is 360° can be derived algebraically from, or lead algebraically to, the Polygon Sum Conjecture that the sum of measures of the interior angles is $180°(n - 2)$. In the case of equiangular polygons, each interior angle has measure $180° - \frac{360°}{n}$. If students still need help in understanding these ideas, you might use Exercise 4 or 10 for a demonstration.

9. $a = 162°$, $b = 83°$, $c = 102°$, $d = 39°$, $e = 129°$, $f = 51°$, $g = 55°$, $h = 97°$, $k = 83°$

Technology CONNECTION

The aperture of a camera is an opening shaped like a regular polygon surrounded by thin sheets that form a set of exterior angles. These sheets move together or apart to close or open the aperture, limiting the amount of light passing through the camera's lens. How does the sequence of closing apertures shown below demonstrate the Exterior Angle Sum Conjecture? Does the number of sides make a difference in the opening and closing of the aperture?

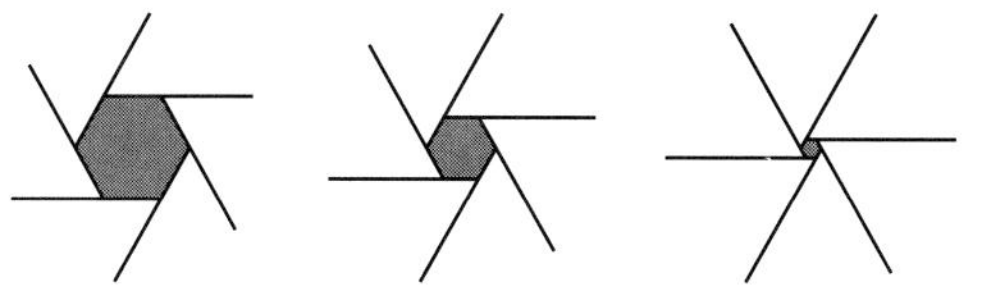

Review

5.1 **13.** Name the regular polygons that appear in the tiling below. Find the measures of the angles that surround point A in the tiling.

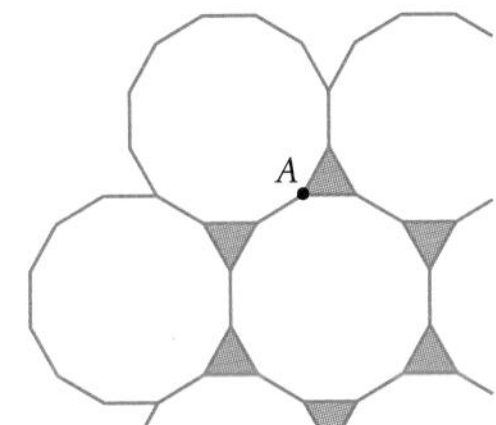

Regular polygons: equilateral triangle and regular dodecagon. Angle measures: 60°, 150°, and 150°.

5.1 **14.** Name the regular polygons that appear in the tiling below. Find the measures of the angles that surround any vertex point in the tiling.

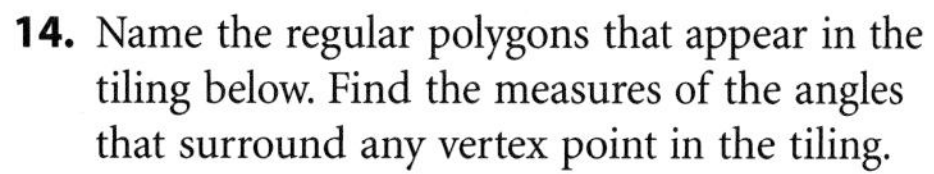

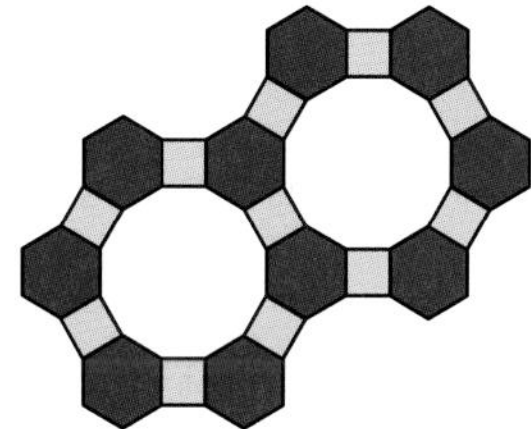

Regular polygons: square, regular hexagon, and regular dodecagon. Angle measures: 90°, 120°, and 150°.

4.6 **15.** $\angle RAC \cong \angle DCA$, $\overline{CD} \cong \overline{AR}$, $\overline{AC} \parallel \overline{DR}$. Is $\overline{AD} \cong \overline{CR}$? Why? ⓗ Yes. $\triangle RAC \cong \triangle DCA$ by SAS. $\overline{AD} \cong \overline{CR}$ by CPCTC.

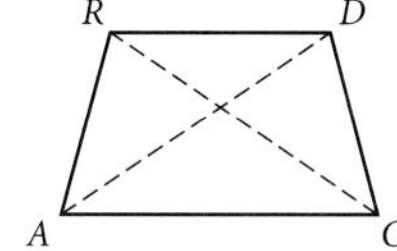

4.6 **16.** $\overline{DT} \cong \overline{RT}$, $\overline{DA} \cong \overline{RA}$. Is $\angle D \cong \angle R$? Why? ⓗ Yes. $\triangle DAT \cong \triangle RAT$ by SSS. $\angle D \cong \angle R$ by CPCTC.

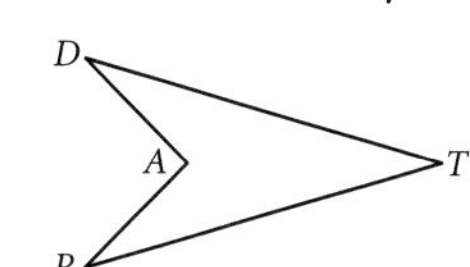

IMPROVING YOUR VISUAL THINKING SKILLS

Dissecting a Hexagon II

Make six copies of the hexagon at right by tracing it onto your paper. Then divide each hexagon into twelve identical parts in a different way.

IMPROVING VISUAL THINKING SKILLS

Eleven possible answers are shown.

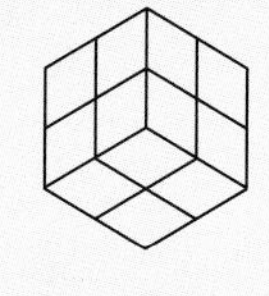
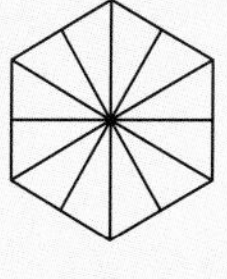
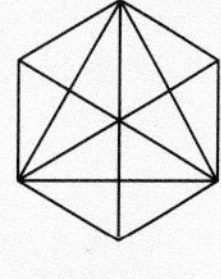
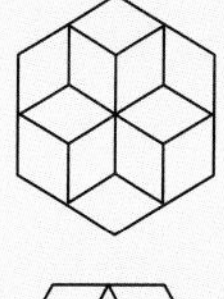
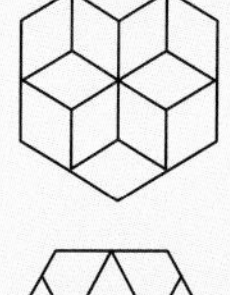
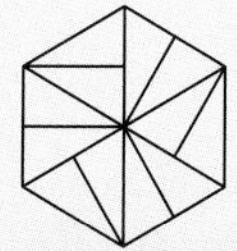
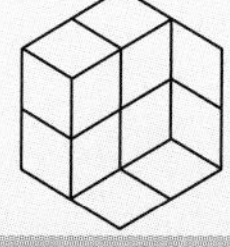
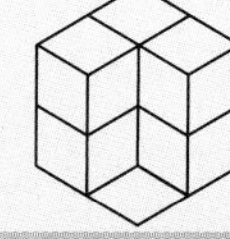
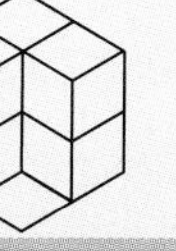
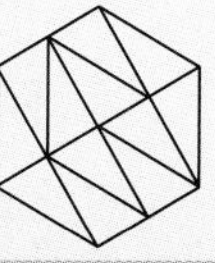

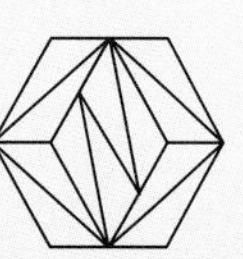

BUILDING UNDERSTANDING

As always, encourage students to support their solutions by being ready to state the conjecture(s) they have used to solve the exercises.

ASSIGNING HOMEWORK

Essential	1–10
Performance assessment	8
Portfolio	9
Journal	12
Group	1
Review	11, 13–16

Helping with the Exercises

Exercise 10 Students may need reminding that *regular* means "equilateral and equiangular."

Exercise 12 As appropriate, remind students to think of concave polygons. This exercise may require extra time and even scissors or patty paper. It can be used as a group activity to close the day's lesson or as a warm-up activity the next day.

Exercises 13, 14 These exercises preview Chapter 7 on tessellations.

EXTENSIONS

A. Have students try to construct regular polygons with up to 20 sides using compass and straightedge. (They will not be able to construct all of them!)

B. Use Take Another Look activity 3, 4, or 5 on page 304. For activity 4, on concave polygons, students should state a clear definition of *interior angle* and *exterior angle* at points where the interior angle measure is greater than 180°.

EXPLORATION

PLANNING

LESSON OUTLINE

One day:

45 min Activity

MATERIALS

- calculators
- The Geometer's Sketchpad

TEACHING

Star polygons have interesting angle sums and expand students' understanding of what a polygon can be.

Guiding the Activity

The convention used to name polygons by listing consecutive vertices is not followed in the student book for star polygons. If it makes more sense to you and your students to name star polygons by listing the vertices in consecutive order, you might choose to follow that convention in your classroom and refer to the 5-pointed star as star *ACEBD*. The 6-pointed star has two sets of vertices and could be called star *FHJ,GIK* to show that there is no side between vertices *J* and *G*.

You might do the first few steps as a class.

Step 1 The points don't actually need to be on a circle, as long as connecting them in order would make a convex polygon.

Step 3 Ask whether students could have found the sum by imagining walking around the star.

Step 4 The sum will change if the vertices are dragged out of order (so that every second point is no longer connected).

Exploration

Star Polygons

If you arrange a set of points roughly around a circle or an oval, and then you connect each point to the next with segments, you should get a convex polygon like the one at right. What do you get if you connect every second point with segments? You get a star polygon like the ones shown in the activity below.

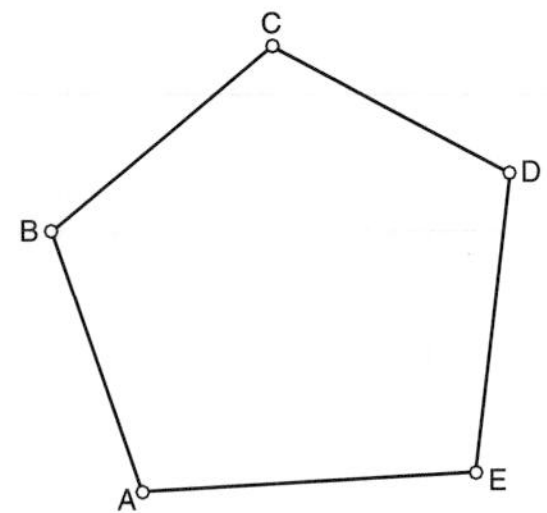

In this activity, you'll investigate the angle measure sums of star polygons.

Activity
Exploring Star Polygons

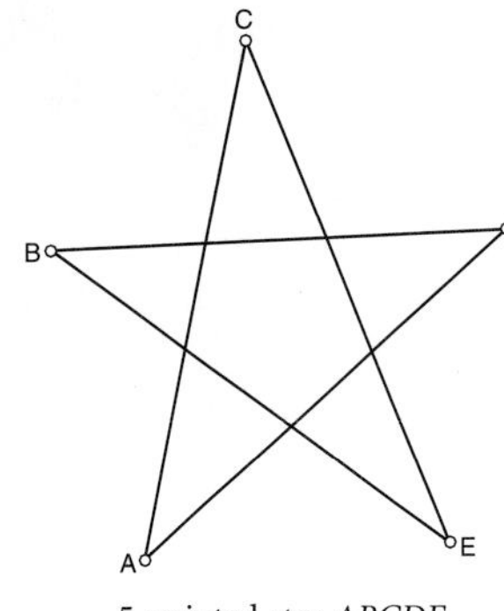

5-pointed star *ABCDE*

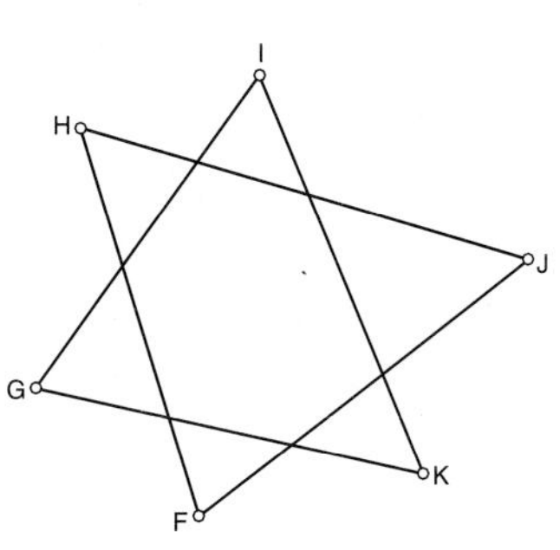

6-pointed star *FGHIJK*

Step 1 Draw five points *A* through *E* in a circular path, clockwise.

Step 2 Connect every second point with $\overline{AC}$, $\overline{CE}$, $\overline{EB}$, $\overline{BD}$, and $\overline{DA}$.

Step 3 Measure the five angles *A* through *E* at the star points. Use the calculator to find the sum of the angle measures. 180°

Step 4 Drag each vertex of the star and observe what happens to the angle measures and the calculated sum. Does the sum change? What is the sum? no; 180°

Step 5 Copy the table on page 265. Use the Polygon Sum Conjecture to complete the first column. Then enter the angle sum for the 5-pointed star.

LESSON OBJECTIVES

- Explore angle measures of star polygons
- Develop skill at using technology to explore geometry

NCTM STANDARDS

CONTENT		PROCESS	
✓	Number	✓	Problem Solving
✓	Algebra	✓	Reasoning
✓	Geometry	✓	Communication
✓	Measurement		Connections
	Data/Probability	✓	Representation

Step 6 Repeat Steps 1–5 for a 6-pointed star. Enter the angle sum in the table. Complete the column for each n-pointed star with every second point connected.

Step 7 What happens if you connect every third point to form a star? What would be the sum of the angle measures in this star? Complete the table column for every third point. three intersecting lines; 0°

Step 8 Use what you have learned to complete the table. What patterns do you notice? Write the rules for n-pointed stars.

Step 8 Some patterns: 180° is a factor; total measure decreases (to 0° or 180°) then increases; numbers are repeated in the opposite order after the minimum. For n-pointed stars: if the points of an n-gon are connected every pth point, then the angle measure sum is $180°|n - 2p|$.

	Angle measure sums by how the star points are connected					
Number of star points	Every point	Every 2nd point	Every 3rd point	Every 4th point	Every 5th point	
5	540°	180°	180°	540°	not a star	
6	720°	360°	0°	360°	720°	
7	900°	540°	180°	180°	540°	900°

Step 9 Let's explore Step 4 a little further. Can you drag the vertices of each star polygon to make it convex? Describe the steps for turning each one into a convex polygon, and then back into a star polygon again, in the fewest steps possible.

Step 10 In Step 9, how did the sum of the angle measure change when a polygon became convex? When did it change?

Step 9 Yes; for even numbers of vertices the two overlapping polygons can be dragged to be non-overlapping. For odd numbers the star needs to be uncrossed. The process can be reversed.

Step 10 Total angle measures are not changed for those made up of overlapping polygons. For others the sum increases as each angle "turns inside out" (for example in $ABCDE$ it changes when A crosses $\overline{DE}$ and the sides of $\angle D$ cross.

This blanket by Teresa Archuleta-Sagel is titled *My Blue Vallero Heaven.* Are these star polygons? Why?

Step 6 [Ask] "How was drawing a five-pointed star different from drawing a six-pointed star?" [The 5-pointed star is a continuous curve; the 6-pointed star has two unconnected pieces.] Different students in each group might take on different numbers of points, or jigsaw among groups. Students probably will need to consider more than 7 points in order to see a pattern. Students might predict the sums before calculating. They will need to extend their tables to allow for the number of points in each star.

Step 7 [Ask] "For what number of points does connecting every third point result in a sum of zero?" [6] "Why?" [It does not form a star.] "For what number of points is the star for every second point the same as the star for every third point?" [5] "Why?" [2 + 3 = 5]

Step 8 Numbers diminish and then increase. It's as if some quantity is decreasing but is being considered only as nonnegative. **[Ask]** "How can you turn any number into a nonnegative number?" [Take the absolute value.] Students may write a short report explaining why the angle measure sums are what they are for any particular polygon stars.

The figures in the star quilt are not star polygons because the eight vertices have not all been connected in the same way.

Step 8

Points	Every point	Every 2nd point	Every 3rd point	Every 4th point	Every 5th point	Every 6th point	Every 7th point	Every 8th point	Every 9th point	Every 10th point	Every 11th point
8	1080°	720°	360°	0°	360°	720°	1080°				
9	1260°	900°	540°	180°	180°	540°	900°	1260°			
10	1440°	1080°	720°	360°	0°	360°	720°	1080°	1440°		
11	1620°	1260°	900°	540°	180°	180°	540°	900°	1260°	1620°	
12	1800°	1440°	1080°	720°	360°	0°	360°	720°	1080°	1440°	1800°

LESSON

5.3

PLANNING

LESSON OUTLINE

One day:

20 min Investigation

10 min Sharing

5 min Closing

10 min Exercises

MATERIALS

- double-edged straightedges with parallel edges
- compasses or patty paper
- protractors

TEACHING

Angles and diagonals of kites and isosceles trapezoids have some interesting properties.

One step Ask students (with their books closed) to discover all they can about the angles and diagonals of kites, trapezoids, and isosceles trapezoids. They might be experienced enough by now to come up with all seven of this lesson's conjectures on their own.

Guiding Investigation 1

Students can explore the properties of kites and complete the conjectures in Investigation 1 using the dynamic geometry exploration at www.keymath.com/DG.

Step 2 Students may find it convenient to label with words the vertex and nonvertex angles.

LESSON 5.3

Kite and Trapezoid Properties

Imagination is the highest kite we fly.

LAUREN BACALL

Recall that a **kite** is a quadrilateral with exactly two distinct pairs of congruent consecutive sides.

If you construct two different isosceles triangles on opposite sides of a common base and then remove the base, you have constructed a kite. In an isosceles triangle, the vertex angle is the angle between the two congruent sides. Therefore, let's call the two angles between each pair of congruent sides of a kite the **vertex angles** of the kite. Let's call the other pair the **nonvertex angles.**

For an interactive version of this sketch, visit www.keymath.com/DG .

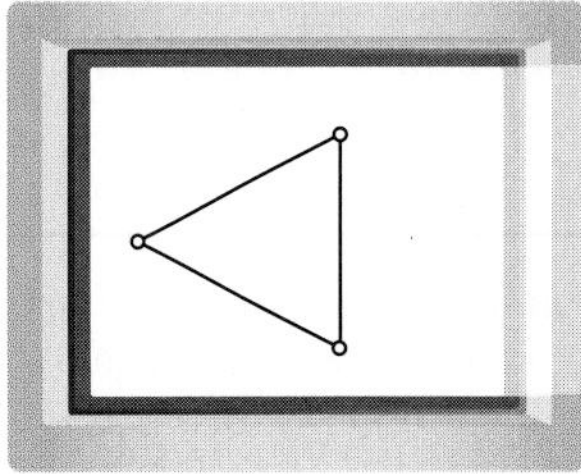

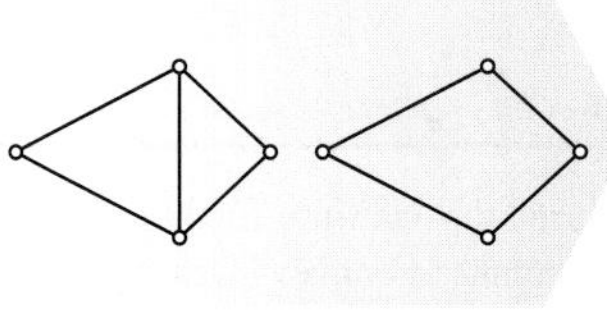

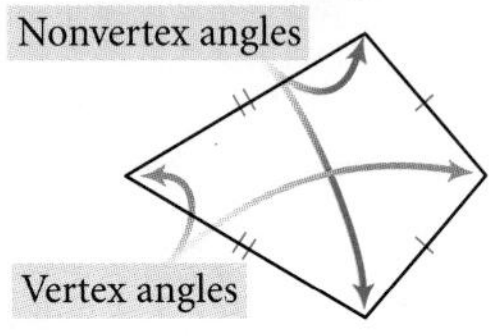

A kite also has one line of reflectional symmetry, just like an isosceles triangle. You can use this property to discover other properties of kites. Let's investigate.

Investigation 1
What Are Some Properties of Kites?

You will need
- patty paper

In this investigation you will look at angles and diagonals in a kite to see what special properties they have.

Step 1 On patty paper, draw two connected segments of different lengths, as shown. Fold through the endpoints and trace the two segments on the back of the patty paper.

Step 2 Compare the size of each pair of opposite angles in your kite by folding an angle onto the opposite angle. Are the vertex angles congruent? Are the nonvertex angles congruent? Share your observations with others near you and complete the conjecture.

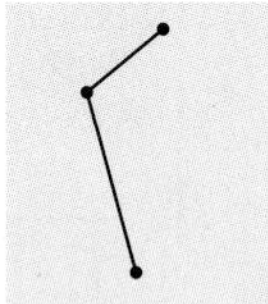

Step 1

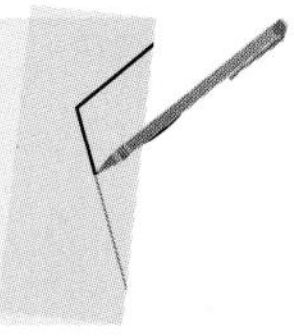

Step 2

LESSON OBJECTIVES

- Discover properties of kites and trapezoids
- Learn new vocabulary
- Practice construction skills

NCTM STANDARDS

CONTENT		PROCESS	
	Number	✓	Problem Solving
	Algebra	✓	Reasoning
✓	Geometry	✓	Communication
✓	Measurement	✓	Connections
	Data/Probability		Representation

Kite Angles Conjecture

C-35

The nonvertex angles of a kite are congruent.

Step 3 Draw the diagonals. How are the diagonals related? Share your observations with others in your group and complete the conjecture.

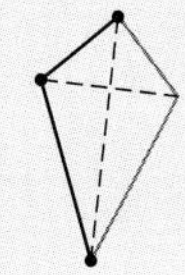

Kite Diagonals Conjecture

C-36

The diagonals of a kite are perpendicular.

What else seems to be true about the diagonals of kites?

Step 4 Compare the lengths of the segments on both diagonals. Does either diagonal bisect the other? Share your observations with others near you. Copy and complete the conjecture.

Kite Diagonal Bisector Conjecture

C-37

The diagonal connecting the vertex angles of a kite is the perpendicular bisector of the other diagonal.

Step 5 Fold along both diagonals. Does either diagonal bisect any angles? Share your observations with others and complete the conjecture.

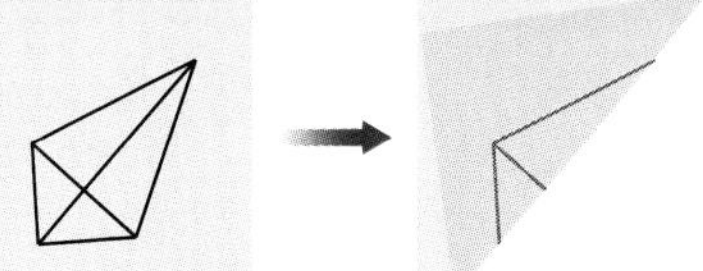

Kite Angle Bisector Conjecture

C-38

The vertex angles of a kite are bisected by a diagonal.

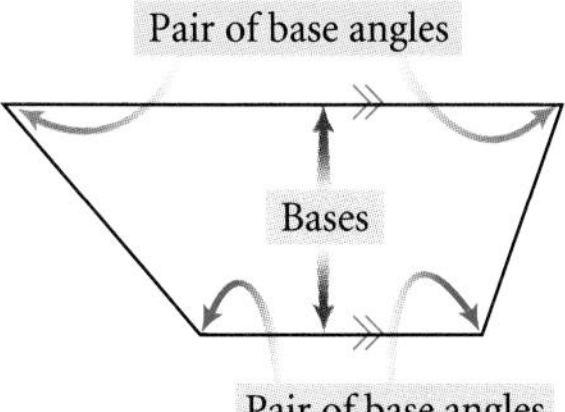

You will prove the Kite Diagonal Bisector Conjecture and the Kite Angle Bisector Conjecture as exercises after this lesson.

Let's move on to trapezoids. Recall that a **trapezoid** is a quadrilateral with exactly one pair of parallel sides.

In a trapezoid the parallel sides are called **bases.** A pair of angles that share a base as a common side are called **base angles.**

In the next investigation, you will discover some properties of trapezoids.

Guiding Investigation 2

Step 2 Consecutive angles share a side—in this case, one of the nonparallel sides of the trapezoid.

Step 4 Students may construct an isosceles trapezoid with the help of its line of symmetry, which goes through the midpoints of the bases.

SHARING IDEAS

Have students read aloud selected conjectures for critique. Reach consensus about which statements students will record in their notebooks.

[Ask] "What are consecutive sides in a polygon?" [sides that share a vertex] "What are consecutive angles in a polygon?" [angles that share a side] "Are consecutive angles the same as adjacent angles?" [Adjacent angles share a side, but they also share a vertex—not possible for distinct angles in a polygon.] "What symmetry does a kite have?" [It has reflectional symmetry over the diagonal through its vertex angles.] "Can the properties of a kite be seen from that symmetry?" [The line of symmetry bisects the vertex angles. Because each nonvertex angle is reflected to the other one through a line perpendicular to the line of symmetry, the diagonals are perpendicular. And, as reflections of each other, the nonvertex angles are congruent.] To preview properties of other figures, you might also ask whether the symmetry guarantees that consecutive angles, adjacent sides, or vertex angles are congruent or whether the diagonals are congruent or bisect each other. [The kite has none of these properties.]

Wonder aloud whether the observation about consecutive angles of a trapezoid extends to consecutive interior angles formed by any line cutting any pair of parallel lines. Students can see that it does by considering linear pairs in which one angle is an opposite interior angle to another.

[Ask] "What kind of symmetry does the isosceles trapezoid have?" [reflectional symmetry over a line through the midpoints of the parallel sides] "What properties of the figure can be seen from this symmetry?" [The base angles are reflections of each other, so they're congruent.] Some students may have more difficulty seeing that the diagonals are also reflections of each other, because the two parts of each diagonal are reflected in different directions. As with the kite, you might ask whether the symmetry guarantees the properties that the figure doesn't have.

Ask whether students could prove the Isosceles Trapezoid Conjecture from the Isosceles Triangle Conjecture. They might say that if they extend the nonparallel sides of the trapezoid to their intersection point, they'll have an isosceles triangle, so the base angles (which are also the base angles of the trapezoid) will be congruent. Ask why the triangle is isosceles; students may say that it is because its

---

Science CONNECTION

A *trapezium* is a quadrilateral with *no* two sides parallel. The words *trapezoid* and *trapezium* come from the Greek word *trápeza,* meaning table. There are bones in your wrists that anatomists call trapezoid and trapezium because of their geometric shapes.

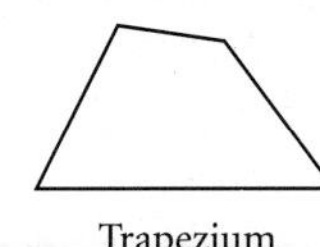

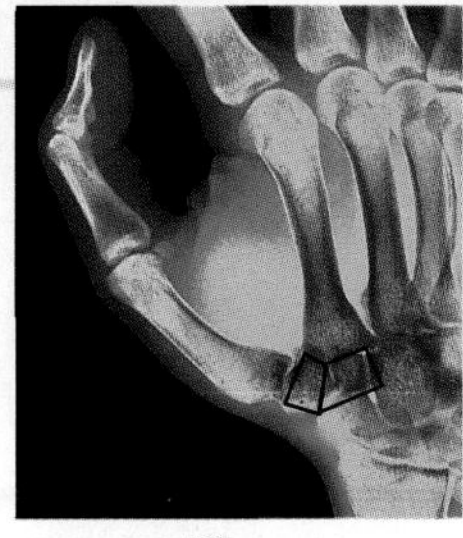

Investigation 2
What Are Some Properties of Trapezoids?

You will need
- a straightedge
- a protractor
- a compass

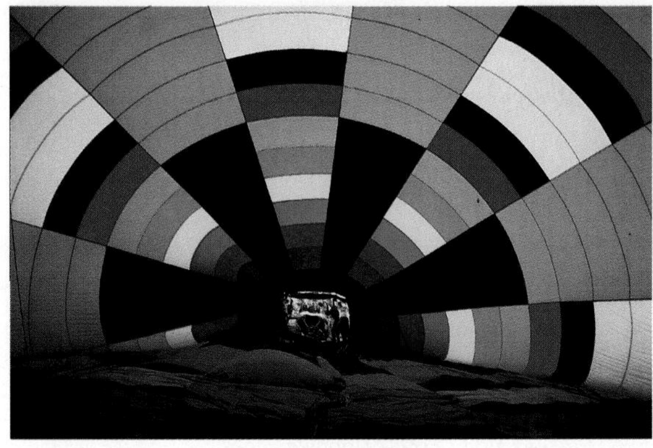

This is a view inside a deflating hot-air balloon. Notice the trapezoidal panels that make up the balloon.

Step 1 Use the two edges of your straightedge to draw parallel segments of unequal length. Draw two nonparallel sides connecting them to make a trapezoid.

Step 2 Use your protractor to find the sum of the measures of each pair of consecutive angles between the parallel bases. What do you notice about this sum? Share your observations with your group.

Step 3 Copy and complete the conjecture.

> **Trapezoid Consecutive Angles Conjecture** C-39
>
> The consecutive angles between the bases of a trapezoid are __?__. supplementary

Recall from Chapter 3 that a trapezoid whose two nonparallel sides are the same length is called an **isosceles trapezoid.** Next, you will discover a few properties of isosceles trapezoids.

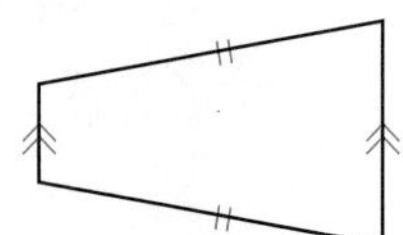

Like kites, isosceles trapezoids have one line of reflectional symmetry. Through what points does the line of symmetry pass?

Step 4 Use both edges of your straightedge to draw parallel lines. Using your compass, construct two congruent segments. Connect the four segments to make an isosceles trapezoid.

Step 5 Measure each pair of base angles. What do you notice about the pair of base angles in each trapezoid? Compare your observations with others near you.

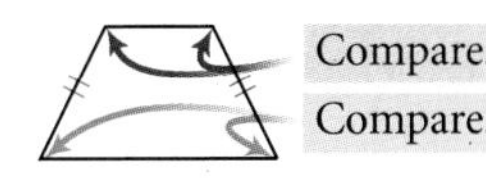

Step 6 Copy and complete the conjecture.

Isosceles Trapezoid Conjecture C-40

The base angles of an isosceles trapezoid are _?_. congruent

What other parts of an isosceles trapezoid are congruent? Let's continue.

Step 7 Draw both diagonals. Compare their lengths. Share your observations with others near you.

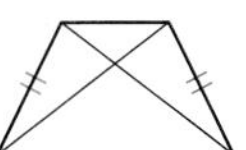

Step 8 Copy and complete the conjecture.

Isosceles Trapezoid Diagonals Conjecture C-41

The diagonals of an isosceles trapezoid are _?_. congruent

Suppose you assume that the Isosceles Trapezoid Conjecture is true. What pair of triangles and which triangle congruence conjecture would you use to explain why the Isosceles Trapezoid Diagonals Conjecture is true?
the triangles formed by the diagonals, SAS

EXERCISES

You will need

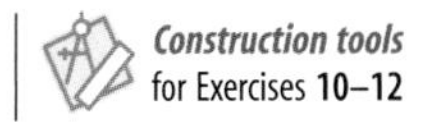

Use your new conjectures to find the missing measures.

1. Perimeter = _?_ 64 cm

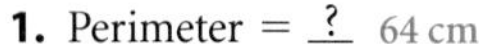

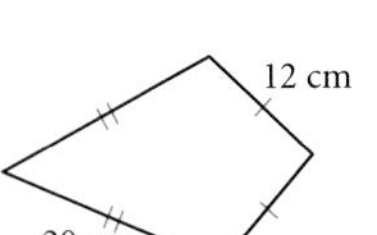

2. $x =$ _?_ 21°
$y =$ _?_ 146°

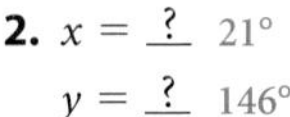

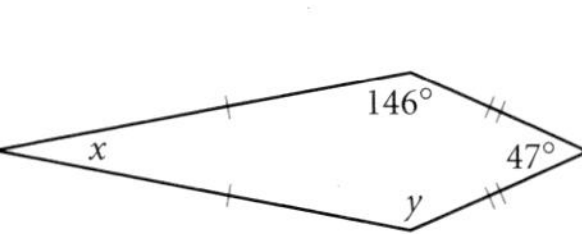

3. $x =$ _?_ 52°
$y =$ _?_ 128°

128°
y
x

Closing the Lesson

Reiterate the main conjectures of this lesson: Nonvertex angles of kites and base angles of trapezoids are congruent; diagonals of kites are perpendicular, and the diagonal between the vertex angles bisects the other diagonal and the vertex angles; diagonals of isosceles trapezoids are congruent; and consecutive angles of any trapezoid (not just isosceles ones) between the parallel sides are supplementary. You might also mention that the vertex angles of kites are not congruent, the diagonals of kites are not congruent and the diagonal between the nonvertex angles doesn't bisect the other diagonal or the nonvertex angles, and the diagonals of isosceles trapezoids don't bisect angles or each other. Urge students to learn to draw and mark pictures from which they can quickly observe what is and isn't true about these figures.

Sharing Ideas (continued)
base angles, or the base angles of the triangle not including the trapezoid, are congruent. This discussion can provide a good example of circular reasoning. (Students are asked to prove the Isosceles Trapezoid Conjecture in the exercises of Lesson 5.7.)

If they assume the truth of the Isosceles Trapezoid Conjecture, however, students can prove the Isosceles Trapezoid Diagonals Conjecture using SAS. As needed, help them see how to use the overlapping triangles to explain why the diagonals are congruent.

Assessing Progress
In this lesson, you can assess students' understanding of kites, trapezoids, diagonals, and parallel and nonparallel lines. You can also monitor their ability to use a protractor and to copy a segment and compare lengths of segments with a compass.

BUILDING UNDERSTANDING

The exercises include a proof of the Kite Angle Bisector Conjecture. As always, encourage students to support all solutions by stating relevant conjectures.

ASSIGNING HOMEWORK

Essential	1–10, 13
Performance assessment	15
Portfolio	14
Journal	12
Group	10–12
Review	17

MATERIALS

- Exercise 14 (T), *optional*
- Exercise 17 (T), *optional*

▶ Helping with the Exercises

Exercises 7–9 These exercises ask students only to sketch the figures. Students can thus visualize the concepts before they get to the next step of constructing some of the figures, in Exercises 10–12.

7. possible answer:

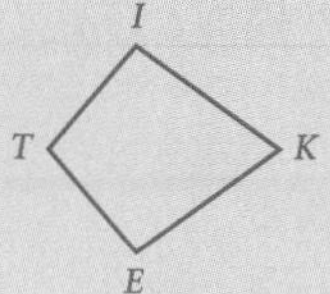

$\angle E \cong \angle I$

8. possible answer:

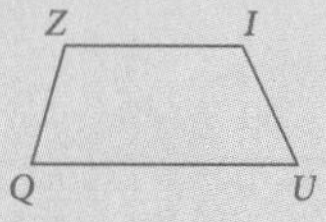

The other base is $\overline{ZI}$. $\angle Q$ and $\angle U$ are a pair of base angles. $\angle Z$ and $\angle I$ are a pair of base angles.

9. possible answer:

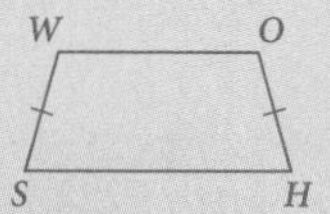

$\overline{OW}$ is the other base. $\angle S$ and $\angle H$ are a pair of base angles. $\angle O$ and $\angle W$ are a pair of base angles. $\overline{SW} \cong \overline{HO}$.

Exercises 10–12 If students make sketches of these figures before beginning the constructions, they'll find it easier to visualize the various parts being given to them.

10.

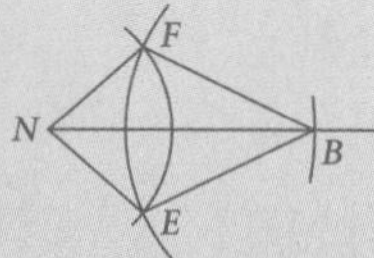

Only one kite is possible because three sides determine a triangle.

11.

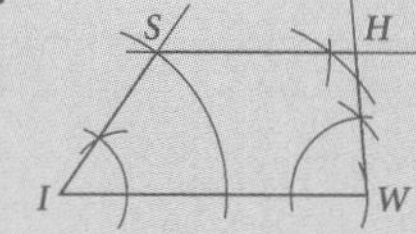

4. $x = \underline{\ ?\ }$ 15 cm

Perimeter = 85 cm

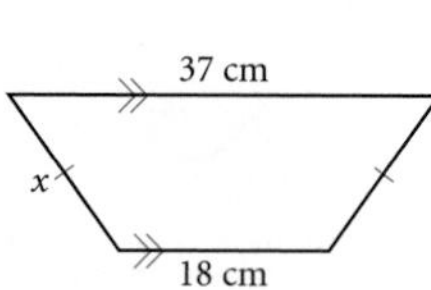

5. $x = \underline{\ ?\ }$ 72°

$y = \underline{\ ?\ }$ 61°

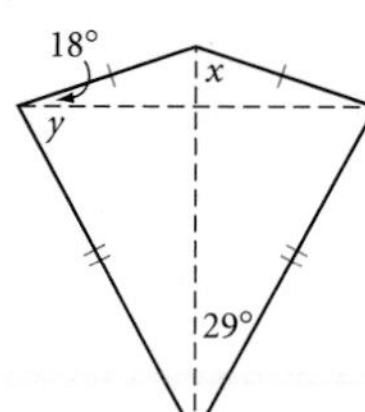

6. $x = \underline{\ ?\ }$ 99°

$y = \underline{\ ?\ }$ 38 cm

Perimeter = 164 cm

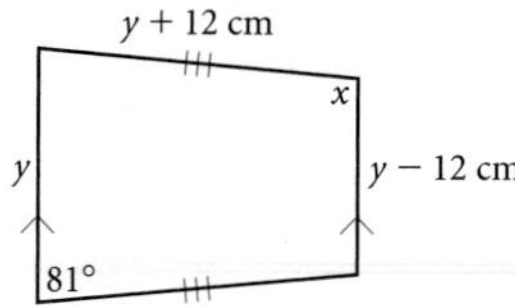

7. Sketch and label kite *KITE* with vertex angles $\angle K$ and $\angle T$ and $KI > TE$. Which angles are congruent?

8. Sketch and label trapezoid *QUIZ* with one base $\overline{QU}$. What is the other base? Name the two pairs of base angles.

9. Sketch and label isosceles trapezoid *SHOW* with one base $\overline{SH}$. What is the other base? Name the two pairs of base angles. Name the two sides of equal length.

In Exercises 10–12, use the properties of kites and trapezoids to construct each figure. You may use either patty paper or a compass and a straightedge.

10. ***Construction*** Construct kite *BENF* given sides $\overline{BE}$ and $\overline{EN}$ and diagonal $\overline{BN}$. How many different kites are possible?

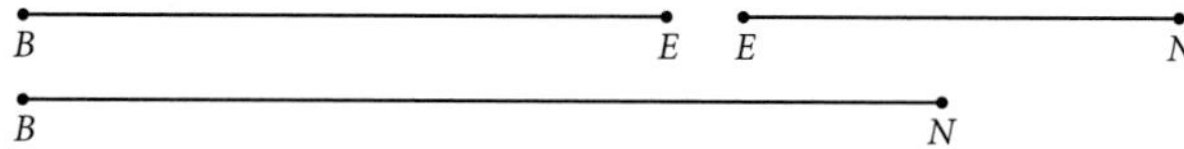

11. ***Construction*** Given $\angle W$, $\angle I$, base $\overline{WI}$, and nonparallel side $\overline{IS}$, construct trapezoid *WISH*. ⓗ

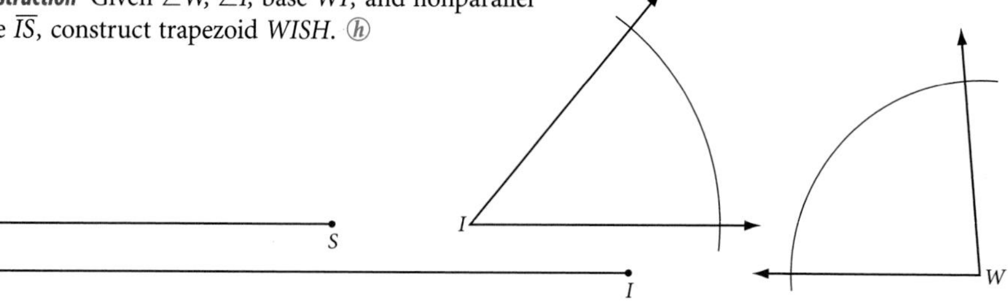

12. ***Construction*** Construct a trapezoid *BONE* with $\overline{BO} \parallel \overline{NE}$. How many different trapezoids can you construct?

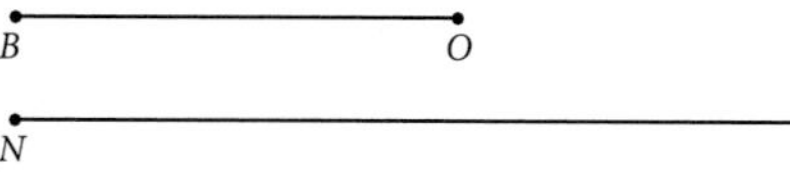

13. Write a paragraph proof or flowchart proof showing how the Kite Diagonal Bisector Conjecture logically follows from the Converse of the Perpendicular Bisector Conjecture. ⓗ

12. possible construction:

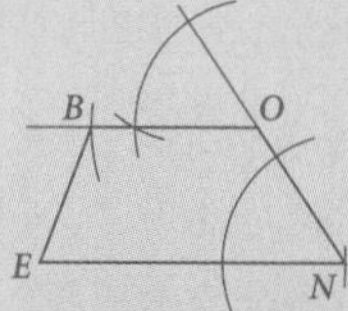

infinitely many

13. The definition of a kite says that $\overline{KI} \cong \overline{IT}$ and $\overline{TE} \cong \overline{EK}$. So point *I* is equidistant from points *K* and *T*. Likewise, point *E* is equidistant from points *K* and *T*. Therefore, both *I* and *E* lie on the perpendicular bisector of $\overline{KT}$. So the diagonal $\overline{IE}$ is the perpendicular bisector of diagonal $\overline{KT}$.

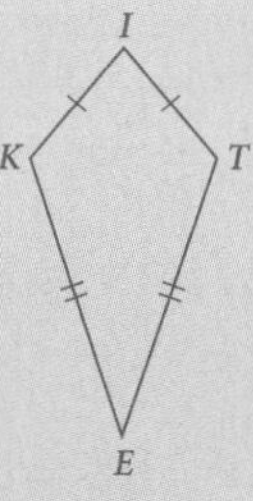

14. Copy and complete the flowchart to show how the Kite Angle Bisector Conjecture follows logically from one of the triangle congruence conjectures.

Given: Kite $BENY$ with $\overline{BE} \cong \overline{BY}$, $\overline{EN} \cong \overline{YN}$

Show: $\overline{BN}$ bisects $\angle B$

$\overline{BN}$ bisects $\angle N$

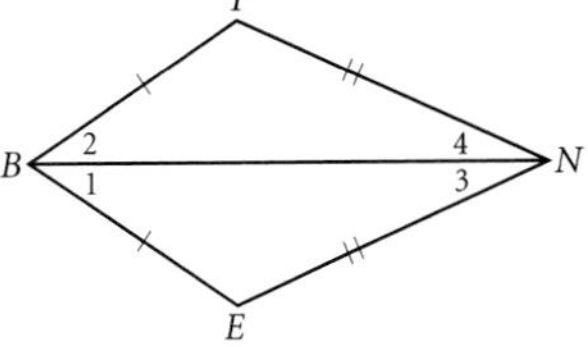

Flowchart Proof

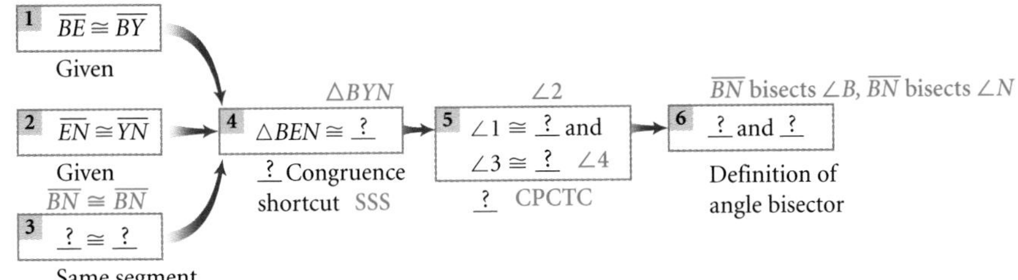

Architecture CONNECTION

The Romans used the classical arch design in bridges, aqueducts, and buildings in the early centuries of the Common Era. The classical semicircular arch is really half of a regular polygon built with wedge-shaped blocks whose faces are isosceles trapezoids. Each block supports the blocks surrounding it.

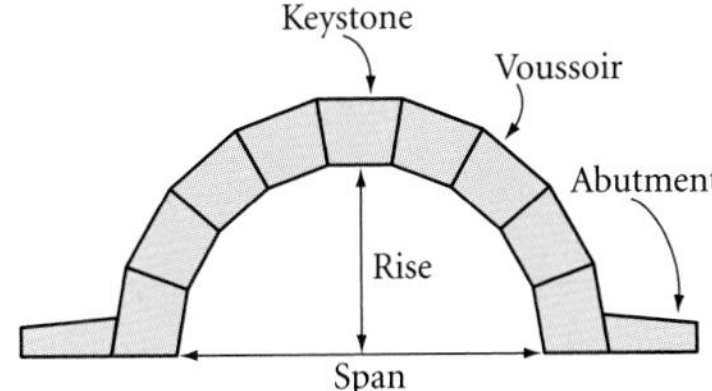

15. **APPLICATION** The inner edge of the arch in the diagram above right is half of a regular 18-gon. Calculate the measures of all the angles in the nine isosceles trapezoids making up the arch. Then use your geometry tools to accurately draw a nine-stone arch like the one shown.

80°, 80°, 100°, 100°

This carton is shaped like an isosceles trapezoid block.

16. The figure below shows the path of light through a trapezoidal prism, and how an image is inverted. For the prism to work as shown, the trapezoid must be isosceles, $\angle AGF$ must be congruent to $\angle BHE$, and $\overline{GF}$ must be congruent to $\overline{EH}$. Show that if these conditions are met, then $\overline{AG}$ will be congruent to $\overline{BH}$. ⓗ

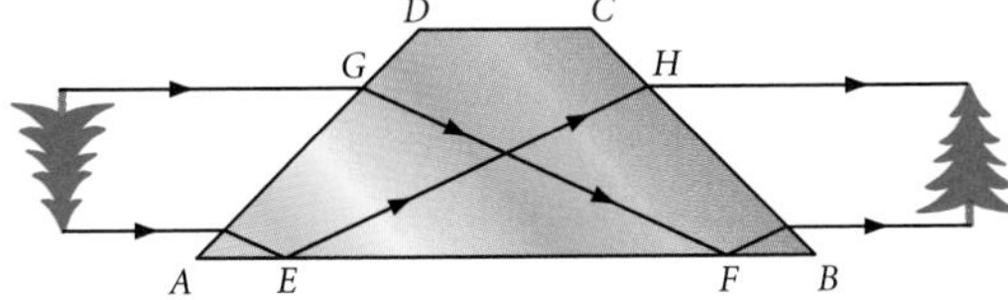

Because $ABCD$ is an isosceles trapezoid, $\angle A \cong \angle B$. $\triangle AGF \cong \triangle BHE$ by SAA. Thus, $\overline{AG} \cong \overline{BH}$ by CPCTC.

Science CONNECTION

The magnifying lenses of binoculars invert the objects you view through them, so trapezoidal prisms are used to flip the inverted images right-side-up again.

Exercise 15 The project Building an Arch in Lesson 5.4 is an extension of this exercise.

EXTENSION

Use Take Another Look activity 4 on page 304.

Parametric Equations
Graphing calculators are used mostly for graphing equations in which y is a function of x; but y is not a function of x in a graph that's a circle or a polygon, because most values of x in the domain correspond to more than one value of y. Therefore to graph a circle or a polygon we use a third variable, usually called t, and write x as a function of t and also write y as a function of t. Students can think of t as giving a time and x and y as giving the positions of a bug crawling on the screen. These functions are called *parametric equations.*

[Link] Students will learn more about parametric equations and trigonometric functions in a later math course.

The focus of the project is on the central angles of a regular polygon. Help students keep the mathematical ideas in mind even while they are immersed in the details of graphing.

Friendly Windows
To help students understand friendly calculator windows, explain that *pixels* are dots on the screen. Pictures are made by turning selected pixels dark and leaving the rest light. If a window has 94 pixels across and you select the x-window to be $[-4.7, 4.7]$, then every pixel represents a distance across of $\frac{9.4}{94} = 0.1$ unit. Or, if a screen has 62 pixels vertically, you could select a y-window of $[-31, 31]$ to give a vertical value of 1 unit per pixel. If you set the window so that each pixel represents a different number vertically than horizontally, figures will appear distorted. Avoiding this distortion may not be important when you are graphing functions. But if you want a regular hexagon to look regular, you need to use a friendly window, that is, one in which each pixel represents the same number of units vertically as horizontally.

Review

17. Trace the figure below. Calculate the measure of each lettered angle. $a = 80°, b = 20°, c = 160°, d = 20°, e = 80°, f = 80°, g = 110°, h = 70°, m = 110°, n = 100°$

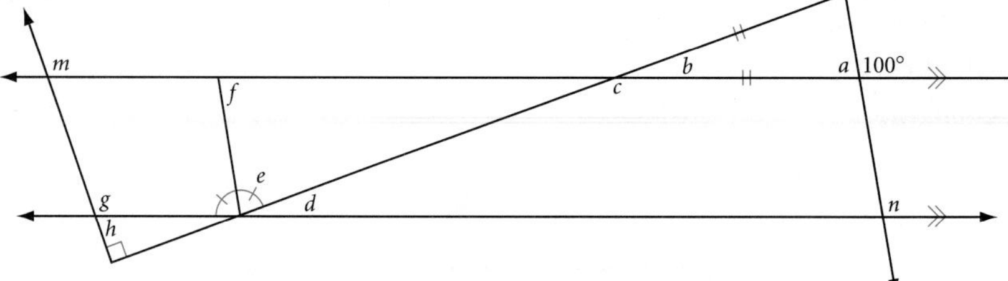

project

DRAWING REGULAR POLYGONS

You can draw a regular polygon's central angle by extending segments from the center of the polygon to its consecutive vertices. For example, the measure of each central angle of a hexagon is 60°.

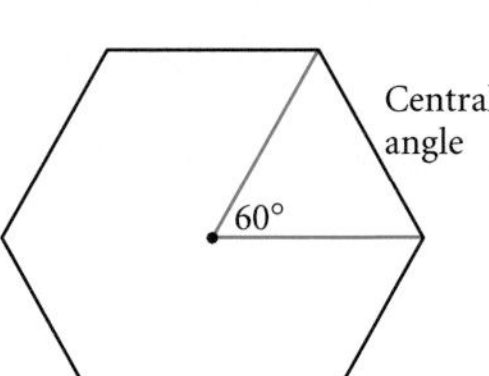

Using central angles, you can draw regular polygons on a graphing calculator. This is done with parametric equations, which give the x- and y-coordinates of a point in terms of a third variable, or parameter, t.

Set your calculator's mode to degrees and parametric. Set a friendly window with an x-range of -4.7 to 4.7 and a y-range of -3.1 to 3.1. Set a t-range of 0 to 360, and t-step of 60. Enter the equations $x = 3\cos t$ and $y = 3\sin t$, and graph them. You should get a hexagon.

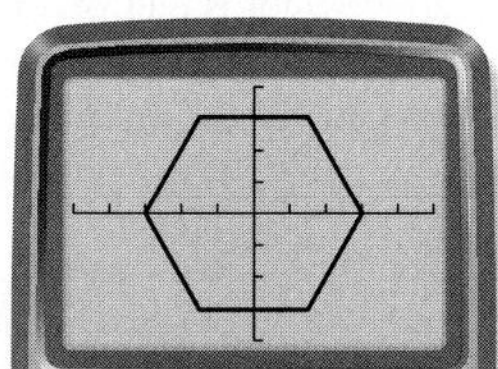

The equations you graphed are actually the parametric equations for a circle. By using a t-step of 60 for t-values from 0 to 360, you tell the calculator to compute only six points for the circle.

Use your calculator to investigate the following. Summarize your findings.

- Choose different t-steps to draw different regular polygons, such as an equilateral triangle, a square, a regular pentagon, and so on. What is the measure of each central angle of an n-gon?
- What happens as the measure of each central angle of a regular polygon decreases?
- What happens as you draw polygons with more and more sides?
- Experiment with rotating your polygons by choosing different t-min and t-max values. For example, set a t-range of -45 to 315, then draw a square.
- Find a way to draw star polygons on your calculator. Can you explain how this works?

Supporting the project

If the steps were infinitely small, the two parametric equations would generate a circle. Considering this case can help students see how the calculator is using the central angle to draw a polygon.

OUTCOMES

- The polygons are regular. (A friendly window was used.)
- The measure of the central angle of each polygon is given, and answers to the questions are clear.
- Rotated polygons are shown.
- Star polygons are created and explained.

LESSON

5.4 Properties of Midsegments

Research is formalized curiosity. It is poking and prying with a purpose.

ZORA NEALE HURSTON

As you learned in Chapter 3, the segment connecting the midpoints of two sides of a triangle is the midsegment of a triangle. The segment connecting the midpoints of the two nonparallel sides of a trapezoid is also called the midsegment of a trapezoid.

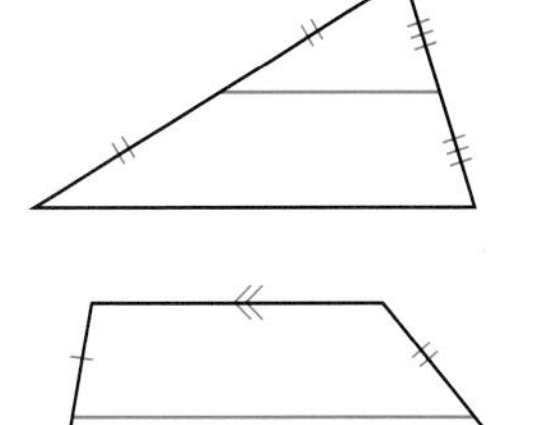

In this lesson you will discover special properties of midsegments.

Investigation 1
Triangle Midsegment Properties

You will need
- patty paper

In this investigation you will discover two properties of the midsegment of a triangle. Each person in your group can investigate a different triangle.

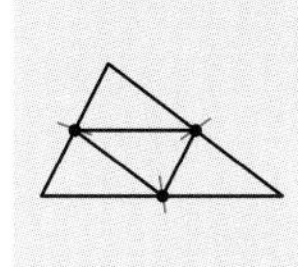

Step 1

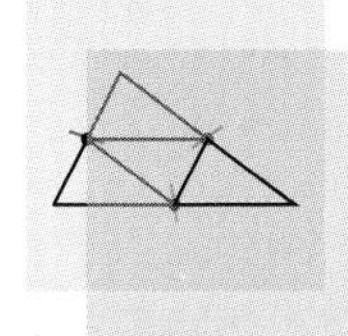

Step 2

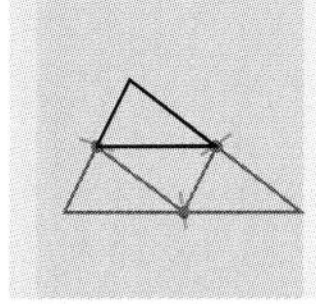

Step 3

Step 1 Draw a triangle on a piece of patty paper. Pinch the patty paper to locate midpoints of the sides. Draw the midsegments. You should now have four small triangles.

Step 2 Place a second piece of patty paper over the first and copy one of the four triangles.

Step 3 Compare all four triangles by sliding the copy of one small triangle over the other three triangles. Compare your results with the results of your group. Copy and complete the conjecture.

Three Midsegments Conjecture C-42

The three midsegments of a triangle divide it into _?_. four congruent triangles

Step 4 Each midsegment is parallel to the third side.

Step 4 Mark all the congruent angles in your drawing. What conclusions can you make about each midsegment and the large triangle's third side, using the Corresponding Angles Conjecture and the Alternate Interior Angles Conjecture? What do the other students in your group think?

NCTM STANDARDS

CONTENT		PROCESS	
	Number	✓	Problem Solving
✓	Algebra	✓	Reasoning
✓	Geometry	✓	Communication
✓	Measurement	✓	Connections
	Data/Probability		Representation

LESSON OBJECTIVES

- Define and discover properties of midsegments in triangles and trapezoids
- Practice construction skills

LESSON 5.4

PLANNING

LESSON OUTLINE

One day:

25 min Investigation

5 min Sharing

5 min Closing

10 min Exercises

MATERIALS

- construction tools
- protractors

TEACHING

A midsegment of a triangle or a trapezoid is closely related to the side or sides it parallels. The one-step investigation replaces both investigations.

Guiding Investigation 1

Step 1 [Alert] Students may have forgotten what a midsegment is.

Step 3 To see that all four triangles are congruent, students will rotate as well as translate the sliding triangle.

Step 5 Students can use patty paper or a compass to see that the midsegment fits twice on the large triangle's third side.

One step Pose this problem: "You are trying to predict how long a road tunnel through a hill will be. You're at one end of the tunnel's path. You can drive along a straight road to a point two miles west and one mile north of the other end of the tunnel. Or, from your starting point, you can go the same distance in the other direction along the road to an intersection that's three miles west and one mile south of the tunnel's other end. Is this enough information for you to determine the

One step (continued)
length of the tunnel?" As you circulate, be sure each group has a sketch of the trapezoidal figure; ask that each group member check it before beginning work. Encourage students to generalize their guess to a conjecture about all trapezoids. As groups finish, encourage them to think about what would happen if one of the trapezoid's parallel sides shrank to a point, so that the figure became a triangle. During Sharing, extend the problem to drawing all midsegments of the triangle and deriving the Three Midsegments Conjecture.

Guiding Investigation 2

Define the midsegment of a trapezoid and ask student groups to discover and conjecture about two special properties of a midsegment of a trapezoid. Circulate to check on the correctness of each group's Trapezoid Midsegment Conjecture.

Step 1 You might emphasize that students should leave plenty of room on the right side of the patty paper. In Step 5, they'll need that space to add the two bases together.

Step 8 Students may say that the length of the midsegment is "half the sum of the bases" or "the average of the bases." For students careful about detail, you might mention during Sharing that the conjecture should refer to the *lengths* of the bases rather than the bases themselves.

Step 5 Compare the length of the midsegment to the large triangle's third side. How do they relate? Copy and complete the conjecture.

Triangle Midsegment Conjecture C-43

A midsegment of a triangle is __?__ to the third side and __?__ the length of __?__.
parallel half the third side

In the next investigation, you will discover two properties of the midsegment of a trapezoid.

Investigation 2
Trapezoid Midsegment Properties

You will need
- patty paper

Each person in your group can investigate a different trapezoid. Make sure you draw the two bases perfectly parallel.

Step 1

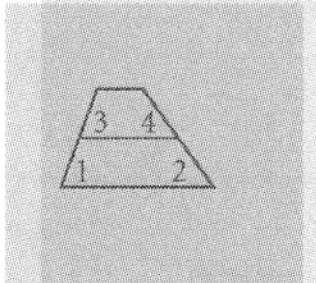

Step 2

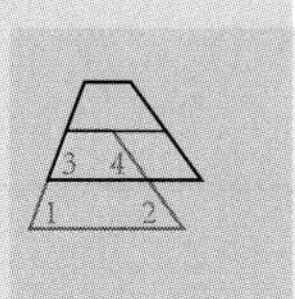

Step 3

Step 1 Draw a small trapezoid on the left side of a piece of patty paper. Pinch the paper to locate the midpoints of the nonparallel sides. Draw the midsegment.

Step 2 Label the angles as shown. Place a second piece of patty paper over the first and copy the trapezoid and its midsegment.

Step 3 Compare the trapezoid's base angles with the corresponding angles at the midsegment by sliding the copy up over the original.

Step 4 Are the corresponding angles congruent? What can you conclude about the midsegment and the bases? Compare your results with the results of other students.

Step 4 Yes; the midsegment is parallel to the base.

The midsegment of a triangle is half the length of the third side. How does the length of the midsegment of a trapezoid compare to the lengths of the two bases? Let's investigate.

Step 5 On the original trapezoid, extend the longer base to the right by at least the length of the shorter base.

Step 6 Slide the second patty paper under the first. Show the sum of the lengths of the two bases by marking a point on the extension of the longer base.

SHARING IDEAS

Have students share the variety of conjecture statements they've come up with. As needed, encourage them to use the words *midsegment* and *average* in improving their conjectures, and lead the class to agree on the wording to be written in their notebooks. Point out that, although every triangle has three midsegments, any trapezoid has only one.

[Ask] "Are triangles trapezoids?" [They're not.] Yet their midsegments seem to have similar properties. Elicit the idea that if one of the parallel edges of the trapezoid is shrunk to a point and the height is kept the same length, the trapezoid shrinks to a triangle that shares the midsegment. **[Ask]** "Can it be said that the length of a triangle's midsegment is the average of the lengths of the two bases?" [Yes, if one of the bases is considered to have length 0. In both the triangle and the trapezoid, the midsegment is parallel to a side.] "What can be said about the change in angles as the trapezoid's base shrinks to a point?" [The corresponding angles remain congruent to each other even while changing measure.]

[Ask] "The term we are using for the line segment that connects the midpoints of the nonparallel sides of a trapezoid is *midsegment.* This segment is also called *the median of a trapezoid.* Which do you think is a better name for the segment, and why?" Each group might write a letter about its views to be read aloud to the class.

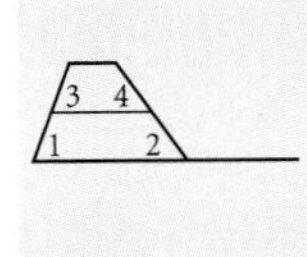

Step 5

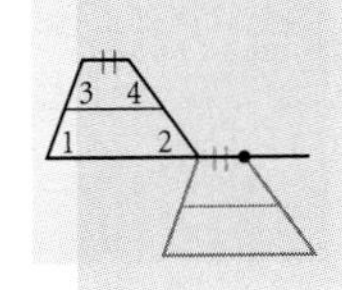

Step 6

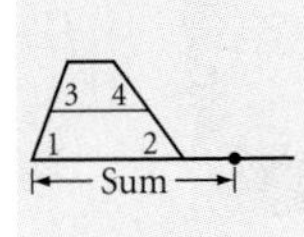

Step 7

Step 7 twice; half the sum of the lengths of the bases

Step 7 How many times does the midsegment fit onto the segment representing the sum of the lengths of the two bases? What do you notice about the length of the midsegment and the sum of the lengths of the two bases?

Step 8 Combine your conclusions from Steps 4 and 7 and complete this conjecture.

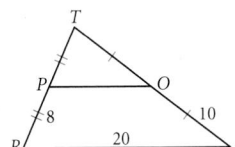

Trapezoid Midsegment Conjecture C-44

The midsegment of a trapezoid is _?_ to the bases and is equal in length to _?_.

parallel; the average of the lengths of the bases

What happens if one base of the trapezoid shrinks to a point? Then the trapezoid collapses into a triangle, the midsegment of the trapezoid becomes a midsegment of the triangle, and the Trapezoid Midsegment Conjecture becomes the Triangle Midsegment Conjecture. Do both of your midsegment conjectures work for the last figure?

For an interactive version of this sketch, visit www.keymath.com/DG .

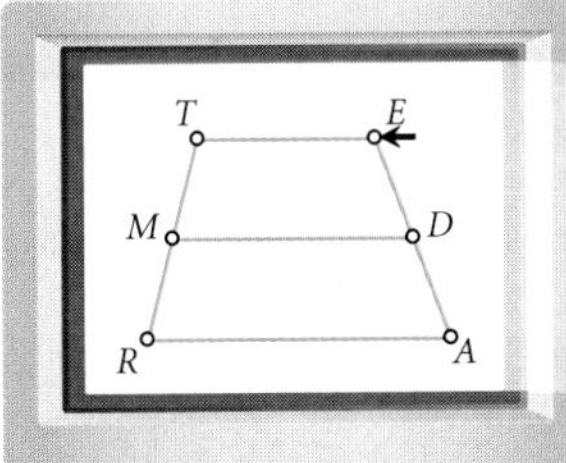

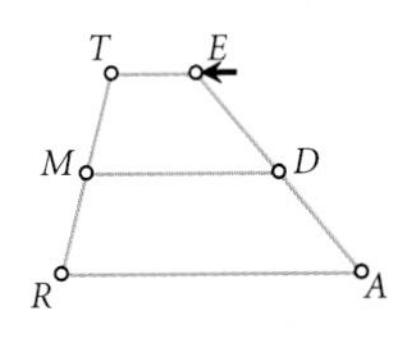

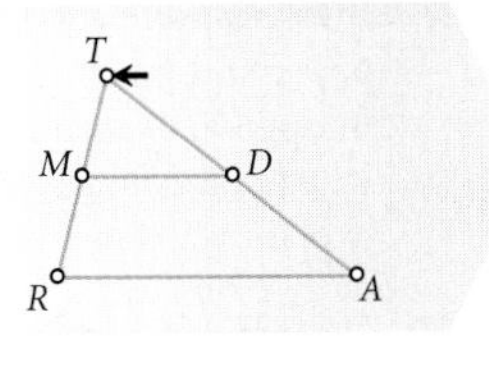

Exercises

You will need

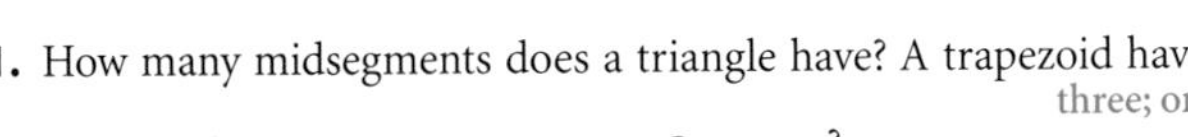

1. How many midsegments does a triangle have? A trapezoid have? three; one

2. What is the perimeter of $\triangle TOP$? ⓗ 28

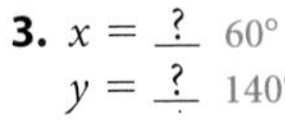

3. $x = \underline{?}$ 60°
   $y = \underline{?}$ 140°

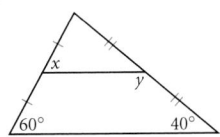

4. $z = \underline{?}$ ⓗ 65°

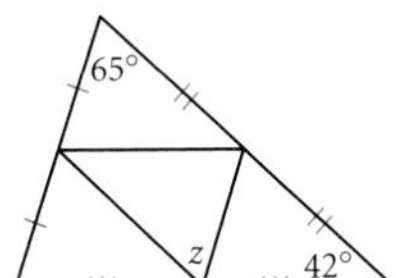

Assessing Progress

Assess students' understanding of trapezoid, midpoint, midsegments of triangles, congruent triangles, and average of lengths. You can also see how well they understand corresponding angles formed by parallel lines and a transversal and the Converse of the Parallel Lines Conjecture. Also check how well they can construct the midpoint of a line segment on patty paper.

Closing the Lesson

The midsegment of any trapezoid is parallel to the bases, and its length is the average of their lengths. If one of the bases shrinks to a point to make a triangle, the midsegment remains parallel to the remaining base, and its length becomes half the length of that side of the triangle. The three midsegments of a triangle divide it into four congruent triangles.

Students can investigate the properties of the midsegment of a trapezoid using the dynamic geometry exploration at www.keymath.com/DG.

BUILDING UNDERSTANDING

The exercises include applications and extensions of the conjectures in this lesson about midsegments. As always, encourage students to support their solutions by being ready to state the conjecture(s) they have used to solve the exercises.

ASSIGNING HOMEWORK

Essential	1–9
Performance assessment	10
Portfolio	9
Journal	11
Group	8
Review	12–18

MATERIALS

- Exercise 11 (T), *optional*

▶ Helping with the Exercises

Exercise 9 If students are having difficulty, ask how they might make triangles so they can apply the Triangle Midsegment Conjecture. [Draw one diagonal to see two triangles.]

9. Parallelogram. Draw a diagonal of the original quadrilateral. The diagonal forms two triangles. Each of the two midsegments is parallel to the diagonal, and thus the midsegments are parallel to each other. Now draw the other diagonal of the original quadrilateral. By the same reasoning, the second pair of midsegments is parallel. Therefore, the quadrilateral formed by joining the midpoints is a parallelogram.

Exercise 10 Students may use the equation $\frac{52 + x}{2} = 41$, or they may simply realize that the other edge is 11 meters shorter than the midsegment, just as 41 is 11 less than 52.

10. The length of the edge of the top base measures 30 m. We know this by the Trapezoid Midsegment Conjecture.

5. What is the perimeter of $\triangle TEN$? 23

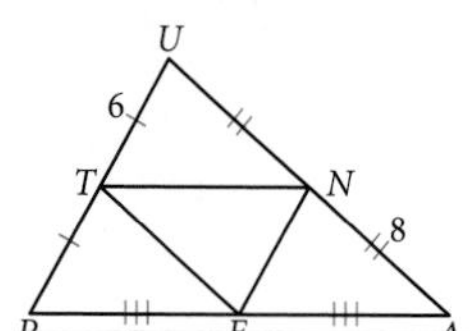

6. $m = \underline{?}$ 129°
$n = \underline{?}$ 73°
$p = \underline{?}$ 42 cm

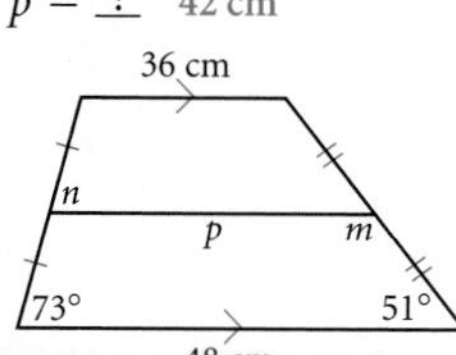

7. $q = \underline{?}$ 35

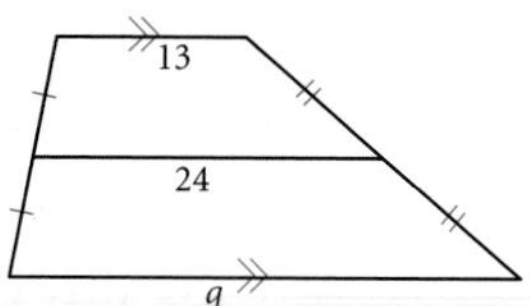

8. Copy and complete the flowchart to show that $\overline{LN} \parallel \overline{RD}$.

Given: Midsegment $\overline{LN}$ in $\triangle FOA$
Midsegment $\overline{RD}$ in $\triangle IOA$

Show: $\overline{LN} \parallel \overline{RD}$

Flowchart Proof

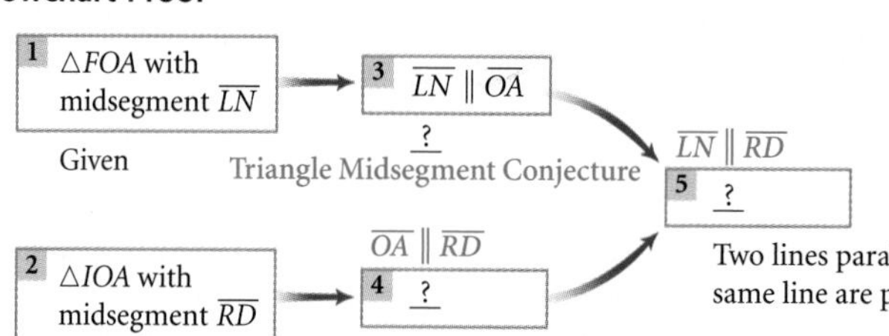

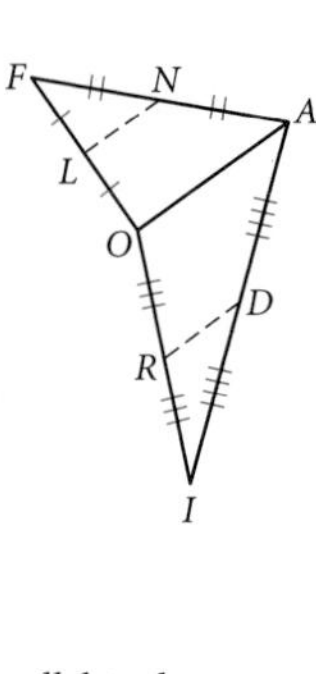

9. *Construction* When you connected the midpoints of the three sides of a triangle in Investigation 1, you created four congruent triangles. Draw a quadrilateral on patty paper and pinch the paper to locate the midpoints of the four sides. Connect the midpoints to form a quadrilateral. What special type of quadrilateral do you get when you connect the midpoints? Use the Triangle Midsegment Conjecture to explain your answer. ⓗ

10. Deep in a tropical rain forest, archaeologist Ertha Diggs and her assistant researchers have uncovered a square-based truncated pyramid (a square pyramid with the top part removed). The four lateral faces are isosceles trapezoids. A line of darker mortar runs along the midsegment of each lateral face. Ertha and her co-workers make some measurements and find that one of these midsegments measures 41 meters and each bottom base measures 52 meters. Now that they have this information, Ertha and her team can calculate the length of the top base without having to climb up and measure it. Can you? What is the length of the top edge? How do you know?

11. Ladie and Casey pride themselves on their estimation skills and take turns estimating distances. Casey claims that two large redwood trees visible from where they are sitting are 180 feet apart, and Ladie says they are 275 feet apart.

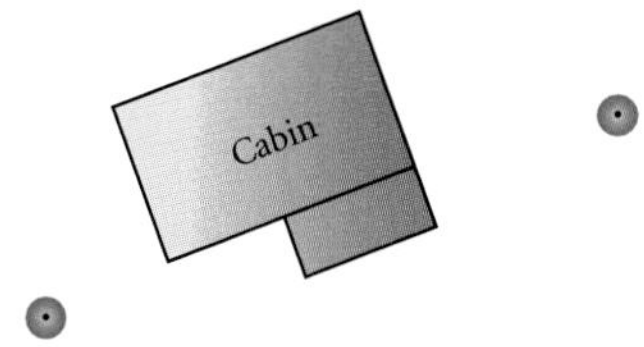

The problem is, they can't measure the distance to see whose estimate is better, because their cabin is located between the trees. All of a sudden, Ladie recalls her geometry: "Oh yeah, the Triangle Midsegment Conjecture!" She collects a tape measure, a hammer, and some wooden stakes. What is she going to do?

Review

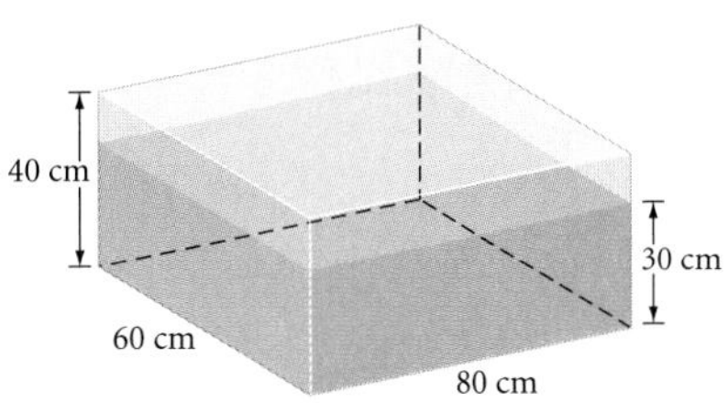

1.8 **12.** The 40-by-60-by-80 cm sealed rectangular container shown at right is resting on its largest face. It is filled with a liquid to a height of 30 cm. Sketch the container resting on its smallest face. Show the height of the liquid in this new position.

5.3 **13.** Write the converse of this statement: If exactly one diagonal bisects a pair of opposite angles of a quadrilateral, then the quadrilateral is a kite. Is the converse true? Is the original statement true? If either conjecture is not true, sketch a counterexample.

14. Trace the figure below. Calculate the measure of each lettered angle.
$a = 54°, b = 72°, c = 108°, d = 72°, e = 162°, f = 18°, g = 81°,$
$h = 49.5°, i = 130.5°, k = 49.5°, m = 162°, n = 99°$

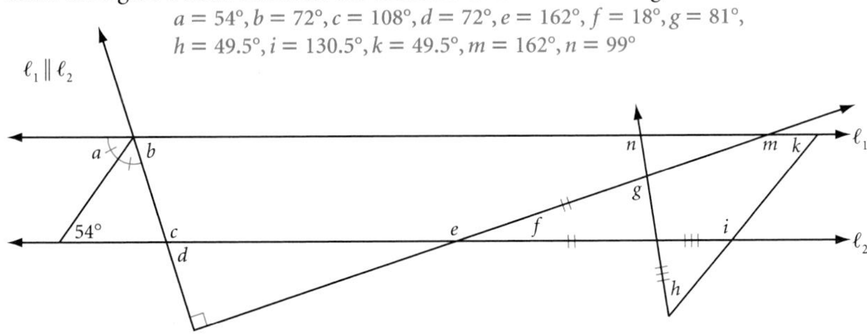

5.3 **15.** *CART* is an isosceles trapezoid. What are the coordinates of point *T*? (3, 8)

5.3 **16.** *HRSE* is a kite. What are the coordinates of point *R*? (0, −8)

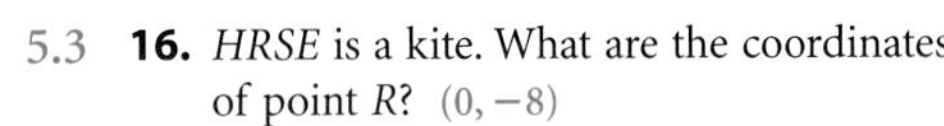

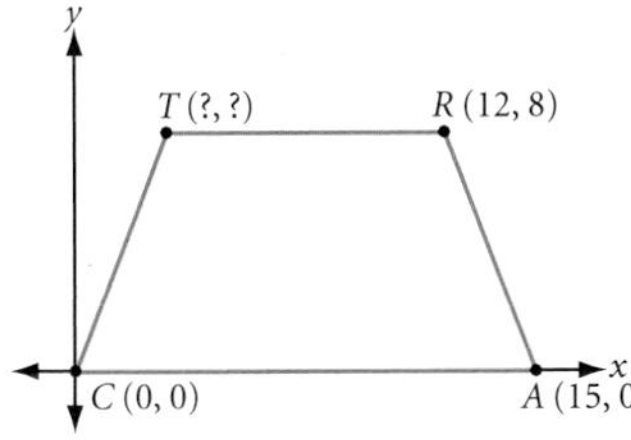

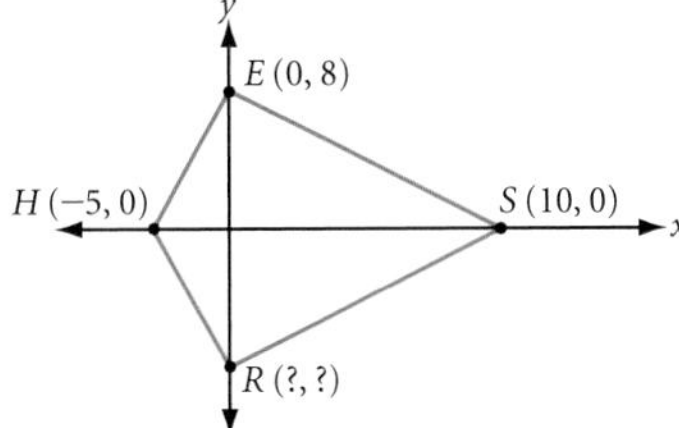

11. Ladie drives a stake into the ground to create a triangle for which the trees are the other two vertices. She finds the midpoint from the stake to each tree. The distance between these midpoints is half the distance between the trees.

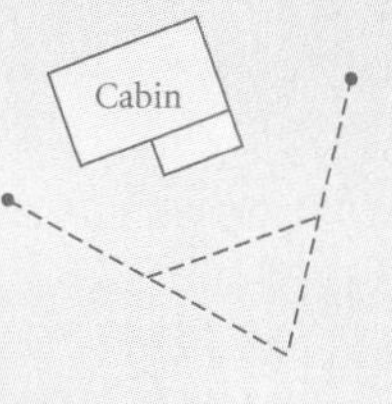

12.

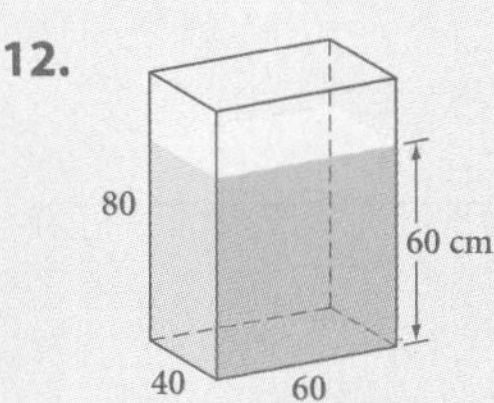

13. If a quadrilateral is a kite, then exactly one diagonal bisects a pair of opposite angles. Both the original and converse statements are true.

EXTENSION

Challenge students to use coordinate geometry to confirm that the midsegment of a triangle is parallel to the third side and that the midsegment of a trapezoid is parallel to the two bases.

18.

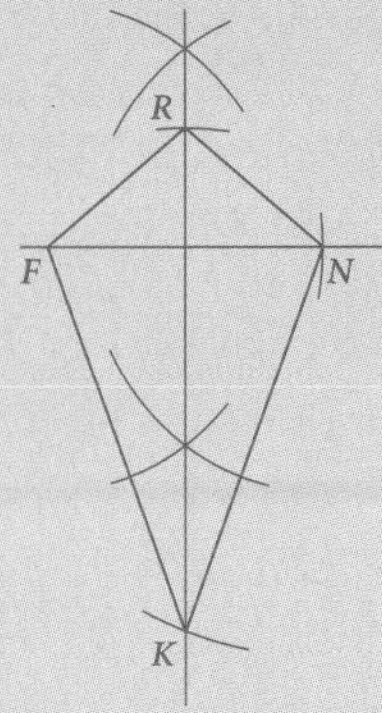

There is only one kite, but more than one way to construct it.

UYAS 3 **17.** Find the coordinates of midpoints E and Z. Show that the slope of the line containing midsegment $\overline{EZ}$ is equal to the slope of the line containing $\overline{YT}$. coordinates: $E(2, 3.5)$, $Z(6, 5)$; the slope of $\overline{EZ} = \frac{3}{8}$, and the slope of $\overline{YT} = \frac{3}{8}$

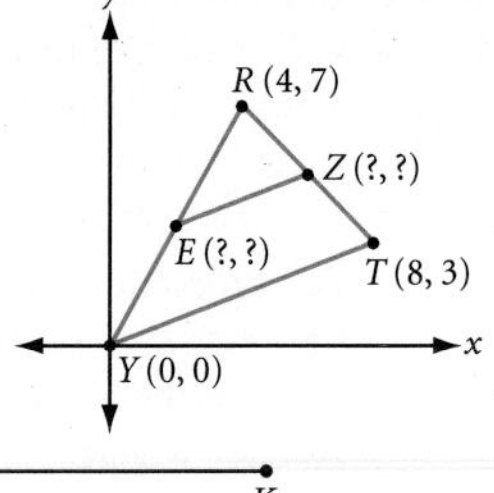

5.3 **18.** ***Construction*** Use the kite properties you discovered in Lesson 5.3 to construct kite $FRNK$ given diagonals $\overline{RK}$ and $\overline{FN}$ and side $\overline{NK}$. Is there only one solution?

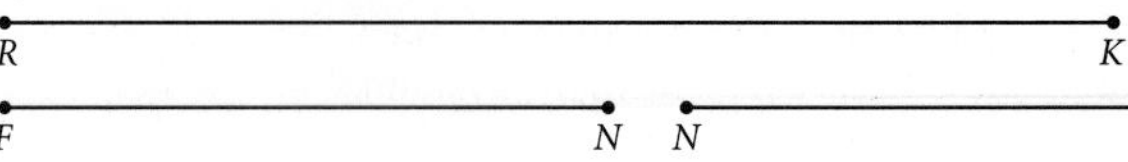

project

BUILDING AN ARCH

In this project, you'll design and build your own Roman arch.

Horseshoe Arch

Basket Arch

Tudor Arch

Lancet Arch

Arches can have a simple semicircular shape, or a pointed "broken arch" shape.

In arch construction, a wooden support holds the voussoirs in place until the keystone is placed (see arch diagram on page 271). It's said that when the Romans made an arch, they would make the architect stand under it while the wooden support was removed. That was one way to be sure architects carefully designed arches that wouldn't fall!

The arches in this Roman aqueduct, above the Gard River in France, are typical of arches you can find throughout regions that were once part of the Roman Empire. An arch can carry a lot of weight, yet it also provides an opening. The abutments on the sides of the arch keep the arch from spreading out and falling down.

What size arch would you like to build? Decide the dimensions of the opening, the thickness of the arch, and the number of voussoirs. Decide on the materials you will use. You should have your trapezoid and your materials approved by your group or your teacher before you begin construction.

Your project should include

- A scale diagram that shows the exact size and angle of the voussoirs and the keystone.
- A template for your voussoirs.
- Your arch.

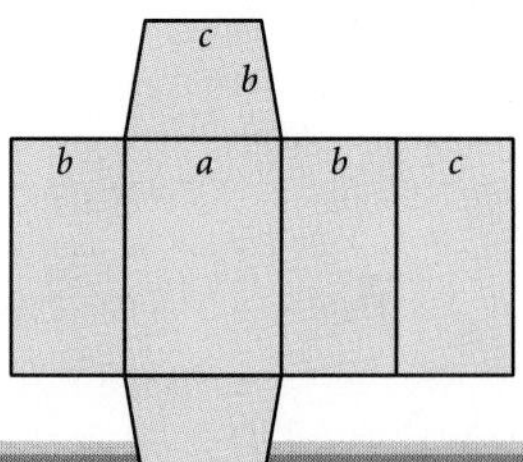

Supporting the project

Students may use folded cardboard, wood, foam, or take-out containers (purchased from a restaurant supply store) to make trapezoidal prisms for the voussoirs.

[Language] *Voussoir* is pronounced [vü-'swär].

OUTCOMES

- The project shows knowledge of the properties of isosceles trapezoids.
- The diagram includes the measure of one voussoir and the number in the arch.
- Measurement of each angle is determined from the number of sides of the circle that contains the arch's arc.
- There is an estimate of the rise and the span. (To actually calculate the rise and the span of an arch requires trigonometry.)

LESSON 5.5

Properties of Parallelograms

If there is an opinion, facts will be found to support it.

JUDY SPROLES

In this lesson you will discover some special properties of parallelograms. A parallelogram is a quadrilateral whose opposite sides are parallel.

Rhombuses, rectangles, and squares all fit this definition as well. Therefore, any properties you discover for parallelograms will also apply to these other shapes. However, to be sure that your conjectures will apply to *any* parallelogram, you should investigate parallelograms that don't have any other special properties, such as right angles, all congruent angles, or all congruent sides.

Investigation
Four Parallelogram Properties

You will need

- graph paper
- patty paper or a compass
- a straightedge
- a protractor

First you'll create a parallelogram.

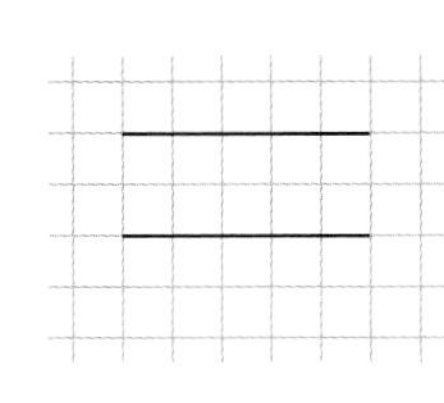

Step 1

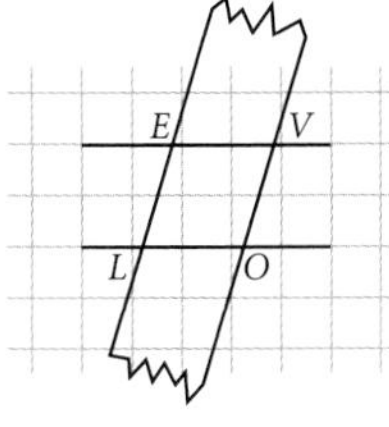

Step 2

Step 1 Using the lines on a piece of graph paper as a guide, draw a pair of parallel lines that are at least 6 cm apart. Using the parallel edges of your straightedge, make a parallelogram. Label your parallelogram *LOVE.*

Step 2 Let's look at the opposite angles. Measure the angles of parallelogram *LOVE.* Compare a pair of opposite angles using patty paper or your protractor.

Compare results with your group. Copy and complete the conjecture.

Parallelogram Opposite Angles Conjecture C-45

The opposite angles of a parallelogram are _?_. congruent

Two angles that share a common side in a polygon are consecutive angles. In parallelogram *LOVE,* $\angle LOV$ and $\angle EVO$ are a pair of consecutive angles. The consecutive angles of a parallelogram are also related.

Step 3 Find the sum of the measures of each pair of consecutive angles in parallelogram *LOVE.* 180°

NCTM STANDARDS

CONTENT		PROCESS	
	Number	✓	Problem Solving
	Algebra	✓	Reasoning
✓	Geometry	✓	Communication
✓	Measurement	✓	Connections
	Data/Probability		Representation

LESSON OBJECTIVES

- Discover properties of parallelograms
- Learn new vocabulary
- Practice construction skills
- Develop inductive reasoning and cooperative behavior

LESSON 5.5

PLANNING

LESSON OUTLINE

One day:

25 min	Investigation
10 min	Sharing
5 min	Closing
5 min	Exercises

MATERIALS

- double-edged straightedges
- compasses or patty paper
- protractors
- graph paper
- Avoiding Hot Water (T) for One step

TEACHING

In this lesson students discover four conjectures about parallelograms. The one-step investigation is on page 280.

Students can also explore the properties of parallelograms using the dynamic geometry exploration at www.keymath.com/DG.

Guiding the Investigation

Step 1 To draw the parallelogram without using a double-edged straightedge, students may draw lines between points on the graph paper if they are careful to apply what they know about slope triangles and slopes of parallel lines. Encourage them to look beyond the special case of rectangles. If possible, help them draw the parallelograms without using the fact that the opposite sides have the same length.

Step 3 As needed, remind students that two angles are called *supplementary* if the sum of their measures is 180°.

Step 7 Students may conjecture that the diagonals are congruent, or are perpendicular, or intersect in the middle of the parallelogram, or go through their midpoints, or bisect each other, or are bisectors. Have them report their conjectures during Sharing, when the class can critique them.

One step Show the Avoiding Hot Water transparency and pose this problem: "Your supervisor wants you to design a mechanism that allows workers to raise and lower pans of water from a heater. The supervisor has rejected the idea of a cranelike device, because a tilting pan might cause dangerous sloshing. You suggest a linkage as in the picture, but your supervisor is skeptical, saying that the nonhorizontal sides would have to change lengths as the pan moved up and down. The supervisor also suggests putting in a diagonal piece for more stability. Do you agree?" If students have difficulty, encourage them to cut pieces out of paper or use wooden sticks to replicate the device. Encourage students to generalize their claims to conjectures about the opposite sides and diagonals of parallelograms. Then ask them to investigate relationships among various angles of the changing parallelogram.

[Link] Students will encounter vectors in physics and in future algebra and calculus classes. The symbol notation for a vector is a half arrow. For example, wind velocity can be written $\vec{V}_w$.

[Language] *Magnitude* means "size" or "amount." It is expressed as a number with its dimensions. In a velocity vector, the magnitude is the speed, which might be the number of miles per hour or meters per second. A student who has seen vectors in science courses may be able to describe the parallelogram rule for finding resultant vectors.

Share your observations with your group. Copy and complete the conjecture.

Parallelogram Consecutive Angles Conjecture C-46

The consecutive angles of a parallelogram are ? . supplementary

Step 4 The opposite angle will have the same measure and the two consecutive angles will have measure 180° minus the measure of the angle.

Step 4 Describe how to use the two conjectures you just made to find all the angles of a parallelogram with only one angle measure given.

Step 5 Next let's look at the opposite sides of a parallelogram. With your compass or patty paper, compare the lengths of the opposite sides of the parallelogram you made.

Share your results with your group. Copy and complete the conjecture.

Parallelogram Opposite Sides Conjecture C-47

The opposite sides of a parallelogram are ? . congruent

Step 6 Finally, let's consider the diagonals of a parallelogram. Construct the diagonals $\overline{LV}$ and $\overline{EO}$, as shown below. Label the point where the two diagonals intersect point *M*.

Step 7 Measure *LM* and *VM*. What can you conclude about point *M*? Is this conclusion also true for diagonal $\overline{EO}$? How do the diagonals relate?

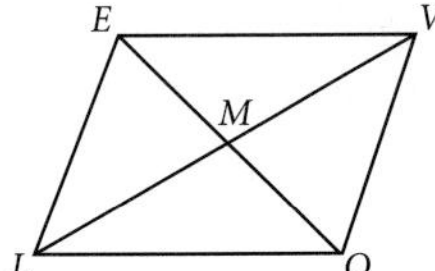

Share your results with your group. Copy and complete the conjecture.

Parallelogram Diagonals Conjecture C-48

The diagonals of a parallelogram ? . bisect each other

Parallelograms are used in vector diagrams, which have many applications in science. A **vector** is a quantity that has both magnitude and direction.

Vectors describe quantities in physics, such as velocity, acceleration, and force. You can represent a vector by drawing an arrow. The length and direction of the arrow represent the magnitude and direction of the vector. For example, a velocity vector tells you an airplane's speed and direction. The lengths of vectors in a diagram are proportional to the quantities they represent.

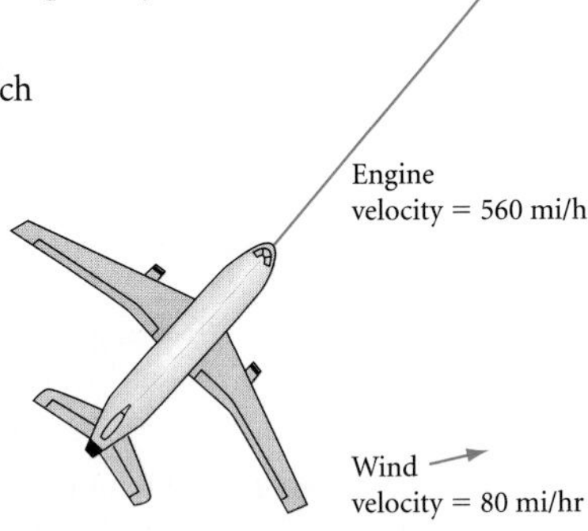

SHARING IDEAS

As students are making conjectures about a parallelogram, urge them to justify their responses. For example, they might justify their conjecture about consecutive angles using the Parallel Lines Conjecture. Your goal is to help them understand the conjectures, not to achieve some particular answer. Ask for explanations when you think anyone in the class might not understand the concepts deeply enough.

[Ask] "What symmetry does a parallelogram have?" [2-fold rotational symmetry about the "middle," the intersection of its diagonals] "How does the symmetry show the properties of a parallelogram?" [Because the symmetry is rotational, opposite sides are congruent, opposite angles are congruent, and the diagonals bisect each other.]

Also ask what false conjectures someone might make. For example, the diagonals of a parallelogram are not congruent and do not bisect the opposite angles. Nothing about the rotational symmetry of the figure guarantees these properties.

In many physics problems, you combine vector quantities acting on the same object. For example, the wind current and engine thrust vectors determine the velocity of an airplane. The **resultant vector** of these vectors is a single vector that has the same effect. It can also be called a **vector sum.** To find a resultant vector, make a parallelogram with the vectors as sides. The resultant vector is the diagonal of the parallelogram from the two vectors' tails to the opposite vertex.

In the diagram at right, the resultant vector shows that the wind will speed up the plane, and will also blow it slightly off course.

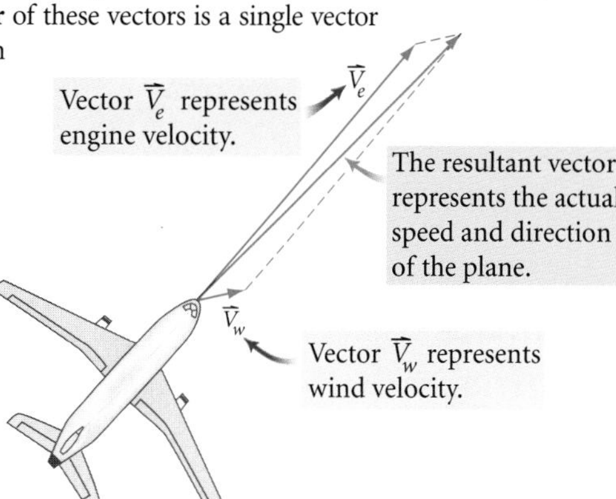

EXERCISES

You will need

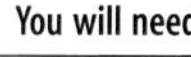

Construction tools for Exercises **7** and **8**

Geometry software for Exercises **21** and **22**

Use your new conjectures in the following exercises. In Exercises 1–6, each figure is a parallelogram.

1. $c = \underline{?}$ 34 cm
$d = \underline{?}$ 27 cm

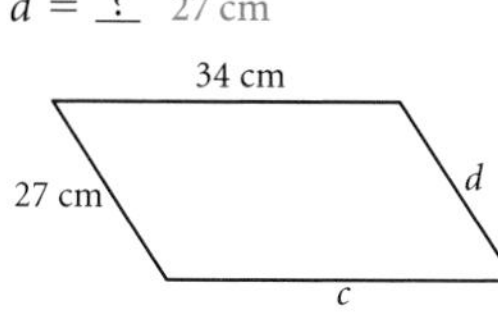

2. $a = \underline{?}$ 132°
$b = \underline{?}$ 48°

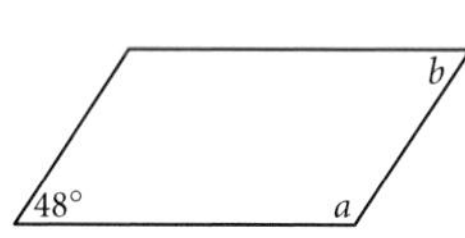

3. $g = \underline{?}$ 16 in.
$h = \underline{?}$ 14 in.

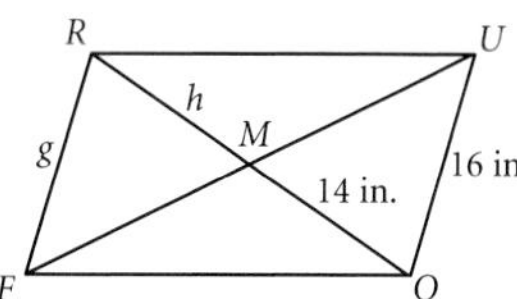

4. $VF = 36$ m
$EF = 24$ m
$EI = 42$ m
What is the perimeter of $\triangle NVI$? (h) 63 m

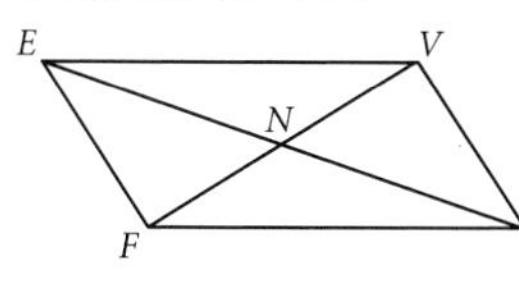

5. What is the perimeter? 80

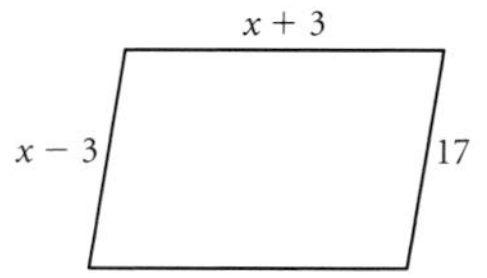

6. $e = \underline{?}$ 63°
$f = \underline{?}$ 78°

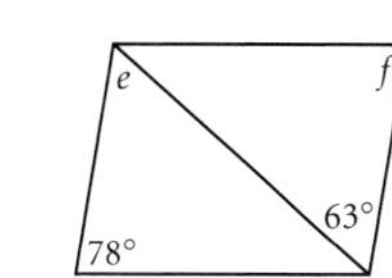

7. *Construction* Given side $\overline{LA}$, side $\overline{AS}$, and $\angle L$, construct parallelogram *LAST.*

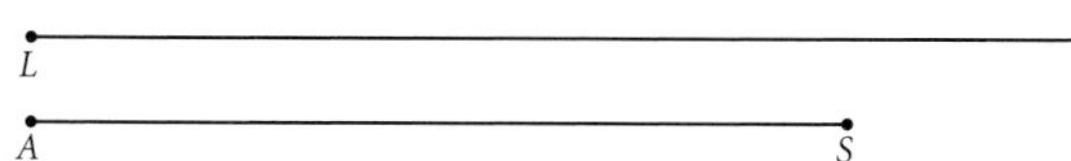

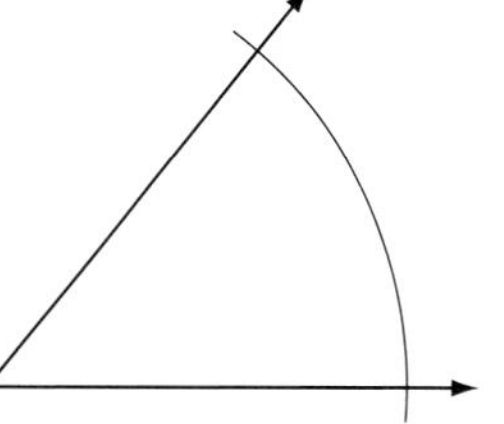

Closing the Lesson

Reiterate the four main conjectures about parallelograms: Opposite angles are congruent, consecutive angles are supplementary, opposite sides are congruent, and diagonals bisect each other. If students aren't comfortable with these conjectures, you might discuss Exercise 4 before they begin working on the exercises.

Students can explore a dynamic version of the vector illustration at left using the dynamic geometry exploration at www.keymath.com/DG.

BUILDING UNDERSTANDING

The exercises give students practice in applying the four conjectures about parallelograms.

ASSIGNING HOMEWORK

Essential	1–8
Performance assessment	12
Portfolio	8
Journal	14
Group	9–11, 13
Review	15–22

MATERIALS

- scissors (Exercise 12)
- Exercises 9 and 10 (T), *optional*
- Exercise 13 (T), *optional*

Sharing Ideas (continued)

[Ask] "Can you make a conjecture about consecutive sides of a parallelogram? They're not always congruent, but can they be?" [If so, the figure would be a rhombus.] "Can kites be parallelograms?" [No; *kite* is defined as having exactly two pairs of congruent consecutive sides.]

Every trapezoid has only one pair of opposite sides parallel; wonder aloud whether trapezoids have the consecutive angles property. [They do.] Do trapezoids have the other properties of parallelograms found in this lesson?

Assessing Progress

You can assess students' understanding of congruent segments, supplementary angles, and diagonals and their ability to compare lengths of segments with a compass and to measure angles with a protractor.

Helping with the Exercises

Exercises 7, 8 Encourage students to make and label sketches.

7.

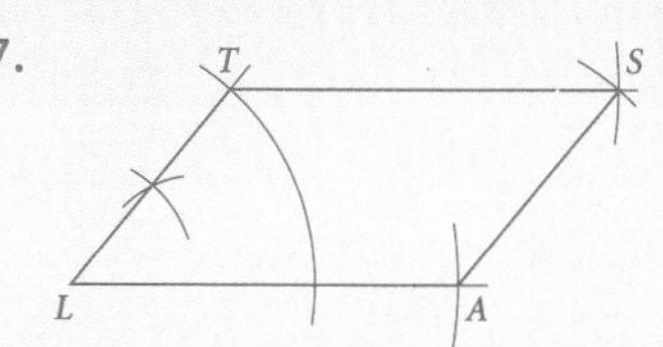

8.

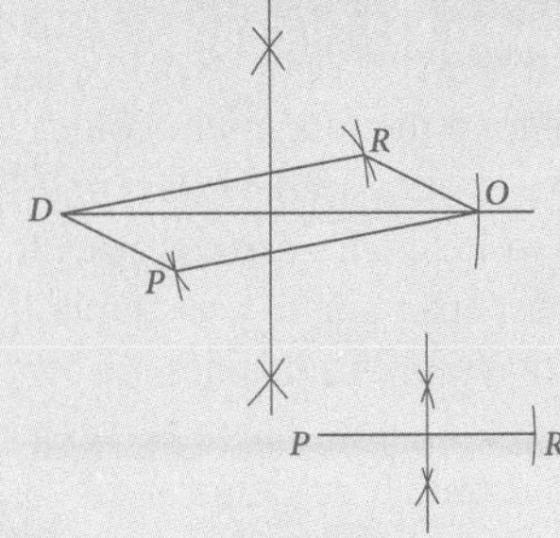

Exercise 11 Suggest to any students having difficulty that they think about how much the right side of the parallelogram has moved horizontally and vertically between points R and A. To be parallel, the left side must make the same amount of change to move the same amount.

Exercise 12 If students are having difficulty, encourage them to label the sides, diagonals, and angles of both quadrilaterals and then match up edges with the same label. **[Ask]** "Which four angles will fit around a point?" [the four angles of the quadrilateral]

12. possible answer:

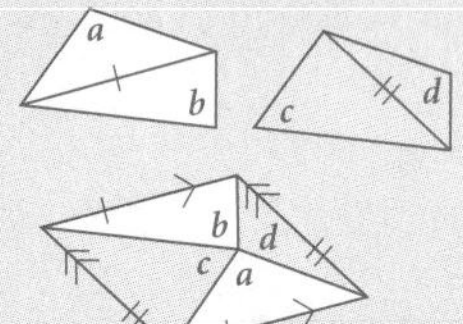

8. ***Construction*** Given side $\overline{DR}$ and diagonals $\overline{DO}$ and $\overline{PR}$, construct parallelogram $DROP$. ⓗ

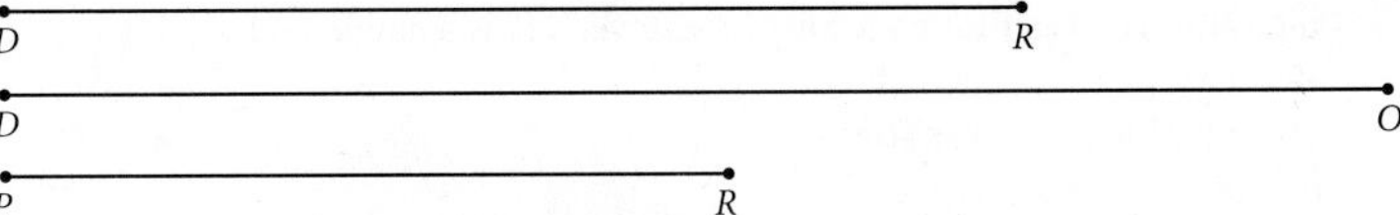

In Exercises 9 and 10, copy the vector diagram and draw the resultant vector.

9.

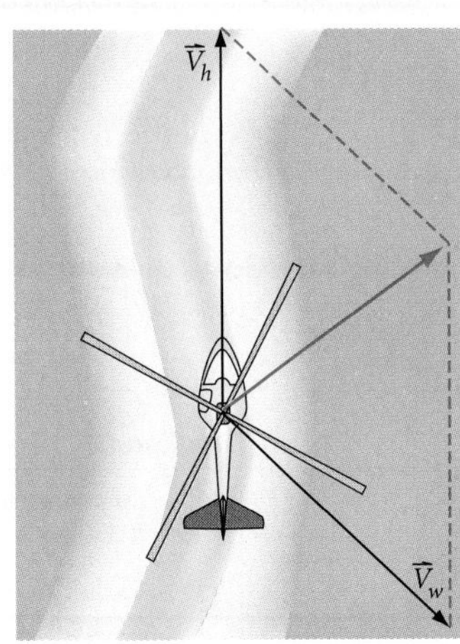

10. ⓗ

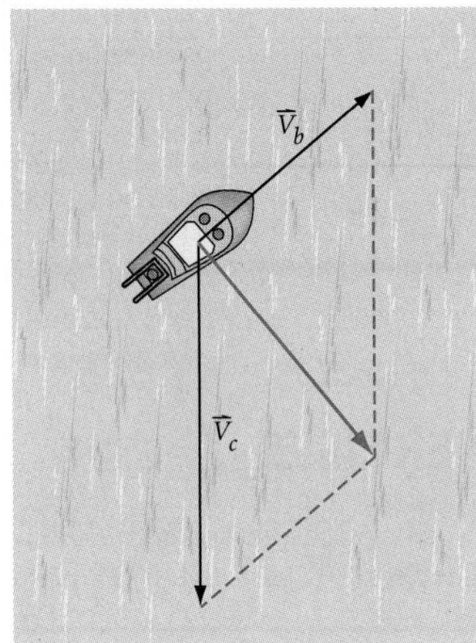

11. Find the coordinates of point M in parallelogram $PRAM$. ⓗ
$(b - a, c)$

12. Draw a quadrilateral. Make a copy of it. Draw a diagonal in the first quadrilateral. Draw the *other* diagonal in the duplicate quadrilateral. Cut each quadrilateral into two triangles along the diagonals. Arrange the four triangles into a parallelogram. Make a sketch showing how you did it.

y
M (?, ?)
A (b, c)
P
R (a, 0)
x

13. Copy and complete the flowchart to show how the Parallelogram Diagonals Conjecture follows logically from other conjectures.

Given: $LEAN$ is a parallelogram

Show: $\overline{EN}$ and $\overline{LA}$ bisect each other

E A T L N

Flowchart Proof

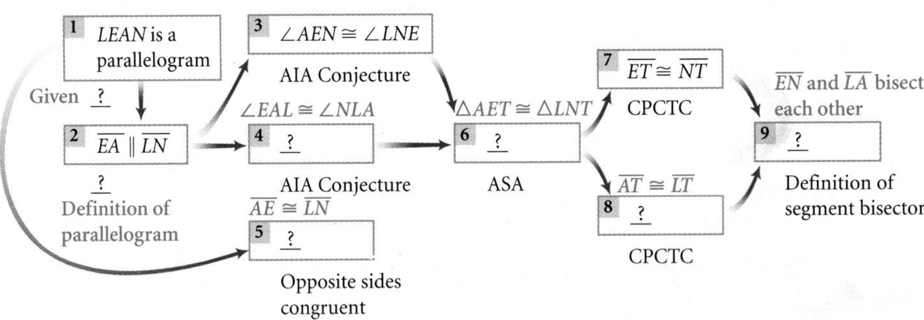

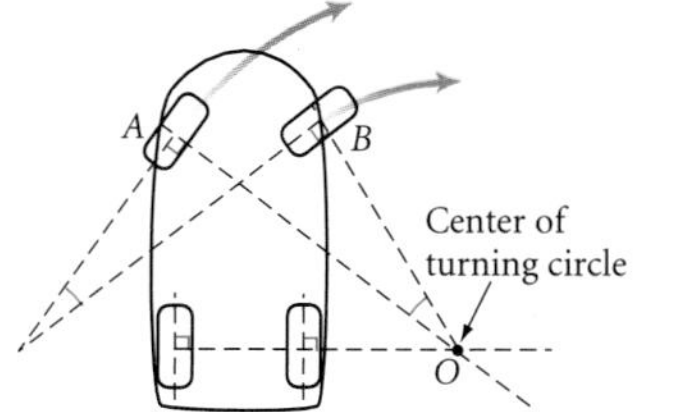

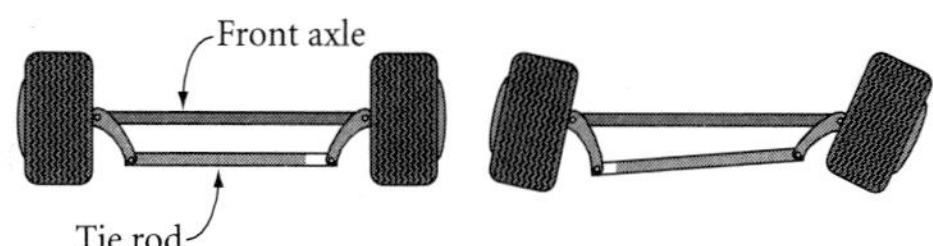

Trapezoid linkage (Top view)

Quadrilateral linkages are used in mechanical design, robotics, the automotive industry, and toy making. In cars, they are used to turn each front wheel the right amount for a smooth turn.

14. Study the sewing box pictured here. Sketch the box as viewed from the side, and explain why a parallelogram linkage is used.

Review

5.1 **15.** Find the measures of the lettered angles in this tiling of regular polygons.
$a = 135°, b = 90°$

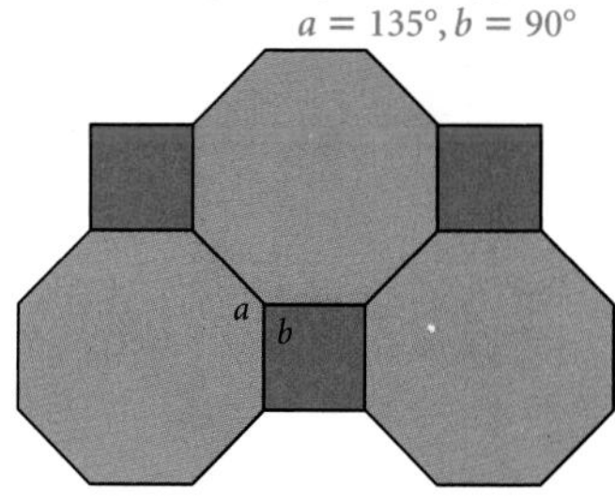

5.1 **16.** Trace the figure below. Calculate the measure of each lettered angle. $a = 120°, b = 108°, c = 90°, d = 42°, e = 69°$

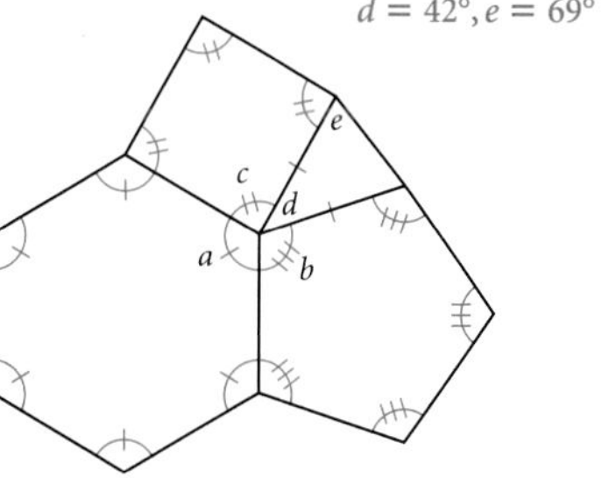

5.3 **17.** Find x and y. Explain.

$x = 104°, y = 98°$. The quadrilaterals on the left and right sides are kites. Nonvertex angles are congruent. The quadrilateral at the bottom is an isosceles trapezoid. Base angles are congruent, and consecutive angles between the bases are supplementary.

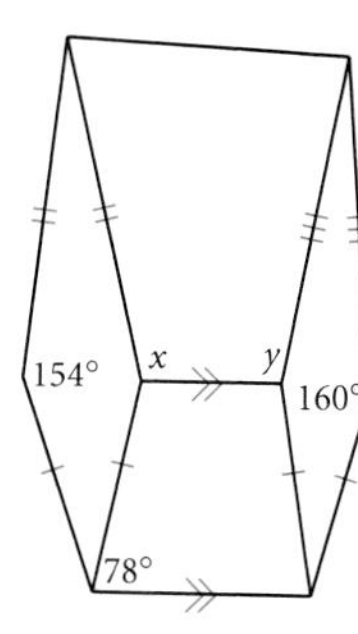

5.3 **18.** What is the measure of each angle in the isosceles trapezoid face of a voussoir in this 15-stone arch? $a = 84°, b = 96°$

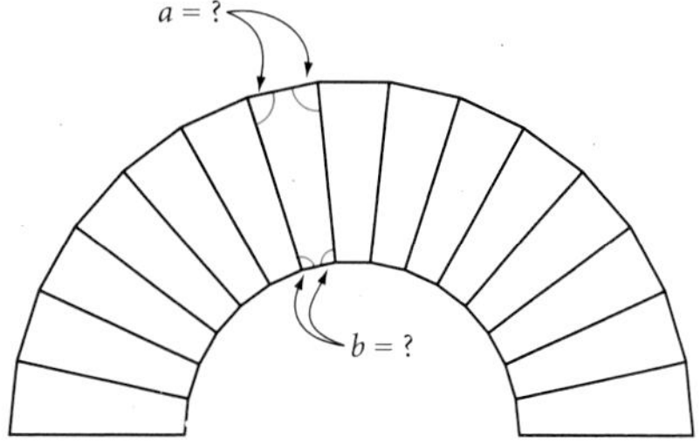

Exercise 14 As needed, have students think about the conjectures made in this lesson.

14. The parallelogram linkage is used for the sewing box so that the drawers remain parallel to each other (and to the ground) so that the contents cannot fall out.

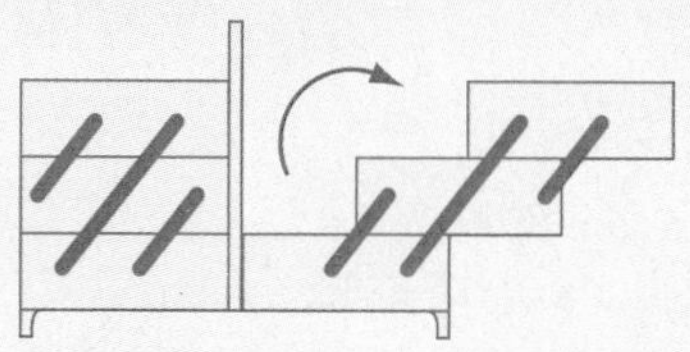

20. 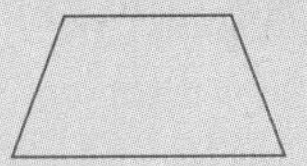

21. Parallelogram. Because triangles are congruent by SAS, $\angle 1 \cong \angle 2$. So lines are parallel and by CPCTC the parallel sides are also congruent.

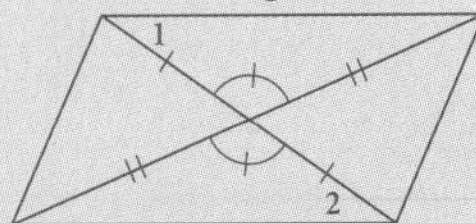

Exercise 22 [Ask] "When is the figure a dart?" [when the line segment between the intersection points, the chord, is not between the two centers] "Can the figure be a triangle?" [yes] "When is the figure a rhombus?" [when the circles are congruent and the chord is between the centers]

22. Kite or dart. Radii of the same circle are congruent. If the circles have equal radii, a rhombus is formed.

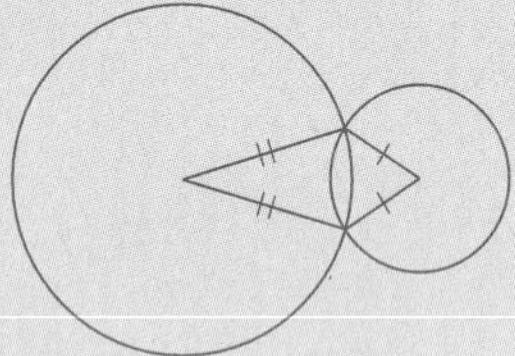

EXTENSIONS

A. Are the converses of the parallelogram conjectures true? Have students choose a tool and devise an investigation to decide.

B. Have students use coordinate geometry to verify one of the parallelogram conjectures.

4.6 **19.** Is $\triangle XYW \cong \triangle WYZ$? Explain.

No. The congruent angles and side do not correspond.

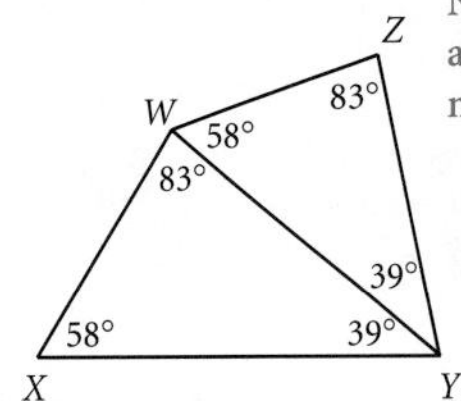

1.8 **20.** Sketch the section formed when this pyramid is sliced by the plane.

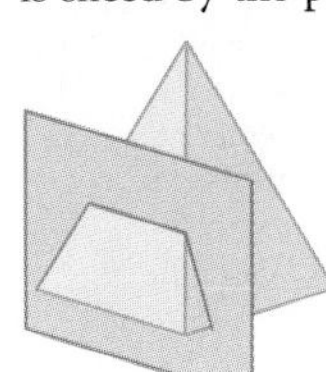

4.4 **21.** ***Technology*** Construct two segments that bisect each other. Connect their endpoints. What type of quadrilateral is this? Draw a diagram and explain why.

5.3 **22.** ***Technology*** Construct two intersecting circles. Connect the two centers and the two points of intersection to form a quadrilateral. What type of quadrilateral is this? Draw a diagram and explain why.

IMPROVING YOUR VISUAL THINKING SKILLS

A Puzzle Quilt

Fourth-grade students at Public School 95, the Bronx, New York, made the puzzle quilt at right with the help of artist Paula Nadelstern. Each square has a twin made of exactly the same shaped pieces. Only the colors, chosen from traditional Amish colors, are different. For example, square A1 is the twin of square B3. Match each square with its twin.

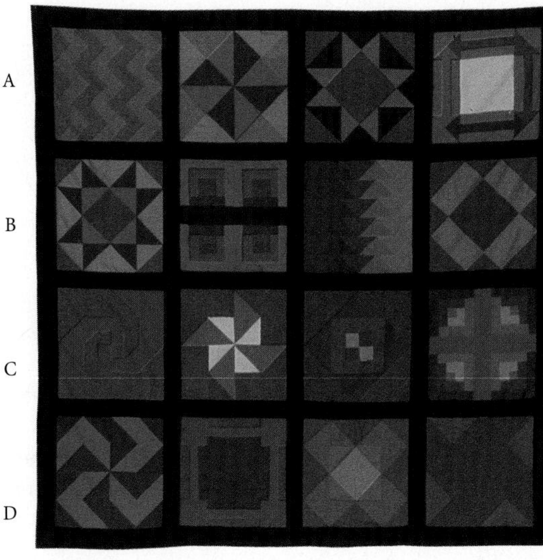

PUZZLE

IMPROVING VISUAL THINKING SKILLS

Matching pairs:
(A1, B3)(B1, D3)(A2, C2)(B2, C4)(A3, B4)
(C1, C3)(A4, D2)(D1, D4)

Solving Systems of Linear Equations

A *system of equations* is a set of two or more equations with the same variables. The solution of a system is the set of values that makes all the equations in the system true. For example, the system of equations below has solution $(2, -3)$. Verify this by substituting 2 for x and -3 for y in both equations.

$$\begin{cases} y = 2x - 7 \\ y = -3x + 3 \end{cases}$$

Graphically, the solution of a system is the point of intersection of the graphs of the equations.

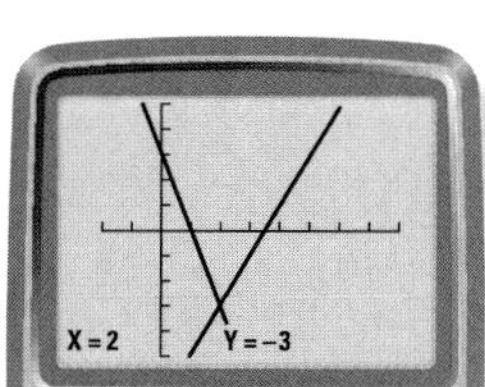

You can estimate the solution of a system by graphing the equations. However, the point of intersection may not have convenient integer coordinates. To find the exact solution, you can use algebra. Examples A and B review how to use the *substitution* and *elimination* methods for solving systems of equations.

EXAMPLE A Use the substitution method to solve the system $\begin{cases} 3y = 12x - 21 \\ 12x + 2y = 1 \end{cases}$.

▶ Solution Start by solving the first equation for y to get $y = 4x - 7$.

Now, substitute the expression $4x - 7$ from the resulting equation for y in the second original equation.

$12x + 2y = 1$	Second original equation.
$12x + 2(4x - 7) = 1$	Substitute $4x - 7$ for y.
$x = \frac{3}{4}$	Solve for x.

To find y, substitute $\frac{3}{4}$ for x in either original equation.

$3y = 12\left(\frac{3}{4}\right) - 21$	Substitute $\frac{3}{4}$ for x in the first original equation.
$y = -4$	Solve for y.

The solution of the system is $\left(\frac{3}{4}, -4\right)$. Verify by substituting these values for x and y in each of the original equations.

EXAMPLE B The band sold calendars to raise money for new uniforms. Aisha sold 6 desk calendars and 10 wall calendars for a total of \$100. Ted sold 12 desk calendars and 4 wall calendars for a total of \$88. Find the price of each type of calendar by writing a system of equations and solving it using the elimination method.

USING YOUR ALGEBRA SKILLS 5

PLANNING

LESSON OUTLINE

One day:

20 min Examples

10 min Sharing and Closing

15 min Exercises

MATERIALS

- graph paper

TEACHING

This lesson reviews solving systems of two linear equations.

▶ *EXAMPLES A AND B*

To help students make connections, show them alternative approaches, and allow a check for reasonableness of the solution. You might also show a graphical approach to solving this system. For further review, change the second equation to $12x - 3y = 1$ and then to $12x - 3y = 21$, demonstrating how a system can have zero or infinitely many solutions and how those cases are reflected on the graphs.

You might have students work on Example B with partners or in groups. Encourage them to graph the equations in addition to solving them algebraically.

SHARING IDEAS

Ask what a solution to a system of equations actually is. Elicit the fact that it's a pair of numbers that satisfies each of the equations.

If no student mentions it, ask the class to critique the reasoning of this nonsymbolic way of solving the problem in Example B: "If Aisha had sold twice as many of

NCTM STANDARDS

CONTENT		PROCESS	
	Number	✓	Problem Solving
✓	Algebra	✓	Reasoning
✓	Geometry		Communication
	Measurement		Connections
✓	Data/Probability	✓	Representation

LESSON OBJECTIVE

- Review finding the solution to a system of linear equations in two variables

Sharing Ideas (continued)
each item, she would have made \$200. She would have sold the same number of desk calendars as Ted but earned \$112 more. That \$112 would have come from where? From her selling 16 wall calendars more than Ted. So wall calendars must sell for \$7 each. The 4 wall calendars Ted sold, then, brought in \$28 of his \$88, so he must have sold his 12 desk calendars for \$60, or for \$5 each." Almost any puzzle or real-life problem that can be solved with a system of equations can be solved with reasoning like this. Point out how it mirrors the symbolic approach of the elimination method.

[Ask] "Under what conditions might you prefer the substitution method to the elimination method, or vice versa?" [If one variable has a coefficient of 1 in one of the equations, it's pretty easy to solve that equation for that variable and substitute in the other equation. If a variable has the same coefficient in both equations, the elimination method can be used to get rid of that variable.]

▸ *Solution*

Let d be the price of a desk calendar, and let w be the price of a wall calendar. You can write this system to represent the situation.

$$\begin{cases} 6d + 10w = 100 & \text{Aisha's sales.} \\ 12d + 4w = 88 & \text{Ted's sales.} \end{cases}$$

Solving a system by elimination involves adding or subtracting the equations to eliminate one of the variables. To solve this system, first multiply both sides of the first equation by 2.

$$\begin{cases} 6d + 10w = 100 \\ 12d + 4w = 88 \end{cases} \rightarrow \begin{cases} 12d + 20w = 200 \\ 12d + 4w = 88 \end{cases}$$

Now, subtract the second equation from the first to eliminate d.

$$\begin{array}{r} 12d + 20w = 200 \\ -(12d + 4w = 88) \\ \hline 16w = 112 \\ w = 7 \end{array}$$

To find the value of d, substitute 7 for w in either original equation. The solution is $w = 7$ and $d = 5$, so a wall calendar costs \$7 and a desk calendar costs \$5.

EXERCISES

Solve each system of equations algebraically.

1. $\begin{cases} y = -2x + 2 \\ 6x + 2y = 3 \end{cases}$ $\left(-\frac{1}{2}, 3\right)$

2. $\begin{cases} x + 2y = 3 \\ 2x - y = 16 \end{cases}$ $(7, -2)$

3. $\begin{cases} 5x - y = -1 \\ 15x = 2y \end{cases}$ $\left(\frac{2}{5}, 3\right)$

4. $\begin{cases} -4x + 3y = 3 \\ 7x - 9y = 6 \end{cases}$ $(-3, -3)$

For Exercises 5 and 6 solve the systems. What happens? Graph each set of equations and use the graphs to explain your results.

5. $\begin{cases} x + 6y = 10 \\ \frac{1}{2}x + 3y = 5 \end{cases}$

6. $\begin{cases} 2x + y = 30 \\ y = -2x - 1 \end{cases}$

7. A snowboard rental company offers two different rental plans. Plan A offers \$4/hr for the rental and a \$20 lift ticket. Plan B offers \$7/hr for the rental and a free lift ticket.

a. Write the two equations that represent the costs for the two plans, using x for the number of hours. Solve for x and y.

b. Graph the two equations. What does the point of intersection represent?

c. Which is the better plan if you intend to snowboard for 5 hours? What is the most number of hours of snowboarding you can get for \$50? Plan B; $7\frac{1}{2}$ hours, with Plan A

8. The lines $y = 3 + \frac{2}{3}x$, $y = -\frac{1}{3}x$, and $y = -\frac{4}{3}x + 3$ intersect to form a triangle. Find the vertices of the triangle. $(-3, 1), (0, 3), (3, -1)$

BUILDING UNDERSTANDING

Encourage students to solve the exercises both algebraically and graphically and to check their solutions by substitution.

ASSIGNING HOMEWORK

Essential	1–7
Performance assessment	8

Closing the Lesson

Summarize by saying that the substitution method, the elimination method, graphing, and reasoning are four ways of solving systems of two equations in two variables.

If students seem weak at these skills, have them work at least one of the exercises in class, using both symbols and a graph.

5. All the variables cancel out and you're left with a true statement.

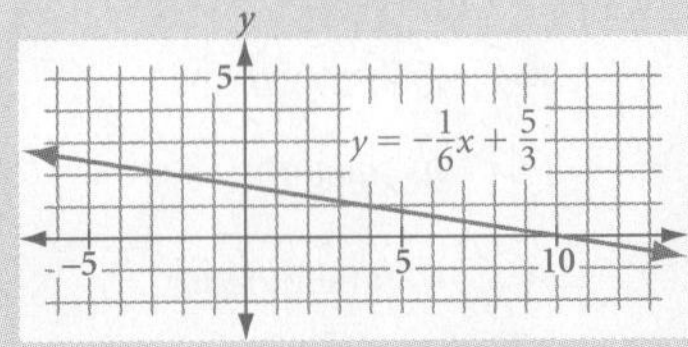

The lines are the same. There are infinitely many solutions.

See page 772 for answers to Exercises 6 and 7.

LESSON 5.6

Properties of Special Parallelograms

You must know a great deal about a subject to know how little is known about it.

LEO ROSTEN

The legs of the lifting platforms shown at right form rhombuses. Can you visualize how this lift would work differently if the legs formed parallelograms that weren't rhombuses?

In this lesson you will discover some properties of rhombuses, rectangles, and squares. What you discover about the diagonals of these special parallelograms will help you understand why these lifts work the way they do.

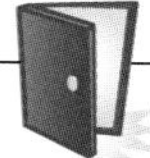

Investigation 1
What Can You Draw with the Double-Edged Straightedge?

You will need

- patty paper
- a double-edged straightedge

In this investigation you will discover the special parallelogram that you can draw using just the parallel edges of a straightedge.

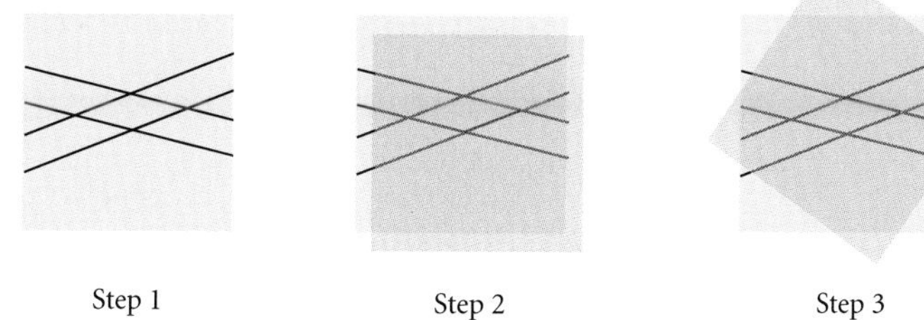
Step 1 Step 2 Step 3

Step 1 On a piece of patty paper, use a double-edged straightedge to draw two pairs of parallel lines that intersect each other.

Step 2 Assuming that the two edges of your straightedge are parallel, you have drawn a parallelogram. Place a second patty paper over the first and copy one of the sides of the parallelogram.

Step 3 Compare the length of the side on the second patty paper with the lengths of the other three sides of the parallelogram. How do they compare? Share your results with your group. Copy and complete the conjecture.

Double-Edged Straightedge Conjecture C-49

If two parallel lines are intersected by a second pair of parallel lines that are the same distance apart as the first pair, then the parallelogram formed is a ?. rhombus

LESSON 5.6

PLANNING

LESSON OUTLINE

One day:

20 min Investigation

15 min Sharing

5 min Closing

5 min Exercises

MATERIALS

- construction tools
- protractors
- graph paper

TEACHING

In this lesson students study diagonals of rhombuses and rectangles.

You can replace or extend Investigations 1–3 with the dynamic geometry exploration at www.keymath.com/DG.

Guiding Investigation 1

If you do not do the one-step investigation (page 288), you might use Investigation 1 as a follow-along activity. Be sure students are following along, not just watching.

NCTM STANDARDS

CONTENT		PROCESS	
	Number	✓	Problem Solving
	Algebra	✓	Reasoning
✓	Geometry	✓	Communication
✓	Measurement		Connections
	Data/Probability		Representation

LESSON OBJECTIVES

- Discover properties of rectangles, rhombuses, and squares
- Practice construction skills

One step Direct students' attention to the photograph of platforms at the beginning of the lesson. Then pose this problem from Exercise 21: "What properties of geometric figures guarantee that the platforms remain horizontal?" In their discussions, students may mention the rhombuses of the figure. You might ask what properties the diagonals of a rhombus have, though their perpendicularity is not relevant to the horizontal aspect of the platforms. As needed, wonder aloud whether parallelograms other than rhombuses are hidden in the picture. As students see diagonals of rectangles, ask whether the diagonals of all the rectangles are the same length. While students' attention is on diagonals, ask how the diagonals relate to the angles of the parallelograms under consideration. Urge students to phrase their ideas as conjectures about the general figures.

Guiding Investigation 2

If students found this result in Exercise 15 of Lesson 3.7, you might skip the first two steps.

In Chapter 3, you learned how to construct a rhombus using a compass and straightedge, or using patty paper. Now you know a quicker and easier way, using a double-edged straightedge. To construct a parallelogram that is *not* a rhombus, you need two double-edged staightedges of different widths.

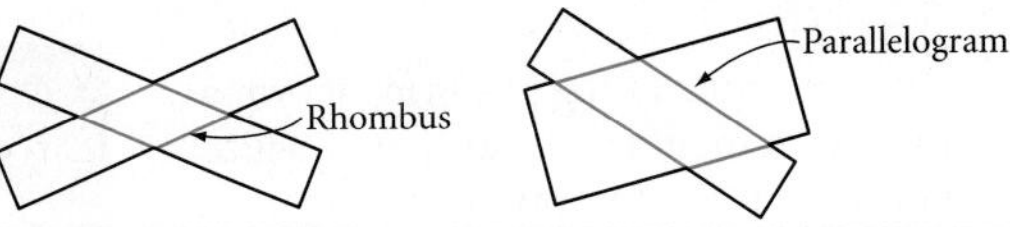

Now let's investigate some properties of rhombuses.

Investigation 2
Do Rhombus Diagonals Have Special Properties?

You will need

- patty paper

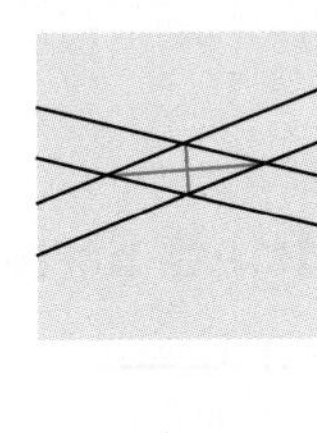

Step 1

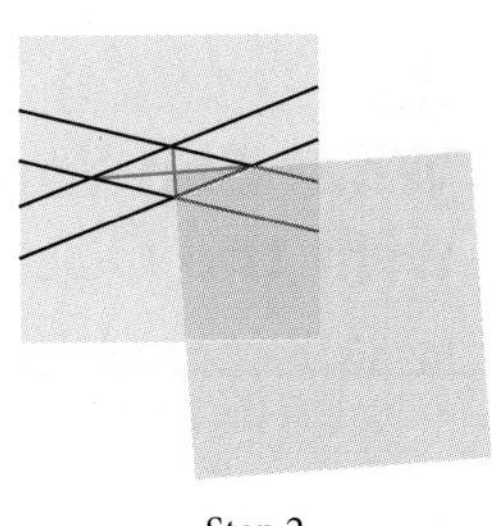

Step 2

Step 1 Draw in both diagonals of the rhombus you created in Investigation 1.

Step 2 Place the corner of a second patty paper onto one of the angles formed by the intersection of the two diagonals. Are the diagonals perpendicular?

Compare your results with your group. Also, recall that a rhombus is a parallelogram and that the diagonals of a parallelogram bisect each other. Combine these two ideas into your next conjecture.

Rhombus Diagonals Conjecture C-50

The diagonals of a rhombus are ?, and they ?.

perpendicular bisect each other

Step 3 The diagonals and the sides of the rhombus form two angles at each vertex. Fold your patty paper to compare each pair of angles. What do you observe? Compare your results with your group. Copy and complete the conjecture.

Rhombus Angles Conjecture C-51

The ? of a rhombus ? the angles of the rhombus.

diagonals bisect

So far you've made conjectures about a quadrilateral with four congruent sides. Now let's look at quadrilaterals with four congruent angles. What special properties do they have?

Recall the definition you created for a rectangle. A **rectangle** is an equiangular parallelogram.

Here is a thought experiment. What is the measure of each angle of a rectangle? The Quadrilateral Sum Conjecture says all four angles add up to 360°. They're congruent, so each angle must be 90°, or a right angle.

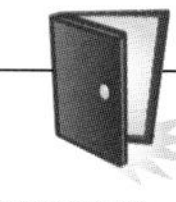

Investigation 3
Do Rectangle Diagonals Have Special Properties?

You will need

- graph paper
- a compass

Now let's look at the diagonals of rectangles.

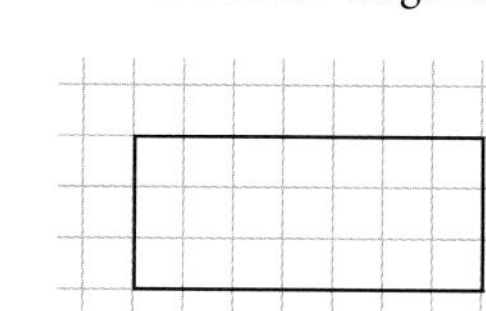

Step 1

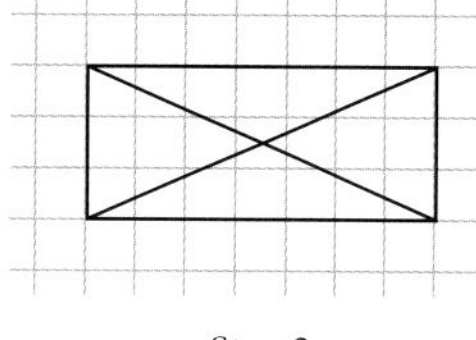

Step 2

Step 1 Draw a large rectangle using the lines on a piece of graph paper as a guide.

Step 2 Draw in both diagonals. With your compass, compare the lengths of the two diagonals.

Compare results with your group. In addition, recall that a rectangle is also a parallelogram. So its diagonals also have the properties of a parallelogram's diagonals. Combine these ideas to complete the conjecture.

Rectangle Diagonals Conjecture C-52

The diagonals of a rectangle are _?_ and _?_.
congruent bisect each other

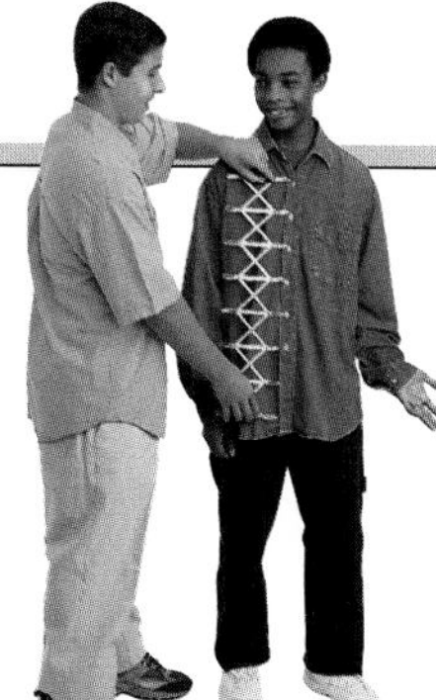

Career CONNECTION

A tailor uses a button spacer to mark the locations of the buttons. The tool opens and closes, but the tips always remain equally spaced. What quadrilateral properties make this tool work correctly?

Guiding Investigation 3

Step 1 As needed, encourage students to draw rectangles that aren't squares.

SHARING IDEAS

After groups share a variety of conjectures and agree on the wording for the five conjectures in this lesson, ask which of these properties of rhombuses, rectangles, and squares hold for all parallelograms. [none of them] Ask what special features of these figures result in their having the special properties. [Some of them come from equal angles, some from equal sides.]

[Ask] "When we draw a rhombus with a double-edged straightedge, is the constant distance between the parallel edges of the straightedge the length of each side of the rhombus?" Help students see that the distance across the straightedge is perpendicular to the opposite edges of the rhombus. Ask whether that distance is ever the length of one side of the rhombus. [It is for a square.] Is every square a rhombus then?

Refer students to Lesson 1.3 and the definition "A square is a 4-sided figure that has all sides congruent and all angles measuring 90°." The book promises better definitions later. Later is now. To encourage students to grapple with the ideas, ask them to critique the two definitions of *square* proposed in this lesson. Then ask what these definitions allow them to conclude about squares from the conjectures of this lesson.

Working through Exercises 1–10 as a class can help you see how well students are understanding the ideas. You might gain insight into a common misunderstanding if you don't move on from Exercise 1 as soon as a student offers the answer "false." Instead, ask the class what it thinks of that answer. Another

Sharing Ideas (continued)

student might say the statement is true if the parallelogram is a rectangle. A class discussion of this disagreement can lead to the realization that in these exercises, as is often the case in mathematics, the word *a* means "any" or "every" or "each." **[Alert]** If students are having other difficulties, suggest that they look back at their drawings from this lesson and the previous lesson.

Assessing Progress

See how well students voluntarily use the terms *parallel, rhombus, rectangle, diagonal, equiangular, equilateral, perpendicular, segment bisector,* and *angle bisector.* You can also assess students' ability to compare lengths using patty paper and how well they understand that properties of a larger class (rectangles or rhombuses) are inherited by members of a subclass (squares).

Closing the Lesson

Reiterate that the diagonals of any rhombus are perpendicular bisectors of each other and bisect opposite angles but are not necessarily congruent to each other. On the other hand, the diagonals of any rectangle are congruent and are bisectors but are not necessarily perpendicular and are not necessarily angle bisectors. The diagonals have all four properties in the case of a rhombus that is also a rectangle—that is, the diagonals of a square are congruent, are perpendicular bisectors of each other, and bisect opposite angles. More important than remembering all this is being able to figure it out from quick sketches. If students are struggling, you might work Exercise 12 or 13 with them.

BUILDING UNDERSTANDING

The exercises involve using all the conjectures from this lesson.

ASSIGNING HOMEWORK

Essential	2–18 evens
Portfolio	17–19
Journal	20, 21
Group	1–19 odds, 22–24
Review	25–31

MATERIALS

- Exercise 25 (T), *optional*

Helping with the Exercises

Exercises 1–5, 8–10 [Language] In these exercises, the word *a* means "any." For the statement to be true, it must be true for any parallelogram, rectangle, or square.

What happens if you combine the properties of a rectangle and a rhombus? We call the shape a square, and you can think of it as a regular quadrilateral. So you can define it in two different ways.

A **square** is an equiangular rhombus.

Or

A **square** is an equilateral rectangle.

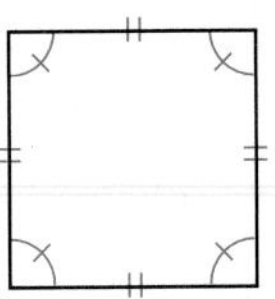

A square is a parallelogram, as well as both a rectangle and a rhombus. Use what you know about the properties of these three quadrilaterals to copy and complete this conjecture.

Square Diagonals Conjecture C-53

The diagonals of a square are _?_, _?_, and _?_. congruent, perpendicular, bisect each other

EXERCISES

You will need

Construction tools for Exercises 17–19, 23, 24, and 30

For Exercises 1–10 identify each statement as true or false. For each false statement, sketch a counterexample or explain why it is false.

1. The diagonals of a parallelogram are congruent. ⓗ false
2. The consecutive angles of a rectangle are congruent and supplementary. true
3. The diagonals of a rectangle bisect each other. true
4. The diagonals of a rectangle bisect the angles. false
5. The diagonals of a square are perpendicular bisectors of each other. true
6. Every rhombus is a square. false
7. Every square is a rectangle. true
8. A diagonal divides a square into two isosceles right triangles. true
9. Opposite angles in a parallelogram are always congruent. true
10. Consecutive angles in a parallelogram are always congruent. False. Consecutive angles are supplementary.

11. *WREK* is a rectangle.
 $CR = 10$
 $WE = \underline{?}$ 20

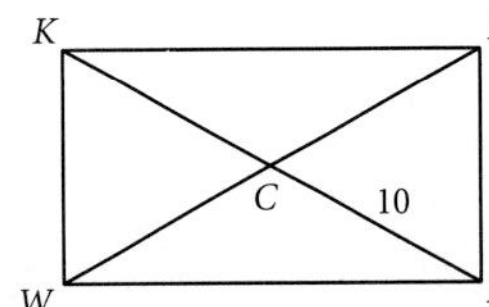

12. *PARL* is a parallelogram.
 $y = \underline{?}$ ⓗ 37°

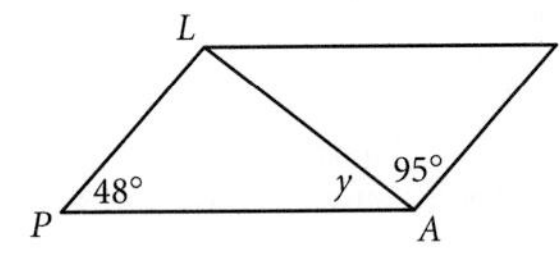

13. *SQRE* is a square.
 $x = \underline{?}$ 45°
 $y = \underline{?}$ 90°

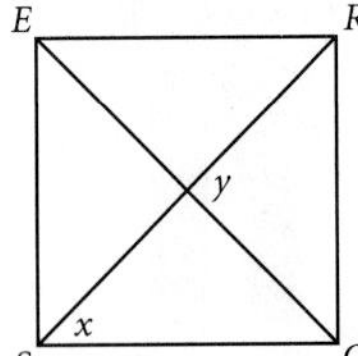

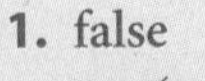

1. false

4. false

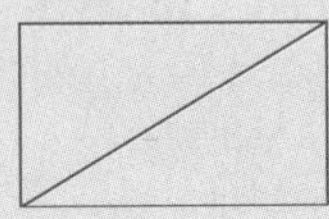

6. false

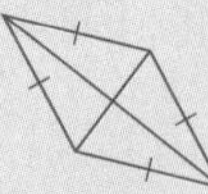

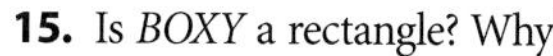

14. Is *DIAM* a rhombus? Why?

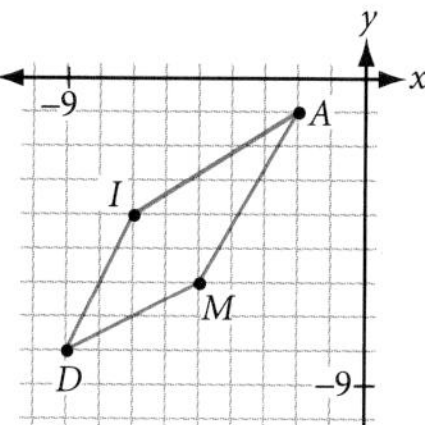

15. Is *BOXY* a rectangle? Why?

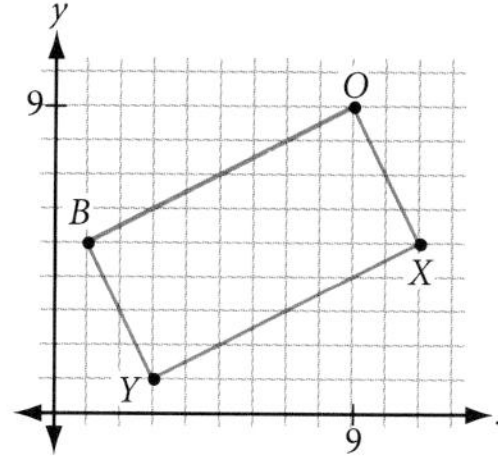

16. Is *TILE* a parallelogram? Why?

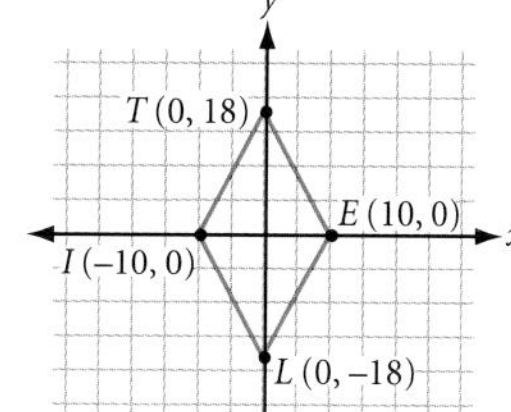

17. ***Construction*** Given the diagonal $\overline{LV}$, construct square *LOVE*. ⓗ

L ———— V

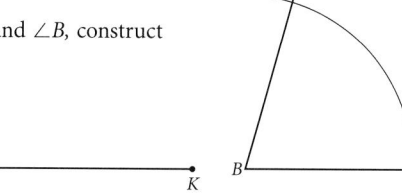

18. ***Construction*** Given diagonal $\overline{BK}$ and $\angle B$, construct rhombus *BAKE*. ⓗ

19. ***Construction*** Given side $\overline{PS}$ and diagonal $\overline{PE}$, construct rectangle *PIES*.

P ———— S

P ———— E

20. To make sure that a room is rectangular, builders check the two diagonals of the room. Explain what they must check, and why this works. If the diagonals are congruent and bisect each other, then the room is rectangular (Rectangle Diagonals Conjecture).

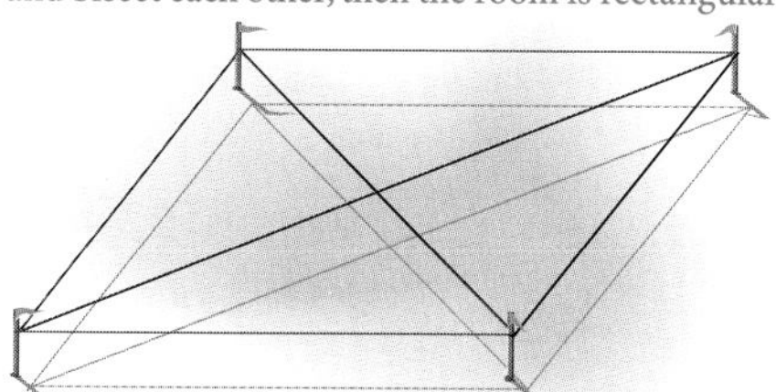

21. The platforms shown at the beginning of this lesson lift objects straight up. The platform also stays parallel to the floor. You can clearly see rhombuses in the picture, but you can also visualize the frame as the diagonals of three rectangles. Explain why the diagonals of a rectangle guarantee this vertical movement. The platform stays parallel to the floor because opposite sides of a rectangle are parallel (a rectangle is a parallelogram).

Exercises 14–16 Be sure students explain their reasoning on these exercises.

14. *DIAM* is not a rhombus because it is not equilateral and opposite sides are not parallel.

15. *BOXY* is a rectangle because its sides are perpendicular.

16. Yes. *TILE* is a rhombus, and a rhombus is a parallelogram.

Exercise 17 If students are having difficulty, suggest that they think about what properties diagonals of squares have. In this and later exercises, they might make a sketch first to help with the construction.

17.

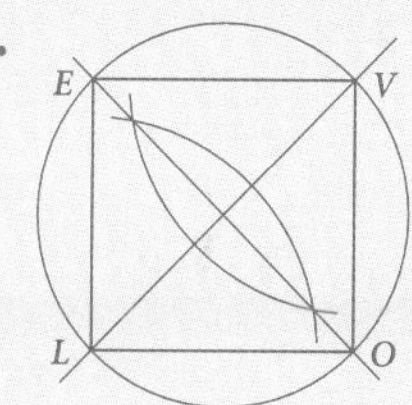

Exercise 18 As needed, wonder aloud how a rhombus's diagonal is related to one of its angles.

18. Constructions will vary.

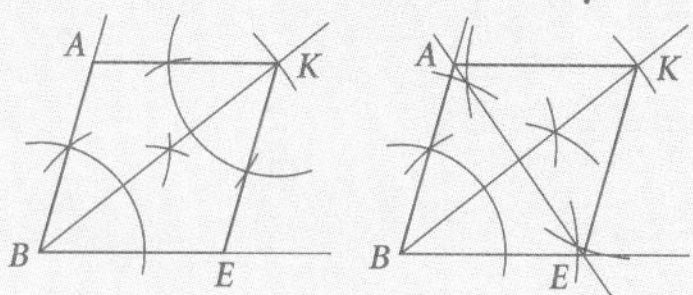

Exercise 19 Students having difficulty might find it useful to start with perpendicular lines and draw the diagonal from the other end of the given side.

19. one possible construction:

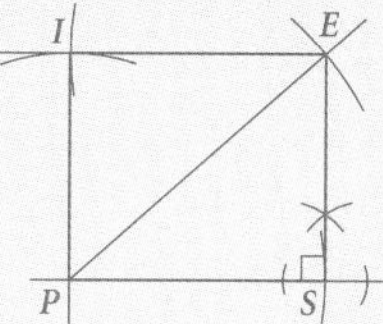

Exercise 21 This exercise is the one-step investigation.

22. The crosswalks form a parallelogram: The streets are of different widths, so the crosswalks are of different lengths. The streets would have to meet at right angles for the crosswalks to form a rectangle. The corners would have to be right angles and the streets would also have to be of the same width for the crosswalk to form a square.

Exercises 23, 24 As needed, ask students what kind of figure they must construct so that a diagonal of that figure solves the problem.

23. Place one side of the ruler along one side of the angle. Draw a line with the other side of the ruler. Repeat with the other side of the angle. Draw a line from the vertex of the angle to the point where the two lines meet.

24. Rotate your ruler so that each endpoint of the segment barely shows on each side of the ruler. Draw the parallel lines on each side of your ruler. Now rotate your ruler the other way and repeat the process to get a rhombus. The original segment is one diagonal of the rhombus. The other diagonal will be the perpendicular bisector of the original segment.

22. At the street intersection shown at right, one of the streets is wider than the other. Do the crosswalks form a rhombus or a parallelogram? Explain. What would have to be true about the streets if the crosswalks formed a rectangle? A square?

In Exercises 23 and 24, use only the two parallel edges of your double-edged straightedge. You may not fold the paper or use any marks on the straightedge.

23. ***Construction*** Draw an angle on your paper. Use your double-edged straightedge to construct the bisector of the angle. ⓗ

24. ***Construction*** Draw a segment on your paper. Use your double-edged straightedge to construct the perpendicular bisector of the segment. ⓗ

Review

25. Trace the figure below. Calculate the measure of each lettered angle.

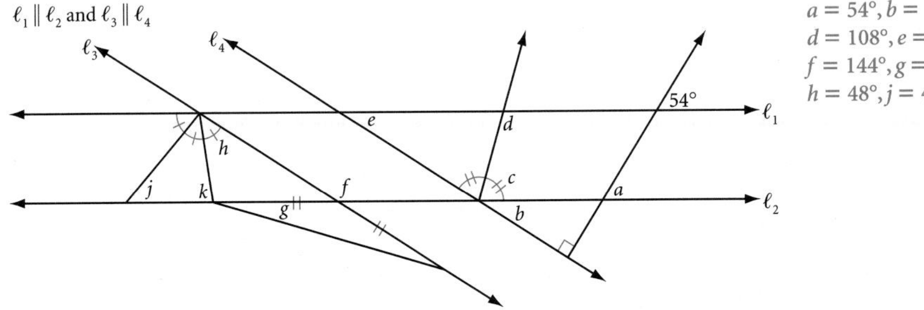

$a = 54°, b = 36°, c = 72°,$
$d = 108°, e = 36°,$
$f = 144°, g = 18°,$
$h = 48°, j = 48°, k = 84°$

4.6 **26.** Complete the flowchart proof below to demonstrate logically that if a quadrilateral has four congruent sides then it is a rhombus. One possible proof for this argument has been started for you.

Given: Quadrilateral *QUAD* has $\overline{QU} \cong \overline{UA} \cong \overline{AD} \cong \overline{DQ}$ with diagonal $\overline{DU}$

Show: *QUAD* is a rhombus

Flowchart Proof

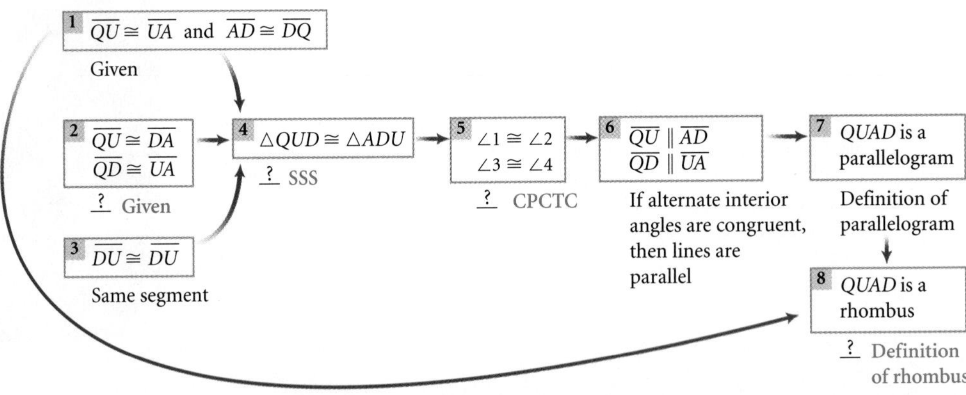

UYAS 5 **27.** Find the coordinates of three more points that lie on the line passing through the points $(2, -1)$ and $(-3, 4)$. possible answers: $(1, 0)$; $(0, 1)$; $(-1, 2)$; $(-2, 3)$

3.7 **28.** Find the coordinates of the circumcenter and the orthocenter for $\triangle RGT$ with vertices $R(2, -1)$, $G(5, 2)$, and $T(-3, 4)$. $(1, 3)$, $(2, -1)$

4.2 **29.** Draw a counterexample to show that this statement is false: If a triangle is isosceles, then its base angles are not complementary. Counterexample: The base angles of an isosceles right triangle measure 45°; thus they are complementary.

5.5 **30.** ***Construction*** Oran Boatwright is rowing at a 60° angle from the upstream direction as shown. Use a ruler and a protractor to draw the vector diagram. Draw the resultant vector and measure it to find his actual velocity and direction. velocity = 1.8 mi/hr. angle of path = 106.1° clockwise from the north

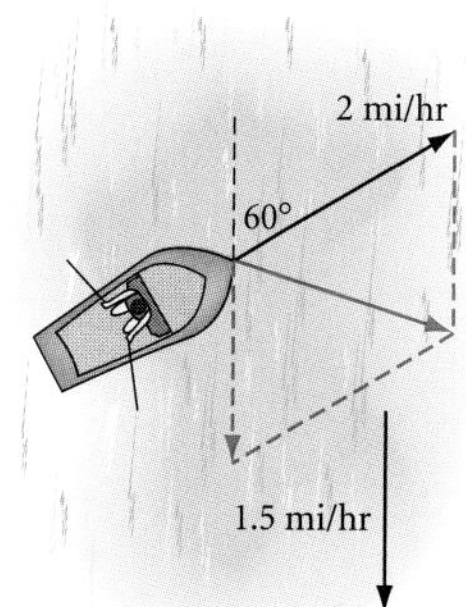

5.5 **31.** In Exercise 26, you proved that if the four sides of a quadrilateral are congruent, then the quadrilateral is a rhombus. So, when we defined rhombus, we did not need the added condition of it being a parallelogram. We only needed to say that it is a quadrilateral with all four sides congruent. Is this true for rectangles? Your conjecture would be, "If a quadrilateral has all four angles congruent, it must be a rectangle." Can you find a counterexample that proves it false? If you cannot, try to create a proof showing that it is true. ⓗ

IMPROVING YOUR REASONING SKILLS

How Did the Farmer Get to the Other Side?

A farmer was taking her pet rabbit, a basket of prize-winning baby carrots, and her small—but hungry—rabbit-chasing dog to town. She came to a river and realized she had a problem. The little boat she found tied to the pier was big enough to carry only herself and one of the three possessions. She couldn't leave her dog on the bank with the little rabbit (the dog would frighten the poor rabbit), and she couldn't leave the rabbit alone with the carrots (the rabbit would eat all the carrots). But she still had to figure out how to cross the river safely with one possession at a time. How could she move back and forth across the river to get the three possessions safely to the other side?

31. Yes, it is true for rectangles.

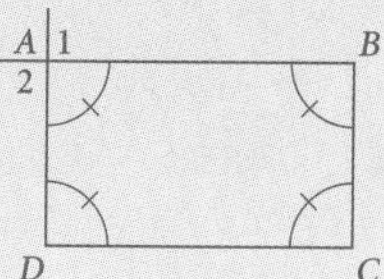

Given: $\angle BAD \cong \angle B \cong \angle C \cong \angle D$

Prove: $ABCD$ is a rectangle

By the Quadrilateral Sum Conjecture, $m\angle BAD + m\angle B + m\angle C + m\angle D = 360°$. Since all four angles are congruent, each measure is $\frac{360°}{4} = 90°$. $m\angle 1 + m\angle BAD = 180°$ because they are a linear pair. We already know $m\angle BAD = 90°$, so $m\angle 1 = 90°$ by subtraction. By definition of congruence and by substitution, $\angle 1 \cong \angle B$. Therefore $\overline{AD} \parallel \overline{BC}$ by AIA. $m\angle 2 + m\angle BAD = 180°$ because they are a linear pair. $m\angle 2 = 90°$ by subtraction. By definition of congruence and by substitution, $\angle 2 \cong \angle D$. Therefore $\overline{AB} \parallel \overline{DC}$ by AIA. Thus $ABCD$ is a parallelogram by definition of parallelogram. Because it is also equiangular, $ABCD$ is a rectangle.

IMPROVING REASONING SKILLS

If students are having difficulty, encourage them to think about which pairs of items can be together. One solution: Take the rabbit across and leave it there. Go back. Take the carrots across and return with the rabbit. Leave the rabbit on the original side. Take the dog across, leave it there, and go back. Finally, bring the rabbit across again.

LESSON 5.7

PLANNING

LESSON OUTLINE

One day:

10 min Example

30 min Exercises

5 min Closing

MATERIALS

- Jananese Puzzle Quilts (W) for project

TEACHING

This lesson gives students practice in thinking backward to write a flowchart proof.

One step Before saying anything about working backward, give students the puzzle in Exercise 1. If some groups solve it working forward, have groups share their approaches so that they all realize the power of backward thinking. Then have them work on the example and exercises.

▶ EXAMPLE

The underlying question students will be asking themselves as they work backward is, "What could I use to prove this?" As they answer that question, they have a reason for the corresponding step in the proof.

LESSON 5.7

Proving Quadrilateral Properties

"For instance" is not a "proof."

JEWISH SAYING

Most of the paragraph proofs and flowchart proofs you have done so far have been set up for you to complete. Creating your own proofs requires a great deal of planning. One excellent planning strategy is "thinking backward." If you know where you are headed but are unsure where to start, start at the end of the problem and work your way back to the beginning one step at a time.

The firefighter below asks another firefighter to turn on one of the water hydrants. But which one? A mistake could mean disaster—a nozzle flying around loose under all that pressure. Which hydrant should the firefighter turn on?

Did you "think backward" to solve the puzzle? You'll find it a useful strategy as you write proofs.

To help plan a proof and visualize the flow of reasoning, you can make a flowchart. As you think backward through a proof, you draw a flowchart backward to show the steps in your thinking.

Work with a partner when you first try planning your geometry proof. Think backward to make your plan: start with the conclusion and reason back to the given. Let's look at an example.

A concave kite is sometimes called a **dart.**

EXAMPLE

Given: Dart $ADBC$ with $\overline{AC} \cong \overline{BC}$, $\overline{AD} \cong \overline{BD}$

Show: $\overline{CD}$ bisects $\angle ACB$

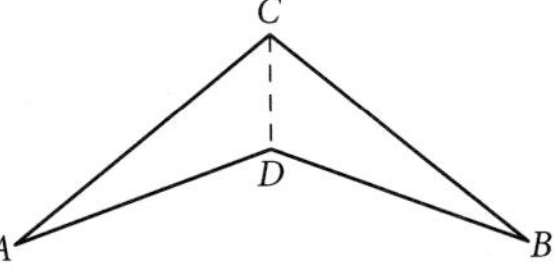

▶ Solution

Plan: Begin by drawing a diagram and marking the given information on it. Next, construct your proof by reasoning backward. Then convert this reasoning into a flowchart. Your flowchart should start with boxes containing the given information and end with what you are trying to demonstrate. The arrows indicate the flow of your logical argument. Your thinking might go something like this:

LESSON OBJECTIVES

- Practice writing flowchart and paragraph proofs
- Develop deductive reasoning skills
- Review properties of quadrilaterals

NCTM STANDARDS

	CONTENT		PROCESS
	Number	✓	Problem Solving
	Algebra	✓	Reasoning
✓	Geometry	✓	Communication
	Measurement		Connections
	Data/Probability	✓	Representation

"I can show $\overline{CD}$ is the bisector of $\angle ACB$ if I can show $\angle ACD \cong \angle BCD$."

$\angle ACD \cong \angle BCD$ → $\overline{CD}$ is the bisector of $\angle ACB$

"I can show $\angle ACD \cong \angle BCD$ if they are corresponding angles in congruent triangles."

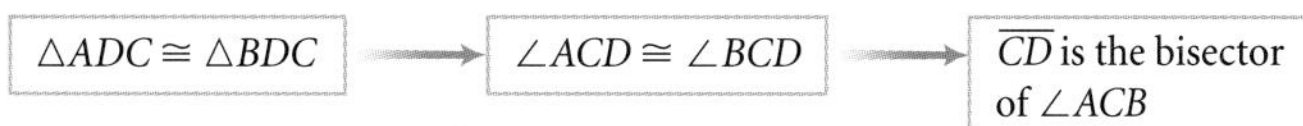

"Can I show $\triangle ADC \cong \triangle BDC$? Yes, I can, by SSS, because it is given that $\overline{AC} \cong \overline{BC}$ and $\overline{AD} \cong \overline{BD}$, and $\overline{CD} \cong \overline{CD}$ because it is the same segment in both triangles."

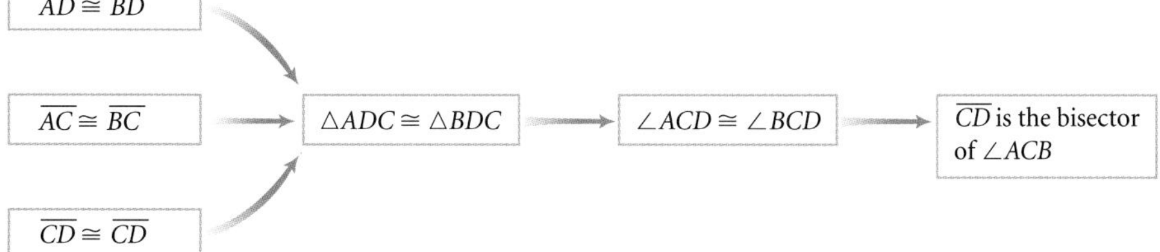

By adding the reason for each statement below each box in your flowchart, you can make the flowchart into a complete flowchart proof.

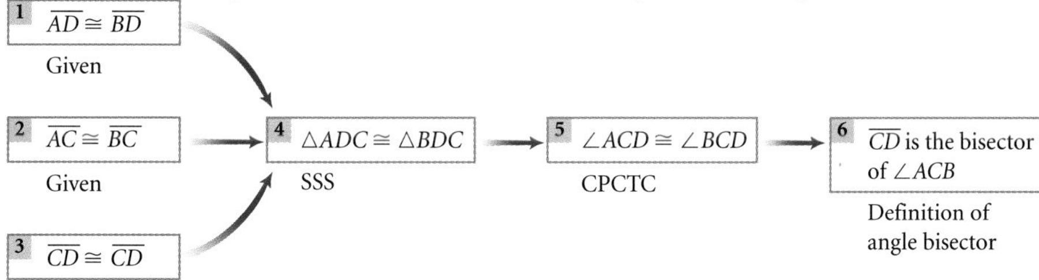

Some students prefer to write their proofs in a flowchart format, and others prefer to write out their proof as an explanation in paragraph form. By reversing the reasoning in your plan, you can make the plan into a complete paragraph proof.

"It is given that $\overline{AC} \cong \overline{BC}$ and $\overline{AD} \cong \overline{BD}$. $\overline{CD} \cong \overline{CD}$ because it is the same segment in both triangles. So, $\triangle ADC \cong \triangle BDC$ by the SSS Congruence Conjecture. So, $\angle ACD \cong \angle BCD$ by the definition of congruent triangles (CPCTC). Therefore, by the definition of angle bisectors, $\overline{CD}$ is the bisector of $\angle ACB$. Q.E.D."

The abbreviation Q.E.D. at the end of a proof stands for the Latin phrase *quod erat demonstrandum,* meaning "which was to be demonstrated." You can also think of Q.E.D. as a short way of saying "Quite Elegantly Done" at the conclusion of your proof.

In the exercises you will prove some of the special properties of quadrilaterals discovered in this chapter.

Assessing Progress

Most of your assessment opportunities in this lesson will come through observation of student work on the exercises. You can assess students' understanding of many major mathematical concepts encountered in this course so far.

Closing the Lesson

The main point of this lesson is that proofs are often written by working backward. If you think students will have difficulty with the exercises, you may want to work through Exercise 2 with them.

BUILDING UNDERSTANDING

The exercises allow students to practice thinking backward to develop proofs of some properties of various quadrilaterals. Urge students to copy all diagrams and to mark and label them accordingly.

ASSIGNING HOMEWORK

Essential	**1–11 odds**
Performance assessment	**5**
Portfolio	**7**
Journal	**12**
Group	**2–10 evens**
Review	**13–16**

▶ Helping with the Exercises

Many students will be unsure of whether a reason they want to cite is a definition or a conjecture. Begin to encourage them to think about the identification question.

You may wish to jigsaw, giving different exercises to different groups, after all groups have completed Exercise 2.

Exercise 1 If students work backward from 100, there's a single path. If they work forward, they may have to track one or two paths until they're stuck before finding the correct path. This exercise is the one-step investigation.

1. work backward: $100 - 5$; $95 \div 5$; $19 - 5$; $14 \cdot 2$; $28 + 2$; $30 \div 5$; $6 + 2$; $8 - 5$; $3 - 2$; 1

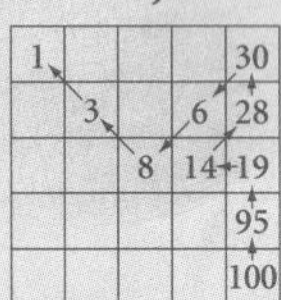

Exercise 3 The given proof depends on the conjecture in Exercise 2.

EXERCISES

1. Let's start with a puzzle. Copy the 5-by-5 puzzle grid at right. Start at square 1 and end at square 100. You can move to an adjacent square horizontally, vertically, or diagonally if you can add, subtract, multiply, or divide the number in the square you occupy by 2 or 5 to get the number in that square.

   For example, if you happen to be in square 11, you could move to square 9 by subtracting 2 or to square 55 by multiplying by 5. When you find the path from 1 to 100, show it with arrows.

   Notice that in this puzzle you may start with different moves. You could start with 1 and go to 5. From 5 you could go to 10 or 3. Or you could start with 1 and go to 2. From 2 you could go to 4. Which route should you take? ⓗ

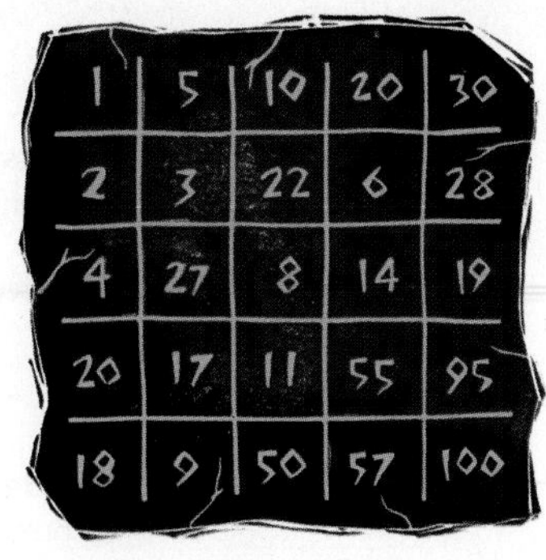

In Exercises 2–10, each conjecture has also been stated as a "given" and a "show." Any necessary auxiliary lines have been included. Complete a flowchart proof or write a paragraph proof.

2. Prove the conjecture: The diagonal of a parallelogram divides the parallelogram into two congruent triangles.

   Given: Parallelogram $SOAK$ with diagonal $\overline{SA}$

   Show: $\triangle SOA \cong \triangle AKS$

   Flowchart Proof

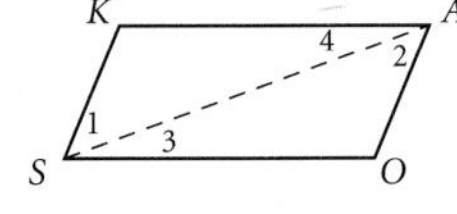

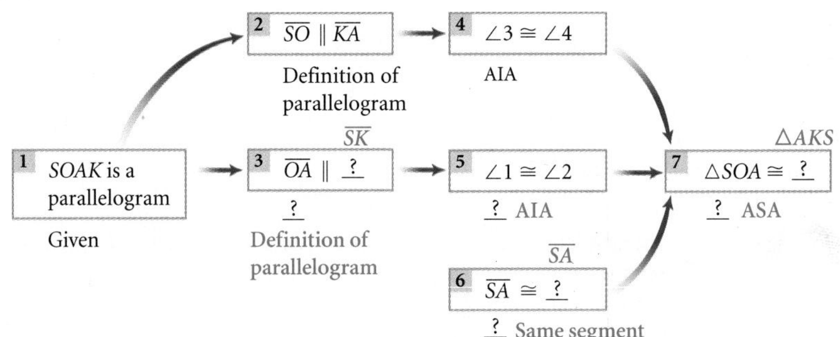

3. Prove the conjecture: The opposite angles of a parallelogram are congruent.

   Given: Parallelogram $BATH$ with diagonals $\overline{BT}$ and $\overline{HA}$

   Show: $\angle HBA \cong \angle ATH$ and $\angle BAT \cong \angle THB$

   Flowchart Proof

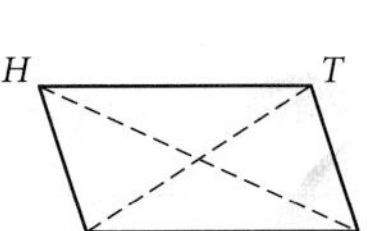

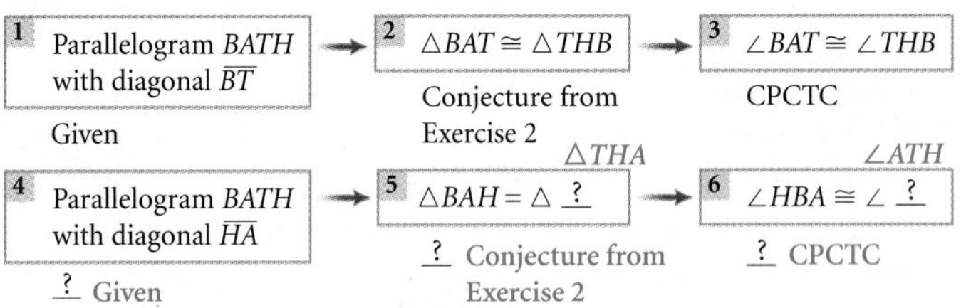

4. Prove the conjecture: If the opposite sides of a quadrilateral are congruent, then the quadrilateral is a parallelogram.

Given: Quadrilateral $WATR$, with $\overline{WA} \cong \overline{RT}$ and $\overline{WR} \cong \overline{AT}$, and diagonal $\overline{WT}$

Show: $WATR$ is a parallelogram

Flowchart Proof

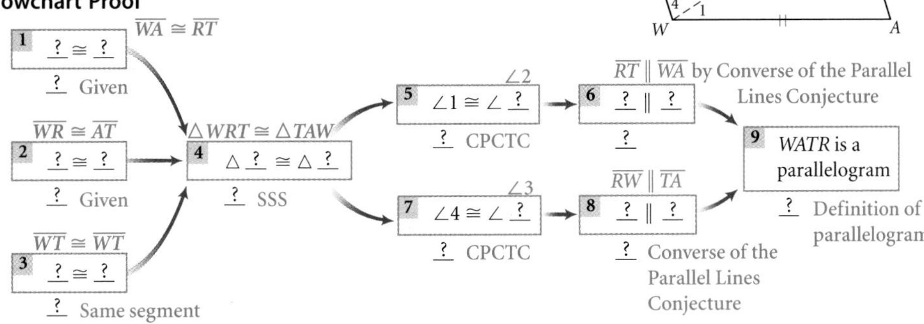

5. Write a flowchart proof to demonstrate that quadrilateral $SOAP$ is a parallelogram.

Given: Quadrilateral $SOAP$ with $\overline{SP} \parallel \overline{OA}$ and $\overline{SP} \cong \overline{OA}$

Show: $SOAP$ is a parallelogram

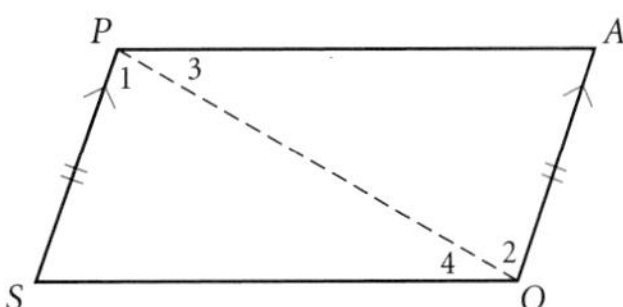

6. The results of the proof in Exercise 5 can now be stated as a proved conjecture. Complete this statement beneath your proof: "If one pair of opposite sides of a quadrilateral are both parallel and congruent, then the quadrilateral is a __?__." parallelogram

7. Prove the conjecture: The diagonals of a rectangle are congruent. ⓗ

Given: Rectangle $YOGI$ with diagonals $\overline{YG}$ and $\overline{OI}$

Show: $\overline{YG} \cong \overline{OI}$

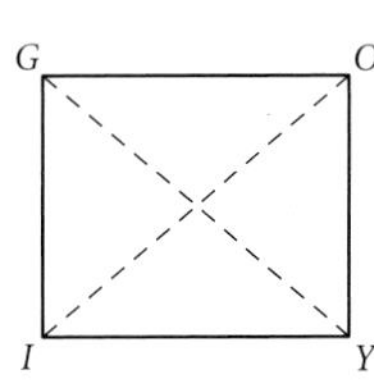

8. Prove the conjecture: If the diagonals of a parallelogram are congruent, then the parallelogram is a rectangle. ⓗ

Given: Parallelogram $BEAR$, with diagonals $\overline{BA} \cong \overline{ER}$

Show: $BEAR$ is a rectangle

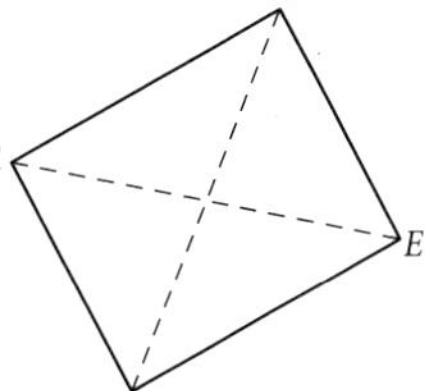

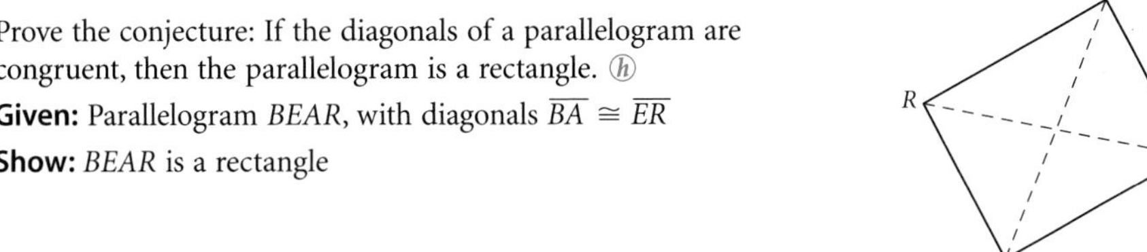

9. Prove the Isosceles Trapezoid Conjecture: The base angles of an isosceles trapezoid are congruent.

Given: Isosceles trapezoid $PART$ with $\overline{PA} \parallel \overline{TR}$, $\overline{PT} \cong \overline{AR}$, and $\overline{TZ}$ constructed parallel to $\overline{RA}$

Show: $\angle TPA \cong \angle RAP$

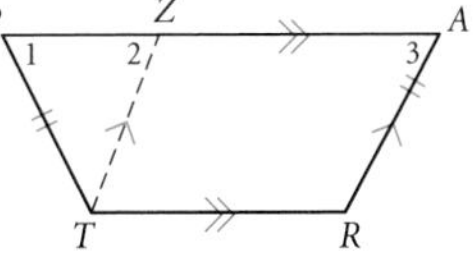

Exercise 4 Students may list given information in a different order.

Exercise 7 Students may use the fact that every rectangle is a parallelogram so they can use the property that opposite sides are congruent. Students may have difficulty realizing that the two triangles they want to prove congruent are overlapping.

Exercise 8 Students may question what they need to prove because they're accustomed to thinking about rectangles as having many different properties. They need to show that the figure satisfies the book's definition of *rectangle* as a parallelogram with four congruent angles.

Exercise 9 This is the Isosceles Trapezoid Conjecture of Lesson 5.3. Students may miss a subtle aspect of this proof: that the auxiliary line segment TZ is different from the trapezoid's side $\overline{PT}$. If point Z could be concurrent with point T, the same proof would apply to showing the congruence of the base angles of a parallelogram, a false conclusion.

9. Because $\overline{AR}$ is parallel to $\overline{ZT}$, corresponding $\angle 3$ and $\angle 2$ are congruent. Opposite sides of parallelogram $ZART$ are equal so $AR = TZ$. Since the trapezoid is isosceles, $AR = PT$, and substituting gives $ZT = PT$ making $\triangle PTZ$ isosceles and $\angle 1$ and $\angle 2$ congruent. By substitution $\angle 1$ and $\angle 3$ are congruent.

5.

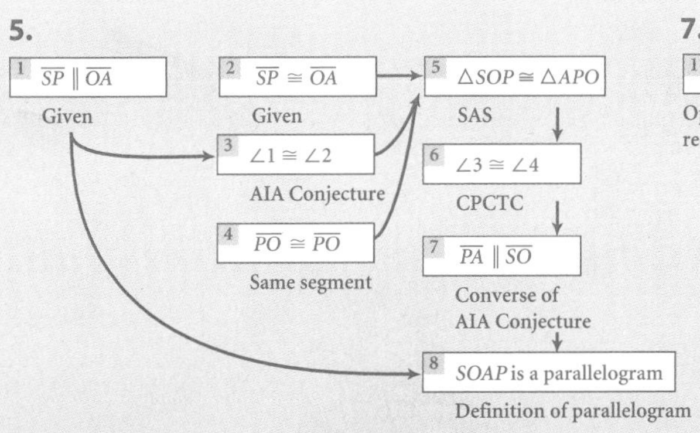

7. sample flowchart proof:

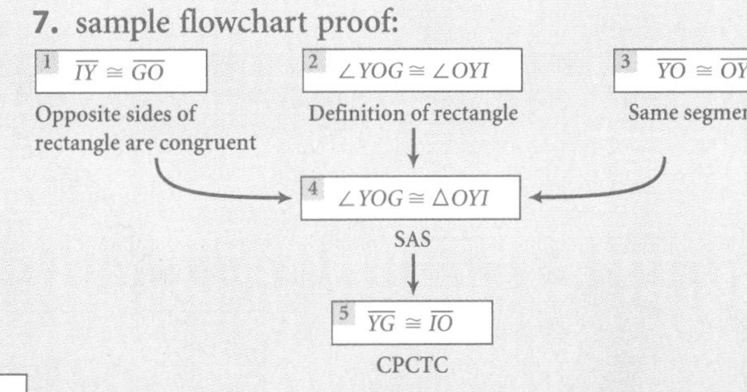

See page 772 for answers to Exercise 8.

Exercise 10 You might skip this problem if students proved the Isosceles Trapezoid Diagonals Conjecture in Lesson 5.3.

Exercise 11 Students may want to say that the lamp is parallel to the vertical holder because the shape is a parallelogram. The real question is, Why is the shape a parallelogram?

12. If the fabric is pulled along the warp or the weft, nothing happens. However, if the fabric is pulled along the bias, it can be stretched because the rectangles are pulled into parallelograms.

10. Prove the Isosceles Trapezoid Diagonals Conjecture: The diagonals of an isosceles trapezoid are congruent.

Given: Isosceles trapezoid *GTHR* with $\overline{GR} \cong \overline{TH}$ and diagonals $\overline{GH}$ and $\overline{TR}$

Show: $\overline{GH} \cong \overline{TR}$

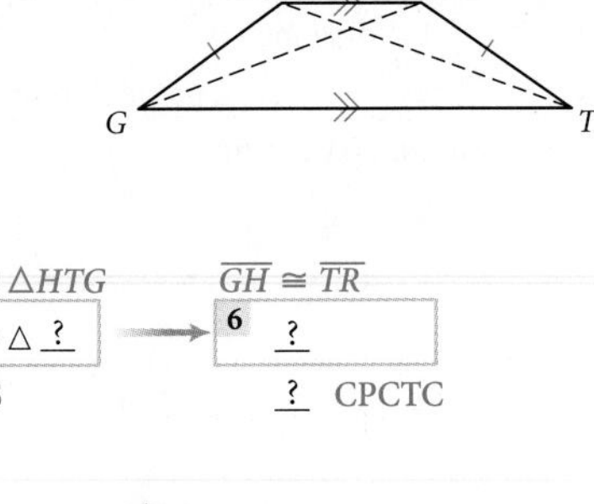

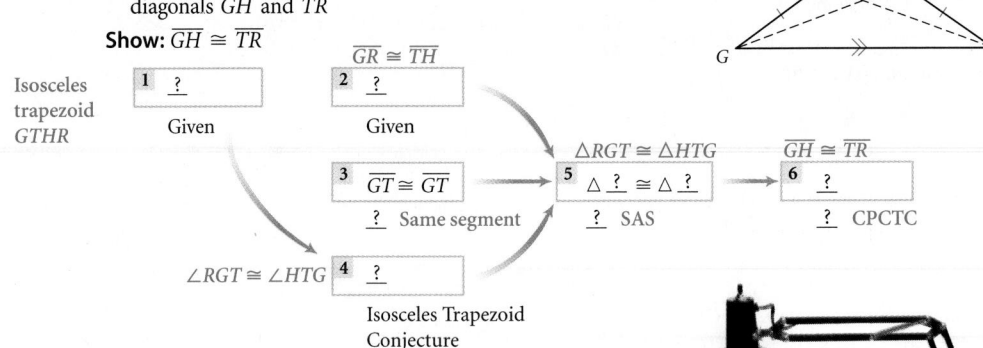

Isosceles trapezoid *GTHR* → 1 ? (Given)

$\overline{GR} \cong \overline{TH}$ → 2 ? (Given)

3 $\overline{GT} \cong \overline{GT}$ (? Same segment)

$\angle RGT \cong \angle HTG$ → 4 ? (Isosceles Trapezoid Conjecture)

$\triangle RGT \cong \triangle HTG$ → 5 $\triangle$? $\cong \triangle$? (? SAS)

$\overline{GH} \cong \overline{TR}$ → 6 ? (? CPCTC)

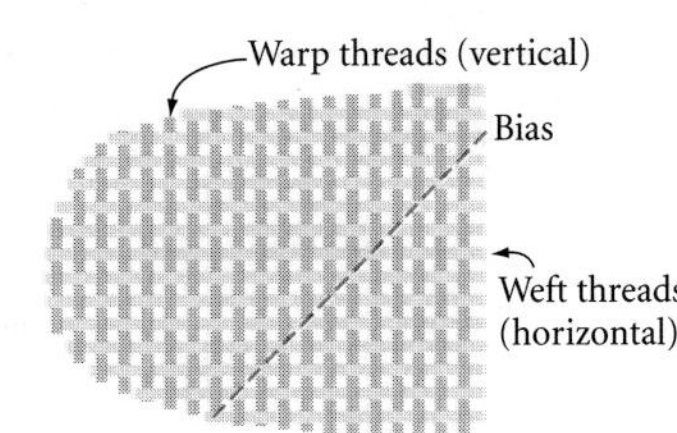

11. If an adjustable desk lamp, like the one at right, is adjusted by bending or straightening the metal arm, it will continue to shine straight down onto the desk. What property that you proved in the previous exercises explains why? Opposite sides of a parallelogram are parallel.

12. You have discovered that triangles are rigid but parallelograms are not. This property shows up in the making of fabric, which has warp threads and weft threads. Fabric is constructed by weaving thread at right angles, creating a grid of rectangles. What happens when you pull the fabric along the warp or weft? What happens when you pull the fabric along a diagonal (the *bias*)? ⓗ

Warp threads (vertical)
Bias
Weft threads (horizontal)

Review

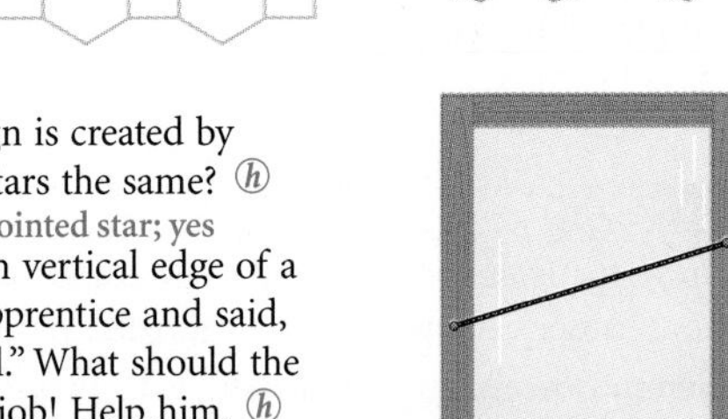

5.2 **13.** Find the measure of the acute angles in the 4-pointed star in the Islamic tiling shown at right. The polygons are squares and regular hexagons. Find the measure of the acute angles in the 6-pointed star in the Islamic tiling on the far right. The 6-pointed star design is created by arranging six squares. Are the angles in both stars the same? ⓗ
30° angles in 4-pointed star, 30° angles in 6-pointed star; yes

2.6 **14.** A contractor tacked one end of a string to each vertical edge of a window. He then handed a protractor to his apprentice and said, "Here, find out if the vertical edges are parallel." What should the apprentice do? No, he can't quit, he wants this job! Help him. ⓗ

He should measure the alternate interior angles to see whether they're congruent. If they are, the edges are parallel.

15. The last bus stops at the school some time between 4:45 and 5:00. What is the probability that you will miss the bus if you arrive at the bus stop at 4:50? ⓗ $\frac{1}{3}$

1.8 **16.** The 3-by-9-by-12-inch clear plastic sealed container shown is resting on its smallest face. It is partially filled with a liquid to a height of 8 inches. Sketch the container resting on its middle-sized face. What will be the height of the liquid in the container in this position? ⓗ

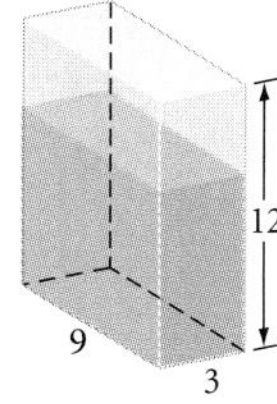

project

JAPANESE PUZZLE QUILTS

When experienced quilters first see Japanese puzzle quilts, they are often amazed (or puzzled?) because the straight rows of blocks so common to block quilts do not seem to exist. The sewing lines between apparent blocks seem jagged. At first glance, Japanese puzzle quilts look like American crazy quilts that must be handsewn and that take forever to make!

However, Japanese puzzle quilts do contain straight sewing lines. Study the Japanese puzzle quilt at right. Can you find the basic quilt block? What shape is it?

Mabry Benson designed this puzzle quilt, *Red and Blue Puzzle* (1994). Can you find any rhombic blocks that are the same? How many different types of fabric were used?

The puzzle quilt shown above is made of four different-color kites sewn into rhombuses. The rhombic blocks are sewn together with straight sewing lines as shown in the diagram at left. Look closely again at the puzzle quilt.

Now for your project. You will need copies of the Japanese puzzle quilt grid, color pencils or markers, and color paper or fabrics.

1. To produce the zigzag effect of a Japanese puzzle quilt, you need to avoid pseudoblocks of the same color sharing an edge. How many different colors or fabrics do you need in order to make a puzzle quilt?
2. How many different types of rhombic blocks do you need for a four-color Japanese puzzle quilt? What if you want no two pseudoblocks of the same color to touch at either an edge or a vertex?
3. Can you create a four-color Japanese puzzle quilt that requires more than four different color combinations in the rhombic blocks?
4. Plan, design, and create a Japanese puzzle quilt out of paper or fabric, using the Japanese puzzle quilt technique.

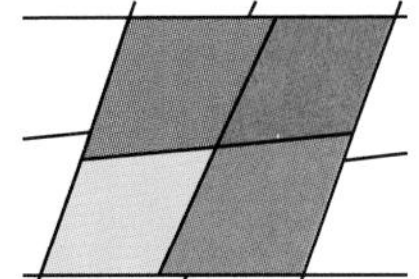

Detail of a pseudoblock

Detail of an actual block

Exercise 15 The exercise reviews the Exploration Geometric Probability I, on page 86.

16.

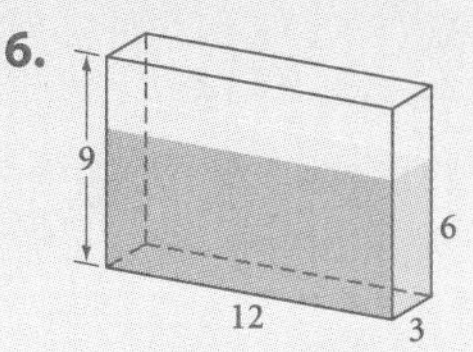

6 inches

Project Question Answers

1. At least two colors are needed.
2. In a quilt of four colors, around any pseudoblock of one color there can be six different arrangements of pseudoblocks of the other three colors (not counting rotations); three of these arrangements require four different quilt blocks. If four colors are used with no touching, then the quilt can be made with two different quilt blocks, each with kites of all four colors. If the colors of one block are considered in clockwise order beginning with a kite in the smaller angle of the rhombus, then the other block will have the same colors in counterclockwise order beginning with a kite in the larger angle of the rhombus.
3. None of the four-color quilts requires more than four different quilt blocks.

Supporting the project

Each student needs eight to ten copies of the worksheet. **[Language]** The *pseudoblocks* are false, jagged blocks of one color, not the rhombic building blocks of two or four colors.

OUTCOMES

- ▸ Project questions are answered.
- ▸ A two- or four-color quilt is correctly assembled.
- • A quilt is designed with five or six colors.

PLANNING

LESSON OUTLINE

First day:

15 min Reviewing

30 min Exercises

Second day:

30 min Exercises

15 min Student self-assessment

REVIEWING

Ask that each student draw a concept map relating different kinds of quadrilaterals. Have students check each other's maps to be sure that they reflect the hierarchy of the student book: The three main kinds of quadrilaterals are trapezoids, kites, and parallelograms; the two main kinds of parallelograms are rhombuses and rectangles; and every square is a rhombus and a rectangle.

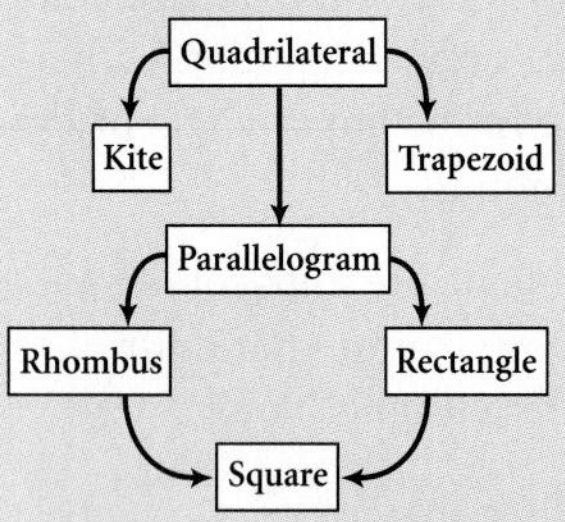

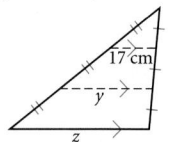

Then ask what properties can be assigned to each category but to none containing it. For example, all sides of a rhombus are congruent, but that is not true for parallelograms in general. Keep stressing that any property of a category is inherited by more specific quadrilaterals; for example, the fact that the diagonals of a parallelogram bisect each other is inherited by rhombuses, rectangles, and squares. In this way you can review most of the conjectures of this chapter. Try to get students to figure out how to fit in the other conjectures. They may want to add "isosceles trapezoids" as a subcategory of trapezoids in order to include conjectures related to those quadrilaterals, and to add a category for polygons (including all quadrilaterals) to fit in the earliest conjectures of the chapter.

CHAPTER 5 REVIEW

In this chapter you extended your knowledge of triangles to other polygons. You discovered the interior and exterior angle sums for all polygons. You investigated the midsegments of triangles and trapezoids and the properties of parallelograms. You learned what distinguishes various quadrilaterals and what properties apply to each class of quadrilaterals.

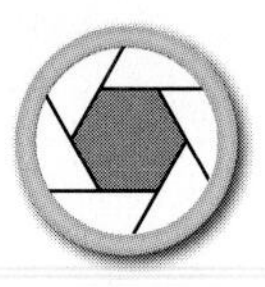

Along the way you practiced proving conjectures with flowcharts and paragraph proofs. Be sure you've added the new conjectures to your list. Include diagrams for clarity.

How has your knowledge of triangles helped you make discoveries about other polygons?

EXERCISES

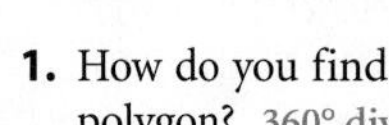

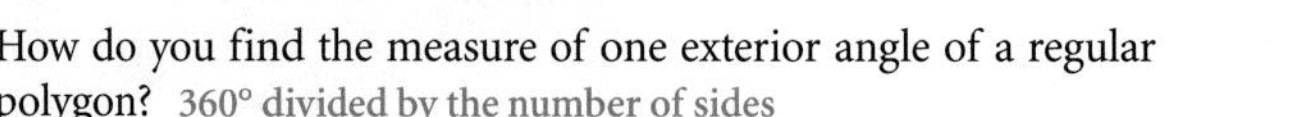

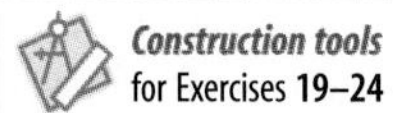

You will need

Construction tools for Exercises **19–24**

1. How do you find the measure of one exterior angle of a regular polygon? 360° divided by the number of sides

2. How can you find the number of sides of an equiangular polygon by measuring one of its interior angles? By measuring one of its exterior angles?

3. How do you construct a rhombus by using only a ruler or double-edged straightedge?

4. How do you bisect an angle by using only a ruler or double-edged straightedge?

5. How can you use the Rectangle Diagonals Conjecture to determine if the corners of a room are right angles? Sample answer: Measure the diagonals with string to see if they are congruent and bisect each other.

6. How can you use the Triangle Midsegment Conjecture to find a distance between two points that you can't measure directly? Draw a triangle so that the two points are midpoints of the sides. Then measure the side parallel to the midsegment.

7. Find x and y. $x = 10°, y = 40°$

8. Perimeter = 266 cm. Find x. $x = 60$ cm

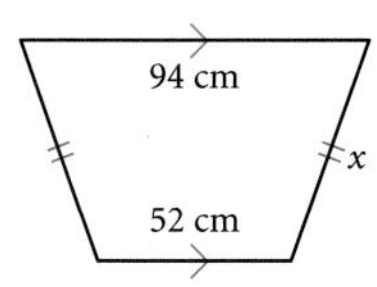

9. Find a and c. $a = 116°, c = 64°$

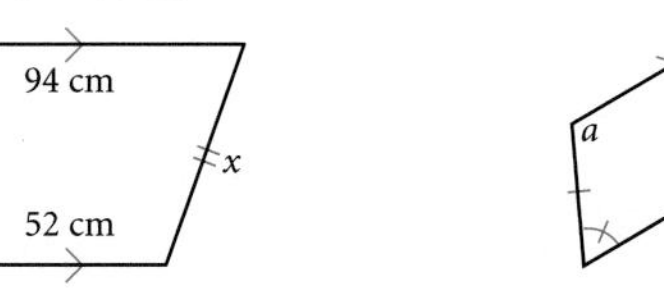

10. $\overline{MS}$ is a midsegment. Find the perimeter of $MOIS$. 100

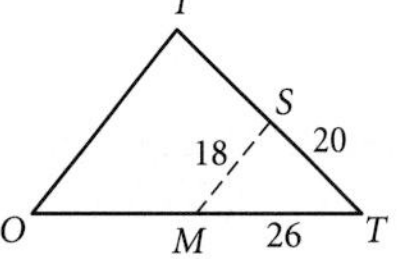

11. Find x. $x = 38$ cm

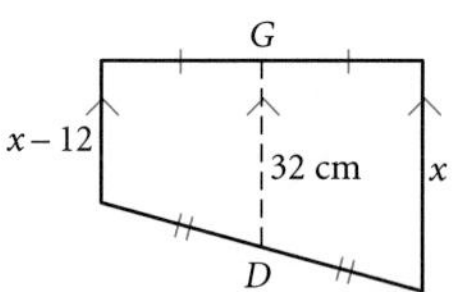

12. Find y and z. $y = 34$ cm, $z = 51$ cm

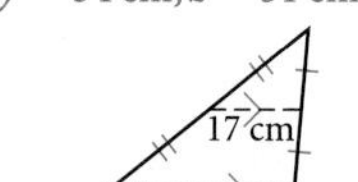

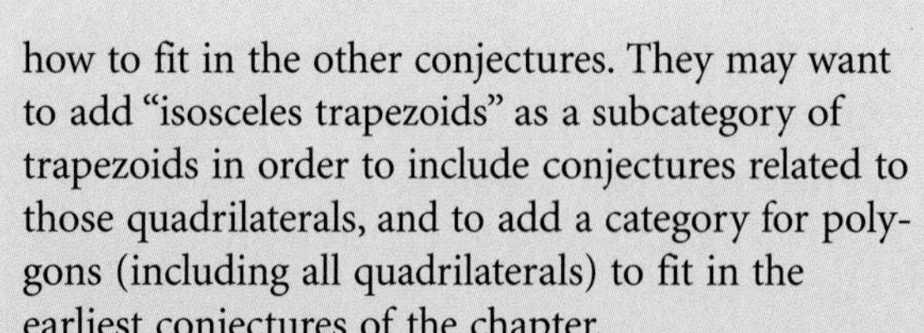

2. Sample answers: Using interior angle, set interior angle measure formula equal to the angle and solve for n. Using exterior angle, divide into 360°. Or find interior angle measure and go from there.

3. Trace both sides of the ruler as shown below.

13. Copy and complete the table below by placing a yes (to mean always) or a no (to mean not always) in each empty space. Use what you know about special quadrilaterals.

	Kite	Isosceles trapezoid	Parallelogram	Rhombus	Rectangle
Opposite sides are parallel	No	No	Yes	Yes	Yes
Opposite sides are congruent	No	No	Yes	Yes	Yes
Opposite angles are congruent	No	No	Yes	Yes	Yes
Diagonals bisect each other	No	No	Yes	Yes	Yes
Diagonals are perpendicular	Yes	No	No	Yes	No
Diagonals are congruent	No	Yes	No	No	Yes
Exactly one line of symmetry	Yes	Yes	No	No	No
Exactly two lines of symmetry	No	No	No	Yes	Yes

14. APPLICATION A 2-inch-wide frame is to be built around the regular decagonal window shown. At what angles a and b should the corners of each piece be cut? $a = 72°, b = 108°$

15. Find the measure of each lettered angle. $a = 120°, b = 60°, c = 60°, d = 120°, e = 60°, f = 30°, g = 108°, m = 24°, p = 84°$

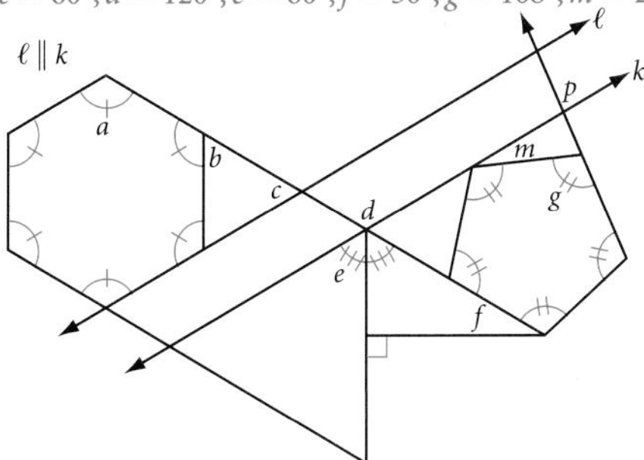

16. Archaeologist Ertha Diggs has uncovered one stone that appears to be a voussoir from a semicircular stone arch. On each isosceles trapezoidal face, the obtuse angles measure 96°. Assuming all the stones were identical, how many stones were in the original arch? 15 stones

ASSIGNING HOMEWORK

If you have skipped any lessons of this chapter, be selective as to which exercises you assign. Students will get a good review if they do odds or evens in groups and the others individually.

▶ Helping with the Exercises

Exercise 13 [Ask] "What can you say about a quadrilateral if it has perpendicular diagonals?" [It could be a kite, a rhombus, or a general quadrilateral.] ". . . exactly one line of symmetry?" [It is a kite or isosceles trapezoid.] ". . . perpendicular diagonals and exactly one line of symmetry?" [It is a kite.] ". . . exactly two lines of symmetry?" [rhombus or rectangle] ". . . perpendicular diagonals and two lines of symmetry?" [rhombus] ". . . perpendicular diagonals and four lines of symmetry?" [square]

4. Make a rhombus using the double-edged straightedge, and draw a diagonal connecting the angle vertex to the opposite vertex.

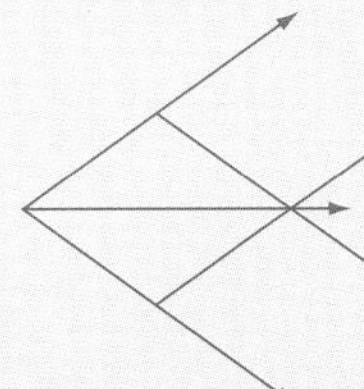

18. When the swing is motionless, the seat, the bar at the top, and the chains form a rectangle. When you swing left to right, the rectangle changes to a parallelogram. The opposite sides stay equal in length, so they stay parallel. The seat and the bar at the top are also parallel to the ground.

20.

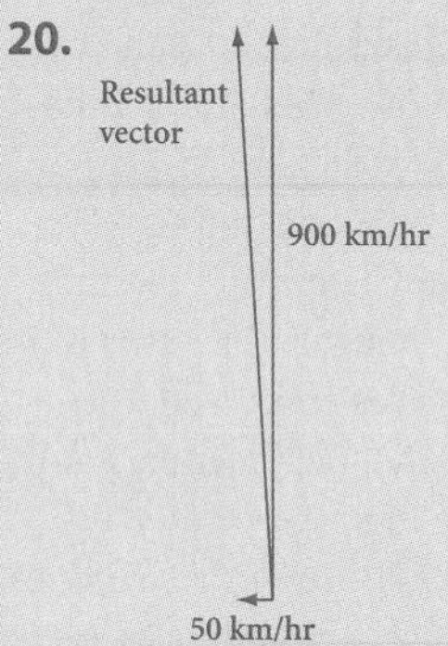

Speed: ≈ 901.4 km/hr. Direction: slightly west of north. Figure is approximate.

Exercise 21 Students may use the diagonals in a different order and have a figure with different labels.

21.

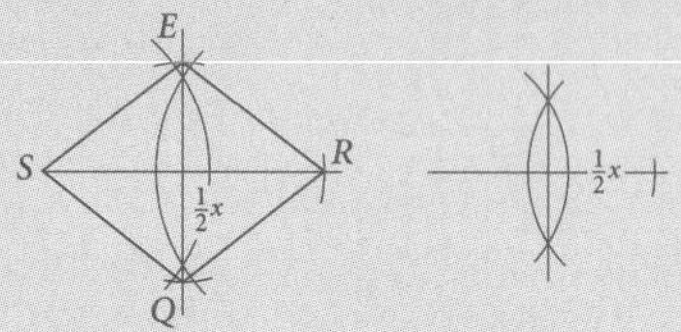

22. possible answers:

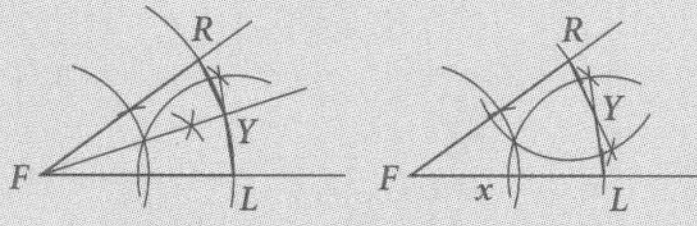

23.

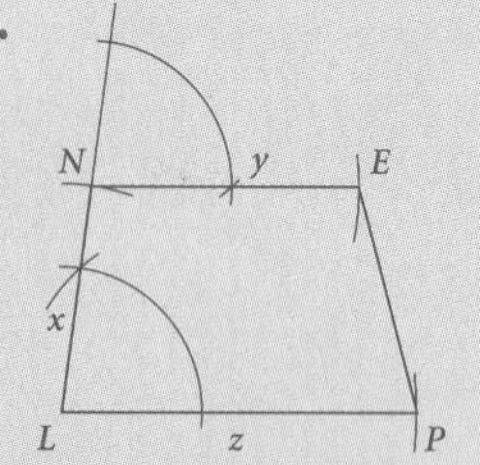

17. Kite $ABCD$ has vertices $A(-3, -2)$, $B(2, -2)$, $C(3, 1)$, and $D(0, 2)$. Find the coordinates of the point of intersection of the diagonals. (1, 0)

18. When you swing left to right on a swing, the seat stays parallel to the ground. Explain why.

19. ***Construction*** The tiling of congruent pentagons shown below is created from a honeycomb grid (tiling of regular hexagons). What is the measure of each lettered angle? Re-create the design with compass and straightedge. $a = 60°, b = 120°$

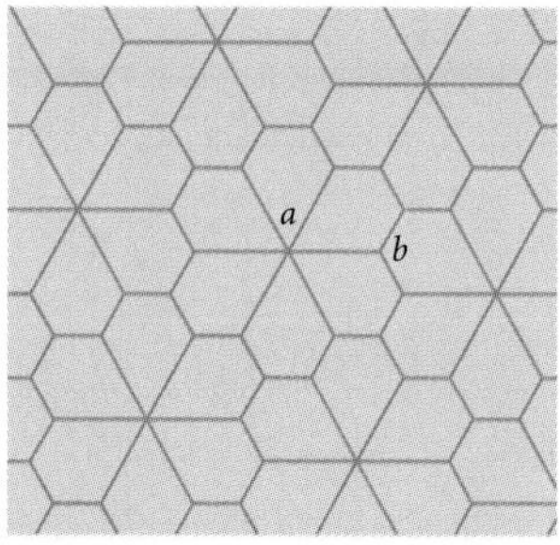

20. ***Construction*** An airplane is heading north at 900 km/hr. However, a 50 km/hr wind is blowing from the east. Use a ruler and a protractor to make a scale drawing of these vectors. Measure to find the approximate resultant velocity, both speed and direction (measured from north). ⓗ

Construction In Exercises 21–24, use the given segments and angles to construct each figure. Use either patty paper or a compass and a straightedge. The small letter above each segment represents the length of the segment.

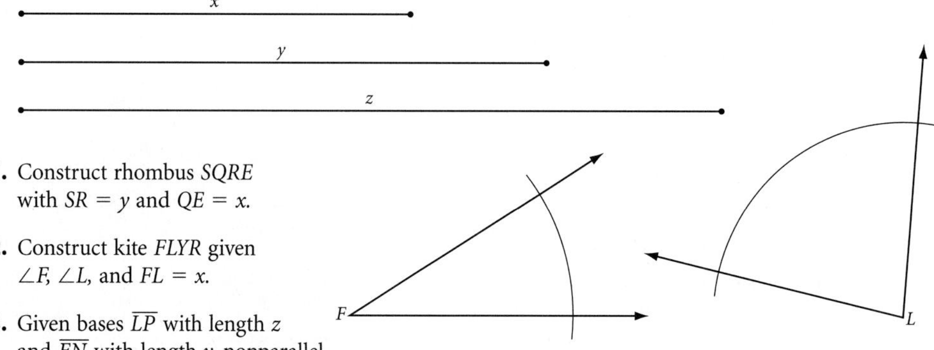

21. Construct rhombus $SQRE$ with $SR = y$ and $QE = x$.

22. Construct kite $FLYR$ given $\angle F$, $\angle L$, and $FL = x$.

23. Given bases $\overline{LP}$ with length z and $\overline{EN}$ with length y, nonparallel side $\overline{LN}$ with length x, and $\angle L$, construct trapezoid $PENL$. ⓗ

24. Given $\angle F$, $FR = x$, and $YD = z$, construct two trapezoids $FRYD$ that are not congruent to each other.

24. possible answers:

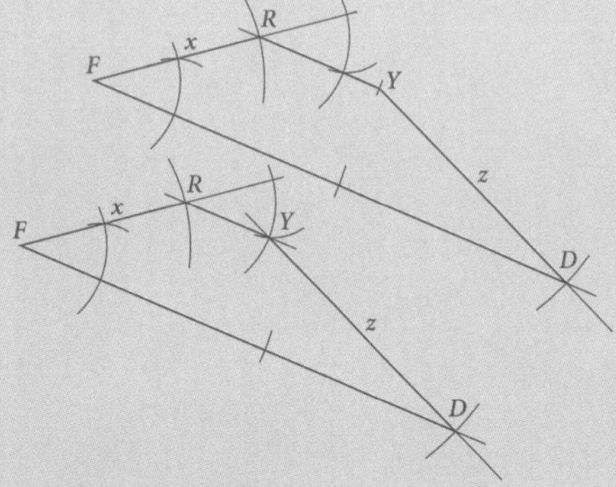

25. Three regular polygons meet at point B. Only four sides of the third polygon are visible. How many sides does this polygon have? 20 sides

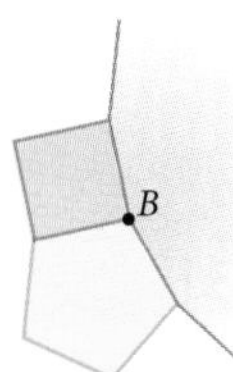

26. Find x. 12 cm

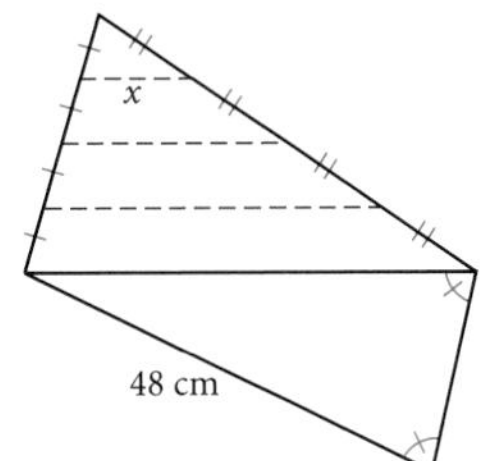

27. Prove the conjecture: The diagonals of a rhombus bisect the angles.

Given: Rhombus $DENI$, with diagonal $\overline{DN}$

Show: Diagonal $\overline{DN}$ bisects $\angle D$ and $\angle N$

Flowchart Proof

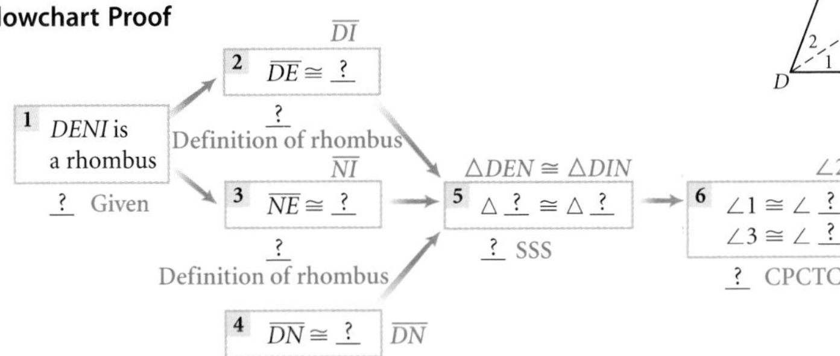

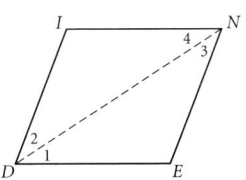

TAKE ANOTHER LOOK

1. Draw several polygons that have four or more sides. In each, draw all the diagonals from one vertex. Explain how the Polygon Sum Conjecture follows logically from the Triangle Sum Conjecture. Does the Polygon Sum Conjecture apply to concave polygons?

2. A triangle on a sphere can have three right angles. Can you find a "rectangle" with four right angles on a sphere? Investigate the Polygon Sum Conjecture on a sphere. Explain how it is related to the Triangle Sum Conjecture on a sphere. Be sure to test your conjecture on polygons with the smallest and largest possible angle measures.

The small, precise polygons in the painting, *Boy With Birds* (1953, oil on canvas), by American artist David C. Driskell (b 1931), give it a look of stained glass.

Take Another Look

1. This activity extends to general polygons the proof for quadrilaterals in Lesson 5.1. Sample answer: There are $n - 2$ triangles and for each triangle the sum of angle measures is 180°, so the total is $180°(n - 2)$. The proof, with adaptations in particular cases, holds for concave polygons.

2. It's not possible for a "rectangle" on a sphere to have four right angles, because the sum of the angles of any quadrilateral on a sphere is greater than 360°. The proof from activity 1 extends to the sphere, on which the sum of angle measures of each triangle is more than 180°. Sample answer: On a sphere, the sum of the angle measures of an n-sided polygon is greater than $180°(n - 2)$.

3. Arranging the angles about a point is one way of finding their sum. Because this arrangement forms a complete circle about the point, the sum of the angle measures is 360°.

4. In Lesson 5.2, students may have seen the generality of the Exterior Angle Sum Conjecture by imagining walking around the figure. In effect, the measure of an exterior angle on a concave side is 180° minus the measure of the interior angle and thus is negative. Other definitions of *exterior angle* are possible, so results may vary.

All the kite conjectures also hold for darts (if the diagonal joining the vertices is extended to intersect the diagonal lying outside the figure).

5. Because the sum of the angle measures at a vertex is still 360°, the same reasoning that applies in a plane shows that the exterior angle sum is less than 360°.

ASSESSING

Use either form of the chapter test, or substitute one or two Constructive Assessment Options for part of the test. If your students are struggling with proof, give them flowchart proofs to complete. If your students are comfortable with proof, ask them to do an entire proof.

FACILITATING SELF-ASSESSMENT

Discuss norms for group presentation and for equal participation by team members.

Choose topics, or give students a choice. Investigations, projects, explorations, Take Another Look activities, and even some Improving Your Skills puzzles can all be good topics.

3. Draw a polygon and one set of its exterior angles. Label the exterior angles. Cut out the exterior angles and arrange them all about a point. Explain how this activity demonstrates the Exterior Angle Sum Conjecture.

4. Is the Exterior Angle Sum Conjecture also true for concave polygons? Are the kite conjectures also true for darts (concave kites)? Choose your tools and investigate.

5. Investigate exterior angle sums for polygons on a sphere. Be sure to test polygons with the smallest and largest angle measures.

Assessing What You've Learned

GIVING A PRESENTATION

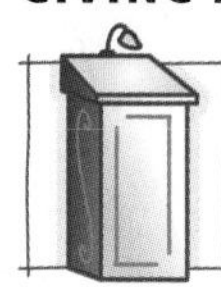

Giving a presentation is a powerful way to demonstrate your understanding of a topic. Presentation skills are also among the most useful skills you can develop in preparation for almost any career. The more practice you can get in school, the better.

Choose a topic to present to your class. There are a number of things you can do to make your presentation go smoothly.

- Work with a group. Make sure your group presentation involves all group members so that it's clear everyone contributed equally.
- Choose a topic that will be interesting to your audience.
- Prepare thoroughly. Make an outline of important points you plan to cover. Prepare visual aids—like posters, models, handouts, and overhead transparencies—ahead of time. Rehearse your presentation.
- Communicate clearly. Speak up loud and clear, and show your enthusiasm about your topic.

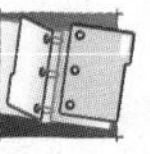

ORGANIZE YOUR NOTEBOOK Your conjecture list should be growing fast! Review your notebook to be sure it's complete and well organized. Write a one-page chapter summary.

WRITE IN YOUR JOURNAL Write an imaginary dialogue between your teacher and a parent or guardian about your performance and progress in geometry.

UPDATE YOUR PORTFOLIO Choose a piece that represents your best work from this chapter to add to your portfolio. Explain what it is and why you chose it.

PERFORMANCE ASSESSMENT While a classmate, a friend, a family member, or a teacher observes, carry out one of the investigations from this chapter. Explain what you're doing at each step, including how you arrived at the conjecture.

Give students pointers on public speaking:

- Don't try to memorize everything. Prepare an outline and visual aids.
- Rehearse your presentation in front of your group or family or with a tape recorder or video camera.
- Look at everyone in your audience. Don't hide behind your poster or projector.
- Most important, speak clearly and show your enthusiasm about your topic!

CHAPTER

6

Discovering and Proving Circle Properties

Overview

In this chapter students use geometry tools to explore relationships among the angles and line segments in and around circles, starting with properties of chords and central angles in **Lesson 6.1** and tangents in **Lesson 6.2.** Students discover relationships between central angles, inscribed angles, and certain polygons in **Lesson 6.3** and prove those conjectures in **Lesson 6.4.** Students find the coordinates of the circumcenter of a circle in **Using Your Algebra Skills 6.** The ratio of the circumference of a circle to the length of its diameter is explored in **Lesson 6.5,** and word problems involving that ratio are solved in **Lesson 6.6.** Arc lengths are calculated in **Lesson 6.7.** The Geometer's Sketchpad **exploration** at the end of the chapter introduces cycloids.

The Mathematics

Circles

The term *circle* has several meanings in English, including both the mathematical meaning and what we call a *disk* in mathematics (the circle and the interior of the circle). Even within mathematics, the terms *radius* and *diameter* have two meanings: as line segments and as the lengths of those line segments. Sometimes the word *circumference* is used to refer to the circle itself, but usually it means the distance around the circle.

The number known as π (pi) may be familiar to students, perhaps even as the ratio of circumference to diameter of any circle. But students are often under the misapprehension that it equals 3.14 or $\frac{22}{7}$, or on the other hand that it "can't be written exactly" or "is infinite." It can be written exactly, as π, but it can't be written exactly as a fraction or a finite decimal. This does not mean that the number itself is infinite, but rather that the exact decimal name would have infinitely many digits.

Besides exploring the constant ratio of circumference to diameter, this chapter includes ideas about chords, angles, arcs, and tangents. The conjecture that a radius is perpendicular to a chord if and only if it bisects the chord allows students to locate the center of a circle from one piece of it: They can find two chords and see where their perpendicular bisectors intersect. The most important conjecture about angles is that the measure of an inscribed angle is half that of the arc it intercepts; four logical implications of this conjecture appear in the book. Working with arc length and measure helps deepen students' understanding of ratios. Exploration of tangent lines and related segments allows students to see what happens when chords are extended and moved around toward a limiting case.

Significant Digits

Lesson 6.5 includes measurements used to approximate values of π, so the use of significant digits becomes important. In general, a result shouldn't be expressed using more significant digits than are in the contributing measurement with the fewest significant digits. For example, a student who measures the diameter of a circle as 12.3 might be tempted to use a calculator to multiply 12.3 times π and report the circumference as 38.64158964. Because the measurement 12.3 has only three significant digits, only three digits of the circumference are significant; it should be rounded to 38.6. It is important that the numbers not be rounded until the final step of a calculation.

Using This Chapter

As an alternative to a lesson-per-day schedule, you might have each group do the investigations for one of the first three lessons (with two groups dividing the investigations in Lesson 6.3) on one day and then share their results over the next one or two days. Return to completing one lesson a day with Lesson 6.4. The last lessons, on circumference and arc length, form a good base for problem solving in the chapters that follow. For any lesson with several investigations, you can jigsaw the groups; during Sharing as students present conjectures, the class can agree on the wording or propose alternative wordings.

If you don't get to this chapter in the first semester, you might want to begin the second semester with Chapter 7, return to Chapter 6, and then proceed to Chapter 8. When you are reviewing student work, keep in mind that constructions made from given parts have been reduced in the Teacher's Edition.

Cooperative Learning

As students become more comfortable working in groups, you might begin to have them take more responsibility for one another's understanding. The method of "numbered heads together" assigns each group member a whole number—from 1 to 4, for example, in a group of four. For Sharing, you randomly pick a number in the range (by spinner, random number generator, or die), and students with that number have the privilege of presenting their groups' ideas. You might give all members of each group bonus points depending on the performance of the selected group member, to encourage groups to be sure all their members understand the ideas.

Resources

Discovering Geometry Resources

Teaching and Worksheet Masters
Lessons 6.1, 6.3, 6.5, and 6.7

Sketchpad Demonstrations
Lessons 6.2 and 6.5

Discovering Geometry with The Geometer's Sketchpad
Lessons 6.1–6.3, 6.5

Assessment Resources A and B
Quiz 1 (Lessons 6.1 and 6.2)
Quiz 2 (Lessons 6.3 and 6.4)
Quiz 3 (Lessons 6.5–6.7)
Chapter 6 Test
Chapter 6 Constructive Assessment Options
Chapters 4–6 Exam

Practice Your Skills for Chapter 6

Condensed Lessons for Chapter 6

Other Resources

www.keypress.com/DG

Materials

- construction tools
- protractors
- calculators
- metersticks
- tape measures, or metersticks and string
- circular objects, *optional*
- geometry software, *optional*

Pacing Guide

	day 1	day 2	day 3	day 4	day 5	day 6	day 7	day 8	day 9	day 10
standard	6.1	6.2	quiz, 6.3	6.3	6.4	quiz, Algebra 6	6.5	6.6	6.7	quiz, review
enriched	6.1	6.2	quiz, 6.3	6.3	6.4	quiz, Algebra 6	6.5	6.6	6.7	quiz, Exploration
block	6.1, 6.2	quiz, 6.3	6.4, Algebra 6	quiz, 6.5	6.6	6.7, review	assessment, TAL	review	assessment	

	day 11	day 12	day 13	day 14	day 15	day 16	day 17	day 18	day 19	day 20
standard	project	review	assessment	review	assessment					
enriched	project	review	assessment, TAL	review, TAL	assessment, TAL					

CHAPTER 6

Discovering and Proving Circle Properties

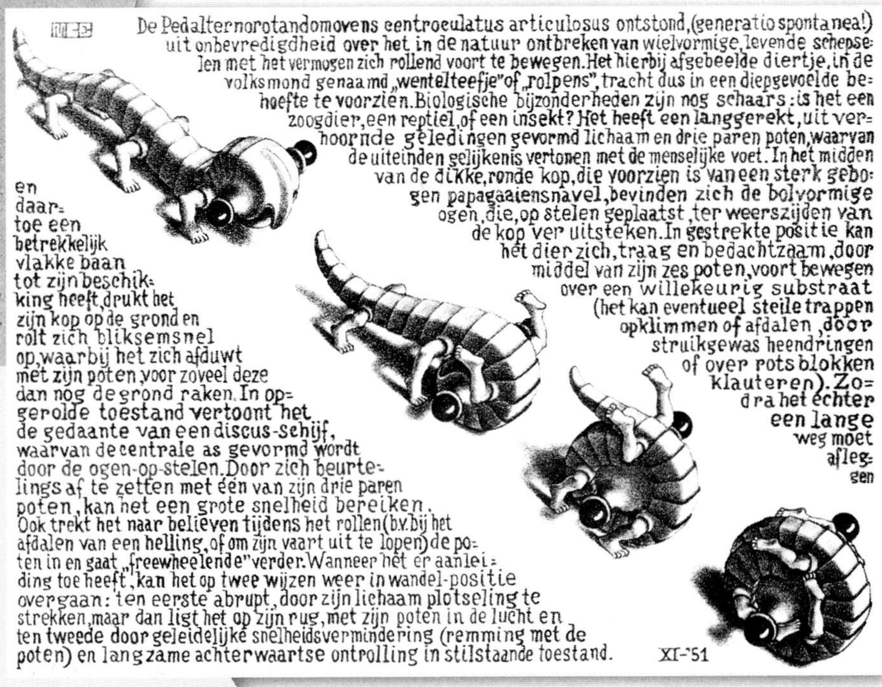

I am the only one who can judge how far I constantly remain below the quality I would like to attain.

M. C. ESCHER

Curl-Up, M. C. Escher, 1951
©2002 Cordon Art B. V.–Baarn–Holland.
All rights reserved.

OBJECTIVES

In this chapter you will

- learn relationships among chords, arcs, and angles
- discover properties of tangent lines
- learn how to calculate the length of an arc
- prove circle conjectures

CHAPTER 6 OBJECTIVES

- Discover properties of chords of circles
- Discover properties of tangents to a circle
- Explore common tangents and tangent circles
- Learn applications of tangents
- Discover relationships between the measure of an inscribed angle of a circle and the measure of its intercepted arc
- Understand π as the relationship between the circumference of a circle and its diameter
- Apply the formula for the circumference of a circle
- Discover and apply a formula for finding the length of an arc of a circle
- Practice visual thinking
- Learn new vocabulary
- Practice construction skills
- Increase cooperative learning skills

Escher uses the circle in his fanciful idea of a creature with its own built-in wheel transportation. The text (in Dutch) around the creature gives it a humorous Latin name: *pedalternorotandomovens* and a nickname, "rolpens." The text describes the creature as able to quickly travel a long, flat path by rolling up and pushing off with its three pairs of legs. The text describes two methods of stopping: fast by uncurling and slowly by braking with its feet. A circle is sometimes described as a "segment connected." In Escher's *Curl-Up*, a creature that starts out long like a line segment gradually becomes connected in a circle.

[Context] Use of the wheel and axle for transportation dates from 3500 B.C.E. in Mesopotamia; the potter's wheel was widely used by 2500 B.C.E. Other uses of the wheel and axle to transfer motion and multiply force include the winch, gears (first used in windmills and waterwheels), and belts.

LESSON
6.1

PLANNING

LESSON OUTLINE

One day:

25 min	Investigation
5 min	Sharing
5 min	Closing
10 min	Exercises

MATERIALS

- construction tools
- protractors
- Gear Fragment (W) for One step

TEACHING

In this lesson students discover some properties relating central angles, chords, and arcs of circles. Begin with the one-step investigation, or ask groups to work through Investigations 1–4.

The terms in the box were first introduced in Chapter 1. **[Language]** The word *chord* is used in music as well as mathematics; in both cases, it probably came from the word referring to a string of a musical instrument. The words *radius* and *diameter* can refer either to the line segments or to their length.

LESSON 6.1

Chord Properties

Learning by experience is good, but in the case of mushrooms and toadstools, hearsay evidence is better.
ANONYMOUS

Let's review some basic terms before you begin discovering the properties of circles. You should be able to identify the terms below.

Match the figures at the right with the terms at the left.

1. Congruent circles
2. Concentric circles
3. Radius
4. Chord
5. Diameter
6. Tangent
7. Minor arc
8. Major arc
9. Semicircle

A. $\overline{DC}$
B. $\overleftrightarrow{TG}$
C. $\overline{OE}$
D. $\overline{AB}$
E.
F.
G. $\overset{\frown}{RQ}$
H. $\overset{\frown}{PRQ}$
I. $\overset{\frown}{PQR}$

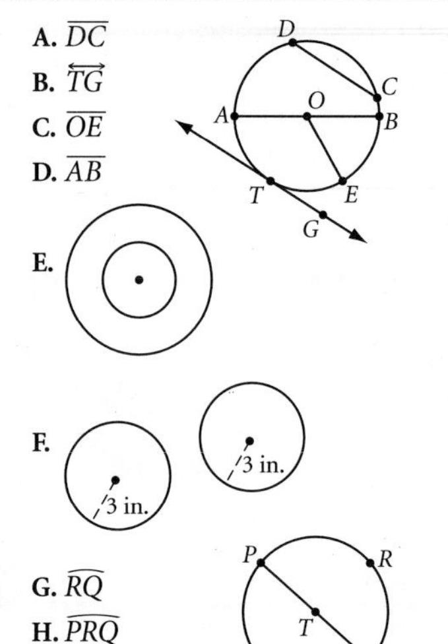

Check your answers: (1.F, 2.E, 3.C, 4.A, 5.D, 6.B, 7.G, 8.I, 9.H)

In addition to these terms, you will become familiar with two more, central angle and inscribed angle, in the next investigation.

Double Splash Evidence, part of modern California artist Gerrit Greve's *Water Series,* uses brushstrokes to produce an impression of concentric ripples in water.

Can you find parts of the water wheel that match the circle terms above?

LESSON OBJECTIVES

- Review basic properties of a circle
- Discover properties of chords of circles
- Practice construction skills

NCTM STANDARDS

	CONTENT		PROCESS
	Number		Problem Solving
	Algebra	✓	Reasoning
✓	Geometry	✓	Communication
✓	Measurement		Connections
	Data/Probability		Representation

Investigation 1
How Do We Define Angles in a Circle?

Look at the examples and non-examples for each term. Then write a definition for each. Discuss your definitions with others in your class. Agree on a common set of definitions and add them to your definition list. In your notebook, draw and label a picture to illustrate each definition.

Step 1 A central angle has its vertex at the center of the circle.

Step 1 Define *central angle.*

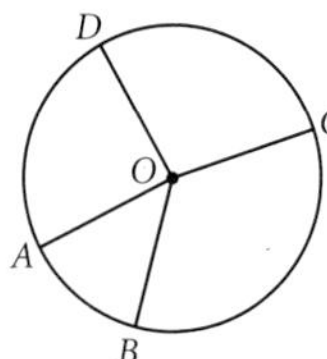

$\angle DOC$ intercepts arc $\widehat{DC}$. $\angle AOB$, $\angle BOC$, $\angle COD$, $\angle DOA$, and $\angle DOB$ are central angles of circle *O*.

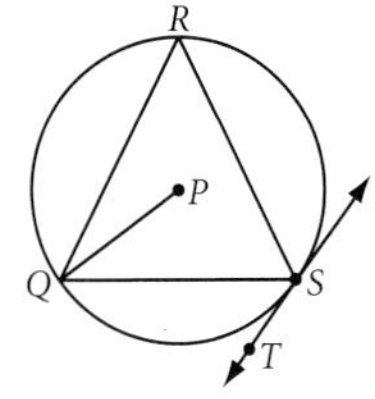

$\angle PQR$, $\angle PQS$, $\angle RST$, $\angle QST$, and $\angle QSR$ are not central angles of circle *P*.

Step 2 An inscribed angle has its vertex on the circle and its sides are chords.

Step 2 Define *inscribed angle.*

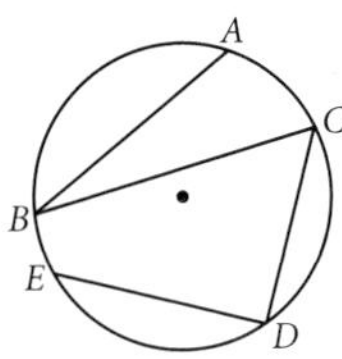

$\angle ABC$, $\angle BCD$, and $\angle CDE$ are inscribed angles. $\angle ABC$ is inscribed in $\widehat{ABC}$ and intercepts (or determines) $\widehat{AC}$.

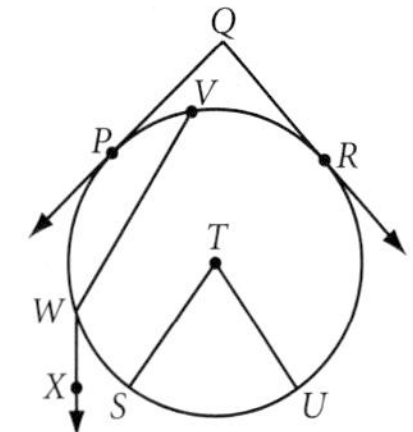

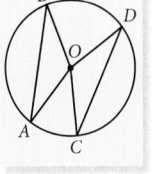

$\angle PQR$, $\angle STU$, and $\angle VWX$ are not inscribed angles.

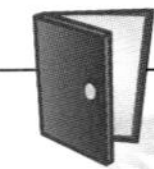

Investigation 2
Chords and Their Central Angles

You will need
- a compass
- a straightedge
- a protractor

Next you will discover some properties of chords and central angles. You will also see a relationship between chords and arcs.

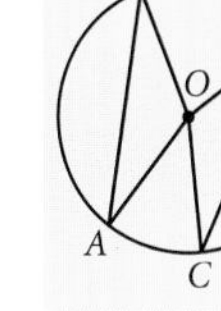

Step 1 Construct a large circle. Label the center *O*. Using your compass, construct two congruent chords in your circle. Label the chords $\overline{AB}$ and $\overline{CD}$, then construct radii $\overline{OA}$, $\overline{OB}$, $\overline{OC}$, and $\overline{OD}$.

Step 2 With your protractor, measure $\angle BOA$ and $\angle COD$. How do they compare? Share your results with others in your group. Then copy and complete the conjecture.

You can replace or extend Investigations 1 and 2 with the dynamic geometry exploration at www.keymath.com/DG.

Guiding Investigation 1

One step Hand out the Gear Fragment worksheet and pose this problem: "In repairing a machine, you find a fragment of a circular gear. To replace the gear, you need to know its diameter. How can you find the gear's diameter?" You may need to review the term *diameter* right away. As you circulate, wonder aloud as needed whether the center is somehow related to the chords of the circle, pointing out what you mean by *chord.*

Step 2 If groups are having difficulty defining *inscribed angle,* **[Ask]** "Where have you heard the word *inscribed* before?" [A triangle inscribed in a circle (whose center is the circumcenter of the triangle) has all three vertices on the circle, and its sides are chords of the circle. An inscribed triangle has three inscribed angles.]

Guiding Investigation 2

[Alert] If you find that all or most students in a group are using a central angle that measures 60° (because they didn't change the compass setting after drawing the circle), point out that they don't have enough information for good inductive reasoning; then have them all change their settings from the circle's radius and begin again.

[Alert] Students may have trouble constructing congruent chords. Challenge them to find the endpoints without using a ruler. They might mark two points on the circle and then use a constant compass opening to locate two other points on the circle the same distance apart.

Step 3 If their paper is too thick to see through when folded, students may want to copy their figure to patty paper.

If you notice confusion, **[Ask]** "Why do you subtract from 360 degrees?" [A circle has a measure of 360°.]

Students may find this investigation and the next two investigations fairly straightforward and begin writing conjectures without going through the steps or comparing results with others in their group. Remind them that the process is more important than the results. If students finish early you might challenge them with the one-step problem.

Chord Central Angles Conjecture C-54

If two chords in a circle are congruent, then they determine two central angles that are _?_. congruent

Step 3 Fold it so that $\overline{OD}$ coincides with $\overline{OB}$ and $\overline{OC}$ coincides with $\overline{OA}$.

Step 3 How can you fold your circle construction to check the conjecture?

As you learned in Chapter 1, the measure of an arc is defined as the measure of its central angle. For example, the central angle, $\angle BOA$ at right, has a measure of 40°, so $m\overset{\frown}{AB} = 40°$. The measure of a major arc is 360° minus the measure of the minor arc making up the remainder of the circle. For example, the measure of major arc $\overset{\frown}{BCA}$ is 360° − 40°, or 320°.

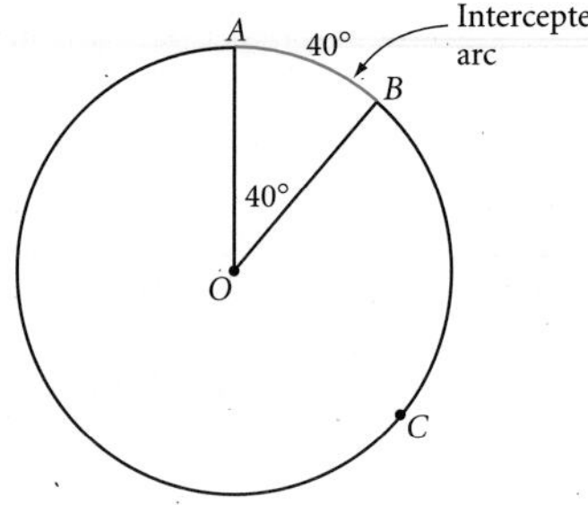

Your next conjecture follows from the Chord Central Angles Conjecture and the definition of arc measure.

Step 4 Two congruent chords in a circle determine two central angles that are congruent. If two central angles are congruent, their intercepted arcs must be congruent. Combine these two statements to complete the conjecture.

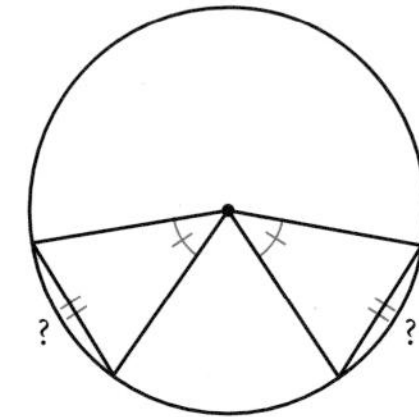

Chord Arcs Conjecture C-55

If two chords in a circle are congruent, then their _?_ are congruent. intercepted arcs

"Pull the cord?! Don't I need to construct it first?"

Investigation 3
Chords and the Center of the Circle

You will need

- a compass
- a straightedge

In this investigation, you will discover relationships about a chord and the center of its circle.

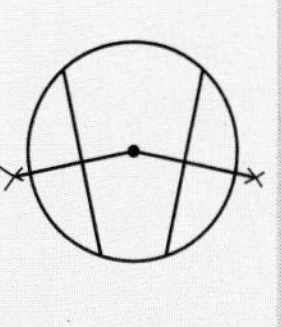

Step 1 On a sheet of paper, construct a large circle. Mark the center. Construct two nonparallel congruent chords. Then, construct the perpendiculars from the center to each chord.

Step 2 How does the perpendicular from the center of a circle to a chord divide the chord? Copy and complete the conjecture.

Perpendicular to a Chord Conjecture C-56

The perpendicular from the center of a circle to a chord is the __?__ of the chord. bisector

Let's continue this investigation to discover a relationship between the length of congruent chords and their distances from the center of the circle.

Step 3 With your compass, compare the distances (measured along the perpendicular) from the center to the chords. Are the results the same if you change the size of the circle and the length of the chords? State your observations as your next conjecture.

Chord Distance to Center Conjecture C-57

Two congruent chords in a circle are __?__ from the center of the circle. equidistant

Investigation 4
Perpendicular Bisector of a Chord

You will need

- a compass
- a straightedge

Next you will discover a property of perpendicular bisectors of chords.

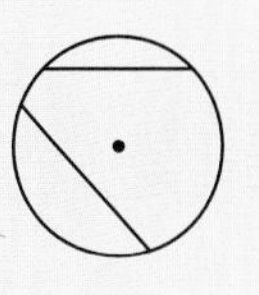

Step 1 On another sheet of paper, construct a large circle and mark the center. Construct two nonparallel chords that are not diameters. Then, construct the perpendicular bisector of each chord and extend the bisectors until they intersect.

Guiding Investigation 3

Step 1 Students can use the same two congruent chords and the same drawing for Investigations 2 and 3. **[Alert]** Students may need some review in how to construct perpendiculars. Using compass constructions to complete all four investigations may be too time-consuming, but this construction and the next can be completed quickly using patty-paper constructions. The perpendicular through the center of the circle to the chord can be folded.

Guiding Investigation 4

The perpendicular bisectors of the chords can be constructed by simply folding the chord in half. The Perpendicular Bisector of a Chord Conjecture is the converse of the Perpendicular to a Chord Conjecture.

SHARING IDEAS

As usual, for presentations select groups that have a variety of statements of the conjectures. As students present, encourage them to put the ideas in their own words, not just those of the conjectures as presented in the student book. Help the class reach consensus on the wording to record in their notebooks.

[Ask] "How would you define congruent arcs?" Although the measure of an arc was first defined in Chapter 1, some students may still be wondering why arcs are measured in degrees based on their central angle. Drawing a central angle of 90° may help some students relate the central angle to a quarter of a circle. But one source of difficulty may be a natural tendency to think that *measure* means "size" in some direct way, and the measure of an arc doesn't give its length. In fact, in different circles, arcs with the same

Sharing Ideas (continued)

measure can have very different lengths. Ask whether having the same measure is enough to make two arcs congruent, as is the case for line segments and angles. **[Ask]** "What's needed to ensure that two arcs have the same size and shape?" [Congruent arcs must be on the same or congruent circles.] (Some students may think that an arc of a larger circle will have the same size and shape as an arc of a smaller circle. To the extent possible, let other students convince them that the curvature will be different.)

[Ask] "Congruent chords are equidistant from the center. Can we say anything about distance from the center if one chord is longer than the other?" [In the same circle, shorter chords are farther from the center.]

Step 2 | What do you notice about the point of intersection? Compare your results with the results of others near you. Copy and complete the conjecture.

Perpendicular Bisector of a Chord Conjecture C-58

The perpendicular bisector of a chord _?_. passes through the center of the circle

With the perpendicular bisector of a chord, you can find the center of any circle, and therefore the vertex of the central angle to any arc. All you have to do is construct the perpendicular bisectors of nonparallel chords.

EXERCISES

You will need

Construction tools for Exercises **13–15, 17,** and **21**

Solve Exercises 1–7. State which conjecture or definition you used to support your conclusion.

1. $x =$ _?_

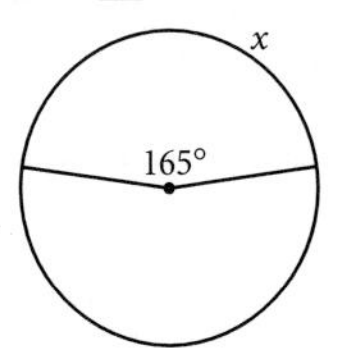

$x = 165°$, definition of measure of an arc

2. $z =$ _?_

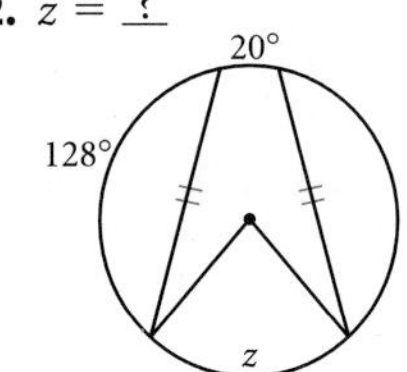

$z = 84°$, Chord Arcs Conj.

3. $w =$ _?_

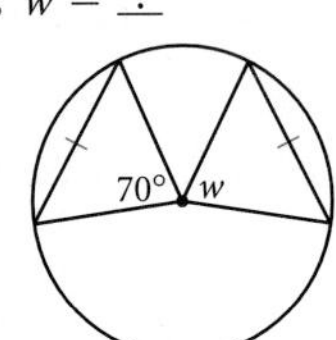

$w = 70°$, Chord Central Angles Conj.

4. $y =$ _?_ ⓗ

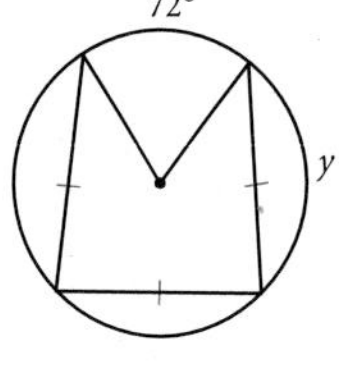

$y = 96°$, Chord Arcs Conj.

5. $AB = CD$
$PO = 8$ cm
$OQ =$ _?_

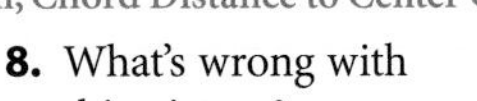

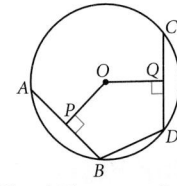

8 cm, Chord Distance to Center Conj.

6. $AB = 6$ cm $OP = 4$ cm
$CD = 8$ cm $OQ = 3$ cm
$BD = 6$ cm
What is the perimeter of $OPBDQ$?

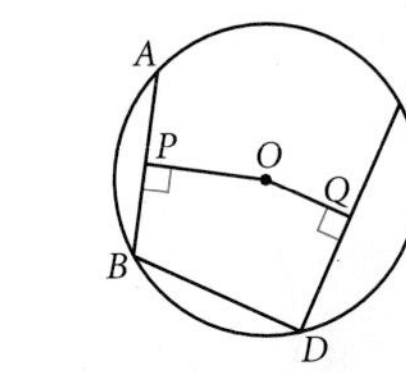

20 cm, Perpendicular to a Chord Conj.

7. $\overline{AB}$ is a diameter. Find $m\overarc{AC}$ and $m\angle B$.

$m\overarc{AC} = 68°$; $m\angle B = 34°$ (Since $\triangle OBC$ is isosceles, $m\angle B = m\angle C$, $m\angle B + m\angle C = 68°$, and therefore $m\angle B = 34°$.)

8. What's wrong with this picture?

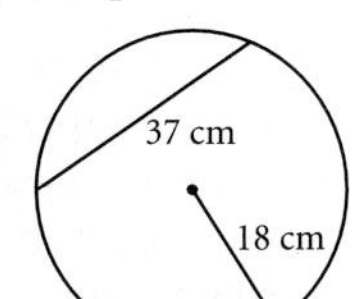

The length of the chord is greater than the length of the diameter.

9. What's wrong with this picture?

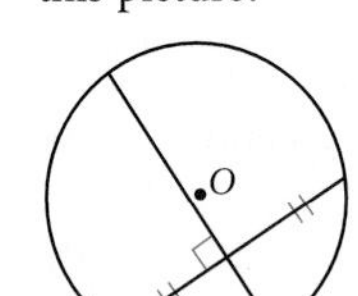

The perpendicular bisector of the segment does not pass through the center of the circle.

Assessing Progress
While watching students work and present, you can assess their understanding of *congruent circles, radius, diameter,* and *chord.* You can also check their skill at writing definitions from examples and counterexamples, transferring lengths with a compass, measuring angles with a protractor, chaining two if-then sentences into one if-and-only-if sentence, constructing perpendiculars to a line through a point, and constructing the perpendicular bisector of a segment. Also observe how well they are labeling their constructions and working with their groups.

Closing the Lesson

Summarize that the major conjectures of this lesson are about congruent chords of a circle: They determine congruent central angles, they intercept congruent arcs, and they are equidistant from the center. Another pair of conjectures about chords forms a biconditional: A line through the center of a circle is perpendicular to a chord if and only if it bisects the chord. If students are still shaky about these ideas, you might want to use one of Exercises 1–6 as an example.

BUILDING UNDERSTANDING

The exercises focus on applying the conjectures about chords. Encourage students to sketch pictures on their own papers. They can then mark and label all information accordingly.

ASSIGNING HOMEWORK

Essential	1–11, 14–17
Performance assessment	14, 15
Portfolio	16
Journal	10, 11, 13
Group	12, 18
Review	19–23

MATERIALS

- circular objects and patty paper (Exercise 14)
- Exercises 15 and 17 (T), *optional*

10. Draw a circle and two chords of unequal length. Which is closer to the center of the circle, the longer chord or the shorter chord? Explain.

11. Draw two circles with different radii. In each circle, draw a chord so that the chords have the same length. Draw the central angle determined by each chord. Which central angle is larger? Explain.

12. Polygon *MNOP* is a rectangle inscribed in a circle centered at the origin. Find the coordinates of points *M*, *N*, and *O*.
$M(-4, 3), N(-4, -3), O(4, -3)$

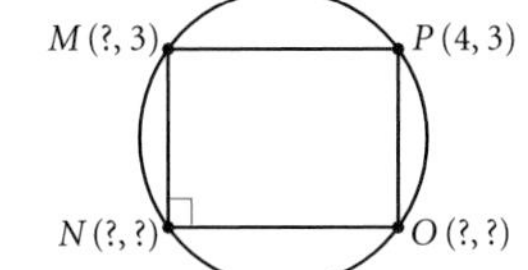

13. *Construction* Construct a triangle. Using the sides of the triangle as chords, construct a circle passing through all three vertices. Explain. Why does this seem familiar?

14. *Construction* Trace a circle onto a blank sheet of paper without using your compass. Locate the center of the circle using a compass and straightedge. Trace another circle onto patty paper and find the center by folding.

15. *Construction* Adventurer Dakota Davis digs up a piece of a circular ceramic plate. Suppose he believes that some ancient plates with this particular design have a diameter of 15 cm. He wants to calculate the diameter of the original plate to see if the piece he found is part of such a plate.

He has only this piece of the circular plate, shown at right, to make his calculations. Trace the outer edge of the plate onto a sheet of paper. Help him find the diameter.

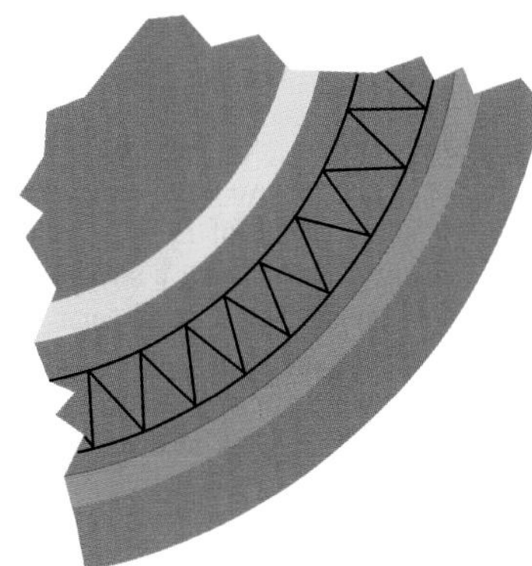

16. Complete the flowchart proof shown, which proves that if two chords of a circle are congruent, then they determine two congruent central angles.

Given: Circle *O* with chords $\overline{AB} \cong \overline{CD}$

Show: $\angle AOB \cong \angle COD$

Flowchart Proof

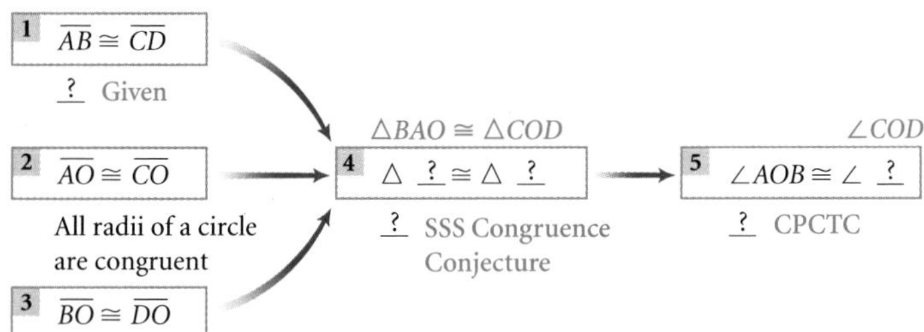

17. *Construction* The satellite photo at right shows only a portion of a lunar crater. How can cartographers use the photo to find its center? Trace the crater and locate its center. Using the scale shown, find its radius. To learn more about satellite photos, go to **www.keymath.com/DG** . They can draw two chords and locate the intersection of their perpendicular bisectors. The radius is just over 5 km.

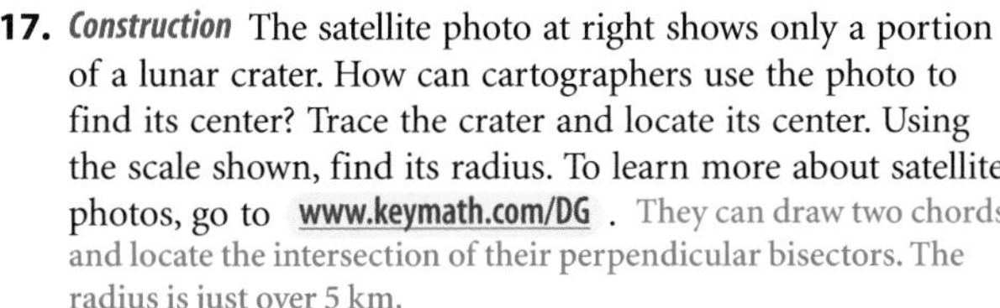

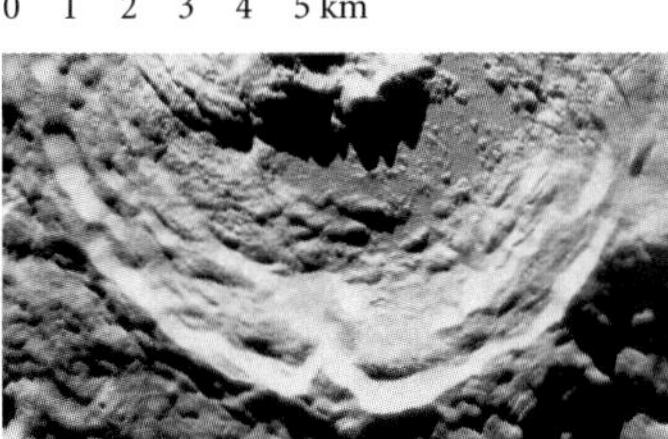

▶ Helping with the Exercises

Exercise 4 As needed, **[Ask]** "What do the measures of all the arcs add up to?" [360°]

Exercise 6 **[Alert]** Some students may neglect to add on the length *OQ*.

Exercise 9 If students are having difficulty, **[Ask]** "What does the perpendicular bisector have to go through?" [the center of the circle]

10. The longer chord is closer to the center; the longest chord, which is the diameter, passes through the center.

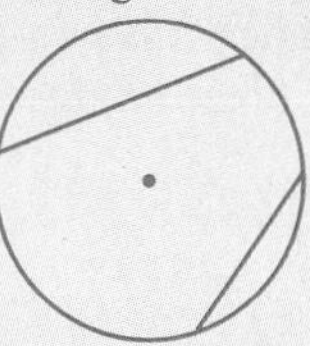

11. The central angle of the smaller circle is larger, because the chord is closer to the center.

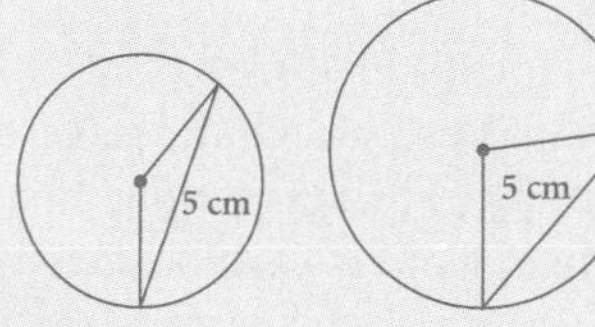

Exercise 13 As needed, remind students of the meaning of a triangle inscribed in a circle (or a circle circumscribed around a triangle).

13. The center of the circle is the circumcenter of the triangle. Possible construction:

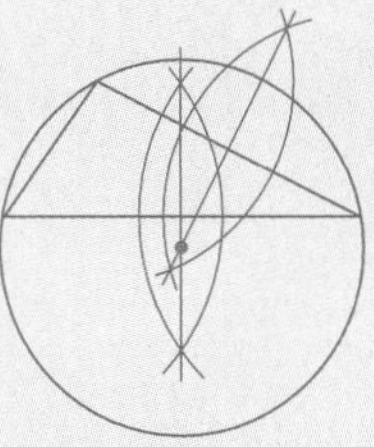

Exercise 14 Have available round objects larger than coins for tracing.

14. possible construction:

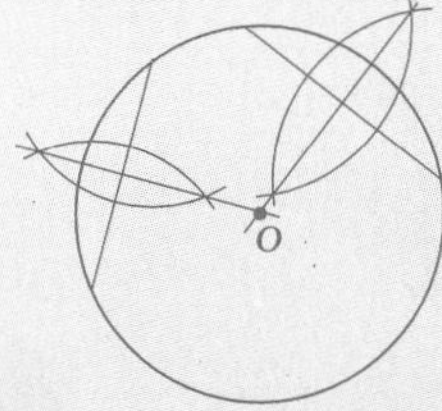

Exercises 14–16 If students are having difficulty, wonder aloud whether there's a conjecture that ends with something about the center of a circle. [Perpendicular Bisector of a Chord]

15. ≈ 13.8 cm

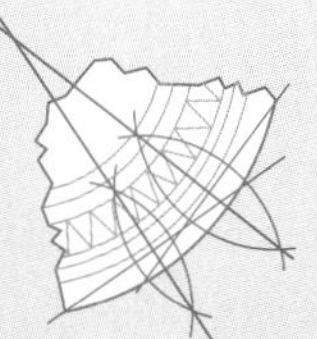

Exercise 20 You might want to advise students that in complicated diagrams it sometimes helps to construct auxiliary lines to make triangles.

Exercise 23 As needed, suggest that students consider the number of possible triangles with right angles at corners of the grid, at the middle of sides, and in the middle. [Four distinct triangles have right angles at each corner (16), 5 triangles (including one tilted) have right angles at the middle dot on each side (20), and 8 triangles (four tilted) have right angles at the middle dot. The total, 44, is divided by the number of ways of choosing three dots from the nine dots, which is $\frac{9(8)(7)}{1(2)(3)} = 84$.]

EXTENSIONS

A. Have students use geometry software to confirm one of the chord conjectures.

B. Ask students to explain why the perpendicular bisector of a chord passes through the center of the circle. [The reasoning here is subtle. This claim differs from the last three conjectures of the lesson, in which the line is assumed to go through the circle's center. If a line is drawn from the center of the circle to the midpoint of the chord, then it must be perpendicular to the chord, so it coincides with the given perpendicular bisector, forcing the latter to go through the circle's center.]

18. Circle O has center (0, 0) and passes through points $A(3, 4)$ and $B(4, -3)$. Find an equation to show that the perpendicular bisector of $\overline{AB}$ passes through the center of the circle. Explain your reasoning. ⓗ $y = \frac{1}{7}x$; (0, 0) is a point on this line.

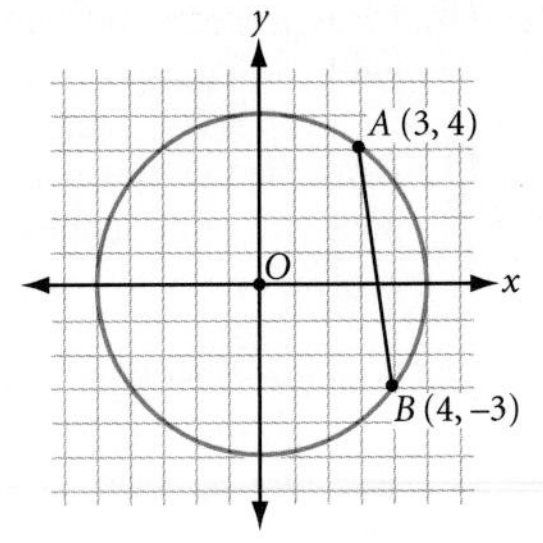

Review

Chapter 5 **19.** Identify each quadrilateral from the given characteristics.

a. Diagonals are perpendicular and bisect each other. rhombus

b. Diagonals are congruent and bisect each other, but it is not a square. rectangle

c. Only one diagonal is the perpendicular bisector of the other diagonal. kite

d. Diagonals bisect each other. parallelogram

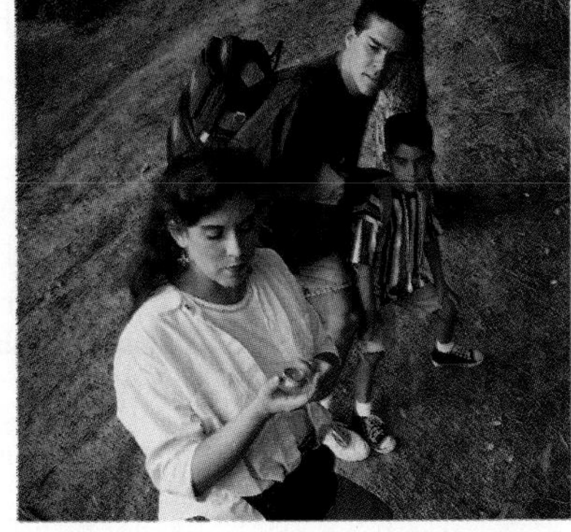

4.4 **20.** A family hikes from their camp on a bearing of 15°. (A **bearing** is an angle measured clockwise from the north, so a bearing of 15° is 15° east of north.) They hike 6 km and then stop for a swim in a lake. Then they continue their hike on a new bearing of 117°. After another 9 km, they meet their friends. What is the measure of the angle between the path they took to arrive at the lake and the path they took to leave the lake? ⓗ 78°

4.4 **21.** ***Construction*** Use a protractor and a centimeter ruler to make a careful drawing of the route the family in Exercise 20 traveled to meet their friends. Let 1 cm represent 1 km. To the nearest tenth of a kilometer, how far are they from their first camp? 9.7 km

4.2 **22.** Explain why x equals y. $x + 55° + 55° = 180°$ and $40° + y + y = 180°$, so $x = y = 70°$

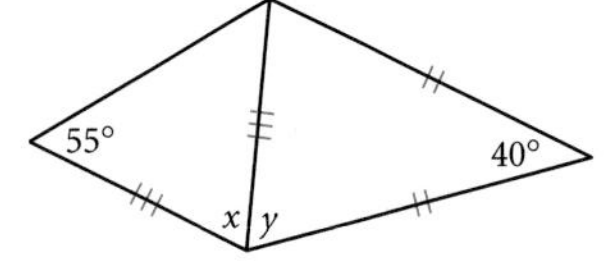

23. What is the probability of randomly selecting three points from the 3-by-3 grid below that form the vertices of a right triangle? $\frac{11}{21}$

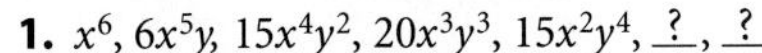

IMPROVING YOUR ALGEBRA SKILLS

Algebraic Sequences II

Find the next two terms of each algebraic pattern.

1. $x^6, 6x^5y, 15x^4y^2, 20x^3y^3, 15x^2y^4,$? , ?
2. $x^7, 7x^6y, 21x^5y^2, 35x^4y^3, 35x^3y^4, 21x^2y^5,$? , ?
3. $x^8, 8x^7y, 28x^6y^2, 56x^5y^3, 70x^4y^4, 56x^3y^5, 28x^2y^6,$? , ?

IMPROVING ALGEBRA SKILLS

These terms occur in expansions of $(x + y)^n$ for $n = 6, 7,$ and 8, respectively. Students who are familiar with Pascal's triangle can see the pattern in the coefficients. The exponents move up or down by 1 in each subsequent term. Or students might find a missing exponent by symmetry. Or they might see a different pattern: To calculate the kth term in a sequence, they multiply the coefficient and first exponent of the previous term and divide by $k - 1$. For example, the sixth term of the first sequence has coefficient $\frac{(15)(2)}{5} = 6$.

1. $6xy^5, y^6$
2. $7xy^6, y^7$
3. $8xy^7, y^8$

LESSON 6.2

Tangent Properties

We are, all of us, alone
Though not uncommon
In our singularity.
Touching,
We become tangent to
Circles of common experience,
Co-incident,
Defining in collective tangency
Circles
Reciprocal in their subtle
Redefinition of us.
In tangency
We are never less alone,
But no longer
Only.
GENE MATTINGLY

Each wheel of a train theoretically touches only one point on the rail. Rails act as tangent lines to the wheels of a train. Each point where the rail and the wheel meet is a point of tangency. Why can't a train wheel touch more than one point at a time on the rail? Can a car wheel touch more than one point at a time on the road?

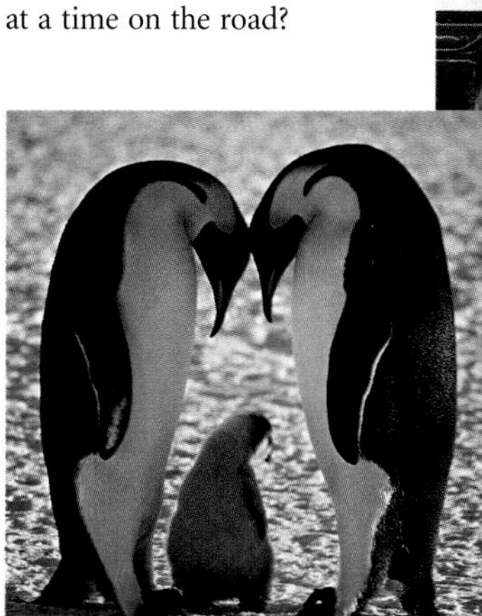

The rail is tangent to the wheels of the train.
The penguins' heads are tangent to each other.

Investigation 1
Going Off on a Tangent

You will need

- a compass
- a straightedge

In this investigation, you will discover the relationship between a tangent line and the radius drawn to the point of tangency.

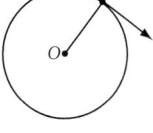

Step 1 Construct a large circle. Label the center O.

Step 2 Using your straightedge, draw a line that appears to touch the circle at only one point. Label the point T. Construct $\overline{OT}$.

Step 3 Use your protractor to measure the angles at T. What can you conclude about the radius $\overline{OT}$ and the tangent line at T?

Step 4 Share your results with your group. Then copy and complete the conjecture.

Tangent Conjecture C-59

A tangent to a circle __?__ the radius drawn to the point of tangency.
is perpendicular to

LESSON 6.2

PLANNING

LESSON OUTLINE

One day:

25 min	Investigation
10 min	Sharing
5 min	Closing
5 min	Exercises

MATERIALS

- construction tools
- protractors
- Intersecting Secants (T) for One step
- geometry software, *optional*
- Sketchpad demonstration Tangent Segments, *optional*

TEACHING

In this lesson students discover two conjectures about tangent lines to a circle. Make sure students realize a tangent has exactly one point in common with a circle.

An inflated car wheel does touch the road at more than one point. But a perfectly round steel train wheel is closer to touching the track at only one point.

Guiding Investigation 1

The one-step investigation is on page 314. As students begin the steps of the investigation, remind them that they need to complete each investigation before writing their conjecture, even if the conjecture may seem obvious.

Step 2 If necessary, note that the instructions say "draw" rather than "construct." Students can draw the tangent line by sliding the ruler toward the circle until it appears that the ruler is touching the circle at just one point.

NCTM STANDARDS

CONTENT		PROCESS	
	Number	✓	Problem Solving
✓	Algebra	✓	Reasoning
✓	Geometry	✓	Communication
✓	Measurement	✓	Connections
	Data/Probability		Representation

LESSON OBJECTIVES

- Discover properties of tangents to a circle
- Explore common tangents and tangent circles
- Learn applications of tangents
- Learn new vocabulary
- Practice construction skills

[Alert] If students' tangent lines appear to touch the circle in several spots, ask them to redraw the line to touch only one point.

One step Show the Intersecting Secants transparency or the Sketchpad demonstration and pose this problem: "Draw two nonparallel but congruent chords in a circle. Then extend them until they meet outside the circle. Keep the point of intersection fixed, and move the original chords away from the center of the circle but keep them congruent. What do you think happens as the chords get shorter and shorter? What happens to the perpendicular bisectors of the chords?" As you circulate, start referring to the extensions of the chords as *secants.* During Sharing, bring out the ideas that the secant segments were congruent and turned into congruent tangent segments and that the radii that were perpendicular bisectors of the chords become perpendicular to the tangent segments at the point of tangency.

MAKING THE CONNECTION

If students have trouble understanding how a satellite stays in orbit, you might explain that the satellite is being pulled by gravity toward the earth in a direction perpendicular to the direction of its velocity, and when the two forces are added the resultant force moves the satellite in a circle.

Tangential Velocity
Discuss the book's description of tangential velocity just enough for students to have an intuitive understanding of it and to see an application of tangent lines.

Guiding Investigation 2

Step 3 To draw the tangent segments, students can line up their ruler to pass through the exterior point and then rotate the ruler about that point until it just touches the circle.

Technology CONNECTION

A series of rockets burning chemical fuels provide the thrust to launch satellites into orbit. Once the satellite reaches its proper orientation in space, it provides its own power for the duration of its mission, sometimes staying in space for five to ten years with the help of solar energy and a battery backup. At right is the Mir space station and the space shuttle *Atlantis* in orbit in 1995. According to the United States Space Command, there are over 8,000 objects larger than a softball circling Earth at speeds of over 18,000 miles per hour! If gravity were suddenly "turned off" somehow, these objects would travel off into space on a straight line tangent to their orbits, and not continue in a curved path.

The Tangent Conjecture has important applications related to circular motion. For example, a satellite maintains its velocity in a direction tangent to its circular orbit. This velocity vector is perpendicular to the force of gravity, which keeps the satellite in orbit.

Investigation 2
Tangent Segments

You will need
- a compass
- a straightedge

In this investigation, you will discover something about the lengths of segments tangent to a circle from a point outside the circle.

Step 1 Construct a circle. Label the center E.

Step 2 Choose a point outside the circle and label it N.

Step 3 Draw two lines through point N tangent to the circle. Mark the points where these lines appear to touch the circle and label them A and G.

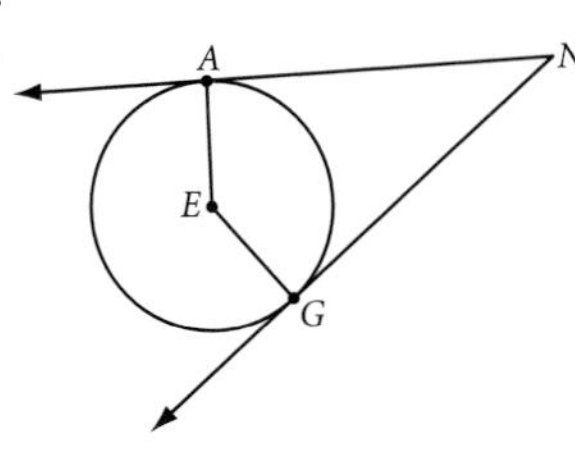

Step 4 Use your compass to compare segments NA and NG. These segments are called **tangent segments.**

Step 5 Share your results with your group. Copy and complete the conjecture.

Tangent Segments Conjecture C-60

Tangent segments to a circle from a point outside the circle are __?__. congruent

To show another approach, put an angle on a transparency and move it up to a circle so that each side of the angle touches the circle in one point. Compare the lengths of the tangent segments. Repeat with one or more different angles.

SHARING IDEAS

As students share whatever variety of conjectures they came up with, some may refer to 90° angles rather than perpendicular lines. As you lead the discussion to agree on wording, encourage the expansion of their vocabularies to include the word *perpendicular.* In the discussion of the Tangent Segments Conjecture, try to raise the question of how a tangent line, which extends indefinitely, can have a length. Your goal is to help students see that the conjecture refers to tangent segments, not lines.

Many students conjecture that if a spinning object is suddenly released, its path will be a spiral, not straight along a tangent line. In preparation for Exercise 6, you might give a demonstration suitable to your space. Be aware that students tend to see

Tangent circles are two circles that are tangent to the same line at the same point. They can be **internally tangent** or **externally tangent,** as shown.

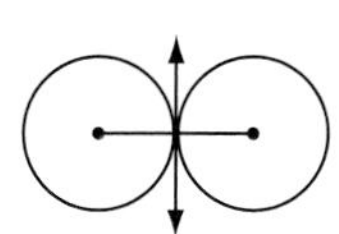
Externally tangent circles

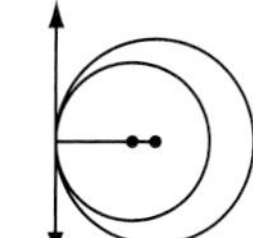
Internally tangent circles

EXERCISES

You will need

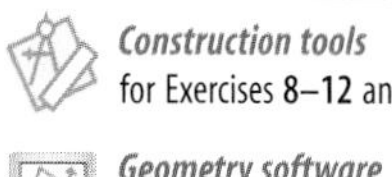
Construction tools for Exercises 8–12 and 15

Geometry software for Exercises 13 and 26

1. Rays m and n are tangent to circle P. $w = \underline{?}$ ⓗ 50°

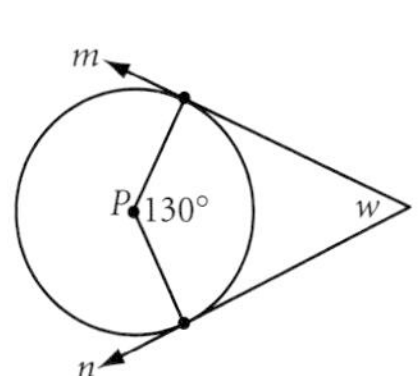
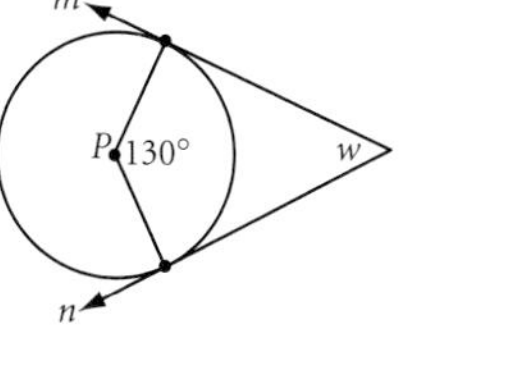

2. Rays r and s are tangent to circle Q. $x = \underline{?}$ ⓗ 55°

3. Ray k is tangent to circle R. $y = \underline{?}$ 30°

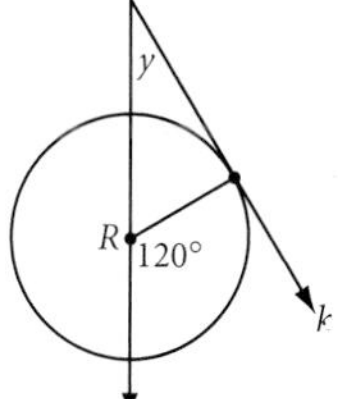

4. Line t is tangent to both circles. $z = \underline{?}$ 105°

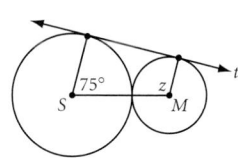

5. Quadrilateral $POST$ is circumscribed about circle Y. $OR = 13$ and $ST = 12$. What is the perimeter of $POST$? ⓗ 76

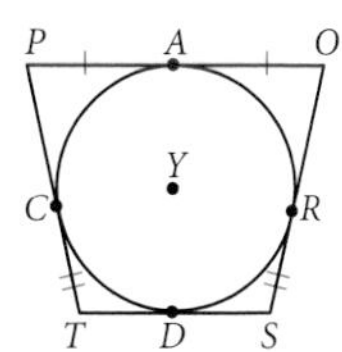

6. Pam participates in the hammer-throw event. She swings a 16 lb ball at arm's length, about eye-level. Then she releases the ball at the precise moment when the ball will travel in a straight line toward the target area. Draw an overhead view that shows the ball's circular path, her arms at the moment she releases it, and the ball's straight path toward the target area.

7. Explain how you could use only a T-square, like the one shown, to find the center of a Frisbee. Possible answer: The perpendicular to the tangent passes through the center of the circle. Use the T-square to find two diameters of the Frisbee. The intersection of these two lines is the center.

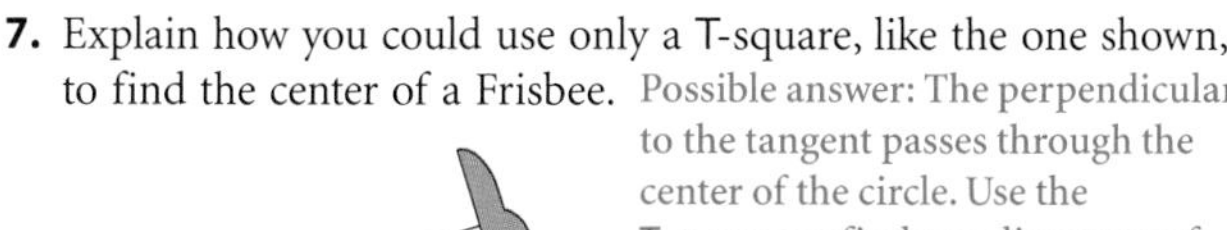

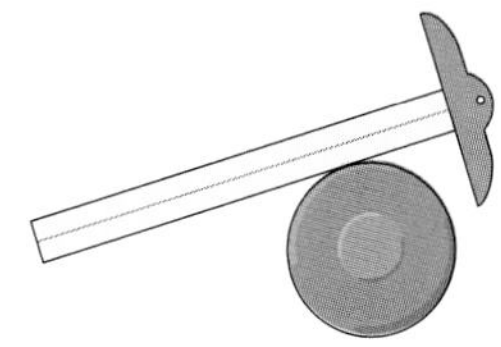

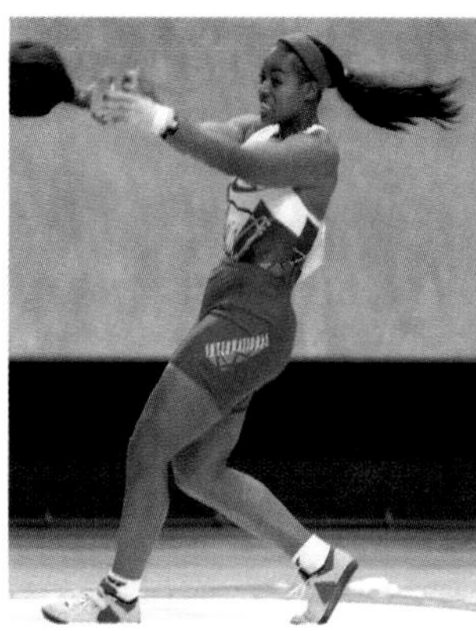
Pam Dukes competes in the hammer-throw event.

Sharing Ideas (continued)

what they expect to see rather than what you want them to see!

[Ask] "How would you construct a tangent line through a point on a circle?" [Help students see that guessing isn't sufficient for a construction; they need to construct a radius to that point and then a line perpendicular to the radius.]

If you have time, **[Ask]** "How would you construct a tangent line through a point outside a circle?" (They drew these rather than constructing them in the investigations.) The ensuing conversation should produce the idea that the conjectures won't help with this construction because the relevant radii aren't known. Plan to return to this topic after consideration of angles inscribed in semicircles in Lesson 6.3.

Assessing Progress

You can assess students' understanding of (and use of the vocabulary for) *tangent line, tangent segment, radius,* and *perpendicular,* and their skill at constructing a circle, measuring an angle with a protractor, and comparing segments with a compass. You might also see how well they understand the difference between drawing and constructing.

Closing the Lesson

The main points of this lesson are that every line tangent to a circle is perpendicular to the radius at the point of tangency and that the two tangent segments from a point outside the circle are congruent. If you think students need more help, you might work through Exercise 5 together.

ASSIGNING HOMEWORK

Essential	1–6, 8, 9, 17–19
Performance assessment	16
Portfolio	6, 12
Journal	7
Group	10–15
Review	20–26

Helping with the Exercises

Exercise 1 **[Ask]** "Do we know any other angle measurements, or something about the sum of the measures of the interior angles of a quadrilateral?" [There are two right angles, and the sum is 360°.]

Exercise 2 As needed, **[Ask]** "Don't we know something about a triangle with two congruent sides?" [It's isosceles, and the base angles are congruent.]

6. See page 316.

BUILDING UNDERSTANDING

Students practice working with tangent lines to a circle.

Exercise 4 **[Ask]** "How is t related to the radii?" [perpendicular]

Exercise 5 Suggest as necessary that students begin with the given information and work their way around the polygon. Students who refuse to believe that $\overline{DT} \cong \overline{DS}$ "just because they look equal" are doing good thinking; it's the facts that $\overline{DS} \cong \overline{RS}$, $\overline{DT} \cong \overline{CT}$, and $\overline{RS} \cong \overline{CT}$ that make $\overline{DT} \cong \overline{DS}$.

Exercise 6 When viewed from the side, the ball's path is actually a parabola, but the overhead view shows a tangent line.

6. possible answer:

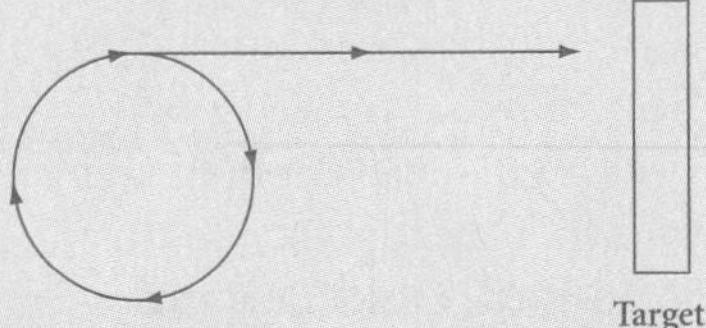

8. Construct $\overrightarrow{OT}$. Construct a line through point T perpendicular to $\overrightarrow{OT}$.

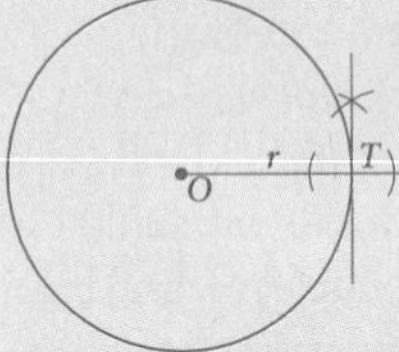

9. Construct $\overrightarrow{OX}$, $\overrightarrow{OY}$, and $\overrightarrow{OZ}$. Construct tangents through points X, Y, and Z.

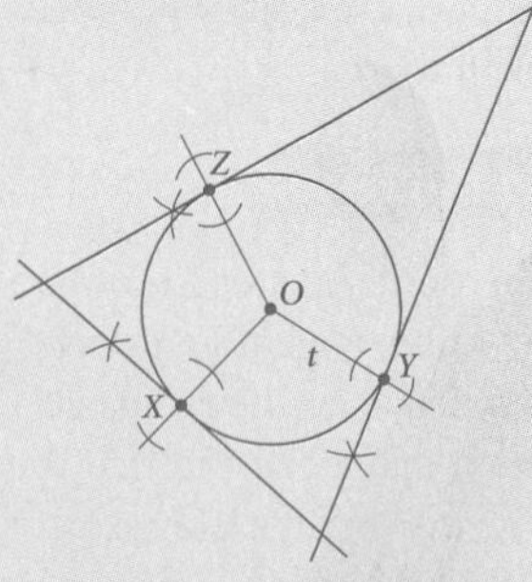

Exercises 10–12 You may need to suggest that students sketch the circles and look for how they might find the center of the unknown circle from the information given.

Construction For Exercises 8–12, first make a sketch of what you are trying to construct and label it. Then use the segments below, with lengths r, s, and t.

r ——— s ——— t ———

8. Construct a circle with radius r. Mark a point on the circle. Construct a tangent through this point. ⓗ

9. Construct a circle with radius t. Choose three points on the circle that divide it into three minor arcs and label points X, Y, and Z. Construct a triangle that is circumscribed about the circle and tangent at points X, Y, and Z.

10. Construct two congruent, externally tangent circles with radius s. Then construct a third circle that is both congruent and externally tangent to the two circles.

11. Construct two internally tangent circles with radii r and t.

12. Construct a third circle with radius s that is externally tangent to both the circles you constructed in Exercise 11.

13. ***Technology*** Use geometry software to construct a circle. Label three points on the circle and construct tangents through them. Drag the three points and write your observations about where the tangent lines intersect and the figures they form.

14. Find real-world examples (different from the examples shown below) of two internally tangent circles and of two externally tangent circles. Either sketch the examples or make photocopies from a book or a magazine for your notebook.

The teeth in the gears shown extend from circles that are externally tangent.

This astronomical clock in Prague, Czech Republic, has one pair of internally tangent circles. What other circle relationships can you find in the clock photo?

15. ***Construction*** In Taoist philosophy, all things are governed by one of two natural principles, yin and yang. Yin represents the earth, characterized by darkness, cold, or wetness. Yang represents the heavens, characterized by light, heat, or dryness. The two principles, when balanced, combine to produce the harmony of nature. The symbol for the balance of yin and yang is shown at right. Construct the yin-and-yang symbol. Start with one large circle. Then construct two circles with half the diameter that are internally tangent to the large circle and externally tangent to each other. Finally, construct small circles that are concentric to the two inside circles. Shade or color your construction. ⓗ

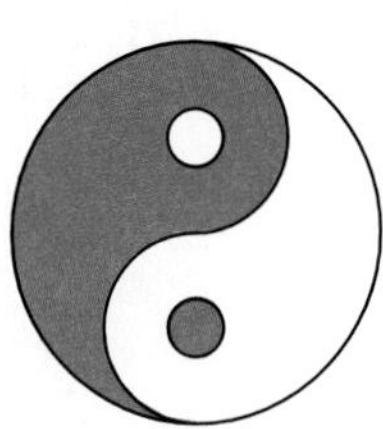

Constructions will vary.

10. Construct tangent circles M and N. Construct equilateral $\triangle MNP$. Construct circle P with radius s.

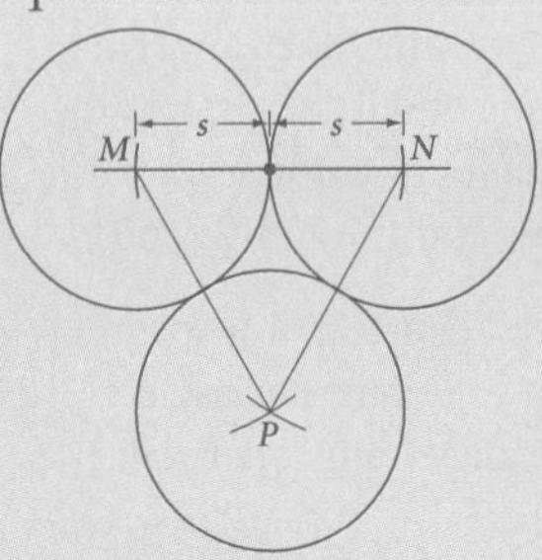

11. Construct a line and label a point T on it. On the line, mark off two points, L and M, each on the same side of T at distances r and t from T, respectively. Construct circle L with radius r. Construct circle M with radius t.

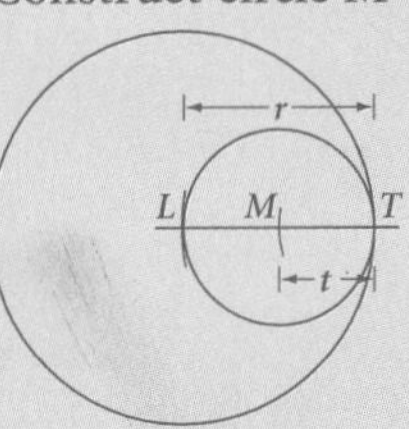

16. A satellite in geostationary orbit remains above the same point on the earth's surface even as the earth turns. If such a satellite has a 30° view of the equator of the earth, what percentage of the equator is observable from the satellite? ⓗ

$360° - 30° - 90° - 90° = 150°$

and $\frac{150°}{360°} = 41.\overline{6}\%$

17. Circle P is centered at the origin. $\overleftrightarrow{AT}$ is tangent to circle P at $A(8, 15)$. Find the equation of $\overleftrightarrow{AT}$. $y = -\frac{8}{15}x + \frac{289}{15}$

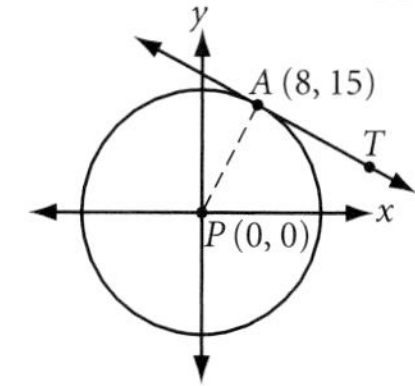

18. $\overrightarrow{PA}$ is tangent to circle Q. The line containing chord $\overline{CB}$ passes through P. Find $m\angle P$. 45°

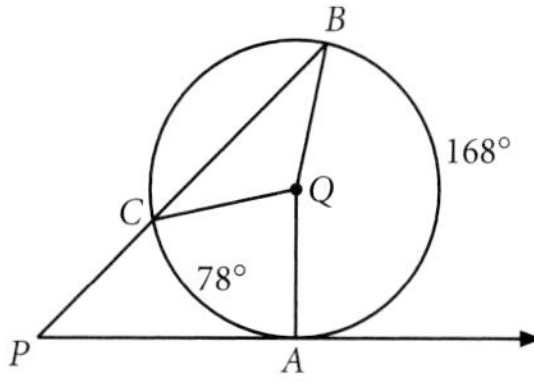

19. $\overrightarrow{TA}$ and $\overrightarrow{TB}$ are tangent to circle O. What's wrong with this picture? Angles A and B must be right angles, but this would make the sum of the angle measures in the quadrilateral shown greater than 360°.

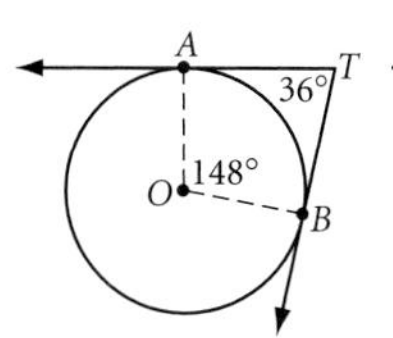

Review

6.1 **20.** Circle U passes through points $(3, 11)$, $(11, -1)$, and $(-14, 4)$. Find the coordinates of its center. Explain your method.

6.1 **21.** Complete the flowchart proof or write a paragraph proof of the Perpendicular to a Chord Conjecture: The perpendicular from the center of a circle to a chord is the bisector of the chord.

Given: Circle O with chord $\overline{CD}$, radii $\overline{OC}$ and $\overline{OD}$, and $\overline{OR} \perp \overline{CD}$

Show: $\overline{OR}$ bisects $\overline{CD}$

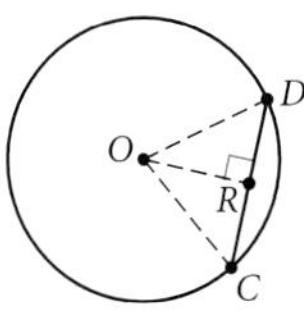

Flowchart Proof

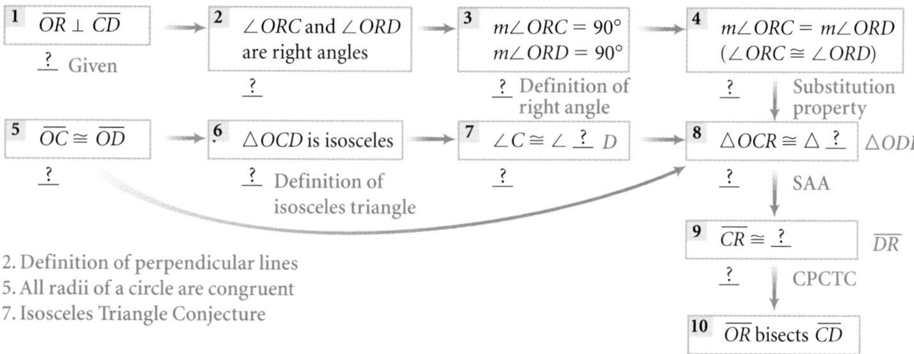

2. Definition of perpendicular lines
5. All radii of a circle are congruent
7. Isosceles Triangle Conjecture

12. Start with the construction from Exercise 11. On line $\overleftrightarrow{LM}$, mark off length TK so that $TK = s$ and K is on the opposite side of T from L and M. Construct circle K with radius s.

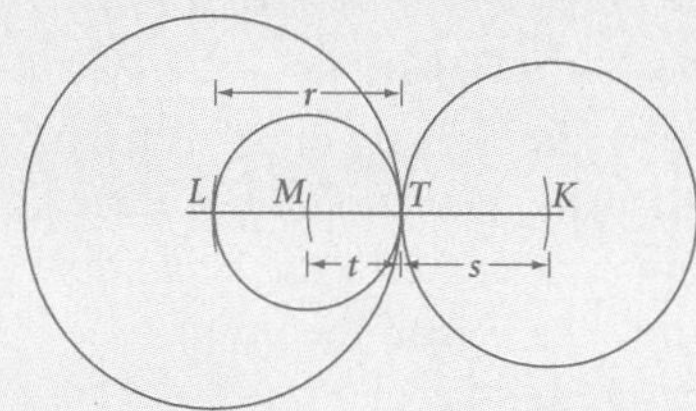

13. Sample answer: If the three points do not lie on the same semicircle, the tangents form a circumscribed triangle. If the points lie on the same semicircle, they form a triangle outside the circle, with one side touching (called an *exscribed triangle*).

Exercise 14 Sample answers include tangent spheres whose great circles through the point of tangency are tangent.

14. Sample answer: Internally tangent: wheels on a roller-coaster car in a loop, one bubble inside another. Externally tangent: touching coins, a snowman, a computer mouse ball and its roller balls.

Exercise 15 Students may need a reminder of what concentric circles are. Students may make intricate yin-and-yang designs that you might display on a bulletin board.

Exercise 16 As needed, wonder aloud if the view from a satellite relates to tangent lines of the circular earth.

20. $(-2, -1)$; Possible method: Plot the three points. Construct the midpoint and the perpendicular bisector of the segments connecting two different pairs of points. The center is the point of intersection of the two lines. To check, construct the circle through the three given points.

22a. If the diagonals were perpendicular bisectors of each other, it would be a square. Because only one diagonal bisects the other, opposite sides can't be the same length.

Exercise 25 [Alert] Students may think the bearing of 38° is from the plane to station. Encourage students to sketch the situation and then reread the problem to check the sketch.

25. Station Beta is closer.

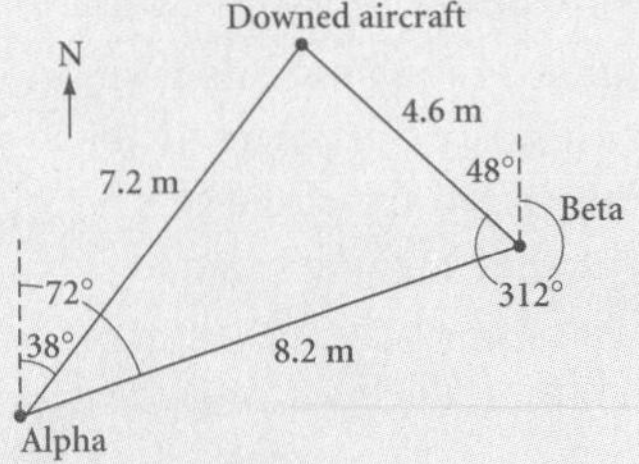

EXTENSIONS

A. Have students use geometry software or patty paper to confirm one of their tangent conjectures.

B. Pose this problem: State a conjecture for segments in space tangent to a sphere. Make a sketch. Test your conjecture with physical objects and explain why you think your conjecture is true.

C. Use Take Another Look activity 1 or 2 on page 355.

Chapter 5 **22.** Identify each of these statements as true or false. If the statement is true, explain why. If it is false, give a counterexample.

a. If the diagonals of a quadrilateral are congruent, but only one is the perpendicular bisector of the other, then the quadrilateral is a kite. true

b. If the quadrilateral has exactly one line of reflectional symmetry, then the quadrilateral is a kite. false; isosceles trapezoid

c. If the diagonals of a quadrilateral are congruent and bisect each other, then it is a square. false; rectangle

3.7 **23.** Rachel and Yulia are building an art studio above their back bedroom. There will be doors on three sides leading to a small deck that surrounds the studio. They need to place an electrical junction box in the ceiling of the studio so that it is equidistant from the three light switches shown by the doors. Copy the diagram of the room and find the most efficient location for the junction box. ⓗ the circumcenter of the triangle formed by the three light switches

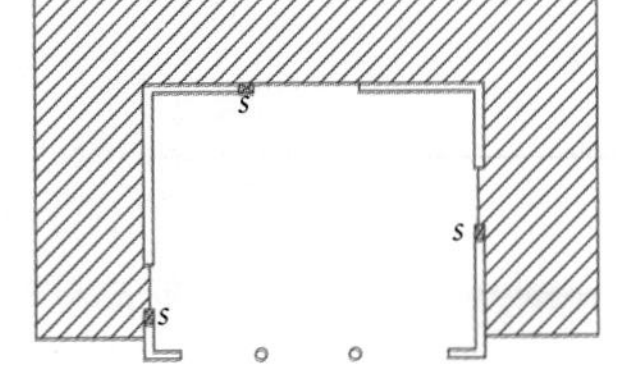

2.3 **24.** What will the units digit be when you evaluate 3^{23}? ⓗ 7

Chapter 2 **25.** A small light-wing aircraft has made an emergency landing in a remote portion of a wildlife refuge and is sending out radio signals for help. Ranger Station Alpha receives the signal on a bearing of 38° and Station Beta receives the signal on a bearing of 312°. (Recall that a bearing is an angle measured clockwise from the north.) Stations Alpha and Beta are 8.2 miles apart, and Station Beta is on a bearing of 72° from Station Alpha. Which station is closer to the downed aircraft? Explain your reasoning. ⓗ

3.7 **26.** *Technology* Use geometry software to pick any three points. Construct an arc through all three points. (Can it be done?) How do you find the center of the circle that passes through all three points? Yes, as long as the three points are noncollinear; possible answer: connect the points with segments, then find the point of concurrency of the perpendicular bisectors (same as circumcenter construction).

IMPROVING YOUR VISUAL THINKING SKILLS

Colored Cubes

Sketch the solid shown, but with the red cubes removed and the blue cube moved to cover the starred face of the green cube.

IMPROVING VISUAL THINKING SKILLS

LESSON

6.3

Arcs and Angles

You will do foolish things, but do them with enthusiasm.

SIDONIE GABRIELLA COLETTE

Many arches that you see in structures are semicircular, but Chinese builders long ago discovered that arches don't have to have this shape. The Zhaozhou bridge, shown below, was completed in 605 C.E. It is the world's first stone arched bridge in the shape of a minor arc, predating other minor-arc arches by about 800 years.

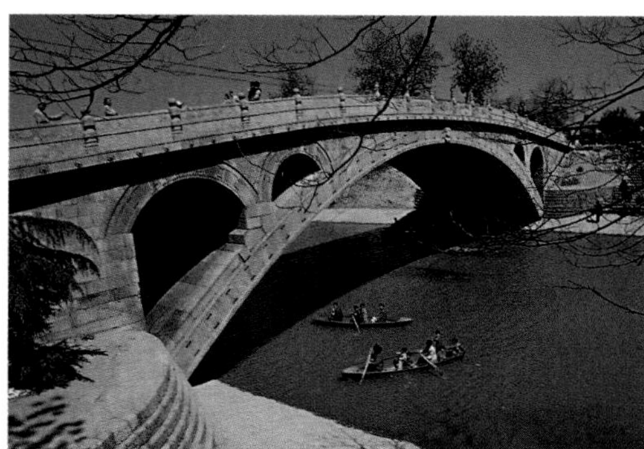

In this lesson you'll discover properties of arcs and the angles associated with them.

Investigation 1
Inscribed Angle Properties

You will need

- a compass
- a straightedge
- a protractor

In this investigation, you will compare an inscribed angle and a central angle, both inscribed in the same arc. Refer to the diagram of circle *O*, with central angle *COR* and inscribed angle *CAR*.

Step 1 100°; 50°; $m\angle CAR = \frac{1}{2}m\angle COR$

Step 1 Measure $\angle COR$ with your protractor to find $m\overset{\frown}{CR}$, the intercepted arc. Measure $\angle CAR$. How does $m\angle CAR$ compare with $m\overset{\frown}{CR}$?

Step 2 Construct a circle of your own with an inscribed angle. Draw the central angle that intercepts the same arc. What is the measure of the inscribed angle? How do the two measures compare?

Step 3 Share your results with others near you. Copy and complete the conjecture.

Inscribed Angle Conjecture C-61

The measure of an angle inscribed in a circle __?__. is one-half the measure of the central angle

NCTM STANDARDS

CONTENT		PROCESS	
	Number	✓	Problem Solving
	Algebra	✓	Reasoning
✓	Geometry	✓	Communication
✓	Measurement	✓	Connections
	Data/Probability		Representation

LESSON OBJECTIVE

- Discover relationships between an inscribed angle of a circle and its intercepted arc

LESSON

6.3

PLANNING

LESSON OUTLINE

First day:

45 min Investigations 1–3 and 5 (if time permits)

Second day:

25 min Investigation 4 (and 5)

15 min Sharing

5 min Closing

MATERIALS

- construction tools
- protractors
- geometry software, *optional*

TEACHING

Investigation 4 and the one-step investigation (page 320) lend themselves to exploration with geometry software. If you have only one day for this lesson, you might demonstrate Investigation 1 and jigsaw Investigations 2 through 5. (Select the group most likely to finish first to take on Investigation 4.)

Guiding Investigation 1

You may need to review the idea of an inscribed angle.

Step 1 [Alert] Students may still have difficulty naming angles using three letters. You may need to offer students assistance in tracing these angles and noticing that the middle letter denotes the vertex and the other two letters denote the endpoints of the intercepted arc. **[Alert]** Sometimes students can see an inscribed angle better if they extend its sides as rays. **[Alert]** If students are not seeing a pattern, encourage them to measure more carefully.

Guiding Investigation 1 (continued)

Step 3 The conjecture can also be completed with "is one-half the measure of the intercepted arc." Another way students may fill in the blank is to say that the measure of the inscribed angle bisects the measure of the central angle. Have this conjecture presented for critique during Sharing to make the point that measures are numbers and thus don't bisect each other. Keeping track of what kind of mathematical object something is (such as a number, segment, polygon, matrix, or function) is a skill you want students to develop.

One step Pose this problem: "Draw any triangle and construct its circumscribed circle. Look at the arcs of the circumscribed circle and the angles of the triangle. Now replace one side of the triangle with two sides that meet on the circle to make a quadrilateral inscribed in the circle. This quadrilateral is called a *cyclic quadrilateral.* What can you say about all cyclic quadrilaterals?" As students work, encourage them to draw various cyclic quadrilaterals, to make measurements (of sides and angles), to try to circumscribe special kinds of quadrilaterals, to consider central angles and chords of the circle, and to think about various angles inscribed in the circle. As students decide that opposite angles are supplementary, challenge them to explain why. During Sharing, be sure to emphasize the measures of inscribed angles, the measures of angles inscribed in a semicircle, and the relationship between opposite pairs of angles.

Investigation 2

Inscribed Angles Intercepting the Same Arc

You will need

- a compass
- a straightedge
- a protractor

Next, let's consider two inscribed angles that intercept the same arc. In the figure at right, $\angle AQB$ and $\angle APB$ both intercept $\overset{\frown}{AB}$. Angles AQB and APB are both inscribed in $\overset{\frown}{APB}$.

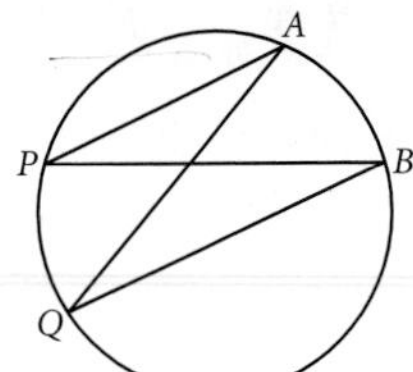

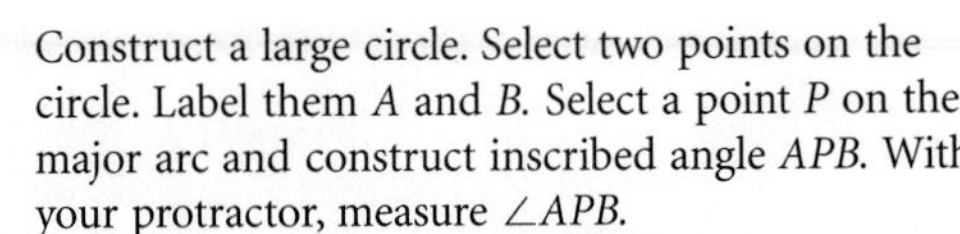

Step 1 Construct a large circle. Select two points on the circle. Label them A and B. Select a point P on the major arc and construct inscribed angle APB. With your protractor, measure $\angle APB$.

Step 2 Select another point Q on $\overset{\frown}{APB}$ and construct inscribed angle AQB. Measure $\angle AQB$.

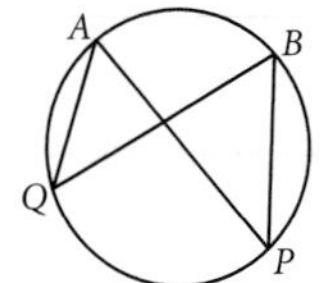

Step 3 How does $m\angle AQB$ compare with $m\angle APB$? equal

Step 4 Repeat Steps 1 and 2 with points P and Q selected on minor arc AB. Compare results with your group. Then copy and complete the conjecture.

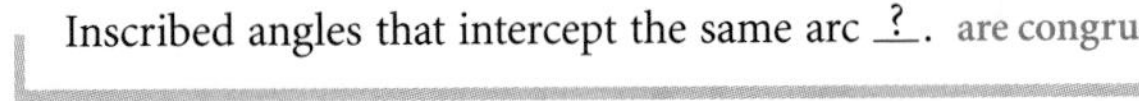

Inscribed Angles Intercepting Arcs Conjecture C-62

Inscribed angles that intercept the same arc __?__. are congruent

Investigation 3

Angles Inscribed in a Semicircle

You will need

- a compass
- a straightedge
- a protractor

Next, you will investigate a property of angles inscribed in semicircles. This will lead you to a third important conjecture about inscribed angles.

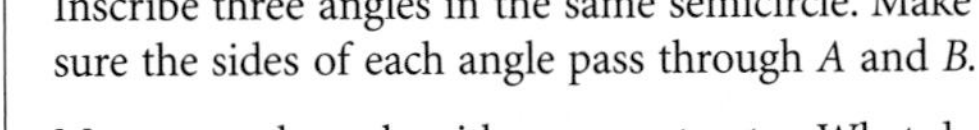

Step 1 Construct a large circle. Construct a diameter $\overline{AB}$. Inscribe three angles in the same semicircle. Make sure the sides of each angle pass through A and B.

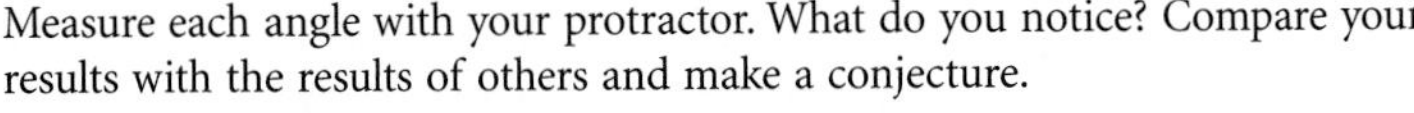

Step 2 Measure each angle with your protractor. What do you notice? Compare your results with the results of others and make a conjecture.

Angles Inscribed in a Semicircle Conjecture C-63

Angles inscribed in a semicircle __?__. are right angles

Now you will discover a property of the angles of a quadrilateral inscribed in a circle.

Guiding Investigation 2

Step 1 [Alert] If students are consistently choosing angles with one side as a diameter, encourage them to experiment with more variety.

Step 4 Some students may say that this conjecture is obvious because of the Inscribed Angle Conjecture. Have them explain their reasoning during Sharing.

Guiding Investigation 3

Step 1 Have students clearly mark the center of the circle so that diameters are obvious. Students then may be more likely to observe that centers are marked this way in the exercises.

Investigation 4
Cyclic Quadrilaterals

You will need

- a compass
- a straightedge
- a protractor

A quadrilateral inscribed in a circle is called a **cyclic** quadrilateral. Each of its angles is inscribed in the circle, and each of its sides is a chord of the circle.

Step 1 Construct a large circle. Construct a cyclic quadrilateral by connecting four points anywhere on the circle.

Step 2 Measure each of the four inscribed angles. Write the measure in each angle. Look carefully at the sums of various angles. Share your observations with students near you. Then copy and complete the conjecture.

Cyclic Quadrilateral Conjecture C-64

The ? angles of a cyclic quadrilateral are ?. opposite; supplementary

Investigation 5
Arcs by Parallel Lines

You will need

- patty paper
- a compass
- a double-edged straightedge

Next, you will investigate arcs formed by parallel lines that intersect a circle.

A line that intersects a circle in two points is called a **secant.** A secant contains a chord of the circle, and passes through the interior of a circle, while a tangent line does not.

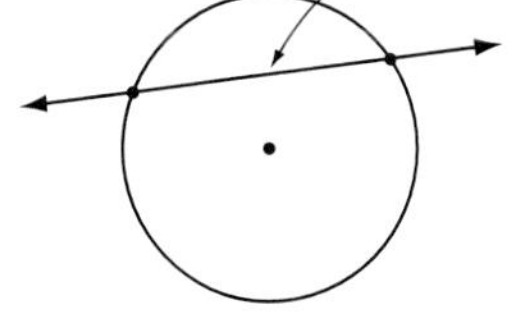

Step 1 On a piece of patty paper, construct a large circle. Lay your straightedge across the circle so that its parallel edges pass through the circle. Draw secants $\overline{AB}$ and $\overline{DC}$ along both edges of the straightedge.

Step 2 Fold your patty paper to compare $\widehat{AD}$ and $\widehat{BC}$. What can you say about $\widehat{AD}$ and $\widehat{BC}$?

Step 2 The arcs are congruent.

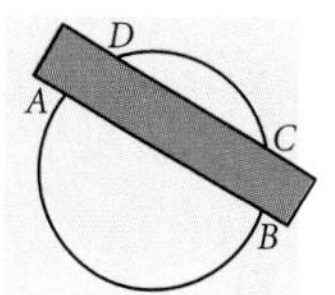

Step 3 Repeat Steps 1 and 2, using either lined paper or another object with parallel edges to construct different parallel secants. Share your results with other students. Then copy and complete the conjecture.

Parallel Lines Intercepted Arcs Conjecture C-65

Parallel lines intercept ? arcs on a circle. congruent

Sharing Ideas (continued)

[Ask] "Can you use the Inscribed Angle Conjecture to explain *why* the other conjectures are true?" [An angle inscribed in a semicircle intercepts a 180° arc, so its measure will be 90°. Opposite angles of a cyclic quadrilateral intercept arcs whose measures sum to 360°, so the sum of the angle measures will be half that, or 180°. And a diagonal is drawn across the quadrilateral-like shape formed by two parallel lines and their intercepted arcs, the two inscribed angles will be congruent by the Parallel Lines Conjecture, so the intercepted arcs will be congruent.]

These observations are informal proofs and lead naturally to the question of why the Inscribed Angle Conjecture is true and motivate Lesson 6.4.

If there's time, you might ask students to pose some questions. Some might be "What if the vertex of an angle is in the interior of the circle (or on the exterior of the circle) but is not the center?" "How does the measure of the angle relate to the measure of the intercepted arc?" The goal is to pose problems, not to solve them.

Guiding Investigation 4

Step 1 **[Alert]** As needed, encourage students to draw different-shaped quadrilaterals.

Guiding Investigation 5

Step 1 If all students are drawing their parallel lines symmetric about a diameter, encourage more variety.

SHARING IDEAS

As students present candidates for the Inscribed Angle Conjecture, ask whether they checked their conjectures for inscribed angles that are obtuse. If not, have them do so. **[Ask]** "What is the measure of the intercepted arc?" [more than 180°]

As students discuss various conjectures, make the point that arcs can't be measured directly. We have measured them through central angles and inscribed angles.

When you come to Investigation 3, you might point out that the Angles Inscribed in a Semicircle Conjecture is useful in constructing right angles when you don't know the vertex. Students may have seen its necessity in Lesson 6.2 when trying to construct a tangent line to a circle from an exterior point. They want the radius to the point of tangency and the tangent segment to form a right angle; the right angle could be in a semicircle whose diameter is on the segment from the exterior point to the circle's center. The semicircle will intersect the original circle at the point of tangency.

In discussing cyclic quadrilaterals, **[Ask]** "Which quadrilaterals are cyclic?" [all squares and rectangles and some kites, trapezoids, and nonspecial quadrilaterals] "Can a parallelogram be a cyclic quadrilateral?" [only if it's a rectangle] "If two sides of a cyclic quadrilateral are parallel, what kind of quadrilateral can it be?" [rectangle, square, or isosceles trapezoid]

Assessing Progress
Through your observations you can assess students' understanding of *inscribed angle, central angle, diameter, semicircle, quadrilateral,* kinds of quadrilaterals, supplementary angles, and congruent angles. You can also see how well they measure angles with a protractor and how well they figure out which angles and arcs are associated with a given string of three letters.

Closing the Lesson

This lesson includes five conjectures, the last four of which are consequences of the first: that the measure of any angle inscribed in a circle is half the measure of the central angle or the intercepted arc. The other conjectures result from applying this conjecture to two angles intercepting the same arc, to angles inscribed in a semicircle, to cyclic quadrilaterals, and to arcs intercepted by parallel lines.

BUILDING UNDERSTANDING

If students need more confidence before starting on the exercises, work together through one or two of the first 15 exercises.

ASSIGNING HOMEWORK

Essential	1–17
Performance assessment	14
Portfolio	20
Journal	18
Group	19–21
Review	22–26

Review these conjectures and ask yourself which quadrilaterals can be inscribed in a circle. Can any parallelogram be a cyclic quadrilateral? If two sides of a cyclic quadrilateral are parallel, then what kind of quadrilateral will it be?

EXERCISES

You will need

Geometry software for Exercises **19** and **21**

Construction tools for Exercise **24**

Use your new conjectures to solve Exercises 1–17.

1. $a = \underline{?}$ 65°

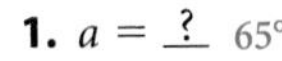
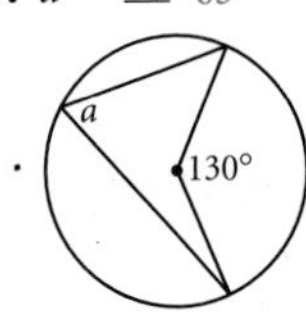

2. $b = \underline{?}$ 30°

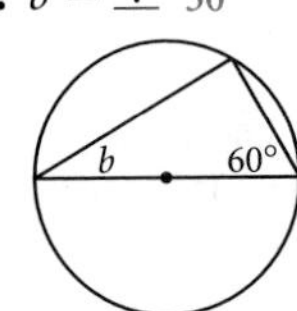

3. $c = \underline{?}$ ⓗ 70°

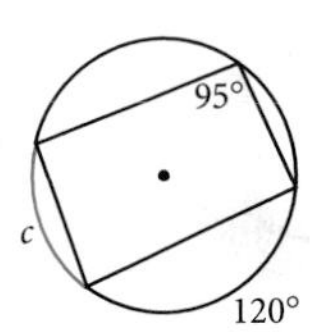

4. $h = \underline{?}$ ⓗ 50°

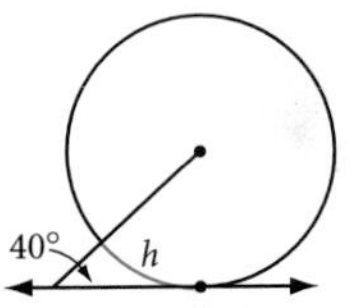

5. $d = \underline{?}$ 140°
$e = \underline{?}$ 42°

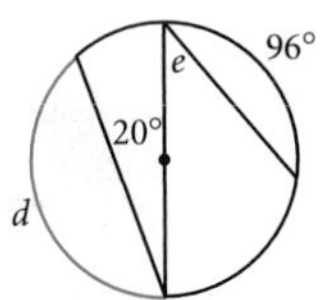

6. $f = \underline{?}$ 90°
$g = \underline{?}$ 100°

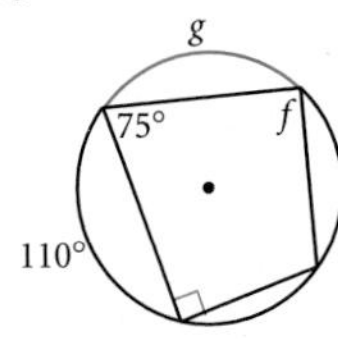

7. *JUST* is a rhombus.
$w = \underline{?}$ 50°

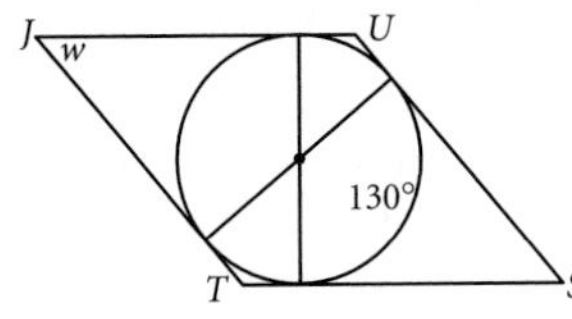

8. *CALM* is a rectangle.
$x = \underline{?}$ 148°

9. *DOWN* is a kite.
$y = \underline{?}$ 44°

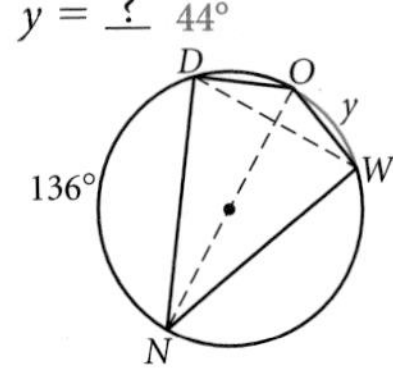

10. $k = \underline{?}$ 142°

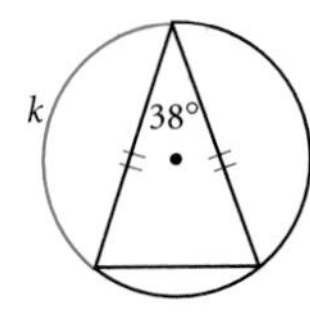

11. $r = \underline{?}$ 120°
$s = \underline{?}$ 60°

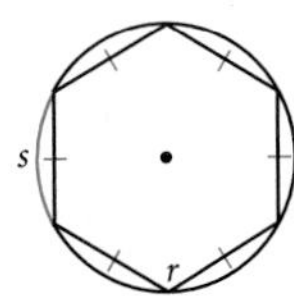

12. $m = \underline{?}$ 140°
$n = \underline{?}$ 111°

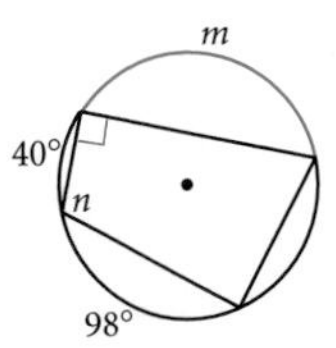

13. $\overline{AB} \parallel \overline{CD}$
$p = \underline{?}$ 71°
$q = \underline{?}$ 41°

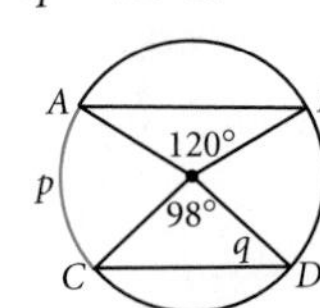

14. What is the sum of *a, b, c, d,* and *e*? ⓗ 180°

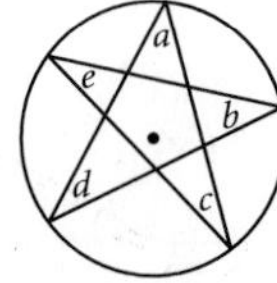

▶ Helping with the Exercises

Exercise 3 If students are having difficulty, **[Ask]** "Will inscribed angles help?" [$c + 120 = 2(95)$]

Exercise 4 40° is the measure of the angle; *h* is the measure of the arc. **[Ask]** "What angle is needed to measure the arc?" [To see the needed central angle, students can draw in a radius to the point of tangency.]

Exercise 13 If students are struggling, wonder aloud whether they know something about arcs intercepted by parallel lines. They also may not be using the fact that all radii of a circle are congruent.

Exercise 14 Students may approach this problem by using inscribed angles or what they learned earlier about star pentagons.

15. $y = \underline{\ ?\ }$ ⓗ 75°

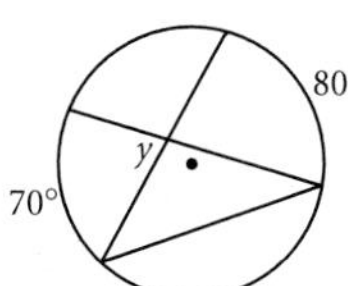

16. What's wrong with this picture?

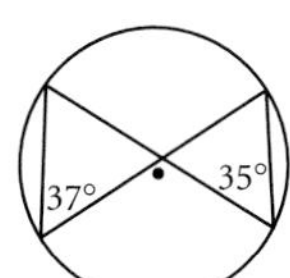

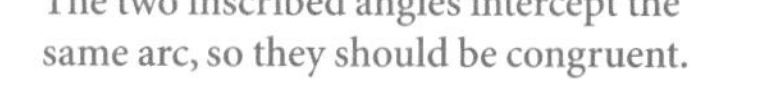
The two inscribed angles intercept the same arc, so they should be congruent.

17. Explain why $\overparen{AC} \cong \overparen{CE}$.

D A H F O B G C E

18. How can you find the center of a circle, using only the corner of a piece of paper?

19. ***Technology*** Chris Chisholm, a high school student in Whitmore, California, used the Angles Inscribed in a Semicircle Conjecture to discover a simpler way to find the orthocenter in a triangle. Chris constructs a circle using one of the sides of the triangle as the diameter, then he immediately finds an altitude to each of the triangle's other two sides. Use geometry software and Chris's method to find the orthocenter of a triangle. Does this method work on all kinds of triangles? ⓗ

20. **APPLICATION** The width of a view that can be captured in a photo depends on the camera's *picture angle.* Suppose a photographer takes a photo of your class standing in one straight row with a camera that has a 46° picture angle. Draw a line segment to represent the row. Draw a 46° angle on a piece of patty paper. Locate at least eight different points on your paper where a camera could be positioned to include all the students, filling as much of the picture as possible. What is the locus of all such camera positions? What conjecture does this activity illustrate? ⓗ

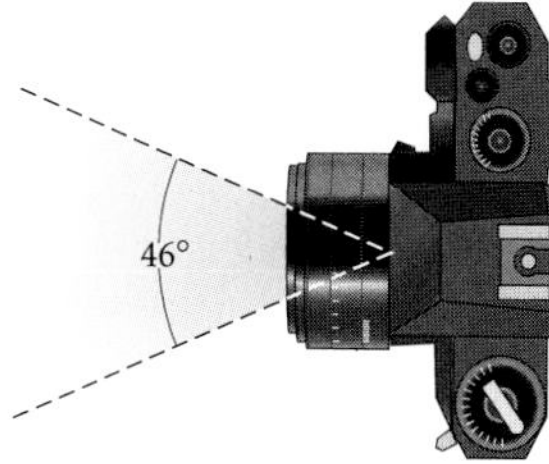

21. ***Technology*** Construct a circle and a diameter. Construct a point on one of the semicircles, and construct two chords from it to the endpoints of the diameter to create a right triangle. Locate the midpoint of each of the two chords. Predict, then sketch the locus of the two midpoints as the vertex of the right angle is moved around the circle. Finally, use your computer to animate the point on the circle and trace the locus of the two midpoints. What do you get?

Review

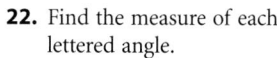

22. Find the measure of each lettered angle.

$a = 108°$; $b = 72°$; $c = 36°$; $d = 108°$; $e = 108°$; $f = 72°$; $g = 108°$; $h = 90°$; $l = 36°$; $m = 18°$; $n = 54°$; $p = 36°$

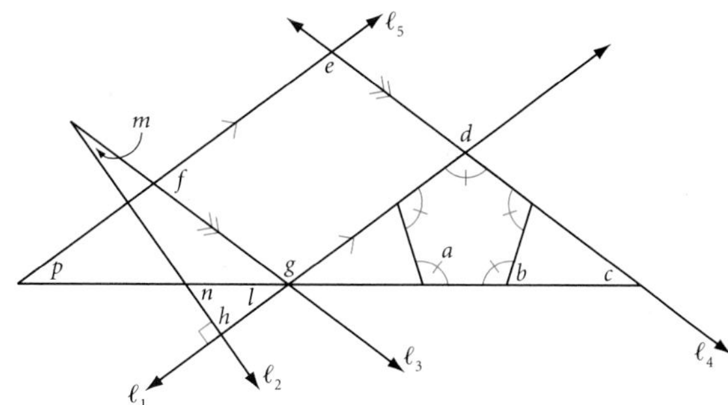

21. two congruent externally tangent circles with half the diameter of the original circle

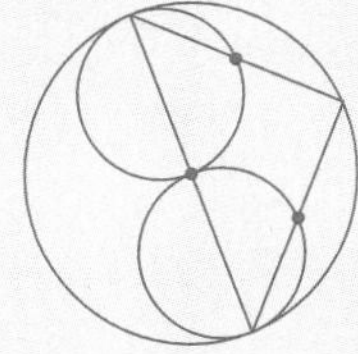

Exercise 15 Keep students focused on inscribed angles and their intercepted arcs.

17. $\angle BFE \cong \angle DFA$ (Vertical Angles Conjecture). $\angle BGD \cong \angle FHD$ (all right angles congruent). Therefore, $\angle B \cong \angle D$ (Third Angle Conjecture)

$m\angle B = \frac{1}{2}\, m\overparen{AC}$

$m\angle D = \frac{1}{2}\, m\overparen{EC}$

$\overparen{AC} \cong \overparen{EC}$

Exercise 18 It helps if the sides of the corner are longer than the radius of the circle.

18. Possible answer: Place the corner so that it is an inscribed angle. Trace the inscribed angle. Use the side of the paper to construct the hypotenuse of the right triangle (which is the diameter). Repeat the process. The place where the two diameters intersect is the center.

Exercise 19 To use this method on an obtuse triangle, you must construct the circle having the longest side as the diameter; the altitudes will intersect the circle at the extensions of the sides.

19. possible answer:

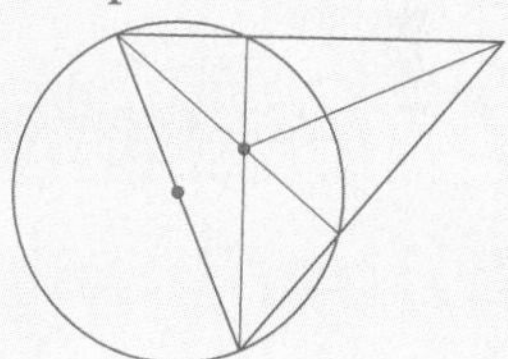

It works on acute and right triangles.

Exercises 20, 21 If necessary, remind students that *locus* means "possible locations."

20. The camera can be placed anywhere on the major arc (measuring 268°) of a circle such that the row of students is a chord intersecting the circle to form a minor arc measuring 92°. This illustrates the conjecture that inscribed angles that intercept the same arc are congruent (Inscribed Angles Intercepting Arcs Conjecture).

23. It is given that $\overline{PQ} \cong \overline{RS}$. $\overline{OP} \cong \overline{OQ} \cong \overline{OR} \cong \overline{OS}$ because all radii in a circle are congruent. Therefore, $\triangle OPQ \cong \triangle ORS$ by SSS and $\angle 2 \cong \angle 1$ by CPCTC. Now we move on to the smaller right triangles inside $\triangle OPQ$ and $\triangle ORS$. It is given that $\overline{OT} \perp \overline{PQ}$ and $\overline{OV} \perp \overline{RS}$. Therefore, $\angle OTQ$ and $\angle OVS$ are right angles by the definition of perpendicular lines and $\angle OTQ \cong \angle OVS$ because all right angles are congruent. Thus, $\triangle OTQ \cong \triangle OVS$ by SAA and $\overline{OT} \cong \overline{OV}$ by CPCTC.

24. Start with an equilateral triangle whose vertices are the centers of the three congruent circles. Then locate the incenter/circumcenter/orthocenter/centroid (all the same point because the triangle is equilateral) to find the center of the larger circle. To find the radius, construct a segment from the incenter of the triangle through the vertex of the triangle to a point on the circle.

EXTENSIONS

A. Students might investigate one or more of the conjectures in this lesson on the surface of a sphere. The Lénárt Sphere is an excellent tool for this extension. Encourage students interested in exploring conjectures on a sphere to keep a section of their notebooks for geometry on a sphere.

B. Use Take Another Look activity 3 or 4 on page 355.

6.1 **23.** Use the diagram at right and the flowchart below to write a paragraph proof explaining why two congruent chords in a circle are equidistant from the center of the circle. ⓗ

Given: Circle O with $\overline{PQ} \cong \overline{RS}$ and $\overline{OT} \perp \overline{PQ}$ and $\overline{OV} \perp \overline{RS}$

Show: $\overline{OT} \cong \overline{OV}$

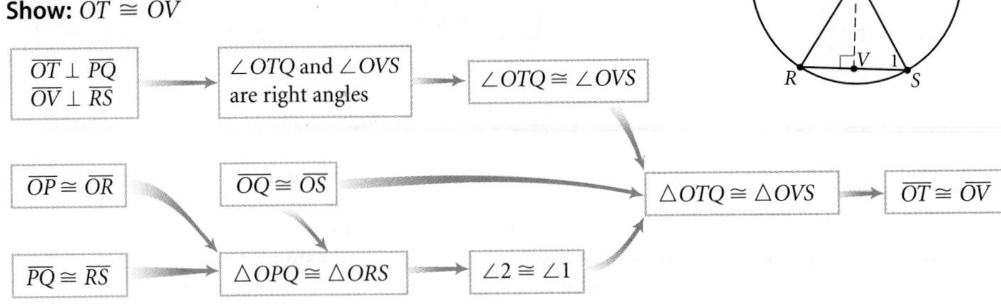

3.7 **24.** ***Construction*** Use your construction tools to re-create this design of three congruent circles all tangent to each other and internally tangent to a larger circle. ⓗ

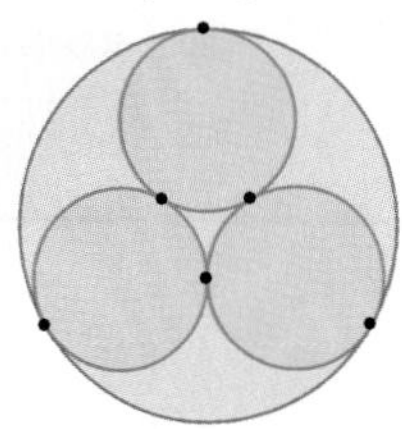

5.2 **25.** What's wrong with this picture?

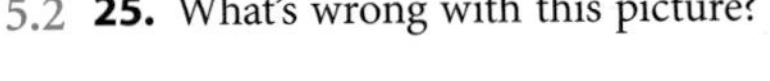

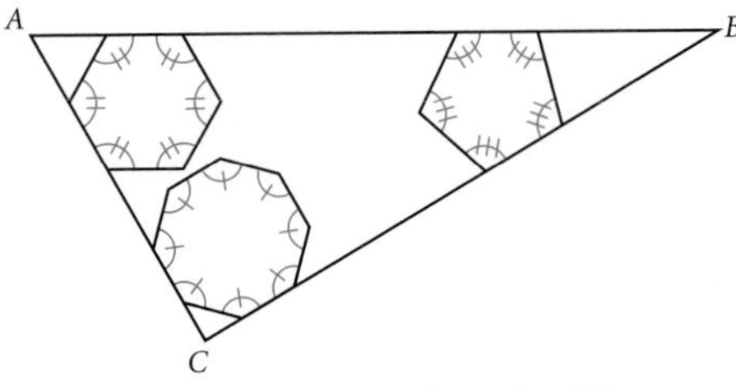

$m\angle A = 60°, m\angle B = 36°, m\angle C = 90°;$
$60° + 36° + 90° \neq 180°$

26. Consider the figure at right with line $\ell \parallel \overline{AB}$. As P moves from left to right along line ℓ, which of these lengths or distances always increases? E

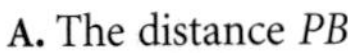

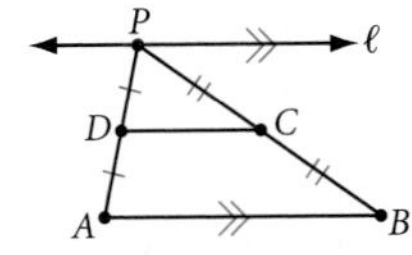

A. The distance PB

B. The distance from D to $\overleftrightarrow{AB}$

C. DC

D. Perimeter of $\triangle ABP$

E. None of the above

IMPROVING YOUR REASONING SKILLS

Think Dinosaur

If the letter in the word *dinosaur* that is three letters after the word's second vowel is also found before the sixteenth letter of the alphabet, then print the word *dinosaur* horizontally. Otherwise, print the word *dinosaur* vertically and cross out the second letter after the first vowel.

IMPROVING REASONING SKILLS

Solution: d
i
n
~~o~~
s
a
u
r

LESSON 6.4

Proving Circle Conjectures

Mistakes are a fact of life. It's the response to the error that counts.

NIKKI GIOVANNI

In Lesson 6.3, you discovered the Inscribed Angle Conjecture: The measure of an angle inscribed in a circle equals half the measure of its intercepted arc. Many other circle conjectures are logical consequences of the Inscribed Angle Conjecture. Let's start this lesson by proving it.

When you inscribe an angle in a circle, the angle will relate to the circle's center in one of the three ways described below. These three possible relationships to the center are the three cases for which you prove the Inscribed Angle Conjecture. To prove the conjecture, you must prove all three cases.

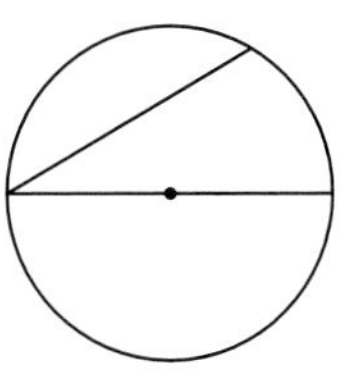

Case 1

The circle's center is on the angle.

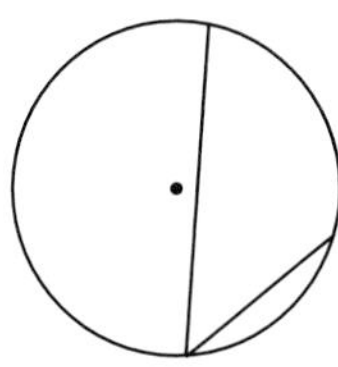

Case 2

The center is outside the angle.

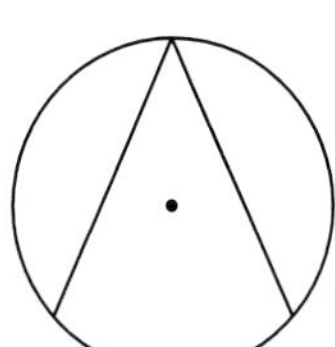

Case 3

The center is inside the angle.

You will first prove that the conjecture is true for Case 1.

Case 1 Conjecture: The measure of an inscribed angle in a circle equals half the measure of its intercepted arc when a side of the angle passes through the center of the circle.

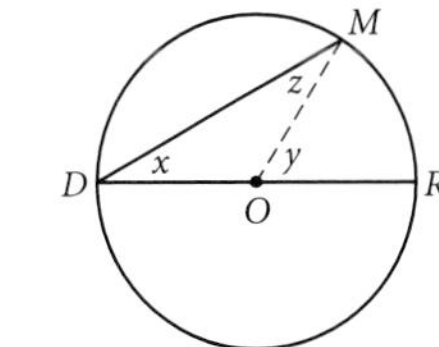

Given: Circle O with inscribed angle MDR on diameter $\overline{DR}$

Let $z = m\angle DMO$, $x = m\angle MDR$, and $y = m\angle MOR$ ($y = m\widehat{MR}$)

Show: $m\angle MDR = \frac{1}{2}m\widehat{MR}$

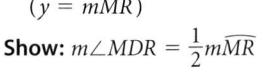

Work backward to formulate a plan. Ask yourself what you're trying to show and what you would need to do that.

Plan

- You need to show that $m\angle MDR = \frac{1}{2}m\widehat{MR}$. Using the variables defined in the given, this can be restated as $x = \frac{1}{2}y$.
- You want to show that $x = \frac{1}{2}y$, so you need to show that $2x = y$.
- You know that $y = x + z$ because of the Exterior Angle Conjecture.
- You also know that $x = z$ because $\triangle DOM$ is isosceles.
- So, start your flowchart proof by establishing that $\triangle DOM$ has two congruent sides.

From this plan you create a flowchart proof.

NCTM STANDARDS

CONTENT		PROCESS	
	Number		Problem Solving
✓	Algebra	✓	Reasoning
✓	Geometry	✓	Communication
✓	Measurement		Connections
	Data/Probability	✓	Representation

LESSON OBJECTIVES

- Review properties of inscribed angles and polygons
- Practice flowchart proofs

PLANNING

LESSON OUTLINE

One day:

20 min	Proofs
5 min	Sharing
5 min	Closing
15 min	Exercises

MATERIALS

none

TEACHING

This lesson presents deductive proofs of the Inscribed Angle Conjecture and some of its logical consequences. Here the conjecture is stated in terms of the intercepted arc rather than the equivalent central angle.

One step Ask students to prove the Inscribed Angle Conjecture, beginning with the assumption that one side of the angle goes through the center of the circle. If you see that students are stuck ask what angle is to be twice the inscribed angle and get students to draw in this central angle. They will discover how it forms an exterior angle to an isosceles triangle. Encourage them to write a flowchart proof. Then ask if inscribed angles that don't have one side along a diameter can be moved somehow (without changing their measure) to fit into the case already proved. This will preview Case 2.

INTRODUCTION

You may need to help students understand the three different cases needed to prove the conjecture. They can see that Case 1 is special because most chords do not pass through the center of the circle.

Proofs

Case 1 Help students see how to reason backward to come up with the proof. After labeling the picture to match the given, **[Ask]** "What is it we want to show?" $\left[x = \frac{1}{2}y\right]$ "Can we connect x and y with an equation?" [$y = x + z$ by the Exterior Angle Sum Conjecture] "What could allow us to conclude that x is half of y?" [Knowing that $z = x$ would imply that $y = 2x$, the same thing.] "Under what conditions could we conclude that z equals x?" [if the triangle is isosceles] "Is there anything to indicate that the sides opposite these angles are congruent?" [The radii are equal.]

Then have students read through the flowchart to see how it encapsulates their reasoning. A similar proof of a different conjecture arises in a review exercise of Lesson 6.6, so students should understand this proof well.

Case 2 Again, you might work as a class to see how the proof might be put together before reading it. **[Ask]** "What are we trying to prove, using arcs so we don't have to draw central angles?" $\left[x = \frac{b}{2}\right]$ "What line segment might you add to this picture to help you include Case 1 as part of the picture?" $\left[\text{diameter } \overline{DR}\right]$ "Does Case 1 apply to any arc in this picture?" [two: arc RK and arc MR] "What does Case 1 tell us about those arcs?" $\left[w = \frac{a+b}{2} \text{ and } z = \frac{a}{2}\right]$ "Can you get from this to what we want to prove?" [yes, through $x = w - z$] Now have students read the book's paragraph proof to see how well it captures their reasoning.

If you have time, you might ask groups to try to prove Case 3 rather than waiting for the exercises.

Flowchart Proof of Case 1

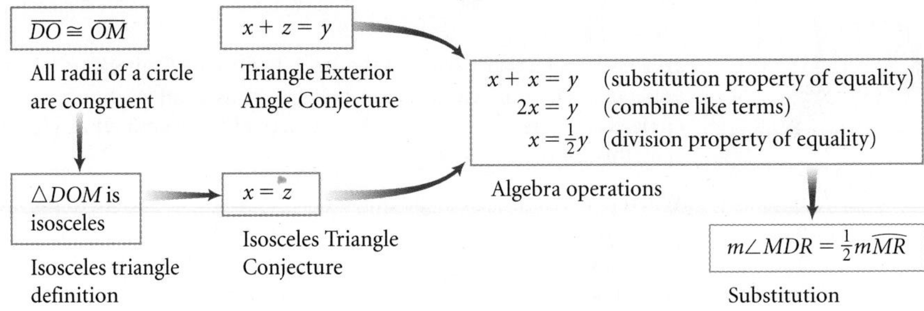

You will use Case 1 to write a paragraph proof for Case 2.

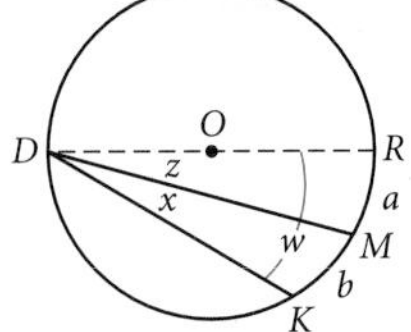

Case 2 Conjecture: The measure of an inscribed angle in a circle equals half the measure of its intercepted arc when the center of the circle is outside the angle.

Given: Circle O with inscribed angle MDK on one side of diameter $\overline{DR}$

Show: $m\angle MDK = \frac{1}{2}m\overset{\frown}{MK}$

Paragraph Proof of Case 2

Let $z = m\angle MDR$, $x = m\angle MDK$, and $w = m\angle KDR$.
Then, $m\angle KDR = m\angle MDR + m\angle MDK$, so $w = x + z$.
Let $a = m\overset{\frown}{MR}$ and $b = m\overset{\frown}{MK}$. Then, $m\overset{\frown}{MR} + m\overset{\frown}{MK} = m\overset{\frown}{KR}$.
So, $m\overset{\frown}{KR} = a + b$.

Stated in terms of x and b, you wish to show that $x = \frac{b}{2}$. From Case 1, you know that $w = \frac{(a+b)}{2}$ and that $z = \frac{a}{2}$. You know that $w = x + z$, so $x = w - z$ by the subtraction property of equality. Substitute $\frac{(a+b)}{2}$ for w and $\frac{a}{2}$ for z to get $x = \frac{(a+b)}{2} - \frac{a}{2} = \frac{(a+b)-a}{2} = \frac{b}{2}$. Therefore, $m\angle MDK = \frac{1}{2}m\overset{\frown}{MK}$. ■

You will prove Case 3 in the exercises.

Light rays from distant objects are focused on the retina of a normal eye. The rays converge short of the retina on a myopic (near-sighted) eye, causing blurry vision. With the proper lens, light rays from distant objects will focus sharply on the retina, giving the near-sighted person clear vision. When the rays are focused on the retina, what kind of angle do they form inside the eye?

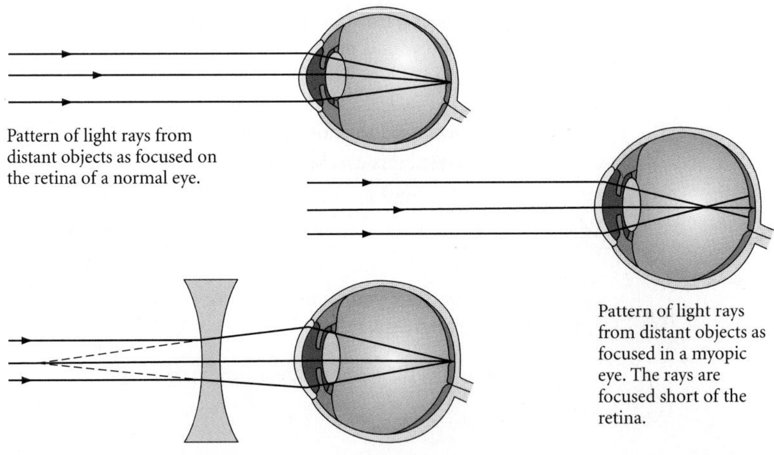

Pattern of light rays from distant objects as focused on the retina of a normal eye.

Pattern of light rays from distant objects as focused in a myopic eye. The rays are focused short of the retina.

SHARING IDEAS

Ask what the big idea is in Cases 2 and 3. Elicit the idea that the addition or subtraction compensates for the angle's not being included in Case 1. It's equivalent to rotating the angle about its vertex until one side is a diameter.

Assessing Progress

As you work through the proofs, you can assess whether students understand the Exterior Angle Sum Conjecture and the Isosceles Triangle Conjecture deeply enough to apply them in the context of "How could we prove . . . ?" Also assess how well they generate the idea that radii of a circle are congruent and how well they can treat overlapping angles as distinct. Check their skill at reading proofs and at finding angles on diagrams to match written symbols. Students' work on the exercises can give you insight into how well they understand the Inscribed Angle Conjecture.

Exercises

1. Prove Case 3 of the Inscribed Angle Conjecture. ⓗ

Case 3 Conjecture: The measure of an inscribed angle in a circle equals half the measure of its intercepted arc when the center of the circle is inside the angle.

Given: Circle O with inscribed angle MDK whose sides $\overline{DM}$ and $\overline{DK}$ lie on either side of diameter $\overline{DR}$

Show: $m\angle MDK = \frac{1}{2}m\widehat{MK}$

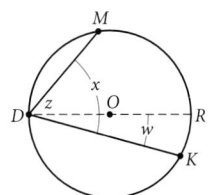

In Exercises 2–5 the four conjectures are consequences of the Inscribed Angle Conjecture. Prove each conjecture by writing a paragraph proof or a flowchart proof.

2. Inscribed angles that intercept the same arc are congruent.

Given: Circle O with $\angle ACD$ and $\angle ABD$ inscribed in $\widehat{ACD}$

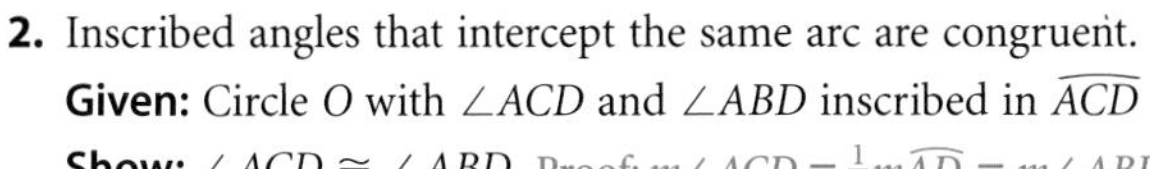

Show: $\angle ACD \cong \angle ABD$ Proof: $m\angle ACD = \frac{1}{2}m\widehat{AD} = m\angle ABD$ by the Inscribed Angle Conjecture. $\therefore \angle ACD \cong \angle ABD$.

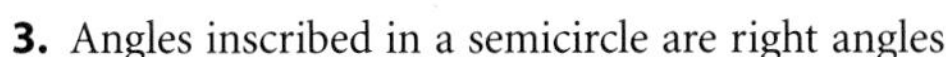

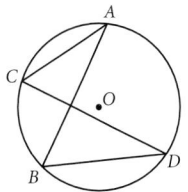

3. Angles inscribed in a semicircle are right angles.

Given: Circle O with diameter $\overline{AB}$, and $\angle ACB$ inscribed in semicircle ACB

Show: $\angle ACB$ is a right angle Proof: By the Inscribed Angle Conjecture, $m\angle ACB = \frac{1}{2}m\widehat{ADB} = \frac{1}{2}(180°) = 90°$. $\therefore \angle ACB$ is a right angle.

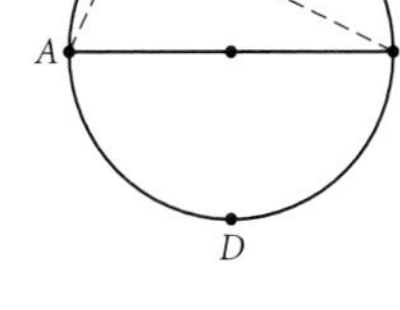

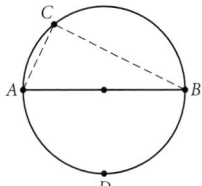

4. The opposite angles of a cyclic quadrilateral are supplementary. ⓗ

Given: Circle O with inscribed quadrilateral $LICY$

Show: $\angle L$ and $\angle C$ are supplementary Proof: By the Inscribed Angle Conjecture, $m\angle C = \frac{1}{2}m\widehat{YLI}$ and $m\angle L = \frac{1}{2}m\widehat{YCI} = \frac{1}{2}(360° - m\widehat{YLI}) = 180° - \frac{1}{2}m\widehat{YLI} = 180° - m\angle C$. $\therefore \angle L$ and $\angle C$ are supplementary. (A similar proof can be used to show that $\angle I$ and $\angle Y$ are supplementary.)

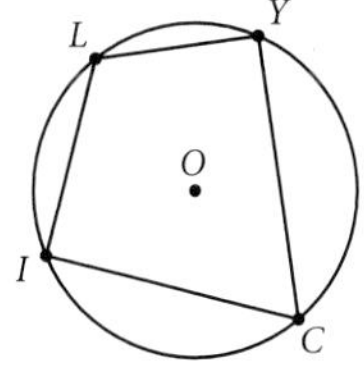

5. Parallel lines intercept congruent arcs on a circle. ⓗ

Given: Circle O with chord $\overline{BD}$ and $\overleftrightarrow{AB} \parallel \overleftrightarrow{CD}$

Show: $\widehat{BC} \cong \widehat{DA}$ Proof: $\angle 1 \cong \angle 2$ by AIA. $m\widehat{BC} = 2m\angle 2 = 2m\angle 1 = m\widehat{AD}$ by the Inscribed Angle Conjecture. $\therefore \widehat{BC} \cong \widehat{AD}$.

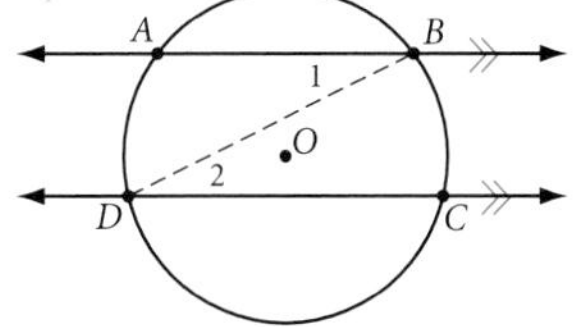

For Exercises 6 and 7, determine whether each conjecture is true or false. If the conjecture is false, draw a counterexample. If the conjecture is true, prove it by writing either a paragraph or flowchart proof.

6. If a parallelogram is inscribed within a circle, then the parallelogram is a rectangle. ⓗ

Given: Circle Y with inscribed parallelogram $GOLD$

Show: $GOLD$ is a rectangle

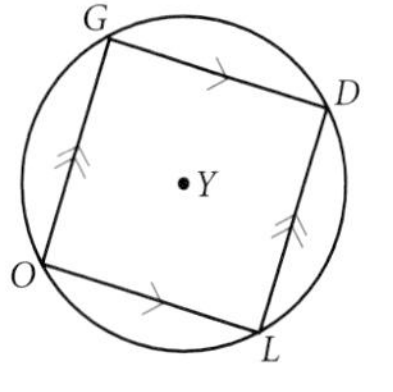

Exercise 6 If students are confused about what to prove, you might remind them that the definition of *rectangle* is "a parallelogram with four congruent angles." Because consecutive angles of all parallelograms are supplementary, rectangularity can be proved by showing that opposite angles are supplementary as well.

6. True. Opposite angles of a parallelogram are congruent. If it is inscribed in a circle, the opposite angles are also supplementary. So they are right angles, and the parallelogram is indeed equiangular, or a rectangle.

Exercises 6, 7 These exercises depend on knowledge of the conjectures for Lesson 6.3 but not on their proofs in Exercises 2–5.

Closing the Lesson

The standard proof of the Inscribed Angle Conjecture involves three cases. The cases in which the center of the circle is inside or outside the angle can be reduced to the case in which the center lies on one side of the angle.

BUILDING UNDERSTANDING

The exercises examine logical consequences of the Inscribed Angle Conjecture. You may wish to jigsaw exercises after the first.

ASSIGNING HOMEWORK

Essential	1–7
Performance assessment	6
Portfolio	7
Group	1
Review	8–11

Helping with the Exercises

1. Proof: Let $z = m\angle MDR$, $x = m\angle MDK$, and $w = m\angle KDR$. $m\angle KDM = m\angle KDR + m\angle RDM$ (or $x = w + z$) by angle addition. $m\widehat{MR} + m\widehat{RK} = m\widehat{MK}$ by arc addition. $z = \frac{1}{2}m\widehat{MR}$ and $w = \frac{1}{2}m\widehat{RK}$ by Case 1. $x = \frac{1}{2}m\widehat{RK} + \frac{1}{2}m\widehat{MR}$ by substitution. $x = \frac{1}{2}(m\widehat{RK} + m\widehat{MR})$ by factoring out the greatest common factor. $x = \frac{1}{2}m\widehat{MK}$ by substitution. $m\angle MDK = \frac{1}{2}m\widehat{MK}$ by substitution.

Exercise 5 As needed, have students review properties of parallel lines.

7. If a trapezoid is inscribed within a circle, then the trapezoid is isosceles. ⓗ
Given: Circle R with inscribed trapezoid $GATE$
Show: $GATE$ is an isosceles trapezoid

Review

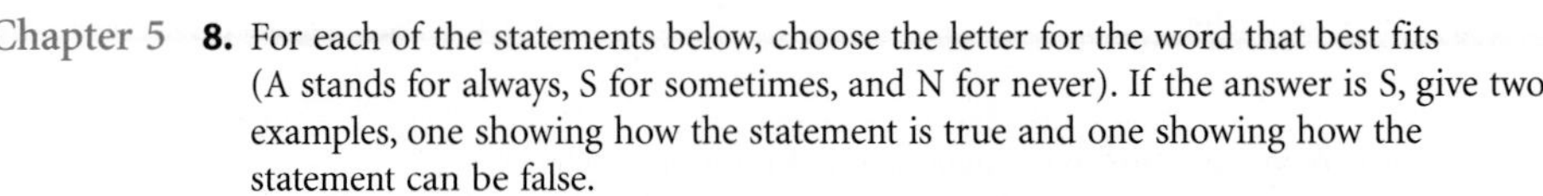

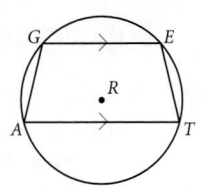

Chapter 5 **8.** For each of the statements below, choose the letter for the word that best fits (A stands for always, S for sometimes, and N for never). If the answer is S, give two examples, one showing how the statement is true and one showing how the statement can be false.

a. An equilateral polygon is (A/S/N) equiangular. S

b. If a triangle is a right triangle, then the acute angles are (A/S/N) complementary. A

c. The diagonals of a kite are (A/S/N) perpendicular bisectors of each other. N

d. A regular polygon (A/S/N) has both reflectional symmetry and rotational symmetry. A

e. If a polygon has rotational symmetry, then it (A/S/N) has more than one line of reflectional symmetry. S

2.6 **9.** Explain why m is parallel to n. ⓗ

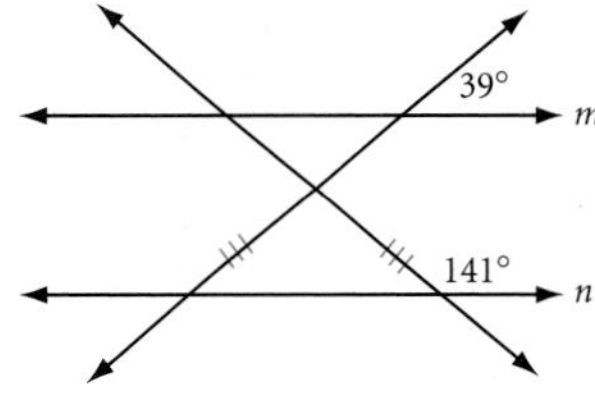

10. What is the probability of randomly selecting three collinear points from the points in the 3-by-3 grid below? ⓗ $\frac{2}{21}$

11. How many different 3-edge routes are possible from R to G along the wire frame shown? ⓗ 6

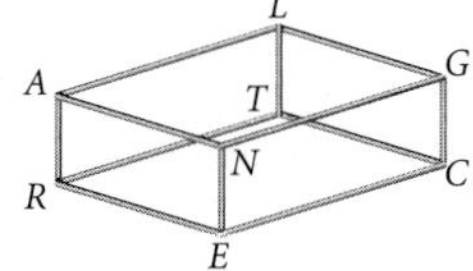

IMPROVING YOUR VISUAL THINKING SKILLS

Rolling Quarters

One of two quarters remains motionless while the other rotates around it, never slipping and always tangent to it. When the rotating quarter has completed a turn around the stationary quarter, how many turns has it made around its own center point? Try it!

7. True. $m\widehat{GA} = m\widehat{ET}$ by Parallel Lines Intercepted Arcs Conjecture. Therefore, the chords that intercept these arcs are congruent (Converse of the Chord Arcs Conjecture), that is $\overline{GA} \cong \overline{ET}$. $\therefore$ $GATE$ is isosceles.

8a. An equilateral triangle is equiangular, but a rhombus is not equiangular.

8c. Only one diagonal is the perpendicular bisector of the other.

8e. An equilateral triangle has rotational symmetry and three lines of symmetry; a parallelogram has rotational symmetry but no line of symmetry.

9. The base angles of the isosceles triangle have a measure of 39°. Because the corresponding angles are congruent, m is parallel to n.

Exercise 10 The only points under consideration are the nine shown. You might refer students to their work in Exercise 23 of Lesson 6.1, in which they calculated that the number of ways of choosing three dots from the nine dots is 84. There are eight triples of collinear dots.

IMPROVING VISUAL THINKING SKILLS

The rotating quarter makes two full turns.

Ask students to try to visualize this puzzle and make a conjecture before trying it. As they question why the rolling quarter turns around twice, suggest that they visualize what would happen if the two quarters were enmeshed gears and were turning together. Both would be facing the same way after a half turn. The same thing happens when one of the two is stationary.

Finding the Circumcenter

Suppose you know the coordinates of the vertices of a triangle. How can you find the coordinates of the circumcenter? You can graph the triangle, construct the perpendicular bisectors of the sides, and then *estimate* the coordinates of the point of concurrency. However, to find the exact coordinates, you need to use algebra. Let's look at an example.

EXAMPLE Find the coordinates of the circumcenter of $\triangle ZAP$ with $Z(0, -4)$, $A(-4, 4)$, and $P(8, 8)$.

Solution To find the coordinates of the circumcenter, you can write equations for the perpendicular bisectors of two of the sides of the triangle and then find the point where the bisectors intersect.

To review midpoint, slopes of perpendicular lines, or solving systems of equations, see the Table of Contents for those Using Your Algebra Skills topics.

To find the equation for the perpendicular bisector of $\overline{ZA}$, first find the midpoint of $\overline{ZA}$, then find its slope.

$$\text{Midpoint of } \overline{ZA} = \left(\frac{0 + (-4)}{2}, \frac{-4 + 4}{2}\right) = (-2, 0)$$

$$\text{Slope of } \overline{ZA} = \frac{4 - (-4)}{-4 - 0} = \frac{8}{-4} = -2$$

The slope of the perpendicular bisector of $\overline{ZA}$ is the negative reciprocal of -2, or $\frac{1}{2}$, and it passes through point $(-2, 0)$. So the equation of the perpendicular bisector is $\frac{y - 0}{x - (-2)} = \frac{1}{2}$. Solving for y gives the equation $y = \frac{1}{2}x + 1$.

You can use the same technique to find the equation of the perpendicular bisector of $\overline{ZP}$. The midpoint of ZP is $(4, 2)$, and the slope is $\frac{3}{2}$. So the slope of the perpendicular bisector of $\overline{ZP}$ is $-\frac{2}{3}$ and it passes through the point $(4, 2)$. The equation of the perpendicular bisector is $\frac{y - 2}{x - 4} = -\frac{2}{3}$, or $y = -\frac{2}{3}x + \frac{14}{3}$.

Since all the perpendicular bisectors intersect at the same point, you can solve these two equations to find that point. To find the point where the perpendicular bisectors intersect, solve this system by substitution.

$$\begin{cases} y = \frac{1}{2}x + 1 & \text{Perpendicular bisector of } \overline{ZA}. \\ y = -\frac{2}{3}x + \frac{14}{3} & \text{Perpendicular bisector of } \overline{ZP}. \end{cases}$$

$$y = \frac{1}{2}x + 1 \qquad \text{Original first equation.}$$

$$-\frac{2}{3}x + \frac{14}{3} = \frac{1}{2}x + 1 \qquad \text{Substitute } -\tfrac{2}{3}x + \tfrac{14}{3} \text{ (from the second equation) for } y.$$

NCTM STANDARDS

CONTENT		PROCESS	
	Number	✓	Problem Solving
✓	Algebra		Reasoning
✓	Geometry		Communication
	Measurement	✓	Connections
	Data/Probability	✓	Representation

LESSON OBJECTIVE

- Use algebra to find the circumcenter of a triangle

USING YOUR ALGEBRA SKILLS 6

PLANNING

LESSON OUTLINE

One day:

15 min Example

10 min Sharing

20 min Exercises

MATERIALS

none

TEACHING

Students find the circumcenter of a triangle analytically.

One step Display the coordinates of the triangle in the example and ask students to use coordinate geometry to find its circumcenter. As they work, ask them to describe the circumcenter. Students may need to review how to solve a system of equations (page 285), how to find the midpoint (page 36), or slope (page 133), and characteristics of perpendicular lines (page 165). If students choose to set up equations using distances to the vertices, they may need a reminder of the distance formula and help in squaring both sides of an equation to eliminate the square root.

EXAMPLE

Students may have difficulty seeing the big picture. The solution has three major steps: finding the equations of the perpendicular bisectors of two sides and finding their intersection. In turn, finding each perpendicular bisector involves three steps: finding the midpoint of the side, the slope of the side, and the equation of the line through that midpoint whose slope is the negative reciprocal of the slope of the side.

SHARING IDEAS

Ask how students might check the reasonableness of their solutions. Graphing is a good way.

[Ask] "Why is the circumcenter of the triangle the center of the circumscribed circle?" [All points on a perpendicular bisector of a segment are equidistant from its endpoints. A point at which two perpendicular bisectors meet is equidistant from all three vertices, so a circle centered at that point will circumscribe the triangle.]

[Ask] "Does it matter which two sides you choose for finding perpendicular bisectors?" [Any pair will work, but some pairs may involve easier algebra.]

If students have not presented the method of using equal distances, you might work through it with them.

As a preview of Using Your Algebra Skills 7, wonder aloud whether there's an easier way to find the coordinates of the circumcenter. Might they be the averages of the coordinates of the vertices? Why? [No, the averages of the coordinates give the centroid.]

Closing the Lesson

The point of this lesson is how to find the **circumcenter** of a triangle analytically (with algebra).

BUILDING UNDERSTANDING

Encourage students to write coordinates as fractions instead of decimals.

$-4x + 28 = 3x + 6$	Multiply both sides by 6.
$22 = 7x$	Add $4x$ to both sides. Subtract 6 from both sides.
$\frac{22}{7} = x$	Divide both sides by 7.
$y = \frac{1}{2}\left(\frac{22}{7}\right) + 1$	Substitute 2 for x in the first equation.
$y = \frac{18}{7}$	Simplify.

The circumcenter is $\left(\frac{22}{7}, \frac{18}{7}\right)$. You can check this result by writing the equation for the perpendicular bisector of $\overline{AP}$ and verifying that $\left(\frac{22}{7}, \frac{18}{7}\right)$ is a point on this line.

EXERCISES

1. Triangle RES has vertices $R(0, 0)$, $E(4, -6)$, and $S(8, 4)$. Find the equation of the perpendicular bisector of $\overline{RE}$. $y = \frac{2}{3}x - \frac{13}{3}$

In Exercises 2–5, find the coordinates of the circumcenter of each triangle.

2. Triangle TRM with vertices $T(-2, 1)$, $R(4, 3)$, and $M(-4, -1)$ $(4, -7)$
3. Triangle FGH with vertices $F(0, -6)$, $G(3, 6)$, and $H(12, 0)$ $\left(\frac{69}{14}, -\frac{6}{7}\right)$
4. Right triangle MNO with vertices $M(-4, 0)$, $N(0, 5)$, and $O(10, -3)$ $\left(3, -1\frac{1}{2}\right)$
5. Isosceles triangle CDE with vertices $C(0, 6)$, $D(0, -6)$, and $E(12, 0)$ $\left(4\frac{1}{2}, 0\right)$
6. If a triangle is a right triangle, there is a shorter method to finding the circumcenter. What is it? Explain. The midpoint of the hypotenuse is the circumcenter.
7. If a triangle is an isosceles triangle, then there is a different, perhaps shorter method to finding the circumcenter. Explain. The intersection of the altitude from the vertex angle and the perpendicular bisector of one equal side is the circumcenter.
8. Circle P with center at $(-6, -6)$ and circle Q with center at $(11, 0)$ have a common internal tangent $\overleftrightarrow{AB}$. Find the coordinates of B if A has coordinates $(-3, -2)$. $(5, -8)$

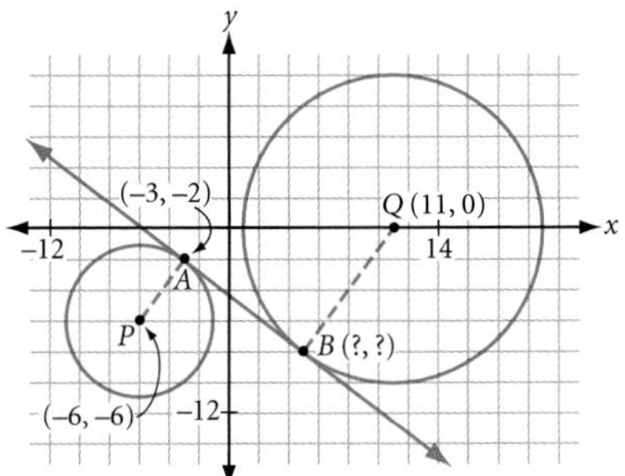

ASSIGNING HOMEWORK

Essential	1–5
Performance assessment	7, 8
Portfolio	3
Journal	6

▶ Helping with the Exercises

Exercise 6 This exercise relates to the Angles Inscribed in a Semicircle Conjecture and to the fact that in a right triangle the midpoint of the hypotenuse is equidistant from the vertices.

Exercise 8 To help students get started, **[Ask]** "How can you find the slope of line AB?" [Find the negative reciprocal of the slope of the line through points $(-6, -6)$ and $(-3, -2)$.]

LESSON

6.5 The Circumference/ Diameter Ratio

No human investigations can ever be called true science without going through mathematical tests.

LEONARDO DA VINCI

The distance around a polygon is called the perimeter. The distance around a circle is called the **circumference.** Here is a nice visual puzzle. Which is greater, the height of a tennis-ball can or the circumference of the can? The height is approximately three tennis-ball diameters tall. The diameter of the can is approximately one tennis-ball diameter. If you have a tennis-ball can handy, try it. Wrap a string around the can to measure its circumference, then compare this measurement with the height of the can. Surprised?

If you actually compared the measurements, you discovered that the circumference of the can is greater than three diameters of the can. In this lesson you are going to discover (or perhaps rediscover) the relationship between the diameter and the circumference of every circle. Once you know this relationship, you can measure a circle's diameter and calculate its circumference.

If you measure the circumference and diameter of a circle and divide the circumference by the diameter, you get a number slightly larger than 3. The more accurate your measurements, the closer your ratio will come to a special number called π (pi), pronounced "pie," like the dessert.

History CONNECTION

In 1897, the Indiana state assembly tried to legislate the value of π. The vague language of the state's House Bill No. 246, which became known as the "Indiana Pi Bill," implies several different incorrect values for π—3.2, 3.232, 3.236, 3.24, and 4. With a unanimous vote of 67-0, the House passed the bill to the state senate, where it was postponed indefinitely.

LESSON 6.5

PLANNING

LESSON OUTLINE

One day:

25 min Investigation

10 min Sharing

5 min Closing

5 min Exercises

MATERIALS

- tape measures, or metersticks and string
- circular objects
- calculators
- penny
- drinking straw
- can of tennis balls
- Sketchpad demonstration The Circumference and Diameter, *optional*

TEACHING

You may want to ask students what they know about the number π. If students are comfortable with finding a circle's circumference from its diameter and vice versa, use the one-step investigation.

INTRODUCTION

Start with a penny and a straw. **[Ask]** "Which is greater, the thickness of the penny or the circumference of the base of the penny?" [the circumference] "Which is greater, the height of the straw or the circumference of the base of the straw?" [the height] Now introduce the can of three tennis balls. **[Ask]** "Which is greater, the height of the can or the circumference?" Many students will say that the height is greater. Demonstrate that the circumference is noticeably greater.

NCTM STANDARDS

CONTENT		PROCESS	
	Number	✓	Problem Solving
	Algebra	✓	Reasoning
✓	Geometry	✓	Communication
✓	Measurement	✓	Connections
✓	Data/Probability		Representation

LESSON OBJECTIVE

- Calculate π, the ratio of the circumference of a circle to its diameter

One step Pose this problem: "Imagine a steel belt fitting tightly around the earth's equator. Now imagine cutting the belt and splicing in a piece to make the belt forty feet longer. Make the longer belt stand out evenly around the equator. What's the largest object that will fit under the belt: An atom? An ant? An anteater? An elephant?" If students say they know the answer, push them to defend it algebraically or explain it intuitively. As students work, they may want to know the radius of the earth (4,000 miles will do) or the earth's circumference (about 24,000 miles). If working with large numbers is causing difficulty, suggest that students use scientific notation or temporarily represent the earth's radius by r. For an intuitive explanation, suggest that students think about a basketball or even a point instead of the earth (but still with an increase in belt length of 40 feet). The goal is to get to the explanation that a circle's circumference varies directly with its radius, with 2π the constant of variation, so that an increase of x in circumference results in an increase in the radius of $\frac{x}{2\pi}$. [The band with 40 feet added would stand out from the earth more than 6 feet.]

Guiding the Investigation

As an alternative to this investigation, take the class outside and draw a large circle on the asphalt with a piece of chalk tied on the end of a string (the radius). To approximate π, have the whole class help hold another string in place around the circumference and compare its length with the diameter. (If a trundle wheel is available, use it for a more accurate result.) The goal is not so much for students to see that $\frac{C}{d}$ is a constant as to get a good approximation to the value of this constant (π), so accurate measurements are extremely important.

Investigation
A Taste of Pi

You will need

- several round objects (cans, mugs, bike wheel, plates)
- a meterstick or metric measuring tape
- sewing thread or thin string

In this investigation you will find an approximate value of π by measuring circular objects and calculating the ratio of the circumference to the diameter. Let's see how close you come to the actual value of π.

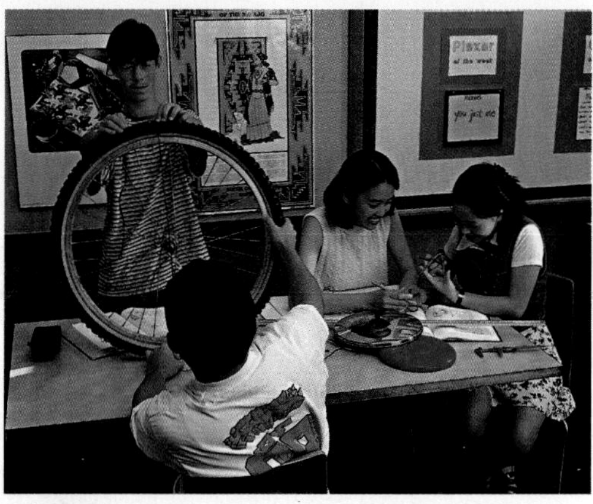

Step 1 Measure the circumference of each round object by wrapping the measuring tape, or string, around its perimeter. Then measure the diameter of each object with the meterstick or tape. Record each measurement to the nearest millimeter (tenth of a centimeter).

Step 2 Make a table like the one below and record the circumference (C) and diameter (d) measurements for each round object.

Object	Circumference (C)	Diameter (d)	Ratio $\frac{C}{d}$
Can			
Mug			
Wheel			

Step 3 Calculate the ratio $\frac{C}{d}$ for each object. Record the answers in your table.

Step 4 Calculate the average of your ratios of $\frac{C}{d}$.

Compare your average with the averages of other groups. Are the $\frac{C}{d}$ ratios close? You should now be convinced that the ratio $\frac{C}{d}$ is very close to 3 for every circle. We define π as the ratio $\frac{C}{d}$. If you solve this formula for C, you get a formula for the circumference of a circle in terms of the diameter, d. The diameter is twice the radius ($d = 2r$), so you can *also* get a formula for the circumference in terms of the radius, r.

Step 5 Copy and complete the conjecture.

Circumference Conjecture C-66

If C is the circumference and d is the diameter of a circle, then there is a number π such that $C =$ __?__. If $d = 2r$ where r is the radius, then $C =$ __?__. $2\pi r$

πd

As students work in groups, they can share the tasks of measuring, recording, and calculating. You might want to display a table summarizing the information about C, d, and $\frac{C}{d}$ so students can see what other groups are getting for their data.

Step 1 Instead of measuring, students might roll some objects until they've made a complete revolution. **[Alert]** You may need to help some groups decide on a method for finding a circle's center so they can determine a diameter to measure.

Mathematics
CONNECTION

The number π is an irrational number—its decimal form never ends. It is also a transcendental number—the pattern of digits does not repeat. The symbol π is a letter of the Greek alphabet. Perhaps no other number has more fascinated mathematicians throughout history. Mathematicians in ancient Egypt used $\left(\frac{4}{3}\right)^4$ as their approximation of circumference to diameter. Early Chinese and Hindu mathematicians used $\sqrt{10}$. By 408 C.E., Chinese mathematicians were using $\frac{355}{113}$. Today, computers have calculated approximations of π to billions of decimal places, and there are websites devoted to π! See **www.keymath.com/DG** .

Accurate approximations of π have been of more interest intellectually than practically. Still, what would a carpenter say if you asked her to cut a board 3π feet long? Most calculators have a π button that gives π to eight or ten decimal places. You can use this value for most calculations, then round your answer to a specified decimal place. If your calculator doesn't have a π button, or if you don't have access to a calculator, use the value 3.14 for π. If you're asked for an exact answer instead of an approximation, state your answer in terms of π.

How do you use the Circumference Conjecture? Let's look at two examples.

EXAMPLE A

If a circle has diameter 3.0 meters, what is the circumference? Use a calculator and state your answer to the nearest 0.1 meter.

▶ Solution

$C = \pi d$ Original formula.

$C = \pi(3.0)$ Substitute the value of d.

In terms of π, the answer is 3π. The circumference is about 9.4 meters.

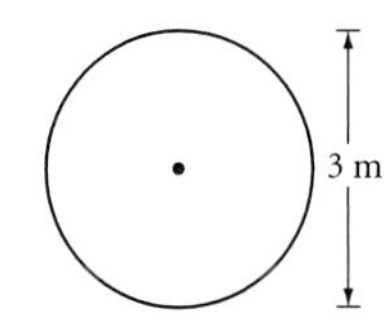

EXAMPLE B

If a circle has circumference 12π meters, what is the radius?

▶ Solution

$C = 2\pi r$ Original formula.

$12\pi = 2\pi r$ Substitute the value of C.

$r = 6$ Solve.

The radius is 6 meters.

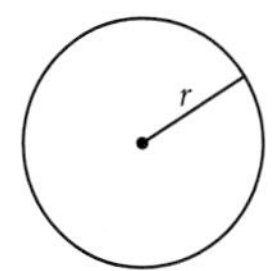

EXERCISES

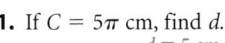

You will need

A calculator for Exercises 7–10

Use the Circumference Conjecture to solve Exercises 1–12. In Exercises 1–6, leave your answer in terms of π.

1. If $C = 5\pi$ cm, find d. $d = 5$ cm

2. If $r = 5$ cm, find C. $C = 10\pi$ cm

3. If $C = 24$ m, find r. $r = \frac{12}{\pi}$ m

4. If $d = 5.5$ m, find C. $C = 5.5\pi$ or $\frac{11\pi}{2}$

5. If a circle has a diameter of 12 cm, what is its circumference? $C = 12\pi$ cm

6. If a circle has a circumference of 46π m, what is its diameter? $d = 46$ m

▶ EXAMPLE A

This example is a good one for students who haven't grasped the idea of multiplying the diameter by π to get the circumference. Because the diameter's measurement (3.0) is given to only two significant digits, the decimal value of the circumference is rounded to two significant digits as well (9.4).

▶ EXAMPLE B

This example shows how to determine the radius from the circumference. It also demonstrates how π can be part of a measurement.

SHARING IDEAS

As students present results, ask about averaging the different ratios calculated for $\frac{C}{d}$ to get a result closer to π than any one ratio. Wonder aloud whether a better average might come from adding up all the circumferences and dividing by the sum of the lengths of the diameters, and let students try it.

[Ask] "Why would anyone work with π as a symbol rather than immediately approximating it with a decimal?" [Even if the numbers are based on measurements, which are not exact, the result is more exact if π isn't approximated.] If students need to find a decimal value of their result, they can substitute an approximation at the end. Ask what approximation they should use. Normally, they use the approximation given by their calculators and round off to the appropriate number of significant digits. If they are without a calculator, they might use $\frac{22}{7}$ or 3.14. For very quick mental approximations, they can replace π with 3.

Point out that the equation $C = \pi d$ has the form $y = kx$, where k is a constant. Ask students the term for that kind of equation. Direct variations are investigated in Chapter 3 of *Discovering Algebra.*

Assessing Progress

You can assess students' skill at measuring lengths, recording data systematically, filling out tables, and calculating ratios and averages.

Closing the Lesson

You might show the Sketchpad demonstration Circumference and Diameter. Restate the idea that π is a constant and is defined to be the ratio of circumference to diameter of any circle. That is, the circumference varies directly with the diameter so that an increase in the diameter by some amount results in an increase in the circumference by π times that amount. The symbol π should be left in calculations until the end; then, if a decimal answer is needed, a substitution can be made and the result rounded to an appropriate number of significant digits.

BUILDING UNDERSTANDING

Students find diameters, circumferences, and radii.

ASSIGNING HOMEWORK

Essential	1–11
Performance assessment	12, 13
Group	14, 15
Review	16–22

MATERIALS

- Exercise 19 (T), *optional*

▶ Helping with the Exercises

Exercise 13 If students ask for help, **[Ask]** "How is the diameter of the circle related to the side of the square?" [It is a diagonal of the square.]

14. Trees grow more in years with more rain.

In Exercises 7–10, use a calculator. Round your answer to the nearest 0.1 unit. Use the symbol $\approx$ to show that your answer is an approximation.

7. If $d = 5$ cm, find C. $C \approx 15.7$ cm

8. If $r = 4$ cm, find C. $C \approx 25.1$ cm

9. If $C = 44$ m, find r. ⓗ $r \approx 7.0$ m

10. What's the circumference of a bicycle wheel with a 27-inch diameter? $C \approx 84.8$ in.

11. If the distance from the center of a Ferris wheel to one of the seats is approximately 90 feet, what is the distance traveled by a seated person, to the nearest foot, in one revolution? 565 ft

12. If a circle is inscribed in a square with a perimeter of 24 cm, what is the circumference of the circle? ⓗ $C = 6\pi$ cm

13. If a circle with a circumference of 16π inches is circumscribed about a square, what is the length of a diagonal of the square? 16 in.

14. Each year a growing tree adds a new ring to its cross section. Some years the ring is thicker than others. Why do you suppose this happens?

Suppose the average thickness of growth rings in the Flintstones National Forest is 0.5 cm. About how old is "Old Fred," a famous tree in the forest, if its circumference measures 766 cm? 244 yr

Trees can live hundreds to thousands of years, and we can determine the age of one tree by counting its growth rings. A pair of rings—a light ring formed in the spring and summer and a dark one formed in the fall and early winter—represent the growth for one year. We can learn a lot about the climate of a region over a period of years by studying tree growth rings. This study is called *dendroclimatology.*

15. Pool contractor Peter Tileson needs to determine the number of 1-inch tiles to put around the edge of a pool. The pool is a rectangle with two semicircular ends as shown. How many tiles will he need? 1399 tiles

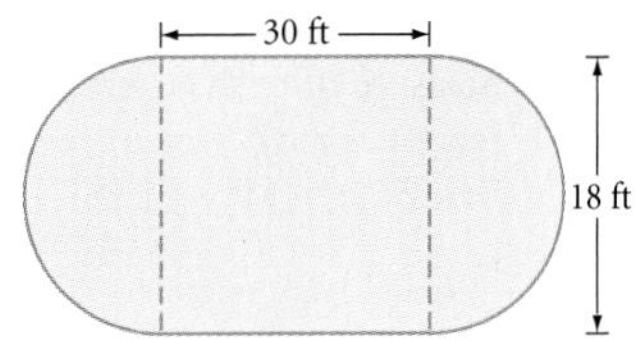

Review

6.3 **16.** ***Mini-Investigation*** Use these diagrams to find a relationship between $\angle AEN$ and the sum of the intercepted arc measures. Then copy and complete the conjecture.

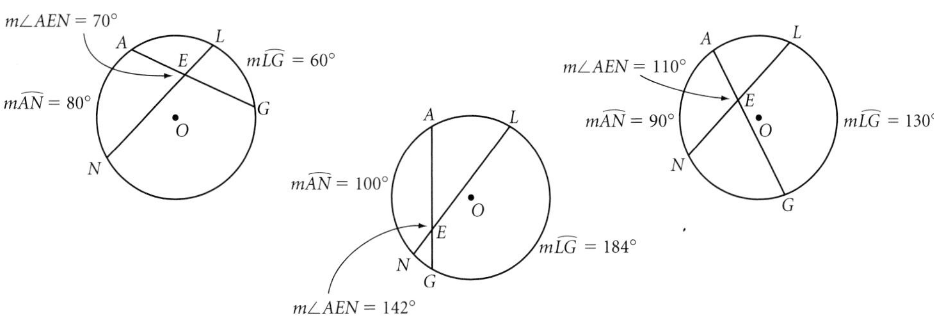

Conjecture: The measure of an angle formed by two intersecting chords is _?_ of the two intercepted arcs.

6.4 **17.** Copy the diagram at right and draw $\overline{AL}$. Prove the conjecture you made in Exercise 16. ⓗ

$m\angle ALN = \frac{1}{2}m\widehat{AN}$ and $m\angle LAG = \frac{1}{2}m\widehat{LG}$ by the Inscribed Angle Conjecture.

$m\angle NEA = m\angle ALN + m\angle LAG$ by the Triangle Exterior Angle Conjecture.

So, $m\angle NEA = \frac{1}{2}(m\angle\widehat{AN} + m\angle\widehat{GL})$ by substitution.

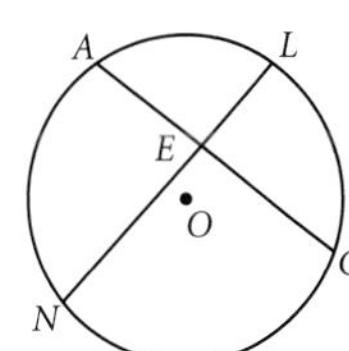

6.4 **18.** **Conjecture:** If two circles intersect at two points, then the segment connecting the centers is the perpendicular bisector of the common chord, the segment connecting the points of intersection.

Complete the flowchart proof of the conjecture.

Given: Circle M and circle S intersect at points A and T with radii $\overline{MA} \cong \overline{MT}$ and $\overline{SA} \cong \overline{ST}$

Show: $\overline{MS}$ is the perpendicular bisector of $\overline{AT}$

Flowchart Proof

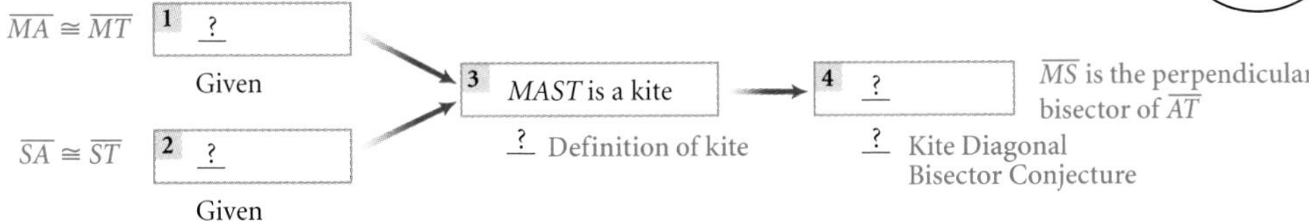

Exercises 16, 17 Students can use the dynamic geometry exploration at www.keymath.com/DG to help complete Exercises 16 and 17.

16. Conjecture: The measure of the angle formed by two intersecting chords is equal to one-half the sum of the measures of the two intercepted arcs. In the diagrams, $m\angle NEA = \frac{1}{2}(m\widehat{AN} + m\widehat{GL})$.

Exercise 20 This exercise reviews probability.

22. $10x + 2y$

EXTENSIONS

A. Students can use geometry software to construct a circle and its diameter, measure them, and calculate the ratio. Have them observe the ratio as they change the size of the circle and explain how what they observe confirms the Circumference Conjecture.

B. Suggest this investigation: Blow one large breath into a high-quality spherical balloon. With string, measure the balloon's circumference; with bow calipers, measure its diameter. Repeat the measurements after blowing into the balloon a second full breath, a third full breath, and so on, until the balloon is near breaking. For each pair of measurements, calculate the ratio of the circumference to the diameter and explain what you observe.

C. Use Take Another Look activity 5 on page 355.

D. Challenge students to write a π poem where the number of letters in successive words is the value of successive digits of π. Go to www.keymath.com/DG to find a link to a π poem that is also a pie poem.

6.3 **19.** Trace the figure below. Calculate the measure of each lettered angle.
$b = 90°, c = 42°, d = 70°, e = 48°, f = 132°, g = 52°$

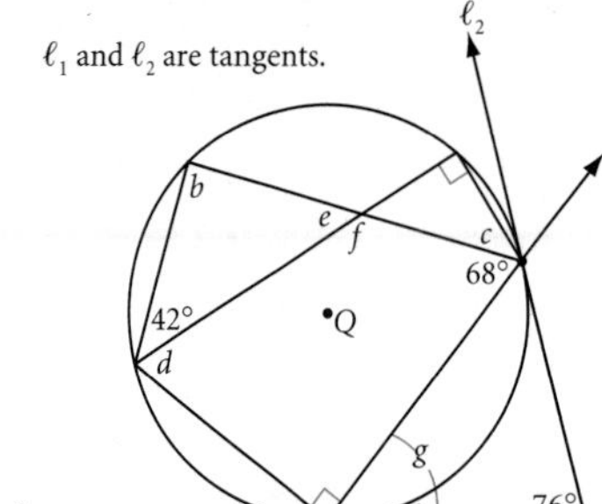

6.3 **20.** What is the probability that a flea strolling along the circle shown below will stop randomly on either $\overset{\frown}{AB}$ or $\overset{\frown}{CD}$? (Because you're probably not an expert in flea behavior, assume the flea will stop exactly once.) $\frac{150°}{360°}$ or $\frac{5}{12}$

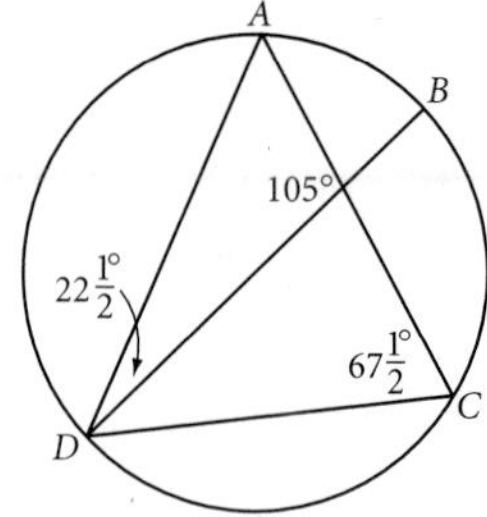

2.5 **21.** Explain why a and b are complementary.
$a + b + b + a = 180°$, so $a + b = 90°$

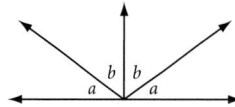

2.3 **22.** Assume the pattern below will continue. Write an expression for the perimeter of the tenth shape in this picture pattern.

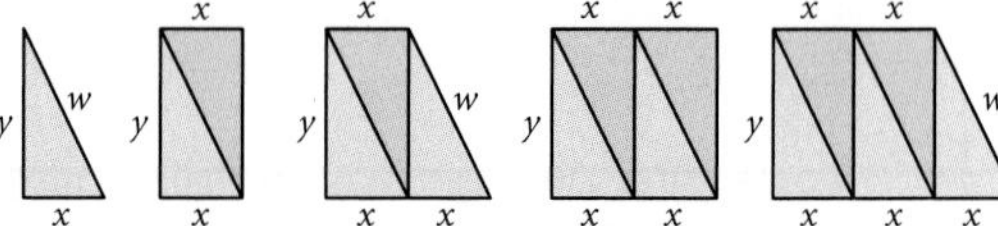

project

NEEDLE TOSS

If you randomly toss a needle on lined paper, what is the probability that the needle will land on one or more lines? What is the probability it will not land on any lines? The length of the needle and the distance between the lines will affect these probabilities.

Start with a toothpick of any length L as your "needle" and construct parallel lines a distance L apart. Write your predictions, then experiment. Using N as the number of times you dropped the needle, and C as the number of times the needle crossed the line, enter your results into the expression $2N/C$. As you drop the needle more and more times, the value of this expression seems to be getting close to what number?

Your project should include

- Your predictions and data.
- The calculated probabilities and your prediction of the theoretical probability.
- Any other interesting observations or conclusions.

Fathom

Using Fathom, you can simulate many experiments. See the demonstration Buffon's Needle that comes with the software package.

Supporting the project

The French mathematician and scientist George Louis Leclerc, Comte de Buffon (1707–1788) was the first to propose this problem. See the www.keymath.com/DG for demonstration Fathom simulations and links to interesting Web sites on Buffon's needle problem.

OUTCOMES

- For a large number of trials, the ratio $\frac{2N}{C}$ will be close to π.
- Explanations will take into account that the experiment involved lines and segments, but the result suggests a circle. They might suggest that the different possible orientations of the toothpick lie in a circle.
- Student does experiments with different line widths and finds for a toothpick with length L tossed on lines a distance D apart ($L < D$) $P(\text{crossing a line}) = \frac{2L}{\pi D}$. (If L is longer than D, however, calculating the probability is more complicated and requires calculus.)

LESSON

6.6

Around the World

Love is like π—natural, irrational, and very important.

LISA HOFFMAN

Many application problems are related to π. Satellite orbits, the wheels of a vehicle, tree trunks, and round pizzas are just a few of the real-world examples that involve the circumference of circles. Here is a famous example from literature.

Literature CONNECTION

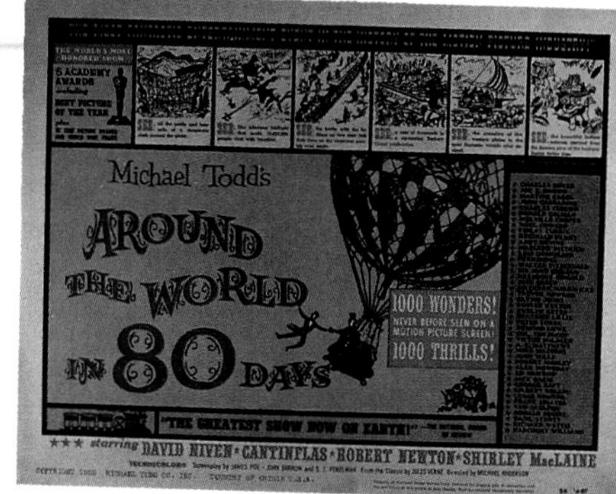

In the novel *Around the World in Eighty Days* (1873), Jules Verne (1828–1905) recounts the adventures of brave Phileas Fogg and his servant Passerpartout. They begin their journey when Phileas bets his friends that he can make a trip around the world in 80 days. Phileas's precise behavior, such as monitoring the temperature of his shaving water or calculating the exact time and location of his points of travel, reflects Verne's interest in the technology boom of the late nineteenth century. His studies in geology, engineering, and astronomy aid the imaginative themes in this and his other novels, including *A Journey to the Center of the Earth* (1864) and *Twenty Thousand Leagues Under the Sea* (1870).

EXAMPLE If the diameter of the earth is 8000 miles, find the average speed in miles per hour Phileas Fogg needs to circumnavigate the earth about the equator in 80 days.

► ***Solution*** To find the speed, you need to know the distance and the time. The distance around the equator is equal to the circumference C of a circle with a diameter of 8,000 miles.

$C = \pi d$ — The equation for circumference.

$= \pi(8{,}000)$ — Substitute 8,000 for d.

$\approx 25{,}133$ — Round to nearest mile.

So, Phileas must travel 25,133 miles in 80 days. To find the speed v in mi/hr, you need to divide distance by time and convert days into hours.

$v = \frac{\text{distance}}{\text{time}}$ — The formula for speed, or velocity.

$\approx \frac{25{,}133 \text{ mi}}{80 \text{ days}} \cdot \frac{1 \text{ day}}{24 \text{ hr}}$ — Substitute values and convert units of time.

≈ 13 mi/hr — Evaluate and round to the nearest mile per hour.

If the earth's diameter were *exactly* 8,000 miles, you could evaluate $\frac{8{,}000\pi}{80 \cdot 24}$ and get an exact answer of $\frac{25\pi}{6}$ in terms of π.

LESSON

6.6

PLANNING

LESSON OUTLINE

One day:

10 min	Example
10 min	Sharing
5 min	Closing
20 min	Exercises

MATERIALS

- calculators

TEACHING

In this lesson students see applications of the Circumference Conjecture.

One step Have students read the Connection, or tell them the story. Then ask them to solve the problem in the Example, with their books closed. As you circulate, encourage the use of dimensional analysis to convert days into hours. You may need to ask how to find speed (in miles per hour) from distance (in miles) and time (in hours). You need not insist that students use any particular approximation of π; variability in answers can lead to better discussion during Sharing.

► ***EXAMPLE***

Students may not recall how to find speed from distance and time, though if you remind them of a more familiar situation such as "You've gone one hundred eighty miles in three hours" they will probably realize what to do. Emphasize how the dimensions (units) work out: mph stands for miles per hour, and to derive it they divide the number of miles by the number of hours. A similar use of units as fractions arises in deciding whether to multiply by $\frac{\text{hours}}{\text{day}}$ or $\frac{\text{days}}{\text{hour}}$ in

NCTM STANDARDS

CONTENT		PROCESS	
	Number	✓	Problem Solving
✓	Algebra	✓	Reasoning
✓	Geometry	✓	Communication
✓	Measurement	✓	Connections
	Data/Probability	✓	Representation

LESSON OBJECTIVES

- Apply the formula for the circumference of a circle
- Practice visual thinking

Example (continued)

converting days to hours. As in multiplying fractions, the numerator of $\frac{\text{days}}{\text{hour}}$ cancels with the denominator of $\frac{\text{miles}}{\text{days}}$ to get $\frac{\text{miles}}{\text{hour}}$: $\left(\frac{\cancel{\text{days}}}{\text{hour}}\right)\left(\frac{\text{miles}}{\cancel{\text{days}}}\right) = \frac{\text{miles}}{\text{hour}}$.

SHARING IDEAS

As students present their findings, consider what would happen if different approximations of π were used.

Ask whether students remember some other equations relating distance, time, and speed. Keep stressing dimensional analysis: In the equation $d = vt$, the units mi/hr and hr are multiplied to get mi, for distance. In the equation $t = \frac{d}{v}$, miles are being divided by mi/hr; when the denominator is inverted to multiply, the miles units cancel to leave hours, for time: $(\cancel{\text{miles}})\left(\frac{\text{hours}}{\cancel{\text{miles}}}\right) = \text{hours}$.

While discussing dimensions, you might have students discuss what dimension π has in finding the circumference from the diameter. Because the diameter and the circumference have the same units, π has no units; it's just a number.

Assessing Progress

You can assess students' familiarity with equations relating distance, speed, and time; their comfort in using dimensional analysis; and their understanding of the Circumference Conjecture. From students' work on the exercises, you can assess how well they understand how and when to approximate the value of π.

Closing the Lesson

The Circumference Conjecture can be very useful, especially in calculating rates, times, or distances of motion. You might go through some exercises, pointing out where this conjecture is used.

EXERCISES

You will need

A calculator for Exercises **1–8**

In Exercises 1–6, round answers to the nearest unit. You may use 3.14 as an approximate value of π. If you have a π button on your calculator, use that value and then round your final answer.

1. A satellite in a nearly circular orbit is 2000 km above Earth's surface. The radius of Earth is approximately 6400 km. If the satellite completes its orbit in 12 hours, calculate the speed of the satellite in kilometers per hour. ⓗ $\approx$ 4398 km/hr

2. Wilbur Wrong is flying his remote-control plane in a circle with a radius of 28 meters. His brother, Orville Wrong, clocks the plane at 16 seconds per revolution. What is the speed of the plane? Express your answer in meters per second. The brothers may be wrong, but you could be right! $\approx$ 11 m/sec

3. Here is a tiring problem. The diameter of a car tire is approximately 60 cm (0.6 m). The warranty is good for 70,000 km. About how many revolutions will the tire make before the warranty is up? More than a million? A billion? (1 km = 1000 m) 37,000,000 revolutions

4. If the front tire of this motorcycle has a diameter of 50 cm (0.5 m), how many revolutions will it make if it is pushed 1 km to the nearest gas station? In other words, how many circumferences of the circle are there in 1000 meters? $\approx$ 637 revolutions

5. Goldi's Pizza Palace is known throughout the city. The small Baby Bear pizza has a 6-inch radius and sells for $9.75. The savory medium Mama Bear pizza sells for $12.00 and has an 8-inch radius. The large Papa Bear pizza is a hefty 20 inches in diameter and sells for $16.50. The edge is stuffed with cheese, and it's the best part of a Goldi's pizza. What size has the most pizza edge per dollar? What is the circumference of this pizza? Mama; $C \approx$ 50 in.

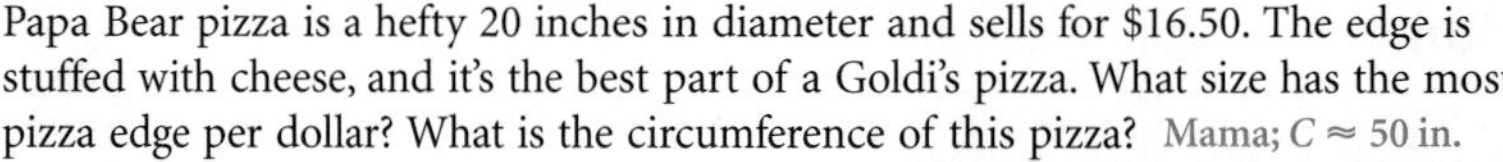

6. Felicia is a park ranger, and she gives school tours through the redwoods in a national park. Someone in every tour asks, "What is the diameter of the giant redwood tree near the park entrance?"

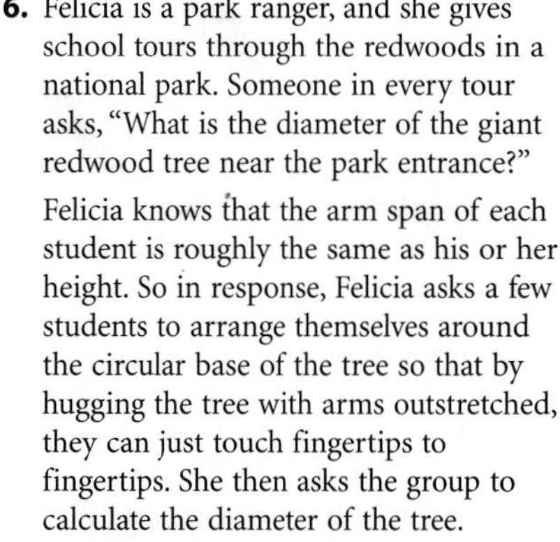

Felicia knows that the arm span of each student is roughly the same as his or her height. So in response, Felicia asks a few students to arrange themselves around the circular base of the tree so that by hugging the tree with arms outstretched, they can just touch fingertips to fingertips. She then asks the group to calculate the diameter of the tree.

In one group, four students with heights of 138 cm, 136 cm, 128 cm, and 126 cm were able to ring the tree. What is the approximate diameter of the redwood? $\approx$ 168 cm

7. APPLICATION Zach wants a circular table so that 12 chairs, each 16 inches wide, can be placed around it with at least 8 inches between chairs. What should be the diameter of the table? Will the table fit in a 12-by-14-foot dining room? Explain.

Calvin and Hobbes **by Bill Watterson**

8. A 45 rpm record has a 7-inch diameter and spins at 45 revolutions per minute. A 33 rpm record has a 12-inch diameter and spins at 33 revolutions per minute. Find the difference in speeds of a point on the edge of a 33 rpm record to that of a point on the edge of a 45 rpm record, in ft/sec. ⓗ 0.35 ft/sec.

Recreation CONNECTION

Using tinfoil records, Thomas Edison (1847–1931) invented the phonograph, the first machine to play back recorded sound, in 1877. Commonly called record players, they weren't widely reproduced until high-fidelity amplification (hi-fi) and advanced speaker systems came along in the 1930s. In 1948, records could be played at slower speeds to allow more material on the disc, creating longer-playing records (LPs). When compact discs became popular in the early 1990s, most record companies stopped making LPs. Some disc jockeys still use records instead of CDs.

Review

6.3 **9.** ***Mini-Investigation*** In these diagrams of circle *O*, find the relationship between $\angle ECA$ formed by the secants and the difference of the intercepted arc measures. Then copy and complete the conjecture.

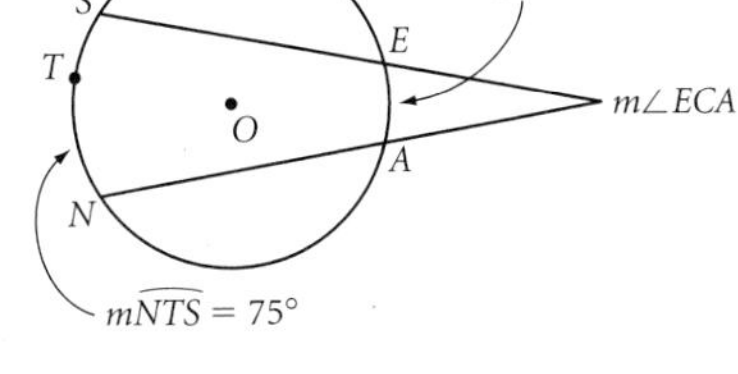

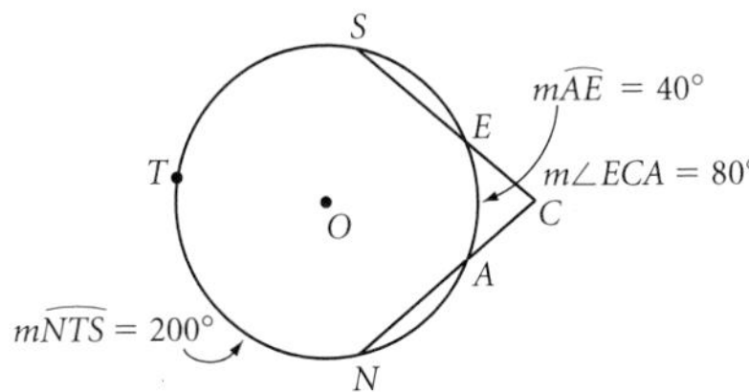

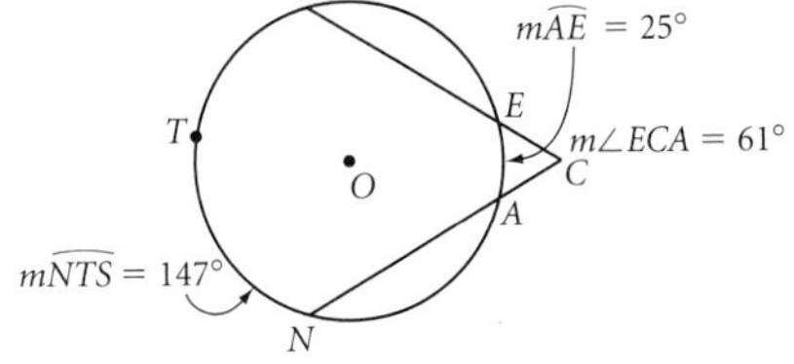

Conjecture: The measure of an angle formed by two secants through a circle is _?_.

BUILDING UNDERSTANDING

In the exercises students see many situations that incorporate the ideas of circumference, diameter, and π. You may want to select several problems for the groups to consider and others for students to complete as part of their assignment. If groups work on the exercises in class, you might have a few students share their solutions with the class before they all work alone.

ASSIGNING HOMEWORK

Essential	1–8
Performance assessment	5
Portfolio	6
Journal	7
Group	1–8
Review	9–17

Helping with the Exercises

Exercises 1–8 The answers given use a calculator π key. If students are using 3.14, their answers may be smaller.

Exercise 1 If students are having difficulty, suggest that drawing a picture often helps. They can see from a picture that the radius of the orbit is the sum of 2000 km and the earth's radius.

Exercises 3, 4 Some students may not realize that in one revolution a wheel rolls a distance equal to its circumference. Roll a cylinder to demonstrate this.

7. $d \approx 7.6$ ft. The table will fit, but the chairs may be a little tight in a 12-by-14 ft room. 12 chairs = 192 in., 12 spaces = 96 in., $C \approx 288$ in., $d \approx 91.7$ in. ≈ 7.6 ft.

Exercise 9 Although this exercise is a review of the Inscribed Angle Conjecture, it extends it to a new conjecture. The proof of this conjecture is similar to the proof of Case 1 of the Inscribed Angle Conjecture.

Students can use the dynamic geometry exploration at www.keymath.com/DG to help complete Exercise 9.

9. $m\angle ECA = \frac{1}{2}(m\widehat{SN} - m\widehat{EA})$
Conjecture: The measure of an angle formed by two secants through a circle is equal to one-half the difference of the larger arc measure and the smaller arc measure.

Exercise 10 For a different proof using a different auxiliary line, draw $\overline{AT}$ parallel to $\overline{SE}$ with point T on the circle. $m\angle TAN = m\angle ACE$, by corresponding angles. $m\widehat{ST} = m\widehat{AE}$, because the lines are parallel. $m\widehat{NT} = m\widehat{NS} - m\widehat{ST}$.

10. $m\angle ESA = \frac{1}{2}m\widehat{EA}$ and $m\angle SAN = \frac{1}{2}m\widehat{SN}$ by the Inscribed Angle Conjecture. $m\angle SAN = m\angle ESA + m\angle ECA$ by the Triangle Exterior Angle Conjecture. So, $\frac{1}{2}m\widehat{SN} = \frac{1}{2}m\widehat{EA} + m\angle ECA$ by substitution. With a little more algebra, $m\angle ECA = \frac{1}{2}(m\widehat{SN} - m\widehat{EA})$.

11. Both triangles are isosceles so the base angles in each triangle are congruent. But one of each base angle is part of a vertical pair. So, $a = b$ by the Vertical Angles Conjecture and transitivity.

Exercise 13 If students did not do the Mini-Investigation in Exercise 16 on page 335, suggest they draw an auxiliary line to complete a triangle below the chords; one angle is $\frac{1}{2}(32°)$ another is $\frac{1}{2}(44°)$ and the third angle is the supplement of a.

Exercise 16 [Language] The abbreviation *rpm* stands for "revolutions per minute." **[Alert]** Students may miss the step of converting minutes to seconds.

16. $\frac{400 \text{ rev}}{1 \text{ min}} \cdot \frac{26\pi \text{ ft}}{1 \text{ rev}} \cdot \frac{1 \text{ min}}{60 \text{ sec}} \approx$ 544.5 ft/sec

EXTENSION

Students can create their own application problems for classmates to solve.

6.4 **10.** Copy the diagram below. Construct $\overline{SA}$. Prove the conjecture you made in Exercise 9. ⓗ

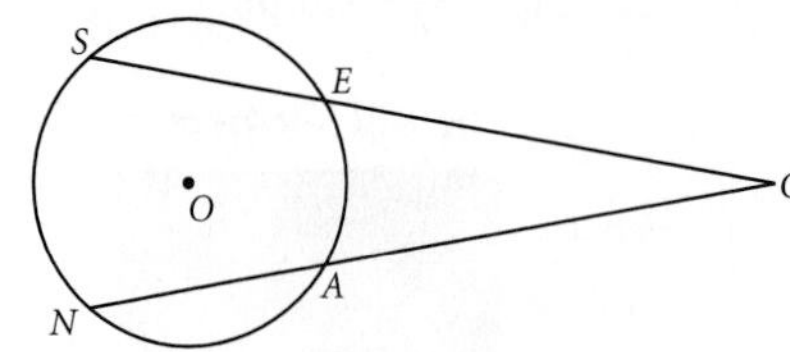

2.5 **11.** Explain why a equals b.

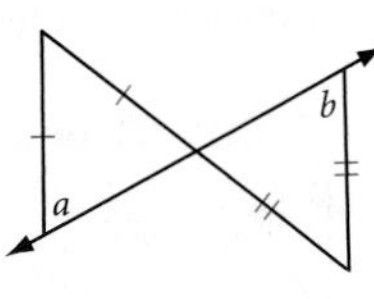

6.3 **12.** As P moves from A to B along the semicircle $\widehat{ATB}$, which of these measures constantly increases? C

A. The perimeter of $\triangle ABP$

B. The distance from P to $\overleftrightarrow{AB}$

C. $m\angle ABP$

D. $m\angle APB$

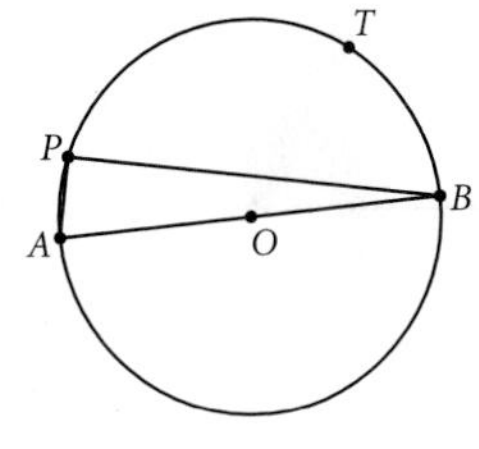

6.3 **13.** $a = \underline{?}$ 38°

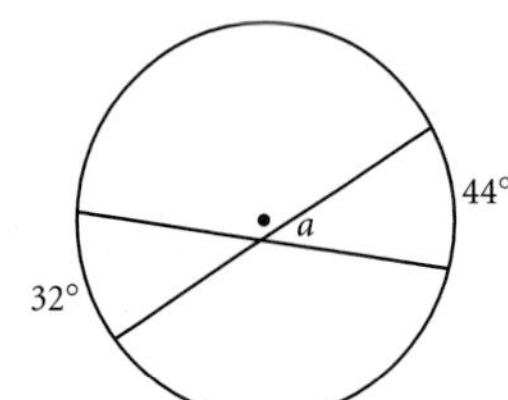

6.3 **14.** $b = \underline{?}$ 48°

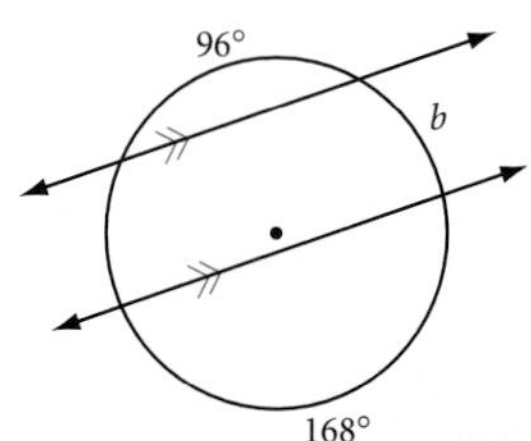

5.4 **15.** $d = \underline{?}$ 30 cm

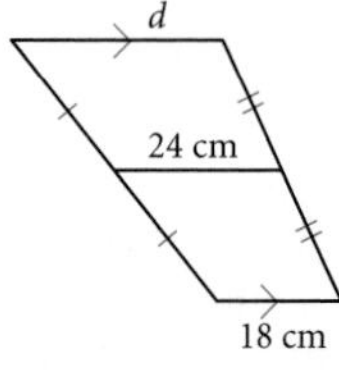

6.5 **16.** A helicopter has three blades each measuring about 26 feet. What is the speed in feet per second at the tips of the blades when they are moving at 400 rpm?

4.3 **17.** Two sides of a triangle are 24 cm and 36 cm. Write an inequality that represents the range of values for the third side. Explain your reasoning.
12 cm < third side < 60 cm. This is based on the Triangle Inequality Conjecture.

IMPROVING YOUR VISUAL THINKING SKILLS

Picture Patterns I

Draw the next picture in each pattern. Then write the rule for the total number of squares in the *n*th picture of the pattern.

1. 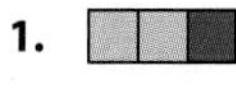 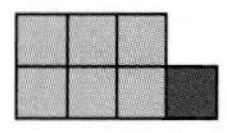 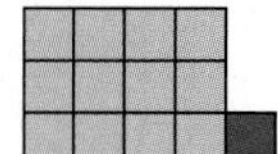

2. 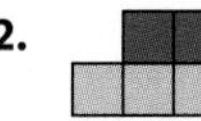  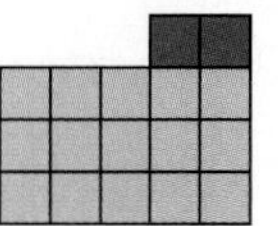

IMPROVING VISUAL THINKING SKILLS

1. Rule: $(n + 1)n + 1 = n^2 + n + 1$

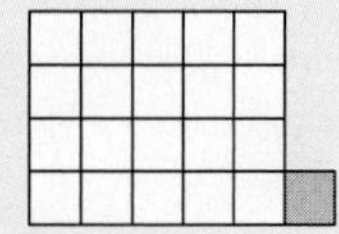

2. Rule: $(n + 2)n + 2 = n^2 + 2n + 2$

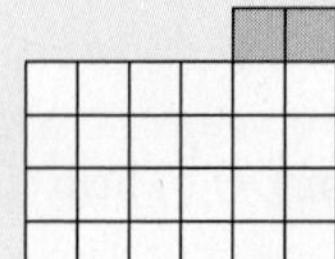

LESSON

6.7

Arc Length

You have learned that the *measure* of an arc is equal to the measure of its central angle. On a clock, the measure of the arc from 12:00 to 1:00 is equal to the measure of the angle formed by the hour and minute hands. A circular clock is divided into 12 equal arcs, so the measure of this arc is $\frac{360°}{12}$, or 30°.

Some people transform the sun into a yellow spot, others transform a yellow spot into the sun.

PABLO PICASSO

Notice that because the minute hand is longer, the tip of the minute hand must travel farther than the tip of the hour hand even though they both move 30° from 12 to 1. So the arc length is different even though the arc *measure* (the degree measure) is the same!

Let's take another look at the arc measure.

EXAMPLE A

What fraction of its circle is each arc?

a. $\overset{\frown}{AB}$ is what fraction of circle T?

b. $\overset{\frown}{CED}$ is what fraction of circle O?

c. $\overset{\frown}{EF}$ is what fraction of circle P?

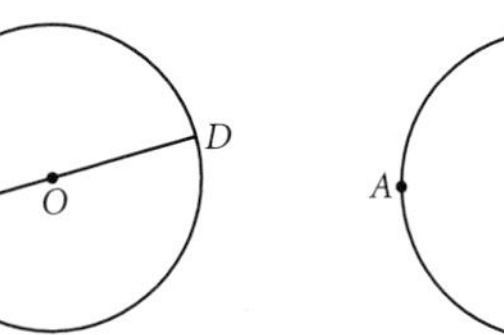

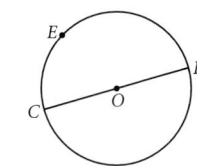

▶ Solution

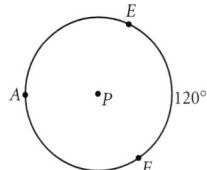

In part a, you probably "just knew" that the arc is one-fourth of the circle because you have seen one-fourth of a circle so many times. Why is it one-fourth? The arc measure is 90°, a full circle measures 360°, and $\frac{90°}{360°} = \frac{1}{4}$. The arc in part b is half of the circle because $\frac{180°}{360°} = \frac{1}{2}$. In part c, you may or may not have recognized right away that the arc is one-third of the circle. The arc is one-third of the circle because $\frac{120°}{360°} = \frac{1}{3}$.

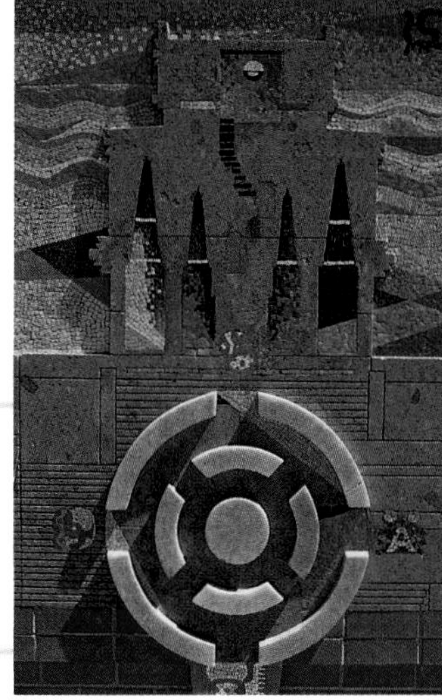

Cultural CONNECTION

This modern mosaic shows the plan of an ancient Mayan observatory. On certain days of the year light would shine through openings, indicating the seasons. This sculpture includes blocks of marble carved into arcs of concentric circles.

NCTM STANDARDS

CONTENT		PROCESS	
	Number	✓	Problem Solving
✓	Algebra	✓	Reasoning
✓	Geometry	✓	Communication
✓	Measurement		Connections
	Data/Probability		Representation

LESSON OBJECTIVES

- Discover a formula for finding the length of an arc of a circle
- Apply the formula for arc length

LESSON 6.7

PLANNING

LESSON OUTLINE

One day:

25 min Investigation or Examples

5 min Closing

15 min Exercises

MATERIALS

- construction tools
- calculators

TEACHING

Start with the one-step investigation or discuss Example A before students begin the step-by-step investigation.

▶ EXAMPLE A

[Alert] Students may have difficulty distinguishing between the arc measure and the arc length. You might draw two concentric circles, one with a radius of 1 and one with a radius of 2, and a 90° arc of each circle.

[Ask] "What is the measure of each arc?" [90°] "What is the length of each arc?" $\left[\frac{\pi}{2}\right.$ and π, respectively$\left.\right]$ The arc measure equals the central angle measure, and the arc length is the proportional part of the circumference.

One step Pose this problem, adapted from Exercise 10: "Astronaut Polly Hedra circles the earth every ninety minutes in a path above the equator. Do you have enough information to calculate the distance along the equator she passes directly over while eating a quick fifteen-minute lunch?" Some students may say no initially because they don't know the astronaut's height. Rather than pointing out that the question is asking about a

One step (continued)
distance on the earth, ask them to make up a height and see how to use that information. Other students may say no because they don't know the circumference of the earth. **[Ask]** "Have you seen a derivation of that number recently?" [yes, in Lesson 6.6] Challenge students to articulate a method for expressing the length of any arc of a circle given the measure of the arc and the circle's diameter.

Guiding the Investigation

Step 4 Encourage groups to try out their conjecture on other circles and arcs or to test the clarity of their wording by exchanging their conjectures with other groups.

SHARING IDEAS

As students present their ideas for finding arc length, keep emphasizing that the goal is not to remember the formula but to have it make sense. The arc is some part of the circle. What part? The arc is the same part of the full circle as the arc measure (or central angle) is of the full circle. So the length of the arc is that same part of the circle's circumference (distance around). The idea will be obvious to some students who may be confused by the formula. Others may still be confused because of difficulty understanding ratios.

If students have difficulty understanding the idea, go through Example B or Example C.

▶ ***EXAMPLES B AND C***

Example B integrates arc length with the Inscribed Angle Conjecture by moving from an inscribed angle through an arc measure to an arc length. Example C moves from an arc length to a radius.

What do these fractions have to do with arc length? If you traveled halfway around a circle, you'd cover $\frac{1}{2}$ of its perimeter, or circumference. If you went a quarter of the way around, you'd travel $\frac{1}{4}$ of its circumference. The **length of an arc,** or arc length, is some fraction of the circumference of its circle.

The measure of an arc is calculated in units of degrees, but arc length is calculated in units of distance.

Investigation
Finding the Arcs

In this investigation you will find a method for calculating the arc length.

Steps 1–3
Circle T $\frac{90}{360} = \frac{1}{4}$, so $\overset{\frown}{AB}$ is $\frac{1}{4}$ of the circle. The radius is 12 meters, so the circumference is 24π meters. $\frac{1}{4}$ of 24π is 6π, so the arc length of $\overset{\frown}{AB}$ is 6π meters.

Circle O $\frac{180}{360} = \frac{1}{2}$, so $\overset{\frown}{CED}$ is $\frac{1}{2}$ of the circle. The diameter is 8 inches, so the circumference is 8π inches. $\frac{1}{2}$ of 8π is 4π, so the arc length of $\overset{\frown}{CED}$ is 4π inches.

Circle P $\frac{140}{360} = \frac{7}{18}$, so $\overset{\frown}{GH}$ is $\frac{7}{18}$ of the circle. The radius is 36 feet, so the circumference is 72π feet. $\frac{7}{18}$ of 72π is 28π, so the arc length of $\overset{\frown}{GH}$ is 28π feet.

Step 1 For $\overset{\frown}{AB}$, $\overset{\frown}{CED}$, and $\overset{\frown}{GH}$, find what fraction of the circle each arc is.

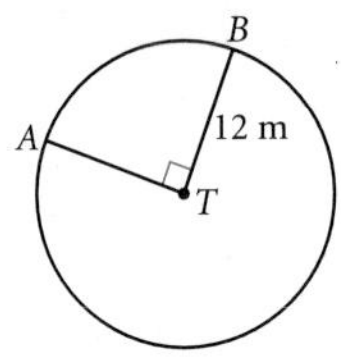

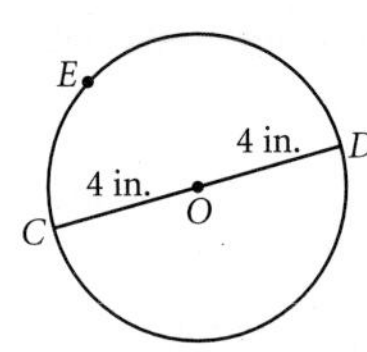

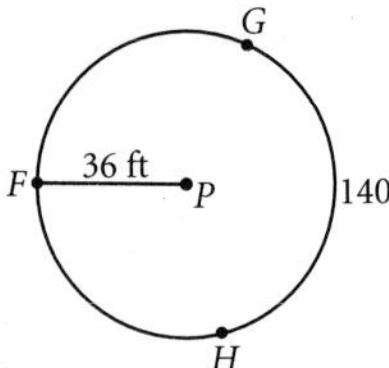

Step 2 Find the circumference of each circle.

Step 3 Combine the results of Steps 1 and 2 to find the length of each arc.

Step 4 Share your ideas for finding the length of an arc. Generalize this method for finding the length of *any* arc, and state it as a conjecture.

Arc Length Conjecture C-67

The length of an arc equals the ___?___. circumference times the measure of the central angle divided by 360°

How do you use this new conjecture? Let's look at a few examples.

EXAMPLE B If the radius of the circle is 24 cm and $m\angle BTA = 60°$, what is the length of $\overset{\frown}{AB}$?

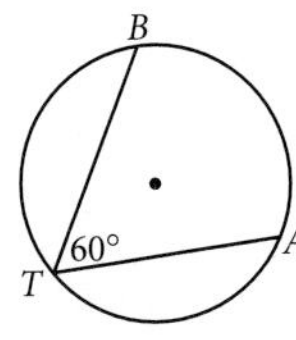

▶ ***Solution*** $m\angle BTA = 60°$, so $m\overset{\frown}{AB} = 120°$ by the Inscribed Angle Conjecture. Then $\frac{120}{360} = \frac{1}{3}$, so the arc length is $\frac{1}{3}$ of the circumference, by the Arc Length Conjecture.

$$\text{Arc length} = \frac{1}{3}C$$

$$= \frac{1}{3}(48\pi) \qquad \text{Substitute } 2\pi r \text{ for } C\text{, where } r = 24.$$

$$= 16\pi \qquad \text{Simplify.}$$

The arc length is 16π cm, or approximately 50.3 cm.

EXAMPLE C If the length of $\overset{\frown}{ROT}$ is 116π meters, what is the radius of the circle?

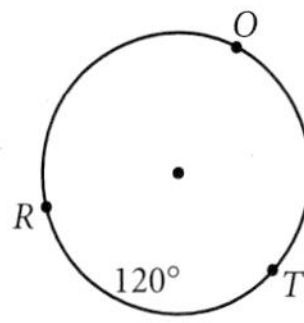

▶ Solution $m\overset{\frown}{ROT} = 240°$, so $\overset{\frown}{ROT}$ is $\frac{240}{360}$, or $\frac{2}{3}$ of the circumference.

$116\pi = \frac{2}{3}C$ Apply the Arc Length Conjecture.

$116\pi = \frac{2}{3}(2\pi r)$ Substitute $2\pi r$ for C.

$348\pi = 4\pi r$ Multiply both sides by 3.

$87 = r$ Divide both sides by 4π.

The radius is 87 m.

EXERCISES

You will need

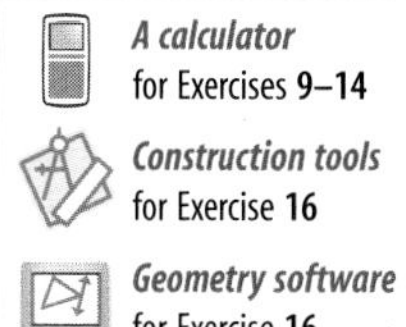

A calculator for Exercises **9–14**

Construction tools for Exercise **16**

Geometry software for Exercise **16**

For Exercises 1–8, state your answers in terms of π.

1. Length of $\overset{\frown}{CD}$ is _?_. $\frac{4\pi}{3}$ in.

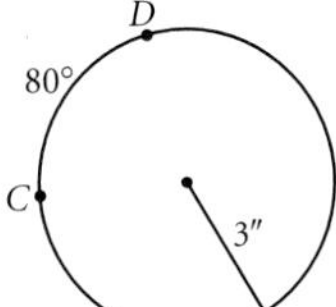

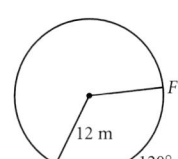

2. Length of $\overset{\frown}{EF}$ is _?_. 8π m

3. Length of $\overset{\frown}{BIG}$ is _?_. ⓗ 14π cm

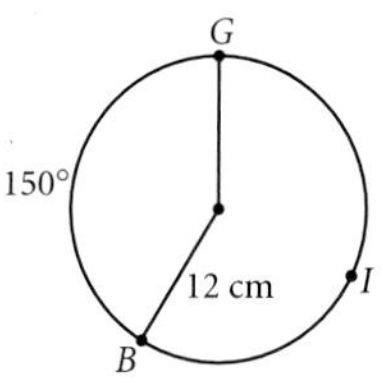

4. Length of $\overset{\frown}{AB}$ is 6π m. The radius is _?_. 9 m

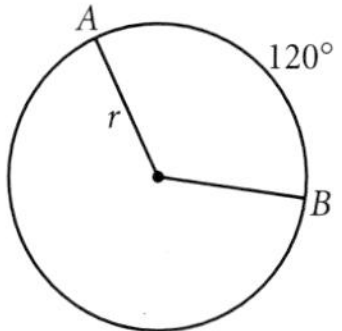

5. The radius is 18 ft. Length of $\overset{\frown}{RT}$ is _?_. 6π ft

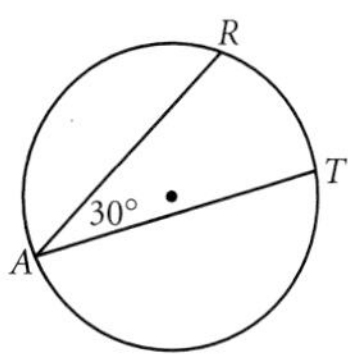

6. The radius is 9 m. Length of $\overset{\frown}{SO}$ is _?_. 4π m

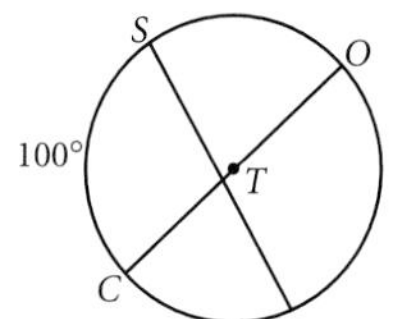

7. Length of $\overset{\frown}{TV}$ is 12π in. The diameter is _?_. 27 in.

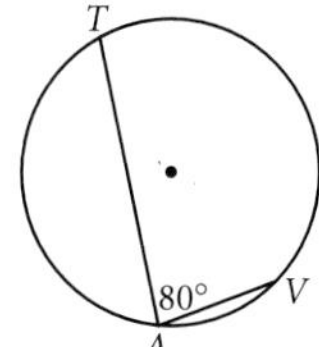

8. Length of $\overset{\frown}{AR}$ is 40π cm. $\overleftrightarrow{CA} \parallel \overleftrightarrow{RE}$. The radius is _?_. ⓗ 100 cm

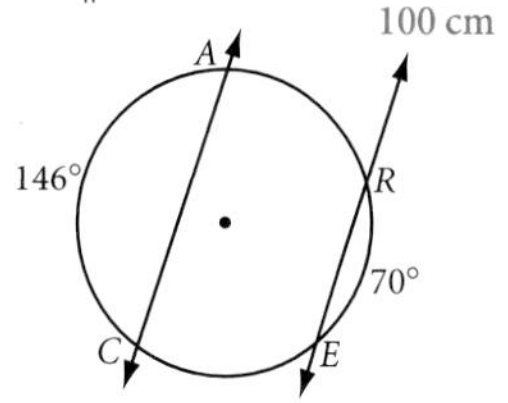

Assessing Progress
You can assess students' understanding of arc measure, ratios, the Inscribed Angle Conjecture, and the Circumference Conjecture.

Closing the Lesson

Reiterate that the length of an arc, or **arc length,** is different from **arc measure.** The length of an arc is in distance units, the part of the circumference corresponding to the part the arc measure is of 360°.

BUILDING UNDERSTANDING

You might have a few students share solutions to early exercises before students move on to solving the rest of them.

ASSIGNING HOMEWORK

Essential	1–10
Performance assessment	12
Portfolio	8
Journal	11
Group	9, 10
Review	13–17

MATERIALS

- Exercise 16 (T), *optional*

▶ Helping with the Exercises

Exercise 1 Students may wonder why the radius is drawn so far from the arc. The radius is drawn only to provide information about its length.

Exercise 3 As needed, wonder aloud whether the measure of arc *BIG* can be calculated. [360° − 150° = 210°]

Exercises 5–8 These exercises integrate the Arc Length Conjecture with conjectures from earlier in the course.

Exercise 9 Encourage any students having difficulty to make a sketch. Ask what they need to know to find the speed. To calculate the distance of one lap, they'll need to apply the Arc Length Conjecture.

Exercise 10 This exercise is the one-step investigation.

Exercise 11 Encourage students to draw a sketch of a view from above.

11. Desks are about 17 meters from the center. About four desks will fit because an arc with one-half the radius and the same central angle will be one-half as long as the outer arc.

Exercise 12 If students protest that the sun's rays won't be parallel, you can point out that the sun is far enough away that its rays will be parallel for practical purposes like this. For exactness, the two cities would have needed to experience noon at the same time; the fact that Syene was a little east of Alexandria introduced a small error. **[Context]** The calculation based on 7.2° is only off by 0.4%, but this calculation was lost and a later calculation that the circumference was 17,000 miles made it seem short enough for Columbus to attempt the trip.

9. A go-cart racetrack has 100-meter straightaways and semicircular ends with diameters of 40 meters. Calculate the average speed in meters per minute of a go-cart if it completes 4 laps in 6 minutes. Round your answer to the nearest m/min. ⓗ 217 m/min

10. Astronaut Polly Hedra circles Earth every 90 minutes in a path above the equator. If the diameter of Earth is approximately 8000 miles, what distance along the equator will she pass directly over while eating a quick 15-minute lunch? $\approx$ 4200 miles

11. APPLICATION The Library of Congress reading room has desks along arcs of concentric circles. If an arc on the outermost circle with eight desks is about 12 meters long and makes up $\frac{1}{9}$ of the circle, how far are these desks from the center of the circle? How many desks would fit along an arc with the same central angle but that is half as far from the center? Explain. ⓗ

The Library of Congress, Washington, D.C.

12. A Greek mathematician who lived in the third century B.C.E., Eratosthenes, devised a clever method to calculate the circumference of Earth. He knew that the distance between Aswan (then called Syene) and Alexandria was 5000 Greek stadia (a stadium was a unit of distance at that time), or about 500 miles. At noon of the summer solstice, the Sun cast no shadow on a vertical pole in Syene, but at the same time in Alexandria a vertical pole did cast a shadow. Eratosthenes found that the angle between the vertical pole and the ray from the tip of the pole to the end of the shadow was 7.2°. From this he was able to calculate the ratio of the distance between the two cities to the circumference of Earth. Use this diagram to explain Eratosthenes' method, then use it to calculate the circumference of Earth in miles.

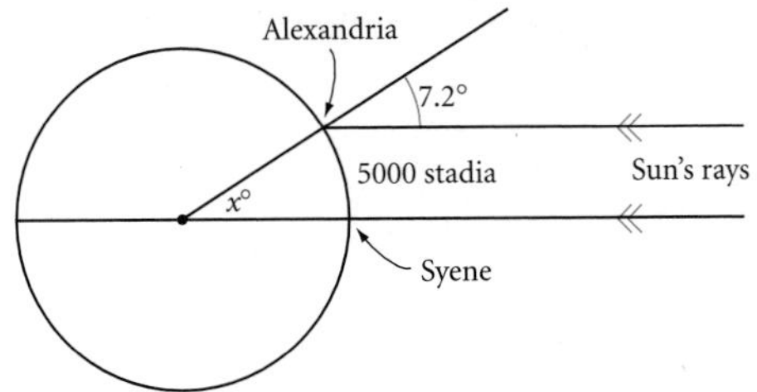

The measure of the central angle is 7.2° because of the Corresponding Angles Conjecture. Therefore, $500 = \frac{7.2}{360} \cdot C$, so $C \approx 25{,}000$ miles.

Review

6.5 **13.** **Angular velocity** is a measure of the rate at which an object revolves around an axis, and can be expressed in degrees per second. Suppose a carousel horse completes a revolution in 20 seconds. What is its angular velocity? Would another horse on the carousel have a different angular velocity? Why or why not? 18°/sec. No, the angular velocity is measured in degrees per second not in distance per second, so it is the same at every point on the carousel.

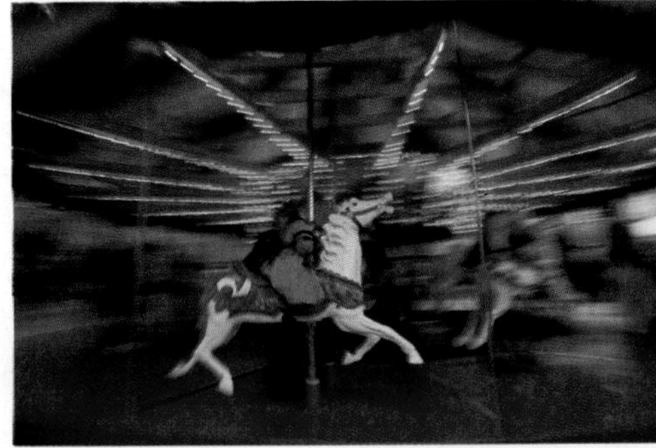

6.5 **14.** **Tangential velocity** is a measure of the distance an object travels along a circular path in a given amount of time. Like speed, it can be expressed in meters per second. Suppose two carousel horses complete a revolution in 20 seconds. The horses are 8 m and 6 m from the center of the carousel, respectively. What are the tangential velocities of the two horses? Round your answers to the nearest 0.1 m/sec. Explain why the horses have equal angular velocities but different tangential velocities.

15. Calculate the measure of each lettered angle. ⓗ

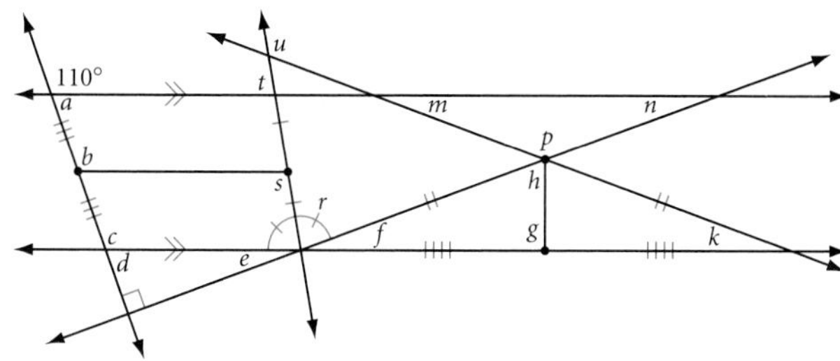

Art
CONNECTION

The traceries surrounding rose windows in Gothic cathedrals were constructed with only arcs and straight lines. The photo at right shows a rose window from Reims cathedral, which was built in the thirteenth century, in Reims, a city in northeastern France. The overlaid diagram shows its constructions.

Chapter 3 **16.** ***Construction*** Read the Art Connection above. Reproduce the constructions shown with your compass and straightedge or with geometry software. ⓗ

1.2 **17.** Find the measure of the angle formed by a clock's hands at 10:20. ⓗ 170°

project

RACETRACK GEOMETRY

If you had to start and finish at the same line of a racetrack, which lane would you choose? The inside lane has an obvious advantage. For a race to be fair, runners in the outside lanes must be given head starts, as shown in the photo.

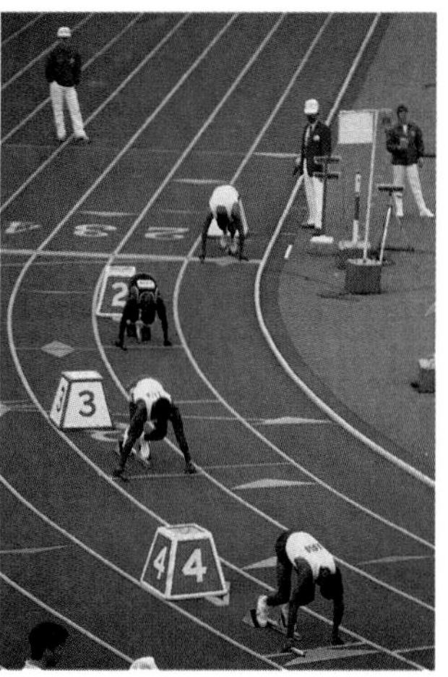

Design a four-lane oval track with straightaways and semicircular ends. Show start and finish lines so that an 800-meter race can be run fairly in all four lanes. The semicircular ends must have inner diameters of 50 meters. The distance of one lap in the inner lane must be 800 meters.

Your project should contain

- A detailed drawing with labeled lengths.
- An explanation of the part that radius, lane width, and straightaway length plays in the design.

14. Outer horse ≈ 2.5 m/sec, inner horse ≈ 1.9 m/sec. One horse has traveled farther in the same amount of time (tangential velocity), but both horses have rotated the same number of times (angular velocity).

15. $a = 70°, b = 110°, c = 110°, d = 70°, e = 20°, f = 20°, g = 90°, h = 70°, k = 20°, m = 20°, n = 20°, p = 140°, r = 80°, s = 100°, t = 80°, u = 120°$

16. possible answer:

EXTENSION

Present this challenge: Using geometry software, construct a circle and an arc on the circle. Measure only the circle's circumference and the arc's central angle. Calculate an expression for the arc's length. Now measure the arc length to confirm that your calculation is correct. Write a paragraph explaining what you did.

Supporting the project

Step-by-step details for completing the project are found in *More Projects and Explorations.*

OUTCOMES

- The track will have straightaways with lengths about 320 meters.
- The runner in the inner lane starts at the finish line.
- Assumptions about the width of the lanes are stated.
- If the lanes are 1 meter wide, the runner in the outer lane will start about 9.4 meters ahead of the runner in the inner lane.
- Complete explanations of all the factors used in the calculations are given.

EXPLORATION

PLANNING

LESSON OUTLINE

One day:

35 min Activity

5 min Sharing

5 min Closing

MATERIALS

- The Geometer's Sketchpad

TEACHING

[Ask] "If a bug is sitting right at the edge of a wheel while the wheel is rolling, what path will the bug follow?" Take all student conjectures without comment before starting the Sketchpad exploration.

Guiding the Activity

You might want to have students work in pairs so one can read the directions as the other runs the software. If so, have them switch roles after Step 9. You may want to have selected students show you their work after Steps 4, 9, and 13.

Step 5 [Alert] If students construct segment *DE* going from left to right, the circle will move in that direction in Step 13, although the radius will indicate that the circle is rolling from right to left.

Steps 5–8 In these steps students make a copy, a translation, of the original circle. Having point *G* along a line allows moving it onto and off of the circle in Step 15. The original circle is still needed.

THE GEOMETER'S SKETCHPAD

Exploration

Cycloids

Imagine a bug gripping your bicycle tire as you ride down the street. What would the bug's path look like? What path does the Moon make as it rotates around Earth while Earth rotates around the Sun? Using animation in Sketchpad, you can model a rotating wheel.

Activity

Turning Wheels

In this activity, you'll investigate the path of a point on a wheel as it rolls along the ground or around another wheel. You'll start by constructing a stationary circle with a rotating spoke.

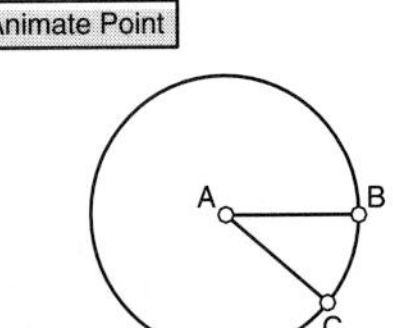

Step 1 Construct two points *A* and *B*. Select them in that order, and choose **Circle By Center+Point** from the Construct menu. Construct radius $\overline{AB}$.

Step 2 Construct a second radius, $\overline{AC}$.

Step 3 Select point *C* and choose **Animation** from the Action Buttons submenu of the Edit menu. Make point *C* move **counterclockwise** around the circle at **fast** speed.

Step 4 Press the Animation button. Now you have a circle with one spoke that rotates in a counterclockwise direction. (Press it again to stop.)

How can you make a wheel that will roll? You can't roll your circle with the spinning spoke because if the circle moves, the spoke would have to move with it. But you can make a different circle and, as you move it, use circle *A* to rotate it. Here's how.

Step 5 Construct a long horizontal segment *DE* going from right to left and a point *F* on the segment.

Step 6 Select points *A* and *F*, in order, and choose **Mark Vector** from the Transform menu.

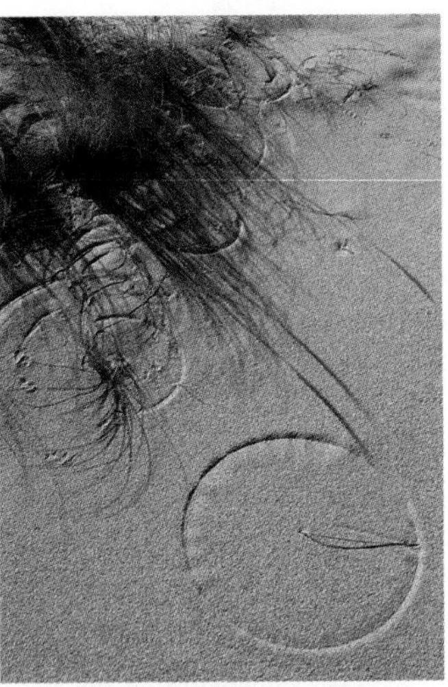

These circles in the sand were created by the wind blowing blades of grass as if they were spokes on a wheel.

LESSON OBJECTIVE

- Understand the construction of a cycloid

NCTM STANDARDS

CONTENT		PROCESS	
	Number		Problem Solving
	Algebra		Reasoning
✓	Geometry	✓	Communication
	Measurement		Connections
	Data/Probability	✓	Representation

Step 7 Select circle A, point C, and $\overline{AC}$, and use the Transform menu to translate by the marked vector.

Step 8 Construct a line FC' overlapping $\overline{FC'}$ and a point G anywhere on the line. Hide the line and construct $\overline{FG}$.

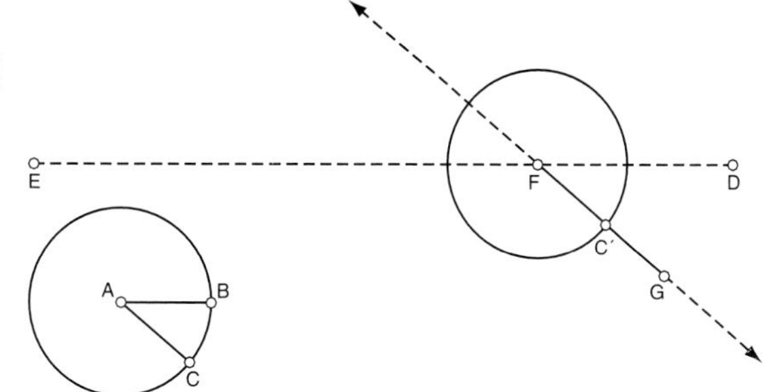

Step 9 Press the animation button. The rotating spoke $\overline{AC}$ should cause the spoke $\overline{FG}$ to spin at the same time.

Now you're ready to make that circle roll.

Step 10 Select $\overline{DE}$ and point F, and choose **Perpendicular Line** from the Construct menu.

Step 11 To construct the road, select point H, the lower point where the line intersects the circle, and $\overline{DE}$ and choose **Parallel Line** from the Construct menu. Hide the perpendicular line and point H.

Step 12 Select points F and C and create an action button that animates both point F backward along the segment at **fast** speed and point C **counterclockwise** around the circle at **fast** speed.

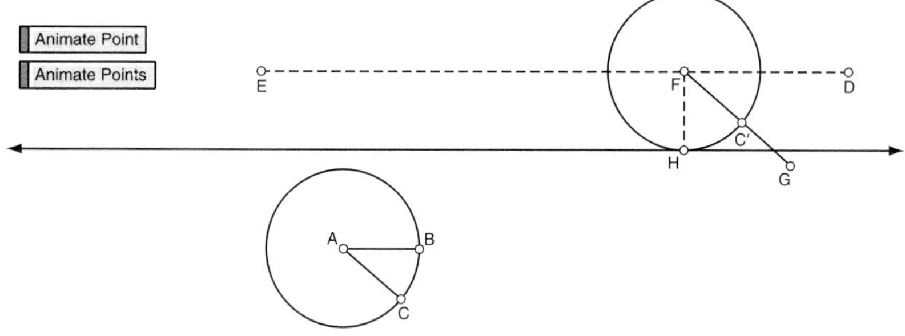

Step 13 Press this new animation button. Circle F should move to the left, rotating at the same time so that it appears to be rolling. Drag point G so that it is on the circle and choose **Trace Point** from the Display menu.

Investigate these questions.

Step 14 What does the path of a point on a rolling circle look like? On your paper, sketch the curve point G makes as the circle rolls. This curve is called a **cycloid.**

Steps 10, 11 These steps construct the path parallel to the path that the center of the circle is to follow.

Step 14 To help students see the shape, you might encourage them to shrink the original circle until it's small compared to segment DE.

Step 14

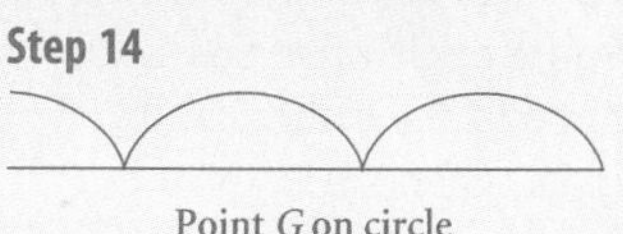

Point G on circle

SHARING IDEAS

As students share their results, **[Ask]** "What does *periodic* mean? What is a *cycle*?" You might mention that the length of a cycle is called its *period.* **[Language]** *Periodic* and *periodical* have the same root. A periodical is a publication, such as a newspaper or magazine, that comes at regular intervals.

[Context] Historically, cycloids were very common curves and were studied in great detail. A ramp that gets a rolling marble from a higher to a lower point in the least amount of time follows a cycloid. Moreover, no matter where you release a marble on such a ramp, it will take the same amount of time to reach the bottom.

[Connection] If you observe the location of planets at the same time each night, they will appear to move backward as well as forward over time. To explain this "retrograde" motion, for about 1000 years people believed that the planets were, in effect, points on circles rolling around circles—that is, that their paths were epicycloids. The idea of Copernicus that the planets revolved around the sun rather than around the earth simplified the model. Kepler's notion that the planets' paths were ellipses rather than circles eliminated altogether the need for epicycloids.

Step 15

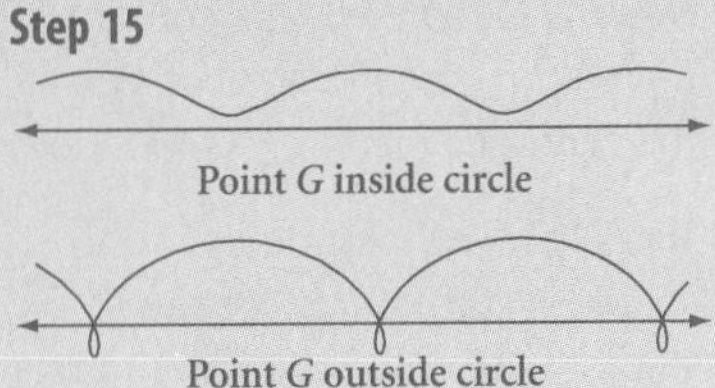

[Link] If students realize that the coordinates of a point moving around a circle of radius 1 centered at the origin can be given as $(\cos t, \sin t)$, then you might ask whether they can find the coordinates of a point generating a cycloid. Imagine a circle of radius 1 in the bottom right corner of Quadrant II, tangent to both axes and ready to roll to the right. The point generating the cycloid is $(0, 1)$. If the center of the rolling circle has a horizontal coordinate of t after the circle has rolled for t seconds, then the horizontal coordinate of the generating point is $x = t + \cos t$, and its vertical coordinate is $y = 1 + \sin t$. (When the curve is translated so that the generating point begins at the origin, these equations become the more standard $x = t - \sin t$ and $y = 1 - \cos t$.)

Closing the Lesson

The main idea of this lesson is that the shape of the path followed by a point on the circumference of a rolling circle is called a **cycloid.**

EXTENSION

What would happen if the "rolling circle" moved along the *inside* of another circle? Investigate this trace by changing the radius of the inner rolling circle. This path is a curve called a *hypocycloid.*

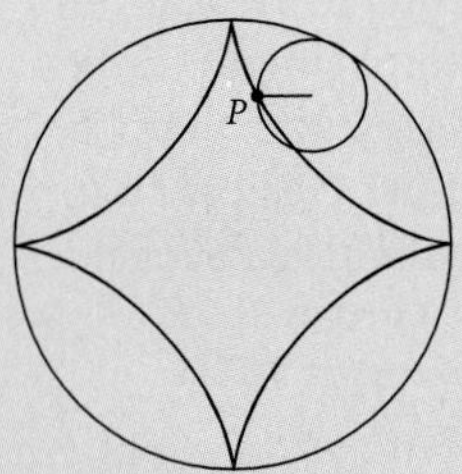

Step 15 Experiment with different cycloids made when point G is inside the circle and outside the circle. Sketch these curves onto your paper.

Step 16 A cycloid is an example of a **periodic** curve. What do you think that means? Adjust the radius AB or the length DE so that point G traces one period, or **cycle,** of the curve. Adjust these lengths so that point G traces two cycles or three cycles. How are the lengths DE and AB related to the number of cycles of the curve?

Step 16 A periodic curve has a shape that repeats. Point G will make one cycle if $DE = (2\pi)AB$, two cycles if $DE = (2)(2\pi)AB$, three if $DE = (3)(2\pi)AB$, and so on.

Step 17 If you apply a car's brakes on a slippery road, you'll skid, because your wheels won't turn fast enough to keep up with the car's movement down the road. If you try to accelerate on a slippery road, your wheels will spin—they'll turn faster than the car is able to go. Experiment with different speeds for points C and F by selecting the animation button and choosing **Properties** from the Edit menu. What combinations cause the wheel to spin? To skid? Explain why the wheel has good traction when the animation speeds are the same.

Step 17 The wheel spins when point C moves faster than point F and skids when point F moves faster than point C. When the speeds are the same, the wheel makes one revolution in the time it takes to travel a distance equal to its circumference, so it has good traction.

Step 18 Add to your sketch so that it shows a traveling bicycle or car. To make a second wheel, you can simply translate the wheel you have by a fixed distance. When you construct the vehicle on these wheels, you'll need to make sure all the parts move when the wheels do!

Step 19 The figure below shows an **epicycloid,** the path of a point on a circle that is rolling around another circle. See if you can make a construction that traces an epicycloid. (Hint: The dashed circle is important in the construction. The circle inside it is just drawn for show.)

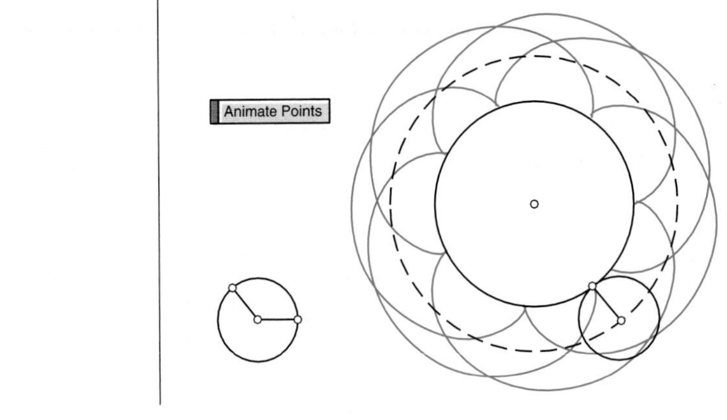

CHAPTER 6 REVIEW

In this chapter you learned some new circle vocabulary and solved real-world application problems involving circles. You discovered the relationship between a radius and a tangent line. You discovered special relationships between angles and their intercepted arcs. And you learned about the special ratio π and how to use it to calculate the circumference of a circle and the length of an arc.

You should be able to sketch these terms from memory: *chord, tangent, central angle, inscribed angle,* and *intercepted arc.* And you should be able to explain the difference between arc measure and arc length.

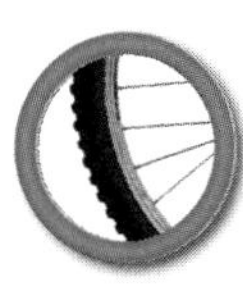

EXERCISES

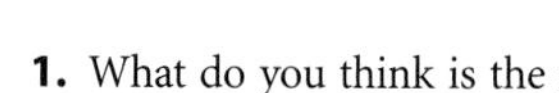

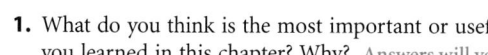

You will need

Construction tools for Exercises **21–24, 67,** and **70**

A calculator for Exercises **11, 12,** and **27–33**

1. What do you think is the most important or useful circle property you learned in this chapter? Why? Answers will vary.

2. How can you find the center of a circle with a compass and a straightedge? With patty paper? With the right-angled corner of a carpenter's square?

3. What does the path of a satellite have to do with the Tangent Conjecture? The velocity vector is always perpendicular to the radius at the point of tangency to the object's circular path.

4. Explain the difference between the degree measure of an arc and its arc length. Sample answer: An arc measure is between 0° and 360°. An arc length is proportional to arc measure and depends on the radius of the circle.

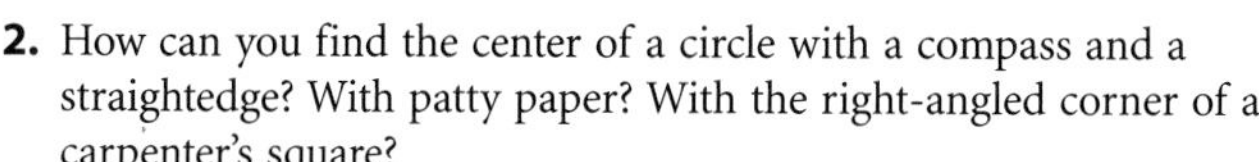

Solve Exercises 5–19. If the exercise uses the "=" sign, answer in terms of π. If the exercise uses the "≈" sign, give your answer accurate to one decimal place.

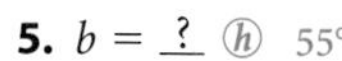

5. $b = \underline{?}$ ⓗ 55°

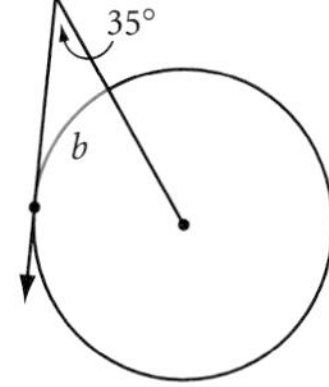

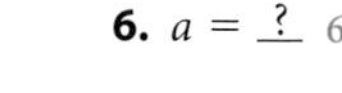

6. $a = \underline{?}$ 65°

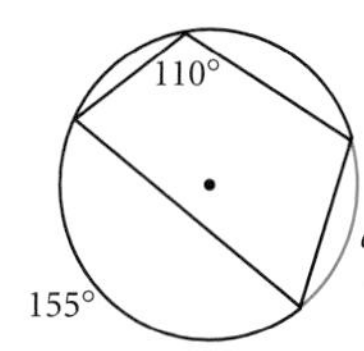

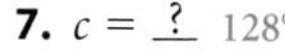

7. $c = \underline{?}$ 128°

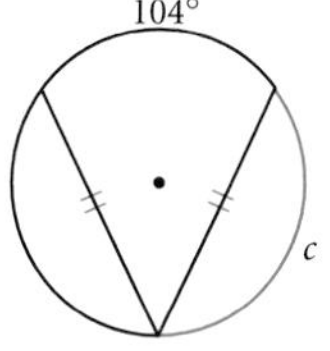

8. $e = \underline{?}$ ⓗ 118°

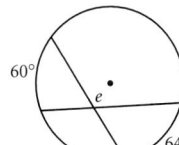

9. $d = \underline{?}$ 91°

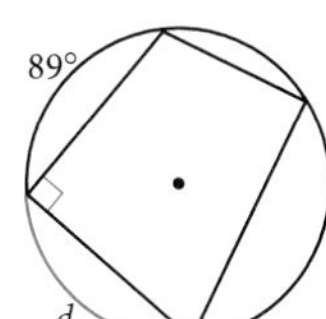

10. $f = \underline{?}$ ⓗ 66°

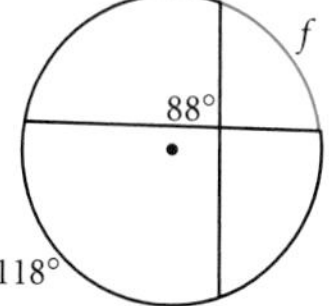

2. Draw two nonparallel chords. The intersection of their perpendicular bisectors is the center of the circle.

Fold the paper so that two semicircles coincide. Repeat with two different semicircles. The center is the intersection of the two folds.

Place the outside or inside corner of the L in the circle so that it is an inscribed right angle. Trace the sides of the corner. Draw the hypotenuse of the right triangle (which is the diameter of the circle). Repeat. The center is the intersection of the two diameters.

CHAPTER REVIEW 6

PLANNING

LESSON OUTLINE

10 min Reviewing
25 min Exercises
10 min Student self-assessment

REVIEWING

Draw a picture of a circle with a central angle intercepting an arc. **[Ask]** "What is pictured?" [central angle, intercepted arc, arc measure, arc length] Have students imagine moving the vertex of the angle away from the center and the intercepted arc. **[Ask]** "Does the angle measure increase or decrease?" [It decreases.] "When the vertex has moved to a point on the circumference of the center, what can be named?" [chord, inscribed angle] "How much has the angle measure shrunk?" [by half] "How has the intercepted arc changed?" [not at all] So the measure of an inscribed angle is half that of the intercepted arc. Move the angle's vertex outside the circle. **[Ask]** "How does the angle measure change?" [It keeps diminishing.] Now move one end of the original intercepted arc around the circle until the angle side through it intersects the circle only once. What can students see now? [a tangent line perpendicular to the radius to the point of tangency] Exercise 1 is a good discussion question.

ASSIGNING HOMEWORK

You might ask students to complete the even-numbered problems on their own and then to discuss Exercises 2 and 4 with their group before completing the odd-numbered problems in groups.

▶ Helping with the Exercises

Exercise 5 As needed, suggest that students draw a radius to the point of tangency.

Exercises 8–10 If students are encountering difficulties, remind them to look for ways to make angles that relate to the arcs with given measures.

20. Ertha can trace the incomplete circle on paper. She can lay the corner of the pad on the circle to trace an inscribed right angle. Then Ertha should mark the endpoints of the intercepted arc and use the pad to construct the hypotenuse of the right triangle, which is the diameter of the circle.

21. Sample answer: Construct perpendicular bisectors of two sides of the triangle. The point at which they intersect (the circumcenter) is the center of the circle. The distance from the circumcenter to each vertex is the radius.

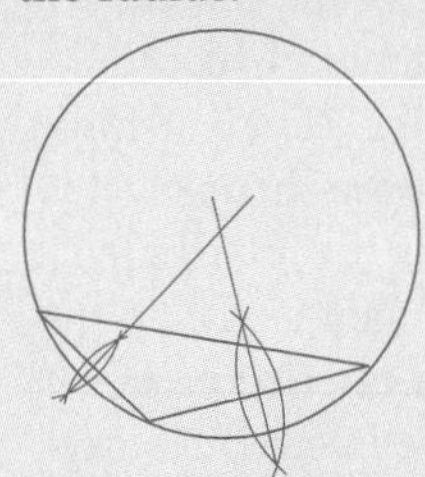

22. Sample answer: Construct the incenter (from the angle bisectors) of the triangle. From the incenter, which is the center of the circle, construct a perpendicular to a side. The distance from the incenter to the foot of the perpendicular is the radius.

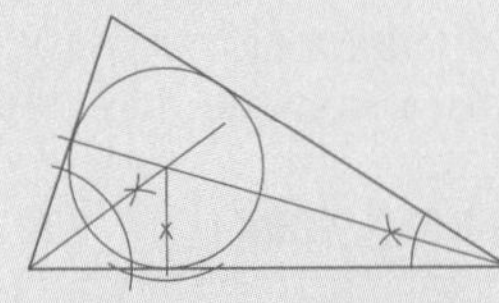

See page 772 for answer to Exercise 23.

11. Circumference ≈ ___?___ 125.7 cm

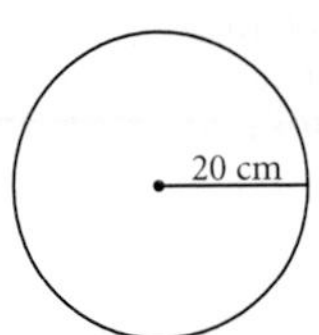

12. Circumference is 132 cm. $d \approx$ ___?___ Ⓗ 42.0 cm

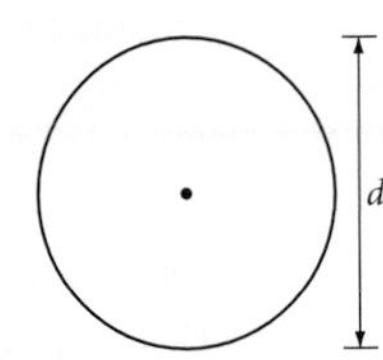

13. $r = 27$ cm. The arc length of $\widehat{AB}$ is ___?___. Ⓗ 15π cm

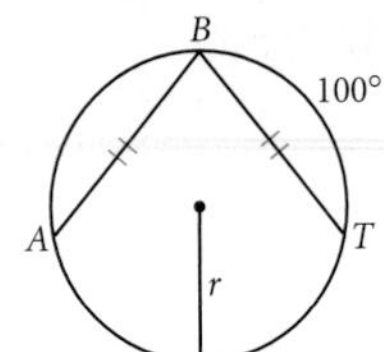

14. $r = 36$ ft. The arc length of $\widehat{CD}$ is ___?___. Ⓗ 14π ft

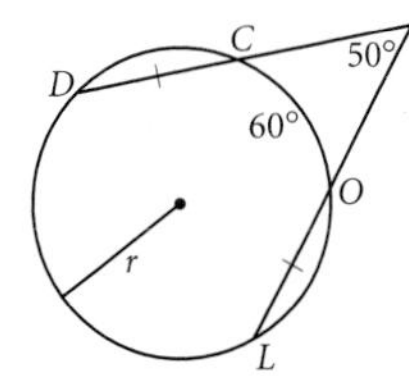

15. What's wrong with this picture? $2 \cdot 57° + 2 \cdot 35° \neq 180°$

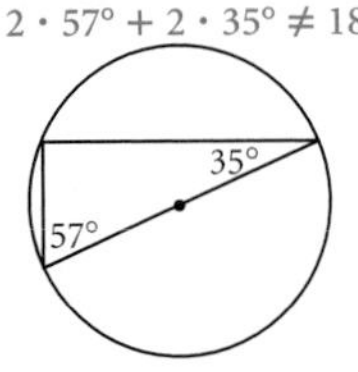

16. What's wrong with this picture?

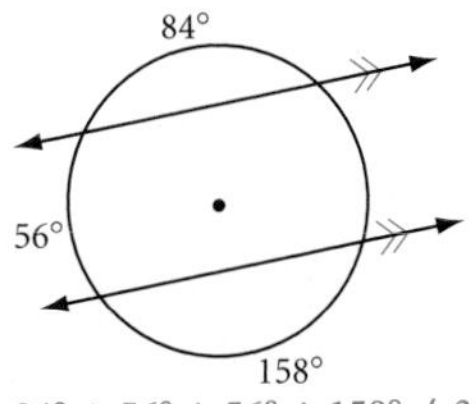

$84° + 56° + 56° + 158° \neq 360°$

17. Explain why $\overline{KE} \parallel \overline{YL}$.

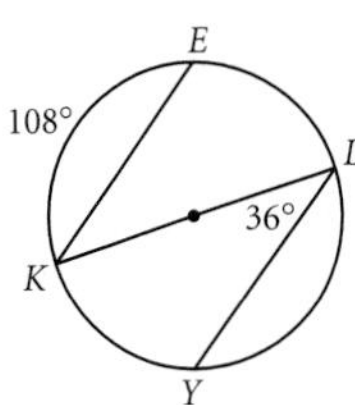

18. Explain why $\triangle JIM$ is isosceles.

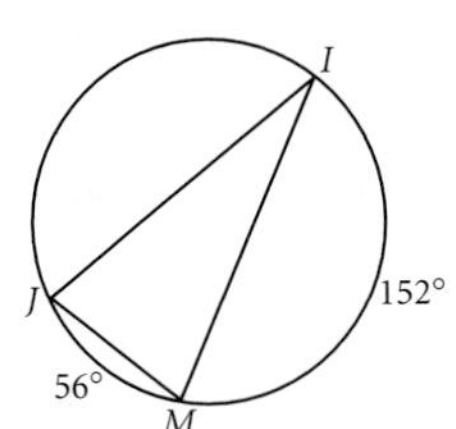

19. Explain why $\triangle KIM$ is isosceles.

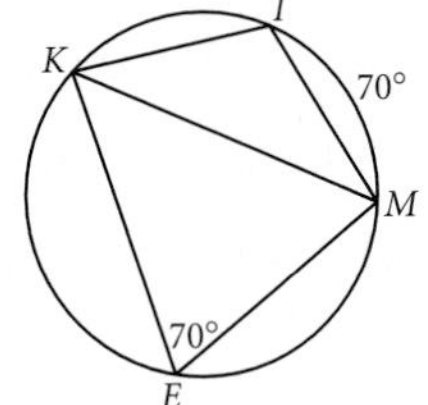

20. On her latest archaeological dig, Ertha Diggs has unearthed a portion of a cylindrical column. All she has with her is a pad of paper. How can she use it to locate the diameter of the column?

21. ***Construction*** Construct a scalene obtuse triangle. Construct the circumscribed circle.

22. ***Construction*** Construct a scalene acute triangle. Construct the inscribed circle.

23. ***Construction*** Construct a rectangle. Is it possible to construct the circumscribed circle, the inscribed circle, neither, or both?

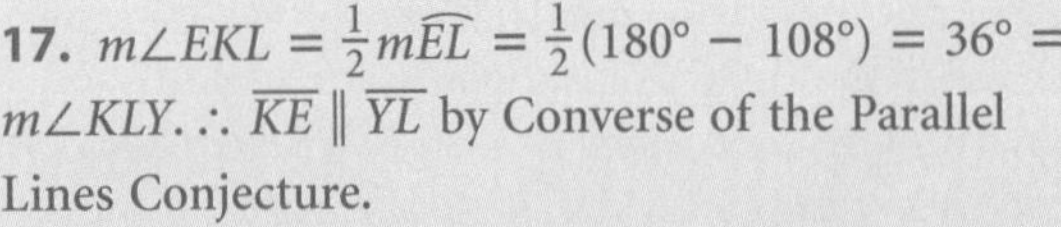

17. $m\angle EKL = \frac{1}{2}m\widehat{EL} = \frac{1}{2}(180° - 108°) = 36° = m\angle KLY$. $\therefore \overline{KE} \parallel \overline{YL}$ by Converse of the Parallel Lines Conjecture.

18. $m\widehat{JI} = 360° - 56° - 152° = 152° = m\widehat{MI}$. $\therefore m\angle JMI = \frac{1}{2}m\widehat{JI} = \frac{1}{2}m\widehat{MI} = m\angle MJI$. $\therefore \triangle JIM$ is isosceles.

19. $m\widehat{KIM} = 2m\angle KEM = 140°$. $\therefore m\widehat{KI} = 140° - 70° = 70° = m\widehat{MI}$. $\therefore m\angle IKM = \frac{1}{2}m\widehat{MI} = \frac{1}{2}m\widehat{KI} = m\angle IMK$. $\therefore \triangle KIM$ is isosceles.

24. ***Construction*** Construct a rhombus. Is it possible to construct the circumscribed circle, the inscribed circle, neither, or both?

24. Sample answer: Construct acute angle R. Mark off equal lengths RM and RH. From points M and H, swing arcs of lengths equal to RM. Label the intersection of the arcs as O. Construct $RHOM$. The intersection of the diagonals is the center of the inscribed circle. Construct a perpendicular to a side to find the radius. It is not possible to construct a circumscribed circle unless the rhombus is a square.

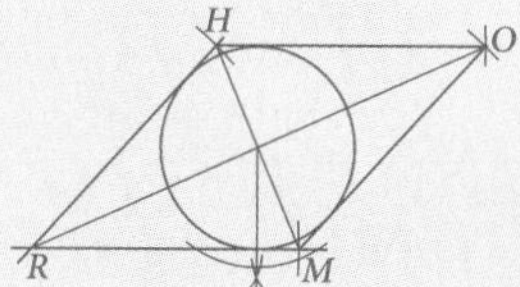

25. Find the equation of the line tangent to circle S centered at $(1, 1)$ if the point of tangency is $(5, 4)$. $4x + 3y = 32$

26. Find the center of the circle passing through the points $(-7, 5)$, $(0, 6)$, and $(1, -1)$. $(-3, 2)$

27. Rashid is an apprentice on a road crew for a civil engineer. He needs to find a trundle wheel similar to but larger than the one shown at right. If each rotation is to be 1 m, what should be the diameter of the trundle wheel? $d = 0.318$ m

28. Melanie rides the merry-go-round on her favorite horse on the outer edge, 8 meters from the center of the merry-go-round. Her sister, Melody, sits in the inner ring of horses, 3 meters in from Melanie. In 10 minutes, they go around 30 times. What is the average speed of each sister?

28. Melanie: 151 m/min or 9 km/hr; Melody: 94 m/min or 6 km/hr.

29. Read the Geography Connection below. Given that the polar radius of Earth is 6357 kilometers and that the equatorial radius of Earth is 6378 kilometers, use the original definition to calculate one nautical mile near a pole and one nautical mile near the equator. Show that the international nautical mile is between both values. ⓗ

$$\frac{2\pi(6357)}{360 \cdot 60} \approx 1.849 < 1.852 < 1.855 \approx \frac{2\pi(6378)}{360 \cdot 60}$$

Geography CONNECTION

One nautical mile was originally defined to be the length of one minute of arc of a great circle of Earth. (A great circle is the intersection of the sphere and a plane that cuts through its center. There are 60 minutes of arc in each degree.) But Earth is not a perfect sphere. It is wider at the great circle of the equator than it is at the great circle through the poles. So defined as one minute of arc, one nautical mile could take on a range of values. To remedy this, an international nautical mile was defined as 1.852 kilometers (about 1.15 miles).

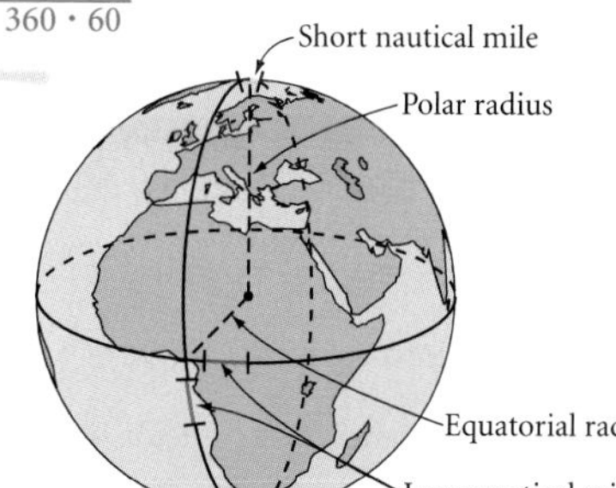

30. While talking to his friend Tara on the phone, Dmitri sees a lightning flash, and 5 seconds later he hears thunder. Two seconds after that, Tara, who lives 1 mile away, hears it. Sound travels at 1100 feet per second. Draw and label a diagram showing the possible locations of the lightning strike. ⓗ

30.

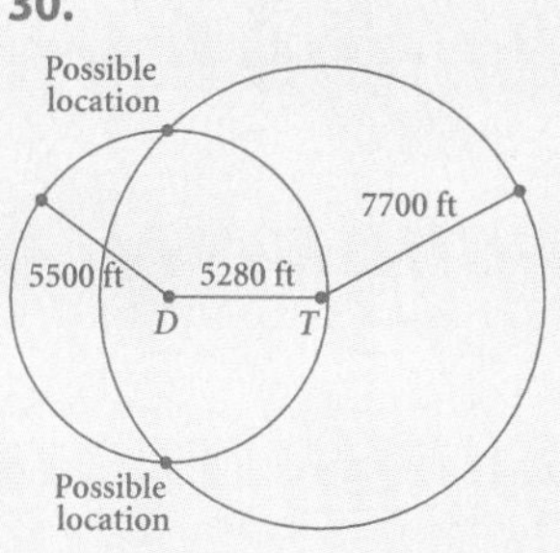

31. King Arthur wishes to seat all his knights at a round table. He instructs Merlin to design and create an oak table large enough to seat 100 people. Each knight is to have 2 ft along the edge of the table. Help Merlin calculate the diameter of the table. ⓗ $\frac{200}{\pi}$ ft ≈ 63.7 ft

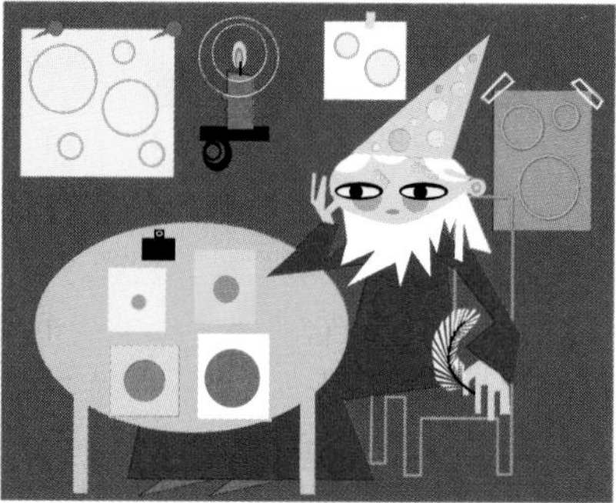

Exercise 32 The question "how much greater?" can mean different things to different students. Students might answer that the longer circumference is $20\pi - 12\pi = 8\pi$ meters longer than the shorter circumference. Or they might say that it's $\frac{20\pi}{12\pi} = \frac{5}{3}$ as long (just as the radius is $\frac{5}{3}$ as long). Both of these answers correctly tell "how much greater."

33. The circumference is $\frac{48}{360} \cdot 2\pi(45) = 12\pi$; 12 cm is the diameter.

34. False. $20° + 20° + 140° = 180°$. An angle with measure 140° is obtuse.

36. false

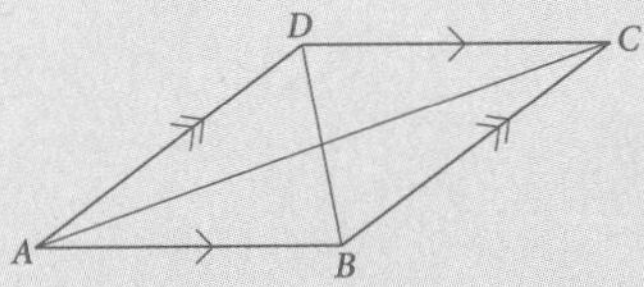

41. False. $(7 - 2) \cdot 180° = 900°$. It could have seven sides.

42. False. The sum of the measures of any triangle is 180°.

43. False. The sum of the measures of one set of exterior angles for any polygon is 360°. The sum of the measures of the interior angles of a triangle is 180° and of a quadrilateral is 360°. Neither is greater than 360°, so these are two counterexamples.

32. If the circular moat should have been a circle of radius 10 meters instead of radius 6 meters, how much greater should the larger moat's circumference have been? 8π m $\approx$ 25.1 m

33. The part of a circle enclosed by a central angle and the arc it intercepts is called a **sector.** The sector of a circle shown below can be curled into a cone by bringing the two straight 45-cm edges together. What will be the diameter of the base of the cone?

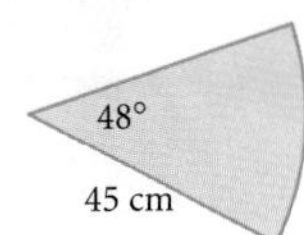

THE FAR SIDE® By GARY LARSON

Suddenly, a heated exchange took place between the king and the moat contractor.

MIXED REVIEW

In Exercises 34–56, identify the statement as true or false. For each false statement, explain why it is false or sketch a counterexample.

4.1 **34.** If a triangle has two angles of equal measure, then the third angle is acute.

4.3 **35.** If two sides of a triangle measure 45 cm and 36 cm, then the third side must be greater than 9 cm and less than 81 cm. true

5.5 **36.** The diagonals of a parallelogram are congruent.

5.1 **37.** The measure of each angle of a regular dodecagon is 150°. true

6.1 **38.** The perpendicular bisector of a chord of a circle passes through the center of the circle. true

5.4 **39.** If $\overline{CD}$ is the midsegment of trapezoid *PLYR* with $\overline{PL}$ one of the bases, then $CD = \frac{1}{2}(PL + YR)$. true

4.4 **40.** In $\triangle BOY$, $BO = 36$ cm, $m\angle B = 42°$, and $m\angle O = 28°$. In $\triangle GRL$, $GR = 36$ cm, $m\angle R = 28°$, and $m\angle L = 110°$. Therefore, $\triangle BOY \cong \triangle GRL$. true

5.1 **41.** If the sum of the measures of the interior angles of a polygon is less than 1000°, then the polygon has fewer than seven sides.

4.1 **42.** The sum of the measures of the three angles of an obtuse triangle is greater than the sum of the measures of the three angles of an acute triangle.

5.2 **43.** The sum of the measures of one set of exterior angles of a polygon is always less than the sum of the measures of interior angles.

5.3 **44.** Both pairs of base angles of an isosceles trapezoid are supplementary.

4.2 **45.** If the base angles of an isosceles triangle each measure 48°, then the vertex angle has a measure of 132°. False. $48° + 48° + 132° \neq 180°$

6.3 **46.** Inscribed angles that intercept the same arc are supplementary.

6.3 **47.** The measure of an inscribed angle in a circle is equal to the measure of the arc it intercepts.

5.6 **48.** The diagonals of a rhombus bisect the angles of the rhombus. true

5.6 **49.** The diagonals of a rectangle are perpendicular bisectors of each other.

4.2 **50.** If a triangle has two angles of equal measure, then the triangle is equilateral. False. It could be isosceles.

5.6 **51.** If a quadrilateral has three congruent angles, then it is a rectangle. False. $100° + 100° + 100° + 60° = 360°$

6.1 **52.** In two different circles, arcs with the same measure are congruent.

6.5 **53.** The ratio of the diameter to the circumference of a circle is π.

5.3 **54.** If the sum of the lengths of two consecutive sides of a kite is 48 cm, then the perimeter of the kite is 96 cm.

5.3 **55.** If the vertex angles of a kite measure 48° and 36°, then the nonvertex angles each measure 138°. true

The concentric circles in the sky are actually a time exposure photograph of the movement of the stars in a night.

56. All but seven statements in Exercises 34–56 are false. This is a paradox.

57. Find the measure of each lettered angle in the diagram below.

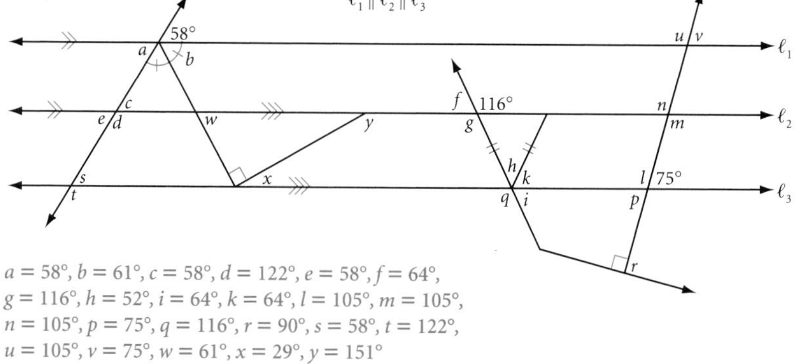

$a = 58°, b = 61°, c = 58°, d = 122°, e = 58°, f = 64°,$
$g = 116°, h = 52°, i = 64°, k = 64°, l = 105°, m = 105°,$
$n = 105°, p = 75°, q = 116°, r = 90°, s = 58°, t = 122°,$
$u = 105°, v = 75°, w = 61°, x = 29°, y = 151°$

44. False. The consecutive angles between the bases are supplementary.

46. False. Inscribed angles that intercept the same arc are congruent.

47. False. The measure of an inscribed angle is half the measure of the arc.

49. False. $\overline{AC}$ and $\overline{BD}$ bisect each other but $\overline{AC}$ is not perpendicular to $\overline{BD}$.

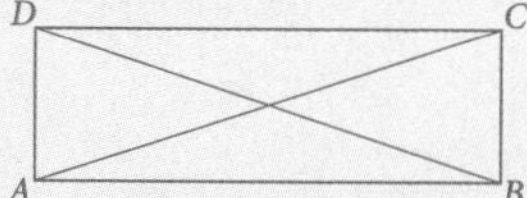

52. False. $\overset{\frown}{AB} \ncong \overset{\frown}{CD}$

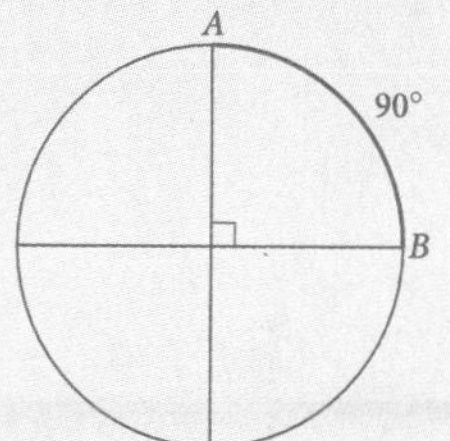

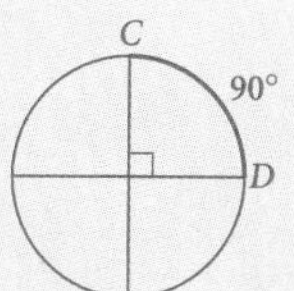

53. False. The ratio of the circumference to the diameter is π.

54. False.
$24 + 24 + 48 + 48 \neq 96$

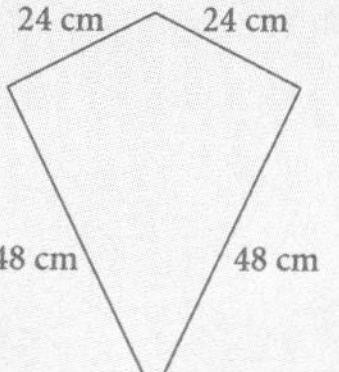

59. $\triangle FTO \cong \triangle YTO$ by SAA
$\triangle FLO \cong \triangle YLO$ by SAA
$\triangle FTL \cong \triangle YTL$ by SSS

In Exercises 58–60, from the information given, determine which triangles, if any, are congruent. State the congruence conjecture that supports your congruence statement.

4.4 **58.** *STARY* is a regular pentagon.

$\triangle TAR \cong \triangle YRA$ by SAS

4.4 **59.** *FLYT* is a kite.

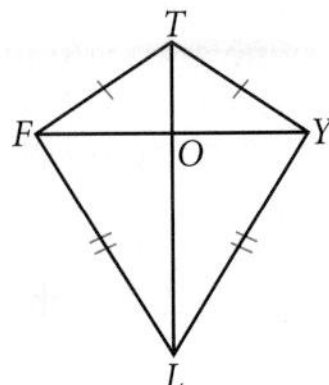

4.4 **60.** *PART* is an isosceles trapezoid.

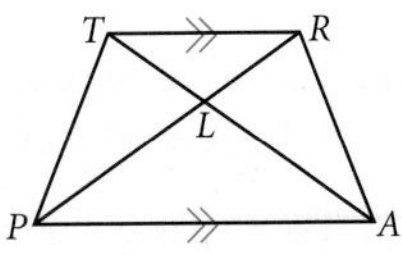

$\triangle PTR \cong \triangle ART$ by SAS
$\triangle TPA \cong \triangle RAP$ by SAS

4.5 **61.** Adventurer Dakota Davis has uncovered a piece of triangular tile from a mosaic. A corner is broken off. Wishing to repair the mosaic, he lays the broken tile piece down on paper and traces the straight edges. With a ruler he then extends the unbroken sides until they meet. What triangle congruence shortcut guarantees that the tracing reveals the original shape? ASA

6.7 **62.** Circle O has a radius of 24 inches. Find the measure and the length of $\overset{\frown}{AC}$.

$m\overset{\frown}{AC} = 84°$, length of $\overset{\frown}{AC} = 11.2\pi \approx 35.2$ in.

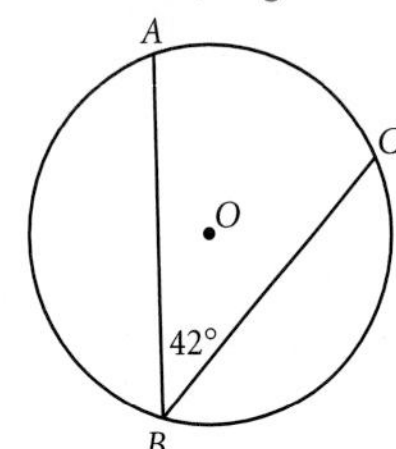

6.3 **63.** $\overrightarrow{EC}$ and $\overrightarrow{ED}$ are tangent to the circle, and $AB = CD$. Find the measure of each lettered angle. $x = 63°, y = 27°, w = 126°$

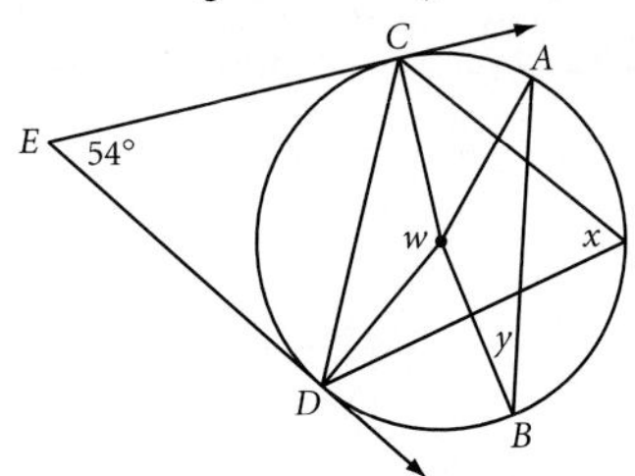

1.3 **64.** Use your protractor to draw and label a pair of supplementary angles that is not a linear pair.

64. sample answer:

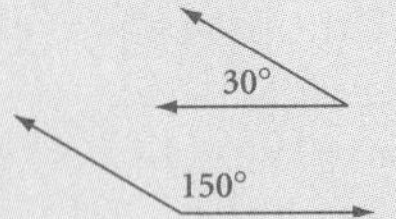

2.3 **65.** Find the function rule $f(n)$ of this sequence and find the 20th term.

n	1	2	3	4	5	6	...	n	...	20
$f(n)$	5	1	−3	−7	−11	−15	...		...	−71

$9 - 4n$

Chapter 0 **66.** The design at right shows three hares joined by three ears, although each hare appears to have two ears of its own.

a. Does the design have rotational symmetry?

b. Does the design have reflectional symmetry?
No, it does not have reflectional symmetry.

Private Collection, Berkeley, California
Ceramist, Diana Hall

Chapter 3 **67.** ***Construction*** Construct a rectangle whose length is twice its width.

UYAS 1 **68.** If $AB = 15$ cm, C is the midpoint of $\overline{AB}$, D is the midpoint of $\overline{AC}$, and E is the midpoint of $\overline{DC}$, what is the length of $\overline{EB}$? 9.375 cm

2.1 **69.** Draw the next shape in this pattern.

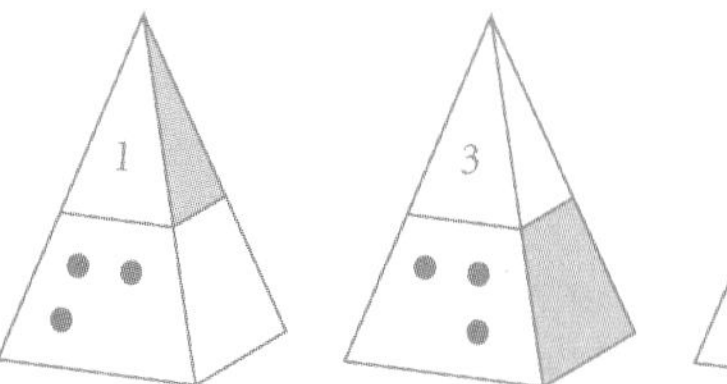

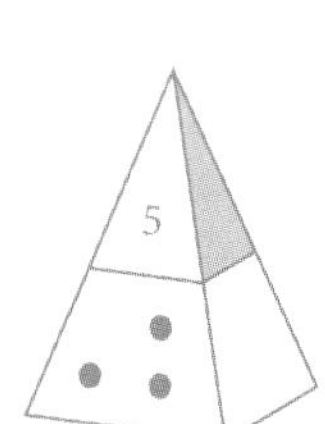

3.8 **70.** ***Construction*** Construct any triangle. Then construct its centroid.

TAKE ANOTHER LOOK

1. Show how the Tangent Segments Conjecture follows logically from the Tangent Conjecture and the converse of the Angle Bisector Conjecture.

2. Investigate the quadrilateral formed by two tangent segments to a circle and the two radii to the points of tangency. State a conjecture. Explain why your conjecture is true, based on the properties of radii and tangents.

3. State the Cyclic Quadrilateral Conjecture in "if-then" form. Then state the converse of the conjecture in "if-then" form. Is the converse also true?

4. A quadrilateral that *can* be inscribed in a circle is also called a cyclic quadrilateral. Which of these quadrilaterals are always cyclic: parallelograms kites, isosceles trapezoids, rhombuses, rectangles, or squares? Which ones are never cyclic? Explain why each is or is not always cyclic.

5. Use graph paper or a graphing calculator to graph the data collected from the investigation in Lesson 6.5. Graph the diameter on the x-axis and the circumference on the y-axis. What is the slope of the best-fit line through the data points? Does this confirm the Circumference Conjecture? Explain.

Exercise 66 [Context] The motif of three rabbits sharing three ears appears in several medieval churches in the Dartmoor section of England. The design is also found in Chinese art from a millennium earlier.

66a. The circle with its contents has 3-fold rotational symmetry, the entire tile does not.

67.

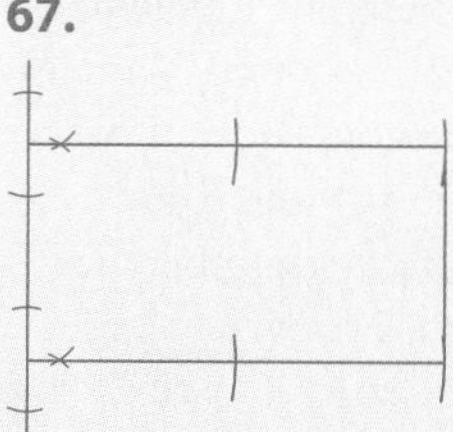

69.

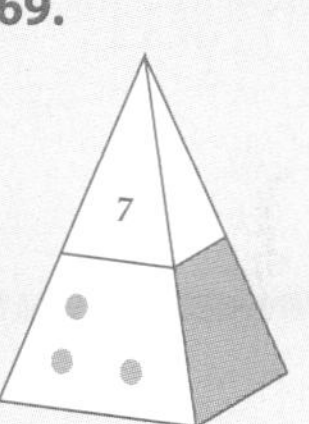

70.

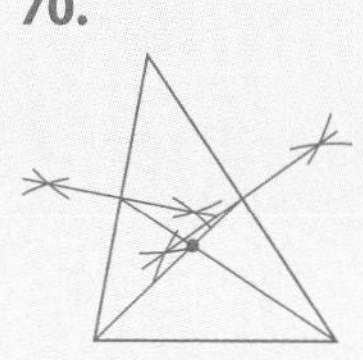

Take Another Look

1. $\angle EAN$ and $\angle EGN$ are right angles because the Tangent Conjecture says that a tangent is perpendicular to the radius. $\overline{EA} \cong \overline{EG}$ because all radii in a circle are congruent. Because point E is equidistant from the sides of $\angle ANG$, the converse of the Angle Bisector Conjecture says that $\angle ANE \cong \angle GNE$. Therefore $\triangle ANE \cong \triangle GNE$ by SAA, so $\overline{AN} \cong \overline{GN}$ by CPCTC. Thus the tangent segments are congruent.

2. Sample answer: The quadrilateral is a kite because $\overline{EA} \cong \overline{EG}$ (all radii in a circle are congruent) and $\overline{AN} \cong \overline{GN}$ (Tangent Segments Conjecture).

3. The converse of the conjecture "If a quadrilateral is inscribed in a circle, then its opposite angles are supplementary" is "If the opposite angles of a quadrilateral are supplementary, then the quadrilateral can be inscribed in a circle." Students might be convinced that this converse is true if they construct a circle through three of the four vertices. For quadrilateral $ABCD$, draw a circle containing A, B, and C and show D is also on the circle. We know $m\widehat{ABC} + m\widehat{AC} = 360°$, $m\angle B + m\angle D = 180°$, and $m\angle B = \frac{1}{2}m\widehat{AC}$. Combining these equations we get the result $m\widehat{ABC} = 2m\angle D$. This is true only if D is on the circle.

4. Rectangles and squares are always cyclic because their opposite angles are right angles and thus are supplementary. An isosceles trapezoid is always cyclic.

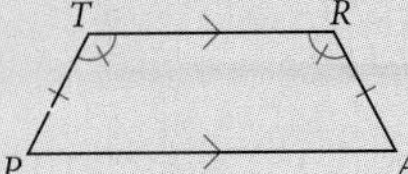

In isosceles trapezoid *PART*, $\angle A$ and $\angle R$ are consecutive interior angles and therefore supplementary. $\angle R$ and $\angle T$ are base angles and therefore congruent. Thus opposite angles *A* and *T* are supplementary. A rhombus has opposite angles congruent, so a rhombus inscribed in a circle is a square. A kite is cyclic only if its nonvertex angles are right angles.

5. Possible answer: $y = a + bx$; thus $C = 0 + 3.1d$, or $C = 3.1d$. This confirms the Circumference Conjecture.

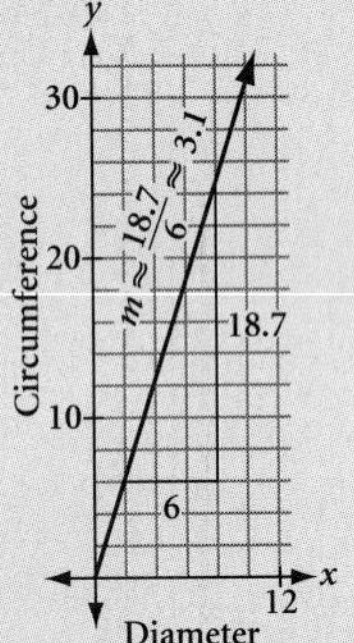

ASSESSING

You can use either of the chapter tests available in the Assessment Resources, use some of the constructive assessment items for this chapter, or create your own test using the items in the Test Generator and Worksheet Builder. There is a unit test covering Chapters 4–6 that you can use after students have completed the mixed review.

Assessing What You've Learned

With the different assessment methods you've used so far, you should be getting the idea that assessment means more than a teacher giving you a grade. All the methods presented so far could be described as self-assessment techniques. Many are also good study habits. Being aware of your *own* learning and progress is the best way to stay on top of what you're doing and to achieve the best results.

WRITE IN YOUR JOURNAL

- You may be at or near the end of your school year's first semester. Look back over the first semester and write about your strengths and needs. What grade would you have given yourself for the semester? How would you justify that grade?
- Set new goals for the new semester or for the remainder of the year. Write them in your journal and compare them to goals you set at the beginning of the year. How have your goals changed? Why?

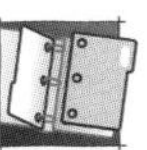

ORGANIZE YOUR NOTEBOOK Review your notebook and conjectures list to be sure they are complete and well organized. Write a one-page chapter summary.

UPDATE YOUR PORTFOLIO Choose a piece of work from this chapter to add to your portfolio. Document the work according to your teacher's instructions.

PERFORMANCE ASSESSMENT While a classmate, a friend, a family member, or a teacher observes, carry out one of the investigations or Take Another Look activities from this chapter. Explain what you're doing at each step, including how you arrived at the conjecture.

WRITE TEST ITEMS Divide the lessons from this chapter among group members and write at least one test item per lesson. Try out the test questions written by your classmates and discuss them.

GIVE A PRESENTATION Give a presentation on an investigation, exploration, Take Another Look project, or puzzle. Work with your group, or try giving a presentation on your own.

FACILITATING SELF-ASSESSMENT

In each of Chapters 0 through 5, students were introduced to a different way of assessing what they learned. You may or may not have assigned all six of these methods. From this chapter on, no new methods of assessment will be introduced. Instead, we offer brief suggestions of ways to use the assessment methods already introduced.

To help students complete the portfolio described in Assessing What You've Learned, suggest that they consider for evaluation their work on Lesson 6.3, Exercise 20; Lesson 6.4, Exercise 7; Using Your Algebra Skills, Exercise 3; Lesson 6.6, Exercise 6; and Lesson 6.7, Exercise 12.

CHAPTER

7

Transformations and Tessellations

Overview

In **Lessons 7.1–7.3,** students examine some basic properties of transformations and symmetry. These lessons review Chapter 0 and include more detail about symmetry and compositions of transformations. Students explore tessellations of regular polygons in **Lesson 7.4** and of nonregular polygons in **Lesson 7.5.** They use symmetry to create interesting tessellations from translations in **Lesson 7.6,** from rotations in **Lesson 7.7,** and from glide reflections in **Lesson 7.8.** The chapter ends with **Using Your Algebra Skills 7,** in which students find the coordinates of the orthocenter and centroid of a triangle.

The Mathematics

Transformations

Intuitively, a *transformation* transforms a geometric figure, shifting it around, flipping it over, rotating it, stretching it, or deforming it. Although technically a transformation acts on the entire plane, this chapter concentrates on transformations of individual shapes. The resulting figure is the *image* of the original figure.

Most common transformations are *isometries,* which don't change the size or shape of the figure. The three major kinds of isometries are *reflection* (over a line), *translation* (along a vector), and *rotation* (about a point), though the latter two can be considered as repeated reflections. This book also includes a composition of a reflection and a translation: the *glide reflection.*

We can use geometric transformations in many ways, such as:

- Defining symmetry. For example, if there's a reflection under which the image of the figure coincides with the figure, then we say the figure has reflectional symmetry.
- Building an axiom system. After defining *isometry,* we might define two figures to be congruent if one is the image of the other under some isometry. Then we could prove the Isosceles Triangle Conjecture by showing that there's a reflection under which one of the base angles is the image of the other. Students at van Hiele levels 1 and 2 are not yet ready to appreciate this use of transformations.
- Organizing geometric ideas. We say that a property, such as perpendicularity, is *preserved* under a transformation if the image of any figure having that property also has that property. In *Discovering Geometry,* the properties studied through Chapter 10 (such as parallelism, angle measurement, distance, area, volume) are preserved by all isometries. These properties are the core of Euclidean geometry. Chapter 11 of the book addresses similarity. Unlike isometries, similarity transformations, or *dilations,* may stretch or shrink the plane. They don't necessarily preserve distance or area. They do, however, preserve angle measurement and hence perpendicularity.

Beyond this course, we can consider what properties are preserved by more general transformations. For example, linear transformations (studied in college linear algebra courses) preserve parallelism but not necessarily angle measurement. (To include translations of the plane, the linear transformations must be in three dimensions.) This kind of exploration leads to the idea that there are different geometries, each a study of properties preserved under some set of transformations. More general than linear transformations are projective transformations, which don't necessarily preserve angle measurement and whose associated geometry is *projective geometry.* Some sets of projective transformations are quite different from linear transformations; the study of properties preserved under these transformations is called *non-Euclidean geometry.* (See the exploration on non-Euclidean geometry on page 718.)

Tessellations

The symmetry of wallpaper designs and friezes has long intrigued mathematicians as well as artists. A design in which one or more shapes repeat to fill the plane is a *tessellation* or *tiling*. In this chapter, students learn how to combine geometric shapes to make tessellations and how to change these shapes to make their own unique tessellations.

It might seem that all tessellations, when considered as unbounded figures of infinitely many tiles, have translational symmetry; that is, if you apply a translation, the image coincides with the original. Such tessellations are called *periodic,* but we could also take a tessellation of squares and cut the squares into congruent trapezoids in ways that gave a *nonperiodic tiling.* As described in Lesson 7.5, Roger Penrose found a pair of tiles that will always make a nonperiodic tessellation if you allow only designated vertices to touch each other.

Using This Chapter

Chapter 7 is optional. It follows logically from the polygon angle sum conjectures of Chapter 5 and precedes Chapter 8 on area. Use it for a motivational start to the second term before or after Chapter 6. If you have time for only part of the chapter, you could concentrate either on transformations and symmetry (Lessons 7.1–7.3) or on tessellations (Lessons 7.4–7.8).

The Geometer's Sketchpad and Kaleidomania are excellent computer tools for exploring transformations. Graphics software can be very useful in creating unusual tessellations.

Resources

Discovering Geometry Resources

Teaching and Worksheet Masters
Lessons 7.1, 7.2, 7.4–7.8, and Chapter 7 Review

Sketchpad Demonstrations
Lessons 7.3, 7.4–7.8

Discovering Geometry with The Geometer's Sketchpad
Lessons 7.1–7.3, 7.6, and 7.7

Assessment Resources A and B
Quiz 1 (Lessons 7.1 and 7.2)
Quiz 2 (Lessons 7.3–7.5)
Chapter 7 Test
Chapter 7 Constructive Assessment Options

Practice Your Skills for Chapter 7

Condensed Lessons for Chapter 7

Other Resources

Kaleidomania™ software.

Inversions by Scott Kim.

For complete references on these and other sources see www.keypress.com/DG.

Materials

- construction tools
- protractors
- rulers
- pattern blocks
- scissors
- crayons or colored markers
- patty paper
- tracing paper
- graph paper
- small mirrors, *optional*
- dominoes, *optional*
- carbon paper, *optional*

Pacing Guide

	day 1	day 2	day 3	day 4	day 5	day 6	day 7	day 8	day 9	day 10
standard	7.1	7.2	7.3, quiz	7.4	7.5	quiz	7.6	7.7	7.8	Algebra 7
enriched	7.1	7.2	quiz, project	7.3	7.4	quiz, project	7.5	7.6	7.7	7.8
block	7.1, 7.2	7.3, quiz, project	7.4, 7.5	quiz, project, 7.6	7.7, 7.8	Algebra 7, review	assessment			
	day 11	**day 12**	**day 13**	**day 14**	**day 15**	**day 16**	**day 17**	**day 18**	**day 19**	**day 20**
standard	review	assessment								
enriched	Algebra 7	review	assessment							

CHAPTER

7 Transformations and Tessellations

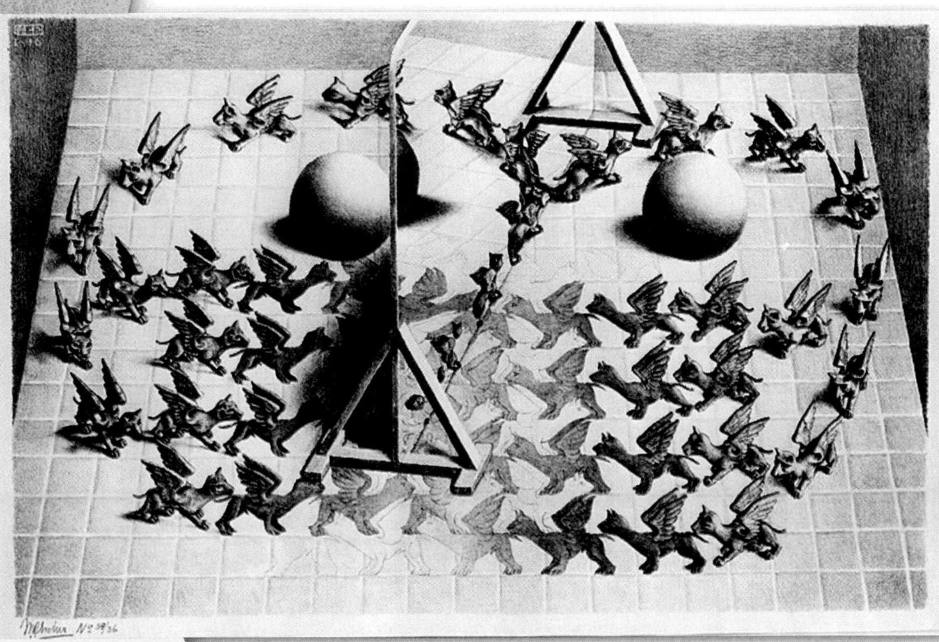

I believe that producing pictures, as I do, is almost solely a question of wanting so very much to do it well.

M. C. ESCHER

Magic Mirror, M. C. Escher, 1946

OBJECTIVES

In this chapter you will
- discover some basic properties of transformations and symmetry
- learn more about symmetry in art and nature
- create tessellations

CHAPTER 7 OBJECTIVES

- Learn about transformations
- Identify and create translations, rotations, and reflections of figures in the plane
- Discover isometries that result from the composition of other isometries
- Find a minimal path using reflection
- Apply concepts of reflectional, rotational, translational, and glide-reflectional symmetry
- Classify and identify monohedral, regular, and semiregular tessellations
- Explore tessellations with regular and nonregular polygons
- Create Escher-type tessellations with translations, rotations, and reflections
- Learn new vocabulary
- Practice construction skills
- Develop visual thinking, problem-solving skills, and cooperative behavior

In this chapter students will be studying basic properties of transformations and symmetry. Escher used many of these properties in his artwork. *Magic Mirror* illustrates several of these properties. **[Ask]** "What geometry do you find in the drawing?" [reflection, tiling (tessellation), squares, triangles, spheres, repetition]

LESSON

7.1

PLANNING

LESSON OUTLINE

One day:

25 min Investigation

5 min Sharing

5 min Closing

10 min Exercises

MATERIALS

- construction tools
- patty paper
- graph paper
- small mirrors, *optional*
- Q-rious (T) for One step

TEACHING

This lesson concerns the three rigid transformations (isometries) of the plane: translations, rotations, and reflections. **[Language]** *Isometry* [ī-'sä-mə-trē] is Greek for "same measure." (Dilations, a kind of nonrigid transformation, appear in Chapter 11.) Two of these isometries, reflection and rotation, help describe symmetry that students may have seen in Chapter 0.

One step Cut the Q-rious transparency in half, and show it with the single letter to the left of the three. Ask groups to discuss what they'd have to do to the Q on the left to make it coincide with each of the figures on the right. If needed, encourage groups to simplify their description of the second transformation to be purely a reflection (or, as they might say, a "flip"). As groups finish, suggest that they connect each point on the Q with its corresponding point on each of the first two images and look for patterns.

LESSON 7.1

Transformations and Symmetry

Symmetry is one idea by which man through the ages has tried to comprehend and create order, beauty, and perfection.

HERMANN WEYL

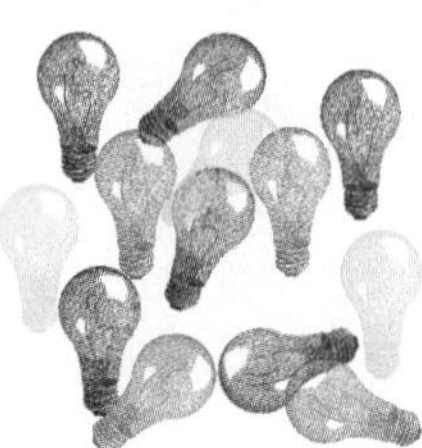

Each light bulb is an image of every other light bulb.

Frieze of bowmen from the Palace of Artaxerxes II in Susa, Iran

By moving all the points of a geometric figure according to certain rules, you can create an **image** of the original figure. This process is called **transformation.** Each point on the original figure corresponds to a point on its image. The image of point A after a transformation of any type is called point A' (read "A prime"), as shown in the transformation of $\triangle ABC$ to $\triangle A'B'C'$ on the facing page.

If the image is congruent to the original figure, the process is called **rigid transformation,** or **isometry.** A transformation that does not preserve the size and shape is called **nonrigid transformation.** For example, if an image is reduced or enlarged, or if the shape changes, its transformation is nonrigid.

Three types of rigid transformation are translation, rotation, and reflection. You have been doing translations, rotations, and reflections in your patty-paper investigations and in exercises on the coordinate plane, using (x, y) rules.

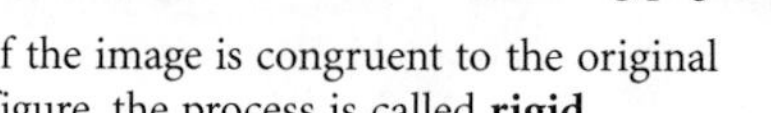

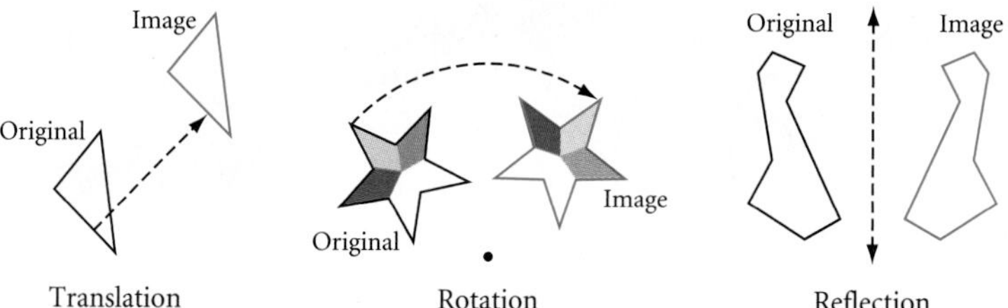

Translation is the simplest type of isometry. You can model a translation by tracing a figure onto patty paper, then sliding it along a straight path without turning it. Notice that when you slide the figure, all points move the same distance along parallel paths to form its image. That is, each point in the image is equidistant from the point that corresponds to it in the original figure. This distance, because it is the same for all points, is called the **distance** of the translation. A translation also has a particular **direction.** So you can use a **translation vector** to describe the translation.

LESSON OBJECTIVES

- Learn about transformations
- Identify and create translations, rotations, and reflections of figures in the plane
- Apply concepts of reflectional, rotational, and translational symmetry
- Discover symmetries of regular polygons
- Learn new vocabulary
- Develop visual thinking and problem-solving skills

NCTM STANDARDS

	CONTENT		PROCESS
	Number	✓	Problem Solving
✓	Algebra		Reasoning
✓	Geometry	✓	Communication
	Measurement	✓	Connections
	Data/Probability	✓	Representation

Translation vector

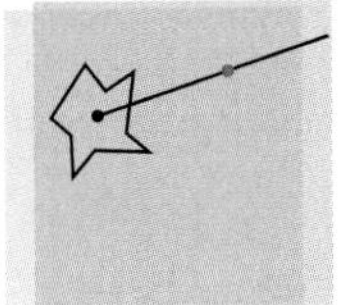

Translating with patty paper

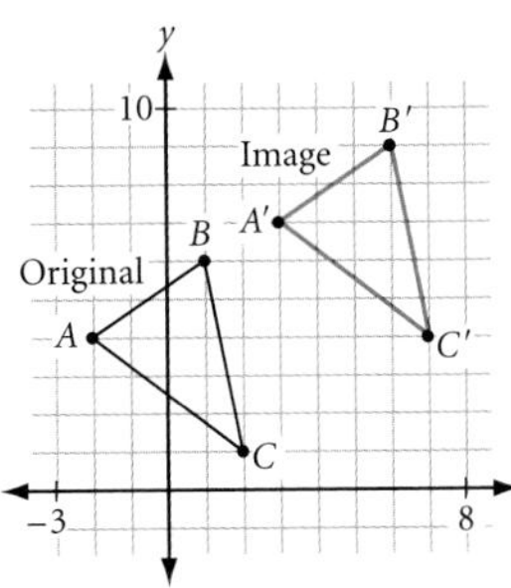

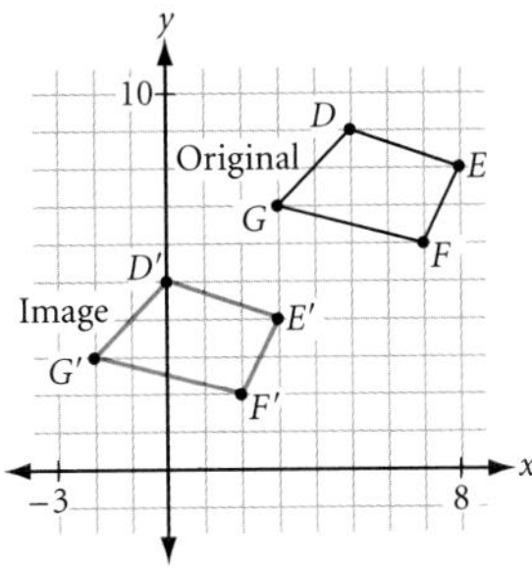

Translations on a coordinate grid

Rotation is another type of isometry. In a rotation, all the points in the original figure rotate, or turn, an identical number of degrees about a fixed center point. You can define a rotation by its center point, the number of degrees it's turned, and whether it's turned clockwise or counterclockwise. If no direction is given, assume the direction of rotation is counterclockwise.

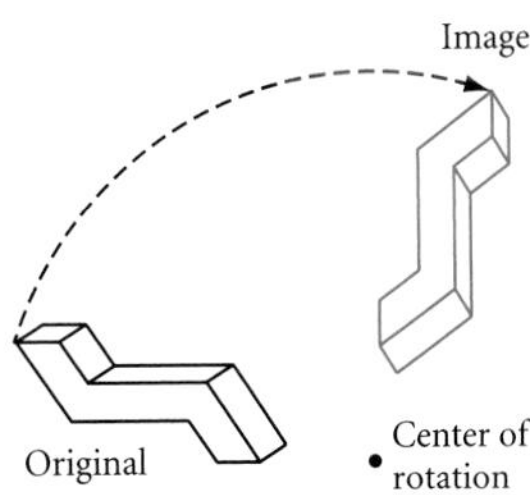

You can model a rotation by tracing over a figure, then putting your pencil point on a point on the patty paper and rotating the patty paper about the point.

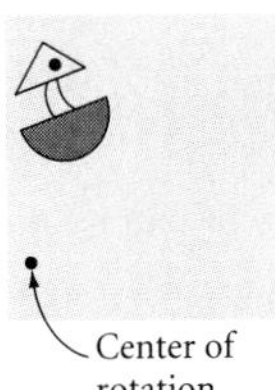

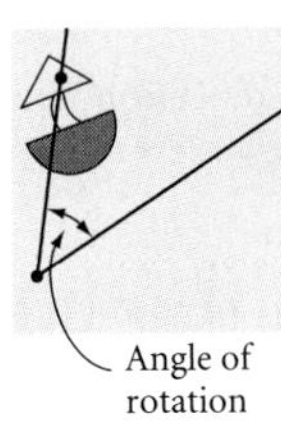

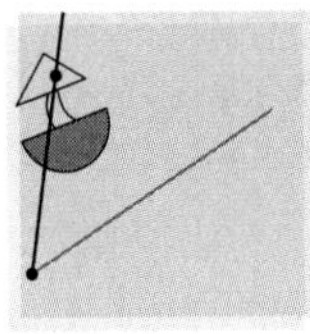

Rotating with patty paper

One step (continued)
During Sharing, have groups demonstrate their ideas by moving the transparencies around. Introduce the names for the three kinds of isometries after students have described them.

INTRODUCTION

Have students read pages 358–360 to themselves and then aloud in their groups. Let them have fun with the paragraphs that have been translated (page 358), rotated (page 359), and reflected (page 360). They may need mirrors to read about reflections. Ask how and why the paragraphs are different from normal.

Reflection is a type of isometry that produces a figure's "mirror image." If you draw a figure onto a piece of paper, place the edge of a mirror perpendicular to your paper, and look at the figure in the mirror, you will see the reflected image of the figure. The line where the mirror is placed is called the **line of reflection.**

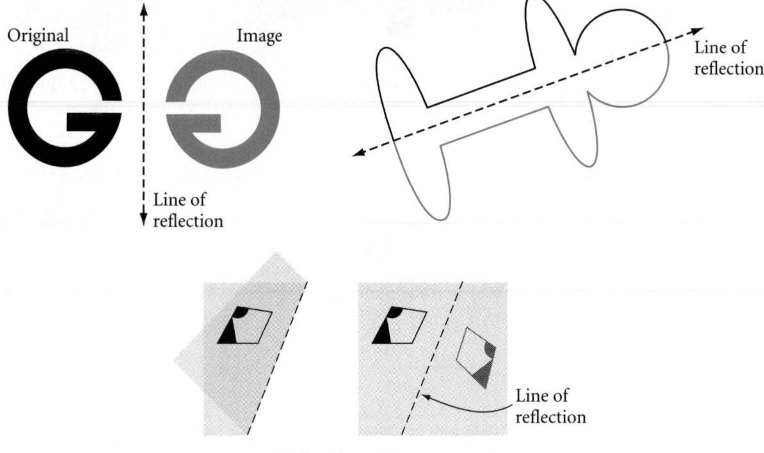

Reflecting with patty paper

History CONNECTION

Leonardo da Vinci (1452–1519, Italy) wrote his scientific discoveries backward so that others couldn't read them and punish him for his research and ideas. His knowledge and authority in almost every subject is astonishing even today. Scholars marvel at his many notebooks containing research into anatomy, mathematics, architecture, geology, meteorology, machinery, and botany, as well as his art masterpieces, like the *Mona Lisa*. Notice his plans for a helicopter in the manuscript at right!

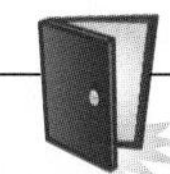

Investigation
The Basic Property of a Reflection

You will need
- patty paper

In this investigation you'll model reflection with patty paper and discover an important property of reflections.

Step 1 Draw a polygon and a line of reflection next to it on a piece of patty paper.

Step 2 Fold your patty paper along the line of reflection and create the reflected image of your polygon by tracing it.

Step 3 Draw segments connecting each vertex with its image point. What do you notice?

Step 3 The line of reflection is the perpendicular bisector of each segment.

Guiding the Investigation

Step 1 If the line of symmetry is drawn through the polygon rather than next to it, the original and the image overlap. **[Alert]** Students will need to restart if they've made their polygon too large to allow it to be reflected over a line while remaining on the paper.

Step 3 The phrase *image point* is used for clarity; the word *image* is sufficient. Suggest that students label the original vertices with letters and label their images with the same letters followed by a prime. They can use compass and protractor or patty paper to compare distances and angles.

SHARING IDEAS

Have the class reach consensus about the Reflection Line Conjecture, using terms like *perpendicular bisector* rather than just stating that a right angle is formed and that two equal segments are created. **[Ask]** "If you are given two figures (original and image) but the line of reflection is missing, how could you determine that a reflection has taken place?" [mirror image] "How could you use this conjecture to help you locate the line of reflection?"

[Ask] "Why are reflections described by mirrors instead of 'flipping?'" [The notion of flipping requires moving outside the plane, while reflecting occurs within the plane.]

While discussing reflections, you might ask why a mirror reflects side to side but not up and down. Be prepared for a great deal of discussion!

Show a picture with reflectional symmetry and **[Ask]** "What does this have to do with transformations?" [Elicit the idea that when a reflection is applied to this picture along the axis of symmetry, the image coincides with the original figure.]

Now do the same with rotational symmetry. **[Ask]** "Which letters of the English alphabet have rotational symmetry?" [H, I, N, O, S, X, and Z all have 2-fold rotational symmetry. If O is perfectly circular, it has rotational symmetry of every fold. Similarly, X can have 4-fold rotational symmetry in some fonts.]

[Ask] "Is a rotation through 0° a rotation?" [It is, mathematically, and is called the *identity transformation.*] In fact, a *symmetry* is a transformation of a figure under which the image of the figure coincides with the original figure, and the identity transformation is considered a symmetry of every figure. So, for example, we can say that the letter H has four symmetries: the identity, one 2-fold rotation, and two reflections.

Wonder aloud, "We've seen symmetry associated with two of these three isometries. What's an example of a figure with translational symmetry?" Leave the answer to this question for Lesson 7.4, when students will see tessellations.

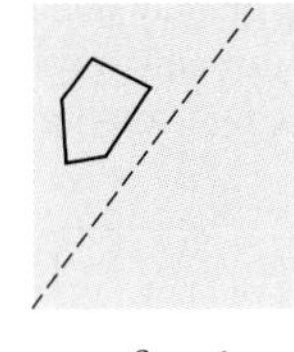

Step 1

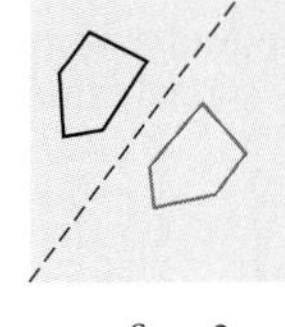

Step 2

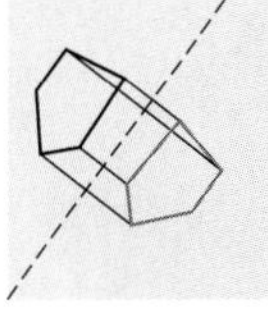

Step 3

Step 4 Compare your results with those of your group members. Copy and complete the following conjecture.

Reflection Line Conjecture

C-68

The line of reflection is the _?_ of every segment joining a point in the original figure with its image. perpendicular bisector

If a figure can be reflected over a line in such a way that the resulting image coincides with the original, then the figure has **reflectional symmetry.** The reflection line is called the **line of symmetry.** The Navajo rug shown below has two lines of symmetry.

The letter *T* has reflectional symmetry. You can test a figure for reflectional symmetry by using a mirror or by folding it.

Navajo rug (two lines of symmetry)

The letter *Z* has 2-fold rotational symmetry. When it is rotated 180° and 360° about a center of rotation, the image coincides with the original figure.

If a figure can be rotated about a point in such a way that its rotated image coincides with the original figure before turning a full 360°, then the figure has **rotational symmetry.** Of course, every image is identical to the original figure after a rotation of any multiple of 360°. However, we don't call a figure symmetric if this is the only kind of symmetry it has. You can trace a figure to test it for rotational symmetry. Place the copy exactly over the original, put your pen or pencil point on the center to hold it down, and rotate the copy. Count the number of times the copy and the original coincide until the copy is back in its original position. Two-fold rotational symmetry is also called **point symmetry.**

Assessing Progress

You can assess students' understanding of perpendicular bisectors and their skill at measuring angles and lengths. If they did Chapter 0, you can assess their understanding of reflectional and rotational symmetry.

Closing the Lesson

A **transformation** is a movement of a geometric figure. Three kinds of **rigid transformations (isometries)**—transformations that don't change the size or shape of the figure—are **translations, rotations,** and **reflections.** The **identity transformation** is also an isometry. For a reflection, the **line of reflection** is the perpendicular bisector of all segments joining points on the figure with corresponding points on its **image.** A figure has **rotational symmetry** if there's a rotation under which its image coincides with the original figure. The **symmetries** of a figure are the rotations and reflections associated with the figure's symmetry.

BUILDING UNDERSTANDING

You might have students work in groups on the Mini-Investigation (Exercise 16) before they work alone on exercises.

ASSIGNING HOMEWORK

Essential	1–14
Performance assessment	13
Portfolio	16
Journal	9
Group	15, 16
Review	17–22

MATERIALS

- Exercises 4–6 (W), *optional*

▶ Helping with the Exercises

Exercises 1–3 You might use these exercises to start a discussion. **[Ask]** "What are some examples of rigid transformations?" [translations, rotations, reflections] "Nonrigid transformations?" [movie images on film projected onto the movie screen, images on an overhead transparency projected onto the screen, designs on a balloon that change size when the balloon is blown up, a candy bar that melts in the sun, various map projections such as a Mercator projection]

Exercises 4–6 Hand out copies of the worksheets to assist students in completing these exercises.

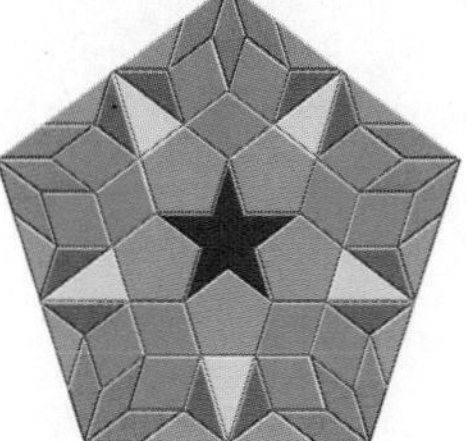

This tile pattern has both 5-fold rotational symmetry and 5-fold reflectional symmetry.

Some polygons have no symmetry, or only one kind of symmetry. Regular polygons, however, are symmetric in many ways. A square, for example, has 4-fold reflectional symmetry and 4-fold rotational symmetry.

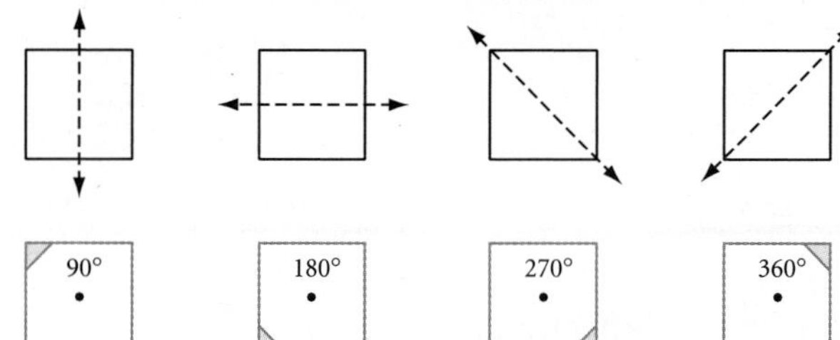

Art CONNECTION

Reflecting and rotating a letter can produce an unexpected and beautiful design. With the aid of graphics software, a designer can do this quickly and inexpensively. To see how, go to www.keymath.com/DG . This design was created by geometry student Michelle Cotter.

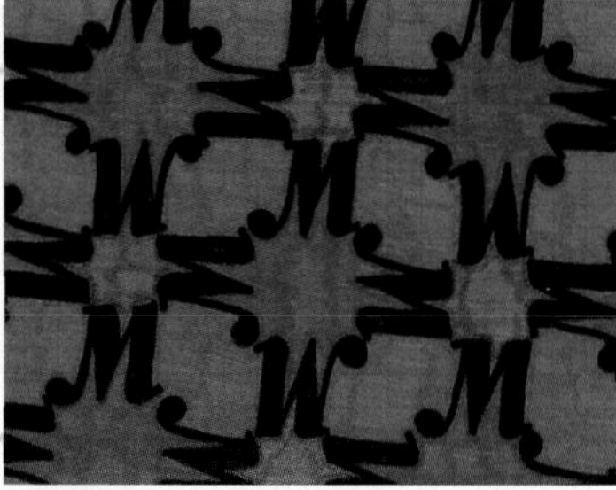

EXERCISES

You will need

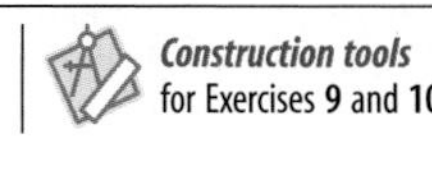

Construction tools for Exercises **9** and **10**

▶ In Exercises 1–3, say whether the transformations are rigid or nonrigid. Explain how you know.

1.

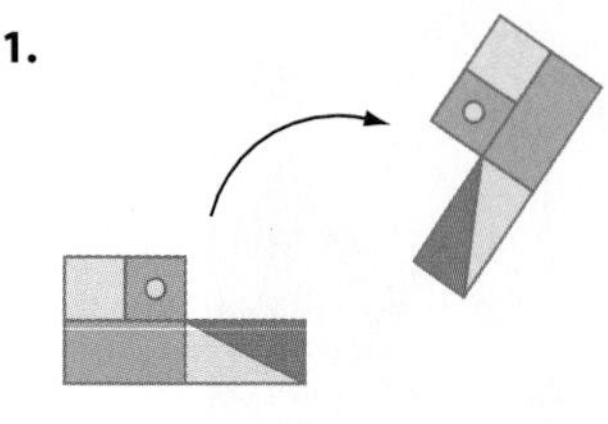

Rigid; reflected, but the size and shape do not change.

2.

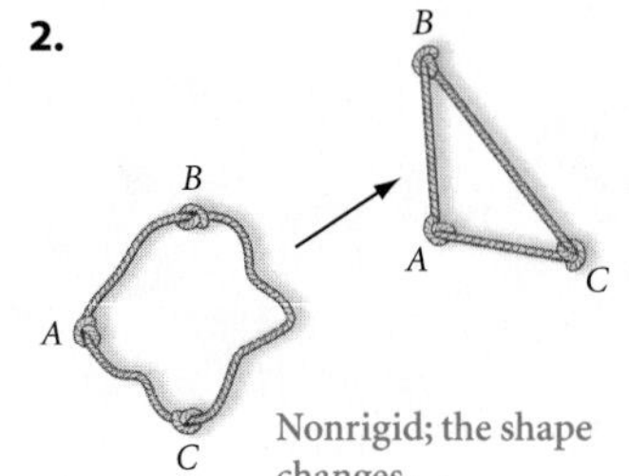

Nonrigid; the shape changes.

3.

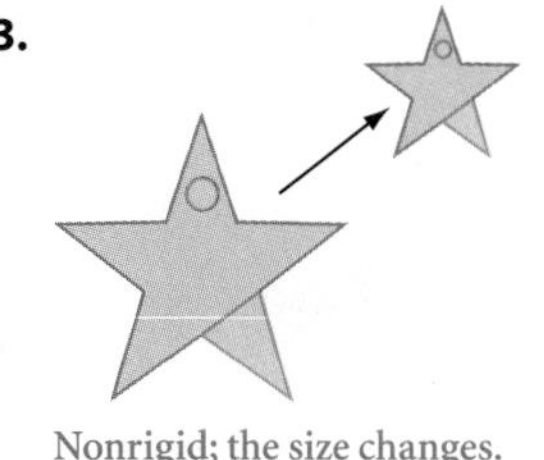

Nonrigid; the size changes.

In Exercises 4–6, copy the figure onto graph or square dot paper and perform each transformation.

4. Reflect the figure over the line of reflection, line ℓ.

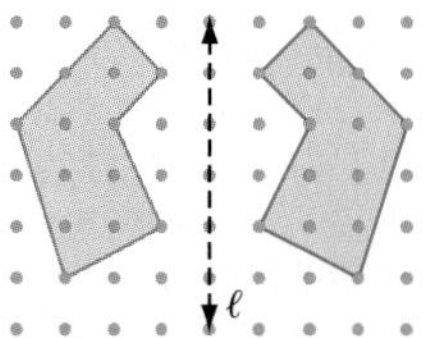

5. Rotate the figure 180° about the center of rotation, point P.

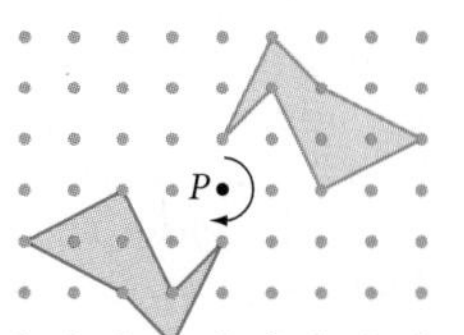

6. Translate the figure by the translation vector.

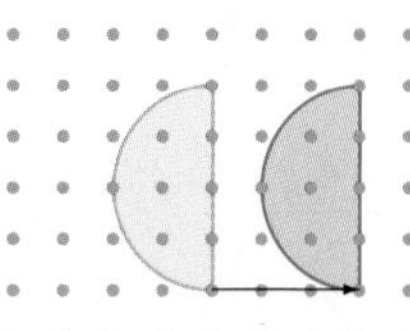

7. An ice skater gliding in one direction creates several translation transformations. Give another real-world example of translation.

8. An ice skater twirling about a point creates several rotation transformations. Give another real-world example of rotation.
possible answer: a Ferris wheel

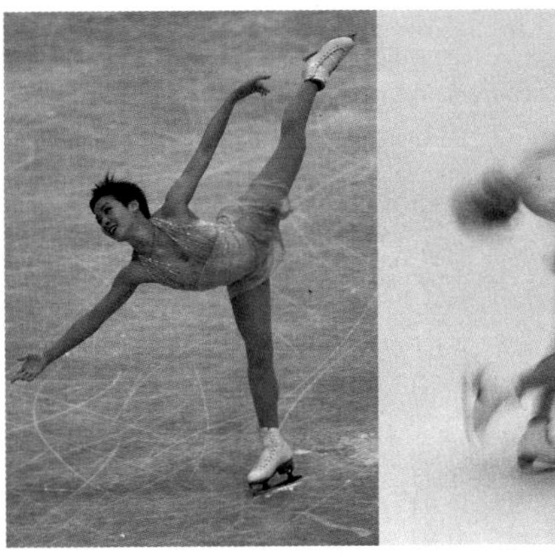

In Exercises 9–11, perform each transformation. Attach your patty paper to your homework.

9. ***Construction*** Use the semicircular figure and its reflected image.

   a. Copy the figure and its reflected image onto a piece of patty paper. Locate the line of reflection. Explain your method.

   b. Copy the figure and its reflected image onto a sheet of paper. Locate the line of reflection using a compass and straightedge. Explain your method.

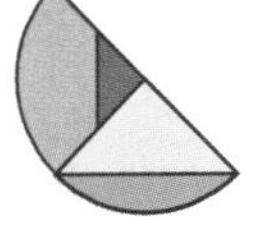
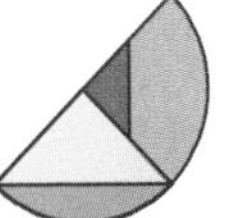

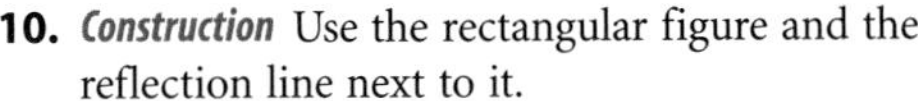

10. ***Construction*** Use the rectangular figure and the reflection line next to it.

    a. Copy the figure and the line of reflection onto a sheet of paper. Use a compass and straightedge to construct the reflected image. Explain your method.

    b. Copy the figure and the line of reflection onto a piece of patty paper. Fold the paper and trace the figure to construct the reflected image.

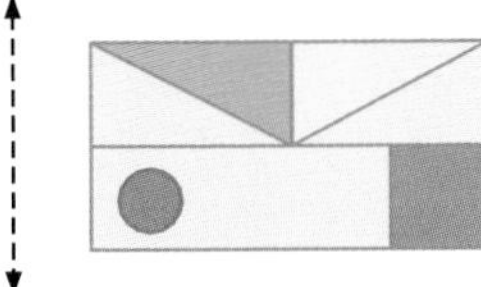

11. Trace the circular figure and the center of rotation, *P*. Rotate the design 90° clockwise about point *P*. Draw the image of the figure, as well as the dotted line.

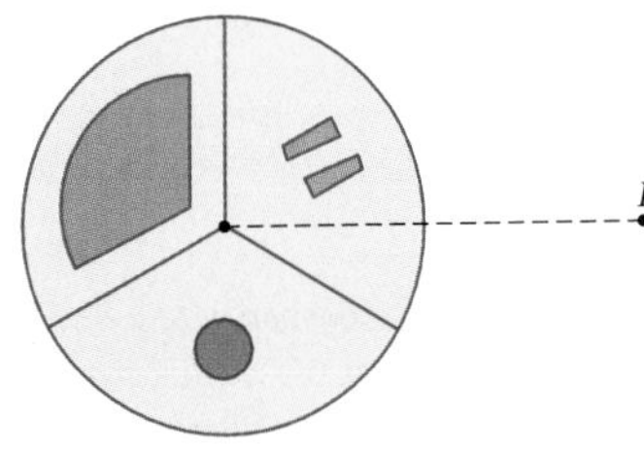

In Exercises 12–14, identify the type (or types) of symmetry in each design.

12.

Butterfly
reflectional symmetry

13.
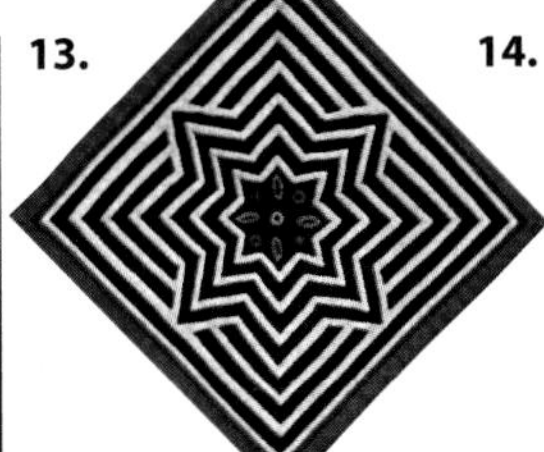
Hmong textile, Laos
4-fold rotational and reflectional symmetry

14.

The Temple Beth Israel, San Diego's first synagogue, built in 1889
reflectional symmetry

7. possible answer: a boat moving across the water

9a. Sample answer: Fold the paper so that the images coincide, and crease.

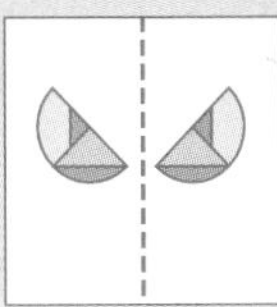

9b. Construct a segment that connects two corresponding points. Construct the perpendicular bisector of that segment.

10a. Extend the three horizontal segments onto the other side of the reflection line. Use your compass to measure lengths of segments and distances from the reflection line.

10b.

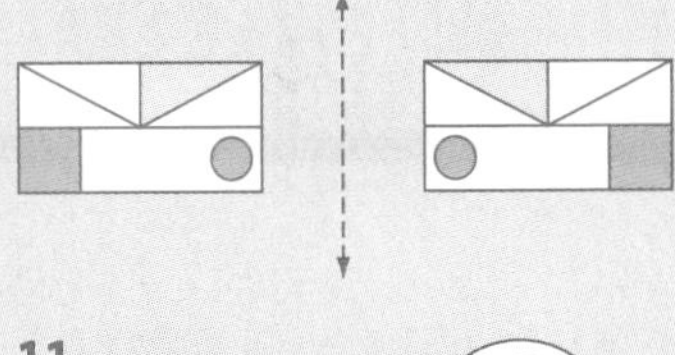

11.

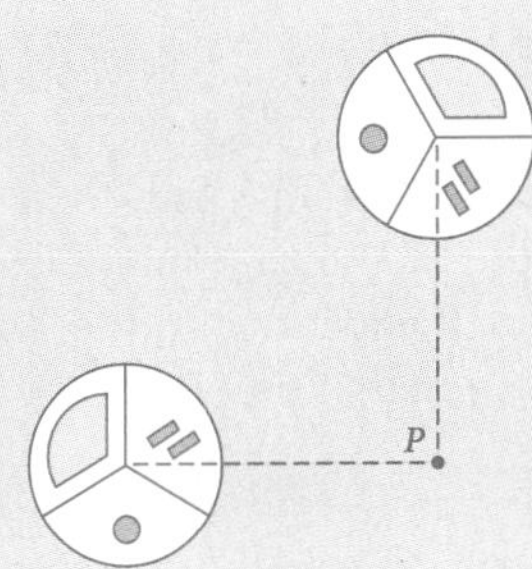

15. 7-fold symmetry: possible answers are F or J. 9-fold symmetry: possible answers are E or H. Basket K has 3-fold rotational symmetry but not reflectional symmetry.

15. All of the woven baskets from Botswana shown below have rotational symmetry and most have reflectional symmetry. Find one that has 7-fold symmetry. Find one with 9-fold symmetry. Which basket has rotational symmetry but not reflectional symmetry? What type of rotational symmetry does it have?

Cultural CONNECTION

For centuries, women in Botswana, a country in southern Africa, have been weaving baskets like the ones you see above, to carry and store food. Each generation passes on the tradition of weaving choice shoots from the mokola palm and decorating them in beautiful geometric patterns with natural dyes. In the past 40 years, international demand for the baskets by retailers and tourists has given economic stability to hundreds of women and their families.

Exercise 16 Students may forget that the rotational symmetries include the identity transformation, a rotation through 0°.

16. ***Mini-Investigation*** Copy and complete the table below. If necessary, use a mirror to locate the lines of symmetry for each of the regular polygons. To find the number of rotational symmetries, you may wish to trace each regular polygon onto patty paper and rotate it. Then copy and complete the conjecture.

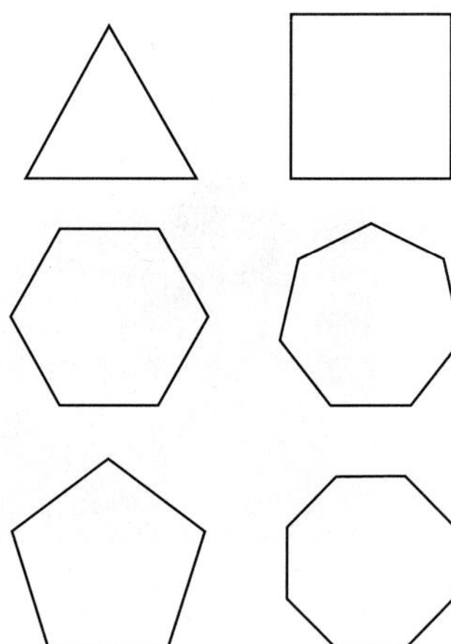

Number of sides of regular polygon	3	4	5	6	7	8	...	n
Number of reflectional symmetries	3	4	5	6	7	8	...	n
Number of rotational symmetries (≤ 360°)	3	4	5	6	7	8	...	n

A regular polygon of n sides has $\underset{?}{n}$ reflectional symmetries and $\underset{n}{?}$ rotational symmetries.

Review

In Exercises 17 and 18, sketch the next two figures.

2.1 **17.** 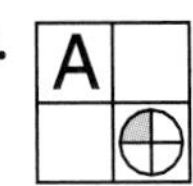 CƆ, Dᗡ, E∃, Fꟻ, GƎ, ?, ?

2.1 **18.** 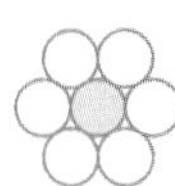 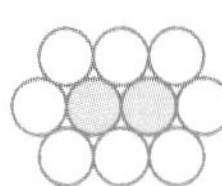 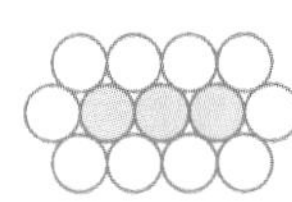

UYAS 3 **19.** Polygon *PQRS* is a rectangle inscribed in a circle centered at the origin. The slope of $\overline{PS}$ is 0. Find the coordinates of points *P*, *Q*, and *R* in terms of *a* and *b*. $P(-a, b), Q(-a, -b), R(a, -b)$

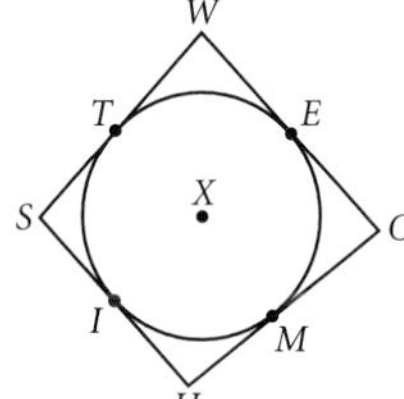

3.2 **20.** Use a circular object to trace a large minor arc. Using either compass-and-straightedge construction or patty-paper construction locate a point on the arc equally distant from the arc's endpoints. Label it *P*.

2.3 **21.** If the circle pattern continues, how many total circles (shaded and unshaded) will there be in the 50th figure? How many will there be in the *n*th figure?

50th figure: 154 (50 shaded, 104 unshaded); *n*th figure: $3n + 4$ (n shaded, $2(n + 2)$ unshaded)

6.2 **22.** Quadrilateral *SHOW* is circumscribed about circle *X*. $WO = 14$, $HM = 4$, $SW = 11$, and $ST = 5$. What is the perimeter of *SHOW*? 46

IMPROVING YOUR ALGEBRA SKILLS

The Difference of Squares

$17^2 - 16^2 = 33$ $\quad 25.5^2 - 24.5^2 = 50$ $\quad 34^2 - 33^2 = 67$

$58^2 - 57^2 = 115$ $\quad 62.1^2 - 61.1^2 = 123.2$ $\quad 76^2 - 75^2 = 151$

Can you use algebra to explain why you can just add the two base numbers to get the answer? (For example, $17 + 16 = 33$.)

17. 

18. 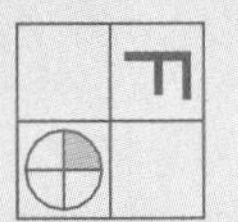 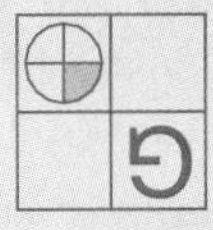

20. possible answer:

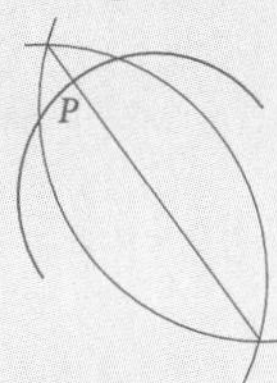

EXTENSIONS

A. Have students discuss topology, or properties preserved by nonrigid transformations.

B. Pose this problem: The numbers 11, 16, 18, 19, 61, 66, 68, 69, 81, 86, 88, 89, 91, 96, 98, and 99 all either have rotational symmetry or can be rotated to create other numbers in the list. Create a 4-by-4 magic square using all 16 numbers. The completed magic square will still be a magic square when rotated 180°, even though 89 becomes 68, 91 becomes 16, 66 becomes 99, and so on. The four corner squares and the four middle squares each add to the magic sum, as do both of the diagonals.

[*Hint*: Any number *x* and the number formed by rotating *x* 180° are both in the same 2-by-2 corner square. For example, the numbers 96 and 69 are in the same corner square. To help students more, give them the boldface numbers in the solution on page 773.]

IMPROVING ALGEBRA SKILLS

If students have seen the formula $a^2 - b^2 = (a - b)(a + b)$ for factoring differences of squares, then they can see that in the case where $a - b = 1$ we can find $a^2 - b^2$ by adding *a* and *b*.

Or students might use the fact that the numbers are consecutive so $a = b + 1$, which students can substitute into the expression $a^2 - b^2$ and show that $(b + 1)^2 - b^2 = 2b + 1 = a + b$.

Another explanation uses a picture:

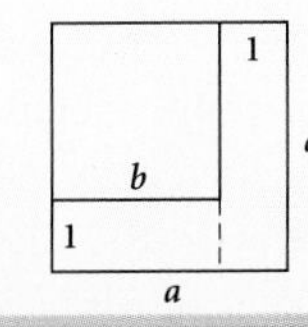

The quantity $a + b$ represents $a(1) + b(1)$, the sum of the areas of the rectangles between the perimeters of the two squares.

LESSON
7.2

PLANNING

LESSON OUTLINE

One day:

5 min Example A
20 min Investigation
5 min Sharing
5 min Example B
10 min Exercises

MATERIALS

- patty paper
- graph paper
- protractors
- rulers, *optional*

TEACHING

Two properties of isometries are the ordered pair rules for some basic rotations and reflections and how the shortest path between points via a line can be determined by using a reflection.

One Step Pose this problem: "Imagine a pool table with corners having coordinates (0, 0), (0, 6), (12, 6), and (12, 0). You want to hit a ball at (4, 2) with the cue ball, which is at (8, 5). Unfortunately, you need to bounce the cue ball off the cushion that lies along the *y*-axis. At what point on that cushion should the cue ball bounce so that it follows the shortest path possible from its current location to the edge and then to the target ball?" [0, 3] Encourage a variety of approaches. During Sharing, if needed, ask what points the first line of the path would go through if it were extended. After students determine that one of those points is (−4, 2), ask if they can use that fact to determine the path initially. Then ask what kind of transformation takes (x, y) to $(-x, y)$ and how, and then ask the same question about other images, including $(x, -y)$, $(-x, -y)$, and (y, x).

INTRODUCTION

So far, ordered pair rules have appeared only in exercises (of Lessons 1.5, 1.6, 1.7, and 4.2). If your students haven't done those exercises, you may need to discuss the idea of such a rule. **[Link]** Ordered pair rules can also be used to transform the graphs of functions, including quadratic, linear, and exponential functions.

► EXAMPLE A

Students can re-create this example using any polygon.

LESSON 7.2

Properties of Isometries

"Why it's a looking-glass book, of course! And, if I hold it up to the glass, the words will all go the right way again."

ALICE IN *THROUGH THE LOOKING-GLASS*
BY LEWIS CARROLL

In many earlier exercises, you used **ordered pair rules** to transform polygons on a coordinate plane by relocating their vertices. For any point on a figure, the ordered pair rule $(x, y) \rightarrow (x + h, y + k)$ results in a horizontal move of h units and a vertical move of k units for any numbers h and k. That is, if (x, y) is a point on the original figure, $(x + h, y + k)$ is its corresponding point on the image. Let's look at an example.

EXAMPLE A

Transform the polygon at right using the rule $(x, y) \rightarrow (x + 2, y - 3)$. Describe the type and direction of the transformation.

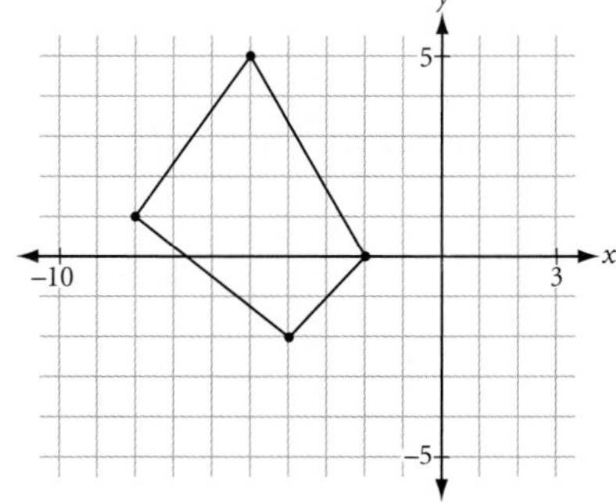

► Solution

Apply the rule to each ordered pair. Every point of the polygon moves right 2 units and down 3 units. This is a translation of $(2, -3)$.

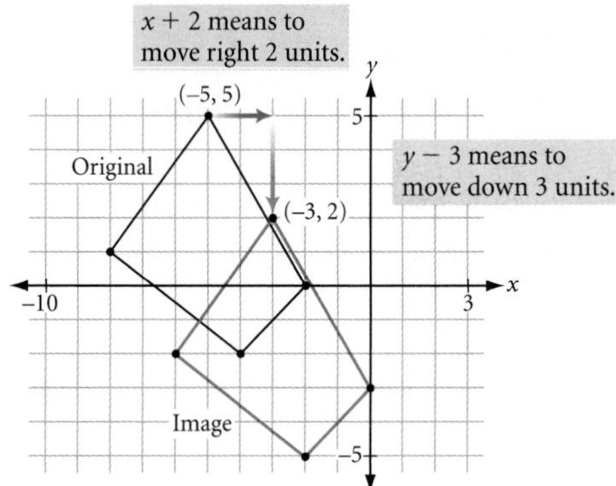

So the ordered pair rule $(x, y) \rightarrow (x + h, y + k)$ results in a translation of (h, k).

Investigation 1
Transformations on a Coordinate Plane

You will need

- graph paper
- patty paper

In this investigation you will discover (or rediscover) how four ordered pair rules transform a polygon. Each person in your group can choose a different polygon for this investigation.

Step 1 On graph paper, create and label four sets of coordinate axes. Draw the same polygon in the same position in a quadrant of each of the four graphs. Write one of these four ordered pair rules below each graph.

a. $(x, y) \rightarrow (-x, y)$
b. $(x, y) \rightarrow (x, -y)$
c. $(x, y) \rightarrow (-x, -y)$
d. $(x, y) \rightarrow (y, x)$

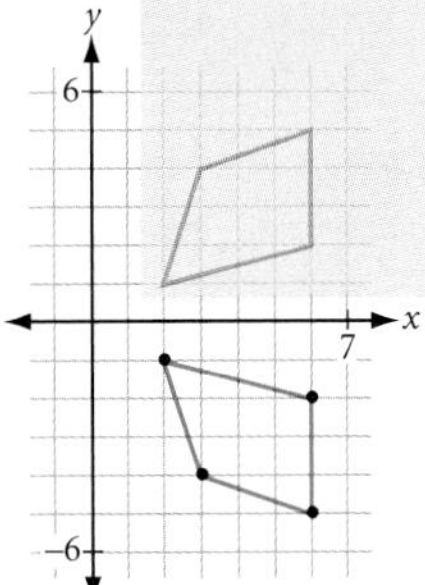

Step 2 Use the ordered pair rule you assigned to each graph to relocate the vertices of your polygon and create its image.

Step 3 Use patty paper to see if your transformation is a reflection, translation, or rotation. Compare your results with those of your group members. Complete the conjecture.

Coordinate Transformations Conjecture C-69

The ordered pair rule $(x, y) \rightarrow (-x, y)$ is a _?_ over _?_. reflection; the y-axis
The ordered pair rule $(x, y) \rightarrow (x, -y)$ is a _?_ over _?_. reflection; the x-axis
The ordered pair rule $(x, y) \rightarrow (-x, -y)$ is a _?_ about _?_. rotation; the origin
The ordered pair rule $(x, y) \rightarrow (y, x)$ is a _?_ over _?_. reflection; $y = x$

Let's revisit "poolroom geometry." When a ball rolls without spin into a cushion, the outgoing angle is congruent to the incoming angle. This is true because the outgoing and incoming angles are reflections of each other.

Investigation 2
Finding a Minimal Path

You will need

- patty paper
- a protractor

In Chapter 1, you used a protractor to find the path of the ball. In this investigation, you'll discover some other properties of reflections that have many applications in science and engineering. They may even help your pool game!

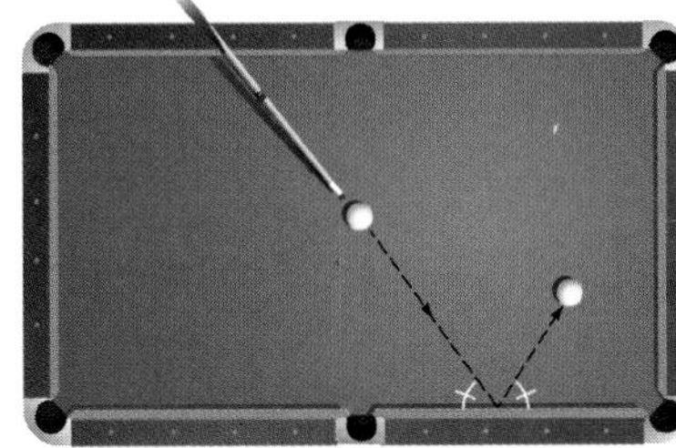

Guiding Investigation 1

Step 1 If students place their figure completely in one quadrant, it will be easier for them to draw conclusions about the action of the transformation.

Step 3 Students can use the patty paper to trace the original polygon.

NCTM STANDARDS

CONTENT		PROCESS	
	Number	✓	Problem Solving
✓	Algebra		Reasoning
✓	Geometry	✓	Communication
	Measurement	✓	Connections
	Data/Probability	✓	Representation

LESSON OBJECTIVES

- Find a minimal path using reflections
- Develop visual thinking and problem-solving skills

Guiding Investigation 2

Step 2 Students are looking for the one location where the incoming angle equals the outgoing angle.

Step 4 The idea of labeling the image with a prime might be new to students.

SHARING IDEAS

As students present their ideas, encourage them to use the terms *reflection* and *rotation*.

If needed, ask what the main idea is in the pool table investigation. Students may not yet have seen that they can work backward, using the reflection of the target to determine the first line of the moving ball's path, which in turn determines a point on the cushion and thus the second line of the path. Ask what students observe in the picture of the situation. They can see several pairs of congruent angles.

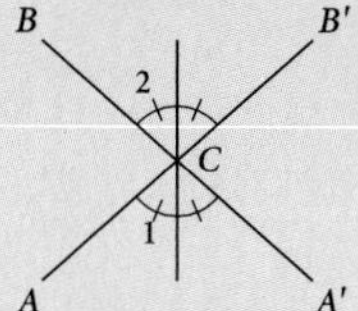

If they connect points A and A', they can probably spot congruent triangles that allow them to prove that the length of the ball's path is indeed the length of the line segment AB', which is the shortest path. They can also show that the incoming and outgoing angles are congruent.

[Ask] "What other real-world applications use the Minimal Path Conjecture?" Be sure to give students plenty of time to think before proceeding; in fact, someone will usually volunteer an idea within half a minute. Some other applications appear in the exercises. One application is to bounce a golf ball off two walls. This idea leads to Example B.

Step 1 Draw a segment, representing a pool table cushion, near the center of a piece of patty paper. Draw two points, A and B, on one side of the segment.

Step 2 Imagine you want to hit a ball at point A so that it bounces off the cushion and hits another ball at point B. Use your protractor to find the point C on the cushion that you should aim for.

Step 3 Draw $\overline{AC}$ and $\overline{CB}$ to represent the ball's path.

Step 4 Fold your patty paper to draw the reflection of point B. Label the image point B'.

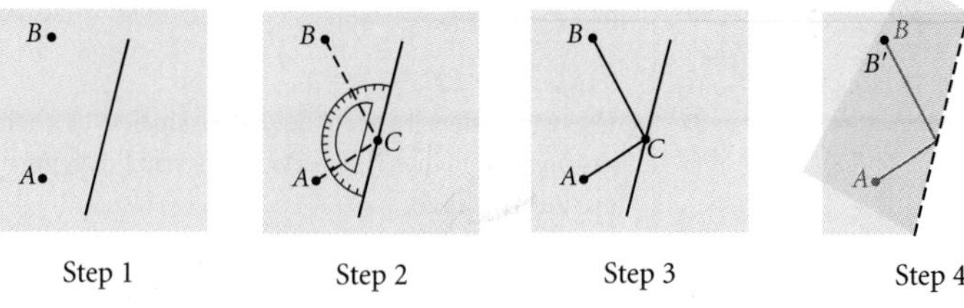

Step 1 Step 2 Step 3 Step 4

Step 5 Unfold the paper and draw a segment from point A to point B'. What do you notice? Does point C lie on segment $\overline{AB'}$? How does the path from A to B' compare to the two-part path from A to C to B?

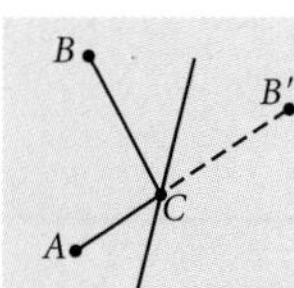

Step 5 Yes. They are the same length.

Step 6 Can you draw any other path from point A to the cushion to point B that is shorter than $AC + CB$? Why or why not? The shortest path from point A to the cushion to point B is called the **minimal path.** Copy and complete the conjecture.

Step 6 No. If the cushion was not there, the ball would travel in a straight line from A to B'. Because it is, the ball is reflected at an equal angle back to B. Any other path between A and B', and therefore between A and B, would be longer.

Minimal Path Conjecture — C-70

If points A and B are on one side of line ℓ, then the minimal path from point A to line ℓ to point B is found by __?__.

reflecting point B over line ℓ, drawing segment AB', then drawing segments AC and CB where point C is the point of intersection of segment AB' and line ℓ

How can this discovery help your pool game? Suppose you need to hit a ball at point A into the cushion so that it will bounce off the cushion and pass through point B. To what point on the cushion should you aim? Visualize point B reflected across the cushion. Then aim directly at the reflected image.

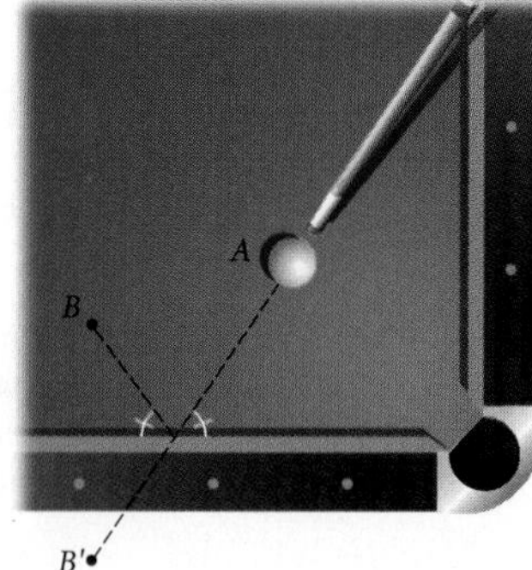

Let's look at a miniature-golf example.

EXAMPLE B

How can you hit the ball at T around the corner and into the hole at H in one shot?

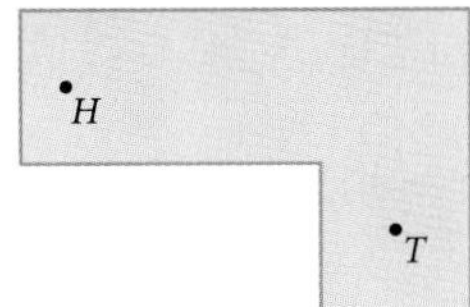

▶ Solution

First, try to get a hole-in-one with a direct shot or with just one bounce off a wall. For one bounce, decide which wall the ball should hit. Visualize the image of the hole across that wall and aim for the reflected hole. There are two possibilities.

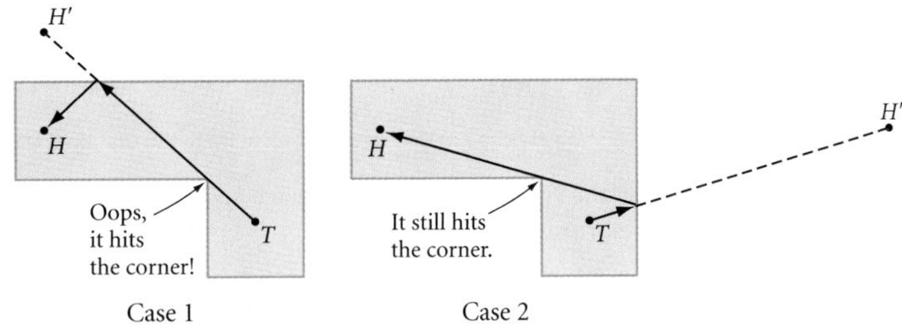

Case 1 Case 2

In both cases the path is blocked. It looks like you need to try two bounces. Visualize a path from the tee hitting two walls and into the hole.

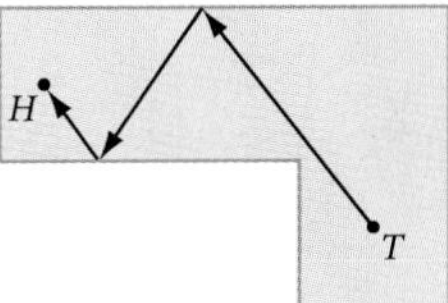

Visualize the path.

Now you can work backward. Which wall will the ball hit last? Reflect the hole across that wall creating image H'.

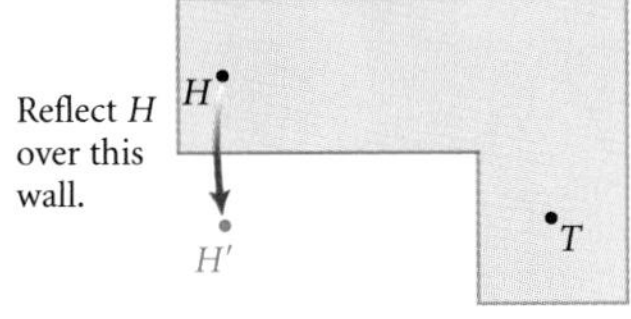

▶ EXAMPLE B

[ESL] In golf, the *tee* is the place from which you take your first shot.

Students may need to use a protractor to locate the bounce-off point on the wall, but encourage them to think about the wall as a line of reflection. They might think about reflecting the entire picture across each wall and drawing a straight line from the ball to the image of the hole.

Assessing Progress

As students work and present their ideas, you can assess their understanding of reflections and rotations, using coordinate graphs, and measuring angles with a protractor.

Closing the Lesson

Restate the two properties of isometries: (1) Rotations and reflections can be represented by some standard ordered pair rules. (2) The shortest path between points via a line can be determined by using a reflection of the target over the line.

BUILDING UNDERSTANDING

The exercises include work with ordered pair rules and transformations as well as applications of the Minimal Path Conjecture.

ASSIGNING HOMEWORK

Essential	1–12
Performance assessment	8, 12
Portfolio	11
Group	15
Review	13–22

MATERIALS

- Exercises 10 and 11 (T), *optional*

▶ Helping with the Exercises

2. reflection

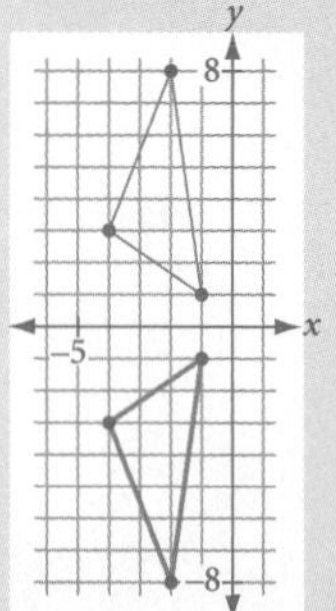

Exercise 4 Some students may find this exercise difficult because the reflection is over a line that is not an axis. It is also correct to think of this as a reflection over the y-axis then a translation. In the next lesson students will investigate combining transformations.

Which wall will the ball hit before it approaches the second wall? Reflect the image of the hole H' across that wall creating image H'' (read "H double prime").

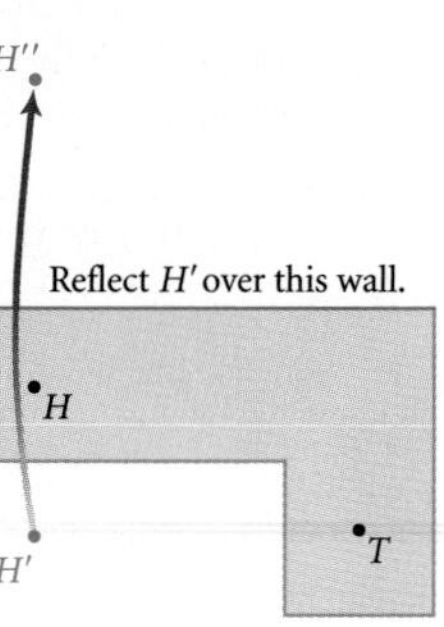

H''
Reflect H' over this wall.
H
T
H'

Draw the path from the tee to H'', H', and H. Can you visualize other possible paths with two bounces? Three bounces? What do you suppose is the minimal path from T to H?

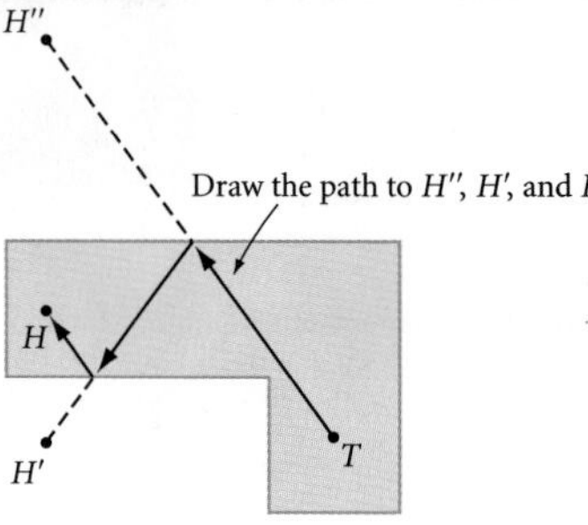

H''
Draw the path to H'', H', and H.
H
H'
T

EXERCISES

You will need

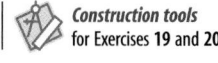

Construction tools for Exercises **19** and **20**

▶ In Exercises 1–5, copy the figure and draw the image according to the rule. Identify the type of transformation.

1. $(x, y) \rightarrow (x + 5, y)$

translation

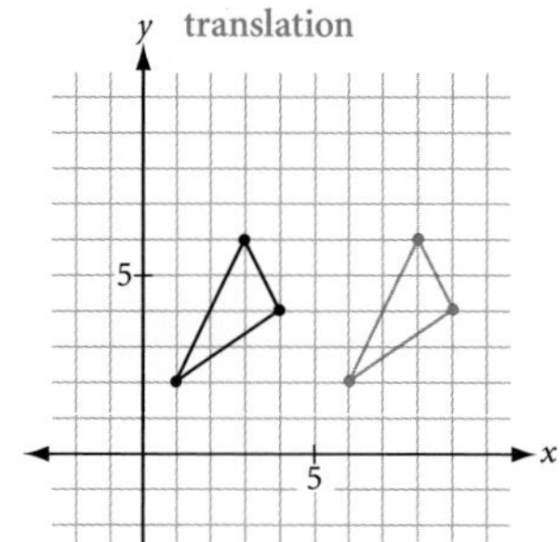

2. $(x, y) \rightarrow (x, -y)$ ⓗ

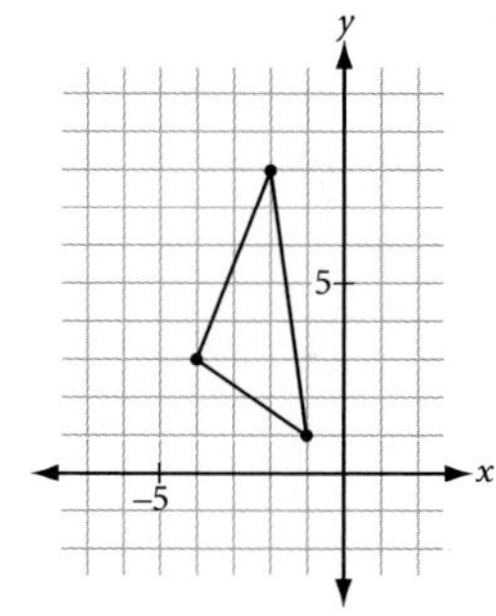

3. $(x, y) \rightarrow (y, x)$

reflection

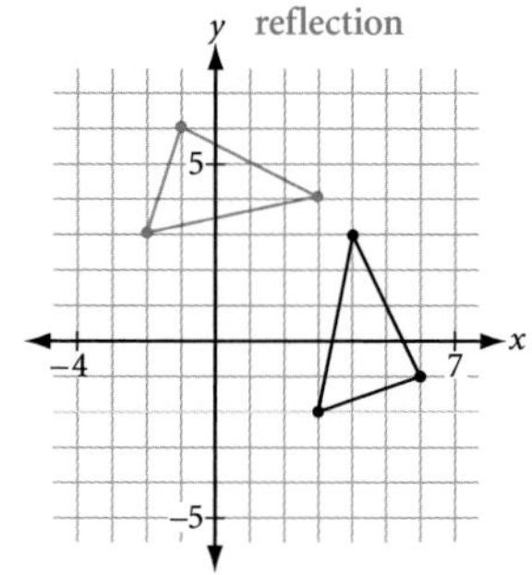

4. $(x, y) \rightarrow (8 - x, y)$

reflection

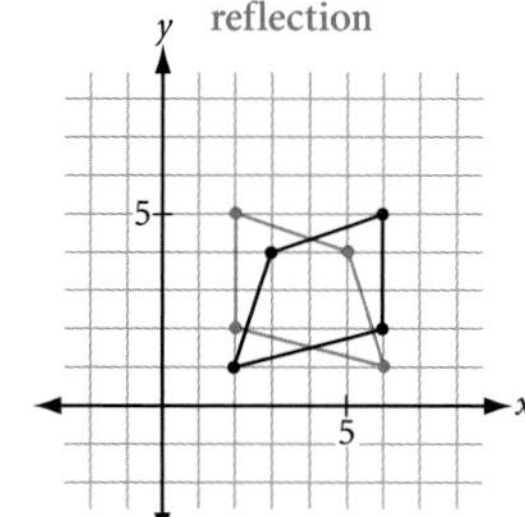

5. $(x, y) \rightarrow (-x, -y)$

rotation

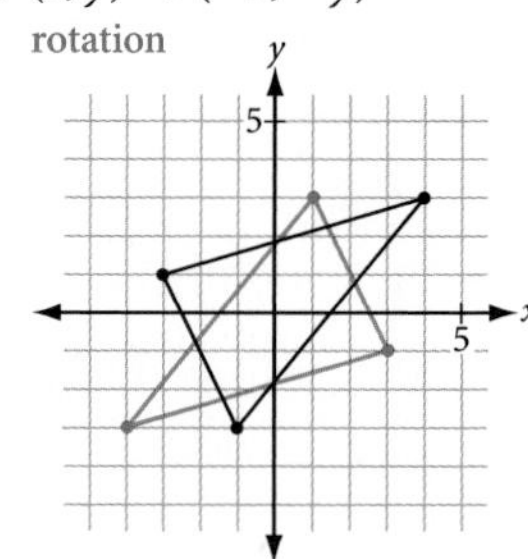

6. Look at the rules in Exercises 1–5 that produced reflections. What do these rules have in common? How about the ones that produce translations? Rotations?

Rules that involve x or y changing signs, or switching places, produce reflections. Rules that produce translations involve a constant being added to the x and/or y terms. If both x and y change signs, the rule produces a rotation.

In Exercises 7 and 8, complete the ordered pair rule that transforms the black triangle to its image, the red triangle.

7. $(x, y) \rightarrow (\underline{?}, \underline{?})$ ⓗ $(x, y) \rightarrow (x, -y)$

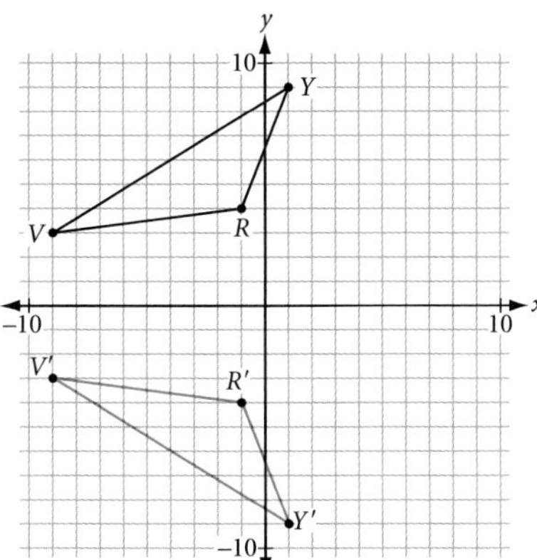

8. $(x, y) \rightarrow (\underline{?}, \underline{?})$ $(x, y) \rightarrow (-x, -y)$

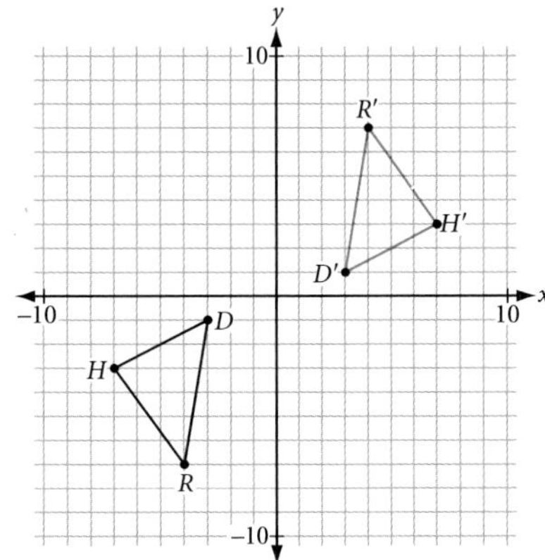

In Exercises 9–11, copy the position of each ball and hole onto patty paper and draw the path of the ball.

9. What point on the W cushion can a player aim for so that the cue ball bounces and strikes the 8-ball? What point can a player aim for on the S cushion? See below.

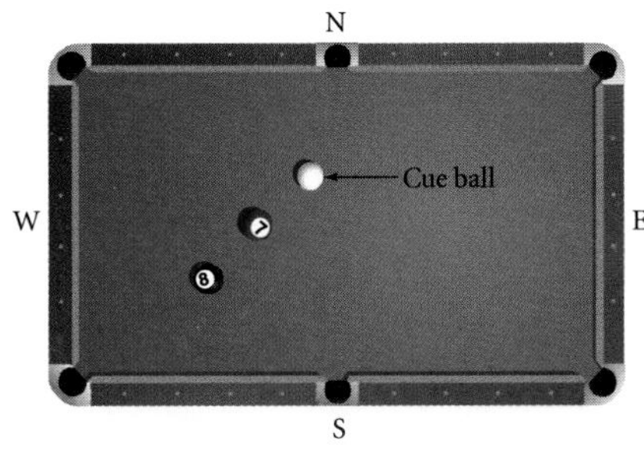

10. Starting from the tee (point T), what point on a wall should a player aim for so that the golf ball bounces off the wall and goes into the hole at H?

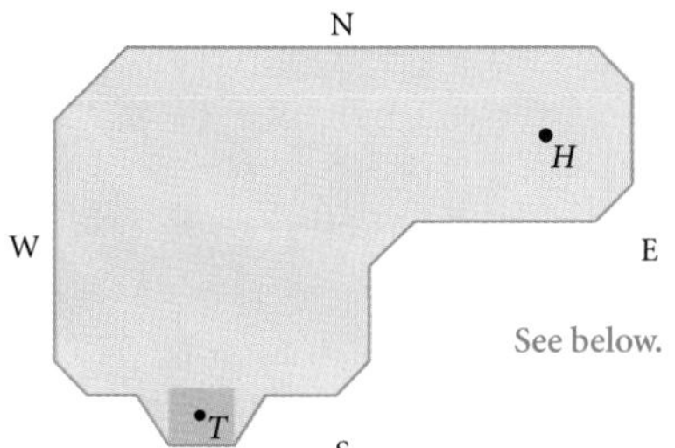

See below.

11. Starting from the tee (point T), plan a shot so that the golf ball goes into the hole at H. Show all your work.

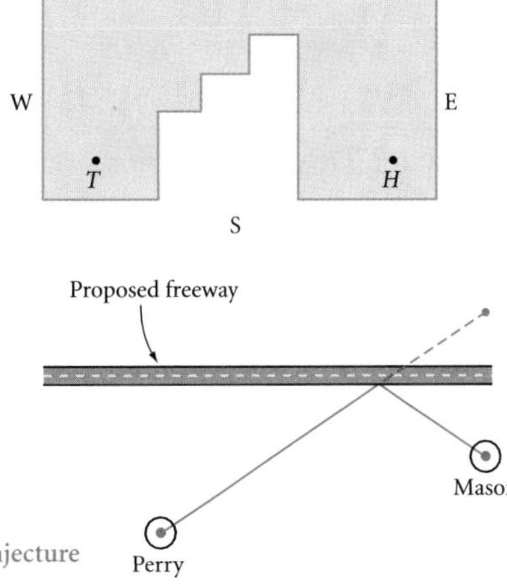

12. A new freeway is being built near the two towns of Perry and Mason. The two towns want to build roads to one junction point on the freeway. (One of the roads will be named Della Street.) Locate the junction point and draw the minimal path from Perry to the freeway to Mason. How do you know this is the shortest path? by the Minimal Path Conjecture

11.

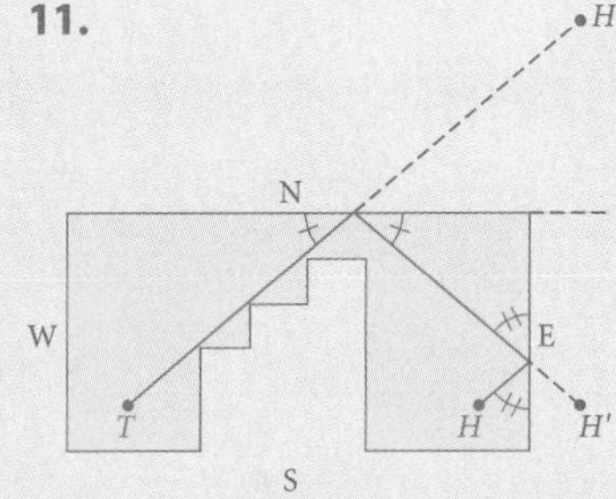

Exercise 12 The answer art is drawn to the edge of the freeway and will vary slightly from answers using the center of the freeway.

9.

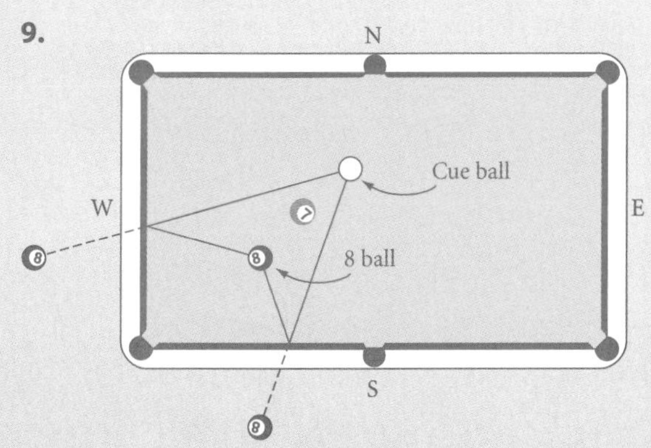

10.

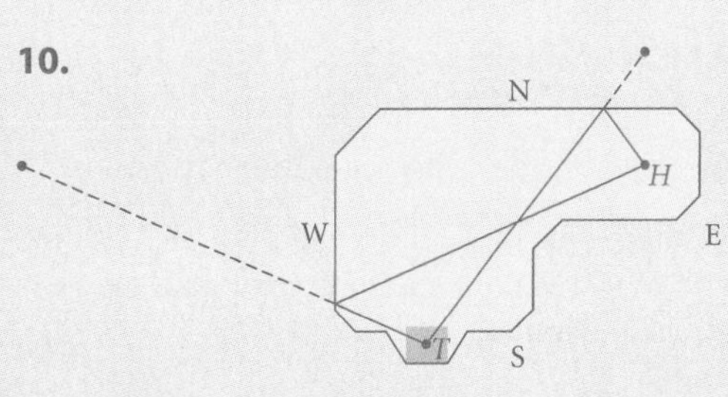

13. 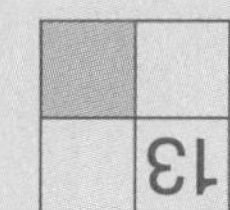

14. 11 13

Exercise 15 You might keep a class list for several days or hold a contest to find the longest word with a horizontal line of symmetry.

18. YOUR TEE SHIRT IS INSIDE OUT

19. sample construction:

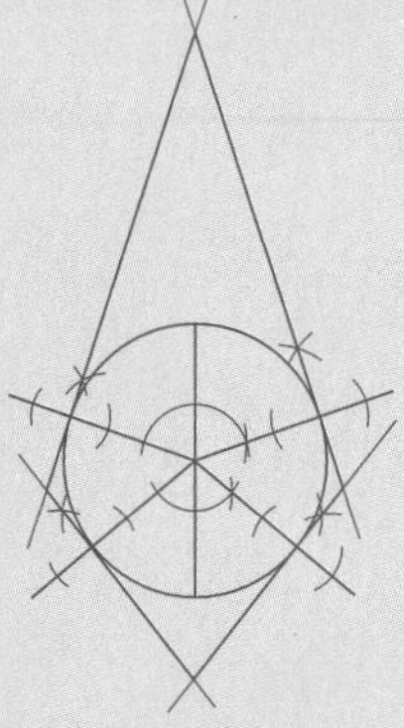

20. sample construction:

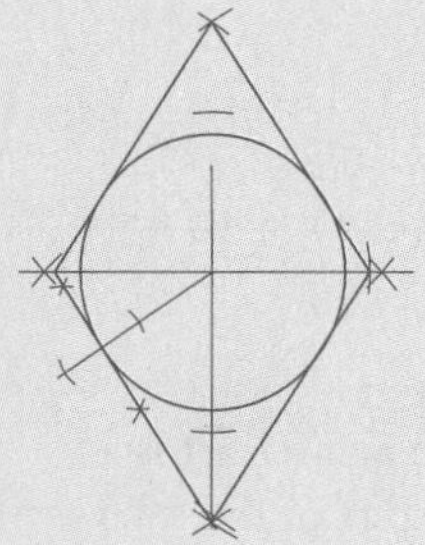

Review

In Exercises 13 and 14, sketch the next two figures.

2.1 **13.** _?_, _?_

2.1 **14.** 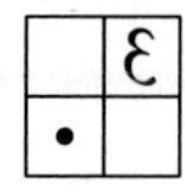 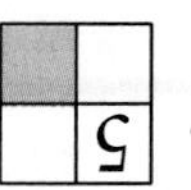 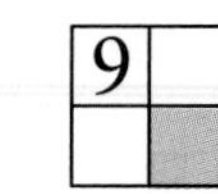 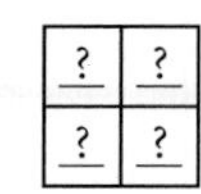 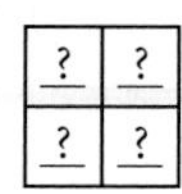

7.1 **15.** The word DECODE remains unchanged when it is reflected over its horizontal line of symmetry. Find another such word with at least five letters. possible answer: HIKED

DECODE

7.1 **16.** How many reflectional symmetries does an isosceles triangle have? One unless it is equilateral, in which case it has three.

7.1 **17.** How many reflectional symmetries does a rhombus have? Two unless it is a square, in which case it has four.

7.1 **18.** Write what is actually on the T-shirt shown at right.

6.2 **19.** ***Construction*** Construct a kite circumscribed about a circle.

6.2 **20.** ***Construction*** Construct a rhombus circumscribed about a circle.

By Holland. ©1976, Punch Cartoon Library.

In Exercises 21 and 22, identify each statement as true or false. If true, explain why. If false, give a counterexample.

5.6 **21.** If two angles of a quadrilateral are right angles, then it is a rectangle. false; possible counterexample: trapezoid with two right angles

5.6 **22.** If the diagonals of a quadrilateral are congruent, then it is a rectangle. false; possible counterexample: isosceles trapezoid

IMPROVING YOUR REASONING SKILLS

Chew on This for a While

If the third letter before the second consonant after the third vowel in the alphabet is in the twenty-sixth word of this puzzle, then print the fortieth word of this puzzle and then print the twenty-second letter of the alphabet after this word. Otherwise, list three uses for chewing gum.

EXTENSIONS

A. Have students determine what kind of ordered pair rule would create a nonrigid transformation.

B. Pose this problem: A line is the minimal path in the plane. What would be the minimal path on a sphere? On a cylinder?

C. Challenge students to find words with more than one type of symmetry.

IMPROVING REASONING SKILLS

You might mention that a hyphenated word is counted as one word.

alphabet v

LESSON

7.3 Compositions of Transformations

There are things which nobody would see unless I photographed them.
DIANE ARBUS

In Lesson 7.2, you reflected a point, then reflected it again to find the path of a ball. When you apply one transformation to a figure and then apply another transformation to its image, the resulting transformation is called a **composition** of transformations. Let's look at an example of a composition of two translations.

EXAMPLE

Triangle ABC with vertices $A(-1, 0)$, $B(4, 0)$, and $C(2, 6)$ is first translated by the rule $(x, y) \rightarrow (x - 6, y - 5)$, and then its image, $\triangle A'B'C'$, is translated by the rule $(x, y) \rightarrow (x + 14, y + 3)$.

a. What single translation is equivalent to the composition of these two translations?

b. What single translation brings the second image, $\triangle A''B''C''$, back to the position of the original triangle, $\triangle ABC$?

Solution

Draw $\triangle ABC$ on a set of axes and relocate its vertices using the first rule to get $\triangle A'B'C'$. Then relocate the vertices of $\triangle A'B'C'$ using the second rule to get $\triangle A''B''C''$.

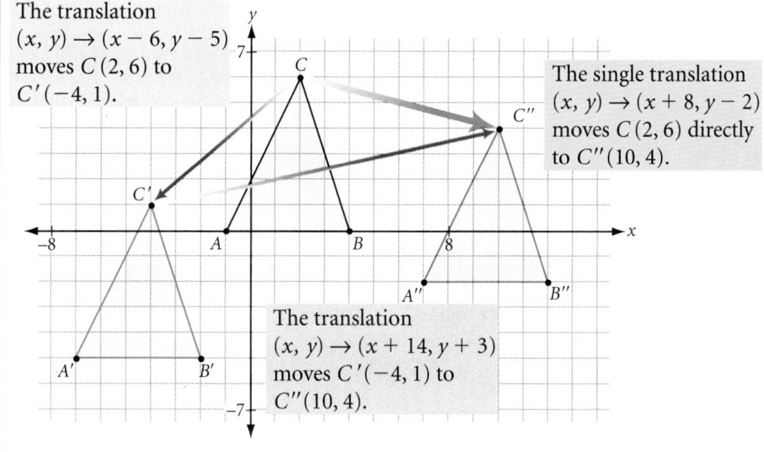

The translation
(x, y) → (x − 6, y − 5)
moves C (2, 6) to
C′(−4, 1).
The single translation
(x, y) → (x + 8, y − 2)
moves C (2, 6) directly
to C″(10, 4).
The translation
(x, y) → (x + 14, y + 3)
moves C′(−4, 1) to
C″(10, 4).
y
x
7
−7
−8
8
C
C′
C″
A
B
A′
B′
A″
B″

a. Each vertex is moved left 6 then right 14, and down 5 then up 3. So the equivalent single translation would be $(x, y) \rightarrow (x - 6 + 14, y - 5 + 3)$ or $(x, y) \rightarrow (x + 8, y - 2)$. You can also write this as $\langle 8, -2 \rangle$.

NCTM STANDARDS

CONTENT		PROCESS	
	Number		Problem Solving
✓	Algebra	✓	Reasoning
✓	Geometry	✓	Communication
	Measurement	✓	Connections
	Data/Probability	✓	Representation

LESSON OBJECTIVES

- Discover the result of reflecting a figure over two parallel lines
- Discover the result of reflecting a figure over two intersecting lines
- Learn about glide reflections
- Develop visual thinking

LESSON 7.3

PLANNING

LESSON OUTLINE

One day:

20 min	Investigation
10 min	Sharing
5 min	Closing
10 min	Exercises

MATERIALS

- patty paper
- protractors
- compasses, *optional*
- Sketchpad demonstration Reflections over Lines, *optional*

TEACHING

Students see that pairs of reflections can yield a translation or a rotation and that a reflection and a translation can be combined as well.

One step Ask what happens if you follow one reflection by another over two intersecting lines. As you circulate, encourage students to experiment with moving the object being reflected farther and farther away from the point of intersection of the two lines of reflection, approximating the case in which the lines are parallel. Have them incorporate measurements of distances and angles into their conjectures. During Sharing, introduce the term *composition of transformations*.

EXAMPLE

[Language] *Equivalent* here means "having the same result."

After they graph the triangle and perform the two translations, students will quickly notice how the second image can be produced from the original with a single translation.

Guiding Investigation 1

Step 1 [Alert] Students should plan to make the original image simple and small, because its images through two reflections should remain on the patty paper.

Step 2 To help them see how the reflected figures relate to the original, students might label points of the original and of their images in each reflection.

Step 3 To keep the figure on the patty paper, the second reflection line shouldn't be too far from the first; to keep things simple, it shouldn't pass through the first image.

Step 7 Instead of saying only that the composition is equivalent to a single translation, students can give the direction of that translation.

b. Reversing the steps, the translation $(-8, 2)$ brings the second image, $\triangle A''B''C''$, back to $\triangle ABC$.

In the investigations you will see what happens when you compose reflections.

Investigation 1
Reflections over Two Parallel Lines

You will need

- patty paper

First consider the case of parallel lines of reflection.

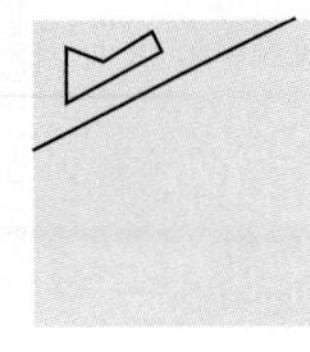

Step 1

Step 2

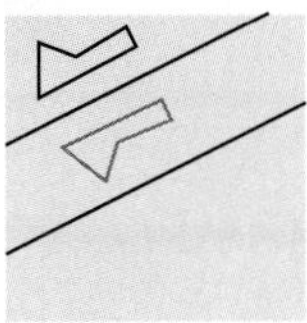

Step 3

Step 1 On a piece of patty paper, draw a figure and a line of reflection that does not intersect it.

Step 2 Fold to reflect your figure over the line of reflection and trace the image.

Step 3 On your patty paper, draw a second reflection line parallel to the first so that the image is between the two parallel reflection lines.

Step 4 Fold to reflect the image over the second line of reflection. Turn the patty paper over and trace the second image.

Step 5 How does the second image compare to the original figure? Name the single transformation that transforms the original to the second image.

Step 5 They are congruent; translations.

Step 6 Use a compass or patty paper to measure the distance between a point in the original figure and its second image point. Compare this distance with the distance between the parallel lines. How do they compare?

Step 6 Distance between the points is twice the distance between the lines.

Step 7 Compare your findings with others in your group and state your conjecture.

Reflections over Parallel Lines Conjecture C-71

A composition of two reflections over two parallel lines is equivalent to a single _?_. In addition, the distance from any point to its second image under the two reflections is _?_ the distance between the parallel lines.
translation twice

Is a composition of reflections always equivalent to a single reflection? If you reverse the reflections in a different order, do you still get the original figure back? Can you express a rotation as a set of reflections?

Investigation 2
Reflections over Two Intersecting Lines

You will need

- patty paper
- a protractor

Next, you will explore the case of intersecting lines of reflection.

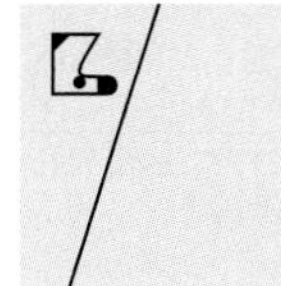
Step 1

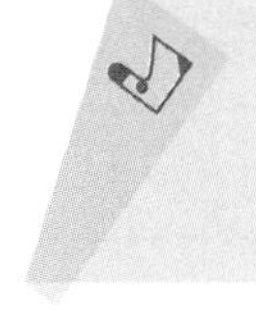
Step 2

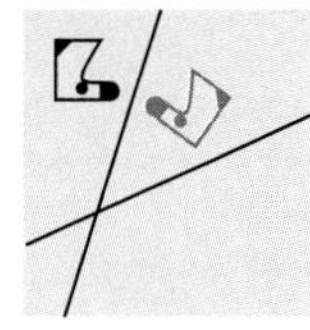
Step 3

Step 1 On a piece of patty paper, draw a figure and a reflection line that does not intersect it.

Step 2 Fold to reflect your figure over the line and trace the image.

Step 3 On your patty paper, draw a second reflection line intersecting the first so that the image is in an acute angle between the two intersecting reflection lines.

Step 4 Fold to reflect the first image over the second line and trace the second image.

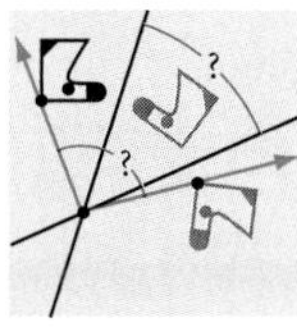

Step 5

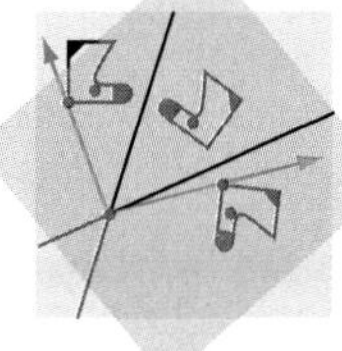
Step 6

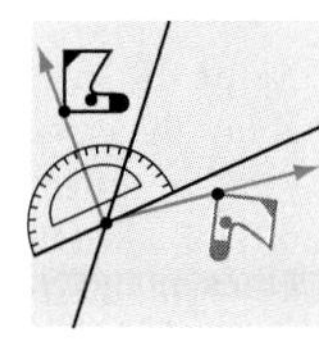
Step 7

Step 5 Draw two rays that start at the point of intersection of the two intersecting lines and that pass through corresponding points on the original figure and its second image.

Step 6 How does the second image compare to the original figure? Name the single transformation from the original to the second image.

Step 6 They are congruent. The image is rotated about the point of intersection.

Step 7 With a protractor or patty paper, compare the angle created in Step 5 with the acute angle formed by the intersecting reflection lines. How do the angles compare?

Step 7 Angle between the rays is twice the angle formed by the intersecting lines.

Step 8 Compare findings in your group and state your next conjecture.

Reflections over Intersecting Lines Conjecture  C-72

A composition of two reflections over a pair of intersecting lines is equivalent to a single _?_. The angle of _?_ is _?_ the acute angle between the pair of intersecting reflection lines.

rotation rotation twice

Guiding Investigation 2

Step 1 The original figure should be simple and not too large.

Step 2 Lettering points will help students see how the figure is changing.

Step 8 Students should specify the center of the rotation as well as saying that the transformation is a rotation.

SHARING IDEAS

As students present ideas about the second investigation, **[Ask]** "What will happen if you change the order in which the two lines of reflection are used?" [The direction of rotation changes.]

[Ask] "What will happen if a translation is followed by a reflection along a line in the direction of the transformation?" [This is a *glide reflection.*] Point out the picture of footprints in the book. **[Ask]** "Does the same result occur if you reverse the order of the isometries?" [yes] Ask if you can reverse the order of any composition of isometries and get the same result. You need not answer this question; it motivates Exercise 3.

Ask students if they think that the converses of the Reflections over Parallel Lines Conjecture and the Reflections over Intersecting Lines Conjecture hold. Discussion of this question helps students see that the conjectures themselves are not claiming that every translation and rotation is the composition of reflections. Leave the question open; students will consider the converses of the conjectures in Exercises 7 and 8.

Assessing Progress
You can assess students' understanding of ordered pair rules, coordinates of points, translations, reflections, rotations, parallel lines, rays, and acute angles. You can also see how well they can find reflected images by folding patty paper and tracing.

Closing the Lesson

A pair of reflections about parallel lines a distance d apart is equivalent to a single translation through a distance $2d$ perpendicular to the two parallel lines. A pair of reflections about lines that intersect at an angle with measure m is equivalent to a single rotation through an angle with measure $2m$.

BUILDING UNDERSTANDING

ASSIGNING HOMEWORK

Essential	1–9
Performance assessment	7
Portfolio	5
Journal	14
Group	13, 15
Review	10–16

Helping with the Exercises

Exercise 2 Students may have difficulty considering the result if the centers of rotation differ. Ask whether the total amount of rotation differs and how they can get from one center to the next. Or students may want to think about breaking down the rotations into compositions of reflections to see that they need only a translation appended to the composition.

There are many other ways to combine transformations. Combining a translation with a reflection gives a special two-step transformation called a **glide reflection.** A sequence of footsteps is a common example of a glide reflection. You will explore a few other examples of glide reflection in the exercises and later in this chapter.

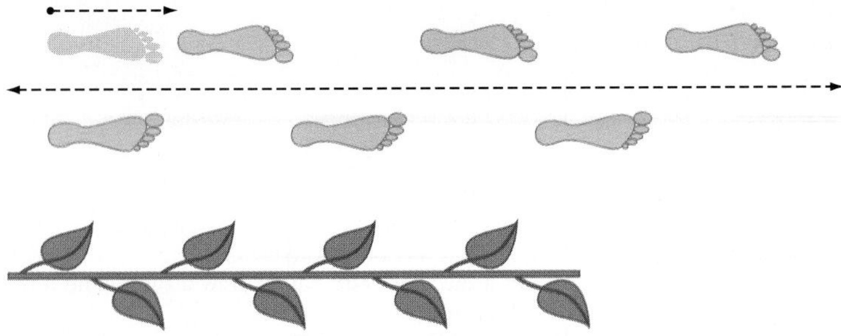

Glide-reflectional symmetry

EXERCISES

1. Name the single translation that can replace the composition of these three translations: (2, 3), then (−5, 7), then (13, 0). (10, 10)

2. Name the single rotation that can replace the composition of these three rotations about the same center of rotation: 45°, then 50°, then 85°. What if the centers of rotation differ? Draw a figure and try it. A 180° rotation. If the centers of rotation differ, rotate 180° and add a translation.

3. Lines m and n are parallel and 10 cm apart.

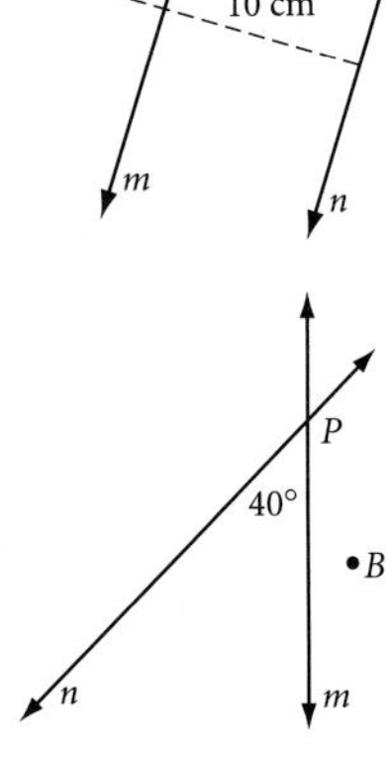

a. Point A is 6 cm from line m and 16 cm from line n. Point A is reflected over line m, then its image, A', is reflected over line n to create a second image, point A''. How far is point A from point A''? 20 cm

b. What if A is reflected over n, and then its image is reflected over m? Find the new image and distance from A. 20 cm, but in the opposite direction

4. Two lines m and n intersect at point P, forming a 40° angle.

a. You reflect point B over line m, then reflect the image of B over line n. What angle of rotation about point P rotates the second image of point B back to its original position? 80° counterclockwise

b. What if you reflect B first over n, and then reflect the image of B over m? Find the angle of rotation that rotates the second image back to the original position. 80° clockwise

P
40°
B
n
m

5. Copy the figure and $\angle PAL$ onto patty paper. Reflect the figure over $\overrightarrow{AP}$. Reflect the image over $\overrightarrow{AL}$. What is the equivalent rotation? 180°

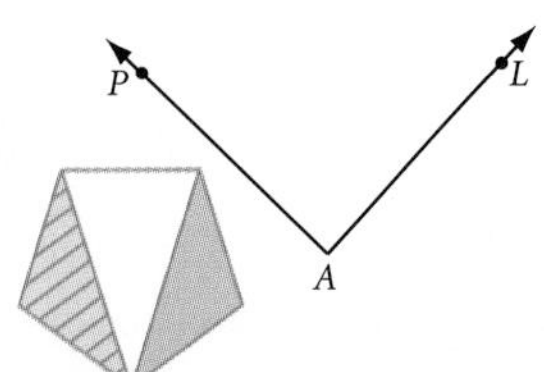

6. Copy the figure and the pair of parallel lines onto patty paper. Reflect the figure over $\overleftrightarrow{PA}$. Reflect the image over $\overleftrightarrow{RL}$. What is the length of the equivalent translation vector? 3 cm

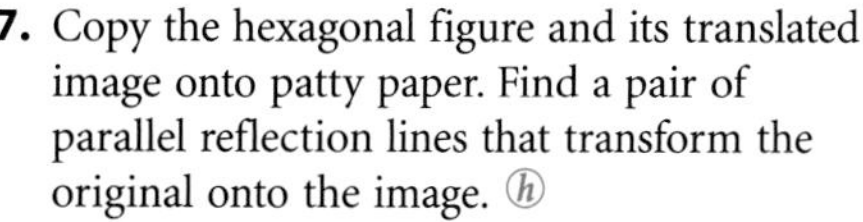

7. Copy the hexagonal figure and its translated image onto patty paper. Find a pair of parallel reflection lines that transform the original onto the image. ⓗ

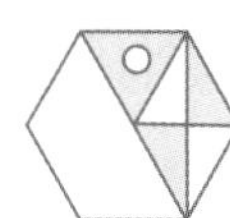

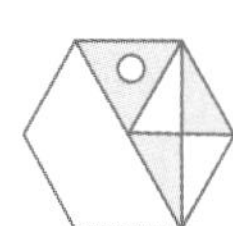

Exercises 7, 8 These exercises explore the converses of the Reflections over Parallel Lines Conjecture and the Reflections over Intersecting Lines Conjecture.

7. possible answer:

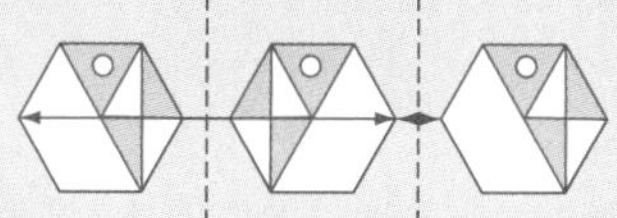

8. Copy the original figure and its translated image onto patty paper. Find a pair of intersecting reflection lines that transform the original onto the image.

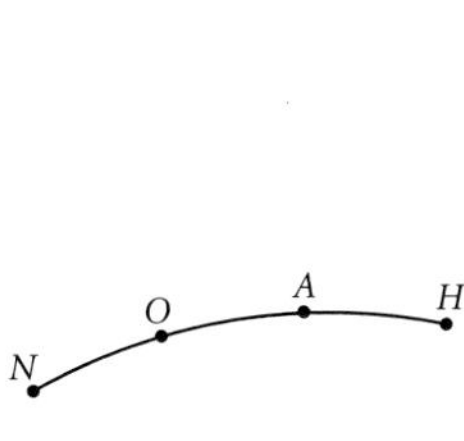

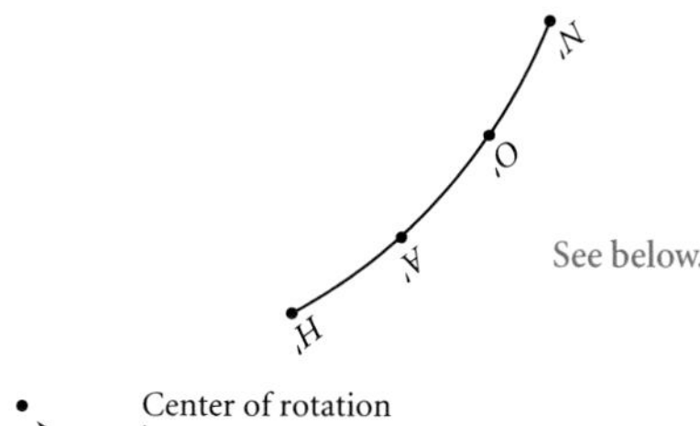

See below.

9. Copy the two figures below onto graph paper. Each figure is the glide-reflected image of the other. Continue the pattern with two more glide-reflected figures.

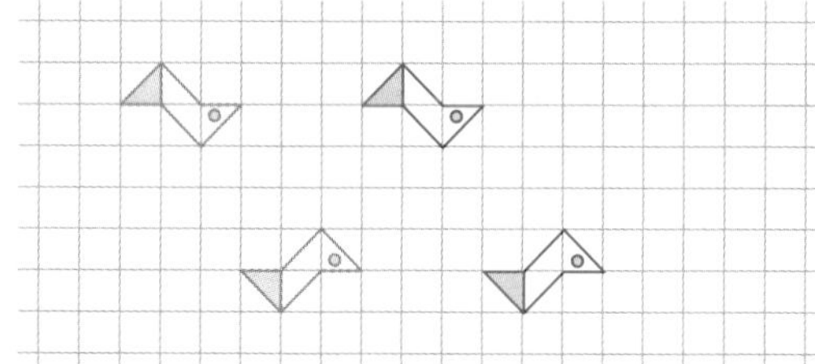

Review

In Exercises 10 and 11, sketch the next two figures.

2.1 **10.** ___, ___, ___, ___, ___, ?, ?

2.1 **11.**

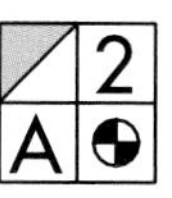

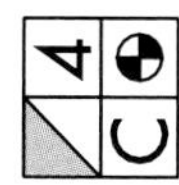

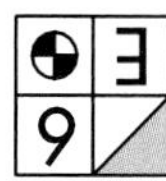

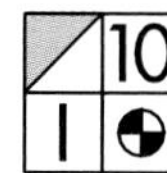

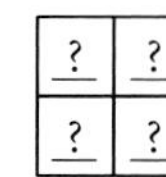

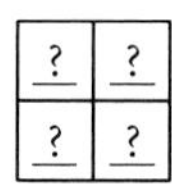

10.

11.

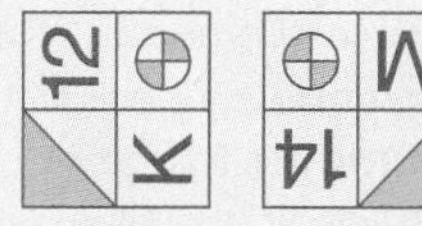

8. possible answer:

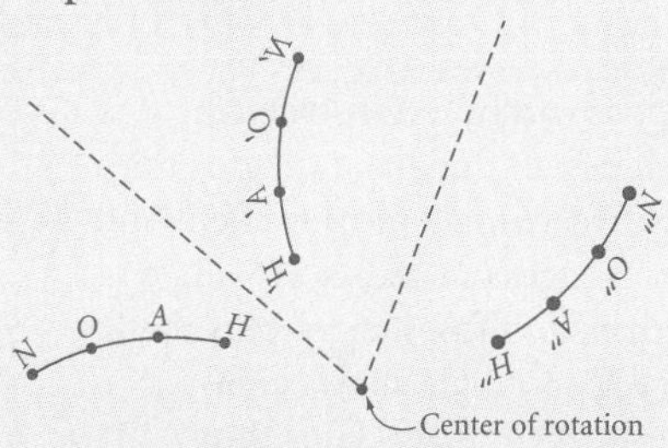

14. Two reflections about intersecting lines yield a rotation. The measure of the angle of rotation is twice the measure of the angle between the lines of reflection, or twice 90°, or 180°.

15. one: yes; two: no; three: yes

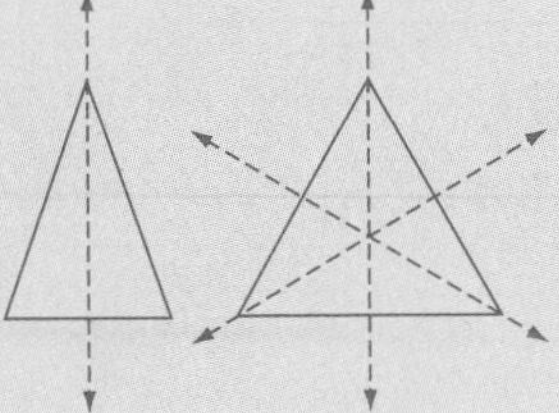

16. possible answer:

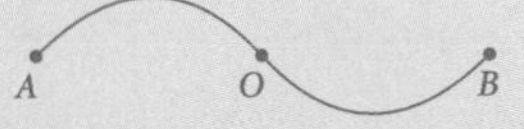

Visualizing Kaleidoscope Reflections

It often helps to think of an image of an object in a mirror as being an actual object on the other side of the mirror—a mathematical reflection of the original object. Thus, if you place an object in front of a mirror and look at it through the mirror, you can think of the image as being an actual object the same distance behind the mirror as the original object is in front of the mirror. By the same reasoning, if you hinge another mirror at a right angle to the first, the image of the second mirror appears to be behind the first and will form a right angle with it. Any object placed in the angle between these mirrors will have an image behind the second mirror; this image, as well as the second mirror itself and the original object, will have an image in the first mirror. So you can see the object four times—the original object and three images. The middle image will be reflected twice and will appear normal.

If the angle between mirrors is somewhat smaller, the image of each mirror in the other is reflected back to itself, again at the same angle as that of the two mirrors, so more images of any object between the mirrors appear.

7.1 **12.** If you draw a figure on an uninflated balloon and then blow up the balloon the figure will undergo a nonrigid transformation. Give another example of a nonrigid transformation. Sample answer: Draw a figure on an overhead transparency and then project the image onto a screen.

7.1 **13.** List two objects in your home that have rotational symmetry but not reflectional symmetry. List two objects in your classroom that have reflectional symmetry but not rotational symmetry. possible answers: rotational: playing card, ceiling fan, propeller blade; reflectional: human body, backpack

7.1 **14.** Have you noticed that some letters have both horizontal and vertical symmetries? Have you also noticed that all the letters that have both horizontal and vertical symmetries also have point symmetry? Is this a coincidence? Use what you have learned about transformations to explain why.

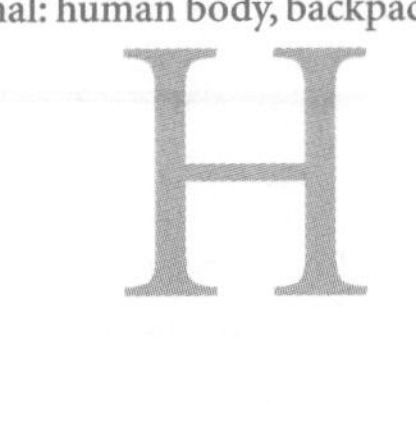

7.1 **15.** Is it possible for a triangle to have exactly one line of symmetry? Exactly two? Exactly three? Support your answers with sketches.

7.1 **16.** Draw two points onto a piece of paper and connect them with a curve that is point symmetric. ⓗ

project

KALEIDOSCOPES

You have probably looked through kaleidoscopes and enjoyed their beautiful designs, but do you know how they work? For a simple kaleidoscope, hinge two mirrors with tape, place a small object or photo between the mirrors and adjust them until you see four objects (the original and three images). What is the angle between the mirrors? At what angle should you hold the mirrors to see six objects? Eight objects?

The British physicist Sir David Brewster invented the tube kaleidoscope in 1816. Some tube kaleidoscopes have colored glass or plastic pieces that tumble around in their end chambers. Some have colored liquid. Others have only a lens in the chamber—the design you see depends on where you aim it.

Design and build your own kaleidoscope using a plastic or cardboard cylinder and glass or plastic as reflecting surfaces. Try various items in the end chamber. Your project should include

- Your kaleidoscope (pass it around!).
- A report with diagrams that show the geometry properties you used, a list of the materials and tools you used, and a description of problems you had and how you solved them.

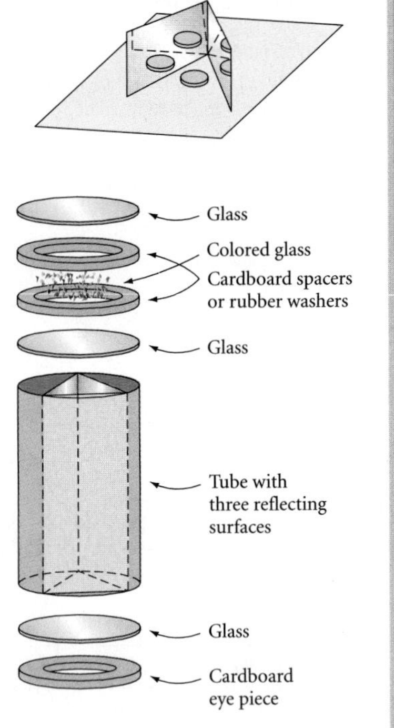

Supporting the project

The tube can be a cardboard cylinder or plastic plumbing pipe (PVC). The round clear pieces can be glass, lenses, or clear plastic. The reflecting surfaces can be mirror glass, or glass or clear plastic painted black on one side.

OUTCOMES

- A kaleidoscope is carefully constructed.
- The student shows an understanding of the relationship between angle measurement and the number of images created. A 60° angle shows six mirrors and five images plus the original object; a 45° angle shows eight mirrors and the seven images plus the original object.

LESSON 7.4

Tessellations with Regular Polygons

I see a certain order in the universe and math is one way of making it visible.

MAY SARTON

Honeycombs are remarkably geometric structures. The hexagonal cells that bees make are ideal because they fit together perfectly without any gaps. The regular hexagon is one of many shapes that can completely cover a plane without gaps or overlaps. Mathematicians call such an arrangement of shapes a **tessellation** or a **tiling.** A tessellation that uses only one shape is called a **monohedral tiling.**

You can find tessellations in every home. Decorative floor tiles have tessellating patterns of squares. Brick walls, fireplaces, and wooden decks often display creative tessellations of rectangles. Where do you see tessellations every day?

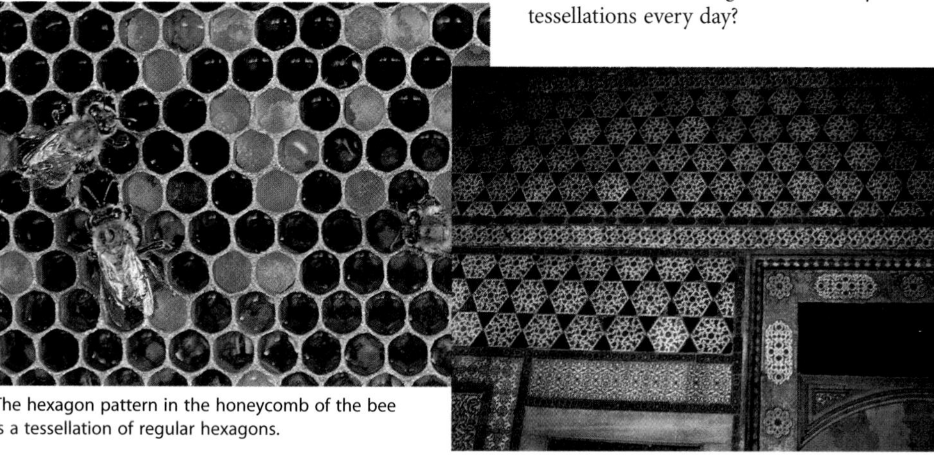

The hexagon pattern in the honeycomb of the bee is a tessellation of regular hexagons.

Regular hexagons and equilateral triangles combine in this tiling from the 17th-century Topkapi Palace in Istanbul, Turkey.

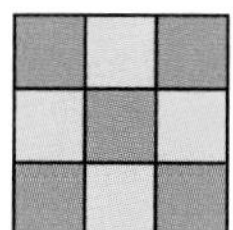

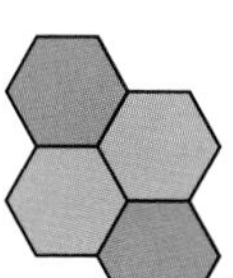

You already know that squares and regular hexagons create monohedral tessellations. Because each regular hexagon can be divided into six equilateral triangles, we can logically conclude that equilateral triangles also create monohedral tessellations. Will other regular polygons tessellate? Let's look at this question logically.

For shapes to fill the plane without gaps or overlaps, their angles, when arranged around a point, must have measures that add up to exactly 360°. If the sum is less than 360°, there will be a gap. If the sum is greater, the shapes will overlap. Six 60° angles from six equilateral triangles add up to 360°, as do four 90° angles from four squares or three 120° angles from three regular hexagons. What about regular pentagons? Each angle in a regular pentagon measures 108°, and 360 is not divisible by 108. So regular pentagons cannot be arranged around a point without overlapping or leaving a gap. What about regular heptagons?

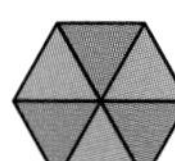

Triangles

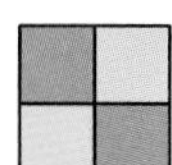

Squares

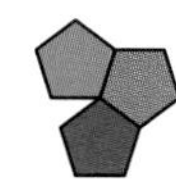

Pentagons

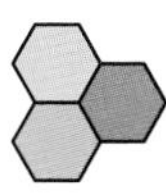

Hexagons

?

Heptagons

NCTM STANDARDS

CONTENT		PROCESS	
✓	Number		Problem Solving
	Algebra	✓	Reasoning
✓	Geometry	✓	Communication
✓	Measurement	✓	Connections
	Data/Probability		Representation

LESSON OBJECTIVES

- Learn about tessellations of regular polygons
- Classify and identify monohedral, regular, and semiregular tessellations
- Learn new vocabulary
- Develop visual thinking

LESSON 7.4

PLANNING

LESSON OUTLINE

One day:

25 min	Investigation
5 min	Sharing
5 min	Closing
10 min	Exercises

MATERIALS

- patty paper
- pattern blocks or Regular Polygons (W) and scissors
- Tessellations (T) for One step
- Sketchpad demonstration Tessellations, *optional*

TEACHING

In this lesson students explore regular and semiregular tessellations.

Pattern blocks or drawing templates for regular polygons will save time during the investigation. If you don't have these, make six to eight copies of the two Regular Polygons worksheets for each group and provide students with scissors.

One step Show the Tessellations transparency, define tessellation to be a repeating pattern of shapes that covers the plane, point out that at each vertex the sum of the polygons' angles is 360°, and show where the vertex arrangements come from. Then ask students to find all tessellations that use only equilateral triangles, squares, and hexagons, labeling each with its vertex arrangement. As students work, suggest that they begin with tessellations that use only one of the three shapes and that they systematically write

One step (continued)
all possible sums of 60°, 90°, and 120° that total 360°. Some of these, such as 3.3.6.6, represent ways that the shapes can be clustered around a point but cannot be replicated indefinitely on the plane. Encourage students to make sure their pattern extends. Let them see for themselves why, for example, 3.3.4.3.4 gives the same tessellation as 3.4.3.3.4 but a different one from 3.3.3.4.4. During Sharing introduce the terms *monohedral* [mä-nō-'hē-drəl], *regular,* and *semiregular* tessellations.

INTRODUCTION

[Language] The word *tessellation* comes from the small square ceramic tiles, called *tesserae,* that the Romans used to create mosaic tile designs.

A shape is said to *tessellate* the plane if repeated copies of it form a tessellation. Students will be most familiar with regular tessellations of squares and hexagons. **[Language]** The terms *tessellation* and *tiling* are used interchangeably.

Students may not recall the measures of interior angles of various regular polyhedra. Remind them that the sum of the measures of the exterior angles is 360° and they can find the measure of each of the n interior angles by taking the supplement of $\frac{360°}{n}$.

Vertex Arrangements
It is important to list the shapes in order; 3.4.3.3.4 is different from 3.3.3.4.4. The convention is to start with the fewest number of sides, for example, 4.8.8 instead of 8.8.4 or 8.4.8. **[Ask]** "What is the vertex arrangement of the tessellation of the Topkapi Palace tiling on page 379?" [3.6.3.6]

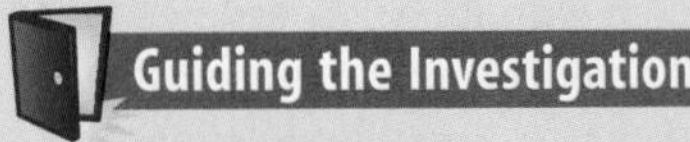

Guiding the Investigation

In preparation for the investigation, point out the three semiregular tessellations shown in the book and stress that the vertices are identical. Otherwise, students might start listing other kinds of tessellations, and the investigation will become lengthy. You might want to have students find the different kinds of vertices in the pictures of 2-uniform and 3-uniform tessellations on page 381 to emphasize that in the investigation they are trying to avoid such tilings.

Steps 1, 2 Students find four of the five remaining semiregular tessellations in Step 1. Encourage them to mark the angle measurements on their pictures so they can check that the sum at each vertex is 360°.

Step 3 Give a few groups blank transparencies on which to draw one of their tessellations, making sure to include all five plus any such as 3.3.6.6 or 3.4.4.6 that appear correct at one vertex but don't extend to tessellations. Let the class critique these during Sharing.

In any regular polygon with more than six sides, each angle has a measure greater than 120°, so no more than two angles can fit about a point without overlapping. So the only regular polygons that create monohedral tessellations are equilateral triangles, squares, and regular hexagons. A monohedral tessellation of congruent regular polygons is called a **regular tessellation.**

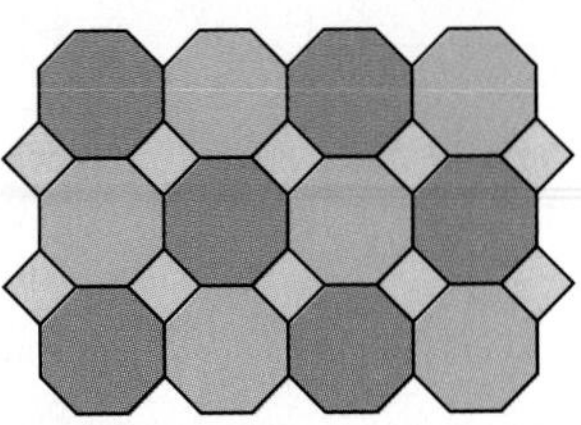

Tessellations can have more than one type of shape. You may have seen the octagon-square combination at right. In this tessellation, two regular octagons and a square meet at each vertex. Notice that you can put your pencil on any vertex and that the point is surrounded by one square and two octagons. So you can call this a 4.8.8 or a 4.8^2 tiling. The numbers give the **vertex arrangement,** or **numerical name** for the tiling.

When the same combination of regular polygons (of two or more kinds) meet in the same order at each vertex of a tessellation, it is called a **semiregular tessellation.** Below are two more examples of semiregular tessellations.

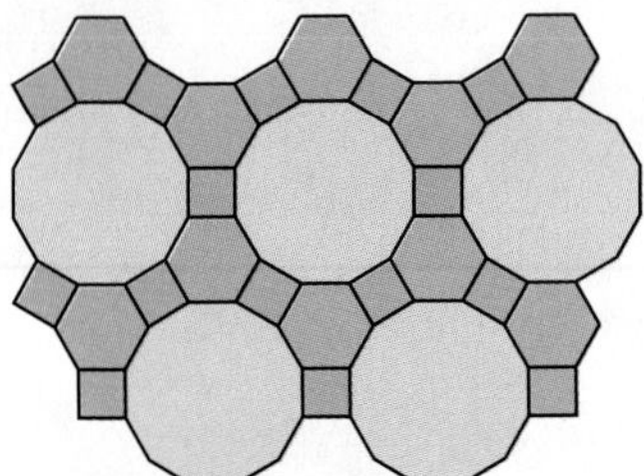
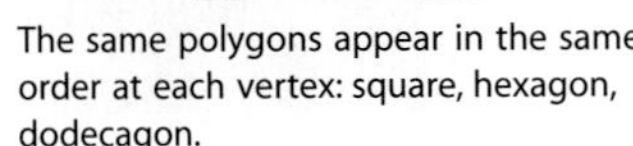

The same polygons appear in the same order at each vertex: square, hexagon, dodecagon.

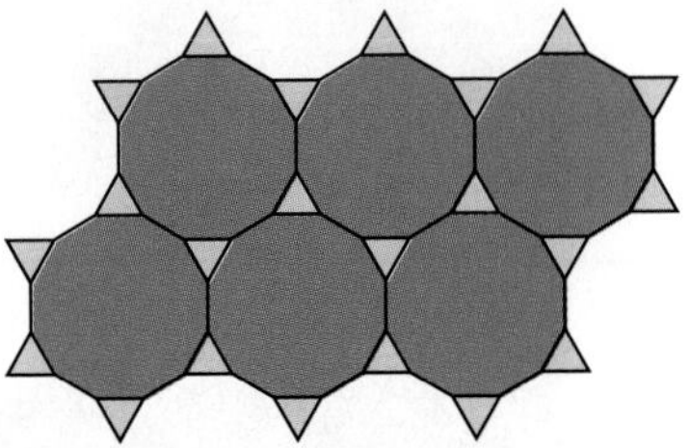

The same polygons appear in the same order at each vertex: triangle, dodecagon, dodecagon.

There are eight different semiregular tessellations. Three of them are shown above. In this investigation, you will look for the other five. To make this easier, the remaining five use only combinations of triangles, squares, or hexagons.

Investigation
The Semiregular Tessellations

You will need
- triangles, squares and hexagons from a set of pattern blocks or,
- geometry software such as GSP or,
- a set of triangles, squares and hexagons created from the set shown

Find or create a set of regular triangles, squares, and hexagons for this investigation. Then work with your group to find the remaining five of the eight semiregular tessellations. Remember, the same combination of regular polygons must meet in the same order at each vertex for the tiling to be semiregular. Also remember to check that the sum of the measures at each vertex is 360°.

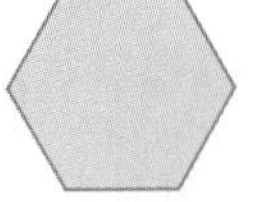

Step 1 Investigate which combinations of two kinds of regular polygons you can use to create a semiregular tessellation.

Step 2 Next, investigate which combinations of three kinds of regular polygons you can use to create a semiregular tessellation.

Step 3 Summarize your findings by sketching all eight semiregular tessellations and writing their vertex arrangements (numerical names).

The three regular tessellations and the eight semiregular tessellations you just found are called the **Archimedean tilings.** They are also called 1-uniform tilings because all the vertices in a tiling are identical.

Mathematics CONNECTION

Greek mathematician and inventor Archimedes (ca. 287–212 B.C.E.) studied the relationship between mathematics and art with tilings. He described 11 plane tilings made up of regular polygons, with each vertex being the same type. Plutarch (ca. 46–127 C.E.) wrote of Archimedes' love of geometry, ". . . he neglected to eat and drink and took no care of his person; that he was often carried by force to the baths, and when there he would trace geometrical figures in the ashes of the fire."

Often, different vertices in a tiling do not have the same vertex arrangement. If there are two different types of vertices, the tiling is called 2-uniform. If there are three different types of vertices, the tiling is called 3-uniform. Two examples are shown below.

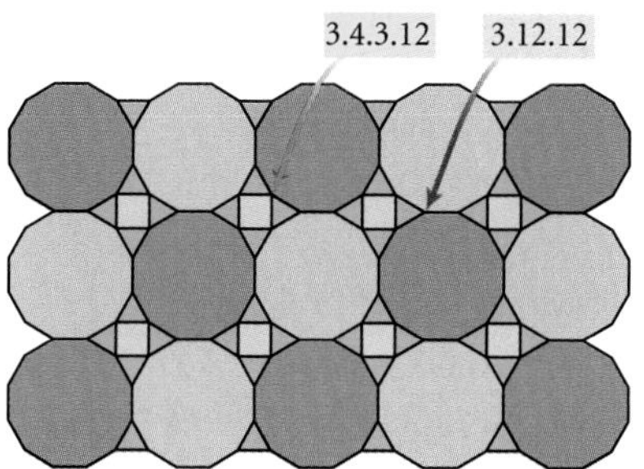

A 2-uniform tessellation: $3.4.3.12 / 3.12^2$

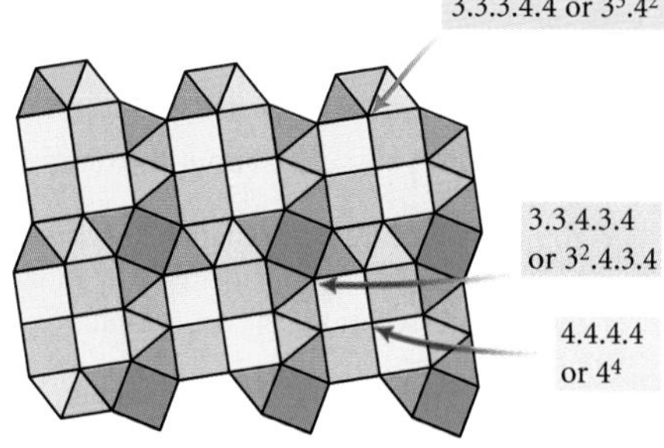

A 3-uniform tessellation: $3^3.4^2 / 3^2.4.3.4 / 4^4$

There are 20 different 2-uniform tessellations of regular polygons, and 61 different 3-uniform tilings. The number of 4-uniform tessellations of regular polygons is still an unsolved problem.

Closing the Lesson

Tessellations, or tilings, are patterns of repeated shapes that cover the plane. A **regular tessellation** consists of only one repeated shape, a regular polygon (in fact, an equilateral triangle, a square, or a regular hexagon). A **semiregular tessellation** contains two or more regular polygons, and each vertex is surrounded by the same kinds of shapes in the same order. Other tessellations, such as **2-uniform** and **3-uniform** tilings, have more than one type of vertex. A tiling can be described by a sequence of numbers, called the **vertex arrangement,** representing each type of vertex. All the tessellations we've seen so far have translational symmetry.

SHARING IDEAS

As groups present their ideas, keep asking if the measures of the angles at each vertex sum to 360°, to help any students who might not understand this idea yet.

Ask what kinds of symmetry one of these tessellations has. It might very well have reflectional and rotational symmetry, over infinitely many lines and about infinitely many points. (Remind students that the tessellation, unlike the picture, covers the entire plane.) The third major kind of transformation is translation; ask whether the tessellation also has translational symmetry. Because the tessellation goes on forever in all directions, its images under infinitely many translations coincide with the original. Wonder aloud whether there are tessellations that don't have translational symmetry. Students will see an answer to this question in the project on Penrose tilings following Lesson 7.5.

Remind students that some valid vertex arrangements, such as 3.3.6.6, couldn't occur at each vertex of a tessellation. **[Ask]** "What if we allowed more than one kind of vertex in a tessellation? Could a tessellation be made, for example, with 3.3.6.6 and 3.3.3.3.3.3 vertices?" Have students read their book's description of 2-uniform and 3-uniform tessellations in preparation for the exercises.

Assessing Progress

You can assess students' understanding of regular polygons and their knowledge of the measures of the interior angles of regular polygons.

See page 773 for answers to Step 3.

BUILDING UNDERSTANDING

The exercises give practice in both analyzing and creating tessellations.

ASSIGNING HOMEWORK

Essential	1–8
Performance assessment	14
Portfolio	9, 11, 12
Journal	10
Group	9, 12, 13
Review	15–18

▶ Helping with the Exercises

Exercise 8 Students can give one vertex arrangement equivalent to either 3.3.4.12 or 3.3.12.4.

9a. The dual of a square tessellation is a square tessellation.

9b. The dual of a hexagon tessellation is a triangle tessellation.

9c. If tessellation A is the dual of tessellation B then tessellation B is the dual of tessellation A.

11.

12.

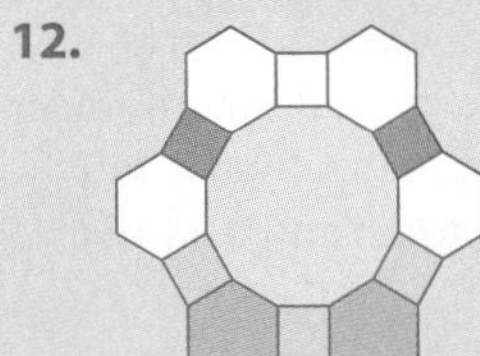

EXERCISES

You will need

Geometry software for Exercises 11–14

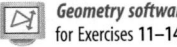

1. Sketch two objects or designs you see every day that are monohedral tessellations. Answers will vary.

2. List two objects or designs outside your classroom that are semiregular tessellations. Answers will vary.

In Exercises 3–5, write the vertex arrangement for each semiregular tessellation in numbers.

3.

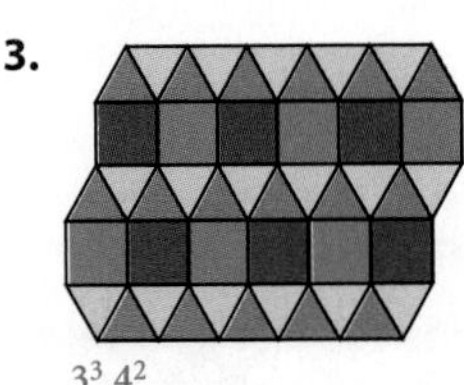

$3^3.4^2$

4.

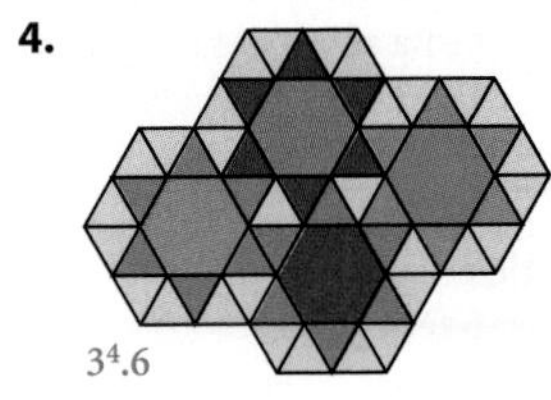

$3^4.6$

5.

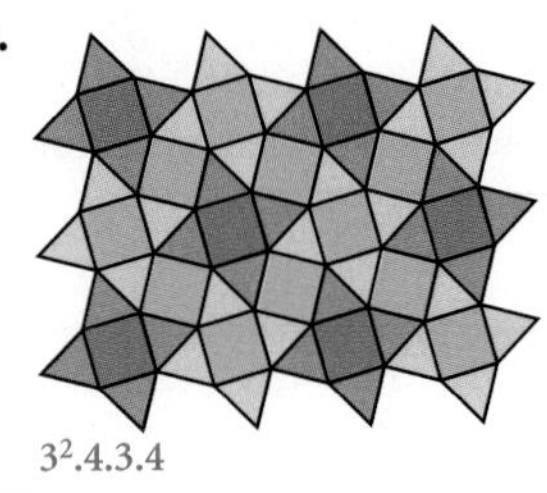

$3^2.4.3.4$

In Exercises 6–8, write the vertex arrangement for each 2-uniform tessellation in numbers.

6.

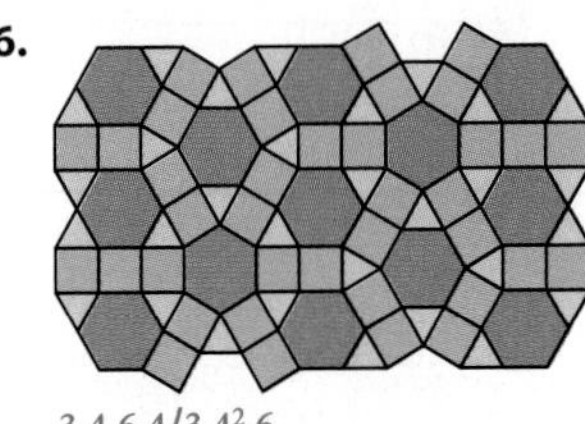

$3.4.6.4/3.4^2.6$

7.

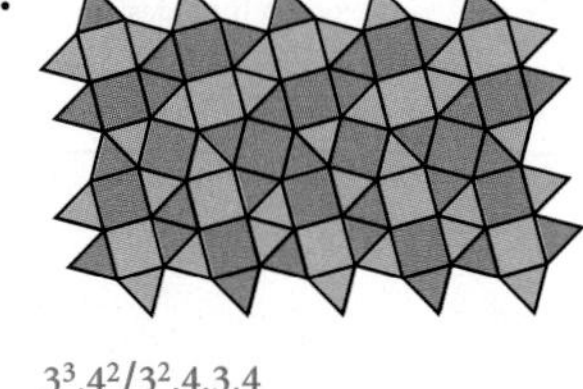

$3^3.4^2/3^2.4.3.4$

8.

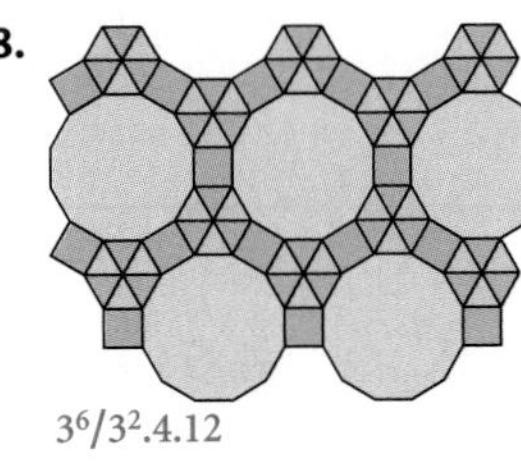

$3^6/3^2.4.12$

9. When you connect the center of each triangle across the common sides of the tessellating equilateral triangles at right, you get another tessellation. This new tessellation is called the **dual** of the original tessellation. Notice the dual of the equilateral triangle tessellation is the regular hexagon tessellation. Every regular tessellation of regular polygons has a dual.

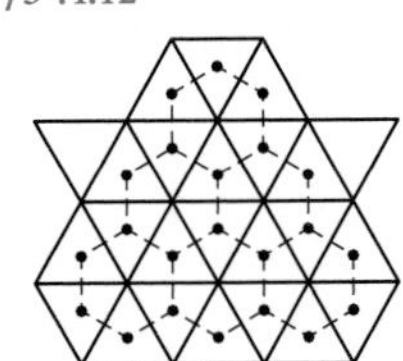

a. Draw a regular square tessellation and make its dual. What is the dual?

b. Draw a hexagon tessellation and make the dual of it. What is the dual?

c. What do you notice about the duals?

10. You can make dual tessellations of semiregular tessellations, but they may not be tessellations of regular polygons. Try it. Sketch the dual of the 4.8.8 tessellation, shown at right. Describe the dual.
The dual is a $3^4/3^8$ tessellation of isosceles right triangles.

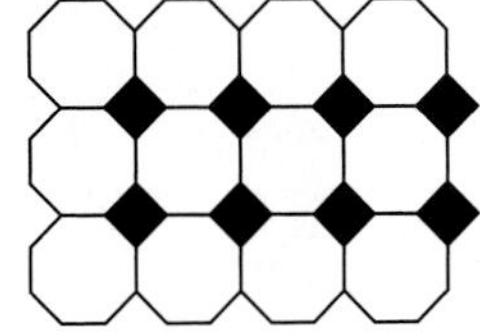

Technology In Exercises 11–14, use geometry software, templates of regular polygons, or pattern blocks.

11. Sketch and color the 3.6.3.6 tessellation. Continue it to fill an entire sheet of paper.

12. Sketch the 4.6.12 tessellation. Color it so it has reflectional symmetry but not rotational symmetry.

13. Show that two regular pentagons and a regular decagon fit about a point but that 5.5.10 does not create a semiregular tessellation. ⓗ

14. Create the tessellation 3.12.12/3.4.3.12. Draw your design onto a full sheet of paper. Color your design to highlight its symmetries.

Review

7.1 **15.** Design a logo with rotational symmetry for Happy Time Ice Cream Company. Or design a logo for your group or for a made-up company. Answers will vary.

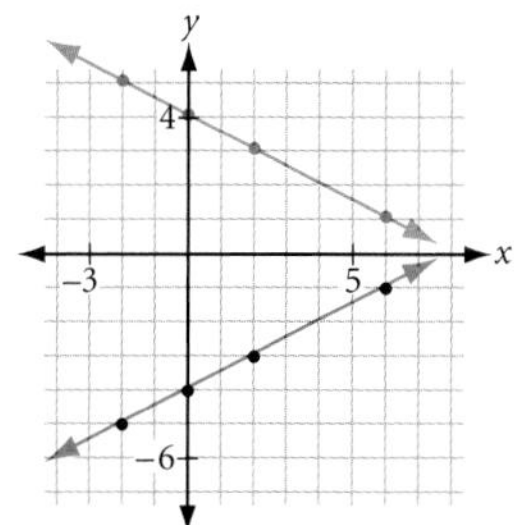

7.2 **16.** Reflect $y = \frac{1}{2}x - 4$ over the x-axis and find the equation of the image line.

7.1 **17.** Words like MOM, WOW, TOOT, and OTTO all have a vertical line of symmetry when you write them in capital letters. Find another word that has a vertical line of symmetry. possible answer: TOT

The design at left comes from *Inversions,* a book by Scott Kim. Not only does the design spell the word *mirror,* it does so with mirror symmetry!

7.2 **18.** Frisco Fats needs to sink the 8-ball into the NW corner pocket, but he seems trapped. Can he hit the cue ball to a point on the N cushion so that it bounces out, strikes the S cushion, and taps the 8-ball into the corner pocket? Copy the table and construct the path of the ball. ⓗ

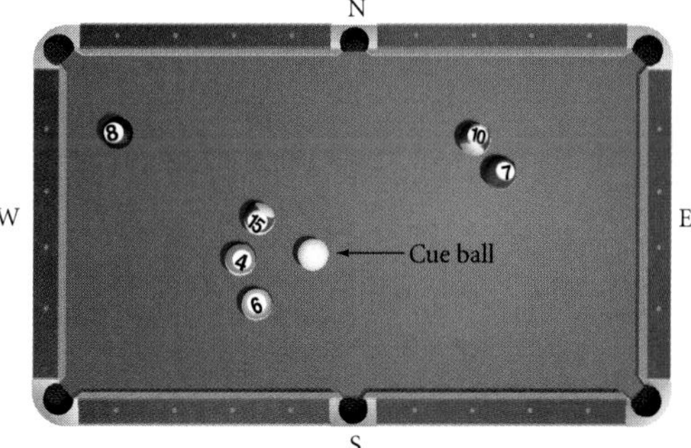

IMPROVING YOUR REASONING SKILLS

Scrambled Arithmetic

In the equation 65 + 28 = 43, all the digits are correct but they are in the wrong places! Written correctly, the equation is 23 + 45 = 68. In each of the three equations below, the operations and the digits are correct, but some of the digits are in the wrong places. Find the correct equations.

1. 11 + 66 = 457

2. 39 · 11 = 75

3. $\frac{78}{523} = 31$

13. A ring of ten pentagons fits around a decagon, and another decagon can fit into any two of the pentagons. But another ring of pentagons around the second decagon doesn't leave room for a third decagon.

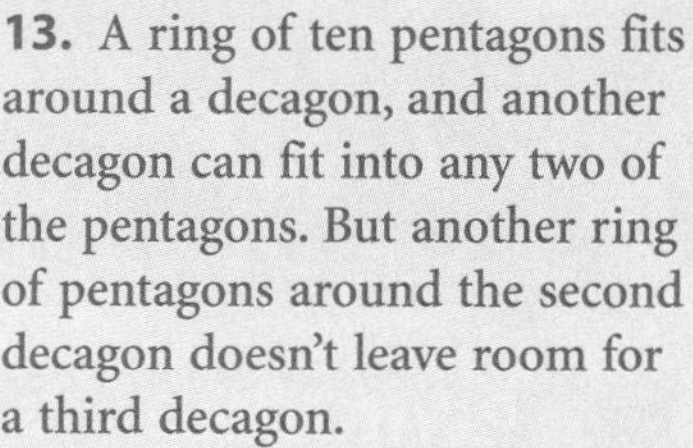

14.

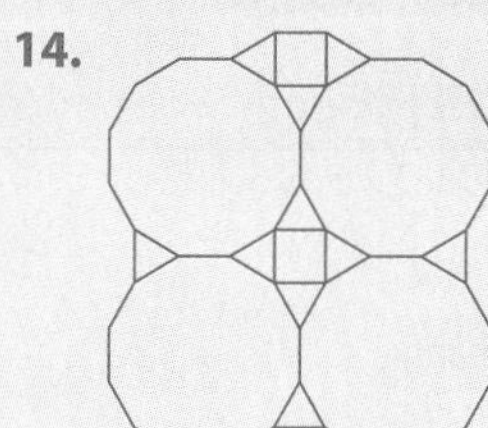

16. $y = -\frac{1}{2}x + 4$

Exercise 17 If students are having difficulty, wonder aloud whether it would help to think first about letters that have a vertical line of symmetry.

Exercise 18 As needed, remind students of how they worked backward to solve similar problems in Lesson 7.2.

18.

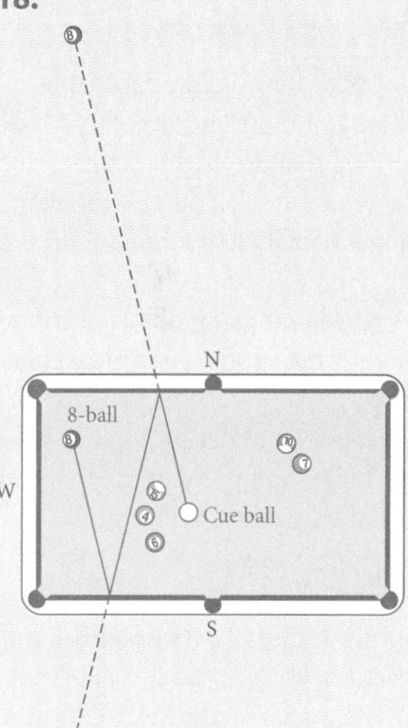

IMPROVING REASONING SKILLS

Some students may point out other possible solutions, such as 25 + 43 = 68, 34 + 52 = 86, or 54 + 32 = 86.

1. Possible answers: 65 + 76 = 141; 66 + 75 = 141

2. Because it is not possible to multiply a two-digit number by a two-digit number and get a two-digit number, the answer must be a two-digit number times a one-digit number giving a three-digit number. Possible answers: 17 · 9 = 153; 9 · 17 = 153

3. Possible answers: $\frac{851}{37} = 23$; $\frac{851}{23} = 37$

LESSON

7.5

PLANNING

LESSON OUTLINE

One day:

20 min Investigation

10 min Sharing

5 min Closing

10 min Exercises

MATERIALS

- construction tools
- scissors
- Penrose Tilings (W) for Project

TEACHING

All triangles, all quadrilaterals, and some pentagons can create monohedral tessellations.

One step Remind students that there are three monohedral tessellations that are regular. Ask if there are any that aren't regular. Suggest that each student cut out 12 copies of some figure and experiment, using different figures within the group. As you circulate, encourage the use of various kinds of triangles and quadrilaterals, including concave quadrilaterals. As needed, suggest that students number the vertices of their figures, using the same numbering for corresponding vertices on all copies. As appropriate, focus students' attention on the vertices and the sum of the angle measures at each vertex.

Guiding Investigation 1

Step 1 [Alert] Students may try surrounding a vertex with several copies of the same angle rather than two copies of each angle. If they seem stuck on this idea, encourage them to number the vertices, using the same numbering for corresponding vertices on all copies. **[Ask]** "What's needed to make that angle fit exactly around that point?" [The angle measure must be a factor of 360°. This doesn't guarantee that the other angle measures in the triangles will also be factors of 360° or that side lengths will be equal.]

[Ask] "How can you get the other vertices of the triangle to coincide?" [Congruent sides of the triangles must be aligned.]

LESSON OBJECTIVES

- Explore tessellations with nonregular polygons
- Practice construction skills
- Develop visual and creative thinking, problem-solving skills, and cooperative behavior

LESSON 7.5

Tessellations with Nonregular Polygons

The most uniquely personal of all that he knows is that which he has discovered for himself.

JEROME BRUNER

In Lesson 7.4, you tessellated with regular polygons. You drew both regular and semi-regular tessellations with them. What about tessellations of nonregular polygons? For example, will a scalene triangle tessellate? Let's investigate.

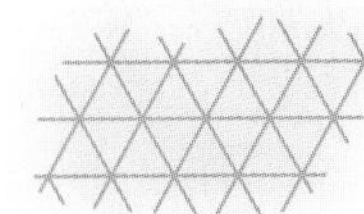

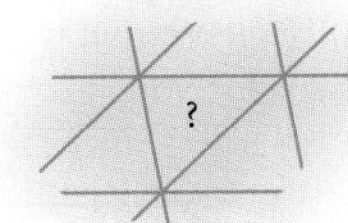

Investigation 1
Do All Triangles Tessellate?

Step 1 Make 12 congruent scalene triangles and use them to try to create a tessellation.

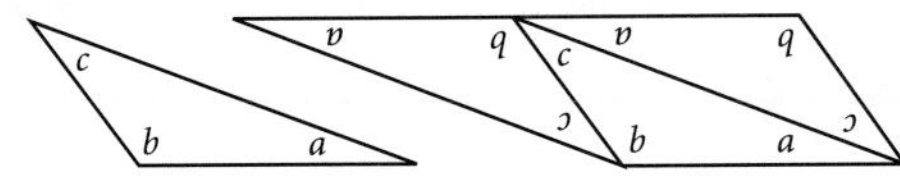

Step 2 Look at the angles about each vertex point. What do you notice?

Step 3 What is the sum of the measures of the three angles of a triangle? What is the sum of the measures of the angles that fit around each point? Compare your results with the results of others and state your next conjecture.

Step 2 Each angle of the triangle fits about the point two times.

Step 3 180°, 360°

Procedure Note

Making Congruent Triangles

1. Stack three pieces of paper and fold them in half.
2. Draw a scalene triangle on the top half-sheet and cut it out, cutting through all six layers to get six congruent scalene triangles.
3. Use one triangle as a template and repeat. You now have 12 congruent triangles.
4. Label the corresponding angles of each triangle *a*, *b*, and *c*, as shown.

Tessellating Triangles Conjecture C-73

__?__ triangle will create a monohedral tessellation.

Any

You have seen that squares and rectangles tile the plane. Can you visualize tiling with parallelograms? Will any quadrilateral tessellate? Let's investigate.

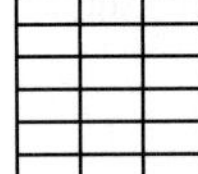

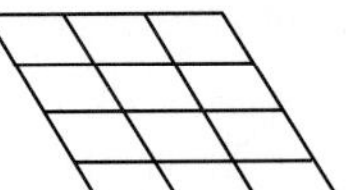

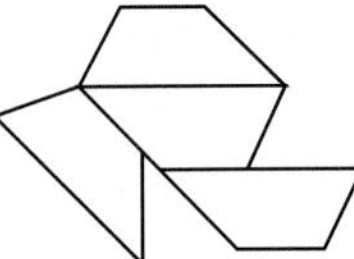

Investigation 2
Do All Quadrilaterals Tessellate?

You want to find out if *any* quadrilateral can tessellate, so you should *not* choose a special quadrilateral for this investigation.

Step 1 Cut out 12 congruent quadrilaterals. Label the corresponding angles in each quadrilateral *a, b, c,* and *d.*

Step 2 Using your 12 congruent quadrilaterals, try to create a tessellation.

Step 3 one time, 360° Step 3 Notice the angles about each vertex point. How many times does each angle of your quadrilateral fit at each point? What is the sum of the measures of the angles of a quadrilateral? Compare your results with others. State a conjecture.

Tessellating Quadrilaterals Conjecture C-74

? (Any) quadrilateral will create a monohedral tessellation.

A regular pentagon does not tessellate, but are there *any* pentagons that tessellate? How many?

Mathematics CONNECTION

In 1975, when Martin Gardner wrote about pentagonal tessellations in *Scientific American,* experts thought that only eight kinds of pentagons would tessellate. Soon another type was found by Richard James III. After reading about this new discovery, Marjorie Rice began her own investigations.

With no formal training in mathematics beyond high school, Marjorie Rice investigated the tessellating problem and discovered four more types of pentagons that tessellate. Mathematics professor Doris Schattschneider of Moravian College verified Rice's research and brought it to the attention of the mathematics community. Rice had indeed discovered what professional mathematicians had been unable to uncover!

In 1985, Rolf Stein, a German graduate student, discovered a fourteenth type of tessellating pentagon. Are *all* the types of convex pentagons that tessellate now known? The problem remains unsolved.

Shown at right are Marjorie Rice (left) and Dr. Doris Schattschneider.

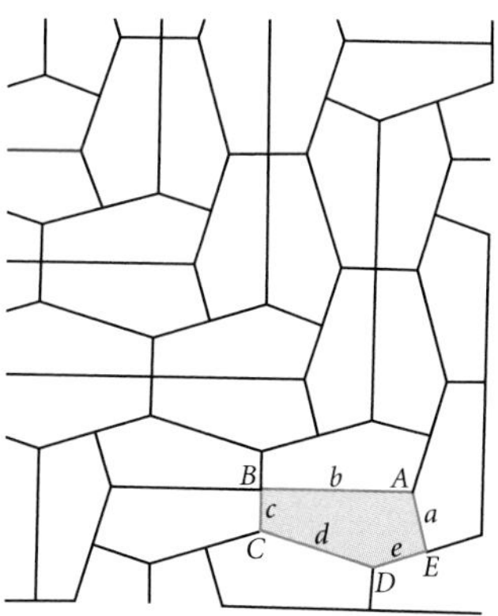

Type 13, discovered in December 1977

$B = E = 90°, 2A + D = 360°$

$2C + D = 360°$

$a = e, a + e = d$

One of the pentagonal tessellations discovered by Marjorie Rice. Capital letters represent angle measures in the shaded pentagon. Lowercase letters represent lengths of sides.

You will experiment with some pentagon tessellations in the exercises.

Guiding Investigation 2

Step 1 Encourage experimentation with concave quadrilaterals as well as with convex quadrilaterals.

Step 2 [Alert] Again, students may try surrounding a vertex with several copies of the same angle. Focus on the sum of the angle measures and on matching up congruent sides of the quadrilaterals.

SHARING IDEAS

After a student or group has demonstrated how to put a scalene triangle about a point, **[Ask]** "Is there more than one way your triangles will fit around this point?" [If the sides have different lengths, then all arrangements are essentially the same, because congruent sides must be aligned.] "How do you know that this arrangement can be repeated to make a tessellation?" [At each unfilled vertex, the angles already there have different measures; it's just a matter of filling in the missing angles.]

As students present their ideas about quadrilaterals, they may use the word *quadrilateral* to mean a nonspecial quadrilateral, in contrast to, say, kites. Remind them that kites, trapezoids, and parallelograms (including squares and other rectangles) are also quadrilaterals.

Have students read the text concerning pentagons. To have students practice algebra skills, ask how they might conclude that $A = C$ and $d = 2a$ in Marjorie Rice's 1977 tessellation. The 14 known ways of tiling a plane with pentagons can be found through links at http://www.keymath.com/DG.

You might have each group make a full-page decorated tessellation for display on a bulletin board.

NCTM STANDARDS

CONTENT		PROCESS	
	Number		Problem Solving
✓	Algebra		Reasoning
✓	Geometry	✓	Communication
✓	Measurement	✓	Connections
	Data/Probability		Representation

Assessing Progress

You can assess students' understanding of scalene triangles, congruent angles and sides, and the sum of the measures of the interior angles of a triangle and of a quadrilateral.

Closing the Lesson

All triangles and quadrilaterals can be used to create monohedral tessellations, by surrounding each vertex with one (in the case of quadrilaterals) or two (for triangles) copies of each angle and by matching up congruent sides. Some nonregular pentagons can also tessellate the plane.

BUILDING UNDERSTANDING

The exercises allow practice in making and analyzing nonregular monohedral tessellations.

ASSIGNING HOMEWORK

Essential	any two from 1–7
Performance assessment	4
Portfolio	2
Journal	5
Group	6
Review	6–8

MATERIALS

- graph paper (Exercise 6)
- dominoes (Exercises 6, 7), *optional*

Helping with the Exercises

Exercise 1 These pentagons are equilateral without being regular; not all their angles are congruent.

2. The dual is a $5^3/5^4$ tessellation.

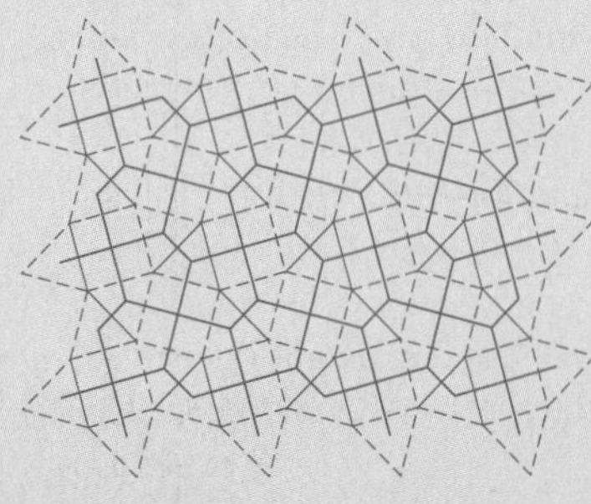

EXERCISES

You will need

Construction tools **for Exercise 1**

1. ***Construction*** The beautiful Cairo street tiling shown below uses equilateral pentagons. One pentagon is shown below left. Use a ruler and a protractor to draw the equilateral pentagon on poster board or heavy cardboard. (For an added challenge, you can try to *construct* the pentagon, as Egyptian artisans likely would have done.) Cut out the pentagon and tessellate with it. Color your design. Answers will vary.

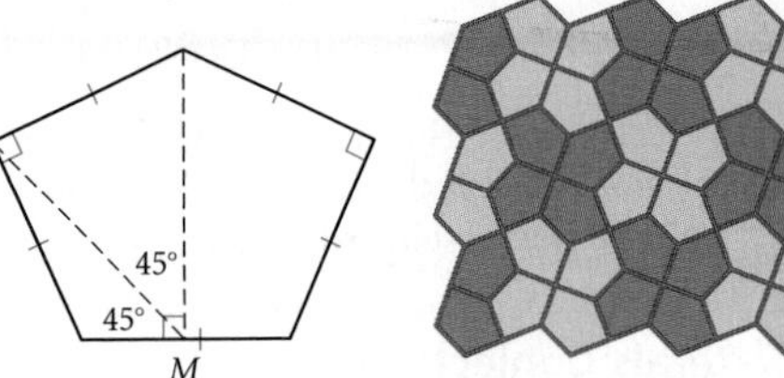

Point M is the midpoint of the base.

2. At right is Marjorie Rice's first pentagonal tiling discovery. Another way to produce a pentagonal tessellation is to make the dual of the tessellation shown in Lesson 7.4, Exercise 5. Try it. ⓗ

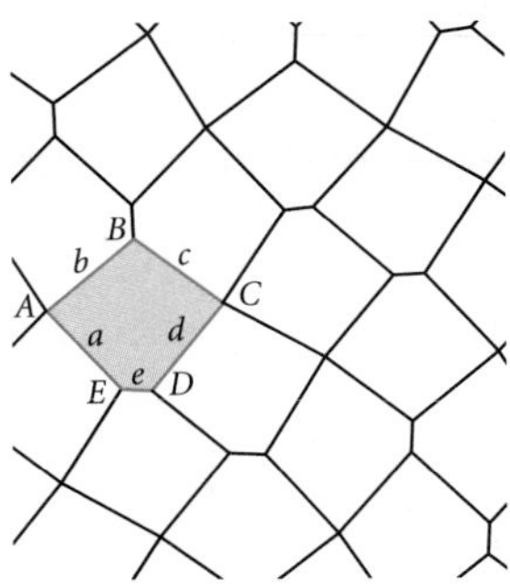

Rice's first discovery, February 1976

$2E + B = 2D + C = 360°$
$a = b = c = d$

3. A tessellation of regular hexagons can be used to create a pentagonal tessellation by dividing each hexagon as shown. Create this tessellation and color it.

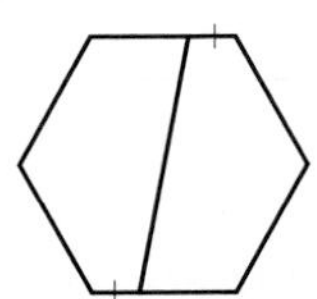

Cultural CONNECTION

Mats called *tatami* are used as a floor covering in traditional Japanese homes. *Tatami* is made from rush, a flowering plant with soft fibers, and has health benefits, such as removing carbon dioxide and regulating humidity and temperature. When arranging *tatami,* you want the seams to form T-shapes. You avoid arranging four at one vertex forming a cross because it is difficult to get a good fit within a room this way. You also want to avoid fault lines—straight seams passing all the way through a rectangular arrangement—because they make it easier for the *tatami* to slip. Room sizes are often given in *tatami* numbers (for example, a 6-mat room or an 8-mat room).

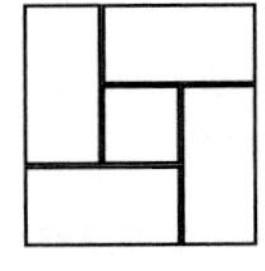

4.5-mat room

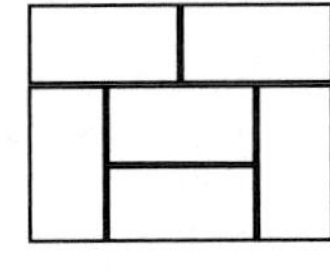

6-mat room

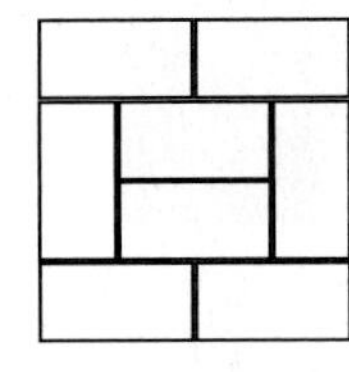

8-mat room

Exercise 3 The infinitely many ways of splitting a hexagon into two congruent pentagons make up just one type of pentagonal tessellation.

3.

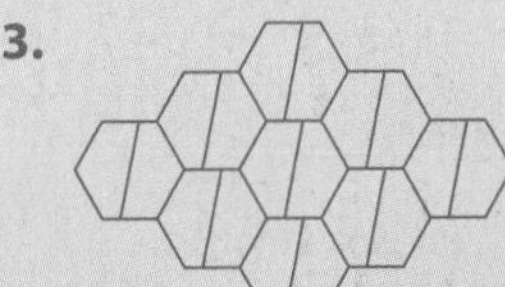

4. Can a concave quadrilateral like the one at right tile the plane? Try it. Create your own concave quadrilateral and try to create a tessellation with it. Decorate your drawing. yes

5. Write a paragraph proof explaining why you can use any triangle to create a monohedral tiling.

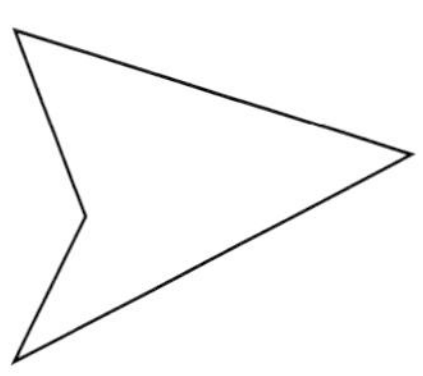

Review

Refer to the Cultural Connection on page 386 for Exercises 6 and 7.

7.4 **6.** Use graph paper to design an arrangement of *tatami* for a 10-mat room. In how many different ways can you arrange the mats so that there are no places where four mats meet at a point (no cross patterns)? Assume that the mats measure 3-by-6 feet and that each room must be at least 9 feet wide. Show all your solutions.

7.4 **7.** There are at least two ways to arrange a 15-mat rectangle with no fault lines. One is shown. Can you find the other?

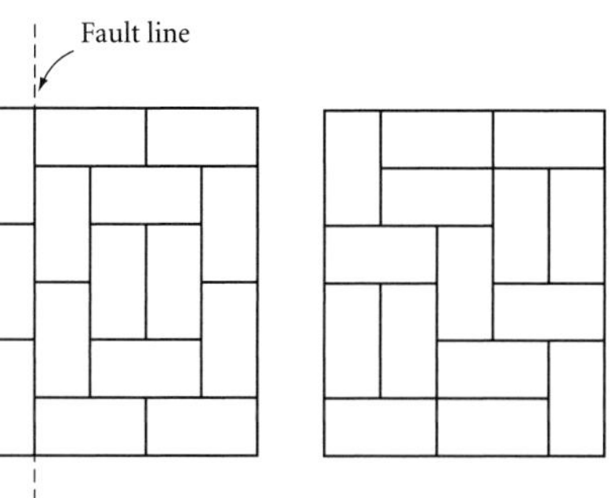

7.2 **8.** Reflect $y = 2x + 3$ across the y-axis and find the equation of the image line.

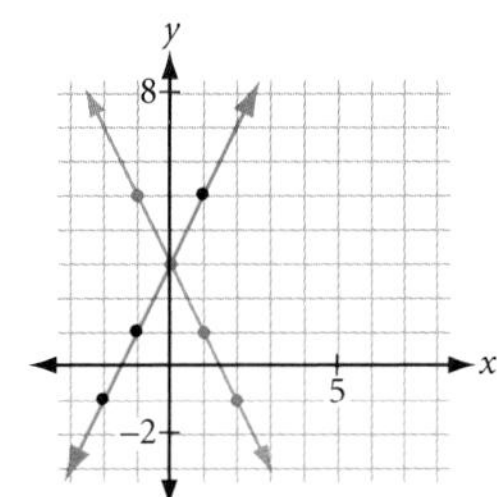

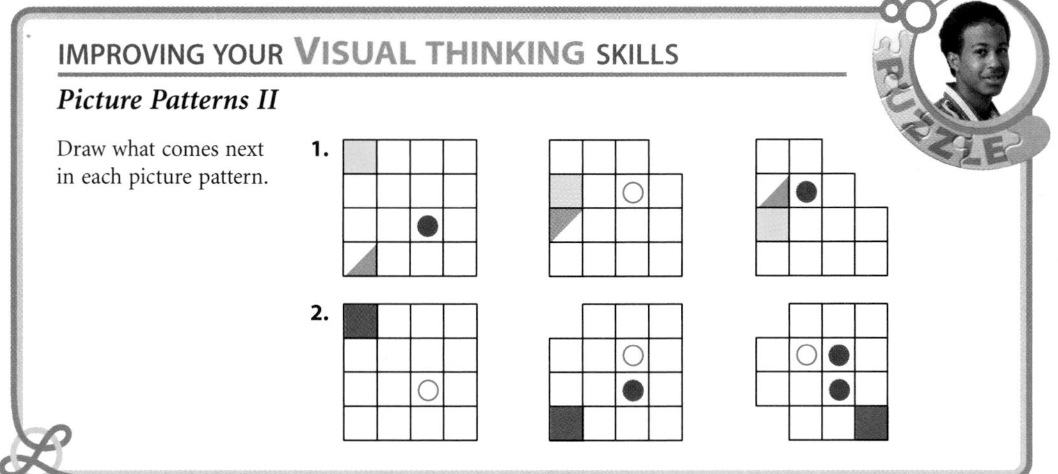

IMPROVING YOUR VISUAL THINKING SKILLS
Picture Patterns II
Draw what comes next in each picture pattern.
1.
2.
PUZZLE

4. The four angles of the quadrilateral will be around each point of intersection in the tessellation.

5.

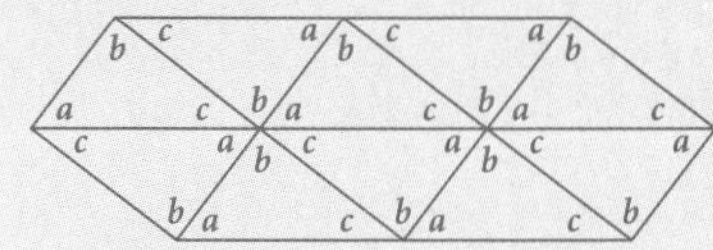

By the Triangle Sum Conjecture, $a + b + c = 180°$. Around each point, we have $2(a + b + c) = 2 \cdot 180° = 360°$. Therefore, a triangle will fill the plane edge to edge without gaps or overlaps. Thus a triangle can be used to create a monohedral tiling.

Exercises 6, 7 Dominoes, like *tatami,* have one side that is half the length of the other. Some students might benefit from working with dominoes rather than graph paper for these exercises.

6. three ways

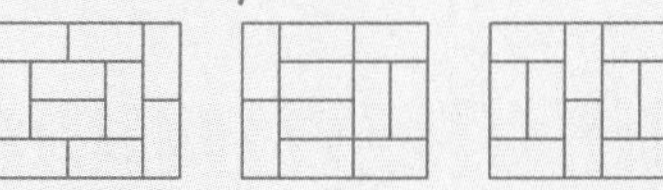

7.

8. $y = -2x + 3$

EXTENSION

Investigate nonperiodic tessellations, Islamic tilings, or tessellations that include star polygons.

IMPROVING VISUAL THINKING SKILLS

Students can justify several answers. Here are two:

1.

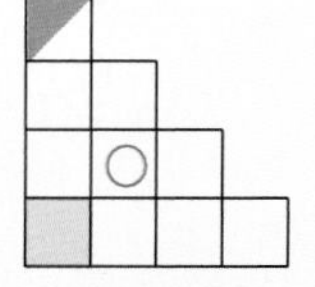

2.

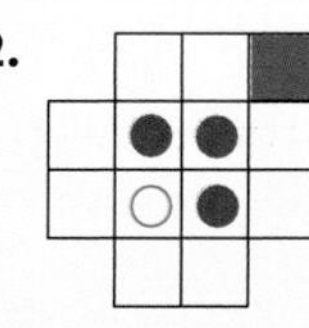

project

PENROSE TILINGS

When British scientist Sir Roger Penrose of the University of Oxford is not at work on quantum mechanics or relativity theory, he's inventing mathematical games. Penrose came up with a special tiling that uses two shapes, a kite and a dart. (The *dart* is a concave kite.) The tiles must be placed so that each vertex with a dot always touches only other vertices with dots. By adding this extra requirement, Penrose's tiles make a *nonperiodic tiling*. That is, as you tessellate, the pattern does not repeat by translations.

Penrose tilings decorate the Storey Hall building in Melbourne, Australia.

Penrose tiling at the Center for Mathematics and Computing, Carleton College, Northfield, Minnesota

Try it. Copy the two tiles shown below—the kite and the dart with their dots—onto patty paper. Use the patty-paper tracing to make two cardboard tiles. Create your own unique Penrose tiling and color it. Or, use geometry software to create and color your design.

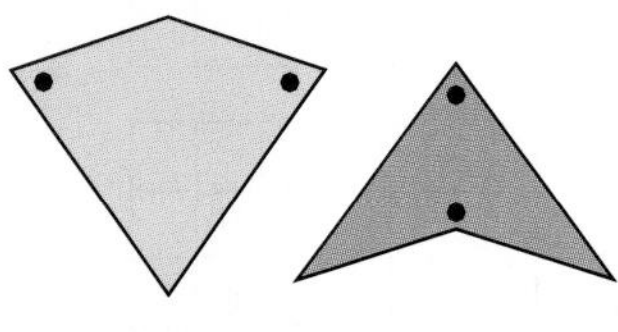

Supporting the project

Use the Penrose Tilings worksheet for many copies of the two shapes.

OUTCOMES

- ▸ The tessellation has no gaps or overlaps.
- ▸ Dots are correctly placed so that the tiling is nonperiodic.
- • Exceptional creativity and care are shown in the coloring.

LESSON 7.6

Tessellations Using Only Translations

There are three kinds of people in this world: those who make things happen, those who watch things happen, and those who wonder what happened.

ANONYMOUS

In 1936, M. C. Escher traveled to Spain and became fascinated with the tile patterns of the Alhambra. He spent days sketching the tessellations that Islamic masters had used to decorate the walls and ceilings. Some of his sketches are shown at right. Escher wrote that the tessellations were "the richest source of inspiration" he had ever tapped.

Brickwork, Alhambra, M. C. Escher

Symmetry Drawing E105, M. C. Escher, 1960

Escher spent many years learning how to use translations, rotations, and glide reflections on grids of equilateral triangles and parallelograms. But he did not limit himself to pure geometric tessellations.

The four steps below show how Escher may have created his Pegasus tessellation, shown at left. Notice how a partial outline of the Pegasus is translated from one side of a square to another to complete a single tile that fits with other tiles like itself.

You can use steps like this to create your own unique tessellation. Start with a tessellation of squares, rectangles, or parallelograms, and try translating curves on opposite sides of the tile. It may take a few tries to get a shape that looks like a person, animal, or plant. Use your imagination!

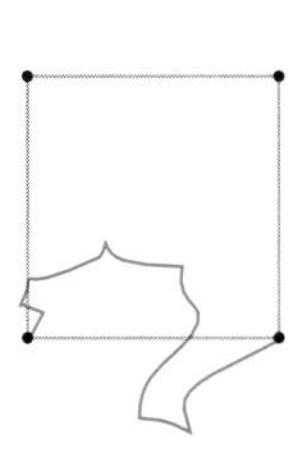

Step 1

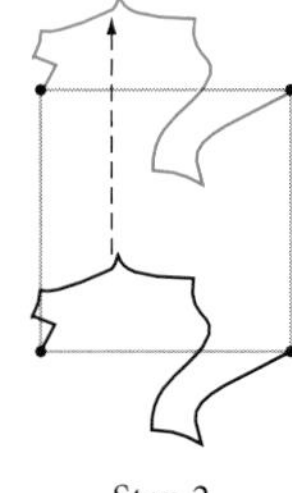

Step 2

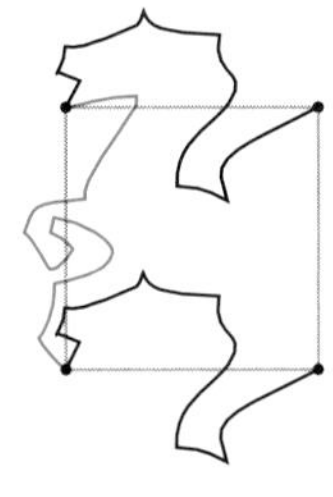

Step 3

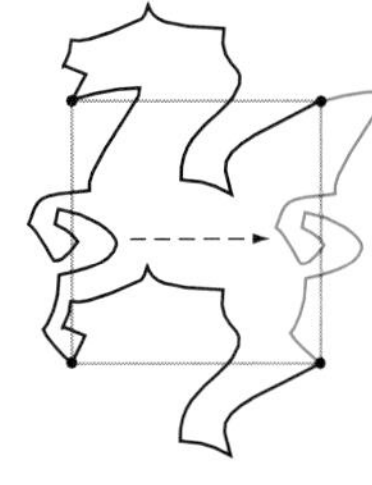

Step 4

NCTM STANDARDS

CONTENT		PROCESS	
	Number		Problem Solving
	Algebra	✓	Reasoning
✓	Geometry		Communication
✓	Measurement	✓	Connections
	Data/Probability		Representation

LESSON OBJECTIVES

- Create Escher-type translation tessellations
- Develop visual and creative thinking

LESSON 7.6

PLANNING

LESSON OUTLINE

One day:

10 min	Sharing
5 min	Closing
30 min	Exercises

MATERIALS

- Cats and Bats (W) for One step

TEACHING

Students can make tessellations by translating curves that replace edges of geometric shapes. You might introduce Lessons 7.6, 7.7, and 7.8 on one day and on the following days have groups work on creating and decorating various tessellations.

[Context] Pegasus was an immortal winged horse of Greek legend.

One step Give out the Cats and Bats worksheet and ask students to determine the irregular shape used as a basis for each tessellation. Have graph paper and patty paper available. As you circulate, encourage students to figure out the basic polygon generating each picture [hexagon] and decide how the student artist might have adapted it to another shape that would tile the plane. During Sharing, have students read the explanation in the book for the pegasus and the bat and see how closely its suggested steps resemble their own.

INTRODUCTION

Escher had done drawings and etchings before, but his trip to the Alhambra sparked a new interest in geometric art and sent him in a completely new direction. Today, he is most famous for his geometric art. For more on Islamic art and the Alhambra, see Lesson 0.6.

Lead the class through the steps needed to create either the pegasus tessellation or the *Monster Mix* tessellation. Show students how to use patty paper and graph paper.

SHARING IDEAS

Sharing can come after work on the one-step investigation or after students do some exercises. As students display their tessellations, ask them to talk about the challenges they met. Students may say it is easier to decide what an already-created shape could represent than to make a shape to match a predetermined image.

[Alert] Students may embellish their shapes, creating figures that appear to be overlapping. Just as a tessellation does not overlap, drawings made on tessellating tiles should not show shapes that overlap or have gaps (such as a background).

[Ask] "What kind of transformation did you apply to curves on the figure?" [translations] "Would other transformations have been possible in order to make a tessellating shape?" You need not answer this question; it motivates the next two lessons.

[Ask] "How much does the area of the shape change as it is re-arranged?" You do not yet need to reach class consensus on this question; it lays the groundwork for Chapter 8.

Assessing Progress

Assess students' understanding of tessellations and translations and of which polygons tessellate the plane.

You can also use the translation technique with regular hexagons. The only difference is that there are three sets of opposite sides on a hexagon. So you'll need to draw three sets of curves and translate them to opposite sides. The six steps below show how student Mark Purcell created his tessellation, *Monster Mix*.

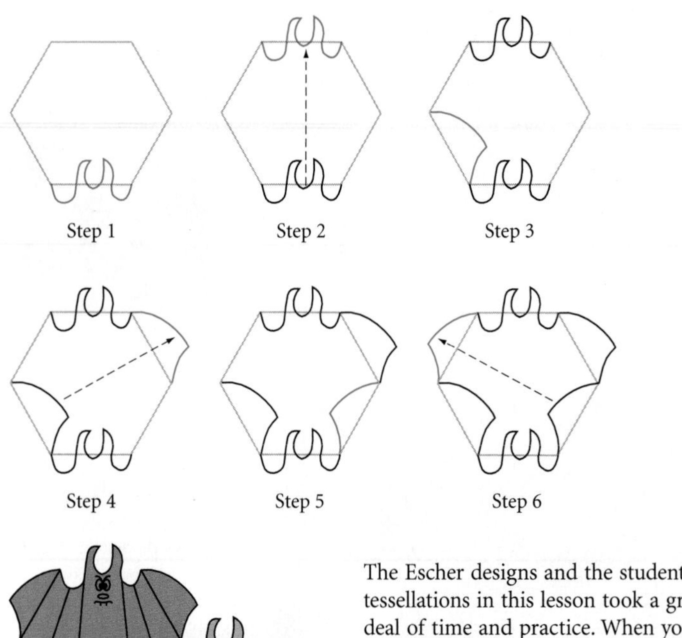

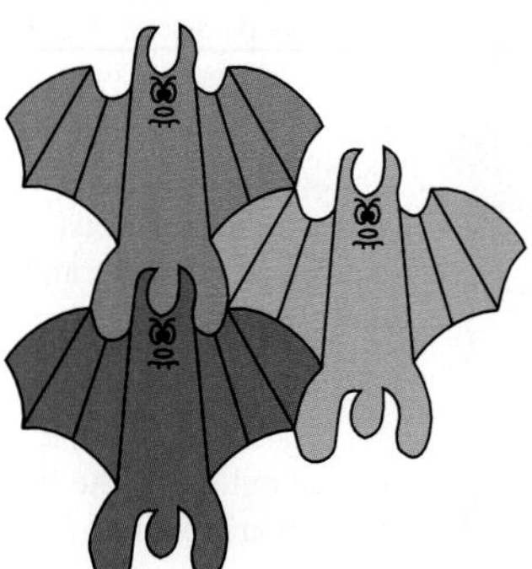

The Escher designs and the student tessellations in this lesson took a great deal of time and practice. When you create your own tessellating designs of recognizable shapes, you'll appreciate the need for this practice! For more about tessellations, and resources to help you learn how to make them, go to www.keymath.com/DG .

Monster Mix, Mark Purcell

EXERCISES

In Exercises 1–3, copy each tessellating shape and fill it in so that it becomes a recognizable figure.

1.

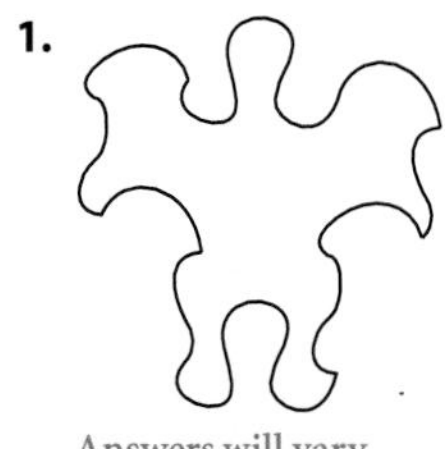

Answers will vary.

2.

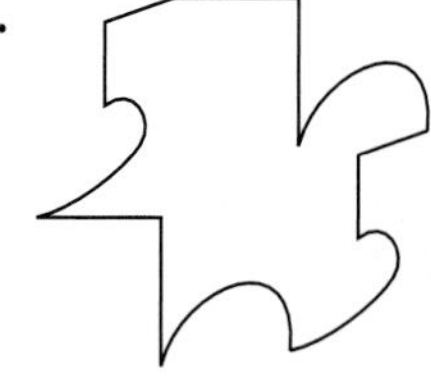

Answers will vary.

3.

Answers will vary.

Closing the Lesson

A tessellating shape can be formed from a square or a regular hexagon by changing two or three adjacent sides and then translating those pieces to replace the opposite sides. The resulting tessellation consists of translations of the basic shape.

In Exercises 4–6, identify the basic tessellation grid (squares, parallelograms, or regular hexagons) that each geometry student used to create each translation tessellation.

4. **5.** **6.**

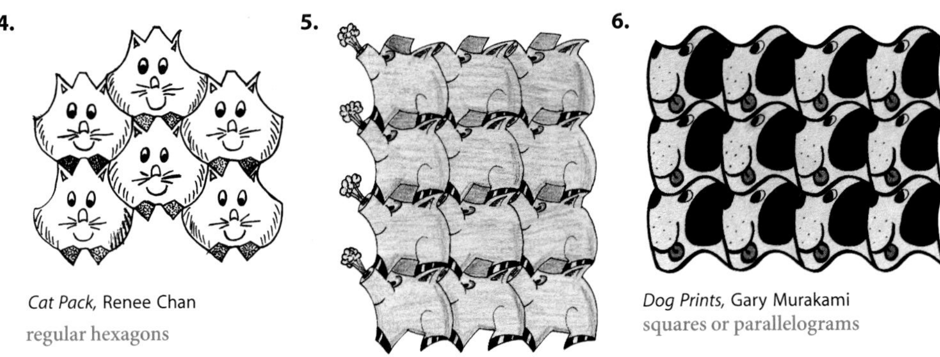

Cat Pack, Renee Chan
regular hexagons

Snorty the Pig, Jonathan Benton
squares or parallelograms

Dog Prints, Gary Murakami
squares or parallelograms

In Exercises 7 and 8, copy the figure and the grid onto patty paper. Create a tessellation on the grid with the figure.

7. **8.**

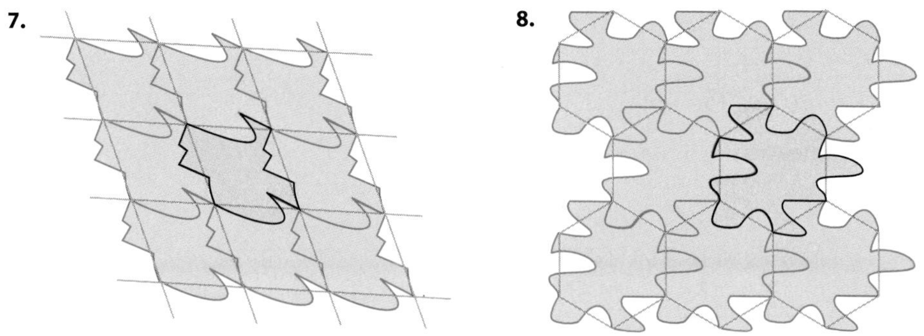

Now it's your turn. In Exercises 9 and 10, create a tessellation of recognizable shapes using the translation method you learned in this lesson. At first, you will probably end up with shapes that look like amoebas or spilled milk, but with practice and imagination, you will get recognizable images. Decorate and title your designs.

9. Use squares as the basic structure. ⓗ Answers will vary.

10. Use regular hexagons as the basic structure. Answers will vary.

Review

7.2 **11.** The route of a rancher takes him from the house at point *A* to the south fence, then over to the east fence, then to the corral at point *B*. Copy the figure at right onto patty paper and locate the points on the south and east fences that minimize the rancher's route.

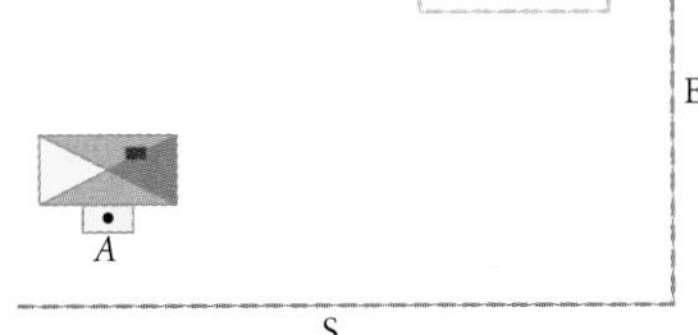

11.

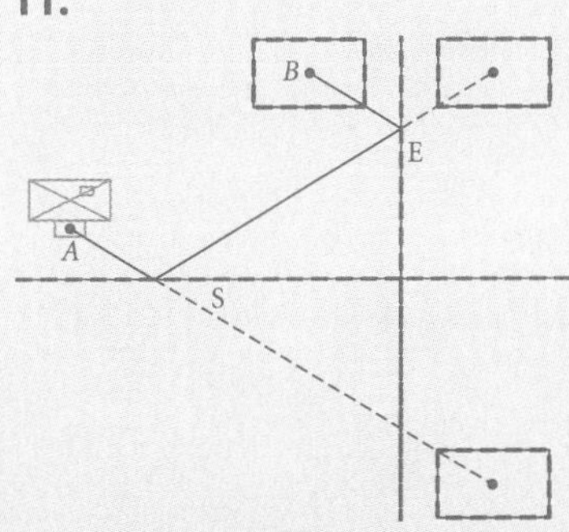

BUILDING UNDERSTANDING

To minimize frustration with unrealistic-looking tessellating designs, Exercises 1–8 give students some experience before they attempt Exercises 9 and 10, in which they actually design their own tessellations. These two exercises will need extra time, and you might assess them separately.

ASSIGNING HOMEWORK

Essential	1–8
Performance assessment	9, 10
Portfolio	9, 10
Journal	15
Review	11–15

MATERIALS

- tracing paper or patty paper
- crayons or colored markers
- Square Dot Paper (W)
- Hexagon Grid Paper (W)

Helping with the Exercises

Exercises 1–3 Encourage imagination here.

Exercises 7, 8 Students may need to be reminded to use a second piece of patty paper for translating the figures.

Exercises 9, 10 Square dot paper and hexagon grid paper for these exercises can be found in the Geometry Materials section of Teaching and Worksheet Masters. As you evaluate students' work, be sure that they are not making pictures in which the figures overlap or have gaps.

12. $y = -\frac{2}{3}x - 3$; the slope is the opposite sign.

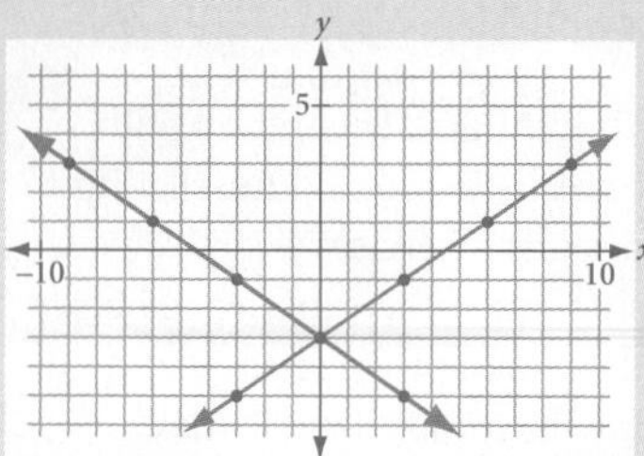

Exercise 14 If students have difficulty, suggest that they use dimensional analysis; remind them that *rpm* stands for "rotations per minute" and can be written as rotations/min.

14.
$\frac{400 \text{ rev}}{1 \text{ min}} \cdot 2\pi \cdot \frac{26 \text{ ft}}{1 \text{ rev}} \cdot \frac{1 \text{ min}}{60 \text{ sec}} \approx$
1089 ft/sec

15. Explanations of the truth of statements might include:

a. The kite diagonal between vertex angles is the perpendicular bisector of the other diagonal; in a square diagonals would bisect each other

d. Parallel lines cut off congruent arcs of a circle, so inscribed angles (the base angles of the trapezoid) are congruent.

EXTENSION

Have students use graphics software, geometry software, or Kaleidomania to create tessellations.

7.2 **12.** Reflect $y = \frac{2}{3}x - 3$ over the y-axis. Write an equation for the image. How does it compare with the original equation?

7.4 **13.** Give the vertex arrangement for the tessellation at right. 3.4.6.4/4.6.12

6.5 **14.** A helicopter has four blades. Each blade measures about 26 feet from the center of rotation to the tip. What is the speed in feet per second at the tips of the blades when they are moving at 400 rpm?

15. Identify each of the following statements as true or false. If true, explain why. If false, give a counterexample explaining why it is false.

5.3 **a.** If the two diagonals of a quadrilateral are congruent but only one is the perpendicular bisector of the other, then the quadrilateral is a kite. true

7.1 **b.** If the quadrilateral has exactly one line of reflectional symmetry, then the quadrilateral is a kite. False; it could be an isosceles trapezoid.

5.6 **c.** If the diagonals of a quadrilateral are congruent and bisect each other, then it is a square. False; it could be a rectangle.

6.3 **d.** If a trapezoid is cyclic, then it is isosceles. true

IMPROVING YOUR VISUAL THINKING SKILLS

3-by-3 Inductive Reasoning Puzzle I

Sketch the figure missing in the lower right corner of this 3-by-3 pattern.

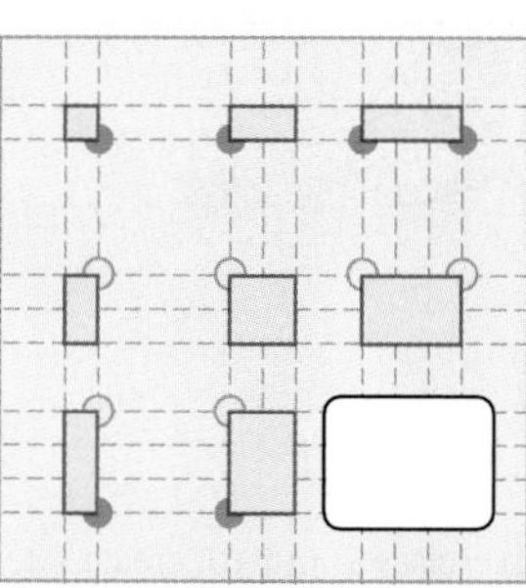

IMPROVING VISUAL THINKING SKILLS

If students are struggling, **[Ask]** "How does the pattern change from one row to the next?"

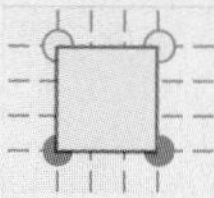

LESSON

7.7

Tessellations That Use Rotations

Einstein was once asked, "What is your phone number?" He answered, "I don't know, but I know where to find it if I need it."

ALBERT EINSTEIN

In Lesson 7.6, you created recognizable shapes by translating curves from opposite sides of a regular hexagon or square. In tessellations using only translations, all the figures face in the same direction. In this lesson you will use rotations of curves on a grid of parallelograms, equilateral triangles, or regular hexagons. The resulting tiles will fit together when you rotate them, and the designs will have rotational symmetry about points in the tiling. For example, in this Escher print, each reptile is made by rotating three different curves about three alternating vertices of a regular hexagon.

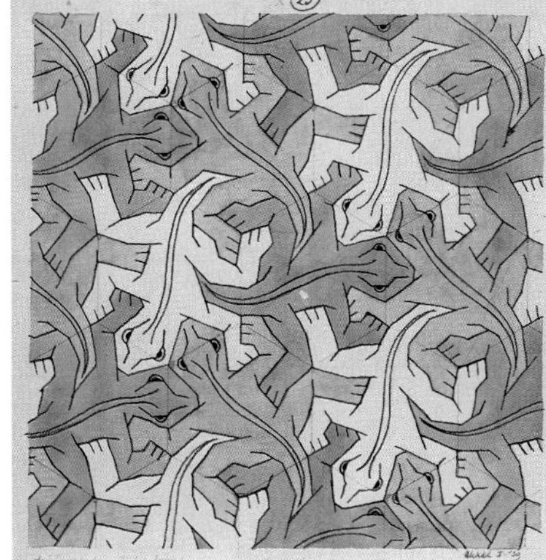

Symmetry Drawing E25, M. C. Escher, 1939

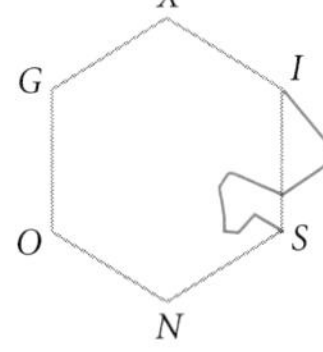

Step 1

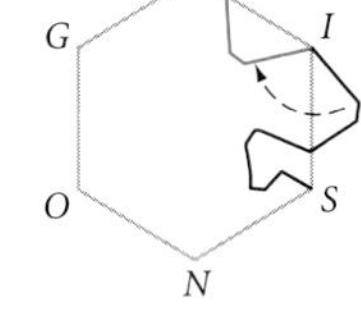

Step 2

Step 3

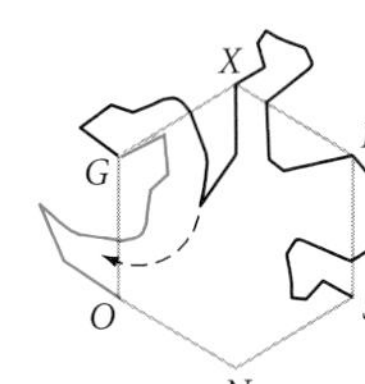

Step 4

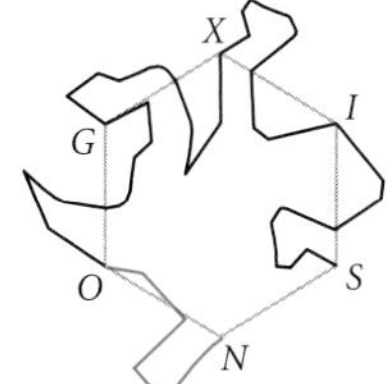

Step 5

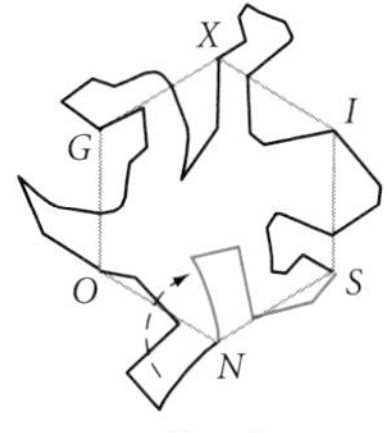

Step 6

Step 1	Connect points S and I with a curve.
Step 2	Rotate curve SI about point I so that point S rotates to coincide with point X.
Step 3	Connect points G and X with a curve.
Step 4	Rotate curve GX about point G so that point X rotates to coincide with point O.
Step 5	Create curve NO.
Step 6	Rotate curve NO about point N so that point O rotates to coincide with point S.

NCTM STANDARDS

CONTENT		PROCESS	
	Number		Problem Solving
	Algebra		Reasoning
✓	Geometry	✓	Communication
	Measurement	✓	Connections
	Data/Probability		Representation

LESSON OBJECTIVES

- Create Escher-type rotation tessellations
- Develop visual and creative thinking

LESSON

7.7

PLANNING

LESSON OUTLINE

One day:

10 min	Sharing
5 min	Closing
30 min	Exercises

MATERIALS

- Merlin (W) for One step

TEACHING

Students learn to make tessellations through rotating curves that replace sides of a geometric shape.

One step Hand out the Merlin worksheet and ask each group to decide on the basic tessellating shape. Have available patty paper and hexagon and isometric grid paper. As students work, ask what the underlying geometric shape is and how the student artist might have changed it. If students are stuck on trying to move shapes by translation, ask what other transformations might be used. During Sharing, have students read the explanation of Escher's drawing of the lizard to see how closely its suggested steps resemble those for Merlin.

INTRODUCTION

Demonstrate how to create either or both of the tessellations of reptiles and flying fish. The steps used to create a tessellating reptile apply to tiles with an even number of sides. For an odd number of sides, one side has to be point-rotated about its midpoint, as in the flying fish

Introduction (continued)
tiling. You may want to demonstrate how to place a pencil point on the center of rotation and rotate the bottom sheet of patty paper.

[Alert] Help students realize that they are changing regular polygons that they already know tessellate.

SHARING IDEAS

[Ask] "How is using the equilateral triangle different from using the hexagon?" [Elicit the idea that when the number of sides is odd one side must be bisected to create a pair for a point-symmetric curve.] "Can you apply this technique to isosceles triangles to create an isosceles triangle tessellation? If so, how?" [Yes; you would apply Step 3 to the base of the isosceles triangle.]

Remind students that in the previous lesson the shapes replacing edges were translated to opposite sides. Here the shapes replacing edges are rotated. **[Ask]** "How do these rotations affect the tessellation as a whole?" [The shapes are rotated to fit together.] Ask what other kinds of transformations there are and whether students might also use these to make tessellations. You need not answer this question; it motivates the next lesson.

You might also ask how the area of the polygon is changing in anticipation of Chapter 8.

Assessing Progress
You can assess students' understanding of tessellations and rotations and of the idea of changing a geometric shape that tessellates.

Escher worked long and hard to adjust each curve until he got what he recognized as a reptile. When you are working on your own design, keep in mind that you may have to redraw your curves a few times until something you recognize appears.

Escher used his reptile drawing in this famous lithograph. Look closely at the reptiles in the drawing. Escher loved to play with our perceptions of reality!
Reptiles, M. C. Escher, 1943

Another method used by Escher utilizes rotations on an equilateral triangle grid. Two sides of each equilateral triangle have the same curve, rotated about their common point. The third side is a curve with point symmetry. The following steps demonstrate how you might create a tessellating flying fish like that created by Escher.

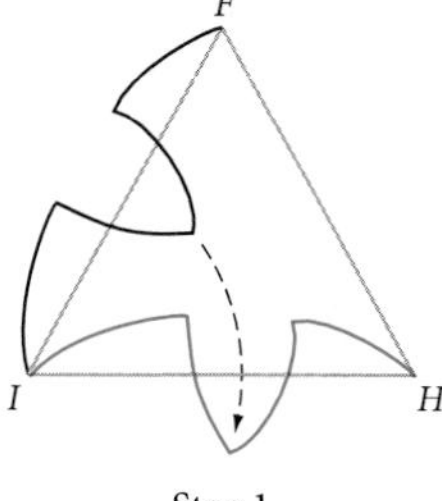

Step 1

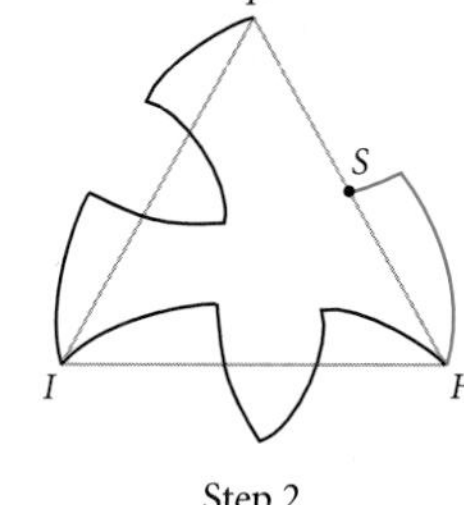

Step 2

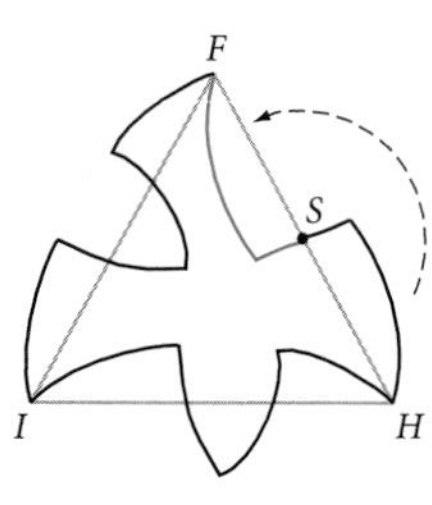

Step 3

Step 1 Connect points F and I with a curve. Then rotate the curve 60° clockwise about point I so that it becomes curve IH.

Step 2 Find the midpoint S of $\overline{FH}$ and draw curve SH.

Step 3 Rotate curve SH 180° about S to produce curve FS. Together curve FS and curve SH become the point-symmetric curve FH.

With a little added detail, the design becomes a flying fish.

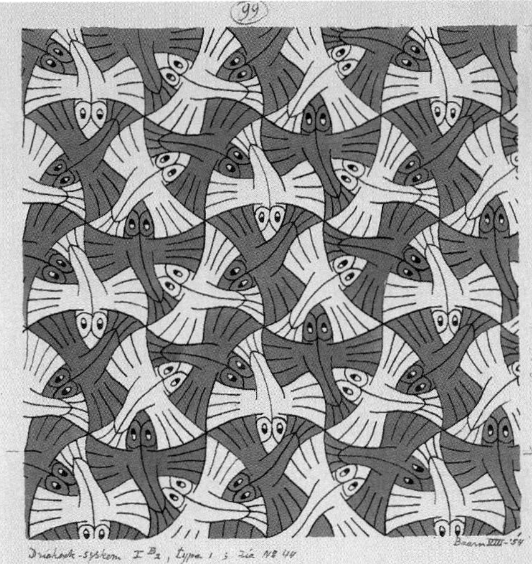

Symmetry Drawing E99,
M. C. Escher, 1954

Or, with just a slight variation in the curves, the resulting shape will appear more like a bird than a flying fish.

Closing the Lesson

A tessellating shape can be formed from a geometric tessellating shape by changing a side (or part of a side) and replacing other sides (or parts of sides) with rotations of the changed side. The resulting tessellation consists of rotations of the basic shape.

BUILDING UNDERSTANDING

The exercises build up to Exercises 5 and 6, in which students make their own designs; you might treat these two exercises as a project and assess them separately. In creating tessellation designs, the segments (sides of polygons) are not needed, only the points. Thus, for neater work, students may want to use dot paper to create their designs.

ASSIGNING HOMEWORK

Essential	1–4
Performance assessment	5, 6
Portfolio	5, 6
Review	7–13

MATERIALS

- tracing paper or patty paper
- isometric or square dot paper
- crayons or colored markers
- Hexagon Grid Paper (W)
- Isometric Grid Paper (W)

EXERCISES

You will need

Geometry software for Exercise **13**

In Exercises 1 and 2, identify the basic grid (equilateral triangles or regular hexagons) that each geometry student used to create the tessellation.

1.

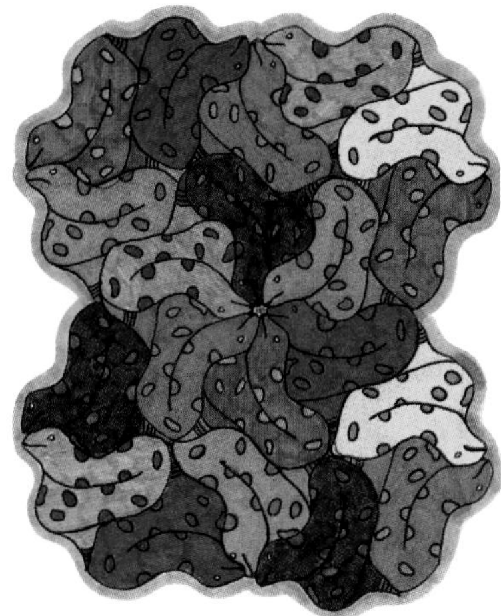

Snakes, Jack Chow
equilateral triangles

2.

Merlin, Aimee Plourdes
regular hexagons

Helping with the Exercises

Exercises 5, 6 Grid paper for these exercises can be found in the Geometry Materials section of Teaching and Worksheet Masters. **[Alert]** Watch for student art that, when colored, uses images that overlap or show gaps (such as a background).

Exercise 7 This exercise builds on investigations in Lesson 0.5.

7. sample design:

In Exercises 3 and 4, copy the figure and the grid onto patty paper. Show how you can use other pieces of patty paper to tessellate the figure on the grid.

3.

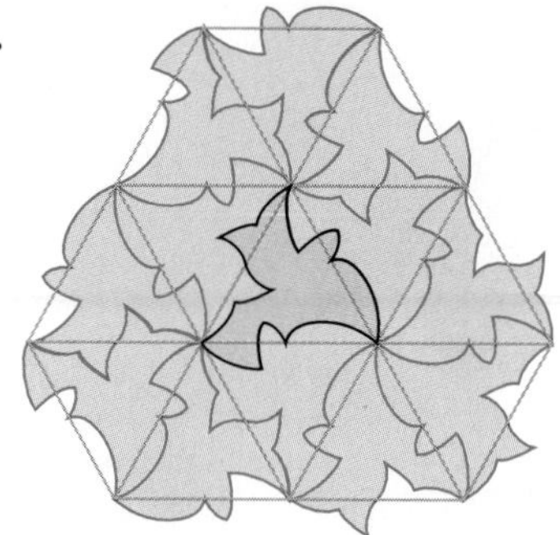

4.

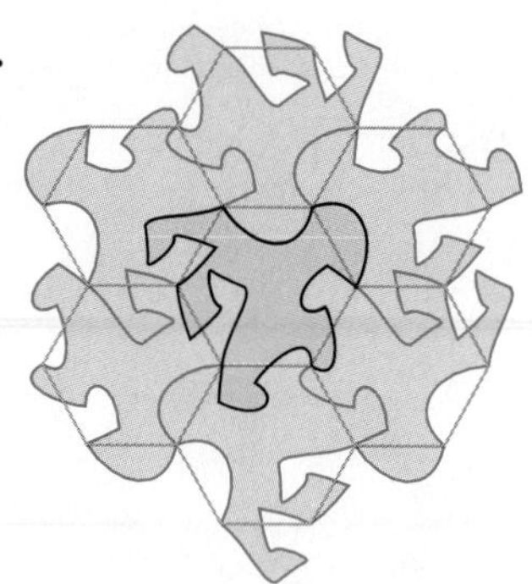

In Exercises 5 and 6, create tessellation designs by using rotations. You will need patty paper, tracing paper, or clear plastic, and grid paper or isometric dot paper.

5. Create a tessellating design of recognizable shapes by using a grid of regular hexagons. Decorate and color your art. Answers will vary.

6. Create a tessellating design of recognizable shapes by using a grid of equilateral or isosceles triangles. Decorate and color your art. Answers will vary.

Review

0.5 **7.** Study these knot designs by Rinus Roelofs. Now try creating one of your own. Select a tessellation. Make a copy and thicken the lines. Make two copies of this thick-lined tessellation. Lay one of them on top of the other and shift it slightly. Trace the one underneath onto the top copy. Erase where they overlap. Then create a knot design using what you learned in Lesson 0.5.

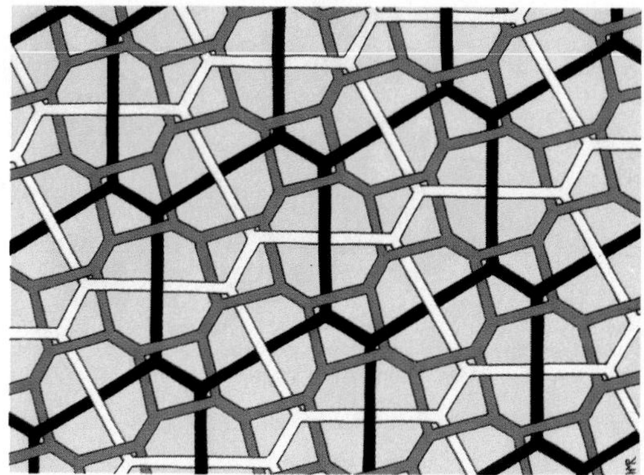

Dutch artist Rinus Roelofs (b 1954) experiments with the lines between the shapes rather than looking at the plane-filling figures. In these paintings, he has made the lines thicker and created intricate knot designs.

(Above) *Impossible Structures–III, structure 24*
(At left) *Interwoven Patterns–V, structure 17*

For Exercises 8–11, identify the statement as true or false. For each false statement, explain why it is false or sketch a counterexample.

5.5 **8.** If the diagonals of a quadrilateral are congruent, the quadrilateral is a parallelogram.

5.6 **9.** If the diagonals of a quadrilateral are congruent and bisect each other, the quadrilateral is a rectangle. true

5.6 **10.** If the diagonals of a quadrilateral are perpendicular and bisect each other, the quadrilateral is a rhombus. true

5.3 **11.** If the diagonals of a quadrilateral are congruent and perpendicular, the quadrilateral is a square.

6.5 **12.** Earth's radius is about 4000 miles. Imagine that you travel from the equator to the South Pole by a direct route along the surface. Draw a sketch of your path. How far will you travel? How long will the trip take if you travel at an average speed of 50 miles per hour?

7.1 **13.** ***Technology*** Use geometry software to construct a line and two points A and B not on the line. Reflect A and B over the line and connect the four points to form a trapezoid.

a. Is it isosceles? Why?

b. Choose a random point C inside the trapezoid and connect it to the four vertices with segments. Calculate the sum of the distances from C to the four vertices. Drag point C around. Where is the sum of the distances the greatest? The least?

8. False; they must bisect each other in a parallelogram.

11. False; it could be a kite or an isosceles trapezoid.

12. The path would be $\frac{1}{4}$ of Earth's circumference, approximately 6280 miles, which will take 126 hours, or around $5\frac{1}{4}$ days.

13a. Yes; it has reflectional symmetry, so legs and base angles are congruent.

13b. greatest: near each of the acute vertices; least: at the intersection of the diagonals (where A, C, and B' become collinear and A', C, and B become collinear)

IMPROVING YOUR REASONING SKILLS

PUZZLE

Logical Liars

Five students have just completed a logic contest. To confuse the school's reporter, Lois Lang, each student agreed to make one true and one false statement to her when she interviewed them. Lois was clever enough to figure out the winner. Are you? Here are the students' statements.

Frances: Kai was second. I was fourth.
Leyton: I was third. Charles was last.
Denise: Kai won. I was second.
Kai: Leyton had the best score. I came in last.
Charles: I came in second. Kai was third.

IMPROVING REASONING SKILLS

Here's a sample of the kind of reasoning required: Both Denise and Charles claim to be second, so at least one of them is lying; therefore Kai must be either first or third. Kai claims to have been last and that Leyton was best; because Kai can't be last, Leyton was best. Continuing with reasoning of this kind leads to the conclusion that, from first to last, the order of finish was Leyton, Denise, Kai, Frances, and Charles.

LESSON

7.8

PLANNING

LESSON OUTLINE

One day:

10 min	Sharing
5 min	Closing
30 min	Exercises

MATERIALS

- More Tessellations (W) for One step

TEACHING

Students can use glide reflections to create tessellations from geometric shapes.

One step Hand out the More Tessellations worksheet and ask each group to decide on the basic tessellating shape for one of the drawings. Have available patty paper, grid paper, and dot paper. As students work, ask what the underlying geometric shapes are and how the artists might have changed them. Be prepared to suggest that they treat different sides differently. During Sharing, have students read the explanations of the Escher drawings in the student book to see how the suggested steps resemble their own.

INTRODUCTION

Discuss the example of a glide-reflection tessellation. **[Ask]** "In this tessellation, are the lines of reflection horizontal or vertical?" [All happen to be vertical.]

Help students understand the two transformations being performed to create the horseman: one glide reflection from one short kite side to the other and another glide reflection from one long kite side to the other. **[Ask]** "Is this Escher drawing possible to make from paper, or impossible?" [It is possible; the horsemen are a little out of perspective. Try making a paper model.]

SHARING IDEAS

[Ask] "How does the transformation of side shapes affect the way the tessellation is put together?" [Elicit the idea that two glide reflections were used to make the soldier's figure, so assembling it into a tessellation requires two reflections. On the other hand, only a glide reflection and a translation were used to create the figure generating the bird drawing, so the tessellation is assembled through reflections and translations.]

Direct students' attention to the design in Exercise 1 and ask if it's symmetric; then ask if it has symmetry other than glide-reflectional symmetry. Its translational symmetry is generated by a pair of heads facing opposite directions. Ask if all figures generated by glide reflections have translational symmetry. You need not answer this question; let students look at several pictures and make conjectures.

LESSON 7.8

Tessellations That Use Glide Reflections

The young do not know enough to be prudent, and therefore they attempt the impossible, and achieve it, generation after generation.

PEARL S. BUCK

In this lesson you will use glide reflections to create tessellations. In Lesson 7.6, you saw Escher's translation tessellation of the winged horse Pegasus. All the horses are facing in the same direction. In the drawings below and below left, Escher used glide reflections on a grid of glide-reflected kites to get his horsemen facing in opposite directions.

Horseman, M. C. Escher, 1946

The steps below show how you can make a tessellating design similar to Escher's *Horseman*. (The symbol ⤉ indicates a glide reflection.)

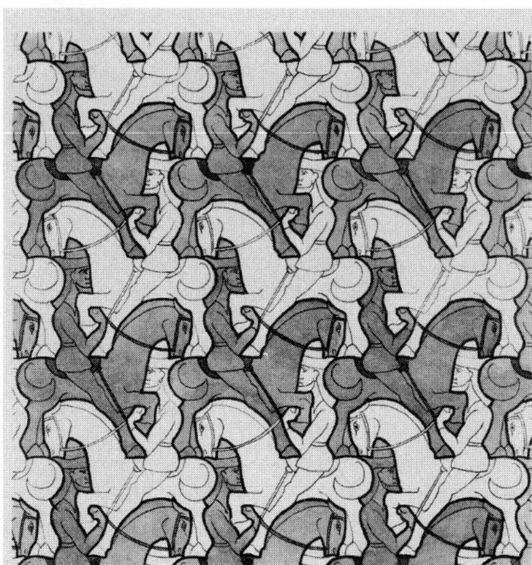

Horseman Sketch, M. C. Escher

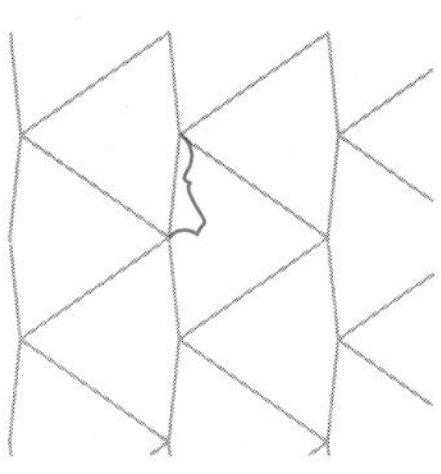

Step 1

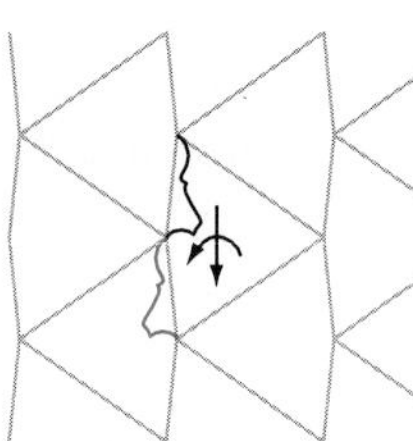

Step 2

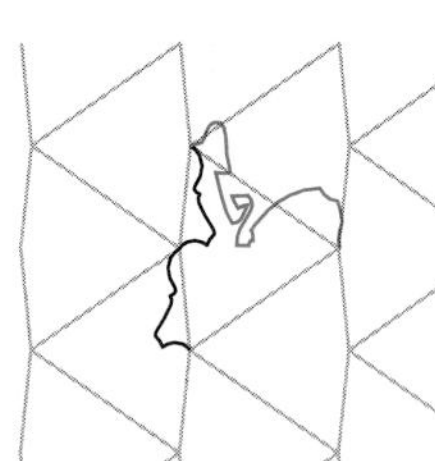

Step 3

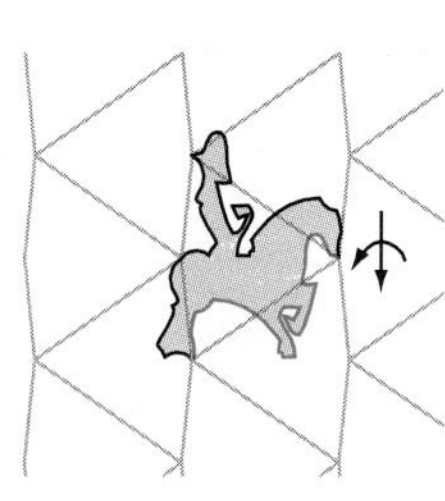

Step 4

In the tessellation of birds below left, you can see that Escher used a grid of squares. You can use the same procedure on a grid of any type of glide-reflected parallelograms. The steps below show how you might create a tessellation of birds or fishes on a parallelogram grid.

Symmetry Drawing E108, M. C. Escher, 1967

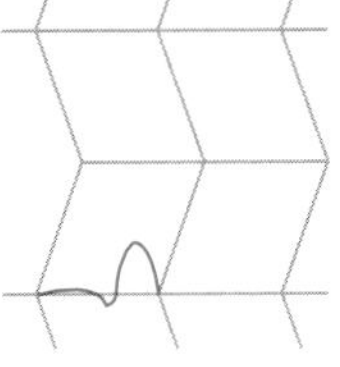

Step 1

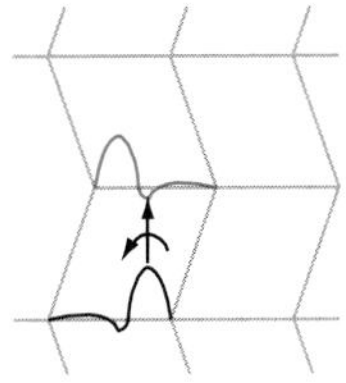

Step 2

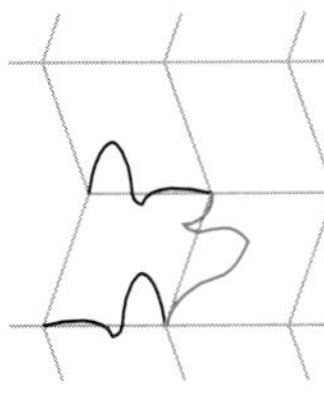

Step 3

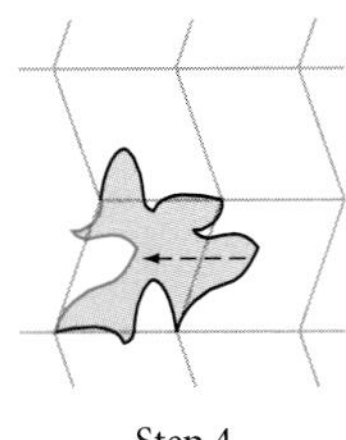

Step 4

EXERCISES

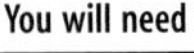

You will need

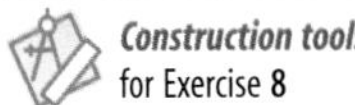

Construction tools for Exercise 8

In Exercises 1 and 2, identify the basic tessellation grid (kites or parallelograms) that the geometry student used to create the tessellation.

1.

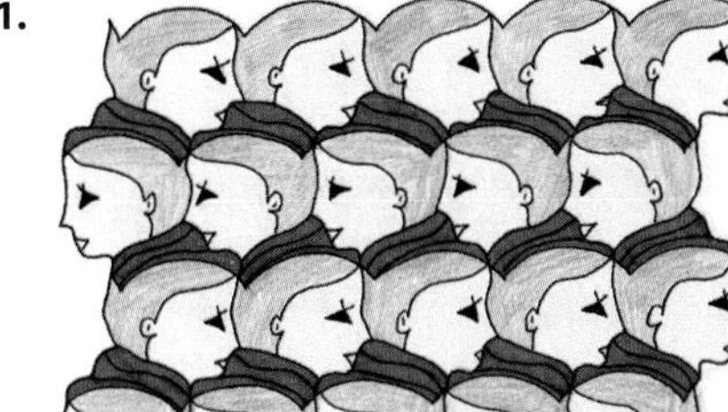

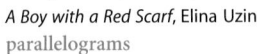

A Boy with a Red Scarf, Elina Uzin

parallelograms

2.

Glide Reflection, Alice Chan

parallelograms

Sharing Ideas (continued)

As in earlier lessons, you might ask a question to bring out the idea that the area of the original geometric shape is preserved by the changes.

Because the tessellation of birds involved two different kinds of transformations (glide reflections and translations), you might challenge students to create tessellations involving all three kinds of transformations (including rotations as well).

Assessing Progress

Assess how well students understand tessellations, translations, and glide reflections.

Closing the Lesson

A tessellating shape can be formed from a geometric tessellating shape by changing a side and replacing other sides with glide reflections of the changed side. The resulting tessellation consists of glide reflections of the basic shape.

BUILDING UNDERSTANDING

The first four exercises prepare students to create their own tessellations in Exercises 5 and 6, which you might treat as a project and assess separately.

ASSIGNING HOMEWORK

Essential	1–4
Performance assessment	5, 6
Portfolio	5, 6
Review	7–10

MATERIALS

- tracing paper or patty paper
- crayons or colored markers
- Parallelogram Grid Paper (W)
- Kite Grid Paper (W)

NCTM STANDARDS

CONTENT		PROCESS	
	Number		Problem Solving
	Algebra		Reasoning
✓	Geometry	✓	Communication
	Measurement	✓	Connections
	Data/Probability		Representation

LESSON OBJECTIVES

- Create Escher-type reflection tessellations
- Develop visual and creative thinking

▶ Helping with the Exercises

Exercises 5, 6 Grid paper for these exercises can be found in the Geometry Materials section of Teaching and Worksheet Masters. You might allow students to use other underlying shapes.

Exercise 7 Students may need to be reminded that the circumcenter of a triangle is at the intersection of the perpendicular bisectors of the sides and is equidistant from the vertices.

Exercise 8 Students may take several approaches to this construction. Encourage variety. You may need to remind some students that guess-and-check is not a valid construction method.

8.

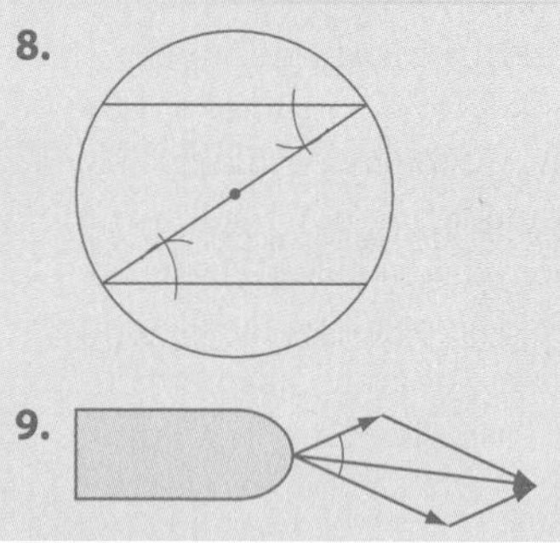

9.

Exercise 10 If students are having difficulty, ask how many blocks high the combined structure is. (They may need to count all the blocks.) If necessary, ask where the L-shaped piece could go. If a Soma Cube puzzle is available, display it for visual help, or let students build the shapes with Multilink cubes.

10.

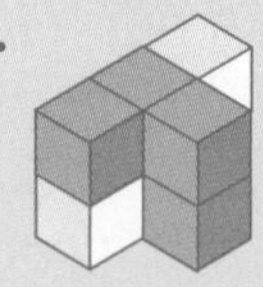

In Exercises 3 and 4, copy the figure and the grid onto patty paper. Show how you can use other patty paper to tessellate the figure on the grid.

3.

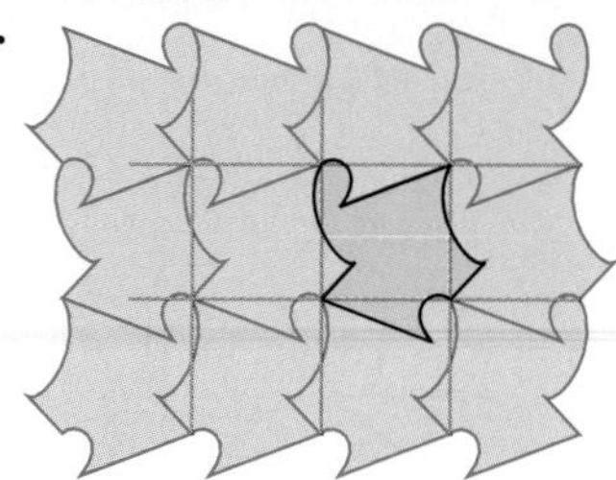

4.

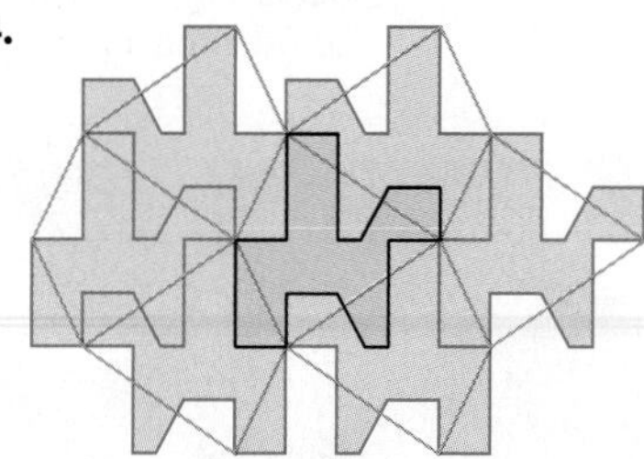

5. Create a glide-reflection tiling design of recognizable shapes by using a grid of kites. Decorate and color your art. ⓗ Answers will vary.

6. Create a glide-reflection tiling design of recognizable shapes by using a grid of parallelograms. Decorate and color your art. Answers will vary.

Review

3.7 **7.** Find the coordinates of the circumcenter and orthocenter of $\triangle FAN$ with $F(6, 0)$, $A(7, 7)$, and $N(3, 9)$. circumcenter is $(3, 4)$; orthocenter is $(10, 8)$

6.1 **8.** ***Construction*** Construct a circle and a chord of the circle. With compass and straightedge construct a second chord parallel and congruent to the first chord.

5.5 **9.** Remy's friends are pulling him on a sled. One of his friends is stronger and exerts more force. The vectors in this diagram represent the forces his two friends exert on him. Copy the vectors, complete the vector parallelogram, and draw the resultant vector force on his sled.

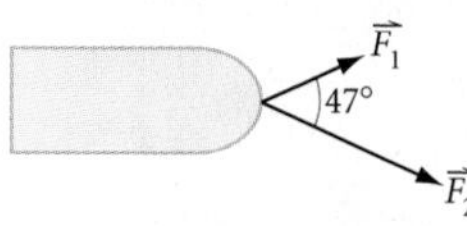

1.8 **10.** The green prism below right was built from the two solids below left. Copy the figure on the right onto isometric dot paper and shade in one of the two pieces to show how the complete figure was created.

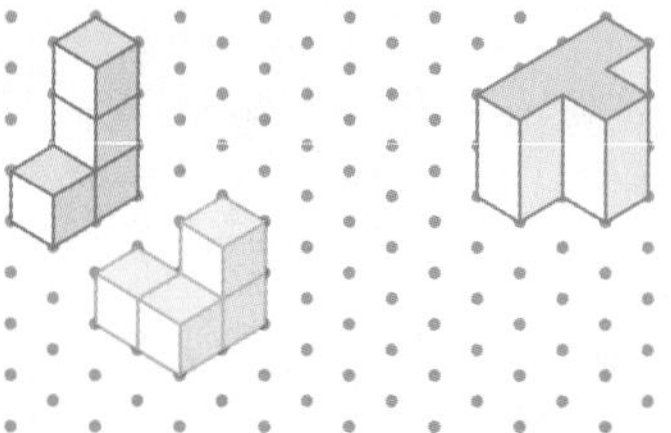

IMPROVING YOUR ALGEBRA SKILLS

Fantasy Functions

If $a \circ b = a^b$ then $3 \circ 2 = 3^2 = 9$,

and if $a \triangle b = a^2 + b^2$ then $5 \triangle 2 = 5^2 + 2^2 = 29$.

If $8 \triangle x = 17 \circ 2$, find x.

IMPROVING ALGEBRA SKILLS

A binary operation is a way of combining two things to get a third. The standard binary operations on numbers are addition, subtraction, multiplication, division, and exponentiation, but this activity shows how to create others out of these standard operations. Solution: $x = \pm 15$

Finding the Orthocenter and Centroid

Suppose you know the coordinates of the vertices of a triangle. You have seen that you can find the coordinates of the circumcenter by writing equations for the perpendicular bisectors of two of the sides and solving the system. Similarly, you can find the coordinates of the orthocenter by finding equations for two lines containing altitudes of the triangle and solving the system.

EXAMPLE A Find the coordinates of the orthocenter of $\triangle PDQ$ with $P(0, -4)$, $D(-4, 4)$, and $Q(8, 4)$.

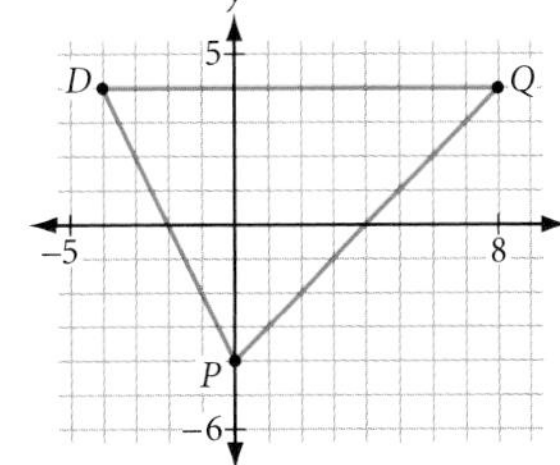

▸ ***Solution*** The altitude of a triangle passes through one vertex and is perpendicular to the opposite side. To find the equation for the altitude from Q to $\overline{PD}$, first you calculate the slope of $\overline{PD}$, getting -2. So the slope of the altitude to $\overline{PD}$ is $\frac{1}{2}$, the negative reciprocal of -2.

The altitude from Q to $\overline{PD}$ passes through point $Q(8, 4)$, so its equation is $\frac{y-4}{x-8} = \frac{1}{2}$. Solving for y gives $y = \frac{1}{2}x$.

Use the same technique to find the equation of the altitude from D to $\overline{PQ}$. The slope of $\overline{PQ}$ is 1. So, the slope of the altitude to $\overline{PQ}$ is -1. The altitude passes through point $D(-4, 4)$, so its equation is $\frac{y-4}{x-(-4)} = -1$, or $y = -x$.

To find the point where the altitudes intersect, use elimination to solve this system.

$$\begin{cases} y = \frac{1}{2}x \\ y = -x \end{cases}$$ Equation of the line containing the altitude from Q to $\overline{PD}$. Equation of the line containing the altitude from D to $\overline{PQ}$.

$0 = \frac{3}{2}x$ Subtract the second equation from the first equation to eliminate y.

$0 = x$ Multiply both sides by $\frac{2}{3}$.

The x-coordinate of the point of the intersection is 0. Substitute 0 for x in either original equation and you will get $y = 0$. So, the orthocenter is $(0, 0)$. You can verify your result by writing the equation of the line containing the third altitude and making sure $(0, 0)$ satisfies it.

You can also find the coordinates of the centroid of a triangle by solving a system of two lines containing medians. However, as you will see in the next example, there is a more efficient method.

USING YOUR ALGEBRA SKILLS 7

PLANNING

LESSON OUTLINE

Partial day:

10 min Examples

5 min Sharing

5 min Closing

15 min Exercises

TEACHING

The orthocenter and centroid of a triangle can be found using coordinate geometry.

▸ ***EXAMPLE A***

The first example reviews the property that the slopes of perpendicular lines are negative reciprocals of each other. Rather than finding the second altitude from vertex D to segment PQ, students might prefer to use the fact that the altitude from vertex P to segment DQ is on the y-axis so the orthocenter must have an x-coordinate of 0. Encourage good observations that can save calculations.

NCTM STANDARDS

CONTENT		PROCESS	
	Number	✓	Problem Solving
✓	Algebra		Reasoning
✓	Geometry		Communication
	Measurement		Connections
	Data/Probability	✓	Representation

LESSON OBJECTIVES

- Use algebra to find the coordinates of a triangle's orthocenter
- Use algebra to find the coordinates of a triangle's centroid

▶ EXAMPLE B

Students may ask why they should find the centroid the hard way when there's an easier way. Remind them that the method of finding centroid by taking the means of the coordinates of the vertices might have grown out of inductive reasoning from data generated the hard way.

SHARING IDEAS

[Ask] "*Why* are the coordinates of the centroid the means of the coordinates of the vertices?" Give students time to discuss this question. You might suggest that students think about the mean of three numbers on a number line to gain insight. The mean is the balance point if the numbers are considered as weights on a beam, just as the centroid of a triangle is its center of mass.

Assessing Progress

You can assess how well students understand the notions of a triangle's centroid and orthocenter, the slopes of perpendicular lines, writing the equation of a line from knowledge of its slope and a point on it, and solving systems of equations.

Closing the Lesson

You can find the coordinates of the orthocenter of a triangle by finding equations of lines perpendicular to two sides and through the opposite vertices and then finding the intersection of these lines. You can find the coordinates of a triangle's centroid by finding the means of its vertices' coordinates.

EXAMPLE B

Consider $\triangle ABC$ with $A(-5, -3)$, $B(3, -5)$, and $C(-1, 2)$.

a. Find the coordinates of the centroid of $\triangle ABC$ by writing equations for two lines containing medians and finding their point of intersection.

b. Find the mean of the x-coordinates and the mean of the y-coordinates of the triangle's vertices. What do you notice?

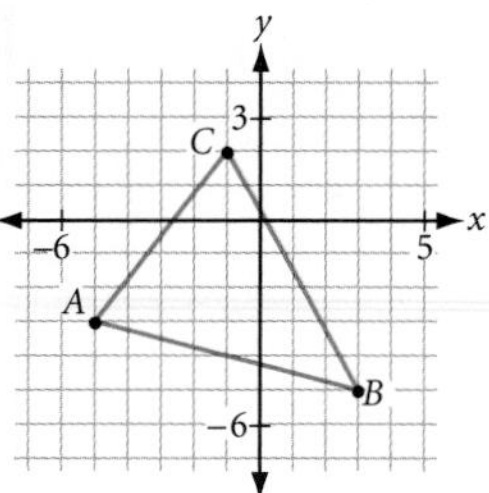

▶ Solution

The median of a triangle joins a vertex with the midpoint of the opposite side.

a. First, find the equation of the line containing the median from A to $\overline{BC}$. The midpoint of $\overline{BC}$ is $\left(1, -\frac{3}{2}\right)$. The slope from $A(-5, -3)$ to this midpoint is $\frac{-3-\left(\frac{-3}{2}\right)}{-5-1}$, or $\frac{1}{4}$. The equation of the line is $\frac{y-(-3)}{x-(-5)} = \frac{1}{4}$. Solving for y gives $y = \frac{1}{4}x - \frac{7}{4}$ as the equation for the median.

Next, find the equation of the line containing the median from $B(3, -5)$ to $\overline{AC}$. The midpoint of $\overline{AC}$ is $\left(-3, -\frac{1}{2}\right)$. The slope is $\frac{-3}{4}$. So you get the equation $\frac{y-(-5)}{x-3} = -\frac{3}{4}$. Solving for y gives $y = -\frac{3}{4}x - \frac{11}{4}$ as the equation for the median.

Finally, use elimination to solve this system.

$$\begin{cases} y = \frac{1}{4}x - \frac{7}{4} \\ y = -\frac{3}{4}x - \frac{11}{4} \end{cases}$$ Equation of the line containing the median from A to $\overline{BC}$. Equation of the line containing the median from B to $\overline{AC}$.

$0 = x + 1$ Subtract the second equation from the first.

$-1 = x$ Subtract 1 from both sides.

The x-coordinate of the point of intersection is -1. Use substitution to find the y-coordinate.

$y = \frac{1}{4}(-1) - \frac{7}{4}$ Substitute -1 for x in the first equation.

$y = -2$ Simplify.

The centroid is $(-1, -2)$. You can verify your result by writing the equation for the third median and making sure $(-1, -2)$ satisfies it.

b. The mean of the x-coordinates is $\frac{-5+3+(-1)}{3} = \frac{-3}{3} = -1$.

The mean of the y-coordinates is $\frac{-3+(-5)+2}{3} = \frac{-6}{3} = -2$.

Notice that these means give you the coordinates of the centroid: $(-1, -2)$.

You can generalize the findings from Example B to all triangles. The easiest way to find the coordinates of the centroid is to find the mean of the vertex coordinates.

EXERCISES

In Exercises 1 and 2, use $\triangle RES$ with vertices $R(0, 0)$, $E(4, -6)$, and $S(8, 4)$.

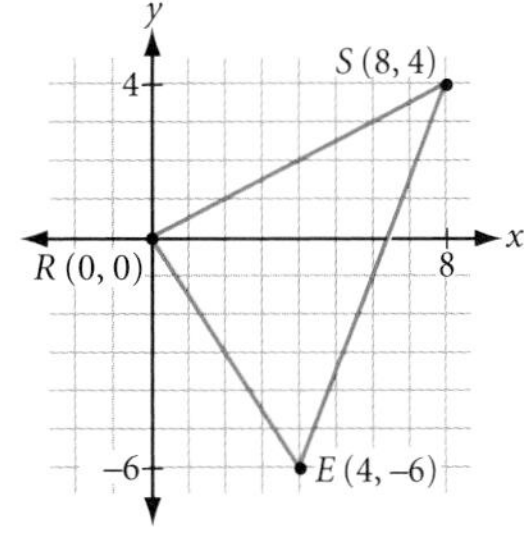

1. Find the equation of the line containing the median from R to $\overline{ES}$. $y = -\frac{1}{6}x$

2. Find the equation of the line containing the altitude from E to $\overline{RS}$. $y = -2x + 2$

In Exercises 3 and 4, use algebra to find the coordinates of the centroid and the orthocenter for each triangle.

3. Right triangle *MNO*

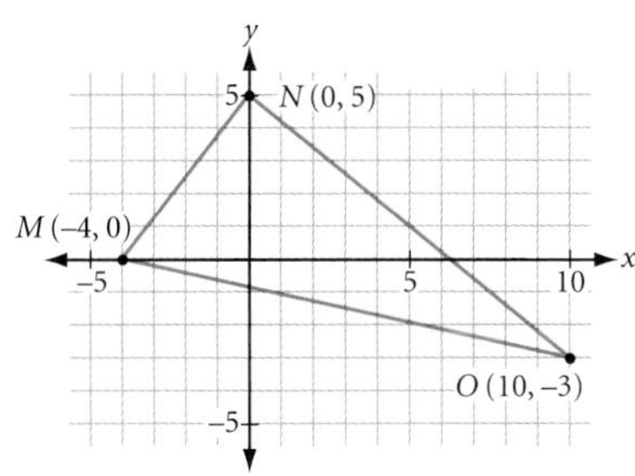

Centroid is $\left(2, \frac{2}{3}\right)$; orthocenter is $(0, 5)$.

4. Isosceles triangle *CDE*

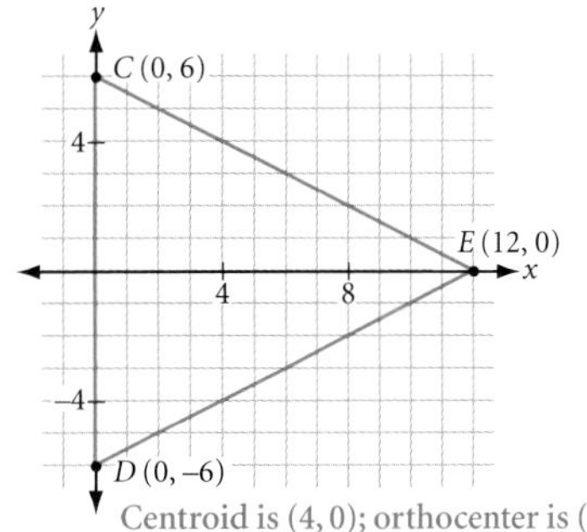

Centroid is $(4, 0)$; orthocenter is $(3, 0)$.

5. Find the coordinates of the centroid of the triangle formed by the x-axis, the y-axis, and the line $12x + 9y = 36$. $\left(1, \frac{4}{3}\right)$

6. The three lines $8x + 3y = 12$, $6y - 7x = 24$, and $x + 9y + 33 = 0$ intersect to form a triangle. Find the coordinates of its centroid. $(-1, -1)$

IMPROVING YOUR VISUAL THINKING SKILLS

Painted Faces I

Suppose some unit cubes are assembled into a large cube, then some of the faces of this large cube are painted. After the paint dries, the large cube is disassembled into the unit cubes and you discover that 32 of these have no paint on any of their faces. How many faces of the large cube were painted?

BUILDING UNDERSTANDING

The exercises give students practice in finding the centroid and orthocenter of various triangles.

ASSIGNING HOMEWORK

Essential	1, 2, 3, 5
Performance assessment	6
Group	4

Helping with the Exercises

Exercises 3–5 Students might graph the special points and then approximate their coordinates by reading the graph.

Exercise 3 Remind students that the legs of a right triangle are two of the altitudes.

Exercise 4 Remind students that in an isosceles triangle the median from the vertex angle is also an altitude. In isosceles triangles, this median/altitude lies on the Euler line. Therefore both the centroid and the orthocenter lie on that segment.

Exercise 5 Refer to Example B, part b.

Exercise 6 Encourage students to graph the triangle. If students are confused, **[Ask]** "What do you need to know to proceed?" [the coordinates of the vertices, which are intersections of lines]

IMPROVING VISUAL THINKING SKILLS

Inside the cube is a smaller cube with two fewer unit cubes on each side; these will have no painted faces. The large cube has more than 3 cubes on each edge, because 32 is more than $3^3 = 27$. And it doesn't have 6 cubes on each edge, because then $4^3 = 64$ cubes in the middle would be completely unpainted. Thus the cube contains $4^3 = 64$ or $5^3 = 125$ unit cubes. In the latter case, there will be 27 unpainted interior cubes so the painting must avoid exactly 5 cubes in the outer layer. If even one face is unpainted, 9 cubes will remain clear. Therefore the large cube must be 4 by 4 by 4. If one face of this large cube is painted, then 16 unit cubes are painted on one face. If two opposite faces are painted, then 32 unit cubes are painted, so 32 remain unpainted. Alternatively, students might consider the 8 interior cubes that are necessarily unpainted and see how to arrive at 24 unpainted unit cubes in the outer layer.

PLANNING

LESSON OUTLINE

One day:

10 min Reviewing

25 min Exercises

10 min Student self-assessment

MATERIALS

- Reviewing Tessellations (T) for Review

REVIEWING

To review the ideas of this chapter, show the Reviewing Tessellations transparency. **[Ask]** "What are pictures like this called?" [tessellations] "What geometric shape makes up the underlying grid?" [parallelograms or rhombuses] Then turn students' attention to how the figure was made. **[Ask]** "What isometries were used?" [reflection, translation, rotation] "How could the tessellation have been done with just reflections?" [reflecting over parallel lines to get a translation; reflecting over intersecting lines to achieve a rotation] "How does the construction of each tile determine the kind of symmetry the entire tessellation has?" [Because of reflections, translations, and rotations, it has glide-reflectional, translational, and rotational symmetry.]

Also review the Reflection Line Conjecture and the Minimal Path Conjecture.

CHAPTER 7 REVIEW

How is your memory? In this chapter you learned about rigid transformations in the plane—called isometries—and you revisited the principles of symmetry that you first learned in Chapter 0. You applied these concepts to create tessellations. Can you name the three rigid transformations? Can you describe how to compose transformations to make other transformations? How can you use reflections to improve your miniature-golf game? What types of symmetry do regular polygons have? What types of polygons will tile the plane? Review this chapter to be sure you can answer these questions.

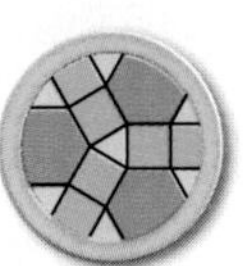

EXERCISES

For Exercises 1–12, identify each statement as true or false. For each false statement, sketch a counterexample or explain why it is false.

1. The two transformations in which the orientation (the order of points as you move clockwise) does not change are translation and rotation. true
2. The two transformations in which the image has the opposite orientation from the original are reflection and glide reflection. true
3. A translation of (5, 12) followed by a translation of $(-8, -6)$ is equivalent to a single translation of $(-3, 6)$. true
4. A rotation of 140° followed by a rotation of 260° about the same point is equivalent to a single rotation of 40° about that point. true
5. A reflection across a line followed by a second reflection across a parallel line that is 12 cm from the first is equivalent to a translation of 24 cm. true
6. A regular n-gon has n reflectional symmetries and n rotational symmetries. true
7. The only three regular polygons that create monohedral tessellations are equilateral triangles, squares, and regular pentagons.
8. Any triangle can create a monohedral tessellation. true
9. Any quadrilateral can create a monohedral tessellation. true
10. No pentagon can create a monohedral tessellation. False; two counterexamples are given in Lesson 7.5.
11. No hexagon can create a monohedral tessellation.
12. There are at least three times as many true statements as false statements in Exercises 1–12.

King by Minnie Evans (1892–1987)

ASSIGNING HOMEWORK

All the problems are good opportunities for group discussion, but you may want to assign the odd exercises for individual work and the even exercises for group work.

7. False; a regular pentagon does not create a monohedral tessellation and a regular hexagon does.

11. False; any hexagon with all opposite sides parallel and congruent will create a monohedral tessellation.

12. This statement can be both true and false.

In Exercises 13–15, identify the type or types of symmetry, including the number of symmetries, in each design. For Exercise 15, describe how you can move candles on the menorah to make the colors symmetrical, too.

13.

Mandala,
Gary Chen, geometry student
6-fold rotational symmetry

14.

translational symmetry

15.

16. The façade of Chartres Cathedral in France does not have reflectional symmetry. Why not? Sketch the portion of the façade that does have bilateral symmetry.

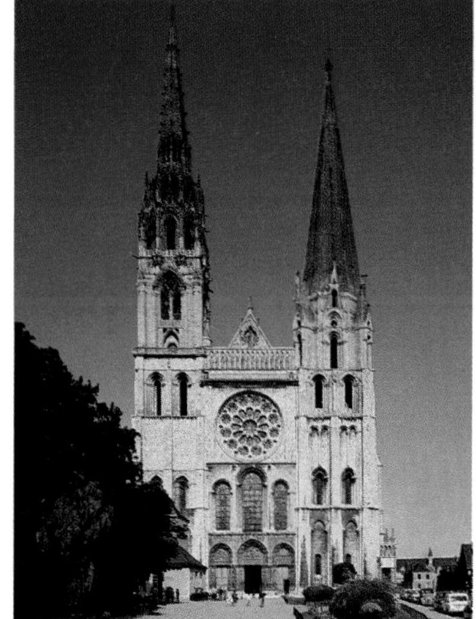

17. Find or create a logo that has reflectional symmetry. Sketch the logo and its line or lines of reflectional symmetry. Answers will vary.

18. Find or create a logo that has rotational symmetry but not reflectional symmetry. Sketch it. Answers will vary.

In Exercises 19 and 20, classify the tessellation and give the vertex arrangement.

19. $3^6/3^2.4.3.4$; 2-uniform

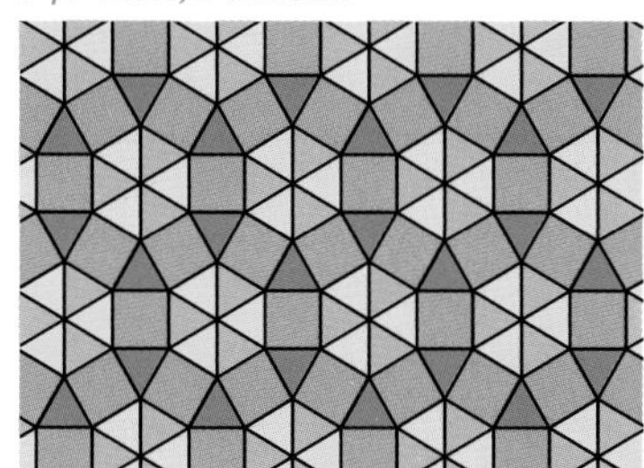

20. 4.8^2; semiregular

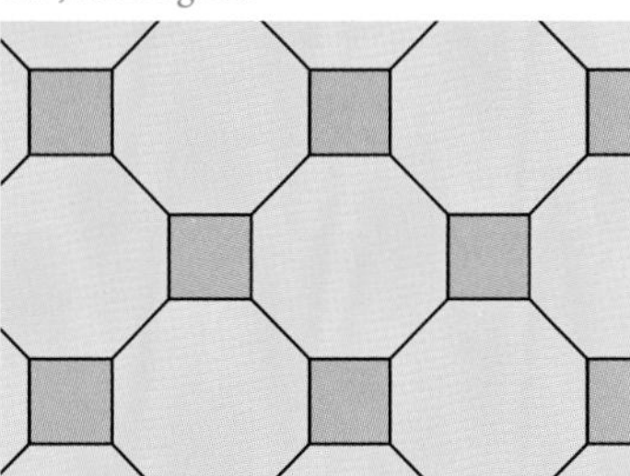

▶ Helping with the Exercises

Exercise 12 This statement could be either true or false. (In contrast a paradox can be neither true nor false because if it's true it's false, and if it's false it's true.) If you say this statement is true, then 9 of the 12 statements are true, making at least three times as many true. If you say it's false, then only 8 of the 12 statements are true, so fewer than three times as many are true.

15. Reflectional; color arrangements will vary, but the white candle must be in the middle.

16. The two towers are not the reflection (or even the translation) of each other. Each tower individually has bilateral symmetry. The center portion has bilateral symmetry.

21, 22. Explanations might be visual (see below) but should also include a text reference to the Minimal Path Conjecture.

21. Experiment with a mirror to find the smallest vertical portion (y) in which you can still see your full height (x). How does y compare to x? Can you explain, with the help of a diagram and what you know about reflections, why a "full-length" mirror need not be as tall as you? See below.

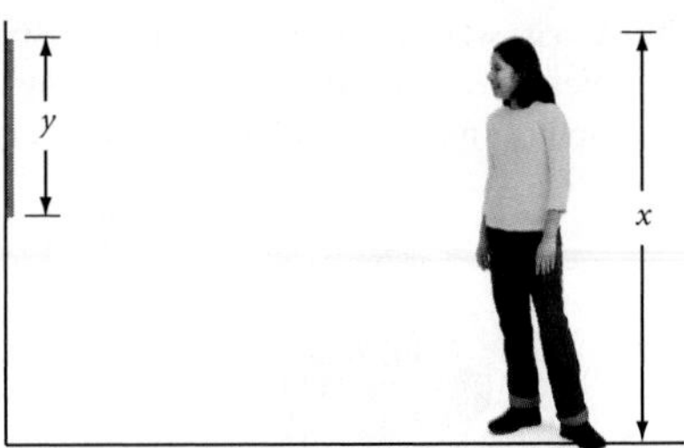

22. Miniature-golf pro Sandy Trapp wishes to impress her fans with a hole in one on the very first try. How should she hit the ball at T to achieve this feat? Explain. See below.

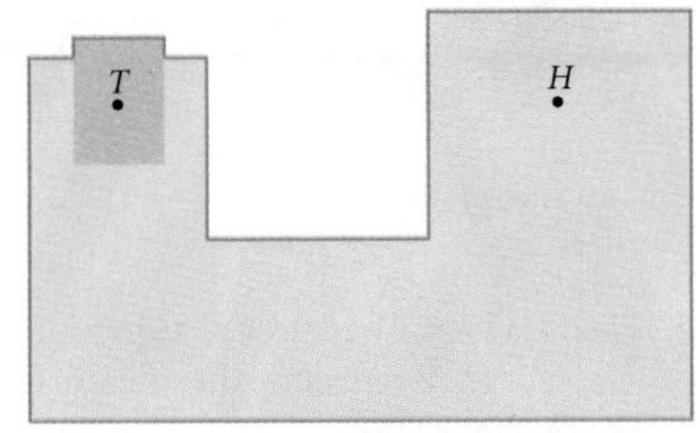

In Exercises 23–25, identify the shape of the tessellation grid and a possible method that the student used to create each tessellation.

23.

Perian Warriors, Robert Bell
Use a grid of squares. Tessellate by translation.

24.

Doves, Serene Tam
Use a grid of equilateral triangles. Tessellate by rotation.

25.

Sightings,
Peter Chua and Monica Grant
Use a grid of parallelograms. Tessellate by glide reflection.

In Exercises 26 and 27, copy the figure and grid onto patty paper. Determine whether or not you can use the figure to create a tessellation on the grid. Explain your reasoning.

26.

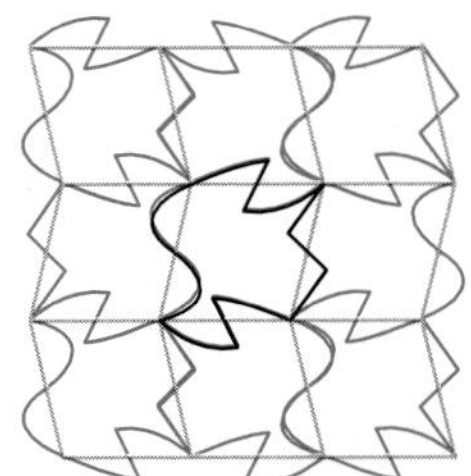

27.

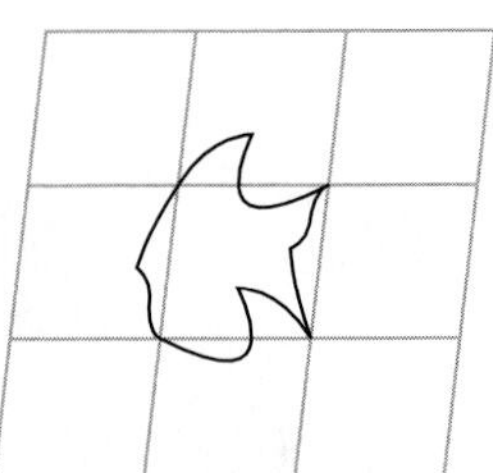

26. Yes. It is a glide reflection for one pair of sides and midpoint rotation for the other two sides.

27. No. Because the shape is suitable for glide reflection, the rows of parallelograms should alternate the direction in which they lean (row 1 leans right, row 2 leans left, row 3 leans right, and so on).

21. $y = \frac{1}{2}x$ **22.**

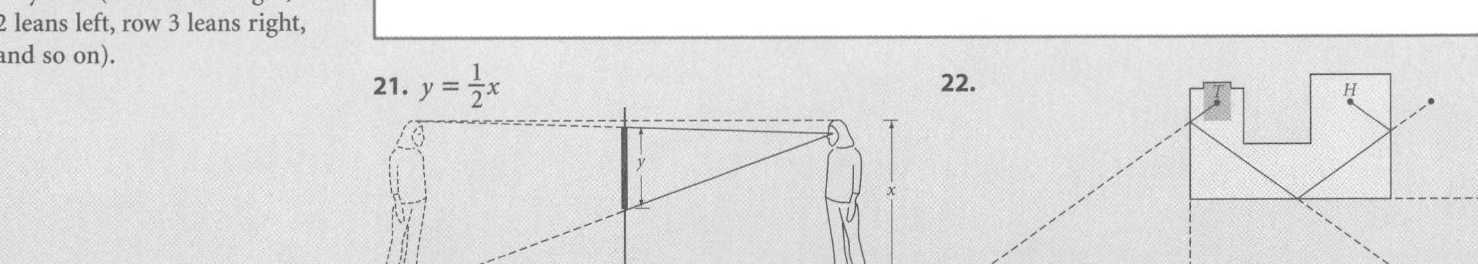

28.

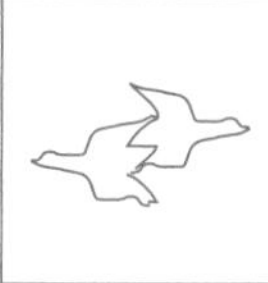

28. In his woodcut *Day and Night,* Escher gradually changes the shape of the patches of farmland into black and white birds. The birds are flying in opposite directions, so they appear to be glide reflections of each other. But notice that the tails of the white birds curve down, while the tails of the black birds curve up. So, on closer inspection, it's clear that this is not a glide-reflection tiling at all!

When two birds are taken together as one tile (a 2-motif tile), they create a translation tessellation. Use patty paper to find the 2-motif tile.

Day and Night, M. C. Escher, 1938

Career **CONNECTION**

Commercial tile contractors use tessellating polygons to create attractive designs for their customers. Some designs are 1-uniform or 2-uniform, and others are even more complex.

ASSESSING

Although a test is available for this chapter, you would do well to grade your students' tessellation artwork as equivalent to a chapter test grade. Then you could use the unit test on Chapters 4–6, if you didn't after Chapter 6.

FACILITATING SELF-ASSESSMENT

To help students complete the portfolio described in Assessing What You've Learned, suggest that they consider for evaluation their work on Lesson 7.4, Exercise 9, 11, or 12; Lesson 7.5, Exercise 2; Lesson 7.6, Exercise 9 or 10; Lesson 7.7, Exercise 5 or 6; and Lesson 7.8, Exercise 5 or 6.

Assessing What You've Learned

Try one or more of these assessment suggestions.

UPDATE YOUR PORTFOLIO Choose one of the tessellations you did in this chapter and add it to your portfolio. Describe why you chose it and explain the transformations you used and the types of symmetry it has.

ORGANIZE YOUR NOTEBOOK Review your notebook to be sure it's complete and well organized. Are all the types of transformation and symmetry included in your definition list or conjecture list? Write a one-page chapter summary.

WRITE IN YOUR JOURNAL This chapter emphasizes applying geometry to create art. Write about connections you see between geometry and art. Does creating geometric art give you a greater appreciation for either art or geometry? Explain.

PERFORMANCE ASSESSMENT While a classmate, a friend, a family member, or a teacher observes, carry out one of the investigations from this chapter. Explain what you're doing at each step, including how you arrive at the conjecture.

GIVE A PRESENTATION Give a presentation about one of the investigations or projects you did or about one of the tessellations you created.

CHAPTER

8

Area

Overview

In **Lessons 8.1, 8.2, 8.4,** and **8.5,** students discover formulas for finding the areas of rectangles, parallelograms, triangles, trapezoids, kites, regular polygons, and circles by cutting apart and rearranging these figures to derive new formulas from previously discovered ones. Beyond simply plugging numbers into formulas, students should be able to describe the process by which they arrived at the formulas. Advanced students should also be able to demonstrate the algebra that supports the discoveries.

Problem solving is emphasized in **Lesson 8.3,** where the problems may require several steps. Be prepared to offer extra help to students whose English skills are limited, but don't shy away from assigning the problems. The **exploration** on Pick's formula introduces a way to estimate area. Students combine formulas from earlier lessons as they explore areas of parts of circles in **Lesson 8.6** and surface area in **Lesson 8.7.** An **exploration** on probability precedes Lesson 8.7, and a Sketchpad **exploration** examining other ways of calculating area concludes the chapter.

The Mathematics

Area

Some students will say, "Oh, area. That's *lw.*" An emphasis on memorizing area formulas may have misled your students into thinking they understand area. The meaning lies not in *what* the formulas are but rather in understanding *why* the formulas are what they are. You can open your students' minds to ideas about area that go beyond formulas they may already have seen. Here are some examples:

- The statement "A rectangle does not have area" is true. The rectangle consists of four line segments, each with area zero. In particular, the shapes we've been studying don't include their interiors. So the phrase "the area of a rectangle" is shorthand for "the area of the region bounded by the rectangle."
- Can a figure have more than one area? A quick response might be "Of course not." But isn't the area of a figure in square centimeters different from its area in square yards? On the other hand, if a shape can have different areas, why do we instinctively feel that it has only one? Could it be that we're using the term *area* in a different sense, to mean a region rather than a number that denotes the measure of a region?
- What happens to formulas if the measurement units are converted to other units? Does the formula for the area of a trapezoid, memorized with great effort, continue to apply when we change the length measurements from centimeters to miles? If so, why? Students may not have a deep understanding of this idea.
- Even the ancient Greeks knew that the ratio of the circumference of a circle to its diameter was constant, the value we now call π. But they did not realize that π also appears in a formula for the area of a circle. Why does it?

An abstract definition of *area,* beyond the understanding of most students at van Hiele level 2, is as a function that assigns to each two-dimensional geometric shape a nonnegative real number so that (1) the area of every point is zero, (2) the areas of congruent figures are equal, and (3) if a shape is partitioned into subregions, then the sum of the areas of those subregions equals the area of the shape. There are infinitely many such functions, so shapes can have infinitely many areas. Despite its abstraction, this definition points to two other ideas about areas that might surprise some of your students:

- If a triangle or parallelogram is rotated so that a different side is considered the base, does the area formula necessarily give the same result? In general, under what transformations is the area conserved? Some students may not be too sure.
- What if a rectangle is cut into pieces that are then rearranged to make, say, a parallelogram? Will the area really be the same? If you pause to raise the question, you may find that your students have a lot of doubt.

Surface Area

Just as a rectangle doesn't include its area, a geometric solid doesn't include its interior. We can talk about the volume of a solid—as we will in Chapter 10—but we won't mean the volume of the solid itself but rather the volume of the region enclosed by the solid. In most uses of the term *solid,* its boundary (the interiors of the polygons formed by its edges) is part of the solid. Surface area is the area of that boundary.

Help students learn the terminology of solids. The term *sides* applies to polygons. For solids, refer to *faces* and *edges* as well as *vertices.*

Using This Chapter

Near the end of the chapter, assign and discuss Improving Your Visual Thinking Skills: Cover the Square as preparation for Chapter 9. Plan to use two days for the chapter review, perhaps doing the explorations in class on one of those days and sharing results and questions about the review on the other day.

Resources

Discovering Geometry Resources

Teaching and Worksheet Masters
  Lessons 8.1, 8.3, 8.6, and 8.7
  Exploration: Pick's Formula for Area

Sketchpad Demonstration
  Lesson 8.2

Discovering Geometry with The Geometer's Sketchpad
  Lessons 8.1, 8.2, 8.4, and 8.5

Assessment Resources A and B
  Quiz 1 (Lessons 8.1 and 8.2)
  Quiz 2 (Lessons 8.3–8.5)
  Quiz 3 (Lessons 8.6 and 8.7)
  Chapter 8 Test
  Chapter 8 Constructive Assessment Options

Practice Your Skills for Chapter 8

Condensed Lessons for Chapter 8

Other Resources

Data in Depth by Tim Erickson.

For complete references to this and other resources, see www.keypress.com/DG.

Materials

- construction tools
- scissors
- heavy paper or cardboard
- rulers
- protractors
- calculators
- geoboards, *optional*
- graph paper, *optional*

Pacing Guide

	day 1	day 2	day 3	day 4	day 5	day 6	day 7	day 8	day 9	day 10
standard	8.1	8.2	quiz, 8.3	8.4	Exploration	8.5	quiz, 8.6	Exploration	8.7	Exploration
enriched	8.1	8.2, project	quiz, 8.3	8.4	Exploration	8.5	quiz, 8.6	project, Exploration	8.7	Exploration, quiz
block	8.1, 8.2	quiz, 8.3, 8.4	Exploration, 8.5	quiz, 8.6, Exploration	8.7	Exploration, IYVTS, quiz	review, TAL	TAL, assessment		

	day 11	day 12	day 13	day 14	day 15	day 16	day 17	day 18	day 19	day 20
standard	quiz, IYVTS	review	review	assessment						
enriched	IYVTS, Exploration	review, TAL	review, TAL	assessment						

CHAPTER

8 Area

I could fill an entire second life with working on my prints.

M. C. ESCHER

Square Limit, M. C. Escher, 1964

OBJECTIVES

In this chapter you will

- discover area formulas for rectangles, parallelograms, triangles, trapezoids, kites, regular polygons, circles, and other shapes
- use area formulas to solve problems
- learn how to find the surface areas of prisms, pyramids, cylinders, and cones

In *Square Limit,* Escher refers to a geometry in which the external and internal measurements of size differ. Viewed externally, the areas of the fish change as they move away from the center. But so would the lengths of any rulers they were carrying. Therefore the fish themselves internally could detect no change in their sizes. There is much to be learned about size (area) beyond formulas.

[Ask] "At the center is a square consisting of fins from four fish. Where and how is that square repeated?" [along the diagonals with one white fin, two red (or green) fins, and one green (or red) fin] "Why do you think the artist chose the title *Square Limit*?" [The artwork is square; the size of the fish approaches a limit of zero near the outside edges.] **[Link]** Limit is a fundamental concept in calculus.

CHAPTER 8 OBJECTIVES

- Develop the concept of area
- Derive formulas and methods for finding the areas of rectangles, parallelograms, triangles, trapezoids, kites, regular polygons, circles, sectors, segments, and annuluses
- Discover Pick's formula for finding the area of an irregular figure drawn on a grid
- Discover methods for finding the surface areas of solids
- Review terminology for solids
- Learn new vocabulary
- Solve area application problems using various problem-solving strategies
- Clarify approximation concepts
- Practice visual thinking in three dimensions
- Develop reading comprehension and cooperative behavior
- Practice using geometry tools
- Practice measuring
- Practice estimation

LESSON

8.1

PLANNING

LESSON OUTLINE

One day:

10 min Investigation

5 min Examples

15 min Sharing

15 min Closing and Exercises

MATERIALS

- construction tools
- scissors
- heavy paper
- graph paper, *optional*
- geoboards, *optional*
- Parallelogram (W) for One step

TEACHING

In this lesson you can deepen students' understanding of the area of a figure while they encounter some formulas that might already be familiar to them.

One step Hand out a copy of the Parallelogram worksheet to each student. Challenge groups to find the area of the figure in as many ways as they can. Some students may remember a formula but have difficulty deciding which edge should be the base. Others may see the figure as a union of triangles or as the result of removing triangles from a rectangle. Others may copy it onto graph paper and count squares. Others may cut it up and rearrange pieces. If some of these ideas aren't emerging from any group, you might plant the ideas when you visit groups that are ahead of the others. During Sharing, **[Ask]** "Should all the answers be the same?" [Answers might differ due to the inexactness in counting or measuring. They will also differ if different measurement units are used.]

LESSON

8.1

Areas of Rectangles and Parallelograms

A little learning is a dangerous thing—almost as dangerous as a lot of ignorance.

ANONYMOUS

People work with areas in many occupations. Carpenters calculate the areas of walls, floors, and roofs before they purchase materials for construction. Painters calculate surface areas so that they know how much paint to buy for a job. Decorators calculate the areas of floors and windows to know how much carpeting and drapery they will need. In this chapter you will discover formulas for finding the areas of the regions within triangles, parallelograms, trapezoids, kites, regular polygons, and circles.

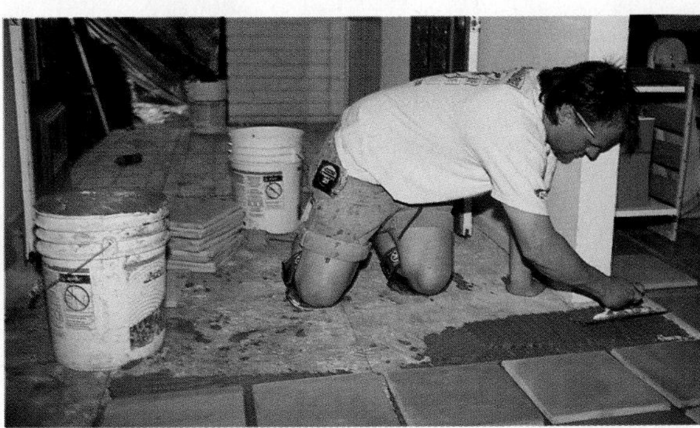

Tile layers need to find floor area to determine how many tiles to buy.

The **area** of a plane figure is the measure of the region enclosed by the figure. You measure the area of a figure by counting the number of square units that you can arrange to fill the figure completely.

1

Length: 1 unit

1 1

Area: 1 square unit

You probably already know many area formulas. Think of the investigations in this chapter as physical demonstrations of the formulas that will help you understand and remember them.

It's easy to find the area of a rectangle.

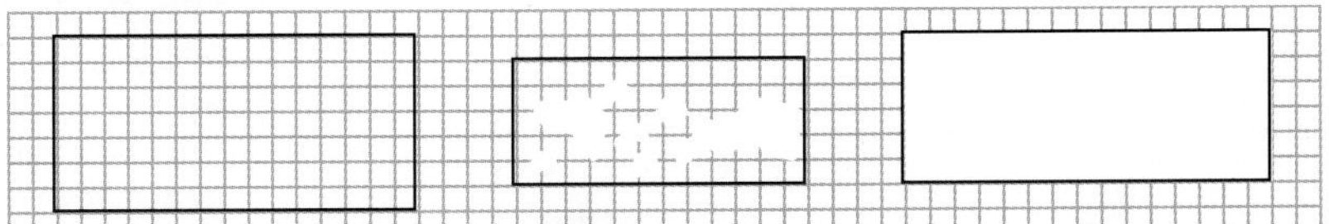

To find the area of the first rectangle, you can simply count squares. To find the areas of the other rectangles, you could draw in the lines and count the squares, but there's an easier method.

INTRODUCTION

Ask what students know about area. Many will say, "Area is lw." Bring out the idea that they may be thinking of a formula for measuring the area of a rectangle. Discuss the idea that *area* often means a number associated with the region enclosed by the shape. If students find the area by counting the number of squares, they may not get an integer. You might challenge students to draw on graph paper a rectangle whose sides don't have integer lengths and see how the fractional parts accumulate with the whole numbers when the rows are counted.

Any side of a rectangle can be called a **base.** A rectangle's **height** is the length of the side that is perpendicular to the base. For each pair of parallel bases, there is a corresponding height.

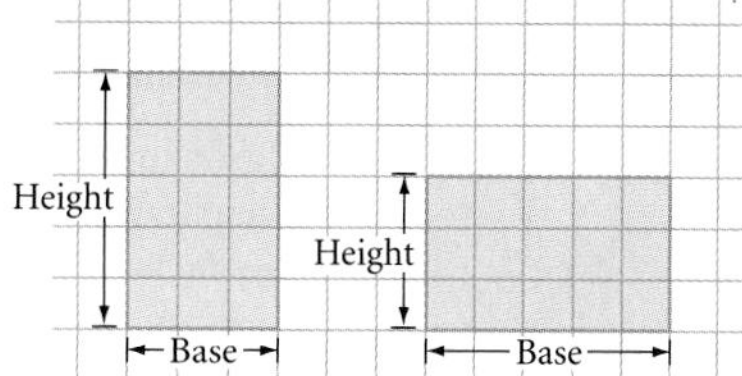

If we call the bottom side of each rectangle in the figure the base, then the length of the base is the number of squares in each row and the height is the number of rows. So you can use these terms to state a formula for the area. Add this conjecture to your list.

Rectangle Area Conjecture

C-75

The area of a rectangle is given by the formula $\underline{?}$ ($A = bh$), where A is the area, b is the length of the base, and h is the height of the rectangle.

The area formula for rectangles can help you find the areas of many other shapes.

EXAMPLE A

Find the area of this shape.

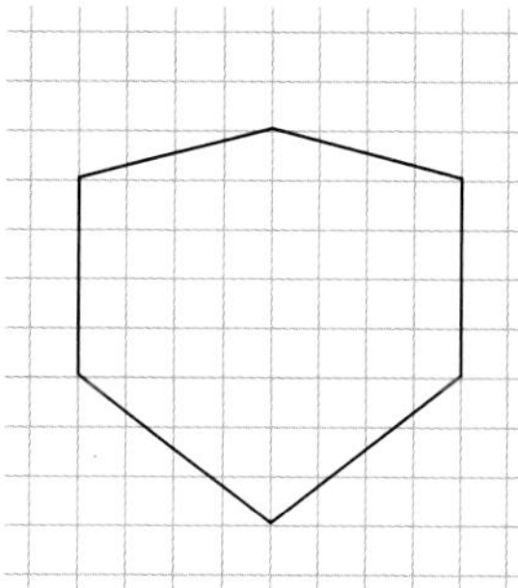

Solution

The middle section is a rectangle with an area of $4 \cdot 8$, or 32 square units.

You can divide the remaining pieces into right triangles, so each piece is actually half a rectangle.

The area of the figure is $32 + 2(2) + 2(6) = 48$ square units.

There are other ways to find the area of this figure. One way is to find the area of an 8-by-8 square and subtract the areas of four right triangles.

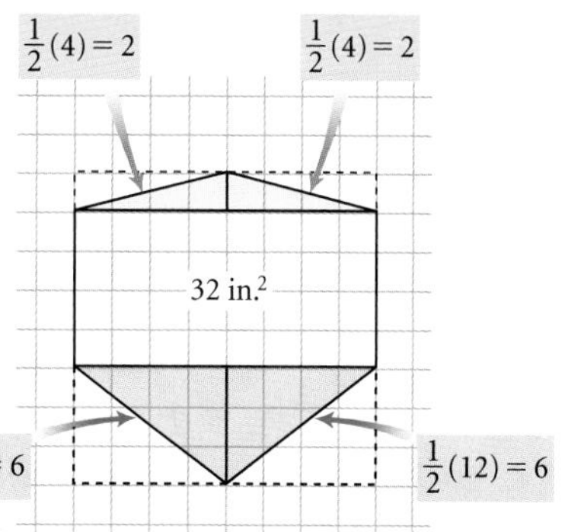

Going back to the familiar formula, **[Ask]** "What do l and w stand for?" Then ask students how they figure out which side is the length and which is the width. **[Language]** The dictionary defines *length* as "the measure of the greatest dimension of a plane or solid figure." *Width* is often used for the shorter of the two sides. Because the area of a rectangle is the product of two adjacent sides' lengths, this book uses *base* and *height* to eliminate associating a term with a particular size. **[Language]** *Base* refers both to the segment and to its measure. Caution students that a base segment might not be horizontal; in fact, the figure might be drawn with no horizontal sides.

The number of squares does not have to be an integer. Have students draw and explain another example.

EXAMPLE A

Encourage students to estimate the area before reading the solution.

[Ask] "What would the area of the shape be if the bottom vertex were moved two units to the left?" [The area remains the same. 48 in.²]

NCTM STANDARDS

CONTENT	PROCESS
Number	✓ Problem Solving
✓ Algebra	✓ Reasoning
✓ Geometry	✓ Communication
✓ Measurement	✓ Connections
✓ Data/Probability	✓ Representation

LESSON OBJECTIVES

- Develop the concept of area
- Derive formulas for the areas of a rectangle and a parallelogram
- Apply area formulas to solve problems
- Review vocabulary

You can also use the area formula for a rectangle to find the area formula for a parallelogram.

Just as with a rectangle, any side of a parallelogram can be called a base. But the height of a parallelogram is not necessarily the length of a side. An **altitude** is any segment from one side of a parallelogram perpendicular to a line through the opposite side. The length of the altitude is the **height.**

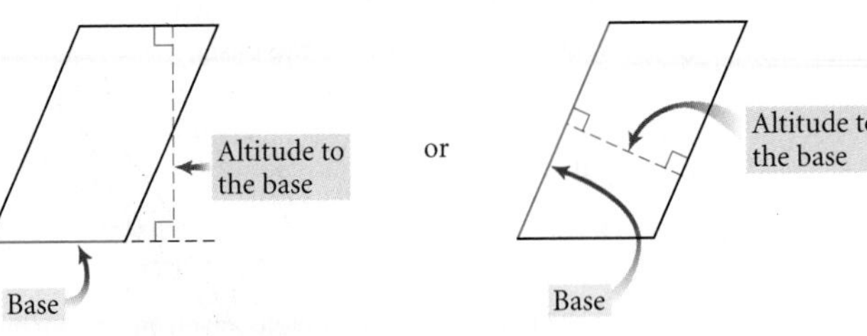

The altitude can be inside or outside the parallelogram. No matter where you draw the altitude to a base, its height should be the same, because the opposite sides are parallel.

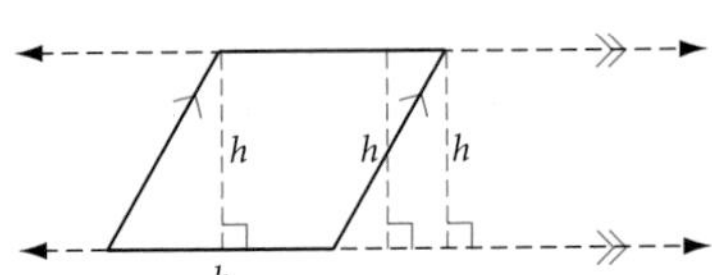

Investigation
Area Formula for Parallelograms

You will need

- heavy paper or cardboard
- a straightedge
- a compass

Using heavy paper, investigate the area of a parallelogram. Can the area be rearranged into a more familiar shape? Different members of your group should investigate different parallelograms so you can be sure your formula works for all parallelograms.

Step 1 Construct a parallelogram on a piece of heavy paper or cardboard. From the vertex of the obtuse angle adjacent to the base, draw an altitude to the side opposite the base. Label the parallelogram as shown.

Step 2 Cut out the parallelogram and then cut along the altitude. You will have two pieces—a triangle and a trapezoid. Try arranging the two pieces into other shapes without overlapping them. Is the area of each of these new shapes the same as the area of the original parallelogram? Why?

Step 2 Yes, because no area was lost or gained.

Step 3 Is one of your new shapes a rectangle? Calculate the area of this rectangle. What is the area of the original parallelogram? State your next conjecture.

Parallelogram Area Conjecture C-76

The area of a parallelogram is given by the formula _?_ ($A = bh$), where A is the area, b is the length of the base, and h is the height of the parallelogram.

Guiding the Investigation

You might use the investigation as a follow-along activity or have a student demonstrate it to the class. You might also wish to extend or replace this investigation with the dynamic geometry exploration at www.keymath.com/DG.

Step 1 As needed, remind students that an altitude of a parallelogram is a perpendicular segment from one side to a non-adjacent side (or to a line containing the side).

Step 2 If students cut along a perpendicular that's not through a vertex, ask them to present their approach for critique during Sharing.

SHARING IDEAS

As students present their ideas, ask *why* the parallelogram and the rectangle have the same area. The area of each is the sum of the areas of its parts. (You might mention that this is often called the *Area Addition Postulate.* It is the basis of most of the informal derivations of area formulas in the chapter.)

[Ask] "Is there more than one way to cut up the parallelogram so that its pieces can be rearranged into a rectangle?" [Cut through the parallelogram along any altitude from one base to the other.]

Ask which of the sides of the parallelogram could be taken to be the base. Draw an altitude to another side and ask whether the product of that base and height will be the same as the product of the original base and height. You need not answer this question now; it can be revisited in Chapter 9.

Ask whether it's easier to count squares to find the area of the rectangle than it is to count squares of the parallelogram. Some students may think so, but let them see that, as in a rectangle, each row of the parallelogram has the same number of squares. In fact, they may see that those rows can simply be shifted and lined up to make the corresponding rows of the rectangle.

Bring up the idea of measurement units. **[Ask]** "When we say that a parallelogram has area ninety, what are the units?" [It depends on the units of length by which the linear dimensions are measured. If the base and height are in cm, then the area is in cm^2; 90 cm^2 means that 90 squares 1 cm on a side could fit into the parallelogram, with cutting and rearranging.] "What's the difference between ninety square centimeters and ninety centimeters squared?" [The former refers to 90 squares, each 1 centimeter on a side. The latter is the square of 90 cm, or 8100 cm^2.] The exponent on the unit cm^2 refers to the cm, not to the number. To reduce confusion, the notation cm^2 should be read "square centimeters," not "centimeters squared."

[Ask] "How are the parallelogram and the rectangle the same, and how are they different?" [One pair of

If the dimensions of a figure are measured in inches, feet, or yards, the area is measured in in.^{2} (square inches), ft^2 (square feet), or yd^2 (square yards). If the dimensions are measured in centimeters or meters, the area is measured in cm^2 (square centimeters) or m^2 (square meters). Let's look at an example.

EXAMPLE B

Find the height of a parallelogram that has area 7.13 m^2 and base length 2.3 m.

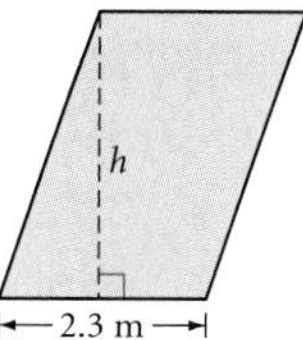

▶ Solution

$A = bh$ Write the formula.

$7.13 = (2.3)h$ Substitute the known values.

$\frac{7.13}{2.3} = h$ Solve for the height.

$h = 3.1$ Divide.

The height measures 3.1 m.

EXERCISES

In Exercises 1–6, each quadrilateral is a rectangle. A represents area and P represents perimeter. Use the appropriate unit in each answer.

1. $A =$? 228 m^2

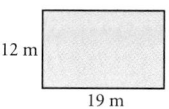

2. $A =$? 41.85 cm^2

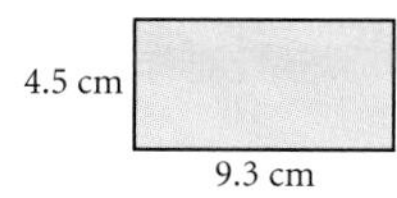

3. $A = 96$ yd^2
$b =$? 8 yd

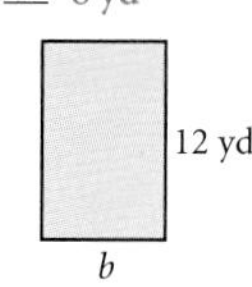

4. $A = 273$ cm^2
$h =$? 21 cm

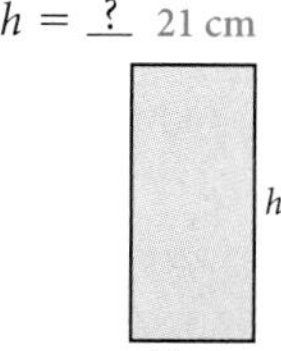

5. $P = 40$ ft
$A =$? 91 ft^2

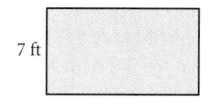

6. Shaded area = ? 182 m^2

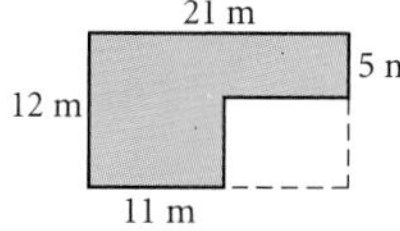

In Exercises 7–9, each quadrilateral is a parallelogram.

7. $A =$? 96 in.^{2}

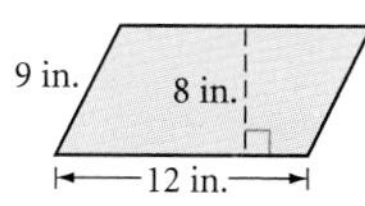

8. $A = 2508$ cm^2
$P =$? 210 cm

44 cm
48 cm

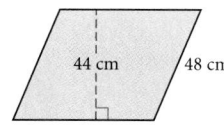

9. Find the area of the shaded region. $A = 42$ ft^2

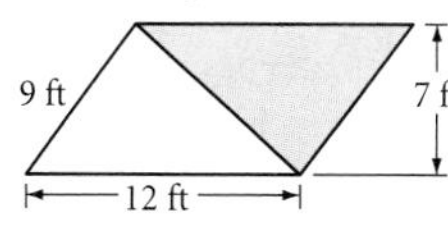

Sharing Ideas (continued)

opposite sides of the parallelogram is congruent to a pair of opposite sides of the rectangle, the heights and areas are the same, but the angles and nonbase sides of the parallelogram are not congruent to their corresponding parts on the rectangle.] **[Alert]** Students can measure the side lengths to find the area of a rectangle, but the side lengths of a parallelogram don't necessarily help them find its area; they must determine the height. **[Ask]** "Is it ever the case that a side length equals the height?" [yes, for a rectangle] "If you rotate the parallelogram, how does its area change?" Don't accept too quickly the answer "It doesn't" and move on. Some students may be unsure.

[Ask] "What do you think of a claim that the area of any parallelogram is zero, because the parallelogram consists only of four line segments, each of which has area zero?" Although we usually refer to the area of a geometric figure, we mean the area of the region inside the figure. **[Language]** In English, the word *area* often means "region." Suggest that students use the word *region* in this context so that they won't be saying things like "the area of the area."

Pose the reverse problem: "If we know the area, can we find the base and height?" Or "If we know the area and base, can we find the height?" Discussion of this question can lead to Example B.

[Ask] "Do all rectangles with the same perimeter have the same area?" Students might think they do, yet not say so. Draw pictures, or take a loop of string, to form rectangles that get longer and narrower while maintaining the same perimeter. At some point most students will decide that the area does change. A few may need to do calculations to be convinced.

▶ EXAMPLE B

[Alert] Some confusion could arise over the measurement units. Point out that 7.13 m^2 is not 7.13 meters squared, but 7.13 square meters. Dimensional analysis might help students see that the height is $\frac{3.1 \text{ m}^2}{\text{m}}$, or 3.1 m.

To help students understand square units, **[Ask]** "What is the area of a rectangle with dimensions 3 meters by 4 meters?" [12 square meters (m^2)] "What is twelve meters squared?" [It represents the area of a square 12 meters on a side and has an area of 144 m^2.]

[Ask] "How would you check the answer to Example B?" [You could multiply height times base to see that you get 7.13 m^2.]

Assessing Progress

You can assess students' understanding of rectangles, parallelograms, and triangles, as well as their comfort with the conservation of area as a figure is broken into pieces that are then rearranged into another shape.

Closing the Lesson

Restate the major points of the lesson: The **area** of a figure is a measure of the region inside the figure. If the figure is broken into parts, the area of the original figure is the sum of the areas of those parts and equals the area of any rearrangement of the parts. Area is measured in **square units** and is the number of unit squares that can be fit into the figure, perhaps after it has been broken into pieces. The areas of a rectangle and a parallelogram can be calculated by multiplying the length of the **base** by the **height,** where any side can be considered the base and the height is the length of an **altitude** to that base.

BUILDING UNDERSTANDING

The exercises provide opportunities to practice applying the area concepts.

ASSIGNING HOMEWORK

Essential	1–14, 16, 19, 23, 24
Performance assessment	18, 25
Portfolio	17
Group	15, 18–22
Review	26–28

▶Helping with the Exercises

Exercise 5 [Alert] Students may confuse perimeter with area. **[Ask]** "Is the perimeter always less than the area or always more than the area?" [neither] Emphasize that you're asking about the numbers here; the units are different.

Exercise 7 [Alert] Students might multiply the height by the noncorresponding base.

Exercise 9 As needed, remind students that the altitude may not always be in the interior of the figure.

10. Sketch and label two different rectangles, each with area 48 cm². ⓗ

In Exercises 11 and 12, find the area of the figure and explain your method.

11. 6 square units

12. 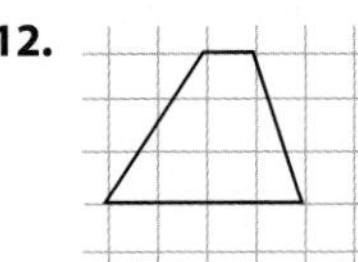 $7\frac{1}{2}$ square units

13. Sketch and label two different parallelograms, each with area 64 cm².

14. Draw and label a figure with area 64 cm² and perimeter 64 cm.

15. The photo shows a Japanese police *koban.* An arch forms part of the roof and one wall. The arch is made from rectangular panels that each measure 1 m by 0.7 m. The arch is 11 panels high and 3 panels wide. What's the total area of the arch? 23.1 m²

Cultural CONNECTION

Koban is Japanese for "mini-station," a small police station. These stations are located in several parts of a city, and officers who work in them know the surrounding neighborhoods and people well. The presence of *kobans* in Japan helps reduce crime and provides communities with a sense of security.

16. What is the total area of the four walls of a rectangular room 4 meters long by 5.5 meters wide by 3 meters high? Ignore all doors and windows. $2(4)(3) + 2(5.5)(3) = 57$ m²

17. APPLICATION Ernesto plans to build a pen for his pet iguana. What is the area of the largest rectangular pen that he can make with 100 meters of fencing?
For a constant perimeter, area is maximized by a square. 100 m ÷ 4 = 25 m per side; $A = 625$ m².

18. The big event at George Washington High School's May Festival each year is the Cow Drop Contest. A farmer brings his well-fed bovine to wander the football field until—well, you get the picture. Before the contest, the football field, which measures 53 yards wide by 100 yards long, is divided into square yards. School clubs and classes may purchase square yards. If one of their squares is where the first dropping lands, they win a pizza party. If the math club purchases 10 squares, what is the probability that the club wins? $\frac{1}{530}$

19. APPLICATION Sarah is tiling a wall in her bathroom. It is rectangular and measures 4 feet by 7 feet. The tiles are square and measure 6 inches on each side. How many tiles does Sarah need? ⓗ 112

Exercises 10, 13, 14 Encourage a variety of answers.

10. sample answer:

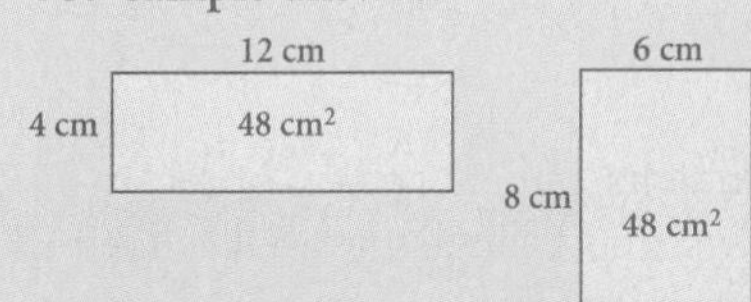

13. sample answers:

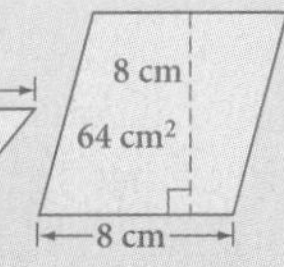

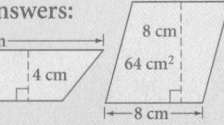

Exercise 14 There are many solutions, including a very skinny parallelogram with base and height 8 and other sides with length 24.

Exercises 11, 12 Student explanations of their methods may include counting squares and fractions of squares.

14. possible answer:

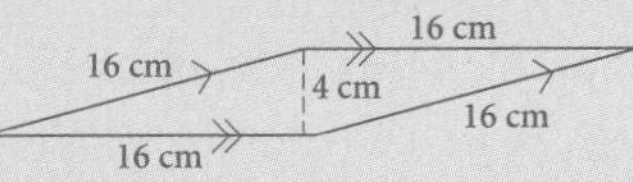

The figure at right demonstrates that $(a + b)^2 = a^2 + 2ab + b^2$. In Exercises 20 and 21, sketch and label a rectangle that demonstrates each algebraic expression.

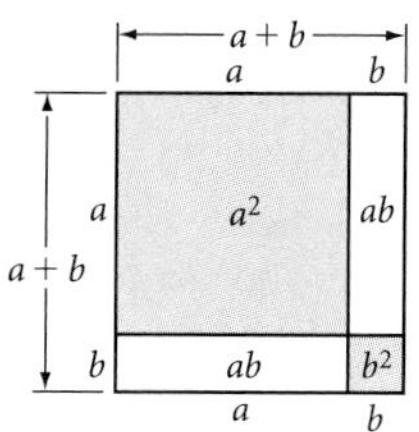

20. $(x + 3)(x + 5) = x^2 + 8x + 15$

21. $(3x + 2)(2x + 5) = 6x^2 + 19x + 10$

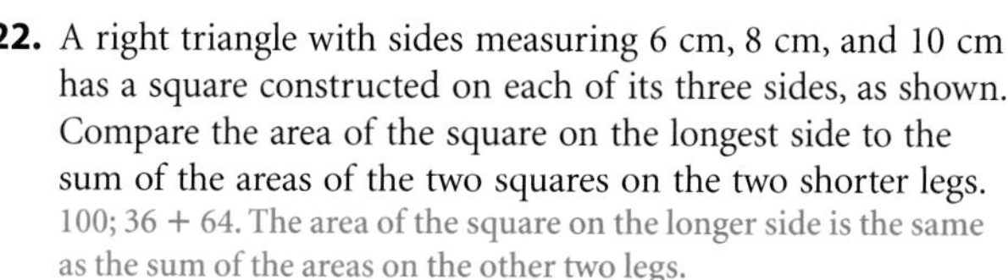

22. A right triangle with sides measuring 6 cm, 8 cm, and 10 cm has a square constructed on each of its three sides, as shown. Compare the area of the square on the longest side to the sum of the areas of the two squares on the two shorter legs.
100; 36 + 64. The area of the square on the longer side is the same as the sum of the areas on the other two legs.

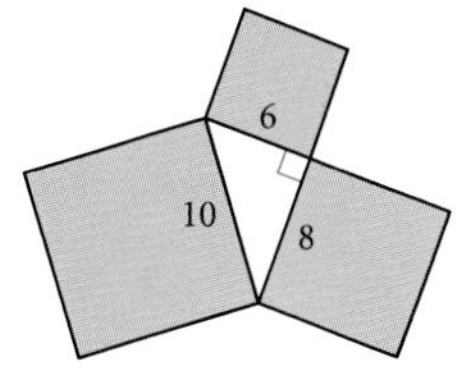

23. What is the area of the parallelogram?
96 square units

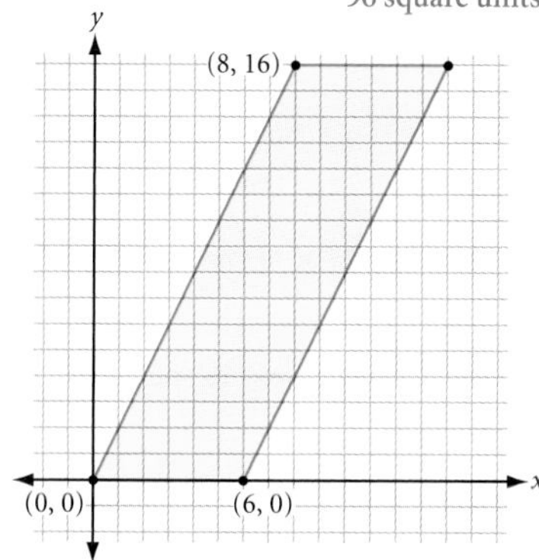

24. What is the area of the trapezoid?
500 cm^2

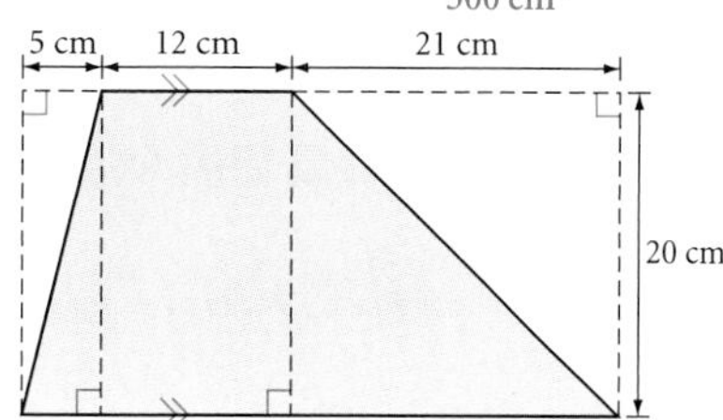

Art

CONNECTION

The design at right is a quilt design called the Ohio Star. Traditional quilt block designs range from a simple nine-patch, based on 9 squares, to more complicated designs like Jacob's Ladder or Underground Railroad, which are based on 16, 25, or even 36 squares. Quiltmakers need to calculate the total area of each different type of material before they make a complete quilt.

25. APPLICATION The Ohio Star is a 16-square quilt design. Each block measures 12 inches by 12 inches. One block is shown above. Assume you will need an additional 20% of each fabric to allow for seams and errors.

a. Calculate the sum of the areas of all the red patches, the sum of the areas of all the blue patches, and the area of the yellow patch in a single block.

b. How many Ohio Star blocks will you need to cover an area that measures 72 inches by 84 inches, the top surface area of a king-size mattress?

c. How much fabric of each color will you need? How much fabric will you need for a 15-inch border to extend beyond the edges of the top surface of the mattress?

Exercise 17 Encourage students to try various bases and heights and to look for a pattern in those dimensions that give the largest area and those that give the smallest, or to graph base versus area. **[Link]** If students graph base versus area, they might notice that the function appears quadratic.

Exercise 18 This exercise connects area with probability. Geometric probability is calculated by dividing the area of the selected region by the area of the entire region.

Exercises 20, 21 These exercises help make connections between algebra and geometry. Students might use algebra tiles instead of sketches.

20.

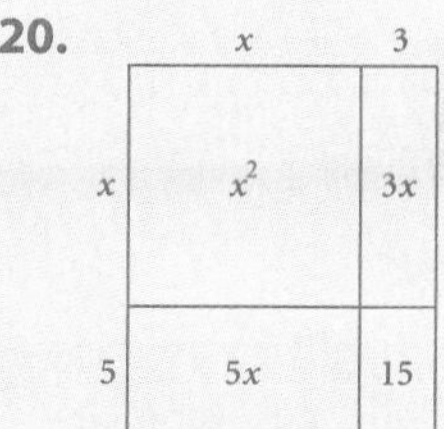

21.

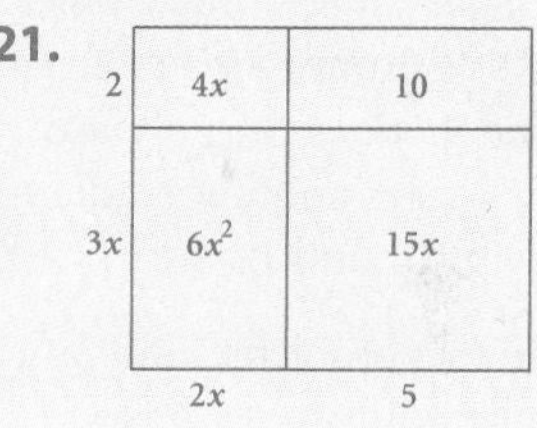

25a. In one Ohio Star block, the sum of the red patches is 36 in.^{2}, the sum of the blue patches is 72 in.^{2}, and the yellow patch is 36 in.^{2}.

25b. The complete quilt requires 42 blocks.

25c. About 1814 in.^{2} of red fabric, about 3629 in.^{2} of blue fabric, and about 1814 in.^{2} of yellow fabric. The border requires 5580 in.^{2} (if it does not need the extra 20%).

Exercise 26 Some students may be intimidated by the complexity of the diagram. Encourage them to start small, with what they can conclude from the given information, and later point out how well they overcame the challenge. After they begin, their biggest challenge may be to find values for *a* and *b*. As needed, focus their attention on *b* and the inscribed angle whose vertex is at *B*. Once they see that the latter is a right angle (by either the Inscribed Angle Conjecture or the Cyclic Quadrilateral Conjecture), they can proceed in several ways. The value of *b* is the difference between a right angle (by the Tangent Segments Conjecture) and the angle at *B* of a small triangle, as is the given angle measure, 52°. Or they can actually find the angle measure of the small triangle by the Isosceles Triangle and Triangle Sum Conjectures. If the question arises of an easy way to find the measure of an angle between tangent segments, encourage students to investigate, perhaps using geometry software. They should measure both the arc labeled *k* in this figure and the arc that forms the rest of the circle.

Exercise 26 See teaching note at the bottom of page 415.

Exercise 27 If students are having difficulty locating the sides of the triangle that aren't perpendicular to the altitude, ask what angles they make with the altitude [30°] and how to find those angles [bisect a 60° angle].

27. sample construction:

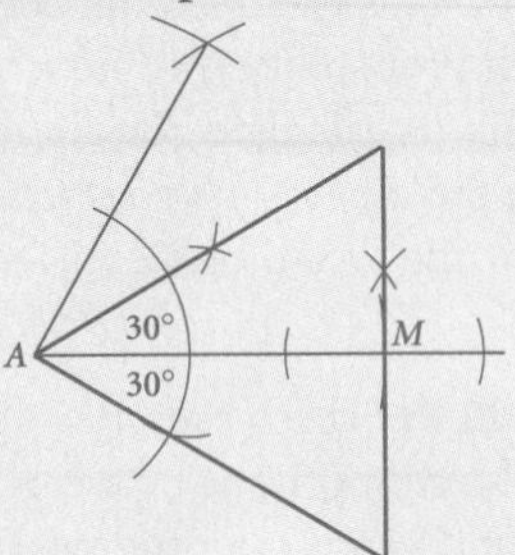

28a.

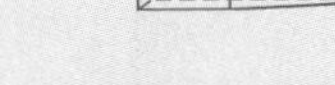

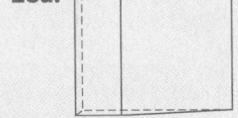

EXTENSIONS

A. Students might enjoy creating geoboard challenges for each other or for other groups. One student (or group) creates an irregular shape on a geoboard and challenges another student (or group) to find its area.

B. Pose this problem: Find rectangles with sides whose lengths are whole numbers in which the number of square units in the area equals the number of units in the perimeter. [For students who find the two answers, 4 by 4 and 3 by 6, **[Ask]** "Why are those the only two rectangles?"]

C. Estimate the area of Tennessee, Utah, or Wyoming. [approximate areas: Tennessee: 42,000 mi^2; Utah: 85,000 mi^2; Wyoming: 98,000 mi^2]

Review

26. Copy the figure at right. Find the lettered angle measures and arc measures. $\overrightarrow{AB}$ and $\overrightarrow{AC}$ are tangents. $\overline{CD}$ is a diameter.
$a = 76°, b = 52°, c = 104°, d = 52°, e = 76°, f = 47°, g = 90°, h = 43°, k = 104°, m = 86°$

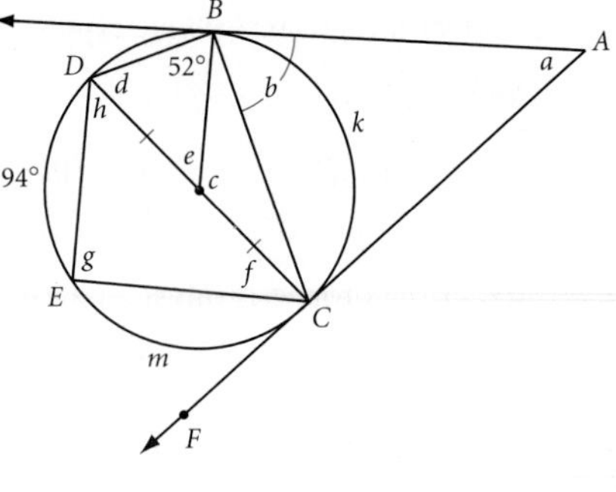

3.3 **27.** Given AM as the length of the altitude of an equilateral triangle, construct the triangle.

1.8 **28.** Sketch what the figure at right looks like when viewed from

a. Above the figure, looking straight down

b. In front of the figure, that is, looking straight at the red-shaded side

c. The side, looking at the blue-shaded side

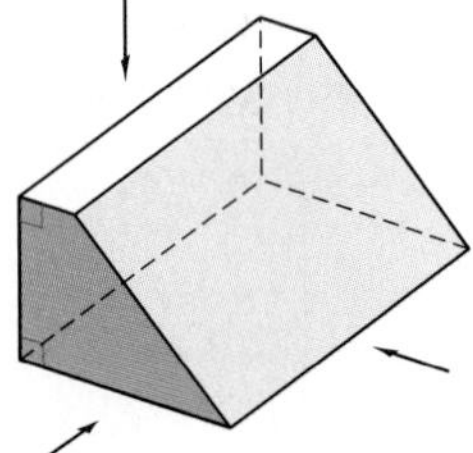

project

RANDOM RECTANGLES

What does a typical rectangle look like? A randomly generated rectangle could be long and narrow, or square-like. It could have a large perimeter, but a small area. Or it could have a large area, but a small perimeter. In this project you will randomly generate rectangles and study their characteristics using scatter plots and histograms.

Your project should include

- A description of how you created your random rectangles, including any constraints you used.
- A scatter plot of base versus height, a perimeter histogram, an area histogram, and a scatter plot of perimeter versus area.
- Any other studies or graphs you think might be interesting.
- Your predictions about the data before you made each graph.
- An explanation of why each graph looks the way it does.

Fathom™

You can use Fathom to generate random base and height values from 0 to 10. Then you can sort them by various characteristics and make a wide range of interesting graphs.

Supporting the project

Students may need to be reminded that a histogram is similar to a bar graph with the bars adjacent; each bar represents a range of values.

[Ask] "How many rectangles are enough?" Discuss sample size.

OUTCOMES

- Student provides clear descriptions, constraints, explanations, and predictions.
- Student includes graphs similar to those in the answer section on pages 773–774.
- Other graphs and relationships are presented.

See pages 773–774 for answers to Exercises 28b and c and graphs for the project.

LESSON

8.2 Areas of Triangles, Trapezoids, and Kites

When you add to the truth, you subtract from it.

THE TALMUD

In Lesson 8.1, you learned the area formula for rectangles, and you used it to discover an area formula for parallelograms. In this lesson you will use those formulas to discover or demonstrate the formulas for the areas of triangles, trapezoids, and kites.

Investigation 1
Area Formula for Triangles

You will need

- heavy paper or cardboard

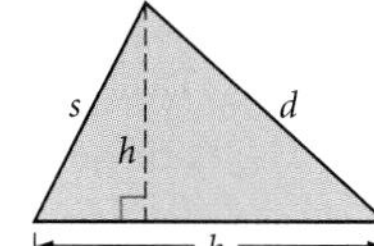

Step 1 Cut out a pair of congruent triangles. Label their corresponding parts as shown.

Step 2 Arrange the triangles to form a figure for which you already have an area formula. Calculate the area of the figure.

Step 3 What is the area of one of the triangles? Make a conjecture. Write a brief description in your notebook of how you arrived at the formula. Include an illustration.

Triangle Area Conjecture C-77

$A = \frac{1}{2}bh$

The area of a triangle is given by the formula ___?___, where A is the area, b is the length of the base, and h is the height of the triangle.

Investigation 2
Area Formula for Trapezoids

You will need

- heavy paper or cardboard

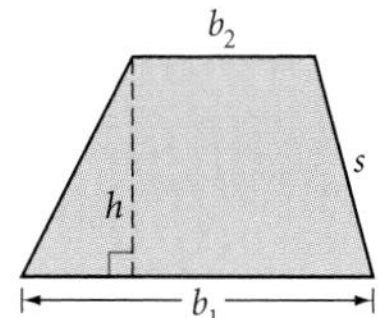

Step 1 Construct any trapezoid and an altitude perpendicular to its bases. Label the trapezoid as shown.

Step 2 Cut out the trapezoid. Make and label a copy.

NCTM STANDARDS

CONTENT		PROCESS	
	Number	✓	Problem Solving
✓	Algebra	✓	Reasoning
✓	Geometry	✓	Communication
✓	Measurement	✓	Connections
	Data/Probability		Representation

LESSON OBJECTIVES

- Derive formulas for the areas of triangles, trapezoids, and kites
- Apply area formulas to solve problems
- Develop cooperative behavior

LESSON

8.2

PLANNING

LESSON OUTLINE

One day:

25 min Investigation
10 min Sharing
5 min Closing
5 min Exercises

MATERIALS

- heavy paper or cardboard
- scissors
- Sketchpad demonstration Areas of Triangles and Trapezoids, *optional*

TEACHING

If you don't use the one-step investigation (page 417), you might jigsaw the investigations. Or, you might prefer to replace these investigations with the dynamic geometry exploration at www.keymath.com/DG.

Guiding Investigation 1

You might do Investigation 1 as a follow-along activity.

Step 1 Encourage students in each group to make different kinds of triangles.

Step 3 **[Alert]** Students may have some difficulty going backward from the area of two triangles to the area of one. Some students may realize from Lesson 8.1 that the area of a right triangle is half the area of a rectangle. Encourage them to see whether the formula generalizes to all triangles.

Guiding Investigation 2

Step 1 Encourage students in each group to make a variety of kinds of trapezoids, including right and isosceles trapezoids.

Step 3 Students may be confused by the number of variables needed to write the formula. If necessary, **[Ask]** "What lengths need variable names? What are some good names for those lengths?" [Looking at the Trapezoid Area Conjecture will help.]

One step To combine the investigations, pose this problem: "Find formulas for the area of triangles, trapezoids, and kites." Many students may already know a formula for the area of a triangle; encourage them to derive it from the area formulas for other figures by copying, cutting, and assembling triangles. Encourage a variety of approaches. For example, some students may derive the formula for the area of a trapezoid by dividing it into pieces, others by putting two copies end to end, and others by making a rectangle of the same area whose length is the midsegment.

Guiding Investigation 3

If students are stuck, **[Ask]** "Is it helpful to use some properties of kites that you know?" [Properties include that one diagonal divides the kite into two congruent triangles, the other diagonal divides the kite into two isosceles triangles, and the diagonals of a kite are perpendicular to each other and thus divide the kite into four right triangles.]

Encourage a variety of approaches. Students may wish to turn over two of the four triangular pieces. Others may consider the kite as a rectangle with triangular pieces removed. Others may think of the kite as two congruent triangles. As needed, ask whether students are using the diagonals or parts of the diagonals.

Remind students to define the formula's variables within the conjecture, as in all the area conjectures.

Step 3 A parallelogram with base $b_1 + b_2$; $h(b_1 + b_2)$

Step 3 Arrange the two trapezoids to form a figure for which you already have an area formula. What type of polygon is this? What is its area? What is the area of one trapezoid? State a conjecture.

Trapezoid Area Conjecture $A = \frac{1}{2}(b_1 + b_2)h$ **C-78**

The area of a trapezoid is given by the formula __?__, where A is the area, b_1 and b_2 are the lengths of the two bases, and h is the height of the trapezoid.

Investigation 3
Area Formula for Kites

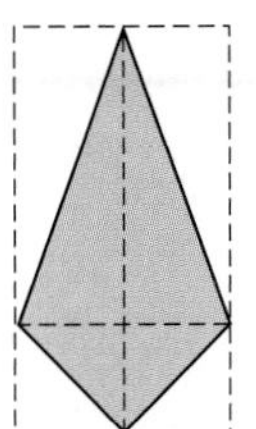

Can you rearrange a kite into shapes for which you already have the area formula? Do you recall some of the properties of a kite?

Create and carry out your own investigation to discover a formula for the area of a kite. Discuss your results with your group. State a conjecture.

Kite Area Conjecture **C-79**

The area of a kite is given by the formula __?__. $A = \frac{1}{2}d_1d_2$, where d_1 and d_2 are the lengths of the diagonals

EXERCISES

In Exercises 1–12, use your new area conjectures to solve for the unknown measures.

1. $A =$ __?__ 20 cm²

2. $A =$ __?__ 49.5 m²

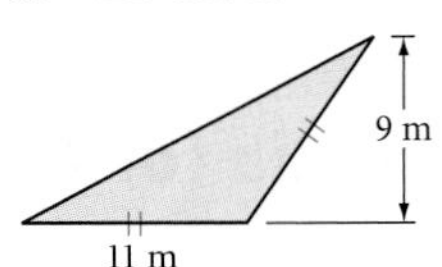

3. $A =$ __?__ 300 square units

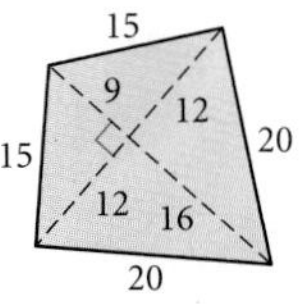

4. $A =$ __?__ 60 cm²

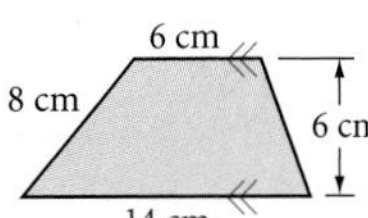

5. $A = 39$ cm²
$h =$ __?__ 6 cm

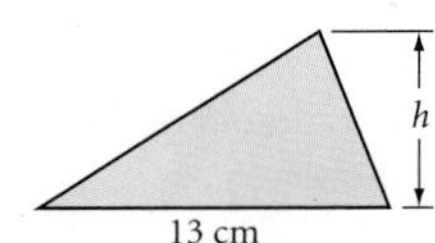

6. $A = 31.5$ ft²
$b =$ __?__ 7 ft

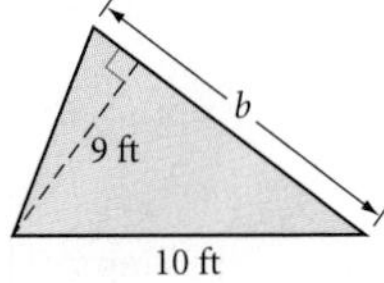

SHARING IDEAS

As students share ideas about the Triangle Area Conjecture, **[Ask]** "How do you know what side is the base of the triangle?" Try joining different sides to see how the resulting parallelograms differ. Students may have difficulty seeing that these three parallelograms have the same area. Suggest that they look at each base-altitude pair of one parallelogram and see how it's a base-altitude pair of another one of the parallelograms.

For the Trapezoid Area Conjecture, **[Ask]** "Is a parallelogram formed for any trapezoid? How do you know?" [Yes; the consecutive angles of the doubled figure are supplementary, because consecutive angles of a trapezoid are supplementary.] "Does it make a difference which base is labeled b_1?" [No; their sum is the same in the parallelogram.] "Does $\frac{1}{2}(b_1 + b_2)$ sound familiar to you?" [It's the average of the lengths of the bases; the length of the trapezoid's midsegment]

7. $A = 420\ \text{ft}^2$
$LE = \underline{?}$ 30 ft

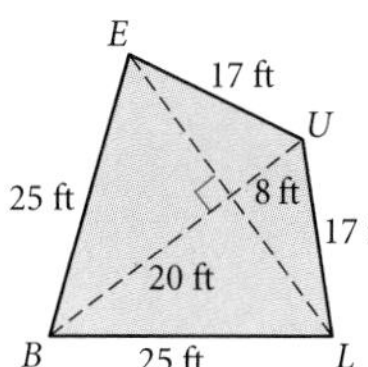

8. $A = 50\ \text{cm}^2$ ⓗ
$h = \underline{?}$ 5 cm

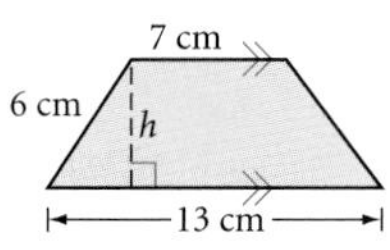

9. $A = 180\ \text{m}^2$
$b = \underline{?}$ 16 m

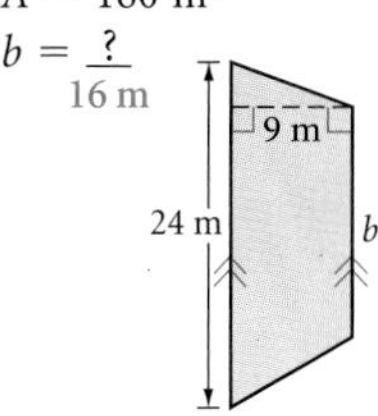

10. $A = 924\ \text{cm}^2$
$P = \underline{?}$ 168 cm

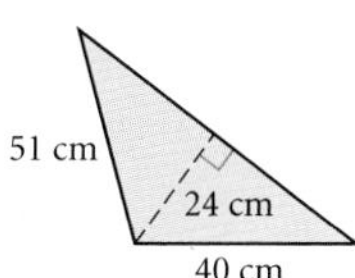

11. $A = 204\ \text{cm}^2$
$P = 62\ \text{cm}$
$h = \underline{?}$ 12 cm

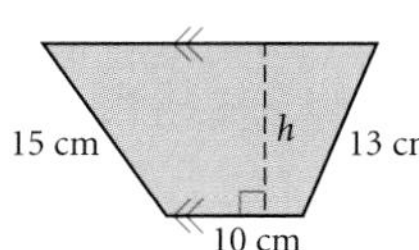

12. $x = \underline{?}$ ⓗ 3.6 ft
$y = \underline{?}$ 10.8 ft

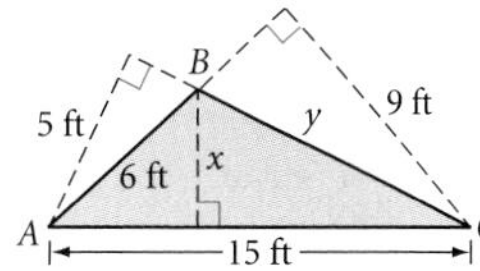

13. Sketch and label two different triangles, each with area $54\ \text{cm}^2$.

14. Sketch and label two different trapezoids, each with area $56\ \text{cm}^2$.

15. Sketch and label two different kites, each with area $1092\ \text{cm}^2$.

16. Sketch and label a triangle and a trapezoid with equal areas and equal heights. How does the base of the triangle compare with the two bases of the trapezoid?

17. P is a random point on side $\overline{AY}$ of rectangle $ARTY$. The shaded area is what fraction of the area of the rectangle? Why?

$\frac{1}{2}$ (To see why, draw altitude $\overline{PQ}$.)

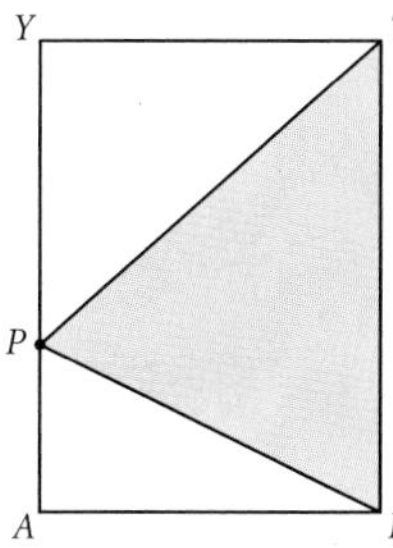

18. One playing card is placed over another, as shown. Is the top card covering half, less than half, or more than half of the bottom card? Explain. more than half, because the top card completely covers one corner of the bottom card

19. APPLICATION Eduardo has designed this kite for a contest. He plans to cut the kite from a sheet of Mylar plastic and use balsa wood for the diagonals. He will connect all the vertices with string, and fold and glue flaps over the string.

a. How much balsa wood and Mylar will he need?

b. Mylar is sold in rolls 36 inches wide. What length of Mylar does Eduardo need for this kite?

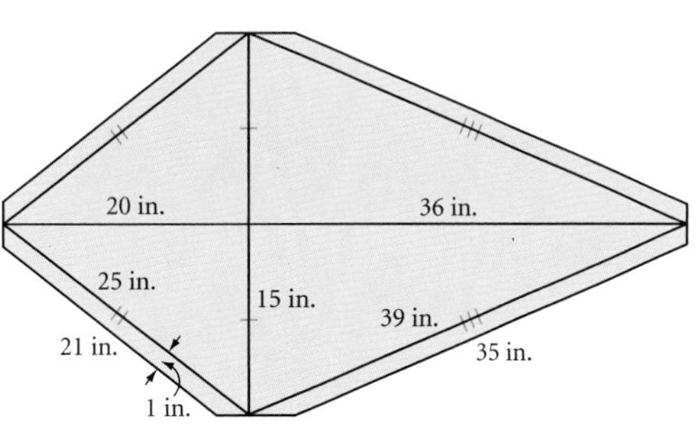

Sharing Ideas (continued)

[Ask] "What happens to the area of a trapezoid if one of the bases shrinks to length zero?" [The trapezoid becomes a triangle with the same height, the midsegment becomes a midsegment of the triangle, and the area becomes half the remaining base times the height.]

BUILDING UNDERSTANDING

Students may wish to show how they used their cut-outs to help them solve the problem, rather than just using the formula in their conjecture.

ASSIGNING HOMEWORK

Essential	1–15
Performance assessment	19, 20
Portfolio	14
Journal	16–18, 21, 22
Group	18–22
Review	23–30

▶ Helping with the Exercises

Exercises 1–12 [Alert] Many of the pictures include extraneous information, so students may use irrelevant numbers.

Exercise 7 If students haven't yet come up with the Kite Area Conjecture, suggest that they use the Triangle Area Conjecture

Exercise 12 This is the most challenging exercise of the lesson. Students may be intimidated by the extra lines sticking out and may not realize that they are altitudes. Wonder aloud whether there are different ways to express the area of the triangle. $\left[\frac{1}{2}(6)(9), \frac{1}{2}(5)y, \frac{1}{2}(15)x\right]$

See page 774 for answers to Exercises 13–16, and 19.

Assessing Progress

As you observe students working and presenting, assess their understanding of the areas of rectangles and parallelograms. You can also check their understanding of area as the number of squares that will cover the shape and their comfort with the conservation of area.

Closing the Lesson

Summarize the major points of this lesson: Every triangle is half a parallelogram with the same base and height, so the area of a triangle is $\frac{1}{2}bh$. Every trapezoid is half a parallelogram whose base is the sum of the bases of the trapezoid and whose height is the same, so the area of a trapezoid is $\frac{1}{2}(b_1 + b_2)h$; this is the same as the length of the midsegment times the height. Every kite is half a rectangle whose base and height are the kite's diagonals, so the area of a kite is $\frac{1}{2}(d_1 \cdot d_2)$.

As needed, you might work several exercises as demonstrations.

Exercise 13 [Alert] Students may look for whole numbers whose product is 54 rather than numbers *half* of whose product is 54.

Exercise 18 If students are having difficulty, ask whether this picture relates to that of Exercise 17. The rounded edges can be ignored.

Exercise 21 Students may be confused because the trapezoid's bases aren't horizontal. To preview the Pythagorean Theorem, **[Ask]** "Create an equation of the two area formulas. After multiplying and combining like terms, what is the equation?"

$$\left[\tfrac{1}{2}(a+b)(a+b) = \tfrac{1}{2}c^2 + ab\right.$$
$$\tfrac{1}{2}(a^2+2ab+b^2) = \tfrac{1}{2}c^2 + ab$$
$$\tfrac{1}{2}a^2 + ab + \tfrac{1}{2}b^2 = \tfrac{1}{2}c^2 + ab$$
$$\left.a^2 + b^2 = c^2\right]$$

21. The isosceles triangle is a right triangle because the angles on either side of the right angle are complementary. If you use the trapezoid area formula, the area of the trapezoid is $\frac{1}{2}(a+b)(a+b)$. If you add the areas of the three triangles, the area of the trapezoid is $\frac{1}{2}c^2 + ab$.

Exercise 22 This approach may repeat what students have already done. If not, **[Ask]** "How does the answer compare with the formula found in Investigation 2?"

22. Given: trapezoid $ABCD$ with height h. Area of $\triangle ABD = \frac{1}{2}hb_1$. Area of $\triangle BCD = \frac{1}{2}hb_2$. Area of trapezoid = sum of areas of two triangles $= \frac{1}{2}h(b_1 + b_2)$.

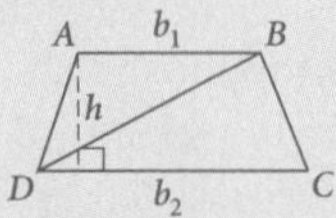

Exercise 27 This puzzle is similar to the complex one from the previous lesson. The main difficulty students may have is finding d, e, and g. Encourage them to look for congruent triangles (to show $d = e$, so they can use the fact that $d + e$ is the same as the measure of $\overset{\frown}{BC}$).

28.

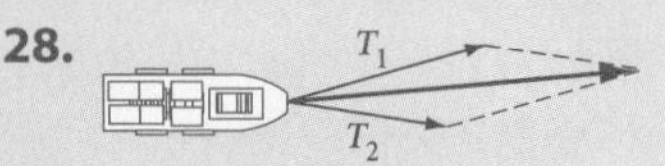

20. APPLICATION The roof on Crystal's house is formed by two congruent trapezoids and two congruent isosceles triangles, as shown. She wants to put new wood shingles on her roof. Each shingle will cover 0.25 square foot of area. (The shingles are 1 foot by 1 foot, but they overlap by 0.75 square foot.) How many shingles should Crystal buy?
3600 shingles (to cover an area of 900 ft²)

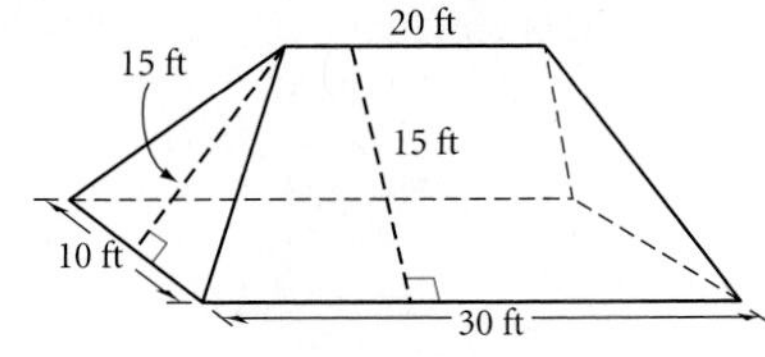

21. A trapezoid has been created by combining two congruent right triangles and an isosceles triangle, as shown. Is the isosceles triangle a right triangle? How do you know? Find the area of the trapezoid two ways: first by using the trapezoid area formula, and then by finding the sum of the areas of the three triangles.

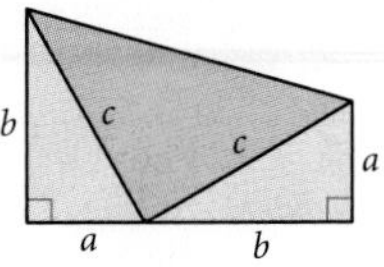

22. Divide a trapezoid into two triangles. Use algebra to derive the formula for the area of the trapezoid by expressing the area of each triangle algebraically and finding their algebraic sum. ⓗ

Review

8.1 **23.** $A = \underline{?}$

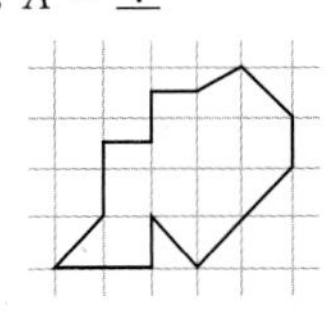

$11\frac{1}{4}$ square units

24. $A = \underline{?}$

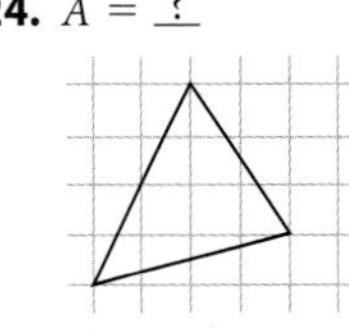

7 square units

25. $A = 264\text{ m}^2$
$P = \underline{?}$ 70 m

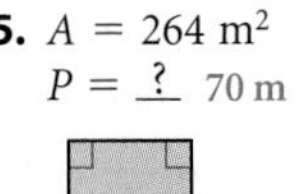

26. $P = 52$ cm
$A = \underline{?}$ 144 cm²

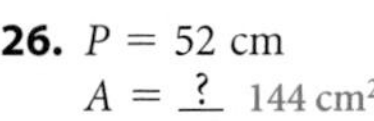

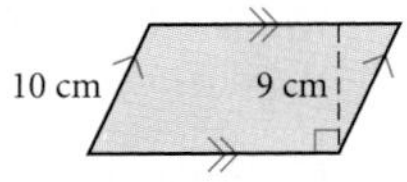

27. Trace the figure at right. Find the lettered angle measures and arc measures. $\overrightarrow{AB}$ and $\overrightarrow{AC}$ are tangents. $\overline{CD}$ is a diameter.
$a = 34°, b = 68°, c = 68°, d = 56°, e = 56°, f = 90°, g = 34°, h = 56°, m = 56°, n = 90°, p = 34°$

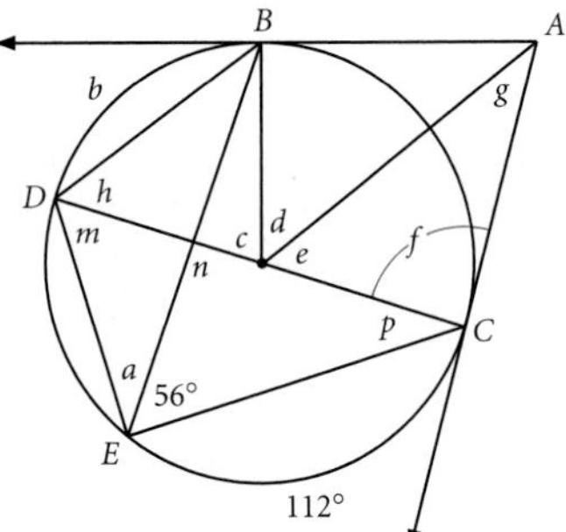

5.5 **28.** Two tugboats are pulling a container ship into the harbor. They are pulling at an angle of 24° between the tow lines. The vectors shown in the diagram represent the forces the two tugs are exerting on the container ship. Copy the vectors and complete the vector parallelogram to determine the resultant vector force on the container ship.

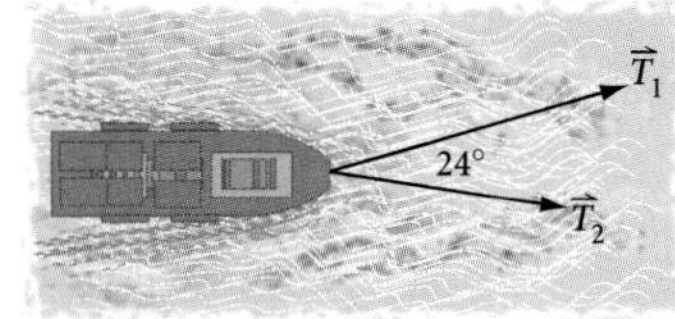

EXTENSIONS

A. Develop the formula for the area of a triangle and a trapezoid as (midsegment) · (height).

B. Find more methods for arriving at the formula for the area of a trapezoid. Consider ways of dividing the trapezoid into pieces (triangles, rectangles, parallelograms) for which you already know the area formula. [possible answers (all use trapezoid $ABCD$ as shown):

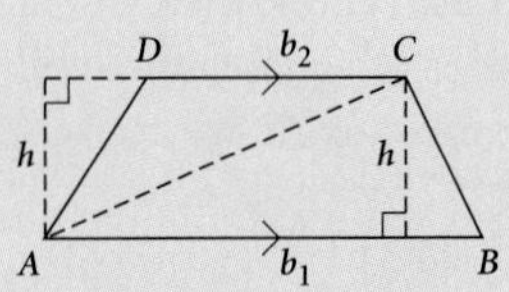

area = area($\triangle ABC$) + area($\triangle CDA$) = $\frac{1}{2}b_1h + \frac{1}{2}b_2h = \frac{1}{2}h(b_1 + b_2)$

29. Two paths from C to T (traveling on the surface) are shown on the 8 cm-by-8 cm-by-4 cm prism below. M is the midpoint of edge $\overline{UA}$. Which is the shorter path from C to T: C-M-T or C-A-T? Explain. ⓗ

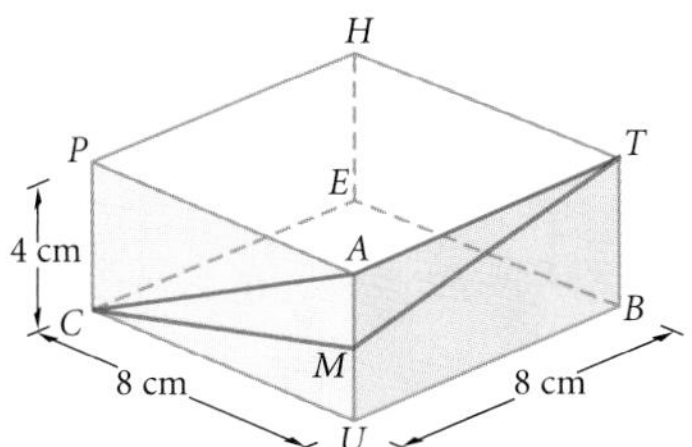

7.4 **30.** Give the vertex arrangement for this 2-uniform tessellation. $3^2.6^2/3.6.3.6$

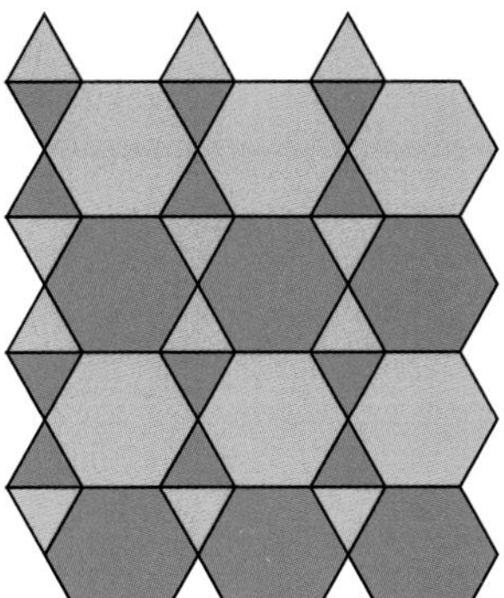

project

MAXIMIZING AREA

A farmer wants to fence in a rectangular pen using the wall of a barn for one side of the pen and the 10 meters of fencing for the remaining three sides. What dimensions will give her the maximum area for the pen?

You can use the trace feature on your calculator to find the value of x that gives the maximum area. Use your graphing calculator to investigate this problem and find the best arrangement.

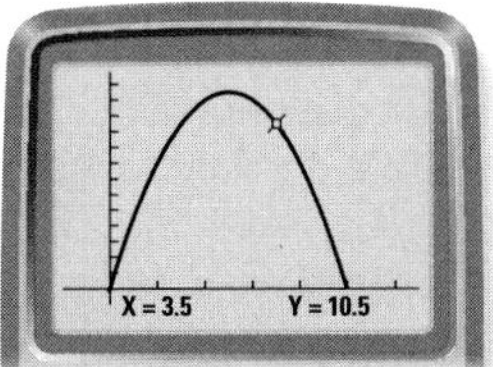

Your project should include

- An expression for the third side length, in terms of the variable x in the diagram.
- An equation and graph for the area of the pen.
- The dimensions of the best rectangular shape for the farmer's pen.

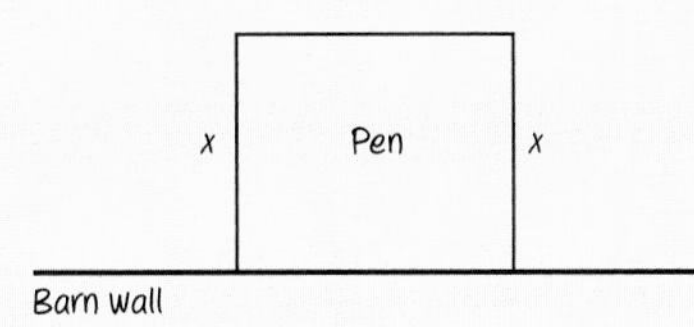

B Solutions (continued)

Construct point E on $\overline{AB}$ so that $\overline{ED}$ is parallel to $\overline{BC}$.

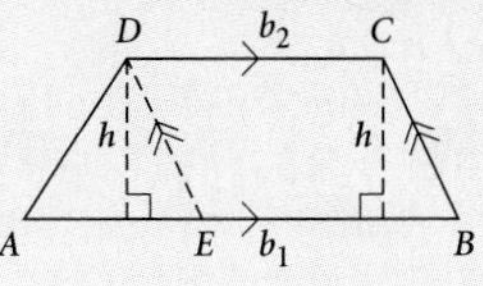

$\therefore$ area $= \frac{1}{2}h(b_1 - b_2) + hb_2 = \frac{1}{2}h(b_1 + b_2)$

Construct $\overline{DE} \perp \overline{AB}$ and $\overline{CF} \perp \overline{AB}$, with points E and F on $\overline{AB}$. Let $c = AE$.

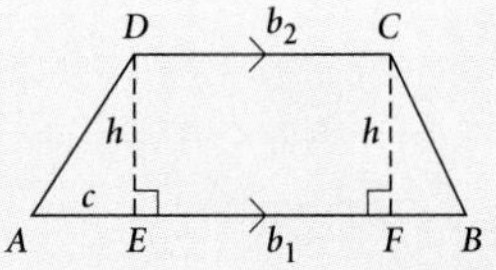

$\therefore$ area $= \frac{1}{2}ch + b_2h + \frac{1}{2}h(b_1 - b_2 - c) = \frac{1}{2}h(b_1 + b_2)$

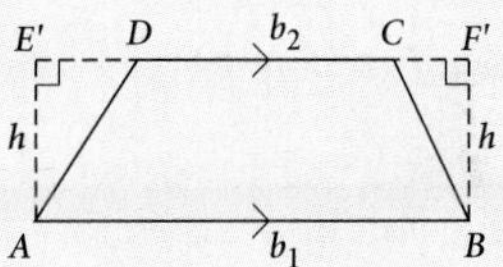

Start as you did in the previous method, then duplicate $\triangle AED$ as $\triangle DE'A$ and $\triangle FBC$ as $\triangle CF'B$, forming rectangle $ABF'E'$.]

C. Estimate the area of California, Texas, or Nevada. [approximate areas: California: 164,000 mi²; Texas: 269,000 mi²; Nevada: 111,000 mi²]

29. The path from C to M to T lies on a straight line, and therefore must be shorter than the path from C to A to T.

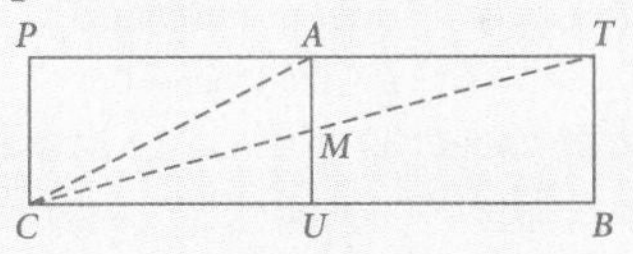

Supporting the project

If they wish, students might gather some data points and use quadratic regression rather than finding and graphing a function expression.

OUTCOMES

- The expression and equation are equivalent to $A = x(10 - 2x)$.
- The graph shows the maximum area at $x = 2.5$.
- The project includes an explanation of why the maximum area is 12.5 m². One reason, not using the graph, is that if there were twice as much fencing available and no barn, then the region of maximum area would be a square (by Exercise 17, Lesson 8.1); the barn wall can be considered a line of symmetry, cutting the amount of fencing in half but making the shape half a square, with width $\frac{1}{4}$ the total amount of fencing.

LESSON

8.3

PLANNING

LESSON OUTLINE

One day:

30 min Investigation

10 min Sharing and Closing

5 min Exercises

MATERIALS

- rulers
- calculators
- Finding Areas (T)

TEACHING

Areas of a variety of shapes can be found if you know how to find the areas of the standard shapes of the previous lessons.

Guiding the Investigation

One step Pose this problem, taken from *Discovering Algebra*: "You are surveying a four-sided piece of land. From your Geographic Information System you have found that one corner of the land is at a tree 638 feet due north of the corner that's next to the large rock. A third corner is at a post 138 feet south and 550 feet east of that tree. The fourth corner is at the edge of a pond. The rock is 400 feet west and 100 feet north of the corner by the pond. What's the area of the plot of land?" As you circulate, encourage graphing and viewing the shape in lots of different ways: as the union of familiar shapes (including small squares), as the result of taking away shapes from a rectangle, and as approximately a right trapezoid.

LESSON 8.3

Area Problems

Optimists look for solutions, pessimists look for excuses.

SUE SWENSON

By now, you know formulas for finding the areas of rectangles, parallelograms, triangles, trapezoids, and kites. Now let's see if you can use these area formulas to approximate the areas of irregularly shaped figures.

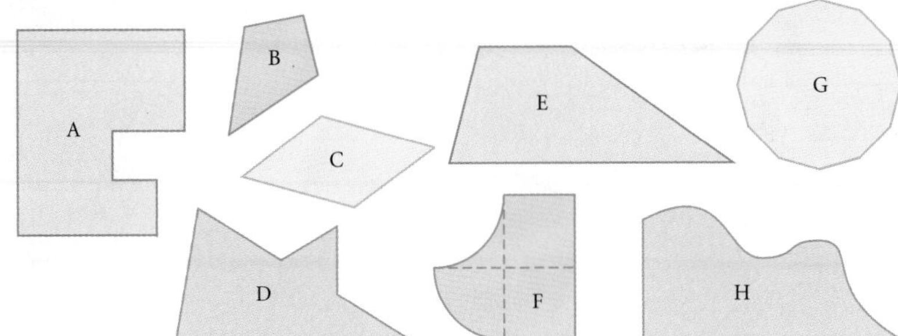

Investigation
Solving Problems with Area Formulas

You will need

- figures A–H
- centimeter rulers or meterstick

Find the area of each geometric figure your teacher provides. Before you begin to measure, discuss with your group the best strategy for each step. Discuss what units you should use. Different group members might get different results. However, your results should be close. You may average your results to arrive at one group answer. For each figure, write a sentence or two explaining how you measured the area and how accurate you think it is.

Now that you have practiced measuring and calculating area, you're ready to try some application problems. Many everyday projects require you to find the areas of flat surfaces on three-dimensional objects. You'll learn more about surface area in Lesson 8.7.

Career CONNECTION

Professional housepainters have a unique combination of skills: For large-scale jobs, they begin by measuring the surfaces that they will paint and use measurements to estimate the quantity of materials they will need. They remove old coating, clean the surface, apply sealer, mix color, apply paint, and add finishes. Painters become experienced and specialize their craft through the on-the-job training they receive during their apprenticeships.

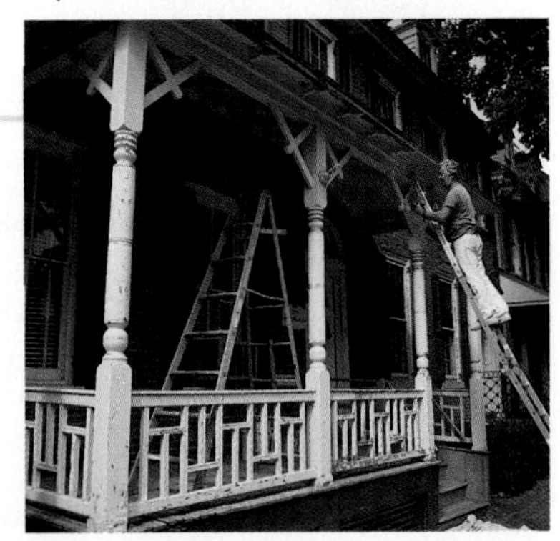

In preparation for the investigation use the three Finding Areas transparencies to project the images onto large sheets of butcher paper and make large copies that can be reused each year. An alternative is to use actual nonrectangular regions in your classroom if they exist and are easily measured.

The task of each group is to find the area of the figures assigned. Encourage groups to think about what is the best strategy. Shared tasks and team effort are important.

As students work, encourage a variety of approaches. For example, some students may decide to subdivide Figure G into congruent triangles, while others will divide it into quadrilaterals and triangles. Similarly, Figure H particularly lends itself to a variety of approaches. Offer advice only if a student becomes frustrated to the point of giving up; one goal is to have students feel the exhilaration of meeting challenges. Groups or students who want to extend the investigation can also find the perimeter of each shape.

In the exercises you will learn how to use area in buying rolls of wallpaper, gallons of paint, bundles of shingles, square yards of carpet, and square feet of tile. Keep in mind that you can't buy $12\frac{11}{16}$ gallons of paint! You must buy 13 gallons. If your calculations tell you that you need 5.25 bundles of shingles, you have to buy 6 bundles. In this type of rounding, you must always round upward.

EXERCISES

1. **APPLICATION** Tammy is estimating how much she should charge for painting 148 rooms in a new motel with one coat of base paint and one coat of finishing paint. The four walls and the ceiling of each room must be painted. Each room measures 14 ft by 16 ft by 10 ft high.
   a. Calculate the total area of all the surfaces to be painted with each coat. Ignore doors and windows. 121,952 ft^2
   b. One gallon of base paint covers 500 square feet. One gallon of finishing paint covers 250 square feet. How many gallons of each will Tammy need for the job? 244 gal of base paint and 488 gal of finishing paint.

2. **APPLICATION** Rashad wants to wallpaper the four walls of his bedroom. The room is rectangular and measures 11 feet by 13 feet. The ceiling is 10 feet high. A roll of wallpaper at the store is 2.5 feet wide and 50 feet long. How many rolls should he buy? (Wallpaper is hung from ceiling to floor. Ignore the doors and windows.) He should buy at least four rolls of wallpaper. (The area of each roll is 125 ft^2. The total surface area to be papered is 480 ft^2.) If paper cut off at the corners is wasted, he'll need 5 rolls.

3. **APPLICATION** It takes 65,000 solar cells, each 1.25 in. by 2.75 in., to power the Helios Prototype, shown below. How much surface area, in square feet, must be covered with the cells? The cells on Helios are 18% efficient. Suppose they were only 12% efficient, like solar cells used in homes. How much more surface area would need to be covered to deliver the same amount of power? 1552 ft^2; 776 ft^2 more surface area

In August 2001, the Helios Prototype, a remotely controlled, nonpolluting solar-powered aircraft, reached 96,500 feet—a record for nonrocket aircraft. Soon, the Helios will likely sustain flight long enough to enable weather monitoring and other satellite functions. For news and updates, go to www.keymath.com/DG .

NCTM STANDARDS

CONTENT		PROCESS	
	Number	✓	Problem Solving
✓	Algebra	✓	Reasoning
✓	Geometry	✓	Communication
✓	Measurement	✓	Connections
	Data/Probability		Representation

LESSON OBJECTIVES

- Practice measuring
- Practice estimation
- Solve area application problems using various problem-solving strategies
- Develop reading comprehension and cooperative behavior

SHARING IDEAS

This is a good chance to have presentations from students who aren't always successful and have found values for the areas of one or more of the first five figures. Figures F and G motivate the next two lessons. Look at inscribed and circumscribed figures in Figure H.

Answers for all figures may vary. Some students, despite having centimeter rulers available, might use other measuring units. Or differences in precision might lead to different numbers. **[Ask]** "Does this mean that a figure can have different areas?" [For any measurement unit, each figure has a unique area. (An area function assigns each shape a single nonnegative number.) How close the area you find is to that unique area depends on the precision of your measurement.]

You might monitor the use of significant figures. For example, if the base and height of a triangle are measured to be 13.6 cm and 18 cm, respectively, then the area is accurate to two significant figures, 120 cm^2, rather than 122.4 cm^2 or 122 cm^2. If both measurements were taken to the same level of accuracy, 18.0 cm should have been stated, and the answer would be 122 cm^2.

[Ask] "Does an interior decorator need to use more or less accuracy when estimating how much carpet is needed for a home than a carpet layer needs to use when measuring how to cut carpet for a single room?" [The interior decorator can be less precise.] "How can you get more accurate results?" [measuring with more precise tools; reading the measurement to a smaller unit]

Assessing Progress
Assess how well students recognize and find the areas of rectangles, parallelograms, triangles, trapezoids, and kites. Also check up on teamwork skills.

Closing the Lesson

Being able to find the areas of some basic shapes allows you to find, or at least approximate, the areas of a wide variety of shapes. To help find areas of figures such as F and G in the investigation, future lessons will investigate finding the areas of other basic shapes.

BUILDING UNDERSTANDING

Introduce the exercise set by talking about situations in which it's appropriate to round all numbers up. [If 160 students are traveling in buses that carry 70, then you need 3 buses, not $2\frac{2}{7}$.] Though the set contains only 11 problems, doing them all will take a lot of time. You might have different groups work on different problems and prepare to present their ideas to the class.

ASSIGNING HOMEWORK

Essential	1–8
Portfolio	6
Group	1–8
Review	9–11

▶ Helping with the Exercises

Exercise 1 As needed, encourage students to draw a top view of the room.

Exercise 3 Students might reason that if the cells are $\frac{2}{3}$ as efficient then there will be $\frac{3}{2}$ as many.

For Exercises 4 and 5, refer to the floor plan at right.

Bedroom 10 ft × 9 ft
Bath 10 ft × 6 ft
Bath 7 ft × 9 ft
Hallway
Bedroom 10 ft × 8 ft
Master bedroom 13 ft × 8 ft
Entryway
Living room 13 ft × 13 ft
Kitchen 10 ft × 18 ft
Dining room 13 ft × 9 ft

4. **APPLICATION** Dareen's family is ready to have wall-to-wall carpeting installed. The carpeting they chose costs \$14 per square yard, the padding \$3 per square yard, and the installation \$3 per square yard. What will it cost them to carpet the three bedrooms and the hallway shown? ⓗ \$760

5. **APPLICATION** Dareen's family now wants to install 1-foot-square terra cotta tiles in the entryway and kitchen, and 4-inch-square blue tiles on each bathroom floor. The terra cotta tiles cost \$5 each, and the bathroom tiles cost 45¢ each. How many of each kind will they need? What will the tiles cost? 220 terra cotta tiles, 1107 blue tiles; \$1598.15

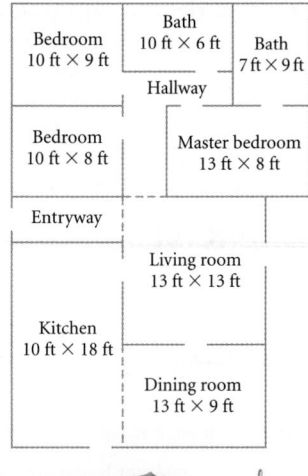

6. **APPLICATION** Harold works at a state park. He needs to seal the redwood deck at the information center to protect the wood. He measures the deck and finds that it is a kite with diagonals 40 feet and 70 feet. Each gallon of sealant covers 400 square feet, and the sealant needs to be applied every six months. How many gallon containers should he buy to protect the deck for the next three years? 21

40 ft
70 ft

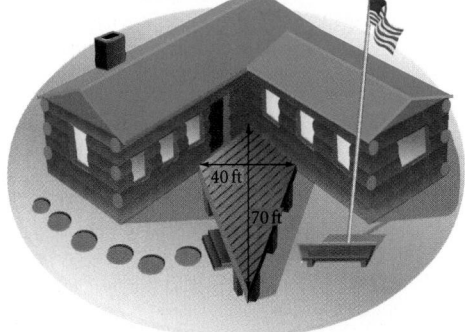

7. **APPLICATION** A landscape architect is designing three trapezoidal flowerbeds to wrap around three sides of a hexagonal flagstone patio, as shown. What is the area of the entire flowerbed? The landscape architect's fee is \$100 plus \$5 per square foot. What will the flowerbed cost? 336 ft^2; \$1780

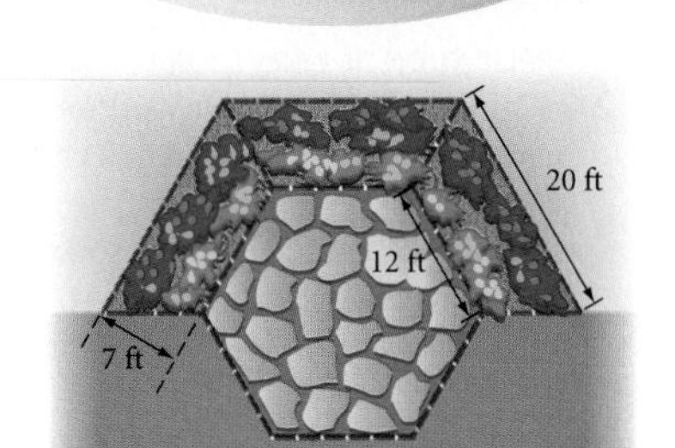
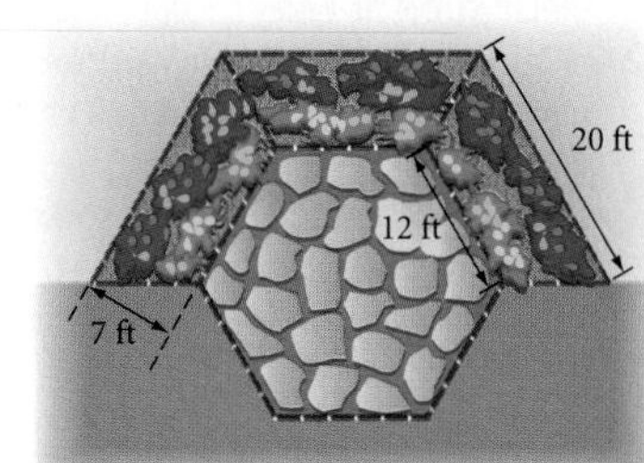

Career

Landscape architects have a keen eye for natural beauty. They study the grade and direction of land slopes, stability of the soil, drainage patterns, and existing structures and vegetation. They look at the various social, economic, and artistic concerns of the client. They also use science and engineering to plan environments that harmonize land features with structures, reducing the impact of urban development upon nature.

Exercise 4 Students may be confused about the widths of hallways. Wonder aloud whether those widths can be found from given dimensions. **[Alert]** Students may have difficulty changing square feet to square yards. Suggest that they draw a square yard and subdivide it into square feet.

Exercise 5 If students are not sure how to convert between square feet and square inches, again have them draw a picture.

Exercise 6 This is a good problem to model for the class; it might generate some interesting disagreements. Some students may miss the condition "for the next three years." Most students may assume that sealant left over after one application can be used six months later. This possibility should be discussed and agreed upon as a class.

8. APPLICATION Tom and Betty are planning to paint the exterior walls of their cabin (all vertical surfaces). The paint they have selected costs \$24 per gallon and, according to the label, covers 150 to 300 square feet per gallon. Because the wood is very dry, they assume the paint will cover 150 square feet per gallon. How much will the project cost? (All measurements shown are in feet.) ⓗ \$384 (16 gal)

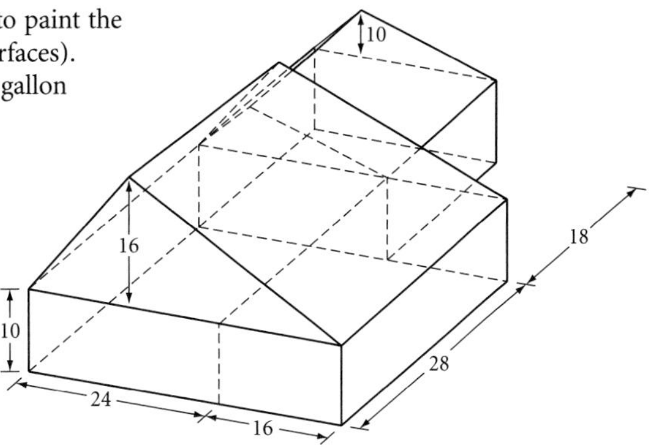

Review

8.2 **9.** A first-century Greek mathematician named Hero is credited with the following formula for the area of a triangle: $A = \sqrt{s(s-a)(s-b)(s-c)}$, where A is the area of the triangle, a, b, and c are the lengths of the three sides of the triangle, and s is the semiperimeter (half of the perimeter). Use Hero's formula to find the area of this triangle. Use the formula $A = \frac{1}{2}bh$ to check your answer. 60 cm² by either method

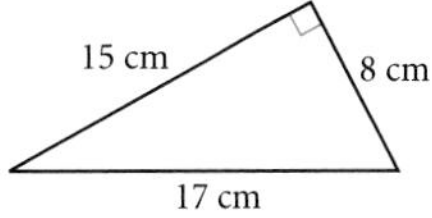

6.3 **10.** Explain why x must be 69° in the diagram at right. Because $\triangle AOB$ is isosceles, $m\angle A = 20°$ and $m\angle AOB = 140°$. $m\widehat{AB} = 140°$ and $m\widehat{CD} = 82°$. $m\widehat{AC} = m\widehat{BD}$ because parallel lines intercept congruent arcs on a circle. $\frac{360° - 140° - 82°}{2} = 69°$.

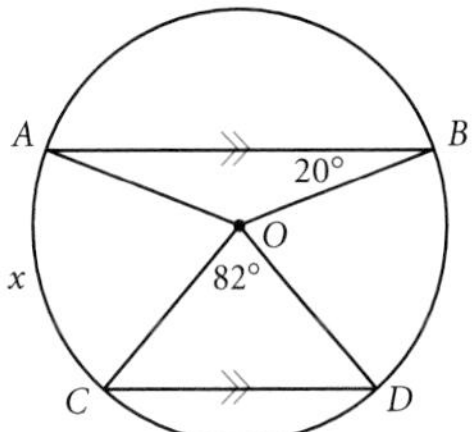

8.1 **11.** As P moves from left to right along ℓ, which of the following values changes? E

A. The area of $\triangle ABP$

B. The area of $\triangle PDC$

C. The area of trapezoid $ABCD$

D. $m\angle A + m\angle PCD + m\angle CPD$

E. None of these

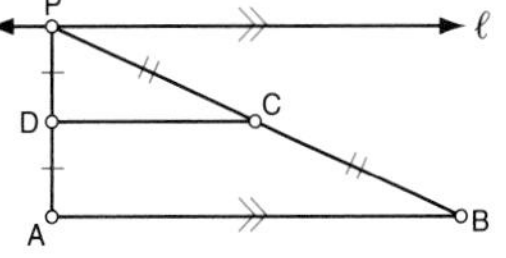

IMPROVING YOUR VISUAL THINKING SKILLS

Four-Way Split

How would you divide a triangle into four regions with equal areas? There are at least six different ways it can be done! Make six copies of a triangle and try it.

Exercise 8 If students aren't seeing the dimensions of a particular figure, suggest that they follow the projection lines from that figure to one of the walls where dimensions are given. Painting will not take place on the part of the wall of the larger section that is against the smaller section.

Exercise 9 This exercise previews the Exploration following Lesson 8.7. **[Ask]** "When is Hero's formula most helpful in finding the area of a triangle?" [when the triangle's three side lengths are given without any given altitude]

EXTENSIONS

A. For Figure H in the investigation, show how by breaking the curve into more pieces you will come closer to the actual area under the curve. **[Link]** This is a topic that will be dealt with in integral calculus.

B. Have a model of a building available with different surfaces to be painted, stained, shingled, or tiled. Provide the cost of each material and ask the students to calculate the total expense for each job.

IMPROVING VISUAL THINKING SKILLS

Encourage creative thinking here. This problem can be done in hundreds of ways. One unusual way if disconnected regions are allowed is to rearrange pieces of the triangle to make a rectangle of the same area, divide the resulting rectangle into four pieces of equal area, and then rearrange those pieces back into a triangle.

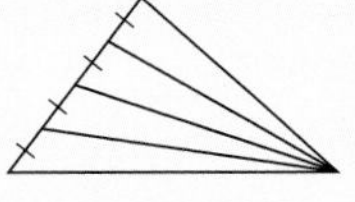

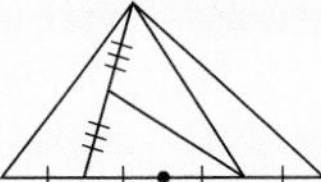

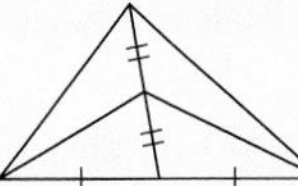

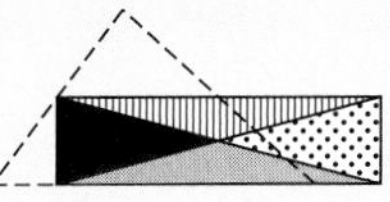

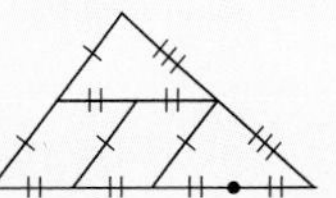

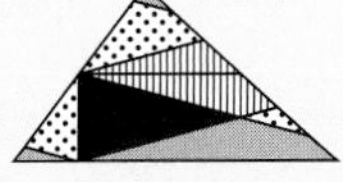

LESSON 8.4

PLANNING

LESSON OUTLINE

One day:

15 min Investigation

10 min Sharing

10 min Closing

10 min Exercises

MATERIALS

- construction tools
- calculators

TEACHING

The area of any regular polygon can be determined by finding areas of triangles. The circles around the polygons in the book foreshadow Lesson 8.5.

One step Challenge students to find a formula for the area of any regular n-gon (regular polygon with n sides). Some may devise different methods for polygons with an even and an odd number of sides. In the unlikely event that no group is thinking of dividing the polygon into congruent isosceles triangles, comment on the awkwardness of one group's approach and plant the idea of congruent isosceles triangles.

INTRODUCTION

If students found the area of Figure G in Lesson 8.3, **[Ask]** "What were some of the ways you found that area?" Lead the class to agree that the most generalizable method of dividing up any regular polygon is to partition it into isosceles triangles radiating from the center.

[Language] *Apothem* is pronounced ['a-pə-them].

LESSON 8.4

Areas of Regular Polygons

If I had to live my life again, I'd make the same mistakes, only sooner.

TALLULAH BANKHEAD

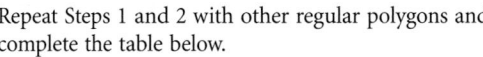

You can divide a regular polygon into congruent isosceles triangles by drawing segments from the center of the polygon to each vertex. The center of the polygon is actually the center of a circumscribed circle.

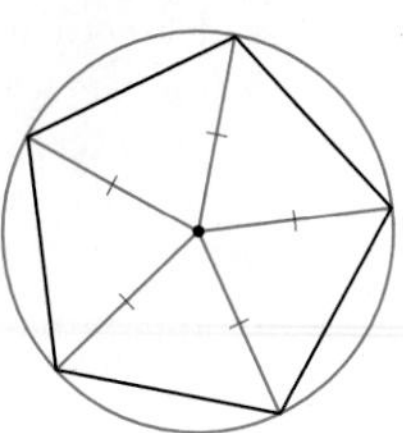

In this investigation you will divide regular polygons into triangles. Then you will write a formula for the area of any regular polygon.

Investigation
Area Formula for Regular Polygons

Consider a regular pentagon with side length s, divided into congruent isosceles triangles. Each triangle has a base s and a height a.

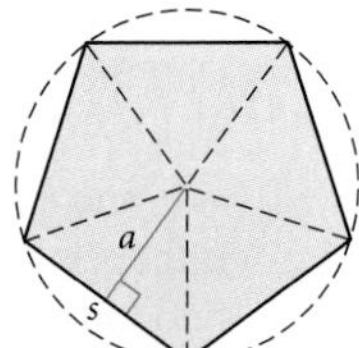

Regular pentagon

Step 1 $\frac{1}{2}as$

Step 2 $5 \cdot \frac{1}{2}as$

Step 1 What is the area of one isosceles triangle in terms of a and s?

Step 2 What is the area of this pentagon in terms of a and s?

Step 3 Repeat Steps 1 and 2 with other regular polygons and complete the table below.

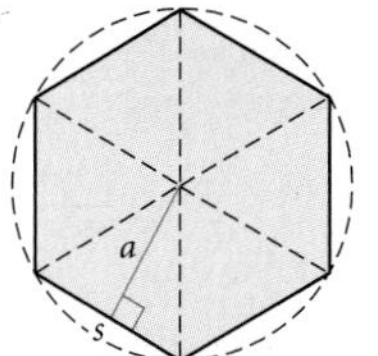

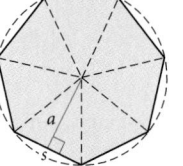

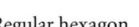

Regular hexagon Regular heptagon

Number of sides	5	6	7	8	9	10	...	12	...	n
Area of regular polygon	$\frac{5}{2}as$	$3as$	$\frac{7}{2}as$	$4as$	$\frac{9}{2}as$	$5as$	...	$6as$	...	$\frac{1}{2}asn$

The distance a always appears in the area formula for a regular polygon, and it has a special name—apothem. An **apothem** of a regular polygon is a perpendicular segment from the center of the polygon's circumscribed circle to a side of the polygon. You may also refer to the length of the segment as the apothem.

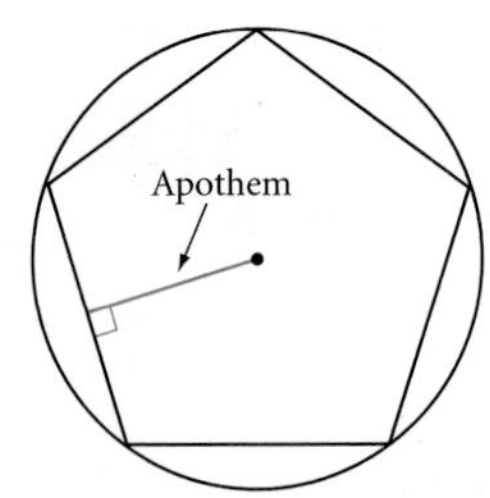

LESSON OBJECTIVES

- Derive the formula for the area of a regular polygon
- Apply area formulas to solve problems
- Learn new vocabulary
- Clarify approximation concepts
- Develop problem-solving skills and cooperative behavior

NCTM STANDARDS

CONTENT		PROCESS	
	Number	✓	Problem Solving
✓	Algebra	✓	Reasoning
✓	Geometry	✓	Communication
✓	Measurement		Connections
	Data/Probability		Representation

You can restate your last entry in the table as your next conjecture.

Regular Polygon Area Conjecture C-80

$A = \frac{1}{2}asn$

The area of a regular polygon is given by the formula __?__, where A is the area, a is the apothem, s is the length of each side, and n is the number of sides. The length of each side times the number of sides is the perimeter, P, so $sn = P$. Thus you can also write the formula for area as $A =$ __?__ P. $A = \frac{1}{2}aP$

EXERCISES

You will need

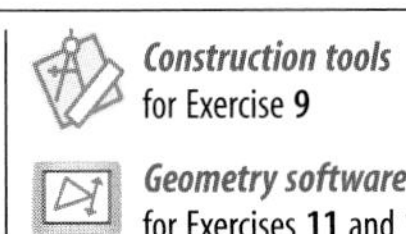

Construction tools for Exercise **9**

Geometry software for Exercises **11** and **17**

In Exercises 1–8, use the Regular Polygon Area Conjecture to find the unknown length accurate to the nearest unit, or the unknown area accurate to the nearest square unit. Recall that you use the symbol $\approx$ when your answer is an approximation.

1. $A \approx$ __?__ 2092 cm²
$s = 24$ cm
$a = 24.9$ cm

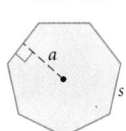

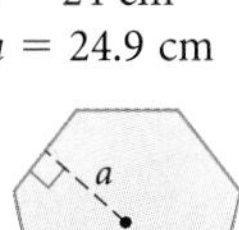

2. $a \approx$ __?__ 74 cm
$s = 107.5$ cm
$A = 19{,}887.5\ \text{cm}^2$

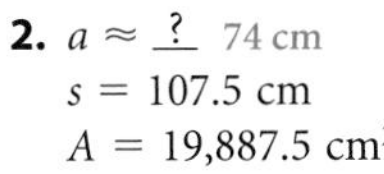

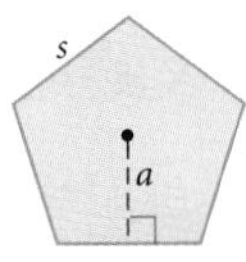

3. $P \approx$ __?__ 256 cm
$a = 38.6$ cm
$A = 4940.8\ \text{cm}^2$

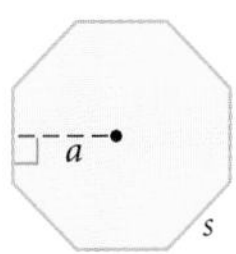

4. Regular pentagon: $a = 3$ cm and $s = 4.4$ cm, $A \approx$ __?__ 33 cm²

5. Regular nonagon: $a = 9.6$ cm and $A = 302.4\ \text{cm}^2$, $P \approx$ __?__ 63 cm

6. Regular n-gon: $a = 12$ cm and $P = 81.6$ cm, $A \approx$ __?__ 490 cm²

7. Find the perimeter of a regular polygon if $a = 9$ m and $A \approx 259.2\ \text{m}^2$. 57.6 m

8. Find the length of each side of a regular n-gon if $a = 80$ feet, $n = 20$, and $A \approx 20{,}000$ square feet. 25 ft

9. *Construction* Use a compass and straightedge to construct a regular hexagon with sides that measure 4 cm. Use the Regular Polygon Area Conjecture and a centimeter ruler to approximate the hexagon's area. ⓗ $\approx 42\ \text{cm}^2$

10. Draw a regular pentagon with apothem 4 cm. Use the Regular Polygon Area Conjecture and a centimeter ruler to approximate the pentagon's area. ⓗ $\approx 58\ \text{cm}^2$

11. *Technology* Use geometry software to construct a circle. Inscribe a pentagon that looks regular and measure its area. Now drag the vertices. How can you drag the vertices to increase the area of the inscribed pentagon? To decrease its area? It is impossible to increase its area, because a regular pentagon maximizes the area. Any dragging of the vertices decreases the area. (Although subsequent dragging to space them out more evenly can increase the area again, but never beyond that of the regular pentagon.)

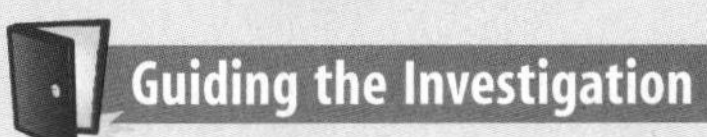

Guiding the Investigation

Step 1 [Alert] Some students may have missed the assumption that the pentagon is regular.

Step 3 Groups may want to divide up the work.

For students who finish early, challenge them to predict and then graph on their calculators these ordered pairs for n-gons inscribed in circles with radius 1: (n, *area*) [approaches π]; (n, a) [approaches 1]; (n, *perimeter*) [approaches 2π].

SHARING IDEAS

First call on students to fill in blanks in the table. Then have students show a variety of formulas, and let them find algebraic equivalents.

[Ask] "Why do the isosceles triangles all have the same area? How would you show that they are congruent?" [Two sides of each triangle are congruent radii of the circumscribed circle. The regularity of the polygon assures that the third sides are congruent, so use SSS. Or regularity gives the congruence of the central angles, so use SAS.]

The table begins with $n = 5$. **[Ask]** "Does the conjecture apply to regular 3-gons or 4-gons?" [Yes. In the case of the triangle, the center coincides with the four points of concurrency. For a square $a = \frac{1}{2}s$, so $\frac{1}{2}asn = \frac{1}{2} \cdot \left(\frac{1}{2}\right)s \cdot s \cdot 4 = s^2$.]

You can link to Lesson 8.5 by wondering aloud how close the polygonal areas are to the area of the circumscribed circle. Elicit the idea that, for a large number of sides, the apothem is close to the radius and the perimeter is close to the circumference. You can leave unanswered for now the question of finding the area of a circle.

Assessing Progress

You can assess students' understanding of regular polygons, congruence, and the area of a figure as the sum of areas of its parts. You can also check students' ability to calculate areas of triangles, use square units in area measurements, and reason inductively.

Closing the Lesson

Reiterate the main point of this lesson: The area of a regular polygon is half the product of the **apothem** and the perimeter. It's equivalent to $\frac{1}{2}nas$, where n is the number of sides, s is each side length, and a is the apothem.

BUILDING UNDERSTANDING

The exercises provide practice in applying the formulas for the area of regular polygons.

ASSIGNING HOMEWORK

Essential	**1–8, 14**
Performance assessment	**8**
Portfolio	**13**
Group	**9–12**
Review	**15–19**

▶ Helping with the Exercises

Exercise 3 If students are having trouble, ask what the formulas are and what happens when the given measurements are substituted. They will be solving the equation $4940.8 = \frac{1}{2}(38.6)P$.

Exercise 9 If students are stuck, **[Ask]** "Didn't we see a way of constructing regular hexagons back in Chapter 0 or Chapter 1?" [Lesson 0.3 and Lesson 1.6]

Exercise 10 The instructions here are to draw, not construct.

Exercise 13 Students will feel best if, on their own, they can get the idea of subtracting the area of the small hexagon from that of the larger.

15. Area is 20 square units.

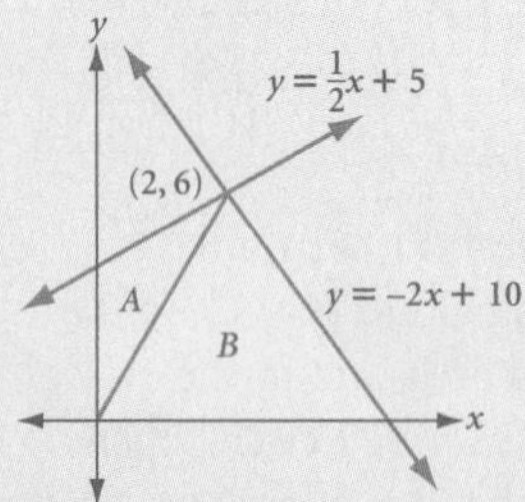

16. Area is 36 square units.

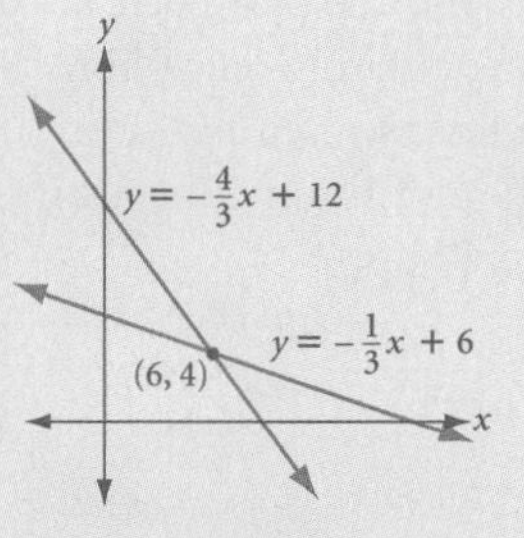

12. Find the shaded area of the regular octagon *ROADSIGN*. The apothem measures about 20 cm. Segment *GI* measures about 16.6 cm. $\approx 996\ \text{cm}^2$

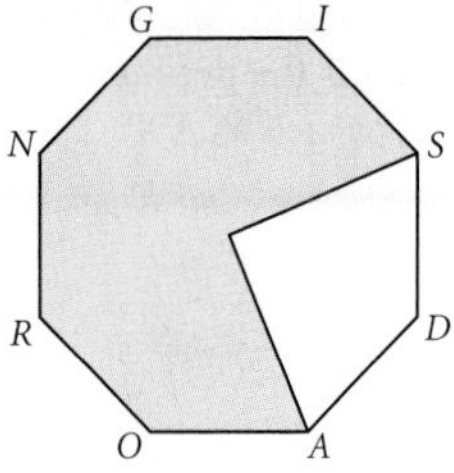

13. Find the shaded area of the regular hexagonal donut. The apothem and sides of the smaller hexagon are half as long as the apothem and sides of the large hexagon. $a \approx 6.9$ cm and $r \approx 8$ cm Ⓗ $\approx 497\ \text{cm}^2$

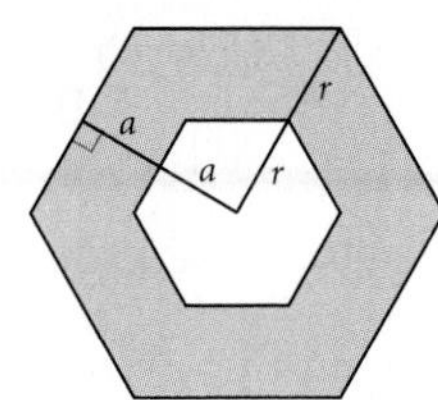

Career CONNECTION

Interior designers, unlike interior decorators, are concerned with the larger planning and technical considerations of interiors, as well as with style and color selection. They have an intuitive sense of spatial relationships. They prepare sketches, schedules, and budgets for client approval and inspect the site until the job is complete.

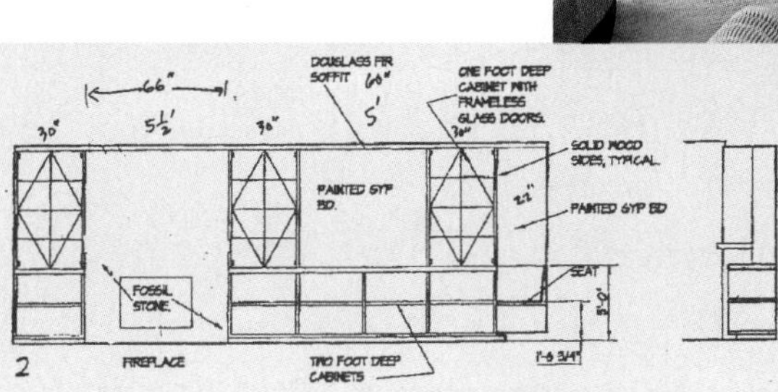

14. **APPLICATION** An interior designer created the kitchen plan shown. The countertop will be constructed of colored concrete. What is its total surface area? If concrete countertops 1.5 inches thick cost \$85 per square foot, what will be the total cost of this countertop?
total surface area = 13,680 in.^{2} = 95 ft^2
cost = \$8075

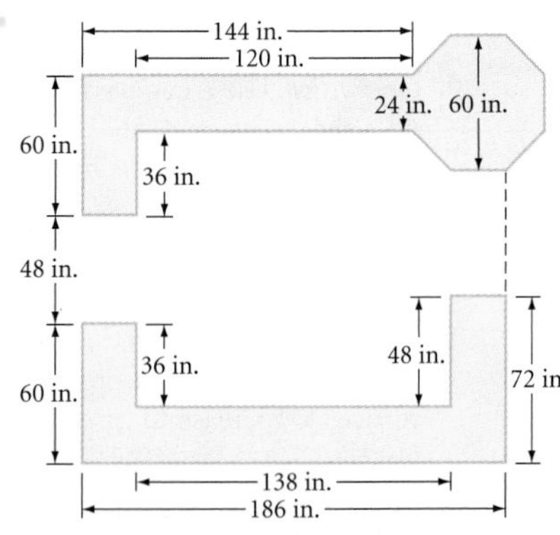

17. Conjecture: The three medians of a triangle divide the triangle into six triangles of equal area. Argument: Triangles 1 and 2 have equal area because they have equal bases and the same height. Because the centroid divides each median into thirds, the height of triangles 1 and 2 is $\frac{1}{3}$ the height of the whole triangle. Each has an area $\frac{1}{6}$ the area of the whole triangle. By the same argument, the other small triangles also have areas of $\frac{1}{6}$ the area of the whole triangle.

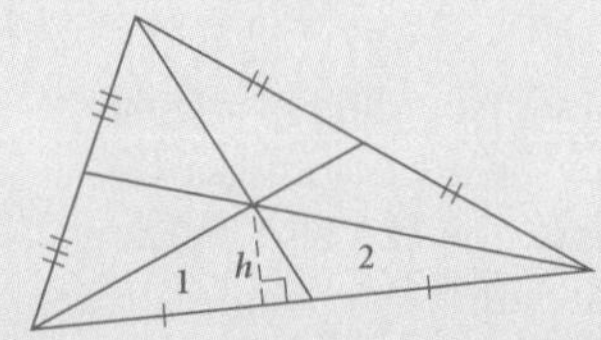

Review

8.1 In Exercises 15 and 16, graph the two lines, then find the area bounded by the x-axis, the y-axis, and both lines.

15. $y = \frac{1}{2}x + 5, y = -2x + 10$ ⓗ

16. $y = -\frac{1}{3}x + 6, y = -\frac{4}{3}x + 12$

3.2 **17.** *Technology* Construct a triangle and its three medians. Compare the areas of the six small triangles that the three medians formed. Make a conjecture, and support it with a convincing argument.

2.3 **18.** If the pattern continues, write an expression for the perimeter of the nth figure in the picture pattern. $nw + ny + 2x$

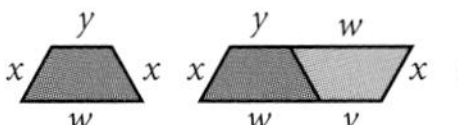

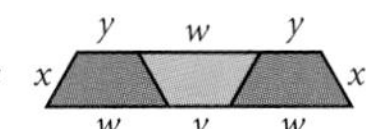

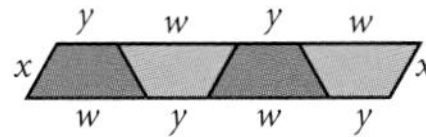

3.7 **19.** Identify the point of concurrency from the construction marks.

a.

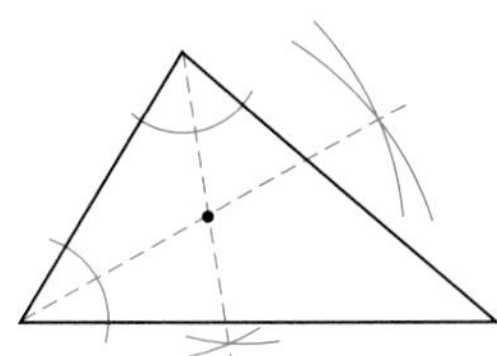

incenter

b.

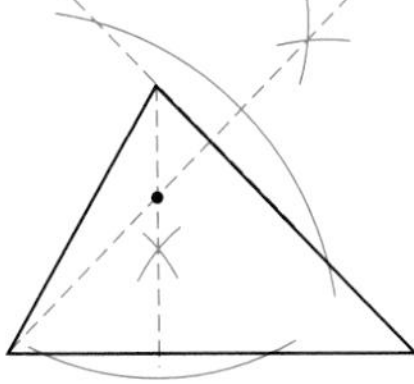

orthocenter

c.

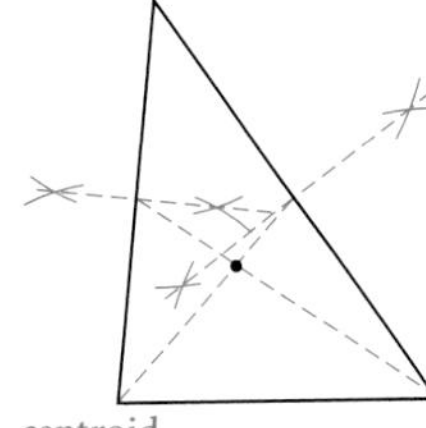

centroid

IMPROVING YOUR VISUAL THINKING SKILLS

The Squared Square Puzzle

The square shown is called a "squared square." A square 112 units on a side is divided into 21 squares. The area of square X is 50^2, or 2500, and the area of square Y is 4^2, or 16. Find the area of each of the other squares.

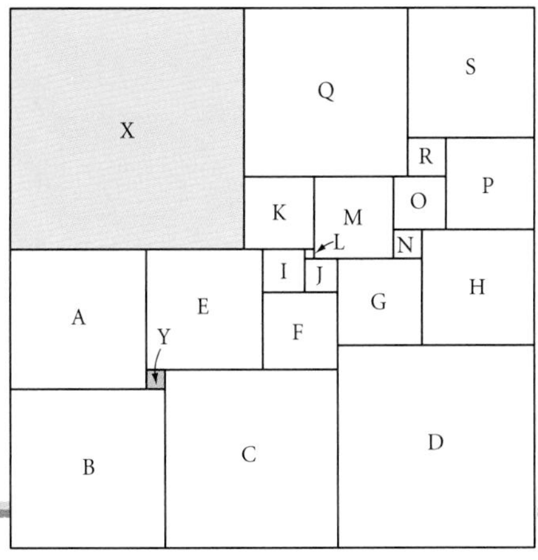

EXTENSIONS

A. Challenge students to create another method for arriving at the formula for the area of a regular polygon. Consider ways of dividing a regular polygon into isosceles triangles and rearranging the triangular pieces into shapes for which they already know the area. [Use a point at the center and divided into triangles with each side as a base, where a is the apothem, s is the length of each side, and n is the number of sides in the regular polygon. If the polygon has an odd number of sides, the triangles can be arranged into a trapezoid with long base $\frac{n+1}{2}s$, short base $\frac{n-1}{2}s$, height a, and area $\left(\frac{\frac{n+1}{2}s + \frac{n-1}{2}s}{2}\right)a = \frac{1}{2}nas$.

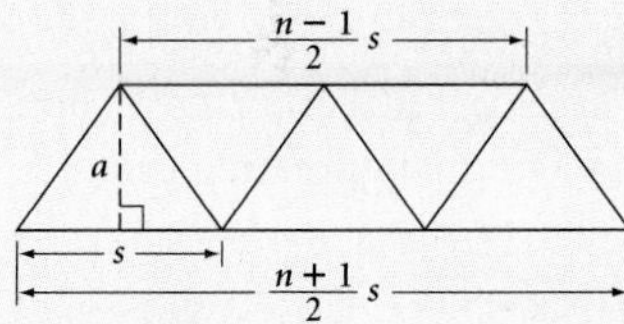

If the polygon has an even number of sides, the triangles can be arranged into a parallelogram with base $\frac{n}{2}s$, height a, and area $\frac{1}{2}nas$.]

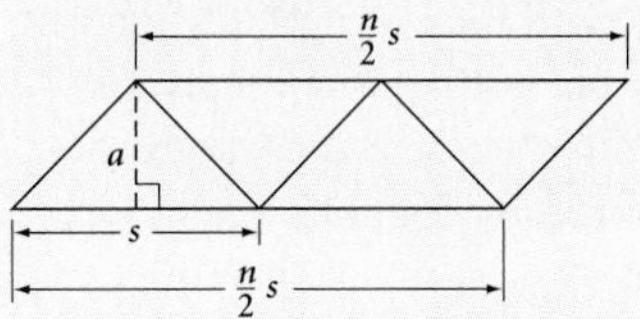

B. Use geometry software to demonstrate the Regular Polygon Area Conjecture.

IMPROVING VISUAL THINKING SKILLS

Students may have difficulty beginning this puzzle, but once they get started they will find the rest manageable. If they have trouble at the beginning, help them see that they know two things about the sides of squares A and B: the sum of their measures and the difference. (They might use lower-case letters for the sides of the squares.) No further manipulation of two variables is needed.

These are the areas of the squares.

A: $29^2 = 841$; B: $33^2 = 1089$; C: $37^2 = 1369$; D: $42^2 = 1764$; E: $25^2 = 625$; F: $16^2 = 256$; G: $18^2 = 324$; H: $24^2 = 576$; I: $9^2 = 81$; J: $7^2 = 49$; K: $15^2 = 225$; L: $2^2 = 4$; M: $17^2 = 289$; N: $6^2 = 36$; O: $11^2 = 121$; P: $19^2 = 361$; Q: $35^2 = 1225$; R: $8^2 = 64$; S: $27^2 = 729$.

EXPLORATION

PLANNING

LESSON OUTLINE

One day:

35 min Investigation

5 min Sharing

5 min Closing

MATERIALS

- square dot paper or graph paper
- geoboards, *optional*
- Pick's Formula for Area (T), *optional*

TEACHING

Areas of irregular figures, polygonal and curved, can be estimated by placing the figure on a grid.

INTRODUCTION

Polygon A can be subdivided into a square and three triangles and the areas of these figures added to get 16. Polygon B can be seen as the result of removing from a rectangle with area 40 four triangles with total area 21, so polygon B's area is 19. **[Alert]** Students might try to find the length of a segment by counting the number of dots on it rather than the number of units between dots.

Exploration

Pick's Formula for Area

You know how to find the area of polygon regions, but how would you find the area of the dinosaur footprint at right?

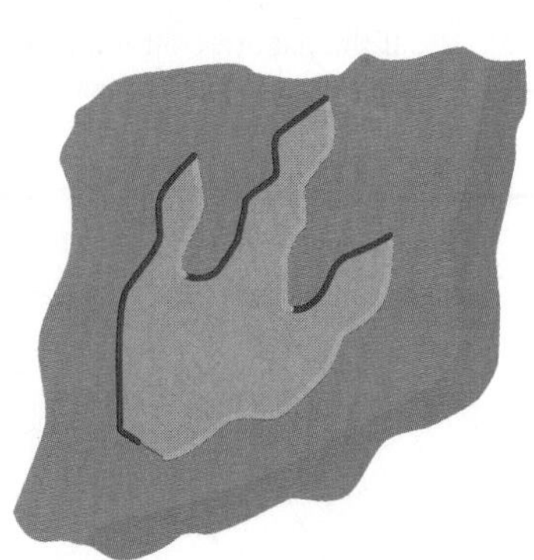

You know how to place a polygon on a grid and count squares to find the area. About a hundred years ago, Austrian mathematician Georg Alexander Pick (1859–1943) discovered a relationship, now known as Pick's formula, for finding the area of figures on a square dot grid.

Let's start by looking at polygons on a square dot grid. The dots are called lattice points. Let's count the lattice points in the interior of the polygon and those on its boundary and compare our findings to the areas of the polygon that you get by counting squares, as you did in Lesson 8.1.

Polygon A

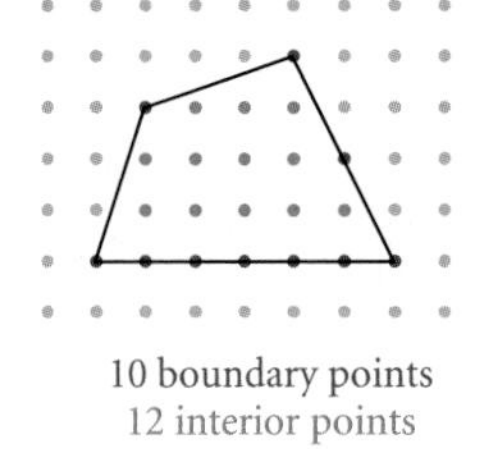

10 boundary points
12 interior points

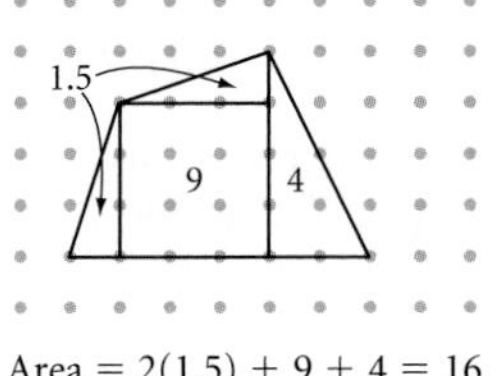

Area = $2(1.5) + 9 + 4 = 16$

Polygon B

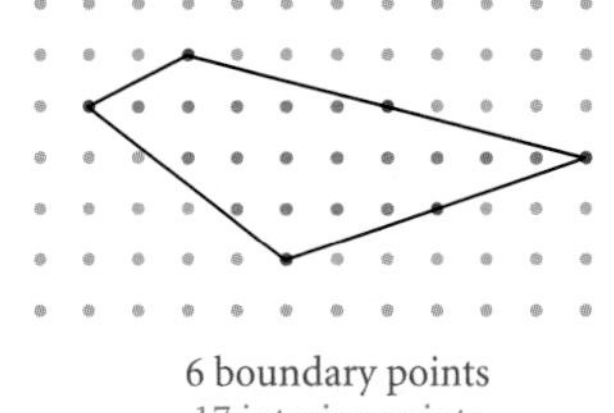

6 boundary points
17 interior points

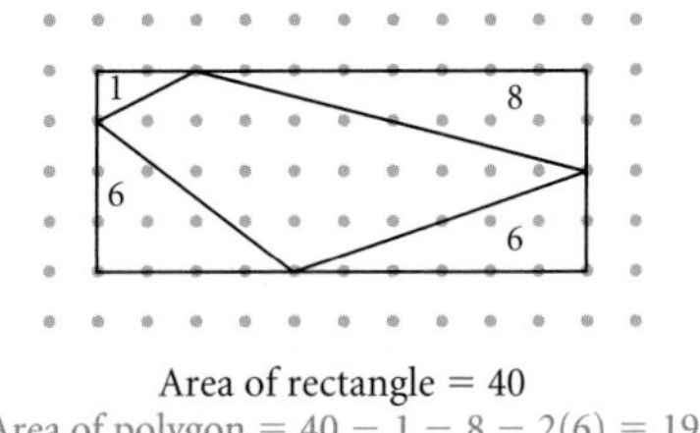

Area of rectangle = 40
Area of polygon = $40 - 1 - 8 - 2(6) = 19$

LESSON OBJECTIVE

- Discover Pick's formula for finding the area of an irregular figure drawn on a grid

NCTM STANDARDS

CONTENT		PROCESS	
✓	Number	✓	Problem Solving
	Algebra		Reasoning
✓	Geometry	✓	Communication
✓	Measurement	✓	Connections
✓	Data/Probability	✓	Representation

How can the boundary points and interior points help us find the area? There are a lot of things to look at. It seems too difficult to find a pattern with our results. An important technique for finding patterns is to hold one variable constant and see what happens with the other variables. That's what you'll do in the activity below.

Activity

Dinosaur Footprints and Other Shapes

You will need

- square dot paper or graph paper
- geoboards (optional)

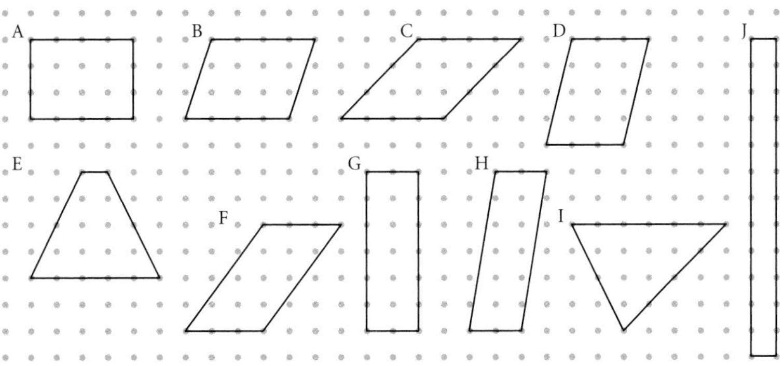

Step 1 Confirm that each polygon A through J above has area $A = 12$.

Step 2 Let b be the number of boundary points and i be the number of interior points. Create and complete a table like this one for polygons A through J.

Polygon ($A = 12$)	A	B	C	D	E	F	G	H	I	J
Number of boundary points (b)	14	10	14	8	10	8	16	6	12	26
Number of interior points (i)	6	8	6	9	8	9	5	10	7	0

Step 3 Study the table for patterns. Do you see a relationship between b and i when $A = 12$? Graph the pairs (b, i) from your table and label each point with its name A through J. What do you notice? Write an equation that fits the points.

Step 4 Consider several polygons with an area of 8. Graph points (b, i) and write an equation.

Step 4 $i = 9 - \frac{1}{2}b$

Step 5 Generalize the formula you found in Steps 3 and 4. When you feel you have enough data, copy and complete the conjecture.

Pick's Formula

If A is the area of a polygon whose vertices are lattice points, b is the number of lattice points on the boundary of the polygon, and i is the number of interior lattice points, then $A = \underset{\frac{1}{2}}{\underline{\ ?\ }}\,b + \underset{1}{\underline{\ ?\ }}\,i + \underset{-1}{\underline{\ ?\ }}$.

Step 3

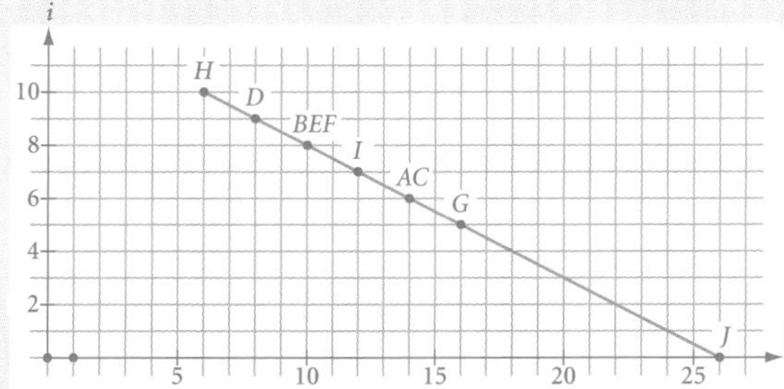

The points lie on the line $i = 13 - \frac{1}{2}b$.

Guiding the Activity

Geoboards might help with this exploration.

Step 3 Students should label the axes. As needed, **[Ask]** "What do you want to figure out to determine the equation of the line?" The equation is $i = 13 + \left(-\frac{1}{2}\right)b$.

Step 5 Students may wonder what to write as a coefficient of i, claiming that "it has no number in front of it" in the formula they derived. Help them see that the coefficient is 1.

Step 6 Students may need help in realizing that they need to measure to find the scale for the map of Texas. If students' calculations disagree with one another, ask if they're counting dots or units when measuring lengths. Pick's formula is accurate for polygons with vertices on grid points. It is not very accurate for these irregular shapes.

SHARING IDEAS

Students might refer to the Pick's Formula transparency as they share.

[Ask] "Are the areas calculated in Step 6 precise?" [All of them are approximate. Pick's formula gives an exact area only of a polygon whose vertices are at grid points, so the areas calculated here are the result of approximating the area of polygons.]"What would happen if you moved one shape on the grid?" [The numbers of boundary and interior points could change, but the area covered by the shape would not change.]

You might mention that Pick's formula is one of many methods for approximating areas of irregular figures. Some methods use counting, while others use probability or calculus.

Sharing Ideas (continued)

To get at the meaning of the coefficients in the formula, especially $\frac{1}{2}$, you might suggest that students start by drawing the smallest possible triangle on the grid $\left(\text{with area } \frac{1}{2}\right)$ and then see how the area changes as they add one grid point at a time to the boundary without introducing any interior points. They can then experiment with introducing interior points one at a time. Another way of thinking about it is that each grid point in the interior represents an entire unit square of area, whereas each grid point on the boundary represents half of a unit square.

Step 6 sample answers: dinosaur: 71 units^2 or about 160 in.^{2}; leaf: 88 units^2 or about 40 in.^{2}; Texas: 84 units^2 or about 313,000 miles^2; oil spill: 114 units^2 or about 2.6 mi^2

Assessing Progress

You can assess students' understanding of area and area conservation and their skill at gathering data systematically and reasoning inductively.

Closing the Lesson

You can find or approximate the area of an irregular shape by first putting it on a grid and then using **Pick's formula,** $A = \left(\frac{1}{2}\right)b + i - 1$. The formula will determine exactly the area of any polygon whose vertices are at grid points.

Pick's formula is especially useful when you apply it to the areas of irregularly shaped regions. Since it relies only on lattice points, you do not need to divide the shape into rectangles or triangles.

Step 6 | Use Pick's formula to find the approximate areas of these irregular shapes.

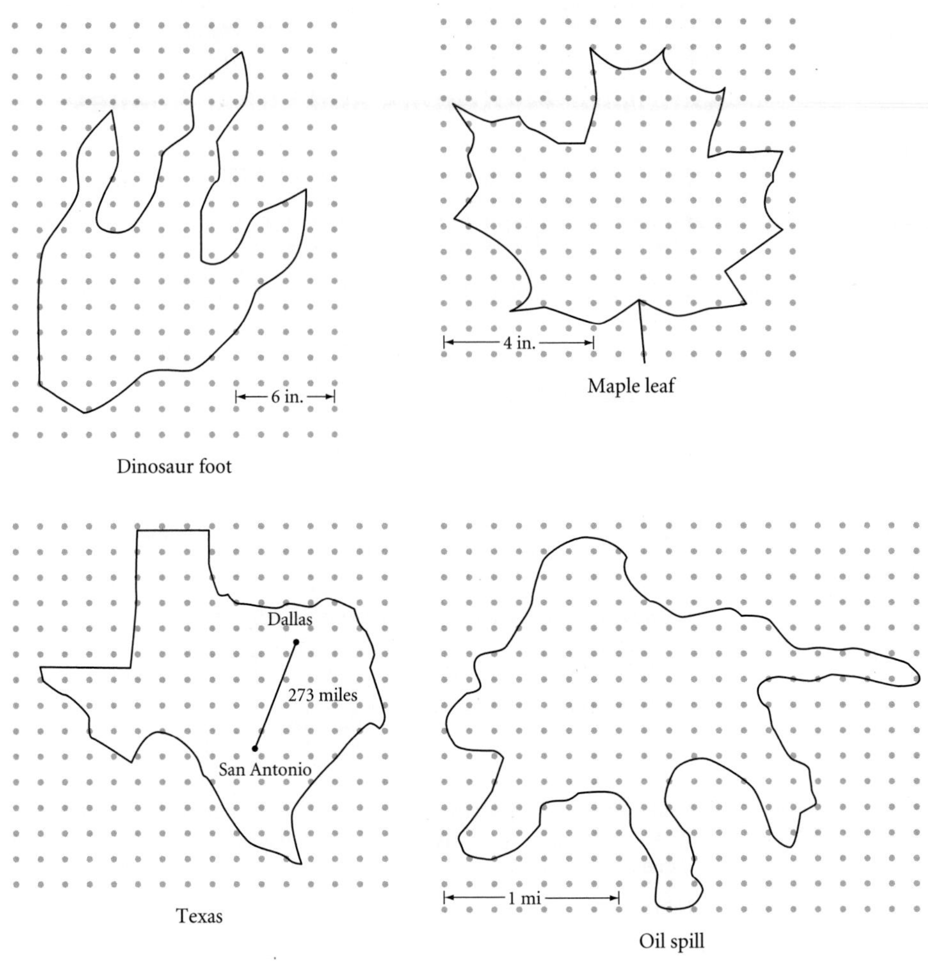

LESSON

8.5

Areas of Circles

So far, you have discovered the formulas for the areas of various polygons. In this lesson, you'll discover the formula for the area of a circle. Most of the shapes you have investigated in this chapter could be divided into rectangles or triangles. Can a circle be divided into rectangles or triangles? Not exactly, but in this investigation you will see an interesting way to think about the area of a circle.

The moon is a dream of the sun.

PAUL KLEE

Investigation
Area Formula for Circles

You will need

- a compass
- scissors

Circles do not have straight sides like polygons do. However, the area of a circle can be rearranged. Let's investigate.

Step 1 Use your compass to make a large circle. Cut out the circular region.

Step 2 Fold the circular region in half. Fold it in half a second time, then a third time and a fourth time. Unfold your circle and cut it along the folds into 16 wedges.

Step 3 Arrange the wedges in a row, alternating the tips up and down to form a shape that resembles a parallelogram.

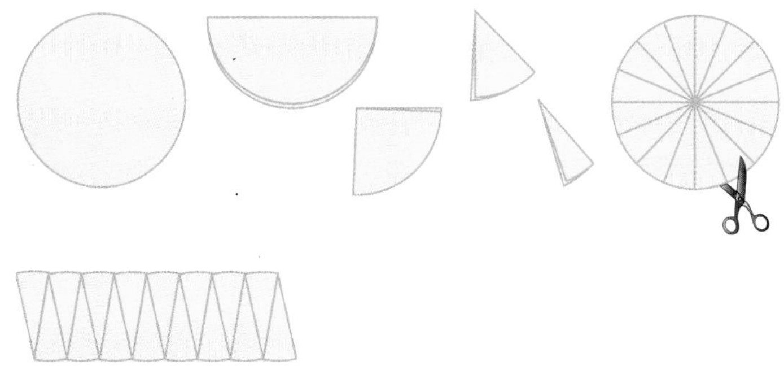

If you cut the circle into more wedges, you could rearrange these thinner wedges to look even more like a rectangle, with fewer bumps. You would not lose or gain any area in this change, so the area of this new "rectangle," skimming off the bumps as you measure its length, would be closer to the area of the original circle.

If you could cut infinitely many wedges, you'd actually have a rectangle with smooth sides. What would its base length be? What would its height be in terms of C, the circumference of the circle?

Step 4 The radius of the original circle is r and the circumference is $2\pi r$. Give the base and the height of a rectangle made of a circle cut into infinitely many wedges. Find its area in terms of r. State your next conjecture.

LESSON 8.5

PLANNING

LESSON OUTLINE

One day:

20 min	Investigation
10 min	Sharing and Examples
5 min	Closing
10 min	Exercises

MATERIALS

- construction tools
- calculators
- scissors

TEACHING

The area of a circle can be expressed in terms of its circumference and therefore in terms of π.

Guiding the Investigation

One step Ask students to derive a formula for the area of a circle. Ask any students who remember some formula to give a justification. Some may divide the circle into pieces. Ask students who can't think of anything whether they have seen something recently about relating circles to inscribed polygons.

You might demonstrate the investigation as students follow along.

Step 1 Make the circle large.

Step 3 Students can tape (or glue) the wedges onto a sheet of paper and label the base and height of the parallelogram in terms of the circumference and radius of the circle. **[Link]** Looking for the limit as the number of divisions approaches infinity is the basis of calculus.

NCTM STANDARDS

CONTENT		PROCESS	
	Number	✓	Problem Solving
✓	Algebra	✓	Reasoning
✓	Geometry	✓	Communication
✓	Measurement	✓	Connections
✓	Data/Probability	✓	Representation

LESSON OBJECTIVES

- Derive the formula for the area of a circle
- Apply area formulas to solve problems
- Develop cooperative behavior

SHARING IDEAS

Have students present whatever variety of statements they've come up with for the Circle Area Conjecture. Some may have derived $\left(\frac{1}{2}\right)Cr$, while others may have found $\pi\left(\frac{d^2}{4}\right)$ or the more familiar πr^2.

[Ask] "How can you remember that the area is πr^2 and the circumference is $2\pi r$?" Let students propose various ways. One way uses dimensional analysis; $2\pi r$ has the same linear units as r, whereas πr^2 has square units.

[Ask] "Does it make sense for π to be in a formula for the area of a circle?" Students may see why a circle has area about three times the area of a square built on its radius, but why should that factor be π? This fact eluded the classical Greek mathematicians, despite their knowledge that the ratio of circumference to diameter was constant.

Assessing Progress

You can assess students' understanding of area, of parallelograms and how to find their areas, of radius, and of circumference as a constant multiple of diameter.

▶ EXAMPLE A

The diameter of the small pie and the radius of the large pie are given. Students may discuss whether "larger" refers to diameter, perimeter, area, or volume. [It is meant to refer to area.] The question "How much larger?" can refer to either a difference or a ratio. The solution gives both. The ratio of large area to small area is not 10 to 8 (125%) but 100 to 64 (156%).

[Alert] Students may not understand when to express their answers using the symbol π and when to use an approximation for π. As with perimeters, they should use the symbol until the end and then approximate if they need a decimal value.

Circle Area Conjecture C-81

The area of a circle is given by the formula __?__, where A is the area and r is the radius of the circle. $A = \pi r^2$

How do you use this new conjecture? Let's look at a few examples.

EXAMPLE A

The small apple pie has a diameter of 8 inches, and the large cherry pie has a radius of 5 inches. How much larger is the large pie?

▶ Solution

First, find each area.

Small pie	Large pie
$A = \pi r^2$	$A = \pi r^2$
$= \pi(4)^2$	$= \pi(5)^2$
$= \pi(16)$	$= \pi(25)$
≈ 50.2	≈ 78.5

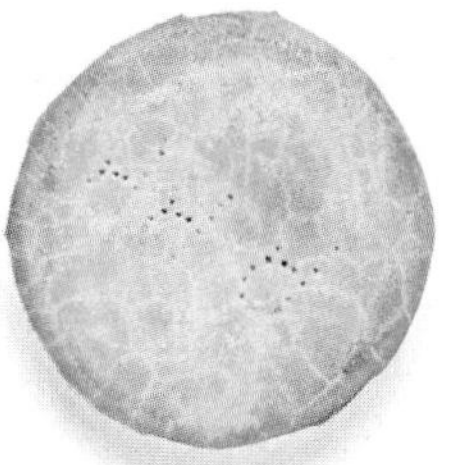

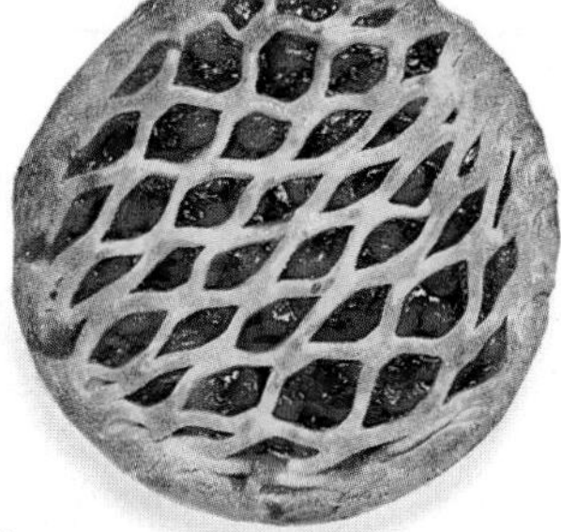

The large pie is 78.5 in^2, and the small pie is 50.2 in^2. The difference in area is about 28.3 square inches. So the large pie is more than 50% larger than the small pie, assuming they have the same thickness. Notice that we used 3.14 as an approximate value for π.

EXAMPLE B

If the area of the circle at right is 256π m^2, what is the circumference of the circle?

▶ Solution

Use the area to find the radius, then use the radius to find the circumference.

$$A = \pi r^2 \qquad C = 2\pi r$$
$$256\pi = \pi r^2 \qquad = 2\pi(16)$$
$$256 = r^2 \qquad = 32\pi$$
$$r = 16 \qquad \approx 100.5 \text{ m}$$

The circumference is 32π meters, or approximately 100.5 meters.

▶ EXAMPLE B

This example demonstrates the convenience of having results in terms of π and not approximating until the end. If students reach for their calculators in the first step, they'll miss the easy cancellation of 2π and perhaps fail to arrive at the exact value for r.

Closing the Lesson

The area of a circle can be found in several ways, all involving π either directly or indirectly. The most common formula is $A = \pi r^2$. The formula $A = \left(\frac{1}{2}\right)rC$ comes either from wedges or from seeing the circle as the limit of inscribed regular polygons.

EXERCISES

You will need

Geometry software for Exercise 19

Use the Circle Area Conjecture to solve for the unknown measures in Exercises 1–8. Leave your answers in terms of π, unless the problem asks for an approximation. For approximations, use the π key on your calculator.

1. If $r = 3$ in., $A = \underline{?}$. 9π in.^{2}

2. If $r = 7$ cm, $A = \underline{?}$. 49π cm^2

3. If $r = 0.5$ m, $A \approx \underline{?}$. 0.79 m^2

4. If $A = 9\pi$ cm^2, then $r = \underline{?}$. 3 cm

5. If $A = 3\pi$ in^2, then $r = \underline{?}$. $\sqrt{3}$ in.

6. If $A = 0.785$ m^2, then $r \approx \underline{?}$. 0.5 m

7. If $C = 12\pi$ in., then $A = \underline{?}$. 36π in.^{2}

8. If $C = 314$ m, then $A \approx \underline{?}$. 7846 m^2

9. What is the area of the shaded region between the circle and the rectangle? $25\pi - 48$ or about 30.5 square units

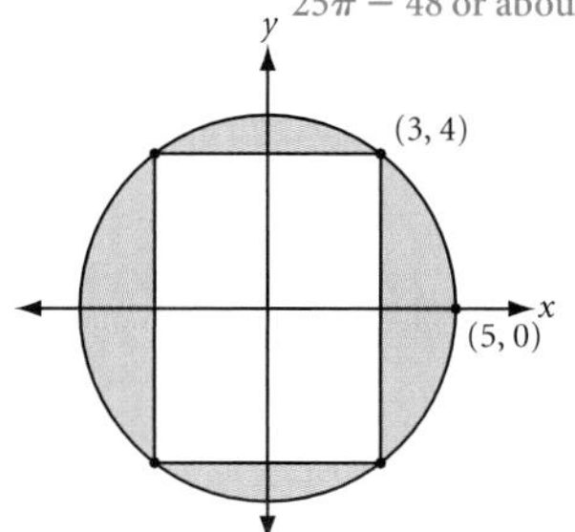

10. What is the area of the shaded region between the circle and the triangle? $100\pi - 128$ or about 186 square units

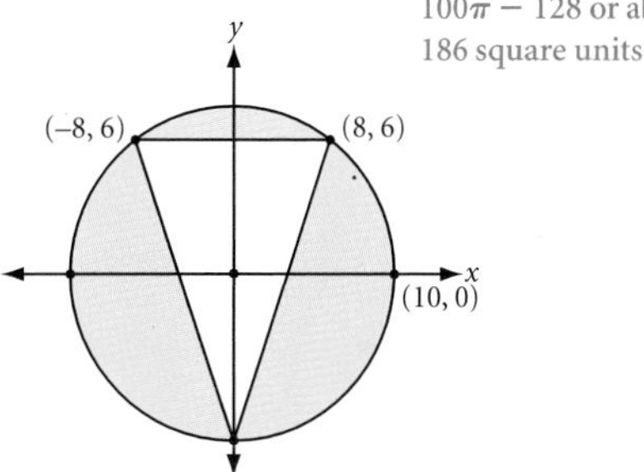

11. Sketch and label a circle with an area of 324π cm^2. Be sure to label the length of the radius.

12. APPLICATION The rotating sprinkler arms in the photo at right are all 16 meters long. What is the area of each circular farm? Express your answer to the nearest square meter. 804 m^2

13. APPLICATION A small college TV station can broadcast its programming to households within a radius of 60 kilometers. How many square kilometers of viewing area does the station reach? Express your answer to the nearest square kilometer. 11,310 km^2

14. Sampson's dog, Cecil, is tied to a post by a chain 7 meters long. How much play area does Cecil have? Express your answer to the nearest square meter. 154 m^2

15. APPLICATION A muscle's strength is proportional to its cross-sectional area. If the cross section of one muscle is a circular region with a radius of 3 cm, and the cross section of a second, identical type of muscle is a circular region with a radius of 6 cm, how many times stronger is the second muscle? ⓗ 4 times

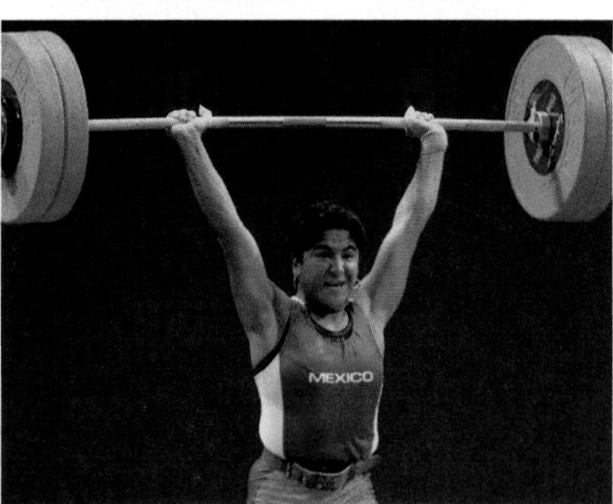

Champion weight lifter Soraya Jimenez extends barbells weighing almost double her own body weight.

Exercise 11 As needed, use an approach similar to that of Exercise 5.

11.

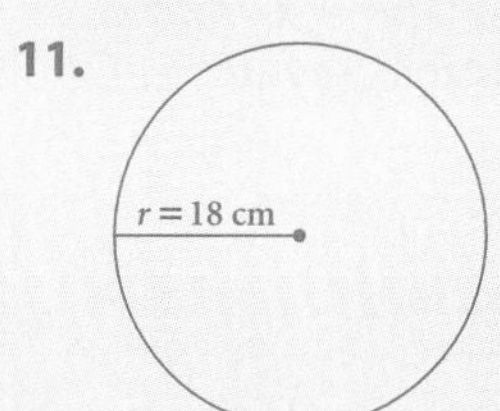

Exercises 12–15 If students are having difficulty, encourage them to draw pictures.

Exercise 15 [Language] A cross section of a three-dimensional object is the intersection of that object with a plane perpendicular to the axis. If you cut a thin slice of an object, you can see a cross section. You may need to explain what it means for the strength of a bone to be "proportional to its cross-sectional area." This idea will be revisited in Chapter 11 in the Exploration Why Elephants Have Big Ears.

BUILDING UNDERSTANDING

As needed, you might have students work on several exercises, especially some in which they need to approximate the value of π, and then share their results.

ASSIGNING HOMEWORK

Essential	1–14
Performance assessment	13
Portfolio	12
Journal	16
Group	15
Review	17–22

Helping with the Exercises

None of the answers involving measurement can be exact. However, when π is left in the answer, an equal sign shows that no rounding has been done. Approximate answers (with an approximation sign, $\approx$) are used for answers that have been rounded. Because π is irrational, calculations with π always require rounding.

Exercise 5 Students may be unfamiliar with radicals and claim that there's no number whose square is 3. Ask whether there's a way to get the radius from the coefficient 9 in Exercise 4 and whether that same method might apply to the coefficient 3 in this exercise. It's better to leave the answer in terms of $\sqrt{3}$, just as with π, but if students want an approximate value they can use a calculator.

Exercise 6 Here finding an approximate square root with a calculator is more important than in Exercise 5.

Exercise 9 If students are stuck, ask whether any methods they've used before could be helpful here. They've often used subtraction.

19. The triangles have equal area when the point is at the intersection of the two diagonals. There is no other location at which all four triangles have equal area.

22.

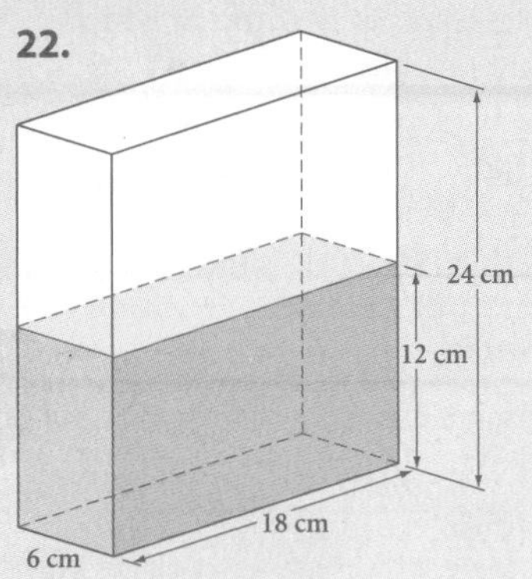

16. What would be a good approximation for the area of a regular 100-gon inscribed in a circle with radius r? Explain your reasoning. ⓗ
$A \approx \pi r^2$ because the 100-gon almost completely fills the circle.

Review

8.1 **17.** $A = \underline{?}$ 456 cm²

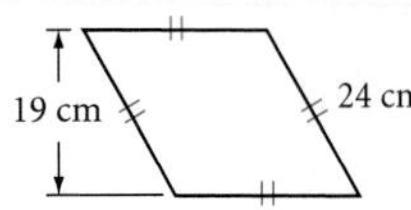

8.2 **18.** $A = \underline{?}$ 36 ft²

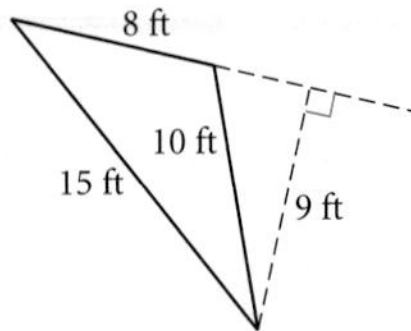

8.3 **19.** ***Technology*** Construct a parallelogram and a point in its interior. Construct segments from this point to each vertex, forming four triangles. Measure the area of each triangle. Move the point to find a location where all four triangles have equal area. Is there more than one such location? Explain your findings.

6.3 **20.** Explain why x must be 48°.
$x = m\widehat{DE} = 2 \cdot 24° = 48°$

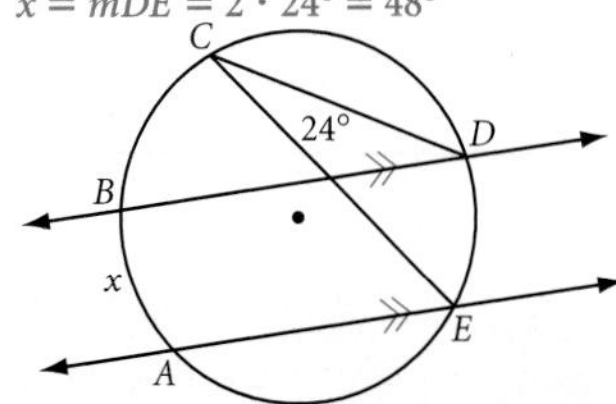

4.1 **21.** What's wrong with this picture?
$90° + 38° + 28° + 28° \neq 180°$

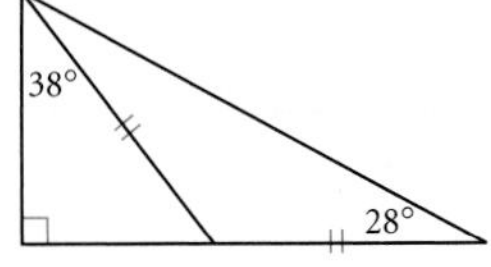

1.8 **22.** The 6-by-18-by-24 cm clear plastic sealed container is resting on a cylinder. It is partially filled with liquid, as shown. Sketch the container resting on its smallest face. Show the liquid level in this position.

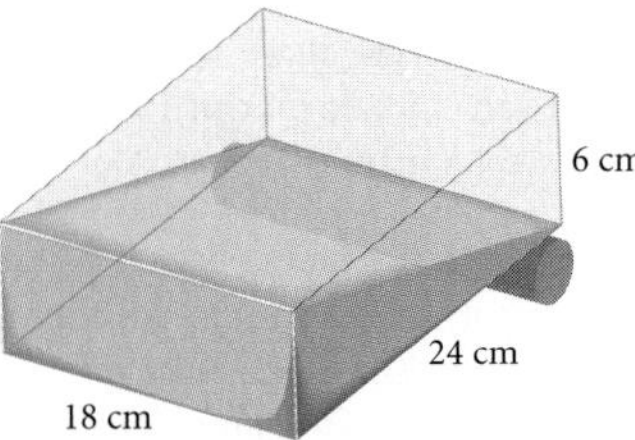

IMPROVING YOUR VISUAL THINKING SKILLS

Random Points

What is the probability of randomly selecting from the 3-by-3 grid at right three points that form the vertices of an isosceles triangle?

IMPROVING VISUAL THINKING SKILLS

To encourage students who need help, **[Ask]** "How many isosceles triangles have their vertex angle at this point?" [2 with vertex angle at each corner, 4 with vertex angle at each side midpoint, and 8 with vertex angle in the center; $2 \cdot 4 + 4 \cdot 4 + 8 = 32$] Students can use symmetry to consider only four points. Familiarity with counting combinations will help them see that there are 84 possible ways to select three points on the grid $\left(\frac{9 \cdot 8 \cdot 7}{2 \cdot 3} = 84\right)$; 32 out of 84 gives a probability of $\frac{8}{21}$.

LESSON 8.6

Any Way You Slice It

Cut my pie into four pieces—
I don't think I could eat eight.
YOGI BERRA

In Lesson 8.5, you discovered a formula for calculating the area of a circle. With the help of your visual thinking and problem-solving skills, you can calculate the areas of different sections of a circle.

Its makers claimed this was the world's largest slice of pizza.

If you cut a slice of pizza, each slice would probably be a sector of a circle. If you could make only one straight cut with your knife, your slice would be a segment of a circle. If you don't like the crust, you'd cut out the center of the pizza; the crust shape that would remain is called an annulus.

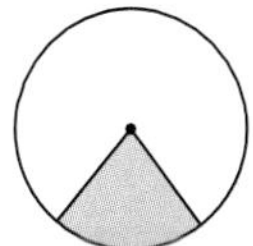

Sector of a circle

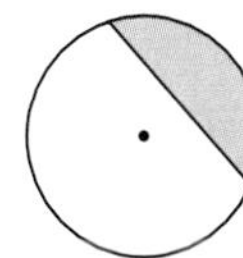

Segment of a circle

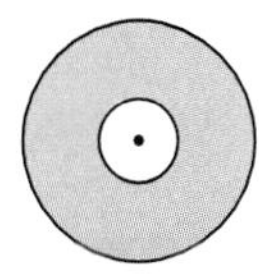

Annulus

A **sector of a circle** is the region between two radii of a circle and the included arc.

A **segment of a circle** is the region between a chord of a circle and the included arc.

An **annulus** is the region between two concentric circles.

"Picture equations" are helpful when you try to visualize the areas of these regions. The picture equations below show you how to find the area of a sector of a circle, the area of a segment of a circle, and the area of an annulus.

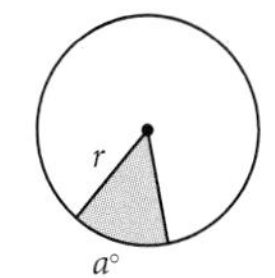

$$\left(\frac{a}{360}\right) \cdot \pi r^2 = A_{\text{sector}}$$

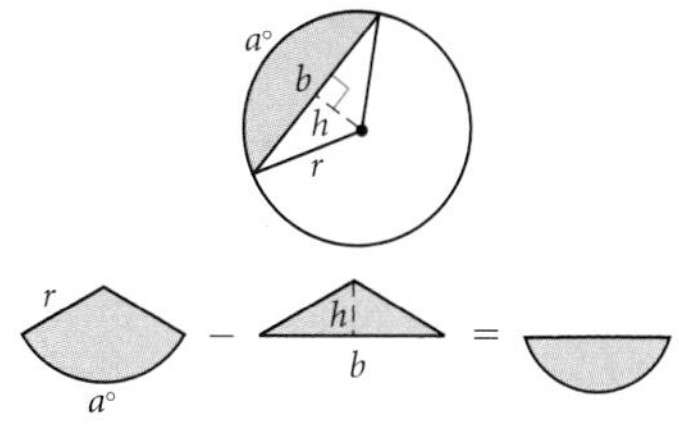

$$\left(\frac{a}{360}\right) \cdot \pi r^2 - \frac{1}{2}bh = A_{\text{segment}}$$

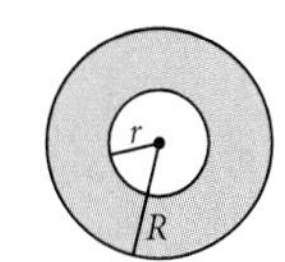

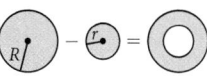

$$\pi R^2 - \pi r^2 = A_{\text{annulus}}$$

NCTM STANDARDS

CONTENT		PROCESS	
✓	Number	✓	Problem Solving
✓	Algebra	✓	Reasoning
✓	Geometry	✓	Communication
✓	Measurement	✓	Connections
	Data/Probability		Representation

LESSON OBJECTIVES

- Discover formulas and methods for calculating the area of annuluses, sectors, and segments of circles
- Learn new vocabulary
- Develop problem-solving skills and cooperative behavior

LESSON 8.6

PLANNING

LESSON OUTLINE

One day:

10 min	Investigation or Examples
5 min	Sharing
5 min	Closing
25 min	Exercises

MATERIALS

none

TEACHING

One step Refer students to the investigation in Lesson 8.5, in which they folded a circle and cut out "wedges." Ask what part of the circle's area was in each wedge. Now you'll consider the reverse question. Pose this problem, adapted from Exercise 13: "Suppose the pointed angle of this slice of pizza is 36°, the long sides have length 20 feet, and one can of tomato sauce will cover 3 square feet of pizza. How many cans would you need to cover this slice?" As needed, encourage students to draw pictures. **[Ask]** "Have you decided whether or not it would help to find the area of the whole circular pizza?" "Is there any way to determine what part this slice is of the whole?" Introduce the terms *sector, segment,* and *annulus* during Sharing, and then consider how to calculate the area of the latter two regions.

INTRODUCTION

[Alert] As you discuss a circle segment, students may be thinking of a cut through the center, a semicircle, which is a segment and a sector. Be sure students' understanding includes all segments.

[Language] *Annulus* is Latin for "ring." As you discuss with students the definition of *annulus,* check that they know what *concentric* means. You might refer back to Lesson 1.6.

▶ EXAMPLE A

If you have a physical model, students would probably benefit from seeing or even handling it.

The picture equation expresses the area of a sector in terms of the arc length of the sector, whereas this example works with only the central angle. Ask how the numbers are related. Because they're the same, you can **[Ask]** "What part of the area of the circle is in the sector?" $\left[\frac{45}{360} = \frac{1}{8}\right]$

▶ EXAMPLE B

Examples A and B appeal to different learning styles. Example A is intentionally presented in two columns for analytical, linear learners, while Example B, in paragraph form, is more verbal. You might also want to show Example B in two columns.

Some students may need to see more details in the derivation:

$A = \left(\frac{a}{360}\right)(\pi r^2) - \left(\frac{1}{2}\right)(b)(h) =$
$\left(\frac{90}{360}\right)(\pi)(6\text{ cm})^2 -$
$\left(\frac{1}{2}\right)(6\text{ cm})(6\text{ cm}) =$
$\left(\frac{1}{4}\right)(36\pi\text{ cm}^2) - \left(\frac{1}{2}\right)(36\text{ cm}^2) =$
$9\pi\text{ cm}^2 - 18\text{ cm}^2 =$
$(9\pi - 18)\text{ cm}^2 \approx 10.3\text{ cm}^2$

A result involving π may not be so useful if you have a concrete reason to know the area. Most students will benefit from learning to estimate. **[Ask]** "To the nearest whole number, what is the value of 9π minus 18?" [π is about 3, so $9\pi - 18$ is about 9.] Or students can use a calculator and round the answer to the appropriate number of significant digits.

EXAMPLE A

Find the area of the shaded sector.

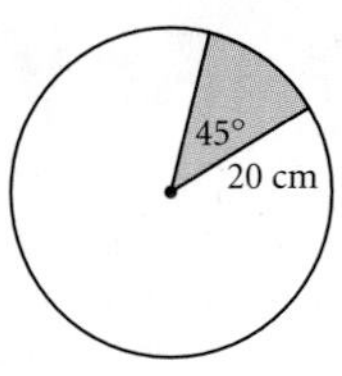

▶ Solution

The sector is $\frac{45°}{360°}$, or $\frac{1}{8}$, of the circle.

$A_{\text{sector}} = \left(\frac{a}{360}\right) \cdot \pi r^2$	The area formula for a sector.
$= \left(\frac{45}{360}\right) \cdot \pi(20)^2$	Substitute $r = 20$ and $a = 45$.
$= \left(\frac{1}{8}\right) \cdot 400\pi$	Reduce the fraction and square 20.
$= 50\pi$	Multiply.

The area is $50\pi\text{ cm}^2$.

EXAMPLE B

Find the area of the shaded segment.

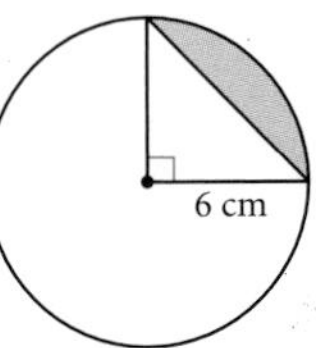

▶ Solution

According to the picture equation on page 437, the area of a segment is equivalent to the area of the sector minus the area of the triangle. You can use the method in Example A to find that the area of the sector is $\left(\frac{1}{4}\right)(36\pi\text{ cm}^2)$, or $9\pi\text{ cm}^2$. The area of the triangle is $\left(\frac{1}{2}\right)(6)(6)$, or 18 cm^2. So the area of the segment is $(9\pi - 18)\text{ cm}^2$.

EXAMPLE C

The shaded area is $14\pi\text{ cm}^2$, and the radius is 6 cm. Find x.

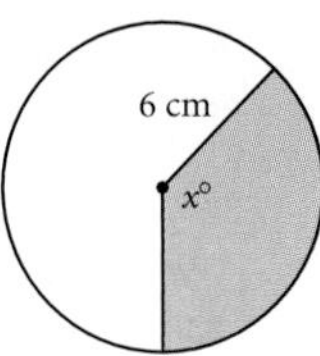

▶ Solution

The sector's area is $\frac{x}{360}$ of the circle's area, which is 36π.

$$14\pi = \left(\frac{x}{360}\right)(36\pi)$$

$$\frac{(360)(14\pi)}{36\pi} = x$$

$$x = 140$$

The central angle measures 140°.

▶ EXAMPLE C

As needed, remind students that the measure of the central angle is the same as the measure of the arc.

You may want to point out that the formula being used is $A = \left(\frac{a}{360}\right)\pi r^2$. For students with weaker algebra skills, you may need to explain that the second step multiplies both sides of the equation by $\frac{360}{36\pi}$, or that this step may be seen as two steps: multiplying both sides by 360 and dividing both sides by 36π.

SHARING IDEAS

You may have Sharing after the one-step investigation or after students have worked on some of the exercises.

Ask what the key idea is in finding the area of a sector. Many students have difficulty with ratios like the one embedded here. Emphasize that they're just finding what part of the area of the whole circle is in the sector. That part is the same as the part of 360° that's in the angle measure of the sector. They encountered similar reasoning when calculating arc

EXERCISES

You will need

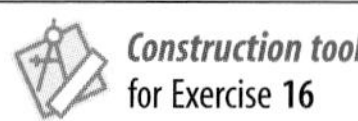

Construction tools for Exercise 16

In Exercises 1–8, find the area of the shaded region. The radius of each circle is r. If two circles are shown, r is the radius of the smaller circle and R is the radius of the larger circle.

1. $r = 6$ cm 6π cm²

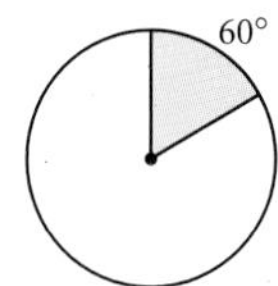

2. $r = 8$ cm $\frac{64\pi}{3}$ cm²

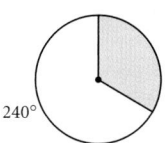

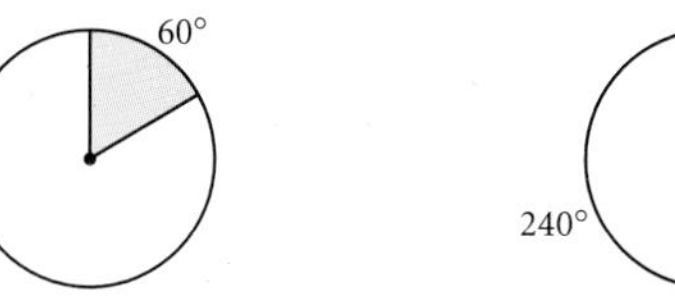

3. $r = 16$ cm 192π cm²

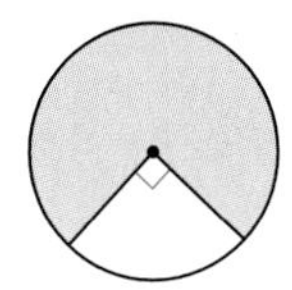

4. $r = 2$ cm $(\pi - 2)$ cm²

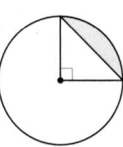

5. $r = 8$ cm $(48\pi + 32)$ cm²

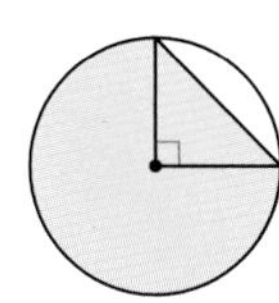

6. $R = 7$ cm
$r = 4$ cm (h) 33π cm²

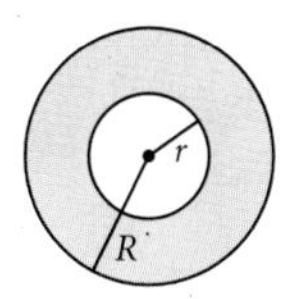

7. $r = 2$ cm 21π cm²

10

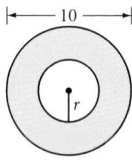

8. $R = 12$ cm
$r = 9$ cm $\frac{105\pi}{2}$ cm²

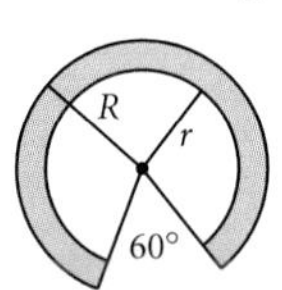

9. The shaded area is 12π cm². Find r. 6 cm

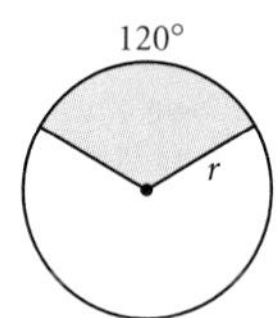

10. The shaded area is 32π cm². Find r. 7 cm

18

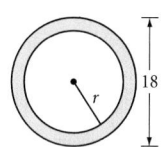

11. The shaded area is 120π cm², and the radius is 24 cm. Find x. 75

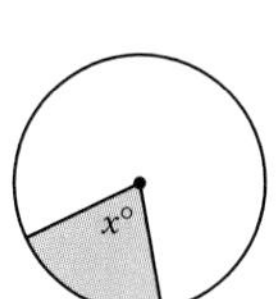

12. The shaded area is 10π cm². The radius of the large circle is 10 cm, and the radius of the small circle is 8 cm. Find x. (h) 100

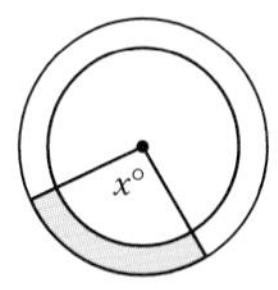

13. Suppose the pizza slice in the photo at the beginning of this lesson is a sector with a 36° arc, and the pizza has a radius of 20 ft. If one can of tomato sauce will cover 3 ft² of pizza, how many cans would you need to cover this slice? 42

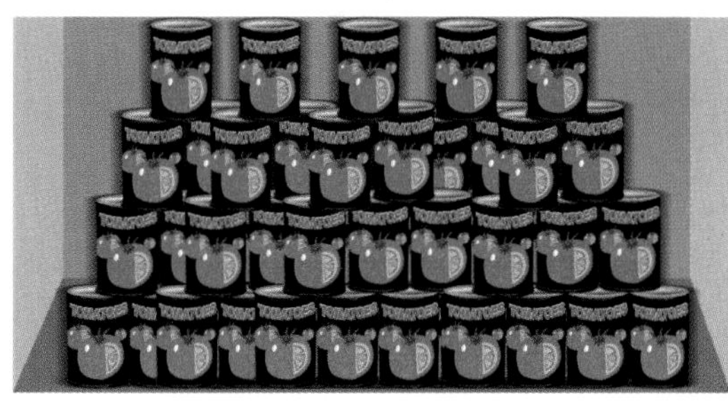

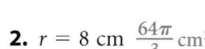

Sharing Ideas (continued)

length. The length of the arc was the same part of the circumference as the measure of the central angle was of 360°.

Ask how segments of circles are related to line segments. They're different because line segments are one-dimensional objects and segments of circles have two dimensions. On the other hand, a line segment across the circle (that is, a chord) cuts off a segment of the circle.

[Ask] "Are sectors and segments of a circle parts of the circle?" [Actually, they're not; they're part of the interior of the circle.]

Ask whether students think they need to memorize formulas for the area of a sector, segment, and annulus. It's much more important that they understand the meaning of the terms and how to find the area from the area of a circle.

Assessing Progress

Through students' work on the exercises, you can assess their understanding of circle circumference and area.

Closing the Lesson

The area of a **sector** of a circle is the same part of the area of the whole circle as the measure of the central angle of the sector is of 360°. The area of a **segment** of a circle can be found by subtracting the area of a triangle from that of the corresponding sector. The area of an **annulus** is the difference in areas of the outside and inside circles.

Because no example of an annulus is given, you may want to work through Exercise 6, 7, 8, 10, or 12.

BUILDING UNDERSTANDING

Students may find these exercises difficult. Be prepared to give plenty of support to keep down the frustration level.

ASSIGNING HOMEWORK

Essential	1–12
Performance assessment	13, 14
Portfolio	13, 14
Group	15, 16
Review	17–22

MATERIALS

- Exercise 15 (T), *optional*
- Exercise 17 (T), *optional*

▶Helping with the Exercises

Exercises 1–8 As needed, suggest that students focus on the unshaded as well as the shaded regions. You might work examples to demonstrate the area of the unshaded regions and then during homework discussion ask for the area of the unshaded regions.

Exercise 3 Ask frustrated students whether this exercise is like Exercise 2, to help them see that they need to subtract the given angle measure from 360°.

Exercise 4 As needed, **[Ask]** "What's needed to find the area of a segment? Can you sketch a picture equation?"

Exercise 8 Students might find the area of the whole annulus first, or they might find the partial areas of the circles and then subtract. This is a good exercise to show that many problems have multiple approaches. Challenge students to find multiple approaches to problems.

See pages 774–775 for answers to Exercises 15 and 16.

14. Utopia Park has just installed a circular fountain 8 meters in diameter. The Park Committee wants to pave a 1.5-meter-wide path around the fountain. If paving costs \$10 per square meter, find the cost to the nearest dollar of the paved path around the fountain. \$448

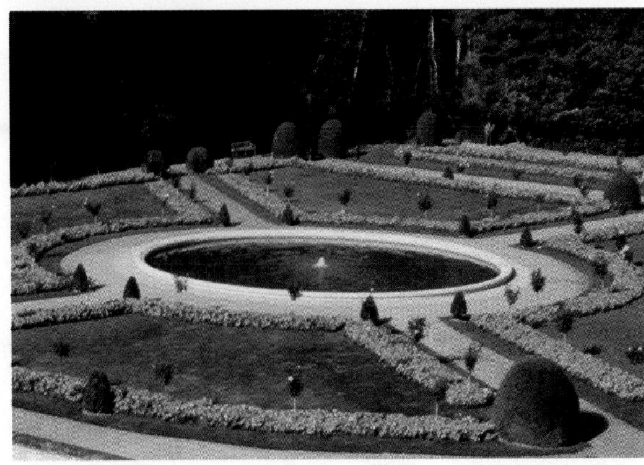

This circular fountain at the Chateau de Villandry in Loire Valley, France, shares a center with the circular path around it. How many concentric arcs and circles do you see in the picture?

Mathematics CONNECTION

Attempts to solve the famous problem of rectifying a circle—finding a rectangle with the same area as a given circle—led to the creation of some special shapes made up of parts of circles. The diagrams below are based on some that Leonardo da Vinci sketched while attempting to solve this problem.

15. The illustrations below demonstrate how to rectify the pendulum.

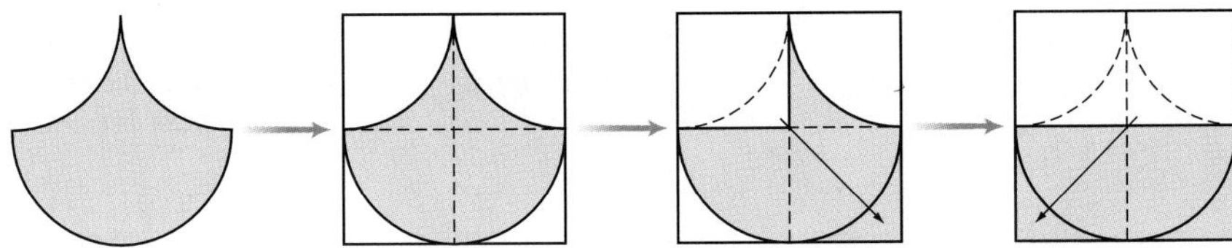

In a series of diagrams, demonstrate how to rectify each figure.

a. 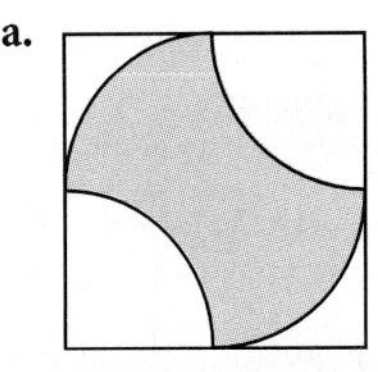

b. 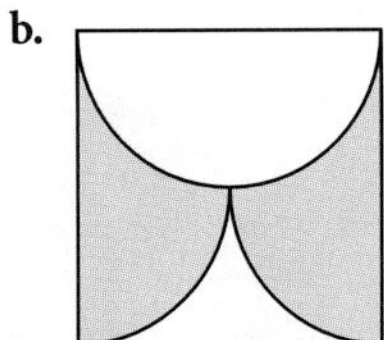

c. 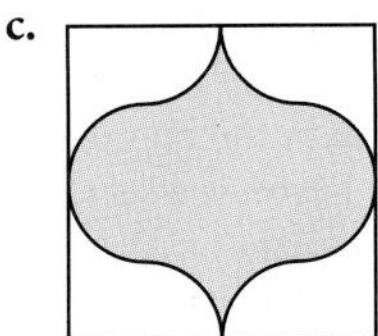

d. 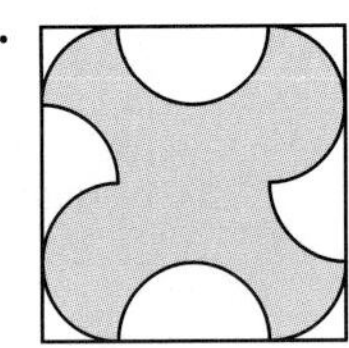

16. *Construction* Reverse the process you used in Exercise 15. On graph paper, draw a 12-by-6 rectangle. Use your compass to divide it into at least four parts, then rearrange the parts into a new curved figure. Draw its outline on graph paper.

Exercises 9–12 These four exercises are the most challenging of the lesson.

Exercise 9 As needed, ask students whether they can express the area, 12π, in terms of r and write an equation.

Exercise 11 If students are having difficulty, wonder aloud whether it would help to use the fact that the shaded area is the same part of the whole area as the angle measure is of 360°. This observation leads to an expression.

Exercise 12 As needed, ask what might be a first step. Students can find the area of the whole annulus first and then consider what part of that area 10π is.

Exercise 15 It might help students to describe in words how the curved region is changed into a rectangular region in the example.

[Context] Leonardo da Vinci (1452–1519) was an Italian painter, draftsman, sculptor, architect, and engineer. His talents were so many and so diverse that many feel he epitomizes the Renaissance ideal.

Review

8.5 **17.** Each set of circles is externally tangent. What is the area of the shaded region in each figure? What percentage of the area of the square is the area of the circle or circles in each figure? All given measurements are in centimeters.

a. 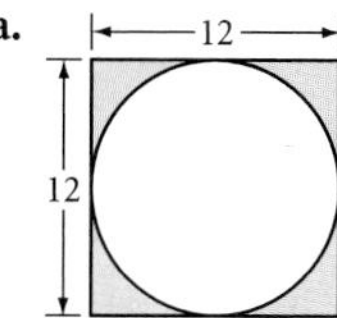

$(144 - 36\pi)$ cm^2; 78.54%

b. 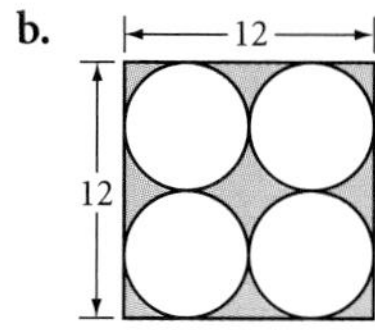

$(144 - 36\pi)$ cm^2; 78.54%

c. 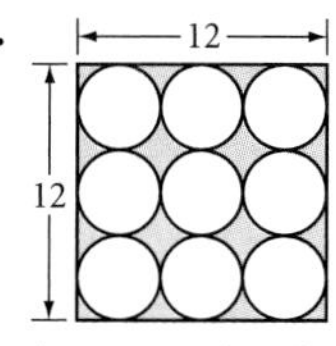

$(144 - 36\pi)$ cm^2; 78.54%

d. 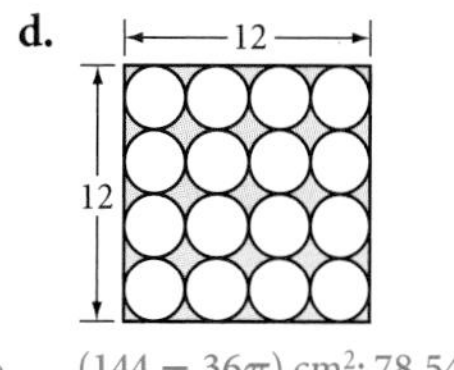

$(144 - 36\pi)$ cm^2; 78.54%

8.2 **18.** The height of a trapezoid is 15 m and the midsegment is 32 m. What is the area of the trapezoid? ⓗ 480 m^2

In Exercises 19–22, identify each statement as true or false. If true, explain why. If false, give a counterexample.

6.7 **19.** If the arc of a circle measures 90° and has an arc length of 24π cm, then the radius of the circle is 48 cm. True. If $24\pi = \frac{90}{360} \cdot 2\pi r$, then $r = 48$ cm.

5.2 **20.** If the measure of each exterior angle of a regular polygon is 24°, then the polygon has 15 sides. True. If $\frac{360}{n} = 24$, then $n = 15$.

5.6 **21.** If the diagonals of a parallelogram bisect its angles, then the parallelogram is a square. False. It could be a rhombus.

4.3 **22.** If two sides of a triangle measure 25 cm and 30 cm, then the third side must be greater than 5 cm but less than 55 cm. true; Triangle Inequality Conjecture

IMPROVING YOUR REASONING SKILLS

Code Equations

Each code below uses the first letters of words that will make the equation true. For example, $12M$ = a Y is an abbreviation of the equation 12 Months = a Year. Find the missing words in each code.

1. $45D$ = an AA of an IRT

2. $7 = SH$

3. $90D$ = each A of a R

4. $5 = D$ in a P

IMPROVING REASONING SKILLS

1. 45 Degrees in an Acute Angle of an Isosceles Right Triangle

2. 7 Sides on a Heptagon

3. 90 Degrees in each Angle of a Rectangle

4. 5 Diagonals in a Pentagon

Exercise 17 Students may be surprised to discover that parts a–d all have the same answer. **[Ask]** "Why are the areas the same?" [Algebraically, $n^2\pi\left(\frac{12}{2n}\right)^2$ is 36π no matter what n is. More insightfully, perhaps, when you divide the linear dimensions of a figure by n, you divide its area by n^2, so n^2 copies of the reduced figure will have the same area as the original.]

EXTENSIONS

A. Have students research the history of the problem of squaring (quadrature of) the circle.

B. Pose this problem: A friend tells you she's found another way to find the area of an annulus. First find the average of the circumferences of the two circles that form the annulus. Then multiply that average by the thickness of the annulus (the difference between the radii) to find the area. Is your friend right? Draw a picture and use algebra to show why this method does or doesn't work. [This method works, because $\frac{2\pi R + 2\pi r}{2}(R - r) = \pi(R + r)(R - r) = \pi(R^2 - r^2) = \pi R^2 - \pi r^2$.]

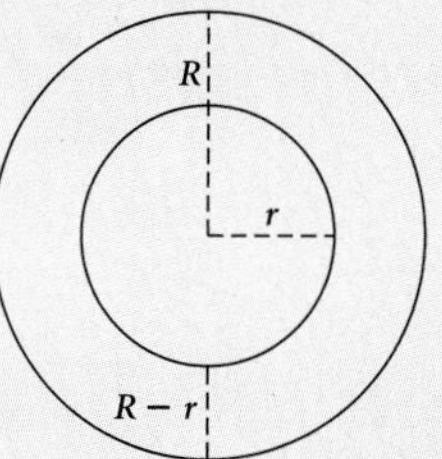

C. The area of a trapezoid can also be seen as the product of its midsegment and its height. Ask students to explain how this idea relates to the area of a portion of an annulus. [$\frac{2\pi R + 2\pi r}{2}$ is the average of the two circumferences.]

EXPLORATION

PLANNING

LESSON OUTLINE

One day:

45 min Activity

MATERIALS

- rulers
- pennies
- dimes
- protractors
- graph paper

TEACHING

Some applications of geometry to probability can be unexpected.

Guiding the Activity

The Shape of Things

Step 1 You may need to emphasize that the computer is picking a point anywhere in the grid, not necessarily in one of the shapes. Students can find the areas of the square and the pentagon by subtracting areas of triangles from the area of an enclosing rectangle.

Step 1 P(trapezoid) $= \frac{15}{144} \approx 0.104$; P(pentagon) $= \frac{15.5}{144} \approx 0.108$; P(square) $= \frac{18}{144} = 0.125$; P(triangle) $= \frac{24}{144} \approx 0.167$

Step 2 Students might interpret the word *quadrilateral* to refer to all of the shapes instead of only to the trapezoid and square. They can either add the two probabilities or add the two areas and divide by 144; the latter method is preferable, because it's exact.

The probability that the computer-selected point is outside all of the shapes can be found from either the sum of the

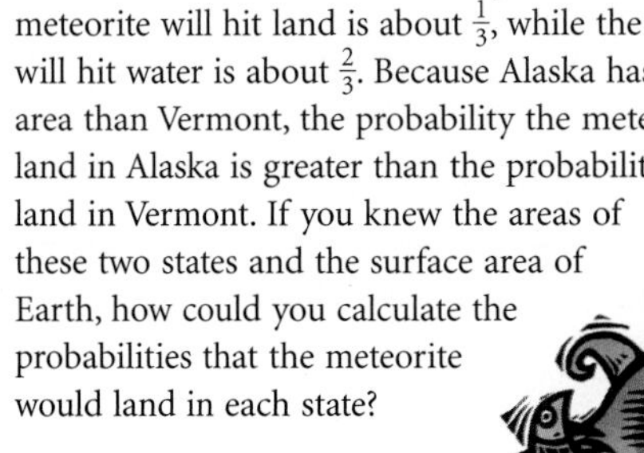

Geometric Probability II

You already know that a probability value is a number between 0 and 1 that tells you how likely something is to occur. For example, when you roll a die, three of the six rolls—namely, 2, 3, and 5—are prime numbers. Since each roll has the same chance of occurring, P(prime number) $= \frac{3}{6}$ or $\frac{1}{2}$.

In some situations, probability depends on area. For example, suppose a meteorite is headed toward Earth. If about $\frac{1}{3}$ of Earth's surface is land, the probability that the meteorite will hit land is about $\frac{1}{3}$, while the probability it will hit water is about $\frac{2}{3}$. Because Alaska has a greater area than Vermont, the probability the meteorite will land in Alaska is greater than the probability it will land in Vermont. If you knew the areas of these two states and the surface area of Earth, how could you calculate the probabilities that the meteorite would land in each state?

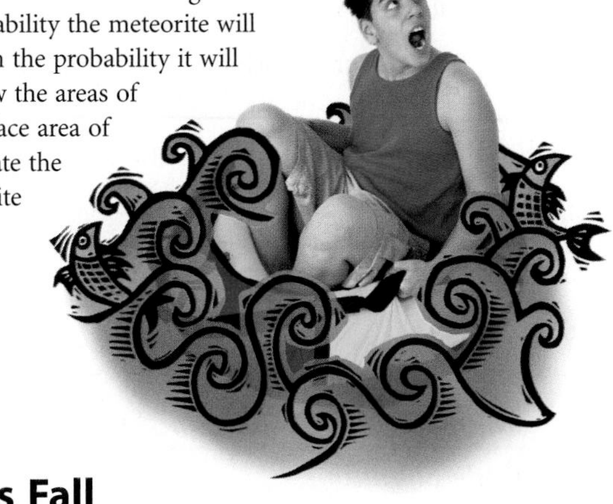

Activity
Where the Chips Fall

You will need

- graph paper
- a ruler
- a penny
- a dime

In this activity, you will solve several probability problems that involve area.

The Shape of Things

At each level of a computer game, you must choose one of several shapes on a coordinate grid. The computer then randomly selects a point *anywhere* on the grid. If the point is outside your shape, you move to the next level. If the point is on or inside your shape, you lose the game.

On the first level, a trapezoid, a pentagon, a square, and a triangle are displayed on a grid that goes from 0 to 12 on both axes. The table below gives the vertices of the shapes.

Shape	Vertices
Trapezoid	(1, 12), (8, 12), (7, 9), (4, 9)
Pentagon	(3, 1), (4, 4), (6, 4), (9, 2), (7, 0)
Square	(0, 6), (3, 9), (6, 6), (3, 3)
Triangle	(11, 0), (7, 4), (11, 12)

LESSON OBJECTIVES

- Use areas of circles and polygons to calculate probability
- Create geometric models to answer probability questions

NCTM STANDARDS

CONTENT		PROCESS	
	Number	✓	Problem Solving
✓	Algebra	✓	Reasoning
✓	Geometry	✓	Communication
	Measurement	✓	Connections
✓	Data/Probability	✓	Representation

Step 2 P(quadrilateral) $= \frac{33}{144} \approx 0.229$; P(outside all shapes) $= \frac{71.5}{144} \approx 0.497$

Step 3 $1 - \text{P(triangle)} \approx 0.833$

Step 4 Trapezoid; the probability that the computer will select a point inside the trapezoid is less than the probability for any other shape.

Step 1 For each shape, calculate the probability the computer will choose a point on or inside that shape. Express each probability to three decimal places.

Step 2 What is the probability the computer will choose a point that is on or inside a quadrilateral? What is the probability it will choose a point that is outside all of the shapes?

Step 3 If you choose a triangle, what is the probability you will move to the next level?

Step 4 Which shape should you choose to have the best chance of moving to the next level? Why?

Right on Target

You are playing a carnival game in which you must throw one dart at the board shown at right. The score for each region is shown on the board. If your dart lands in a Bonus section, your score is tripled. The more points you get, the better your prize will be. The radii of the circles from the inside to the outside are 4 in., 8 in., 12 in., and 16 in. Assume your aim is not very good, so the dart will hit a random spot. If you miss the board completely, you get to throw again.

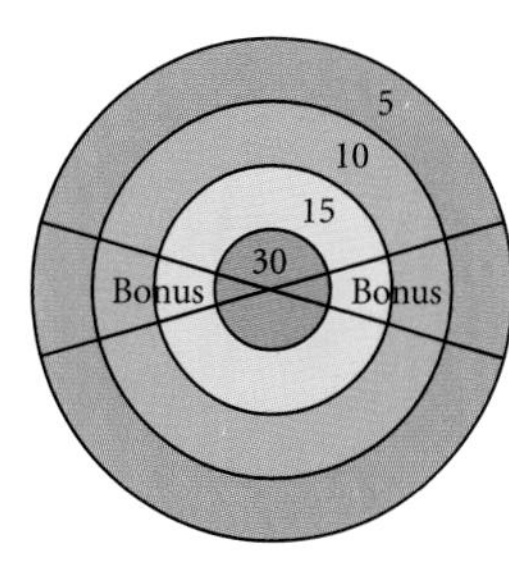

Step 6 Together, the sectors make up $\frac{60}{360}$, or $\frac{1}{6}$, of the total area. So, P(Bonus) $= \frac{1}{6} \approx 0.167$

Step 5 What is the probability your dart will land in the red region? Blue region?

Step 6 Compute the probability your dart will land in a Bonus section. (The central angle measure for each Bonus section is 30°.)

Step 7 If you score 90 points, you will win the grand prize, a giant stuffed emu. What is the probability you will win the grand prize?

Step 8 If you score exactly 30 points, you win an "I ♥ Carnivals" baseball cap. What is the probability you will win the cap?

Step 9 Yes; the dart is no longer equally likely to hit any spot on the board, so you can no longer compute probabilities by simply finding and dividing areas.

Step 9 Now imagine you have been practicing your dart game, and your aim has improved. Would your answers to Steps 5–8 change? Explain.

The Coin Toss

You own a small cafe that is popular with the mathematicians in the neighborhood. You devise a game in which the customer flips a coin onto a red-and-white checkered tablecloth with 1-inch squares. If it lands completely within a square, the customer wins, and doesn't have to pay the bill. If it lands touching or crossing the boundary of a square, the customer loses.

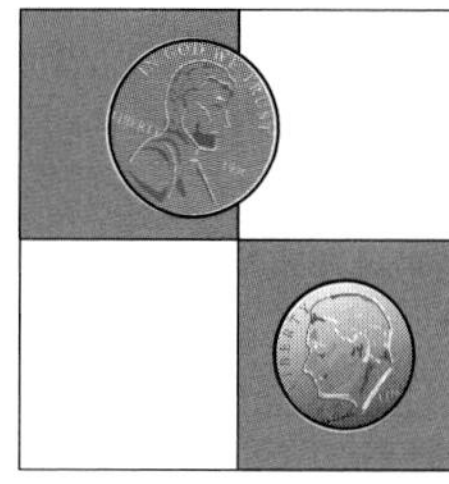

Step 10 Assuming the coin stays on the table, what is the probability of the customer winning by flipping a penny? A dime? (Hint: Where must the center of the coin land in order to win?)

Step 2 (continued) probabilities or the sum of the areas. The former gives a slightly different result due to round-off error.

As when they are working with π, for more accurate results students should wait until the end to do any rounding.

Step 3 As needed, remind students that they move to the next level if the randomly selected point is outside the chosen shape.

Step 5 $\text{P(red)} = \frac{\text{area of red}}{\text{area of target}} = \frac{16\pi}{256\pi} = \frac{1}{16} = 0.0625$; area of blue $= 256\pi - 144\pi = 112\pi$, so P(blue) $= \frac{\text{area of blue}}{\text{area of target}} = \frac{112\pi}{256\pi} = \frac{7}{16} = 0.4375$

Step 7 Students could compute the probability as:

P(red and bonus) $=$ P(red) $\cdot$ P(bonus) $= \frac{1}{16} \cdot \frac{1}{6} = \frac{1}{96}$.

Step 7 The dart must land in the part of the red section within a bonus section. $\frac{1}{6}(16\pi) = \frac{8\pi}{3}$, P(90 points) $= \frac{\frac{8\pi}{3}}{256\pi} = \frac{1}{96} \approx 0.010$

Step 8 To score 30 points, the dart must land either in the part of the red section that is *not* in a Bonus section, $\frac{5}{6}(16\pi) = \frac{40\pi}{3}$, or in the part of the green section that *is* in a Bonus section, $\frac{1}{6}(144\pi - 64\pi) = \frac{40\pi}{3}$.

Step 8 P(30 points) $= \frac{\frac{40\pi}{3} + \frac{40\pi}{3}}{256\pi} = \frac{15}{48} \approx 0.104$

Step 10 Give students graph paper, or have them draw their own "tablecloth," for physical trials. For a coin to be completely inside a square, the distance from its center to a side of the square must be greater than its radius, r. The center of the coin must be within a square of side length $1 - 2r$, or $1 - d$, centered in the 1-inch square.

A penny has a diameter of about $\frac{3}{4}$ in., so the penny would have to land within a square with side length $1 - \frac{3}{4}$, or $\frac{1}{4}$ in.

A dime has a diameter of about $\frac{11}{16}$ in., so it would have to land within a square of side length $1 - \frac{11}{16}$, or $\frac{5}{16}$ in.

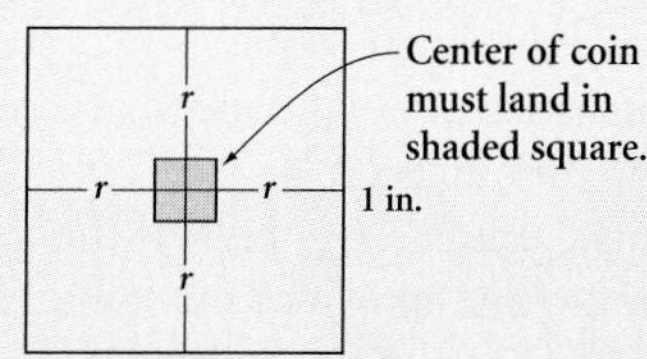

Step 10 P(win with penny) =

$\dfrac{\text{area of center square}}{\text{area of 1-inch square}} = \dfrac{\frac{1}{16}}{1} =$

$\frac{1}{16} = 0.0625$

P(win with dime) =

$\dfrac{\text{area of center square}}{\text{area of 1-inch square}} = \dfrac{\frac{25}{256}}{1} =$

$\frac{25}{256} \approx 0.0977$

Step 11 If the coin must land in a red square, the probabilities determined in Step 10 are multiplied by $\frac{1}{2}$.

Step 13 Before students begin on this step, you might give them a few minutes to try to figure out this probability. Then they might be more impressed by the area process, because the situation apparently has nothing to do with geometry.

Steps 13, 14

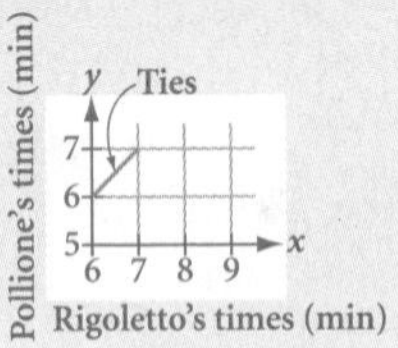

Step 14 P(Rigoletto) =

$\dfrac{\text{area of grid below line}}{\text{area of grid}} =$

$\frac{5.5}{6} \approx 0.917$

[Context] The fictitious opera singers are characters in famous operas by Verdi and Bellini.

Assessing Progress
You can assess students' understanding of probability as a ratio.

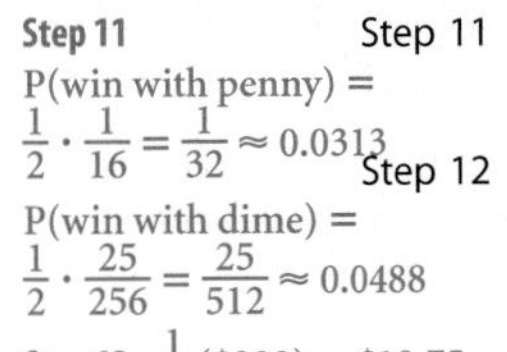

Step 11
P(win with penny) =
$\frac{1}{2} \cdot \frac{1}{16} = \frac{1}{32} \approx 0.0313$
P(win with dime) =
$\frac{1}{2} \cdot \frac{25}{256} = \frac{25}{512} \approx 0.0488$

Step 12 $\frac{1}{16}(\$300) = \$18.75$

Step 11 If the customer wins only if the coin falls within a red square, what is the probability of winning with a penny? A dime?

Step 12 Suppose the game is always played with a penny, and a customer wins if the penny lands completely inside any square (red or white). If your daily proceeds average $300, about how much will the game cost you per day?

On a Different Note

Two opera stars—Rigoletto and Pollione—are auditioning for a part in an upcoming production. Since the singers have similar qualifications, the director decides to have a contest to see which man can hold a note the longest. Rigoletto has been known to hold a note for any length of time from 6 to 9 minutes. Pollione has been known to hold a note for any length of time between 5 and 7 minutes.

Step 13 Draw a rectangular grid in which the bottom side represents the range of times for Rigoletto and the left side represents the range of times for Pollione. Each point in the rectangle represents one possible outcome of the contest.

Step 14 On your grid, mark all the points that represent a tie. Use your diagram to find the probability that Rigoletto will win the contest.

DIFFERENT DICE

Understanding probability can improve your chances of winning a game. If you roll a pair of standard 6-sided dice, are you more likely to roll a sum of 6 or 12? It's fairly common to roll a sum of 6, since many combinations of two dice add up to 6. But a 12 is only possible if you roll a 6 on each die.

If you rolled a pair of standard 6-sided dice over and over again, and recorded the number of times you got each sum, the histogram would look like this:

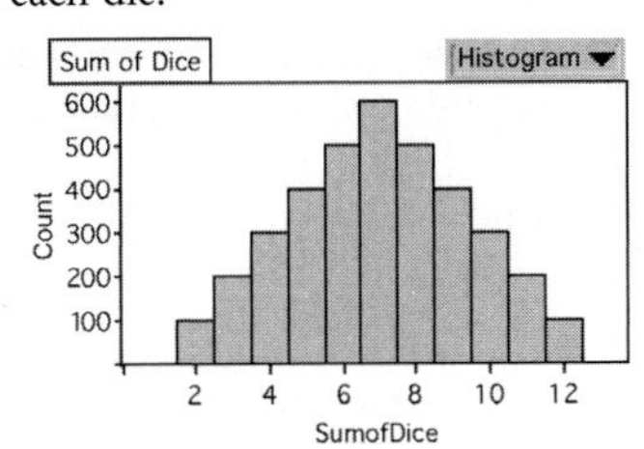

Would the distribution be different if you used different dice? What if one die had odd numbers and the other had even numbers? What if you used 8-sided dice? What if you rolled three 6-sided dice instead of two?

Choose one of these scenarios or one that you find interesting to investigate. Make your dice and roll them 20 times. Predict what the graph will look like if you roll the dice 100 times, then check your prediction.

Your project should include

- Your dice.
- Histograms of your experimental data, and your predictions and conclusions.

Fathom™

You can use Fathom to simulate real events, such as rolling the dice that you have designed. You can obtain the results of hundreds of events very quickly, and use Fathom's graphing capabilities to make a histogram showing the distribution of different outcomes.

Supporting the project

You might connect this project with the Chapter 10 Exploration on Platonic solids. A student who has completed the project with Fathom can demonstrate the results dynamically. Or you can show the demonstrations available at www.keymath.com/DG.

OUTCOMES

- Predictions mention possible outcomes and most likely outcomes.
- Irregularities in weight and shape of dice are minimized.
- The histogram's range reflects the minimum and maximum possible outcomes and has the approximate correct shape.
- Simulation results roughly match the theoretical probability.
- Report makes a connection between the number of trials and how closely the outcomes match the expected values.
- Unusual dice are explored.
- Report compares theoretical outcomes for several kinds of dice.

LESSON

8.7 Surface Area

No pessimist ever discovered the secrets of the stars, or sailed to an uncharted land, or opened a new doorway for the human spirit.

HELEN KELLER

In Lesson 8.3, you calculated the surface areas of walls and roofs. But not all building surfaces are rectangular. How would you calculate the amount of glass necessary to cover a pyramid-shaped building? Or the number of tiles needed to cover a cone-shaped roof?

In this lesson, you will learn how to find the surface areas of prisms, pyramids, cylinders, and cones. The **surface area** of each of these solids is the sum of the areas of all the faces or surfaces that enclose the solid. For prisms and pyramids, the faces include the solid's **bases** and its remaining **lateral faces.**

In a prism, the bases are two congruent polygons and the lateral faces are rectangles or parallelograms.

In a pyramid, the base can be any polygon. The lateral faces are triangles.

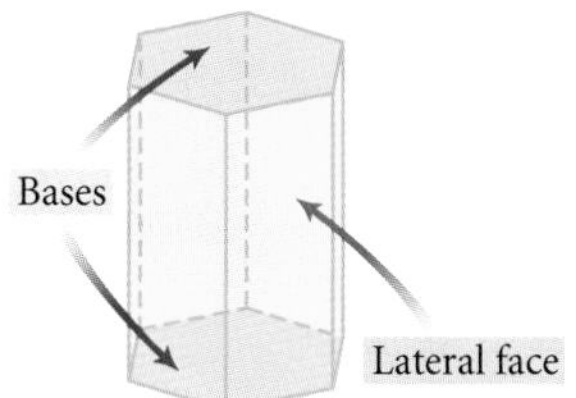

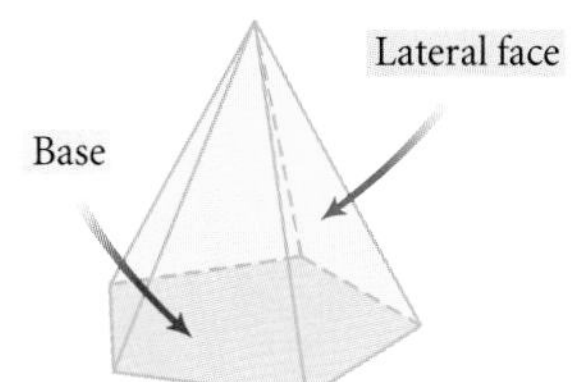

This glass pyramid was designed by I. M. Pei for the entrance of the Louvre museum in Paris, France.

This skyscraper in Chicago, Illinois, is an example of a prism.

A cone is part of the roof design of this Victorian house in Massachusetts.

This stone tower is a cylinder on top of a larger cylinder.

NCTM STANDARDS

CONTENT		PROCESS	
	Number	✓	Problem Solving
✓	Algebra	✓	Reasoning
✓	Geometry	✓	Communication
✓	Measurement	✓	Connections
	Data/Probability		Representation

LESSON OBJECTIVES

- Review terminology for solids
- Discover methods for finding the surface areas of solids
- Practice visual thinking in three dimensions
- Develop problem-solving skills and cooperative behavior

LESSON 8.7

PLANNING

LESSON OUTLINE

One day:

5 min	Examples
20 min	Investigation
5 min	Sharing
5 min	Closing
10 min	Exercises

MATERIALS

- calculators
- prisms, pyramids, and other solids

TEACHING

It's possible to find the surface area of many solids, such as regular prisms, pyramids, cylinders, and cones. We are assuming all the solids are right prisms, pyramids, cylinders, or cones. Having real objects can help students' visualization. Boxes can be cut apart. Cans can be covered with paper, which can then be removed and flattened. You might remind students that they've seen nets earlier in the course. Emphasize that finding surface area is actually finding the area of the net.

One step Remind students of what a prism, a cylinder, a pyramid, and a cone are and explain what their lateral surface area is. Then ask the class to do two things: find a formula for the lateral surface area of a prism whose base is a regular polygon, then see what happens to that formula as the number of sides increases and as one base shrinks to a point. As you circulate, encourage groups to think about cutting the figures to lay them flat, to consider one kind of change at a time, and to divide

One step (continued)
up the labor. During Sharing, introduce the term *slant height* for one length students are using, and ask students how to find the total surface area of each figure, including the areas of the bases.

INTRODUCTION

To focus attention on the surface area of solids, you might ask students, if a brick has six faces, how many faces does a half brick have? At first one or two students may laugh at the spoof on mindless algebraic thinking, but if you persist they may see that splitting a brick in half diagonally can result in a "half brick" with only five faces. Ask whether there are other possible answers, and leave the question open to encourage three-dimensional visualization.

▶ *EXAMPLE A*

[Alert] Some students, thinking of a volume formula, may say that they know a simple formula to find the surface area. They may not realize that surface area is the number of square units that it will take to cover the two-dimensional surface of a three-dimensional figure.

To find the surface areas of prisms and pyramids, follow these steps.

Steps for Finding Surface Area

1. Draw and label each face of the solid as if you had cut the solid apart along its edges and laid it flat. Label the dimensions.
2. Calculate the area of each face. If some faces are identical, you only need to find the area of one.
3. Find the total area of all the faces.

EXAMPLE A Find the surface area of the rectangular prism.

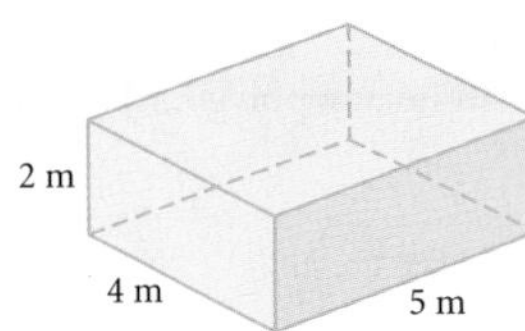

These shipping containers are rectangular prisms.

▶ Solution First, draw and label all six faces.
Then, find the areas of all the rectangular faces.

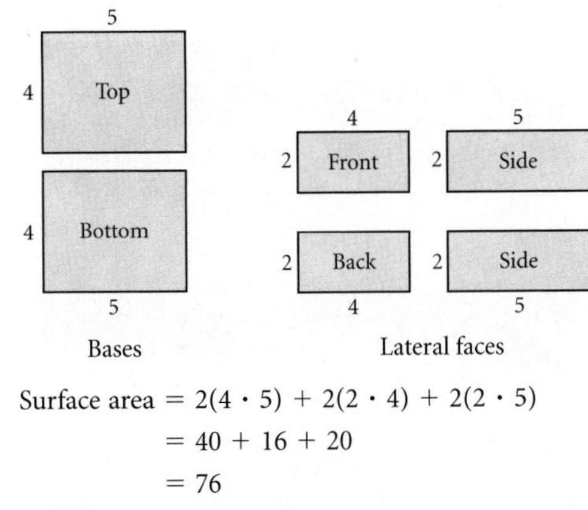

$$\begin{aligned}\text{Surface area} &= 2(4 \cdot 5) + 2(2 \cdot 4) + 2(2 \cdot 5) \\ &= 40 + 16 + 20 \\ &= 76\end{aligned}$$

The surface area of the prism is 76 m^2.

EXAMPLE B Find the surface area of the cylinder.

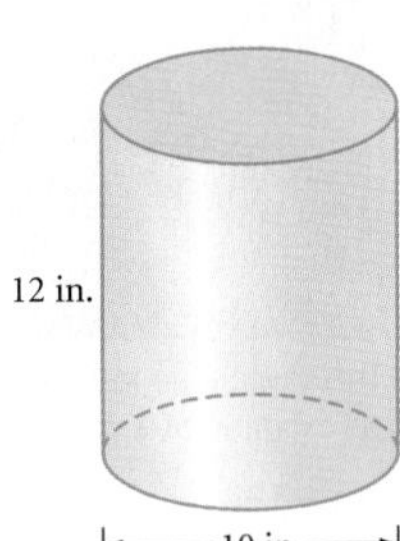

▶ Solution Imagine cutting apart the cylinder. The two bases are circular regions, so you need to find the areas of two circles. Think of the lateral surface as a wrapper. Slice it and lay it flat to get a rectangular region. You'll need the area of this rectangle. The height of the rectangle is the height of the cylinder. The base of the rectangle is the circumference of the circular base.

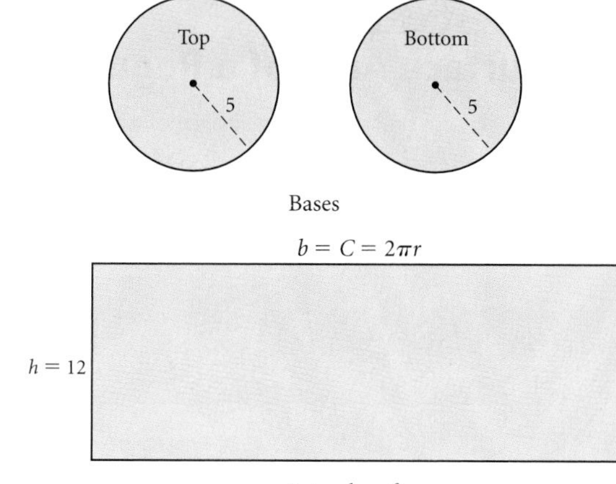

$$\begin{aligned}\text{Surface area} &= 2(\pi r^2) + (2\pi r)h \\ &= 2(\pi \cdot 5^2) + (2 \cdot \pi \cdot 5) \cdot 12 \\ &\approx 534\end{aligned}$$

The surface area of the cylinder is about 534 in^2.

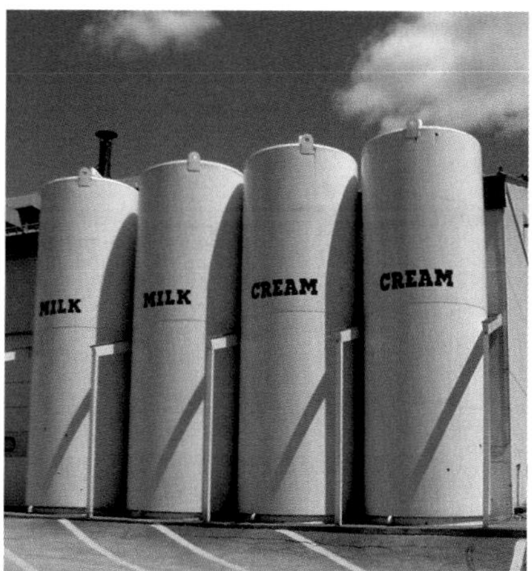

This ice cream plant in Burlington, Vermont, uses cylindrical containers for its milk and cream.

These conservatories in Edmonton, Canada, are glass pyramids.

The surface area of a pyramid is the area of the base plus the areas of the triangular faces. The height of each triangular lateral face is called the **slant height.** To avoid confusing slant height with the height of the pyramid, use l rather than h for slant height.

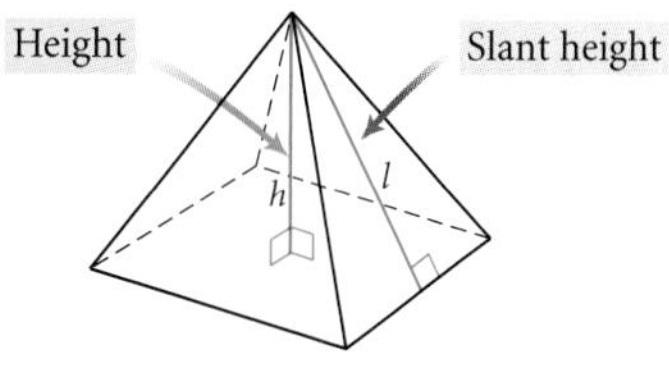

In the investigation you'll find out how to calculate the surface area of a pyramid with a regular polygon base.

▶ EXAMPLE B

Students can make the sides of cylinders out of paper, with no overlaps, and then see how to find the lateral surface area after unrolling the paper.

Slant Height

[Alert] Students may have difficulty differentiating between the *height* (perpendicular to the base), the *slant height* (an altitude of a face), and the length of an edge of a pyramid. Having models available can help.

Guiding Investigation 1

Steps 4, 5 Students may need help in thinking to use the distributive property to get $A = \frac{1}{2}nb(l + a)$ and in realizing that $nb = P$.

Guiding Investigation 2

Step 2 [Alert] You may need to help students see that as the number of triangles increases the lateral surface of the pyramid begins to look like the lateral surface of a cone. Therefore, $\frac{1}{2}Pl$ becomes $\frac{1}{2}Cl$, because the perimeter becomes a circle.

Step 3 Some students might go on to write the expression $\frac{1}{2}Pl + \pi r^2$ as $\frac{1}{2}(2\pi r)l + \pi r^2$, which simplifies to $\pi r(r + l)$.

SHARING IDEAS

As students present ideas, encourage careful use of terminology. These figures are called *solids,* though they're not "filled in." That is, the "solid" is only the surface, a two-dimensional figure whose area you can find. The surface may contain two-dimensional faces surrounded by one-dimensional edges.

[Ask] "When we refer to a particular kind of prism, such as a pentagonal prism, what do we mean?" [The shape of the bases is being specified.]

Ask whether the formulas for lateral surface area are related. Elicit the idea that they're all the same: If you consider a pyramid or a cone as having two bases, one of perimeter 0, then the lateral surface is the slant height times the average of the two base perimeters. This might remind students of how parallelograms can be changed to trapezoids and then to triangles. **[Ask]** "Is there an analogy in three dimensions going from a prism and a pyramid with the same base to the intermediate step of a trapezoid?" [The intermediate step is called a *frustum.*]

Investigation 1
Surface Area of a Regular Pyramid

You can cut and unfold the surface of a regular pyramid into these shapes.

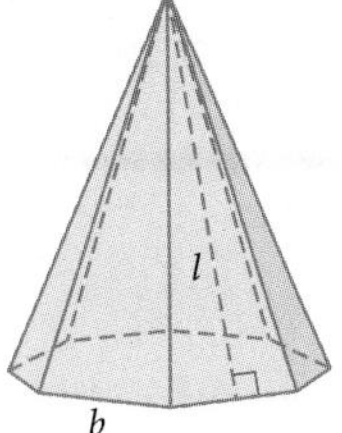
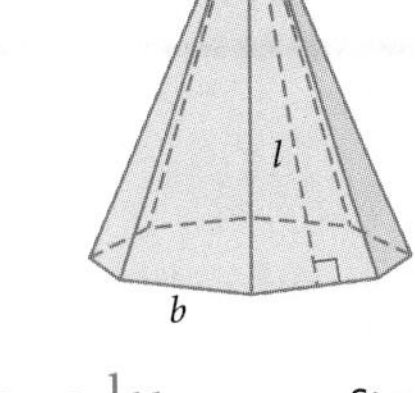
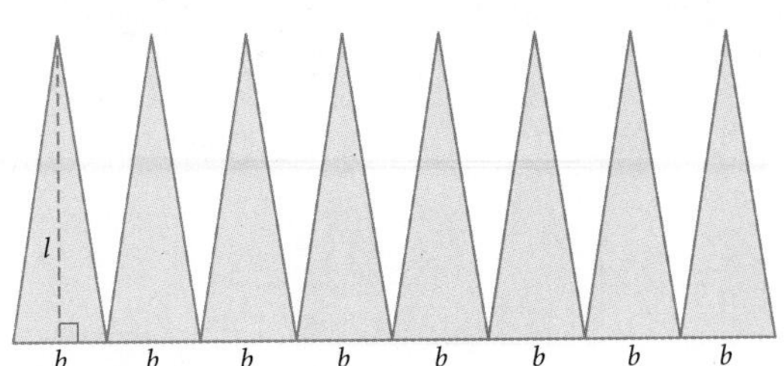

Step 1 $\frac{1}{2}bl$

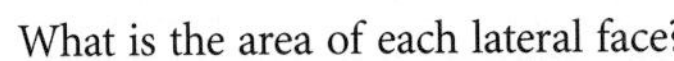

Step 1 What is the area of each lateral face?

Step 2 $8 \cdot \frac{1}{2}bl$, $n\frac{1}{2}bl$

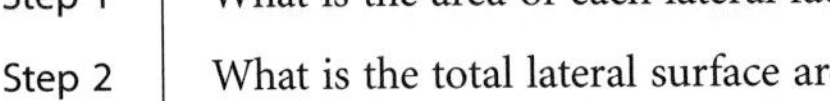

Step 2 What is the total lateral surface area? What is the total lateral surface area for any pyramid with a regular n-gon base?

Step 3 $\frac{1}{2}aP$ or $\frac{1}{2}abn$

Step 3 What is the area of the base for any regular n-gon pyramid?

Step 4 $\frac{1}{2}nb(l + a)$

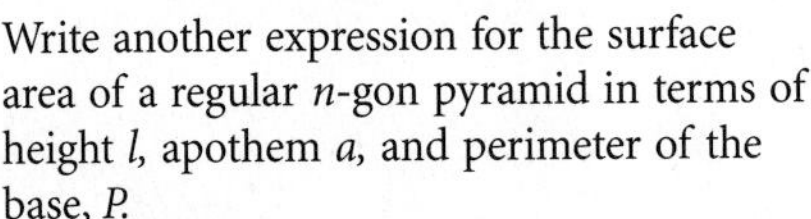

Step 4 Use your expressions from Steps 2 and 3 to write a formula for the surface area of a regular n-gon pyramid in terms of base length b, slant height l, and apothem a.

Step 5 $\frac{1}{2}P(l + a)$

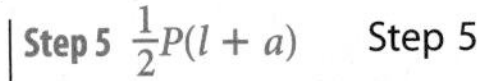

Step 5 Write another expression for the surface area of a regular n-gon pyramid in terms of height l, apothem a, and perimeter of the base, P.

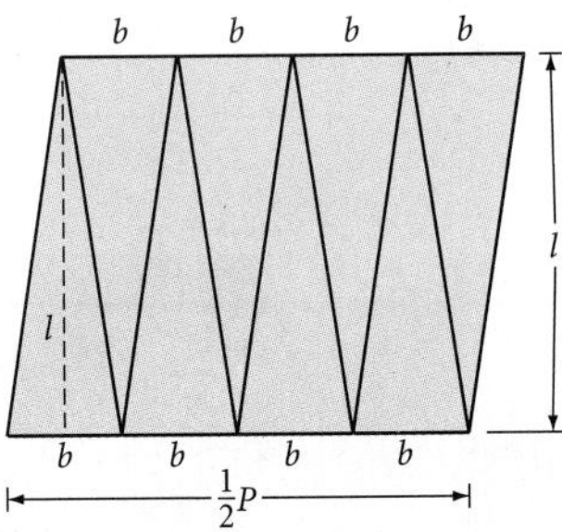

You can find the surface area of a cone using a method similar to the one you used to find the surface area of a pyramid.

Is the roof of this building in Kashan, Iran, a cone or a pyramid? What makes it hard to tell?

Investigation 2
Surface Area of a Cone

As the number of faces of a pyramid increases, it begins to look like a cone. You can think of the lateral surface as many small triangles, or as a sector of a circle.

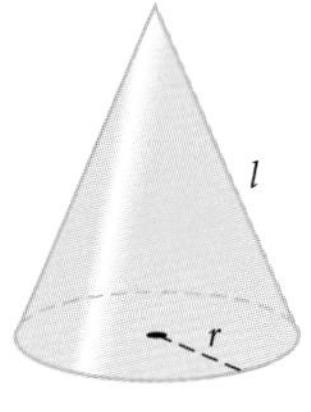

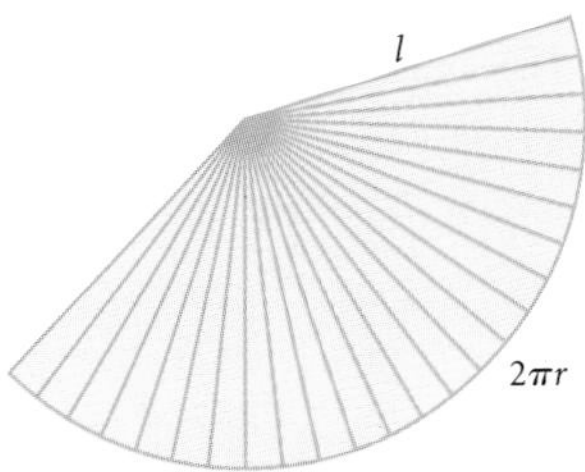

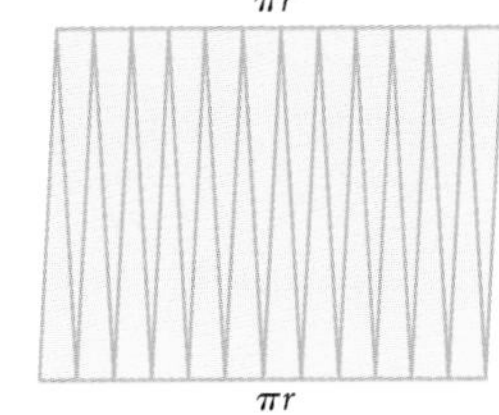

Step 1 πr^2

Step 2 $\frac{2\pi r}{2\pi l} = \frac{r}{l}$; $\pi l^2 \cdot \frac{r}{l} = \pi lr$

Step 3 $\pi r(r + l)$

Step 1 What is the area of the base?

Step 2 What is the lateral surface area in terms of l and r? What portion is the sector of the circle? What is the area of the sector?

Step 3 Write the formula for the surface area of a cone.

This photograph of Sioux tepees was taken around 1902 in North or South Dakota. Is a tepee shaped more like a cone or a pyramid?

EXAMPLE C Find the total surface area of the cone.

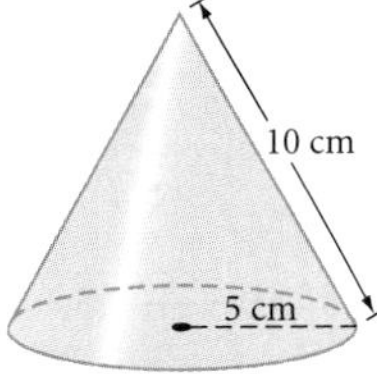

► **Solution**

$$SA = \pi rl + \pi r^2$$
$$= (\pi)(5)(10) + \pi(5)^2$$
$$= 75\pi$$
$$\approx 235.6$$

The surface area of the cone is about 236 cm^2.

Sharing Ideas (continued)

You might mention that there are ways to find the surface area of oblique and nonregular solids as well. Students will study the surface area of spheres in Chapter 10.

[Ask] "What kinds of units do surface area measures have?" [They are measures of area, so they have square units.] Remind students that in Lesson 8.6 they found the area of a sector of a circle by considering what part it was of a whole circle. Now to find the lateral surface area of a cone they thought of cutting the cone and laying out the surface into a sector. Wonder aloud whether the area of this sector can be found in the same way. We don't know the angle or the measure of the arc, but we do know the arc length, which is $2\pi r$. The whole circle would have circumference $2\pi l$, so the area of the sector is $\frac{2\pi r}{2\pi l}$ times the area of the whole circle, which is πl^2. This product simplifies to πrl, as found in Investigation 2.

If you feel students need more practice in finding the surface areas of cones, proceed to Example C. Otherwise, close the lesson and begin on the exercises.

► ***EXAMPLE C***

Students might use any of the formulas they know for the surface area of a cone.

Closing the Lesson

Reiterate the main ideas of this lesson: The **surface area** of any prism, pyramid, cylinder, or cone is its lateral surface area plus the area(s) of its base(s). The **lateral surface area** is the **slant height** times the average of the base perimeters, considering pyramids and cones to have one base of perimeter 0. (The perimeter of a circle is its circumference.)

BUILDING UNDERSTANDING

The exercises give practice in finding surface area.

ASSIGNING HOMEWORK

Essential	**1–10**
Performance assessment	**12**
Portfolio	**10**
Journal	**11**
Group	**13**
Review	**14–18**

MATERIALS

- Exercise 12 (T), *optional*

▶ Helping with the Exercises

Exercises 1–8 As needed, encourage students to cut the solid into the various shapes as illustrated in the examples. Then calculate the area of each plane figure.

EXERCISES

You will need

Construction tools for Exercise **13**

In Exercises 1–10, find the surface area of each solid. All quadrilaterals are rectangles, and all given measurements are in centimeters. Round your answers to the nearest 0.1 cm^2.

1.

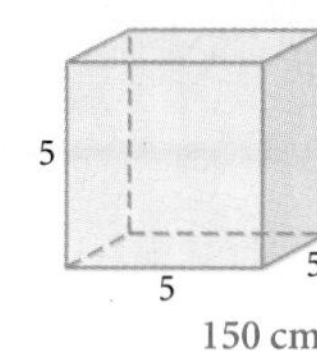

150 cm^2

2.

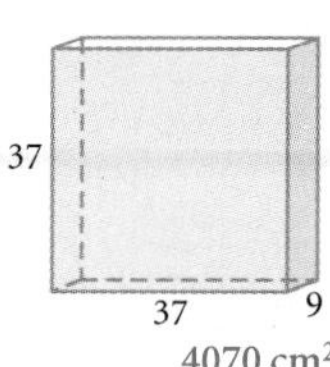

4070 cm^2

3.

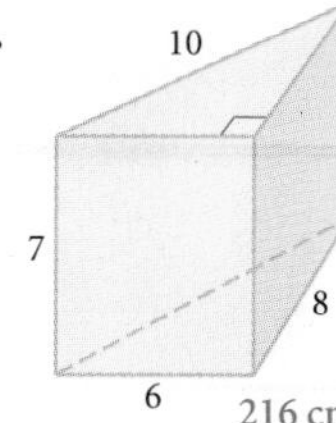

216 cm^2

4.

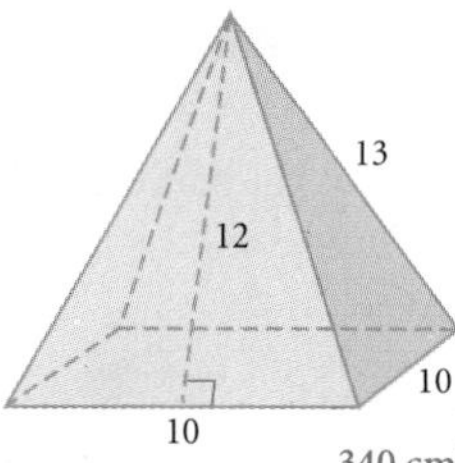

340 cm^2

5.

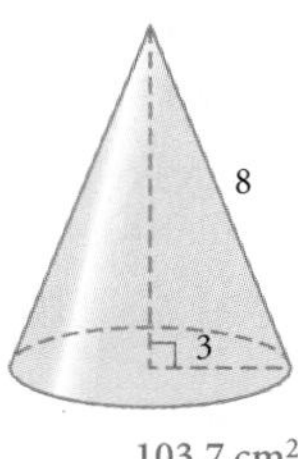

103.7 cm^2

6.

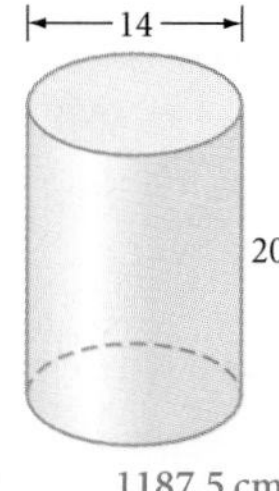

1187.5 cm^2

7. The base is a regular hexagon with apothem $a = 12.1$, side $s = 14$, and height $h = 7$. ⓗ 1604.4 cm^2

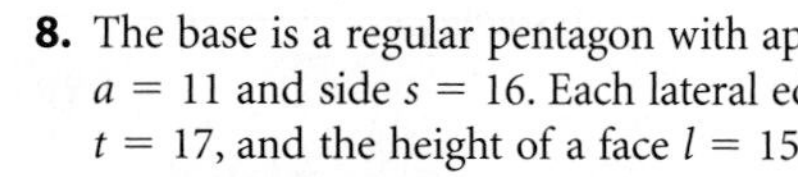

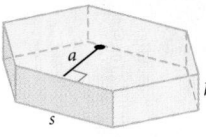

8. The base is a regular pentagon with apothem $a = 11$ and side $s = 16$. Each lateral edge $t = 17$, and the height of a face $l = 15$. 1040 cm^2

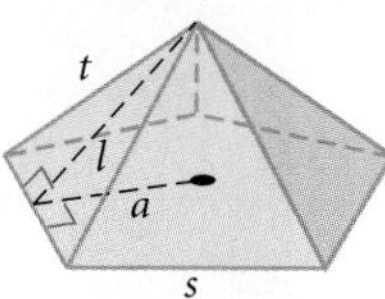

9. $D = 8, d = 4, h = 9$ ⓗ 414.7 cm^2

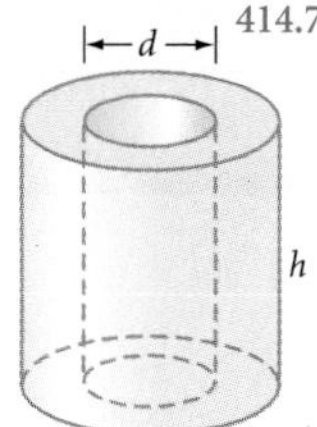

10. $l = 8, w = 4, h = 10, d = 4$ 329.1 cm^2

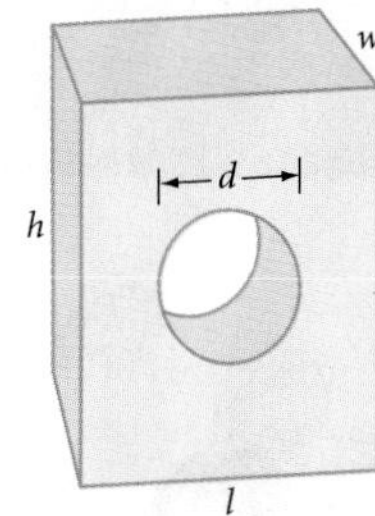

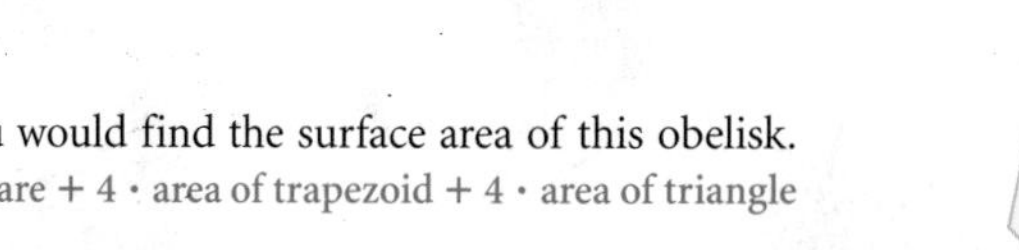

11. Explain how you would find the surface area of this obelisk.
area of square + 4 · area of trapezoid + 4 · area of triangle

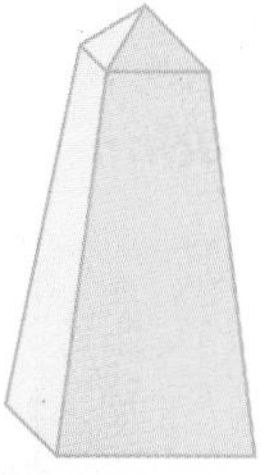

12. APPLICATION Claudette and Marie are planning to paint the exterior walls of their country farmhouse (all vertical surfaces) and to put new cedar shingles on the roof. The paint they like best costs \$25 per gallon and covers 250 square feet per gallon. The wood shingles cost \$65 per bundle, and each bundle covers 100 square feet. How much will this home improvement cost? All measurements are in feet. \$1570

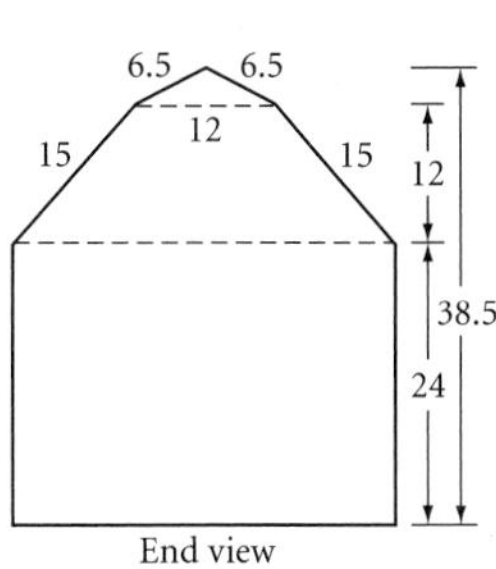

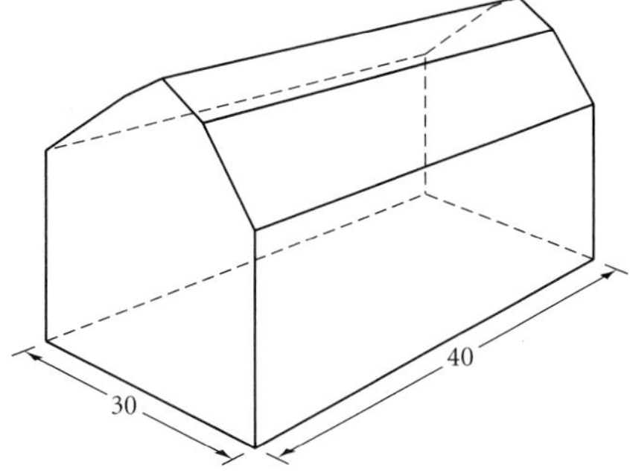

13. *Construction* The shapes of the spinning dishes in the photo are called **frustums** of cones. Think of them as cones with their tops cut off. Use your construction tools to draw pieces that you can cut out and tape together to form a frustum of a cone.

A Sri Lankan dancer balances and spins plates.

Review

7.4 **14.** Use patty paper, templates, or pattern blocks to create a $3^3.4^2/3^2.4.3.4/4^4$ tiling.

6.3 **15.** Trace the figure at right. Find the lettered angle measures and arc measures. $a = 75°, b = 75°, c = 30°, d = 60°, e = 150°, f = 30°$

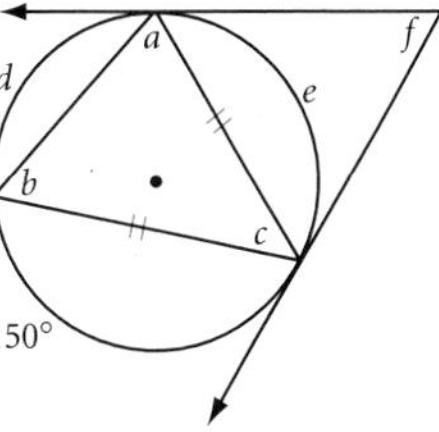

13. sample answer:

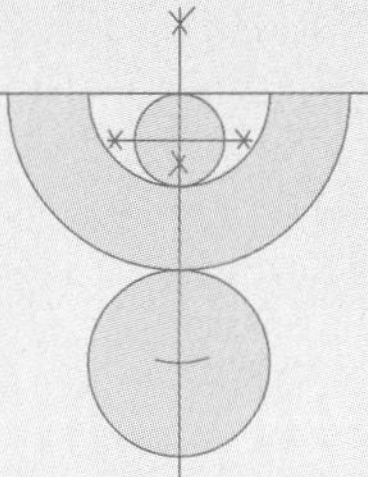

14. sample tiling

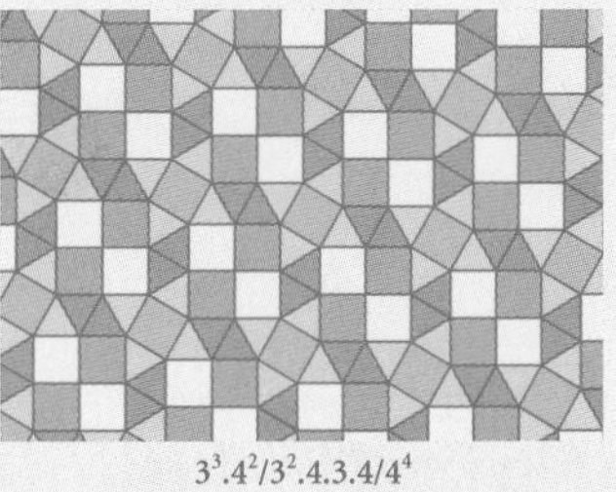

$3^3.4^2/3^2.4.3.4/4^4$

EXTENSION

In this lesson, students found the surface area of a prism, a pyramid, and a cylinder without using surface area formulas. They used area formulas for polygons and circles to find the areas of the different surfaces that made up each solid and then added those areas to find the total surface area. For the cone, they derived a formula for the lateral surface area. Ask students to derive a single formula for the total surface area of each solid in the examples and investigations, using algebra to make the formulas as simple as possible. (In other words, ask them to use as few variables as possible and combine as many terms as possible.) Ask them to write and present examples of their formula. [Prism: $2lw + 2lh + 2wh$ or $2(lw + lh + wh)$; Square-based pyramid: $b^2 + 2bl$ or $b(b + 2l)$; Cylinder: $2\pi r^2 + 2\pi rh$ or $2\pi r(r + h)$; Cone: $\pi r^2 + \pi rl$ or $\pi r(r + l)$]

16. About 23 days. Each sector is around 1.767 km².

8.6 **16.** **APPLICATION** Suppose a circular ranch with a radius of 3 km was divided into 16 congruent sectors. In a one-year cycle, how long would the cattle graze in each sector? What would be the area of each sector?

History CONNECTION

In 1792, visiting Europeans presented horses and cattle to Hawaii's King Kamehameha I. Cattle ranching soon developed when Mexican *vaqueros* came to Hawaii to train Hawaiians in ranching. Today, Hawaiian cattle ranching is big business.

"Grazing geometry" is used on Hawaii's Kahua Ranch. Ranchers divide the grazing area into sectors. The cows are rotated through each sector in turn. By the time they return to the first sector, the grass has grown back and the cycle repeats.

17. $a = 50°$, $b = 50°$, $c = 80°$, $d = 100°$, $e = 80°$, $f = 100°$, $g = 80°$, $h = 80°$, $k = 80°$, $m = 20°$, $n = 80°$

17. Trace the figure at right. Find the lettered angle measures.

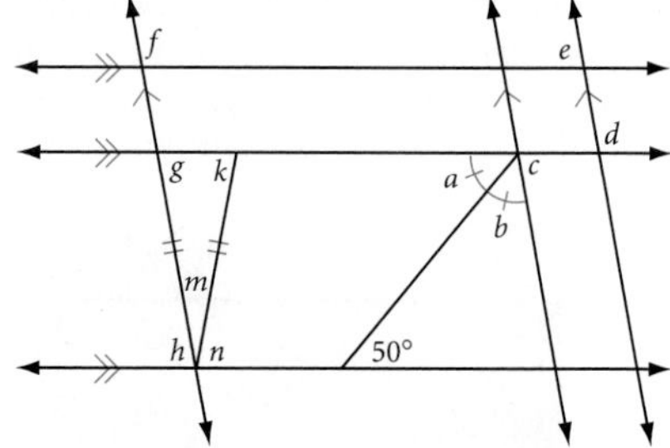

2.3 **18.** If the pattern of blocks continues, what will be the surface area of the 50th solid in the pattern? (Every edge of each block has length 1 unit.)

398 square units

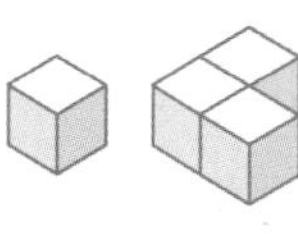
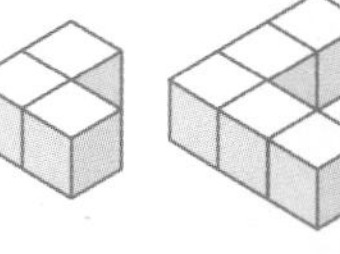

IMPROVING YOUR VISUAL THINKING SKILLS

Moving Coins

Create a triangle of coins similar to the one shown. How can you move exactly three coins so that the triangle is pointing down rather than up? When you have found a solution, use a diagram to explain it.

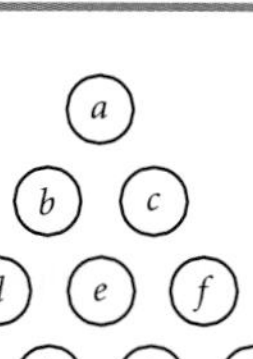

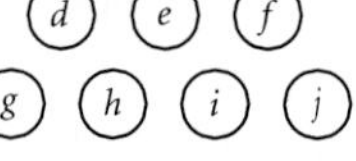

IMPROVING VISUAL THINKING SKILLS

If students are stuck, you might wonder aloud what changing each row to the longest row would mean for the other rows.

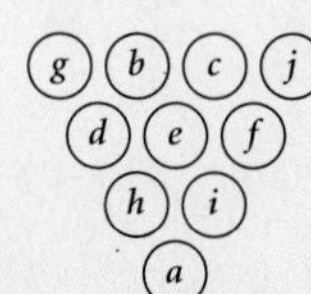

Exploration

Alternative Area Formulas

In ancient Egypt, when the yearly floods of the Nile River receded, the river often followed a different course, so the shape of farmers' fields along the banks could change from year to year. Officials then needed to measure property areas, in order to keep records and calculate taxes. Partly to keep track of land and finances, ancient Egyptians developed some of the earliest mathematics.

Historians believe that ancient Egyptian tax assessors used this formula to find the area of any quadrilateral:

$$A = \frac{1}{2}(a + c) \cdot \frac{1}{2}(b + d)$$

where a, b, c, and d are the lengths, in consecutive order, of the figure's four sides.

In this activity, you will take a closer look at this ancient Egyptian formula, and another formula called Hero's formula, named after Hero of Alexandria.

Activity
Calculating Area in Ancient Egypt

Investigate the ancient Egyptian formula for quadrilaterals.

Step 1 Construct a quadrilateral and its interior.

Step 2 Change the labels of the sides to a, b, c, and d, consecutively.

Step 3 Measure the lengths of the sides and use the Sketchpad calculator to find the area according to the ancient Egyptian formula.

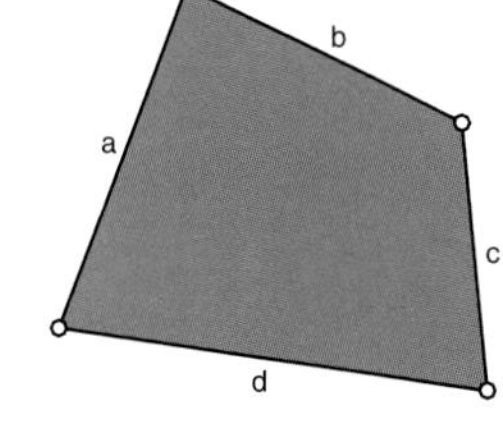

Step 4 Select the polygon interior and measure its area. How does the area given by the formula compare to the actual area? Is the ancient Egyptian formula correct?

Step 5 Does the ancient Egyptian formula always favor either the tax collector or the landowner, or does it favor one in some cases and the other in other cases? Explain.

Step 6 Describe the quadrilaterals for which the formula works accurately. For what kinds of quadrilaterals is it slightly inaccurate? Very inaccurate?

Step 7 State the ancient Egyptian formula in words, using the word *mean.*

Step 4 no

Step 5 The formula favors the tax collector or is fair if the quadrilateral is a rectangle.

Step 6 The formula works only for rectangles.

Step 7 The area of a quadrilateral (rectangle) is equal to the product of the means of the lengths of opposite sides.

NCTM STANDARDS

CONTENT		PROCESS	
	Number		Problem Solving
	Algebra	✓	Reasoning
✓	Geometry	✓	Communication
✓	Measurement	✓	Connections
	Data/Probability		Representation

LESSON OBJECTIVES

- Use geometry software to explore area formulas
- Investigate Hero's formula for the area of triangles
- Explore the Egyptian formula for the area of a quadrilateral

EXPLORATION

PLANNING

LESSON OUTLINE

One day:

35 min Activity
5 min Sharing
5 min Closing

MATERIALS

- The Geometer's Sketchpad

TEACHING

Students investigate proposed formulas for the areas of all quadrilaterals and for the areas of all triangles.

INTRODUCTION

[Context] Egypt had a government, courts of law, and systems of taxation as early as 3000 B.C.E.

Guiding the Activity

Step 1 To investigate an "arbitrary" quadrilateral, students must construct one that has no special characteristics. They can adjust quadrilaterals appropriately using Sketchpad.

Step 7 Help students see that this formula might make intuitive sense to someone thinking of slight deviations from rectangles.

Step 8 If students are having difficulty with accuracy, encourage them to break up the formula into pieces. They certainly won't want to reenter $\frac{a+b+c}{2}$ each time, so they can calculate this quantity first. They might also want to consider the square root of the product as a product of at least two square roots. Hero's formula applies to any triangle.

[Context] Hero (ca. 1–75 C.E.) may have been a lecturer at the Museum in Alexandria. Hero's formula is sometimes called *Heron's formula.*

SHARING IDEAS

Focus on why the ancient Egyptian formula holds for rectangles but not quadrilaterals in general. For example, the area formula for trapezoids involves means. **[Ask]** "Why doesn't the proposed formula apply to trapezoids?" [The mean of the nonbases would have to be the height, but both nonbases are longer than an altitude.] The same reasoning can be used to explain why the formula doesn't apply to any parallelograms other than rectangles: The sides not considered bases are longer than an altitude.

[Ask] "When might Hero's formula be useful?" [when the sides of the triangle are known but no altitude is known] You might suggest that students try extending Hero's formula to quadrilaterals; in what cases, if any, is it accurate?

Assessing Progress

Check students' understanding of special kinds of quadrilaterals, their hierarchy, and their areas.

Closing the Lesson

The **ancient Egyptian formula** for the area of a quadrilateral applies only to rectangles, but **Hero's formula** for the area of a triangle applies to all triangles.

Step 8 Hero's formula always works.

Step 8 According to Hero's formula, if s is half the perimeter of a triangle with side lengths a, b, and c, the area A is given by the formula

$$A = \sqrt{s(s-a)(s-b)(s-c)}$$

Use Sketchpad to investigate Hero's formula. Construct a triangle and its interior. Label the sides a, b, and c, and use the Sketchpad calculator to find the triangle's area according to Hero. Compare the result to the measured area of the triangle. Does Hero's formula work for all triangles?

Step 9 One possible method: Divide the quadrilateral into two triangles, then find the area of each triangle.

Step 9 Devise a way of calculating the area of any quadrilateral. Use Sketchpad to test your method.

IMPROVING YOUR VISUAL THINKING SKILLS

PUZZLE

Cover the Square

Trace each diagram below onto another sheet of paper.

Cut out the four triangles in each of the two small equal squares and arrange them to exactly cover the large square.

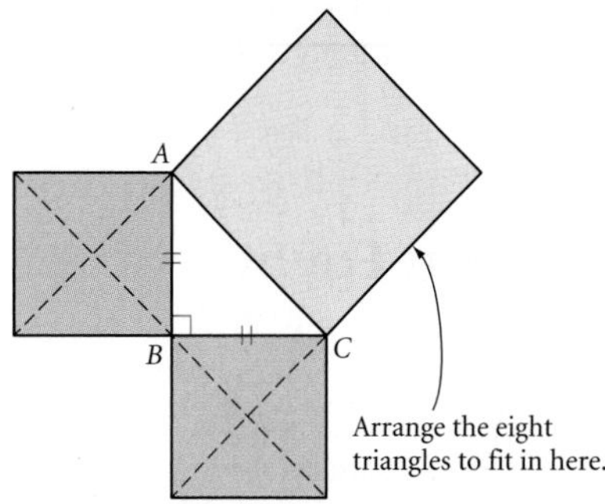

Cut out the small square and the four triangles from the square on leg $\overline{EF}$ and arrange them to exactly cover the large square.

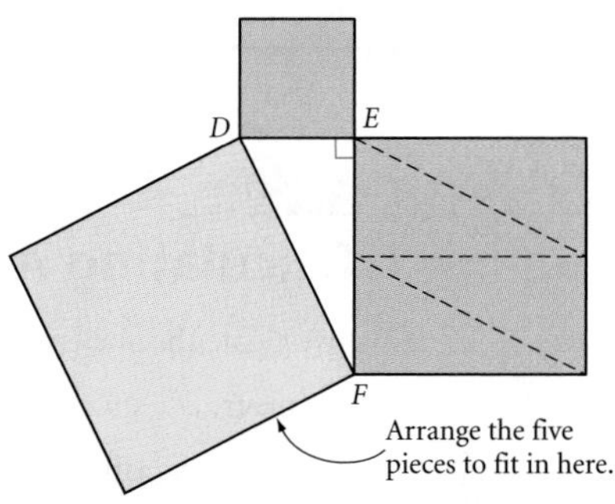

Two squares with areas x^2 and y^2 are divided into the five regions as shown. Cut out the five regions and arrange them to exactly cover a larger square with an area of z^2.

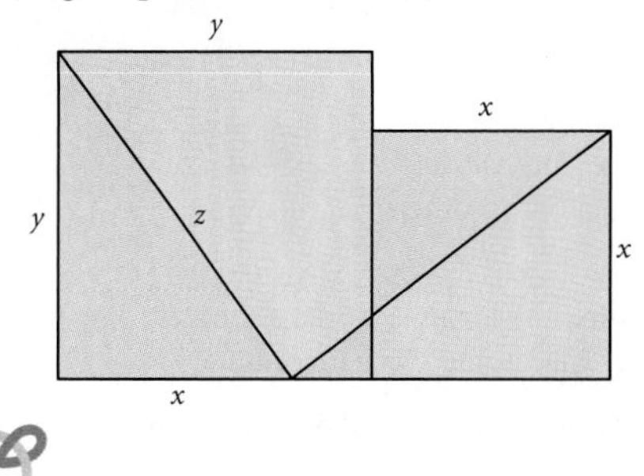

Two squares have been divided into three right triangles and two quadrilaterals. Cut out the five regions and arrange them to exactly cover a larger square.

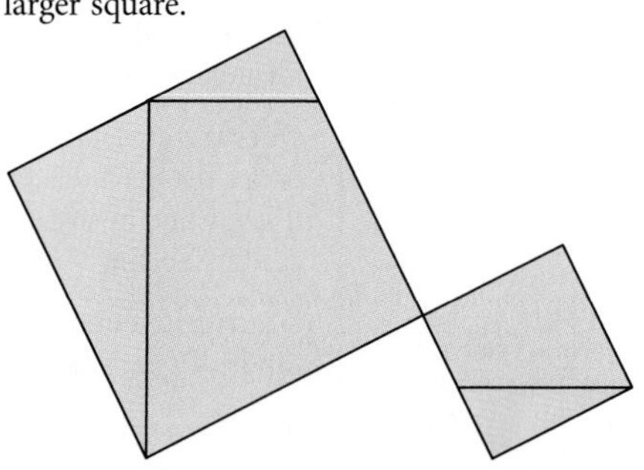

IMPROVING VISUAL THINKING SKILLS

This activity helps prepare students for the Pythagorean Theorem in Chapter 9. Assign it and have students share their results in class.

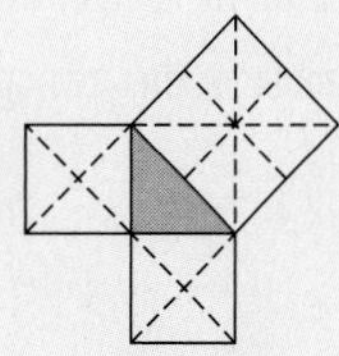

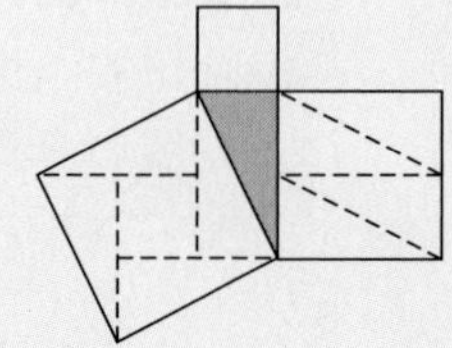

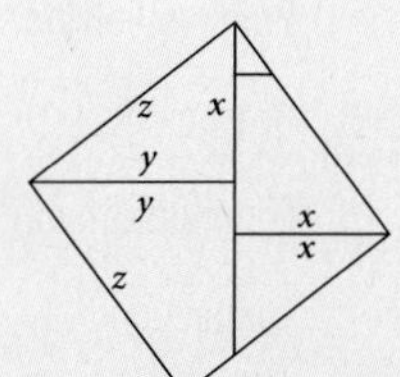

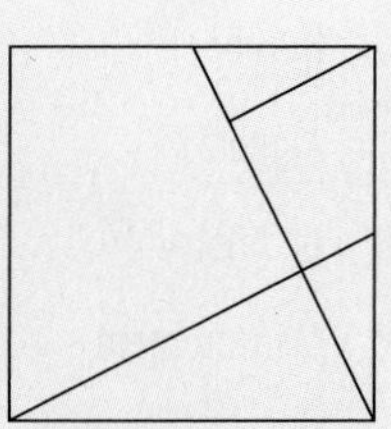

CHAPTER 8 REVIEW

You should know area formulas for rectangles, parallelograms, triangles, trapezoids, regular polygons, and circles. You should also be able to show where these formulas come from and how they're related to one another. Most importantly, you should be able to apply them to solve practical problems involving area, including the surface areas of solid figures. What occupations can you list that use area formulas?

When you use area formulas for real-world applications, you have to consider units of measurement and accuracy. Should you use inches, feet, centimeters, meters, or some other unit? If you work with a circle or a regular polygon, is your answer exact or an approximation?

EXERCISES

For Exercises 1–10, match the area formula with the shaded area.

1. $A = bh$ parallelogram (B)
2. $A = 0.5bh$ triangle (A)
3. $A = 0.5h(b_1 + b_2)$ trapezoid (C)
4. $A = 0.5d_1d_2$ kite (E)
5. $A = 0.5aP$ regular polygon (F)
6. $A = \pi r^2$ circle (D)
7. $A = \left(\frac{x}{360}\right)\pi r^2$ sector (J)
8. $A = \pi(R^2 - r^2)$ annulus (I)
9. $SA = 2\pi rl + 2\pi r^2$ cylinder (G)
10. $LA = \pi rl$ cone (H)

A. 

B. 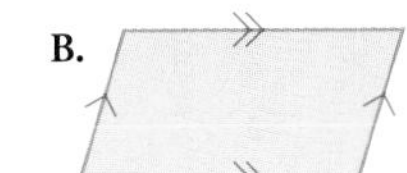

C.

D. 

E. 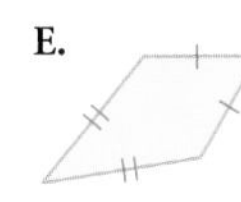

F. 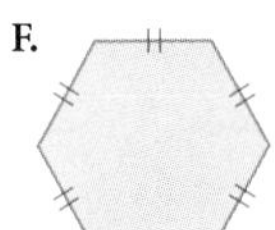

G. 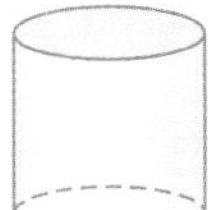

H. 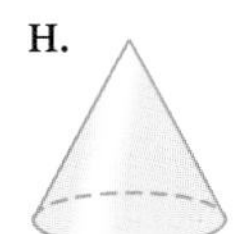

I. 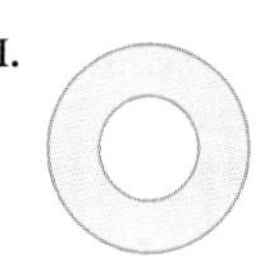

J. 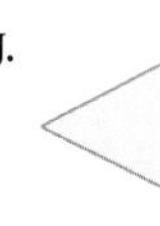

For Exercises 11–13, illustrate each term.

11. Apothem
12. Annulus
13. Sector of a circle

For Exercises 14–16, draw a diagram and explain in a paragraph how you derived the area formula for each figure.

14. Parallelogram
15. Trapezoid
16. Circle

11–16. Answers are on page 456.

Reviewing (continued)

regular n-gon. Then imagine letting the number of sides become infinite, so that the figure becomes a circle. **[Ask]** "What's its area?" Convert the area algebraically to the standard formula. Then consider a piece of the circle, a sector with arc measure (or central angle measure) 60°. **[Ask]** "What's its area?" Find the area of the associated segment.

Going back to the square, imagine moving it straight out from a plane to form a square prism. Analyze its surface area. Add an edge—and more edges—to make regular n-gon prisms, and analyze their surface areas. Shrink the outer n-gon to make a frustum. **[Ask]** "What's its surface area?" Shrink the top all the way to a point. **[Ask]** "What's the surface area of the pyramid?"

Make one more trip back to the square. Again, turn it into a regular n-gon, and move it out to make a prism. This time, let the number of edges get larger to approach a cylinder. **[Ask]** "What's its surface area?" Shrink the outer circle to make a frustum and then a cone, and examine their surface areas.

CHAPTER REVIEW 8

PLANNING

LESSON OUTLINE

One day:

10 min	Reviewing
25 min	Exercises
10 min	Student self-assessment

REVIEWING

You might do a quick dynamic review of the topics in this chapter. Start with a square—using geometry software or drawing on an erasable surface. **[Ask]** "What's its area, and why?" Discuss square units. Expand the square to a rectangle, and discuss its area in terms of square units. Shrink one side, adjusting consecutive sides, to make a trapezoid, and discuss how the square units now have to be cut apart but the area is still the number of units that fit into the space. Shrink the side down to a point, and find the area of the resulting triangle.

Go back to the square and draw in diagonals. **[Ask]** "What larger square has an area equal to the product of the diagonals?" The area of the square is also half the product of the lengths of the diagonals. Now shift one edge to make a rhombus. **[Ask]** "Has the area changed?" "What's the area of a rhombus in terms of its diagonals?" Finally, move one vertex of the rhombus along a diagonal to make a kite. **[Ask]** "What's the area of the kite?"

Again start with a square. This time, divide it into triangles and find its area in terms of its perimeter. Increase the number of sides to make a regular pentagon. **[Ask]** "What's its area in terms of its perimeter?" Generalize to a

ASSIGNING HOMEWORK

You may want to have students work on the exercises over most of two class periods. Most students will benefit from doing some of the exercises in a group and some exercises individually.

MATERIALS

- graph and dot paper

Helping with the Exercises

Exercises 1–10 These exercises are quick, but they could be reviewed more than once.

Exercises 11–16 With sketches, these exercises should become part of each student's notebook.

11.

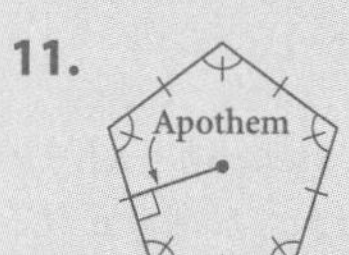

12.

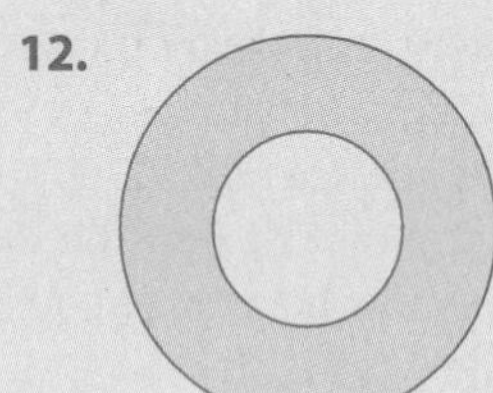

13.

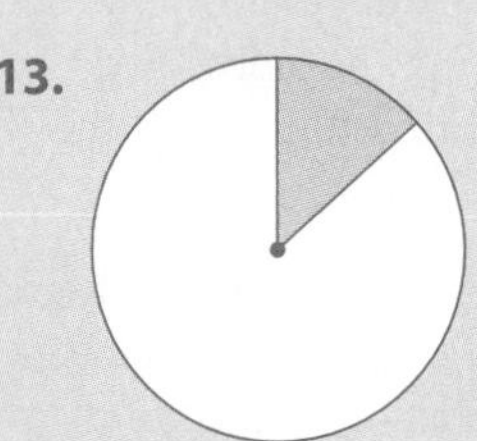

14. Sample answer: Construct an altitude from the vertex of an obtuse angle to the base. Cut off the right triangle and move it to the opposite side, forming a rectangle. Because the parallelogram's area hasn't changed, its area equals the area of the rectangle. Because the area of the rectangle is given by the formula $A = bh$, the area of the parallelogram is also given by $A = bh$.

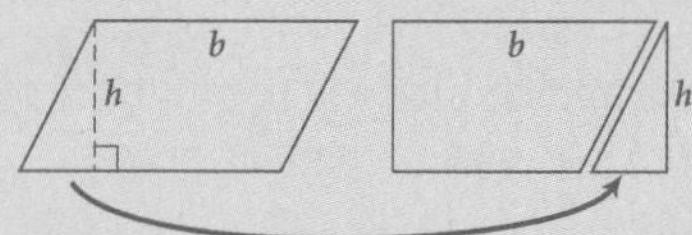

Solve for the unknown measures in Exercises 17–25. All measurements are in centimeters.

17. $A = \underline{?}$ 800 cm²

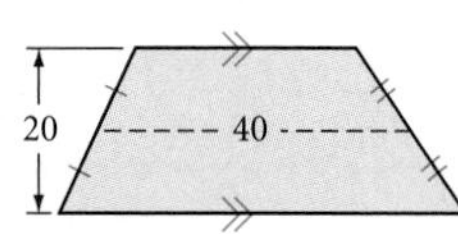

18. $A = \underline{?}$ 5990.4 cm²
$a = 36$
$s = 41.6$

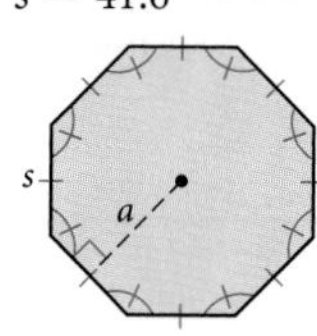

19. $A = \underline{?}$ 60π cm² or 188.5 cm²
$R = 8$
$r = 2$

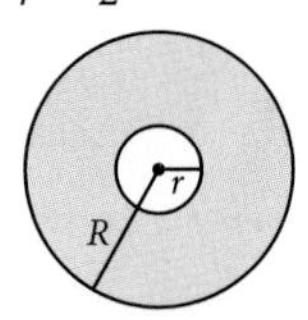

20. $A = 576$ cm²
$h = \underline{?}$ 32 cm

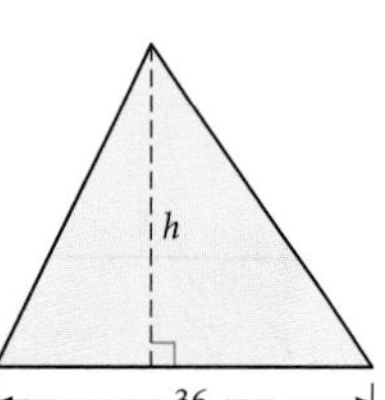
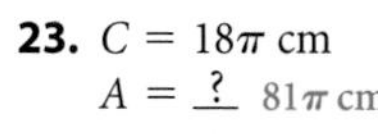

21. $A = 576$ cm²
$d_1 = \underline{?}$ 32 cm

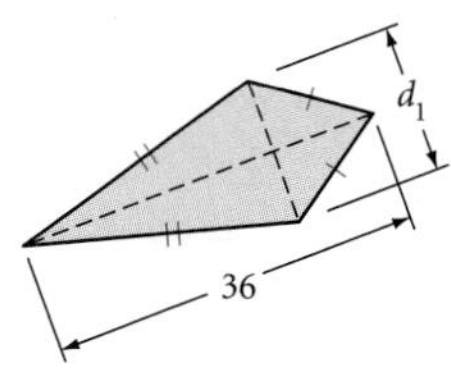

22. $A = 126$ cm²
$a = 13$ cm
$h = 9$ cm
$b = \underline{?}$
15 cm

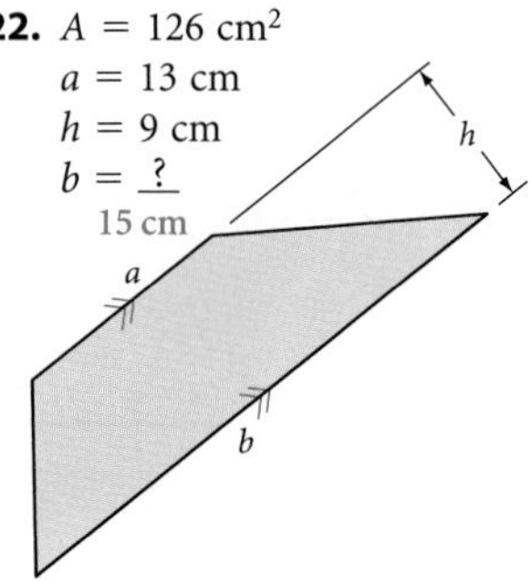

23. $C = 18\pi$ cm
$A = \underline{?}$ 81π cm²

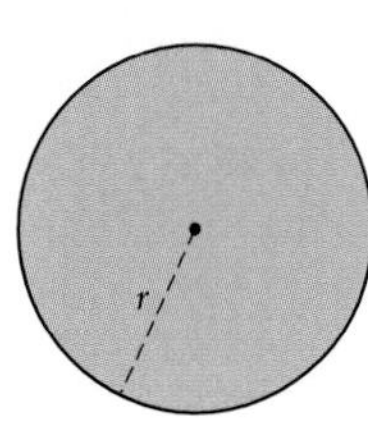

24. $A = 576\pi$ cm²
The circumference is $\underline{?}$.
48π cm

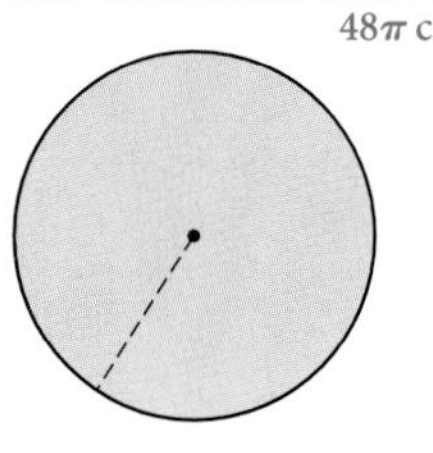

25. $A_{sector} = 16\pi$ cm²
$m\angle FAN = \underline{?}$. 40°

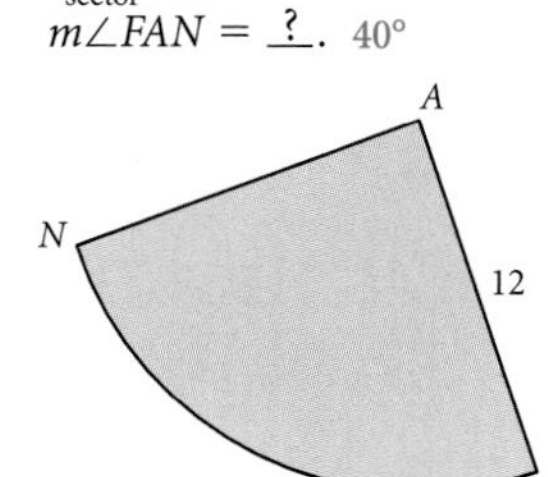

In Exercises 26–28, find the shaded area to the nearest 0.1 cm². In Exercises 27 and 28, the quadrilateral is a square and all arcs are arcs of a circle of radius 6 cm.

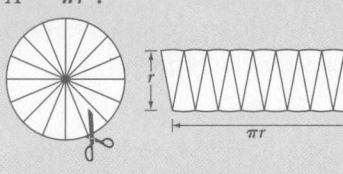

26.

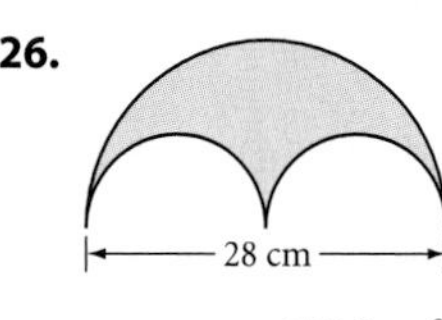

153.9 cm²

27.

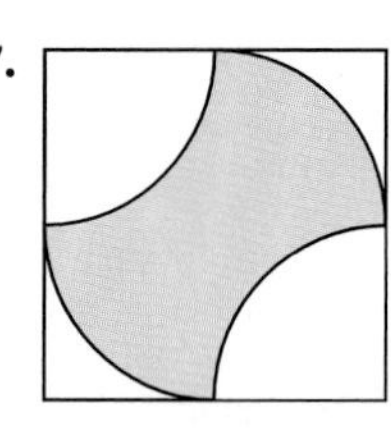

72 cm²

28.

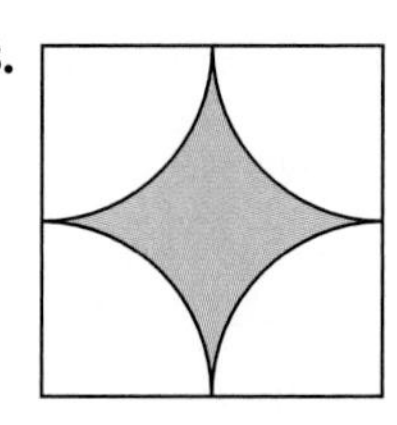

30.9 cm²

15. Sample answer: Make a copy of the trapezoid and put the two copies together to form a parallelogram with base $(b_1 + b_2)$ and height h. Thus the area of one trapezoid is given by the formula $A = \frac{1}{2}(b_1 + b_2)h$.

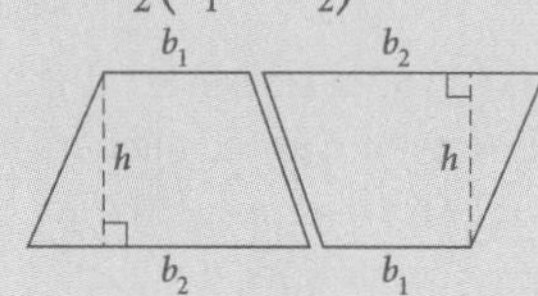

16. Sample answer: Cut a circular region into 16 wedges and arrange them into a shape that resembles a rectangle. The base length of this "rectangle" is πr and the height is r, so its area is πr^2. Thus the area of a circle is given by the formula $A = \pi r^2$.

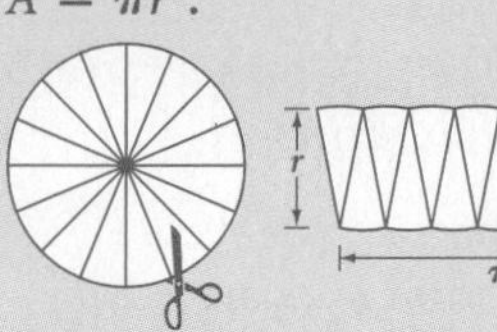

In Exercises 29–31, find the surface area of each prism or pyramid. All given measurements are in centimeters. All quadrilaterals are rectangles, unless otherwise labeled.

29.

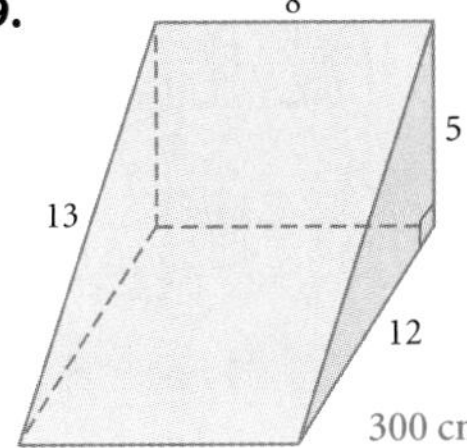

300 cm²

30. The base is a trapezoid.

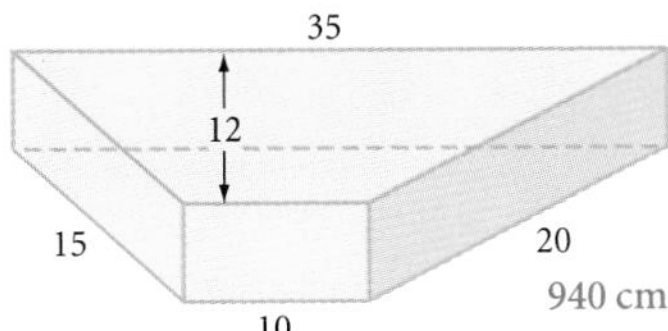

940 cm²

31.

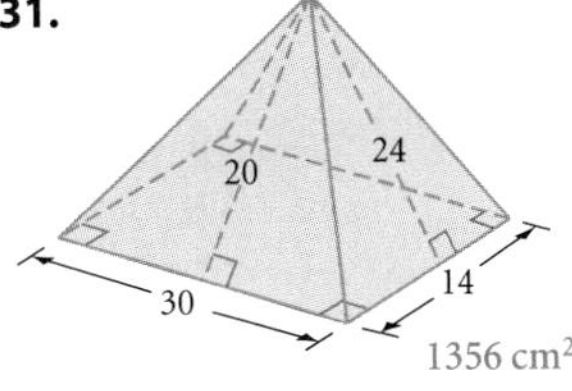

1356 cm²

For Exercises 32 and 33, plot the vertices of each figure on graph paper, then find its area.

32. Parallelogram $ABCD$ with $A(0, 0)$, $B(14, 0)$, and $D(6, 8)$

33. Quadrilateral $FOUR$ with $F(0, 0)$, $O(4, -3)$, $U(9, 5)$, and $R(4, 15)$

34. The sum of the lengths of the two bases of a trapezoid is 22 cm, and its area is 66cm². What is the height of the trapezoid? 6 cm

35. Find the area of a regular pentagon to the nearest tenth of a square centimeter if the apothem measures 6.9 cm and each side measures 10 cm. 172.5 cm²

36. Find three noncongruent polygons, each with an area of 24 square units, on a 6-by-6 geoboard or a 6-by-6 square dot grid.

37. Lancelot wants to make a pen for his pet, Isosceles. What is the area of the largest rectangular pen that Lancelot can make with 100 meters of fencing if he uses a straight wall of the castle for one side of the pen? ⓗ 1250 m²

38. If you have a hundred feet of rope to arrange into the perimeter of either a square or a circle, which shape will give you the maximum area? Explain.

Ropes

39. Which is a better (tighter) fit: a round peg in a square hole or a square peg in a round hole? ⓗ a round peg in a square hole

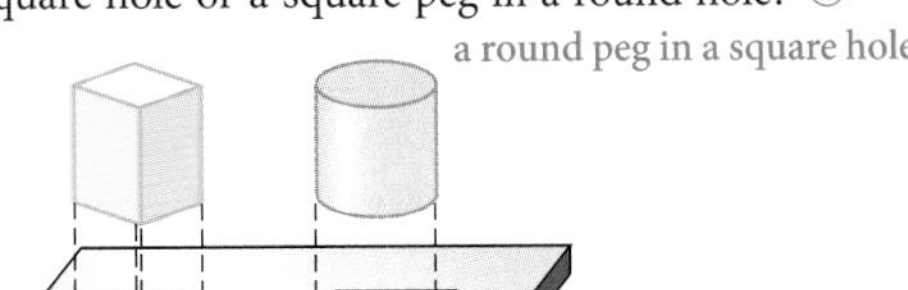

36. sample answers:

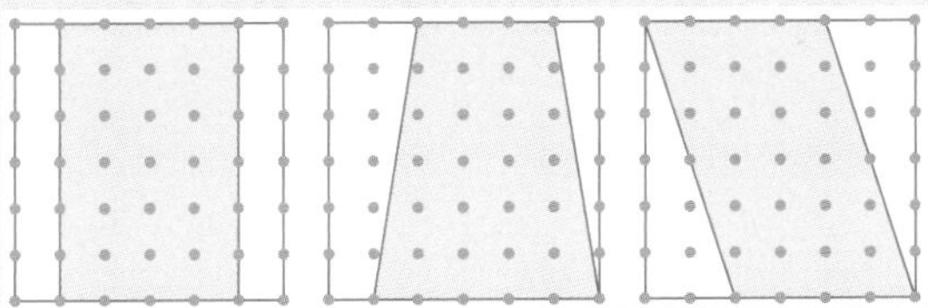

Exercise 32 Both possible parallelograms with these three vertices have the same area.

32. Area is 112 square units.

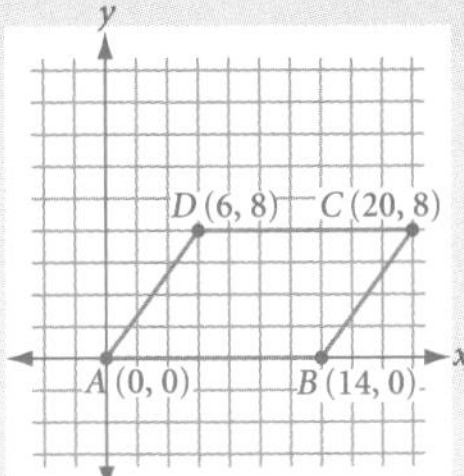

33. Area is 81 square units.

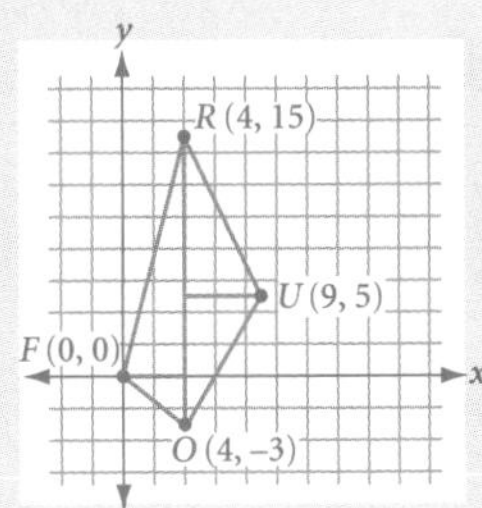

Exercise 38 Some students may have difficulty going from circumference to radius. It might be easier for them to find the diameter by dividing the circumference by π and then halving to get the radius.

38. Circle. For the square, $100 = 4s$, $s = 25$, $A = 25^2 = 625$ ft². For the circle, $100 = 2\pi r$, $r \approx 15.9$, $A \approx \pi(15.9)^2 \approx 795$ ft².

Exercise 39 Students may be tempted to try to solve this problem by subtraction, but differences don't make much sense because the sizes of the holes aren't given. Ratios are needed. If students are having difficulty finding the area of the square peg that's in the round hole, suggest that they draw a square with r as one side and see how much of the original square would fit into this new square. They can then see that the area of the square peg is $2r^2$. They end up comparing $\frac{\pi}{4}$ with $\frac{2}{\pi}$.

Exercise 41 This exercise foreshadows area ratios in Lesson 11.5. A few students may be ready to see that because the ratio of linear dimensions is $\frac{16}{12} = \frac{4}{3}$, the ratio of areas will be $\left(\frac{4}{3}\right)^2 = \frac{16}{9}$.

42. one-eighth of a 12-inch diameter pie; one-fourth of a 6-inch pie and one-eighth of a 12-inch pie both have the same length of crust, and more than one-sixth of an 8-inch pie

Exercise 43 **[Ask]** "Does the model show you what the length of the sides of the squares should be?" [yes, 12 ft]

Exercises 44–46 Encourage the use of dimensional analysis.

40. Al Dente's Pizzeria sells pizza by the slice, according to the sign. Which slice is the best deal (the most pizza per dollar)? giant

41. If you need 8 oz of dough to make a 12-inch diameter pizza, how much dough will you need to make a 16-inch pizza on a crust of the same thickness? about 14 oz

42. Which is the biggest slice of pie: one-fourth of a 6-inch diameter pie, one-sixth of an 8-inch diameter pie, or one-eighth of a 12-inch diameter pie? Which slice has the most crust along the curved edge?

43. The Hot-Air Balloon Club at Da Vinci High School has designed a balloon for the annual race. The panels are a regular octagon, eight squares, and sixteen isosceles trapezoids, and club members will sew them together to construct the balloon. They have built a scale model, as shown at right. The dimensions of three of the four types of panels are below, shown in feet. ⓗ

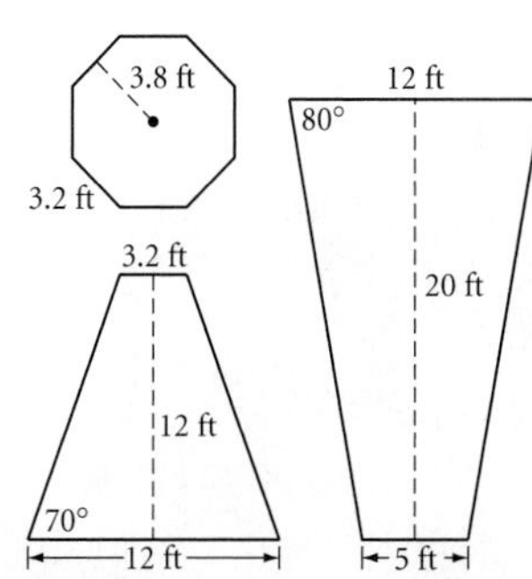

a. What will be the perimeter, to the nearest foot, of the balloon at its widest? What will be the perimeter, to the nearest foot, of the opening at the bottom of the balloon? 96 ft; 40 ft

b. What is the total surface area of the balloon to the nearest square foot? 3290 ft²

For Exercises 44–46, unless the dimensions indicate otherwise, assume each quadrilateral is a rectangle.

44. You are producing 10,000 of these metal wedges, and you must electroplate them with a thin layer of high-conducting silver. The measurements shown are in centimeters. Find the total cost for silver, if silver plating costs $1 for each 200 square centimeters. $3000

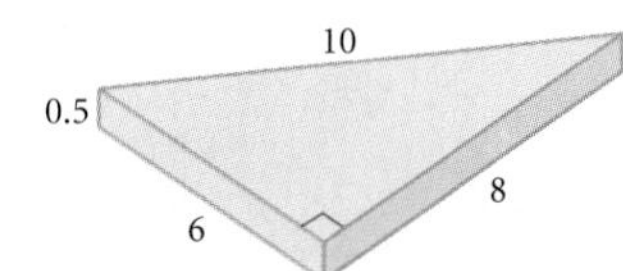

45. The measurements of a chemical storage container are shown in meters. Find the cost of painting the exterior of nine of these large cylindrical containers with sealant. The sealant costs \$32 per gallon. Each gallon covers 18 square meters. Do not paint the bottom faces. \$4160

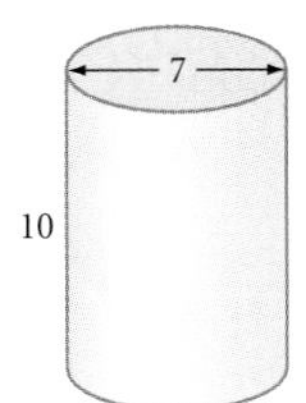

46. The measurements of a copper cone are shown in inches. Find the cost of spraying an oxidizer on 100 of these copper cones. The oxidizer costs \$26 per pint. Each pint covers approximately 5000 square inches. Spray only the lateral surface. \$2002

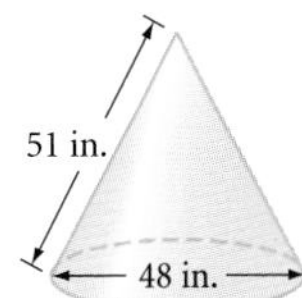

47. Hector is a very cost-conscious produce buyer. He usually buys asparagus in large bundles, each 44 cm in circumference. But today there are only small bundles that are 22 cm in circumference. Two 22 cm bundles are the same price as one 44 cm bundle. Is this a good deal or a bad deal? Why? It's a bad deal. $2\pi r_1 = 44$ cm. $2\pi r_2 = 22$ cm, which implies $4\pi r_2 = 44$ cm. Therefore $r_1 = 2r_2$. The area of the large bundle is $4\pi(r_2)^2$ cm². The combined area of two small bundles is $2\pi(r_2)^2$ cm². Thus he is getting half as much for the same price.

TAKE ANOTHER LOOK

1. Use geometry software to construct these shapes.

a. A triangle whose perimeter can vary, but whose area stays constant

b. A parallelogram whose perimeter can vary, but whose area stays constant

2. True or false? The area of a triangle is equal to half the perimeter of the triangle times the radius of the inscribed circle. Support your conclusion with a convincing argument.

3. Does the area formula for a kite hold for a dart (a concave kite)? Support your conclusion with a convincing argument.

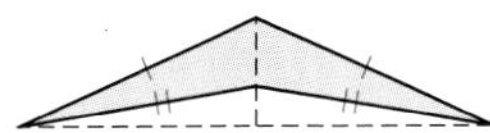

4. How can you use the Regular Polygon Area Conjecture to arrive at a formula for the area of a circle? Use a series of diagrams to help explain your reasoning.

5. Use algebra to show that the total surface area of a prism with a regular polygon base is given by the formula $SA = P(h + a)$, where h is height of the prism, a is the apothem of the base, and P is the perimeter of the base.

6. Use algebra to show that the total surface area of a cylinder is given by the formula $SA = C(h + r)$, where h is the height of the cylinder, r is the radius of the base, and C is the circumference of the base.

7. Here is a different formula for the area of a trapezoid: $A = mh$, where m is the length of the midsegment and h is the height. Does the formula work? Use algebra or a diagram to explain why or why not. Does it work for a triangle?

Exercise 46 The oxidizer creates a green patina on the cones.

Exercise 47 Students might not recognize that they need to compare only the areas of two circles. This exercise foreshadows work with proportions in Lesson 11.5. A bundle with $\frac{1}{2}$ the linear dimensions will have $\left(\frac{1}{2}\right)^2$ the area; it should be $\frac{1}{4}$ the price.

Take Another Look

1. A possible approach for the triangle: To make a base of constant length, construct line j between points A and B. Mark vector AB. Construct point C on line j. Translate point C to C' by the marked vector. Then CC' will be constant. To create a constant altitude, construct point D not on line j. Construct line k through point D parallel to line j. Construct point E on line k. Construct segments to form $\triangle CC'E$ of constant base and height. Then hide points A, B, and D and lines j and k.

2. True. Given $\triangle ABC$ with inscribed circle O as shown:

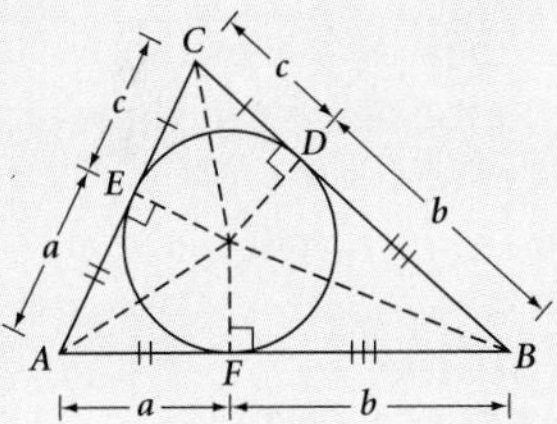

The triangle is composed of three pairs of congruent right triangles. Its area is therefore

$\frac{1}{2}r(a + b + b + c + c + a) = \frac{1}{2}Pr$

3. yes; area of kite $= \frac{1}{2} \cdot d_1 \cdot d_2 = \frac{1}{2} \cdot x \cdot 2y = xy$

area of two triangles $= 2 \cdot \frac{1}{2} \cdot x \cdot y = xy$

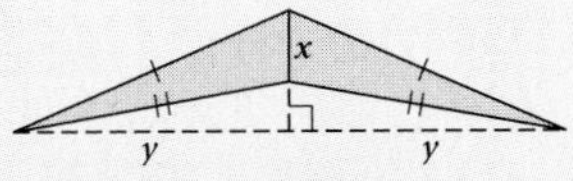

4. See Lesson 8.5, Exercise 16. As $n \to \infty$, $a \to r$. Therefore $A = \frac{1}{2}aP \to A = \frac{1}{2}r \cdot 2\pi r = \pi r^2$.

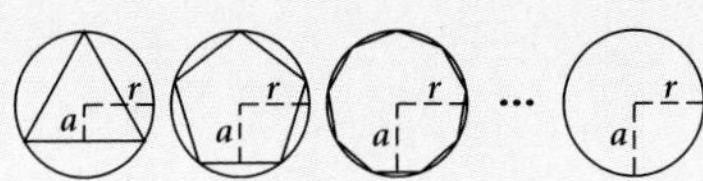

5. area of two bases $= 2 \cdot \frac{1}{2} \cdot a \cdot P = aP$

area of n rectangular sides $= n \cdot$ side length of polygon $\cdot h = P \cdot h$

total surface area $= Ph + aP = P(h + a)$

6. Students may point out that as the number of sides of the base gets larger, the prism approaches a cylinder and a becomes r. Or they might repeat the argument in activity 5, except with C and r:

area of two bases $= 2 \cdot \pi r^2$

area of side $= C \cdot h$

total surface area $= C \cdot h + 2\pi r^2$
$= C \cdot h + 2\pi r \cdot r$
$= C \cdot h + C \cdot r$
$= C(h + r)$

7. Students may have seen these ideas already. The Trapezoid Area Conjecture tells us that $A = \frac{1}{2}(b_1 + b_2)h$. But the Trapezoid Midsegment Conjecture tells us that $m = \frac{1}{2}(b_1 + b_2)$. Thus, if $A = \frac{1}{2}(b_1 + b_2)h$ and $m = \frac{1}{2}(b_1 + b_2)$, then $A = mh$.

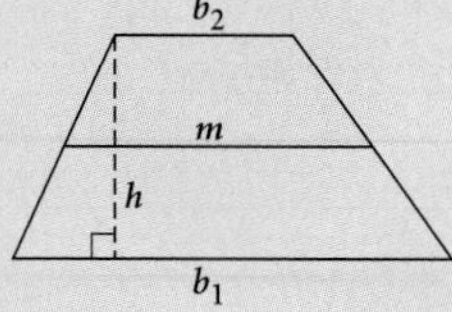

Similarly, the Triangle Area Conjecture says that the formula for the area of a triangle is $A = \frac{1}{2}bh$. But the Triangle Midsegment Conjecture tells us that the length of the midsegment is half the length of the third side $\left(m = \frac{1}{2}b\right)$. Thus, if $A = \frac{1}{2}bh$ and $m = \frac{1}{2}b$, by substitution $A = mh$.

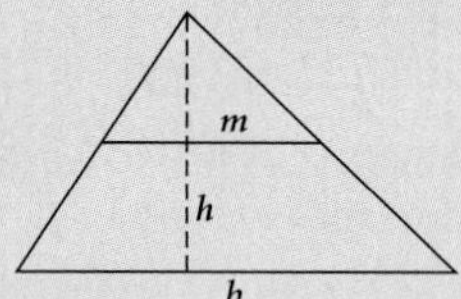

ASSESSING

To de-emphasize the memorization of formulas, you might want to allow students to use their notebooks for the chapter test.

FACILITATING SELF-ASSESSMENT

To help students complete the portfolio described in Assessing What You've Learned, suggest that they consider for evaluation their work on Lesson 8.1, Exercise 17; Lesson 8.2, Exercise 14; Lesson 8.3, Exercise 6; Lesson 8.4, Exercise 13; Lesson 8.5, Exercise 12; Lesson 8.6, Exercises 13, 14; and Lesson 8.7, Exercise 10.

Assessing What You've Learned

UPDATE YOUR PORTFOLIO Choose one of the more challenging problems you did in this chapter and add it to your portfolio. Write about why you chose it, what made it challenging, what strategies you used to solve it, and what you learned from it.

ORGANIZE YOUR NOTEBOOK Review your notebook to be sure it's complete and well organized. Be sure you have included all of this chapter's area formulas in your conjecture list. Write a one-page chapter summary.

WRITE IN YOUR JOURNAL Imagine yourself five or ten years from now, looking back on the influence this geometry class had on your life. How do you think you'll be using geometry? Will this course have influenced your academic or career goals?

PERFORMANCE ASSESSMENT While a classmate, a friend, a family member, or a teacher observes, demonstrate how to derive one or more of the area formulas. Explain each step, including how you arrive at the formula.

WRITE TEST ITEMS Work with group members to write test items for this chapter. Include simple exercises and complex application problems.

GIVE A PRESENTATION Create a poster, a model, or other visual aid, and give a presentation on how to derive one or more of the area formulas. Or present your findings from one of the Take Another Look activities.

CHAPTER

9

The Pythagorean Theorem

Overview

In **Lesson 9.1,** students gain a deeper understanding of the Pythagorean Theorem by dissecting the squares on the legs of a right triangle and fitting the pieces into the square on the hypotenuse. They apply the Pythagorean Theorem to find missing lengths in right triangles, and they can animate an explanation of the theorem in a flip book. Students explore the converse of the Pythagorean Theorem and apply it to three dimensions in **Lesson 9.2.** Radical expressions are reviewed in **Using Your Algebra Skills 8. Lesson 9.3** introduces students to special properties of isosceles right triangles and 30°-60°-90° triangles. In an **exploration,** students build a Pythagorean fractal using The Geometer's Sketchpad. They solve story problems in **Lesson 9.4.** In **Lesson 9.5,** students discover that the distance formula in coordinate geometry is nothing more than the Pythagorean Theorem and then use the distance formula to arrive at the equation of a circle. An **exploration** of a leaning ladder sliding down the side of a building follows. **Lesson 9.6** covers some uses of the Pythagorean Theorem in circle geometry.

The Mathematics

Many students will already "know" the Pythagorean Theorem as $a^2 + b^2 = c^2$. This understanding is limited, for three reasons:

- It includes no conditions. What are a, b, and c? Without saying that a and b are lengths of legs of a right triangle and c is the length of its hypotenuse, the equation is meaningless.
- It ties students to these letters. Students need to be able to use variables other than a, b, and c, for example, in deriving the distance formula and the equation of a circle.
- Even if the conditions are understood, students will see this statement as being about lengths of sides of a right triangle. Indeed, most applications of the theorem are in this algebraic context: the square *of* the hypotenuse equals the sum of the squares *of* the other two sides. But seeing the theorem as being about areas of squares—the square *on* the hypotenuse equals the sum of the squares *on* the other two sides—can lead to a generalization to other, similar figures on those three sides and thus to a deeper understanding of one of the basic ideas of mathematics: that if two figures are similar with scale factor s, then their areas have scale factor s^2.

Special Triangles

Two special right triangles are used so often that they warrant some investigation. The ratios of the lengths of the sides in a 45°-45°-90° triangle are $1:1:\sqrt{2}$. In a 30°-60°-90° triangle those ratios are $1:\sqrt{3}:2$, where the length of the side opposite the 30° angle is half the length of the hypotenuse. Investigation of these special triangles is aided by some facility in working with radical expressions.

A tradition in radical calculation is rationalizing denominators so that no radical expression appears in them. This convention was especially helpful in approximating decimal values before electronic calculators came along. Insistence on following this rule leads to contortions such as $\left(\frac{1}{\sqrt{2}}\right)^2 = \left(\frac{\sqrt{2}}{2}\right)^2 = \frac{2}{4} = \frac{1}{2}$, where doing the calculation directly would be easier.

Distance Formula

In coordinate geometry, you can find the distance between two points by applying the Pythagorean Theorem to a right triangle in which the two points are vertices of the nonright angles. The Pythagorean Theorem gives $d^2 = (x_1 - x_2)^2 + (y_1 - y_2)^2$. The actual distance is $d = \sqrt{(x_1 - x_2)^2 + (y_1 - y_2)^2}$. Taking only the nonnegative square root is allowable here because d is a distance and thus is not negative.

Equation of a Circle

The Pythagorean Theorem says that the coordinates of any point (x, y) on a circle with radius 1 centered at the origin satisfy the equation $x^2 + y^2 = 1^2$. If the circle is dilated by a factor of r (making its radius r), the equation becomes $\left(\frac{x}{r}\right)^2 + \left(\frac{y}{r}\right)^2 = 1$, or more familiarly $x^2 + y^2 = r^2$. If the circle is translated to have center (h, k), then the equation becomes the general form: $(x - h)^2 + (y - k)^2 = r^2$.

For circles, y is not a function of x because vertical lines give two values of y for some values of x. This fact is reflected in the equation; if you solve for y in terms of x, you get two values: $y = \pm\sqrt{r^2 - (x - h)^2}$. Therefore, to graph circles on a calculator, one usually graphs two functions: $y = \sqrt{r^2 - (x - h)^2}$ and $y = -\sqrt{r^2 - (x - h)^2}$. However, it's not quite true to say "circles are not functions." One can consider a circle with radius r as a function of a third variable, usually called t: $f(t) = (r\cos t, r\sin t)$. This idea will come up in the Exploration Trigonometric Ratios and the Unit Circle in Chapter 12.

Using This Chapter

If the weather is nice, you can do the investigation in Lesson 9.2 by going outside with long lengths of string to create large right triangles. After completing Lesson 9.5, advanced classes might be ready for the extension into three-dimensional coordinates and the distance formula in three dimensions.

Resources

Discovering Geometry Resources

Teaching and Worksheet Masters
 Lessons 9.1, 9.5, and 9.6
 Exploration: A Pythagorean Fractal

Sketchpad Demonstrations
 Lesson 9.1
 Exploration: A Pythagorean Fractal

Discovering Geometry with The Geometer's Sketchpad
 Lessons 9.1–9.3 and 9.5

Assessment Resources A and B
 Quiz 1 (Lessons 9.1 and 9.2)
 Quiz 2 (Lessons 9.3 and 9.4)
 Quiz 3 (Lessons 9.5 and 9.6)
 Chapter 9 Test
 Chapter 9 Constructive Assessment Options
 Chapters 7–9 Exam

Practice Your Skills for Chapter 9

Condensed Lessons for Chapter 9

Other Resources

www.keypress.com/DG

Materials

- construction tools
- scissors
- protractors
- rulers
- string
- graphing calculators
- graph paper
- dot paper
- patty paper
- paper clips

Pacing Guide

	day 1	day 2	day 3	day 4	day 5	day 6	day 7	day 8	day 9	day 10
standard	9.1	9.2	Algebra 8	9.3	Exploration	quiz, Exploration	9.4	9.5	Exploration	9.6
enriched	9.1, project	9.2	Algebra 8	9.3	Exploration	quiz, Exploration	9.4	9.5	Exploration	9.6
block	9.1, 9.2	Algebra 8, 9.3	quiz, 9.4	Exploration	9.5, Exploration	9.6, quiz, review	review, TAL	assessment, TAL	mixed review	unit exam

	day 11	day 12	day 13	day 14	day 15	day 16	day 17	day 18	day 19	day 20
standard	quiz, review	review	assessment	mixed review	unit exam					
enriched	quiz, review, TAL	review, TAL	assessment	mixed review	unit exam					

CHAPTER

9 The Pythagorean Theorem

But serving up an action, suggesting the dynamic in the static, has become a hobby of mine . . . . The "flowing" on that motionless plane holds my attention to such a degree that my preference is to try and make it into a cycle.

M. C. ESCHER

Waterfall, M. C. Escher, 1961

OBJECTIVES

In this chapter you will

- discover the Pythagorean Theorem, one of the most important concepts in mathematics
- use the Pythagorean Theorem to calculate the distance between any two points
- use conjectures related to the Pythagorean Theorem to solve problems

CHAPTER 9 OBJECTIVES

- Understand the Pythagorean Theorem more deeply
- Discover the Converse of the Pythagorean Theorem
- Practice working with radical expressions
- Discover relationships among the lengths of the sides of a 45°-45°-90° triangle and among the lengths of the sides of a 30°-60°-90° triangle
- Apply the Pythagorean Theorem and its converse
- Discover and apply the Pythagorean relationship on a coordinate plane (the distance formula)
- Derive the equation of a circle from the distance formula
- Practice using geometry tools
- Develop reading comprehension, problem-solving skills, and cooperative behavior
- Learn new vocabulary

Escher has cleverly used right angles to form his artwork known as *Waterfall*. The picture contains three uses of the impossible tribar created by British mathematician Roger Penrose (b 1931) in 1954. In 1934 Swedish artist Oscar Reutersvard (b 1915), "father of impossible figures," had created an impossible tribar that consisted of a triangular arrangement of cubes.

The shapes topping the towers in Escher's work are, on the left, a compound of three cubes and, on the right, a stellation of the rhombic dodecahedron.

[Ask] "What impossible things do you see?" [Water seems to be traveling up an incline, yet it is running a mill wheel.] "Which surfaces appear to be horizontal? Vertical? Sloped? There are three impossible tribars in the picture; where are they?" [They all have flowing water along two sides; twice one of the bars is replaced by the waterfall, and once one bar is replaced by a group of four columns.]

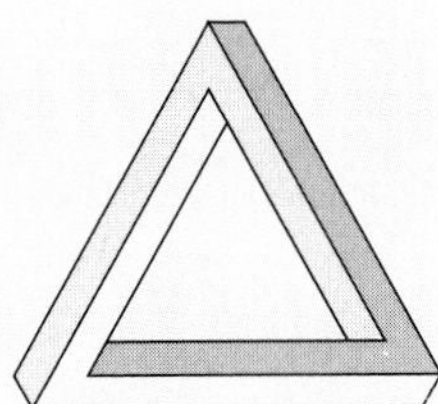

Penrose tribar

LESSON 9.1

PLANNING

LESSON OUTLINE

One day:

15 min Investigation

5 min Sharing

10 min Examples

15 min Closing and Exercises

MATERIALS

- construction tools
- scissors
- Pythagorean Theorem (W) for One step
- Dissection of Squares (W), *optional*
- Sketchpad demonstration Three Triangles, *optional*

TEACHING

Many students may already know the Pythagorean Theorem as $a^2 + b^2 = c^2$. In this lesson they review what the letters stand for and discover proofs showing why the relationship holds for all right triangles.

INTRODUCTION

Direct students' attention to Improving Your Visual Thinking Skills on page 454. Ask what they can conclude about right triangles, and help them state the Pythagorean Theorem using areas of squares and the terms *hypotenuse* and *legs*.

LESSON 9.1

The Theorem of Pythagoras

I am not young enough to know everything.

OSCAR WILDE

In a right triangle, the side opposite the right angle is called the **hypotenuse.** The other two sides are called **legs.** In the figure at right, a and b represent the lengths of the legs, and c represents the length of the hypotenuse.

In a right triangle, the side opposite the right angle is called the **hypotenuse,** here with length c.

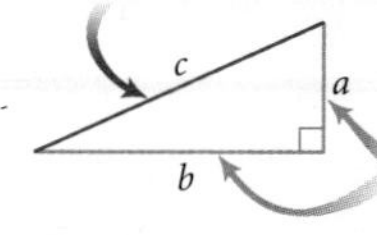

The other two sides are **legs,** here with lengths a and b.

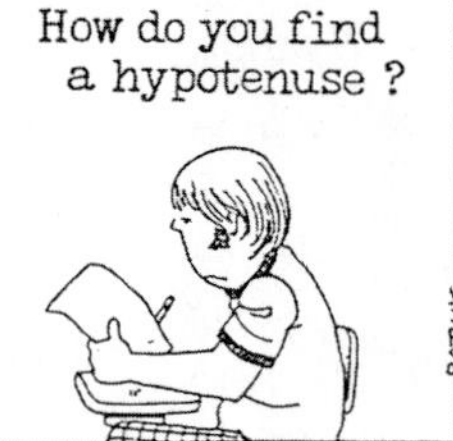

How do you find a hypotenuse ?
BATIUK

Look for tracks around the water hole !

FUNKY WINKERBEAN by Batiuk. Reprinted with special permission of North America Syndicate.

There is a special relationship between the lengths of the legs and the length of the hypotenuse. This relationship is known today as the **Pythagorean Theorem.**

Investigation

The Three Sides of a Right Triangle

You will need

- scissors
- a compass
- a straightedge
- patty paper

The puzzle in this investigation is intended to help you recall the Pythagorean Theorem. It uses a **dissection,** which means you will cut apart one or more geometric figures and make the pieces fit into another figure.

Step 1 Construct a scalene right triangle in the middle of your paper. Label the hypotenuse c and the legs a and b. Construct a square on each side of the triangle.

Step 2 To locate the center of the square on the longer leg, draw its diagonals. Label the center O.

Step 3 Through point O, construct line j perpendicular to the hypotenuse and line k perpendicular to line j. Line k is parallel to the hypotenuse. Lines j and k divide the square on the longer leg into four parts.

Step 4 Cut out the square on the shorter leg and the four parts of the square on the longer leg. Arrange them to exactly cover the square on the hypotenuse.

Guiding the Investigation

One step Hand out a copy of the Pythagorean Theorem worksheet to each group. Challenge students to cut up one or both of the smaller squares and assemble the pieces on top of the largest square. As you circulate, you might remind students of the problem-solving technique of trying a special case first—here, an isosceles right triangle. As needed, point out that good pieces might be formed if they draw lines through the smaller squares parallel to edges of the largest square.

[Language] A *dissection* is the result of separating something into pieces.

Step 1 Using the Dissection of Squares worksheets or the Sketchpad demonstration will speed the investigation, but the use of many different triangles drawn by the students strengthens the inductive conclusion. The constructions are quicker with patty paper than with compass and straightedge. It is also easy to create several examples using geometry software.

Step 2 As needed, remind students that the legs are the sides other than the hypotenuse, so the "longer leg" is not the hypotenuse. Suggest that students minimize clutter by making these diagonals very light or by drawing only the portion near the center of the square.

Step 4 Ask students to take care in drawing and cutting out pieces so they will fit together well. Students may want to tape the pieces together.

Step 5 | State the Pythagorean Theorem.

The Pythagorean Theorem C-82

In a right triangle, the sum of the squares of the lengths of the legs equals the square of the length of the hypotenuse. If a and b are the lengths of the legs, and c is the length of the hypotenuse, then __?__. $a^2 + b^2 = c^2$

History **CONNECTION**

Pythagoras of Samos (ca. 569–475 B.C.E.), depicted in this statue, is often described as "the first pure mathematician." Samos was a principal commercial center of Greece and is located on the island of Samos in the Aegean Sea. The ancient town of Samos now lies in ruins, as shown in the photo at right.

Mysteriously, none of Pythagoras's writings still exist, and we know very little about his life. He founded a mathematical society in Croton, in what is now Italy, whose members discovered irrational numbers and the five regular solids. They proved what is now called the Pythagorean Theorem, although it was discovered and used 1000 years earlier by the Chinese and Babylonians. Some math historians believe that the ancient Egyptians also used a special case of this property to construct right angles.

A **theorem** is a conjecture that has been proved. Demonstrations like the one in the investigation are the first step toward proving the Pythagorean Theorem.

Believe it or not, there are more than 200 proofs of the Pythagorean Theorem. Elisha Scott Loomis's *Pythagorean Proposition,* first published in 1927, contains original proofs by Pythagoras, Euclid, and even Leonardo da Vinci and U. S. President James Garfield. One well-known proof of the Pythagorean Theorem is included below. You will complete another proof as an exercise.

Paragraph Proof: The Pythagorean Theorem

You need to show that $a^2 + b^2$ equals c^2 for the right triangles in the figure at left. The area of the entire square is $(a + b)^2$ or $a^2 + 2ab + b^2$. The area of any triangle is $\left(\frac{1}{2}\right)ab$, so the sum of the areas of the four triangles is $2ab$. The area of the quadrilateral in the center is $(a^2 + 2ab + b^2) - 2ab$, or $a^2 + b^2$.

If the quadrilateral in the center is a square then its area also equals c^2. You now need to show that it is a square. You know that all the sides have length c, but you also need to show that the angles are right angles. The two acute angles in the right triangle, along with any angle of the quadrilateral, add up to 180°. The acute angles in a right triangle add up to 90°. Therefore the quadrilateral angle measures 90° and the quadrilateral is a square. If it is a square with side length c, then its area is c^2. So, $a^2 + b^2 = c^2$, which proves the Pythagorean Theorem. ■

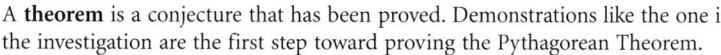

SHARING IDEAS

You might make a transparency of the Dissection of Squares worksheets for students to use in presenting their ideas.

Ask about symmetry in the dissected square on the hypotenuse. The method of the Investigation gives 4-fold rotational symmetry.

[Ask] "What if the triangle isn't a right triangle? Do you think there's still a relationship among the lengths of the sides?" You need not answer this question now; it's addressed later. **[Link]** The Pythagorean Theorem is a special case of the Law of Cosines $\left(c^2 = a^2 + b^2 - 2ab\cos C\right.$, where $\angle C$ is the angle opposite side $\left.c\right)$; when $m\angle C = 90°$, we have $\cos C = 0$.

[Ask] "What is the longest side of a right triangle?" "Is it the same as the longest leg?" [The hypotenuse, not the longest leg, is the longest side.] If you ask why the longest side is always the hypotenuse and what can be said about the longer of the two legs, you can review the Triangle Inequality Conjecture and the Side-Angle Inequality Conjecture.

[Ask] "What is a theorem?" [It's a conjecture that has been proved deductively within a deductive system.] So far in this course no axiom system has been developed, so there are no real theorems; this conjecture is called a theorem in this book because it has been proved within an axiom system and it's so well known by that name.

If students are not very familiar with the Pythagorean Theorem, ask how this theorem about areas of squares might be used to calculate lengths. Direct students' attention to the two examples.

NCTM STANDARDS

CONTENT		PROCESS	
	Number	✓	Problem Solving
✓	Algebra	✓	Reasoning
✓	Geometry	✓	Communication
✓	Measurement	✓	Connections
	Data/Probability	✓	Representation

LESSON OBJECTIVES

- Understand the Pythagorean Theorem more deeply
- Practice using geometry tools
- Learn new vocabulary

▶ EXAMPLE A

After working through the example, ask students what square roots are and how to find them using their calculators. Remind them that many of the square roots they'll find with their calculators are approximations. **[Ask]** "What are some numbers whose square roots are whole numbers?" [4, 9, 16, 25, 36, and so on] Students will begin to recognize more examples of perfect squares as they work through the chapter.

The equation $h^2 = 375$ is not a perfect model for this problem because it has two solutions, one positive and one negative. The negative solution is ignored because all distances in geometry are positive.

▶ EXAMPLE B

In Example A, the book mentions that 19.4 is an approximation of $\sqrt{375}$. Point out that in Example B the calculation is exact. See whether students recognize 256 as a perfect square. Again, the negative square root is being ignored.

Process text (the reason for each algebraic step) is included with each step in Example A. In Example B, it has been left up to students to figure out what algebraic steps are being carried out. **[Ask]** "Why does [this step] follow from the previous step?"

Assessing Progress

You can assess students' understanding of *right triangle, square, diagonal,* and *perpendicular.* Also watch for their ability to follow instructions and to work together in groups. See how well they realize when exact answers are appropriate and when they need to use approximations.

The Pythagorean Theorem works for right triangles, but does it work for all triangles? A quick check demonstrates that it doesn't hold for other triangles.

Acute triangle

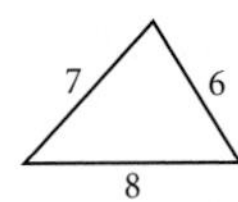

$6^2 + 7^2 > 8^2$

Obtuse triangle

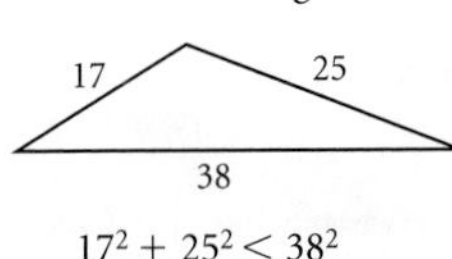

$17^2 + 25^2 < 38^2$

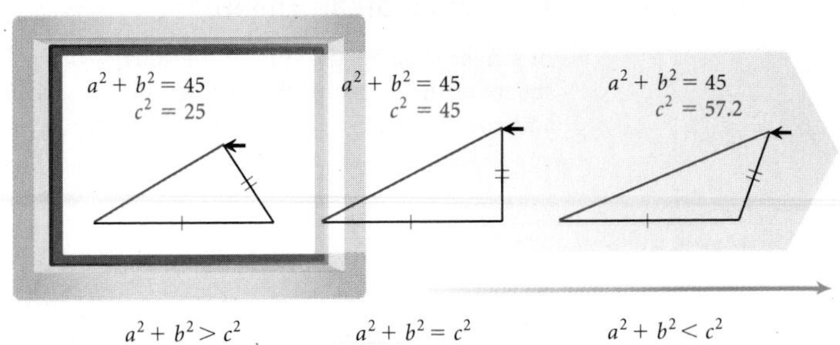

$a^2 + b^2 > c^2$ $a^2 + b^2 = c^2$ $a^2 + b^2 < c^2$

For an interactive version of this sketch, visit www.keymath.com/DG .

Let's look at a few examples to see how you can use the Pythagorean Theorem to find the distance between two points.

EXAMPLE A

How high up on the wall will a 20-foot ladder touch if the foot of the ladder is placed 5 feet from the wall?

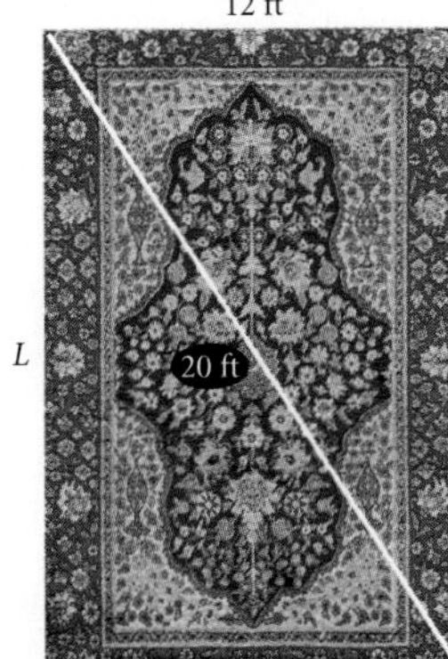

▶ Solution

The ladder is the hypotenuse of a right triangle, so $a^2 + b^2 = c^2$.

$(5)^2 + (h)^2 = (20)^2$	Substitute.
$25 + h^2 = 400$	Multiply.
$h^2 = 375$	Subtract 25 from both sides.
$h = \sqrt{375} \approx 19.4$	Take the square root of each side.

The top of the ladder will touch the wall about 19.4 feet up from the ground.

Notice that the exact answer in Example A is $\sqrt{375}$. However, this is a practical application, so you need to calculate the approximate answer.

EXAMPLE B

Find the area of the rectangular rug if the width is 12 feet and the diagonal measures 20 feet.

12 ft

L

20 ft

▶ Solution

Use the Pythagorean Theorem to find the length.

$$a^2 + b^2 = c^2$$
$$(12)^2 + (L)^2 = (20)^2$$
$$144 + L^2 = 400$$
$$L^2 = 256$$
$$L = \sqrt{256}$$
$$L = 16$$

The length is 16 feet. The area of the rectangle is $12 \cdot 16$, or 192 square feet.

Closing the Lesson

The Pythagorean Theorem is a claim about areas of squares built on the sides of a right triangle: The area of the square on the hypotenuse is the sum of the areas of the squares on the legs. Its primary applications are in finding the length of one side of a right triangle in which the lengths of the other two sides are known. The theorem can be proved by dissection.

You might wish to encourage students to use the dynamic geometry exploration at www.keymath.com/DG to learn more about the Pythagorean Theorem, and explore whether it is true for non-right triangles.

EXERCISES

In Exercises 1–11, find each missing length. All measurements are in centimeters. Give approximate answers accurate to the nearest tenth of a centimeter.

1. $a = \underline{?}$ 12 cm

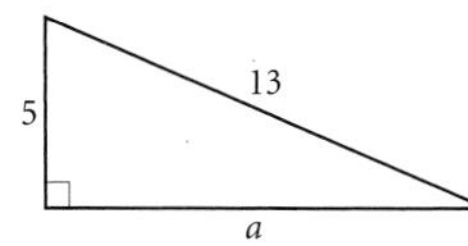

2. $c \approx \underline{?}$ 19.2 cm

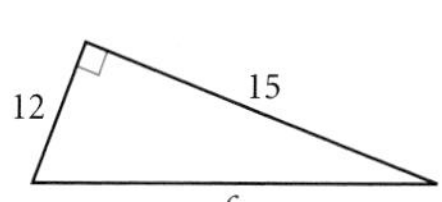

3. $a \approx \underline{?}$ 5.3 cm

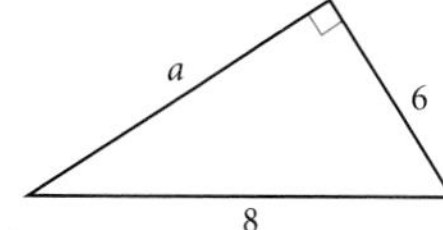

4. $d = \underline{?}$ 10 cm

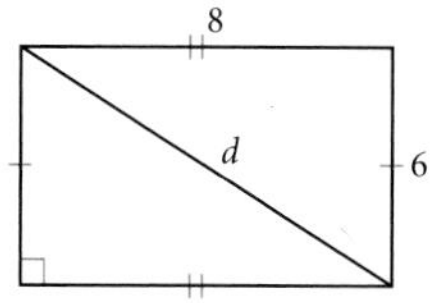

5. $s = \underline{?}$ 26 cm

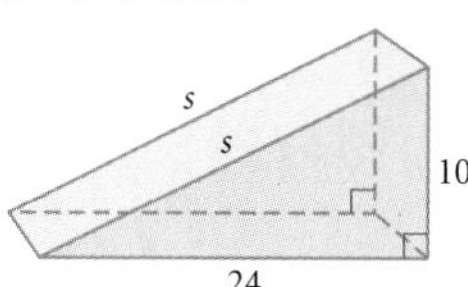

6. $c \approx \underline{?}$ ⓗ 8.5 cm

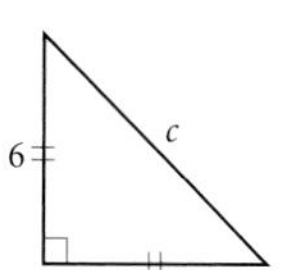

7. $b = \underline{?}$ 24 cm

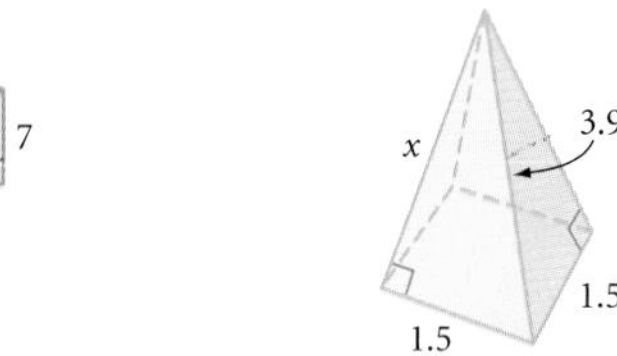

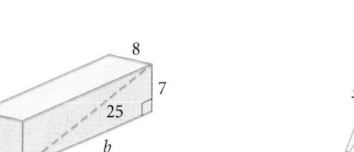

8. $x = \underline{?}$ 3.6 cm

9. The base is a circle.
$x = \underline{?}$ 40 cm

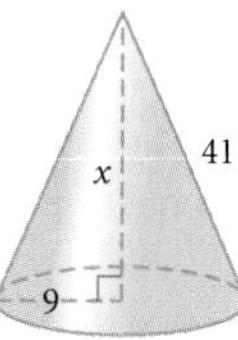

10. $s \approx \underline{?}$ 3.5 cm

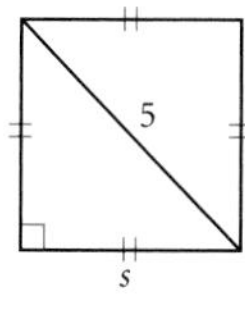

11. $r = \underline{?}$ ⓗ 13 cm

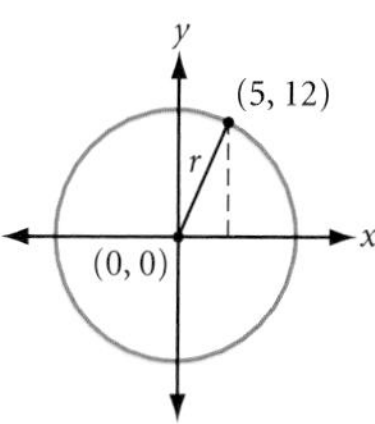

12. A baseball infield is a square, each side measuring 90 feet. To the nearest foot, what is the distance from home plate to second base? 127 ft

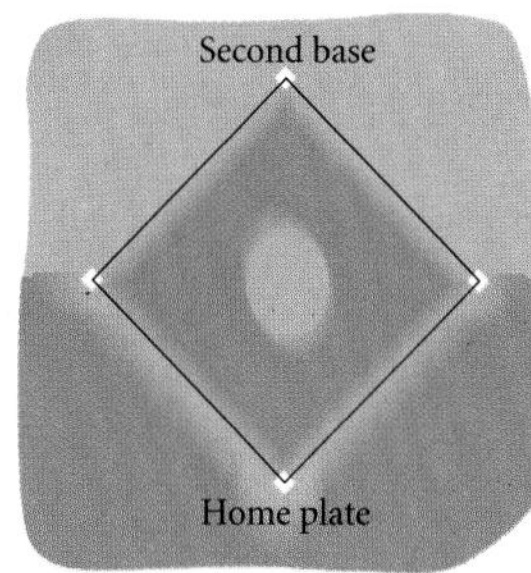

13. The diagonal of a square measures 32 meters. What is the area of the square? ⓗ 512 m^2

14. What is the length of the diagonal of a square whose area is 64 cm^2? 11.3 cm

15. The lengths of the three sides of a right triangle are consecutive integers. Find them. ⓗ 3, 4, 5

16. A rectangular garden 6 meters wide has a diagonal measuring 10 meters. Find the perimeter of the garden. 28 m

BUILDING UNDERSTANDING

After students have solved some exercises, you may want to have several groups report on how they solved them.

ASSIGNING HOMEWORK

Essential	1–16
Portfolio	17, 18
Journal	17, 18
Group	18
Review	19–22

Helping with the Exercises

[Alert] As needed, remind students that the hypotenuse is always the longest side and is opposite the right angle.

Exercise 4 Students might wonder why the upper triangle is a right triangle. **[Ask]** "What kind of figure is the quadrilateral? Do you see congruent triangles?"

Exercise 7 **[Alert]** Some students may want to use the measure 8, which is not needed in the calculation.

Exercise 10 If students are having difficulty, ask what shape the quadrilateral is.

Exercise 11 This is good preparation for work with the unit circle in trigonometry.

Exercises 12–16 Students may find it helpful to draw and label pictures.

Exercise 12 As an extension, you might have students measure the lengths of the distances between the bases on a local baseball field.

17. The area of the large square is 4 · area of triangle + area of small square.

$c^2 = 4 \cdot \frac{1}{2} \cdot ab + (b - a)^2$

$c^2 = 2ab + b^2 - 2ab + a^2$

$c^2 = a^2 + b^2$

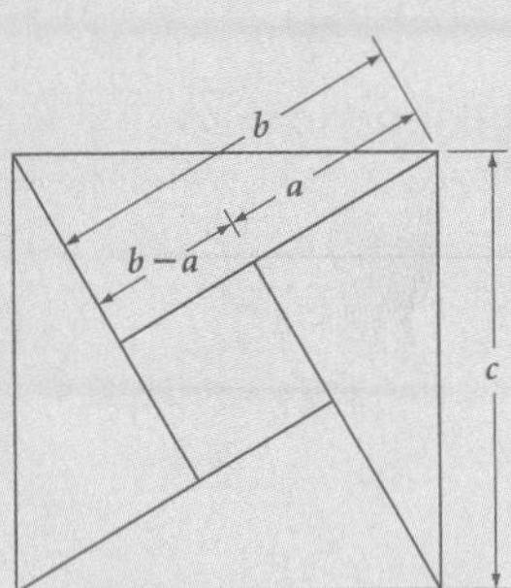

Exercise 18 This problem illustrates a special case in which SSA is a congruence shortcut. That is, when the non-included angle is a right angle, there is only one triangle that can be formed by SSA. This shortcut is sometimes called HL (Hypotenuse-Leg). Students can prove HL using the thinking process used in the solution to this exercise. Given two right triangles with congruent, corresponding hypotenuses with length c and corresponding legs with length a, use the Pythagorean Theorem to show that the other two corresponding legs are congruent; the triangles are congruent by SSS. Students will prove the HL Theorem in Lesson 13.7

21. Mark the unnamed angles as shown in the figure below. By the Linear Pair Conjecture, $p + 120° = 180°$. ∴ $p = 60°$. By AIA, $m = q$. By the Triangle Sum Conjecture, $q + p + n = 180°$. Substitute $m = q$ and $p = 60°$ to get $m + 60° + n = 180°$. ∴ $m + n = 120°$.

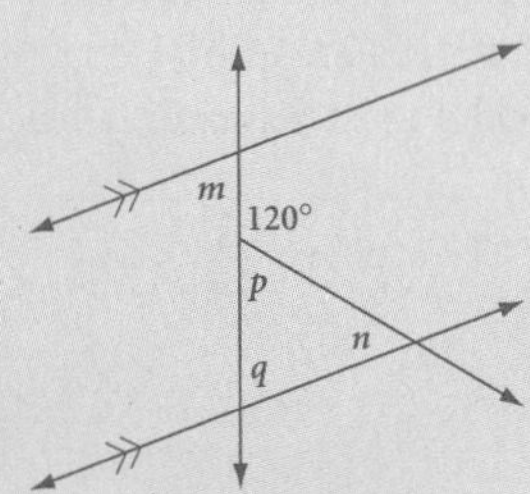

Or use the Exterior Angle Conjecture $q + n = 120°$. By AIA $q = m$. Substituting, $m + n = 120°$.

17. One very famous proof of the Pythagorean Theorem is by the Hindu mathematician Bhaskara. It is often called the "Behold" proof because, as the story goes, Bhaskara drew the diagram at right and offered no verbal argument other than to exclaim, "Behold." Use algebra to fill in the steps, explaining why this diagram proves the Pythagorean Theorem. ⓗ

History CONNECTION

Bhaskara (1114–1185, India) was one of the first mathematicians to gain a thorough understanding of number systems and how to solve equations, several centuries before European mathematicians. He wrote six books on mathematics and astronomy, and led the astronomical observatory at Ujjain.

18. Is $\triangle ABC \cong \triangle XYZ$? Explain your reasoning.
Sample answer: Yes, $\triangle ABC \cong \triangle XYZ$ by SSS. Both triangles are right triangles, so you can use the Pythagorean Theorem to find that $CB = ZY = 3$ cm.

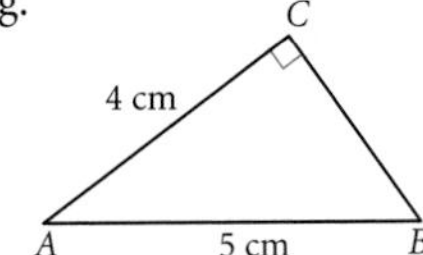

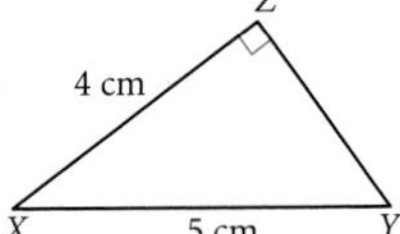

Review

8.1 **19.** The two quadrilaterals are squares. Find x. $x = 21$ cm

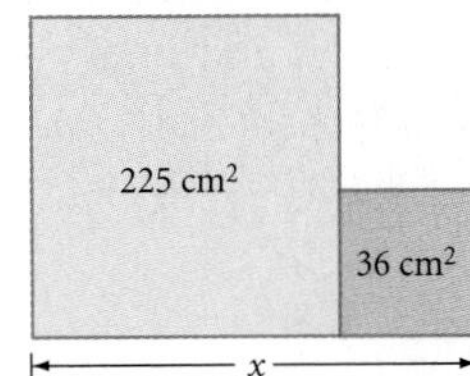

7.4 **20.** Give the vertex arrangement for the 2-uniform tessellation. $3^6/3^2.4.3.4$

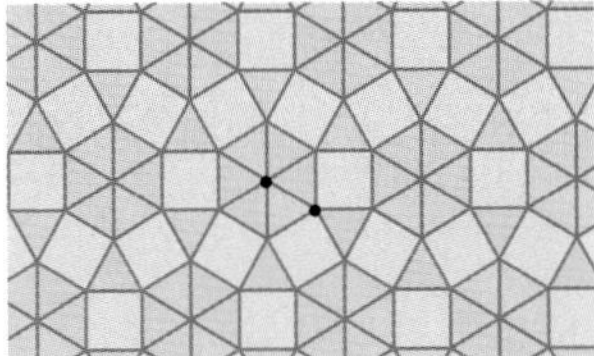

4.1 **21.** Explain why $m + n = 120°$.

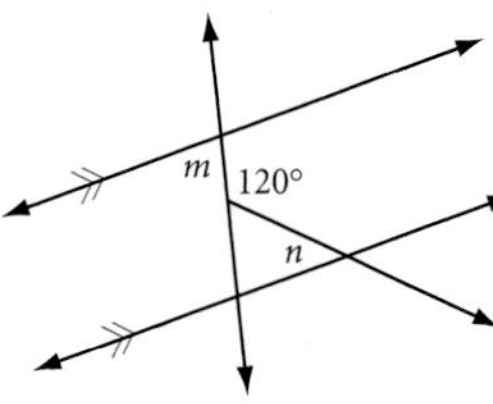

6.3 **22.** Calculate each lettered angle, measure, or arc. $\overline{EF}$ is a diameter; ℓ_1 and ℓ_2 are tangents.

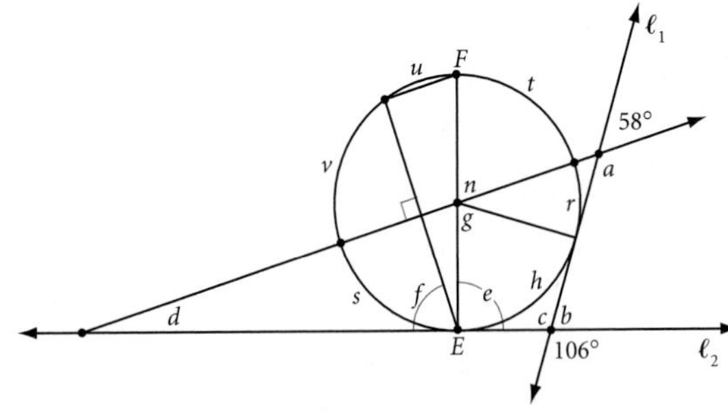

22. $a = 122°, b = 74°, c = 106°, d = 16°, e = 90°, f = 74°, g = 74°, h = 74°, n = 74°, r = 32°, s = 74°, t = 74°, u = 32°, v = 74°$

project

CREATING A GEOMETRY FLIP BOOK

Have you ever fanned the pages of a flip book and watched the pictures seem to move? Each page shows a picture slightly different from the previous one. Flip books are basic to animation technique. For more information about flip books, see www.keymath.com/DG .

These five frames start off the photo series titled *The Horse in Motion,* by photographer, innovator, and motion picture pioneer Eadweard Muybridge (1830–1904).

Here are two dissections that you can animate to demonstrate the Pythagorean Theorem. (You used another dissection in the Investigation The Three Sides of a Right Triangle.)

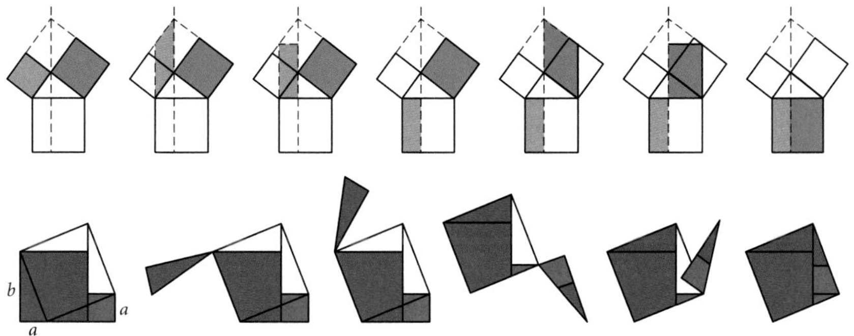

You could also animate these drawings to demonstrate area formulas.

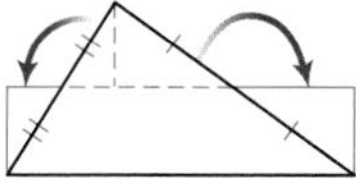

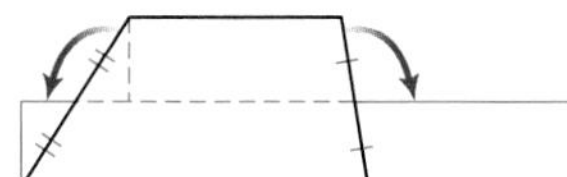

Choose one of the animations mentioned above and create a flip book that demonstrates it. Be ready to explain how your flip book demonstrates the formula you chose.

Here are some practical tips.

- Draw your figures in the same position on each page so they don't jump around when the pages are flipped. Use graph paper or tracing paper to help.
- The smaller the change from picture to picture, and the more pictures there are, the smoother the motion will be.
- Label each picture so that it's clear how the process works.

[Context] Eadweard Muybridge, the man who created *The Horse in Motion,* was born in England but moved to the United States as a boy. As part of scientific research to improve techniques of horseracing, he devised an ingenious method of setting up a dozen or more cameras to go off in rapid sequence. He was a leader in the early days of photography, improving on existing methods, including the art of film developing. He invented a precursor to the movie projector based on the idea of a *zoetrope,* a slitted drum with pictures on the inside that is spun to show the illusion of motion when the pictures are watched through the slits.

EXTENSIONS

A. Have students research and try one of numerous other dissections that demonstrate the Pythagorean Theorem.

B. Use Take Another Look activity 1, 2, or 3 on pages 501–502.

Supporting the project

Suggest that students use a small graph paper tablet to help keep the nonmoving features in the same position from page to page. They can glue tracing papers of the flip book onto cards for a firmer flip.

OUTCOMES

- Movement in the flip book is smooth.
- The student can explain the dissection used.
- The student adds other animation, for example, drawing a hand flipping the pages of a flip book, thus creating a flip book of a flip book!
- An animation is created using geometry software.

LESSON

9.2

PLANNING

LESSON OUTLINE

One day:

20 min Investigation

10 min Sharing

5 min Closing

10 min Exercises

MATERIALS

- rulers
- string (two 1-meter strings per group)
- paper clips (six per group)
- protractors
- patty paper

TEACHING

The Converse of the Pythagorean Theorem can also be proved.

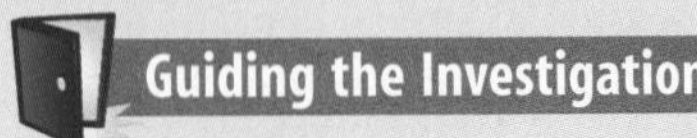

Guiding the Investigation

One step Pose this problem: "What can you say about triangles in which the side lengths satisfy the equation $a^2 + b^2 = c^2$?" As you circulate, encourage groups to try various triples from the list in the student book or to make up their own lengths, perhaps not integers.

As needed, remind students that the converse of a true statement might be false.

The Pythagorean triples are arranged in families. **[Ask]** "How are the triples in a column related?" [They are multiples of the first triple in that column.] "What would be the next triple in the second column?" [15, 36, 39] "Why is 3-4-5 or 5-12-13 called a *primitive Pythagorean triple*?" [The numbers in the triple have no common factor.]

LESSON 9.2

The Converse of the Pythagorean Theorem

Any time you see someone more successful than you are, they are doing something you aren't.

MALCOLM X

In Lesson 9.1, you saw that if a triangle is a right triangle, then the square of the length of its hypotenuse is equal to the sum of the squares of the lengths of the two legs. What about the converse? If *x*, *y*, and *z* are the lengths of the three sides of a triangle and they satisfy the Pythagorean equation, $a^2 + b^2 = c^2$, must the triangle be a right triangle? Let's find out.

Investigation

Is the Converse True?

You will need

- string
- a ruler
- paper clips
- a piece of patty paper

Three positive integers that work in the Pythagorean equation are called **Pythagorean triples.** For example, 8-15-17 is a Pythagorean triple because $8^2 + 15^2 = 17^2$. Here are nine sets of Pythagorean triples.

3-4-5	5-12-13	7-24-25	8-15-17
6-8-10	10-24-26		16-30-34
9-12-15			
12-16-20			

Step 1 Select one set of Pythagorean triples from the list above. Mark off four points, *A*, *B*, *C*, and *D*, on a string to create three consecutive lengths from your set of triples.

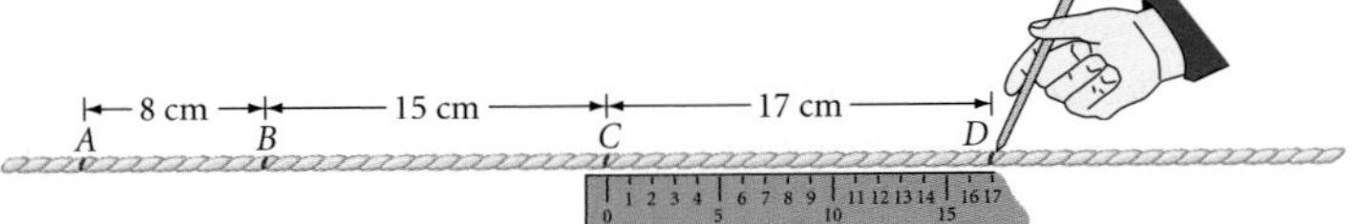

Step 2 Loop three paper clips onto the string. Tie the ends together so that points *A* and *D* meet.

Step 3 Three group members should each pull a paper clip at point *A*, *B*, or *C* to stretch the string tight.

You might let the class do this investigation outside, with the students themselves acting as "rope stretchers" of long ropes.

Step 1 Suggest that leaving excess string at both ends will make it easier to tie the ends together in Step 2.

LESSON OBJECTIVES

- Discover the Converse of the Pythagorean Theorem
- Learn new vocabulary
- Develop reading comprehension, problem-solving skills, and cooperative behavior

Step 4 right triangle

Step 4 With your paper, check the largest angle. What type of triangle is formed?

Step 5 Select another set of triples from the list. Repeat Steps 1–4 with your new lengths.

Step 6 Compare results in your group. State your results as your next conjecture.

Converse of the Pythagorean Theorem C-83

If the lengths of the three sides of a triangle satisfy the Pythagorean equation, then the triangle _?_. is a right triangle

This ancient Babylonian tablet, called Plimpton 322, dates sometime between 1900 and 1600 B.C.E. It suggests several advanced Pythagorean triples, such as 1679-2400-2929.

History CONNECTION

Some historians believe Egyptian "rope stretchers" used the Converse of the Pythagorean Theorem to help reestablish land boundaries after the yearly flooding of the Nile and to help construct the pyramids. Some ancient tombs show workers carrying ropes tied with equally spaced knots. For example, 13 equally spaced knots would divide the rope into 12 equal lengths. If one person held knots 1 and 13 together, and two others held the rope at knots 4 and 8 and stretched it tight, they could have created a 3-4-5 right triangle.

Step 4 Students can also use a corner of a piece of paper (or of some other object such as a carpenter's square) to verify a right angle.

SHARING IDEAS

Have students show their work with a variety of lengths. Let the class discuss measurement errors. Elicit the idea that a slight error in the measurement of a length can result in a measurably different angle. Keep asking students whether they think the converse is always true. Agree on a statement of the conjecture without resolving the question of truth.

[Ask] "Will the conjecture hold if you use different measurement units so that the triples change, possibly to non-integers?"

[Ask] "Suppose one triangle has sides whose lengths are a Pythagorean triple and another triangle has sides whose lengths are a multiple of that Pythagorean triple. How are the triangles related?" [They are similar.] Students can try drawing such triangles and looking for patterns, but you need not answer the question yet. It foreshadows the ideas of similarity in Chapter 11.

Also ask whether students who believe the conjecture is true can prove it deductively. Then have the class read the proof outline in the student book.

MAKING THE CONNECTION

Pythagoras himself is believed to have studied in Egypt, and he may have learned the triangle relationship there. Although some historians discount the rope stretchers tale, there's no doubt that Egyptian mathematicians knew the relationship.

NCTM STANDARDS

CONTENT	PROCESS
✓ Number	✓ Problem Solving
✓ Algebra	✓ Reasoning
✓ Geometry	✓ Communication
✓ Measurement	✓ Connections
Data/Probability	✓ Representation

Proof
Ask students to critique this outline in order to deepen their understanding of it. As they discuss it, monitor their facial expressions and try to include students who seem to have ideas but aren't speaking up. You may want to let the discussion lead to filling in details as a class and then writing up a good model proof. Or, if your students are fairly comfortable with proof, you can challenge them to write up the details as homework.

Assessing Progress
You can check how well students can measure lengths and angles, experiment systematically, and follow a deductive proof.

Closing the Lesson

The Converse of the Pythagorean Theorem is true and can be used to determine right angles. A common proof actually uses the Pythagorean Theorem itself.

BUILDING UNDERSTANDING

These exercises help students practice both the Pythagorean Theorem and its converse.

ASSIGNING HOMEWORK

Essential	1–7, 9–15, 19, 20
Performance assessment	8
Portfolio	16
Journal	20
Group	17, 18
Review	21–25

Helping with the Exercises

Exercise 2 This is a good place to point out the power of recognizing Pythagorean multiples. The triple 50-120-130 is based on the Pythagorean primitive 5-12-13, so sides of those lengths form a right triangle.

The proof of the Converse of the Pythagorean Theorem is very interesting because it is one of the few instances where the original theorem is used to prove the converse. Let's take a look. One proof is started for you below. You will finish it as an exercise.

Proof: Converse of the Pythagorean Theorem

Conjecture: If the lengths of the three sides of a triangle work in the Pythagorean equation, then the triangle is a right triangle.

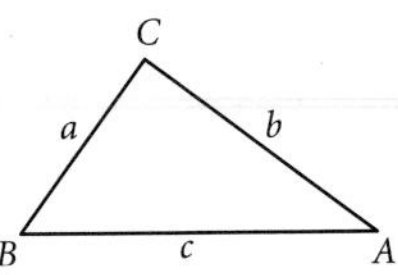

Given: a, b, c are the lengths of the sides of $\triangle ABC$ and $a^2 + b^2 = c^2$

Show: $\triangle ABC$ is a right triangle

Plan: Begin by constructing a second triangle, right triangle DEF (with $\angle F$ a right angle), with legs of lengths a and b and hypotenuse of length x. The plan is to show that $x = c$, so that the triangles are congruent. Then show that $\angle C$ and $\angle F$ are congruent. Once you show that $\angle C$ is a right angle, then $\triangle ABC$ is a right triangle and the proof is complete.

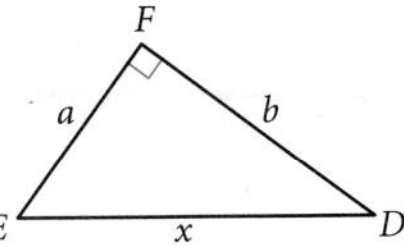

EXERCISES

In Exercises 1–6, use the Converse of the Pythagorean Theorem to determine whether each triangle is a right triangle.

1. yes

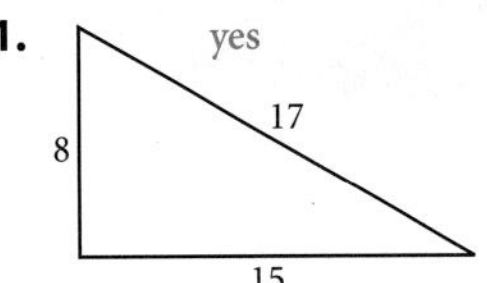

2. yes

3. no

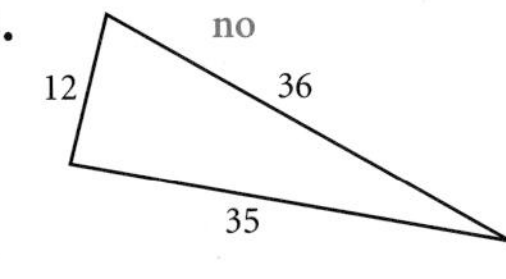

4. no

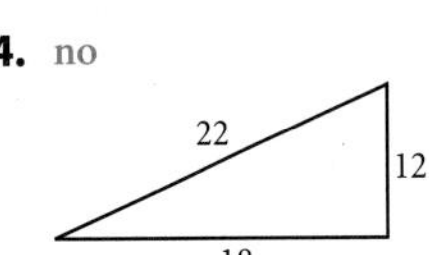

5. no

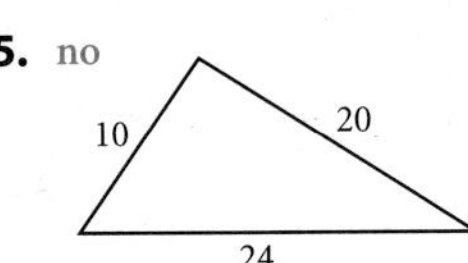

6. ⓗ no

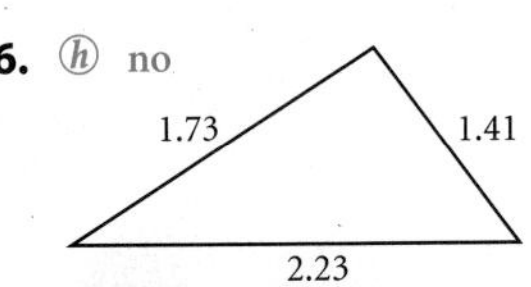

In Exercises 7 and 8, use the Converse of the Pythagorean Theorem to solve each problem.

7. Is a triangle with sides measuring 9 feet, 12 feet, and 18 feet a right triangle? no

8. A window frame that seems rectangular has height 408 cm, length 306 cm, and one diagonal with length 525 cm. Is the window frame really rectangular? Explain.
No, the given lengths are not a Pythagorean triple.

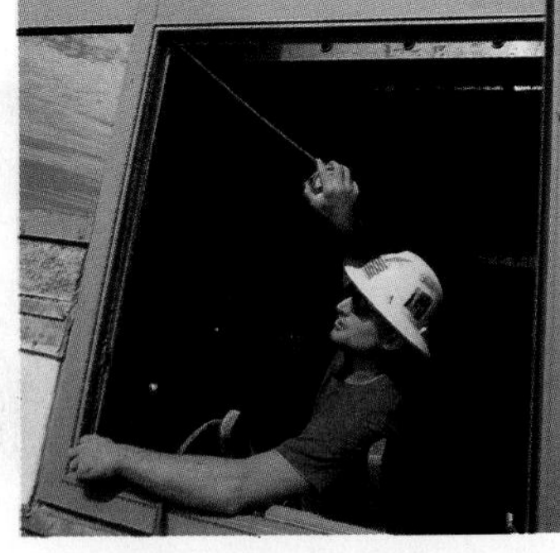

Exercise 7 Students' justifications might cite Pythagorean multiples. The numbers 9, 12, and 18 have a common factor of 3, so a primitive would be 3-4-6. This is not a Pythagorean triple; the familiar 3-4-5 triple says that if the two legs have lengths 3 and 4, the hypotenuse must have length 5 to give a right triangle.

Exercise 8 After students decide that the angle isn't right, you might ask whether students could have known the window frame was rectangular if the angle had turned out to be right. Having one right angle is not a sufficient condition for a quadrilateral to be a rectangle.

In Exercises 9–11, find y.

9. Both quadrilaterals are squares. $y = 25$ cm

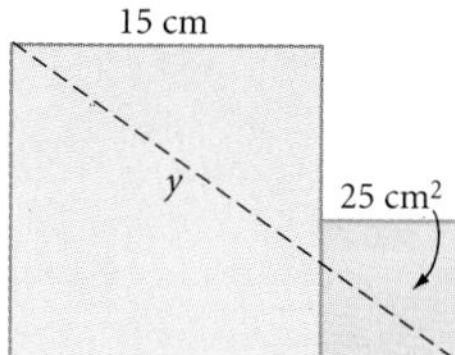

10. ⓗ $y = 24$ units

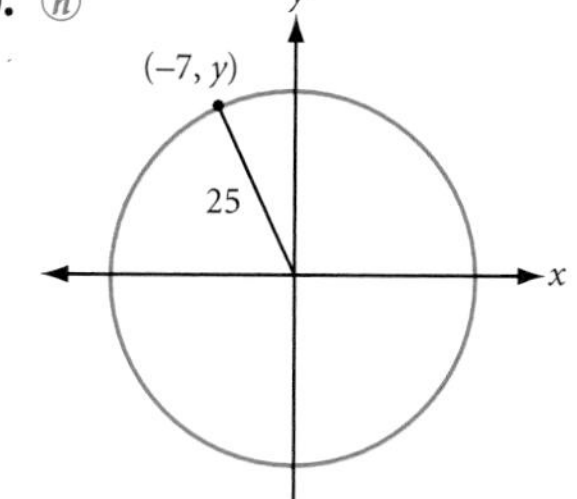

11. $y = 17.3$ m

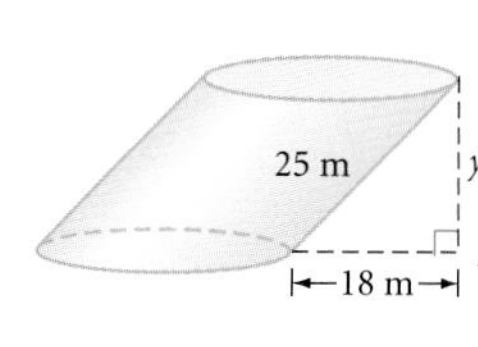

12. The lengths of the three sides of a right triangle are consecutive even integers. Find them. ⓗ 6, 8, 10

13. Find the area of a right triangle with hypotenuse length 17 cm and one leg length 15 cm. 60 cm²

14. How high on a building will a 15-foot ladder touch if the foot of the ladder is 5 feet from the building? 14.1 ft

15. The congruent sides of an isosceles triangle measure 6 cm, and the base measures 8 cm. Find the area. 17.9 cm²

16. Find the amount of fencing in linear feet needed for the perimeter of a rectangular lot with a diagonal length 39 m and a side length 36 m. 102 m

17. A rectangular piece of cardboard fits snugly on a diagonal in this box.

a. What is the area of the cardboard rectangle? 1442 cm²

b. What is the length of the diagonal of the cardboard rectangle? 74.8 cm

20 cm

60 cm

40 cm

18. Look back at the start of the proof of the Converse of the Pythagorean Theorem. Copy the conjecture, the given, the show, the plan, and the two diagrams. Use the plan to complete the proof.

19. What's wrong with this picture?

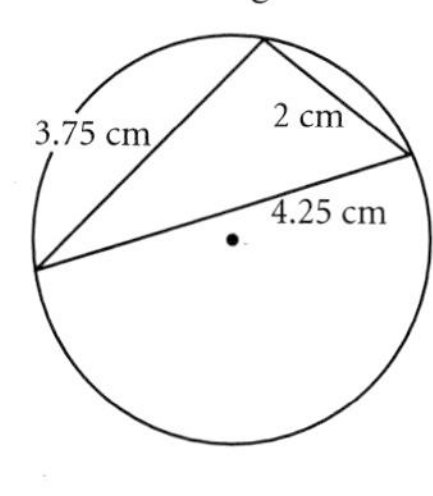

Sample answer: The numbers given satisfy the Pythagorean Theorem, so the triangle is a right triangle; but the right angle should be inscribed in an arc of 180°. Thus the triangle is not a right triangle.

20. Explain why $\triangle ABC$ is a right triangle.

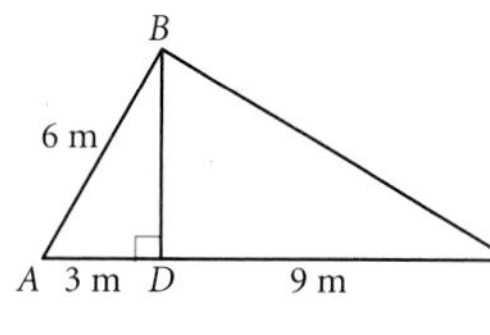

Sample answer: $BD^2 = 6^2 - 3^2 = 27$; $BC^2 = BD^2 + 9^2 = 108$; then $AB^2 + BC^2 = AC^2$ $(36 + 108 = 144)$, so $\triangle ABC$ is a right triangle by the Converse of the Pythagorean Theorem.

Review

3.8 **21.** Identify the point of concurrency from the construction marks. centroid

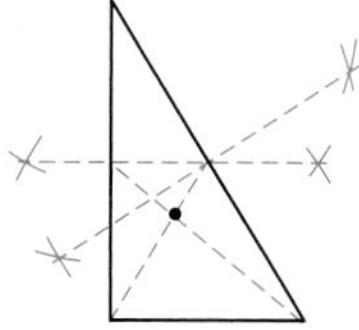

18. Because $\triangle DEF$ is a right triangle, $a^2 + b^2 = x^2$. By substitution, $c^2 = x^2$ and $c = x$. Therefore, $\triangle EFD \cong \triangle BCA$ by SSS and $\angle C \cong \angle F$ by CPCTC. Hence, $\angle C$ is a right angle and $\triangle BCA$ is a right triangle.

Exercise 9 Here is another situation in which Pythagorean triples can be applied. For the triangle with y as the hypotenuse, the legs have lengths 15 cm and 20 cm. Each length has a common factor of 5 cm. Because 3-4-5 is a common Pythagorean primitive, the hypotenuse must have length 5(5 cm) = 25 cm.

Exercise 10 This exercise provides groundwork for Chapter 12 work with the unit circle in trigonometry.

Exercises 12–16 Encourage students to draw pictures.

Exercise 12 Students might miss the condition that the integers are even. If appropriate, **[Ask]** "If x is the first even integer, how would the second integer be described?" [$x + 2$] "Is there only one triple of consecutive even integers?" [Half of any such triple is a triple of consecutive integers, say, $x - 1$, x, and $x + 1$. The algebraic equation $(x - 1)^2 + x^2 = (x + 1)^2$ has only two solutions: $x = 0$ and $x = 4$.]

Exercise 15 **[Ask]** "In an isosceles triangle, what does an altitude from the vertex angle to the base do to the base?" [It is the perpendicular bisector of the base; it is the same as the median.]

Exercise 16 **[Language]** *Linear feet* refers to the length of the fence, whereas *square feet* measures area.

Exercise 17 **[Alert]** Some students will have difficulty visualizing the box. They might create a three-dimensional model. Students are being gradually introduced to the Pythagorean Theorem in three dimensions. As in Exercises 11 and 13–16, exactness of answers will vary. The answers given assume that measurements given in the exercises are exact and thus answers to the nearest square cm or nearest tenth of a cm are reasonable. In real life the exactness of an answer depends on how it will be used and further knowledge of given measurements.

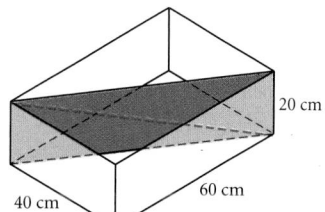

Exercise 22 This exercise can be approached through finding that the complement of x is $90 - \frac{a}{2}$, through using the properties of an isosceles right triangle, or by considering the limit as a secant line through C rotates to become the tangent line (and the intercepted arc becomes the arc with measure a).

Exercise 23 If students are having difficulty, ask how they might count triangles systematically. One approach is to consider where the vertex angle might go. Symmetry helps.

Exercise 24 As needed, focus students' attention on the number of square faces being added at each step.

EXTENSIONS

A. Pose this problem: If the sum of the squares of the lengths of the two shorter sides of a triangle is less than the square of the length of the longest side, what can you conjecture about the angle opposite the longest side? If the sum of the squares of the lengths of the two shorter sides of a triangle is greater than the square of the length of the longest side, what can you conjecture about the angle opposite the longest side? [If the sum is less, the angle is obtuse. If the sum is greater, the angle is acute.]

B. Have students use geometry software to draw triangles. Have them label and measure angles and sides, calculate squares of the lengths of the sides or construct squares on the sides and measure their area, and drag vertices until the sum of the squares of the lengths of the two smallest sides equals the square of the length of the largest side. Students should find a right angle.

See page 775 for answers to Exercises 22 and 25.

6.3 **22.** Line CF is tangent to circle D at C. The arc measure of $\overset{\frown}{CE}$ is a. Explain why $x = \left(\frac{1}{2}\right)a$. ⓗ

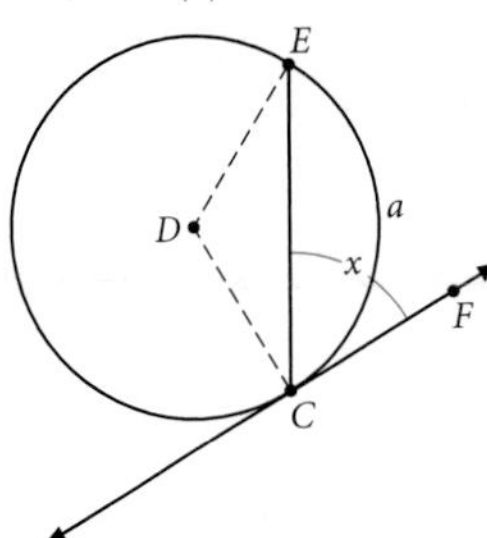

23. What is the probability of randomly selecting three points that form an isosceles triangle from the 10 points in this isometric grid? $\frac{3}{10}$

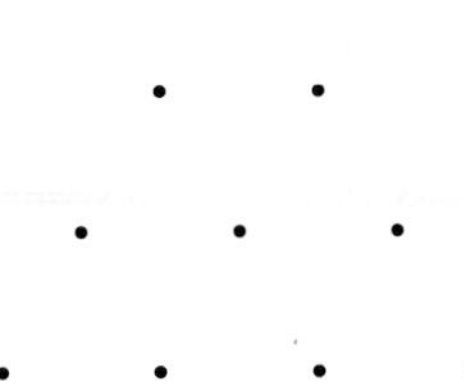

2.3 **24.** If the pattern of blocks continues, what will be the surface area of the 50th solid in the pattern? 790 square units

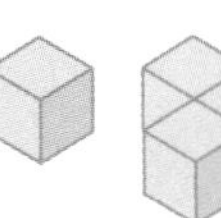 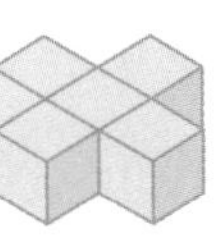 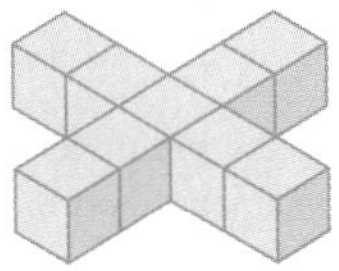 

1.8 **25.** Sketch the solid shown, but with the two blue cubes removed and the red cube moved to cover the visible face of the green cube.

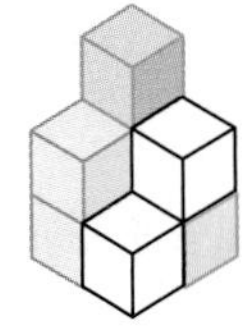

The outlines of stacked cubes create a visual impact in this untitled module unit sculpture by conceptual artist Sol Lewitt.

IMPROVING YOUR ALGEBRA SKILLS

Algebraic Sequences III

Find the next three terms of this algebraic sequence.

$x^9, 9x^8y, 36x^7y^2, 84x^6y^3, 126x^5y^4, 126x^4y^5, 84x^3y^6, \underline{?}, \underline{?}, \underline{?}$

IMPROVING ALGEBRA SKILLS

Students might think of number combinations, Pascal's triangle, or symmetry. Or they might see this pattern: After the first term, each coefficient can be determined by multiplying the previous coefficient by the exponent on x in the previous term and then dividing by the number of the term (counting from zero). For example, the term that includes x^6 is the third term, so its coefficient is $\frac{7(36)}{3} = 84$. The next three terms in the sequence are $36x^2y^7$, $9xy^8$, and y^9.

Radical Expressions

When you work with the Pythagorean Theorem, you often get radical expressions, such as $\sqrt{50}$. Until now you may have left these expressions as radicals, or you may have found a decimal approximation using a calculator. Some radical expressions can be simplified. To simplify a square root means to take the square root of any perfect-square factors of the number under the radical sign. Let's look at an example.

EXAMPLE A | Simplify $\sqrt{50}$.

▶ ***Solution*** One way to simplify a square root is to look for perfect-square factors.

The largest perfect-square factor of 50 is 25.

$$\sqrt{50} = \sqrt{25 \cdot 2} = \sqrt{25} \cdot \sqrt{2} = 5\sqrt{2}$$

25 is a perfect square, so you can take its square root.

Another approach is to factor the number as far as possible with prime factors.

Write 50 as a set of prime factors. Look for any square factors (factors that appear twice).

$$\sqrt{50} = \sqrt{5 \cdot 5 \cdot 2} = \sqrt{5^2 \cdot 2} = \sqrt{5^2} \cdot \sqrt{2} = 5\sqrt{2}$$

Squaring and taking the square root are inverse operations—they undo each other. So, $\sqrt{5^2}$ equals 5.

You might argue that $5\sqrt{2}$ doesn't look any simpler than $\sqrt{50}$. However, in the days before calculators with square root buttons, mathematicians used paper-and-pencil algorithms to find approximate values of square roots. Working with the smallest possible number under the radical made the algorithms easier to use.

Giving an exact answer to a problem involving a square root is important in a number of situations. Some patterns are easier to discover with simplified square roots than with decimal approximations. Standardized tests often express answers in simplified form. And when you multiply radical expressions, you often have to simplify the answer.

NCTM STANDARDS

CONTENT		PROCESS	
✓	Number		Problem Solving
✓	Algebra		Reasoning
	Geometry		Communication
	Measurement		Connections
	Data/Probability	✓	Representation

LESSON OBJECTIVES

- Learn to simplify square roots
- Learn to multiply radical expressions

USING YOUR ALGEBRA SKILLS 8

PLANNING

LESSON OUTLINE

One day or partial day:

15 min Examples

20 min Exercises

MATERIALS

none

TEACHING

Being able to work with radical expressions will help students later see patterns in special right triangles.

One step Draw a right triangle with legs labeled with lengths 4 and 8. Ask what multiple of 4 the length of the hypotenuse is. Students might divide the hypotenuse into four pieces and look at squares of each piece. Or they might rewrite $\sqrt{80}$ as a product of 4 and a square root. During Sharing, ask about working backward, as in Example B.

INTRODUCTION

[Language] The symbol for the nonnegative square root, $\sqrt{\ }$, is an example of a *radical.* Roots to other powers are also called radicals.

▶ *EXAMPLE A*

You might give a definition such as "Prime factors are factors that can't be broken down into smaller factors."

Emphasize that $5\sqrt{2}$ equals $\sqrt{50}$ exactly; it is not an approximation.

▶ EXAMPLE B

You may want to mention that the commutative property of multiplication allows you to rewrite $3 \cdot \sqrt{6} \cdot 5 \cdot \sqrt{2}$ as $3 \cdot 5 \cdot \sqrt{6} \cdot \sqrt{2}$.

SHARING IDEAS

You might ask the class to critique this shortcut for Example A as a shortcut for all cases: $\sqrt{5 \cdot 5 \cdot 2}$ immediately becomes $5\sqrt{2}$ because "you can move any factor that appears twice inside the radical to one appearance outside the radical." Keep asking for justification, using the general rules about square roots of products and of squares.

Ask whether the relationship $\sqrt{a \cdot a \cdot b} = a\sqrt{b}$ can be represented by lengths, remembering that square roots are often represented by sides of squares. This question foreshadows work with area ratios in Lesson 11.5.

Assessing Progress

You can assess students' previous understanding of radical expressions as well as their ability to see and generalize patterns.

Closing the Lesson

Two rules are useful in rewriting square roots and in multiplying radical expressions: The (positive) square root of a product is the product of the square roots, and the square root of the square of a number is the (absolute value of) the number.

BUILDING UNDERSTANDING

Though students are taught to simplify radical expressions, they are not taught to rationalize the denominators. You might decide to teach that also.

ASSIGNING HOMEWORK

Essential	1–21 odds
Group	2–20 evens

EXAMPLE B | Multiply $3\sqrt{6}$ by $5\sqrt{2}$.

▶ Solution | To multiply radical expressions, associate and multiply the quantities outside the radical sign, and associate and multiply the quantities inside the radical sign.

$$(3\sqrt{6})(5\sqrt{2}) = 3 \cdot 5 \cdot \sqrt{6 \cdot 2} = 15 \cdot \sqrt{12} = 15 \cdot \sqrt{4 \cdot 3} = 15 \cdot 2\sqrt{3} = 30\sqrt{3}$$

EXERCISES

In Exercises 1–5, express each product in its simplest form.

1. $(\sqrt{3})(\sqrt{2})$ $\sqrt{6}$ **2.** $(\sqrt{5})^2$ 5 **3.** $(3\sqrt{6})(2\sqrt{3})$ $18\sqrt{2}$ **4.** $(7\sqrt{3})^2$ 147 **5.** $(2\sqrt{2})^2$ 8

In Exercises 6–20, express each square root in its simplest form.

6. $\sqrt{18}$ $3\sqrt{2}$ **7.** $\sqrt{40}$ $2\sqrt{10}$ **8.** $\sqrt{75}$ $5\sqrt{3}$ **9.** $\sqrt{85}$ $\sqrt{85}$ **10.** $\sqrt{96}$ $4\sqrt{6}$

11. $\sqrt{576}$ 24 **12.** $\sqrt{720}$ $12\sqrt{5}$ **13.** $\sqrt{722}$ $19\sqrt{2}$ **14.** $\sqrt{784}$ 28 **15.** $\sqrt{828}$ $6\sqrt{23}$

16. $\sqrt{2952}$ $6\sqrt{82}$ **17.** $\sqrt{5248}$ $8\sqrt{82}$ **18.** $\sqrt{8200}$ $10\sqrt{82}$ **19.** $\sqrt{11808}$ $12\sqrt{82}$ **20.** $\sqrt{16072}$ $14\sqrt{82}$

21. What is the next term in the pattern? $\sqrt{2952}, \sqrt{5248}, \sqrt{8200}, \sqrt{11808}, \sqrt{16072}, \ldots$ $\sqrt{20992} = 16\sqrt{82}$

IMPROVING YOUR VISUAL THINKING SKILLS

PUZZLE

Folding Cubes II

Each cube has designs on three faces. When unfolded, which figure at right could it become?

1. 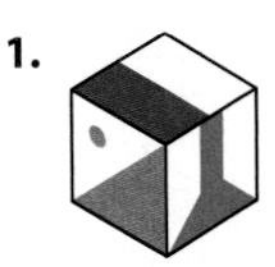 A. 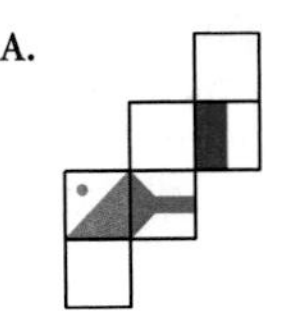 B. 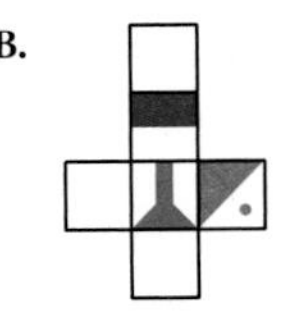 C. 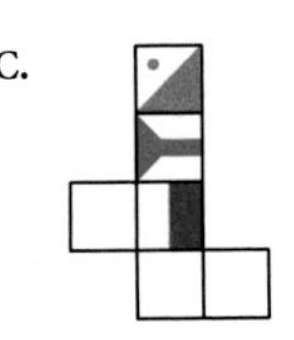 D. 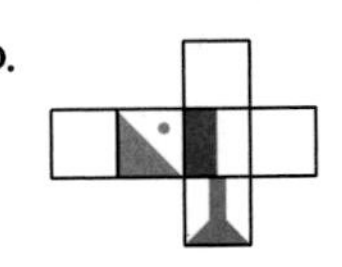

2. 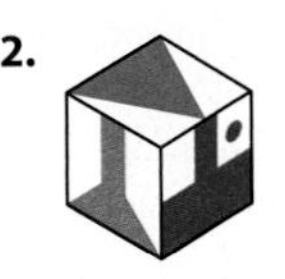 A. 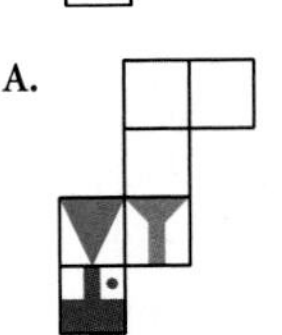 B. 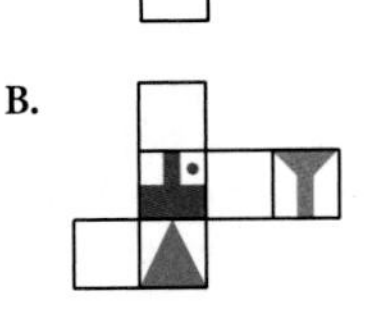 C. 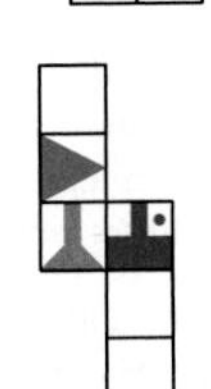 D. 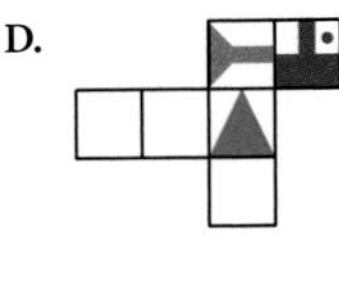

▶ Helping with the Exercises

Exercise 2 Squaring and taking the square root are opposite operations.

Exercise 9 It is possible to factor 85 as $5 \cdot 17$, but neither factor is a perfect square.

Exercise 21 If students are mystified, refer them to Exercises 16–20.

IMPROVING VISUAL THINKING SKILLS

If students are having difficulty, point out that a good problem-solving technique is to eliminate as many choices as possible. For example, 1A can be eliminated because the base of the green face is touching the red face, unlike its position in the original cube.

1. D **2.** C

LESSON

9.3

Two Special Right Triangles

In an isosceles triangle, the sum of the square roots of the two equal sides is equal to the square root of the third side.

THE SCARECROW IN THE 1939 FILM *THE WIZARD OF OZ*

In this lesson you will use the Pythagorean Theorem to discover some relationships between the sides of two special right triangles.

One of these special triangles is an isosceles right triangle, also called a 45°-45°-90° triangle. Each isosceles right triangle is half a square, so they show up often in mathematics and engineering. In the next investigation, you will look for a shortcut for finding the length of an unknown side in a 45°-45°-90° triangle.

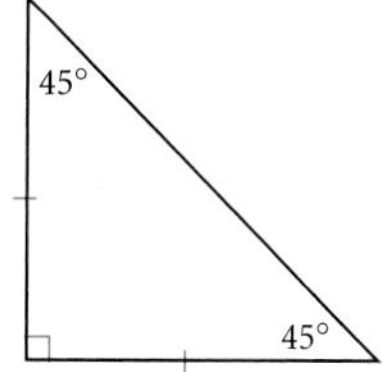

An isosceles right triangle

Investigation 1
Isosceles Right Triangles

Step 1 Sketch an isosceles right triangle. Label the legs l and the hypotenuse h.

Step 2 Pick any integer for l, the length of the legs. Use the Pythagorean Theorem to find h. Simplify the square root.

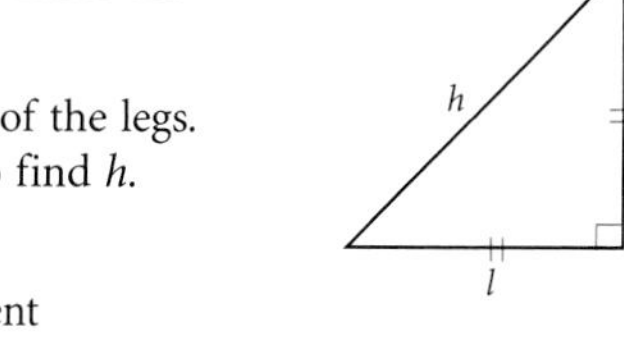

Step 3 Repeat Step 2 with several different values for l. Share results with your group. Do you see any pattern in the relationship between l and h?

Step 4 State your next conjecture in terms of length l.

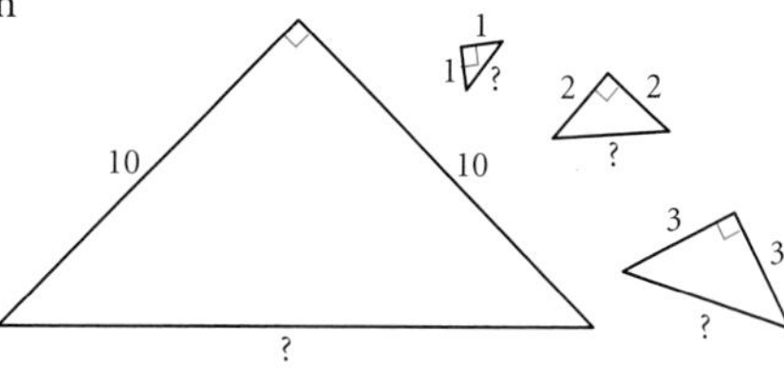

Isosceles Right Triangle Conjecture C-84

In an isosceles right triangle, if the legs have length l, then the hypotenuse has length ? . $l\sqrt{2}$

LESSON

9.3

PLANNING

LESSON OUTLINE

One day:

25 min	Investigation
10 min	Sharing
5 min	Closing
5 min	Exercises

MATERIALS

- square and isometric dot paper

TEACHING

Two special right triangles occur so often in real life (and on college entrance exams and achievement tests) that it's good to know the ratios of their side lengths.

One step Ask students to draw on dot paper right triangles in which the two legs are congruent and right triangles in which the hypotenuse has length twice that of one of the legs. They should look for the length of the third sides of these triangles and measure the angles.

Guiding Investigation 1

Step 3 If students are having difficulty seeing a pattern, suggest that they systematically try consecutive integers and make a table of the results.

NCTM STANDARDS

CONTENT		PROCESS	
	Number	✓	Problem Solving
✓	Algebra	✓	Reasoning
✓	Geometry	✓	Communication
✓	Measurement	✓	Connections
	Data/Probability		Representation

LESSON OBJECTIVES

- Practice simplifying square roots
- Discover relationships among the lengths of the sides of a 45°-45°-90° triangle and a 30°-60°-90° triangle
- Develop problem-solving skills and cooperative behavior

Guiding Investigation 2

Steps 1–3 Students can use patty paper to answer some of the questions in Steps 2 and 3 without doing the measurements in Step 1. They might also recall that every altitude is a median.

SHARING IDEAS

After the class reaches consensus about what conjectures to record in their notebooks, ask how to restate the conjectures using ratios. [For a 45°-45°-90° triangle, the side lengths have the ratio $1:1:\sqrt{2}$; for a 30°-60°-90° triangle, they have the ratio $1:\sqrt{3}:2$.]

Ask whether these ratios can be represented geometrically, remembering that square roots are often shown as sides of squares. Students can draw the triangles on dot paper (or isometric dot paper) and calculate the areas of appropriate squares.

[Ask] "How do you know which angle is the 30° angle in a 30°-60°-90° triangle?" [By the Side-Angle Inequality Conjecture, it's the angle opposite the shortest side.]

[Ask] "How can these special triangles be constructed with straightedge and compass?" [Students can construct perpendicular lines and then lay out equal segments from the intersection point to get a 45°-45°-90° triangle. Now that they know the 30°-60°-90° Triangle Conjecture, they can construct one leg and a hypotenuse to determine the third side.]

Wonder aloud whether the 30°-60°-90° Triangle Conjecture can be proved for all triangles, even if none of the lengths are integers. After students have made suggestions, direct their attention to the proof in the student book, asking them to critique and rewrite the reasoning in order to understand it better.

You can also demonstrate this property on a geoboard or graph paper, as shown at right.

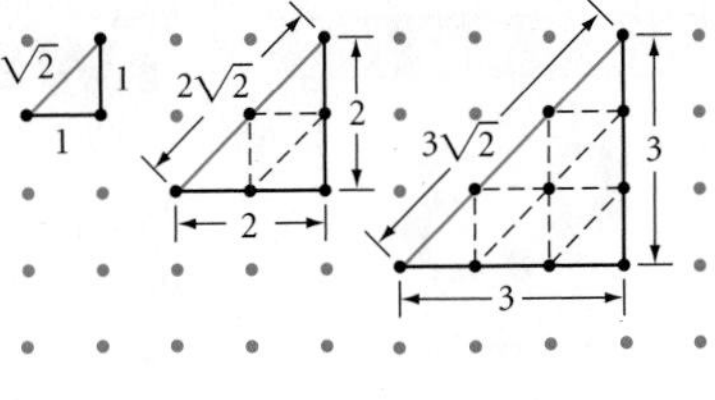

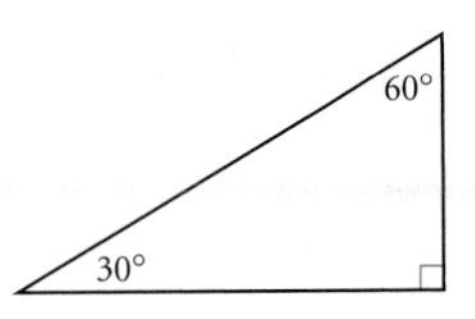

A 30°-60°-90° triangle

The other special right triangle is a 30°-60°-90° triangle. If you fold an equilateral triangle along one of its altitudes, the triangles you get are 30°-60°-90° triangles. A 30°-60°-90° triangle is half an equilateral triangle, so it also shows up often in mathematics and engineering. Let's see if there is a shortcut for finding the lengths of its sides.

Investigation 2
30°-60°-90° Triangles

Let's start by using a little deductive thinking to find the relationships in 30°-60°-90° triangles. Triangle ABC is equilateral, and $\overline{CD}$ is an altitude.

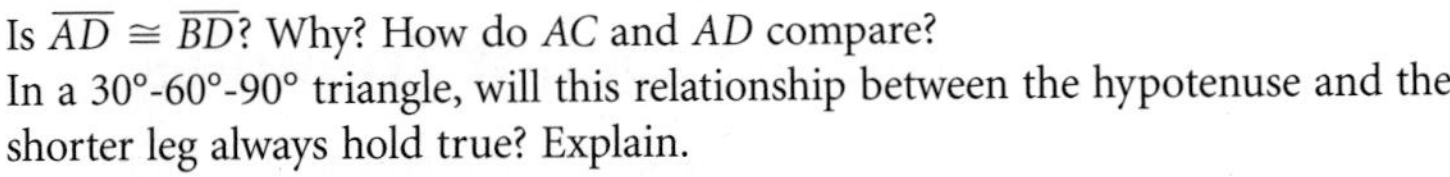

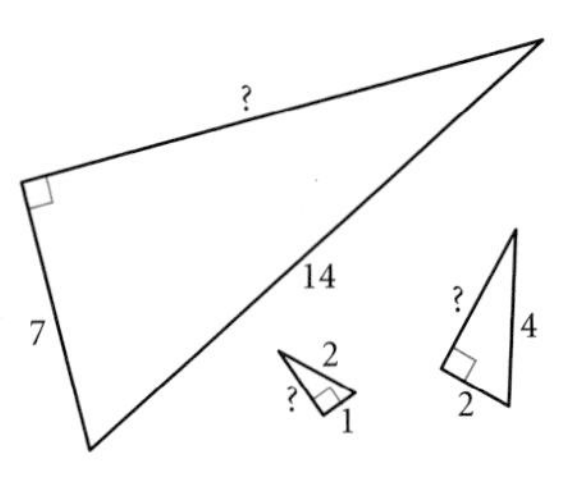

Step 1 60°; 30°; 90°

Step 2 yes, SAS, ASA, or SAA

Step 3 Yes, CPCTC. $AC = 2AD$; yes all 30°-60°-90° triangles are similar.

Step 1 What are $m\angle A$ and $m\angle B$? What are $m\angle ACD$ and $m\angle BCD$? What are $m\angle ADC$ and $m\angle BDC$?

Step 2 Is $\triangle ADC \cong \triangle BDC$? Why?

Step 3 Is $\overline{AD} \cong \overline{BD}$? Why? How do AC and AD compare? In a 30°-60°-90° triangle, will this relationship between the hypotenuse and the shorter leg always hold true? Explain.

Step 4 Sketch a 30°-60°-90° triangle. Choose any integer for the length of the shorter leg. Use the relationship from Step 3 and the Pythagorean Theorem to find the length of the other leg. Simplify the square root.

Step 5 Repeat Step 4 with several different values for the length of the shorter leg. Share results with your group. What is the relationship between the lengths of the two legs? You should notice a pattern in your answers.

Step 6 State your next conjecture in terms of the length of the shorter leg, a.

30°-60°-90° Triangle Conjecture C-85

In a 30°-60°-90° triangle, if the shorter leg has length a, then the longer leg has length _?_ [$a\sqrt{3}$] and the hypotenuse has length _?_. [$2a$]

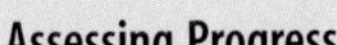

Assessing Progress

Assess students' ability to generate isosceles right triangles and equilateral triangles, to simplify square roots, to measure angles, to find patterns, and to follow a deductive proof. Also check their understanding of altitudes of isosceles triangles, SAS, and the Pythagorean Theorem.

Closing the Lesson

In a 45°-45°-90° triangle, if the legs have length l, then the hypotenuse has length $l\sqrt{2}$. In a 30°-60°-90° triangle, if the leg opposite the 30° angle has length a, then the hypotenuse has length $2a$ and the other leg has length $a\sqrt{3}$.

You can use algebra to verify that the conjecture will hold true for any 30°-60°-90° triangle.

Proof: 30°-60°-90° Triangle Conjecture

$(2a)^2 = a^2 + b^2$	Start with the Pythagorean Theorem.
$4a^2 = a^2 + b^2$	Square $2a$.
$3a^2 = b^2$	Subtract a^2 from both sides.
$a\sqrt{3} = b$	Take the square root of both sides.

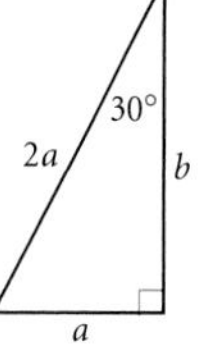

Although you investigated only integer values, the proof shows that any number, even a non-integer, can be used for a. You can also demonstrate this property for integer values on isometric dot paper.

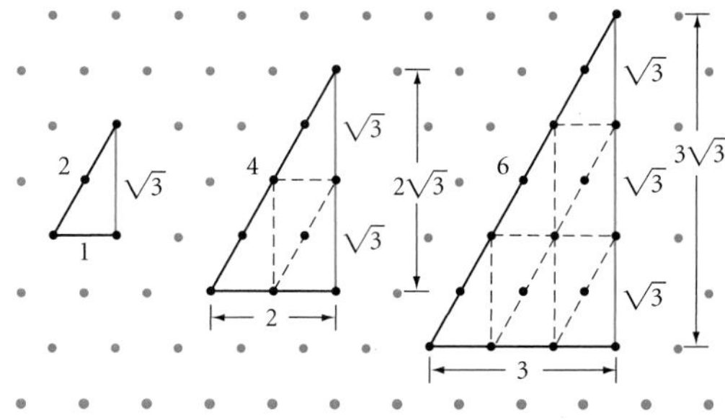

EXERCISES

You will need

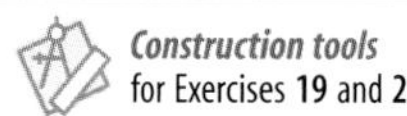

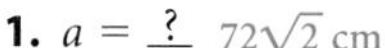

In Exercises 1–8, use your new conjectures to find the unknown lengths. All measurements are in centimeters.

1. $a = \underline{?}$ $72\sqrt{2}$ cm

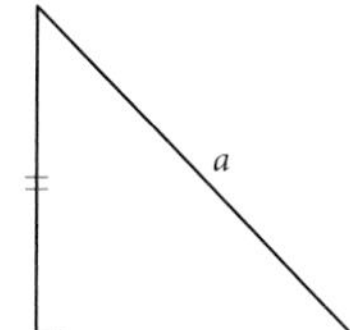

2. $b = \underline{?}$ ⓗ 13 cm

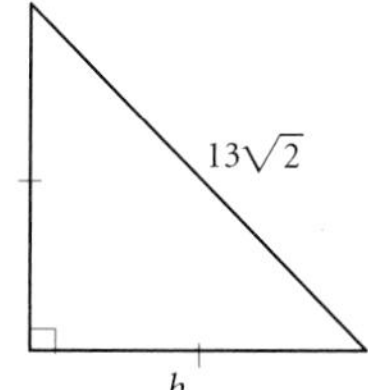

3. $a = \underline{?}$, $b = \underline{?}$
10 cm, $5\sqrt{3}$ cm

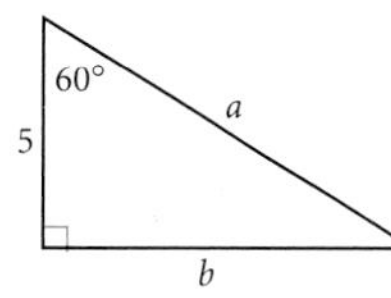

4. $c = \underline{?}$, $d = \underline{?}$ ⓗ
$10\sqrt{3}$ cm, 10 cm

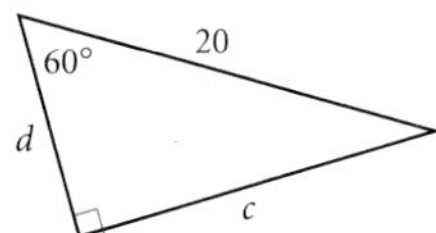

5. $e = \underline{?}$, $f = \underline{?}$
34 cm, 17 cm

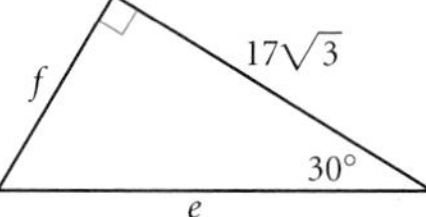

6. What is the perimeter of square $SQRE$? 72 cm

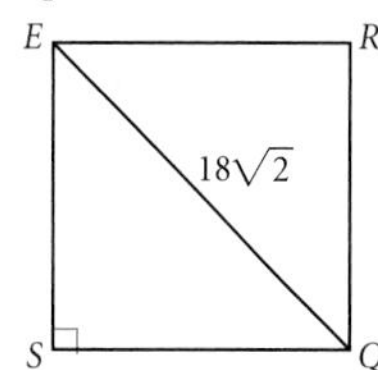

BUILDING UNDERSTANDING

The exercises give practice with the two special right triangles.

ASSIGNING HOMEWORK

Essential	1–11
Performance assessment	18
Portfolio	17
Group	12–16
Review	19–23

▶ Helping with the Exercises

Exercise 3 If students aren't sure what to do, suggest that in a 30°-60°-90° triangle it often helps to locate the shortest side first. **[Ask]** "Where is the 30-degree angle?"

Exercise 7 This is another example of using the Pythagorean Theorem in three dimensions. **[Ask]** "How would you generalize the Pythagorean Theorem to three dimensions?" [In a right rectangular prism, the space diagonal (d) can be found from the three dimensions of the prism (a, b, c): $d^2 = a^2 + b^2 + c^2$.

Exercise 10 In situations in which you want to find the coordinates of a point, it's often useful to draw segments whose lengths are those coordinates. **[Link]** Students will work with the unit circle in trigonometry.

12. possible answer:

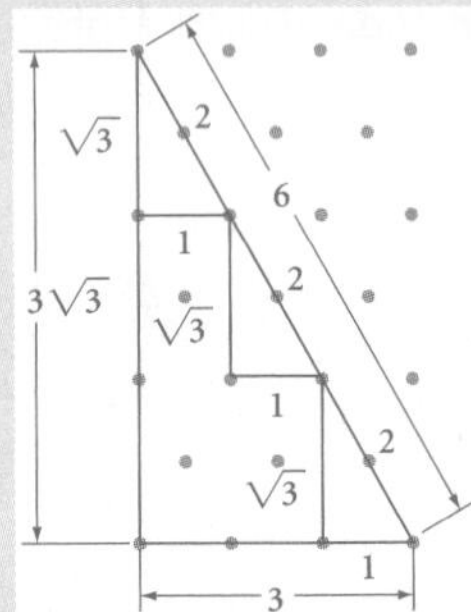

13. possible answer:

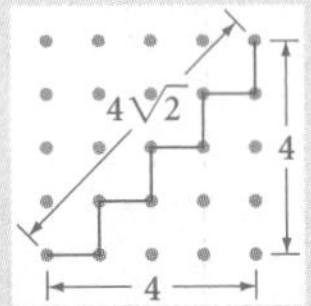

Exercise 16 Ask students how to find a special triangle in a picture of this situation.

Exercise 18 Students using geometry software might discover that letting the hypotenuses (not the right angles) coincide produces a slightly larger triangle.

18. $\frac{\sqrt{3}}{1}$

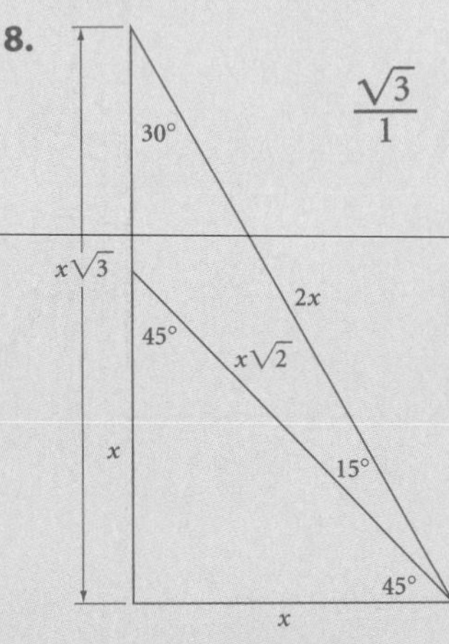

7. The solid is a cube. $d = \underline{?}$ ⓗ $12\sqrt{3}$ cm

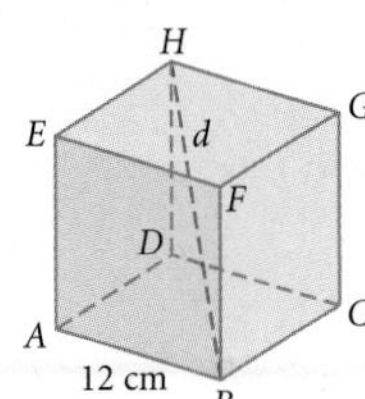

8. $g = \underline{?}$, $h = \underline{?}$ 50 cm, 100 cm

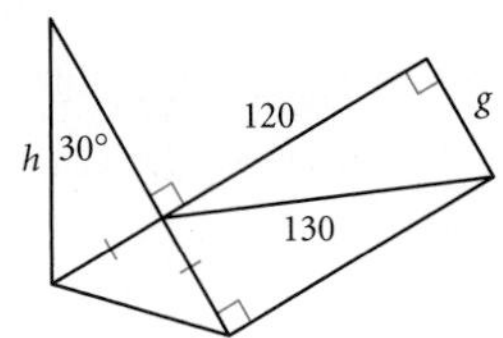

9. What is the area of the triangle? ⓗ 16 cm²

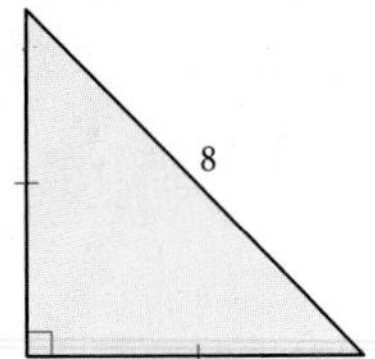

10. Find the coordinates of P. $\left(\frac{1}{\sqrt{2}}, \frac{1}{\sqrt{2}}\right)$

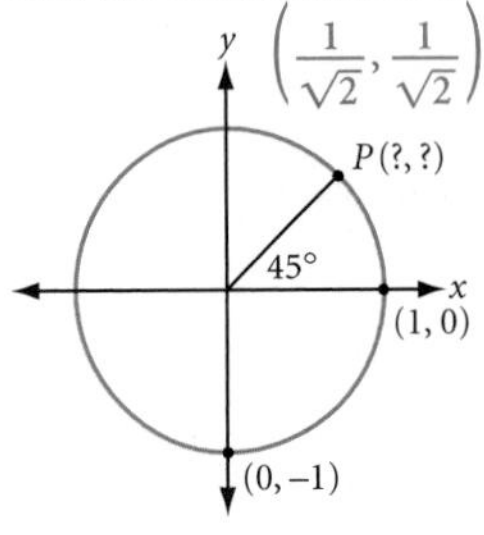

11. What's wrong with this picture? A 30°-60°-90° triangle must have sides whose lengths are multiples of 1, 2, and $\sqrt{3}$. The triangle shown does not reflect this rule.

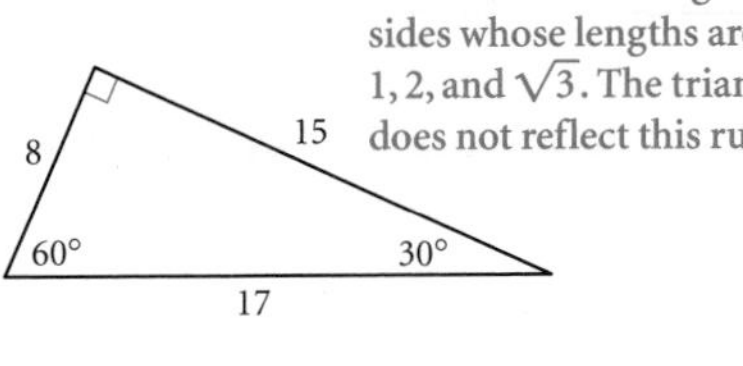

12. Sketch and label a figure to demonstrate that $\sqrt{27}$ is equivalent to $3\sqrt{3}$. (Use isometric dot paper to aid your sketch.) ⓗ

13. Sketch and label a figure to demonstrate that $\sqrt{32}$ is equivalent to $4\sqrt{2}$. (Use square dot paper or graph paper.)

14. In equilateral triangle ABC, $\overline{AE}$, $\overline{BF}$, and $\overline{CD}$ are all angle bisectors, medians, and altitudes simultaneously. These three segments divide the equilateral triangle into six overlapping 30°-60°-90° triangles and six smaller, non-overlapping 30°-60°-90° triangles.

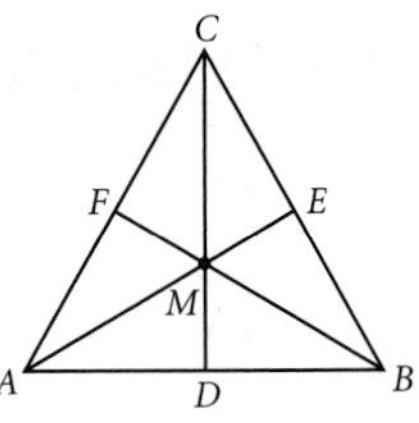

a. One of the overlapping triangles is $\triangle CDB$. Name the other five triangles that are congruent to it. $\triangle CDA, \triangle AEC, \triangle AEB, \triangle BFA, \triangle BFC$

b. One of the non-overlapping triangles is $\triangle MDA$. Name the other five triangles congruent to it. $\triangle MDB, \triangle MEB, \triangle MEC, \triangle MFC, \triangle MFA$

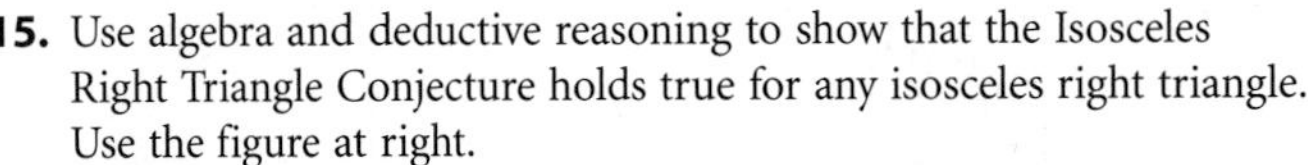

15. Use algebra and deductive reasoning to show that the Isosceles Right Triangle Conjecture holds true for any isosceles right triangle. Use the figure at right.

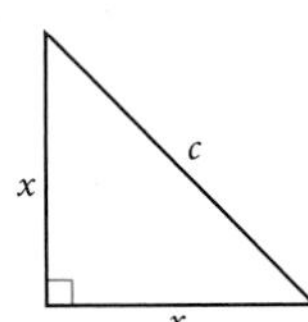

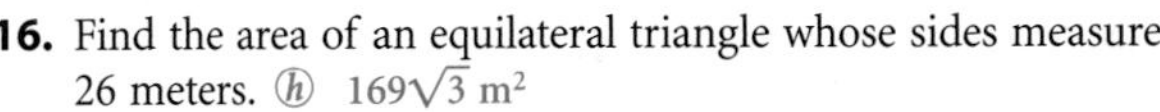

16. Find the area of an equilateral triangle whose sides measure 26 meters. ⓗ $169\sqrt{3}$ m²

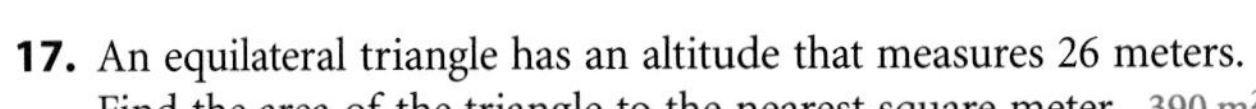

17. An equilateral triangle has an altitude that measures 26 meters. Find the area of the triangle to the nearest square meter. 390 m²

18. Sketch the largest 45°-45°-90° triangle that fits in a 30°-60°-90° triangle. What is the ratio of the area of the 30°-60°-90° triangle to the area of the 45°-45°-90° triangle?

15.

$c^2 = x^2 + x^2$	Start with the Pythagorean Theorem.
$c^2 = 2x^2$	Combine like terms.
$c = x\sqrt{2}$	Take the square root of both sides.

Review

Construction In Exercises 19 and 20, choose either patty paper or a compass and straightedge and perform the constructions.

19. Given the segment with length a below, construct segments with lengths $a\sqrt{2}$, $a\sqrt{3}$, and $a\sqrt{5}$. ⓗ

a

8.5 **20.** ***Mini-Investigation*** Draw a right triangle with sides of lengths 6 cm, 8 cm, and 10 cm. Locate the midpoint of each side. Construct a semicircle on each side with the midpoints of the sides as centers. Find the area of each semicircle. What relationship do you notice among the three areas?

9.1 **21.** The *Jiuzhang suanshu* is an ancient Chinese mathematics text of 246 problems. Some solutions use the *gou gu,* the Chinese name for what we call the Pythagorean Theorem. The *gou gu* reads $(gou)^2 + (gu)^2 = (xian)^2$. Here is a *gou gu* problem translated from the ninth chapter of *Jiuzhang.*

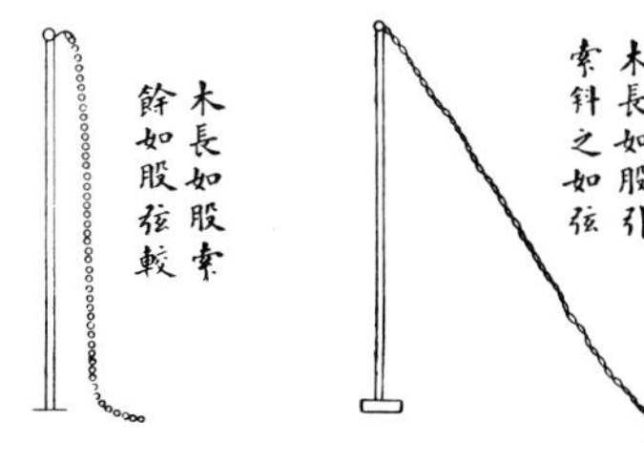

A rope hangs from the top of a pole with three *chih* of it lying on the ground. When it is tightly stretched so that its end just touches the ground, it is eight *chih* from the base of the pole. How long is the rope? $\frac{73}{6} \approx 12.2$ *chih*

2.6 **22.** Explain why $m\angle 1 + m\angle 2 = 90°$. ⓗ

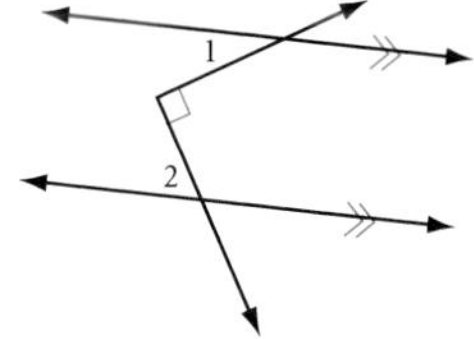

8.7 **23.** The lateral surface area of the cone below is unwrapped into a sector. What is the angle at the vertex of the sector? 80°

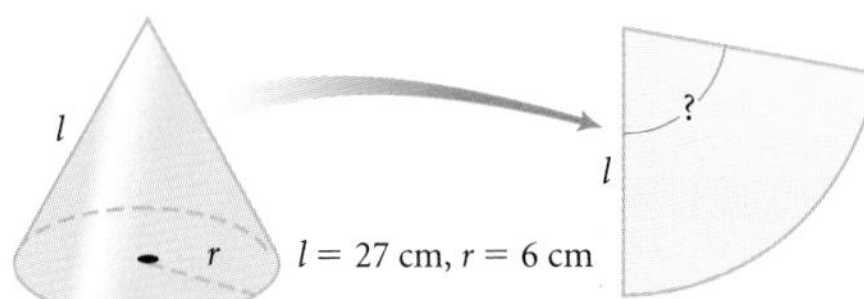

IMPROVING YOUR VISUAL THINKING SKILLS

Mudville Monsters

The 11 starting members of the Mudville Monsters football team and their coach, Osgood Gipper, have been invited to compete in the Smallville Punt, Pass, and Kick Competition. To get there, they must cross the deep Smallville River. The only way across is with a small boat owned by two very small Smallville football players. The boat holds just one Monster visitor or the two Smallville players. The Smallville players agree to help the Mudville players across if the visitors agree to pay $5 each time the boat crosses the river. If the Monsters have a total of $100 among them, do they have enough money to get all players and the coach to the other side of the river?

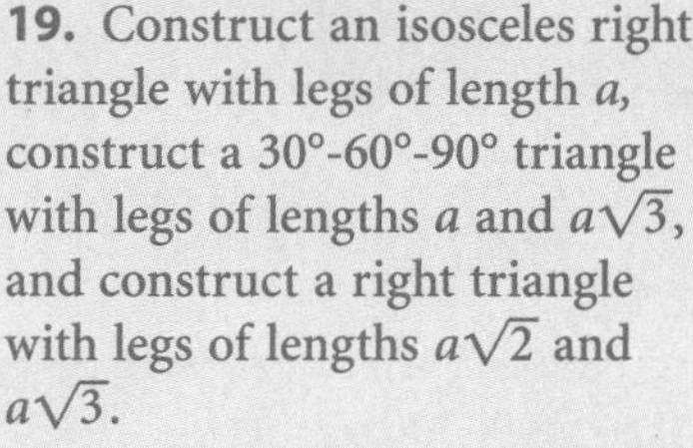

19. Construct an isosceles right triangle with legs of length a, construct a 30°-60°-90° triangle with legs of lengths a and $a\sqrt{3}$, and construct a right triangle with legs of lengths $a\sqrt{2}$ and $a\sqrt{3}$.

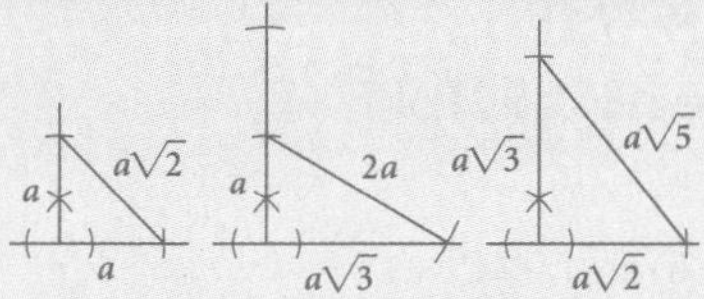

Exercise 20 This mini-investigation foreshadows area ratios in Lesson 11.5.

20. Areas: 4.5π cm^2, 8π cm^2, 12.5π cm^2. $4.5\pi + 8\pi = 12.5\pi$, that is, the sum of the areas of the semicircles on the two legs is equal to the area of the semicircle on the hypotenuse.

22. Extend the rays that form the right angle.
$m\angle 4 + m\angle 5 = 180°$ by the Linear Pair Conjecture, and it's given that $m\angle 5 = 90°$.
$\therefore m\angle 4 = 90°$.
$m\angle 2 + m\angle 3 + m\angle 4 =$
$m\angle 2 + m\angle 3 + 90° = 180°$.
$\therefore m\angle 2 + m\angle 3 = 90°$.
$m\angle 3 = m\angle 1$ by AIA.
$\therefore m\angle 1 + m\angle 2 = 90°$.

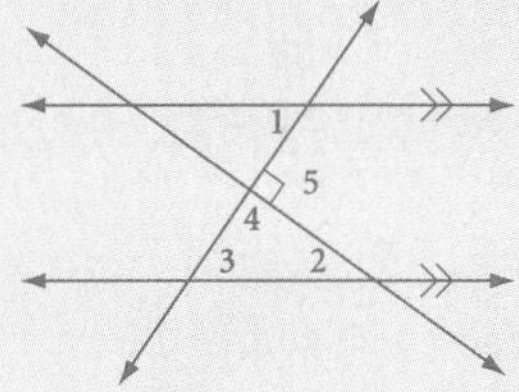

EXTENSION

Use Take Another Look activity 4 or 5 on page 502.

IMPROVING VISUAL THINKING SKILLS

Each Monster visitor must go across alone. It makes no sense for one to return, so before each Monster crosses, the two Smallville players must cross and leave one on the other side to bring the boat back on the next trip. This will require 23 round trips for the 11 players and the coach. The team has enough money for 20 one-way trips. Even without seeing how to arrange the Smallville players to return the boat at least 11 times, the Monsters don't have enough money.

EXPLORATION

PLANNING

LESSON OUTLINE

One day:

45 min Activity

MATERIALS

- The Geometer's Sketchpad
- The Right Triangle Fractal (W), *optional*
- Sketchpad demonstration A Right Triangle Fractal, *optional*

TEACHING

Students construct a fractal based on the Pythagorean Theorem.

The student book includes a very brief mention of similarity. You need not elaborate; the topic will be formally addressed in Chapter 11. Also, a proof of the Pythagorean Theorem based on similar triangles is an exercise in Lesson 13.7.

Guiding the Activity

Sketchpad provides many tools for constructions like this. For example, half of this fractal can be made easily by constructing a square, then constructing a right triangle on one side, and then using the iteration tool. The full fractal can be made with custom tools. If students are not proficient enough using Sketchpad to create the fractal on their own, use The Right Triangle Fractal worksheet with detailed steps for creating the fractal in Sketchpad or use the Sketchpad demonstration.

Step 2 Changing the ratio of the lengths of the legs of the original triangle affects the shape of the fractal. See page 56 for a quilt design that uses isosceles right triangles.

Exploration

A Pythagorean Fractal

If you wanted to draw a picture to state the Pythagorean Theorem without words, you'd probably draw a right triangle with squares on each of the three sides. This is the way you first explored the Pythagorean Theorem in Lesson 9.1.

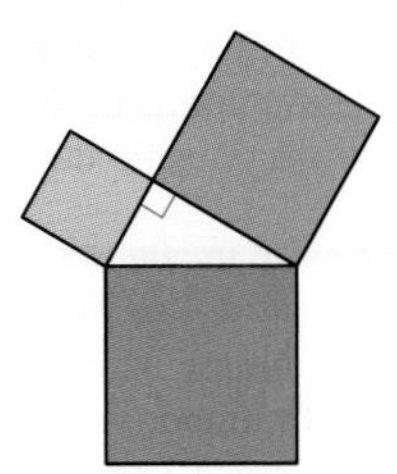

Another picture of the theorem is even simpler: a right triangle divided into two right triangles. Here, a right triangle with hypotenuse c is divided into two smaller triangles, the smaller with hypotenuse a and the larger with hypotenuse b. Clearly, their areas add up to the area of the whole triangle. What's surprising is that all three triangles have the same angle measures. Why? Though different in size, the three triangles all have the same shape. Figures that have the same shape but not necessarily the same size are called **similar figures.** You'll use these similar triangles to prove the Pythagorean Theorem in a later chapter.

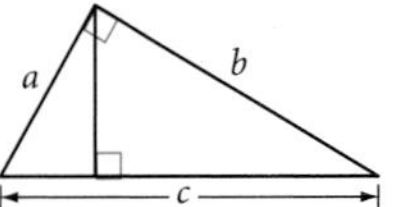

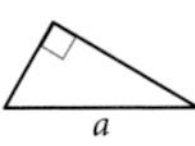

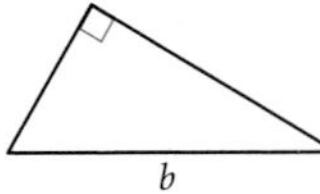

A beautifully complex fractal combines both of these pictorial representations of the Pythagorean Theorem. The fractal starts with a right triangle with squares on each side. Then similar triangles are built onto the squares. Then squares are built onto the new triangles, and so on. In this exploration, you'll create this fractal.

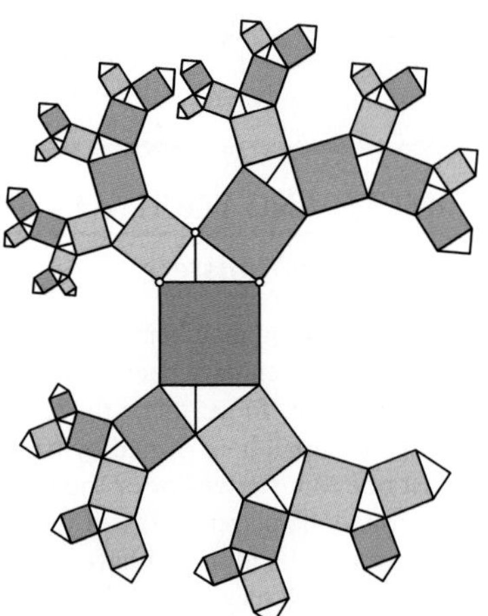

LESSON OBJECTIVES

- Explore a right triangle fractal
- Look for and describe patterns in the fractal

NCTM STANDARDS

	CONTENT		PROCESS
	Number		Problem Solving
	Algebra	✓	Reasoning
✓	Geometry	✓	Communication
✓	Measurement		Connections
	Data/Probability		Representation

Activity

The Right Triangle Fractal

You will need

- the worksheet The Right Triangle Fractal (optional)

The Geometer's Sketchpad software uses custom tools to save the steps of repeated constructions. They are very helpful for fractals like this one.

Procedure Note

1. Use the diameter of a circle and an inscribed angle to make a triangle that always remains a right triangle.
2. It is important to construct the altitude to the hypotenuse in each triangle in order to divide it into similar triangles.
3. Create custom tools to make squares and similar triangles repeatedly.

Step 1 Use The Geometer's Sketchpad to create the fractal on page 480. Follow the Procedure Note.

Notice that each square has two congruent triangles on two opposite sides. Use a reflection to guarantee that the triangles are congruent.

After you successfully make the Pythagorean fractal, you're ready to investigate its fascinating patterns.

Step 2 First, try dragging a vertex of the original triangle.

Step 3 Does the Pythagorean Theorem still apply to the branches of this figure? That is, does the sum of the areas of the branches on the legs equal the area of the branch on the hypotenuse? See if you can answer without actually measuring all the areas. yes

Step 4 Consider your original sketch to be a single right triangle with a square built on each side. Call this sketch Stage 0 of your fractal. Explore these questions.

a. At Stage 1, you add three triangles and six squares to your construction. On a piece of paper, draw a rough sketch of Stage 1. How much area do you add to this fractal between Stage 0 and Stage 1? (Don't measure any areas to answer this.)

b. Draw a rough sketch of Stage 2. How much area do you add between Stage 1 and Stage 2?

c. How much area is added at any new stage?

d. A true fractal exists only after an infinite number of stages. If you could build a true fractal based on the construction in this activity, what would be its total area?

Step 5 Give the same color and shade to sets of squares that are congruent. What do you notice about these sets of squares other than their equal area? Describe any patterns you find in sets of congruent squares.

Step 6 Describe any other patterns you can find in the Pythagorean fractal.

Step 4c At every new stage, the area added equals the area of the Stage 0 figure plus the area of the original triangle.

Step 4d Its area would be infinite.

Step 5 Sample observations: Each square on the hypotenuse branch has a mirror image on one of the leg branches. The squares of equal area on the leg branches all face the same direction; that is, corresponding sides in all the squares are parallel. The number of squares of a particular area on the leg branches is one more than the number of squares of the next largest area on those branches.

Step 3 At each stage, the sum of the areas of the squares added to each branch equals the area of the original square on that branch.

Step 4a

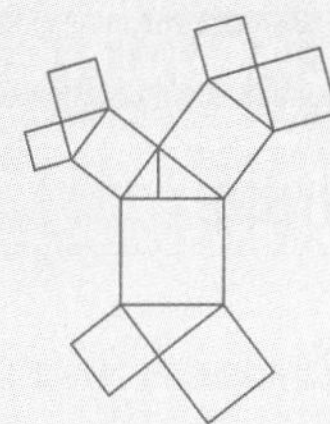

At Stage 1, the area of the triangle on the hypotenuse branch equals the area of the original triangle, and the sum of the areas of the triangles on the other two branches also equals the area of the original triangle. The sum of the two added squares equals the area of one of the original squares by the Pythagorean Theorem. Thus the total added area is twice the area of the original triangle plus the areas of all the original squares, or the area of the Stage 0 figure plus the area of the original triangle.

Step 4b

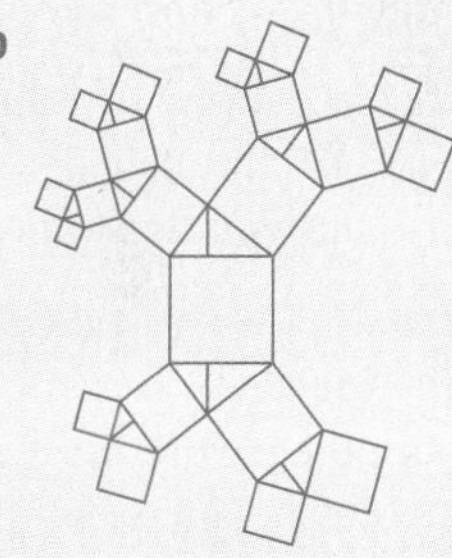

The total added area is, again, the area of the Stage 0 figure plus the area of the original triangle.

Step 4 At each stage, triangles whose total area is twice that of the original are added, and squares whose total area is twice that of the square on the original hypotenuse are added. If the original triangle has the usual lengths a, b, and c, then an area equal to $ab + 2c^2$ is added at each stage. This number becomes larger without bound as the fractal design expands.

Step 5 Students can see many patterns. For example, there is reflectional symmetry over a midsegment of the square on the original hypotenuse.

Step 6 Students' responses will vary. Check them for validity and justification.

LESSON

9.4

PLANNING

LESSON OUTLINE

One day:

25 min Example and Exercises

15 min Sharing

5 min Closing

MATERIALS

- calculators

TEACHING

The Pythagorean Theorem has many applications. This lesson consists primarily of exercises.

One step Pose the problem from the Example and have students discuss it without opening their books.

▶ *EXAMPLE*

The distance x is called the *space diagonal.* To find its length, you need d^2, but you don't need to find d.

Assessing Progress

Through their work on the exercises, you can assess students' understanding of the Pythagorean Theorem.

SHARING IDEAS

Have several groups prepare some of their solutions to the exercises on transparencies and share them with the class. Keep asking whether the results seem reasonable.

Closing the Lesson

Emphasize that a good first step in solving application problems is to draw a picture. Then students should examine the picture for common geometric shapes, such as right triangles, and apply what they know about those shapes.

LESSON 9.4

Story Problems

You may be disappointed if you fail, but you are doomed if you don't try.

BEVERLY SILLS

You have learned that drawing a diagram will help you to solve difficult problems. By now you know to look for many special relationships in your diagrams, such as congruent polygons, parallel lines, and right triangles.

FUNKY WINKERBEAN by Batiuk. Reprinted with special permission of North America Syndicate.

EXAMPLE What is the longest stick that will fit inside a 24-by-30-by-18-inch box?

▶ *Solution* Draw a diagram.

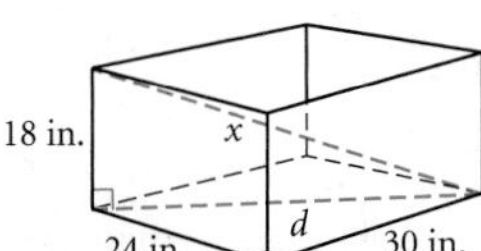

You can lay a stick with length d diagonally at the bottom of the box. But you can position an even longer stick with length x along the diagonal of the box, as shown. How long is this stick?

Both d and x are the hypotenuses of right triangles, but finding d^2 will help you find x.

$$30^2 + 24^2 = d^2$$
$$900 + 576 = d^2$$
$$d^2 = 1476$$

$$d^2 + 18^2 = x^2$$
$$1476 + 18^2 = x^2$$
$$1476 + 324 = x^2$$
$$1800 = x^2$$
$$x \approx 42.4$$

The longest possible stick is about 42.4 in.

EXERCISES

1. A giant California redwood tree 36 meters tall cracked in a violent storm and fell as if hinged. The tip of the once beautiful tree hit the ground 24 meters from the base. Researcher Red Woods wishes to investigate the crack. How many meters up from the base of the tree does he have to climb? ⓗ 10 m

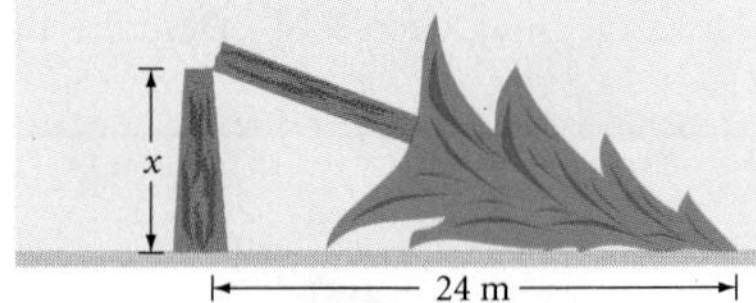

2. Amir's sister is away at college, and he wants to mail her a 34 in. baseball bat. The packing service sells only one kind of box, which measures 24 in. by 2 in. by 18 in. Will the box be big enough? No. The space diagonal of the box is 30.1 in.

LESSON OBJECTIVES

- Apply the Pythagorean Theorem and its converse
- Develop reading comprehension and problem-solving skills

NCTM STANDARDS

CONTENT		PROCESS	
	Number	✓	Problem Solving
✓	Algebra	✓	Reasoning
✓	Geometry		Communication
✓	Measurement	✓	Connections
	Data/Probability	✓	Representation

3. Meteorologist Paul Windward and geologist Rhaina Stone are rushing to a paleontology conference in Pecos Gulch. Paul lifts off in his balloon at noon from Lost Wages, heading east for Pecos Gulch Conference Center. With the wind blowing west to east, he averages a land speed of 30 km/hr. This will allow him to arrive in 4 hours, just as the conference begins. Meanwhile, Rhaina is 160 km north of Lost Wages. At the moment of Paul's lift off, Rhaina hops into an off-roading vehicle and heads directly for the conference center. At what average speed must she travel to arrive at the same time Paul does? ⓗ 50 km/hr

Career
CONNECTION

Meteorologists study the weather and the atmosphere. They also look at air quality, oceanic influence on weather, changes in climate over time, and even other planetary climates. They make forecasts using satellite photographs, weather balloons, contour maps, and mathematics to calculate wind speed or the arrival of a storm.

4. A 25-foot ladder is placed against a building. The bottom of the ladder is 7 feet from the building. If the top of the ladder slips down 4 feet, how many feet will the bottom slide out? (It is not 4 feet.) ⓗ 8 ft

5. The front and back walls of an A-frame cabin are isosceles triangles, each with a base measuring 10 m and legs measuring 13 m. The entire front wall is made of glass 1 cm thick that cost $\$120/\text{m}^2$. What did the glass for the front wall cost? ⓗ area: 60 m^2; cost: $7200

6. A regular hexagonal prism fits perfectly inside a cylindrical box with diameter 6 cm and height 10 cm. What is the surface area of the prism? What is the surface area of the cylinder? ⓗ

surface area of prism $= (27\sqrt{3} + 180)\text{ cm}^2 \approx 226.8\text{ cm}^2$; surface area of cylinder $= 78\pi\text{ cm}^2 \approx 245.0\text{ cm}^2$

7. Find the perimeter of an equilateral triangle whose median measures 6 cm. $\frac{36}{\sqrt{3}}$ cm

8. APPLICATION According to the Americans with Disabilities Act, the slope of a wheelchair ramp must be no greater than $\frac{1}{12}$. What is the length of ramp needed to gain a height of 4 feet? Read the Science Connection on the top of page 484 and then figure out how much force is required to go up the ramp if a person and a wheelchair together weigh 200 pounds. 48.2 ft; 16.6 lb

BUILDING UNDERSTANDING

You may want to divide up the exercises and have different groups work on different exercises.

ASSIGNING HOMEWORK

Essential	1–5
Performance assessment	6
Portfolio	9
Group	7–10
Review	11–20

▶ Helping with the Exercises

Exercise 1 If students are having difficulty, **[Ask]** "If the tree was originally 36 meters tall and it cracked with x meters left standing, how much has fallen?" [$36 - x$] You might also use specific numbers until students see the general case.

Exercise 5 As needed, suggest that students draw altitudes to create right triangles.

Exercise 6 **[Alert]** Some students may have forgotten that a hexagon inscribed in a circle has sides the same length as the circle's radius.

Exercise 7 After students have drawn pictures, you might **[Ask]** "Which side of the 30°-60°-90° triangle do we know?" [the longer leg]

11. 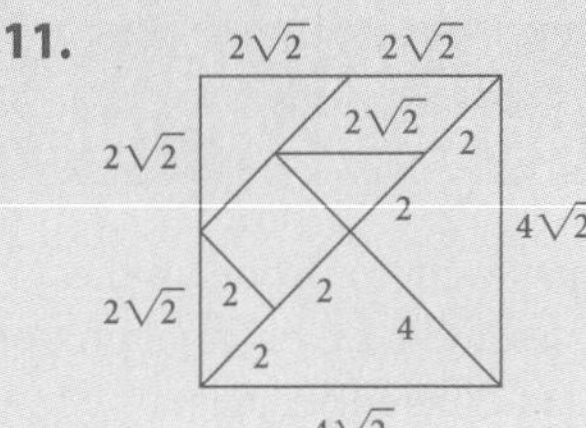

Making the Connection
[Language] *Qi qiao* is pronounced [chē chēaù].

Science CONNECTION

It takes less effort to roll objects up an *inclined plane,* or ramp, than to lift them straight up. *Work* is a measure of force applied over distance, and you calculate it as a product of force and distance. For example, a force of 100 pounds is required to hold up a 100-pound object. The work required to lift it 2 feet is 200 foot-pounds. But if you use a 4-foot-long ramp to roll it up, you'll do the 200 foot-pounds of work over a 4-foot distance. So you need to apply only 50 pounds of force at any given moment.

For Exercises 9 and 10, refer to the above Science Connection about inclined planes.

9. Compare what it would take to lift an object these three different ways.

a. How much work, in foot-pounds, is necessary to lift 80 pounds straight up 2 feet? 160 ft-lb

b. If a ramp 4 feet long is used to raise the 80 pounds up 2 feet, how much force, in pounds, will it take? 40 lb

c. If a ramp 8 feet long is used to raise the 80 pounds up 2 feet, how much force, in pounds, will it take? 20 lb

10. If you can exert only 70 pounds of force and you need to lift a 160-pound steel drum up 2 feet, what is the minimum length of ramp you should set up? 4.6 ft

Review

Recreation CONNECTION

Private collection, Berkeley, California. Photo by Cheryl Fenton.

This set of enameled porcelain *qi qiao* bowls can be arranged to form a 37-by-37 cm square (as shown) or other shapes, or used separately. Each bowl is 10 cm deep. Dishes of this type are usually used to serve candies, nuts, dried fruits, and other snacks on special occasions.

The *qi qiao,* or tangram puzzle, originated in China and consists of seven pieces—five isosceles right triangles, a square, and a parallelogram. The puzzle involves rearranging the pieces into a square, or hundreds of other shapes (a few are shown below).

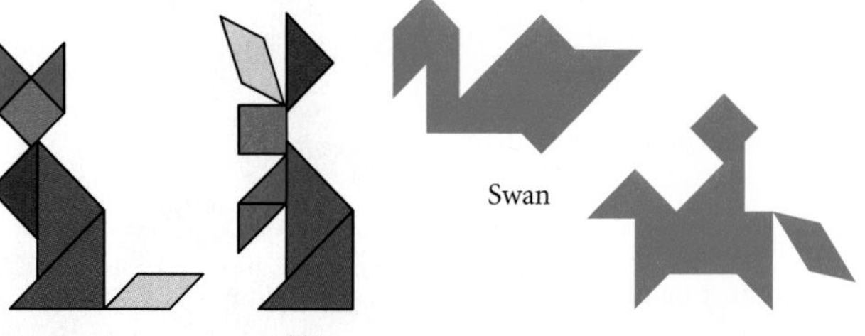

9.1 **11.** If the area of the red square piece is 4 cm², what are the dimensions of the other six pieces?

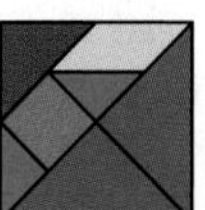

12. Make a set of your own seven tangram pieces and create the Cat, Rabbit, Swan, and Horse with Rider as shown on page 484.

9.3 **13.** Find the radius of circle Q. 12 units

(?, 6), r, 150°, Q, x, y

9.1 **14.** Find the length of $\overline{AC}$. $18\sqrt{2}$ cm

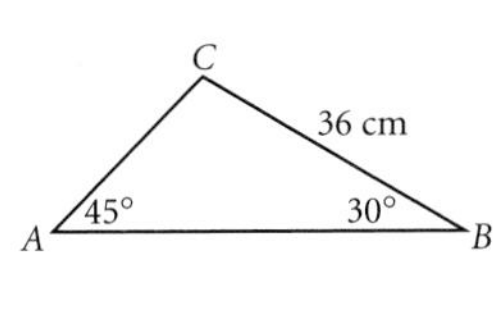

6.2 **15.** The two rays are tangent to the circle. What's wrong with this picture?

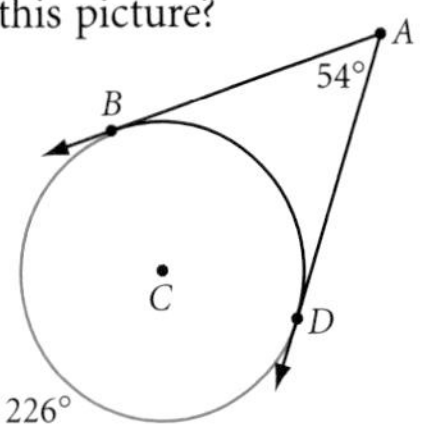

7.1 **16.** In the figure below, point A' is the image of point A after a reflection over $\overrightarrow{OT}$. What are the coordinates of A'? ⓗ $(4, 4\sqrt{3})$

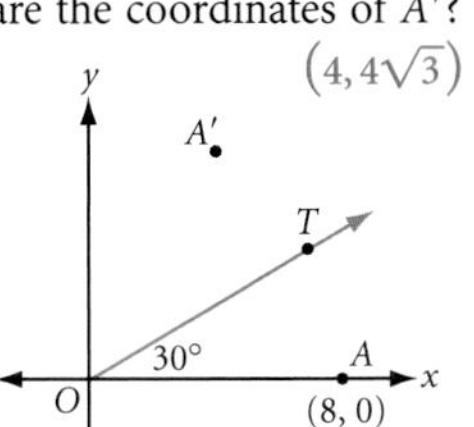

4.5 **17.** Which congruence shortcut can you use to show that $\triangle ABP \cong \triangle DCP$? SAA

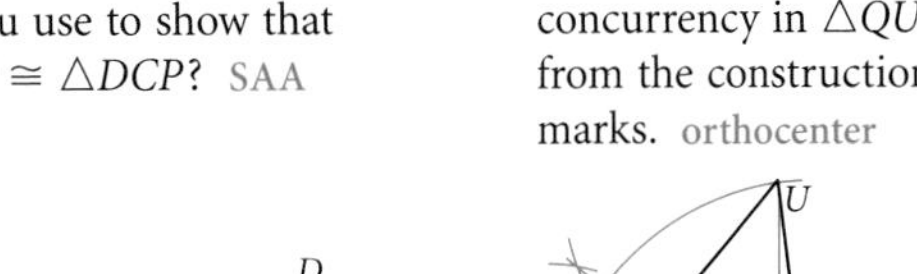

3.7 **18.** Identify the point of concurrency in $\triangle QUO$ from the construction marks. orthocenter

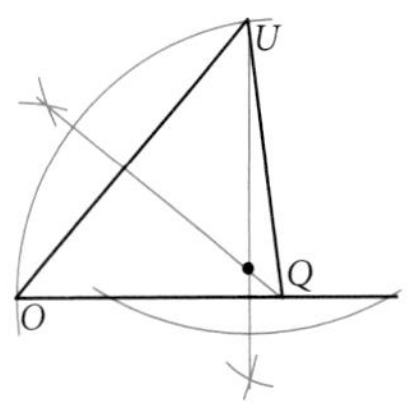

5.5 **19.** In parallelogram $QUID$, $m\angle Q = 2x + 5°$ and $m\angle I = 4x - 55°$. What is $m\angle U$? 115°

4.3 **20.** In $\triangle PRO$, $m\angle P = 70°$ and $m\angle R = 45°$. Which side of the triangle is the shortest? $\overline{PO}$

IMPROVING YOUR VISUAL THINKING SKILLS

PUZZLE

Fold, Punch, and Snip

A square sheet of paper is folded vertically, a hole is punched out of the center, and then one of the corners is snipped off. When the paper is unfolded it will look like the figure at right.

Sketch what a square sheet of paper will look like when it is unfolded after the following sequence of folds, punches, and snips.

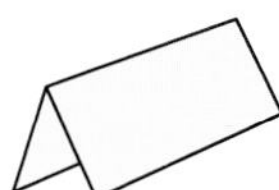

Fold once.

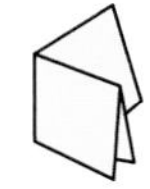

Fold twice.

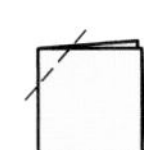

Snip double-fold corner.

Punch opposite corner.

12.

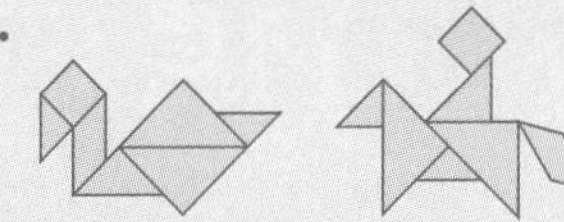

15. Draw radii $\overline{CD}$ and $\overline{CB}$. $\angle ABC = \angle ADC = 90°$. For quadrilateral $ABCD$ $54° + 90° + m\angle C + 90° = 360°$, so $m\angle C = 126°$. $\overset{\frown}{BD} = 126°$ but $126° + 226° \neq 360°$.

Exercises 19, 20, 18 [Language] The figure names in these exercises form a legal phrase: *quid pro quo.* Quid pro quo means "something for something." It's used to mean the consideration for a contract, that is, what each party gets out of it (such as money or advantage). A similar colloquial expression is "tit for tat."

EXTENSION

Have students show algebraically that 3-4-5 is the only Pythagorean triple of consecutive positive integers.

IMPROVING VISUAL THINKING SKILLS

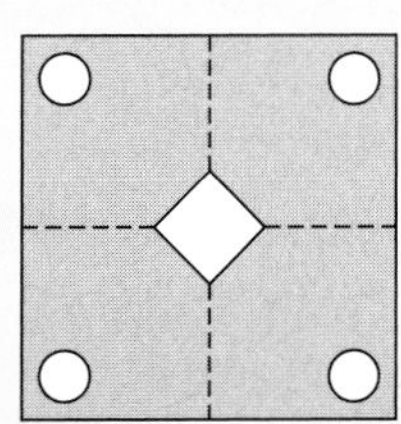

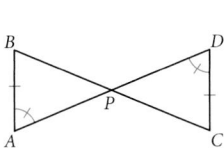

LESSON
9.5

PLANNING

LESSON OUTLINE

One day:

25 min Investigation and Examples

5 min Sharing

5 min Closing

10 min Exercises

MATERIALS

- graph paper
- The Distance Formula (T), *optional*

TEACHING

If your curriculum or your students' background requires that you emphasize both the distance formula and the equation of a circle, you may want to plan two days for this lesson.

One step Pose this problem: "Viki is standing on a street corner and is trying to talk with Scott by walkie-talkie. He says he's also at a corner, but static keeps Viki from understanding which corner. If each block is one-tenth mile long, what are the possible straight-line distances Scott could be from Vicki and still be within a half mile?" As needed, encourage students to draw right triangles to find diagonal distances. During Sharing, ask for an equation describing Scott's possible locations if he's exactly $\frac{1}{2}$ mile away but not necessarily at a corner.

LESSON
9.5

Distance in Coordinate Geometry

We talk too much; we should talk less and draw more.

JOHANN WOLFGANG VON GOETHE

Viki is standing on the corner of Seventh Street and 8th Avenue, and her brother Scott is on the corner of Second Street and 3rd Avenue. To find her shortest sidewalk route to Scott, Viki can simply count blocks. But if Viki wants to know her diagonal distance to Scott, she would need the Pythagorean Theorem to measure across blocks.

8th Ave, 7th Ave, 6th Ave, 5th Ave, 4th Ave, 3rd Ave, 2nd Ave, 1st Ave

First St, Second St, Third St, Fourth St, Fifth St, Sixth St, Seventh St, Eighth St

V S

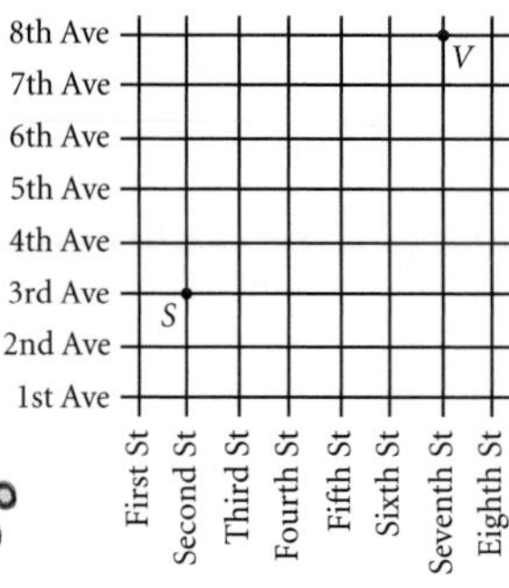

You can think of a coordinate plane as a grid of streets with two sets of parallel lines running perpendicular to each other. Every segment in the plane that is not in the x- or y-direction is the hypotenuse of a right triangle whose legs are in the x- and y-directions. So you can use the Pythagorean Theorem to find the distance between any two points on a coordinate plane.

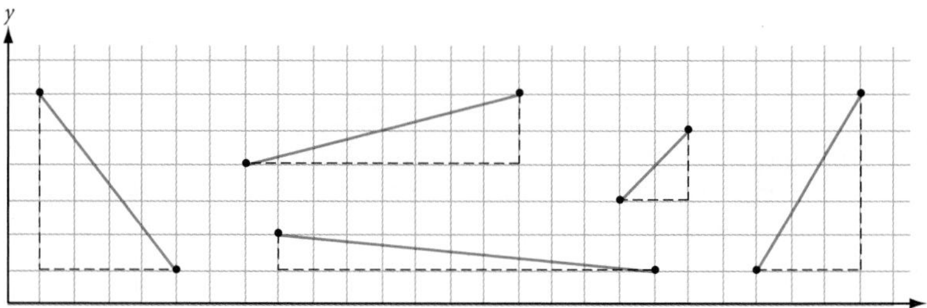

Investigation 1
The Distance Formula

You will need

- graph paper

In Steps 1 and 2, find the length of each segment by using the segment as the hypotenuse of a right triangle. Simply count the squares on the horizontal and vertical legs, then use the Pythagorean Theorem to find the length of the hypotenuse.

Step 1 Copy graphs a–d from the next page onto your own graph paper. Use each segment as the hypotenuse of a right triangle. Draw the legs along the grid lines. Find the length of each segment.

LESSON OBJECTIVES

- Discover the Pythagorean relationship on a coordinate plane (the distance formula)
- Derive the equation of a circle from the distance formula
- Use the distance formula to solve problems
- Develop problem-solving skills and cooperative behavior

NCTM STANDARDS

CONTENT		PROCESS	
	Number	✓	Problem Solving
✓	Algebra	✓	Reasoning
✓	Geometry	✓	Communication
✓	Measurement	✓	Connections
	Data/Probability		Representation

a.

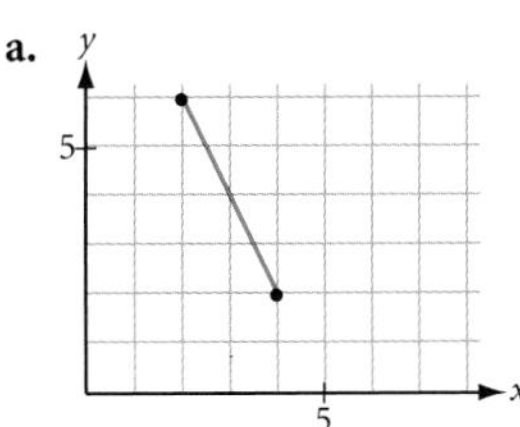

$\sqrt{20} = 2\sqrt{5} \approx 4.5$

b.

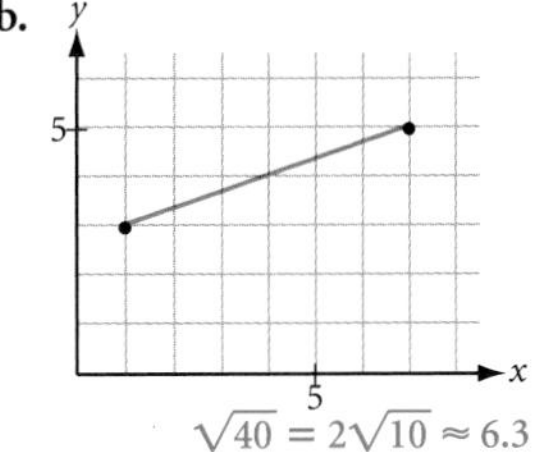

$\sqrt{40} = 2\sqrt{10} \approx 6.3$

c.

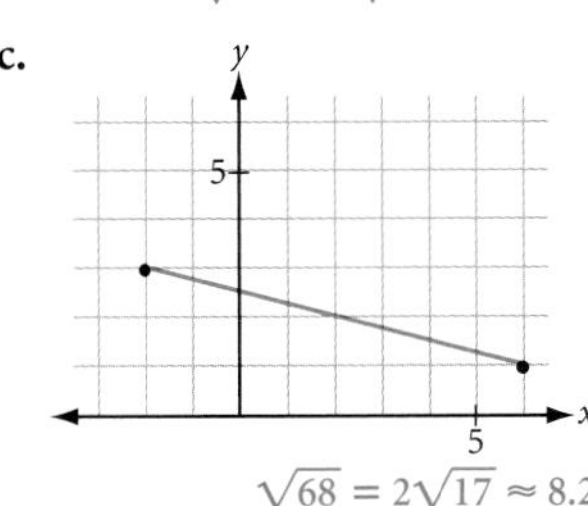

$\sqrt{68} = 2\sqrt{17} \approx 8.2$

d.

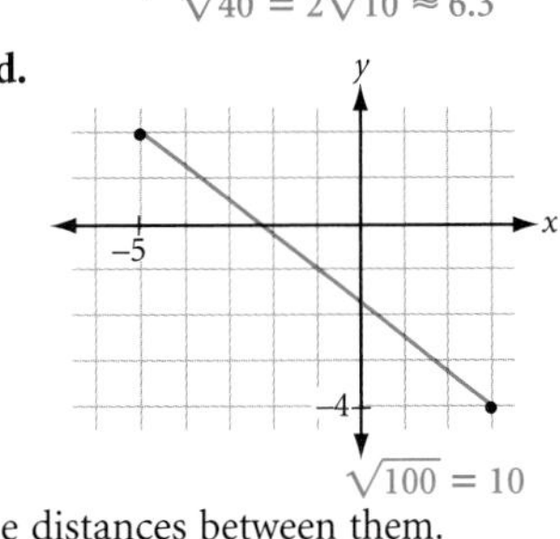

$\sqrt{100} = 10$

Step 2 Graph each pair of points, then find the distances between them.

a. $(-1, -2), (11, -7)$ 13 **b.** $(-9, -6), (3, 10)$ 20

What if the points are so far apart that it's not practical to plot them? For example, what is the distance between the points $A(15, 34)$ and $B(42, 70)$? A formula that uses the coordinates of the given points would be helpful. To find this formula, you first need to find the lengths of the legs in terms of the x- and y-coordinates. From your work with slope triangles, you know how to calculate horizontal and vertical distances.

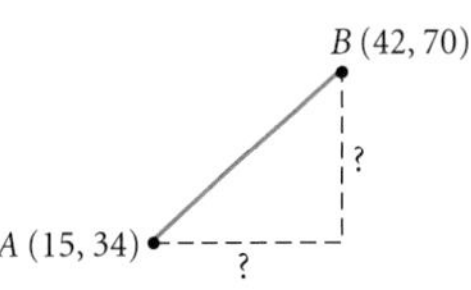

Step 3 Write an expression for the length of the horizontal leg using the x-coordinates.

Step 4 Write a similar expression for the length of the vertical leg using the y-coordinates.

Step 5 Use your expressions from Steps 3 and 4, and the Pythagorean Theorem, to find the distance between points $A(15, 34)$ and $B(42, 70)$.

Step 6 Generalize what you have learned about the distance between two points in a coordinate plane. Copy and complete the conjecture below.

Distance Formula

C-86

The distance between points $A(x_1, y_1)$ and $B(x_2, y_2)$ is given by

$$(AB)^2 = (\underline{?})^2 + (\underline{?})^2 \text{ or } AB = \sqrt{(\underline{?})^2 + (\underline{?})^2}$$

$(x_2 - x_1)^2 + (y_2 - y_1)^2$ $\sqrt{(x_2 - x_1)^2 + (y_2 - y_1)^2}$

Let's look at an example to see how you can apply the distance formula.

Guiding Investigation 1

Step 1 Students used triangles like this earlier in finding slopes of lines. You might provide The Distance Formula worksheet so students aren't tempted to write in their books. You might use pair share within groups or jigsaw between groups to save time.

Step 2 As needed, encourage students to use right triangles so they can see the distance formula as a special application of the Pythagorean Theorem. Pair share works well for this step also.

Step 3 Students may want to discuss how to handle negative distances. Some students may want to take the absolute value so that all distances are positive. Others may be comfortable with negative values as a measure of directed distance. Still other students may advocate always subtracting the smaller x-coordinate from the larger so the distance is always positive.

Step 3 Subtract one x-coordinate from the other.

Step 4 Subtract one y-coordinate from the other.

Step 5 $AB^2 = (42 - 15)^2 + (70 - 34)^2$; $AB = \sqrt{729 + 1296} = 45$

Step 6 Students may remember the distance formula from algebra I, perhaps using d instead of AB.

▶ EXAMPLE A

Because the distance formula is derived directly from the Pythagorean Theorem, the book begins with the $a^2 + b^2 = c^2$ version of the distance formula. You could also show that you can start with $AB = \sqrt{(x_2 - x_1)^2 + (y_2 - y_1)^2}$. **[Alert]** If students are using calculators, they can easily get incorrect answers if parentheses are omitted or not used correctly.

▶ EXAMPLE B

Students may benefit from being reminded that an equation for a geometric figure is satisfied by the coordinates of a point if and only if the point lies on the figure.

Guiding Investigation 2

Step 1 **[Alert]** Students may inattentively think of diameter instead of radius.

Step 1a

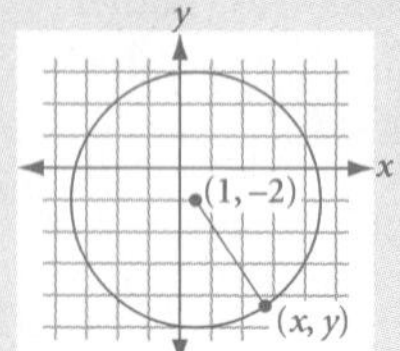

Step 1b

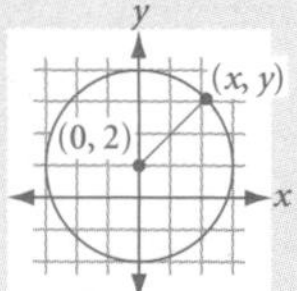

Step 1c

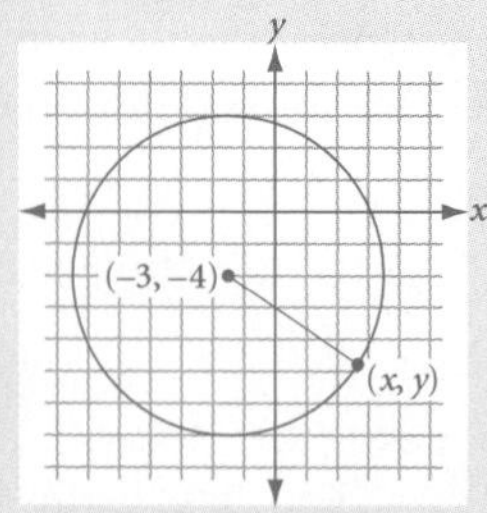

Step 2 As needed, encourage students to use the model in Example B.

After doing this investigation, you may want to work with another example. **[Ask]** "What is the equation for a circle with center (2, −3) and radius 4?" $[(x - 2)^2 + (y + 3)^2 = 16]$

EXAMPLE A | Find the distance between $A(8, 15)$ and $B(-7, 23)$.

▶ Solution

$(AB)^2 = (x_2 - x_1)^2 + (y_2 - y_1)^2$	The distance formula.
$= (-7 - 8)^2 + (23 - 15)^2$	Substitute 8 for x_1, 15 for y_1, −7 for x_2, and 23 for y_2.
$= (-15)^2 + (8)^2$	Subtract.
$(AB)^2 = 289$	Square −15 and 8 and add.
$AB = 17$	Take the square root of both sides.

The distance formula is also used to write the equation of a circle.

EXAMPLE B | Write an equation for the circle with center (5, 4) and radius 7 units.

▶ Solution

Let (x, y) represent any point on the circle. The distance from (x, y) to the circle's center, (5, 4), is 7. Substitute this information in the distance formula.

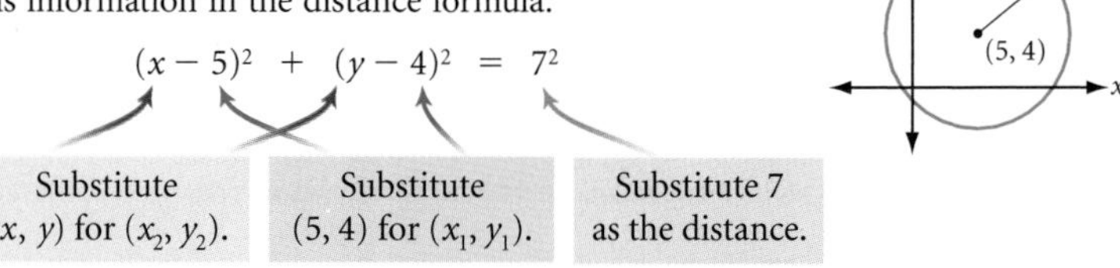

y
(x, y)
(5, 4)
x

So, the equation in standard form is $(x - 5)^2 + (y - 4)^2 = 7^2$.

Investigation 2
The Equation of a Circle

You will need

- graph paper

Find equations for a few more circles and then generalize the equation for any circle with radius r and center (h, k).

Step 1 Given its center and radius, graph each circle on graph paper.

a. Center = (1, −2), $r = 8$ **b.** Center = (0, 2), $r = 6$

c. Center = (−3, −4), $r = 10$

Step 2 Select any point on each circle; label it (x, y). Use the distance formula to write an equation expressing the distance between the center of each circle and (x, y).

Step 3 Copy and complete the conjecture for the equation of a circle.

Step 2a $(x - 1)^2 + (y + 2)^2 = 64$

Step 2b $x^2 + (y - 2)^2 = 36$

Step 2c $(x + 3)^2 + (y + 4)^2 = 100$

Equation of a Circle **C-87**

The equation of a circle with radius r and center (h, k) is

$$(x - \underset{h}{\underline{?}})^2 + (y - \underset{k}{\underline{?}})^2 = (\underset{r}{\underline{?}})^2$$

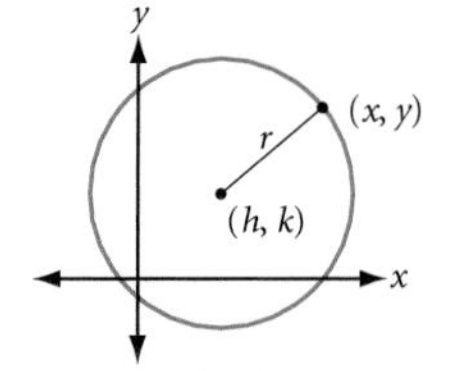

SHARING IDEAS

Students may have come up with a variety of distance formulas. For example, they may have either $x_2 - x_1$ or $y_2 - y_1$ first, or they might have $x_1 - x_2$ in place of $x_2 - x_1$ or $y_1 - y_2$ in place of $y_2 - y_1$. Through student discussion, elicit the idea that these are all the same formula after squaring and adding.

[Ask] "In Example A, how would you know to substitute the coordinates (8, 15) for (x_1, y_1) instead of for (x_2, y_2)?" Student experimentation can lead to the realization that it doesn't matter.

When discussing the equation of a circle, ask whether you could get an equivalent formula by taking the square root, as with the distance formula. Students may say $r = \sqrt{(x - h)^2 + (y - k)^2}$. **[Ask]** "Should the equation include negative values of r, $r = \pm\sqrt{(x - h)^2 + (y - k)^2}$? [No; r is a radius, so it cannot be negative.] The equation with r^2 is called the *standard form.*

Ask how students might use the equation to graph a circle with center at (1, −2) and radius 8. They need to solve the equation for y in terms of x. They'll get $(y + 2)^2 = 64 - (x - 1)^2$, from

Let's look at an example that uses the equation of a circle in reverse.

EXAMPLE C Find the center and radius of the circle $(x+2)^2 + (y-5)^2 = 36$.

▶ ***Solution*** Rewrite the equation of the circle in the standard form.

$$(x-h)^2 + (y-k)^2 = r^2$$
$$(x-(-2))^2 + (y-5)^2 = 6^2$$

Identify the values of h, k, and r. The center is $(-2, 5)$ and the radius is 6.

EXERCISES

In Exercises 1–3, find the distance between each pair of points.

1. (10, 20), (13, 16) 5 units **2.** (15, 37), (42, 73) 45 units **3.** $(-19, -16)$, $(-3, 14)$ 34 units

4. Look back at the diagram of Viki's and Scott's locations on page 486. Assume each block is approximately 50 meters long. What is the shortest distance from Viki to Scott to the nearest meter? 354 m

5. Find the perimeter of $\triangle ABC$ with vertices $A(2, 4)$, $B(8, 12)$, and $C(24, 0)$. 52.4 units

6. Determine whether $\triangle DEF$ with vertices $D(6, -6)$, $E(39, -12)$, and $F(24, 18)$ is scalene, isosceles, or equilateral. isosceles

For Exercises 7 and 8, find the equation of the circle.

7. Center = (0, 0), $r = 4$ $x^2 + y^2 = 16$ **8.** Center = (2, 0), $r = 5$ $(x-2)^2 + y^2 = 25$

For Exercises 9 and 10, find the radius and center of the circle.

9. $(x-2)^2 + (y+5)^2 = 6^2$ center is $(2, -5)$, $r = 6$ **10.** $x^2 + (y-1)^2 = 81$ center is $(0, 1)$, $r = 9$

11. The center of a circle is $(3, -1)$. One point on the circle is $(6, 2)$. Find the equation of the circle. ⓗ $(x-3)^2 + (y+1)^2 = 18$

12. ***Mini-Investigation*** How would you find the distance between two points in a three-dimensional coordinate system? Investigate and make a conjecture. ⓗ

a. What is the distance from the origin (0, 0, 0) to $(2, -1, 3)$? $\sqrt{14}$ units

b. What is the distance between $P(1, 2, 3)$ and $Q(5, 6, 15)$? $\sqrt{176} = 4\sqrt{11}$ units

c. Complete this conjecture: If $A(x_1, y_1, z_1)$ and $B(x_2, y_2, z_2)$ are two points in a three-dimensional coordinate system, then the distance AB is $\sqrt{(\underline{?})^2 + (\underline{?})^2 + (\underline{?})^2}$.

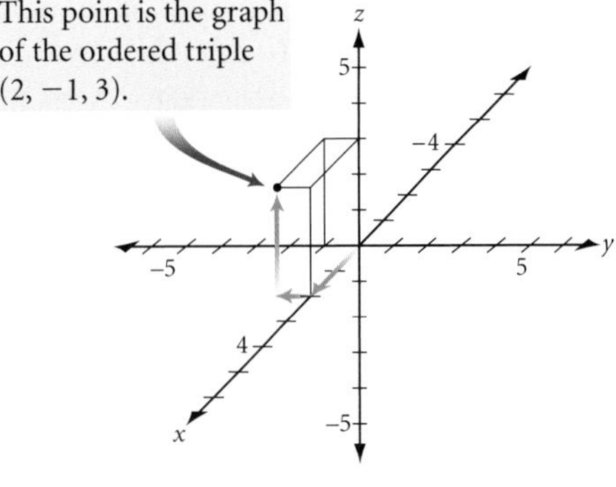
This point is the graph of the ordered triple (2, −1, 3).
z
5
−4
y
−5
5
4
−5
x

▶ ***EXAMPLE C***

Point out that $(x+2)^2$ can be rewritten as $(x-(-2))^2$.

Assessing Progress

You can assess students' familiarity with coordinates of points, circles and their radii, right triangles and their hypotenuses, and the Pythagorean Theorem. Also check students' ability to work separately with the horizontal and vertical distances.

Closing the Lesson

The **distance formula,** $AB = \sqrt{(x_2-x_1)^2 + (y_2-y_1)^2}$, and the related **equation of a circle,** $(x-h)^2 + (y-k)^2 = r^2$, are both derived from the Pythagorean Theorem.

BUILDING UNDERSTANDING

These exercises motivate the need for a formula to find the distance between points when plotting the points is impractical.

ASSIGNING HOMEWORK

Essential	1–10
Performance assessment	12
Portfolio	6
Journal	17
Group	11
Review	13–17

▶ Helping with the Exercises

Exercise 3 [Alert] Students may not be careful enough in substituting the negative numbers into the distance formula.

Exercise 12 As needed, encourage students to break apart the problem and consider a diagonal of a horizontal or vertical rectangle as an intermediate step. Or ask whether the distance could be a space diagonal of an imaginary box.

Sharing Ideas (continued)

which they may want to take square roots to get $y + 2 = \sqrt{64-(x-1)^2}$ and hence $y = -2 + \sqrt{64-(x-1)^2}$. When they graph this function on a calculator, they'll get only a semicircle, because in taking the square root they eliminated negative values of $y + 2$. To graph the other half of the circle, they'll need to graph the second function $y = -2 - \sqrt{64-(x-1)^2}$.

Their graphs still might not look very circular. Suggest that they use a friendly window.

Exercise 11 The radius is determined to be $\sqrt{18}$ or $3\sqrt{2}$. The equation is then $(x-3)^2 + (y+1)^2 = (3\sqrt{2})^2$ or $(x-3)^2 + (y+1)^2 = (\sqrt{18})^2$, or simply $(x-3)^2 + (y+1)^2 = 18$. This is a good example of a case in which the "unsimplified" form $\sqrt{18}$ is more useful than the "simplified" form, because it's easier to square.

12c. $AB = \sqrt{(x_1-x_2)^2 + (y_1-y_2)^2 + (z_1-z_2)^2}$

Exercise 15 As needed, ask whether the triangle is a special kind. If a student rationalizes the denominator, the solutions are $x = 2\sqrt{3}$ and $y = 4\sqrt{3}$.

Exercise 17 If students are having difficulty, ask if they know any properties of the center of a rotation.

Review

9.3 **13.** Find the coordinates of A. $\left(-\frac{\sqrt{3}}{2}, \frac{1}{2}\right)$

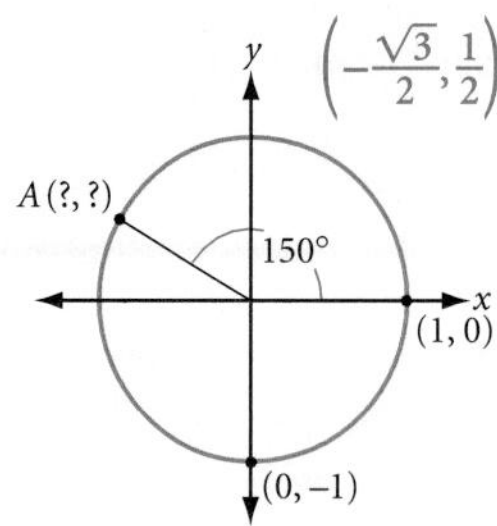

9.1 **14.** $k =$?, $m =$? ⓗ $k = \sqrt{2}, m = \sqrt{6}$

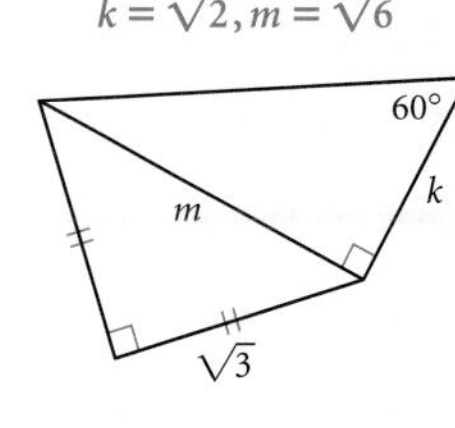

9.1 **15.** The large triangle is equilateral. Find x and y. $x = \frac{6}{\sqrt{3}}, y = \frac{12}{\sqrt{3}}$

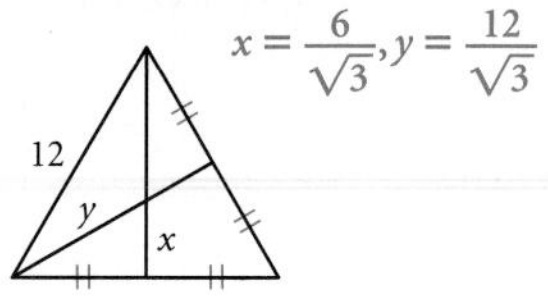

16. Antonio is a biologist studying life in a pond. He needs to know how deep the water is. He notices a water lily sticking straight up from the water, whose blossom is 8 cm above the water's surface. Antonio pulls the lily to one side, keeping the stem straight, until the blossom touches the water at a spot 40 cm from where the stem first broke the water's surface. How is Antonio able to calculate the depth of the water? What is the depth? ⓗ 96 cm

7.1 **17.** $C'U'R'T'$ is the image of $CURT$ under a rotation transformation. Copy the polygon and its image onto patty paper. Find the center of rotation and the measure of the angle of rotation. Explain your method.
The angle of rotation is approximately 77°. Connect two pairs of corresponding points. Construct the perpendicular bisector of each segment. The point where the perpendicular bisectors meet is the center of rotation.

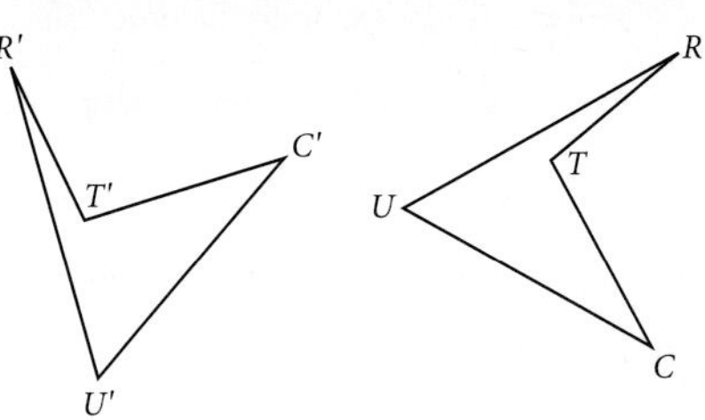

IMPROVING YOUR VISUAL THINKING SKILLS

The Spider and the Fly

(attributed to the British puzzlist Henry E. Dudeney, 1857–1930)

In a rectangular room, measuring 30 by 12 by 12 feet, a spider is at point A on the middle of one of the end walls, 1 foot from the ceiling. A fly is at point B on the center of the opposite wall, 1 foot from the floor. What is the shortest distance that the spider must crawl to reach the fly, which remains stationary? The spider never drops or uses its web, but crawls fairly.

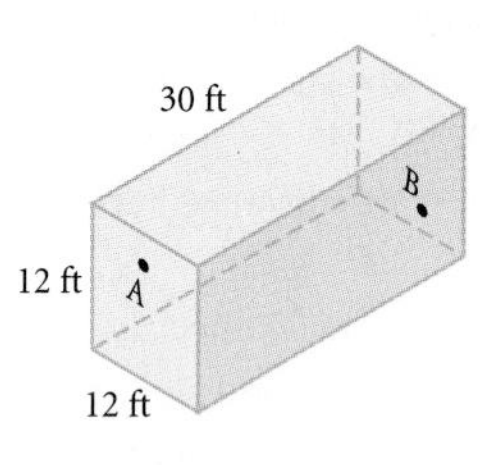

The Spider and the Fly
Here is another path shorter than 42 feet. It is not the shortest.

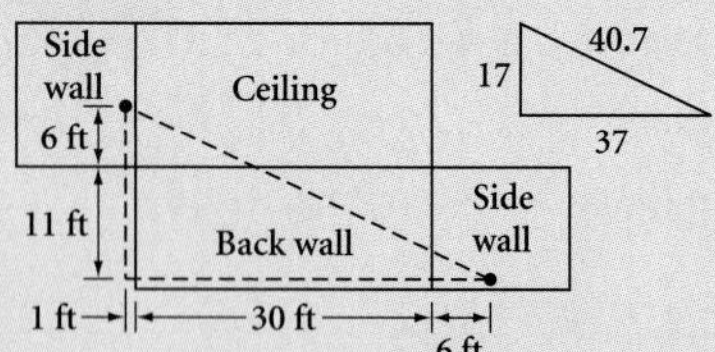

IMPROVING VISUAL THINKING SKILLS

[Context] Henry E. Dudeney (1857–1930, England) was a puzzle inventor whose puzzles continue to challenge people today. His spider-and-fly problem first appeared in an English newspaper.

If students are stuck, wonder aloud whether it would help to think of the problem in two dimensions. They might draw several different nets of the room and draw straight lines between the points on the net. **[Ask]** "Which net will give the shortest distance? What does that mean for the original room?"

The shortest path measures 40 feet.

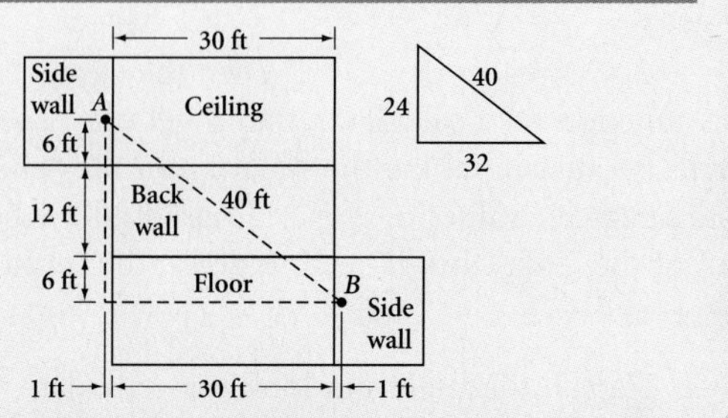

Exploration

Ladder Climb

Suppose a house painter rests a 20-foot ladder against a building, then decides the ladder needs to rest 1 foot higher against the building. Will moving the ladder 1 foot toward the building do the job? If it needs to be 2 feet lower, will moving the ladder 2 feet away from the building do the trick? Let's investigate.

Activity

Climbing the Wall

You will need

- a graphing calculator

Sketch a ladder leaning against a vertical wall, with the foot of the ladder resting on horizontal ground. Label the sketch using y for height reached by the ladder and x for the distance from the base of the wall to the foot of the ladder.

Step 1 $y = \sqrt{400 - x^2}$

Step 2 $0 < x < 20$; $0 < y < 20$

Step 3 a quarter-circle

Step 4 (3, 19.8); (6, 19.1); (9, 17.9); (12, 16) No. At first the height reached by the ladder decreases slowly, but the farther the ladder is pulled out, the faster the height reached by it decreases.

Step 5 When $x = y$ $\left(\text{at } x \approx 14, \text{the length of the ladder divided by } \sqrt{2}\right)$, the ladder forms a 45° angle with the floor and the wall.

Step 1 Write an equation relating x, y, and the length of the ladder and solve it for y. You now have a function for the height reached by the ladder in terms of the distance from the wall to the foot of the ladder. Enter this equation into your calculator.

Step 2 Before you graph the equation, think about the settings you'll want for the graph window. What are the greatest and least values possible for x and y? Enter reasonable settings, then graph the equation.

Step 3 Describe the shape of the graph.

Step 4 Trace along the graph, starting at $x = 0$. Record values (rounded to the nearest 0.1 unit) for the height reached by the ladder when $x = 3, 6, 9$, and 12. If you move the foot of the ladder away from the wall 3 feet at a time, will each move result in the same change in the height reached by the ladder? Explain.

Step 5 Find the value for x that gives a y-value approximately equal to x. How is this value related to the length of the ladder? Sketch the ladder in this position. What angle does the ladder make with the ground?

Step 6 Should you lean a ladder against a wall in such a way that x is greater than y? Explain. How does your graph support your explanation?

NCTM STANDARDS

CONTENT		PROCESS	
	Number		Problem Solving
✓	Algebra		Reasoning
✓	Geometry		Communication
✓	Measurement	✓	Connections
	Data/Probability	✓	Representation

LESSON OBJECTIVES

- Create an algebraic model for the ladder problem
- Review graphing an equation
- Apply the Pythagorean Theorem to understand how rates of change vary

EXPLORATION

PLANNING

LESSON OUTLINE

One day:

25 min Activity

20 min Sharing and Closing

MATERIALS

- rulers
- graphing calculators

TEACHING

[ESL] *Do the trick* means "accomplish the task."

Guiding the Activity

Step 2 Ask students to conjecture whether the amount of change will always be the same and, if not, what it depends on. As needed, help students see where the maximum value of each variable occurs (on an axis).

Step 3 Unless students happened to choose a friendly window in Step 2, they may say that the graph is part of a parabola rather than an arc of a circle.

Step 5 Suggest that students study a table of these data.

SHARING IDEAS

As students present their ideas about Steps 4–6, **[Ask]** "At what point will a one-foot change in x result in a one-foot change in y?" [at the instant $y = x$]

Closing the Lesson

Rates of change of a function will vary if the graph of the function is curved.

See page 775 for answer to Step 6.

LESSON

9.6

PLANNING

LESSON OUTLINE

One day:

10 min Examples

30 min Exercises

5 min Closing

MATERIALS

- graph paper
- Exercise 8 (T) for One step

TEACHING

The Pythagorean Theorem can be powerful when combined with earlier conjectures about circles. You may either start with the one-step investigation; or, for more structure, begin with the examples. The lesson consists primarily of exercises.

▶ EXAMPLE A

Some students might miss the fact that the angle at vertex N has measure 60°. They may also be confused by the proportional reasoning.

▶ EXAMPLE B

Ask students how they know that $\overline{AC}$ is a diameter. [By the Inscribed Angle Conjecture, a right angle inscribed in a circle intercepts a semicircle.]

One step Pose this problem, as you display the transparency for Exercise 8: "In repairing an old machine, you must find a belt that will make one wheel turn another. The wheels' diameters have lengths 36 cm and 24 cm, and their centers are 60 cm apart. Because the wheels turn in opposite directions, the belt has to cross itself; marks indicate that the crossing point is 24 cm from the center of the smaller wheel. What length belt should you locate?" As needed, encourage students to review earlier conjectures about circles and special right triangles.

Assessing Progress

As students discuss the examples and work through the exercises, you can assess their understanding of tangent segments, arc lengths, the Pythagorean Theorem, and special right triangles.

Closing the Lesson

Much of the power of geometry comes from combining different conjectures. For example, using what we know about tangent segments, arc lengths, the Pythagorean Theorem, and special right triangles can help us solve a variety of problems.

LESSON 9.6

Circles and the Pythagorean Theorem

You must do things you think you cannot do.

ELEANOR ROOSEVELT

In Chapter 6, you discovered a number of properties that involved right angles in and around circles. In this lesson you will use the conjectures you made, along with the Pythagorean Theorem, to solve some challenging problems. Let's review two of the most useful conjectures.

Tangent Conjecture: A tangent to a circle is perpendicular to the radius drawn to the point of tangency.

Angles Inscribed in a Semicircle Conjecture: Angles inscribed in a semicircle are right angles.

Here are two examples that use these conjectures along with the Pythagorean Theorem.

EXAMPLE A

$\overrightarrow{TA}$ is tangent to circle N at A. $TA = 12\sqrt{3}$ cm. Find the area of the shaded region.

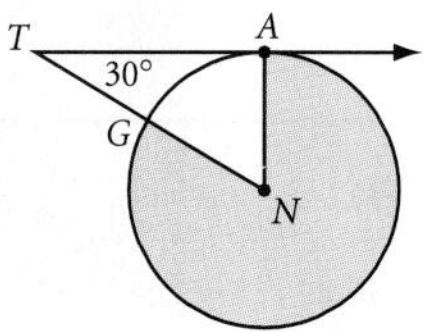

▶ Solution

$\overrightarrow{TA}$ is tangent at A, so $\angle TAN$ is a right angle and $\triangle TAN$ is a 30°-60°-90° triangle. The longer leg is $12\sqrt{3}$ cm, so the shorter leg (also the radius of the circle) is 12 cm. The area of the entire circle is 144π cm^2. The area of the shaded region is $\frac{360-60}{360}$, or $\frac{5}{6}$, of the area of the circle. Therefore the shaded area is $\frac{5}{6}(144\pi)$, or 120π cm^2.

EXAMPLE B

$AB = 6$ cm and $BC = 8$ cm. Find the area of the circle.

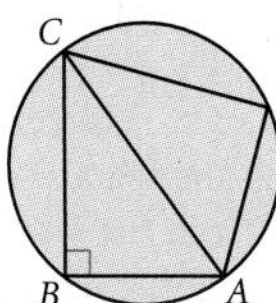

▶ Solution

Inscribed angle ABC is a right angle, so $\overarc{ABC}$ is a semicircle and $\overline{AC}$ is a diameter. By the Pythagorean Theorem, if $AB = 6$ cm and $BC = 8$ cm, then $AC = 10$ cm. Therefore the radius of the circle is 5 cm and the area of the circle is 25π cm^2.

EXERCISES

You will need

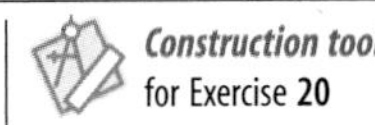

Construction tools for Exercise **20**

In Exercises 1–4, find the area of the shaded region in each figure. Assume lines that appear tangent are tangent at the labeled points.

1. $OD = 24$ cm (h) 456π cm^2

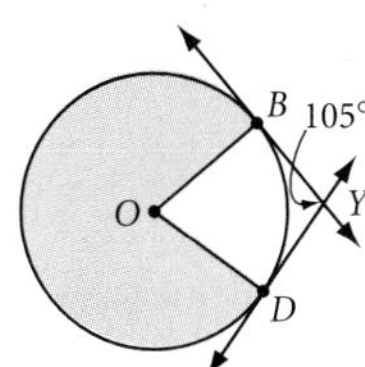

2. $HT = 8\sqrt{3}$ cm $(32\pi - 32\sqrt{3})$ cm^2

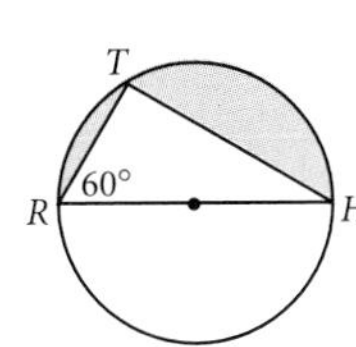

3. $HA = 8\sqrt{3}$ cm (h)

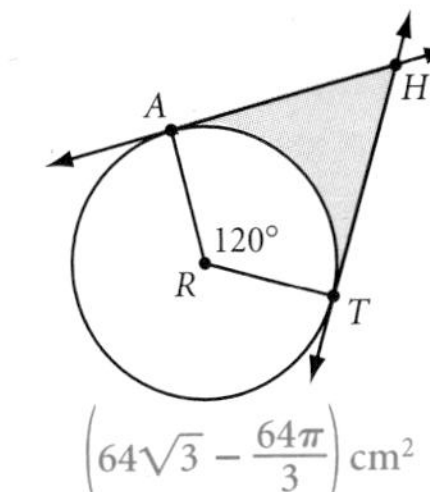

$\left(64\sqrt{3} - \frac{64\pi}{3}\right)$ cm^2

4. $HO = 8\sqrt{3}$ cm $\left(\frac{64\pi}{3} - 16\sqrt{3}\right)$ cm^2

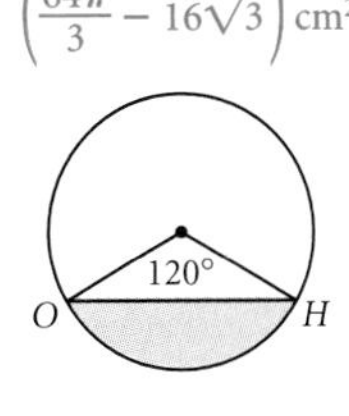

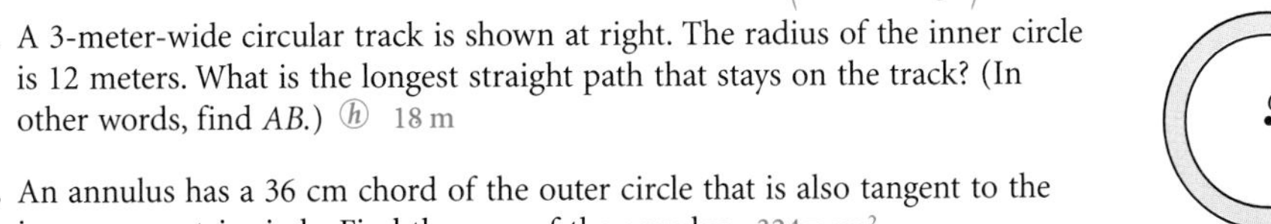

5. A 3-meter-wide circular track is shown at right. The radius of the inner circle is 12 meters. What is the longest straight path that stays on the track? (In other words, find AB.) (h) 18 m

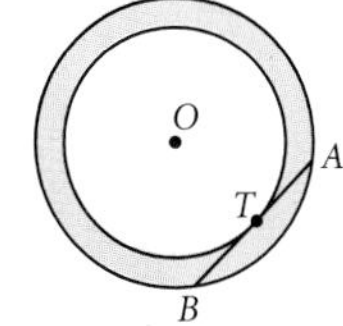

6. An annulus has a 36 cm chord of the outer circle that is also tangent to the inner concentric circle. Find the area of the annulus. 324π cm^2

7. In her latest expedition, Ertha Diggs has uncovered a portion of circular, terra-cotta pipe that she believes is part of an early water drainage system. To find the diameter of the original pipe, she lays a meterstick across the portion and measures the length of the chord at 48 cm. The depth of the portion from the midpoint of the chord is 6 cm. What was the pipe's original diameter? 102 cm

8. APPLICATION A machinery belt needs to be replaced. The belt runs around two wheels, crossing between them so that the larger wheel turns the smaller wheel in the opposite direction. The diameter of the larger wheel is 36 cm, and the diameter of the smaller is 24 cm. The distance between the centers of the two wheels is 60 cm. The belt crosses 24 cm from the center of the smaller wheel. What is the length of the belt? (h) 230 cm

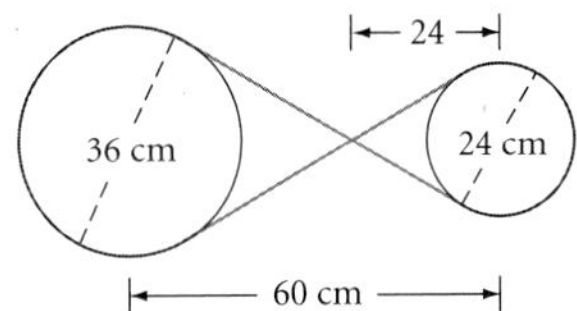

9. A circle of radius 6 has chord $\overline{AB}$ of length 6. If point C is selected randomly on the circle, what is the probability that $\triangle ABC$ is obtuse? $\frac{5}{6}$

NCTM STANDARDS

CONTENT		PROCESS	
	Number	✓	Problem Solving
✓	Algebra		Reasoning
✓	Geometry		Communication
✓	Measurement	✓	Connections
	Data/Probability		Representation

LESSON OBJECTIVE

- Apply the Pythagorean relationship to problems involving circles

BUILDING UNDERSTANDING

You might have several groups present their solutions to a few of the exercises. Distribute transparencies and pens to help students prepare their presentations.

ASSIGNING HOMEWORK

Essential	1–9
Performance assessment	13
Portfolio	14
Group	10–17
Review	18–23

Helping with the Exercises

Exercise 3 If students are having difficulty, wonder aloud whether there's a way to draw auxiliary lines to create right triangles, perhaps special right triangles.

Exercise 4 As needed, remind students that the area of a segment is the difference between the area of a sector and the area of a triangle.

Exercise 6 Students might think they don't have enough information. **[Ask]** "What is the difference in the squares of the radii? Can you use that to find the area of the annulus?" $[R^2 - r^2 = 18^2;$ $A = \pi(R^2 - r^2)]$

Exercise 7 Some students may stop after finding the radius instead of finding the diameter.

Exercise 8 The answer in terms of π is $(40\pi + 60\sqrt{3})$ cm.

Exercise 9 As needed, **[Ask]** "Does a chord that's congruent to a radius remind you of anything?" [Mark the radius six times around a circle to form a hexagon.] "What happens if point C falls in the arcs intercepted by the various sides of the inscribed regular hexagon?" [The arc on the hexagon side opposite side AB would be the only one where the third vertex would create an acute triangle.]

Exercise 12 As in Exercise 8, this exercise represents a physical situation, so an answer in terms of π, $\left(\frac{6400}{3}\pi - 1600\sqrt{3}\right)$ cm², may not be as appropriate as a rounded answer.

Exercise 13 If students are stuck, ask where the marked lengths transfer to on the sides of the rectangle and what they know about the rest of the height.

Exercise 14 You might encourage students to make a model for this exercise.

Exercise 16 Remind students as needed that they haven't worked much with obtuse angles, so they might benefit from drawing an acute triangle with point M at one vertex.

Exercises 16, 17 [Link] This kind of reasoning is used in trigonometry.

In Exercises 10 and 11, each triangle is equilateral. Find the area of the inscribed circle and the area of the circumscribed circle. How many times greater is the area of the circumscribed circle than the area of the inscribed circle?

10. $AB = 6$ cm ⓗ

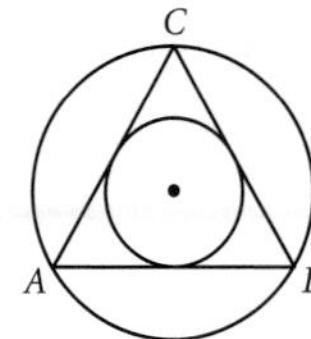

Inscribed circle: 3π cm². Circumscribed circle: 12π cm². The area of the circumscribed circle is four times as great as the area of the inscribed circle.

11. $DE = 2\sqrt{3}$ cm

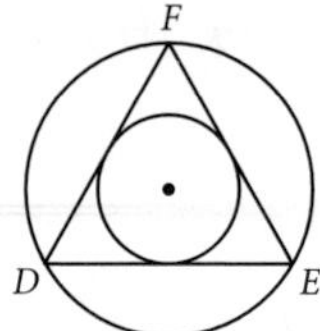

Inscribed circle: π cm². Circumscribed circle: 4π cm². The area of the circumscribed circle is four times as great as the area of the inscribed circle.

12. The Gothic arch is based on the equilateral triangle. If the base of the arch measures 80 cm, what is the area of the shaded region? 3931 cm²

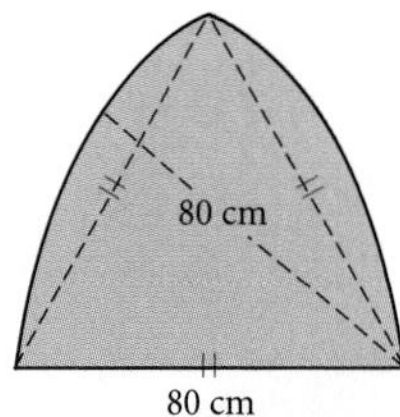

13. Each of three circles of radius 6 cm is tangent to the other two, and they are inscribed in a rectangle, as shown. What is the height of the rectangle? $\left(12 + 6\sqrt{3}\right)$ cm

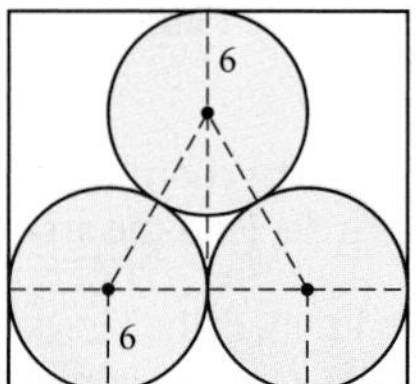

14. Sector ARC has a radius of 9 cm and an angle that measures 80°. When sector ARC is cut out and $\overline{AR}$ and $\overline{RC}$ are taped together, they form a cone. The length of $\overset{\frown}{AC}$ becomes the circumference of the base of the cone. What is the height of the cone? ⓗ $\sqrt{77}$ cm

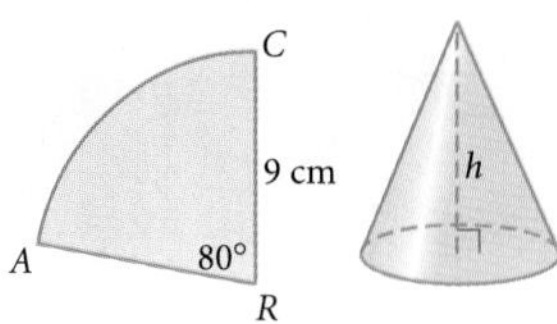

15. **APPLICATION** Will plans to use a circular cross section of wood to make a square table. The cross section has a circumference of 336 cm. To the nearest centimeter, what is the side length of the largest square that he can cut from it? 76 cm

16. Find the coordinates of point M. $\left(-\frac{1}{\sqrt{2}}, \frac{1}{\sqrt{2}}\right)$

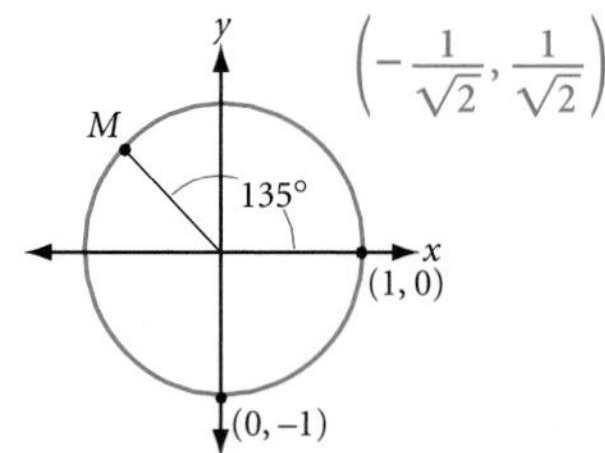

17. Find the coordinates of point K. $\left(-\frac{\sqrt{3}}{2}, -\frac{1}{2}\right)$

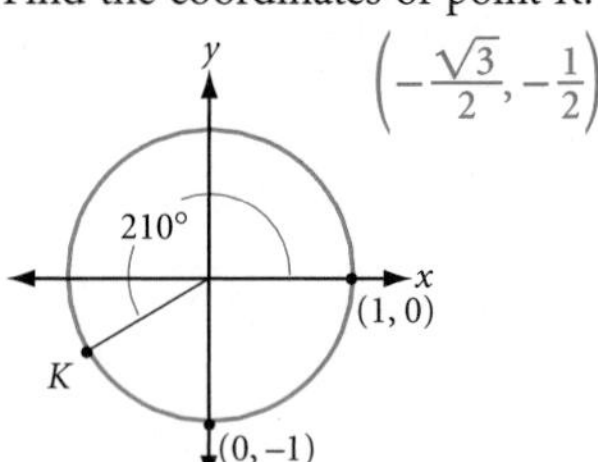

Review

9.5 **18.** Find the equation of a circle with center (3, 3) and radius 6. $(x-3)^2+(y-3)^2=36$

9.5 **19.** Find the radius and center of a circle with the equation $x^2+y^2-2x+1=100$. ⓗ center = (1, 0), $r = 10$

6.3 **20.** *Construction* Construct a circle and a chord in a circle. With compass and straightedge, construct a second chord parallel and congruent to the first chord. Explain your method.

2.6 **21.** Explain why the opposite sides of a regular hexagon are parallel.

2.3 **22.** Find the rule for this number pattern:

$$1\cdot3-3=4\cdot0$$
$$2\cdot4-3=5\cdot1$$
$$3\cdot5-3=6\cdot2$$
$$4\cdot6-3=7\cdot3$$
$$5\cdot7-3=8\cdot4$$
$$\vdots$$
$$n\cdot(\underline{?})-(\underline{?})=(\underline{?})\cdot(\underline{?})$$

$n\cdot(n+2)-3=(n+3)\cdot(n-1)$

6.2 **23.** **APPLICATION** Felice wants to determine the diameter of a large heating duct. She places a carpenter's square up to the surface of the cylinder, and the length of each tangent segment is 10 inches.

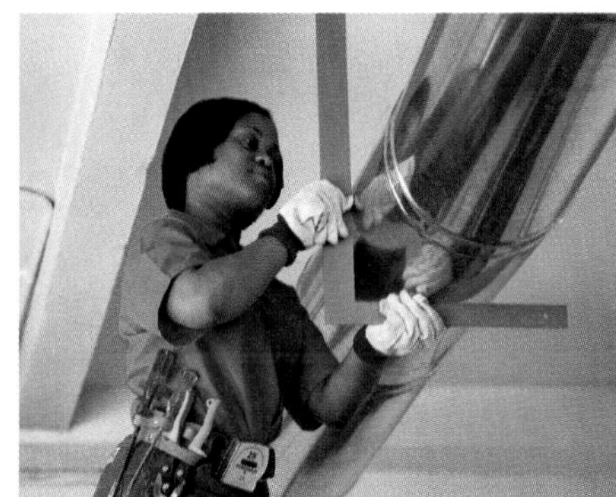

a. What is the diameter? Explain your reasoning.

b. Describe another way she can find the diameter of the duct.
Possible answer: Measure the circumference with string and divide by π.

IMPROVING YOUR REASONING SKILLS

PUZZLE

Reasonable 'rithmetic I

Each letter in these problems represents a different digit.

1. What is the value of B?

```
    3 7 2
    3 8 4
+   9 B 4
---------
  C 7 C A
```

2. What is the value of J?

```
    E F 6
  × D 7
---------
  D D F D
J E D
---------
H G E D
```

IMPROVING REASONING SKILLS

If students are having difficulty, suggest that they make a table of the letters, listing what they can say about each letter.

1. $A = 0$ and $C = 1$, so $B = 5$.

2. $D = 2$; $7F + 4$ ends in F, so F is 1 or 6. Trying each possibility leads to $J = 6$.

EXTENSION

Ask students to show that the shaded area in this figure is equal to the area of the triangle. See *Leonardo's Dessert—No Pi* by Herbert Wills for further study of problems like this.

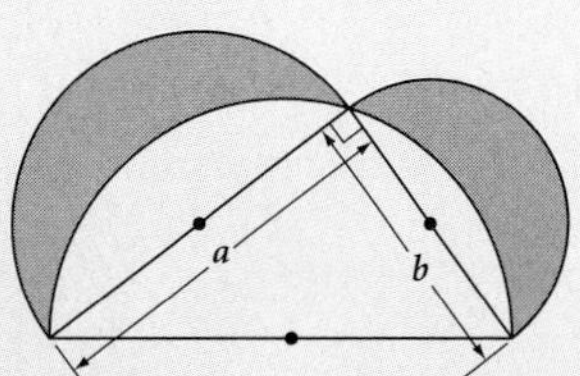

Exercise 19 This exercise requires that students be able to recognize the square of the binomial $(x-1)^2$.

20. The diameter is the transversal, and the chords are parallel by the Converse of the Parallel Lines Conjecture. The chords are congruent because they are the same distance from the center. Sample construction:

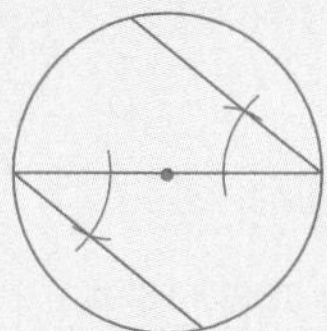

21. Any long diagonal of a regular hexagon divides it into two congruent quadrilaterals. Each angle of a regular hexagon is $\frac{(6-2)\cdot180°}{6}=120°$, and the diagonal divides two of the 120° angles into 60° angles. Look at the diagonal as a transversal.

The alternate interior angles are congruent, thus the opposite sides of a regular hexagon are parallel.

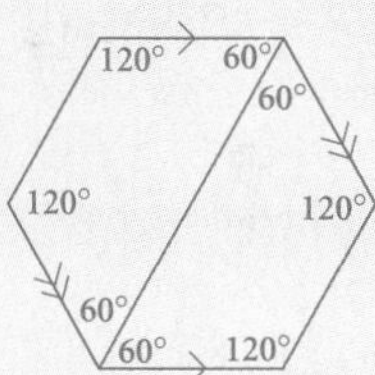

23a. Because a carpenter's square has a right angle and both radii are perpendicular to the tangents, a square is formed. The radius is 10 in., therefore the diameter is 20 in.

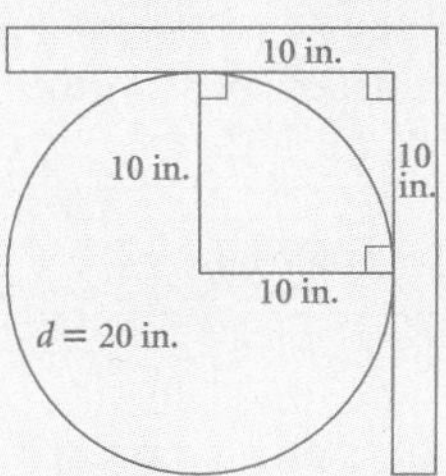

PLANNING

LESSON OUTLINE

First day:
10 min Reviewing
35 min Exercises

Second day:
30 min Exercises
15 min Student self-assessment

REVIEWING

Remind students of the equation of a circle, $(x - h)^2 + (y - k)^2 = r^2$, and ask what that means. Try to elicit the idea that it's the set of all points (x, y) whose coordinates satisfy the equation. Ask why those points form a circle. Bring out the idea of the distance formula. Finally, ask where the distance formula comes from. See that students understand it comes from the Pythagorean Theorem. Wonder aloud how the distance formula can be derived from the Pythagorean Theorem given that there are no *a*'s, *b*'s, or *c*'s in the distance formula but the Pythagorean Theorem is $a^2 + b^2 = c^2$. Elicit the idea that the Pythagorean Theorem includes a condition: $a^2 + b^2 = c^2$ if *a* and *b* are the lengths of the legs of a right triangle and *c* is the length of its hypotenuse. The letters *a*, *b*, and *c* are variables and can be replaced by any other representations of those lengths.

ASSIGNING HOMEWORK

It's probably best to assign every student to work on every problem from Exercises 1–29. The odds 15–29 could be done in groups. Use the mixed review to prepare for a unit exam.

CHAPTER 9 REVIEW

If 50 years from now you've forgotten everything else you learned in geometry, you'll probably still remember the Pythagorean Theorem. (Though let's hope you don't really forget everything else!) That's because it has practical applications in the mathematics and science that you encounter throughout your education.

It's one thing to remember the equation $a^2 + b^2 = c^2$. It's another to know what it means and to be able to apply it. Review your work from this chapter to be sure you understand how to use special triangle shortcuts and how to find the distance between two points in a coordinate plane.

EXERCISES

You will need

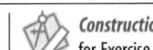

Construction tools for Exercise **30**

For Exercises 1–4, measurements are given in centimeters.

1. $x = \underline{?}$ 20 cm

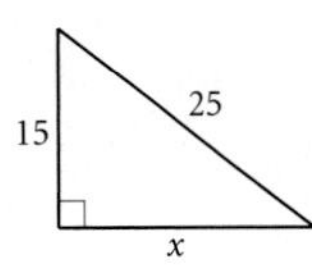

2. $AB = \underline{?}$ 10 cm

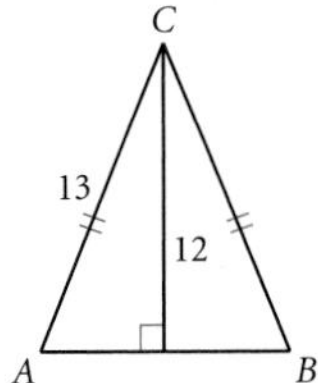

3. Is $\triangle ABC$ an acute, obtuse, or right triangle? obtuse

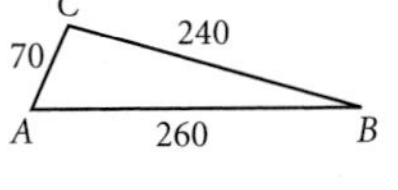

4. The solid is a rectangular prism. $AB = \underline{?}$ 26 cm

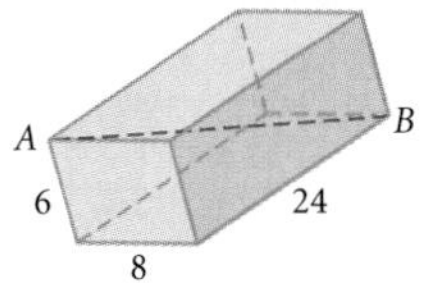

5. Find the coordinates of point *U*. $\left(\frac{\sqrt{3}}{2}, \frac{1}{2}\right)$

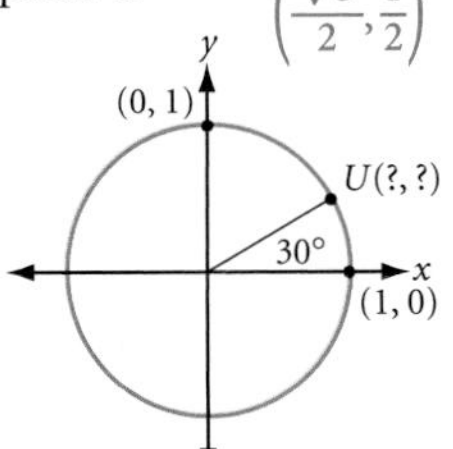

6. Find the coordinates of point *V*. $\left(-\frac{1}{\sqrt{2}}, -\frac{1}{\sqrt{2}}\right)$

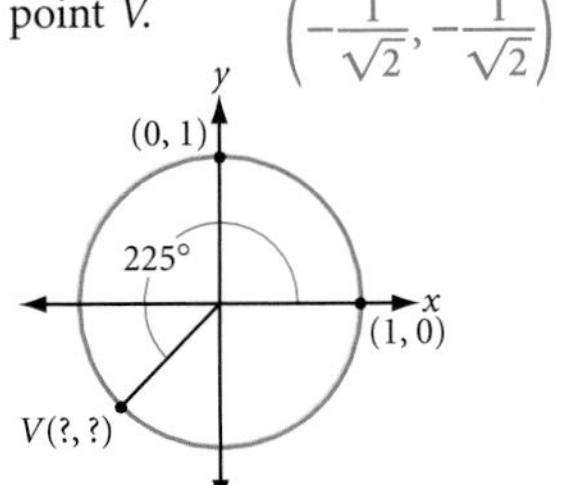

7. What is the area of the triangle? $200\sqrt{3}$ cm²

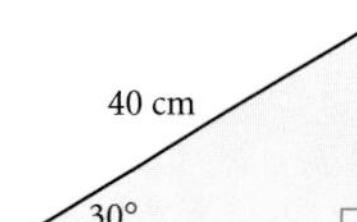

8. The area of this square is 144 cm². Find *d*. $d = 12\sqrt{2}$ cm

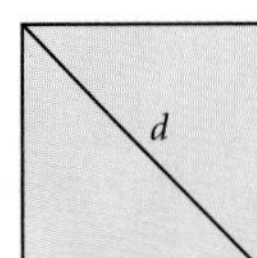

9. What is the area of trapezoid *ABCD*? 246 cm²

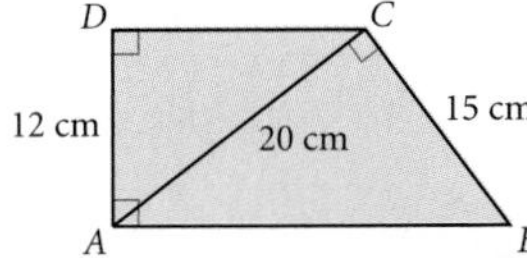

10. The arc is a semicircle. What is the area of the shaded region? ⓗ 72π in.^{2}

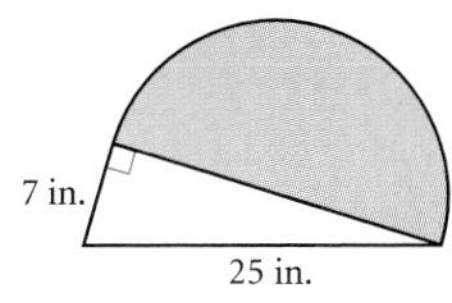

11. Rays TA and TB are tangent to circle O at A and B respectively, and $BT = 6\sqrt{3}$ cm. What is the area of the shaded region? 24π cm^2

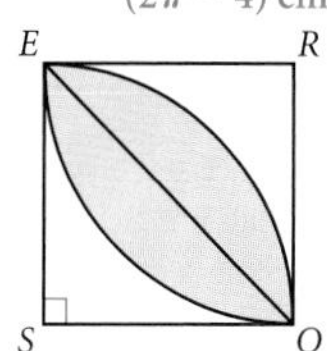

12. The quadrilateral is a square, and $QE = 2\sqrt{2}$ cm. What is the area of the shaded region? ⓗ $(2\pi - 4)$ cm^2

13. The area of circle Q is 350 cm^2. Find the area of square $ABCD$ to the nearest 0.1 cm^2. 222.8 cm^2

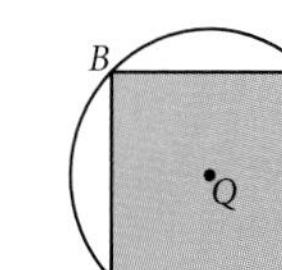

14. Determine whether $\triangle ABC$ with vertices $A(3, 5)$, $B(11, 3)$, and $C(8, 8)$ is an equilateral, isosceles, or isosceles right triangle. isosceles right

15. Sagebrush Sally leaves camp on her dirt bike traveling east at 60 km/hr with a full tank of gas. After 2 hours, she stops and does a little prospecting—with no luck. So she heads north for 2 hours at 45 km/hr. She stops again, and this time hits pay dirt. Sally knows that she can travel at most 350 km on one tank of gas. Does she have enough fuel to get back to camp? If not, how close can she get? ⓗ

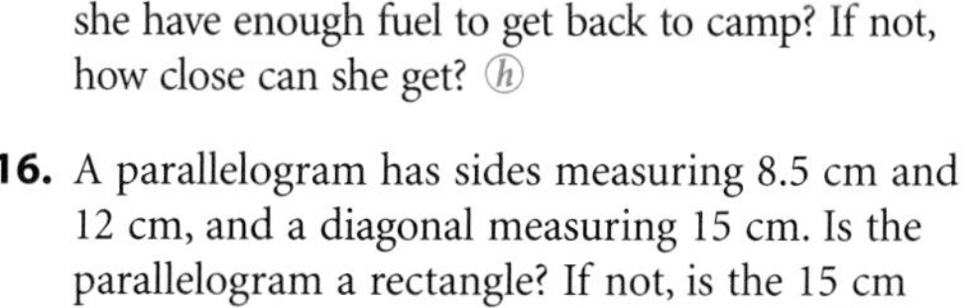

16. A parallelogram has sides measuring 8.5 cm and 12 cm, and a diagonal measuring 15 cm. Is the parallelogram a rectangle? If not, is the 15 cm diagonal the longer or shorter diagonal? ⓗ No. 15 cm is the longer diagonal.

17. After an argument, Peter and Paul walk away from each other on separate paths at a right angle to each other. Peter is walking 2 km/hr, and Paul is walking 3 km/hr. After 20 min, Paul sits down to think. After 30 min, Peter stops. Both decide to apologize. How far apart are they? How long will it take them to reach each other if they both start running straight toward each other at 5 km/hr? 1.4 km; $8\frac{1}{2}$ min

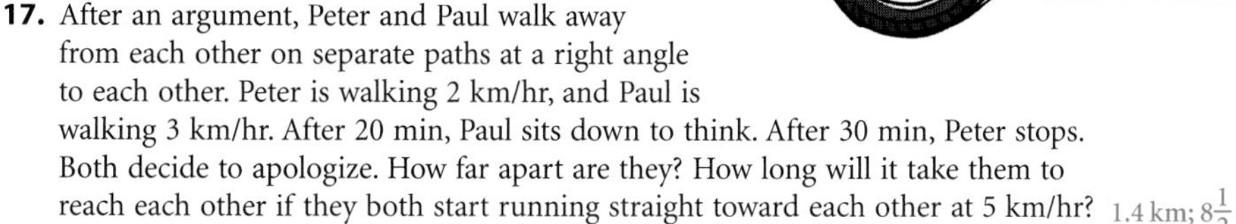

18. Flora is away at camp and wants to mail her flute back home. The flute is 24 inches long. Will it fit diagonally within a box whose inside dimensions are 12 by 16 by 14 inches? yes

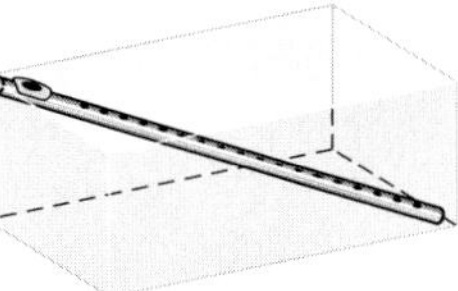

19. To the nearest foot, find the original height of a fallen flagpole that cracked and fell as if hinged, forming an angle of 45 degrees with the ground. The tip of the pole hit the ground 12 feet from its base. 29 ft

▶ Helping with the Exercises

Exercise 11 If students are having difficulty, suggest that they create a right triangle and look for special triangles.

Exercise 14 From the way the problem is stated, students need to do only two calculations to find sides of two different lengths; then they can conclude that the triangle is an isosceles right triangle because it's not equilateral. Encourage them, though, to verify the congruence and perpendicularity of two sides. Slope can help with the latter.

15. No. The closest she can come to camp is 10 km.

Exercise 17 After finding the distance apart to be $\sqrt{2}$ km, students might realize that the second question can be answered easily by using closing speed: Paul and Peter's distance apart is closing at a rate of 10 miles per hour.

Exercise 18 Students have worked enough with space diagonals that they may be ready to generalize and find that the space diagonal of this box has length $\sqrt{12^2 + 16^2 + 14^2}$.

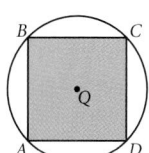

20. You are standing 12 feet from a cylindrical corn-syrup storage tank. The distance from you to a point of tangency on the tank is 35 feet. What is the radius of the tank? ≈ 45 ft

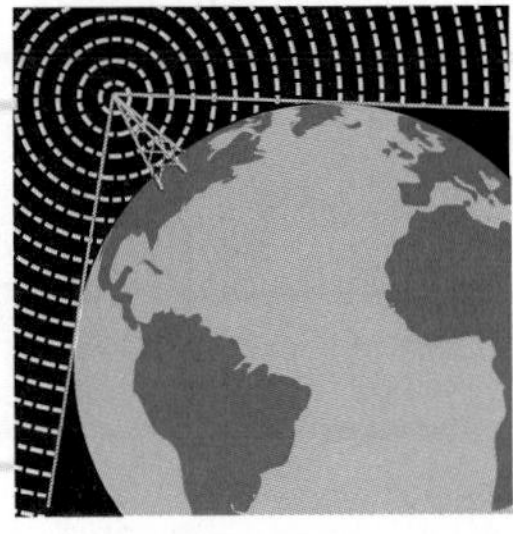

Technology CONNECTION

Radio and TV stations broadcast from high towers. Their signals are picked up by radios and TVs in homes within a certain radius. Because Earth is spherical, these signals don't get picked up beyond the point of tangency.

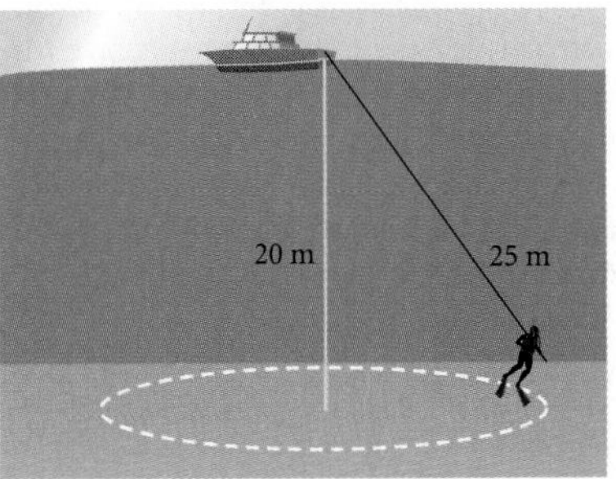

21. **APPLICATION** Read the Technology Connection above. What is the maximum broadcasting radius from a radio tower 1800 feet tall (approximately 0.34 mile)? The radius of Earth is approximately 3960 miles, and you can assume the ground around the tower is nearly flat. Round your answer to the nearest 10 miles. 50 mi

22. A diver hooked to a 25-meter line is searching for the remains of a Spanish galleon in the Caribbean Sea. The sea is 20 meters deep and the bottom is flat. What is the area of circular region that the diver can explore? 707 m^2

23. What are the lengths of the two legs of a 30°-60°-90° triangle if the length of the hypotenuse is $12\sqrt{3}$? $6\sqrt{3}$ and 18

24. Find the side length of an equilateral triangle with an area of $36\sqrt{3}$ m^2. 12 m

25. Find the perimeter of an equilateral triangle with a height of $7\sqrt{3}$. 42

26. Al baked brownies for himself and his two sisters. He divided the square pan of brownies into three parts. He measured three 30° angles at one of the corners so that two pieces formed right triangles and the middle piece formed a kite. Did he divide the pan of brownies equally? Draw a sketch and explain your reasoning.

27. A circle has a central angle AOB that measures 80°. If point C is selected randomly on the circle, what is the probability that $\triangle ABC$ is obtuse? $\frac{7}{9}$

26. No. If you reflect one of the right triangles into the center piece, you'll see that the area of the kite is almost half again as large as the area of each of the other triangles.

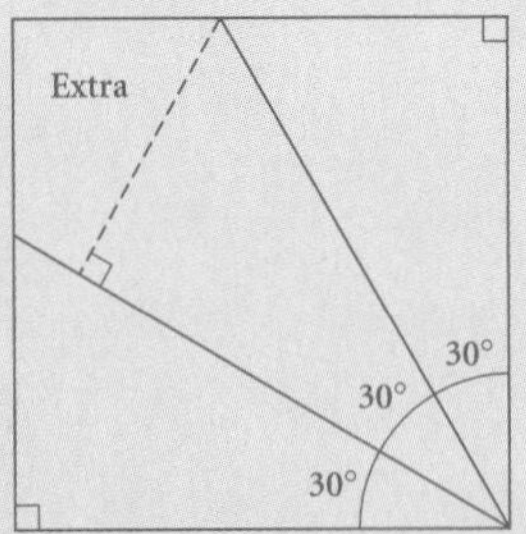

Or students might compare areas by assuming the short leg of the 30°-60°-90° triangle is 1. The area of each triangle is then $\frac{\sqrt{3}}{2}$ and the area of the kite is $3 - \sqrt{3}$.

28. One of the sketches below shows the greatest area that you can enclose in a right-angled corner with a rope of length s. Which one? Explain your reasoning.

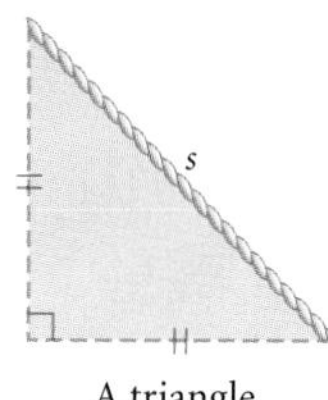

A triangle

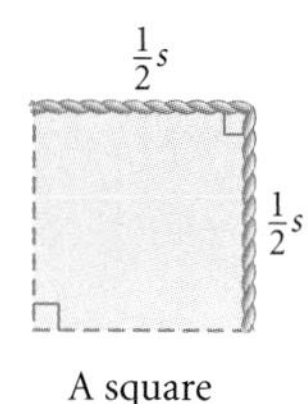

A square

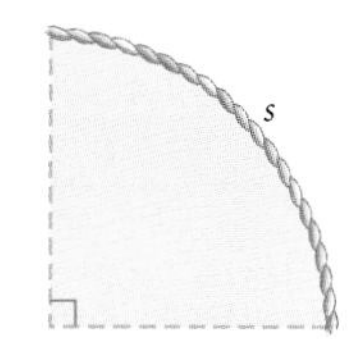

A quarter-circle

29. A wire is attached to a block of wood at point A. The wire is pulled over a pulley as shown. How far will the block move if the wire is pulled 1.4 meters in the direction of the arrow? 1.6 m

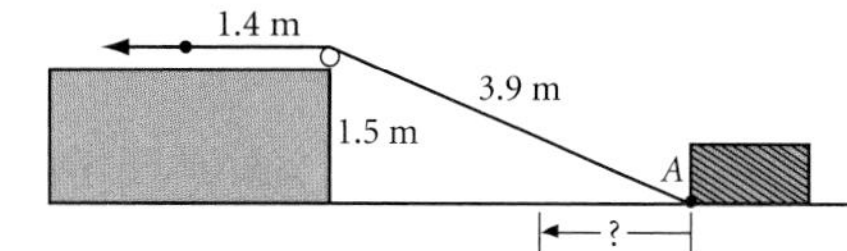

MIXED REVIEW

3.1 **30.** ***Construction*** Construct an isosceles triangle that has a base length equal to half the length of one leg.

2.3 **31.** In a regular octagon inscribed in a circle, how many diagonals pass through the center of the circle? In a regular nonagon? a regular 20-gon? What is the general rule?

6.7 **32.** A bug clings to a point two inches from the center of a spinning fan blade. The blade spins around once per second. How fast does the bug travel in inches per second? 4π, or approximately 12.6 in./sec

In Exercises 33–40, identify the statement as true or false. For each false statement, explain why it is false or sketch a counterexample.

8.1 **33.** The area of a rectangle and the area of a parallelogram are both given by the formula $A = bh$, where A is the area, b is the length of the base, and h is the height. true

7.1 **34.** When a figure is reflected over a line, the line of reflection is perpendicular to every segment joining a point on the original figure with its image. true

9.3 **35.** In an isosceles right triangle, if the legs have length x, then the hypotenuse has length $x\sqrt{3}$. False. The hypotenuse is of length $x\sqrt{2}$.

8.2 **36.** The area of a kite or a rhombus can be found by using the formula $A = (0.5)d_1d_2$, where A is the area and d_1 and d_2 are the lengths of the diagonals. true

9.5 **37.** If the coordinates of points A and B are (x_1, y_1) and (x_2, y_2), respectively, then $AB = \sqrt{(x_1 - y_1)^2 + (x_2 - y_2)^2}$. false; $AB = \sqrt{(x_2 - x_1)^2 + (y_2 - y_1)^2}$

7.3 **38.** A glide reflection is a combination of a translation and a rotation. False. A glide reflection is a combination of a translation and a reflection.

28. The quarter-circle gives the maximum area.

Triangle:

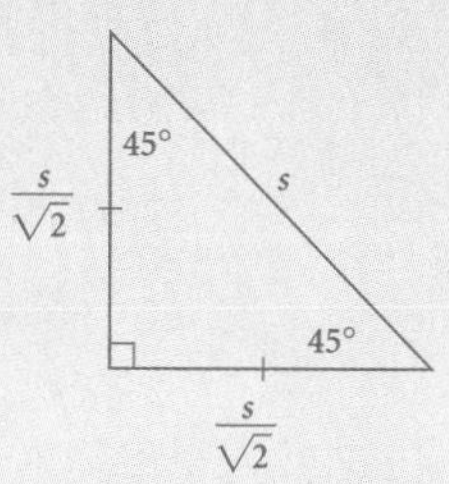

$$A = \frac{1}{2} \cdot \frac{s}{\sqrt{2}} \cdot \frac{s}{\sqrt{2}} = \frac{s^2}{4}$$

Square:

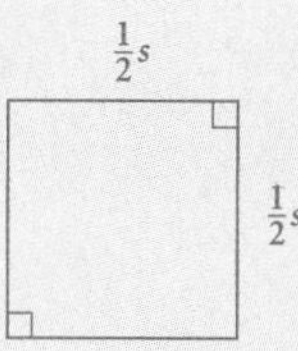

$$A = \frac{1}{2}s \cdot \frac{1}{2}s = \frac{s^2}{4}$$

Quarter-circle:

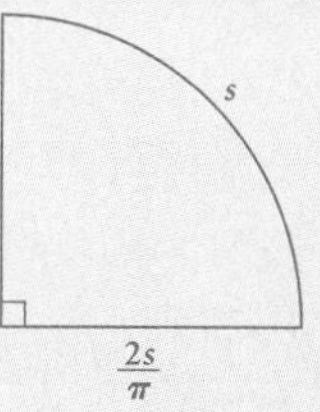

$$s = \frac{1}{4} \cdot 2\pi r$$

$$r = \frac{2s}{\pi}$$

$$A = \frac{1}{4}\pi\left(\frac{2s}{\pi}\right)^2 = \frac{s^2}{\pi}$$

$$\frac{s^2}{\pi} > \frac{s^2}{4}$$

30.

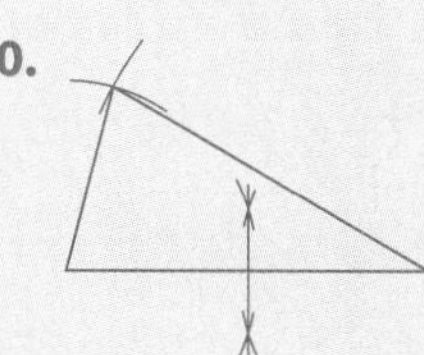

Exercise 31 Encourage students to make a table and look for a pattern.

31. 4; 0; 10. The rule is $\frac{n}{2}$ if n is even, but 0 if n is odd.

7.4 **39.** Equilateral triangles, squares, and regular octagons can be used to create monohedral tessellations. False. Equilateral triangles, squares, and regular *hexagons* can be used to create monohedral tessellations.

9.3 **40.** In a 30°-60°-90° triangle, if the shorter leg has length x, then the longer leg has length $x\sqrt{3}$ and the hypotenuse has length $2x$. true

In Exercises 41–46, select the correct answer.

9.1 **41.** The hypotenuse of a right triangle is always _?_. D

A. opposite the smallest angle and is the shortest side.
B. opposite the largest angle and is the shortest side.
C. opposite the smallest angle and is the longest side.
D. opposite the largest angle and is the longest side.

8.2 **42.** The area of a triangle is given by the formula _?_, where A is the area, b is the length of the base, and h is the height. B

A. $A = bh$ **B.** $A = \frac{1}{2}bh$
C. $A = 2bh$ **D.** $A = b^2h$

9.2 **43.** If the lengths of the three sides of a triangle satisfy the Pythagorean equation, then the triangle must be a(n) _?_ triangle. A

A. right **B.** acute
C. obtuse **D.** scalene

7.2 **44.** The ordered pair rule $(x, y) \rightarrow (y, x)$ is a _?_. C

A. reflection over the x-axis **B.** reflection over the y-axis
C. reflection over the line $y = x$ **D.** rotation 90° about the origin

7.3 **45.** The composition of two reflections over two intersecting lines is equivalent to _?_. C

A. a single reflection **B.** a translation
C. a rotation **D.** no transformation

8.7 **46.** The total surface area of a cone is equal to _?_, where r is the radius of the circular base and l is the slant height. D

A. $\pi r^2 + 2\pi r$ **B.** πrl
C. $\pi rl + 2\pi r$ **D.** $\pi rl + \pi r^2$

5.7 **47.** Create a flowchart proof to show that the diagonal of a rectangle divides the rectangle into two congruent triangles.

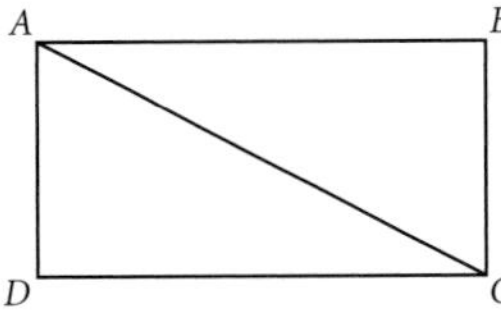

47.

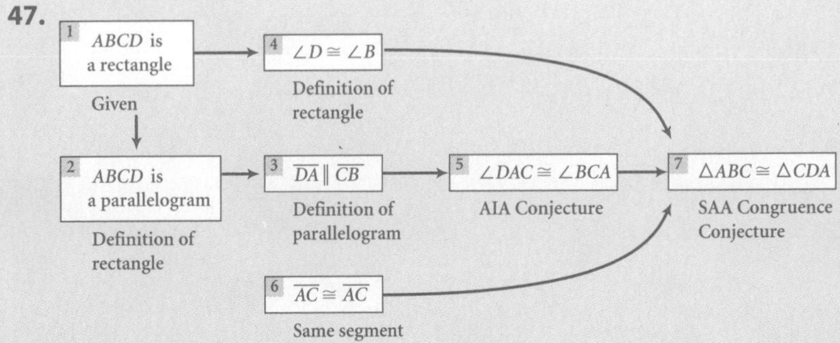

1.2 **48.** Copy the ball positions onto patty paper.

a. At what point on the S cushion should a player aim so that the cue ball bounces off and strikes the 8-ball? Mark the point with the letter *A*.

b. At what point on the W cushion should a player aim so that the cue ball bounces off and strikes the 8-ball? Mark the point with the letter *B*.

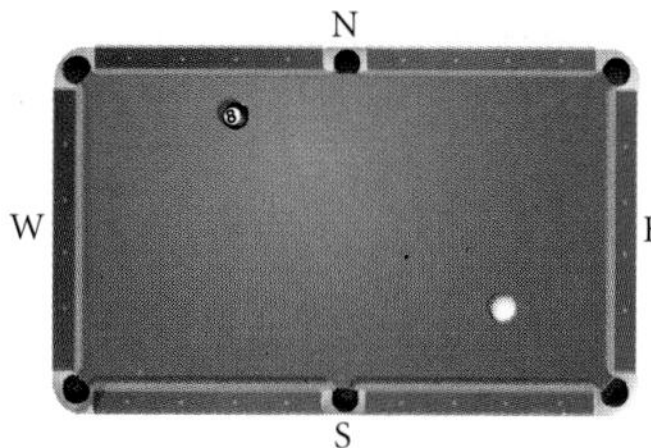

8.2 **49.** Find the area and the perimeter of the trapezoid. 34 cm^2; $22 + 4\sqrt{2} \approx 27.7$ cm

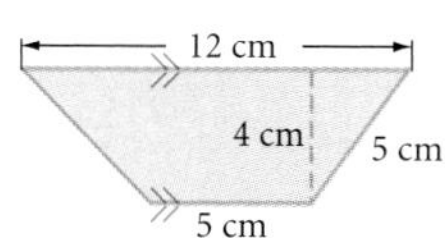

8.6 **50.** Find the area of the shaded region. $\frac{40\pi}{3}\text{ cm}^2$

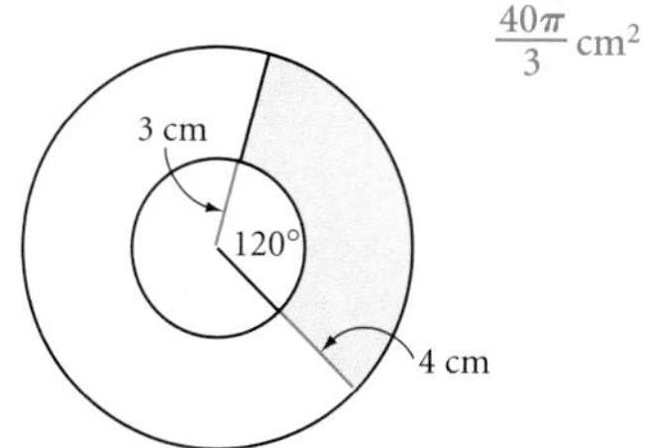

9.1 **51.** An Olympic swimming pool has length 50 meters and width 25 meters. What is the diagonal distance across the pool?

8.4 **52.** The side length of a regular pentagon is 6 cm, and the apothem measures about 4.1 cm. What is the area of the pentagon?

9.1 **53.** The box below has dimensions 25 cm, 36 cm, and *x* cm. The diagonal shown has length 65 cm. Find the value of *x*. 48 cm

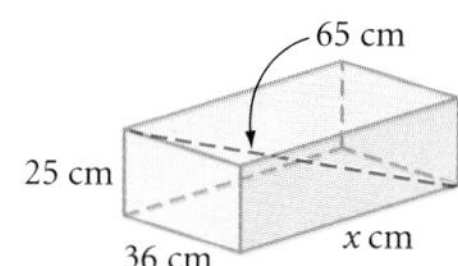

8.7 **54.** The cylindrical container below has an open top. Find the surface area of the container (inside and out) to the nearest square foot. 322 ft^2

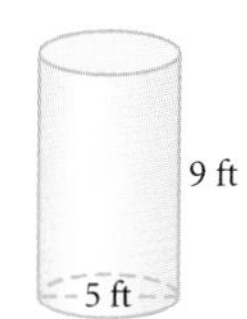

51. about 55.9 m

52. about 61.5 cm^2

TAKE ANOTHER LOOK

1. Use geometry software to demonstrate the Pythagorean Theorem. Does your demonstration still work if you use a shape other than a square—for example, an equilateral triangle or a semicircle?

2. Find Elisha Scott Loomis's *Pythagorean Proposition* and demonstrate one of the proofs of the Pythagorean Theorem from the book.

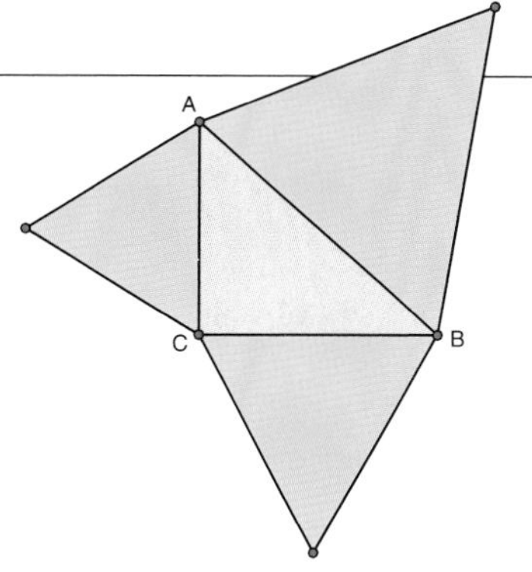

Take Another Look

1. Demonstrations should include shapes other than a square. (Any regular polygon can be used. In fact, any three similar figures will work. Students will study similar figures in Chapter 11.)

2. Demonstrations will vary.

48.

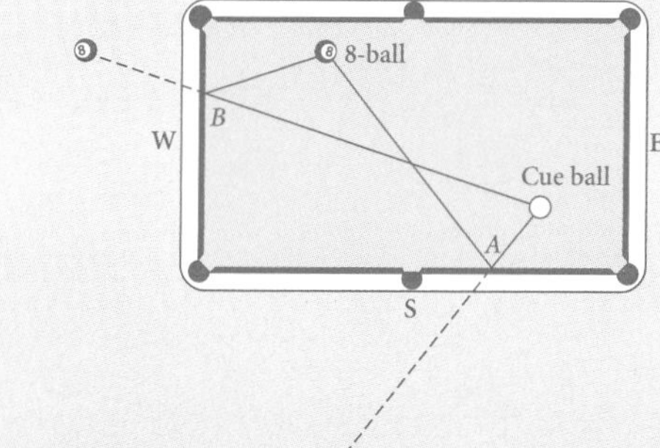

3. The small square in the center has sides of length $b - a$, the slanted square has area c^2, and the triangles each have area $\frac{ab}{2}$. The equation $c^2 = (b - a)^2 + 4\left(\frac{ab}{2}\right)$ simplifies to $c^2 = a^2 + b^2$.

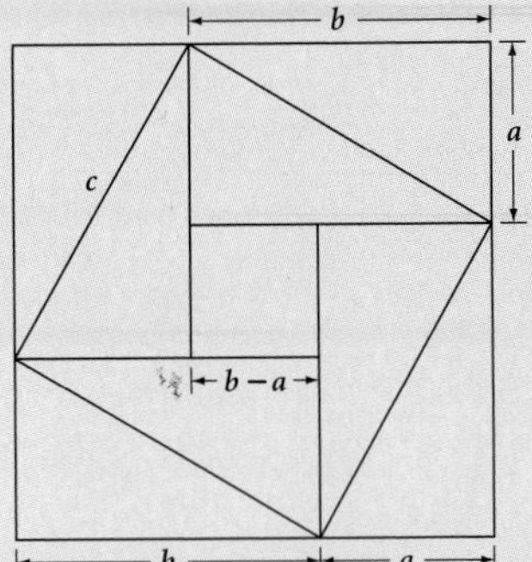

4. One possible proof: Given $\triangle ABC$ with $BC = x$, $AC = x\sqrt{3}$, and $AB = 2x$, construct 30°-60°-90° right triangle DEF with right angle F, 30° angle D, and $EF = x$. $DF = x\sqrt{3}$ and $DE = 2x$, by the 30°-60°-90° Triangle Conjecture. $\triangle ABC \cong \triangle DEF$ by SSS. $\angle C \cong \angle F$ and is a right angle, $\angle A \cong \angle D$ and is a 30° angle, and $\angle B \cong \angle E$ and is a 60° angle.

5.

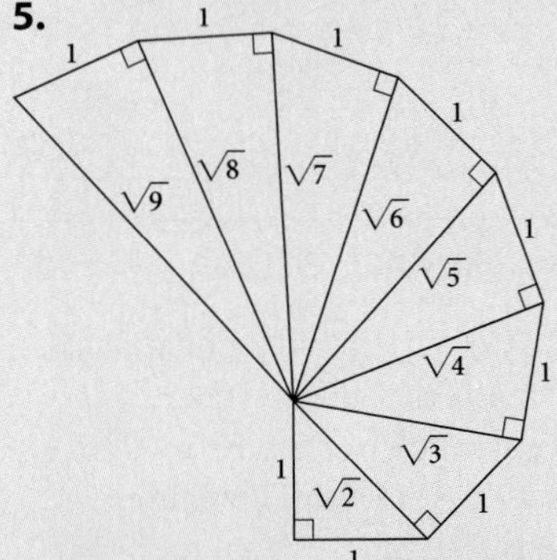

ASSESSING

As part of a final grade, you might ask students to present visual demonstrations or animations of various proofs of the Pythagorean Theorem. (See Take Another Look activities 1–3.) If this presentation replaces the chapter test, you can give a unit exam after working through the mixed review.

3. The *Zhoubi Suanjing,* one of the oldest sources of Chinese mathematics and astronomy, contains the diagram at right demonstrating the Pythagorean Theorem (called *gou gu* in China). Find out how the Chinese used and proved the *gou gu,* and present your findings.

4. Use the SSS Congruence Conjecture to verify the converse of the 30°-60°-90° Triangle Conjecture. That is, show that if a triangle has sides with lengths x, $x\sqrt{3}$, and $2x$, then it is a 30°-60°-90° triangle.

5. Starting with an isosceles right triangle, use geometry software or a compass and straightedge to start a right triangle like the one shown. Continue constructing right triangles on the hypotenuse of the previous triangle at least five more times. Calculate the length of each hypotenuse and leave them in radical form.

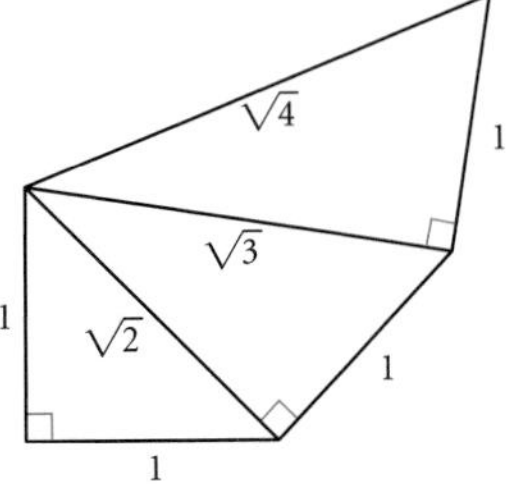

Assessing What You've Learned

UPDATE YOUR PORTFOLIO Choose a challenging project, Take Another Look activity, or exercise you did in this chapter and add it to your portfolio. Explain the strategies you used.

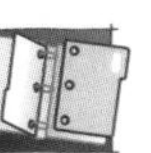

ORGANIZE YOUR NOTEBOOK Review your notebook and your conjecture list to be sure they are complete. Write a one-page chapter summary.

WRITE IN YOUR JOURNAL Why do you think the Pythagorean Theorem is considered one of the most important theorems in mathematics?

WRITE TEST ITEMS Work with group members to write test items for this chapter. Try to demonstrate more than one way to solve each problem.

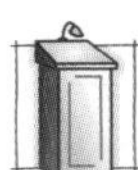

GIVE A PRESENTATION Create a visual aid and give a presentation about the Pythagorean Theorem.

FACILITATING SELF-ASSESSMENT

To help students complete the portfolio described in Assessing What You've Learned, suggest that they consider for evaluation their work on Lesson 9.1, Exercises 17, 18; Lesson 9.2, Exercise 16; Lesson 9.3, Exercise 17; Lesson 9.4, Exercise 9; and Lesson 9.5, Exercise 6.

CHAPTER

10

Volume

Overview

In this chapter, students discover the formulas for finding the volumes of solids, extend their understanding of surface area, and apply what they know to solving problems. In **Lesson 10.1,** students extend their vocabulary of space geometry. The **exploration** on Euler's Formula for Polyhedrons gives students a chance to see relationships among parts of a polyhedron. In **Lesson 10.2,** they investigate formulas for the volumes of prisms and cylinders. In **Lesson 10.3,** students use models to discover the one-third relationship between prisms and pyramids and between cylinders and cones. The activity in the next **exploration** concerns the Platonic solids. **Lesson 10.4** allows students to combine what they have learned about volume with their understanding of area and the Pythagorean Theorem to solve problems. Students are shown how to calculate the volume and density of irregularly shaped solids through displacement in **Lesson 10.5.** Students practice drawing solids in the **exploration** on orthographic drawing. In **Lesson 10.6,** students again use models to discover a volume relationship, this time between a sphere and a cylinder. In **Lesson 10.7,** students use the volume formulas for a sphere and a pyramid to derive the surface area formula for a sphere. A final **exploration** builds students' knowledge of valid forms of reasoning; it is the first of three Explorations that develop basic concepts of symbolic logic.

The Mathematics

A returning college student once said to her math teacher, "As a nurse, I'm always working with cubic centimeters. But the syringes they're in are round; there aren't any cubes in there. What's going on?" This question indicates a safe classroom atmosphere for critical thinking; it also shows a deficiency of understanding of volume shared by many students.

One difficulty your students may have in understanding volume stems from weakness in conditional (if-then) reasoning. The phrase "a cylinder has a volume of 30π cubic centimeters" means "*If* centimeter cubes were broken into small enough pieces and rearranged, *then* it would take 30π of the cubes to fill the cylinder" or "*If* the cylinder were filled with water and the water were poured into a box, filling it exactly, *then* that box would hold 30π centimeter cubes." Another difficulty for some students is that they're not really convinced of the conservation of volume: Do those reassembled centimeter fragments (or that poured water) *really* occupy the same amount of space?

For a deeper understanding, teach volume not only through the formulas. Stretching students' conceptual understanding by repeatedly asking questions about meaning is challenging but worth the effort. Students will retain a deep understanding of volume long after they have forgotten the formulas.

Lesson 10.1 organizes solids into those with flat faces (polyhedrons) and those with "curved faces" (spheres, cylinders, and cones). Another scheme might organize solids into those with two bases (prisms and cylinders), one base (pyramids and cones), and no base (including spheres). In fact, the student book uses this latter organization to explore volume formulas in later lessons: Prisms and cylinders are considered in Lesson 10.2, cones and pyramids in Lesson 10.3, and spheres in Lesson 10.6.

How can you find the volume of solids for which no formula is available? One way, considered in Lesson 10.5, is to submerge them in water. The volume of the object is the same as the volume of water it displaces. Students can find the volume of the displaced water using a standard volume formula based on the shape of the container. Dividing the mass of an object by its volume, however determined, gives its density, by which its composition might be ascertained.

To ensure that you use the language of solids carefully, you should be aware of some subtleties that might affect your students' understanding. Polygons are collections of line segments. When we refer to the area of a polygon, we mean the area of the interior region bounded by the polygon. Similarly, a solid does not contain its interior, though its volume is a measure of the interior. Prisms, pyramids, cylinders, cones, and spheres are the boundaries of three-dimensional regions rather than those regions themselves. Moreover, although we say that a face of a polyhedron is a polygon, the face is actually the polygon and its interior.

These subtleties of language lead to questions about dimensions. A polygon, consisting only of line segments, is a one-dimensional figure, though it exists in a two-dimensional plane. The polygon's interior is two-dimensional. Although a solid exists in three-dimensional space, it is a two-dimensional surface. Its interior is three-dimensional. Its faces, if any, include the interiors of polygons, so they are two-dimensional. A solid's edges, if any, are one-dimensional. Any vertices, being points, are zero-dimensional.

Using This Chapter

Some of these lessons take a fair amount of preparation. You will need to obtain sets of hollow solids, sand (or something else to pour), and large boxes for Lessons 10.3 and 10.6. If you don't already have the plastic models and your budget can afford it, purchase at least one set. Or use the worksheets, copied onto card stock, to make models ahead of time.

Before embarking on Lesson 10.5, you might borrow from the science department a balance, a graduated cylinder, and a variety of metals whose volume and density your class can calculate.

Resources

Discovering Geometry Resources

Teaching and Worksheet Masters
- Lessons 10.1–10.3
- Exploration: The Five Platonic Solids
- Exploration: Orthographic Drawing

Assessment Resources A and B
- Quiz 1 (Lessons 10.1–10.3)
- Quiz 2 (Lessons 10.4 and 10.5)
- Quiz 3 (Lessons 10.6 and 10.7)
- Chapter 10 Test
- Chapter 10 Constructive Assessment Options

Practice Your Skills for Chapter 10

Condensed Lessons for Chapter 10

Other Resources

The Platonic Solids video from Key Curriculum Press.

Zome Geometry by George Hart and Henri Picciotto.

For complete references on these and other sources and for information on plastic models, see www.keypress.com/DG.

Materials

- construction tools
- toothpicks and modeling clay or a building set such as Zome System
- a ream of paper or a stack of cards
- a stack of disks such as coins or chemistry filters
- hollow pairs of prisms and pyramids, and pairs of cylinders and cones
- hollow pairs of hemispheres and cones or cylinders
- sand, rice, or birdseed
- cardboard or file folders
- scissors and glue
- colored pens or pencils
- isometric dot paper
- graph paper
- cubes, 12 per group
- calculators

Pacing Guide

	day 1	day 2	day 3	day 4	day 5	day 6	day 7	day 8	day 9	day 10
standard	10.1	Exploration	10.2	10.3	quiz, Exploration	10.4	10.5	quiz, Exploration	10.6	10.7
enriched	10.1	Exploration	10.2, project	10.3, project	quiz, Exploration	10.4	10.5, project	quiz, Exploration	10.6	10.7
block	10.1, Exploration	10.2, 10.3	quiz, Exploration	10.4, 10.5	quiz, Exploration	10.6, 10.7	quiz, Exploration	review, TAL	assessment	

	day 11	day 12	day 13	day 14	day 15	day 16	day 17	day 18	day 19	day 20
standard	quiz, Exploration	review	review	assessment						
enriched	quiz, Exploration	review	review	assessment						

CHAPTER

10 Volume

Perhaps all I pursue is astonishment and so I try to awaken only astonishment in my viewers. Sometimes "beauty" is a nasty business.

M. C. ESCHER

Verblifa tin, M. C. Escher, 1963

OBJECTIVES

In this chapter you will

- explore and define many three-dimensional solids
- discover formulas for finding the volumes of prisms, pyramids, cylinders, cones, and spheres
- learn how density is related to volume
- derive a formula for the surface area of a sphere

CHAPTER 10 OBJECTIVES

- Learn the vocabulary of solids: polyhedrons (including prisms and pyramids), cylinders, cones, and spheres
- Discover formulas for the volumes of solids and use them to solve applied problems
- Derive the formula for the surface area of a sphere and use it to solve applied problems
- Find volumes of irregularly shaped solids through displacement or density
- Practice three-dimensional visual thinking skills
- Develop reading comprehension, problem-solving skills, and cooperative behavior

This chapter is about the amount of space contained within objects, particularly polyhedrons. The *Verblifa tin* is a regular polyhedron. **[Ask]** "Why did Escher use starfish? [Five edges come together at each vertex.] "Why are there three shells on each face?" [to preserve the rotational symmetry of the triangular faces] "How many faces does the solid have?" [20, an icosahedron] "What kind of symmetry do you see on a face of the solid?" [3-fold rotational] "What other symmetry do you see?" [The solid has 6 axes of 5-fold rotational symmetry about lines through opposite vertices, 15 axes of 2-fold rotational symmetry about lines through midpoints of opposite edges, and 10 axes of 3-fold rotational symmetry about the centers of opposite faces. If the pattern on the faces is not considered, the solid has 15 planes of reflectional symmetry over opposite edges.] "How could you find its surface area?" [20 times the area of one triangle] "Volume?" Don't expect an answer, but come back to the question at the end of the chapter. [20 times the volume of one triangular pyramid with its vertex at the center; or measure the water it displaces.]

LESSON

10.1

PLANNING

LESSON OUTLINE

One day:

15 min Definitions

5 min Sharing

5 min Closing

20 min Exercises

MATERIALS

- Solids (W) for One step

TEACHING

This lesson focuses on the vocabulary of common solids enclosed by polygonal or curved surfaces.

One step Hand out the Solids worksheet and ask students to find as many similarities and differences between pairs of figures as they can. (Each group might consider five or six different pairs.) As you circulate, focus students' attention on symmetry, parallelism, and perpendicularity. During Sharing, lead students to the ideas of flat surfaces and polyhedrons; parallel congruent surfaces and prisms; pyramids, cones, spheres, and cylinders; and right and oblique figures.

INTRODUCTION

Have models of different polyhedrons and cutouts of different polygons available for students to manipulate. Students have seen some of the terminology in Lesson 1.8 and in their study of surface area in Lesson 8.7.

LESSON 10.1

The Geometry of Solids

Everything in nature adheres to the cone, the cylinder, and the cube.

PAUL CEZANNE

Most of the geometric figures you have worked with so far have been flat plane figures with two dimensions—base and height. In this chapter you will work with solid figures with three dimensions—length, width, and height. Most real-world solids, like rocks and plants, are very irregular, but many others are geometric. Some real-world geometric solids occur in nature: viruses, oranges, crystals, the earth itself. Others are human-made: books, buildings, baseballs, soup cans, ice cream cones.

Still Life With a Basket (1888–1890) by French post-impressionist painter Paul Cézanne (1839–1906) uses geometric solids to portray everyday objects.

This amethyst crystal is an irregular solid, but parts of it have familiar shapes.

Science CONNECTION

Three-dimensional geometry plays an important role in the structure of molecules. For example, when carbon atoms are arranged in a very rigid network, they form diamonds, one of the earth's hardest materials. But when carbon atoms are arranged in planes of hexagonal rings, they form graphite, a soft material used in pencil lead.

Carbon atoms can also bond into very large molecules. Named fullerenes, after U.S. engineer Buckminster Fuller (1895–1983), these carbon molecules have the same symmetry as a soccer ball, as shown at left. They are popularly called buckyballs.

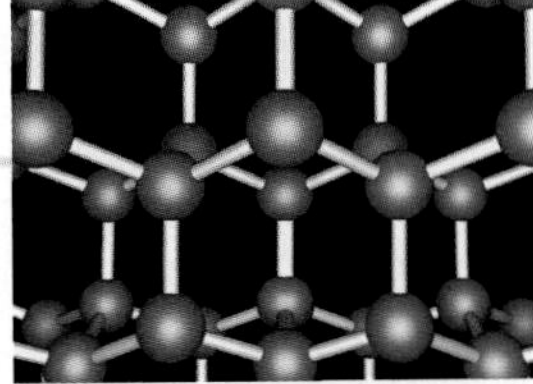

The geometry of diamonds

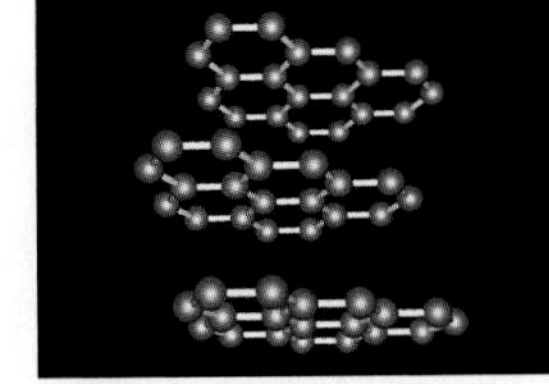

The geometry of graphite

LESSON OBJECTIVES

- Learn the vocabulary of polyhedrons—prisms and pyramids in particular
- Learn the vocabulary of spheres, cylinders, and cones
- Practice three-dimensional visual thinking skills

NCTM STANDARDS

CONTENT		PROCESS	
	Number		Problem Solving
	Algebra		Reasoning
✓	Geometry	✓	Communication
	Measurement	✓	Connections
	Data/Probability	✓	Representation

A solid formed by polygons that enclose a single region of space is called a **polyhedron.** The flat polygonal surfaces of a polyhedron are called its **faces.** Although a face of a polyhedron includes the polygon and its interior region, we identify the face by naming the polygon that encloses it. A segment where two faces intersect is called an **edge.** The point of intersection of three or more edges is called a **vertex** of the polyhedron.

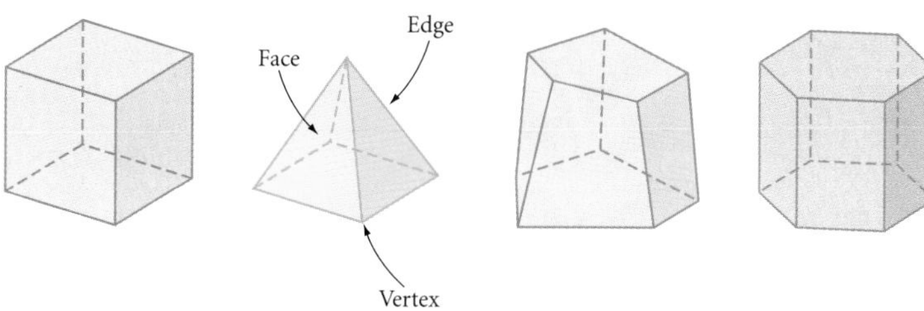

Just as a polygon is classified by its number of sides, a polyhedron is classified by its number of faces. The prefixes for polyhedrons are the same as they are for polygons with one exception: A polyhedron with four faces is called a **tetrahedron.** Here are some examples of polyhedrons.

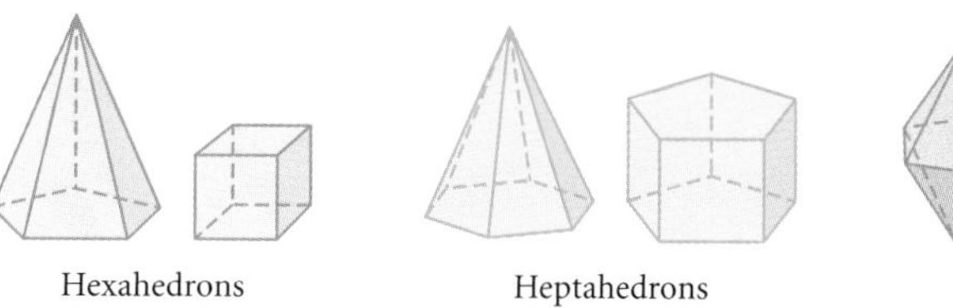

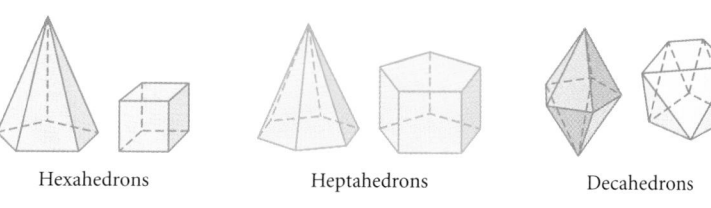

Hexahedrons Heptahedrons Decahedrons

If each face of a polyhedron is enclosed by a regular polygon, and each face is congruent to the other faces, and the faces meet at each vertex in exactly the same way, then the polyhedron is called a **regular polyhedron.** The regular polyhedron shown at right is called a regular dodecahedron because it has 12 faces.

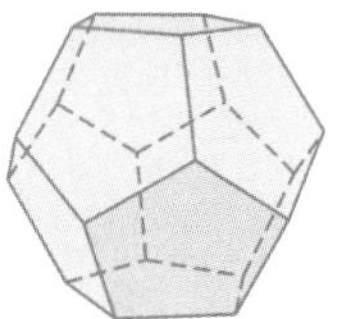

Regular dodecahedron

The Ramat Polin housing complex in Jerusalem, Israel, has many polyhedral shapes.

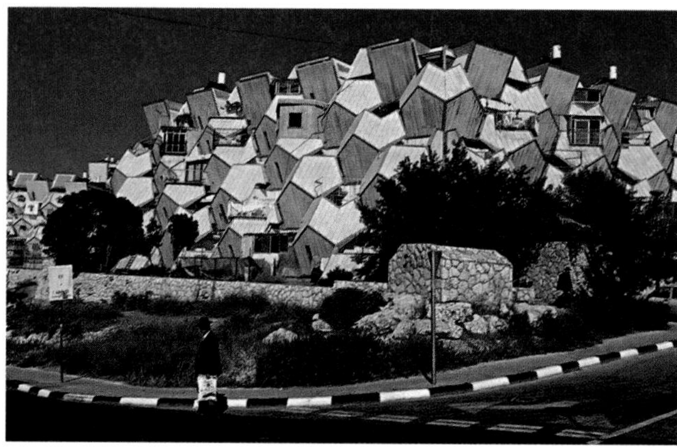

[Language] The plural of *polyhedron* is either *polyhedrons* or *polyhedra.* A polyhedron might have more than one name. Most often a polyhedron's name is based on the number of faces. The name may not describe the figure other than by the number of faces. For example, the prefix *hex-* means "six," and a hexahedron may be a pyramid or a prism or some other figure. If a hexahedron is a pyramid, it has a pentagonal base and five triangular lateral faces. If a hexahedron is a prism, it has two quadrilateral faces and four parallelogram lateral faces. A cube is a hexahedron.

Base, vertex, and *altitude* are familiar terms, but point out that they take on a different meaning in three dimensions. **[Language]** A pyramid has multiple vertices; when we say *the vertex,* we mean the vertex common to the lateral faces.

Point out that lateral edges are segments whose endpoints are corresponding vertices of the polygonal bases. For a right prism, the altitude can be represented simply by a lateral edge.

[ESL] *Ball* and *globe* are two common words for spherical objects. Objects in nature that are spherical include peas, bubbles, pollen, and eyeballs.

[Language] In the sentence on page 507 "Every plane that passes through the center of a sphere determines a great circle," the word *determines* means "there is one and only one."

SHARING IDEAS

As students share ideas, they may refer to the *sides* of the figure. Urge them to use either *faces* or *edges* to communicate more clearly.

[Ask] "What's the difference between a polyhedron and a polygon?" [Polygons exist in a plane, whereas polyhedrons exist only in three-dimensional space.]

[Ask] "How many faces would a pentahedron have? [five] "What would you call a polyhedron with eight faces?" [an octahedron] "What would a regular hexahedron look like? What is a common name for this?" [cube] **[Language]** If students are wondering why the polyhedron with four faces is called a *tetrahedron* instead of a *quadrahedron,* you might mention that *tetra-* is the Greek root for "four," while *quadra-* is the Latin root.

There are right and oblique prisms and pyramids.
[Ask] "How would you identify a right pyramid and an oblique pyramid?" [The vertex of a right pyramid is over the center of the base; the vertex of an oblique pyramid is not over the center of the base.]

A **prism** is a special type of polyhedron, with two faces called **bases,** that are congruent, parallel polygons. The other faces of the polyhedron, called **lateral faces,** are parallelograms that connect the corresponding sides of the bases.

The lateral faces meet to form the **lateral edges.** Each solid shown below is a prism.

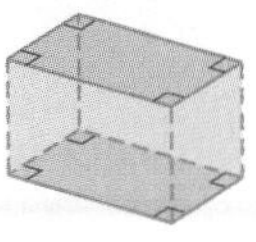
Rectangular prism

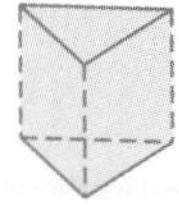
Triangular prism

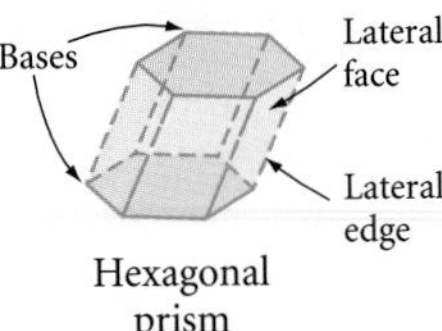

Hexagonal prism

Prisms are classified by their bases. For example, a prism with triangular bases is a triangular prism, and a prism with hexagonal bases is a hexagonal prism.

A prism whose lateral faces are rectangles is called a **right prism.** Its lateral edges are perpendicular to its bases. A prism that is not a right prism is called an **oblique prism.** The **altitude** of a prism is any perpendicular segment from one base to the plane of the other base. The length of an altitude is the **height** of the prism.

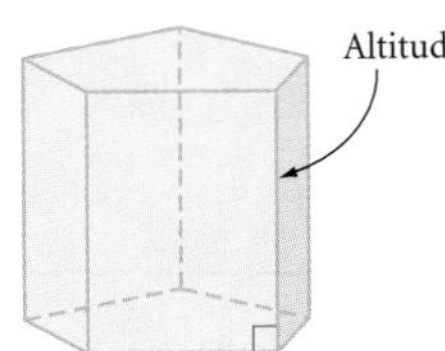

Right pentagonal prism

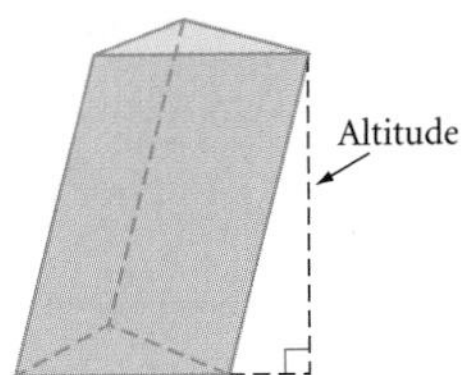

Oblique triangular prism

A **pyramid** is another special type of polyhedron. Pyramids have only one base. Like a prism, the other faces are called the lateral faces, and they meet to form the lateral edges. The common vertex of the lateral faces is the vertex of the pyramid.

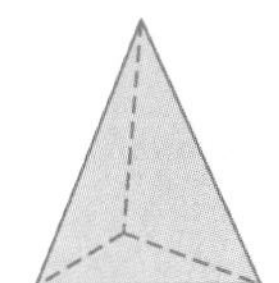
Triangular pyramid

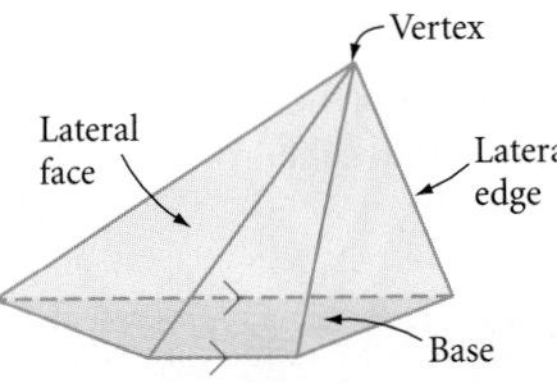

Trapezoidal pyramid

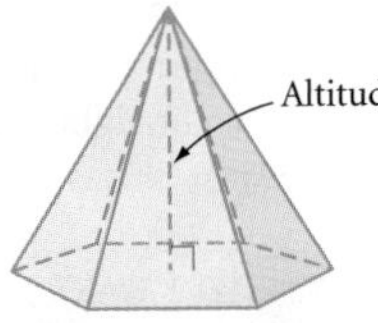

Hexagonal pyramid

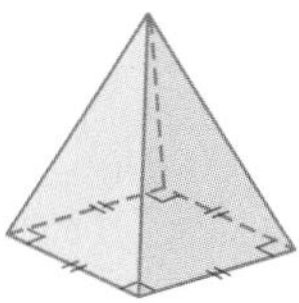
Square pyramid

Like prisms, pyramids are also classified by their bases. The pyramids of Egypt are square pyramids because they have square bases.

The altitude of the pyramid is the perpendicular segment from its vertex to the plane of its base. The length of the altitude is the height of the pyramid.

Polyhedrons are geometric solids with flat surfaces. There are also geometric solids that have curved surfaces. One that all sports fans know well is the ball, or sphere—you can think of it as a three-dimensional circle. An orange is one example of a sphere found in nature. What are some others?

A **sphere** is the set of all points in space at a given distance from a given point.

The given distance is called the **radius** of the sphere, and the given point is the **center** of the sphere. A **hemisphere** is half a sphere and its circular base. The circle that encloses the base of a hemisphere is called a **great circle** of the sphere. Every plane that passes through the center of a sphere determines a great circle. All the longitude lines on a globe of Earth are great circles. The equator is the only latitude line that is a great circle.

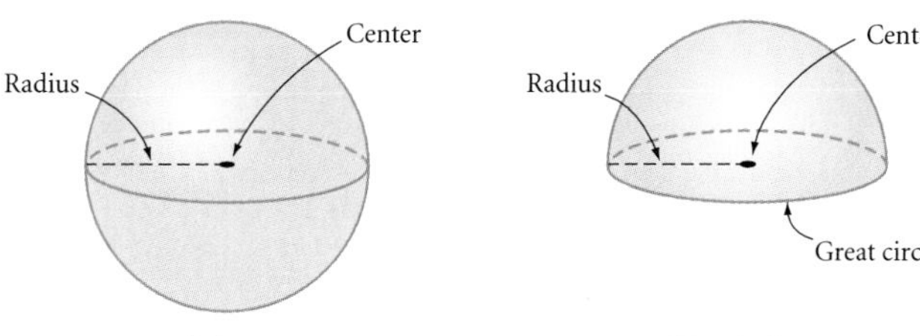

100 Cans (1962 oil on canvas), by pop art artist Andy Warhol (1925–1987), repeatedly uses the cylindrical shape of a soup can to make an artistic statement with a popular image.

Another solid with a curved surface is a **cylinder.** Soup cans, compact discs (CDs), and plumbing pipes are shaped like cylinders. Like a prism, a cylinder has two bases that are both parallel and congruent. Instead of polygons, however, the bases of cylinders are circles and their interiors. The segment connecting the centers of the bases is called the **axis** of the cylinder. The **radius** of the cylinder is the radius of a base.

If the axis of a cylinder is perpendicular to the bases, then the cylinder is a **right cylinder.** A cylinder that is not a right cylinder is an **oblique cylinder.**

The altitude of a cylinder is any perpendicular segment from the plane of one base to the plane of the other. The height of a cylinder is the length of an altitude.

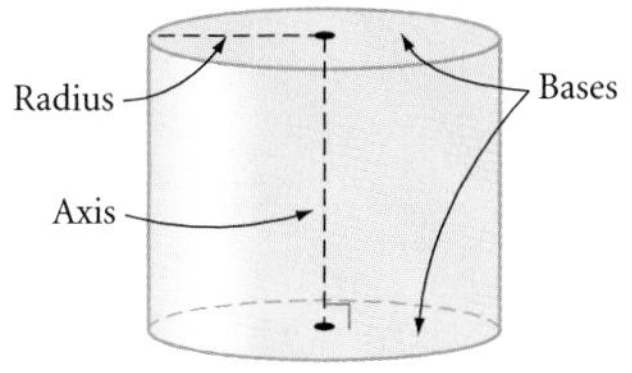

Right cylinder

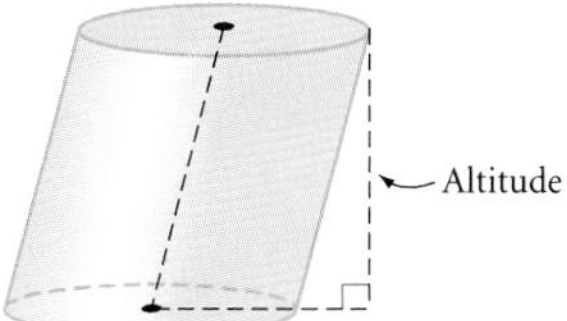

Oblique cylinder

Sharing Ideas (continued)

Latitude and longitude uniquely locate a point on the surface of Earth. The lines of longitude are all great circles, as is the equator; other lines of latitude are not. **[Ask]** "Is it possible for two great circles of a sphere to not intersect?" [no]

"What would a prism with a 100-gon base look like? In what sense is a cylinder a special case of a prism?" [Each base is like a polygon with infinitely many sides.] Like any prism, every slice parallel to the bases is congruent to the bases.

[Ask] "What would a pyramid with a 100-gon base look like? In what sense is a cone a special case of a pyramid?" [Its base is like a polygon with infinitely many sides.] "Slice a pyramid or cone by a plane parallel to the base. How does the cross section compare to the base?" [Every slice parallel to the base has the same shape as the base but is progressively smaller as you move away from the base.]

Draw each figure and **[Ask]** "Do you think this solid fits the definition of a cylinder?"

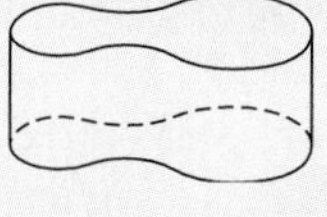

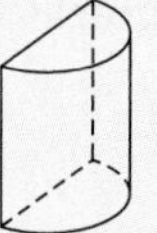

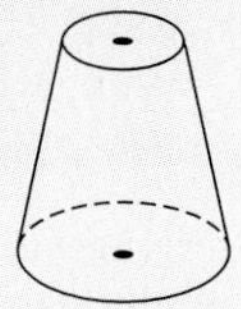

Students may answer yes to the first two if they have been exposed to a more general definition of congruent bases that are closed curves. For the definitions in this book, the bases must be congruent circles.

Assessing Progress

As students discuss the new ideas of this lesson, you can assess their understanding of different kinds of polygons.

Closing the Lesson

The major mathematical idea of this lesson is that terminology can help us classify solids. Either they have only flat faces (in which case they are **polyhedrons**), or they have curved faces and possibly flat faces (**cones, cylinders,** and **spheres**). Polyhedrons can be named according to the number of faces. **Prisms** are polyhedrons with two parallel congruent faces (the **bases**) whose vertices are joined to make parallelograms. **Pyramids** are polyhedrons with one vertex joined to all vertices of another face (the base). The **lateral** (nonbase) **faces** of prisms are parallelograms, while the lateral faces of pyramids are triangles. A prism is **right** if the lateral faces are perpendicular to the bases; a cylinder is right if its **axis**—the line through the centers of its bases—is perpendicular to the bases; a cone is **right** if its axis—the line through its vertex and the center of its base—is perpendicular to the base. An **altitude** of a prism, cylinder, pyramid, or cone is a line segment from a vertex perpendicular to the opposite base; the **height** of the figure is the length of an altitude. A **regular polyhedron** meets three conditions: Each face is a regular polygon, all faces are congruent to each other, and all faces meet at each vertex in the same way.

A third type of solid with a curved surface is a **cone.** Funnels and ice cream cones are shaped like cones. Like a pyramid, a cone has a base and a vertex.

The base of a cone is a circle and its interior. The radius of a cone is the radius of the base. The vertex of a cone is the point that is the greatest perpendicular distance from the base. The altitude of a cone is the perpendicular segment from the vertex to the plane of the base. The length of the altitude is the height of a cone. If the line segment connecting the vertex of a cone with the center of its base is perpendicular to the base, then it is a **right cone.**

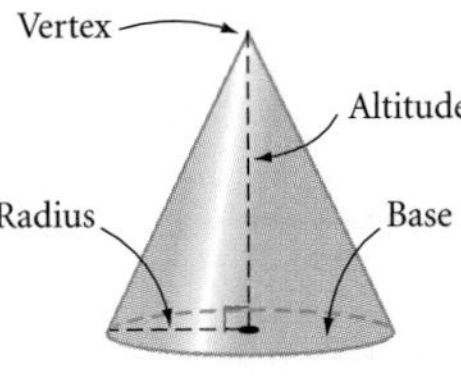

Right cone

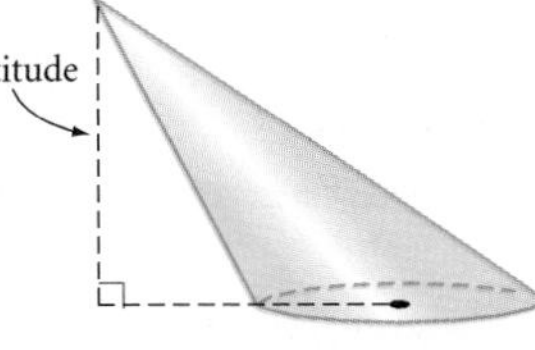

Oblique cone

EXERCISES

1. Complete this definition:
   A pyramid is a _?_ with one _?_ face (called the base) and whose other faces (lateral faces) are _?_ formed by segments connecting the vertices of the base to a common point (the vertex) not on the base. polyhedron; polygonal; triangles

For Exercises 2–9, refer to the figures below. All measurements are in centimeters.

2. Name the bases of the prism. $\triangle PQR$, $\triangle TUS$
3. Name all the lateral faces of the prism. *PQUT, QRSU, RPTS*
4. Name all the lateral edges of the prism. $\overline{QU}$, $\overline{PT}$, $\overline{RS}$
5. What is the height of the prism? 6 cm
6. Name the base of the pyramid. *GYPTAN*
7. Name the vertex of the pyramid. point *E*
8. Name all the lateral edges of the pyramid. $\overline{GE}$, $\overline{YE}$, $\overline{PE}$, $\overline{TE}$, $\overline{AE}$, $\overline{NE}$
9. What is the height of the pyramid? 13 cm

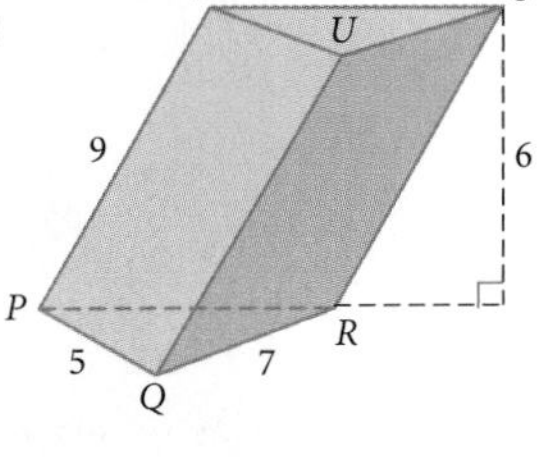

BUILDING UNDERSTANDING

There are many exercises, but each one is short. You might have students check their answers to Exercises 1–9 with their groups.

ASSIGNING HOMEWORK

Essential	1–35
Portfolio	37
Journal	36
Group	27–35, 37
Review	38–41

MATERIALS

- Exercises 2–9 (T), *optional*

For Exercises 10–22, match each real object with a geometry term. You may use a geometry term more than once or not at all.

10. Die C
11. Tomb of Egyptian rulers D
12. Holder for a scoop of ice cream B
13. Wedge or doorstop H
14. Box of breakfast cereal J
15. Plastic bowl with lid M
16. Ingot of silver I

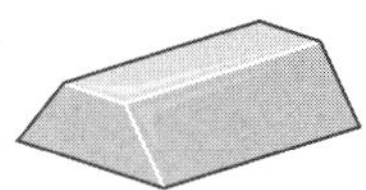

17. Honeycomb L
18. Stop sign G
19. Moon E
20. Can of tuna fish A
21. Book J
22. Pup tent H

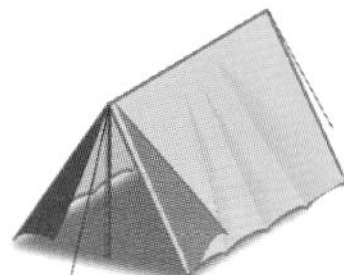

A. Cylinder
B. Cone
C. Square prism
D. Square pyramid
E. Sphere
F. Triangular pyramid
G. Octagonal prism
H. Triangular prism
I. Trapezoidal prism
J. Rectangular prism
K. Heptagonal pyramid
L. Hexagonal prism
M. Hemisphere

For Exercises 23–26, draw and label each solid. Use dashed lines to show the hidden edges.

23. A triangular pyramid whose base is an equilateral triangular region (use the proper marks to show that the base is equilateral)

24. A hexahedron with two trapezoidal faces

25. A cylinder with a height that is twice the diameter of the base (use x and $2x$ to indicate the height and the diameter)

26. A right cone with a height that is half the diameter of the base

For Exercises 27–35, identify each statement as true or false. Sketch a counterexample for each false statement or explain why it is false.

27. A lateral face of a pyramid is always a triangular region. true

28. A lateral edge of a pyramid is always perpendicular to the base. False. This statement is true only for a right prism.

29. Every slice of a prism cut parallel to the bases is congruent to the bases. ⓗ true

30. When the lateral surface of a right cylinder is unwrapped and laid flat, it is a rectangle. true

31. When the lateral surface of a right circular cone is unwrapped and laid flat, it is a triangle. ⓗ False. It is a sector of a circle.

32. Every section of a cylinder, parallel to the base, is congruent to the base. true

33. The length of a segment from the vertex of a cone to the circular base is the height of the cone.

34. The length of the axis of a right cylinder is the height of the cylinder. true

35. All slices of a sphere passing through the sphere's center are congruent. true

26.

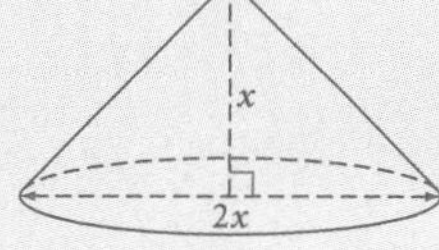

33. false; counterexample:

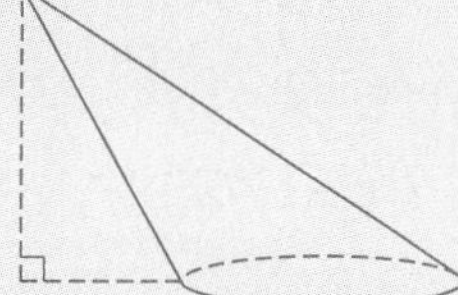

▶ Helping with the Exercises

Exercise 10 [ESL] A *die* is one of a pair of dice.

Exercise 11 If necessary, refer to the photo of an Egyptian pyramid on page 519.

Exercise 13 You may want to illustrate *wedge* with a triangular wedge of cheese.

Exercises 15, 16 [Ask] "Is a bowl always a hemisphere?" [No; it usually is not.] "Is an ingot always a trapezoidal prism?" [Not necessarily; it can be any shape that stacks well.]

Exercise 17 If necessary, refer to the photo of the honeycomb on page 2.

Exercise 19 *Moon* does not refer to what we see from Earth but to the actual shape of the Moon.

Exercises 23–26 You may want to refer students back to the exploration on page 172 for help in drawing solids.

23.

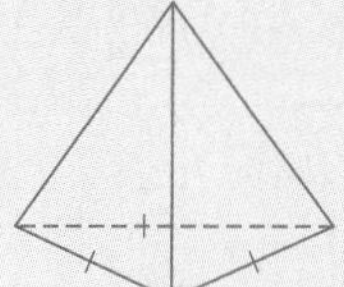

24.

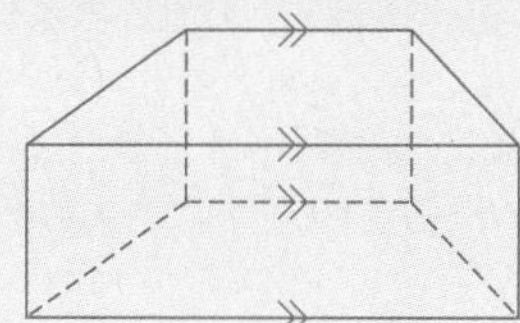

25.

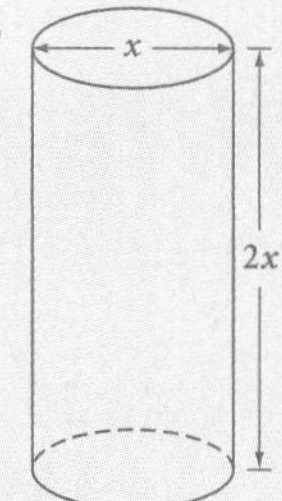

36. Answer should include the idea that the painting "disappears" into the view out the window. Students might also note the effect created by the cone-shaped tower appearing similar to the road disappearing into the distance.

Exercise 37 An antiprism is created by rotating one base of a prism and connecting the vertices so that the lateral faces are triangles.

37. Possible answers include that the number of lateral faces of an antiprism is always twice the number for the related prism; that the number of vertices is the same for each related prism and antiprism; and that the number of edges for a prism is three times the number of faces, while for an antiprism, the number of edges is twice the number of faces.

36. Write a paragraph describing the visual tricks that Belgian artist René Magritte (1898–1967) plays in his painting at right.

The Promenades of Euclid
(1935 oil on canvas),
René Magritte

37. An **antiprism** is a polyhedron with two congruent bases and lateral faces that are triangles. Complete the tables below for prisms and antiprisms. Describe any relationships you see between the number of lateral faces, total faces, edges, and vertices of related prisms and antiprisms.

	Triangular prism	Rectangular prism	Pentagonal prism	Hexagonal prism		*n*-gonal prism
Lateral faces	3	4	5	6	. . .	n
Total faces	5	6	7	8	. . .	$n + 2$
Edges	9	12	15	18	. . .	$3n$
Vertices	6	8	10	12	. . .	$2n$

	Triangular antiprism	Rectangular antiprism	Pentagonal antiprism	Hexagonal antiprism		*n*-gonal antiprism
Lateral faces	6	8	10	12	. . .	$2n$
Total faces	8	10	12	14	. . .	$2n + 2$
Edges	12	16	20	24	. . .	$4n$
Vertices	6	8	10	12	. . .	$2n$

Review

For Exercises 38 and 39, how many cubes measuring 1 cm on each edge will fit into the container?

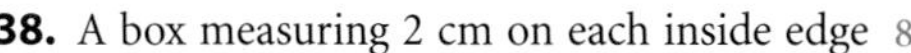

38. A box measuring 2 cm on each inside edge 8

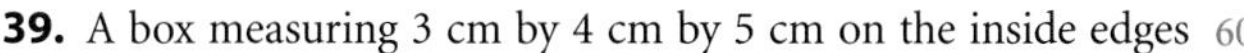

39. A box measuring 3 cm by 4 cm by 5 cm on the inside edges 60

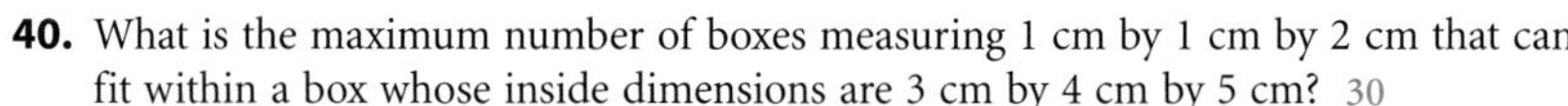

40. What is the maximum number of boxes measuring 1 cm by 1 cm by 2 cm that can fit within a box whose inside dimensions are 3 cm by 4 cm by 5 cm? 30

41. For each net, decide whether it folds to make a box. If it does, copy the net and mark each pair of opposite faces with the same symbol.

a. 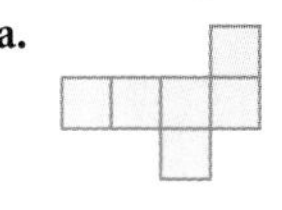 yes

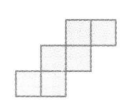

b. 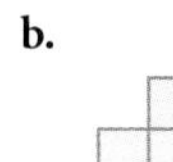 yes

c. 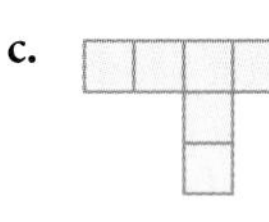 no

d. 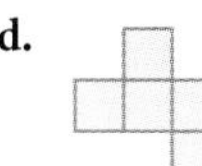 yes

Exercises 38–40 These exercises preview volume concepts.

41a.

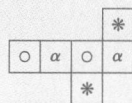

41b.

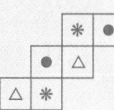

41d.

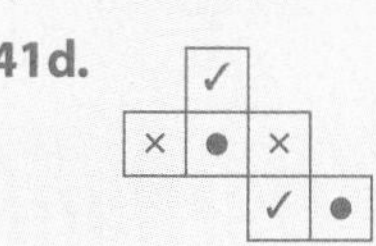

IMPROVING YOUR VISUAL THINKING SKILLS

Piet Hein's Puzzle

In 1936, while listening to a lecture on quantum physics, the Danish mathematician Piet Hein (1905–1996) devised the following visual thinking puzzle:

> What are all the possible nonconvex solids that can be created by joining four or fewer cubes face-to-face?

A nonconvex polyhedron is a solid that has at least one diagonal that is exterior to the solid. For example, four cubes in a row, joined face-to-face, form a convex polyhedron. But four cubes joined face-to-face into an L-shape form a nonconvex polyhedron.

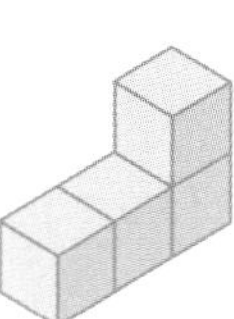

Use isometric dot paper to sketch the nonconvex solids that solve Piet Hein's puzzle. There are seven solids.

IMPROVING VISUAL THINKING SKILLS

This puzzle, which asks for seven shapes, is a three-dimensional equivalent of polyominoes. It is a prerequisite to the Project The Soma Cube in Lesson 10.2.

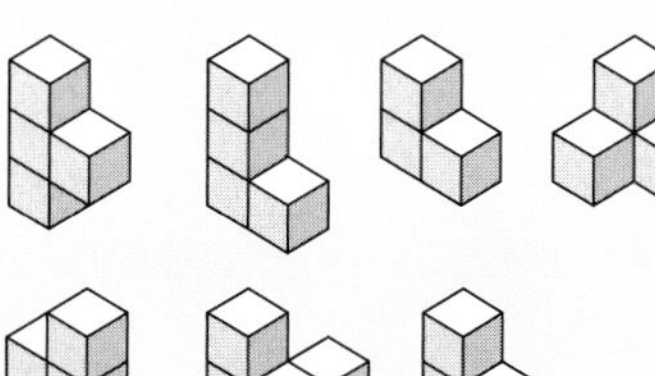

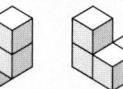

EXPLORATION

PLANNING

LESSON OUTLINE

One day:

30 min Activity

10 min Sharing

5 min Closing

MATERIALS

- toothpicks
- modeling clay (alternatively, gumdrops, small marshmallows, or dried peas)
- a building set such as Zome System, *optional*

TEACHING

If students want to learn more about Euler ['ȯi-lər], refer back to the Exploration The Seven Bridges of Königsberg on page 118. Students might be interested to learn that Euler was blind for the last 15 years of his life but remained mathematically productive.

Guiding the Activity

Each group will need toothpicks (or wooden barbecue skewers) to use as the edges of the models and something to use as vertices: modeling clay (a lump the size of a large egg per group), gumdrops or small marshmallows (about 75 per group), or dried peas (soaked overnight before use).

Step 4 Euler's Formula for Polyhedrons applies only to special polyhedrons. They must have no holes, for example. *Discovering Geometry More Projects and Explorations* has a guided investigation to help students discover a general formula for polyhedrons with various numbers of holes.

Exploration

Euler's Formula for Polyhedrons

In this activity you will discover a relationship among the vertices, edges, and faces of a polyhedron. This relationship is called Euler's Formula for Polyhedrons, named after Leonhard Euler. Let's first build some of the polyhedrons you learned about in Lesson 10.1.

Activity
Toothpick Polyhedrons

You will need

- toothpicks
- modeling clay, gumdrops, or dried peas

First, you'll model polyhedrons using toothpicks as edges and using small balls of clay, gumdrops, or dried peas as connectors.

Step 1 Build and save the polyhedrons shown in parts a–d below and described in parts e–i on the top of page 513. You may have to cut or break some sticks. Share the tasks among the group.

a.

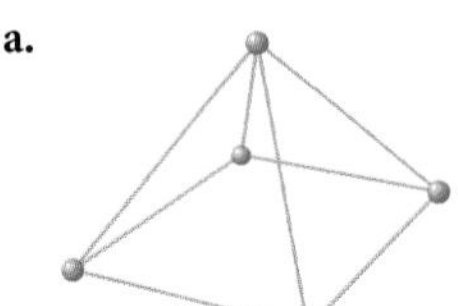

b.

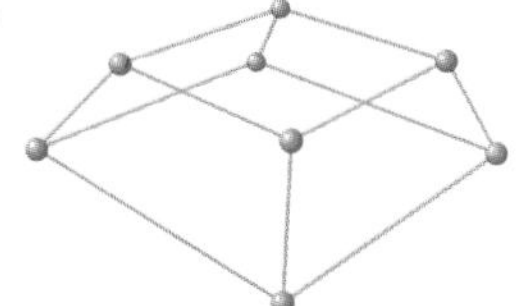

c.

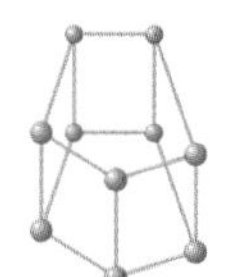

d.

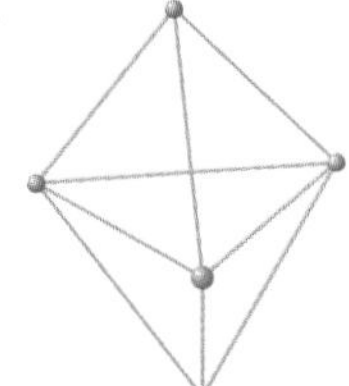

LESSON OBJECTIVES

- Build polyhedrons
- Find a pattern in the number of faces, edges, and vertices of polyhedrons

NCTM STANDARDS

CONTENT		PROCESS	
✓	Number		Problem Solving
	Algebra	✓	Reasoning
✓	Geometry	✓	Communication
	Measurement	✓	Connections
✓	Data/Probability	✓	Representation

e. Build a tetrahedron.
f. Build an octahedron.
g. Build a nonahedron.
h. Build at least two different-shaped decahedrons.
i. Build at least two different-shaped dodecahedrons.

Step 2 Classify all the different polyhedrons your class built as prisms, pyramids, regular polyhedrons, or just polyhedrons.

Next, you'll look for a relationship among the vertices, faces, and edges of the polyhedrons.

Step 3 Count the number of vertices (V), edges (E), and faces (F) of each polyhedron model. Copy and complete a chart like this one.

Polyhedron	Vertices (V)	Faces (F)	Edges (E)
a. pyramid	5	5	8
⋮	⋮	⋮	⋮
b. polyhedron	8	6	12

Step 4 Answers should be equivalent to $V + F = E + 2$.

Step 4 Look for patterns in the table. By adding, subtracting, or multiplying V, F, and E (or a combination of two or three of these operations), you can discover a formula that is commonly known as Euler's Formula for Polyhedrons.

Step 5 Now that you have discovered the formula relating the number of vertices, edges, and faces of a polyhedron, use it to answer each of these questions.

Step 5a Tetrahedron. It is impossible.

a. Which polyhedron has 4 vertices and 6 edges? Can you build another polyhedron with a different number of faces that also has 4 vertices and 6 edges?

Step 5b Octahedron. It is impossible.

b. Which polyhedron has 6 vertices and 12 edges? Can you build another polyhedron with a different number of faces that also has 6 vertices and 12 edges?
c. If a solid has 8 faces and 12 vertices, how many edges will it have? 18
d. If a solid has 7 faces and 12 edges, how many vertices will it have? 7
e. If a solid has 6 faces, what are all the possible combinations of vertices and edges it can have?

Step 5e 5 vertices and 9 edges, 6 vertices and 10 edges, or 8 vertices and 12 edges

Step 5 When students complete Step 5e, they will realize that a solid with six faces can take on more than one shape.

SHARING IDEAS

[Ask] "Is there one kind of part—vertex, edge, or face—that there are more of than any other part?" [edges] "Why?" [It takes at least three edges to add a face and three edges to add a vertex.]

Ask students to calculate $V - E + F$ for twin tetrahedra (joined only at a vertex), for a picture frame, and for a cylinder. Let them discuss what definition of *polyhedron* should be used for Euler's Formula for Polyhedrons.

Ask students if they see *why* Euler's formula holds. Ask students to critique this argument: Imagine the figure as being made of rubber. Remove one face and stretch out the rest, flattening it into a plane like this cube.

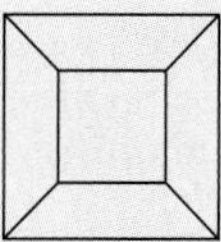

This figure will have the same number of faces, edges, and vertices as the original if the region outside is considered a face. Now draw diagonals to make every face except the outside one a triangle. Drawing a diagonal adds one edge and one face, so the sum $V - E + F$ is not changed. Finally remove triangles systematically, removing either one edge and a face or one face, two edges, and a vertex. In each case the sum is not changed. Eventually you'll be left with a triangle; there are two faces, including the outer one, three edges, and three vertices, so the sum $V - E + F$ is two. But the sum hasn't changed, so it must have been two to begin with.

Challenge students to come up with their own proofs.

Assessing Progress

Check students' ability to work in groups, to construct polyhedrons, to count systematically, and to see patterns in data.

Step 3 sample answers:

Polyhedron	V	F	E
c. prism	10	7	15
d. polyhedron	5	6	9
e. pyramid (tetrahedron)	4	4	6
f. regular polyhedron (octahedron)	6	8	12

Closing the Lesson

Euler's Formula for Polyhedrons states that $V - E + F = 2$, where V is the number of vertices, E is the number of edges, and F is the number of faces. The formula holds for only selected polyhedrons.

LESSON 10.2

PLANNING

LESSON OUTLINE

One day:

20 min Investigation

10 min Sharing

5 min Closing

10 min Exercises

MATERIALS

- a ream of paper or a stack of cards
- a stack of coins or other disks
- Volume of Prisms (T), *optional*
- cubes for One step

TEACHING

Prisms and cylinders have a pair of congruent, parallel bases—and they share the same volume formula. **[Language]** A *unit cube* is a cube that measures 1 unit by 1 unit by 1 unit.

One step Have right cylinders and unit cubes (wooden or sugar) available for each group. **[Ask]** "How many unit cubes would fit into a cylinder?" Some will see how many whole cubes they can squeeze in. As needed, point out that you said "would fit," not "do fit." Let students determine the conditions for "would fit," but encourage them to think of "would fit if the cubes were cut up into small enough pieces to leave no gaps." Help groups focus on the number of unit squares (faces of unit cubes) that would cover a base of the cylinder and then to think about layers of cubes. Keep focusing on the idea of filling the cylinder completely. During Sharing, ask about oblique cylinders and various prisms, and develop a formula that summarizes students' findings.

LESSON 10.2

Volume of Prisms and Cylinders

How much deeper would oceans be if sponges didn't live there?

STEVEN WRIGHT

In real life you encounter many volume problems. For example, when you shop for groceries, it's a good idea to compare the volumes and the prices of different items to find the best buy. When you fill a car's gas tank or when you fit last night's leftovers into a freezer dish, you fill the volume of an empty container.

Many occupations also require familiarity with volume. An engineer must calculate the volume and the weight of sections of a bridge to avoid too much stress on any one section. Chemists, biologists, physicists, and geologists must all make careful volume measurements in their research. Carpenters, plumbers, and painters also know and use volume relationships. A chef must measure the correct volume of each ingredient in a cake to ensure a tasty success.

American artist Wayne Thiebaud (b 1920) painted *Bakery Counter* in 1962.

Volume is the measure of the amount of space contained in a solid. You use cubic units to measure volume: cubic inches (in.^3), cubic feet (ft^3), cubic yards (yd^3), cubic centimeters (cm^3), cubic meters (m^3), and so on. The volume of an object is the number of unit cubes that completely fill the space within the object.

Length: 1 unit

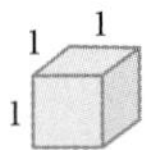

Volume: 1 cubic unit

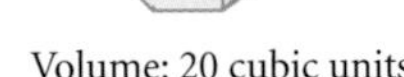

Volume: 20 cubic units

LESSON OBJECTIVES

- Discover formulas for finding the volumes of prisms and cylinders
- Practice three-dimensional visual thinking skills
- Develop problem-solving skills and cooperative behavior

NCTM STANDARDS

	CONTENT		PROCESS
	Number		Problem Solving
✓	Algebra	✓	Reasoning
✓	Geometry	✓	Communication
✓	Measurement	✓	Connections
	Data/Probability		Representation

Investigation
The Volume Formula for Prisms and Cylinders

Step 1a 24 cm^3
Step 1b 288 cm^3
Step 1c 3000 cm^3

Step 1 | Find the volume of each right rectangular prism below in cubic centimeters. That is, how many 1 cm-by-1 cm-by-1 cm cubes will fit into each solid? Within your group, discuss different strategies for finding each volume. How could you find the volume of any right rectangular prism?

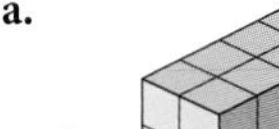

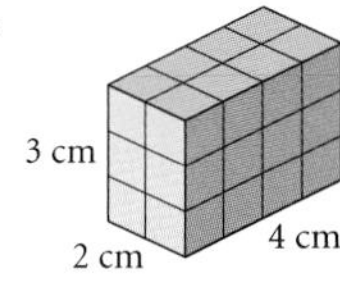

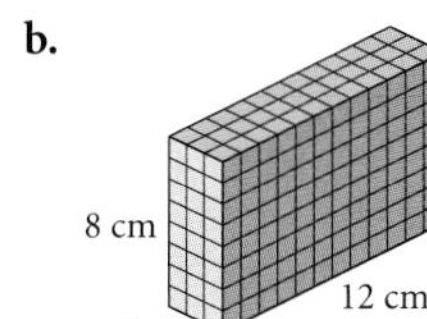

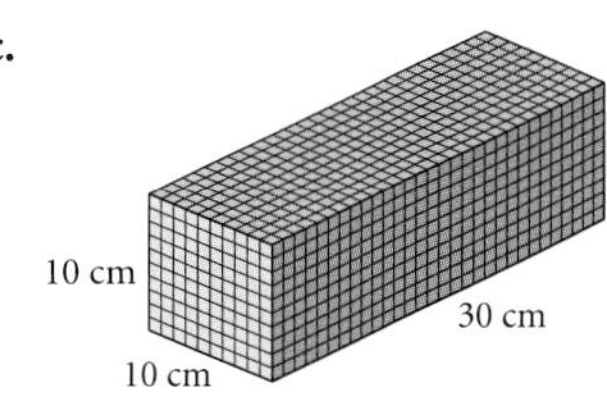

Notice that the number of cubes resting on the base equals the number of square units in the area of the base. The number of layers of cubes equals the number of units in the height of the prism. So you can multiply the area of the base by the height of the prism to calculate the volume.

Step 2 | Complete the conjecture.

Conjecture A C-88a

If B is the area of the base of a right rectangular prism and H is the height of the solid, then the formula for the volume is $V = \underline{?}$. *BH*

In Chapter 8, you discovered that you can reshape parallelograms, triangles, trapezoids, and circles into rectangles to find their area. You can use the same method to find the areas of bases that have these shapes. Then you can multiply the area of the base by the height of the prism to find its volume. For example, to find the volume of a right triangular prism, find the area of the triangular base (the number of cubes resting on the base) and multiply it by the height (the number of layers of cubes).

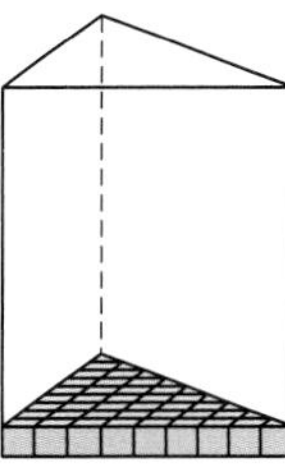

So you can extend Conjecture A (the volume of right rectangular prisms) to all right prisms and right cylinders.

Step 3 | Complete the conjecture.

Conjecture B C-88b

If B is the area of the base of a right prism (or cylinder) and H is the height of the solid, then the formula for the volume is $V = \underline{?}$. *BH*

Guiding the Investigation

You might lead the class through the investigation.

Step 1 Develop the idea of starting with a single layer of cubes that covers some number of square units of area and then filling a volume by stacking multiple layers up to some height. The number of cubes in the bottom layer reflects the area of the base. For Figure a, students might discuss simply counting cubes. For Figures b and c, students should consider strategies such as multiplying length times width times height or multiplying the area of the base times the height. Some students might benefit from building the first two figures from wooden or sugar cubes.

[ESL] A *ream* is a standard measure of paper (either 500 sheets for a printer's ream or 516 sheets for a perfect ream). You might do the stacked paper example as a classroom demonstration.

Step 4 The stack of disks you use to model the cylinder can be coins, chemistry filter papers, old CDs, or other disks.

SHARING IDEAS

Students develop the concept of volume as the number of cubic units. Students might use the Volume of Prisms transparency as they share their ideas.

The demonstration with reams of paper or stacks of disks might produce some confusion that students are unable to articulate without help. A few students may not believe that the volume remains the same when the stack is slanted. More commonly, students will doubt that the height remains the same. **[Ask]** "Does the thickness of each sheet stay the same?" You might measure the height of the stack both straight and slanted. **[Ask]** "Is this situation the same as shifting a rectangle into a parallelogram?" [With a parallelogram, the side lengths don't change, but the height and the area change. With this three-dimensional stack, however, the edge lengths change, but not the height.] **[Link]** This approach to calculating size is a special case of Cavalieri's Principle: If two figures have the same height and the same cross-sectional size at every level, then they have the same size. Bonaventura Cavalieri (1598–1647) was a leader in calculating areas and volumes by considering objects to consist of infinitely many "indivisible" objects of lower dimension, a principle fundamental to calculus.

What about the volume of an oblique prism or cylinder? You can approximate the shape of this oblique rectangular prism with a staggered stack of three reams of 8.5-by-11-inch paper. If you nudge the individual pieces of paper into a slanted stack, then your approximation can be even better.

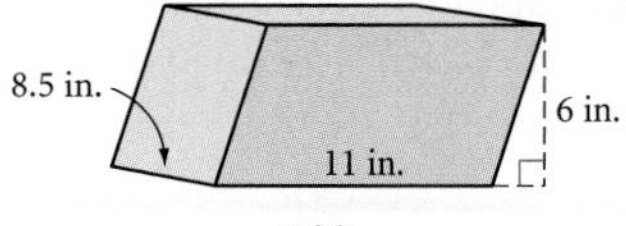

Oblique rectangular prism

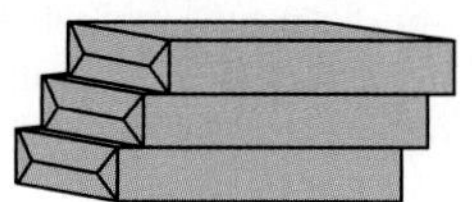
Stacked reams of 8.5-by-11-inch paper

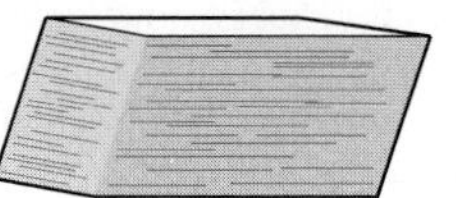
Stacked sheets of paper

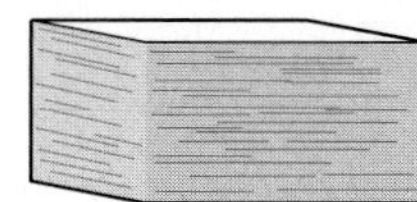
Sheets of paper stacked straight

Rearranging the paper into a right rectangular prism changes the shape, but certainly the volume of paper hasn't changed. The area of the base, 8.5 by 11 inches, didn't change and the height, 6 inches, didn't change, either.

In the same way, you can use coffee filters, coins, candies, or chemistry filter papers to show that an oblique cylinder has the same volume as a right cylinder with the same base and height.

Step 4 | Use the stacking model to extend Conjecture B (the volume of right prisms and cylinders) to oblique prisms and cylinders. Complete the conjecture.

Conjecture C C-88c

The volume of an oblique prism (or cylinder) is the same as the volume of a right prism (or cylinder) that has the same _?_ and the same _?_. height
base area

Finally, you can combine Conjectures A, B, and C into one conjecture for finding the volume of any prism or cylinder, whether it's right or oblique.

Step 5 | Copy and complete the conjecture.

Prism-Cylinder Volume Conjecture C-88

The volume of a prism or a cylinder is the _?_ multiplied by the _?_. height
area of the base

If you successfully completed the investigation, you saw that the same volume formula applies to all prisms and cylinders, regardless of the shapes of their bases. To calculate the volume of a prism or cylinder, first calculate the area of the base using the formula appropriate to its shape. Then multiply the area of the base by the height of the solid. In oblique prisms and cylinders, the lateral edges are no longer at right angles to the bases, so you do *not* use the length of the lateral edge as the height.

Because the formulas are the same for right and oblique figures, you might ask if it's ever useful to know that a prism or a cylinder is right or oblique. That information helps you determine whether or not the slant height can be used as the height in calculating volume.

[Alert] Some students will assume that bases of figures are always on the bottom. You might ask where the bases are in the trapezoidal prism in Exercise 3.

Assessing Progress

You can assess students' ability to use the terminology of prisms and cylinders and to generalize from data. You might also note students' ability to see repeated addition as multiplication.

EXAMPLE A Find the volume of a right trapezoidal prism that has a height of 15 cm. The two bases of the trapezoid measure 4 cm and 8 cm, and its height is 5 cm.

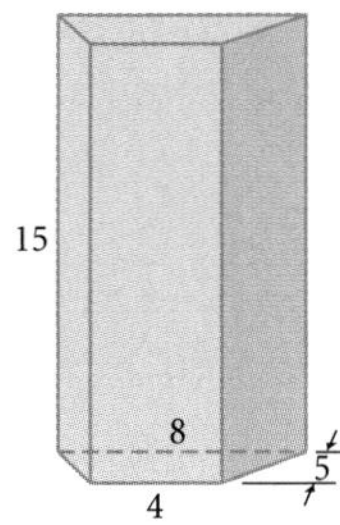

▸ Solution Use $B = \frac{1}{2}h(b_1 + b_2)$ for the area of the trapezoidal base.

$V = BH$	The formula for volume of a prism, where B is the area of its base and H is its height.
$= \frac{1}{2}(5)(4 + 8) \cdot (15)$	Substitute $\frac{1}{2}(5)(4 + 8)$ for B, applying the formula for area of a trapezoid. Substitute 15 for H, the height of the prism.
$= (30)(15)$	Simplify.
$= 450$	

The volume is 450 cm³.

EXAMPLE B Find the volume of an oblique cylinder that has a base with a radius of 6 inches and a height of 7 inches.

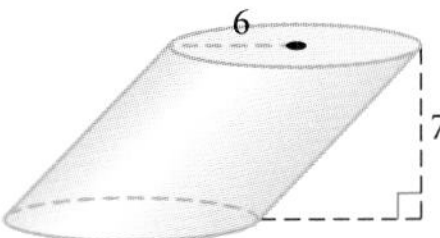

▸ Solution Use $B = \pi r^2$ for the area of the circular base.

$V = BH$	The formula for volume of a cylinder.
$= (\pi \cdot 6^2)(7)$	Substitute $(\pi \cdot 6^2)$ for B, applying the formula for area of a circle.
$= 36\pi(7)$	Simplify.
$= 252\pi \approx 791.68$	Use the π key on your calculator to get an approximate answer.

The volume is 252π in.³, or about 791.68 in.³.

EXERCISES

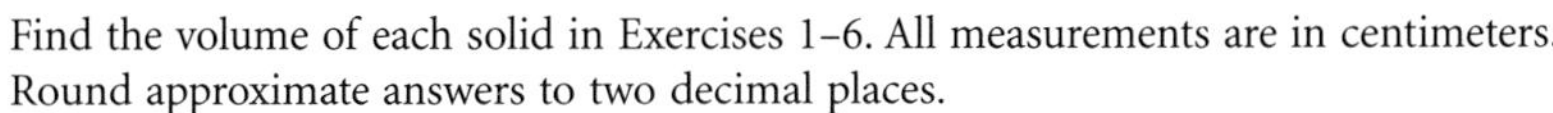

Find the volume of each solid in Exercises 1–6. All measurements are in centimeters. Round approximate answers to two decimal places.

1. Oblique rectangular prism
72 cm³

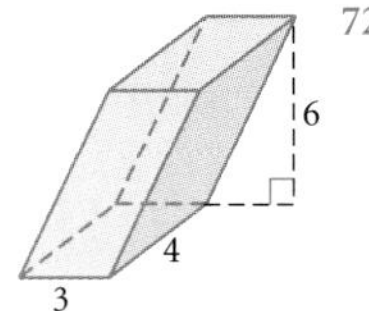

2. Right triangular prism ⓗ
24 cm³

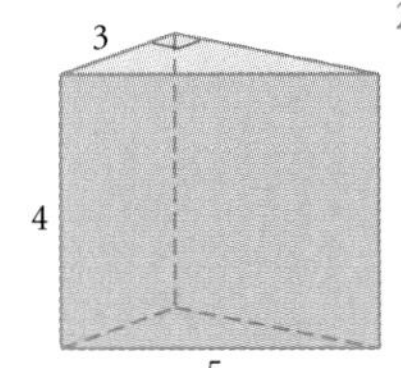

3. Right trapezoidal prism
108 cm³

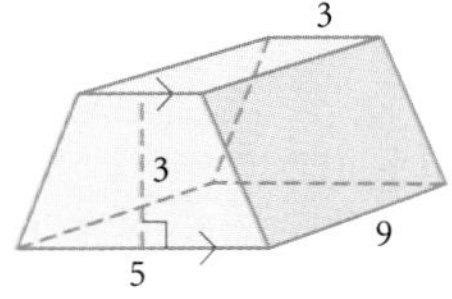

▸ EXAMPLE A

Do this example if students haven't caught on to how to calculate the volume of a prism or are weak at finding the area of a trapezoid. **[Alert]** Students might be confused by the labels B (which represents the area of the trapezoidal base) and b_1 and b_2 (which represent the bases of the trapezoid).

Note that the height is the measure of the perpendicular distance between the two bases of the trapezoid. Using a real solid with this shape might help students understand the figure better.

▸ EXAMPLE B

This example reviews how to calculate the volume of an oblique cylinder. The height is *not* measured along the lateral edge. Note that π can be left in the volume expression. If students want to know the number of cubes that will fill the cylinder, they can find an approximation. Again, using a real model might help some students.

Closing the Lesson

The volume of both a prism and a cylinder—right or oblique—can be found by multiplying the height by the area of the base.

BUILDING UNDERSTANDING

Have students write out formulas for each exercise as was done in the examples.

ASSIGNING HOMEWORK

Essential	**1–10**
Performance assessment	**14**
Portfolio	**24**
Journal	**14**
Group	**11–13, 15–18**
Review	**19–26**

▶ Helping with the Exercises

Exercise 5 [Alert] Students may forget to divide by 2.

Exercise 6 As needed, **[Ask]** "How much of the cylinder is still there?" $\left[\frac{3}{4}\right]$

Exercise 8 Some students might be confused by the two uses of the word *base.* The first use of the word refers to a base of a prism; the second refers to bases of a trapezoid, which are edges of the prism.

8. 960 in.^{3}

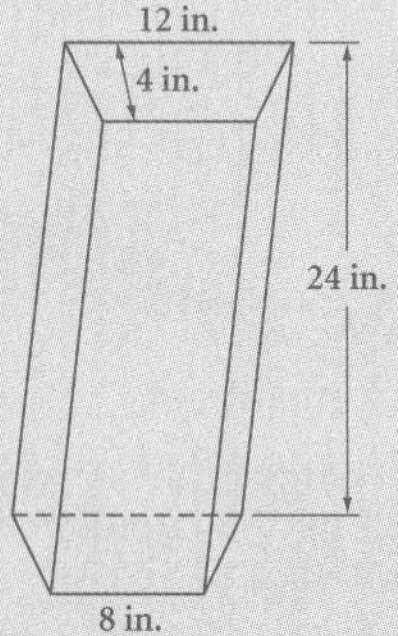

9. $QT\pi$ cubic units

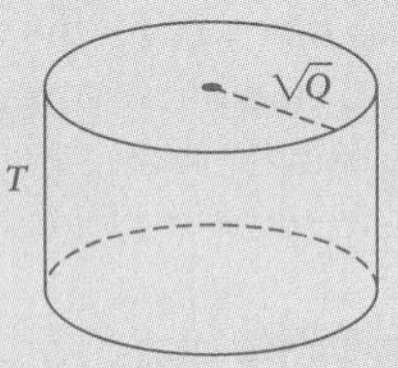

Exercise 10 It is important that students label sketches like these to show they are different figures that meet the criteria, not just sketches that look different.

10. sample answer:

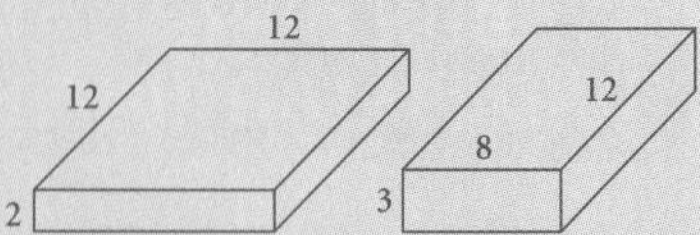

Exercise 14 A box is a right rectangular prism. **[Context]** A *cord of firewood* is measured by rectangular dimensions, typically 8 ft by 4 ft by 4 ft. Gaps are not considered.

4. Right cylinder
160π cm$^3 \approx 502.65$ cm^3

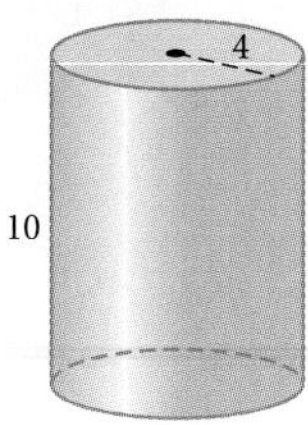

5. Right semicircular cylinder ⓗ
36π cm$^3 \approx 113.10$ cm^3

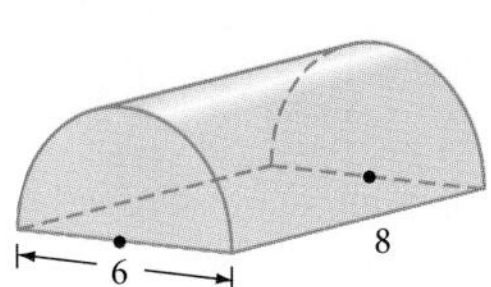

6. Right cylinder with a 90° slice removed ⓗ
324π cm$^3 \approx 1017.88$ cm^3

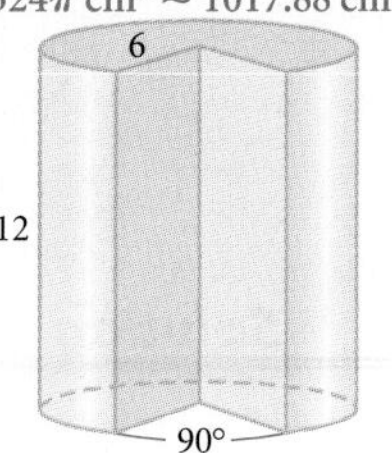

7. Use the information about the base and height of each solid to find the volume. All measurements are given in centimeters.

Information about base of solid	Height of solid	Right triangular prism	Right rectangular prism	Right trapezoidal prism	Right cylinder
		(h, b, H)	(h, b, H)	(b_2, h, b, H)	(r, H)
$b = 6, b_2 = 7,$ $h = 8, r = 3$	$H = 20$	**a.** $V =$ ⓗ 480 cm^3	**d.** $V =$ 960 cm^3	**g.** $V =$ 1040 cm^3	**j.** $V =$ 180π cm^3
$b = 9, b_2 = 12,$ $h = 12, r = 6$	$H = 20$	**b.** $V =$ 1080 cm^3	**e.** $V =$ 2160 cm^3	**h.** $V =$ 2520 cm^3	**k.** $V =$ 720π cm^3
$b = 8, b_2 = 19,$ $h = 18, r = 8$	$H = 23$	**c.** $V =$ 1656 cm^3	**f.** $V =$ 3312 cm^3	**i.** $V =$ 5589 cm^3	**l.** $V =$ 1472π cm^3

For Exercises 8–9, sketch and label each solid described, then find the volume.

8. An oblique trapezoidal prism. The trapezoidal base has a height of 4 in. and bases that measure 8 in. and 12 in. The height of the prism is 24 in.

9. A right circular cylinder with a height of T. The radius of the base is $\sqrt{Q}$. ⓗ

10. Sketch and label two different rectangular prisms each with a volume of 288 cm^3.

In Exercises 11–13, express the volume of each solid with the help of algebra.

11. Right rectangular prism $2x^3$

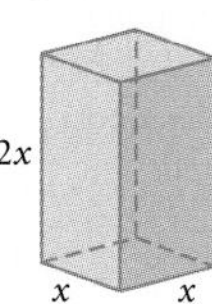

12. Oblique cylinder $3\pi r^3$

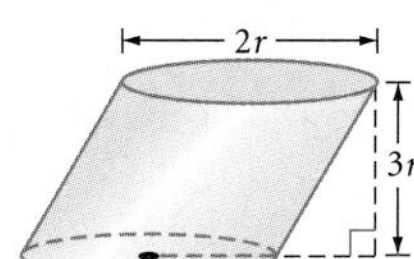

13. Right rectangular prism with a rectangular hole $13x^3$

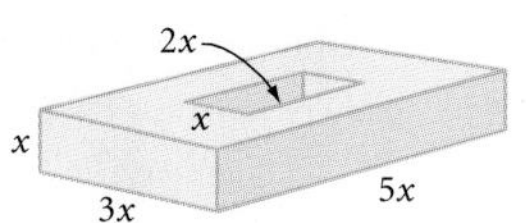

14. APPLICATION A cord of firewood is 128 cubic feet. Margaretta has three storage boxes for firewood that each measure 2 feet by 3 feet by 4 feet. Does she have enough space to order a full cord of firewood? A half cord? A quarter cord? Explain.
Margaretta has room for 0.5625 cord. She should order a half cord.

Career
CONNECTION

In construction and landscaping, sand, rocks, gravel, and fill dirt are often sold by the "yard," which actually means a cubic yard.

15. APPLICATION A contractor needs to build up a ramp as shown at right from the street to the front of a garage door. How many cubic yards of fill will she need? 170 yd^3

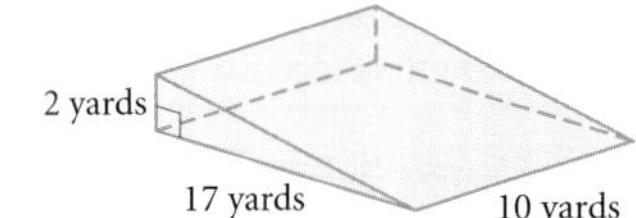

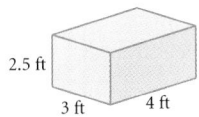

16. If an average rectangular block of limestone used to build the Great Pyramid of Khufu at Giza is approximately 2.5 feet by 3 feet by 4 feet and limestone weighs approximately 170 pounds per cubic foot, what is the weight of one of the nearly 2,300,000 limestone blocks used to build the pyramid? 5100 lb

2.5 ft
3 ft
4 ft

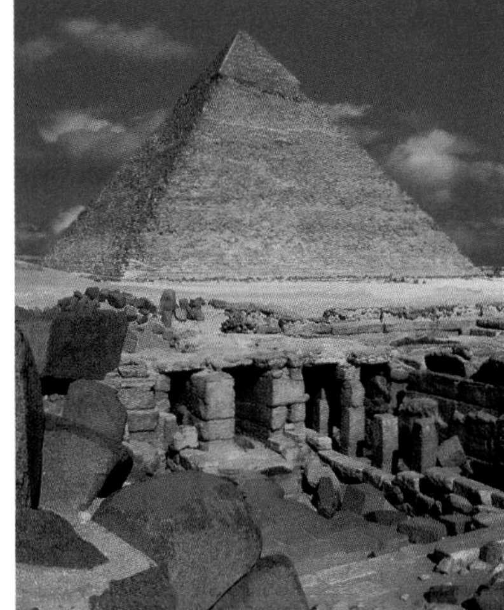

The Great Pyramid of Khufu at Giza, Egypt, was built around 2500 B.C.E.

17. Although the Exxon *Valdez* oil spill (11 million gallons of oil) is one of the most notorious oil spills, it was small compared to the 250 million gallons of crude oil that were spilled during the 1991 Persian Gulf War. A gallon occupies 0.13368 cubic foot. How many rectangular swimming pools, each 20 feet by 30 feet by 5 feet, could be filled with 250 million gallons of crude oil? 11,140

18. When folded, a 12-by-12-foot section of the AIDS Memorial Quilt requires about 1 cubic foot of storage. In 1996, the quilt consisted of 32,000 3-by-6-foot panels. What was the quilt's volume in 1996? If the storage facility had a floor area of 1,500 square feet, how high did the quilt panels need to be stacked?

The NAMES Project AIDS Memorial Quilt memorializes persons all around the world who have died of AIDS. In 1996, the 32,000 panels represented less than 10% of the AIDS deaths in the United States alone, yet the quilt could cover about 19 football fields.

Exercise 15 Large amounts of sand, rocks, gravel, and fill dirt are also sold by the ton.

Exercise 16 If needed, **[Ask]** "How many cubic feet are there in each block?"

Exercise 18 This exercise is rich mathematically because it deals with the volume of an object that is most often thought of in terms of the area it covers. It also demonstrates how mathematical concepts (area and volume) apply to human concerns. You might want to have a discussion on how the volume of the quilt illustrates the human tragedy of AIDS.

18. The volume of the quilt in 1996 was 4000 ft^3. The quilt panels were stacked 2 ft 8 in. high.

19.

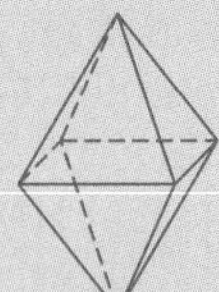

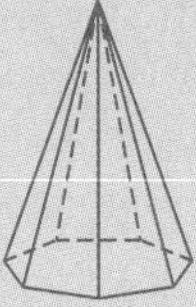

Exercise 20 [Language] *Flush* here means that the base of the cone matches up perfectly with the base of the cylinder.

20.

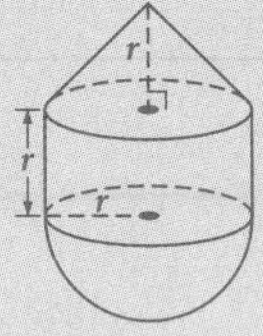

Exercise 22 Another counterexample: If a plane cuts through the midpoints of two adjacent edges on each of the six faces, then the section is a regular hexagon.

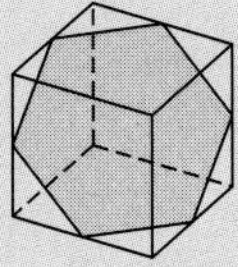

The section can also be a pentagon.

22. false

24. possible solution: prism

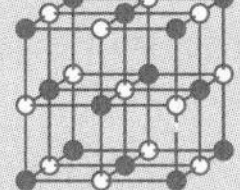

Salt crystal

MAKING THE CONNECTION

Most substances contract in volume (become denser) when they decrease in temperature; water increases in volume when frozen, becoming less dense, so it floats. The molecules move apart into a rigid three-dimensional lattice as the water freezes.

Review

For Exercises 19 and 20, draw and label each solid. Use dashed lines to show the hidden edges.

10.1 **19.** An octahedron with all triangular faces and another octahedron with at least one nontriangular face

10.1 **20.** A cylinder with both radius and height r, a cone with both radius and height r resting flush on one base of the cylinder, and a hemisphere with radius r resting flush on the other base of the cylinder

For Exercises 21 and 22, identify each statement as true or false. Sketch a counterexample for each false statement or explain why it is false.

10.1 **21.** A prism always has an even number of vertices. true

10.1 **22.** A section of a cube is either a square or a rectangle.

1.8 **23.** The tower below is an unusual shape. It's neither a cylinder nor a cone. Sketch a two-dimensional figure and an axis such that if you spin your figure about the axis, it will create a solid of revolution shaped like the tower.

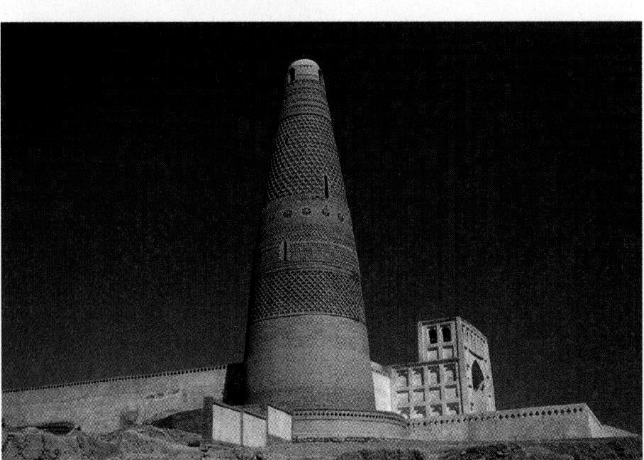

The Sugong Tower Mosque in Turpan, China

23.

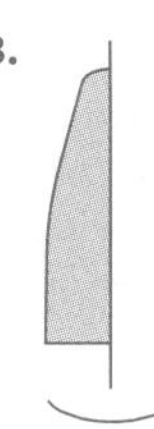

1.8 **24.** Do research to find a photo or drawing of a chemical model of a crystal. Sketch it. What type of polyhedral structure does it exhibit? You will find helpful Internet links at www.keymath.com/DG .

Science CONNECTION

Ice is a well-known crystal structure. If ice were denser than water, it would sink to the bottom of the ocean, away from heat sources. Eventually the oceans would fill from the bottom up with ice, and we would have an ice planet. What a cold thought!

Project Solutions

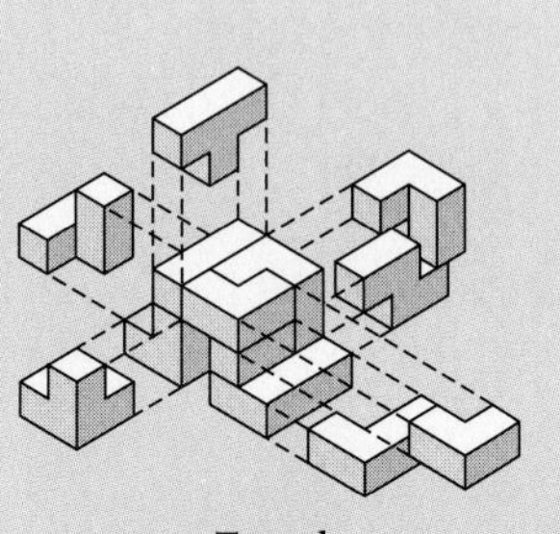

Tunnel

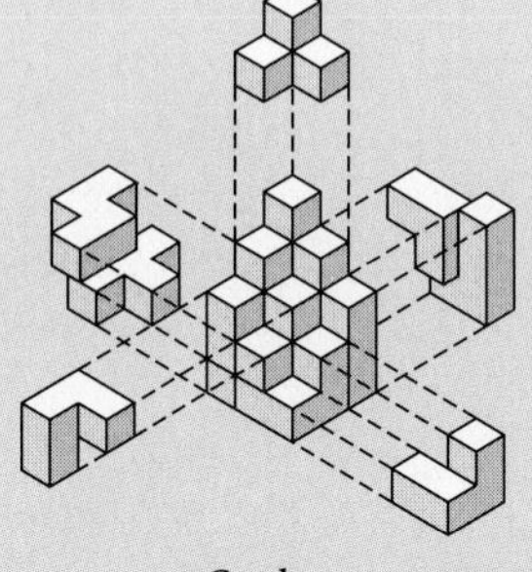

Castle

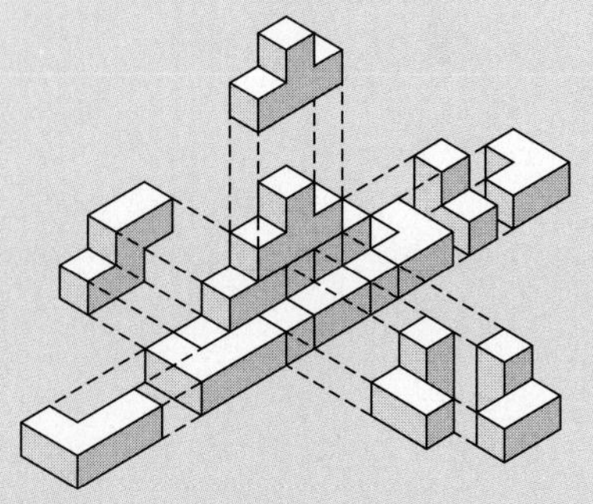

Winners' Podium

6.7 **25.** Six points are equally spaced around a circular track with a 20 m radius. Ben runs around the track from one point, past the second, to the third. Al runs straight from the first point to the second, and then straight to the third. How much farther does Ben run than Al? approximately 1.89 m

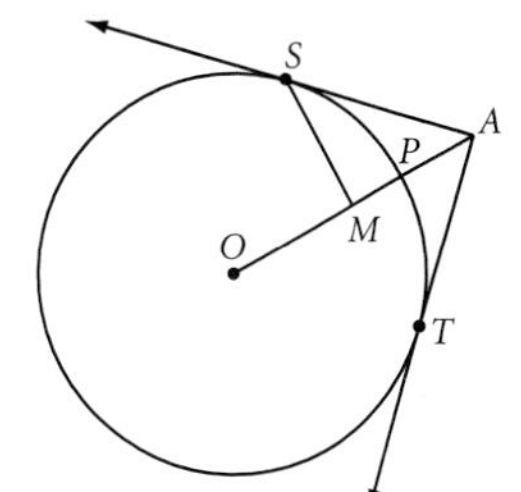

9.3 **26.** $\overrightarrow{AS}$ and $\overrightarrow{AT}$ are tangent to circle O at S and T, respectively. $m\angle SMO = 90°$, $m\angle SAT = 90°$, $SM = 6$. Find the exact value of PA. ⓗ $12 - 6\sqrt{2}$

Exercise 26 As necessary, encourage students to draw in radii to see that they have a square, half of which is bisected into a special right triangle.

EXTENSIONS

A. Have students do research and write current-events problems of their own similar to Exercises 17 and 18.

B. Have students build a three-dimensional solid from heavy paper, determine its volume, and confirm this volume by filling the solid with sand or rice.

Project Solutions

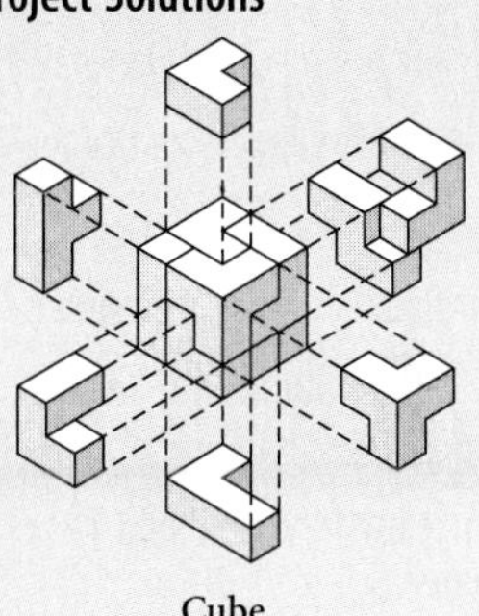

Cube

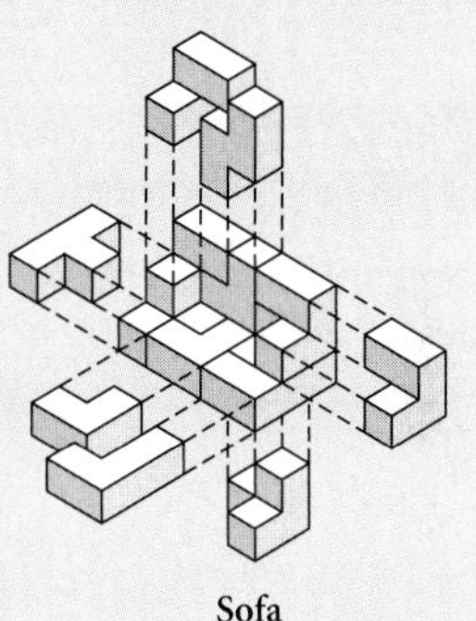

Sofa

project

THE SOMA CUBE

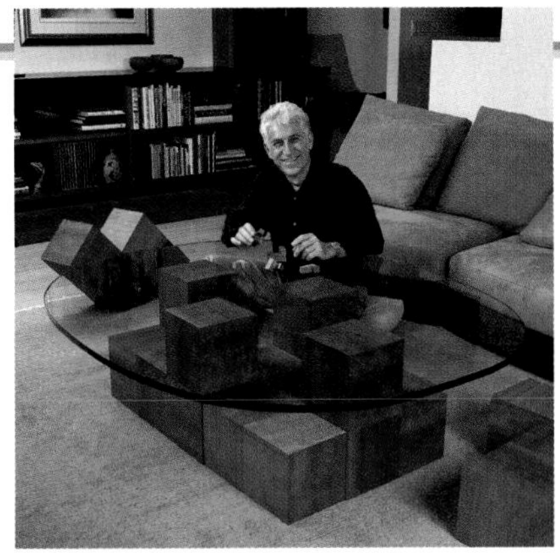

If you solved Piet Hein's puzzle at the end of the previous lesson, you now have sketches of the seven nonconvex polyhedrons that can be assembled using four or fewer cubes. These seven polyhedrons consist of a total of 27 cubes: 6 sets of 4 cubes and 1 set of 3 cubes. You are ready for the next rather amazing discovery. These pieces can be arranged to form a 3-by-3-by-3 cube. The puzzle of how to put them together in a perfect cube is known as the Soma Cube puzzle.

Use cubes (wood, plastic, or sugar cubes) to build one set of the seven pieces of the Soma Cube. Use glue, tape, or putty to connect the cubes.

Solve the Soma Cube puzzle. Put the pieces together to make a 3-by-3-by-3 cube.

Now build these other shapes. How do you build the sofa? The tunnel? The castle? The winners' podium?

Sofa

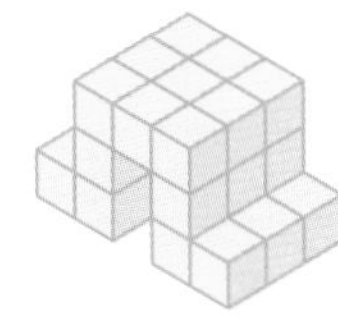

Tunnel

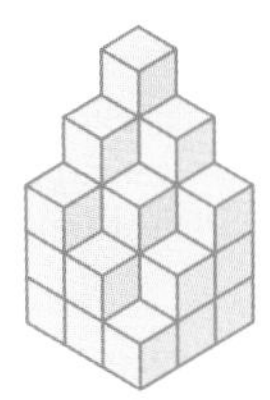

Castle

Winners' Podium

Create a shape of your own that uses all the pieces. Go to www.keymath.com/DG to learn more about the Soma Cube.

Supporting the project

[Context] Piet Hein did not envision a cube and then cut it into seven different shapes; rather, he posed and solved a combinatorial geometry problem, noticed that the total number of cubes was 27, and began to wonder. He developed the puzzle in 1936; in 1969, Parker Brothers Inc. produced it.

OUTCOMES

- The seven unique pieces are built.
- The project shows at least one of the 240 distinct ways to arrange the seven pieces into a cube. (The number exceeds 1,000,000 if rotations are considered.)
- Solutions are given for the four shapes pictured in the book.
- An interesting shape is built and drawn.
- The student completes research on the number and strategies of solutions.

LESSON

10.3

PLANNING

LESSON OUTLINE

One day:

25 min Investigation

10 min Sharing

5 min Examples

5 min Closing

MATERIALS

- hollow pairs of prisms and pyramids
- hollow pairs of cylinders and cones
- sand, rice, birdseed, or water
- cardboard boxes or plastic dishpans
- Square-Based Pyramid and Prism (W), *optional*
- Pentagon-Based Pyramid and Prism (W), *optional*
- Cone and Cylinder (W), *optional*

TEACHING

In this lesson students learn that the volumes of pyramids and cones are closely related to the volumes of their circumscribed prisms or cylinders.

Guiding the Investigation

Whether you demonstrate the investigation or ask students to do it, they will benefit from first estimating the number of times figures with a volume equal to that of the cone or pyramid will fit into a circumscribed figure.

Before class, set up a workstation for each group with the two pairs of models (with congruent bases and equal heights), something to pour, and a box or dishpan to pour over. You may want to save time by combining this investigation with the one on the volume of a sphere in Lesson 10.6.

LESSON 10.3

Volume of Pyramids and Cones

If I had influence with the good fairy . . . I should ask that her gift to each child in the world be a sense of wonder so indestructible that it would last throughout life.

RACHEL CARSON

There is a simple relationship between the volumes of prisms and pyramids with congruent bases and the same height, and between cylinders and cones with congruent bases and the same height. You'll discover this relationship in the investigation.

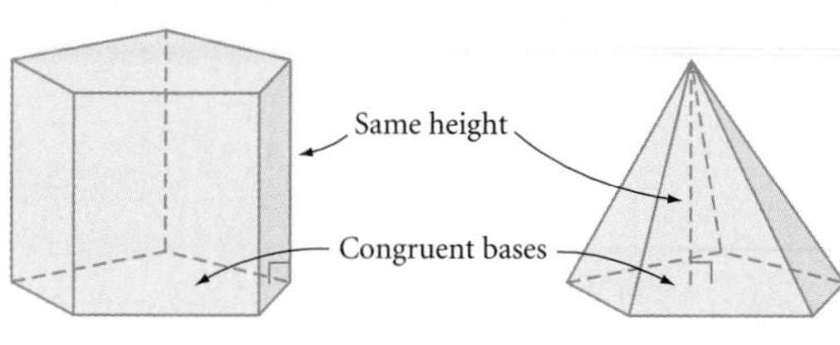

Same volume?

Investigation
The Volume Formula for Pyramids and Cones

You will need

- container pairs of prisms and pyramids
- container pairs of cylinders and cones
- sand, rice, birdseed, or water

Step 1 Choose a prism and a pyramid that have congruent bases and the same height.

Step 2 Fill the pyramid, then pour the contents into the prism. About what fraction of the prism is filled by the volume of one pyramid?

Step 3 Check your answer by repeating Step 2 until the prism is filled.

Step 4 Choose a cone and a cylinder that have congruent bases and the same height and repeat Steps 2 and 3.

Step 5 Compare your results with the results of others. Did you get similar results with both your pyramid-prism pair and the cone-cylinder pair? You should be ready to make a conjecture.

Pyramid-Cone Volume Conjecture C-89

If B is the area of the base of a pyramid or a cone and H is the height of the solid, then the formula for the volume is $V =$ __?__. $\frac{1}{3}BH$

If you cannot get enough hollow plastic models, students can transfer the nets from the Pyramid and Prism and Cone and Cylinder worksheets onto cardboard, cut them out, tape them together, and fill them with something light such as birdseed.

One step Ask groups how the volume of a pyramid or cone relates to the volume of its circumscribed prism or cylinder. As you circulate, encourage conjecturing from the start. Have students check their theoretical conjectures using materials at the workstations.

SHARING IDEAS

Have students share their conjectures. Keep emphasizing that the area of the base describes the number of unit-cube equivalents that fit in one layer of the solid and that the height describes the number of layers that will fill in the solid. For pyramids and cones, the layers closer to the vertex contain fewer unit-cube equivalents than do layers closer to the base. The coefficient $\frac{1}{3}$ will come as a surprise to some students.

If you successfully completed the investigation, you probably noticed that the volume formula is the same for all pyramids and cones, regardless of the type of base they have. To calculate the volume of a pyramid or cone, first find the area of its base. Then find the product of that area and the height of the solid, and multiply by the fraction you discovered in the investigation.

EXAMPLE A

Find the volume of a regular hexagonal pyramid with a height of 8 cm. Each side of its base is 6 cm.

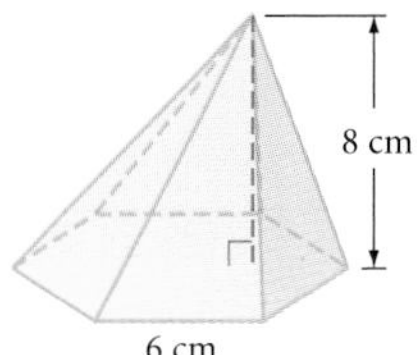

▶ Solution

First find the area of the base. To find the area of a regular hexagon, you need the apothem. By the 30°-60°-90° Triangle Conjecture, the apothem is $3\sqrt{3}$ cm.

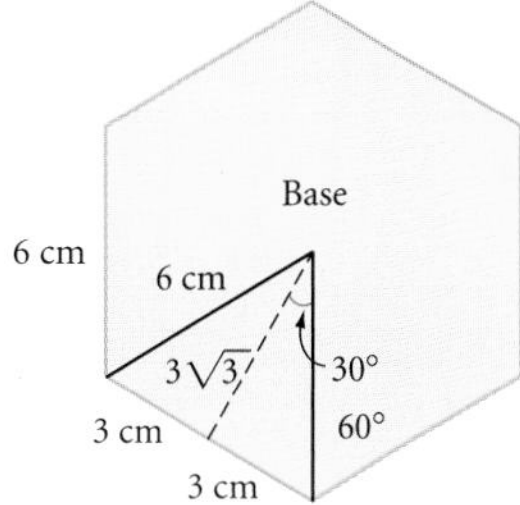

$B = \left(\frac{1}{2}\right)ap$ — The area of a regular polygon is one-half the apothem times the perimeter.

$B = \left(\frac{1}{2}\right)(3\sqrt{3})(36)$ — Substitute $3\sqrt{3}$ for a and 36 for p.

$B = 54\sqrt{3}$ — Multiply.

The base has an area of $54\sqrt{3}$ cm². Now find the volume of the pyramid.

$V = \left(\frac{1}{3}\right)BH$ — The volume of a pyramid is one-third the area of the base times the height.

$V = \left(\frac{1}{3}\right)(54\sqrt{3})(8)$ — Substitute $54\sqrt{3}$ for B and 8 for H.

$V = 144\sqrt{3}$ — Multiply.

The volume is $144\sqrt{3}$ cm³ or approximately 249.4 cm³.

EXAMPLE B

A cone has a base radius of 3 in. and a volume of 24π in.³. Find the height.

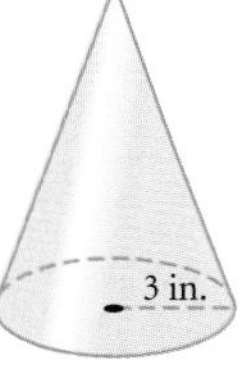

NCTM STANDARDS

CONTENT		PROCESS	
	Number	✓	Problem Solving
	Algebra	✓	Reasoning
✓	Geometry	✓	Communication
✓	Measurement	✓	Connections
	Data/Probability	✓	Representation

LESSON OBJECTIVES

- Discover formulas for the volumes of pyramids and cones
- Practice three-dimensional visual thinking skills
- Develop problem-solving skills and cooperative behavior

Sharing Ideas (continued)

Those who already know the formula might benefit from trying to explain it; ideally, they will all come to realize that $\frac{1}{3}$ is not obvious. Why isn't it $\frac{1}{\pi}$ or $\frac{2}{5}$? You might draw analogies to the dynamic picture of a rectangle in which one side shrinks to a point; when the figure is a trapezoid, the area is equal to the height times the mean of the lengths of the two bases, becoming the height times $\frac{1}{2}$ the remaining base when one base shrinks to a point. Why is the number $\frac{1}{3}$ instead of $\frac{1}{2}$ for volume? Discussion can lead to a deeper understanding of volume, even if you don't find answers that completely satisfy all students.

Ask whether Cavalieri's Principle is helpful in deriving the formula. Because all pyramids and cones with the same base and height have the same area for corresponding cross sections, the figures all have the same volume. If you can show that one particular pyramid, say a triangular pyramid, has volume $\frac{1}{3}$ that of the circumscribed prism, then the same volume formula will apply to all pyramids and cones with the same base and height. See the solution for Take Another Look activity 4 for a picture of three triangular pyramids of equal volume that can be combined to form a prism.

▶ EXAMPLE A

This example combines finding the volume of a pyramid with properties of regular hexagons and the 30°-60°-90° triangle. As needed, **[Ask]** "How might you find the area of the hexagon?" [It is 6 times the area of each equilateral triangle.] "How can you find the area of each equilateral triangle? How can you find its height? Is there a way to find the length of the side opposite the 60° angle if you know the length of the hypotenuse?" [Divide the length in half and multiply by $\sqrt{3}$.]

▶ EXAMPLE B

This example works from the known volume to an unknown height of a cone. Keep stressing that the height gives the number of layers of unit cubes needed to fill the cone, with each layer smaller but not thinner than the one beneath it (closer to the base).

Assessing Progress

You can assess students' knowledge of the terminology of prisms, cylinders, pyramids, and cones and their comfort with the concept of volume as filling space with the equivalent of unit cubes.

Closing the Lesson

The volume of every pyramid and cone is $\frac{1}{3}$ the volume of any prism or cylinder of the same base area and height.

BUILDING UNDERSTANDING

[Alert] Students frequently forget to divide by 3 in the exercises.

ASSIGNING HOMEWORK

Essential	1–12
Performance assessment	14
Portfolio	10
Group	13, 15, 16
Review	17–23

▶ Helping with the Exercises

Exercise 3 If needed, **[Ask]** "What is the height of the trapezoid?" [5 cm]

Exercise 6 Students might not think to subtract the volume of the cone from that of the cylinder.

▶ Solution Start with the volume formula and solve for H.

$V = \frac{1}{3}BH$	Volume formula for pyramids and cones.
$V = \frac{1}{3}(\pi r^2)(H)$	The base of a cone is a circle.
$24\pi = \frac{1}{3}(\pi \cdot 3^2)(H)$	Substitute 24π for the volume and 3 for the radius.
$24\pi = 3\pi H$	Square the 3 and multiply by $\frac{1}{3}$.
$8 = H$	Solve for H.

The height of the cone is 8 in.

EXERCISES

Find the volume of each solid named in Exercises 1–6. All measurements are in centimeters.

1. Square pyramid 192 cm³

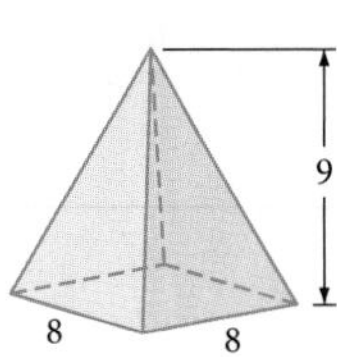

2. Cone 84π cm³

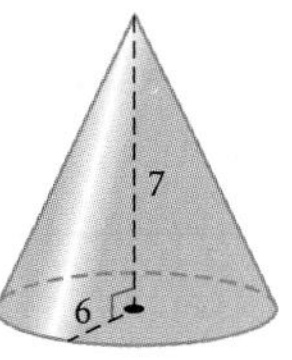

3. Trapezoidal pyramid ⓗ 150 cm³

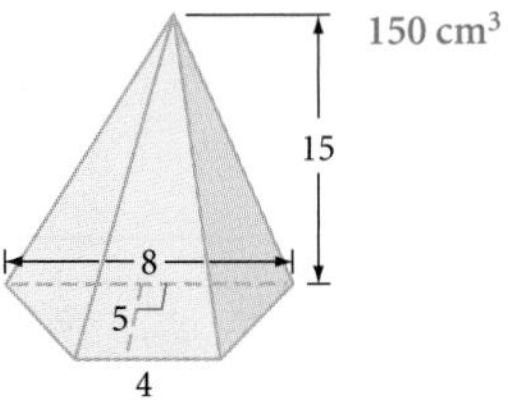

4. Triangular pyramid 60 cm³

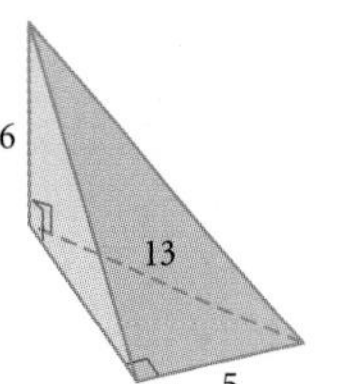

5. Semicircular cone 84π cm³

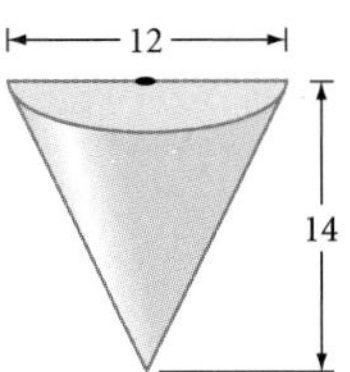

6. Cylinder with cone removed ⓗ 384π cm³

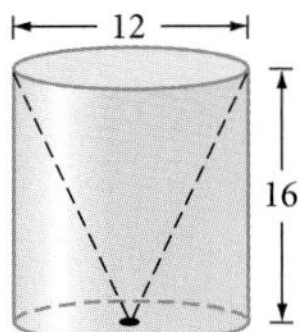

In Exercises 7–9, express the total volume of each solid with the help of algebra. In Exercise 9, what percentage of the volume is filled with the liquid? All measurements are in centimeters.

7. Square pyramid $\frac{m^3}{3}$ cm³

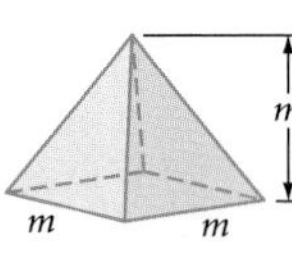

8. Cone $\frac{2}{3}\pi b^3$ cm³

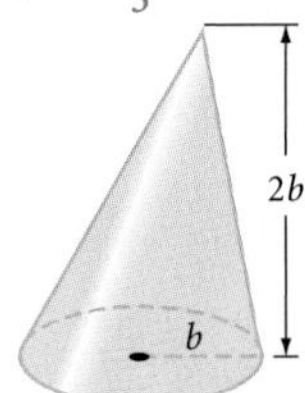

9. Cone $324\pi x^3$ cm³; 29.6%

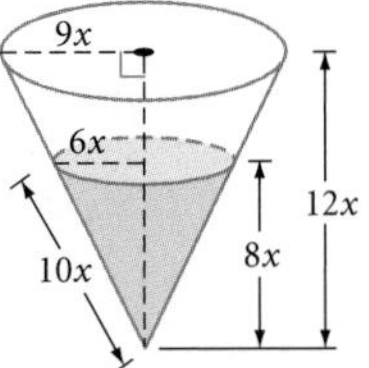

10. Use the information about the base and height of each solid to find the volume. All measurements are given in centimeters.

Information about base of solid	Height of solid	Triangular pyramid	Rectangular pyramid	Trapezoidal pyramid	Cone
$b = 6, b_2 = 7,$ $h = 6, r = 3$	$H = 20$	**a.** $V =$ ⓗ 120 cm^3	**d.** $V =$ 240 cm^3	**g.** $V =$ 260 cm^3	**j.** $V =$ 60π cm^3
$b = 9, b_2 = 22,$ $h = 8, r = 6$	$H = 20$	**b.** $V =$ 240 cm^3	**e.** $V =$ 480 cm^3	**h.** $V = \frac{2480}{3}$ cm^3	**k.** $V =$ 240π cm^3
$b = 13, b_2 = 29,$ $h = 17, r = 8$	$H = 24$	**c.** $V =$ 884 cm^3	**f.** $V =$ 1768 cm^3	**i.** $V =$ 2856 cm^3	**l.** $V =$ 512π cm^3

For Exercises 11 and 12, sketch and label the solids described.

11. Sketch and label a square pyramid with height H feet and each side of the base M feet. The altitude meets the square base at the intersection of the two diagonals. Find the volume in terms of H and M.

12. Sketch two different circular cones each with a volume of 2304π cm^3.

13. Mount Fuji, the active volcano in Honshu, Japan, is 3776 m high and has a slope of approximately 30°. Mount Etna, in Sicily, is 3350 m high and approximately 50 km across the base. If you assume they both can be approximated by cones, which volcano is larger?

Mount Fuji is Japan's highest mountain. Legend claims that an earthquake created it.

14. Bretislav has designed a crystal glass sculpture. Part of the piece is in the shape of a large regular pentagonal pyramid, shown at right. The apothem of the base measures 27.5 cm. How much will this part weigh if the glass he plans to use weighs 2.85 grams per cubic centimeter? 78,375 grams

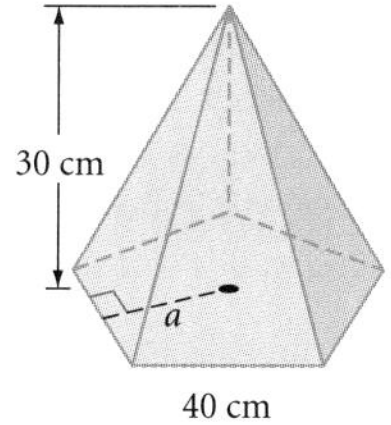

15. Jamala has designed a container that she claims will hold 50 $in.^3$. The net is shown at right. Check her calculations. What is the volume of the solid formed by this net? ⓗ 48 $in.^3$

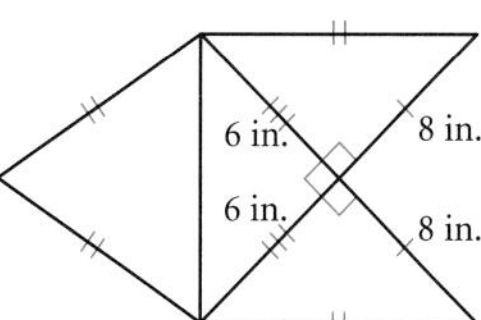

11. $V = \frac{1}{3}M^2H$ ft^3

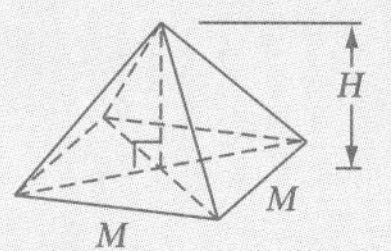

Exercise 12 Labels on the sketches are essential to show the sketches are different cones with the same volume.

12. sample answer:

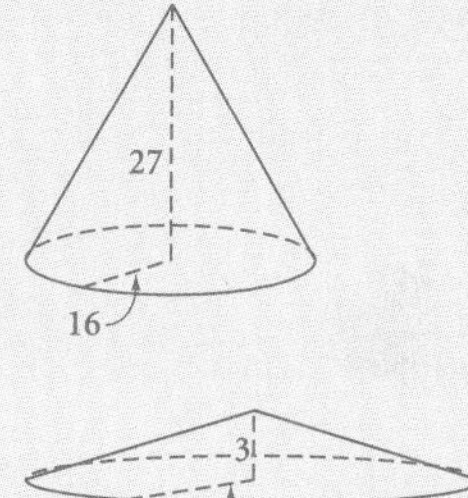

13. Mount Etna is larger. The volume for Mount Etna is approximately 2193 km^3, and the volume for Mount Fuji is approximately 169 km^3.

Exercise 14 [Context] The character is named after the glass sculptor Bretislav Novak (b 1952 in Czechoslovakia).

Exercise 16 Some students might have difficulty seeing that the rotation results in a cone. They think of lines as flat and of cones as curved. In fact, one possible definition of a cone is the figure that results from rotating one line about a line that it intersects.

Exercise 21 The faces of a regular tetrahedron or icosahedron are triangles. The faces of a regular hexahedron are squares. They are pictured on page 528.

16. Find the volume of the solid formed by rotating the shaded figure about the x-axis. 4π units^3

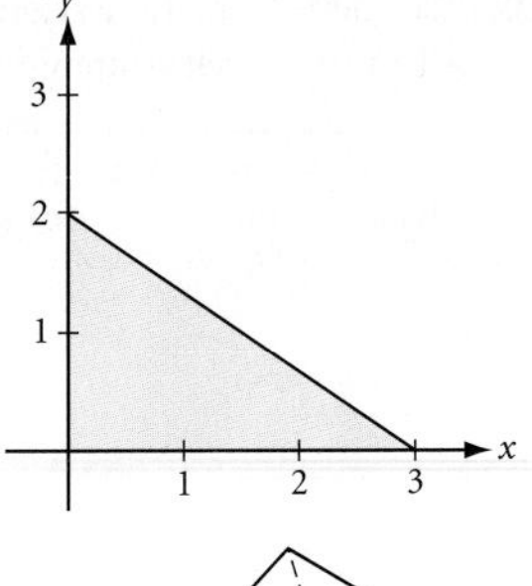

Review

10.2 **17.** Find the volume of the liquid in this right rectangular prism. All measurements are given in centimeters. $144x^3$ cm^3

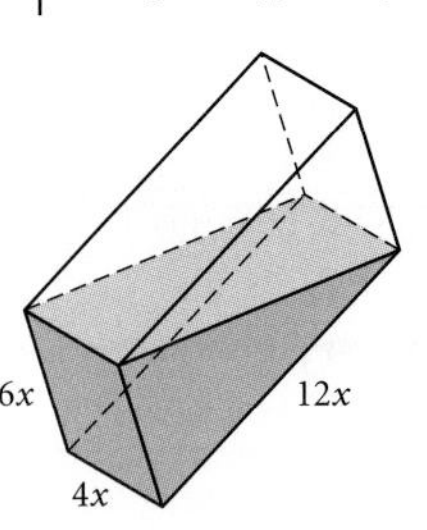

10.2 **18.** **APPLICATION** A swimming pool is in the shape of this prism. A cubic foot of water is about 7.5 gallons. How many gallons of water can the pool hold? If a pump is able to pump water into the pool at a rate of 15 gallons per minute, how long will it take to fill the pool? ⓗ 40,200 gal; 44 hr 40 min

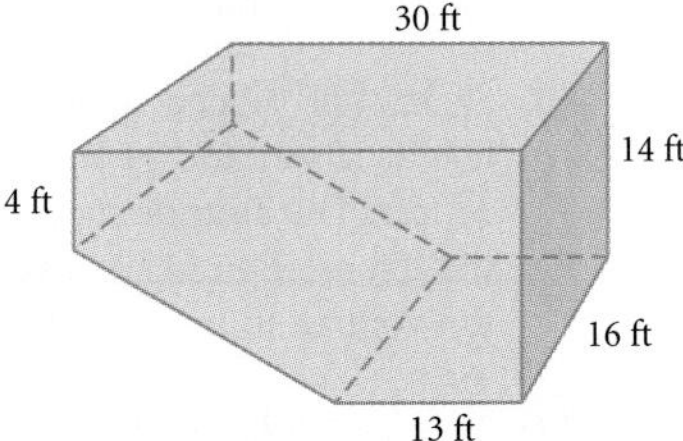

10.2 **19.** **APPLICATION** A landscape architect is building a stone retaining wall as sketched at right. How many cubic feet of stone will she need? 71 ft^3

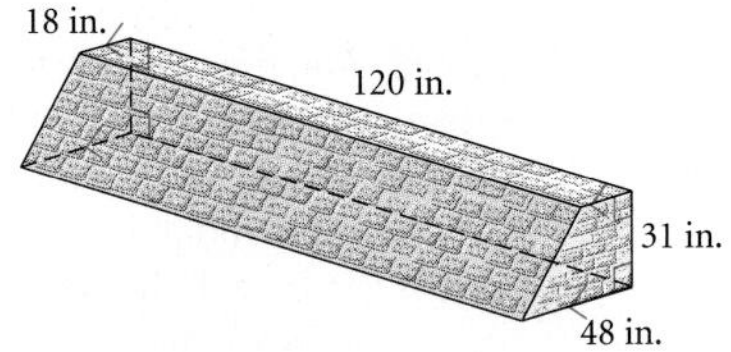

10.2 **20.** As bad as tanker oil spills are, they are only about 12% of the 3.5 million tons of oil that enters the oceans each year. The rest comes from routine tanker operations, sewage treatment plants' runoff, natural sources, and offshore oil rigs. One month's maintenance and routine operation of a single supertanker produces up to 17,000 gallons of oil sludge that gets into the ocean! If a cylindrical barrel is about 1.6 feet in diameter and 2.8 feet tall, how many barrels are needed to hold 17,000 gallons of oil sludge? Recall that a cubic foot of water is about 7.5 gallons. 403 barrels

8.7 **21.** Find the surface area of each of the following polyhedrons. (See the shapes on page 528.) Give *exact* answers.

a. A regular tetrahedron with an edge of 4 cm $16\sqrt{3}$ cm^2

b. A regular hexahedron with an edge of 4 cm 96 cm^2

c. A regular icosahedron with an edge of 4 cm $80\sqrt{3}$ cm^2

d. The dodecahedron shown at right, made of four congruent rectangles and eight congruent triangles $(24\sqrt{13} + 120)$ cm^2

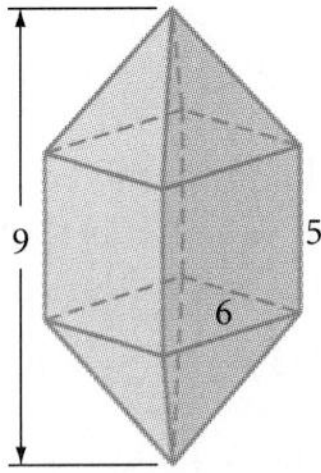

7.1 **22.** Given the triangle at right, reflect D over $\overline{AC}$ to D'. Then reflect D over $\overline{BC}$ to D''. Explain why D', C, D'' are collinear.

5.5 **23.** In each diagram, $WXYZ$ is a parallelogram. Find the coordinates of Y.

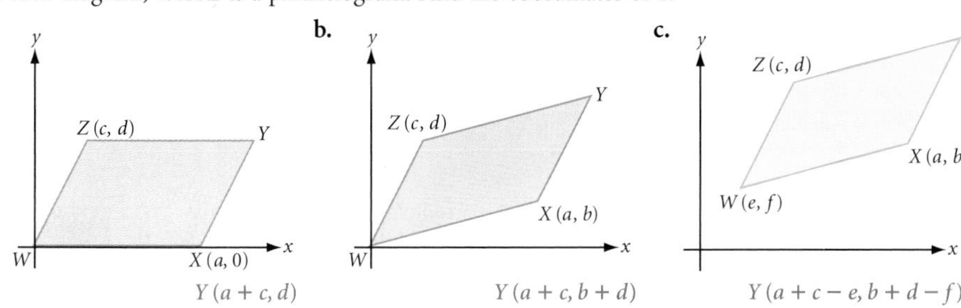

$Y(a + c, d)$ $\quad$ $Y(a + c, b + d)$ $\quad$ $Y(a + c - e, b + d - f)$

22.

Possible answer: From the properties of reflection $\angle 1 \cong \angle 3$ and $\angle 2 \cong \angle 4$. $m\angle 1 + m\angle 2 = 90°$, so $m\angle 3 + m\angle 4 = 90°$, and $m\angle 1 + m\angle 2 + m\angle 3 + m\angle 4 = 180°$. Therefore D', C, and D'' are collinear.

EXTENSION

Lay the groundwork for proportions in Lesson 11.5 by asking students to use algebra to show that if the height of a prism, a cylinder, a pyramid, or a cone is doubled, the volume is doubled, but if you double the dimensions of the base, you increase the volume by more than two times. **[Ask]** "By how much is the volume multiplied if the dimensions of the base are doubled?" [4] "By how much is the volume multiplied if the dimensions of the base are doubled and the height is doubled?" [8]

project

THE WORLD'S LARGEST PYRAMID

The pyramid at Cholula, Mexico, shown at right, was built between the second and eighth centuries C.E. Like most pyramids of the Americas, it has a flat top. In fact, it is really two flat-topped pyramids.

This church in Cholula appears to be on a hill, but it is actually built on top of an ancient pyramid!

Some people claim it is the world's largest pyramid—even larger than the Great Pyramid of Khufu at Giza (shown on page 519) erected around 2500 B.C.E. Is it? Which of the two has the greater volume?

Your project should include

- Volume calculations for both pyramids.
- Scale models of both pyramids.

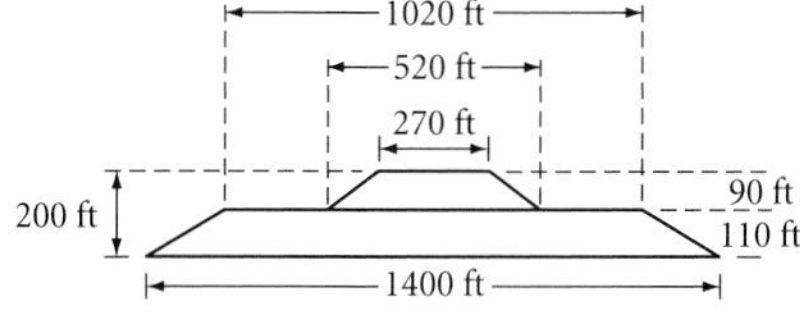

Side view of the two pyramids at Cholula

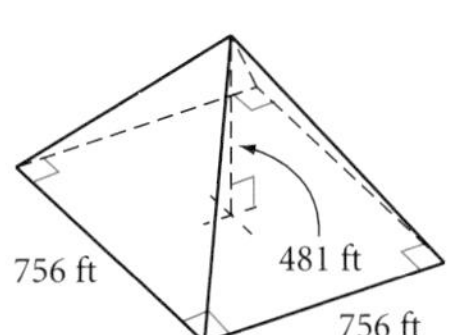

Dimensions of the Great Pyramid at Giza

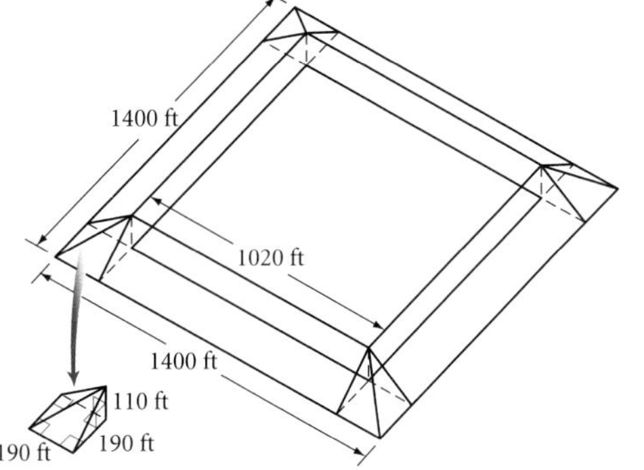

Dissected view of bottom pyramid at Cholula

Supporting the project

Another name for a "flat-topped pyramid" is *frustum*. The volume of a frustum can be found by imagining a pyramid and subtracting the volume of a smaller pyramid removed from the volume of the original pyramid, or by dissecting the frustum into familiar solids.

OUTCOMES

- The volume of the pyramid at Cholula: volume of bottom section is $162{,}374{,}666\frac{1}{3}$ ft^3, volume of top section is 14,511,000 ft^3, total volume is $176{,}885{,}666\frac{1}{3}$ ft$^3 \approx$ 6.6 million yd^3
- The volume of the Great Pyramid at Giza: $V = \frac{1}{3}(756)^2(481) = 91{,}636{,}272$ ft$^3 \approx$ 3.4 million yd^3
- Accurate models are built using the same scale for both pyramids.

EXPLORATION

PLANNING

LESSON OUTLINE

One day:

30 min Activity

10 min Sharing

5 min Closing

MATERIALS

- poster board or cardboard (file folders work well)
- construction tools
- scissors
- glue, paste, or cellophane tape
- colored pens or pencils, *optional*
- The Five Platonic Solids (W)
- *The Platonic Solids* video, *optional*

TEACHING

[Context] According to Plato and Aristotle, all things are composed of five different kinds of atoms. The idea for four of these atoms—earth, air, fire, and water—goes back to Empedocles (ca. 490–430 B.C.E.) and perhaps even earlier. A century later, the fact that there are exactly five regular solids led Plato to believe that a correspondence existed.

Plato and Aristotle considered fire to be the lightest atom; they reasoned that because the tetrahedron has the fewest faces and the sharpest points, fire atoms must be tetrahedral. They reasoned further that fire, air, and water react with one another, so they must be composed of atoms that are similar. The faces of the octahedron, icosahedron, and tetrahedron are equilateral triangles, so air, water, and fire must have these shapes. Air is the second lightest substance, so air atoms must be octahedrons. Earth atoms must be cubes, because the cube is very stable, like earth.

What about the fifth regular solid, the dodecahedron? These two philosophers believed that objects outside Earth—the stars, planets, sun, and moon—consist of matter very different from that on Earth. The dodecahedron is very unlike the other regular polyhedra, because it has pentagonal faces. Therefore the matter of the cosmos must be made of dodecahedral atoms. This conclusion of Plato and Aristotle is consistent with the division of the sky into a zodiac of 12 signs. **[ESL]** The *cosmos* is the universe.

Exploration

The Five Platonic Solids

Regular polyhedrons have intrigued mathematicians for thousands of years. Greek philosophers saw the principles of mathematics and science as the guiding forces of the universe. Plato (429–347 B.C.E.) reasoned that because all objects are three-dimensional, their smallest parts must be in the shape of regular polyhedrons. There are only five regular polyhedrons, and they are commonly called the **Platonic solids.**

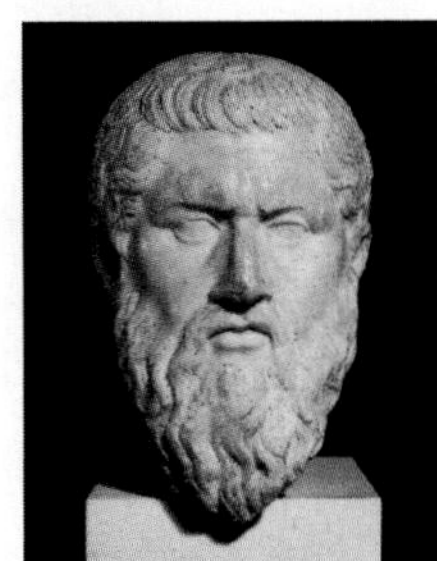

Plato

Plato assigned each regular solid to one of the five "atoms": the tetrahedron to fire, the icosahedron to water, the octahedron to air, the cube or hexahedron to earth, and the dodecahedron to the cosmos.

Fire

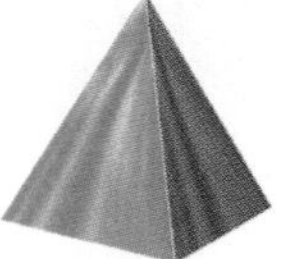

Regular tetrahedron (4 faces)

Water

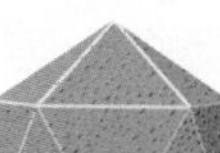

Regular icosahedron (20 faces)

Air

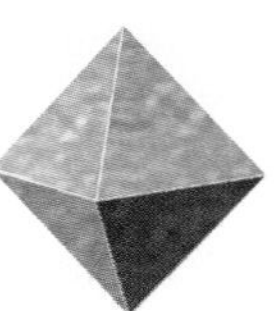

Regular octahedron (8 faces)

Earth

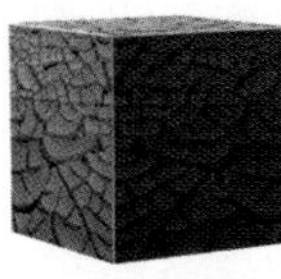

Regular hexahedron (6 faces)

Cosmos

Regular dodecahedron (12 faces)

Activity

Modeling the Platonic Solids

You will need

- poster board or cardboard
- a compass and straightedge
- scissors
- glue, paste, or cellophane tape
- colored pens or pencils for decorating the solids (*optional*)

What would each of the five Platonic solids look like when unfolded? There is more than one way to unfold each polyhedron. Recall that a flat figure that you can fold into a polyhedron is called its net.

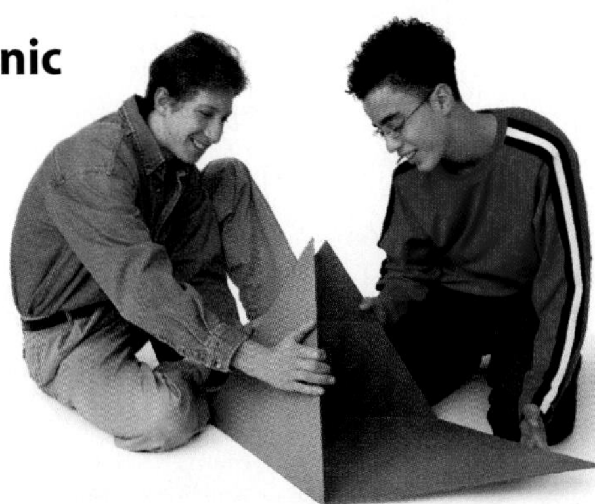

Step 1 | One face is missing in the net at right. Complete the net to show what the regular tetrahedron would look like if it were cut open along the three lateral edges and unfolded into one piece.

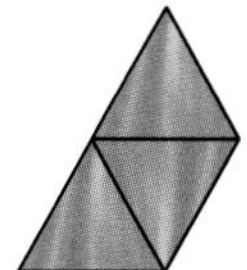

Step 2 | Two faces are missing in the net at right. Complete the net to show what the regular hexahedron would look like if it were cut open along the lateral edges and three top edges, then unfolded.

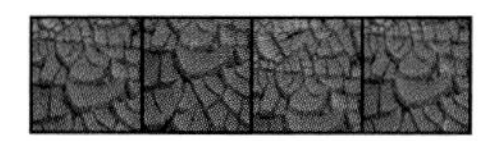

Step 3 | Here is one possible net for the regular icosahedron. When the net is folded together, the five top triangles meet at one top point. Which edge—*a*, *b*, or *c*—does the edge labeled *x* line up with? *b*

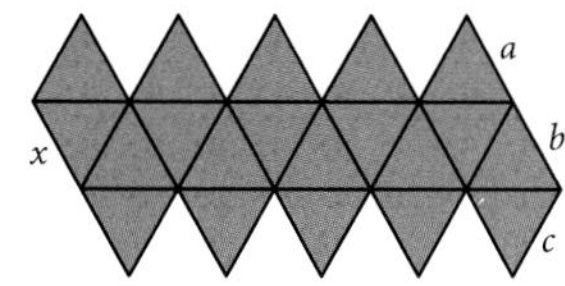

Step 4 | The regular octahedron is similar to the icosahedron but has only eight equilateral triangles. Complete the octahedron net at right. Two faces are missing.

Step 5 | The regular dodecahedron has 12 regular pentagons as faces. If you cut the dodecahedron into two equal parts, they would look like two flowers, each having five pentagon-shaped petals around a center pentagon. Complete the net for half a dodecahedron.

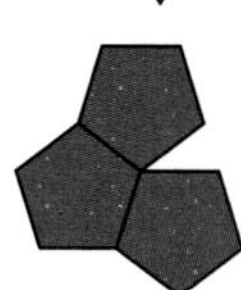

Now you know what the nets of the five Platonic solids could look like. Let's use the nets to construct and assemble models of the five Platonic solids. See the Procedure Note for some tips.

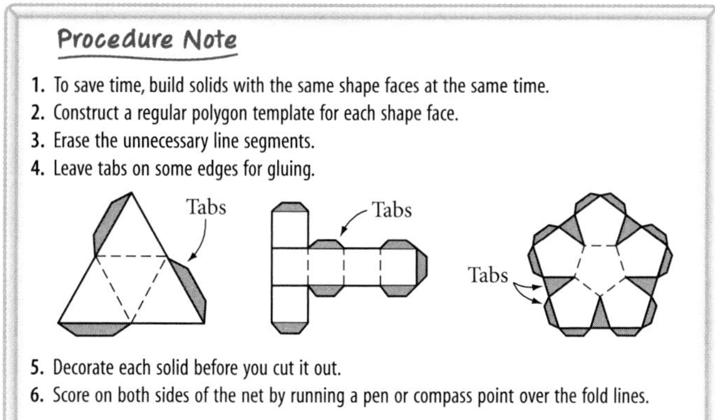
Procedure Note

1. To save time, build solids with the same shape faces at the same time.
2. Construct a regular polygon template for each shape face.
3. Erase the unnecessary line segments.
4. Leave tabs on some edges for gluing.

5. Decorate each solid before you cut it out.
6. Score on both sides of the net by running a pen or compass point over the fold lines.

Step 6 | Construct the nets for icosahedron, octahedron, and tetrahedron with equilateral triangles.

Guiding the Activity

Nets could also be built using geometry software and then printed onto heavy paper. Nets of the Platonic Solids can be found on the worksheets for this exploration, but make sure students still read through the steps.

Step 1

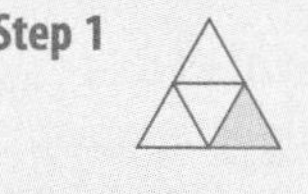

Step 2

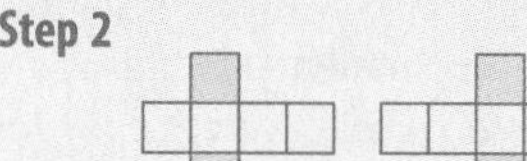

Step 4 possible answers (plus all reflections and rotations of these):

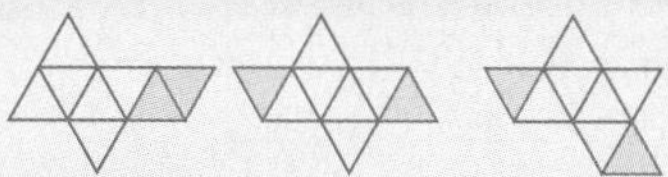

Step 5

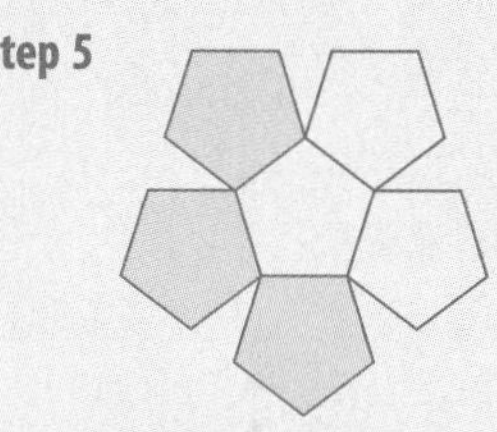

Step 6 Before you begin this step, read through the construction tips in the Procedure Note in the student book.

NCTM STANDARDS

CONTENT		PROCESS	
✓	Number		Problem Solving
	Algebra		Reasoning
✓	Geometry	✓	Communication
✓	Measurement	✓	Connections
	Data/Probability		Representation

LESSON OBJECTIVES

- Learn about the Platonic solids
- Deepen understanding of nets
- Improve visual thinking

Step 8 Using the Pythagorean Theorem twice, students can find that the length of one side of a regular pentagon inscribed in a circle of radius 1 is $\sqrt{\frac{5-\sqrt{5}}{2}}$. This step can be done using a protractor by placing points at 0°, 72°, 144°, 216°, and 288° around a circle.

Step 9 Students may find that minor changes in the placement of a straightedge along the diagonals of the smaller pentagon can lead to significant changes in the larger pentagon formed. Even with careful construction, adjustments might be needed to make this pentagon regular.

Step 10 The sum of angles at each vertex of a net must be less than 360° to allow bending, so the only possible regular polygons that could meet there are 3, 4, or 5 equilateral triangles (each with an interior angle of 60°); 3 squares (with interior angles of 90°); or 3 regular pentagons (with interior angle of 108°).

Step 7 Construct a net for the hexahedron, or cube, with squares.

Step 8 You will construct a net for the dodecahedron with regular pentagons. To construct a regular pentagon, follow Steps A–F below. Construct a circle. Construct two perpendicular diameters. Find M, the midpoint of $\overline{OA}$. Swing an arc with radius BM intersecting $\overline{OC}$ at point D.

Step A

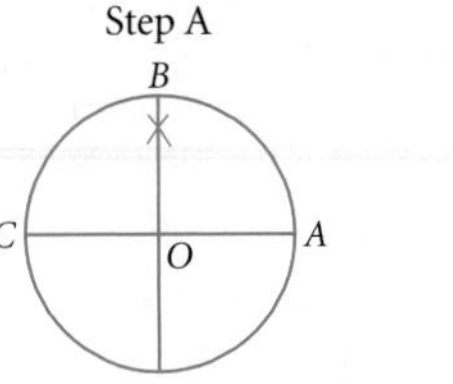

Step B

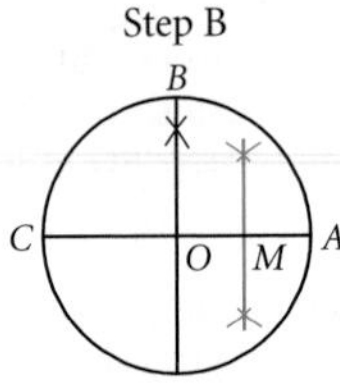

Step C

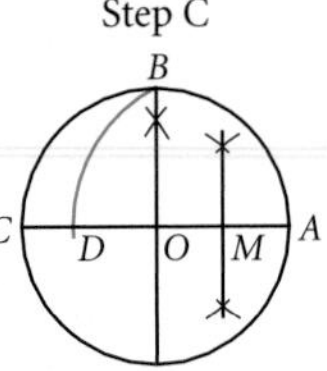

BD is the length of each side of the pentagon. Starting at point B, mark off BD on the circumference five times. Connect the points to form a pentagon.

Step D

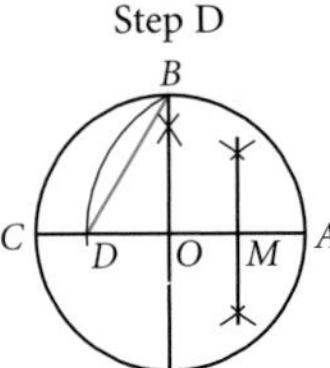

Step E

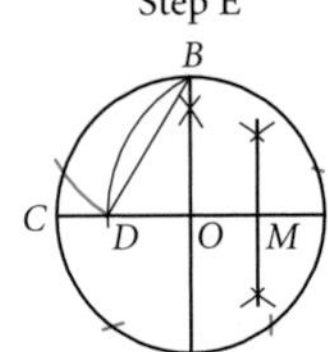

Step F

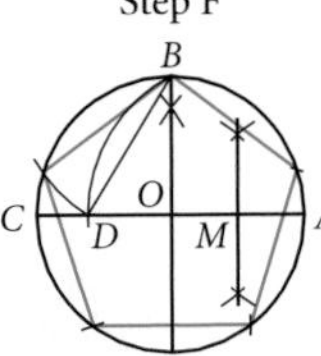

Step 9 Follow Steps A–D below to construct half the net for the dodecahedron. Construct a large regular pentagon. Lightly draw all the diagonals. The smaller regular pentagon will be one of the 12 faces of the dodecahedron.

Step A

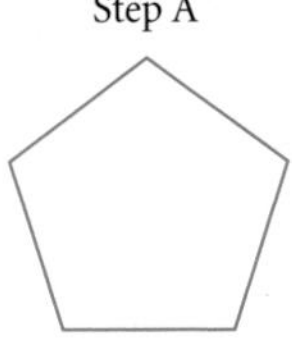

Step B

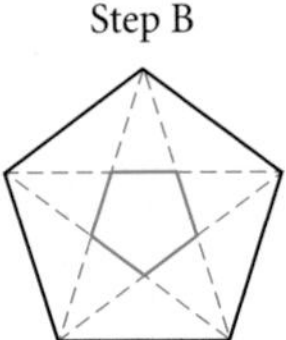

Draw the diagonals of the central pentagon and extend them to the sides of the larger pentagon. Find the five pentagons that encircle the central pentagon.

Step C

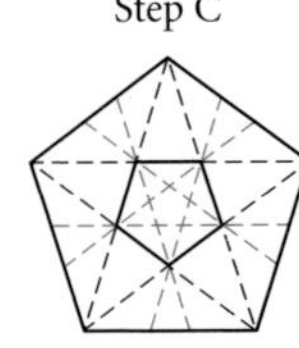

Step D

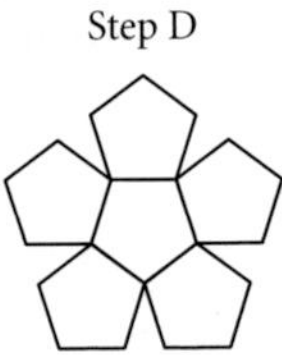

Step 10 Can you explain from looking at the nets why there are only five Platonic solids?

SHARING IDEAS

Have students display their solids around the room. You might ask them to evaluate one another's work on things such as completeness, accuracy, and visual appeal.

You might review the definition of a regular polyhedron from Lesson 10.1. **[Ask]** "Would the definition be complete without each part of the definition? Why or why not?" [At first the long, three-part definition is necessary to determine a regular polyhedron. Claiming that a regular polyhedron is a polyhedron with all faces congruent and regular is not enough. The additional necessary condition can be expressed in several ways: All the vertices lie on a sphere, or all the dihedral angles (angles between face planes) are congruent, or all the vertices are surrounded by the same number of faces.] (For more on regular polyhedrons, see *Polyhedra* by Peter Cromwell.)

You might show a model of a nonregular solid and **[Ask]** "What condition of a regular solid does this solid not meet?"

Assessing Progress

Assess students' understanding of regular polygons and regular polyhedrons and their visualization skills in moving from nets to solids.

Closing the Lesson

If you have time, you might show *The Platonic Solids* video.

LESSON

10.4 Volume Problems

If you have made mistakes . . . there is always another chance for you . . . for this thing we call "failure" is not the falling down, but the staying down.

MARY PICKFORD

Volume has applications in science, medicine, engineering, and construction. For example, a chemist needs to accurately measure the volume of reactive substances. A doctor may need to calculate the volume of a cancerous tumor based on a body scan. Engineers and construction personnel need to determine the volume of building supplies such as concrete or asphalt. The volume of the rooms in a completed building will ultimately determine the size of mechanical devices such as air conditioning units.

Sometimes, if you know the volume of a solid, you can calculate an unknown length of a base or the solid's height. Here are two examples.

EXAMPLE A

The volume of this right triangular prism is 1440 cm^3. Find the height of the prism.

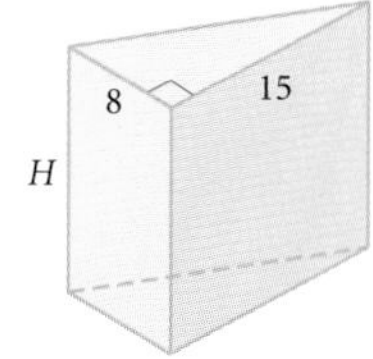

▶ Solution

$V = BH$	Volume formula for prisms and cylinders.
$V = \frac{1}{2}(bh)H$	The base of the prism is a triangle.
$1440 = \frac{1}{2}(8)(15)H$	Substitute 1440 for the volume, 8 for the base of the triangle, and 15 for the height of the triangle.
$1440 = 60H$	Multiply.
$24 = H$	Solve for H.

The height of the prism is 24 cm.

EXAMPLE B

The volume of this sector of a right cylinder is 2814 m^3. Find the radius of the base of the cylinder to the nearest m.

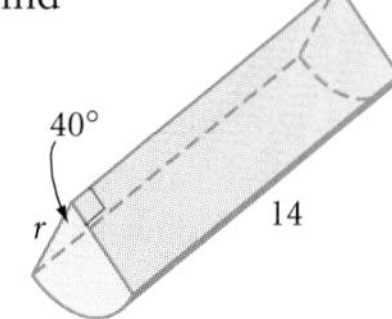

▶ Solution

The volume is the area of the base times the height. To find the area of the sector, you first find what fraction the sector is of the whole circle: $\frac{40}{360} = \frac{1}{9}$.

$$V = BH$$

$$V = \left(\frac{1}{9}\pi r^2\right)H$$

$$2814 = \frac{1}{9}\pi r^2(14)$$

$$\frac{9 \cdot 2814}{14\pi} = r^2$$

$$575.8 \approx r^2$$

$$24 \approx r$$

The radius is about 24 m.

NCTM STANDARDS

CONTENT		PROCESS	
	Number	✓	Problem Solving
✓	Algebra		Reasoning
✓	Geometry	✓	Communication
✓	Measurement		Connections
	Data/Probability	✓	Representation

LESSON OBJECTIVES

- Solve applied problems involving polyhedrons, cones, cylinders, spheres, or hemispheres
- Practice three-dimensional visual thinking skills
- Develop reading comprehension and problem-solving skills

LESSON 10.4

PLANNING

LESSON OUTLINE

One day:

10 min Examples

25 min Exercises

10 min Closing

MATERIALS

none

TEACHING

In this lesson students deepen their understanding of volume by working on a variety of applications. Use the one-step investigation (page 532), or use the examples and allow groups to work on the exercises.

▶ EXAMPLE A

[Language] The term *right triangular prism* means that the prism is not oblique, not necessarily that the triangular base is a right triangle.

You might ask students if the dimensions of the base look familiar. They occur in the 8-15-17 Pythagorean triple. Finding the length of the hypotenuse isn't necessary in order to solve this problem.

▶ EXAMPLE B

[Alert] Students might not see this figure as part of a cylinder. As needed, **[Ask]** "What is a sector of a cylinder?" [a cylinder whose base is a sector of a circle, a region between two radii of a circle and the included arc] "Where are the bases of this cylinder?" [to the left and right in the drawing]

The next-to-last step of the solution uses an approximation of π to obtain an approximation of r. The value of r^2 is very close to the square of 24, or 576. A radius of 24 is a better answer than 23.996 because it contains only two significant digits.

One step Pose this problem, taken from Exercise 13: "A standard juice box holds 8 fluid ounces. A fluid ounce of liquid occupies 1.8 cubic inches. Design cans in the shape of prisms, cylinders, pyramids, and cones that will hold about the same volume as one juice box. Record the advantages and disadvantages of each shape." As you circulate, encourage students to draw pictures. You might also get different groups to focus on different shapes.

SHARING IDEAS

As students share results of the one-step investigation, be sure different volume formulas are revisited. In critiquing the proposed shapes, you can review ideas about the surface areas and discuss efficient stacking and packaging, shelf space, and attractiveness for marketing.

[Ask] "How might you find volumes of irregularly shaped objects?" You need not answer this question; it motivates the next lesson.

Closing the Lesson

Reiterate the main mathematical point of this lesson: Volume formulas can be useful in a variety of circumstances.

EXERCISES

You will need

Construction tools for Exercise **18**

1. If you cut a 1-inch square out of each corner of an 8.5-by-11-inch piece of paper and fold it into a box without a lid, what is the volume of the container? 58.5 in.^{3}

2. The prism at right has equilateral triangle bases with side lengths of 4 cm. The height of the prism is 8 cm. Find the volume. $32\sqrt{3}$ cm^3

3. A triangular pyramid has a volume of 180 cm^3 and a height of 12 cm. Find the length of a side of the triangular base if the triangle's height from that side is 6 cm. 15 cm

4. A trapezoidal pyramid has a volume of 3168 cm^3, and its height is 36 cm. The lengths of the two bases of the trapezoidal base are 20 cm and 28 cm. What is the height of the trapezoidal base? ⓗ 11 cm

5. The volume of a cylinder is 628 cm^3. Find the radius of the base if the cylinder has a height of 8 cm. Round your answer to the nearest 0.1 cm. 5.0 cm

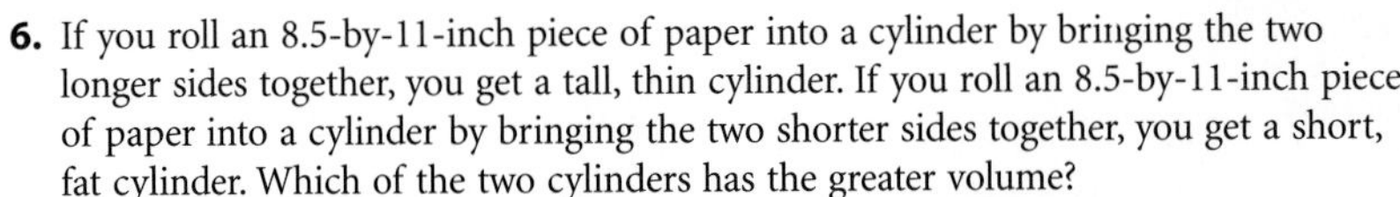

6. If you roll an 8.5-by-11-inch piece of paper into a cylinder by bringing the two longer sides together, you get a tall, thin cylinder. If you roll an 8.5-by-11-inch piece of paper into a cylinder by bringing the two shorter sides together, you get a short, fat cylinder. Which of the two cylinders has the greater volume?

7. Sylvia has just discovered that the valve on her cement truck failed during the night and that all the contents ran out to form a giant cone of hardened cement. To make an insurance claim, she needs to figure out how much cement is in the cone. The circumference of its base is 44 feet, and it is 5 feet high. Calculate the volume to the nearest cubic foot. 257 ft^3

8. A sealed rectangular container 6 cm by 12 cm by 15 cm is sitting on its smallest face. It is filled with water up to 5 cm from the top. How many centimeters from the bottom will the water level reach if the container is placed on its largest face? 4 cm

9. To test his assistant, noted adventurer Dakota Davis states that the volume of the regular hexagonal ring at right is equal to the volume of the regular hexagonal hole in its center. The assistant must confirm or refute this, using dimensions shown in the figure. What should he say to Dakota? ⓗ He must refute the statement.

ASSIGNING HOMEWORK

Essential	1–12
Performance assessment	12
Portfolio	6
Journal	9
Group	1–14
Review	15–19

Helping with the Exercises

Exercises 3, 4, 7 [Alert] Students may forget to divide by 3.

6. $\left(\frac{8.5 \text{ in.}}{2\pi}\right)^2 \pi \cdot 11 \text{ in.} \approx 63.24 \text{ in.}^3$;

$\left(\frac{11 \text{ in.}}{2\pi}\right)^2 \pi \cdot 8.5 \text{ in.} \approx 81.85 \text{ in.}^3$

The short, fat cylinder has greater volume.

BUILDING UNDERSTANDING

Because much of this lesson can be devoted to students' work on the exercises, you might ask students to share selected results. Encourage students to sketch a picture for each exercise.

Use this information to solve Exercises 10–12: Water weighs about 63 pounds per cubic foot, and a cubic foot of water is about 7.5 gallons.

10. APPLICATION A king-size waterbed mattress measures 5.5 feet by 6.5 feet by 8 inches deep. To the nearest pound, how much does the water in this waterbed weigh? ⓗ 1502 lb

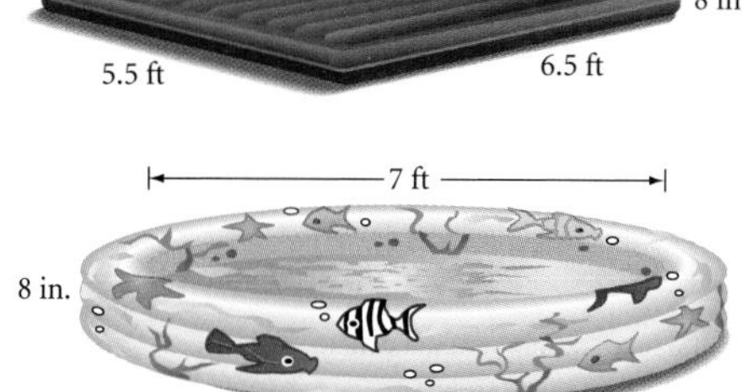

11. A child's wading pool has a diameter of 7 feet and is 8 inches deep. How many gallons of water can the pool hold? Round your answer to the nearest 0.1 gallon. 192.4 gal

12. Madeleine's hot tub has the shape of a regular hexagonal prism. The chart on the hot-tub heater tells how long it takes to warm different amounts of water by 10°F. Help Madeleine determine how long it will take to raise the water temperature from 93°F to 103°F. 13 min

Minutes to Raise Temperature 10°F

Gallons	350	400	450	500	550	600	650	700
Minutes	9	10	11	12	14	15	16	18

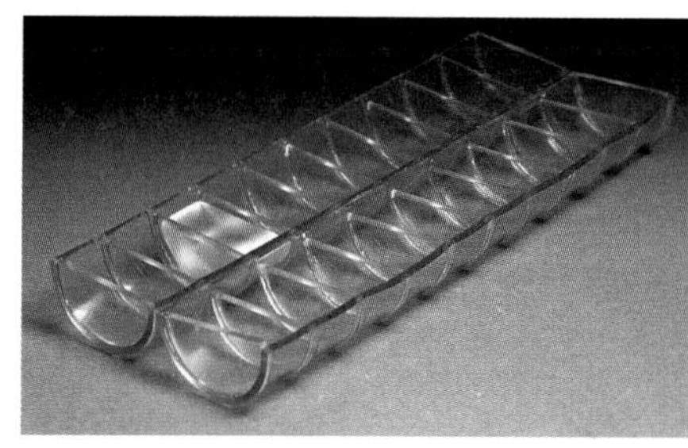

13. A standard juice box holds 8 fluid ounces. A fluid ounce of liquid occupies 1.8 in.^{3}. Design a cylindrical can that will hold about the same volume as one juice box. What are some possible dimensions of the can? Answers will vary, but $\pi r^2 H$ should equal about 14.4 in.^{3}

14. The photo at right shows an ice tray that is designed for a person who has the use of only one hand—each piece of ice will rotate out of the tray when pushed with one finger. Suppose the tray has a length of 12 inches and a height of 1 inch. Approximate the volume of water the tray holds if it is filled to the top. (Ignore the thickness of the plastic.) approximately 38 in.^{3}

Review

10.3 **15.** Find the height of this right square pyramid. Give your answer to the nearest 0.1 cm. 8.2 cm

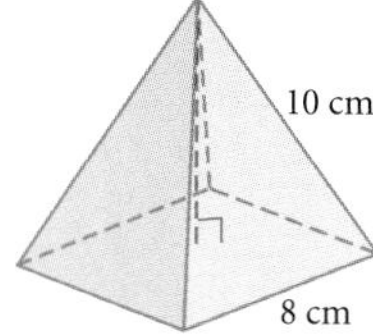

6.2 **16.** $\overleftrightarrow{EC}$ is tangent at C. $\overleftrightarrow{ED}$ is tangent at D. Find x. $x = 140°$

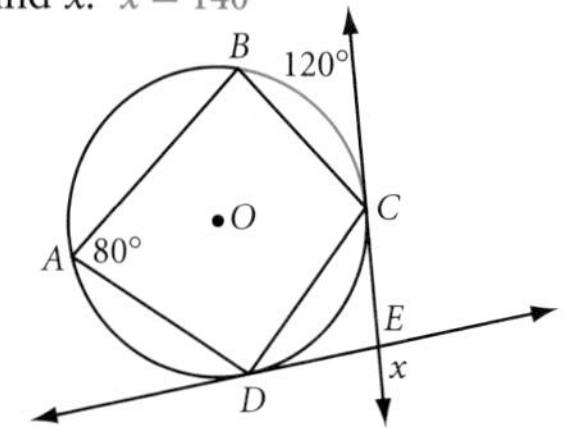

Exercise 8 As needed, **[Ask]** "What does *sitting on its smallest face* mean? Which dimension is the height?" [on one of its 6-by-12 faces; 15]

Exercise 10 **[Alert]** Students may neglect to convert to common units, either inches or feet.

Exercises 12–14 These are the most challenging exercises of the lesson.

Exercise 12 Students might benefit from being reminded that the area of the regular hexagonal base is $\frac{1}{2}aP$.

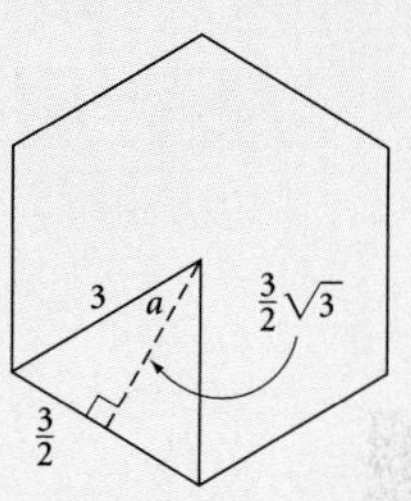

Exercise 15 Students may have difficulty seeing how to apply the Pythagorean Theorem twice. They could first find half the diagonal of the base and use that as one leg of a right triangle with a hypotenuse of 10 cm. Or they could find the slant height and use it along with 4 to find the height.

Exercise 16 If you extended the Tangent Secants Conjecture to include the case where the secants become tangents, students can find $\frac{1}{2}(m\overset{\frown}{CBD} - m\overset{\frown}{CD})$. Or students can complete quadrilateral $OBCD$ and find the measure of $\angle CED$.

17. *AB* equals *EC* because the opposite sides of a parallelogram are congruent. *EC* equals *BD* because the diagonals of a rectangle are congruent. So, *AB* equals *BD* because both are equal to *EC*. Therefore, $\triangle ABD$ is isosceles.

18.

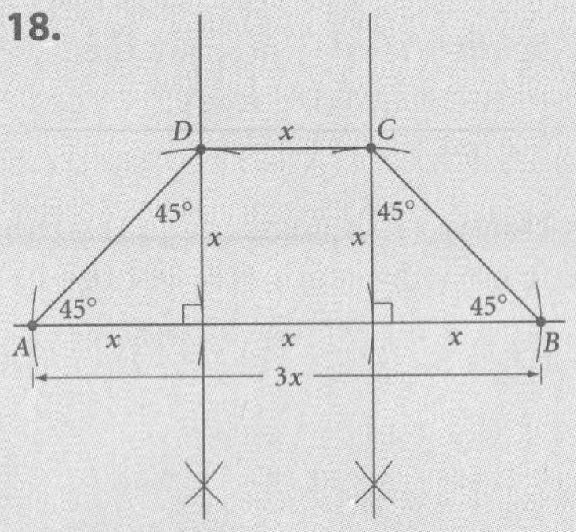

EXTENSION

To extend Exercise 1, students can cut different-size squares out of the corners and find the volume as in the Project Maximizing Volume on page 538.

5.5 **17.** In the figure at right, *ABCE* is a parallelogram and *BCDE* is a rectangle. Write a paragraph proof showing that $\triangle ABD$ is isosceles.

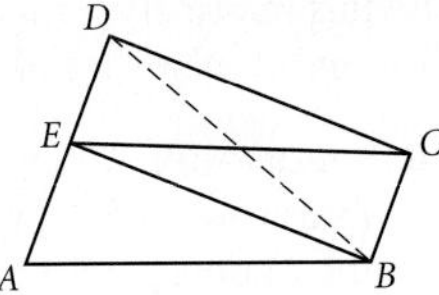

5.3 **18.** ***Construction*** Use your compass and straightedge to construct an isosceles trapezoid with a base angle of 45° and the length of one base three times the length of the other base.

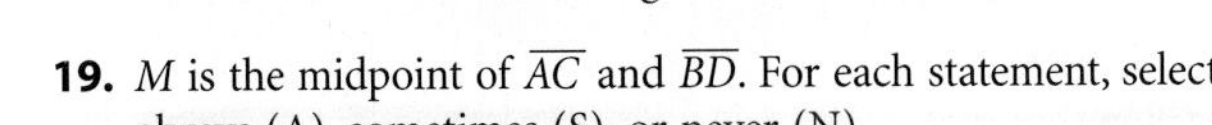

19. *M* is the midpoint of $\overline{AC}$ and $\overline{BD}$. For each statement, select always (A), sometimes (S), or never (N).

a. *ABCD* is a parallelogram. A

b. *ABCD* is a rhombus. S

c. *ABCD* is a kite. N

d. $\triangle AMD \cong \triangle AMB$ S

e. $\angle DAM \cong \angle BCM$ A

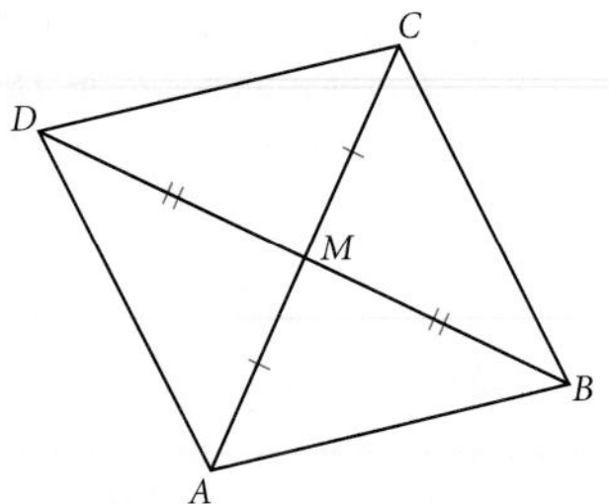

IMPROVING YOUR REASONING SKILLS

Bert's Magic Hexagram

Bert is the queen's favorite jester. He entertains himself with puzzles. Bert is creating a magic hexagram on the front of a grid of 19 hexagons. When Bert's magic hexagram (like its cousin the magic square) is completed, it will have the same sum in every straight hexagonal row, column, or diagonal (whether it is three, four, or five hexagons long). For example, $B + 12 + 10$ is the same sum as $B + 2 + 5 + 6 + 9$, which is the same sum as $C + 8 + 6 + 11$. Bert planned to use just the first 19 positive integers (his age in years), but he only had time to place the first 12 integers before he was interrupted. Your job is to complete Bert's magic hexagram. What are the values for *A, B, C, D, E, F,* and *G*?

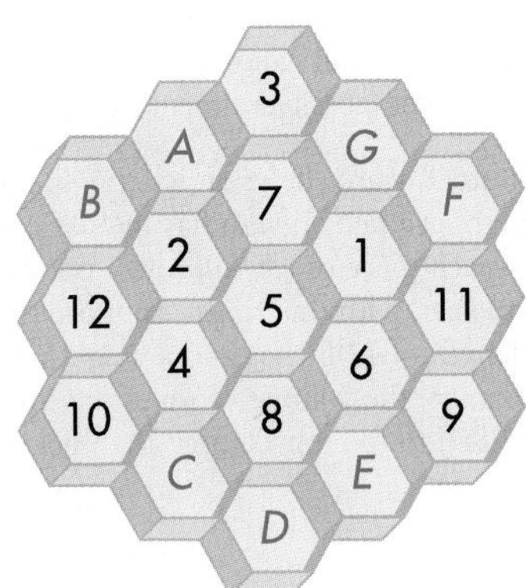

IMPROVING REASONING SKILLS

From the fact that $A + B + 3 = B + 12 + 10$, we can find $A = 19$, so $A + 7 + 1 + 11$ gives the magic sum 38. Because each letter appears at least once in a sum with only numbers and itself, it's not too difficult to find that the other values are $B = 16$, $C = 13$, $D = 15$, $E = 14$, $F = 18$, and $G = 17$.

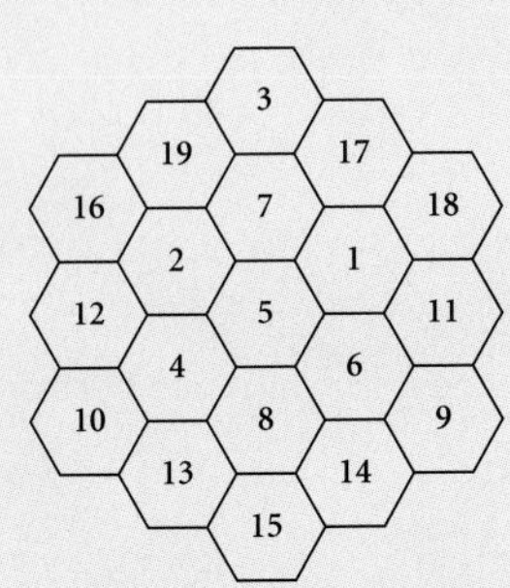

LESSON 10.5

Displacement and Density

Eureka! I have found it!

ARCHIMEDES

What happens if you step into a bathtub that is filled to the brim? If you add a scoop of ice cream to a glass filled with root beer? In each case, you'll have a mess! The volume of the liquid that overflows in each case equals the volume of the solid below the liquid level. This volume is called an object's **displacement.**

EXAMPLE A Mary Jo wants to find the volume of an irregularly shaped rock. She puts some water into a rectangular prism with a base that measures 10 cm by 15 cm. When the rock is put into the container, Mary Jo notices that the water level rises 2 cm because the rock displaces its volume of water. This new "slice" of water has a volume of (2)(10)(15), or 300 cm^3. So the volume of the rock is 300 cm^3.

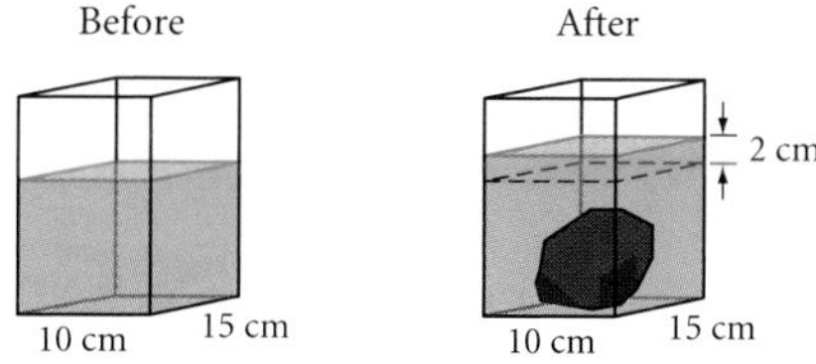

An important property of a material is its density. **Density** is the mass of matter in a given volume. You can find the mass of an object by weighing it. You calculate density by dividing the mass by the volume,

$$\text{density} = \frac{\text{mass}}{\text{volume}}$$

EXAMPLE B A clump of metal weighing 351.4 grams is dropped into a cylindrical container, causing the water level to rise 1.1 cm. The radius of the base of the container is 3.0 cm. What is the density of the metal? Given the table, and assuming the metal is pure, what is the metal?

Metal	Density	Metal	Density
Aluminum	2.81 g/cm^3	Nickel	8.89 g/cm^3
Copper	8.97 g/cm^3	Platinum	21.40 g/cm^3
Gold	19.30 g/cm^3	Potassium	0.86 g/cm^3
Lead	11.30 g/cm^3	Silver	10.50 g/cm^3
Lithium	0.54 g/cm^3	Sodium	0.97 g/cm^3

LESSON

10.5

PLANNING

LESSON OUTLINE

One day:

10 min	Examples
10 min	Sharing
20 min	Exercises
5 min	Closing

MATERIALS

- calculators
- water and pans
- metal samples
- scales, *optional*

TEACHING

For a shape for which we have no formula for calculating volume, it is possible to find the volume by submerging the object in a liquid. Use the examples or start with the one-step investigation on page 536.

[ESL] The *brim* of a tub or pan is the top edge.

▶ ***EXAMPLE A***

[Alert] Students might have difficulty seeing that the water being displaced would fill a rectangular prism with height 2 cm.

▶ ***EXAMPLE B***

The water being displaced forms a cylinder with base area 9π cm^2 and height 1.1 cm. The volume of the displaced water is therefore 9.9π cm^3, making the density $\frac{351.4 \text{ grams}}{9.9\pi \text{ cm}^3} \approx 11.3$ g/cm^3.

NCTM STANDARDS

CONTENT		PROCESS	
	Number	✓	Problem Solving
✓	Algebra		Reasoning
✓	Geometry		Communication
✓	Measurement	✓	Connections
✓	Data/Probability		Representation

LESSON OBJECTIVES

- Apply volume formulas
- Find volumes of irregularly shaped solids through displacement
- Practice three-dimensional visual thinking skills
- Develop reading comprehension, problem-solving skills, and cooperative behavior

One step Give students some irregularly shaped metal samples and either a weighing instrument or the masses of the samples. Ask them to identify the metals, using the table in Example B. As they work, encourage them to find the volumes by putting the samples into a partially filled pan of water that's a cylinder or prism. As needed, refer students to the examples.

SHARING IDEAS

Volume and density can cause a great deal of confusion. **[Ask]** "Will heavier objects displace more water than lighter objects?" [no] Students may think so, perhaps because heavier objects tend to be bigger—that is, have more volume—than lighter objects. **[Ask]** "For two objects with the same volume but different masses, such as a jar full of rocks and a jar of the same size and shape full of cotton, which will displace more volume?" [They displace the same volume of water.] "Would an empty closed jar of the same size and shape displace the same amount of water?" Most students will believe that the empty jar will float, thus displacing much less water even though it has the same volume. Elicit the idea that it's the volume of the part of the object under the water that is equivalent to the volume of displaced water. The part of a floating object under the water level is determined by the density of the object, which is its total mass divided by its total volume—not just the volume beneath the surface. **[Ask]** "Can concrete float?" [It's a heavy material—with lots of mass—so hunks of it sink. But concrete can be formed into a boat whose volume is so large that its density is small.] A lesson on buoyancy appears in *Discovering Geometry More Projects and Explorations.*

▶ ***Solution*** First, find the volume of displaced water. Then, divide the weight by the volume to get the density of the metal.

$$\text{Volume} = \pi(3.0)^2(1.1) = (\pi)(9)(1.1) \approx 31.1$$

$$\text{Density} \approx \frac{351.4}{31.1} \approx 11.3$$

The density is 11.3 g/cm^3. Therefore the metal is lead.

History CONNECTION

Archimedes solved the problem of how to tell if a crown was made of genuine gold by weighing the crown under water. Legend has it that the insight came to him while he was bathing. Thrilled by his discovery, Archimedes ran through the streets shouting "Eureka!" wearing just what he'd been wearing in the bathtub.

EXERCISES

1. When you put a rock into a container of water, it raises the water level 3 cm. If the container is a rectangular prism whose base measures 15 cm by 15 cm, what is the volume of the rock? 675 cm^3

2. You drop a solid glass ball into a cylinder with a radius of 6 cm, raising the water level 1 cm. What is the volume of the glass ball? 36π cm^3

3. A fish tank 10 by 14 by 12 inches high is the home of a large goldfish named Columbia. She is taken out when her owner cleans the tank, and the water level in the tank drops $\frac{1}{3}$ inch. What is Columbia's volume? 47 in.^{3}

For Exercises 4–9, refer to the table on page 535.

4. How much does a solid block of aluminum weigh if its dimensions are 4 cm by 8 cm by 20 cm? 1798.4 g

5. Which weighs more: a solid cylinder of gold with a height of 5 cm and a diameter of 6 cm or a solid cone of platinum with a height of 21 cm and a diameter of 8 cm? The gold weighs 2728.4 g, and the platinum weighs 7529.8 g. The solid cone of platinum weighs more.

6. Chemist Dean Dalton is given a clump of metal and is told that it is sodium. He finds that the metal weighs 145.5 g. He places it into a nonreactive liquid in a square prism whose base measures 10 cm on each edge. If the metal is indeed sodium, how high should the liquid level rise? ⓗ 1.5 cm

7. A square-prism container with a base 5 cm by 5 cm is partially filled with water. You drop a clump of metal that weighs 525 g into the container, and the water level rises 2 cm. What is the density of the metal? Assuming the metal is pure, what is the metal? 10.5 g/cm^3; silver

You might also ask about the difference between weight and mass. The *weight* of an object is measured in relation to the gravitational pull on the object, but the *mass* of an object is independent of the pull of gravity. Your weight would be less on the moon, but your mass would be the same.

Because the lesson consists primarily of exercises, you might have students share their work on the exercises.

Closing the Lesson

You can find the volume of an irregularly shaped object by measuring the amount of liquid it **displaces.** Depending on the shape of the container, you can think of that liquid as occupying a cylinder or a prism, whose volume can be found by a formula. Volumes can be used to find the **density** of objects and thus identify the materials of which they're made. The units of density (g/cm^3) can help students remember that density is mass (g) divided by volume (cm^3).

8. When ice floats in water, one-eighth of its volume floats above the water level and seven-eighths floats beneath the water level. A block of ice placed into an ice chest causes the water in the chest to rise 4 cm. The right rectangular chest measures 35 cm by 50 cm by 30 cm high. What is the volume of the block of ice? Ⓗ 8000 cm^3

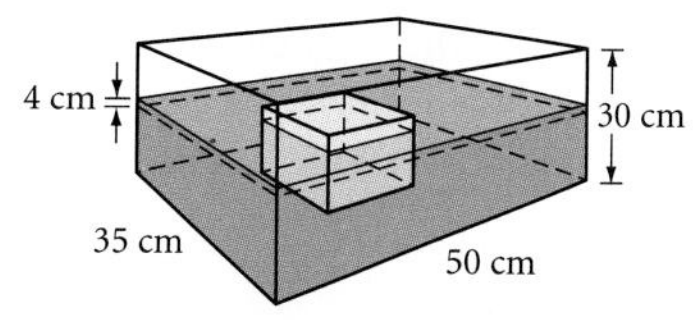

Science
CONNECTION

Buoyancy is the tendency of an object to float in either a liquid or a gas. For an object to float on the surface of water, it must sink enough to displace the volume of water equal to its weight.

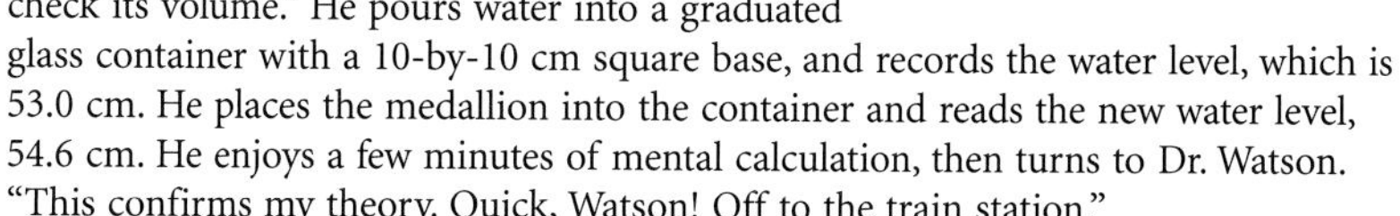

9. Sherlock Holmes rushes home to his chemistry lab, takes a mysterious medallion from his case, and weighs it. "It weighs 3088 grams. Now, let's check its volume." He pours water into a graduated glass container with a 10-by-10 cm square base, and records the water level, which is 53.0 cm. He places the medallion into the container and reads the new water level, 54.6 cm. He enjoys a few minutes of mental calculation, then turns to Dr. Watson. "This confirms my theory. Quick, Watson! Off to the train station."

"Holmes, you amaze me. Is it gold?" questions the good doctor.

"If it has a density of 19.3 grams per cubic centimeter, it is gold," smiles Mr. Holmes. "If it is gold, then Colonel Banderson is who he says he is. If it is a fake, then so is the Colonel."

"Well?" Watson queries.

Holmes smiles and says, "It's elementary, my dear Watson. Elementary geometry, that is."

What is the volume of the medallion? Is it gold? Is Colonel Banderson who he says he is?

The volume of the medallion is 160 cm^3. Yes, it is gold, and the Colonel is who he says he is.

Review

10.2 **10.** What is the volume of the slice removed from this right cylinder? Give your answer to the nearest cm^3. 679 cm^3

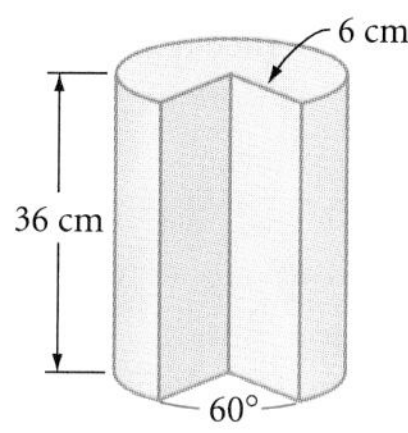

10.2 **11.** APPLICATION Ofelia has brought home a new aquarium shaped like the regular hexagonal prism shown at right. She isn't sure her desk is strong enough to hold it. The aquarium, without water, weighs 48 pounds. How much will it weigh when it is filled? (Water weighs 63 pounds per cubic foot.) If a small fish needs about 180 cubic inches of water to swim around in, about how many small fish can this aquarium house? approximately 194 lb; 22 fish

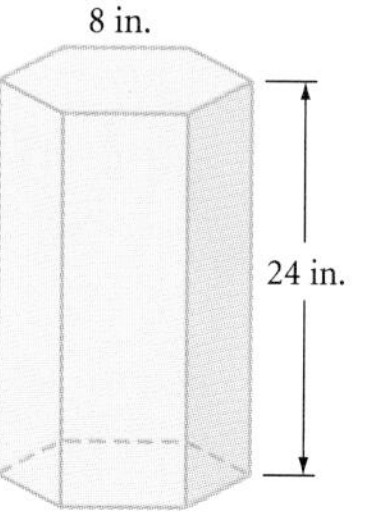

BUILDING UNDERSTANDING

As needed, remind students to use the density table in Example B.

ASSIGNING HOMEWORK

Essential	1–8
Performance assessment	9
Portfolio	3
Review	10–16

Helping with the Exercises

Exercise 6 [Language] *Nonreactive* means it does not react chemically. Displacement works with liquids as long as there is no chemical reaction, which would alter the size of the object. Sodium in water is explosive, so the chemist uses something else.

Exercise 8 Students may be misled by the extraneous information about the height of the ice chest.

Exercise 9 [ESL] A *graduated container* is one marked with units of depth. A *medallion* is a medal of honor given to symbolize an accomplishment.

13. $\angle S \cong \angle R$ by *AIA* because $\overline{SP} \parallel \overline{RQ}$. $\overline{SM} \cong \overline{MR}$ because it is given. $\angle SMP \cong \angle RMQ$ because they are vertical angles. $\triangle SMP \cong \triangle RMQ$ by ASA. $\overline{MP} \cong \overline{MQ}$ because they are corresponding parts of congruent triangles. Therefore, *M* is the midpoint of *PQ* because $\overline{MP} \cong \overline{MQ}$.

Exercise 15 The analytic geometry involved makes this exercise challenging. As needed, remind students how to find the center of a circle from the intersection of the perpendicular bisectors of chords.

Exercise 16 This notation is different from that used in Chapter 2, but the inductive process used to find the function rule is not new.

8.2 **12.** $\triangle ABC$ is equilateral. *M* is the centroid. $AB = 6$ Find the area of $\triangle CEA$. $\frac{9}{2}\sqrt{3}$

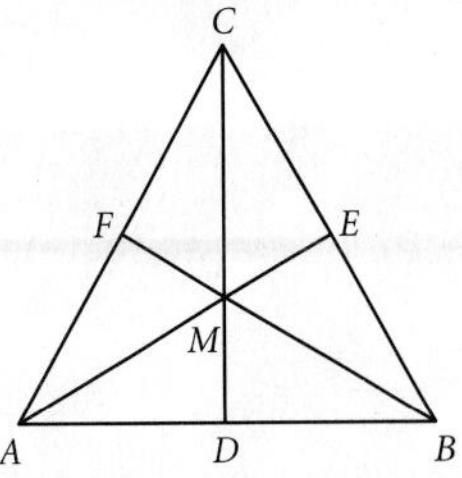

4.6 **13.** Give a paragraph or flowchart proof explaining why *M* is the midpoint of $\overline{PQ}$.

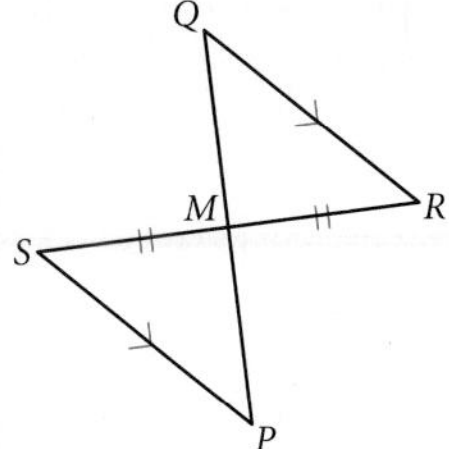

5.1 **14.** The three polygons are regular polygons. How many sides does the red polygon have? 15 sides

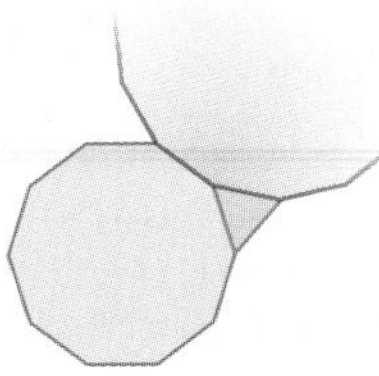

UYAS 6 **15.** A circle passes through the three points (4, 7), (6, 3), and (1, −2).

a. Find the center. (1, 3)

b. Find the equation. $(x-1)^2 + (y-3)^2 = 25$

2.3 **16.** A secret rule matches the following numbers:

$2 \rightarrow 4,\ 3 \rightarrow 7,\ 4 \rightarrow 10,\ 5 \rightarrow 13$

Find $20 \rightarrow$? (58), and $n \rightarrow$? ($3n - 2$).

MAXIMIZING VOLUME

Suppose you have a 10-inch-square sheet of metal and you want to make a small box by cutting out squares from the corners of the sheet and folding up the sides. What size corners should you cut out to get the biggest box possible?

To answer this question, consider the length of the corner cut *x* and write an equation for the volume of the box, *y*, in terms of *x*. Graph your equation using reasonable window values. You should see your graph touch the *x*-axis in at least two places and reach a maximum somewhere in between. Study these points carefully to find their significance.

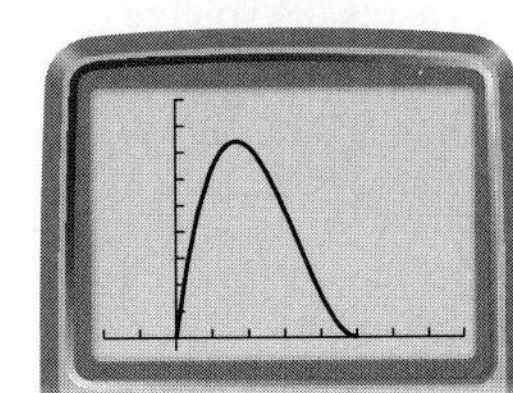

Your project should include

- The equation you used to calculate volume in terms of *x* and *y*.
- A sketch of the calculator graph and the graphing window you used.
- An explanation of important points, for example, when the graph touches the *x*-axis.
- A solution for what size corners make the biggest volume.

Lastly, generalize your findings. For example, what fraction of the side length could you cut from each corner of a 12-inch-square sheet to make a box of maximum volume?

Supporting the project

Students might explore this question by first making physical models to discover an equation that gives the volumes of different boxes. Students can use Fathom software to enter data from each group (corner size, volume), graph the data, and experiment with functions whose graphs fit the points.

OUTCOMES

- The equation $y = x(10 - 2x)(10 - 2x)$ is graphed (on a calculator, in a window such as [0, 6, 1, 0, 80, 10]).
- An interpretation is given of the *x*-intercepts when the volume is zero.
- The maximum point at (1.67, 74.07) is explained as representing a maximum volume of 74.07 in.^{3} when the cut is 1.67 in.
- In general, the maximum volume occurs when the cut equals $\frac{1}{6}$ of the side length. For a 12-inch-square sheet, the cut should be 2 inches to maximize the volume.

Exploration

Orthographic Drawing

If you have ever put together a toy from detailed instructions, or built a birdhouse from a kit, or seen blueprints for a building under construction, you have seen isometric drawings.

Isometric means "having equal measure," so the edges of a cube drawn isometrically all have the same length. In contrast, recall that when you drew a cube in two-point perspective, you needed to use edges of different lengths to get a natural look.

When you buy a product from a catalog or off the Internet, you want to see it from several angles. The top, front, and right side views are given in an **orthographic drawing.** Ortho means "straight," and the views of an orthographic drawing show the faces of a solid as though you are looking at them "head-on."

Top

Front

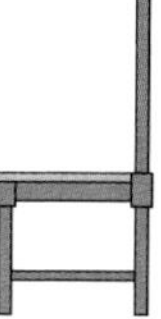

Side

Isometric

An isometric drawing

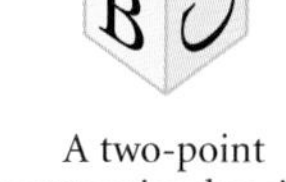

A two-point perspective drawing

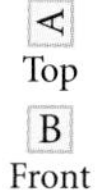

An orthographic drawing

Career CONNECTION

Architects create blueprints for their designs, as shown at right. Architectural drawing plans use orthographic techniques to describe the proposed design from several angles. These front and side views are called building elevations.

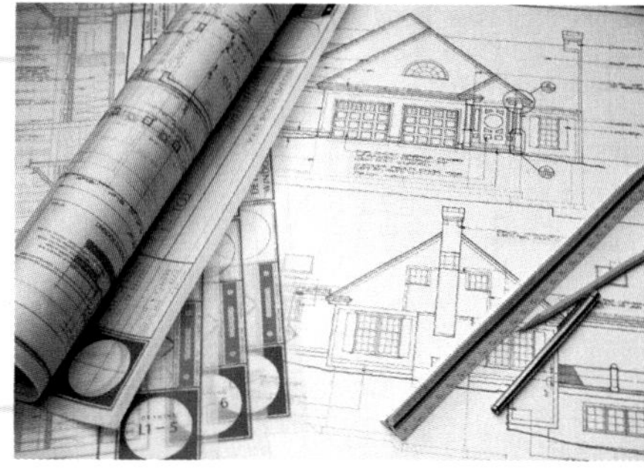

EXPLORATION

PLANNING

LESSON OUTLINE

One day:

10 min	Examples
25 min	Activity
5 min	Sharing
5 min	Closing

MATERIALS

- isometric dot paper
- graph paper
- wooden or sugar cubes, 12 per group
- Isometric and Orthographic Drawings (T) for One step
- Cube Nets (W), *optional*

TEACHING

Isometric drawings are useful in moving to and from orthographic views of an object.

One step Show the Isometric and Orthographic Drawings transparency and ask students what relationships they see. As you circulate, encourage students to build the structure from available cubes so they can view it from different angles. During Sharing ask how students might draw each kind of drawing if they are given the other kind.

NCTM STANDARDS

CONTENT		PROCESS	
	Number	✓	Problem Solving
	Algebra		Reasoning
✓	Geometry	✓	Communication
✓	Measurement	✓	Connections
	Data/Probability	✓	Representation

LESSON OBJECTIVES

- Do isometric and orthographic drawings
- Enhance visualization skills

▶ ***EXAMPLE A***

[Ask] "Are any other dimensions shared?" [The height of the top view must equal the width of the side view.]

▶ ***EXAMPLE B***

Shading shows depth by simulating a light source shining on an object. The object in the solution to Example B shows illumination by a light source from the top left. Isometric drawings omit shadows cast on any surface imagined to be supporting the object.

Guiding the Activity

You can get by with 8 cubes per group, but using 12 is better. You can use sugar cubes, children's blocks, or manipulatives; you might also saw cubes from 1-by-1-inch or 2-by-2-inch wood molding, or build cubes using the Cube Nets worksheet.

Step 3 Some students may prefer to draw the isometric views (following the rules in Example B) and then construct the object from cubes. Others may work on both tasks together. Help students with different learning styles feel comfortable using their preferred approaches.

Step 5 Students get to experiment with drawing slanted planes and circles in isometric drawings and with indicating depth change in orthographic drawings of curves or of plane intersections with angle measures more than 90°. For example, students might doubt their drawing of solid G because the isometric drawing looks like a prism whose base is a rectangle rather than a more general parallelogram.

EXAMPLE A

Make an orthographic drawing of the solid shown in the isometric drawing at right.

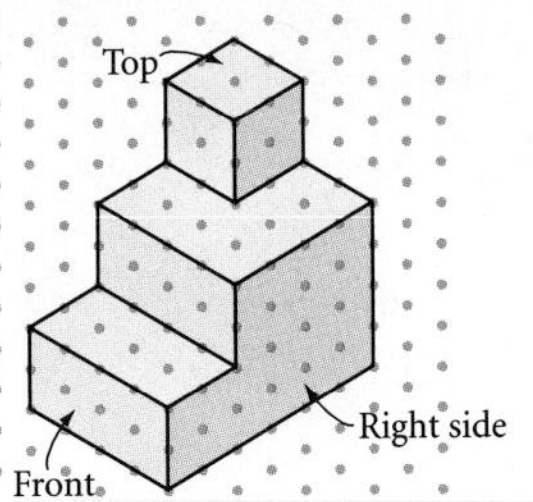

▶ ***Solution***

Visualize how the building would look from the top, the front, and the right side. Draw an edge wherever there is a change of depth. The top and front views must have the same width, and the front and right side views must have the same height.

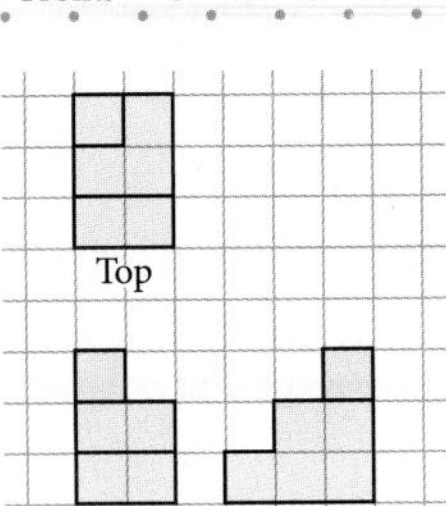

EXAMPLE B

Draw the isometric view of the object shown here as an orthographic drawing. The dashed lines mean that there is an invisible edge.

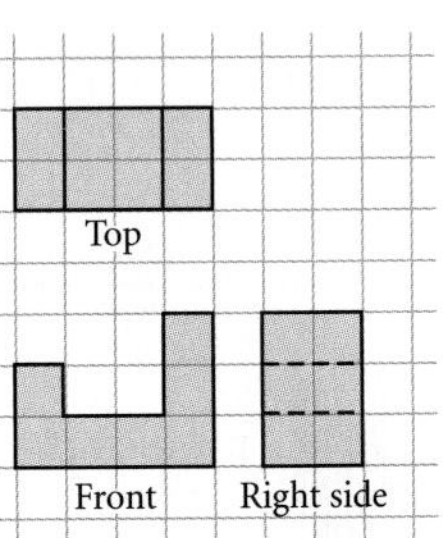

▶ ***Solution***

Find the vertices of the front face and make the shape. Use the width of the side and top views to extend parallel lines. Complete the back edges. You can shade parallel planes to show depth.

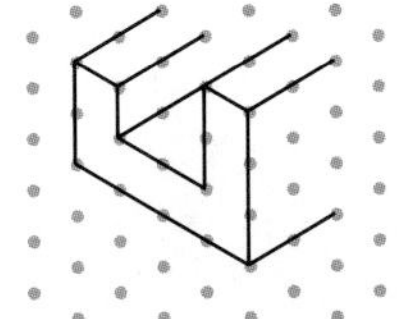

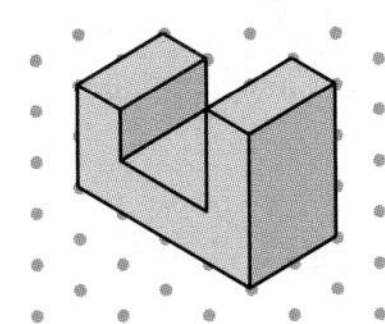

British pop artist David Hockney (b 1937) titled this photographic collage *Sunday Morning Mayflower Hotel, N.Y., Nov-28, 1982.* Each photo shows the view from a different angle, just as an orthographic drawing shows multiple angles at once.

SHARING IDEAS

[Ask] "How is an isometric drawing different from a two-point perspective view?" [In an isometric drawing, all three axes are simultaneously rotated away from the picture plane and maintained at a 30° angle to the picture plane, so all edges of a cube are equally distorted and retain the proportion 1:1:1. By comparison, in two-point perspective, if a cube is placed so that one vertical edge is presented to the viewer, the visible faces recede so that their rear vertical edges are drawn shorter than the common edge in front.]

Activity
Isometric and Orthographic Drawings

You will need

- isometric dot paper
- graph paper
- 12 cubes

In this investigation you'll build block models and draw their isometric and orthographic views.

Step 1 a rhombus; yes, they are congruent; congruent squares

Step 1 Practice drawing a cube on isometric dot paper. What is the shape of each visible face? Are they congruent? What should the orthographic views of a cube look like?

Step 2 Stack three cubes to make a two-step "staircase." Turn the structure so that you look at it the way you would walk up stairs. Call that view the front. Next, identify the top and right sides. How many planes are visible from each view? Make an isometric drawing of the staircase on dot paper and the three orthographic views on graph paper.

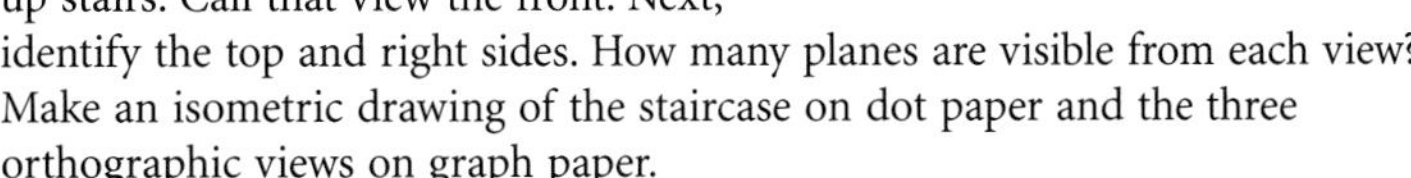

Step 3 Build solids A–D from their orthographic views, then draw their isometric views.

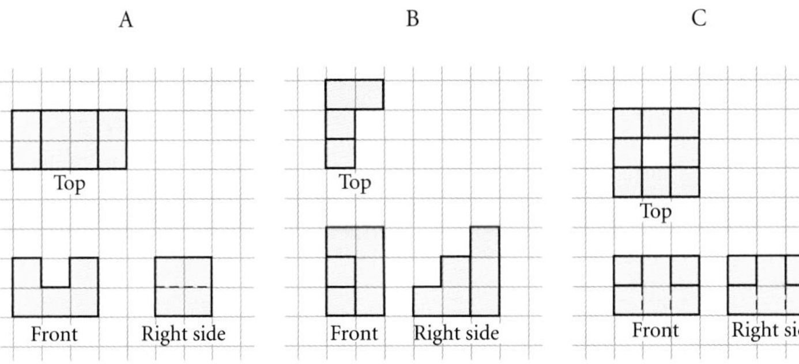

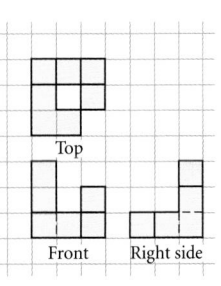

Step 4 Make your own original 8- to 12-cube structure and agree on the orthographic views that represent it. Then, trade places with another group and draw the orthographic views of their structure.

Step 5 Make orthographic views for solids E and F, and sketch the isometric views of solids G and H.

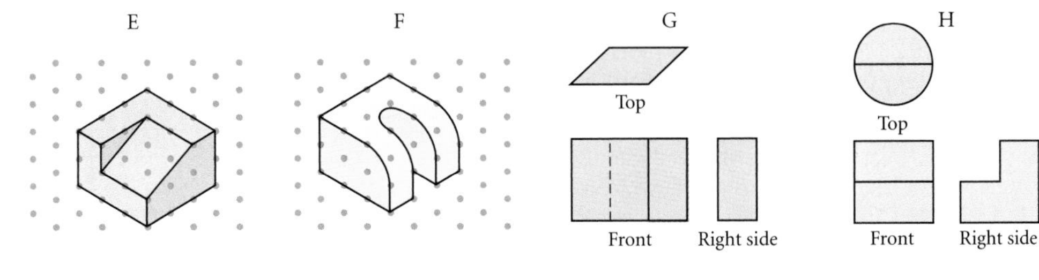

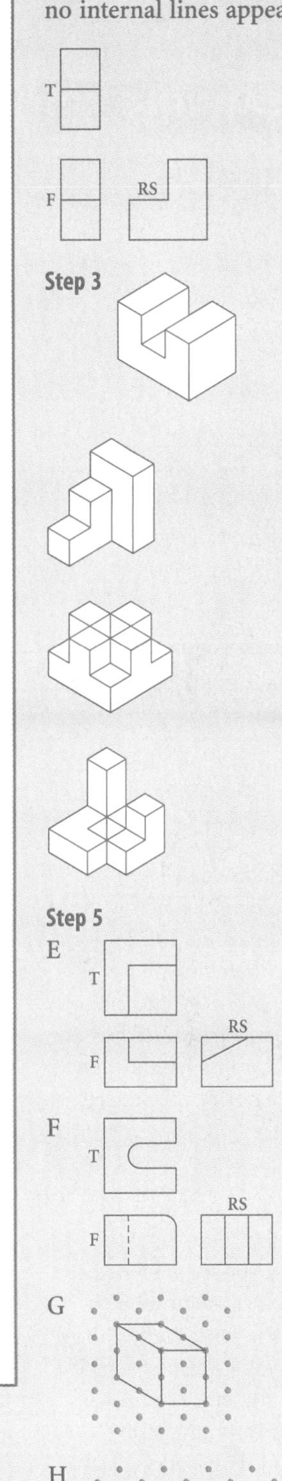

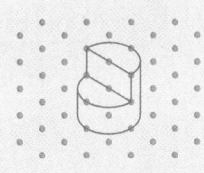

Assessing Progress

You can assess students' understanding of two-point perspective, their three-dimensional visualization skills, and their recognition of congruent rhombuses and other parallelograms.

Closing the Lesson

The main point of this lesson is that **isometric** drawings are useful in moving to and from orthographic views of an object. You might review the procedures for drawing an isometric view from given **orthographic** views.

LESSON
10.6

PLANNING

LESSON OUTLINE

One day:

20 min Investigation

15 min Sharing and Examples

5 min Closing

5 min Exercises

MATERIALS

- a pair of hollow solids for each group
- sand, rice, birdseed, or water
- boxes or dishpans

TEACHING

The volume of a sphere can be found by comparing the sphere to a cylinder or a cone with the same radius and height.

Set up workstations ahead of time with a cylinder/hemisphere pair for each group. (You might use some cone/hemisphere pairs.) The radius of the cylinder (or cone) must be the radius of the sphere, and its height must be the diameter of the sphere.

Guiding the Investigation

One step Ask groups how the volume of a sphere is related to the volume of a cylinder or a cone with the same radius and height. As you circulate, encourage students to state conjectures carefully before testing them with materials at the workstations.

Step 3 If they are using a cylinder/hemisphere pair, students will find that the volume of the sphere seems to be about $\frac{2}{3}$ the volume of the cylinder. Students might fill the hemisphere once more to confirm their estimate. Students using a cone/hemisphere pair will find equal volumes. If they are using a cone/sphere pair, they will need two pourings of the cone to fill the sphere.

Step 5 From the cylinder/hemisphere pair, $V_{\text{sphere}} = \left(\frac{2}{3}\right)\left(V_{\text{cylinder}}\right) = \left(\frac{2}{3}\right)(2\pi r^3) = \left(\frac{4}{3}\right)\pi r^3$.

▶ *EXAMPLE A*

Many students will be surprised by how large the result is. Use their skepticism as reason to check the calculations so that they'll understand them better. Consider together the reasons for not approximating $\frac{4}{3}$ or π by a decimal too early. Having a model available might help some students make sense of the result.

SHARING IDEAS

Have students present a variety of approaches for class critique. For example, if one group using a cylinder guessed $\frac{2}{3}$ or $\frac{3}{4}$, have that group present early, and have any group that checked its estimate present later.

LESSON
10.6 Volume of a Sphere

Satisfaction lies in the effort,
not in the attainment.
Full effort is full victory.
MOHANDAS K. GANDHI

In this lesson you will develop a formula for the volume of a sphere. In the investigation you'll compare the volume of a right cylinder to the volume of a hemisphere.

Investigation
The Formula for the Volume of a Sphere

You will need
- cylinder and hemisphere with the same radius
- sand, rice, birdseed, or water

This investigation demonstrates the relationship between the volume of a hemisphere with radius r and the volume of a right cylinder with base radius r and height $2r$—that is, the smallest cylinder that encloses a given sphere.

Step 1 Fill the hemisphere.

Step 2 Carefully pour the contents of the hemisphere into the cylinder. What fraction of the cylinder does the hemisphere appear to fill? $\frac{1}{3}$

Step 3 Fill the hemisphere again and pour the contents into the cylinder. What fraction of the cylinder do two hemispheres (one sphere) appear to fill? $\frac{2}{3}$

Step 4 If the radius of the cylinder is r and its height is $2r$, then what is the volume of the cylinder in terms of r? $V = 2\pi r^3$

Step 5 The volume of the sphere is the fraction of the cylinder's volume that was filled by two hemispheres. What is the formula for the volume of a sphere? State it as your conjecture.

Sphere Volume Conjecture C-90

The volume of a sphere with radius r is given by the formula __?__. $V = \frac{4}{3}\pi r^3$

EXAMPLE A

As an exercise for her art class, Mona has cast a plaster cube, 12 cm on each side. Her assignment is to carve the largest possible sphere from the cube. What percentage of the plaster will be carved away?

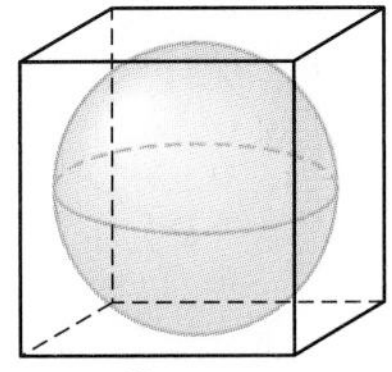

▶ ***Solution***

The largest possible sphere will have a diameter of 12 cm, so its radius is 6 cm. Applying the formula for volume of a sphere, you get $V = \left(\frac{4}{3}\right)\pi r^3 = \left(\frac{4}{3}\right)\pi \cdot 6^3 = \left(\frac{4}{3}\right)\pi \cdot 216 = 288\pi$ or about 905 cm³. The volume of the plaster cube is 12^3 or 1728 cm³. You subtract the volume of the sphere from the volume of the cube to get the amount carved away, which is about 823 cm³. Therefore the percentage carved away is $\frac{823}{1728} \approx 48\%$.

EXAMPLE B

Find the volume of plastic (to the nearest cubic inch) needed for this hollow toy component. The outer-hemisphere diameter is 5.0 in. and the inner-hemisphere diameter is 4.0 in.

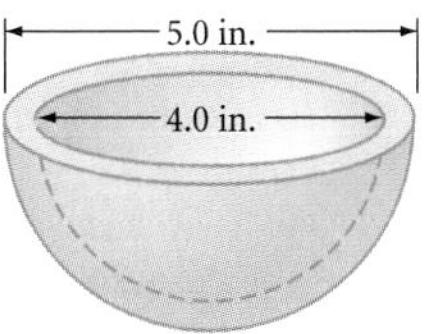

▶ ***Solution***

The formula for volume of a sphere is $V = \left(\frac{4}{3}\right)\pi r^3$, so the volume of a hemisphere is half of that, $V = \left(\frac{2}{3}\right)\pi r^3$. A radius is half a diameter.

Outer Hemisphere	**Inner Hemisphere**
$V_o = \left(\frac{2}{3}\right)\pi r^3$	$V_i = \left(\frac{2}{3}\right)\pi r^3$
$= \left(\frac{2}{3}\right)\pi(2.5)^3$	$= \left(\frac{2}{3}\right)\pi(2)^3$
$= \left(\frac{2}{3}\right)\pi(15.625)$	$= \left(\frac{2}{3}\right)\pi(8)$
≈ 33	≈ 17

Subtracting the volume of the inner hemisphere from the volume of the outer one, 16 in.³ of plastic are needed.

EXERCISES

You will need

Construction tools for Exercise **21**

In Exercises 1–6, find the volume of each solid. All measurements are in centimeters.

1.
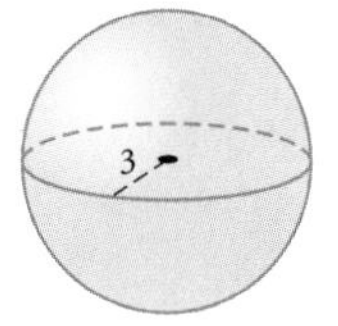

36π cm³

2.
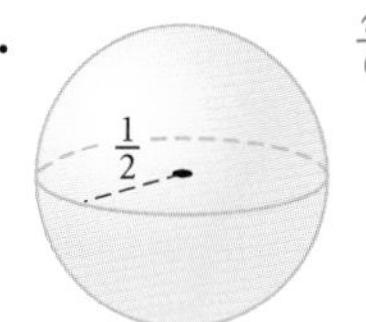

$\frac{\pi}{6}$ cm³

3.
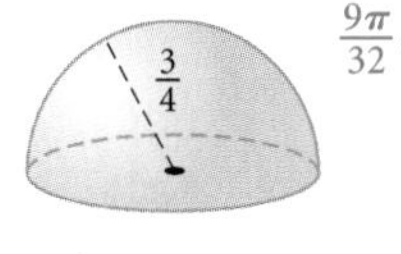

$\frac{9\pi}{32}$ cm³

4. (h)
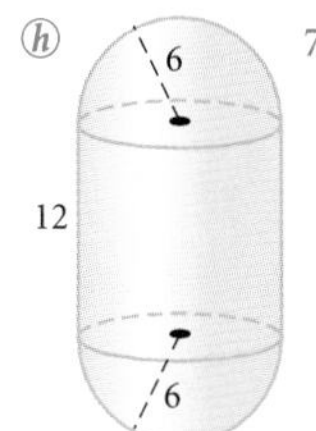

720π cm³

5.
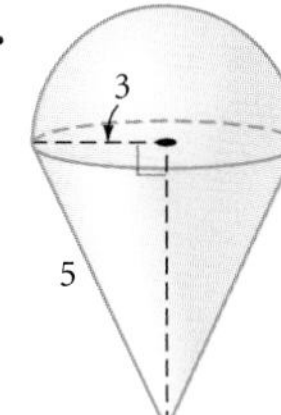

30π cm³

6. (h)
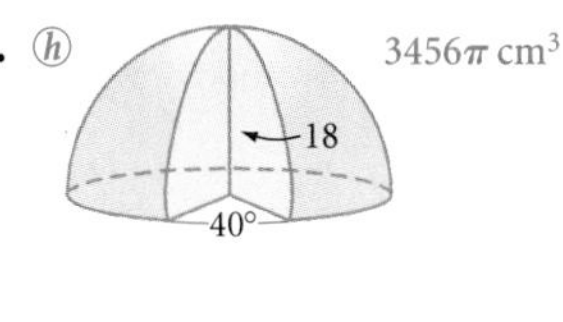

3456π cm³

Sharing Ideas (continued)

You might challenge some students to think about whether Cavalieri's Principle might be applied to find the volume of a hemisphere. By the Pythagorean Theorem, the radius of a cross section h units from the base is $\sqrt{r^2 - h^2}$, so the area of this cross section is $\pi r^2 - \pi h^2$. It's the same area as that of an annulus between a cylinder and a cone, both with radius and height r. So the volume of the hemisphere is the same as the volume of the region between the cone and the cylinder, or $\pi r^3 - \frac{1}{3}\pi r^3 = \frac{2}{3}\pi r^3$.

The cone, sphere, and circumscribed cylinder are represented by this side view on page 616.

The outer figure is a cylinder, not a cube. Here is a three-dimensional sketch.

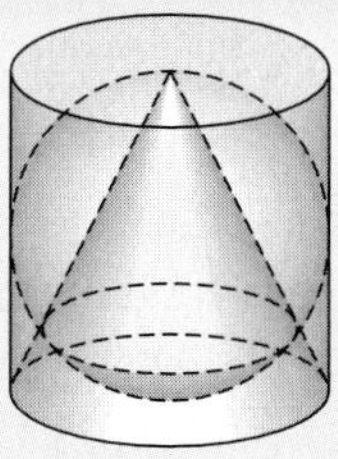

Students might be surprised that these volumes have the ratio 1:2:3. Encourage further exploration through more questions to teach the value and excitement of problem posing beyond problem solving. For example, students might ask what the fourth number in the ratio would be for a circumscribed cube. $\left[\frac{12}{\pi}\right]$ They might also ask about the ratios of surface areas, foreshadowing a surprise in Lesson 10.7.

▶ ***EXAMPLE B***

This example also illustrates the need to put off approximating the fraction and π until the end.

Assessing Progress

Assess the depth of students' understanding of cones, spheres, and cylinders; of radii; and of volume.

NCTM STANDARDS

CONTENT		PROCESS	
	Number	✔	Problem Solving
✔	Algebra	✔	Reasoning
✔	Geometry	✔	Communication
✔	Measurement	✔	Connections
✔	Data/Probability		Representation

LESSON OBJECTIVES

- Derive the formula for the volume of a sphere
- Apply volume formulas to problems involving spheres or hemispheres
- Practice three-dimensional visual thinking skills
- Develop problem-solving skills

Closing the Lesson

The volume of a sphere is $\frac{2}{3}$ that of a circumscribed cylinder, or $\frac{4}{3}\pi r^3$. It's also twice the volume of a cone with the same radius and height.

BUILDING UNDERSTANDING

The exercises give students practice in applying the volume formula for a sphere.

ASSIGNING HOMEWORK

Essential	1–8, 10
Performance assessment	9, 11
Portfolio	15, 17
Group	12–17
Review	18–22

▶ Helping with the Exercises

Exercise 6 If necessary, **[Ask]** "Can you tell what fraction of the hemisphere is still there?" $\left[\frac{8}{9}\right]$

Exercise 7 If students are having trouble, encourage them to draw a picture. The 3-meter side determines the radius of the largest hemisphere.

Exercise 8 Students might find the volume of both the sphere and the cone. Or they might realize that a cone with height 8 cm would hold just half the sphere, so one with height 12 cm will hold $\frac{3}{2}$ as much—still only $\frac{3}{4}$ of the ice cream.

8. No. The volume of the ice cream is $85.\overline{3}\pi$ cm^3, and the volume of the cone is 64π cm^3.

Exercise 9 **[Alert]** Students might incorrectly use the given diameters instead of radii in the formulas.

Exercises 11, 13 **[Alert]** Students might need help in eliminating $\frac{4}{3}$. Some might not know how to find a cube root on a calculator.

7. What is the volume of the largest hemisphere that you could carve out of a wooden block whose edges measure 3 m by 7 m by 7 m? 18π m^3

8. A sphere of ice cream is placed onto your ice cream cone. Both have a diameter of 8 cm. The height of your cone is 12 cm. If you push the ice cream into the cone, will all of it fit?

9. APPLICATION Lickety Split ice cream comes in a cylindrical container with an inside diameter of 6 inches and a height of 10 inches. The company claims to give the customer 25 scoops of ice cream per container, each scoop being a sphere with a 3-inch diameter. How many scoops will each container really hold? only 20 scoops

10. Find the volume of a spherical shell with an outer diameter of 8 meters and an inner diameter of 6 meters. approximately 155 m^3

11. Which is greater, the volume of a hemisphere with radius 2 cm or the total volume of two cones with radius 2 cm and height 2 cm? They have the same volume.

12. A sphere has a volume of 972π in.^{3}. Find its radius. ⓗ 9 in.

13. A hemisphere has a volume of 18π cm^3. Find its radius. 3 cm

14. The base of a hemisphere has an area of 256π cm^2. Find its volume. $\frac{8192\pi}{3}$ cm^3

15. If the diameter of a student's brain is about 6 inches, and you assume its shape is approximately a hemisphere, then what is the volume of the student's brain? 18π in.^{3}

THE FAR SIDE® By GARY LARSON

"Mr. Osborne, may I be excused? My brain is full."

16. A cylindrical glass 10 cm tall and 8 cm in diameter is filled to 1 cm from the top with water. If a golf ball 4 cm in diameter is placed into the glass, will the water overflow?

17. APPLICATION This underground gasoline storage tank is a right cylinder with a hemisphere at each end. How many gallons of gasoline will the tank hold? (1 gallon = 0.13368 cubic foot) If the service station fills twenty 15-gallon tanks from the storage tank per day, how many days will it take to empty the storage tank? approximately 15,704 gallons; 53 days.

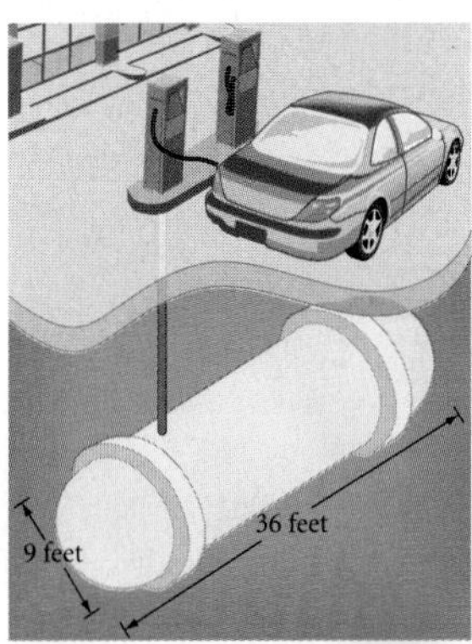

Exercise 16 Students might have to learn by trying that they need to find only the volume of the empty space, not the volume of the entire glass.

16. No. The unused volume is 16π cm^3, and the volume of the golf ball is $10.\overline{6}\pi$ cm^3.

Review

10.5 **18.** Inspector Lestrade has sent a small piece of metal to the crime lab. The lab technician finds that its mass is 54.3 g. It appears to be lithium, sodium, or potassium, all highly reactive with water. Then the technician places the metal into a graduated glass cylinder of radius 4 cm that contains a nonreactive liquid. The metal causes the level of the liquid to rise 2.0 cm. Which metal is it? (Refer to the table on page 535.) lithium

8.6 **19.** City law requires that any one-story commercial building supply a parking area equal in size to the floor area of the building. A-Round Architects has designed a cylindrical building with a 150-foot diameter. They plan to ring the building with parking. How far from the building should the parking lot extend? Round your answer to the nearest foot. 31 ft

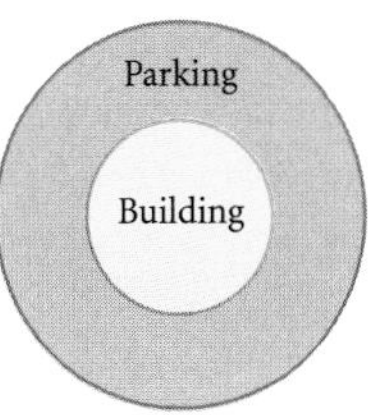

7.1 **20.** Plot A, B, C, and D onto graph paper.

A is $(3, -5)$.

C is the reflection of A over the x-axis.

B is the rotation of C 180° around the origin.

D is a transformation of A by the rule $(x, y) \rightarrow (x + 6, y + 10)$.

What kind of quadrilateral is $ABCD$? Give reasons for your answer.

3.7 **21.** *Construction* Use your geometry tools to construct an inscribed and circumscribed circle for an equilateral triangle.

5.2 **22.** Find w, x, and y. $w = 110°, x = 115°, y = 80°$

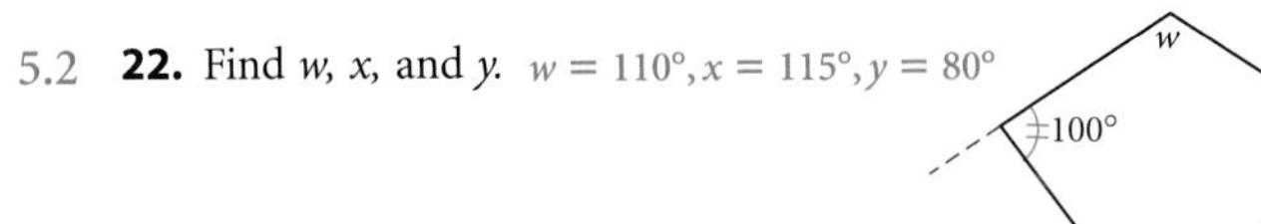

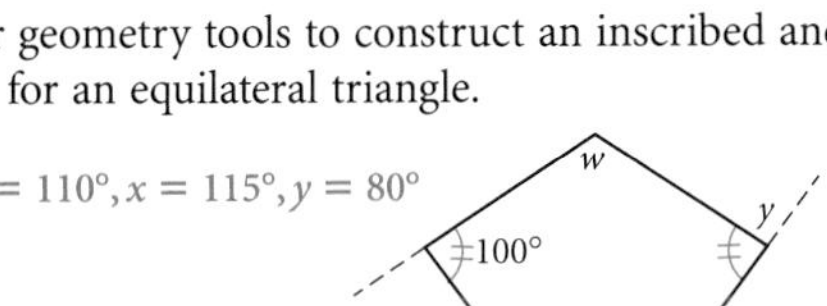

IMPROVING YOUR VISUAL THINKING SKILLS

Patchwork Cubes

The large cube at right is built from 13 double cubes like the one shown plus one single cube. What color must the single cube be, and where must it be positioned?

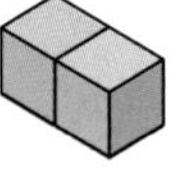

Exercise 19 Students might benefit from seeing that the area of the circle surrounding the entire parking lot is twice the area of the building.

20. $ABCD$ is a parallelogram because the slopes of $\overline{CD}$ and $\overline{AB}$ are both 0 and the slopes of $\overline{BC}$ and $\overline{AD}$ are both $\frac{5}{3}$.

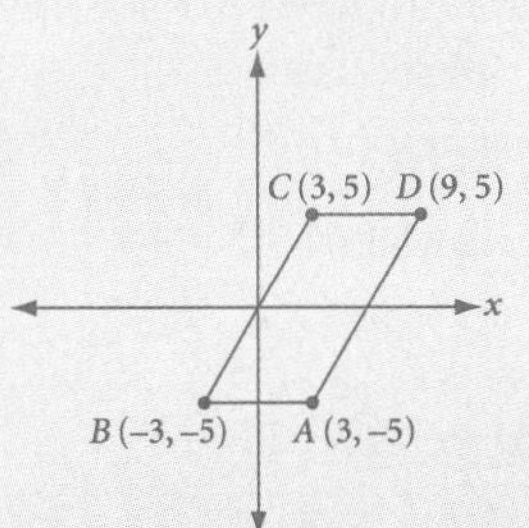

21.

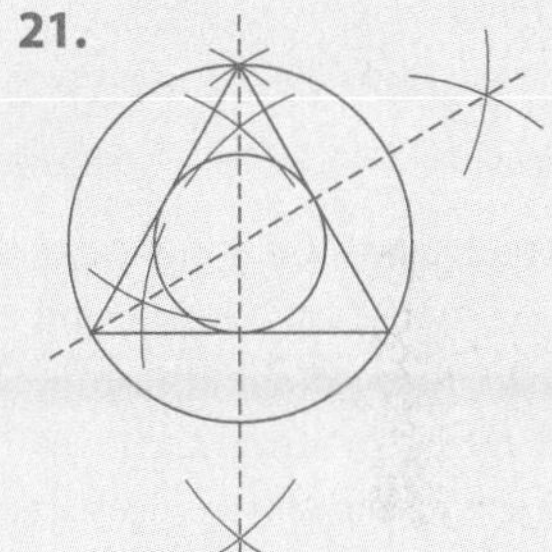

IMPROVING VISUAL THINKING SKILLS

The large cube has an odd number of small cubes. Because of the placement of pink cubes at the corners, there must be one more pink cube than blue cubes, so the single cube must be pink. Students can imagine laying out the pairs so that the empty space occurs at a corner, at the middle of a face, or at the middle of the cube, so any of the pink cubes might be the single cube.

LESSON

10.7

PLANNING

LESSON OUTLINE

One day:

20 min	Investigation
10 min	Sharing
5 min	Closing
10 min	Exercises

MATERIALS

- calculators

TEACHING

The surface area of a sphere can be approximated by considering the surface to be made up of bases of many pyramids whose vertices are at the sphere's center.

Guiding the Investigation

Step 1 There's nothing special about 1000 "nearly polygons." You can use a trillion "nearly polygons," and the reasoning will be the same.

Step 2 A soccer ball might help students visualize the (curved) hexagons and pentagons as bases of pyramids.

Steps 3, 4 Groups might need coaxing and encouragement to do the algebra here.

One step Remind students that the ratio of the volume of a sphere to the volume of a cylinder of the same radius and height is 2:3. **[Ask]** "What's the ratio of surface areas of these figures, and what do we need to know to find it?" As appropriate, remind students that they've seen how to find the surface area of a cylinder and can look up the formula if they don't remember it. Suggest that they think about a sphere as a collection of "almost pyramids" with bases on the surface and vertices at the center of the sphere. If, as you circulate, students are asking what kind of pyramids they should assume, suggest that they choose one kind, although which kind doesn't matter. Note the variety of approaches to be presented during Sharing, by which time you hope students will be amazed that the ratio of the surface areas of the sphere and its circumscribed cylinder is, like the ratio of volumes, 2:3.

LESSON OBJECTIVES

- Derive the formula for the surface area of a sphere
- Apply the surface area formula to solve problems
- Practice three-dimensional visual thinking skills
- Develop reading comprehension, problem-solving skills, and cooperative behavior

LESSON 10.7

Surface Area of a Sphere

Sometimes it's better to talk about difficult subjects lying down; the change in posture sort of tilts the world so you can get a different angle on things.

MARY WILLIS WALKER

Earth is so large that it is reasonable to use area formulas for plane figures—rectangles, triangles, and circles—to find the areas of most small land regions. But, to find Earth's entire surface area, you need a formula for the surface area of a sphere. Now that you know how to find the volume of a sphere, you can use that knowledge to arrive at the formula for the surface area of a sphere.

Earth rises over the Moon's horizon. From there, the Moon's surface seems flat.

Investigation
The Formula for the Surface Area of a Sphere

In this investigation you'll visualize a sphere's surface covered by tiny shapes that are nearly flat. So the surface area, S, of the sphere is the sum of the areas of all the "nearly polygons." If you imagine radii connecting each of the vertices of the "nearly polygons" to the center of the sphere, you are mentally dividing the volume of the sphere into many "nearly pyramids." Each of the "nearly polygons" is a base for a pyramid, and the radius, r, of the sphere is the height of the pyramid. So the volume, V, of the sphere is the sum of the volumes of all the pyramids. Now get ready for some algebra.

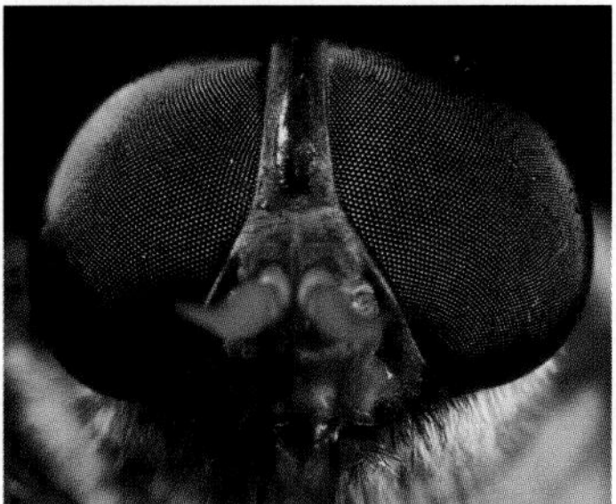

A horsefly's eyes resemble spheres covered by "nearly polygons."

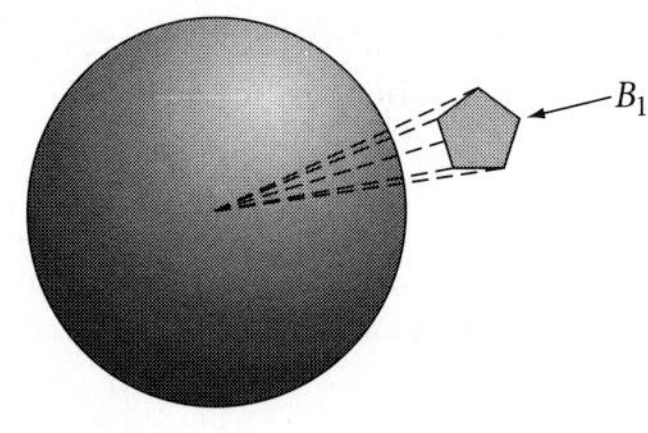

Step 1 Divide the surface of the sphere into 1000 "nearly polygons" with areas $B_1, B_2, B_3, \ldots, B_{1000}$. Then you can write the surface area, S, of the sphere as the sum of the 1000 B's:

$$S = B_1 + B_2 + B_3 + \ldots + B_{1000}$$

Step 2 The volume of the pyramid with base B_1 is $\frac{1}{3}(B_1)(r)$, so the total volume of the sphere, V, is the sum of the volumes of the 1000 pyramids:

$$V = \frac{1}{3}(B_1)(r) + \frac{1}{3}(B_2)(r) + \ldots + \frac{1}{3}(B_{1000})(r)$$

$$V = \frac{1}{3}r(B_1 + B_2 + \ldots + B_{1000})$$

What common expression can you factor from each of the terms on the right side? Rewrite the last equation showing the results of your factoring.

Step 3 $\frac{4}{3}\pi r^3 = \frac{1}{3}rS$

Step 3 But the volume of the sphere is $V = \frac{4}{3}\pi r^3$. Rewrite your equation from Step 2 by substituting $\frac{4}{3}\pi r^3$ for V and substituting for S the sum of the areas of all the "nearly polygons."

Step 4 Solve the equation from Step 3 for the surface area, S. You now have a formula for finding the surface area of a sphere in terms of its radius. State this as your next conjecture and add it to your conjecture list.

Sphere Surface Area Conjecture C-91

The surface area, S, of a sphere with radius r is given by the formula _?_. $S = 4\pi r^2$

EXAMPLE Find the surface area of a sphere whose volume is $12{,}348\pi$ m^3.

▶ Solution First, use the volume formula for a sphere to find its radius. Then, use the radius to find the surface area.

Radius Calculation	Surface Area Calculation
$V = \left(\frac{4}{3}\right)\pi r^3$	$S = 4\pi r^2$
$12{,}348\pi = \left(\frac{4}{3}\right)\pi r^3$	$= 4\pi(21)^2$
$\left(\frac{3}{4}\right)12{,}348 = r^3$	$= 4\pi(441)$
$9261 = r^3$	$S = 1764\pi \approx 5541.8$
$r = 21$	

The radius is 21 m, and the surface area is 1764π m^2, or about 5541.8 m^2.

EXERCISES

You will need

Geometry software for Exercises **20** and **21**

For Exercises 1–3, find the volume and total surface area of each solid. All measurements are in centimeters.

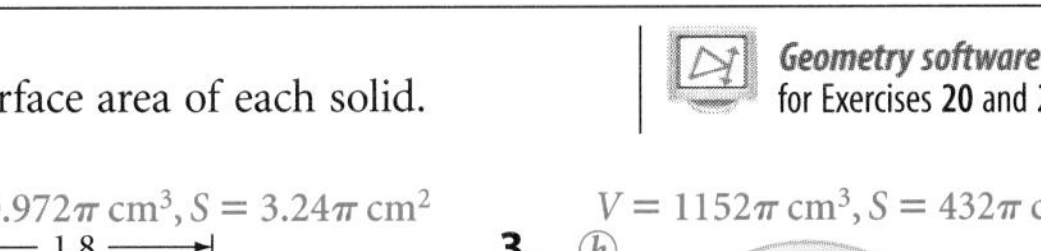

1. (h) $V = 972\pi$ cm^3, $S = 324\pi$ cm^2

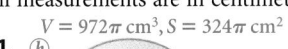

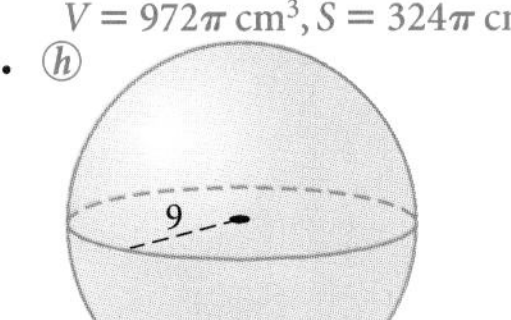

2. $V = 0.972\pi$ cm^3, $S = 3.24\pi$ cm^2

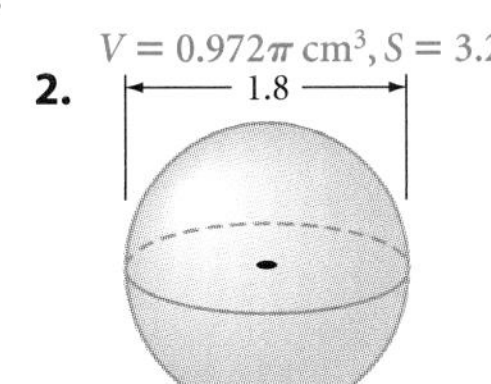

3. (h) $V = 1152\pi$ cm^3, $S = 432\pi$ cm^2

12

▶ EXAMPLE

The example is good practice for students who are still confusing volume and surface area.

SHARING IDEAS

If some students still aren't sure of the algebra after other students present their ideas, you might lead the class through each step. Point out that it doesn't matter how many pyramids are used.

Wonder aloud if the formula is exact. The sum of the bases is exactly the surface area, but the volume of each "nearly pyramid" is only an approximation of the volume of a real pyramid. The approximations improve as the bases of the "nearly pyramids" shrink. At the limit, the sum of the volumes of the "nearly pyramids" is exactly the volume of the sphere, so the formula holds exactly. **[Link]** This process of summing infinitely many infinitely small numbers is the cornerstone of integral calculus.

[Ask] "How might we visually confirm this theoretical result?" One way is to cut out of paper or cloth four circles with the same radius as some spherical object, perhaps a beach ball or an orange. Cover the object with the circles, cutting the circles into pieces and arranging them on the surface of the object. Alternatively, peel an orange and compare the peeling to a circle drawn with the same diameter as that of the orange.

[Context] You might mention that the mathematician Archimedes was so awed by his discovery that both the volume and the surface area of a sphere were equal to $\frac{2}{3}$ those of the circumscribed cylinder that he requested a picture representing that fact to be inscribed on his tombstone.

Point out that the surface area of a sphere equals the *lateral* surface area of the circumscribed cylinder, and ask if that makes sense.

NCTM STANDARDS

CONTENT		PROCESS	
	Number	✓	Problem Solving
✓	Algebra	✓	Reasoning
✓	Geometry	✓	Communication
✓	Measurement	✓	Connections
	Data/Probability	✓	Representation

Sharing Ideas (continued)

As a challenge, ask about the surface area of a cone inscribed in the cylinder. From Lesson 8.7, its surface area is $\pi r^2 + \pi rl$, and in this case, by the Pythagorean Theorem, $l = r\sqrt{5}$. So the ratio of the surface areas of the cone, sphere, and cylinder is $\frac{1+\sqrt{5}}{2}:2:3$. Students who have heard of the Golden Ratio might recognize it in the first of these three numbers.

Assessing Progress
Assess students' understanding of polygons, pyramids, surface area, and the difference between surface area and volume. You can also check their knowledge of the formula for the volume of a sphere, their willingness to think about the reasonableness of their answers, and their algebra skills.

Closing the Lesson

The surface of a sphere can be broken into a large number of "nearly polygons," the sum of whose areas is equal to the surface area of the sphere. The sum of the volumes of the "nearly pyramids" built on those "nearly polygons" and with vertices at the center of the sphere is equal to the volume of the sphere and is approximately $\frac{1}{3}r$(sum of bases). As the number of "nearly polygons" increases, the approximation becomes exact. The equation $\frac{1}{3}r(\text{sum of bases}) = \frac{4}{3}\pi r^3$ implies that the surface area, or sum of the bases, is $4\pi r^2$.

BUILDING UNDERSTANDING

The exercises give students practice in applying ideas about the surface area of a sphere.

ASSIGNING HOMEWORK

Essential	1–8, 13
Performance assessment	9
Portfolio	13
Group	10–12
Review	14–21

▶ Helping with the Exercises

Exercises 2, 4–6 If students are stuck, **[Ask]** "What do you need to know to apply the formula?" [the radius] "How might you find it from the information given?"

4. The shaded circle at right has area 40π cm². Find the surface area of the sphere. ⓗ $S = 160\pi \text{ cm}^2$

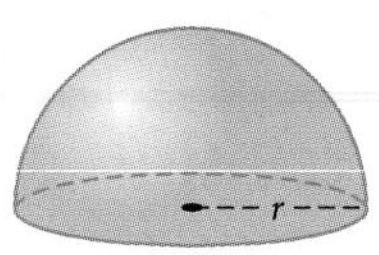

5. Find the volume of a sphere whose surface area is 64π cm². $V = \frac{256\pi}{3} \text{ cm}^3$

6. Find the surface area of a sphere whose volume is 288π cm³. $S = 144\pi \text{ cm}^2$

7. If the radius of the base of a hemisphere (which is bounded by a great circle) is r, what is the area of the great circle? What is the total surface area of the hemisphere, including the base? How do they compare? Area of great circle = πr^2. Total surface area of hemisphere = $3\pi r^2$. Total surface area of hemisphere is three times that of area of great circle.

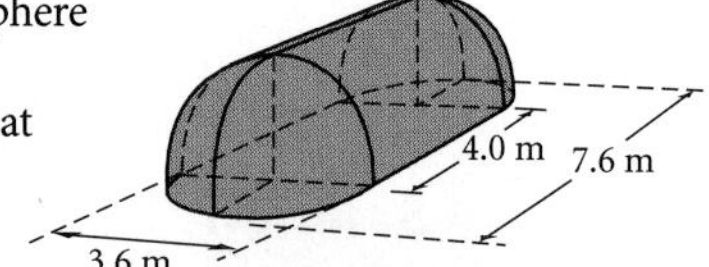

8. If Jose used 4 gallons of wood sealant to cover the hemispherical ceiling of his vacation home, how many gallons of wood sealant are needed to cover the floor? 2 gal

9. Assume a Kickapoo wigwam is a semicylinder with a half-hemisphere on each end. The diameter of the semicylinder and each of the half-hemispheres is 3.6 meters. The total length is 7.6 meters. What is the volume of the wigwam and the surface area of its roof?

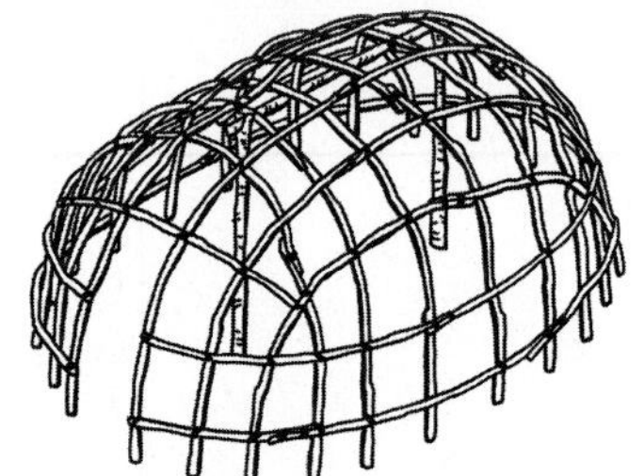

Cultural CONNECTION

A wigwam was a domed structure that Native American woodland tribes, such as the Kickapoo, Iroquois, and Cherokee, used for shelter and warmth in the winter. They designed each wigwam with an oval floor pattern, set tree saplings vertically into the ground around the oval, bent the tips of the saplings into an arch, and tied all the pieces together to support the framework. They then wove more branches horizontally around the building and added mats over the entire dwelling, except for the doorway and smoke hole.

10. APPLICATION A farmer must periodically resurface the interior (wall, floor, and ceiling) of his silo to protect it from the acid created by the silage. The height of the silo to the top of the hemispherical dome is 50 ft, and the diameter is 18 ft.

a. What is the approximate surface area that needs to be treated? approximately 3082 ft²

b. If 1 gallon of resurfacing compound covers about 250 ft², how many gallons are needed? 13 gal

c. There is 0.8 bushel per ft³. Calculate the number of bushels of grain this silo will hold. approximately 9568 bushels

11. About 70% of Earth's surface is covered by water. If the diameter of Earth is about 12,750 km, find the area not covered by water to the nearest 100,000 km². 153,200,000 km²

Exercise 7 Students might need help in recalling that great circles are the largest circles on the surface of the sphere. They have the same center and radius as the sphere itself. Ask if their result makes sense to them.

9. $V = \left(\frac{1}{2}\right)\left(\frac{4}{3}\right)\pi(1.8)^3 + \left(\frac{1}{2}\right)\pi(1.8)^2(4.0) = 10.368\pi \text{ m}^3$, $S = \left(\frac{1}{2}\right)(4)\pi(1.8)^2 + \left(\frac{1}{2}\right)(2)\pi(1.8)(4.0) = 13.68\pi \text{ m}^2$

Exercise 10 As needed, remind students to round up. **[Language]** *Silage* is coarse food (whole plants) for farm animals that is stored and preserved through fermentation in towers called *silos.*

History
CONNECTION

From the early 13th century to the late 17th century, the Medici family of Florence, Italy, were successful merchants and generous patrons of the arts. The Medici family crest, shown here, features six spheres—five red spheres and one that resembles the earth. The use of three gold spheres to advertise a pawnshop could have been inspired by the Medici crest.

12. A sculptor has designed a statue that features six hemispheres (inspired by the Medici crest) and three spheres (inspired by the pawnshop logo). He wants to use gold electroplating on the six hemispheres (diameter 6 cm) and the three spheres (diameter 8 cm), which will cost about 14¢/cm². (The bases of the hemispheres will *not* be electroplated.) Will he be able to stay under his $150 budget? If not, what diameter spheres should he make to stay under budget? The total cost is $131.95. He will stay under budget.

13. Earth has a thin outer layer called the *crust,* which averages about 24 km thick. Earth's diameter is about 12,750 km. What percentage of the volume of Earth is the crust? 1.13%

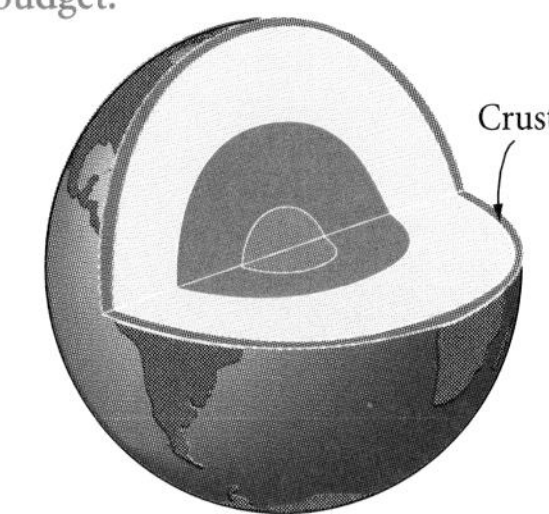

Review

10.5 **14.** A piece of wood placed in a cylindrical container causes the container's water level to rise 3 cm. This type of wood floats half out of the water, and the radius of the container is 5 cm. What is the volume of the piece of wood? 150π cm³

8.5 **15.** Find the ratio of the area of the circle inscribed in an equilateral triangle to the area of the circumscribed circle. $\frac{1}{4}$

8.5 **16.** Find the ratio of the area of the circle inscribed in a square to the area of the circumscribed circle. $\frac{1}{2}$

8.5 **17.** Find the ratio of the area of the circle inscribed in a regular hexagon to the area of the circumscribed circle. $\frac{3}{4}$

18. Make a conjecture as to what happens to the ratio in Exercises 15–17 as the number of sides of the regular polygon increases. Make sketches to support your conjecture. The ratio gets closer to 1.

2.3 **19.** Use inductive reasoning to complete each table.

a.

n	1	2	3	4	5	6	...	n	...	200
$f(n)$	−2	1	4	7	10	13	...	$3n-5$	...	595

b.

n	1	2	3	4	5	6	...	n	...	200
$f(n)$	0	$\frac{1}{3}$	$\frac{1}{2}$	$\frac{3}{5}$	$\frac{2}{3}$	$\frac{5}{7}$	...	$\frac{n-1}{n+1}$	...	$\frac{199}{201}$

MAKING THE CONNECTION

[Language] A *patron of the arts* is someone who supports the arts through contributions and purchases. **[ESL]** A *pawnshop* is a place where money is loaned in exchange for valuable property. If the loan is not paid back, the property is sold.

Exercise 13 Students can use the diameter of Earth given in Exercise 11. They might approximate the volume of the crust by multiplying the surface area (from Exercise 11) by 24 km or by subtracting the volume of the noncrust sphere from the volume of Earth. Or they might find the ratio of the diameter (or radius) of the noncrust to that of the whole Earth, cube it for the ratio of volumes, and subtract from 1 to find the ratio of the volume of the crust to that of the whole Earth. This last approach uses ideas students will see in Lesson 11.5.

Exercises 15–17 One approach is to square the ratios of the circles' radii. This approach foreshadows the ideas of Lesson 11.5.

Exercise 19b As needed, encourage students to think about equivalent forms of the fractions.

Exercise 20 This exercise previews the idea of similarity in Chapter 11.

20. They trace two similar shapes, except that the one traced by C is smaller by a scale factor of 2:1.

21. The line traces an infinite hourglass shape. Or, it traces the region between the two branches of a hyperbola.

20. ***Technology*** Use geometry software to construct a segment $\overline{AB}$, and its midpoint C. Trace C and B, and drag B around to sketch a shape. Compare the shapes they trace.

21. ***Technology*** Use geometry software to construct a circle. Choose a point A on the circle and a point B not on the circle, and construct the perpendicular bisector of $\overline{AB}$. Trace the perpendicular bisector as you animate A around the circle. Describe the locus of points traced.

IMPROVING YOUR REASONING SKILLS

PUZZLE

Reasonable 'rithmetic II

Each letter in these problems represents a different digit.

1. What is the value of C?

$$\begin{array}{rccccc} & & 8 & 7 & 8 & 9 \\ & & 3 & B & A & 7 \\ & & 4 & 8 & 2 & A \\ + & & 7 & A & B & 5 \\ \hline & 2 & C & 2 & 8 & 7 \end{array}$$

2. What is the value of D?

$$\begin{array}{rcccc} & D & E & F & F \\ - & E & 2 & F & 6 \\ \hline & 1 & 9 & 9 & 7 \end{array}$$

3. What is the value of K?

$$\begin{array}{r} G\,J \\ 7\overline{)H\,G\,K} \\ \underline{2\,1} \\ H\,K \\ \underline{H\,K} \end{array}$$

4. What is the value of N?

$$\begin{array}{r} 5\;\,2 \\ LQ\overline{)N\,M\,2} \\ \underline{N\,P} \\ M\,2 \\ \underline{M\,2} \end{array}$$

IMPROVING REASONING SKILLS

Student difficulties with Problem 3 may arise from their neglecting to note that each letter represents a different digit. In Problem 4, they may forget that 5 can be multiplied by numbers other than 0 to get 0 as the second digit.

1. $C = 4$

2. $D = 4$

3. $K = 8$

4. $N = 8$

Exploration

Sherlock Holmes and Forms of Valid Reasoning

"That's logical!" You've probably heard that expression many times. What do we mean when we say someone is thinking logically? One dictionary defines *logical* as "capable of reasoning or using reason in an orderly fashion that brings out fundamental points."

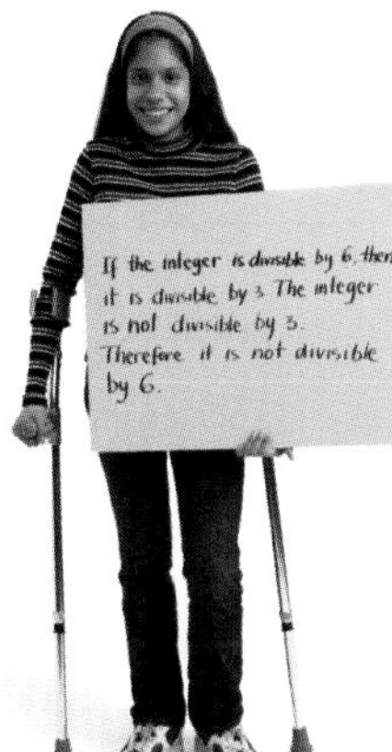

"Prove it!" That's another expression you've probably heard many times. It is an expression that is used by someone concerned with logical thinking. In daily life, proving something often means you can present some facts to support a point.

In Chapter 2 you learned that in geometry—as in daily life—a conclusion is valid when you present rules and facts to support it. You have often used given information and previously proven conjectures to prove new conjectures in paragraph proofs and flowchart proofs.

When you apply deductive reasoning, you are "being logical" like detective Sherlock Holmes. The statements you take as true are called premises, and the statements that follow from them are conclusions.

When you translate a deductive argument into symbolic form, you use capital letters to stand for simple statements. When you write "If *P* then *Q*," you are writing a **conditional statement.** Here are two examples.

English argument	Symbolic translation
If Watson has chalk between his fingers, then he has been playing billiards. Watson has chalk between his fingers. Therefore, Watson has been playing billiards.	*P*: Watson has chalk between his fingers. *Q*: Watson has been playing billiards. If *P* then *Q*. *P* ∴ Q
If triangle *ABC* is isosceles, then the base angles are congruent. Triangle *ABC* is isosceles. Therefore, its base angles are congruent.	*P*: Triangle *ABC* is isosceles. *Q*: Triangle *ABC*'s base angles are congruent. If *P* then *Q*. *P* ∴ Q

NCTM STANDARDS

	CONTENT		PROCESS
	Number		Problem Solving
	Algebra	✓	Reasoning
✓	Geometry	✓	Communication
	Measurement	✓	Connections
	Data/Probability	✓	Representation

LESSON OBJECTIVES

- Use the forms of logical reasoning *Modus Ponens* and *Modus Tollens*
- Learn some symbols used in formal logic
- Distinguish between the validity and the truth of an argument

EXPLORATION

PLANNING

LESSON OUTLINE

One day:

30 min Activity

10 min Sharing

5 min Closing

MATERIALS

none

TEACHING

In this lesson students encounter the basic ideas of the argument forms *Modus Ponens* and *Modus Tollens.* For more lessons on symbolic logic, see www.keypress.com/DG.

Sherlock Holmes is the main character in detective stories set in London over one hundred years ago. The stories were written by physician Sir Arthur Conan Doyle (1859–1930). "It's elementary, my dear Watson" is Holmes' often-quoted reply to questions from his friend Dr. Watson.

[Language] A loose translation of the Latin phrase *Modus Ponens* is "the affirmative method." Some students may be familiar with the phrase *modus operandi,* which means "method of working." *Modus Tollens* is loosely translated as "method of canceling."

The double negation "It is not the case that it is not raining" means "It is raining," analogous to the arithmetic property that the negative of a negative number is positive.

[ESL] In some languages, such as Spanish, a double negation does not always result in a positive. Be sensitive to the fact that students new to English may have difficulty with the concept of double negation.

Some students will wonder whether a valid negation of "It is raining" is "The sun is shining." [no] Negations are not necessarily opposites. However, statements that are negations of each other cannot both be true or both be false. **[Alert]** With *Modus Tollens* students may have difficulty remembering that the order of the statements is reversed in the conclusion. "If *P* then *Q*" and "not *Q*" imply "not *P*." But "If *P* then *Q*" and "not *P*" do not imply "not *Q*."

[Ask] "Why do we know 'not *P*'?" [Because if it were *P* it would have to be *Q*; but it is not *Q*, and it can't be both *Q* and not *Q*.]

Guiding the Activity

Step 2c To show why the argument is not valid, suggest that today is Saturday. There is no school tomorrow yet yesterday was not Thursday.

Step 2d Despite the negations, this is still an example of a *Modus Ponens* argument, not a *Modus Tollens* argument.

Step 3 Students might say that all parts are valid. An example to show that part d isn't valid would be "If it's raining, then it's cloudy. It's cloudy. Therefore it's not raining." (It's not necessarily raining, but we can't conclude that it's not raining.) Similarly, to show that part e is invalid, you could use "If it's raining, then it's cloudy. It's not raining. Therefore it's not cloudy."

Part e is an example of a double negation $\sim\sim Q$ is Q. **[Alert]** Students may be confused by parts *g*, *h*, and *i*, where part of the conditional statement is itself a conditional statement. Any of the variables in *MP* or *MT* might be a single statement or be made up of several statements.

The symbol ∴ means "therefore." So you can read the last two lines "*P*, ∴ *Q*" as "*P*, therefore *Q*" or "*P* is true, so *Q* is true."

Both of these examples illustrate one of the well-accepted forms of valid reasoning. According to ***Modus Ponens*** (MP), if you accept "If *P* then *Q*" as true and you accept *P* as true, then you must logically accept *Q* as true.

In geometry—as in daily life—we often encounter "not" in a statement. "Not *P*" is the **negation** of statement *P*. If *P* is the statement "It is raining," then "not *P*," symbolized $\sim P$, is the statement "It is not raining" or "It is not the case that it is raining." To remove negation from a statement, you remove the not. The negation of the statement "It is not raining" is "It is raining." You can also negate a "not" by adding yet another "not." So you can also negate the statement "It is not raining" by saying "It is not the case that it is not raining." This property is called **double negation.**

According to ***Modus Tollens*** (MT), if you accept "If *P* then *Q*" as true and you accept $\sim Q$ as true, then you must logically accept $\sim P$ as true. Here are two examples.

English argument	Symbolic translation
If Watson wished to invest money with Thurston, then he would have had his checkbook with him. Watson did not have his checkbook with him. Therefore Watson did not wish to invest money with Thurston.	*P*: Watson wished to invest money with Thurston. *Q*: Watson had his checkbook with him. If *P* then *Q*. $\sim Q$ $\therefore \sim P$
If $\overline{AC}$ is the longest side in $\triangle ABC$, then $\angle B$ is the largest angle in $\triangle ABC$. $\angle B$ is not the largest angle in $\triangle ABC$. Therefore $\overline{AC}$ is not the longest side in $\triangle ABC$.	*P*: $\overline{AC}$ is the longest side in $\triangle ABC$. *Q*: $\angle B$ is the largest angle in $\triangle ABC$. If *P* then *Q*. $\sim Q$ $\therefore \sim P$

Activity
It's Elementary!

In this activity you'll apply what you have learned about *Modus Ponens* (MP) and *Modus Tollens* (MT). You'll also get practice using the symbols of logic such as *P* and $\sim P$ as statements and ∴ for "so" or "therefore." To shorten your work even further you can symbolize the conditional "If *P* then *Q*" as $P \rightarrow Q$. Then *Modus Ponens* and *Modus Tollens* written symbolically look like this:

Modus Ponens	***Modus Tollens***
$P \rightarrow Q$	$R \rightarrow S$
P	$\sim S$
$\therefore Q$	$\therefore \sim R$

Step 1 Use logic symbols to translate parts a–e. Tell whether *Modus Ponens* or *Modus Tollens* is used to make the reasoning valid.

a. If Watson was playing billiards, then he was playing with Thurston. Watson was playing billiards. Therefore Watson was playing with Thurston.

b. Every cheerleader at Washington High School is in the 11th grade. Mark is a cheerleader at Washington High School. Therefore, Mark is in the 11th grade.

c. If Carolyn studies, then she does well on tests. Carolyn did not do well on her tests, so she must not have studied.

d. If $\overline{ED}$ is a midsegment in $\triangle ABC$, then $\overline{ED}$ is parallel to a side of $\triangle ABC$. $\overline{ED}$ is a midsegment in $\triangle ABC$. Therefore $\overline{ED}$ is parallel to a side of $\triangle ABC$.

e. If $\overline{ED}$ is a midsegment in $\triangle ABC$, then $\overline{ED}$ is parallel to a side of $\triangle ABC$. $\overline{ED}$ is not parallel to a side of $\triangle ABC$. Therefore $\overline{ED}$ is a not a midsegment in $\triangle ABC$.

Step 1a $P \rightarrow Q$ $P, \therefore Q$; *Modus Ponens*

Step 1b $P \rightarrow Q$ $P, \therefore Q$; *Modus Ponens*

Step 1c $P \rightarrow Q$ $\sim Q, \therefore \sim P$; *Modus Tollens*

Step 1d $P \rightarrow Q$ $P, \therefore Q$; *Modus Ponens*

Step 1e $P \rightarrow Q$ $\sim Q, \therefore \sim P$; *Modus Tollens*

Step 2 Use logic symbols to translate parts a–d. If the two premises fit the valid reasoning pattern of *Modus Ponens* or *Modus Tollens*, state the conclusion symbolically and translate it into English. Tell whether *Modus Ponens* or *Modus Tollens* is used to make the reasoning valid. Otherwise write "no valid conclusion."

a. If Aurora passes her Spanish test, then she will graduate. Aurora passes the test.

b. The diagonals of $ABCD$ are not congruent. If $ABCD$ is a rectangle, then its diagonals are congruent.

c. If yesterday was Thursday, then there is no school tomorrow. There is no school tomorrow. no valid conclusion

d. If you don't use Shining Smile toothpaste, then you won't be successful. You do not use Shining Smile toothpaste.

e. If squiggles are flitz, then ruggles are bodrum. Ruggles are not bodrum.

Step 2a $P \rightarrow Q$ $P, \therefore Q$; *Modus Ponens* She will graduate.

Step 2b $P \rightarrow Q$ $\sim Q, \therefore \sim P$; *Modus Tollens* $ABCD$ is not a rectangle.

Step 2d $P \rightarrow Q$ $P, \therefore Q$; *Modus Ponens* You won't be successful.

Step 2e $P \rightarrow Q$ $\sim Q, \therefore \sim P$; *Modus Tollens* Squiggles are not flitz.

Step 3 Identify each symbolic argument as *Modus Ponens* or *Modus Tollens*. If the argument is not valid, write "no valid conclusion."

a. $P \rightarrow S$ MP
P
$\therefore S$

b. $\sim T \rightarrow P$ MP
$\sim T$
$\therefore P$

c. $R \rightarrow \sim Q$ MT
Q
$\therefore \sim R$

d. $Q \rightarrow S$ no valid conclusion
S
$\therefore \sim Q$

e. $Q \rightarrow P$ no valid conclusion
$\sim Q$
$\therefore \sim P$

f. $\sim R \rightarrow S$ MT
$\sim S$
$\therefore R$

g. $\sim P \rightarrow (R \rightarrow Q)$ MP
$\sim P$
$\therefore (R \rightarrow Q)$

h. $(T \rightarrow \sim P) \rightarrow Q$ MT
$\sim Q$
$\therefore \sim(T \rightarrow \sim P)$

i. $P \rightarrow (\sim R \rightarrow P)$
$(\sim R \rightarrow P)$
$\therefore P$
no valid conclusion

SHARING IDEAS

[Ask] "Do you think all examples of deductive reasoning are in *Modus Ponens* or *Modus Tollens* form?" Have students review some paragraph proofs and see that the reasoning can be more complicated than these forms.

Ask whether all valid arguments are true. A discussion of this intentionally ambiguous statement might lead students to note that an argument can be valid but have false premises, in which case the conclusion isn't necessarily true. An argument that uses even one false premise is *unsound*, even if the method of reasoning is valid and whether or not the conclusion is true.

Assessing Progress

You can assess students' ability to see patterns and their comfort in talking about triangles, midsegments, parallel lines, rectangles, diagonals, and congruence.

Closing the Lesson

Modus Ponens is a form of deductive reasoning in which a **conditional premise** of the form "If *P* then *Q*" combines with the premise *P* to reach the **conclusion** *Q*. In ***Modus Tollens,*** the premises are "If *P* then *Q*" and "not *Q*," and the conclusion is "not *P*."

CHAPTER REVIEW 10

PLANNING

LESSON OUTLINE

First day:

15 min Reviewing

15 min Exercises

15 min Exercises in groups

Second day:

15 min Sharing

15 min Exercises

15 min Student self-assessment

REVIEWING

Ask students to draw concept maps relating various kinds of solids: polyhedrons, prisms, pyramids, spheres, cylinders, and cones. They might come up with something like this:

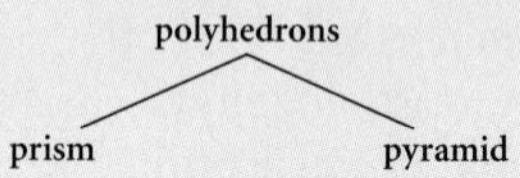

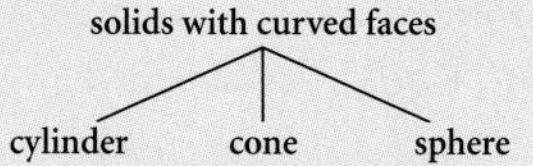

or the Venn diagram:

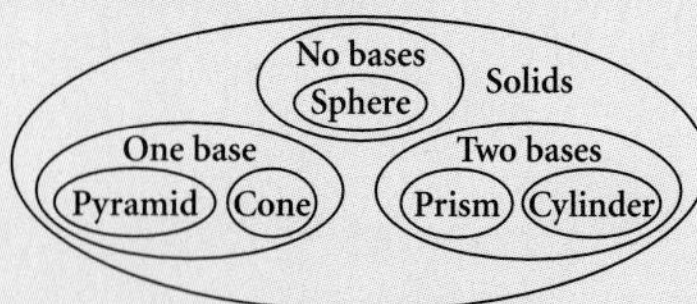

Then ask students to discuss or write about these aspects of each type of solid: edges, faces, regularity, base(s), lateral faces, lateral edges, right and oblique examples, altitude, height, volume, and surface area.

CHAPTER 10 REVIEW

In this chapter you discovered a number of formulas for finding volumes. It's as important to remember how you discovered these formulas as it is to remember the formulas themselves. For example, if you recall pouring the contents of a cone into a cylinder with the same base and height, you may recall that the volume of the cone is one-third the volume of the cylinder. Making connections will help, too. Recall that prisms and cylinders share the same volume formula because their shapes—two congruent bases connected by lateral faces—are alike.

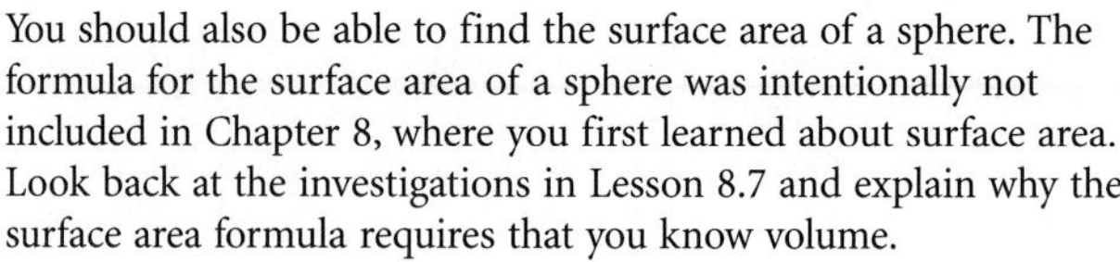

You should also be able to find the surface area of a sphere. The formula for the surface area of a sphere was intentionally not included in Chapter 8, where you first learned about surface area. Look back at the investigations in Lesson 8.7 and explain why the surface area formula requires that you know volume.

As you have seen, volume formulas can be applied to many practical problems. Volume also has many extensions such as calculating displacement and density.

EXERCISES

1. How are a prism and a cylinder alike? They have the same formula for volume: $V = BH$.

2. What does a cone have in common with a pyramid? They have the same formula for volume: $V = \frac{1}{3}BH$.

For Exercises 3–8, find the volume of each solid. Each quadrilateral is a rectangle. All solids are right (not oblique). All measurements are in centimeters.

3.

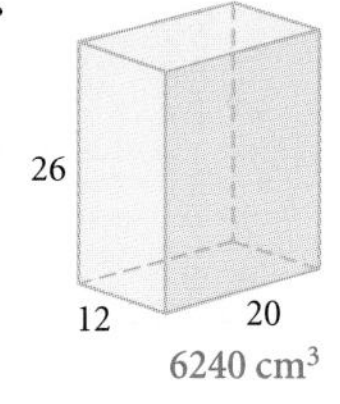

6240 cm^3

4.

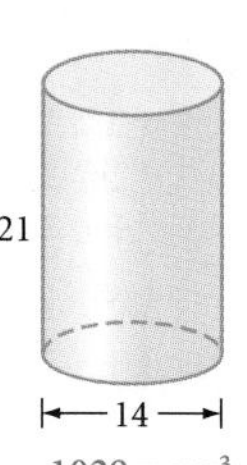

1029π cm^3

5. ⓗ

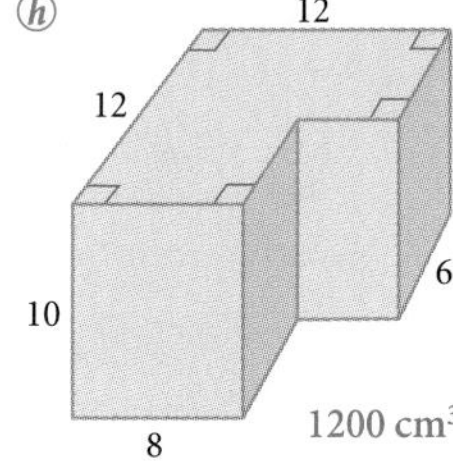

1200 cm^3

6.

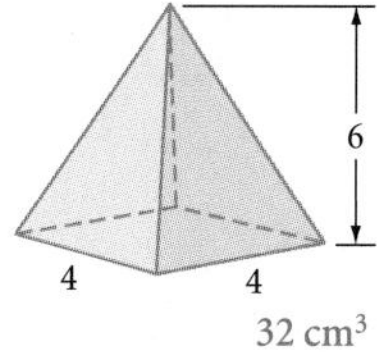

32 cm^3

7.

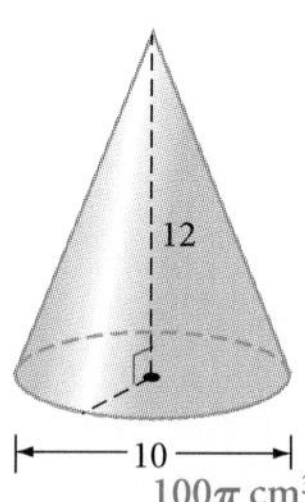

100π cm^3

8.

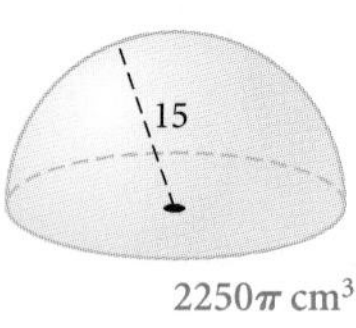

2250π cm^3

[Ask] "How might the volume be determined if the solid is not one of these types?" [through displacement or dissecting the solid into familiar shapes] "How would you find the volume of Escher's *Verblifa tin*? How are the volumes of a cone and a sphere inscribed in a cylinder related?" [The volume of a cone is $\frac{2}{3}\pi r^3$; that of a sphere is $\frac{4}{3}\pi r^3$; and that of the circumscribed cylinder is $2\pi r^3$.] Ask students how they make intuitive sense of these formulas to help their memories.

ASSIGNING HOMEWORK

Ideally, you can assign all the review exercises to all students over a two-day period. You might jigsaw a few of the problems, assigning them to groups for presentation.

For Exercises 9–12, calculate each unknown length given the volume of the solid. All measurements are in centimeters.

9. Find H. $V = 768\text{ cm}^3$

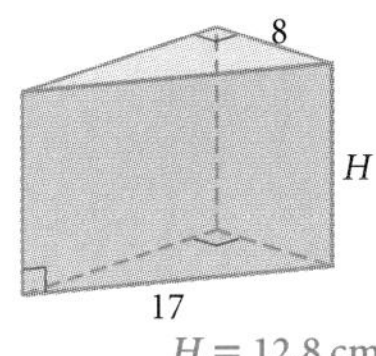
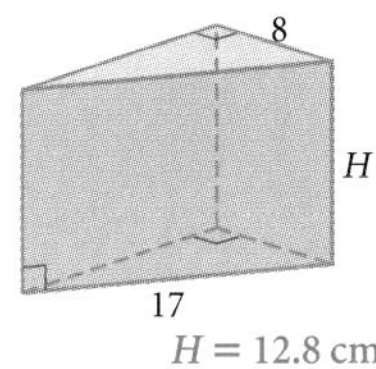

$H = 12.8$ cm

10. Find h. $V = 896\text{ cm}^3$

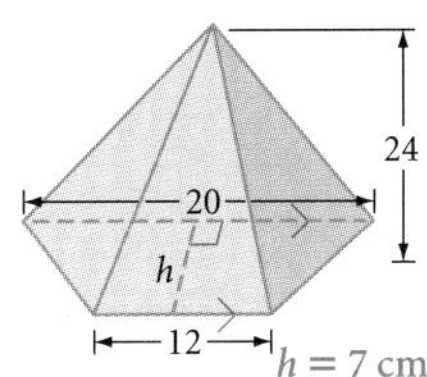
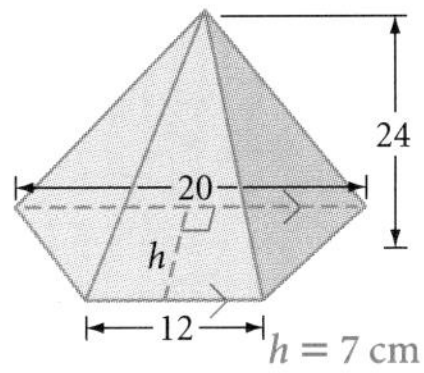

$h = 7$ cm

11. Find r. $V = 1728\pi\text{ cm}^3$ $r = 12$ cm

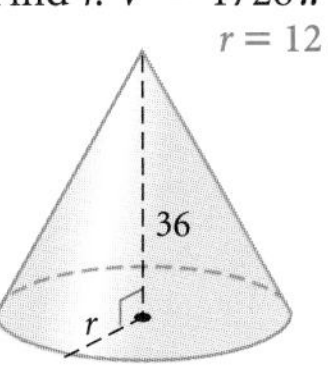

12. Find r. $V = 256\pi\text{ cm}^3$ ⓗ $r = 8$ cm

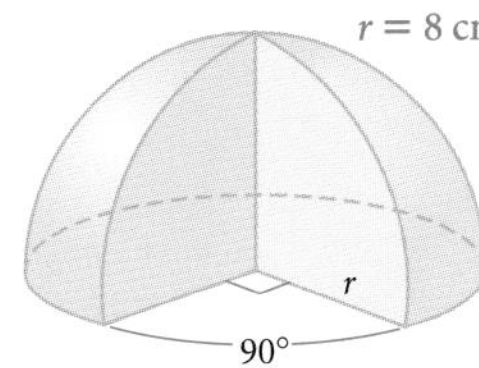

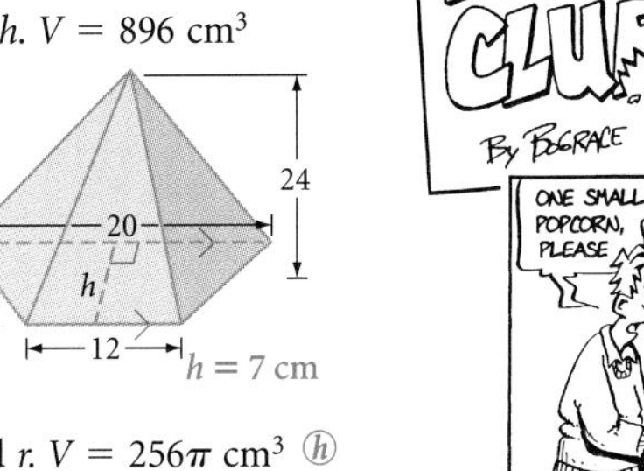

13. Find the volume of a rectangular prism whose dimensions are twice those of another rectangular prism that has a volume of 120 cm^3. 960 cm^3

14. Find the height of a cone with a volume of 138π cubic meters and a base area of 46π square meters. 9 m

15. Find the volume of a regular hexagonal prism that has a cylinder drilled from its center. Each side of the hexagonal base measures 8 cm. The height of the prism is 16 cm. The cylinder has a radius of 6 cm. Express your answer to the nearest cubic centimeter. 851 cm^3

16. Two rectangular prisms have equal heights but unequal bases. Each dimension of the smaller solid's base is half each dimension of the larger solid's base. The volume of the larger solid is how many times as great as the volume of the smaller solid? four times as great

17. The "extra large" popcorn container is a right rectangular prism with dimensions 3 in. by 3 in. by 6 in. The "jumbo" is a cone with height 12 in. and diameter 8 in. The "colossal" is a right cylinder with diameter 10 in. and height 10 in.

a. Find the volume of all three containers.

b. Approximately how many times as great is the volume of the "colossal" than the "extra large"? 14.5 times as great

18. Two solid cylinders are made of the same material. Cylinder A is six times as tall as cylinder B, but the diameter of cylinder B is four times the diameter of cylinder A. Which cylinder weighs more? How many times as much?

▶ Helping with the Exercises

Exercise 13 **[Ask]** "Why is the volume 8 times as large?"

Exercise 17 According to the cartoon, an "extra large" popcorn costs $28. **[Ask]** "How much should a "jumbo" and a "colossal" cost?" [$104 and $407] "Why?" [Those prices are proportional to the volumes.]

17a. $V_{\text{extra large}} = 54\text{ in.}^3$
$V_{\text{jumbo}} \approx 201.1\text{ in.}^3$
$V_{\text{colossal}} \approx 785.4\text{ in.}^3$

18. Cylinder B weighs $\frac{8}{3}$ times as much as cylinder A.

Exercise 19 **[Language]** *Tonne* is synonymous with *metric ton* (1000 kilograms, about 2204.64 lb) and is not the same as *ton* (2000 lb).

20. $H = 2r$. $\frac{V_{\text{sphere}}}{V_{\text{box}}} = \frac{\frac{4}{3}\pi r^3}{(2r)^3}$. Thus, 52.4% of the box is filled by the ball.

Exercise 22 Students can solve the problem without approximating the value of π.

22. No. The unused volume is 98π in.^{3}, and the volume of the meatballs is 32π in.^{3}.

Exercise 23 If students are stuck, **[Ask]** "Is there a way to find the volume of the water displaced?" [It has the same volume as a hexagonal prism with height 4 cm.] Some students may need reminding that the density of an object is its mass divided by its volume. **[Language]** *Art deco* is a style of decorative arts originating in the 1920s and characterized by geometric motifs, curvilinear forms, bold colors, and sharply defined outlines. An example is shown in the photo of a lobby on page 7. **[ESL]** *Fraud* is dishonesty, deceit, trickery.

Exercise 24 Students may need help in seeing that the weight equals the volume times the density. Density is given here with new units $\left(\frac{\text{lb}}{\text{in.}^3}\right)$ not $\frac{\text{grams}}{\text{cm}^3}$, so the data given in the problem do not match the data in the table in Lesson 10.5, Example B.

Exercises 25, 26 Students can find the density of steel in these units from Exercise 24 rather than from the table in Lesson 10.5.

19. **APPLICATION** Rosa Avila is a plumbing contractor. She needs to deliver 200 lengths of steel pipe to a construction site. Each cylindrical steel pipe is 160 cm long, has an outer diameter of 6 cm, and has an inner diameter of 5 cm. Rosa needs to know if her quarter-tonne truck can handle the weight of the pipes. To the nearest kilogram, what is the weight of these 200 pipes? How many loads will Rosa have to transport to deliver the 200 lengths of steel pipe? (Steel has a density of about 7.7 g/cm^3. One tonne equals 1000 kg.) ⓗ 2129 kg; 9 loads

20. A ball is placed snugly into the smallest possible box that will completely contain the ball. What percentage of the box is filled by the ball?

21. **APPLICATION** The blueprint for a cement slab floor is shown at right. How many cubic yards of cement are needed for ten identical floors that are each 4 inches thick? approximately 358 yd^3

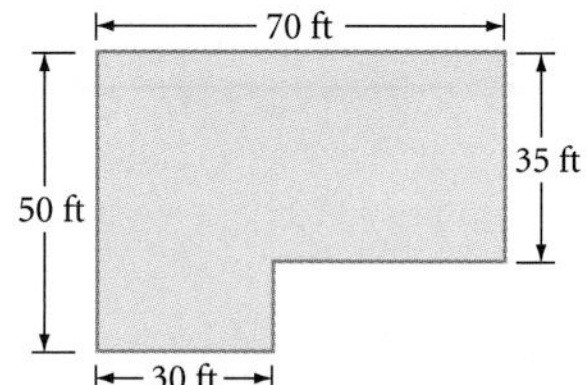

22. A prep chef has just made two dozen meatballs. Each meatball has a 2-inch diameter. Right now, before the meatballs are added, the sauce is 2 inches from the top of the 14-inch-diameter pot. Will the sauce spill over when the chef adds the meatballs to the pot?

23. To solve a crime, Betty Holmes, who claims to be Sherlock's distant cousin, and her friend Professor Hilton Gardens must determine the density of a metal art deco statue that weighs 5560 g. She places it into a graduated glass prism filled with water and finds that the level rises 4 cm. Each edge of the glass prism's regular hexagonal base measures 5 cm. Professor Gardens calculates the statue's volume, then its density. Next, Betty Holmes checks the density table (see page 535) to determine if the statue is platinum. If so, it is the missing piece from her client's collection and Inspector Clouseau is the thief. If not, then the Baron is guilty of fraud. What is the statue made of? platinum

24. Can you pick up a solid steel ball of radius 6 inches? Steel has a density of 0.28 pound per cubic inch. To the nearest pound, what is the weight of the ball? No. The ball weighs 253 lb.

25. To the nearest pound, what is the weight of a hollow steel ball with an outer diameter of 14 inches and a thickness of 2 inches? 256 lb

26. A hollow steel ball has a diameter of 14 inches and weighs 327.36 pounds. Find the thickness of the ball. ⓗ approximately 3 in.

Exercise 27 Students may propose that the volume of the water is $\frac{1}{4}$ that of the barrel because the height of the water is $\frac{1}{4}$ the height of the barrel. Ask them to try to confirm their answer by solving the problem another way. An alternative approach is to multiply the area of the segment of a base by the tank length. Another is to multiply the volume of the barrel by the ratio of the segment area to the area of the whole circle. Students who are stuck might benefit from rotating the picture or drawing a single base. Even then they might have difficulty recognizing the 30°-60°-90° triangles formed by the segment. Students will find it easier to work with fractions in this exercise.

27. A water barrel that is 1 m in diameter and 1.5 m long is partially filled. By tapping on its sides, you estimate that the water is 0.25 m deep at the deepest point. What is the volume of the water in cubic meters? ⓗ

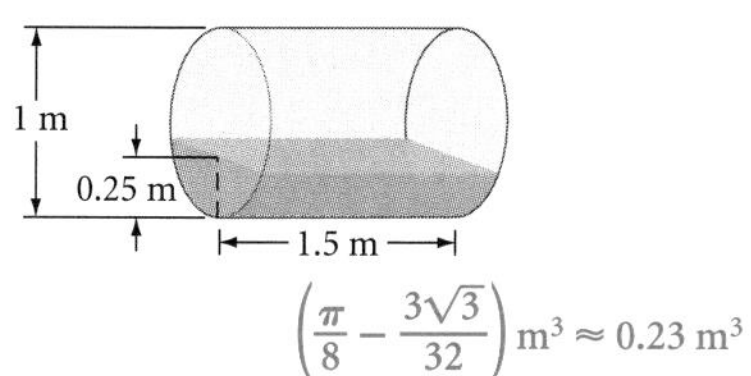

$\left(\frac{\pi}{8} - \frac{3\sqrt{3}}{32}\right)\text{ m}^3 \approx 0.23\text{ m}^3$

28. Find the volume of the solid formed by rotating the shaded figure about the y-axis.

160π cubic units

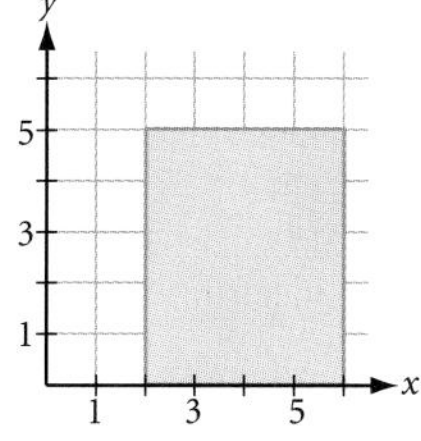

TAKE ANOTHER LOOK

1. You may be familiar with the area model of the expression $(a + b)^2$, shown below. Draw or build a volume model of the expression $(a + b)^3$. How many distinct pieces does your model have? What's the volume of each type of piece? Use your model to write the expression $(a + b)^3$ in expanded form.

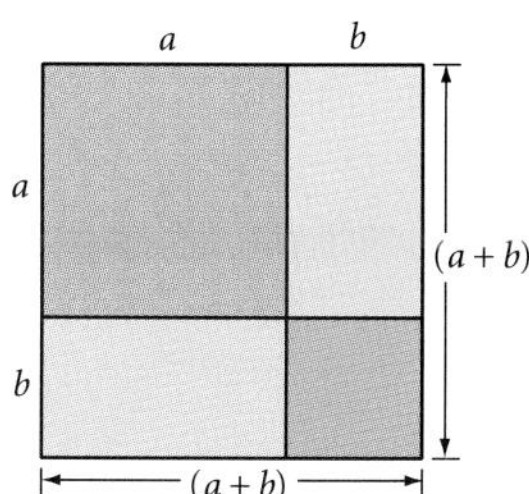

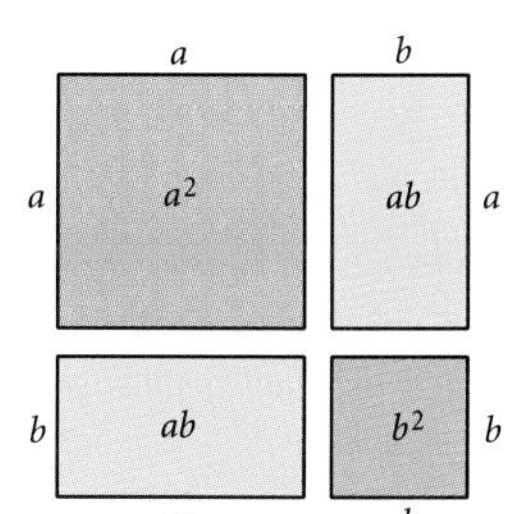

2. Use algebra to show that if you double all three dimensions of a prism, a cylinder, a pyramid, or a cone, the volume is increased eightfold but the surface area is increased only four times.

3. Any sector of a circle can be rolled into a cone. Find a way to calculate the volume of a cone given the radius and central angle of the sector.

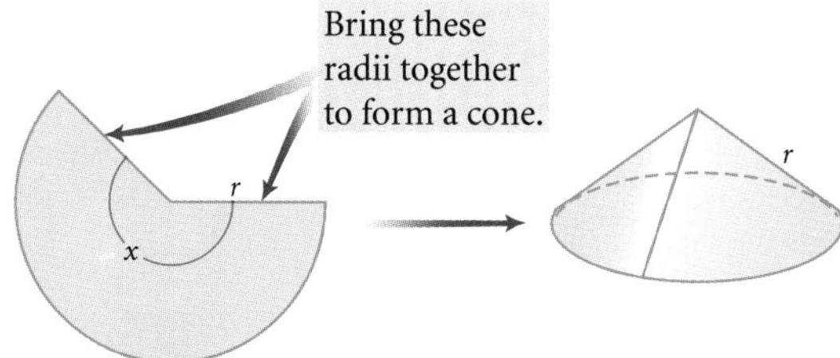

Activity 3 (continued)

Now use the formula to find the volume of a cone:

$$V = \frac{1}{3}\pi R^2 H$$
$$= \frac{1}{3}\pi\left(\frac{x}{360} \cdot r\right)^2\left(r\sqrt{1 - \frac{x^2}{129{,}600}}\right)$$
$$= \frac{1}{3}\pi\left(\frac{x^2}{129{,}600} \cdot r^2\right)\left(r\sqrt{1 - \frac{x^2}{129{,}600}}\right)$$
$$= \frac{x^2}{388{,}800}\pi r^3\sqrt{1 - \frac{x^2}{129{,}600}}$$

Take Another Look

1. The models should have eight pieces. Volumes: one a^3, three a^2b, three ab^2, and one b^3; $(a + b)^3 = a^3 + 3a^2b + 3ab^2 + b^3$.

2. If you double all three dimensions of a rectangular prism, you get $V = (2l)(2w)(2h) = 8(lwh)$ but $S = 2(2l)(2w) + 2(2l)(2h) + 2(2w)(2h) = 4(2lw + 2lh + 2wh)$. Thus the volume increases eightfold, but the surface area is increased only four times. Similarly, for a cylinder, $V = \pi(2r)^2(2h) = 8(\pi r^2 h)$ but $S = 2\pi(2r)^2 + 2\pi(2r)(2H) = 4(2\pi r^2 + 2\pi rH)$. Similarly, for a pyramid or a cone, $V = \frac{1}{3}(4B)(2H) = 8\left(\frac{1}{3}BH\right)$, but $S = 4(rl + 4r^2)$ for a cone and $S = 4\left(B + \frac{1}{2}bhn\right)$ for a pyramid.

3. Let r represent the radius of the sector and x represent the central angle. When the sector is rolled into a cone, the outside edge of the sector becomes the circumference of the base of the cone: $C = \frac{x}{360}(2\pi r)$.

Let R represent the radius of the base of the cone, and find the radius in terms of r: $2\pi R = \frac{x}{360}(2\pi r)$, or $R = \frac{x}{360} \cdot r$.

When the sector is rolled into a cone, the radius of the sector becomes the slant height of the cone. Use the Pythagorean Theorem to find the perpendicular height, H, of the cone:

$$R^2 + H^2 = r^2$$
$$\left(\frac{x}{360} \cdot r\right)^2 + H^2 = r^2$$
$$H = \sqrt{r^2 - \left(\frac{x^2}{360^2}\right) \cdot r^2}$$
$$= \sqrt{r^2\left(1 - \frac{x^2}{129{,}600}\right)}$$
$$= r\sqrt{1 - \frac{x^2}{129{,}600}}$$

4. sample answer:

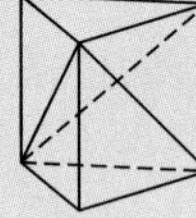

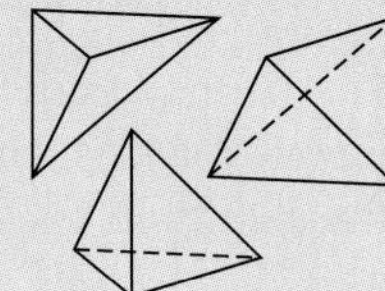

The first two of these pyramids have the same base and height as the prism, so the two have equal volumes. If you consider halves of the front face of the prism as the bases of the second and third pyramids, they also have equivalent bases and heights and hence equal volumes.

For another answer, use three congruent square pyramids each with vertex over a vertex of the square base.

5. Answers will vary depending on the solid. Sample: Almost four hemispheres $\left(\frac{12}{\pi}\right)$ fill a cube of side $2r$.

$8r^3 = \frac{12}{\pi}$

$V_{\text{hemisphere}} = \frac{2}{3}\pi r^2$

6. No; the spheres wouldn't have the same surface area. The surface area of the bumpy sphere would be greater, because the pyramids add a lot of surface.

ASSESSING

Along with the chapter test you might assign a sculpture project. (See Geometry in Sculpture in *Discovering Geometry More Projects and Explorations.*) The sculpture should contain at least five solids, and a written description should contain the dimensions, the surface area, and the volume of each solid. The project can be graded on creativity as well as mathematical accuracy.

4. Build a model of three pyramids with equal volumes that you can assemble into a prism.

5. Derive the Sphere Volume Conjecture by using a pair of hollow shapes different from those you used in the Investigation The Formula for the Volume of a Sphere. Or use two solids made of the same material and compare weights. Explain what you did and how it demonstrates the conjecture.

6. Spaceship Earth, located at the Epcot center in Orlando, Florida, is made of polygonal regions arranged in little pyramids. The building appears spherical, but the surface is not smooth. If a perfectly smooth sphere had the same volume as Spaceship Earth, would it have the same surface area? If not, which would be greater, the surface area of the smooth sphere or of the bumpy sphere? Explain.

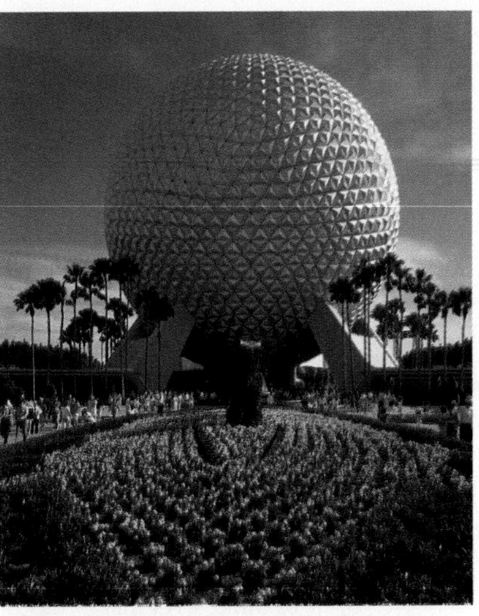

Spaceship Earth, the Epcot center's signature structure, opened in 1982 in Walt Disney World. It features a ride that chronicles the history of communication technology.

Assessing What You've Learned

UPDATE YOUR PORTFOLIO Choose a project, a Take Another Look activity, or one of the more challenging problems or puzzles you did in this chapter to add to your portfolio.

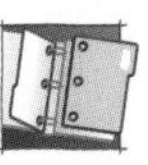

WRITE IN YOUR JOURNAL Describe your own problem-solving approach. Are there certain steps you follow when you solve a challenging problem? What are some of your most successful problem-solving strategies?

ORGANIZE YOUR NOTEBOOK Review your notebook to be sure it's complete and well organized. Be sure you have all the conjectures in your conjecture list. Write a one-page summary of Chapter 10.

PERFORMANCE ASSESSMENT While a classmate, friend, family member, or teacher observes, demonstrate how to derive one or more of the volume formulas. Explain what you're doing at each step.

WRITE TEST ITEMS Work with classmates to write test items for this chapter. Include simple exercises and complex application problems. Try to demonstrate more than one approach in your solutions.

GIVE A PRESENTATION Give a presentation about one or more of the volume conjectures. Use posters, models, or visual aids to support your presentation.

FACILITATING SELF-ASSESSMENT

To help students complete the portfolio described in Assessing What You've Learned, suggest that they consider for evaluation their work on Lesson 10.1, Exercise 37; Lesson 10.2, Exercise 24; Lesson 10.3, Exercise 10; Lesson 10.4, Exercise 6; Lesson 10.5, Exercise 3; Lesson 10.6, Exercise 14 or 16; and Lesson 10.7, Exercise 13.

CHAPTER

11 Similarity

Overview

Chapter 11 begins with **Using Your Algebra Skills 9,** a review of proportions. In **Lessons 11.1** and **11.2,** students explore some of the basic properties of similarity for polygons and for triangles. In an **exploration** students use a Sketchpad construction to demonstrate dilations. Students use similarity for indirect measurement in **Lesson 11.3.** In **Lessons 11.4** and **11.5,** students discover linear, area, and volume relationships between similar figures. The second **exploration** looks at the implications of these relationships for living things. Proportions of segments between parallel lines are investigated in **Lesson 11.6.** The final **exploration** uses the language of symbolic logic to show valid reasoning.

The Mathematics

We see examples of similar figures in paintings, sculptures, scale models for design or recreation, and maps of roads or of silicon chips. We see them whenever we have lines parallel to sides of triangles. But defining what we mean by "similar" can be difficult.

- One definition is that similar figures have the same shape though not necessarily the same size. This definition misleads some students to believe that all rectangles, for example, are similar because they have the same shape (rectangle).
- Another definition is that plane figures are similar if corresponding angles are congruent and corresponding sides are proportional. ("proportional sides" is shorthand for "proportional lengths of sides") and that solids are similar if corresponding faces are similar and corresponding edges are proportional. These definitions work for polygons and polyhedrons, but how they apply to circles and spheres is not completely clear. Other curved shapes can also be similar.
- Lesson 11.1 introduces a kind of transformation called a *dilation,* which enlarges or reduces figures by the same amount (the scale factor) in all directions from the origin. Although in practice we often think of similar figures as dilations of each other (not necessarily centered at the origin), many similar figures are actually dilations of *reflections* of each other. So a definition of similarity would involve composites of dilations with isometries.

The study of similarity strengthens ideas about ratios and proportions, which are weak areas for many students. These ideas have applications primarily in two realms:

- Measuring distances with similar triangles. The distances may be heights or distances across untraversable terrain. Triangles are especially easy to work with because there are several shortcuts to proving their similarity, just as there were for proving congruence.
- Finding areas and volumes. Ratios of two-dimensional parts of figures (surface areas, cross-sectional areas) equal the squares of the scale factors, whereas ratios of three-dimensional parts (volumes) equal the cubes of the scale factors. These relationships not only allow us to find area and volume but also extend to other dimensions, including fractional dimensions.

With the study of similarity, students take their first step away from the heart of Euclidean geometry, which concentrates on congruence. (Euclid himself didn't introduce similar figures until Book VI of *Elements.*) Sometimes a geometry is considered as the study of properties that don't change under some class of transformations. From that perspective, students in this course have so far focused on properties—such as congruence, area, and volume—that don't change under isometries. In this chapter they turn to non-isometric transformations called *similarities,* dilations followed by isometries. These transformations change distance, area, and volume, and they change area and volume in interesting ways. What *don't* they change? They don't change angle measure or ratios of distances.

More general geometries will be considered in an exploration in Chapter 13.

Using This Chapter

Try to integrate Using Your Algebra Skills 9 with Lesson 11.1 over two or three days. If you don't have that much time, skip the second investigation in Lesson 11.1. If you must trim this chapter, skip Lesson 11.6 on the Parallel/Proportionality Conjecture. Lessons 11.4 and 11.5 are especially critical.

Lesson 1.3 offers opportunities for group members to collaborate. Within a group, responsibilities might be divided up—taking measurements, recording them, doing the calculations, and keeping track of the equipment.

If you want to cover more symbolic logic than is included in the last Exploration, use the more detailed explorations in *Discovering Geometry More Projects and Explorations.*

Resources

Discovering Geometry Resources

Teaching and Worksheet Masters
Lesson 11.1

Sketchpad Demonstrations
Exploration: Constructing a Dilation Design
Lesson 11.5

Discovering Geometry with The Geometer's Sketchpad
Lessons 11.1–11.6

Assessment Resources A and B
Quiz 1 (Lessons 11.1–11.3)
Quiz 2 (Lessons 11.4–11.6)
Chapter 11 Test
Chapter 11 Constructive Assessment Options

Practice Your Skills for Chapter 11

Condensed Lessons for Chapter 11

Other Resources

Symmetry: A Unifying Concept by Istvan and Magdolna Hargittai.

For complete references on this and other resources see www.keypress.com/DG.

Materials

- construction tools
- rulers
- protractors
- calculators
- graph paper
- mirrors
- metersticks
- masking tape
- 1000 or more interlocking cubes
- biology and physics reference books, *optional*
- large paper such as poster board or butcher paper, *optional*
- colored pens or pencils, *optional*
- geometry software, *optional*

Pacing Guide

	day 1	day 2	day 3	day 4	day 5	day 6	day 7	day 8	day 9	day 10
standard	Algebra 9	11.1	11.1	11.2	project or Exploration	11.3	quiz, 11.4	11.5	Exploration	11.6
enriched	Algebra 9, 11.1	11.1	11.1, project	project	11.2	Exploration	11.3	quiz, 11.4	11.5	project
block	Algebra 9, 11.1	11.1, 11.2	Exploration, 11.3	quiz, 11.4	11.5, project	Exploration	11.6, Exploration	quiz, review, TAL	review, assessment	

	day 11	day 12	day 13	day 14	day 15	day 16	day 17	day 18	day 19	day 20
standard	quiz, Exploration	review	review	assessment						
enriched	Exploration	11.6	quiz, Exploration	review, TAL	assessment, TAL					

CHAPTER

11 Similarity

Nobody can draw a line that is not a boundary line, every line separates a unity into a multiplicity. In addition, every closed contour no matter what its shape, pure circle or whimsical splash accidental in form, evokes the sensation of "inside" and "outside," followed quickly by the suggestion of "nearby" and "far off," of object and background.

M. C. ESCHER

Path of Life I, M. C. Escher, 1958

OBJECTIVES

In this chapter you will

- review ratio and proportion
- define similar polygons and solids
- discover shortcuts for similar triangles
- learn about area and volume relationships in similar polygons and solids
- use the definition of similarity to solve problems

Starting at the edge of *Path of Life I* and working toward the center, the fishlike creatures decrease in size proportionally.

[ESL] In the Escher quote, a *unity* means a whole quantity or a region; a *multiplicity* means the region divided into multiple regions, or more than one region; *whimsical* suggests that the shape can be any shape, or just curves or lines; *evokes* suggests creating something through doing something else; *sensation* suggests there may not always be a true inside or outside, but perhaps just the hint of an inside and an outside.

[Ask] "What shapes in the print are similar?" [The black-red fish are similar to each other, as are the white-red fish. The boundary three-colored fish are congruent and similar. The flowerlike shapes outlined by the black fish are similar.] "Do you see a spiral? Where?" [Yes; there are eight spirals along the backbones of the white fish to the three-colored fish and eight shorter spirals along black fish in the other direction.]

CHAPTER 11 OBJECTIVES

- Review ratio and proportion and practice solving proportions
- Develop an intuitive concept of similarity and define similar polygons
- Use the definition of similar triangles and other polygons to solve problems
- Discover shortcut methods for determining similar triangles
- Practice using proportions to find measures in similar figures
- Discover a relationship between corresponding parts of similar triangles
- Explore the ratio of the parts into which an angle bisector of a triangle divides the opposite side
- Discover the relationship between the areas and volumes of similar figures
- Apply the similarity conjectures to problems involving area and volume
- Discover the relationship between the ratios of the parts into which parallel lines cut the sides of a triangle
- Discover a construction method for dividing a segment into proportional parts
- Develop reading comprehension, problem-solving skills, and cooperative behavior

Proportion and Reasoning

Working with similar geometric figures involves ratios and proportions. You may be a little rusty with these topics, so let's review.

A **ratio** is an expression that compares two quantities by division. You can write the ratio of quantity a to quantity b in these three ways:

$\frac{a}{b}$ a to b $a{:}b$

In this book you will write ratios in fraction form. As with fractions, you can multiply or divide both parts of a ratio by the same number to get an equivalent ratio.

A **proportion** is a statement of equality between two ratios. The equality $\frac{6}{18} = \frac{1}{3}$ is an example of a proportion. Proportions are useful for solving problems involving comparisons.

EXAMPLE A In a photograph, Dan is 2.5 inches tall and his sister Emma is 1.5 inches tall. Dan's actual height is 70 inches. What is Emma's actual height?

▶ ***Solution*** The ratio of Dan's height to Emma's height is the same in real life as it is in the photo. Let x represent Emma's height and set up a proportion.

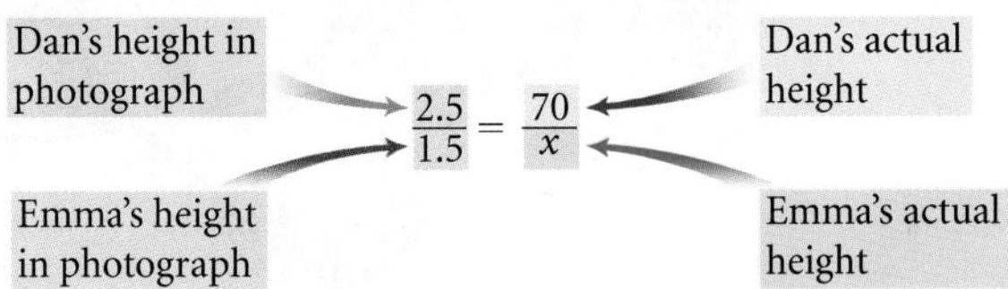

Find Emma's height by solving for x.

$\frac{2.5}{1.5} = \frac{70}{x}$	Original proportion.
$\frac{2.5}{1.5}x = 70$	Multiply both sides by x.
$2.5x = 105$	Multiply both sides by 1.5.
$x = 42$	Divide both sides by 2.5.

Emma is 42 inches tall.

There are other proportions you could have used to solve the problem in Example A. For instance, the ratio of Dan's actual height to his height in the photo is equal to the ratio of Emma's actual height to her height in the photo. So you could have found Emma's height by solving $\frac{70}{2.5} = \frac{x}{1.5}$. What other correct proportion could you use?

USING YOUR ALGEBRA SKILLS 9

PLANNING

LESSON OUTLINE

One day:

10 min Examples

30 min Exercises

5 min Closing

MATERIALS

none

TEACHING

Not only are ratios and proportions essential to working with similarity, but having a "feeling" for ratios is key to learning a great deal of mathematics. You may want to teach this lesson along with Lesson 11.1 over two days, partly because similar figures are concrete representations of ratios, but also so students will see the importance of ratios in a context. When you review out of context, you risk losing students who think they understand the ideas because they've seen them before or students who found the ideas boring or overwhelming in their previous encounter.

One step Pose this problem: "A police department is trying to estimate the number of petty thefts in a neighborhood. It's not easy, because some petty thefts are not reported. The police know that 82 thefts were reported, and they know that 5 of 31 thefts confessed to had not been reported. Are these numbers enough to allow the police to make the estimate they want?" Students' varying intuition may lead to some healthy controversy about this situation. Be aware that intuition can keep students from hearing other points of view and that some students will resist changing their original ideas because they see it as part of their identity. Encourage students to air their ideas, but push them toward careful analytical thinking. Even then, students may appropriately disagree about whether or not the portion of confessed thefts that were not reported is about equal to the portion of total thefts that were not reported. Even after accepting the need for assumptions, some students may object that the result can't be exact. Remain flexible about how students express their reasoning. Writing and solving an actual proportion can wait for Sharing.

▶ **EXAMPLE A**

Other proportions could be used to solve the problem, such as $\frac{x}{70} = \frac{1.5}{2.5}$ or $\frac{1.5}{x} = \frac{2.5}{70}$. To check their work, students can substitute the solution into the original equation and use a calculator to verify that $\frac{2.5}{1.5}$ and $\frac{70}{42}$ are both equivalent to $1.\overline{6}$.

Some students may want to cross multiply—simultaneously multiplying each numerator by the denominator of the other side. What they are doing is justified because it is a shortcut way of thinking about multiplying both sides by the two denominators.

Some proportions require more algebra to solve.

EXAMPLE B Solve $\frac{306}{24} = \frac{x+50}{20}$.

▶ Solution

$\frac{306}{24} = \frac{x+50}{20}$ Original proportion.

$20 \cdot \frac{306}{24} = x + 50$ Multiply both sides by 20.

$255 = x + 50$ Multiply and divide on the left side.

$205 = x$ Subtract 50 from both sides.

EXERCISES

1. Look at the rectangle at right. Find the ratio of the shaded area to the area of the whole figure. Find the ratio of the shaded area to the unshaded area. $\frac{3}{8}, \frac{3}{5}$

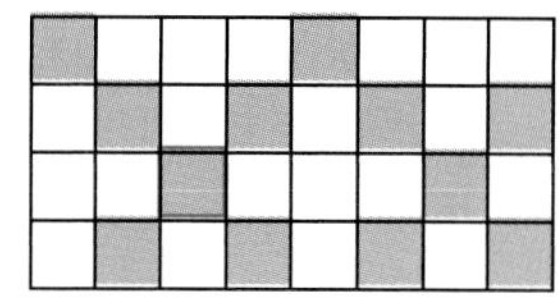

2. Use the figure below to find these ratios: $\frac{AC}{CD}$, $\frac{CD}{BD}$, and $\frac{BD}{BC}$.

A —3 cm— C —5 cm— D —8 cm— B

$\frac{AC}{CD} = \frac{3}{5}, \frac{CD}{BD} = \frac{5}{8}, \frac{BD}{BC} = \frac{8}{13}$

3. Consider these triangles.

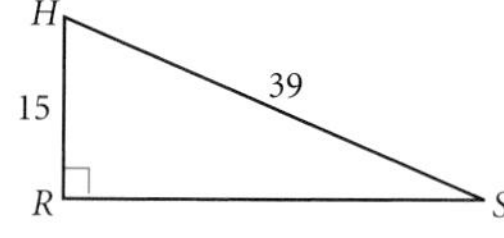

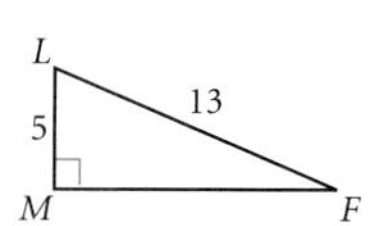

a. Find the ratio of the perimeter of $\triangle RSH$ to the perimeter of $\triangle MFL$. $\frac{3}{1}$

b. Find the ratio of the area of $\triangle RSH$ to the area of $\triangle MFL$. $\frac{9}{1}$

In Exercises 4–12, solve the proportion.

4. $\frac{7}{21} = \frac{a}{18}$ $a = 6$

5. $\frac{10}{b} = \frac{15}{24}$ $b = 16$

6. $\frac{20}{13} = \frac{60}{c}$ $c = 39$

7. $\frac{4}{5} = \frac{x}{7}$ $x = 5.6$

8. $\frac{2}{y} = \frac{y}{32}$ $y = \pm 8$

9. $\frac{14}{10} = \frac{x+9}{15}$ $x = 12$

10. $\frac{10}{10+z} = \frac{35}{56}$ $z = 6$

11. $\frac{d}{5} = \frac{d+3}{20}$ $d = 1$

12. $\frac{y}{y+2} = \frac{15}{21}$ $y = 5$

13. Solve this proportion for x. Assume $c \neq 0$ and $z \neq 0$.

$\frac{x}{c} = \frac{b}{z}$ $x = \frac{bc}{z}$

NCTM STANDARDS

CONTENT	PROCESS
✓ Number	✓ Problem Solving
✓ Algebra	Reasoning
Geometry	Communication
✓ Measurement	✓ Connections
Data/Probability	✓ Representation

LESSON OBJECTIVES

- Learn or review the meanings of *ratio* and *proportion*
- Practice solving proportions
- Use ratios and proportions to solve word problems
- Develop reading comprehension, problem-solving skills, and cooperative behavior

Cross multiplication is often learned as a rote skill with little understanding; press these students to explain their reasoning, and encourage them to separate the steps until they can justify the shortcut.

▶ EXAMPLE B

Ask students to solve the proportion before reading the solution in their books. You can then begin to assess their algebra skills. For example, students might mistakenly reduce the 50 and 20, changing the right side to $\frac{x+5}{2}$. Others might first reasonably reduce $\frac{306}{24}$ to $\frac{51}{4}$.

SHARING IDEAS

As students present their ideas, repeatedly emphasize the variety of ways in which proportions can be solved. One reason why some students panic during standardized mathematics tests is that they can't remember "the right way" to solve a familiar-looking problem.

You might want to have students work on the exercises and present some of the solutions before closing the lesson.

Assessing Progress
You can assess students' intuition about and ability to work with ratios and proportions.

Closing the Lesson

A **proportion** is a statement of the equality of two **ratios.** Variables representing unknown quantities may be involved. You can find values of those variables in various ways, often including multiplying both sides of the equation by denominators.

BUILDING UNDERSTANDING

You might supplement the exercises with some based on exercises students will encounter later in studying similarity.

ASSIGNING HOMEWORK

Essential	1–8
Portfolio	16
Group	9–18

▶ Helping with the Exercises

Exercise 1 Encourage a variety of approaches. If you ask how students did the counting and how they might have done it, you can review several algebraic principles, such as commutativity and distributivity. Without counting all the squares, some students might notice that in every pair of columns 3 of the 8 squares are shaded, or that in each pair of rows 6 of the 16 squares are shaded.

Exercise 3 As needed, **[Ask]** "How might you find missing sides?" [Use the Pythagorean Theorem. Students might find one side using the similarity ratio, even if they haven't studied similarity.]

Exercise 8 **[Alert]** Students may miss the negative result, taking only the positive square root of 64.

Exercise 10 Be open to a variety of approaches. For example, if students first reduce $\frac{35}{56}$ to $\frac{5}{8}$, they might notice that 10 is twice 5 and get the equation $10 + z = 16$.

Exercise 13 **[Alert]** Seeing only letters may confuse students. Some may try to add the variables instead of multiplying them.

Exercise 15 Solutions should include justification of answers. Otherwise, students might simply use one of the many web sites where earned run averages can be calculated.

Exercise 16 Be open to alternatives to setting up two proportions (one for each dimension). For example, students may reason that the long dimension is $\frac{1}{4}$ longer than the short dimension.

In Exercises 14–17, use a proportion to solve the problem.

14. APPLICATION A car travels 106 miles on 4 gallons of gas. How far can it go on a full tank of 12 gallons? 318 mi

15. APPLICATION Ernie is a baseball pitcher. He gave up 34 runs in 152 innings last season. What is Ernie's earned run average—the number of runs he would give up in 9 innings? Give your answer accurate to two decimal places. 2.01

16. APPLICATION The floor plan of a house is drawn to the scale of $\frac{1}{4}$ in. = 1 ft. The master bedroom measures 3 in. by $3\frac{3}{4}$ in. on the blueprints. What is the actual size of the room? 12 ft by 15 ft

17. Altor and Zenor are ambassadors from Titan, the largest moon of Saturn. The sum of the lengths of any Titan's antennae is a direct measure of that Titan's age. Altor has antennae with lengths 8 cm, 10 cm, 13 cm, 16 cm, 14 cm, and 12 cm. Zenor is 130 years old, and her seven antennae have an average length of 17 cm. How old is Altor? almost 80 years old

18. Assume $\frac{AB}{XY} = \frac{BC}{YZ}$. Find AB and BC.

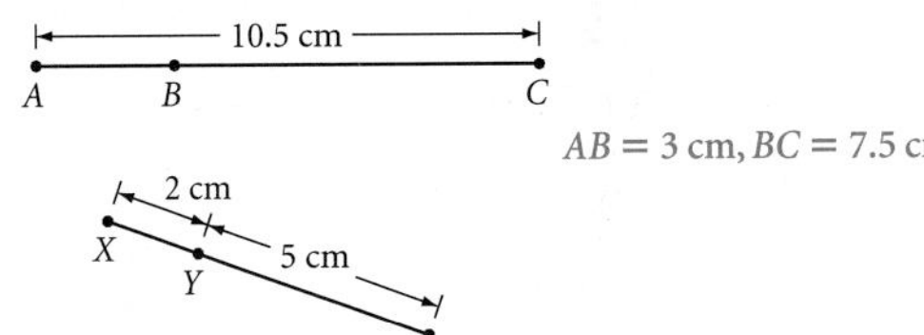

$AB = 3$ cm, $BC = 7.5$ cm

IMPROVING YOUR ALGEBRA SKILLS

Algebraic Magic Squares II

In this algebraic magic square, the sum of the entries in every row, column, and diagonal is the same. Find the value of x.

$8 - x$	15	14	$11 - x$
12	$x - 1$	x	9
8	$x + 3$	$x + 4$	5
$2x - 1$	3	2	$2x + 2$

Exercise 18 If p represents AB, then $10.5 - p = BC$.

EXTENSION

Discuss variation of the square, variation of the cube, and inverse variation.

IMPROVING ALGEBRA SKILLS

Students need only to write equations from two rows or columns in which the coefficients of x are different. In the second and third rows, for example, the coefficients of x are both 2, so the equations would be $2x + 20 = 2x + 20$, not yielding a way to solve for x. Many other pairs of equations lead to the solution, $x = 7$.

LESSON

11.1

Similar Polygons

He that lets
the small things bind him
Leaves the great
undone behind him.
PIET HEIN

You know that figures that have the same shape and size are congruent figures. Figures that have the same shape but not necessarily the same size are **similar figures.** To say that two figures have the same shape but not necessarily the same size is not, however, a precise definition of similarity.

Is your reflection in a fun-house mirror similar to a regular photograph of you? The images have a lot of features in common, but they are not mathematically similar. In mathematics, you can think of similar shapes as enlargements or reductions of each other with no irregular distortions.

Are all rectangles similar? They have common characteristics, but they are not all similar. That is, you could not enlarge or reduce a given rectangle to fit perfectly over every other rectangle. What about other geometric figures: squares, circles, triangles?

The uneven surface of a fun-house mirror creates a distorted image of you. Your true proportions look different in your reflection.

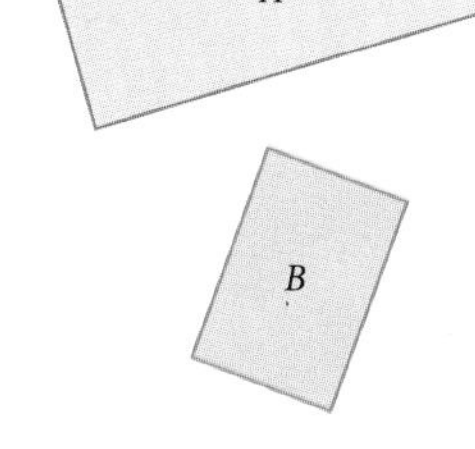

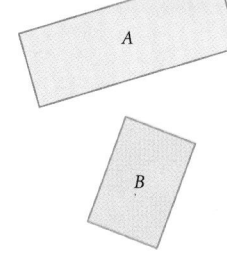

Rectangles *A* and *B* are not similar. You could not enlarge or reduce one to fit perfectly over the other.

Art CONNECTION

Movie scenes are scaled down to small images on strips of film. Then they are scaled up to fit a large screen. So the film image and the projected image are similar. If the distance between the projector and the screen is decreased by half, each dimension of the screen image is cut in half.

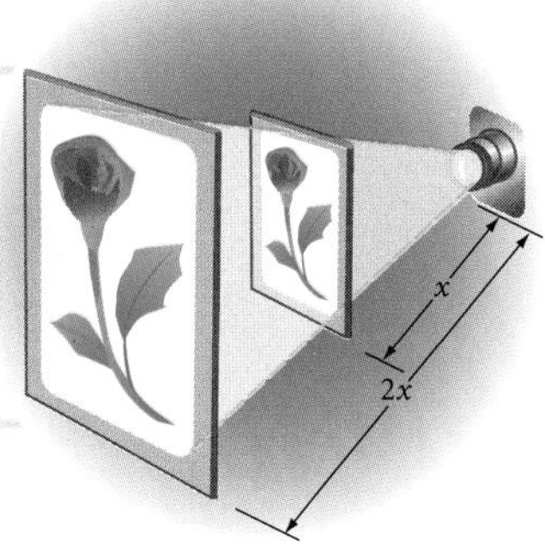

NCTM STANDARDS

CONTENT		PROCESS	
	Number	✓	Problem Solving
✓	Algebra	✓	Reasoning
✓	Geometry	✓	Communication
✓	Measurement	✓	Connections
	Data/Probability		Representation

LESSON OBJECTIVES

- Develop an intuitive concept of similarity
- Define similar polygons
- Use the definition of similar polygons to solve problems
- Develop problem-solving skills and cooperative behavior

LESSON

11.1

PLANNING

LESSON OUTLINE

First day:

10 min Connections
25 min Investigation 1
10 min Sharing

Second day:

20 min Investigation 2
15 min Sharing
5 min Closing
5 min Exercises

MATERIALS

- construction tools
- rulers
- protractors
- calculators
- graph paper
- Similar Polygons (W), *optional*

TEACHING

Examples of similar figures abound. Similar polygons are dilations of each other or isometries of those dilations, and their angle measures and side lengths are closely related.

One step Ask students to pretend they're working for an advertising company and have been assigned to create a design that shows the tripling of a company's sales over two years. They should plot a small polygon (their choice of shape) on graph paper (or using geometry software) to represent sales two years ago. Then they should use the coordinate rule $(x, y) \rightarrow (3x, 3y)$ on each vertex to make a polygon that represents current sales. Finally, they should compare geometric features of the two polygons, including angle measures and side lengths. During Sharing,

One step (continued)
summarize their ideas using the terms *dilation, scale factor,* and *similar figures.* If they note that areas are not proportional, you can lead them into a discussion of misleading advertising.

Guiding Investigation 1

You might use the Similar Polygons worksheet to make measuring easier. Students can use calculators to convert the ratios to decimals for comparison. Some variation should be expected, but if the ratios differ by too much, then students either measured or calculated inaccurately. **[Alert]** Students can usually be more accurate in their measurements if they measure in centimeters and millimeters instead of in inches.

Step 2 $AB \approx 2.3$ cm, $BC \approx 3.0$ cm, $CD \approx 2.3$ cm, $DE \approx 0.5$ cm, $EF \approx 5.2$ cm, $FA \approx 0.5$ cm, $PQ \approx 4.1$ cm, $QR \approx 5.4$ cm, $RS \approx 4.1$ cm, $TU \approx 9.3$ cm, $ST \approx 0.9$ cm, $UP \approx 0.9$ cm

SHARING IDEAS

After students share ideas about Investigation 1, ask about the counterexamples. You might remind them that a counterexample to a conjecture in the form "If *P,* then *Q*" would show how *P* can be true but *Q* false. Students might recognize that the counterexamples make a case only for quadrilaterals. You might want to challenge students to experiment with other polygons, foreshadowing the special case of triangles to be considered in Lesson 11.2.

Ask what is meant by the ratio of sides of figures. The phrase "ratio of the sides" is shorthand for "ratio of the lengths of the sides." **[Ask]** "Can the sides be curved?" [yes] "What if the figure is a circle?" [It has only one side; all circles are similar.]

Investigation 1
What Makes Polygons Similar?

You will need

- patty paper
- a ruler

Let's explore what makes polygons similar. Hexagon *PQRSTU* is an enlargement of hexagon *ABCDEF*—they are similar.

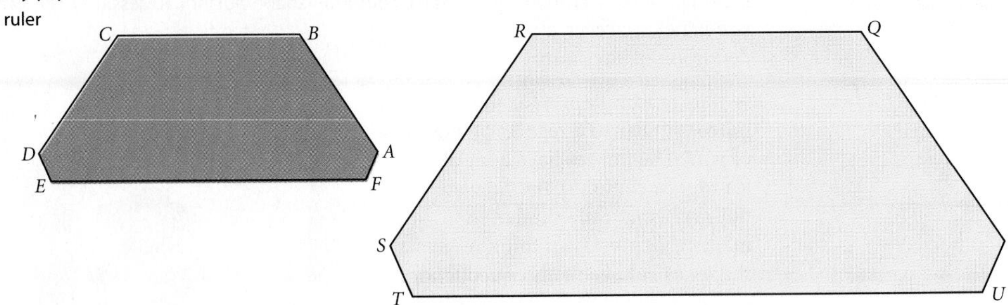

Step 1 Use patty paper to compare all corresponding angles. How do the corresponding angles compare? They are congruent.

Step 2 Measure the corresponding segments in both hexagons.

Step 3 Find the ratios of the lengths of corresponding sides. How do the ratios of corresponding sides compare? The ratios are approximately equal to 0.56.

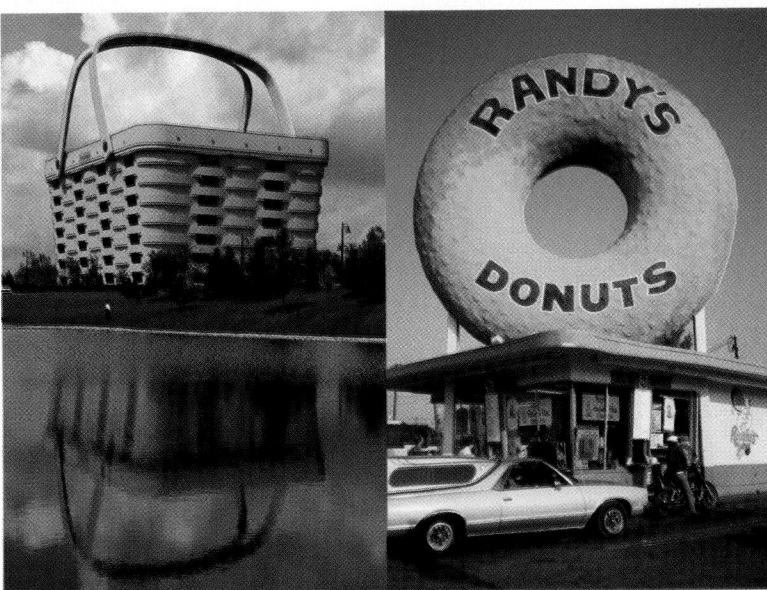

Similar objects are often used to create unique buildings. The giant basket shown here is actually an office building for a basket manufacturer. The giant donut advertises a donut shop in Los Angeles, California.

From the investigation, you should be able to state a mathematical definition of similar polygons. Two polygons are **similar polygons** if and only if the corresponding angles are congruent and the corresponding sides are proportional. Similarity is the state of being similar.

The statement $CORN \sim PEAS$ says that quadrilateral $CORN$ is similar to quadrilateral $PEAS$. Just as in statements of congruence, the order of the letters tells you which segments and which angles in the two polygons correspond.

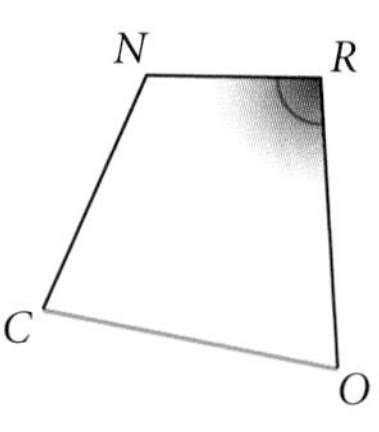

Corresponding angles are congruent:

$\angle C \cong \angle P$ $\quad \angle R \cong \angle A$

$\angle O \cong \angle E$ $\quad \angle N \cong \angle S$

Corresponding segments are proportional:

$$\frac{CO}{PE} = \frac{OR}{EA} = \frac{RN}{AS} = \frac{NC}{SP}$$

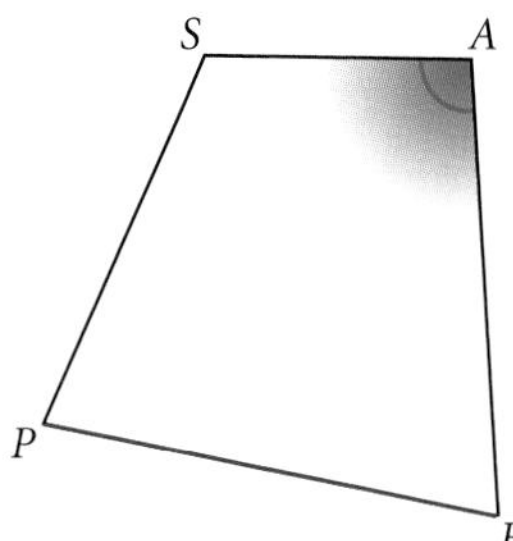

Do you need both conditions—congruent angles and proportional sides—to guarantee that the two polygons are similar? For example, if you know only that the corresponding angles of two polygons are congruent, can you conclude that the polygons have to be similar? Or, if corresponding sides of two polygons are proportional, are the polygons necessarily similar? These counterexamples show that both answers are no.

In the figures below, corresponding angles of square $SQUE$ and rectangle $RCTL$ are congruent, but their corresponding sides are not proportional.

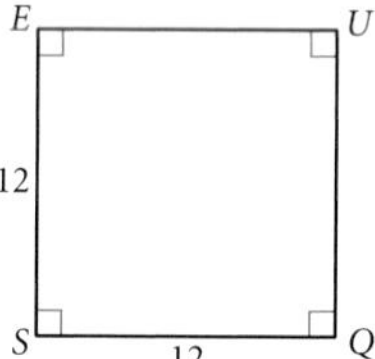

$$\frac{12}{10} \neq \frac{12}{18}$$

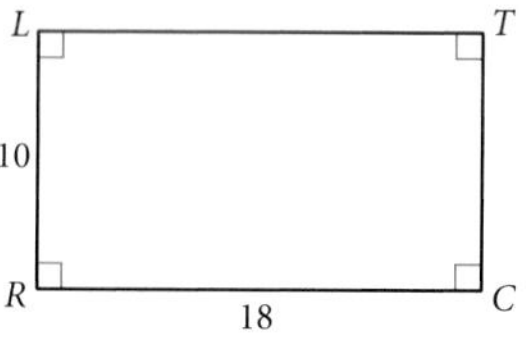

In the figures below, corresponding sides of square $SQUE$ and rhombus $RHOM$ are proportional, but their corresponding angles are not congruent.

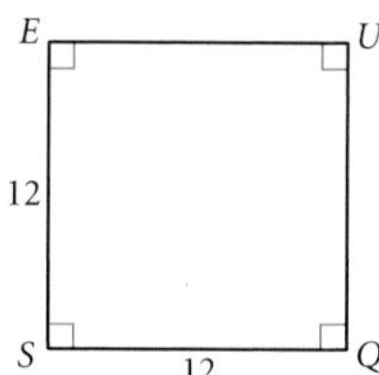

$$\frac{12}{18} = \frac{12}{18}$$

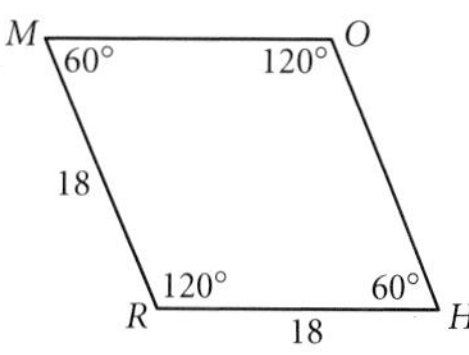

Clearly, neither pair of polygons is similar. You cannot conclude that two polygons are similar given only the fact that their corresponding angles are congruent or given only the fact that their corresponding sides are proportional.

Similarity and Proportions

The symbol $\sim$ is used to indicate that geometric figures are similar. In the logic Exploration at the end of this chapter (page 611), the same symbol is used for negation.

In the series of side proportions $\left(\frac{CO}{PE} = \frac{OR}{EA} = \frac{RN}{AS} = \frac{NC}{SP}\right)$, the measurements from $CORN$ are always in the numerator of the ratios, and the measurements from $PEAS$ are always in the denominator. When you set up the proportions between corresponding sides, you have to be certain to set up the ratios in corresponding fashion.

You can use the definition of similar polygons to find missing measures in similar polygons.

EXAMPLE

SMAL ~ *BIGE*
Find *x* and *y*.

▸ **Solution**

The quadrilaterals are similar, so you can use a proportion to find *x*.

$\frac{18}{24} = \frac{21}{x}$	A proportion of corresponding sides.
$18x = (24)(21)$	Multiply both sides by $24x$ and reduce.
$x = 28$	Divide both sides by 18.

The measure of the side labeled *x* is 28 ft.

In similar polygons, corresponding angles are congruent, so $\angle M \cong \angle I$. The measure of the angle labeled *y* is therefore 83°.

Earlier in this book you worked with translations, rotations, and reflections. These rigid transformations preserve both size and shape—the images are congruent to the original figures. One type of nonrigid transformation is called a **dilation.** Let's look at an image after a dilation transformation.

Investigation 2
Dilations on a Coordinate Plane

You will need

- graph paper
- a straightedge
- patty paper
- a compass

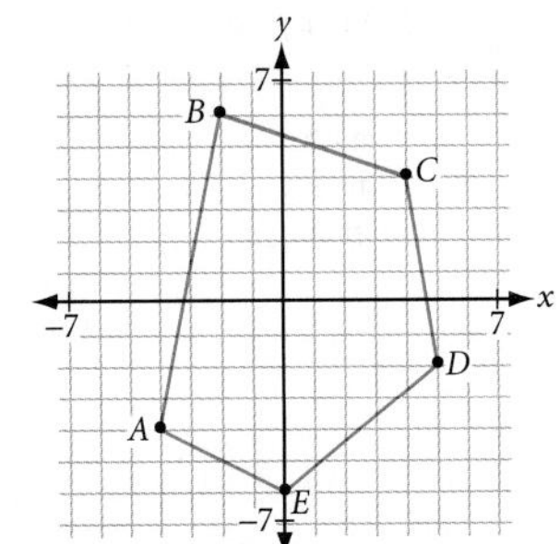

Step 1 To dilate a pentagon on a coordinate plane, first copy this pentagon onto your graph paper.

Step 2 Have each member of your group multiply the coordinates of the vertices by one of these numbers: $\frac{1}{2}$, $\frac{3}{4}$, 2, or 3. Each of these factors is called a **scale factor.**

Step 3 Locate these new coordinates on your graph paper and draw the new pentagon.

▸ ***EXAMPLE***

You might ask students to set up and solve the proportion before looking at the book in order to generate a variety of approaches. For example, they might begin by reducing $\frac{18}{24}$ to $\frac{3}{4}$. Then, rather than multiplying by denominators, they might see the right side of the proportion as the equivalent fraction $\frac{21}{28}$.

Guiding Investigation 2

[Language] Rigid transformations are also called *isometries.* For more on isometries, see Chapter 7.

Step 2 Students who consistently have difficulty with estimating might be assigned a factor such as 2 or 3. Students might find their task easier if they write a mapping rule such as $(x, y) \rightarrow (2x, 2y)$.

SHARING IDEAS

Ask students what sense they made of dilations in Investigation 2. Dilations are enlargements or reductions about some point called the *center of dilation.* That center is not necessarily the origin, although it is in this investigation.

[Language] The pupil of the eye dilates. It gets larger in dim light and smaller in bright light.

To help students make sense of the ideas of dilation and scale factor, you might refer them to the connection that follows Investigation 2 and ask them to guess the scale factor in each example of similarity.

[Ask] "What does similarity have to do with dilations?" Students might say that if one figure is the dilation of another, then the two figures are similar. Reach consensus on this claim, and wonder aloud whether the converse is true. Bring out the idea that one figure may be similar to another but not be only a dilation of the other; rather, it could be a reflection, rotation, or translation as well as a dilation of the other figure. Checking for enlargements of reflections, especially, can be difficult, so we look for other characteristics of similar figures, such as congruent angles and proportional sides.

[Ask] "If two polygons are congruent, must they be similar?" [Yes; each can be obtained from the other through dilation by a scale factor of 1 and an isometry.]

You might want to have the class work on several exercises and share their ideas before closing the lesson.

Step 5 $\frac{1}{2}, \frac{3}{4}, 2$, or 3 times as long

Step 4 Copy the original pentagon onto patty paper. Compare the corresponding angles of the two pentagons. What do you notice? The angles are congruent.

Step 5 Compare the corresponding sides with a compass or with patty paper. The length of each side of the new pentagon is how many times as long as the length of the corresponding side of the original pentagon?

Step 6 Compare results with your group. You should be ready to state a conjecture.

Dilation Similarity Conjecture C-92

If one polygon is the image of another polygon under a dilation, then ? . (the polygons are similar)

History CONNECTION

Similarity plays an important role in human history. For example, accurate maps of regions of China have been found dating back to the second century B.C.E. Neolithic cave paintings 8000–6000 B.C.E. contain small-scale drawings of the animals people hunted. Giant geoglyphs made by the Nazca people of Peru (110 B.C.E.–800 C.E.) are some of the largest scale drawings ever made.

This cave art is part of a grouping of over 15,000 drawings in Tassili N'Ajjier National Park of the Algerian Sahara. Interestingly, these drawings depict animals and landscapes that are absent from the region today, such as these elephants or vast lakes.

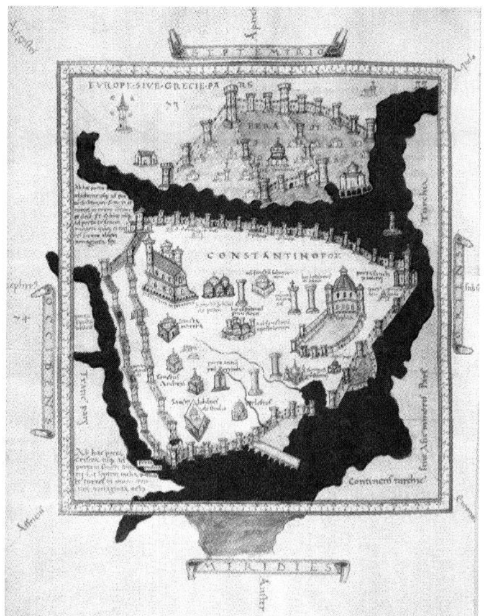

In order for a map to be accurate, cartographers need to use similarity to reduce the earth's attributes to a smaller scale. This sixteenth-century French map, a plan of Constantinople, included a mariner's chart of America, Europe, Africa, and Asia.

This monkey is a geoglyph found in the Pampa region of Peru in 1920. Called the Nazca Lines, the figure measures over 400 feet long and can only be clearly seen from the air.

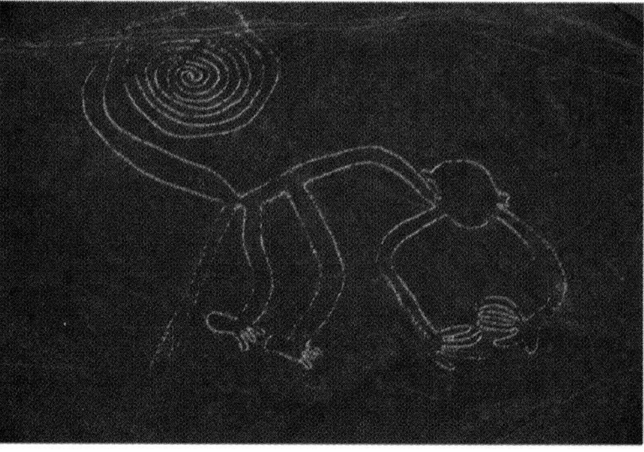

MAKING THE CONNECTION

It's good to spend some time with these connections so students can see how common the phenomenon of similarity is.

Although the cave drawings and geoglyphs demonstrate similarity, they are not accurate scale drawings. Map making, on the other hand, requires a great deal of accuracy. **[Language]** A *cartographer* is a person who makes maps. Maps of small areas can be very accurate, but because Earth is a globe, it is not possible to have exact similarity between a feature on its curved surface and that same feature on a map. Maps distort some distances over large areas.

[Ask] "If the projector is moved three times the fixed distance away from the screen, what would happen?" [The image would be three times as large in each dimension.]

Ask students for other examples of similarity. Some students might mention, for example, images reduced or enlarged by a photocopier or photographs in different sizes.

Assessing Progress

You can assess students' understanding of ratios and their ability to compare angles with patty paper, measure segments, find ratios, plot points, solve proportions, and see patterns in data.

Closing the Lesson

Ask the class for examples of **similar** figures. Similar figures are **dilations** of each other or of isometric images of each other. Any angles are congruent, and lengths of corresponding sides are proportional.

BUILDING UNDERSTANDING

If you think students need more guidance, pick an exercise for a demonstration.

ASSIGNING HOMEWORK

Essential	2–16 evens
Performance assessment	15
Portfolio	16
Journal	8, 10
Group	1–17 odds
Review	18–25

Helping with the Exercises

3. possible answer:

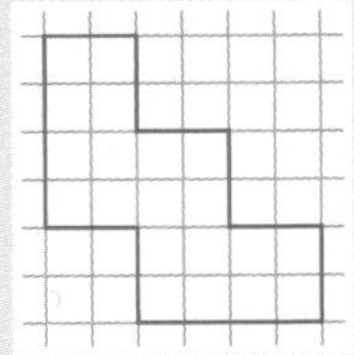

4. possible answer:

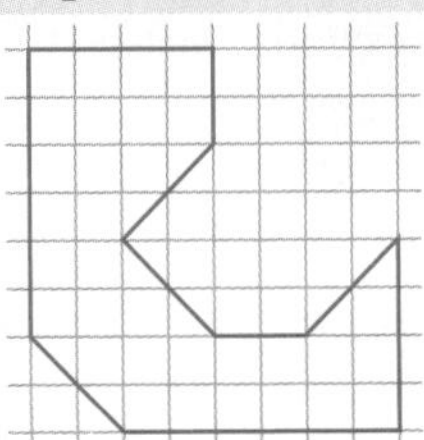

5. possible answer:

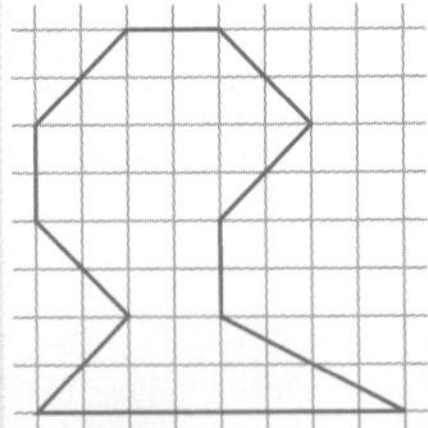

Exercise 6 You may want to label this property the *transitive property of similarity.* It will be used formally in Chapter 13.

6. Figure A is similar to Figure C. Possible answer:

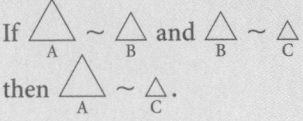

If $\triangle_A \sim \triangle_B$ and $\triangle_B \sim \triangle_C$, then $\triangle_A \sim \triangle_C$.

EXERCISES

You will need
Construction tools for Exercises 22 and 25

For Exercises 1 and 2, match the similar figures.

1. 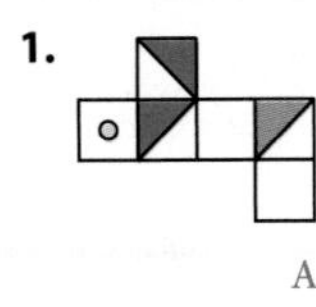 **A.** 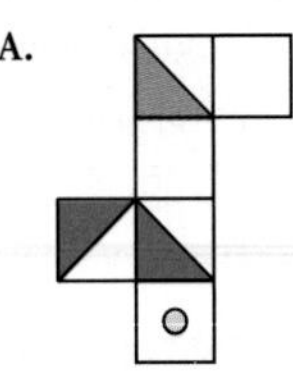 **B.** 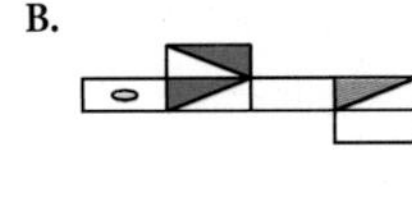 **C.** 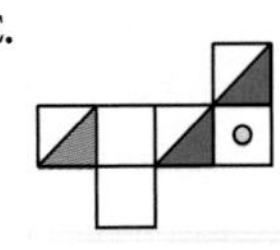

A

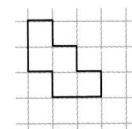

2. **A.** 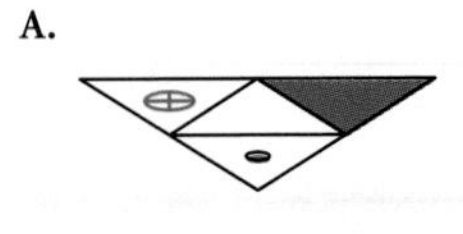 **B.** 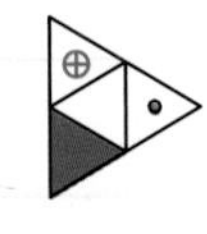 **C.** 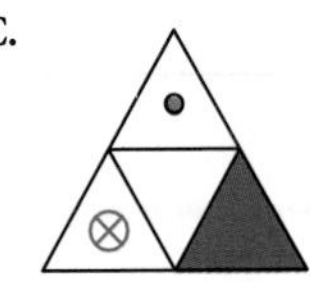

B

For Exercises 3–5, sketch on graph paper a similar, but not congruent, figure.

3. 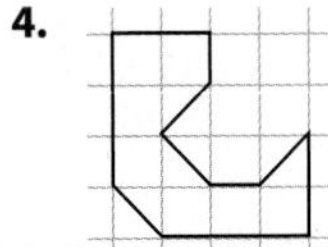 **4.** 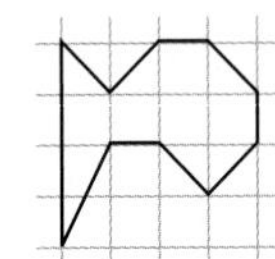 **5.**

6. Complete the statement: If Figure A is similar to Figure B and Figure B is similar to Figure C, then __?__. Draw and label figures to illustrate the statement.

For Exercises 7–14, use the definition of similar polygons. All measurements are in centimeters.

7. $THINK \sim LARGE$
Find AL, RA, RG, and KN.

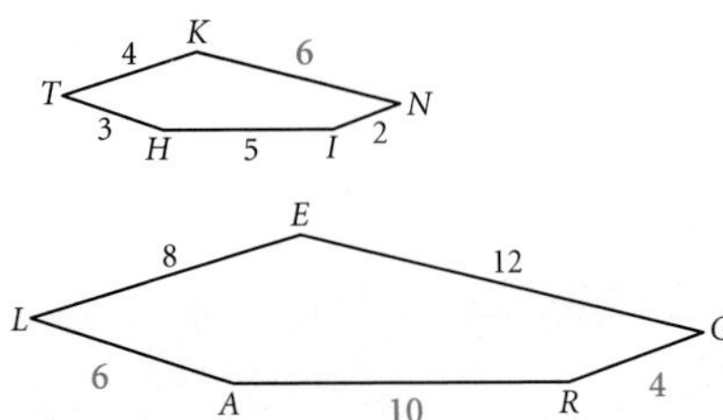

8. Are these polygons similar? Explain why or why not. ⓗ

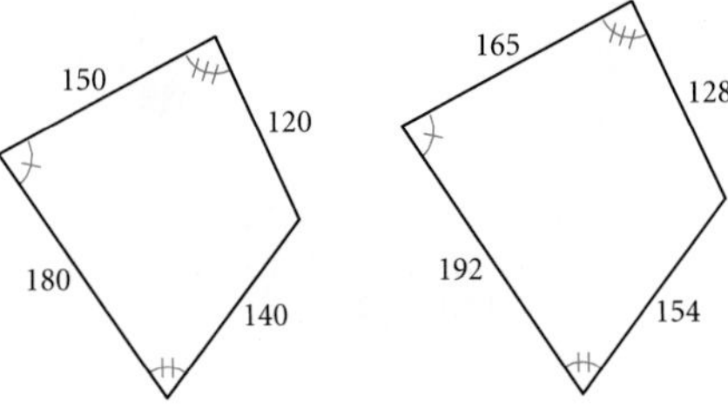

9. $SPIDER \sim HNYCMB$
Find NY, YC, CM, and MB.

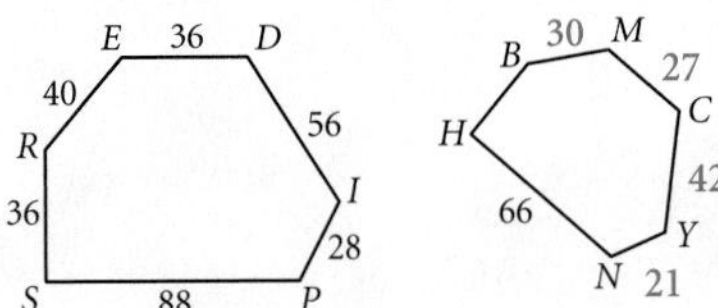

10. Are these polygons similar? Explain why or why not.

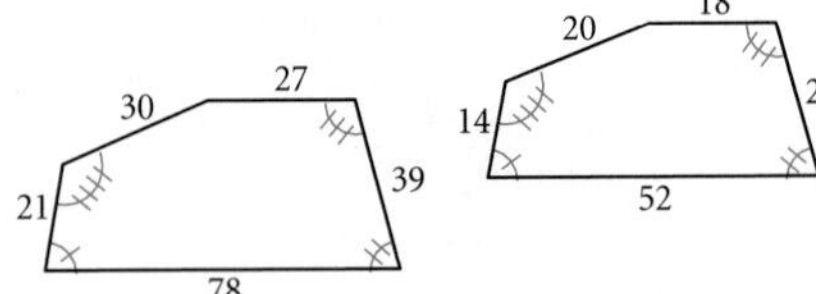

Exercises 7–14 Encourage students to write out possible proportions to determine similarity. Check for equal ratios. It will help some students to first write the proportion in terms of the side labels and then substitute numbers and variables.

Exercise 7 Each ratio can compare lengths either between similar figures or within similar figures.

8. No; the corresponding angles are congruent, but the corresponding sides are not proportional.

Exercise 10 Because four out of five pairs of corresponding angles are congruent, the fifth pair of corresponding angles will be congruent. Challenge students to explain why.

10. Yes; the corresponding angles are congruent, and the corresponding sides are proportional.

project

MAKING A MURAL

A mural is a large work of art that usually fills an entire wall. This project gives you a chance to use similarity and make your own mural.

One way to create a mural from a small picture is to draw a grid of squares lightly over the small picture. Then divide the mural surface into a similar but larger grid. Proceeding square by square, draw the lines and curves of the small grid in each corresponding square of the mural grid. Complete the mural by coloring or painting the regions and erasing the grid lines.

You project should include

- ▶ An original drawing, a cartoon, or a photograph divided into a grid of squares.
- ▶ A finished mural drawn on a large sheet of paper.

You can learn more about the art of mural making through the links at www.keymath.com/DG .

Mural artists use similarity to help them create large artwork. This mural, finished in 1990, is in the North Beach neighborhood of San Francisco, California.

EXTENSIONS

A. Have students make scale drawings or models and describe what they did and how it relates to similarity.

B. Ask students to use geometry software to investigate dilations. **[Ask]** "What happens if you dilate by a scale factor less than zero?" [a dilation plus a rotation of 180°]

C. Use Take Another Look activities 1 and 2 on page 617.

Supporting the project

For a class project, you might use a complicated design, give each student one small square and the numbers of its row and column position in the enlargement, and without showing the original design let students watch as the mural unfolds.

OUTCOMES

- ▶ The grid on the original image contains enough squares so that each square contains only a few lines.
- ▶ The mural accurately depicts the original.
- • A group of students produces a complex piece of art.

Materials for the Project

Students can make their enlarged drawing on poster board, butcher paper, the white side of wrapping paper or wallpaper, or anything big enough to hold the final drawing. For a quick project, choose a simple graphic with few lines.

LESSON

11.2

PLANNING

LESSON OUTLINE

One day:

20 min Investigation

10 min Sharing

5 min Closing

10 min Exercises

MATERIALS

- construction tools
- rulers
- protractors

TEACHING

If you do not use the one-step investigation, you might model an investigation on the overhead and jigsaw the other investigations, or jigsaw all three.

To revisit the shortcuts for showing triangle congruence, **[Ask]** "There were six potential shortcuts for showing triangles to be congruent. Which of them actually were congruence shortcuts? What would it mean to say that one was a shortcut for showing similarity of two triangles?" [SSS, SAS, ASA, and SAA are congruence short cuts. For similarity, we would show angle congruence, but we would also show the proportionality rather than the congruence of side lengths.]

One step Have students examine the six congruence shortcuts to see whether their analogues can serve as similarity shortcuts. You might assign different shortcuts to the various groups.

You might consider extending or replacing Investigations 1–3 with the dynamic geometry exploration at www.keymath.com/DG.

LESSON 11.2

Similar Triangles

Life is change. Growth is optional. Choose wisely.

KAREN KAISER CLARK

In Lesson 11.1, you concluded that you must know about both the angles and the sides of two quadrilaterals in order to make a valid conclusion about their similarity.

However, triangles are unique. Recall from Chapter 4 that you found four shortcuts for triangle congruence: SSS, SAS, ASA, and SAA. Are there shortcuts for triangle similarity as well? Let's first look for shortcuts using only angles.

The figures below illustrate that you cannot conclude that two triangles are similar given that only one set of corresponding angles are congruent.

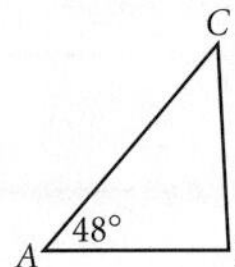

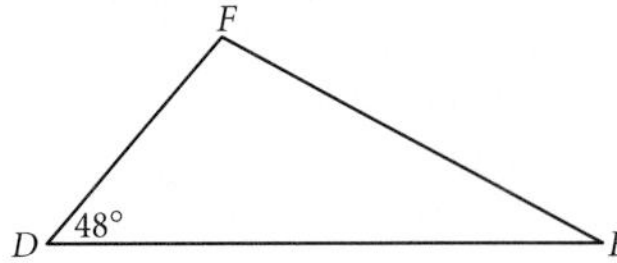

$\angle A \cong \angle D$, but $\triangle ABC$ is not similar to $\triangle DEF$.

How about two sets of congruent angles?

Investigation 1
Is AA a Similarity Shortcut?

You will need

- a compass
- a ruler

If two angles of one triangle are congruent to two angles of another triangle, must the two triangles be similar?

Step 1 Draw any triangle ABC.

Step 2 Construct a second triangle, DEF, with $\angle D \cong \angle A$ and $\angle E \cong \angle B$. What will be true about $\angle C$ and $\angle F$? Why?

Step 3 Carefully measure the lengths of the sides of both triangles. Compare the ratios of the corresponding sides. Is $\frac{AB}{DE} \approx \frac{AC}{DF} \approx \frac{BC}{EF}$?

Step 4 Compare your results with the results of others near you. You should be ready to state a conjecture.

AA Similarity Conjecture C-93

If two ? angles of one triangle are congruent to two ? angles of another triangle, then ? . the triangles are similar

As you may have guessed from Step 2 of the investigation, there is no need to investigate the AAA Similarity Conjecture. Thanks to the Third Angle Conjecture, the AA Similarity Conjecture is all you need.

Guiding Investigation 1

In Chapter 4, students encountered the idea that AAA, while not a congruence shortcut, ensures that the triangles have the same shape.

Step 2 This step reviews the Triangle Sum Conjecture. It's why AAA can be reduced to AA.

Step2 $\angle F$ must be congruent to $\angle C$ because the three angles of each triangle must add up to 180°.

Step 3 The approximations are important. Normal measurement error, and any conversion to decimals, might yield slightly unequal ratios.

Step3 The ratios should be equal.

Now let's look for shortcuts for similarity that use only sides. The figures below illustrate that you cannot conclude that two triangles are similar given that two sets of corresponding sides are proportional.

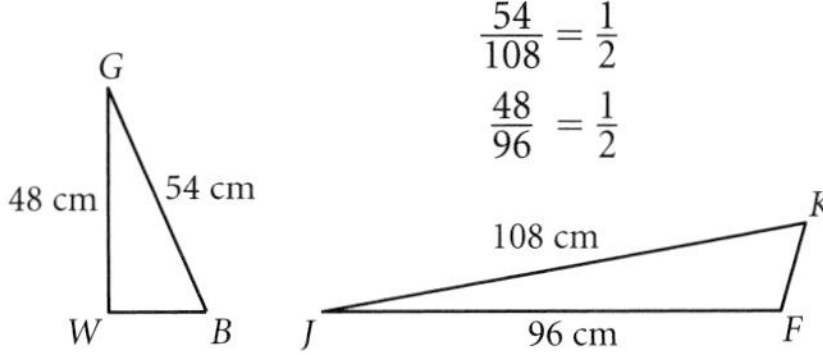

$\frac{GB}{JK} = \frac{GW}{JF}$, but $\triangle GWB$ is not similar to $\triangle JFK$.

How about all three sets of corresponding sides?

Investigation 2
Is SSS a Similarity Shortcut?

You will need

- a compass
- a straightedge
- a protractor

If three sides of one triangle are proportional to the three sides of another triangle, must the two triangles be similar?

Draw any triangle ABC. Then construct a second triangle, DEF, whose side lengths are a multiple of the original triangle. (Your second triangle can be larger or smaller.)

Compare the corresponding angles of the two triangles. Compare your results with the results of others near you and state a conjecture. Corresponding angles should be congruent.

SSS Similarity Conjecture C-94

If the three sides of one triangle are proportional to the three sides of another triangle, then the two triangles are __?__. similar

Many dollhouses and other toys are scale models of real objects.

Guiding Investigation 2

Students could start with $\triangle ABC$ from Investigation 1. **[Alert]** Students may struggle with constructing the second triangle. You might suggest that they copy each side two or three times or bisect each side once or twice, or that they construct a midsegment of their original triangle.

NCTM STANDARDS

CONTENT		PROCESS	
	Number	✓	Problem Solving
✓	Algebra	✓	Reasoning
✓	Geometry	✓	Communication
✓	Measurement	✓	Connections
	Data/Probability		Representation

LESSON OBJECTIVES

- Discover shortcut methods for determining similar triangles
- Practice using proportions to find measures in similar figures
- Develop problem-solving skills and cooperative behavior

Guiding Investigation 3

Students can use some of the techniques they used in Investigation 2 to produce two corresponding sides that are in the same ratio. They can then build these sides on the sides of a copy of the original angle.

SHARING IDEAS

After students reach consensus about the shortcuts and record the conjectures in their notebooks, **[Ask]** "How do the similarity shortcuts compare to the congruence shortcuts?" [All the shortcuts refer to congruent angles; similarity shortcuts refer to proportional rather than congruent sides. All the congruence shortcuts have corresponding similarity shortcuts, and AAA guarantees similarity even though it didn't guarantee congruence.] "How do the comparisons reflect how similarity and congruence are alike and different?" [In both similar and congruent figures, corresponding angles are congruent. In similar figures, corresponding sides are proportional, whereas in congruent figures they're congruent.]

[Ask] "Why is the similarity shortcut called AA instead of AAA?" [Knowing that two angles of a triangle are congruent to two angles of another triangle guarantees that the third angles are congruent, by the Triangle Sum Conjecture.]

As students watch, draw two triangles, one of which is a reflection of an enlargement of the other. Ask whether they're similar. Let students see that the two triangles do satisfy the definition of similar.

Return to the list of all potential shortcuts: AAA, SSS, SAS, SAA, ASA, and SSA. **[Ask]** "You've considered the first three as similarity shortcuts in this lesson; what about the last three?" Students can probably see that SAA and ASA both imply AAA (and hence AA), again by the Triangle Sum Conjecture, so they are similarity shortcuts. SSA may present a little more difficulty. Ask whether it would help to consider cases in which SSA failed as a congruence shortcut. The triangles in those cases were not similar, so SSA is not a similarity shortcut. (In contrast, all pairs of triangles that showed the failing of AAA as a congruence shortcut were in fact similar.) As another example, to preview Lesson 11.4, you might have students draw a triangle, bisect one angle, and look at the ratios of the lengths of the sides of the two smaller triangles.

Assessing Progress

You can assess students' understanding of congruent and similar figures, congruence shortcuts, ratio, proportional sides, congruent angles, and similar polygons. You can also check their memory of what the congruence shortcuts are and their skill at measuring, calculating ratios, and using construction tools.

In Investigations 1 and 2, you discovered two shortcuts for triangle similarity: AA and SSS. But if AA is a shortcut, then so are ASA, SAA, and AAA. That leaves SAS and SSA as possible shortcuts to consider.

Investigation 3
Is SAS a Similarity Shortcut?

You will need

- a compass
- a protractor
- a ruler

Is SAS a shortcut for similarity? Try to construct two different triangles that are not similar but have two pairs of sides proportional and the pair of included angles equal in measure. Corresponding sides should be proportional, and corresponding angles should be congruent.
Compare the measures of corresponding sides and corresponding angles. Share your results with others near you and state a conjecture.

SAS Similarity Conjecture C-95

If two sides of one triangle are proportional to two sides of another triangle and __?__, then the __?__. the included angles are congruent; triangles are similar

One question remains: Is SSA a shortcut for similarity? Recall from Chapter 4 that SSA did not work for congruence because you could create two different triangles. Those two different triangles were neither congruent nor similar. So, no, SSA is not a shortcut for similarity.

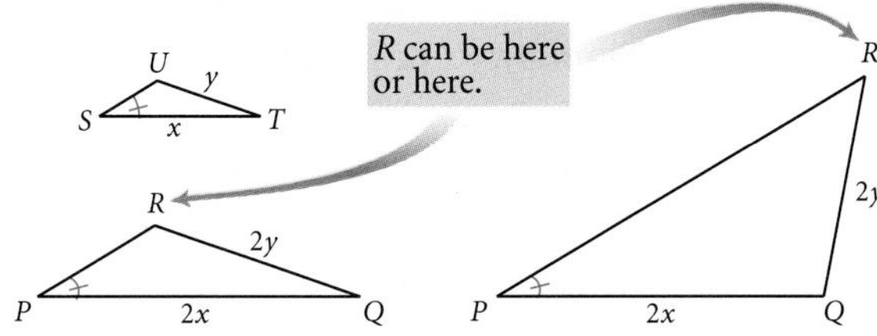

EXERCISES

For Exercises 1–14, use your new conjectures. All measurements are in centimeters.

1. $g = \underline{?}$ 6 cm

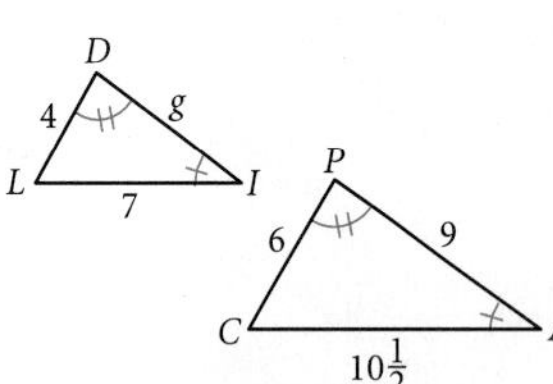

2. $h = \underline{?}$, $k = \underline{?}$
40 cm 40 cm

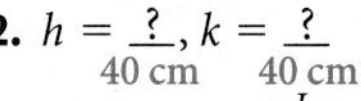

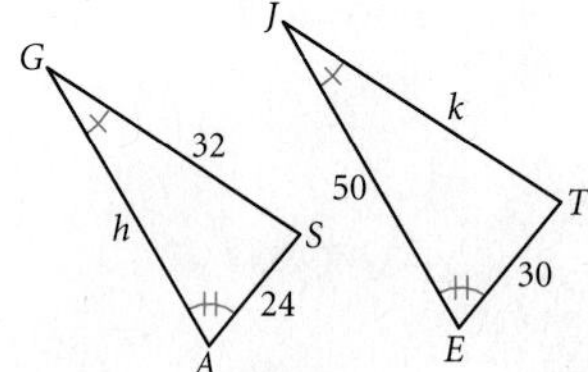

3. $m = \underline{?}$ ⓗ 28 cm

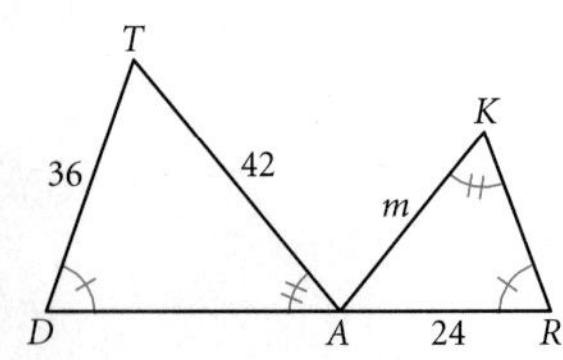

4. $n = \underline{?}$, 54 cm
$s = \underline{?}$ 42 cm

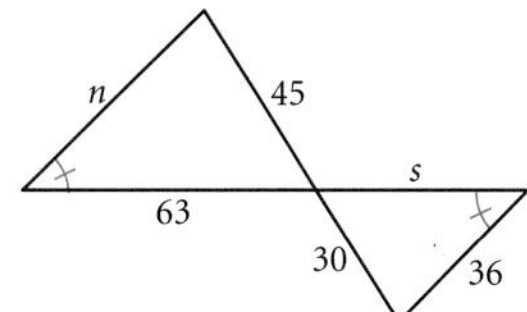

5. Is $\triangle AUL \sim \triangle MST$?
Explain why or why not.
No, $\frac{37}{30} \neq \frac{35}{28}$.

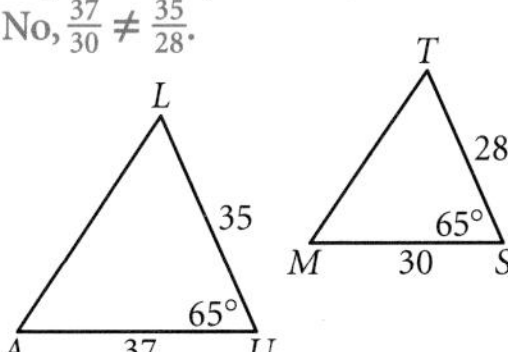

6. Is $\triangle MOY \sim \triangle NOT$?
Explain why or why not.
Yes, $\triangle MOY \sim \triangle NOT$ by SAS.

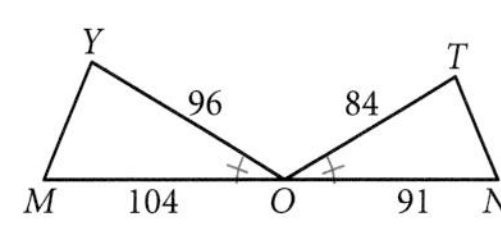

7. Is $\triangle PHY \sim \triangle YHT$?
Is $\triangle PTY$ a right triangle?
Explain why or why not.

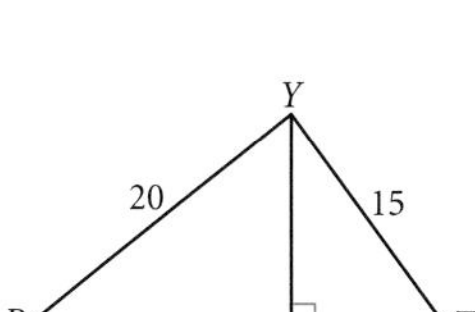

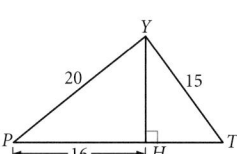

8. Why is $\triangle TMR \sim \triangle THM \sim \triangle MHR$?
Find x, y, and h. ⓗ

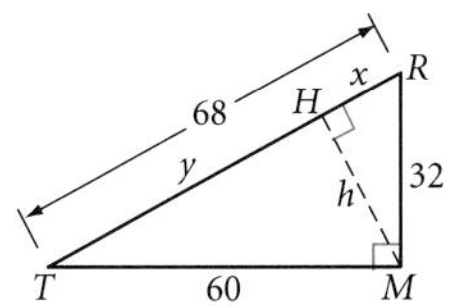

9. $\overline{TA} \parallel \overline{UR}$
Is $\angle QTA \cong \angle TUR$?
Is $\angle QAT \cong \angle ARU$?
Why is $\triangle QTA \sim \triangle QUR$?
$e = \underline{?}$

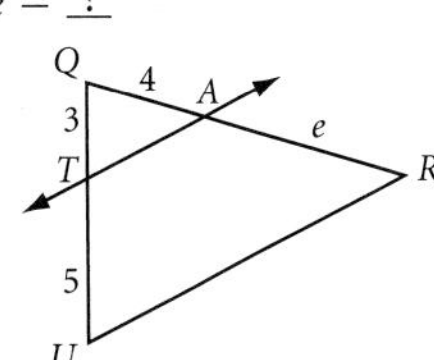

10. $\overline{OR} \parallel \overline{UE} \parallel \overline{NT}$
$f = \underline{?}$, $g = \underline{?}$
24 cm 40 cm

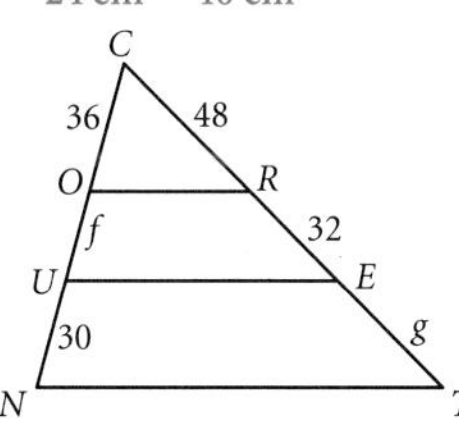

11. Is $\angle THU \cong \angle GDU$?
Is $\angle HTU \cong \angle DGU$?
$p = \underline{?}$, $q = \underline{?}$ ⓗ
52 cm 42 cm

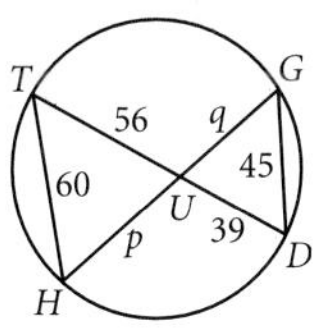

12. Why is $\triangle SUN \sim \triangle TAN$?
$r = \underline{?}$, $s = \underline{?}$
13 cm 20 cm

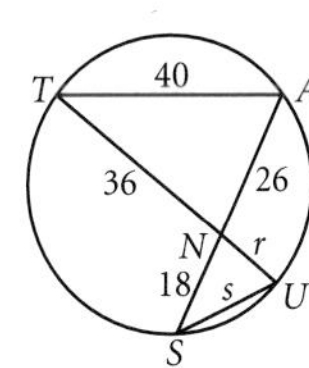

13. *FROG* is a trapezoid.
Is $\angle RGO \cong \angle FRG$?
Is $\angle GOF \cong \angle RFO$?
Why is $\triangle GOS \sim \triangle RFS$?
$t = \underline{?}$, $s = \underline{?}$
28 cm 120 cm

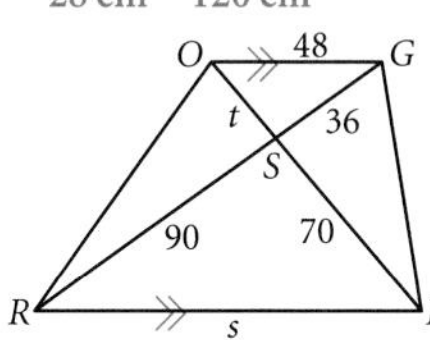

14. *TOAD* is a trapezoid.
$w = \underline{?}$, $x = \underline{?}$
20 21

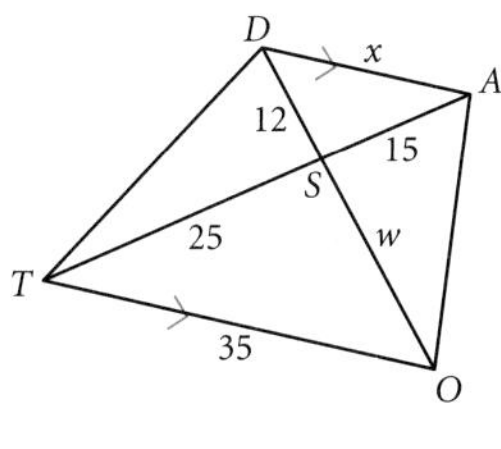

15. Find x and y. ⓗ
$x = 50, y = 9$

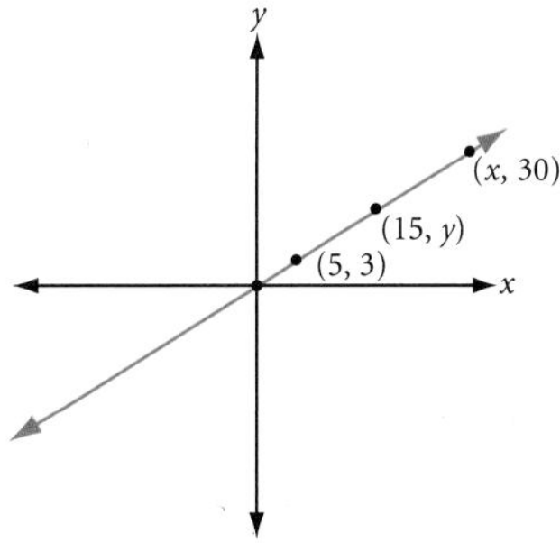

Closing the Lesson

Reiterate the main points of this lesson: Similarity shortcuts for triangles, like congruence shortcuts, refer to congruence of angles, but unlike congruence shortcuts they refer to proportionality rather than congruence of sides. SSS, SAS, and AA (or AAA) are similarity shortcuts, as are AAS and ASA because they imply AA.

BUILDING UNDERSTANDING

If you or your students are still insecure with the depth of their understanding, you might have them work and report on several selected exercises. In many of these exercises, similar triangles are reflections as well as enlargements or reductions of each other. If students are having difficulty seeing corresponding parts, you might suggest that they redraw the triangles with the same orientation.

ASSIGNING HOMEWORK

Essential	**1–15**
Performance assessment	**8, 18**
Portfolio	**5**
Journal	**6, 7, 9, 17, 21**
Group	**12–15**
Review	**16–21**

▶ Helping with the Exercises

Exercises 7, 8 These exercises preview the Pythagorean Theorem similar triangles proof.

7. Yes, $\triangle PHY \sim \triangle YHT$ because $YH = 12$ and $\frac{20}{15} = \frac{16}{12} = \frac{12}{9}$ (SSS). Yes, $\triangle PTY$ is a right triangle because $20^2 + 15^2 = 25^2$.

Exercise 8 [Alert] If students have difficulty identifying the corresponding parts, you might encourage them to separate and redraw all three triangles.

8. $\triangle TMR \sim \triangle THM \sim \triangle MHR$ by AA. $x \approx 15.1$ cm, $y \approx 52.9$ cm, $h \approx 28.2$ cm.

Exercises 9, 10 These exercises preview the Parallel/Proportionality Conjecture that students will discover in Lesson 11.6.

9. Yes, $\angle QTA \cong \angle TUR$ and $\angle QAT \cong \angle ARU$. $\triangle QTA \sim \triangle QUR$ by AA. $e = 6\frac{2}{3}$ cm

Exercises 11, 12 These exercises are a good review of circle properties.

Exercise 11 Students might need help in seeing $\angle THU$ as $\angle THG$.

11. Yes, $\angle THU \cong \angle GDU$ and $\angle HTU \cong \angle DGU$ so $\triangle HUT \sim \triangle DUG$ by AA.

12. $\triangle SUN \sim \triangle TAN$ by AA.

13. Yes, $\angle RGO \cong \angle FRG$ and $\angle GOF \cong \angle RFO$. $\triangle GOS \sim \triangle RFS$ by AA.

Exercise 15 Students can also use similar slope triangles.

Exercise 16 This exercise is very challenging. Students might benefit from reviewing tangent circles in the exercises of Lesson 6.2.

Exercise 17 **[Language]** SPCA is the Society for Prevention of Cruelty to Animals. **[Alert]** Students may not notice that information is given about two months but the question is about three months.

Exercise 18 Students may not have seen, or may not remember, the capture-recapture method:

$$\frac{\text{tagged fish in sample}}{\text{sample size}} = \frac{\text{fish previously tagged}}{\text{estimated population}}$$

[Context] The fish named is the state fish of Hawaii.

20. Yes, $ABCD \sim A'B'C'D'$. The ratio of the perimeters is $\frac{2}{1}$. The ratio of the areas is $\frac{4}{1}$.

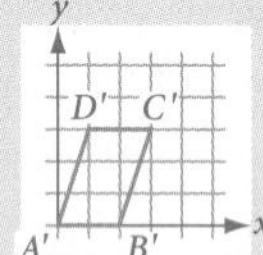

Review

6.2 **16.** In the figure below right, find the radius, r, of one of the small circles in terms of the radius, R, of the large circle. ⓗ $r = R\left(\frac{\sqrt{2}-1}{\sqrt{2}+1}\right) = R(\sqrt{2}-1)^2$

This Tibetan mandala is a complex design with a square inscribed within a circle and tangent circles inscribed within the corners of a larger circumscribed square.

UYAS 9 **17.** APPLICATION Phoung volunteers at an SPCA that always houses 8 dogs. She notices that she uses seven 35-pound bags of dry dog food every two months. A new, larger SPCA facility that houses 20 dogs will open soon. Help Phoung estimate the amount of dry dog food that the facility should order every three months. Explain your reasoning. She should order approximately 919 lb every three months. Explanations will vary. $\frac{8 \text{ dogs}}{367.5 \text{ lb}} = \frac{20 \text{ dogs}}{x \text{ lb}}$

UYAS 9 **18.** APPLICATION Ramon and Sabina are oceanography students studying the habitat of a Hawaiian fish called Humuhumunukunukuapuaʻa. They are going to use the capture-recapture method to determine the fish population. They first capture and tag 84 fish, which they release back into the ocean. After one week, Ramon and Sabina catch another 64. Only 12 have tags. Can you estimate the population of Humuhumunukunukuapuaʻa?

448

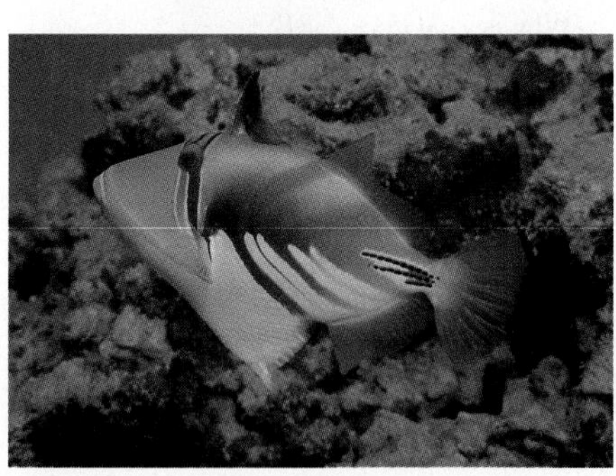

8.2 **19.** Points $A(-9, 5)$, $B(4, 13)$, and $C(1, -7)$ are connected to form a triangle. Find the area of $\triangle ABC$. 118 square units

11.1 **20.** Use the ordered pair rule, $(x, y) \rightarrow \left(\frac{1}{2}x, \frac{1}{2}y\right)$, to relocate the coordinates of the vertices of parallelogram $ABCD$. Call the new parallelogram $A'B'C'D'$. Is $A'B'C'D'$ similar to $ABCD$? If they are similar, what is the ratio of the perimeter of $ABCD$ to the perimeter of $A'B'C'D'$? What is the ratio of their areas? See page 576.

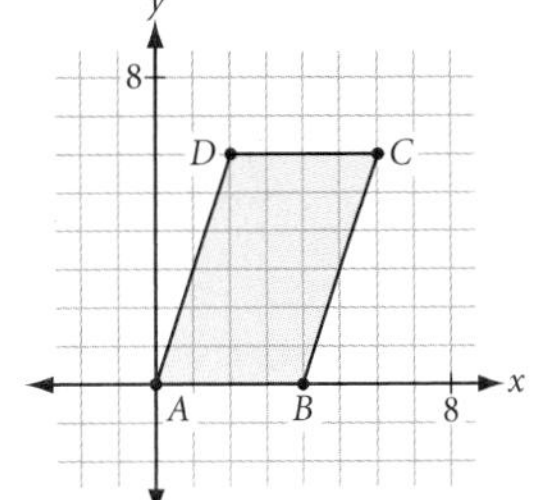

UYAS 9 **21.** The photo below shows a fragment from an ancient statue of the Roman Emperor Constantine. Use this photo to estimate how tall the entire statue was. List the measurements you need to make. List any assumptions you need to make. Explain your reasoning.

History CONNECTION

The Emperor Constantine the Great (Roman Emperor 306–337 C.E.) adopted Christianity as the official religion of the Roman Empire. The Roman Catholic Church regards him as Saint Constantine, and the city of Constantinople was named for him. The colossal statue of Constantine was built between 315 and 330 C.E., and broke when sculptors tried to add the extra weight of a beard to its face. The pieces of the statue remain close to its original location in Rome, Italy.

IMPROVING YOUR VISUAL THINKING SKILLS

Build a Two-Piece Puzzle

Construct two copies of Figure A, shown at right. Here's how to construct the figure.

- Construct a regular hexagon.
- Construct an equilateral triangle on two alternating edges, as shown.
- Construct a square on the edge between the two equilateral triangles, as shown.

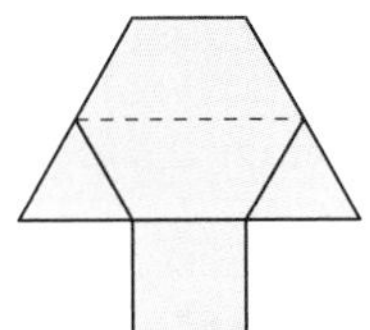
Figure A

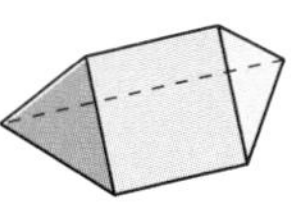
Figure B

Cut out each copy and fold them into two identical solids, as shown in Figure B. Tape the edges. Now arrange your two solids to form a regular tetrahedron.

Exercise 21 This exercise reviews Using Your Algebra Skills 9 and requires an understanding of which measurements to make and the assumptions that go along with that decision.

21. The statue was about 40 feet, or 12 meters, tall. To estimate, you need to approximate the height of a person (or some part of a person) in the picture, measure a part of the statue in the picture, calculate the approximate height of that statue piece, and assume that the statue has the same proportions as the average person.

EXTENSIONS

A. Use Take Another Look activities 4 and 5 on page 618.

B. Have students prove the Pythagorean Theorem using similar triangles. [In outline, the sides of the original triangle are the hypotenuses of the three similar triangles; if their ratio is $a{:}b{:}c$, then the ratio of the areas of similar figures on those sides is $a^2{:}b^2{:}c^2$. Areas of the two smaller triangles sum to the area of the larger one, so $a^2 + b^2 = c^2$. Details about proportionality factors are needed to make the proof complete.]

C. Pose this problem: Are all isosceles triangles similar? Explain why or provide a counterexample to show why not. [Not all isosceles triangles are similar. One possible counterexample is shown here.]

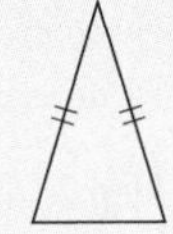

[Ask] "Are all isosceles triangles with base angles that measure 50° similar? Explain." [Yes; by AA the three angles must measure 50°, 50°, and 80°.] "Are all isosceles right triangles similar?" [yes, by the same reasoning]

IMPROVING VISUAL THINKING SKILLS

Students might get stuck trying to make a small triangle one face of the tetrahedron. You can ask whether there's a way to combine one face from each solid to make a triangular face of the tetrahedron. Or **[Ask]** "Which sides might be part of a triangle that is one face of the tetrahedron?" To create the tetrahedron, place the square faces together and rotate one solid until it completes the tetrahedron.

EXPLORATION

PLANNING

LESSON OUTLINE

One day:

40 min Activity

5 min Sharing

MATERIALS

- The Geometer's Sketchpad
- Sketchpad demonstration Dilation Design, *optional*

TEACHING

Even if you don't use geometry software, you might want to introduce the method of dilation described in the introductory paragraph as a convenient way of constructing similar polygons.

[Ask] "Why does marking the distance two more times give you a scale factor of 3?" [The distance from point *P* to the vertex is the scale factor of 1. You add onto this.] To create a scale factor of 2, you would mark off the distance to each vertex once. To create a scale factor of $\frac{1}{2}$, you would bisect the segments between point *P* and each vertex.

Guiding the Activity

Step 1 Students might benefit from making circle *A* much larger than shown in the book.

Step 2 Students might miss the fact that $\overrightarrow{AB'}$ is a ray. Let them try to correct themselves in Step 3. Eventually it will help students to have labels showing; a point's label can be turned on by clicking on the point with the **Text** tool.

Exploration

Constructing a Dilation Design

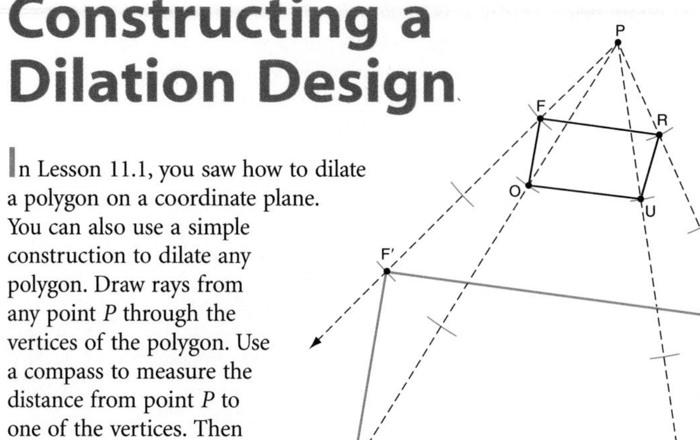

In Lesson 11.1, you saw how to dilate a polygon on a coordinate plane. You can also use a simple construction to dilate any polygon. Draw rays from any point *P* through the vertices of the polygon. Use a compass to measure the distance from point *P* to one of the vertices. Then mark this distance two more times along the ray; that will give you a scale factor of 3. Repeat this process for each of the other vertices using the same scale factor. When you connect the image of each vertex, you will get a similar polygon. Try it yourself. How would you create a similar polygon with a scale factor of 2? Of $\frac{1}{2}$?

Now take a closer look at *Path of Life I,* the M. C. Escher woodcut that begins this chapter. Notice that dilations transform the black fishlike creatures, shrinking them again and again as they approach the picture's center. The same is true for the white fish. (The black-and-white fish around the outside border are congruent to one another, but they're not similar to the other fish.) Also notice that rotations repeat the dilations in eight sectors. With Sketchpad, you can make a similar design.

Activity
Dilation Creations

Step 1 Construct a circle with center point *A* and point *B* on the circle. Construct $\overline{AB}$.

Step 2 Use the Transform menu to mark point *A* as center, then rotate point *B* by an angle of 45°. Your new point is *B*′. Construct $\overrightarrow{AB'}$.

Step 3 Construct a larger circle with center point *A* and point *C* on $\overrightarrow{AB'}$. Hide $\overrightarrow{AB'}$ and construct $\overline{AC}$.

LESSON OBJECTIVE

- Explore dilation by constructing a dilation design

NCTM STANDARDS

CONTENT		PROCESS	
✓	Number		Problem Solving
✓	Algebra		Reasoning
✓	Geometry	✓	Communication
✓	Measurement	✓	Connections
	Data/Probability	✓	Representation

Step 4 Rotate $\overline{AC}$, point B', and point C by an angle of 45°. You now have $\overline{AC'}$, point B'', and point C'.

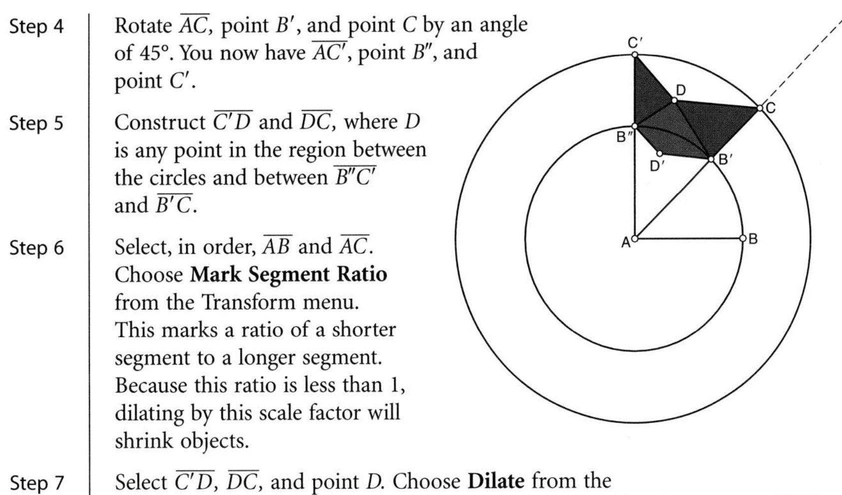

Step 5 Construct $\overline{C'D}$ and $\overline{DC}$, where D is any point in the region between the circles and between $\overline{B''C'}$ and $\overline{B'C}$.

Step 6 Select, in order, $\overline{AB}$ and $\overline{AC}$. Choose **Mark Segment Ratio** from the Transform menu. This marks a ratio of a shorter segment to a longer segment. Because this ratio is less than 1, dilating by this scale factor will shrink objects.

Step 7 Select $\overline{C'D}$, $\overline{DC}$, and point D. Choose **Dilate** from the Transform menu and dilate by the marked ratio. The dilated images are $\overline{B''D'}$, $\overline{D'B'}$, and D'.

Step 8 Construct three polygon interiors—two triangles and a quadrilateral.

Step 9 Select the three polygon interiors and dilate them by the marked ratio. Repeat this process two or three times.

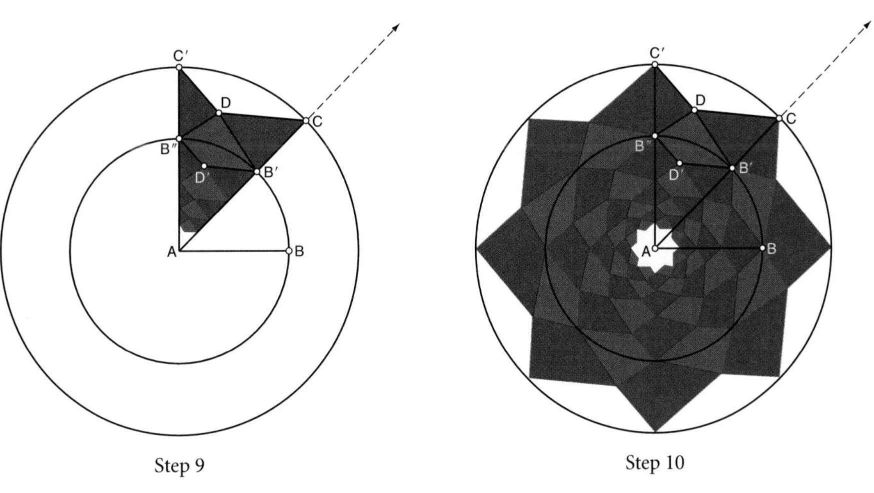

Step 9 Step 10

Step 10 Select all the polygon interiors in the sector and rotate them by an angle of 45°. Repeat the rotation by 45° until you've gone all the way around the circle.

Now you have a design that has the same basic mathematical properties as Escher's *Path of Life I.*

Step 11 Be prepared for exclamations of amazement as students drag points around their sketches.

Step 11a any point on the bisector of $\angle C'AC$

Step 11b Dragging point C away from point A decreases the dilation ratio. The shapes in the figure shrink more rapidly toward its center.

Step 11c Dragging point C toward point A causes the shapes in the figure to increase in size away from the outer circle. This happens because the dilation ratio becomes greater than 1.

SHARING IDEAS

You might want to print out copies of students' designs and display them around the room. Students might add other designs they make later to the display.

[Ask] "What kinds of symmetry did you find, and when?" [8-fold rotational symmetry, and reflectional symmetry over eight reflection lines when $\angle BAD$ measures 67.5°. The 8-fold rotational symmetry is due to the repeated rotations by a 45° angle.]

[Ask] "Can you explain why the dilated set of polygons fits next to the original set without any gap or overlap? How does this dilation construction differ from the one you did by hand at the beginning of this exploration?"

[Ask] "Escher's *Path of Life I* and the design you made in the first part of this exploration also have spiral similarity. Can you color or shade your original design to emphasize the spiral similarity?" The term *spiral similarity* is used to mean symmetry created by a tessellation of a repeated shape or shapes as they rotate and dilate. (See *Symmetry: A Unifying Concept.*)

Step 11 Experiment with changing the design by moving different points. Answer these questions.

a. What locations of point D result in both rotational and reflectional symmetry?

b. Drag point C away from point A. What does this do to the numerical dilation ratio? What effect does that have on the geometric figure?

c. Drag point C toward point A. What happens when the circle defined by point C becomes smaller than the circle defined by point B? Why?

Experiment with other dilation-rotation designs of your own. Try different angles of rotation or different polygons. Here are some examples.

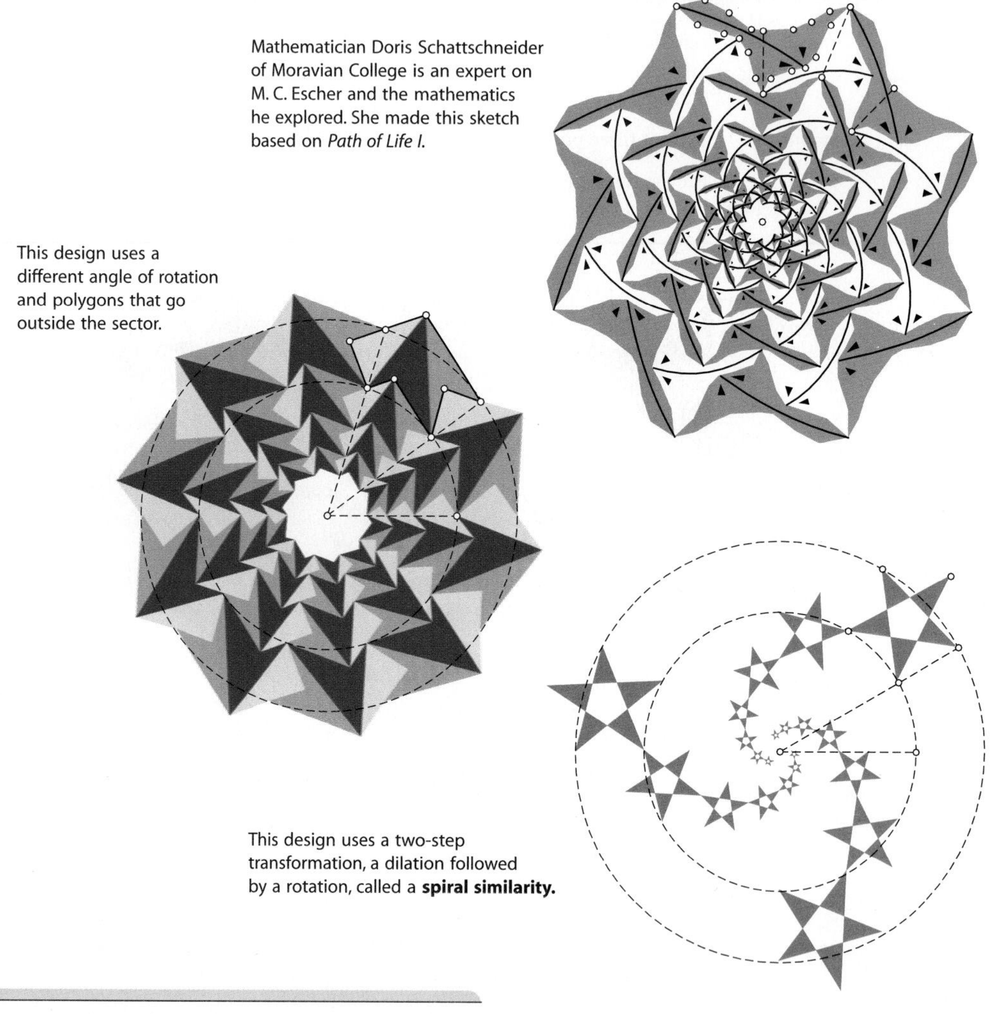

Mathematician Doris Schattschneider of Moravian College is an expert on M. C. Escher and the mathematics he explored. She made this sketch based on *Path of Life I*.

This design uses a different angle of rotation and polygons that go outside the sector.

This design uses a two-step transformation, a dilation followed by a rotation, called a **spiral similarity.**

Assessing Progress

Check students' comfort in using rotations and dilations, in seeing the role of scale factors, and in recognizing similar figures.

Closing the Lesson

Make the point that dilations coupled with isometries (in particular, rotations) can create some fascinating patterns.

LESSON 11.3 Indirect Measurement with Similar Triangles

Never be afraid to sit awhile and think.

LORRAINE HANSBERRY

You can use similar triangles to calculate the height of tall objects that you can't reach. This is called **indirect measurement.** One method uses mirrors. Try it in the next investigation.

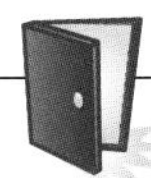

Investigation
Mirror, Mirror

You will need

- metersticks
- masking tape or a soluble pen
- a mirror

Choose a tall object with a height that would be difficult to measure directly, such as a football goalpost, a basketball hoop, a flagpole, or the height of your classroom.

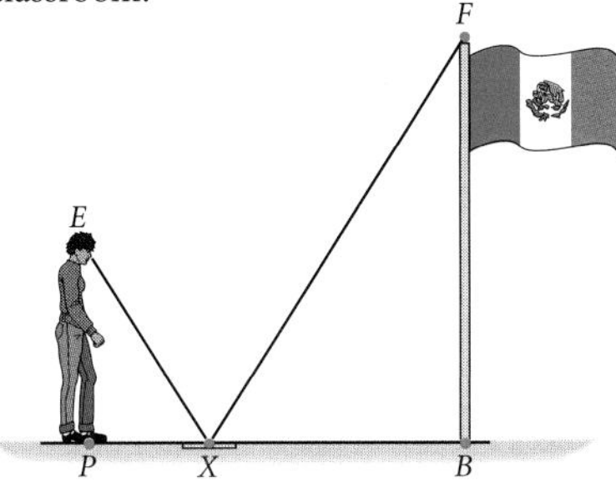

Step 1 Mark crosshairs on your mirror. Use tape or a soluble pen. Call the intersection point X. Place the mirror on the ground several meters from your object.

Step 2 An observer should move to a point P in line with the object and the mirror in order to see the reflection of an identifiable point F at the top of the object at point X on the mirror. Make a sketch of your setup, like this one.

Step 3 Measure the distance PX and the distance from X to a point B at the base of the object directly below F. Measure the distance from P to the observer's eye level, E.

Step 4 Think of $\overline{FX}$ as a light ray that bounces back to the observer's eye along $\overline{XE}$. Why is $\angle B \cong \angle P$? Name two similar triangles. Tell why they are similar.

Step 5 Set up a proportion using corresponding sides of similar triangles. Use it to calculate FB, the approximate height of the tall object.

Step 6 Write a summary of what you and your group did in this investigation. Discuss possible causes for error.

Step 4 Because the flagpole and the person are perpendicular to the ground, $\triangle EPX \sim \triangle FBX$ by AA.

Step 5 The proportion should be equivalent to $\frac{PE}{XP} = \frac{FB}{BX}$.

Step 6 Two possible causes for errors are (1) not measuring on flat ground (which would mean the triangles formed are not truly similar right triangles) and (2) measuring an object when it is difficult to see the top.

Another method of indirect measurement uses shadows.

LESSON 11.3

PLANNING

LESSON OUTLINE

One day:

30 min	Investigation
5 min	Sharing
5 min	Closing
5 min	Exercises

MATERIALS

- mirrors
- metersticks
- masking tape
- graph paper, *optional*

TEACHING

The investigation may take most of a class period, but students' understanding will be deeper if they engage in the activity (or the one-step investigation on page 582) rather than simply discussing or observing it.

Guiding the Investigation

If you are confined to the classroom, have students measure heights such as that of a clock, the top of a window, or the line between the wall and the ceiling.

You might have different groups measure different objects, but if you have each object measured by two groups they can compare results and discuss discrepancies.

Step 1 Grease pencils can also be used to make crosshairs, crossed line segments whose intersection point indicates where to aim.

Step 4 As needed, remind students that the height of a person and the height of a tall object are both measured at right angles to the ground.

NCTM STANDARDS

CONTENT		PROCESS	
	Number	✓	Problem Solving
✓	Algebra		Reasoning
✓	Geometry	✓	Communication
✓	Measurement	✓	Connections
	Data/Probability	✓	Representation

LESSON OBJECTIVES

- Use similar triangles to solve applied problems
- Develop reading comprehension and problem-solving skills

Step 5 If students have trouble understanding why the angles at the mirror are congruent, refer back to the discussion on incoming and outgoing angles in Lesson 1.2. Students may decide that calculations will be easier and move the mirror to an integral distance from the object and remeasure.

Step 6 As needed, prompt students to check the reasonableness of their final answer.

One step Have each group choose an object that's high above the ground or floor. (It might be the top of a tall object such as a building or flagpole, or a clock or the top of a classroom window.) Challenge them to use similar triangles to find the height of that object and of another group's object, without leaving the floor or the ground. Have available metersticks, graph paper, and mirrors. Encourage a variety of approaches; note any invalid ones to be included among those presented for critique during Sharing. If nobody is thinking about using the mirrors, encourage at least one group to do so. If shadows are available, encourage a group to consider them.

▶ *EXAMPLE*

This example is the first time the proportion has been written with each ratio comparing parts within one triangle. Some students will be more comfortable with the proportion $\frac{x}{5.25} = \frac{18}{6}$, because it equates ratios of corresponding sides of the two triangles. The proportions are equivalent. To encourage students to consider the approaches more closely, **[Ask]** "Is the answer reasonable?" [yes]

[Language] The word *shadow* can refer to a three-dimensional region or to a two-dimensional region. In either case, the object blocks light from reaching that region. In the example, the word refers to the two-dimensional region on the ground.

EXAMPLE

A person 5 feet 3 inches tall casts a 6-foot shadow. At the same time of day, a lamppost casts an 18-foot shadow. What is the height of the lamppost?

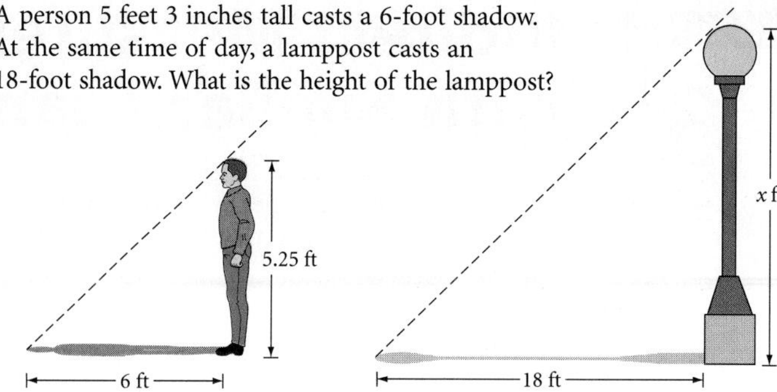

▶ ***Solution***

The light rays that create the shadows hit the ground at congruent angles. Assuming both the person and the lamppost are perpendicular to the ground, you have similar triangles by the AA Similarity Conjecture. Solve a proportion that relates corresponding lengths.

$$\frac{5.25}{6} = \frac{x}{18}$$

$$18 \cdot \frac{5.25}{6} = x$$

$$15.75 = x$$

The height of the lamppost is 15 feet 9 inches.

EXERCISES

You will need

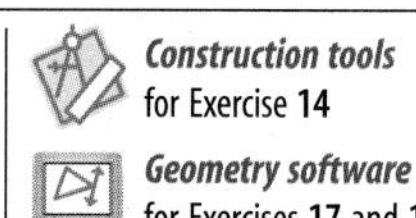

Construction tools for Exercise **14**

Geometry software for Exercises **17** and **18**

1. A flagpole 4 meters tall casts a 6-meter shadow. At the same time of day, a nearby building casts a 24-meter shadow. How tall is the building? 16 m
2. Five-foot-tall Melody casts an 84-inch shadow. How tall is her friend if, at the same time of day, his shadow is 1 foot shorter than hers? 4 ft 3 in.
3. A 10 m rope from the top of a flagpole reaches to the end of the flagpole's 6 m shadow. How tall is the nearby football goalpost if, at the same moment, it has a shadow of 4 m? ⓗ $5\frac{1}{3}$ m
4. Private eye Samantha Diamond places a mirror on the ground between herself and an apartment building and stands so that when she looks into the mirror, she sees into a window. The mirror's crosshairs are 1.22 meters from her feet and 7.32 meters from the base of the building. Sam's eye is 1.82 meters above the ground. How high is the window? 10.92 m

Encourage students to draw the two triangles and explain why they are similar. **[Alert]** You might need to review why 3 in. = 0.25 ft and 0.75 ft = 9 in.

SHARING IDEAS

Have the class compare their results, critique the validity of various approaches, and explain discrepancies in their indirect measurements.

[Ask] "How do you know a particular pair of triangles is similar?" [by AA, SAS, SSS, ASA, or SAA]

Point out that the similar triangles in this lesson are all right triangles, and ask students what they know about right triangles. The Pythagorean Theorem relates the three sides of one right triangle, but in measuring distances we're usually interested in four sides—two sides of each of two triangles.

If you have time, you might ask about how to use similar triangles to make other indirect measurements, such as the width of a river. You need not answer now; instead, have students begin work on Exercise 6 or 7.

5. **APPLICATION** Juanita, who is 1.82 meters tall, wants to find the height of a tree in her backyard. From the tree's base, she walks 12.20 meters along the tree's shadow to a position where the end of her shadow exactly overlaps the end of the tree's shadow. She is now 6.10 meters from the end of the shadows. How tall is the tree? 5.46 m

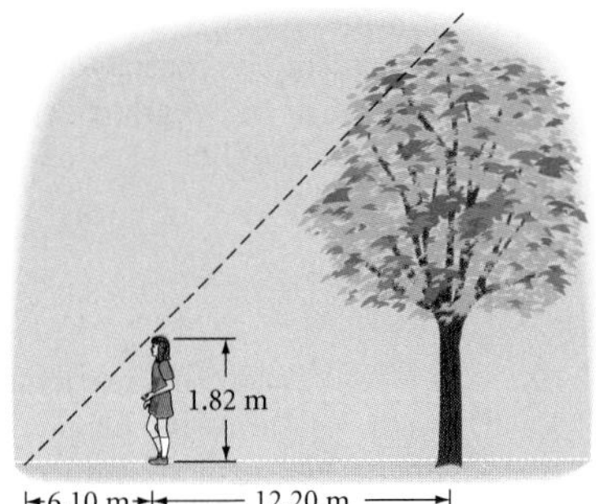

6. While vacationing in Egypt, the Greek mathematician Thales calculated the height of the Great Pyramid. According to legend, Thales placed a pole at the tip of the pyramid's shadow and used similar triangles to calculate its height. This involved some estimating since he was unable to measure the distance from directly beneath the height of the pyramid to the tip of the shadow. From the diagram, explain his method. Calculate the height of the pyramid from the information given in the diagram.

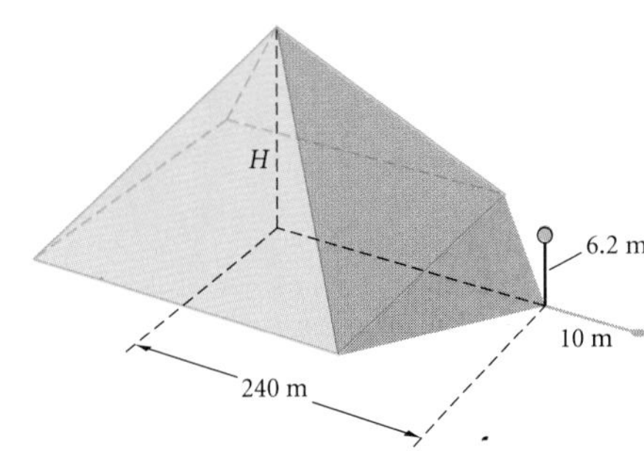

7. Calculate the distance across this river, *PR*, by sighting a pole, at point *P*, on the opposite bank. Points *R* and *O* are collinear with point *P*. Point *C* is chosen so that $\overline{OC} \perp \overline{PO}$. Lastly, point *E* is chosen so that *P*, *E*, and *C* are collinear and that $\overline{RE} \perp \overline{PO}$. Also explain why $\triangle PRE \sim \triangle POC$. ⓗ
90 m; $\angle R$ and $\angle O$ are both right angles and $\angle P$ is the same angle in both triangles, so $\triangle PRE \sim \triangle POC$ by AA.

P
R
E
60 m
45 m
O
C
90 m

8. A pinhole camera is a simple device. Place unexposed film at one end of a shoe box, and make a pinhole at the opposite end. When light comes through the pinhole, an inverted image is produced on the film. Suppose you take a picture of a painting that is 30 cm wide by 45 cm high with a pinhole box camera that is 20 cm deep. How far from the painting should the pinhole be to make an image that is 2 cm wide by 3 cm high? Sketch a diagram of this situation. ⓗ
300 cm; see page 584 for sketch

Assessing Progress

While students work and present, you can assess their understanding of properties of similar triangles and of light rays reflecting off mirrors. You can also assess their skill at measurement, setting up and solving proportions, and group work. See how well they're developing the habits of critical thinking, especially in checking the reasonableness of answers.

Closing the Lesson

Restate the main mathematical point of this lesson: Similar triangles can be used to measure heights indirectly in a variety of ways, including measuring shadows and sighting the object through a mirror on the ground.

BUILDING UNDERSTANDING

Encourage students to sketch diagrams of triangles representing the situations.

ASSIGNING HOMEWORK

Essential	1–7
Portfolio	7
Journal	10
Group	8, 9
Review	11–18

▶ Helping with the Exercises

Exercise 3 If students are having difficulty, be sure they've drawn a diagram. As needed, **[Ask]** "How can you find the vertical leg of the triangle representing the flagpole?" [Pythagorean Theorem]

Exercise 4 **[ESL]** A *private eye* is a private detective.

Exercise 5 Students might think of Juanita's distance from the tree as one side of the larger triangle. Encourage them to sketch a diagram.

Exercise 6 A picture of the Great Pyramid can be found in Lesson 10.2, page 519.

6. Thales used similar right triangles. The height of the pyramid and 240 m are the lengths of the legs of one triangle; 6.2 m and 10 m are the lengths of the corresponding legs of the other triangle; 148.8 m.

Exercise 7 The first word in this exercise is *calculate,* so it's not sufficient for students to only explain similarity.

Exercise 8 Students might solve the problem using both pairs of dimensions before they realize that one pair would have sufficed.

8.

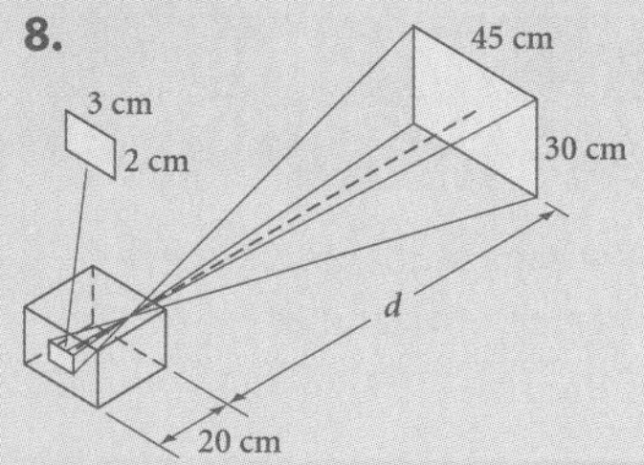

Exercise 9 [ESL] A *guy wire* is a wire attached to something as a brace or guide. Encourage a variety of approaches.

9.

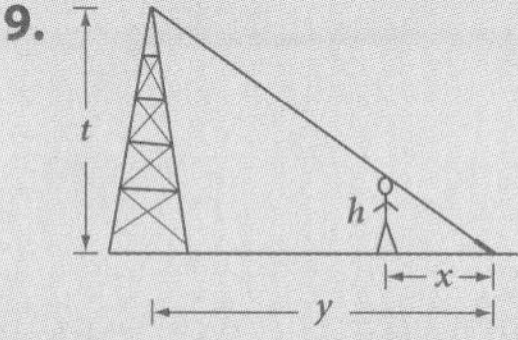

Possible answer: Walk to the point where the guy wire touches your head. Measure your height, h; the distance from you to the end of the guy wire, x; and the distance from the point on the ground directly below the top of the tower to the end of the guy wire, y. Solve a proportion to find the height of the tower, t: $\frac{h}{t} = \frac{x}{y}$. Finally, use the Pythagorean Theorem to find the length of the guy wire: $\sqrt{t^2 + y^2}$.

10. The triangles are similar by AA (because the ruler is parallel to the wall), so Kristin can use the length of string to the ruler, the length of string to the wall, and the length of the ruler to calculate the height of the wall; 144 in., or 12 ft.

Exercise 14 The result has the potential to surprise students. Although they'd all probably agree that the triangle's area will be the same no matter how it's measured, the pairs of segments being measured seem so unrelated that their common product might be startling. Encourage students to express their wonder at mathematical relationships. For many students, the pleasure and awe that arise from seeing unexpected relationships is the most powerful motivation for continuing to study mathematics.

9. **APPLICATION** A guy wire attached to a high tower needs to be replaced. The contractor does not know the height of the tower or the length of the wire. Find a method to measure the length of the wire indirectly. ⓗ

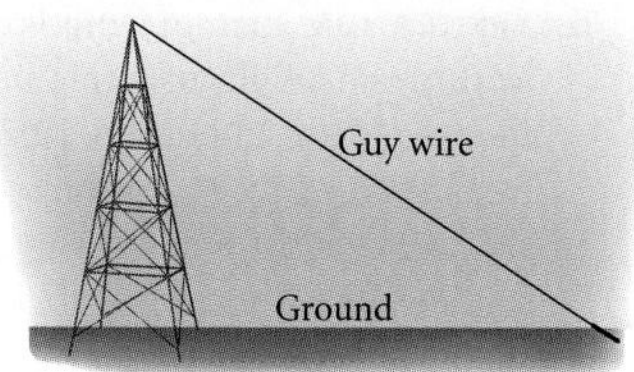

10. Kristin has developed a new method for indirectly measuring the height of her classroom. Her method uses string and a ruler. She tacks a piece of string to the base of the wall and walks back from the wall holding the other end of the string to her eye with her right hand. She holds a 12-inch ruler parallel to the wall in her left hand and adjusts her distance to the wall until the bottom of the ruler is in line with the bottom edge of the wall and the top of the ruler is in line with the top edge of the wall. Now with two measurements, she is able to calculate the height of the room. Explain her method. If the distance from her eye to the bottom of the ruler is 23 inches and the distance from her eye to the bottom of the wall is 276 inches, calculate the height of the room.

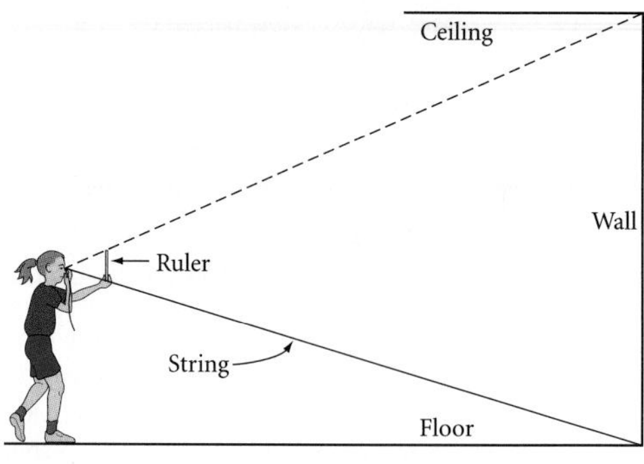

Review

11.2 For Exercises 11–13, first identify similar triangles and explain why they are similar. Then find the missing lengths.

11. Find x. ⓗ

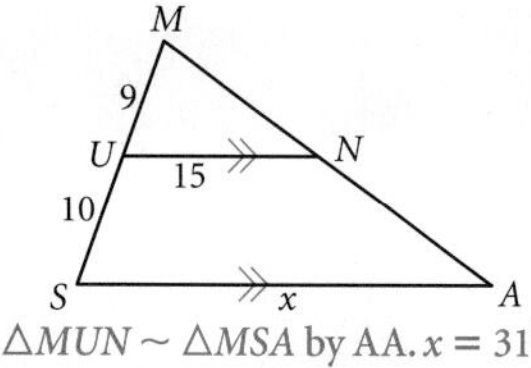

$\triangle MUN \sim \triangle MSA$ by AA. $x = 31\frac{2}{3}$

12. Find y.

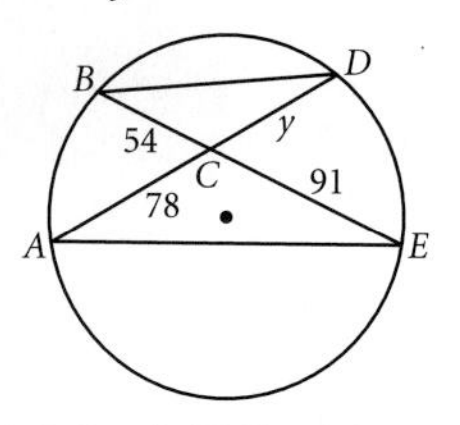

$\triangle BDC \sim \triangle AEC$ by AA. $y = 63$

13. Find x, y, and h. ⓗ

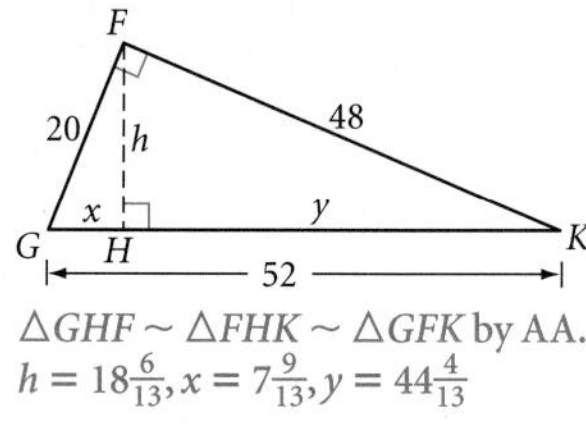

$\triangle GHF \sim \triangle FHK \sim \triangle GFK$ by AA. $h = 18\frac{6}{13}, x = 7\frac{9}{13}, y = 44\frac{4}{13}$

8.2 **14.** ***Construction*** Draw an obtuse triangle.

a. Use a compass and straightedge to construct two altitudes.

b. Use a ruler to measure both altitudes and their corresponding bases.

c. Calculate the area using both altitude-base pairs. Compare your results.

9.6 **15.** Find the radius of the circle. $5\frac{2}{3}$

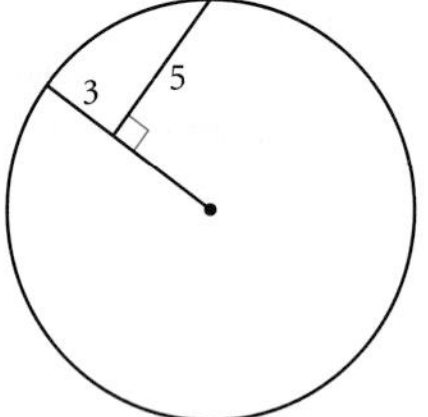

14. possible answer:

$A = \frac{1}{2}(8.2)(1.7)$
$= 6.97 \text{ cm}^2$

$A = \frac{1}{2}(3)(4.6)$
$= 6.9 \text{ cm}^2$

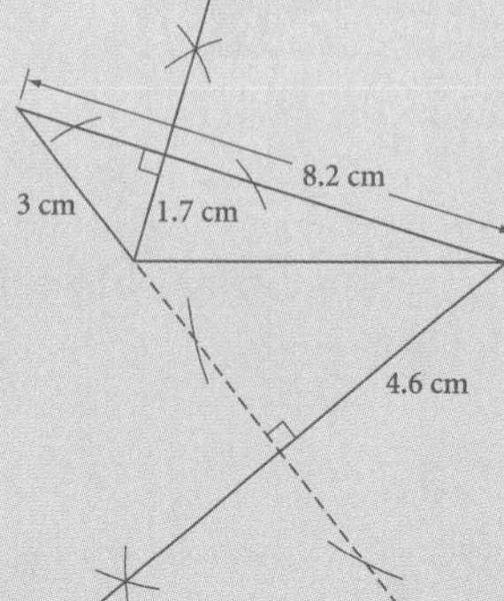

Exercise 15 Students who are still concentrating on similar triangles may spin their wheels for a long time on this review problem. As appropriate, ask students whether they know anything else about right triangles. [Pythagorean Theorem] Students might write an equation using the radius as the variable, $r^2 = 5^2 + (r - 3)^2$, or using the short leg as the variable, $x^2 + 5^2 = (x + 3)^2$.

7.4 **16.** Give the vertex arrangement of each tessellation.

a.

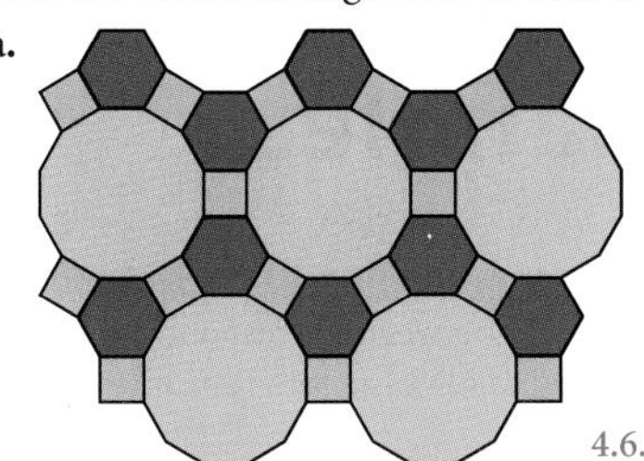

4.6.12

b.

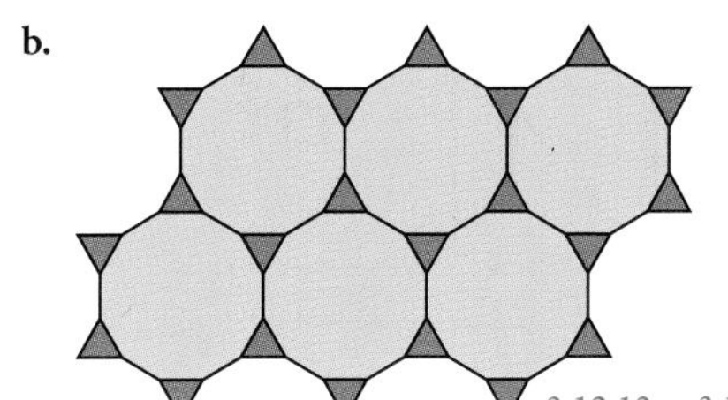

3.12.12 or 3.12^2

17. ***Technology*** On a segment AB, point X is called the **golden cut** if $\frac{AB}{AX} = \frac{AX}{XB}$, where $AX > XB$. The **golden ratio** is the value of $\frac{AB}{AX}$ and $\frac{AX}{XB}$ when they are equal. Use geometry software to explore the location of the golden cut on any segment AB. What is the value of the golden ratio? Find a way to construct the golden cut. ⓗ

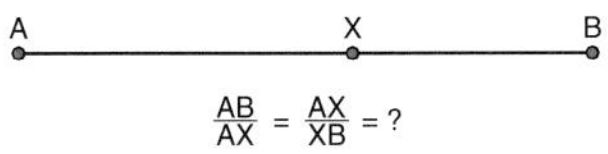

18. ***Technology*** Imagine that a rod of a given length is attached at one end to a circular track and passes through a fixed pivot point. As one endpoint moves around the circular track, the other endpoint traces a curve.

a. Predict what type of curve will be traced. Answers will vary.

b. Model this situation with geometry software. Describe the curve that is traced.

c. Experiment with changing the size of the circular track, the length of the rod, or the location of the pivot point. Describe your results.

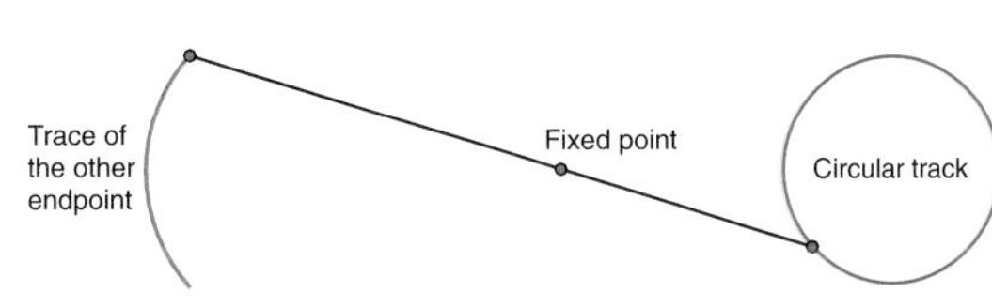

IMPROVING YOUR VISUAL THINKING SKILLS

TIC-TAC-NO!

Is it possible to shade six of the nine squares of a 3-by-3 grid so that no three of the shaded squares are in a straight line (row, column, or diagonal)?

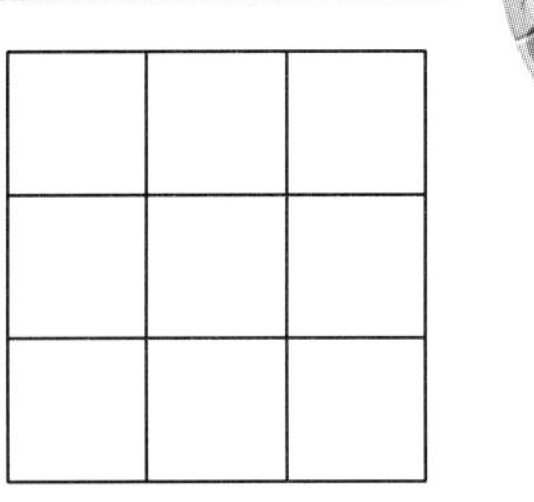

PUZZLE

IMPROVING VISUAL THINKING SKILLS

Students can try to think of how the three unshaded squares must be arranged: one in each row and each column.

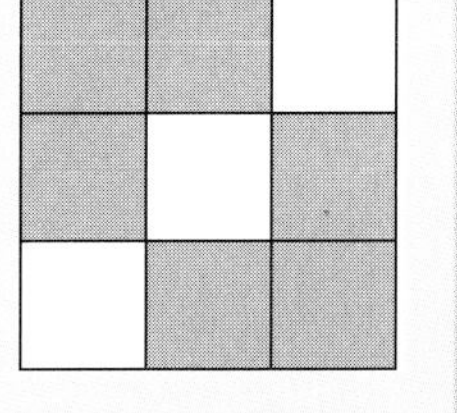

EXTENSIONS

A. Have students devise or research other indirect measuring devices.

B. Students can make pinhole cameras (see Exercise 8) and describe the proportions in their pictures versus the dimensions and proportions of the objects they photograph.

Exercise 17 You might refer interested students to the Fathom project in Lesson 11.5.

17. The golden ratio is approximately 1.618. Here is one possible construction:

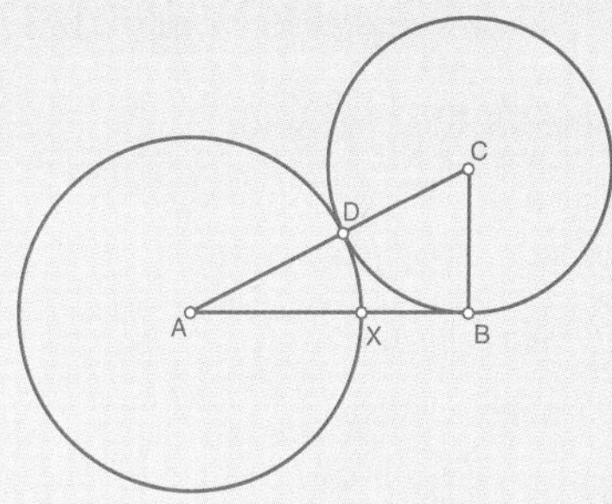

$m\angle B = 90°$

Construct $BC = \frac{1}{2}AB$

$$AC = \frac{\sqrt{5}}{2}AB$$

$$AX = AD = \frac{\sqrt{5}}{2}AB - \frac{1}{2}AB$$

$$= \frac{\sqrt{5}-1}{2}AB$$

$$\frac{AB}{AX} = \frac{2}{\sqrt{5}-1}$$

Therefore, X is the golden cut.

Exercise 18a Students may at first think the curve will be circular.

18b. Possible answer: The shape is an irregular curve. Some students might describe it as a tear or a guitar pick.

18c. Possible answers: As the circular track becomes smaller, the curve becomes more circular; as the track becomes larger, the curve becomes more pointed near the fixed point. As the rod becomes shorter, the curve becomes more pointed near the fixed point; as the rod becomes longer, the curve becomes more like an oval. As the fixed point moves closer to the traced endpoint, the curve becomes more pointed near the fixed point; as the fixed point moves closer to the circular track, the curve begins to look like a crescent moon.

LESSON 11.4

PLANNING

LESSON OUTLINE

One day:

25 min Investigation

10 min Sharing

5 min Closing

5 min Exercises

MATERIALS

- construction tools
- rulers
- calculators
- geometry software, *optional*

TEACHING

In this lesson students encounter two ideas involving similar triangles and the ratios of the lengths of their corresponding sides: the ratios of the lengths of corresponding altitudes, medians, and angle bisectors; and the ratio by which an angle bisector divides the opposite side.

You might have each group work through the steps on one of the two investigations (jigsaw) or use the one-step investigation (page 587).

Guiding Investigation 1

If students have difficulty seeing patterns, suggest that they remeasure more accurately and convert fractions to decimals. If they have access to geometry software tools that construct special triangle points, they might do this investigation using the software, which can measure more precisely and display the ratios of measurements.

LESSON 11.4

Corresponding Parts of Similar Triangles

Big doesn't necessarily mean better. Sunflowers aren't better than violets.

EDNA FERBER

Is there more to similar triangles than just proportional sides and congruent angles? For example, are there relationships between corresponding altitudes, corresponding medians, or corresponding angle bisectors in similar triangles? Let's investigate.

Investigation 1
Corresponding Parts

You will need

- a compass
- a straightedge

Use unlined paper for this investigation.

Step 1 Draw any triangle and construct a triangle of a different size similar to it. State the scale factor you used.

Step 2 Construct a pair of corresponding altitudes and use your compass to compare their lengths. How do they compare? How does the comparison relate to the scale factor you used?

Step 2 The altitudes should compare by the same scale factor. For example, if one triangle is constructed such that each side is three times longer, then the altitude will be three times longer too.

Step 3 Construct a pair of corresponding medians. How do their lengths compare?

Step 3 The medians should compare by the same scale factor.

Step 4 Construct a pair of corresponding angle bisectors. How do their lengths compare?

Step 4 The angle bisectors should compare by the same scale factor.

Step 5 Compare your results with the results of others near you. You should be ready to make a conjecture.

Proportional Parts Conjecture C-96

If two triangles are similar, then the corresponding _?_, _?_, and _?_ are _?_ to the corresponding sides. altitudes; medians; angle bisectors; proportional

The discovery you made in the investigation probably seems very intuitive. Let's see how you can prove one part of your conjecture. You will prove the other two parts in the exercises.

LESSON OBJECTIVES

- Discover a relationship between corresponding parts of similar triangles
- Explore the ratio of the parts into which an angle bisector of a triangle divides the angle's opposite side

NCTM STANDARDS

CONTENT		PROCESS	
	Number	✔	Problem Solving
✔	Algebra	✔	Reasoning
✔	Geometry	✔	Communication
✔	Measurement		Connections
	Data/Probability		Representation

EXAMPLE

Prove that corresponding medians of similar triangles are proportional to corresponding sides.

▶ Solution

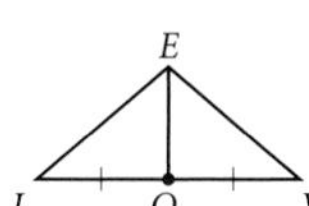

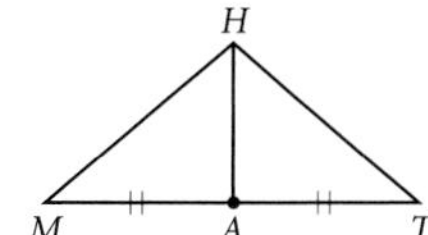

Consider similar triangles $\triangle LVE$ and $\triangle MTH$ with corresponding medians $\overline{EO}$ and $\overline{HA}$. You need to show that the corresponding medians are proportional to corresponding sides, for example $\frac{EO}{HA} = \frac{EL}{HM}$. If you show that $\triangle LOE \sim \triangle MAH$ then you can show that $\frac{EO}{HA} = \frac{EL}{HM}$.

If you accept the SAS Similarity Conjecture as true, then you can show that $\triangle LOE \sim \triangle MAH$. You already know that $\angle L \cong \angle M$. Use algebra to show that $\frac{EL}{HM} = \frac{LO}{MA}$.

$$\frac{EL}{HM} = \frac{LV}{MT}$$ Corresponding sides of similar triangles $\triangle LVE$ and $\triangle MTH$ are proportional.

$$\frac{EL}{HM} = \frac{LO + OV}{MA + AT}$$ $LV = LO + OV$ and $MT = MA + AT$. Substitute.

$$\frac{EL}{HM} = \frac{LO + LO}{MA + MA}$$ Since $\overline{EO}$ and $\overline{HA}$ are medians, O and A are midpoints. Since O and A are midpoints, $OV = LO$ and $AT = MA$. Substitute.

$$\frac{EL}{HM} = \frac{2LO}{2MA}$$ Add.

$$\frac{EL}{HM} = \frac{LO}{MA}$$ Reduce.

So, $\triangle LOE \sim \triangle MAH$ by the SAS Similarity Conjecture. Therefore you can also set up the proportion $\frac{EO}{HA} = \frac{EL}{HM}$, which shows that the corresponding medians are proportional to corresponding sides.

Recall when you first saw an angle bisector in a triangle. You may have thought that the bisector of an angle in a triangle divides the opposite side into two equal parts as well. A counterexample shows that this is not necessarily true. In $\triangle ROE$, $\overline{RT}$ bisects $\angle R$, but point T does not bisect $\overline{OE}$.

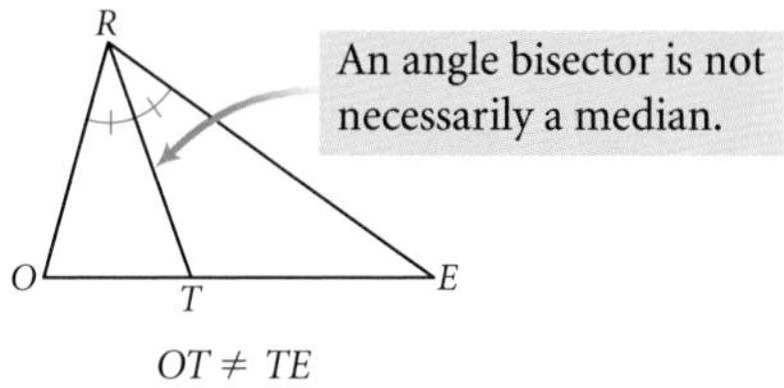

$OT \neq TE$

The angle bisector does, however, divide the opposite side in a particular way.

One step Pose this problem: "On graph paper, draw a triangle and bisect one of its angles. Draw perpendiculars from the other vertices to the angle bisector you just drew. What lengths have the same ratios in the triangle? Now choose a scale factor and use it to dilate the triangle and the special lines. What lengths have the same ratios between triangles?"

▶ EXAMPLE

You might ask students to rewrite the proof using $\triangle VEO$ and $\triangle THA$.

SHARING IDEAS

As students share their work on Investigation 1, keep asking them to think about why the conjecture might be true. Ask about other lengths, such as perimeter. **[Ask]** "Are ratios of the lengths of all corresponding segments the same as the scale factor? Does the conjecture extend to ratios of perimeters? Diagonals? Diagonals of nontriangular polygons?" [yes to all]

After reaching consensus on the Angle Bisector/Opposite Side Conjecture in Investigation 2, ask why it might be true and how it relates to similar figures, the main topic of this chapter. In fact, the proportion indicates that there may be similar figures lurking. **[Ask]** "Are the two smaller triangles similar?" [no] "Can you make figures that *are* similar?" [Drop perpendiculars to the angle bisector. Now you have two pairs of similar triangles by AA.] "Does that help?" [One pair has corresponding sides with lengths in the same ratio as *CA* and *BA*. The other pair has corresponding sides with lengths in the same ratio as *CD* and *BD*. Both have corresponding sides with lengths in the same ratio as the perpendiculars dropped to the angle bisector.] You might have students write up this proof to be sure they understand it.

Guiding Investigation 2

Step 3 Students might use patty paper rather than construction tools to bisect the angle.

Step 5 If students use geometry software for this investigation, they can consider more than two ratios.

Assessing Progress
You can assess students' ability to measure lengths and to construct similar triangles, altitudes, medians, and angle bisectors. You can also monitor their understanding of similarity, scale factors, ratios, and proportional segments and their willingness to check the reasonableness of results.

Closing the Lesson

The main mathematical idea of this lesson is that corresponding one-dimensional parts of similar triangles (and other figures) have the same ratio as the scale factor. One consequence of this phenomenon is that an angle bisector of a triangle divides the opposite side into two segments whose lengths are in the same ratio as the lengths of the triangle's other two sides.

BUILDING UNDERSTANDING

ASSIGNING HOMEWORK

Essential	1–15
Performance assessment	16
Portfolio	19
Journal	22
Group	17–19
Review	20–26

Investigation 2
Opposite Side Ratios

You will need
- a compass
- a ruler

In this investigation you'll discover that there is a proportional relationship involving angle bisectors.

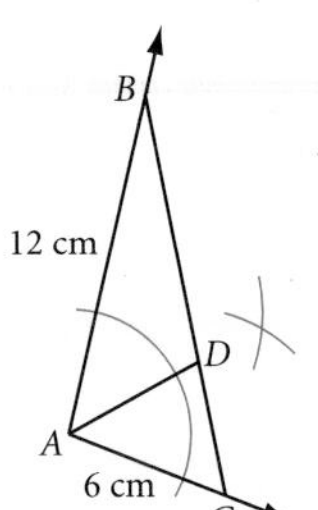

Step 1 Draw any angle. Label it A.

Step 2 On one ray, locate point C so that AC is 6 cm. Use the same compass setting and locate point B on the other ray so that AB is 12 cm. Draw $\overline{BC}$ to form $\triangle ABC$.

Step 3 Construct the bisector of $\angle A$. Locate point D where the bisector intersects side $\overline{BC}$.

Step 4 Measure and compare CD and BD. *Step 4 BD is twice CD.*

Step 5 Calculate and compare the ratios $\frac{CA}{BA}$ and $\frac{CD}{BD}$. *Step 5 They are equal.*

Step 6 Repeat Steps 1–5 with $AC = 10$ cm and $AB = 15$ cm. *Step 6 $BD = \frac{3}{2}CD$ and $\frac{CA}{BA} = \frac{CD}{BD}$*

Step 7 Compare your results with the results of others near you. State a conjecture.

Angle Bisector/Opposite Side Conjecture C-97

A bisector of an angle in a triangle divides the opposite side into two segments whose lengths are in the same ratio as __?__. *the lengths of the two sides forming the angle*

EXERCISES

You will need

For Exercises 1–13, use your new conjectures. All measurements are in centimeters.

1. $\triangle ICE \sim \triangle AGE$
$h = $ __?__ *18 cm*

2. $\triangle SKI \sim \triangle JMP$
$x = $ __?__ *12 cm*

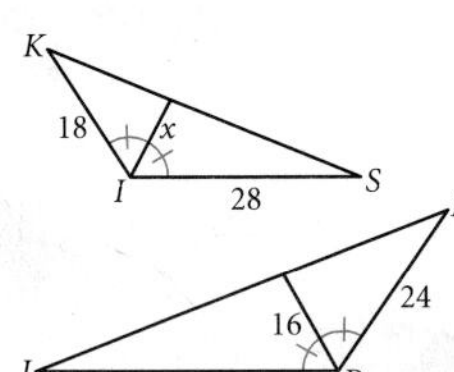

3. $\triangle PIE \sim \triangle SIC$
Point S is the midpoint of PI.
$CL = $ __?__, $CS = $ __?__ ⓗ
21 cm *20 cm*

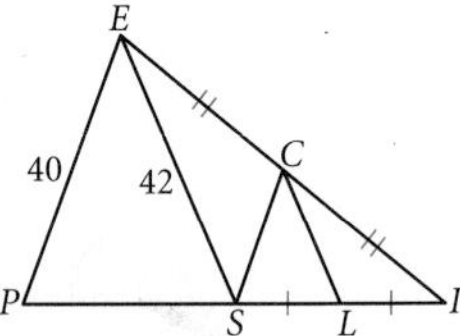

▶Helping with the Exercises

Exercise 2 **[Alert]** One figure is a reflection of a dilation of the other, so students may set up the correspondence incorrectly. You might work through this example, modeling how to check the proportion by looking at the order in which the vertices are named in the similar triangle expression.

Exercise 3 If students are having difficulty, **[Ask]** "Is there anything you can say about the segments?" [Some are medians of the similar triangles.]

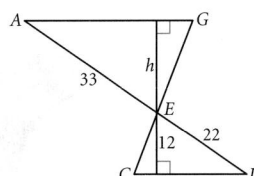

4. $\triangle CAP \sim \triangle DAY$
$FD = \underline{?}$ 15 cm

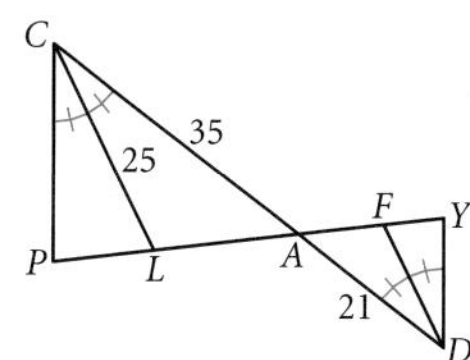

5. $\triangle HAT \sim \triangle CLD$
$x = \underline{?}$ 2.0 cm

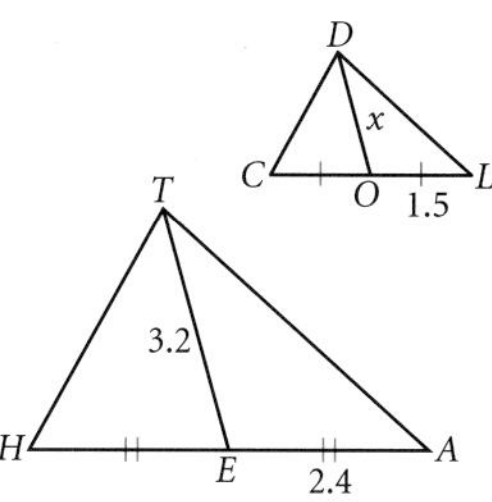

6. $\triangle ARM \sim \triangle LEG$
Area of $\triangle ARM = \underline{?}$ 126 cm^2
Area of $\triangle LEG = \underline{?}$ 504 cm^2

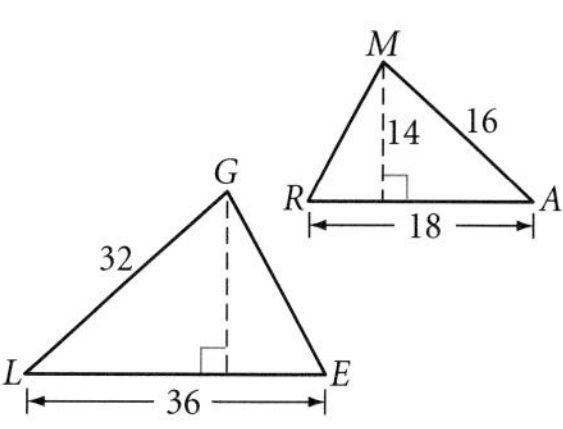

7. $v = \underline{?}$ 16 cm

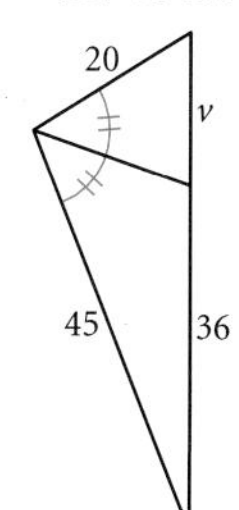

8. $y = \underline{?}$ 60 cm

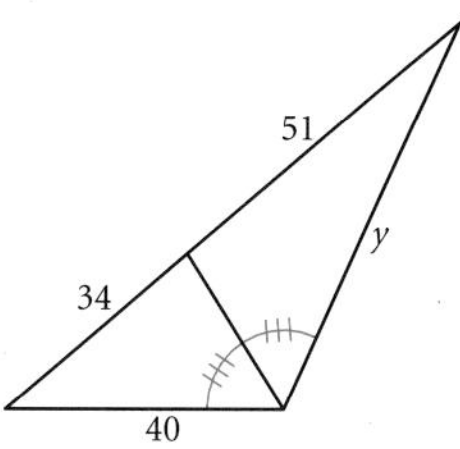

9. $x = \underline{?}$ ⓗ $4\frac{4}{9}$ cm

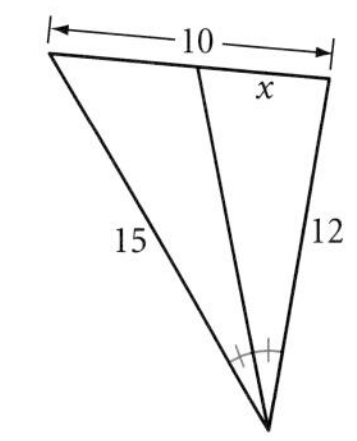

10. $\frac{a}{b} = \frac{?}{?}$, $\frac{a}{p} = \frac{?}{?}$ $\frac{p}{q}$, $\frac{b}{q}$

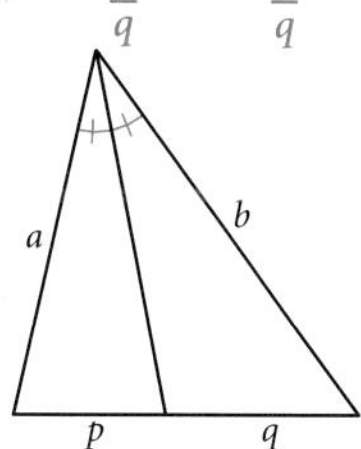

11. $k = \underline{?}$ $6\sqrt{3}$ cm

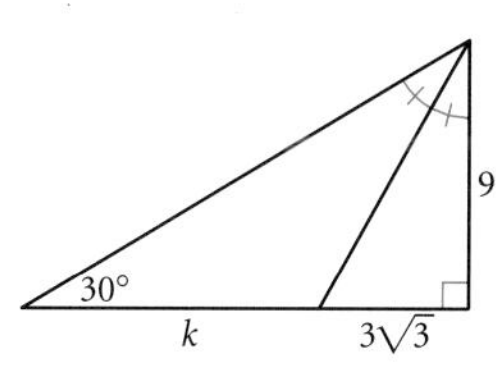

12. $x = \underline{?}$ ⓗ 6 cm

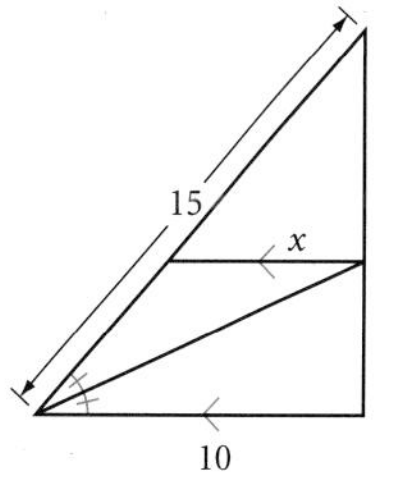

13. $x = \underline{?}$, $y = \underline{?}$ $8\frac{2}{3}$ cm, $\frac{5\sqrt{13}}{3}$ cm

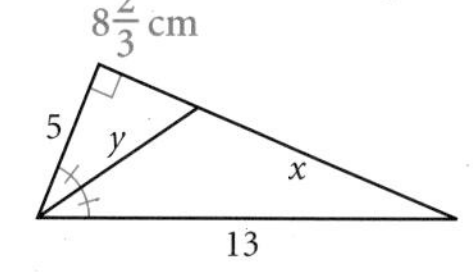

14. Triangle PQR is the image of $\triangle ABC$ under a dilation. Find the coordinates of B and R. Find the ratio $\frac{k}{h}$.
$B = (3, 5)$, $R = \left(1\frac{3}{4}, 7\right)$; $\frac{k}{h} = \frac{7}{4}$

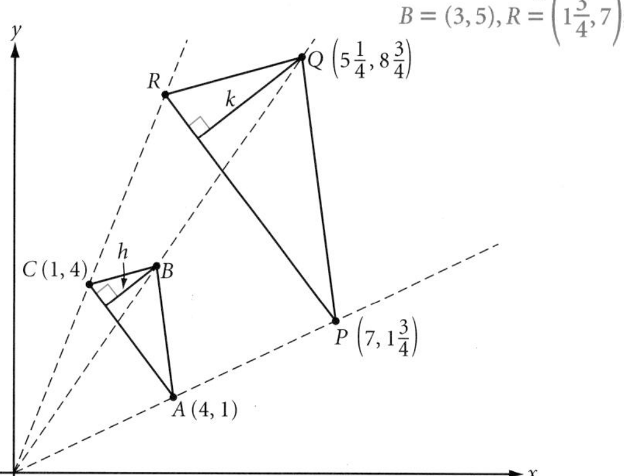

Exercise 6 This exercise is purposely labeled with more information than necessary. AM and LG are unnecessary but might lead students to ask about the lengths of the other sides and to note that the area ratio is the square of the scale factor. This exercise foreshadows Lesson 11.5.

Exercise 11 Encourage students to think creatively. This exercise can be solved in at least two ways other than using proportions based on the angle bisector. (1) By angle sums, you can determine that the left-hand triangle is isosceles, so the length of the angle bisector is also k. Then use the Pythagorean Theorem or 30°-60°-90° triangle properties on the right-hand triangle to find k. (2) Consider the whole triangle. By 30°-60°-90° triangle properties, $k + 3\sqrt{3} = 9\sqrt{3}$. Subtract to find $k = 6\sqrt{3}$.

Exercise 12 Students may use the Angle Bisector/Opposite Side Conjecture, or, if they see the congruence of alternate interior angles between the parallel lines, they can use isosceles triangle properties. This exercise foreshadows Lesson 11.6.

Exercise 13 To work with the smallest triangle, students need to write one leg as $12 - x$.

Exercise 14 The dotted lines show a dilation that guarantees similar triangles. Once students realize that the ratio of altitudes equals the scale factor, they can use the scale factor between the coordinates of A and P.

Exercise 16 Any two of the three lengths $2x$, $3x$, and AB must have a sum greater than the third length. That is, the three segments should make a triangle. This exercise motivates a simpler approach arising from the ideas of Lesson 11.6.

Exercises 17, 18 These student proofs can be somewhat less rigorous than the proof for medians given in the example.

17.

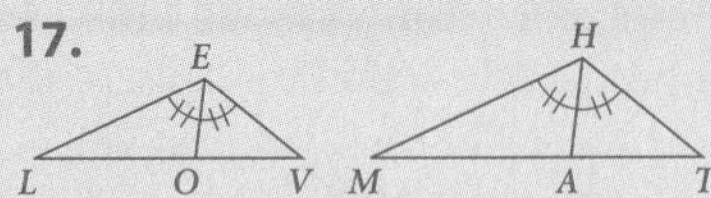

Consider similar triangles $\triangle LVE$ and $\triangle MTH$ with corresponding angle bisectors $\overline{EO}$ and $\overline{HA}$. To show that the corresponding angle bisectors are proportional to corresponding sides, for example $\frac{EO}{HA} = \frac{EL}{HM}$, show by AA that $\triangle LOE \sim \triangle MAH$ then you can show that $\frac{EO}{HA} = \frac{EL}{HM}$. You know that $\angle L \cong \angle M$. Use algebra to show that $\angle LEO \cong \angle MHA$.

18.

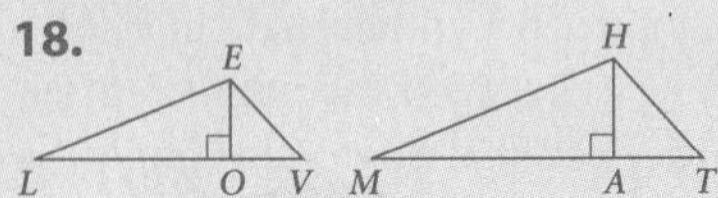

Consider similar triangles $\triangle LVE$ and $\triangle MTH$ with corresponding altitudes $\overline{EO}$ and $\overline{HA}$. Show that $\triangle LOE \sim \triangle MAH$, then $\frac{EO}{HA} = \frac{EL}{HM}$. You know that $\angle L \cong \angle M$. Since $\overline{EO}$ and $\overline{MA}$ are altitudes, $\angle LOE$ and $\angle MAH$ are both right angles, and $\angle LOE \cong \angle MAH$.

So, if you accept the AA Similarity Conjecture, $\triangle LOE \sim \triangle MAH$. You can then write the proportion $\frac{EO}{HA} = \frac{EL}{HM}$, which shows that the corresponding altitudes are proportional to corresponding sides.

15. Aunt Florence has willed to her two nephews a plot of land in the shape of an isosceles right triangle. The land is to be divided into two unequal parts by bisecting one of the two congruent angles. What is the ratio of the greater area to the lesser area? $\frac{\sqrt{2}}{1}$

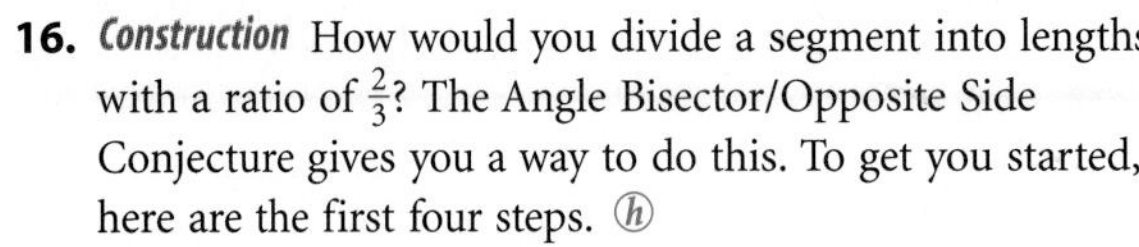

16. ***Construction*** How would you divide a segment into lengths with a ratio of $\frac{2}{3}$? The Angle Bisector/Opposite Side Conjecture gives you a way to do this. To get you started, here are the first four steps. ⓗ

Step 1 | Construct any segment AB.

Step 2 | Construct a second segment. Call its length x.

Step 3 | Construct two more segments with lengths $2x$ and $3x$.

Step 4 | Construct a triangle with lengths $2x$, $3x$, and AB.

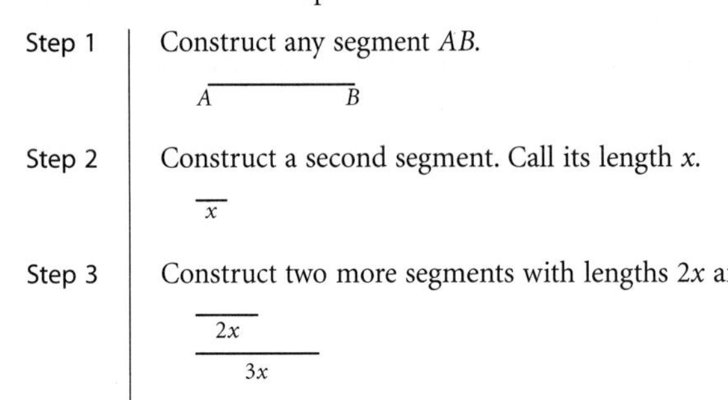

Label the third vertex C. Construct segment CD, which bisects $\angle C$. $\frac{AD}{DB} = \frac{2x}{3x}$

You're on your own from here!

17. Prove that corresponding angle bisectors of similar triangles are proportional to corresponding sides. ⓗ

18. Prove that corresponding altitudes of similar triangles are proportional to corresponding sides.

19. ***Mini-Investigation*** This investigation is in two parts. You will need to complete the conjecture in part a before moving on to part b.

a. The altitude to the hypotenuse has been constructed in each right triangle below. This construction creates two smaller right triangles within each original right triangle. Calculate the measures of the acute angles in each diagram.

i. $a = \underline{?}$ 40°, $b = \underline{?}$ 50°, $c = \underline{?}$ 40° **ii.** $a = \underline{?}$ 60°, $b = \underline{?}$ 30°, $c = \underline{?}$ 60° **iii.** $a = \underline{?}$ 22°, $b = \underline{?}$ 68°, $c = \underline{?}$ 22°

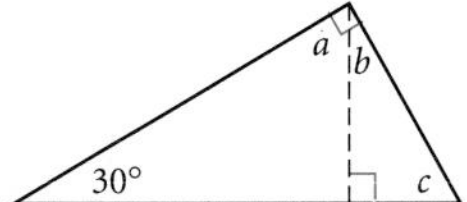

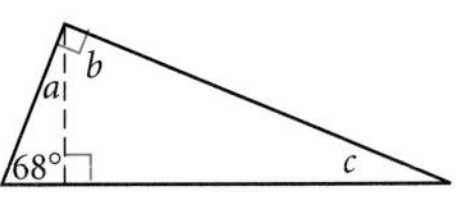

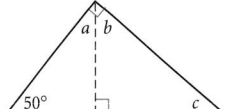

How do the smaller right triangles compare in each diagram? How do they compare to the original right triangle? You should be ready to state a conjecture.

Conjecture: The altitude to the hypotenuse of a right triangle divides the triangle into two right triangles that are $\underline{?}$ (similar) to each other and to the original $\underline{?}$ (right triangle).

Exercise 19 From the conjecture in part b, $h = \sqrt{pq}$. If you add two numbers and divide by 2, you get their average, or *arithmetic mean.* If you multiply two numbers and take the square root, you get what's called their *geometric mean.* The classical Greeks constructed the geometric mean of two numbers by constructing a right triangle with the length of the hypotenuse equal to the sum of the two numbers and constructing an altitude to that hypotenuse.

b. Complete each proportion for these right triangles.

i. $\frac{h}{r} = \frac{s}{?}$ $\frac{s}{h}$ **ii.** $\frac{y}{h} = \frac{?}{x}$ $\frac{h}{x}$ **iii.** $\frac{n}{h} = \frac{?}{?}$ $\frac{h}{m}$ or $\frac{b}{a}$

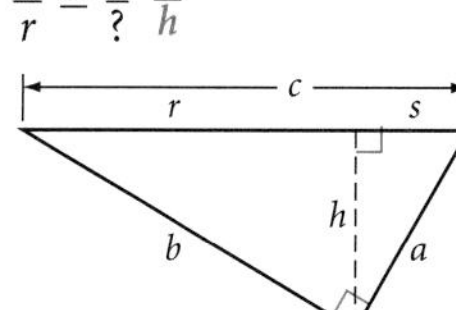

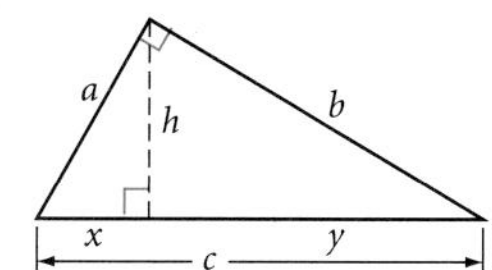

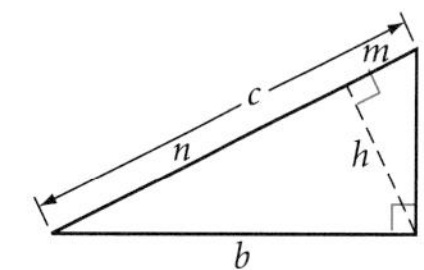

Review the proportions you wrote. How are they alike? You should be ready to state a conjecture.

Conjecture: The altitude (length h) to the hypotenuse of a right triangle divides the hypotenuse into two segments (lengths p and q), such that $\frac{p}{?} = \frac{?}{q}$. $\frac{p}{h} = \frac{h}{q}$

Add these conjectures to your notebook.

Review

UYAS 9 **20.** Use algebra to show that if $\frac{a}{b} = \frac{c}{d}$, then $\frac{a+b}{b} = \frac{c+d}{d}$. ⓗ

11.1 **21.** A rectangle is divided into four rectangles, each similar to the original rectangle. What is the ratio of short side to long side in the rectangles?

11.2 **22.** In Chapter 5, you discovered that when you construct the three midsegments in a triangle, they divide the triangle into four congruent triangles. Are the four triangles similar to the original? Explain why.

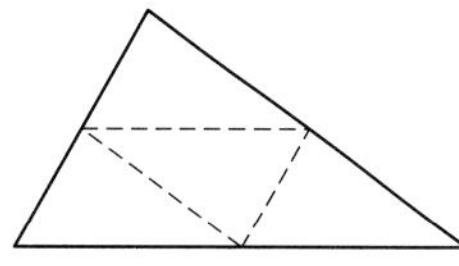

11.2 **23.** ***Construction*** Draw any triangle ABC. Select any point X on $\overline{AB}$. Construct a line through X parallel to $\overline{AC}$ that intersects $\overline{BC}$ in point Y. Find a proportion that relates AX, XB, BY, and YC.

24. A rectangle has sides a and b. For what values of a and b is another rectangle with sides $2a$ and $\frac{b}{2}$

a. Congruent to the original? $2a = b$

b. Equal in perimeter to the original? $2a = b$

c. Equal in area to the original? all values of a and b

d. Similar but not congruent to the original? no values of a and b

10.3 **25.** Find the volume of this truncated cone.
9,120π m^3 or approximately 28,651 m^3

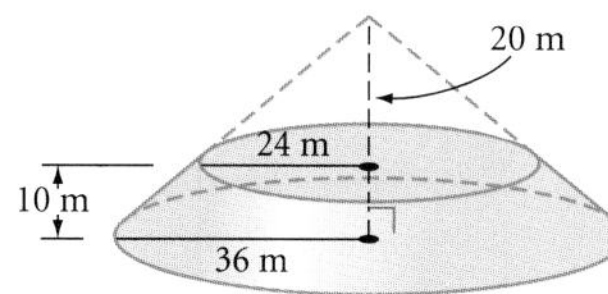

9.3 **26.** The large circles are tangent to the square and tangent to each other. The smaller circle is tangent to each larger circle. Find the radius of the smaller circle in terms of s, the length of each side of the square. ⓗ
$\frac{s}{2\sqrt{2}} - \frac{s}{4}$ or $\frac{s\sqrt{2} - s}{4}$

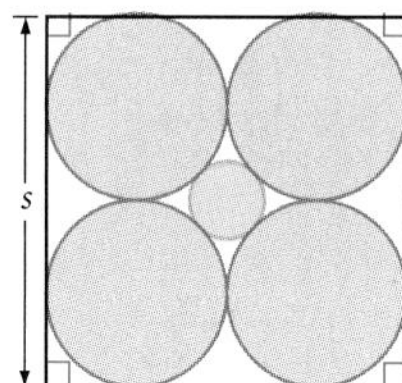

Exercise 20 Remind students that a good proof technique is to work backward at first. They may then see that they can add an equivalent of 1 to each side of the first equation to get the second. Watch for faulty logic. Some students may be satisfied with assuming the second equation and deriving the first. However, they've only proved the converse of what they are asked to prove.

20. $\frac{a}{b} + 1 = \frac{c}{d} + 1$

$\frac{a}{b} + \frac{b}{b} = \frac{c}{d} + \frac{d}{d}$

$\frac{a+b}{b} = \frac{c+d}{d}$

21. The ratio is $\frac{1}{2}$ if it can be divided like this:

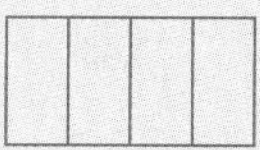

It might be any ratio if divided like this:

22. Yes, by the SSS or the SAS Similarity Conjecture.

Exercise 23 This exercise is a preview of Lesson 11.6.

23. possible answer: $\frac{AX}{XB} = \frac{CY}{YB}$

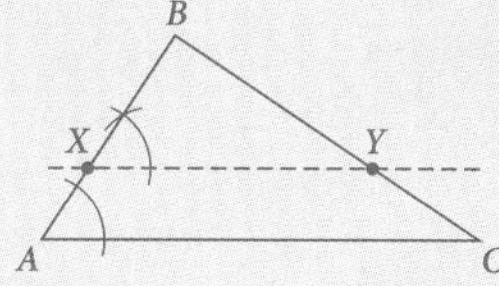

Exercise 24 This exercise asks for a range of numbers that will satisfy each completion of the question.

EXTENSIONS

A. Challenge students to prove or find a counterexample to this claim: If two triangles are similar, then the ratio of the lengths of their corresponding medians is equal to the ratio of the lengths of their corresponding altitudes. [True. The ratio of the lengths of corresponding medians and the ratio of the lengths of corresponding altitudes both equal the ratio of the lengths of corresponding sides, so they equal each other.]

B. Pose this problem: If the corresponding sides of two similar triangles are in the ratio 2 to 3, is the ratio of the perimeters less, greater, or the same? Is the ratio of the areas less, greater, or the same? Explain your reasoning. [The ratio of the perimeters is the same. The ratio of the areas is the square of the ratios of the sides, so it is $\frac{4}{9}$. It is less because the scale factor is less than 1.]

C. Use Take Another Look activity 3 on page 617.

LESSON

11.5

PLANNING

LESSON OUTLINE

One day:

20 min Investigation

10 min Sharing

5 min Closing

10 min Exercises

MATERIALS

- calculators
- graph paper
- interlocking (or other) cubes
- Sketchpad demonstration Area Ratios, *optional*

TEACHING

This lesson addresses some of the most powerful ideas of geometry: how the areas and volumes of similar figures compare. Quite a few exercises have foreshadowed these ideas.

One step Pose this problem: "If you triple the volume of a cake but keep the same shape, by how much do you need to multiply the amount of icing?" Discussion may bring in points about recipes and the practicality of baking the larger cake, and a few students may still claim that all rectangular and all "round" cakes have the "same shape," no matter what their height is. Gently lead groups to consider similar cakes. Encourage a variety of assumptions about the shape and what sides to ice so patterns can emerge during Sharing.

Guiding Investigation 1

Step 1 Because the rectangle might be enlarged later, encourage students to limit the size of the rectangle they draw.

Have each group use a different rectangle, but have all members within a group use the same rectangle.

Step 2 Have each group member use a different scale factor so that students can get different results to compare within their group. Encourage some scale factors of less than 1. During Sharing compare the results of scale factors on different rectangles.

Step 3 As needed, encourage students to reduce ratios in order to recognize and complete the conjecture.

LESSON 11.5

Proportions with Area and Volume

It is easy to show that a hare could not be as large as a hippopotamus, or a whale as small as a herring. For every type of animal there is a most convenient size, and a large change in size inevitably carries with it a change of form.

J. B. S. HALDANE

You can use similarity to find the surface areas and volumes of objects that are geometrically similar. Suppose an artist wishes to gold-plate a sculpture. If it costs \$250 to gold-plate a model that is half as long in each dimension, how much will it cost for the full-size sculpture? Not \$500, but \$1000! If the model weighs 40 pounds, how much will the full-size sculpture weigh? Not 80 pounds, but 320 pounds! In this lesson you will discover why these answers may not be what you expected.

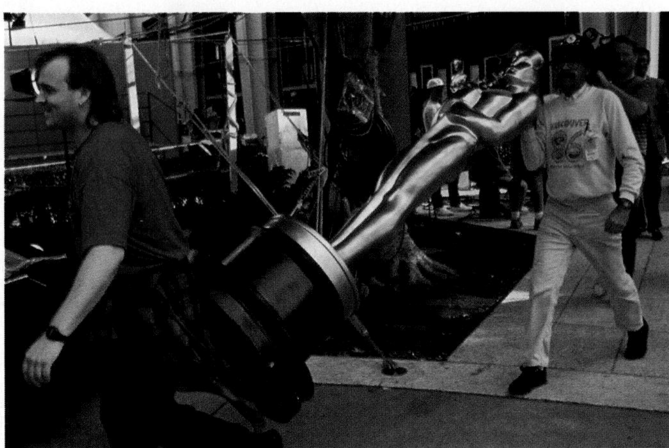

You might recognize this giant golden man as the Academy Awards statuette. Also called the Oscar, smaller versions of the figure are handed out annually for excellence in the motion picture industry. If this statuette were real gold, it would be very expensive and incredibly heavy.

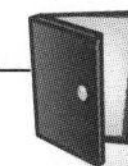

Investigation 1
Area Ratios

You will need

- graph paper

In this investigation you will find the relationship between areas of similar figures.

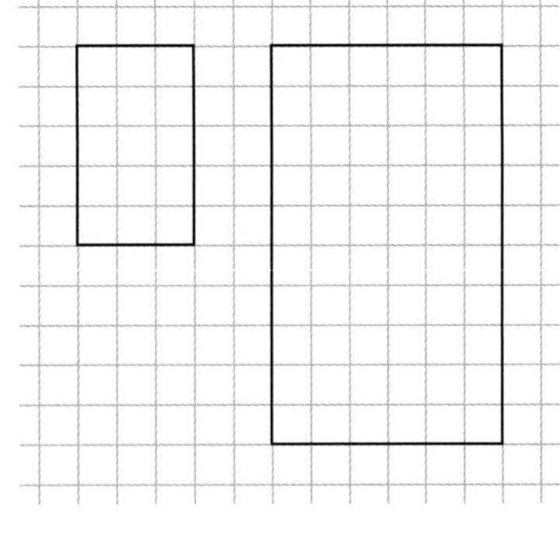

Step 1 Draw a rectangle on graph paper. Calculate its area.

Step 2 Draw a rectangle similar to your first rectangle by multiplying its sides by a scale factor. Calculate this area.

Step 3 What is the ratio of side lengths (larger to smaller) for your two rectangles? What is the ratio of their areas (larger to smaller)?

Step 1 Possible answer: A 3-by-5 rectangle would have an area of 15.

Step 2 Possible answer: Using a scale factor of 2, the new rectangle would be 6 by 10. The area would be 60.

Step 3 Possible answer: Ratio of side lengths is $\frac{2}{1}$. Ratio of areas is $\frac{4}{1}$, or $\frac{2^2}{1^2}$.

Step 4 Possible answer: You would need four copies.

Step 4 | How many copies of the smaller rectangle would you need to fill the larger rectangle? Draw lines in your larger rectangle to show how you would place the copies to fill the area.

Step 5 | Compare your results with the results of others near you.

Step 6 | Repeat Steps 1–5 using triangles instead of rectangles.

Step 7 | Discuss whether or not your findings would apply to any pair of similar polygons. Would they apply to similar circles or other curved figures? You should be ready to state a conjecture.

Proportional Areas Conjecture C-98

If corresponding sides of two similar polygons or the radii of two circles compare in the ratio $\frac{m}{n}$, then their areas compare in the ratio __?__. $\frac{m^2}{n^2}$ or $\left(\frac{m}{n}\right)^2$

Similar solids are solids that have the same shape but not necessarily the same size. All cubes are similar, but not all prisms are similar. All spheres are similar, but not all cylinders are similar. Two polyhedrons are similar if all their corresponding faces are similar and the lengths of their corresponding edges are proportional. Two right cylinders (or right cones) are similar if their radii and heights are proportional.

EXAMPLE A

Are these right rectangular prisms similar?

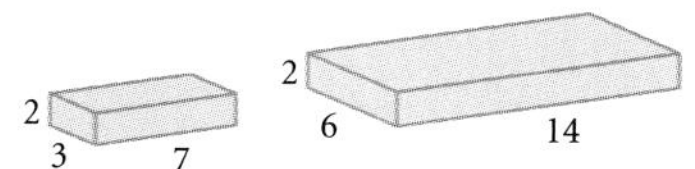

▶ Solution

The two prisms are not similar because the corresponding edges are not proportional.

$$\frac{2}{2} \neq \frac{3}{6} = \frac{7}{14}$$

EXAMPLE B

Are these right circular cones similar?

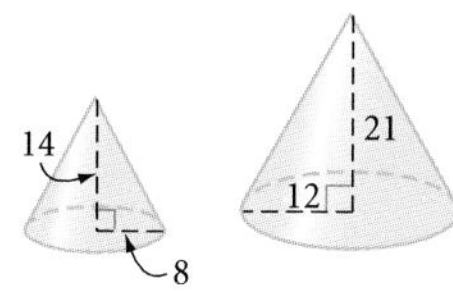

▶ Solution

The two cones are similar because the radii and heights are proportional.

$$\frac{8}{12} = \frac{14}{21}$$

Step 7 Students may wonder what *similar circles* are. All circles are similar to one another, as dilations of one another. **[Ask]** "What other polygons are similar to all others of the same name?" [squares, regular hexagons, equilateral triangles, isosceles right triangles, and so on] If pattern blocks or geometry software is available, students might want to investigate several shapes. Some students, not thinking about exponents, may complete the conjecture with $\frac{m \cdot m}{n \cdot n}$. Save any critique for Sharing.

▶ EXAMPLE A

Students might still be thinking of two-dimensional figures; two pairs of bases of these prisms are indeed similar rectangles.

▶ EXAMPLE B

Students could also consider the ratio of the diameters instead of the ratio of the radii.

NCTM STANDARDS

CONTENT		PROCESS	
✓	Number	✓	Problem Solving
✓	Algebra	✓	Reasoning
✓	Geometry	✓	Communication
✓	Measurement	✓	Connections
	Data/Probability	✓	Representation

LESSON OBJECTIVES

- Discover the relationship between the areas of similar figures
- Discover the relationship between the volumes of similar solids
- Apply the similarity conjectures to problems involving area and volume

Guiding Investigation 2

Each group will need at least 221 cubes. If you use nonconnecting cubes, use tape or poster putty to hold them together. If no cubes are available, students could draw the solids and then draw and cut out the solids' nets from graph paper, but some students will have trouble visualizing the enlarged solids without building them first.

This activity works well in groups of four, with pair share. One subgroup builds the snake, the other subgroup builds the fish, and they share results in Steps 5 and 6.

Steps 1, 2 If you are short on blocks, reduce the snake's original dimensions to 1 by 1 by 3 or reduce the scale factor to 2. **[Alert]** Many students neglect to scale one dimension.

Step 2 Asking how many copies of the original snake would fit into the expanded snake encourages in many students a deeper understanding of volume.

Step 4 You could reduce the dimensions of the fish to 1 by 2 by 3 if you are short on blocks. Some students may be confused about what to do with the single block on top of the rectangle; it has dimensions 1 by 1 by 1, so it needs to expand to a 2-by-2-by-2 cube. Again, you might ask how many of the original fish would fit into the larger fish; they won't fit without being broken up and having their pieces reassembled.

Investigation 2
Volume Ratios

You will need

- interlocking cubes

How does the ratio of lengths of corresponding edges of similar solids compare with the ratio of their volumes? Let's find out.

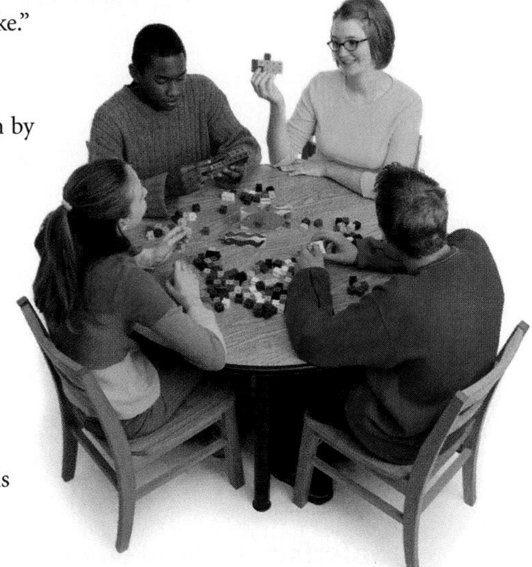

Step 1 The volume is 4.

Step 2 The snake will be 3 by 3 by 12. The volume is 108.

Step 3 The ratio of side lengths is $\frac{3}{1}$. The ratio of volumes is $\frac{27}{1}$, or $\frac{3^3}{1^3}$.

Step 4 The ratio of side lengths is $\frac{2}{1}$. The ratio of volumes is $\frac{8}{1}$, or $\frac{2^3}{1^3}$.

Step 1 Use blocks to build the "snake." Calculate its volume.

Step 2 Build a similar snake by multiplying every dimension by a scale factor of 3. Calculate this volume.

Step 3 What is the ratio of side lengths (larger to smaller) for your two snakes? What is the ratio of volumes (larger to smaller)?

Step 4 As in Steps 1–3, use blocks to build the "fish" and another fish similar to it, this time by a scale factor of 2. Find the ratio of the side lengths and the ratio of the volumes.

Step 5 How do your results compare with the results in Investigation 1? Discuss how you would calculate the volume of a snake increased by a scale factor of 5. Discuss how you would calculate the volume of a fish increased by a scale factor of 4.

Step 6 You should be ready to state a conjecture.

Proportional Volumes Conjecture C-99

If corresponding edges (or radii, or heights) of two similar solids compare in the ratio $\frac{m}{n}$, then their volumes compare in the ratio __?__. $\frac{m^3}{n^3}$ or $\left(\frac{m}{n}\right)^3$

SHARING IDEAS

If no groups have used exponents to write their conjectures, you can demonstrate exponents as shorthand for repeated products. If exponents are really a new idea for students and you plan to do the Exploration Why Elephants Have Big Ears, you might want to look first at some rules for manipulating exponents. At least remind students how to "unsquare" and "uncube" numbers.

Ask what meaning students can make of the conjectures about area and volume ratios of similar figures. *Why* are the ratios, respectively, the square and the cube of the scale factors (sometimes called *length ratios* or *linear ratios*)? Most students are satisfied with thinking of figures, like rectangles and "snakes," that allow them to actually lay out the smaller object several times to fill the larger object. Others will be happier seeing how the formulas of standard figures can give the same results.

Ask how similar polyhedrons might be defined. Then ask students to critique the definition in the book. **[Ask]** "Why does the definition of similar polyhedrons not even mention angles?" [It does so indirectly, through similar polygons.] "Do similar solids have to be dilations of each other?" [No; they might be reflections, rotations, or translations of dilations of each other.]

EXERCISES

1. $\triangle CAT \sim \triangle MSE$
   Area of $\triangle CAT = 72\ \text{cm}^2$
   Area of $\triangle MSE = \underline{?}$ (h) $18\ \text{cm}^2$

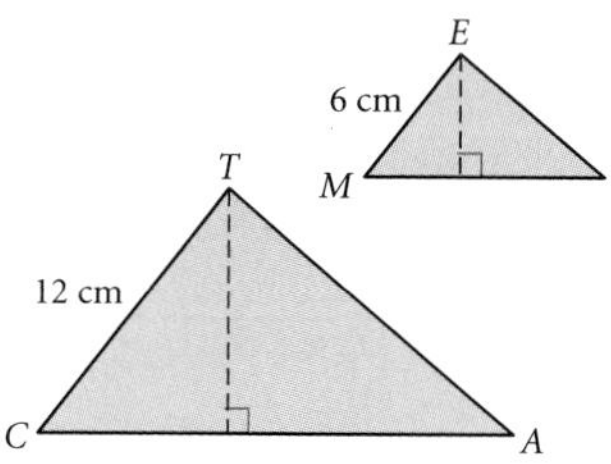

2. $RECT \sim ANGL$
   $\dfrac{\text{Area of } RECT}{\text{Area of } ANGL} = \dfrac{9}{16}$
   $TR = \underline{?}$ 18

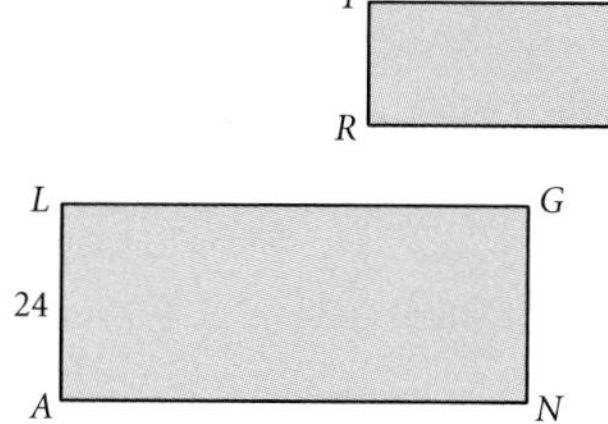

3. $TRAP \sim ZOID$ (h)
   $\dfrac{\text{Area of } ZOID}{\text{Area of } TRAP} = \dfrac{16}{25}$
   $a = \underline{?}$, $b = \underline{?}$
   5, 10

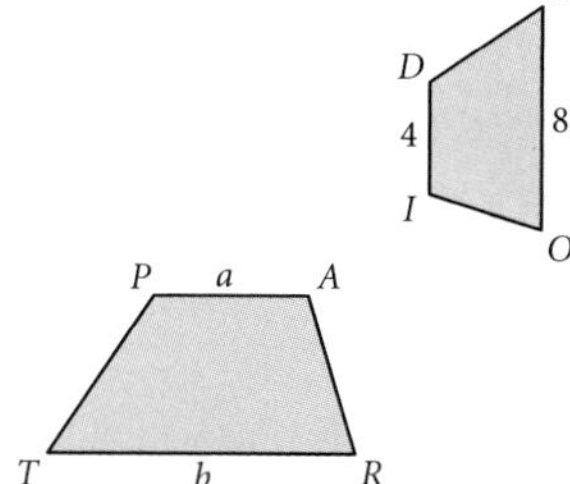

4. semicircle $R \sim$ semicircle S
   $\dfrac{r}{s} = \dfrac{3}{5}$
   Area of semicircle $S = 75\pi\ \text{cm}^2$
   Area of semicircle $R = \underline{?}$ $27\pi\ \text{cm}^2$

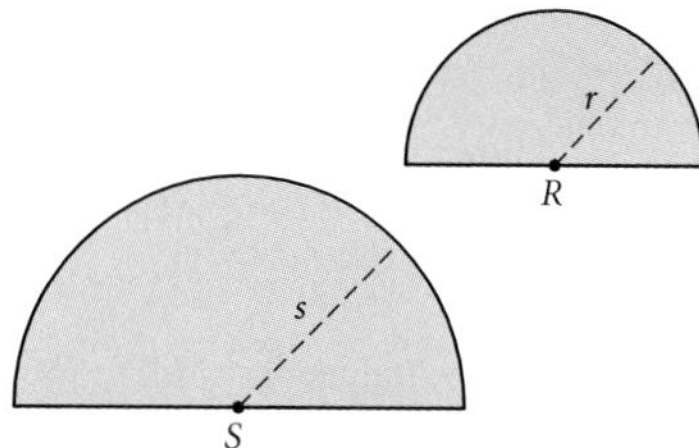

5. The ratio of the lengths of corresponding diagonals of two similar kites is $\frac{1}{7}$. What is the ratio of their areas? $\frac{1}{49}$
6. The ratio of the areas of two similar trapezoids is $\frac{1}{9}$. What is the ratio of the lengths of their altitudes? $\frac{1}{3}$
7. The ratio of the lengths of the edges of two cubes is $\frac{m}{n}$. What is the ratio of their surface areas? (h) $\frac{m^2}{n^2}$ or $\left(\frac{m}{n}\right)^2$
8. The celestial sphere shown at right has radius 9 inches. The planet in the sphere's center has radius 3 inches. What is the ratio of the volume of the planet to the volume of the celestial sphere? What is the ratio of the surface area of the planet to the surface area of the celestial sphere? The ratio of the volumes is $\frac{1}{27}$. The ratio of the surface areas is $\frac{1}{9}$.
9. **APPLICATION** Annie works in a magazine's advertising department. A client has requested that his 5 cm-by-12 cm ad be enlarged: "Double the length and double the width, then send me the bill." The original ad cost \$1500. How much should Annie charge for the larger ad? Explain your reasoning.

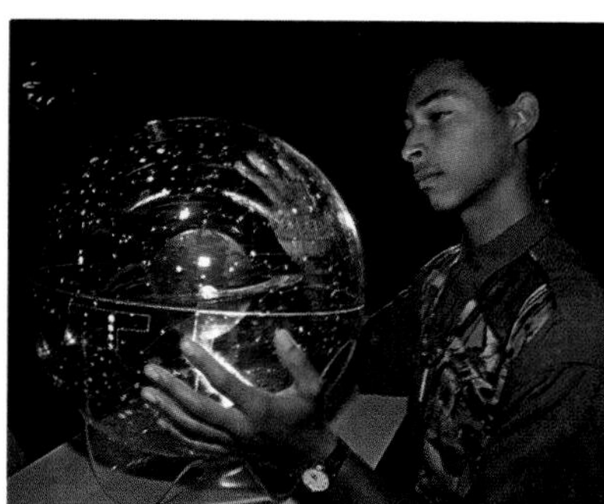

Sharing Ideas (continued)

Ask about other solids. **[Ask]** "If the radii of two cones were the same but the heights were different, would you consider them similar cones? What if the radii were the same and the heights were the same? What about spheres and cylinders?" [As with two-dimensional figures, similar three-dimensional figures have the same ratio of all one-dimensional parts.]

Earlier we saw that the perimeters of similar plane figures had the same ratio as the lengths of the sides. **[Ask]** "What might be an analogy for solids?" [The ratio of sums of the edge lengths is the scale factor; the ratio of surface areas is the square of the scale factor.]

[Ask] "What does it mean when someone says that one object is 'twice as big' as another?" [It could mean having twice the linear dimensions, twice the area, or twice the volume. If it means twice the linear dimensions, then the larger object has four times the area and eight times the volume.] If you don't plan to assign the Exploration Why Elephants Have Big Ears, you might want to discuss some of the questions raised in it at this time.

BUILDING UNDERSTANDING

Have students pay close attention to whether they are comparing large to small or small to large. In the investigations they compared large to small with integer ratios, but the exercises mix it up and use non-integer ratios.

ASSIGNING HOMEWORK

Essential	1–8, 10–16, 18
Portfolio	8, 19, 20
Journal	9
Group	17
Review	21–28

9. See page 596 for solution.

Assessing Progress

You can assess students' understanding of scale factor, area, and volume and of how similar figures can be formed by multiplying all dimensions. You can also check their ability to measure lengths and calculate ratios.

Closing the Lesson

The main mathematical point of this lesson is that if two figures are similar then the ratio of any corresponding two-dimensional parts is the square of the scale factor, and the ratio of any corresponding three-dimensional parts is the cube of the scale factor. You might summarize with the equation ratio of sizes of n-dimensional parts = (scale factor)^n.

▶Helping with the Exercises

Many of these exercises can be solved in several ways, both algebraic and intuitive. **[Alert]** Students often have trouble deciding which dimension(s) to square or cube, and they sometimes "unsquare" by halving instead of by taking a square root.

Exercise 5 In Lesson 11.4, students learned that the lengths of some corresponding parts of similar triangles are proportional to the lengths of corresponding sides. This problem extends the idea to diagonals of a kite. In this particular case, you can justify extending the conjecture because the diagonals of a kite create similar triangles.

Exercise 9 **[ESL]** *Ad* is a shorter word for *advertisement.*

9. Possible answer: Assuming the ad is sold by area, Annie should charge $6000.

Exercise 11 This exercise asks students to verify that the Proportional Volumes Conjecture applies to cones. They can use the Pythagorean Theorem to find *H,* from which they can find *h* by calculating the scale factor.

Exercise 13 **[Alert]** Some students may not recall how to find the volume of a cylinder. [area of base · height]

Exercise 15 A formula-based teaching approach would have students solve the equation $\left(\frac{h}{H}\right)^3 = \frac{8}{125}$ for $\frac{h}{H}$. For an approach that builds understanding, **[Ask]** "How is the ratio of one-dimensional parts related to the ratio of three-dimensional parts?"

10. The pentagonal pyramids are similar.

$\frac{h}{H} = \frac{4}{7}$

Volume of large pyramid = ? 1715 cm³

Volume of small pyramid = 320 cm³

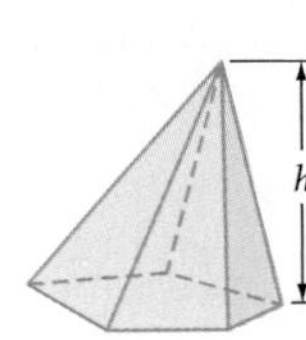

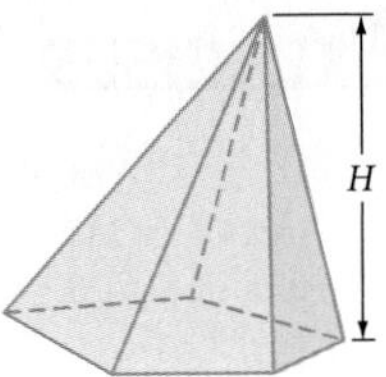

11. These right cones are similar.

$H =$?, $h =$? 16 cm, 4 cm

Volume of large cone = ? 768π cm³ ≈ 2412.7 cm³

Volume of small cone = ? 12π cm³ ≈ 37.7 cm³

$\frac{\text{Volume of large cone}}{\text{Volume of small cone}} =$? $\frac{64}{1}$

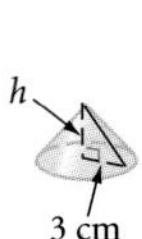

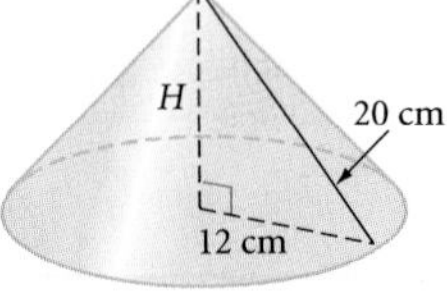

12. These right trapezoidal prisms are similar.

Volume of small prism = 324 cm³

$\frac{\text{Area of base of small prism}}{\text{Area of base of large prism}} = \frac{9}{25}$

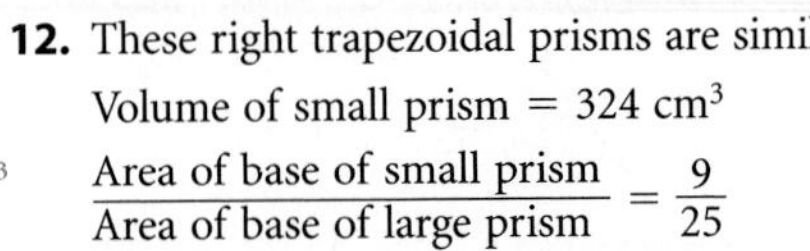

$\frac{h}{H} =$? $\frac{3}{5}$

$\frac{\text{Volume of large prism}}{\text{Volume of small prism}} =$? $\frac{125}{27}$

Volume of large prism = ? ⓗ 1500 cm³

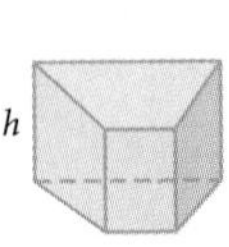

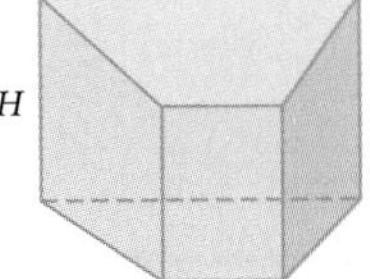

13. These right cylinders are similar.

Volume of large cylinder = 4608π ft³

Volume of small cylinder = ? 1944π ft³ ≈ 6107.3 ft³

$\frac{\text{Volume of large cylinder}}{\text{Volume of small cylinder}} =$? $\left(\frac{H}{24}\right)^3 = \frac{64}{27}$

$H =$? 32 ft

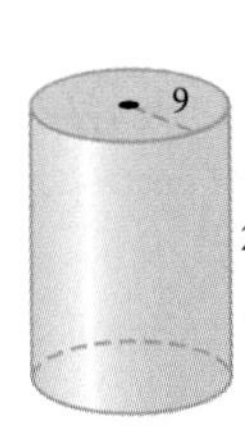

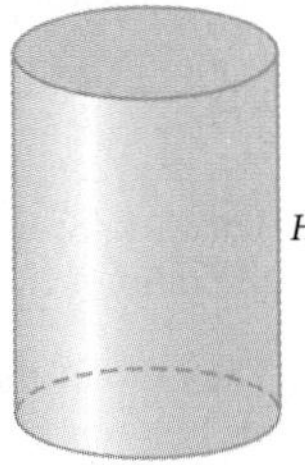

14. The ratio of the lengths of corresponding edges of two similar triangular prisms is $\frac{5}{3}$. What is the ratio of their volumes? $\frac{125}{27}$

15. The ratio of the volumes of two similar pentagonal prisms is $\frac{8}{125}$. What is the ratio of their heights? $\frac{2}{5}$

16. The ratio of the weights of two spherical steel balls is $\frac{8}{27}$. What is the ratio of their diameters? $\frac{2}{3}$

17. APPLICATION The energy (and cost) needed to operate an air conditioner is proportional to the volume of the space that is being cooled. It costs ZAP Electronics about $125 per day to run an air conditioner in their small rectangular warehouse. The company's large warehouse, a few blocks away, is 2.5 times as long, wide, and high as the small warehouse. Estimate the daily cost of cooling the large warehouse with the same model of air conditioner. ⓗ $1953.13

Exercises 16, 18 Although weight, which depends on the force of gravity, is not the same as mass, weight is still proportional to volume for objects made of the same material.

Exercise 17 This model assumes that the cost of cooling a space is proportional to its volume, which (because the shapes of the warehouses are similar) is proportional to the cube of the scale factor.

18. APPLICATION A sculptor creates a small bronze statue that weighs 38 lb. She plans to make a version that will be four times as large in each dimension. How much will this larger statue weigh if it is also bronze? 2432 lb

This bronze sculpture by Camille Claudel (1864–1943) is titled *La Petite Chatelaine.* Claudel was a notable French artist and student of Auguste Rodin, whose famous sculptures include *The Thinker.*

19. A tabloid magazine at a supermarket checkout exclaims, "Scientists Breed 4-Foot Tall Chicken." A photo shows a giant chicken that supposedly weighs 74 pounds and will solve the world's hunger problem. What do you think about this headline? Assuming an average chicken stands 14 inches tall and weighs 7 pounds, would a 4-foot chicken weigh 74 pounds? Is it possible for a chicken to be 4 feet tall? Explain your reasoning.

20. The African goliath frog shown in this photo is the largest known frog—about 0.3 m long and 3.2 kg in weight. The Brazilian gold frog is one of the smallest known frogs—about 9.8 mm long. Approximate the weight of a gold frog. What assumptions do you need to make? Explain your reasoning.

20. Possible answer: Assuming the body types of the goliath frog and the gold frog are similar, the gold frog would weigh about 0.0001 kg, or 0.1 g.

Review

11.1 **21.** Make four copies of the trapezoid at right. Arrange them into a similar but larger trapezoid. Sketch the final trapezoid and show how the smaller trapezoids fit inside it.

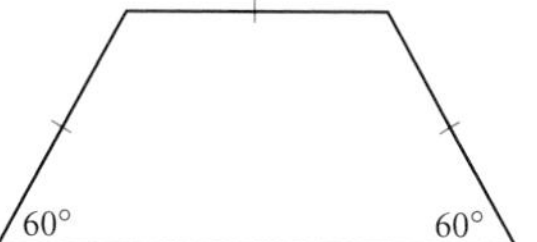

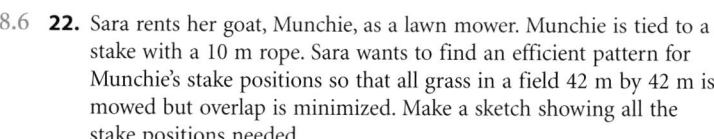

8.6 **22.** Sara rents her goat, Munchie, as a lawn mower. Munchie is tied to a stake with a 10 m rope. Sara wants to find an efficient pattern for Munchie's stake positions so that all grass in a field 42 m by 42 m is mowed but overlap is minimized. Make a sketch showing all the stake positions needed.

Exercise 19 The thinking students do to answer the last question in this exercise is good preparation for the Exploration Why Elephants Have Big Ears. **[ESL]** A *tabloid magazine* publishes sensational stories that are unusual, outrageous, exaggerated, and often not true.

19. Possible answer: No, a 4-foot chicken, similar to a 14-inch 7-pound chicken, would weigh approximately 282 pounds $\left(\frac{14^3}{48^3} = \frac{7}{x}\right)$. It is unlikely that the legs of the giant chicken would be able to support its weight.

Exercise 21 As needed, **[Ask]** "Can you tell anything about the side lengths of the larger trapezoid?" [Because the trapezoids are similar and the ratio of areas is 4, the ratio of side lengths will be 2.]

21.

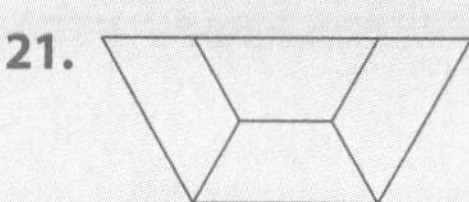

22.

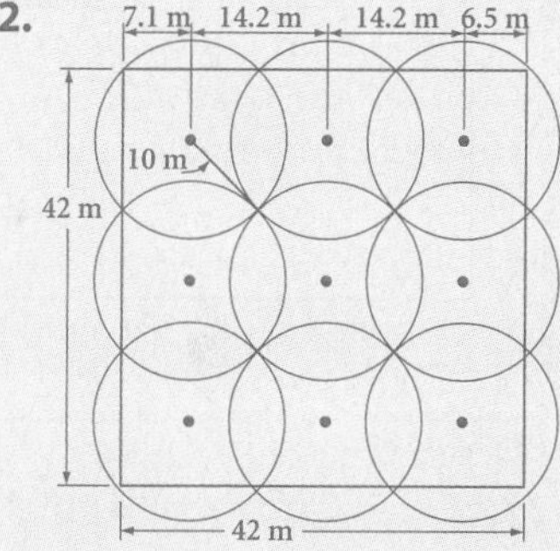

EXTENSIONS

A. Discuss with students the inverse square law in reference to gravitational attraction and to the intensity of light from the sun. [These laws seem to be analogous to the Proportional Areas Conjecture.]

Extensions (continued)

B. Have students investigate the dimensions of the Sierpiński triangle from Chapter 2. [Students can use the relationship:
ratio of sizes of n-dimensional parts = (scale factor)^n
with the understanding that the ratio of the fractal to the next-smaller similar piece (which must have the same dimension) is 3, whereas the corresponding scale factor is 2, so the equation becomes $3 = 2^n$. By approximations or logarithms, the dimension n can be found to be about 1.58.]

C. Ask students to present an algebraic argument showing that if two triangles have lengths of corresponding sides in the ratio $\frac{a}{b}$, then their areas are in the ratio $\left(\frac{a}{b}\right)^2$. [If the base and height of one triangle are B and H, then $\frac{a}{b}B$ and $\frac{a}{b}H$ are the base and height of the other triangle. Its area, then, is $\frac{1}{2}\left(\frac{a}{b}B\right)\left(\frac{a}{b}H\right) = \left(\frac{a}{b}\right)^2\frac{1}{2}BH$, which is $\left(\frac{a}{b}\right)^2$ times the area of the first triangle.]

Exercise 23 If students are having difficulty, ask if they know anything about right triangles with side lengths 3 and 5.

Exercise 24 Students may get hung up trying to find lengths of the diagonals or of pieces of them. Lead them to focus on what they can say about trapezoid and triangle midsegments from the information given.

Exercise 26 Encourage a variety of approaches. Students might use Hero's formula. Or they might draw an altitude to the base of this isosceles triangle and recognize a Pythagorean triplet or use the Pythagorean Theorem to find the third side.

Exercise 27 A cross section is parallel to the base.

Graphs for the Project
In the graph (shorter side, longer side), the slope of the line of best fit represents the ratio of sides.

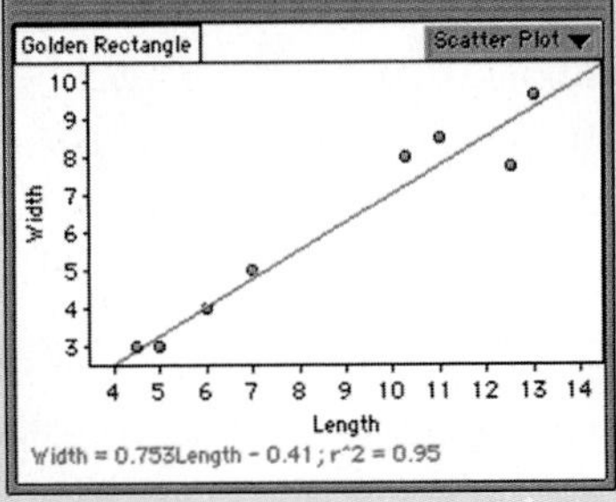

For other graphs, see page 775.

Golden Rectangle Extensions

A. Construct golden rectangles and golden spirals using construction tools or geometry software.

B. How are Fibonacci numbers related to the golden ratio?

11.2 **23.** $x = \underline{?}$, $y = \underline{?}$ $\frac{16}{3}, \frac{20}{3}$

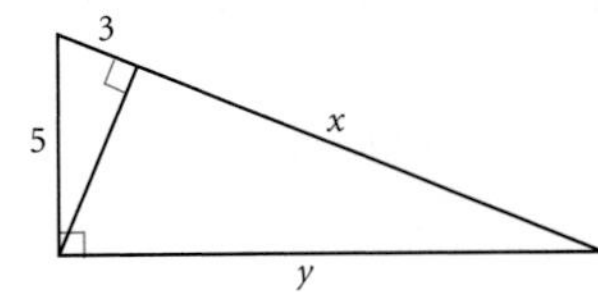

11.2 **24.** $XY = \underline{?}$ 8

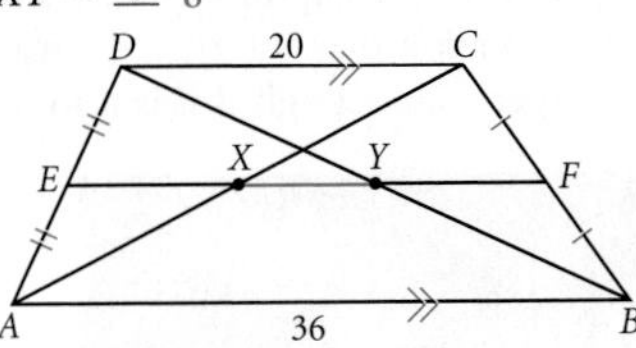

8.5 **25.** Find the area of a regular decagon with an apothem 5.7 cm and a perimeter 37 cm. 105.45 cm²

8.2 **26.** Find the area of a triangle whose sides measure 13 feet, 13 feet, and 10 feet. ⓗ 60 ft²

10.1 **27.** True or false? Every cross section of a pyramid has the same shape as, but a different size from the base. ⓗ true

11.2 **28.** What's wrong with this picture?

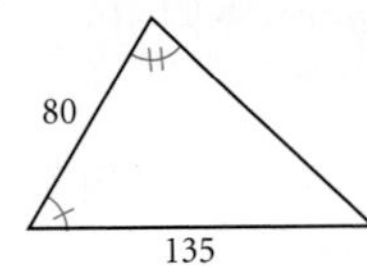

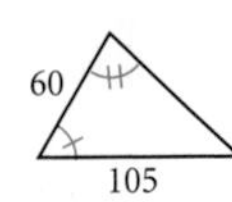

Two angles are congruent, so the triangles are similar by the AA Similarity Conjecture. However, the two sets of corresponding sides are not proportional $\left(\frac{60}{80} \neq \frac{105}{135}\right)$, so the triangles are not similar.

project

IN SEARCH OF THE PERFECT RECTANGLE

A square is a perfectly symmetric quadrilateral. Yet, people rarely make books, posters, or magazines that are square. Instead, most people seem to prefer rectangles. In fact, some people believe that a particular type of rectangle is more appealing because its proportions fit the golden ratio. You can learn more about the historical importance of the golden ratio by doing research with the links at **www.keymath.com/DG** .

Do people have a tendency to choose a particular length/width ratio when they design or build common objects? Find at least ten different rectangular objects in your classroom or home: books, postcards, desks, doors, and other everyday items. Measure the longer side and the shorter side of each one. Predict what a graph of your data will look like.

Now graph your data. Is there a pattern? Find the line of best fit. How well does it fit the data? What is the range of length/width ratios? What ratio do points on the line of best fit represent?

Your project should include

- A table and graph of your data.
- Your predictions and your analysis.
- A paragraph explaining your opinion about whether or not people have a tendency to choose a particular type of rectangle and why.

Fathom™
You can use Fathom to graph your data and find the line of best fit. Choose different types of graphs to get other insights into what your data mean.

Supporting the project

A golden rectangle has a ratio of longer side to shorter side of the golden ratio (approximately 1.618). The side lengths of a golden rectangle satisfy the proportion: $\frac{l}{w} = \frac{w+l}{l}$. Drawing a square on the longer side of a golden rectangle produces a larger golden rectangle, which is similar.

OUTCOMES

- The table of measured objects and the graph of data with the line of best fit are complete. The graph as shown may compare the shorter side to the longer side or compare the length-width ratio to one of the sides.
- The equation of the line of best fit is used to make predictions.
- It is unlikely that students will find the golden ratio, but their explanation might mention it.
  - Predictions are checked with the measurements of other rectangles.
  - Other representations of the data are included.
  - Students combine or gather more data.

Exploration

Why Elephants Have Big Ears

The relationship between surface area and volume is of critical importance to all living things. It explains why elephants have big ears, why hippos and rhinos have short, thick legs and must spend a lot of time in water, and why movie monsters like King Kong and Godzilla can't exist.

Activity
Convenient Sizes

Body Temperature

Every living thing processes food for energy. This energy creates heat that radiates from its surface.

Step 1 Imagine two similar animals, one with dimensions three times as large as those of the other.

Step 2 How would the surface areas of these two animals compare? How much more heat could the larger animal radiate through its surface?

Step 3 How would the volumes of these two animals compare? If the animals' bodies produce energy in proportion to their volumes, how many times as much heat would the larger animal produce?

Step 4 Review your answers from Steps 2 and 3. How many times as much heat must each square centimeter of the larger animal radiate? Would this be good or bad?

Step 5 Use what you have concluded to answer these questions. Consider size, surface area, and volume.

a. Why do large objects cool more slowly than similar small objects?

b. Why is a beached whale more likely than a beached dolphin to experience overheating? A larger object cools more slowly than a smaller object.

c. Why are larger mammals found closer to the poles than the equator?

d. If a woman and a small child fall into a cold lake, why is the child in greater danger of hypothermia? A smaller person cools quicker than a larger person.

Step 2 Ratio of surface areas is 1:9. It could radiate 9 times the heat.

Step 3 Ratio of volumes is 1:27. It could produce 27 times the heat.

Step 4 Each square centimeter radiates 3 times more heat. This is bad; a large animal would more easily overheat.

Step 5a Going back to the example of an animal with dimensions 3 times larger means its surface area is 9 times larger and its volume and amount of heat produced is 27 times larger. Therefore each square unit of surface must radiate 3 times as much heat as the smaller animal. So the larger animal cools more slowly.

Step 5c It is cooler near the poles.

NCTM STANDARDS

CONTENT		PROCESS	
✓	Number	✓	Problem Solving
✓	Algebra		Reasoning
✓	Geometry	✓	Communication
✓	Measurement	✓	Connections
	Data/Probability		Representation

LESSON OBJECTIVES

- Examine the plausibility of giant creatures
- Explore the relationship between size and function in living creatures

EXPLORATION

PLANNING

LESSON OUTLINE

One day:

30 min Activity

10 min Sharing

5 min Closing

MATERIALS

- biology and physics reference books, *optional*

TEACHING

In this exploration, students see and write about applications—in science and art—of the Proportional Areas and Proportional Volumes Conjectures.

You could have all students work through all three parts of the activity or divide the three parts among the groups and have groups report their ideas during Sharing. You might want to have some biology and physics books available for reference.

Guiding the Activity

Step 1 If students have trouble imagining similar creatures with such different body sizes, you might refer them to the frogs described in Exercise 20 of Lesson 11.5.

Step 5 Encourage lots of discussion to help students realize that smaller objects have more surface area per unit of volume than do larger objects, so they cool faster. In symbols, if s is the scale factor between two similar objects (with $s > 1$), then the ratio of surface area to volume of the larger object is $\frac{s^2}{s^3} = \frac{1}{s}$, which is less than 1 times the ratio of surface area to volume of the smaller object. Students may

Step 5 (continued)
argue that bodies of young and adult animals aren't really similar in shape. Although they are correct, an assumption of similarity within each species is good enough for the general discussion here.

[Language] *Hypothermia* is a condition in which the body becomes too cold to sustain life. For part f, note that elephant ears are thin and therefore provide more surface area (for cooling) with relatively little increase in volume (which would generate more heat).

Step 7 Cross sections of bones are considered to be approximately perpendicular to the length. Students can assume similarity in the shapes of the two people compared in this step.

Steps 7, 8 As needed, keep stressing the general principles regarding size ratios for similar figures: The ratio of two-dimensional parts (including surface area) is the square of the scale factor, and the ratio of three-dimensional parts (including volume) is the cube of the scale factor.

Step 9 It is estimated that the human thighbone breaks under 10 times the human body weight.

Dalí's Program Cover
The weight of a heavy body could not stand on spindly legs; the cover evokes imagination.

Students interested in literary or performing arts could research the story of *As You Like It,* or this particular production of the ballet, and then explain why Dalí might have chosen elephants to illustrate the program. **[Ask]** "Where else in the visual arts, the movies, or literature have you seen or read of impossible creatures?" For students interested in the visual arts, suggest research on Salvador Dalí or other artists who have used imaginary or impossible creatures. Students could also investigate stories about Paul Bunyan, or read or see the movie version of *Gulliver's Travels* by Jonathan Swift or *Fantastic Voyage,* about people in a ship traveling through a human body. Keep having students return to the question of why these larger (or smaller) but similar creatures are physically impossible.

Step 5e The smaller iguana will become active first because it warms more quickly. The larger iguana will remain active longer after sunset because it cools more slowly.

e. When the weather is cold, iguanas hardly move. When it warms up, they become active. If a small iguana and a large iguana are sunning themselves in the morning sun, which one will become active first? Why? Which iguana will remain active longer after sunset? Why?

f. Why do elephants have big ears? The large surface area cools their body.

Bone and Muscle Strength

The strength of a bone or a muscle is proportional to its cross-sectional area.

Step 6 Imagine a 7-foot-tall basketball player and a 42-inch-tall child. How would the dimensions of the bones of the basketball player compare to the corresponding bones of the child? 2:1

Step 7 How would the cross-sectional areas of their corresponding bones compare? 4:1

Step 8 How would their weights compare? 8:1

Step 9 Two times as much weight. Since basketball players tend to be thin, it is unlikely the athlete would weigh 8 times that of the child.

Step 9 How many times as much weight would each cross-sectional square inch of bone have to support in the basketball player? What are some factors that may explain why basketball players' bones don't usually break?

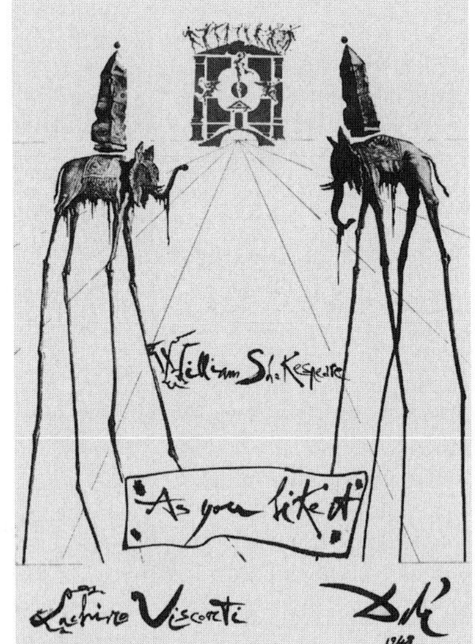

The Spanish artist Salvador Dalí (1904–1989) designed this cover for a 1948 program of the ballet *As You Like It.* What is the effect created by the elephants on long spindly legs? Could these animals really exist? Explain.

LESSON

11.6 Proportional Segments Between Parallel Lines

Mistakes are the portals of discovery.

JAMES JOYCE

In the figure below, $\overleftrightarrow{MT} \parallel \overline{LU}$. Is $\triangle LUV$ similar to $\triangle MTV$? Yes, it is. A short paragraph proof can support this observation.

Given: $\triangle LUV$ with $\overleftrightarrow{MT} \parallel \overline{LU}$

Show: $\triangle LUV \sim \triangle MTV$

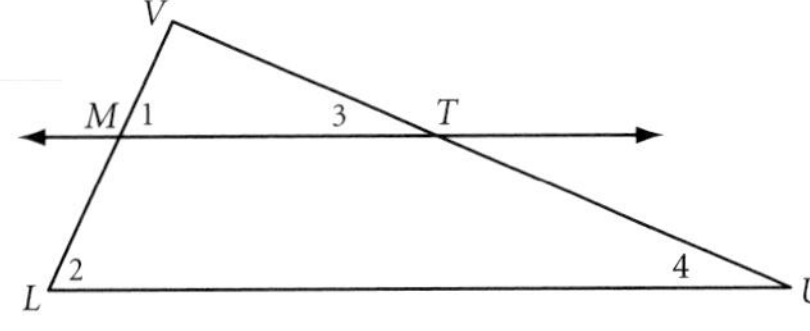

Paragraph Proof

First assume that the Corresponding Angles Conjecture and the AA Similarity Conjecture are true.

If $\overleftrightarrow{MT} \parallel \overline{LU}$, then $\angle 1 \cong \angle 2$ and $\angle 3 \cong \angle 4$ by the Corresponding Angles Conjecture.

If $\angle 1 \cong \angle 2$ and $\angle 3 \cong \angle 4$, then $\triangle LUV \sim \triangle MTV$ by the AA Similarity Conjecture. ■

Let's see how you can use this observation to solve problems.

EXAMPLE A

$\overline{EO} \parallel \overline{LN}$

$y = \underline{\ ?\ }$

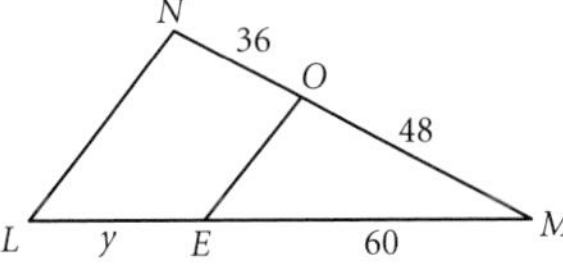

▶ Solution

Use the fact that $\triangle EMO \sim \triangle LMN$ to write a proportion with the lengths of corresponding sides.

$\frac{MO}{MN} = \frac{ME}{ML}$	Corresponding sides of similar triangles are proportional.
$\frac{48}{48 + 36} = \frac{60}{60 + y}$	Substitute lengths given in the figure.
$\frac{4}{7} = \frac{60}{60 + y}$	Reduce the left side of the equation.
$240 + 4y = 420$	Multiply both sides by $7(60 + y)$, reduce, and distribute.
$4y = 180$	Subtract 240 from both sides.
$y = 45$	Divide by 4.

Look back at the figure in Example A. Notice that the ratio $\frac{LE}{EM}$ is the same as the ratio $\frac{NO}{OM}$. So there are more relationships in the figure than the ones we find in similar triangles. Let's investigate.

NCTM STANDARDS

CONTENT		PROCESS	
	Number	✓	Problem Solving
	Algebra	✓	Reasoning
✓	Geometry	✓	Communication
✓	Measurement		Connections
	Data/Probability	✓	Representation

LESSON OBJECTIVES

- Discover the relationship between the ratios of the parts into which parallel lines cut the sides of a triangle
- Extend the Parallel/Proportionality Conjecture to include multiple parallel lines
- Discover a construction method for dividing a segment into proportional parts

LESSON 11.6

PLANNING

LESSON OUTLINE

One day:

30 min	Investigation and Examples
5 min	Sharing
5 min	Closing
5 min	Exercises

MATERIALS

- construction tools
- rulers
- protractors

TEACHING

Students find that lines parallel to one side of a triangle divide the other two sides proportionally and that this fact can be used to divide any segment into any number of congruent pieces. Start with Example A or the one-step investigation on page 604.

Some students may recall the opening proof from Exercise 9 in Lesson 11.2, where they followed all the necessary steps without actually writing a proof.

▶ EXAMPLE A

You might ask students to solve the proportion another way in order to practice their algebra skills. For example, they might invert during the first or second step to get $\frac{48 + 36}{48} = \frac{60 + y}{60}$ and rewrite this as $1 + \frac{36}{48} = 1 + \frac{y}{60}$. Subtracting 1 from both sides and then multiplying by 60 gives a value for y.

One step Pose this problem: "We learned long ago how to use a perpendicular bisector to divide a segment into two congruent pieces. If you kept bisecting the smaller segments, you could divide the segment into 4, 8, 16, and so on congruent parts. In Exercise 16 of Lesson 11.4, you saw how to divide a segment into parts with lengths in the ratio 2:3, and from that you could bisect the shorter piece and lay it out so as to divide the original segment into five congruent pieces. But that approach is unwieldy. Is there a good method for dividing a segment into any number of congruent parts?" As you circulate, if needed, suggest similar triangles. You might encourage groups that finish first to try to write up paragraph proofs of their methods, perhaps referring them back to Exercise 9 in Lesson 11.2. During Sharing, a group that did not write up a proof can present its method, followed by a group that proved the correctness of that method.

Guiding Investigation 1

Step 1 If time is limited, you can distribute parts a, b, and c among groups. Color coding the segments may help visual learners.

Step 2 Students might say that the lengths are proportional or that the ratios of the lengths are equal.

Steps 4, 5 These steps can be completed by using a ruler or by marking off equal units with a compass.

Step 5 You might shorten the investigation by asking different groups to use different lengths as suggested in Step 8 instead of having each group repeat Steps 3–7.

Investigation 1
Parallels and Proportionality

You will need

- a ruler
- a protractor

In this investigation, we'll look at the ratios of segments that have been cut by parallel lines.

Step 1 In each figure below, find x. Then find numerical values for the ratios.

a. $\overleftrightarrow{EC} \parallel \overline{AB}$

$x = \underline{?}$ 24

$\frac{DE}{AE} = \underline{?}$, $\frac{DC}{BC} = \underline{?}$

$\frac{8}{16} = \frac{1}{2}$ $\quad \frac{12}{24} = \frac{1}{2}$

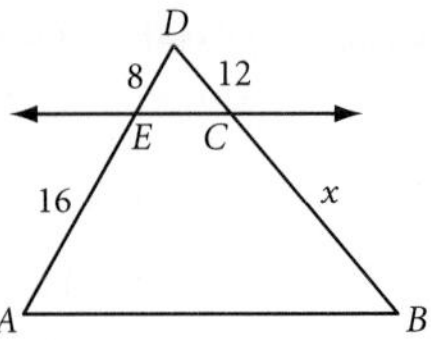

b. $\overleftrightarrow{KH} \parallel \overline{FG}$

$x = \underline{?}$ 36

$\frac{JK}{KF} = \underline{?}$, $\frac{JH}{HG} = \underline{?}$

$\frac{24}{8} = \frac{3}{1}$ $\quad \frac{36}{12} = \frac{3}{1}$

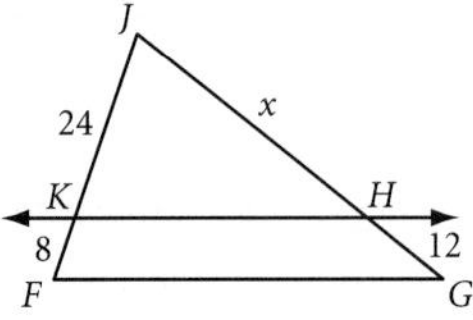

c. $\overleftrightarrow{QN} \parallel \overline{LM}$

$x = \underline{?}$ 36

$\frac{PQ}{QL} = \underline{?}$, $\frac{PN}{MN} = \underline{?}$

$\frac{20}{36} = \frac{5}{9}$ $\quad \frac{25}{45} = \frac{5}{9}$

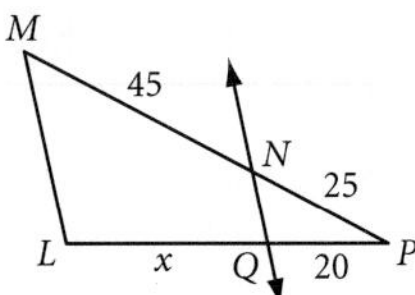

Step 2 What do you notice about the ratios of the lengths of the segments that have been cut by the parallel lines? They are equal.

Is the converse true? That is, if a line divides two sides of a triangle proportionally, is it parallel to the third side? Let's see.

Step 3 Draw an acute angle, P.

Step 4 Beginning at point P, use your ruler to mark off lengths of 8 cm and 10 cm on one ray. Label the points A and B.

Step 5 Mark off lengths of 12 cm and 15 cm on the other ray. Label the points C and D. Notice that $\frac{8}{10} = \frac{12}{15}$.

Step 6 Draw $\overline{AC}$ and $\overline{BD}$.

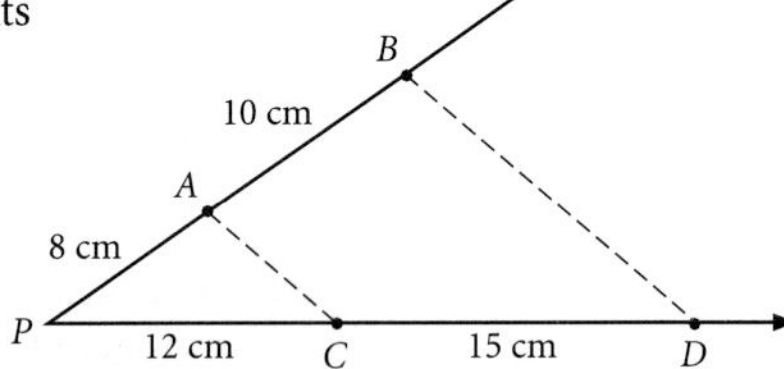

Step 7 With a protractor, measure $\angle PAC$ and $\angle PBD$. Are $\overline{AC}$ and $\overline{BD}$ parallel? yes

Step 8 Repeat Steps 3–7, but this time use your ruler to create your own lengths such that $\frac{PA}{AB} = \frac{PC}{CD}$.

Step 8 Possible answer: Segments of 6 cm, 8 cm, 12 cm, and 16 cm will give $\frac{6}{8} = \frac{12}{16}$.

Step 9 Compare your results with the results of others near you.

You should be ready to combine your observations from Steps 2 and 9 into one conjecture.

Parallel/Proportionality Conjecture C-100

If a line parallel to one side of a triangle passes through the other two sides, then it divides the other two sides __?__ (proportionally). Conversely, if a line cuts two sides of a triangle proportionally, then it is __?__ (parallel) to the third side.

Step 7 Students can determine the congruence of these angles without measuring; they are corresponding angles of triangles that are similar by SAS. As needed, **[Ask]** "Why are the lines parallel?" [by the Corresponding Angles Conjecture]

Step 10 This conjecture is also known as the *side splitter conjecture.*

If you assume that the AA Similarity Conjecture is true, you can use algebra to prove the Parallel/Proportionality Conjecture. Here's the first part.

EXAMPLE B

Given: $\triangle ABC$ with $\overleftrightarrow{XY} \parallel \overline{BC}$

Show: $\frac{a}{c} = \frac{b}{d}$

(Assume that the lengths a, b, c, and d are all nonzero.)

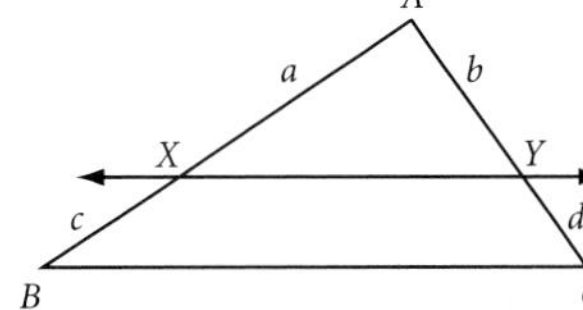

▶ *Solution*

First, you know that $\triangle AXY \sim \triangle ABC$ (see the proof on page 603). Use a proportion of corresponding sides.

$\frac{a}{a+c} = \frac{b}{b+d}$	Lengths of corresponding sides of similar triangles are proportional.
$\frac{a(a+c)(b+d)}{(a+c)} = \frac{b(a+c)(b+d)}{(b+d)}$	Multiply both sides by $(a+c)(b+d)$.
$a(b+d) = b(a+c)$	Reduce.
$ab + ad = ba + bc$	Apply the distributive property.
$ab + ad = ab + bc$	Commute ba to ab.
$ad = bc$	Subtract ab from both sides.
$\frac{ad}{cd} = \frac{bc}{cd}$	We want c and d in the denominator, so divide both sides by cd.
$\frac{a}{c} = \frac{b}{d}$	Reduce.

You'll prove the converse of the Parallel/Proportionality Conjecture in Exercise 18.

Can the Parallel/Proportionality Conjecture help you divide segments into several proportional parts? Let's investigate.

▶ ***EXAMPLE B***

This example provides a proof of the Parallel/Proportionality Conjecture. You might ask students to solve the equation in a different way. Here's one alternative: Because the denominator contains a sum, invert both sides and distribute to get $1 + \frac{c}{a} = 1 + \frac{d}{b}$. Subtracting 1 and inverting again gives the desired equation.

Guiding Investigation 2

Students might separate the nested triangles and label the sides to help them see the similarity behind the equations.

▶ EXAMPLE C

This example is an application of the Extended Parallel/Proportionality Conjecture to a case in which the parallel lines intercept congruent segments.

SHARING IDEAS

After students present their ideas about Investigation 1, ask how they can prove that $\frac{8}{10} = \frac{12}{15}$. One approach is to reduce both sides to $\frac{4}{5}$, reasoning, in effect, that $\frac{8}{10} = \frac{4}{5}$ and $\frac{12}{15} = \frac{4}{5}$, so $\frac{8}{10} = \frac{12}{15}$. Or students can multiply both parts of the left-hand side by 1.5, with the underlying reasoning that $\frac{8}{10} = \frac{8}{10} \cdot 1 = \frac{8}{10} \cdot \frac{1.5}{1.5} = \frac{12}{15}$.

In contrast, a logically invalid proof uses cross multiplication. Its underlying reasoning is that if $\frac{8}{10} = \frac{12}{15}$, then $8 \cdot 15 = 12 \cdot 10$, so $120 = 120$. You might remind students of the exploration on forms of valid reasoning at the end of Chapter 10 and point out that starting with what you want to prove and reaching a true statement, then affirming your assumption is true has the invalid form "If *P*, then *Q*; *Q*; therefore *P*."

Students might be familiar with the analogous invalid reasoning in verifying a solution to an algebraic equation, showing, for example, that -2 is a solution to equation $\sqrt{x+3} = -1$:

$\sqrt{-2+3} = -1$	assumed
$-2 + 3 = 1$	square both sides
$1 = 1$	arithmetic

To conclude that -2 is a solution to the equation is invalid. In fact, it's not a solution; the left side is the square root of a negative number.

Investigation 2
Extended Parallel/Proportionality

Step 1 Use the Parallel/Proportionality Conjecture to find each missing length. Are the ratios equal?

Step 1a $x = 70, y = 56$

a. $\overline{FT} \parallel \overline{LA} \parallel \overline{GR}$

$x = \underline{?}, y = \underline{?}$

Is $\frac{FL}{LG} = \frac{TA}{AR}$? yes

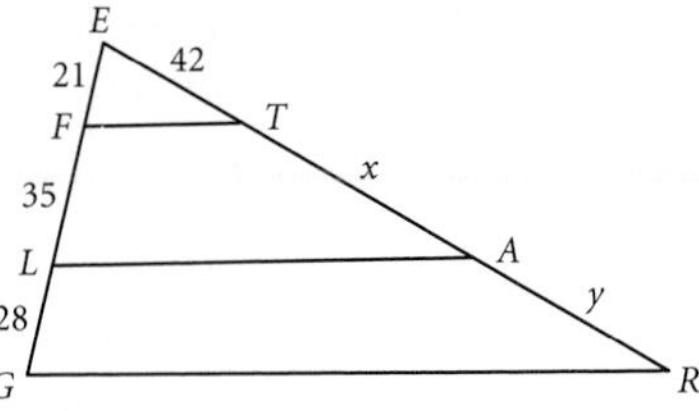

Step 1b $a = 28, b = 35, c = 15$

b. $\overline{ZE} \parallel \overline{OP} \parallel \overline{IA} \parallel \overline{DR}$

$a = \underline{?}, b = \underline{?}, c = \underline{?}$

Is $\frac{DI}{IO} = \frac{RA}{AP}$? Is $\frac{IO}{OZ} = \frac{AP}{PE}$?
yes yes

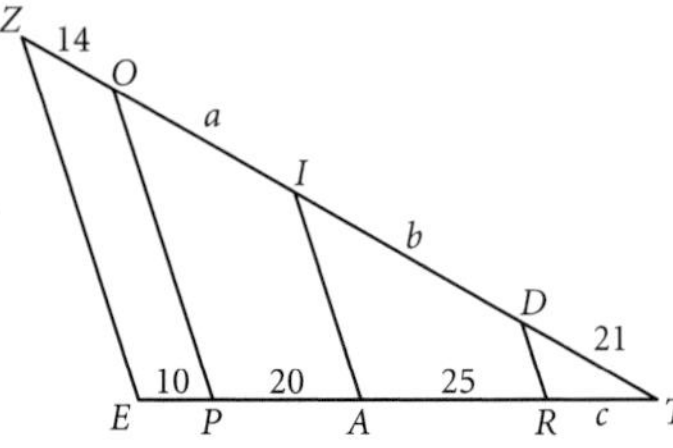

Step 2 Compare your results with the results of others near you. Complete the conjecture below.

> **Extended Parallel/Proportionality Conjecture** C-101
>
> If two or more lines pass through two sides of a triangle parallel to the third side, then they divide the two sides $\underline{?}$. proportionally

Exploring the converse of this conjecture has been left for you as a Take Another Look activity.

You already know how to use a perpendicular bisector to divide a segment into two, four, or eight equal parts. Now you can use your new conjecture to divide a segment into *any* number of equal parts.

EXAMPLE C Divide any segment *AB* into three congruent parts using only a compass and straightedge.

▶ Solution Draw segment *AB*. From one endpoint of $\overline{AB}$, draw any ray to form an angle. On the ray, mark off three congruent segments with your compass. Connect the third compass mark to the other endpoint of $\overline{AB}$ to form a triangle.

Ask students whether they can work backward to produce a valid argument. They might begin with $120 = 120$, rewrite the equation as $8 \cdot 15 = 12 \cdot 10$, divide both sides by 10, and then divide both sides by 15.

Assessing Progress

As you watch students work and present, you can assess their understanding of the Parallel Lines Conjecture, the AA similarity shortcut, and invalid reasoning with conditional sentences. You can also evaluate their ability to follow a paragraph proof, recognize similar triangles when they are nested, construct parallel lines, measure lengths and angles, solve algebraic equations, and calculate and compare ratios.

Finally, through the other two compass marks on the ray, construct lines parallel to the third side of the triangle. The two parallel lines divide $\overline{AB}$ into three equal parts.

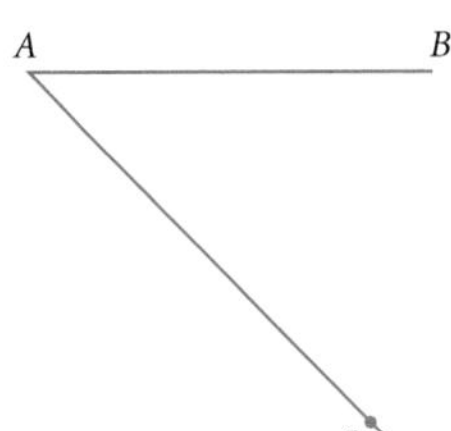

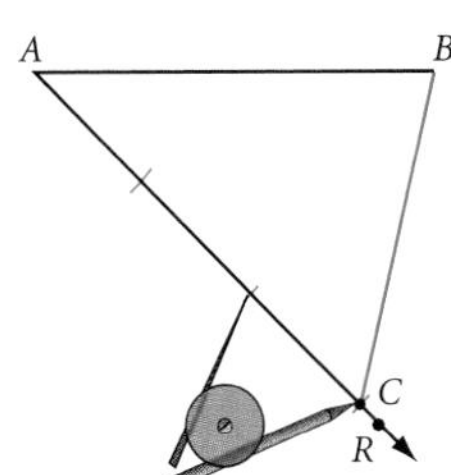

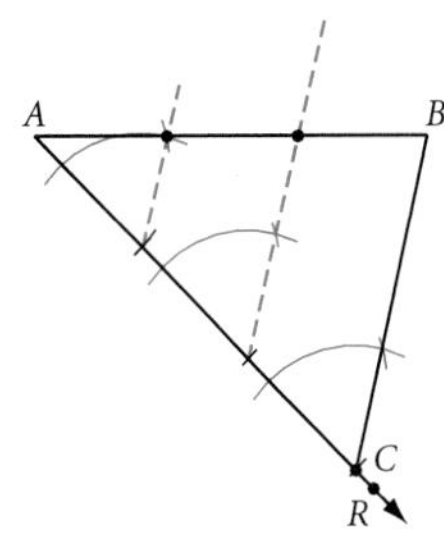

Closing the Lesson

Summarize the main points of the lesson: Lines parallel to one side of a triangle divide the other two sides proportionally, and any segment can be divided into any number of congruent pieces by laying out congruent segments on a ray through an endpoint of the given segment and constructing parallel lines to make similar triangles.

Exercises

You will need

Construction tools for Exercises **13** and **14**

Geometry software for Exercise **26**

For Exercises 1–12, all measurements are in centimeters.

1. $\ell \parallel \overline{WE}$
$a = \underline{?}$ ⓗ 5 cm

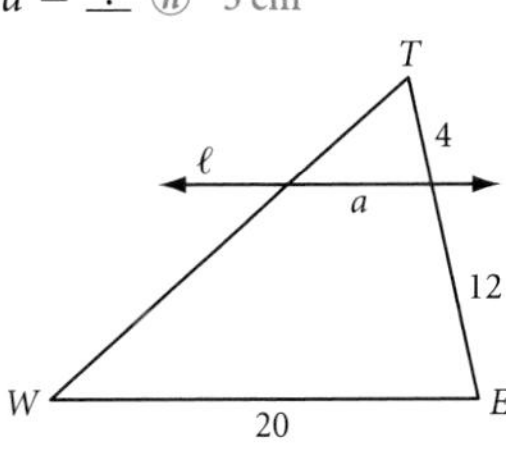

2. $m \parallel \overline{DR}$
$b = \underline{?}$
$33\frac{1}{3}$ cm

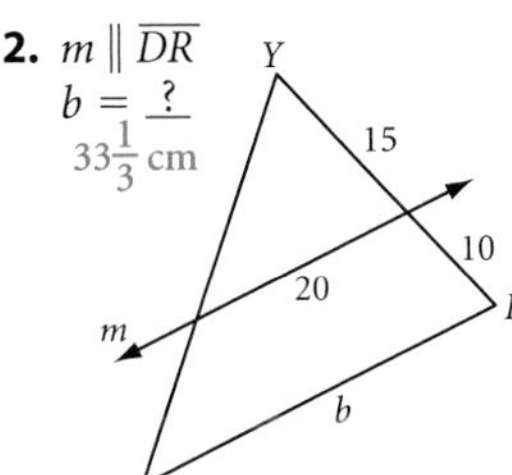

3. $n \parallel \overline{SN}$
$c = \underline{?}$ ⓗ 45 cm

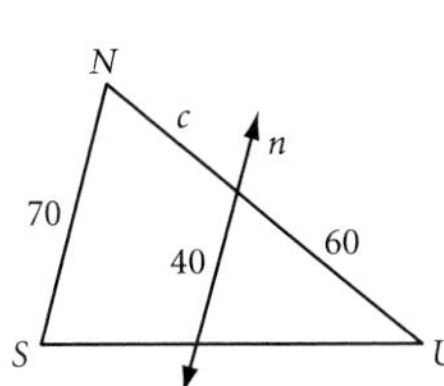

4. $\ell \parallel \overline{RA}$
$d = \underline{?}$ ⓗ 21 cm

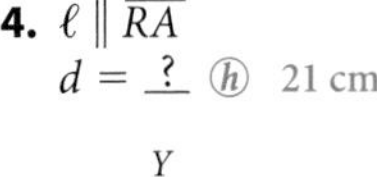
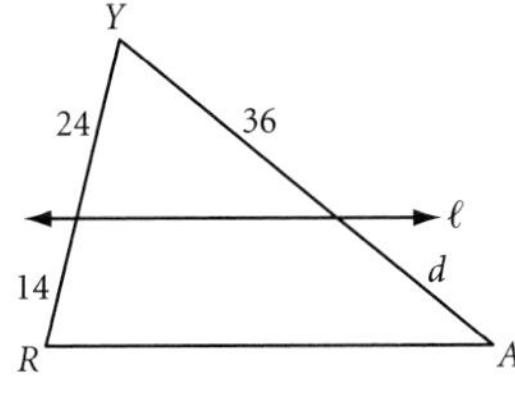

5. $m \parallel \overline{BA}$
$e = \underline{?}$ 28 cm

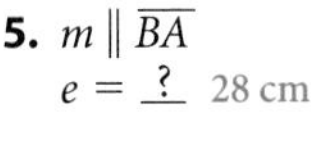
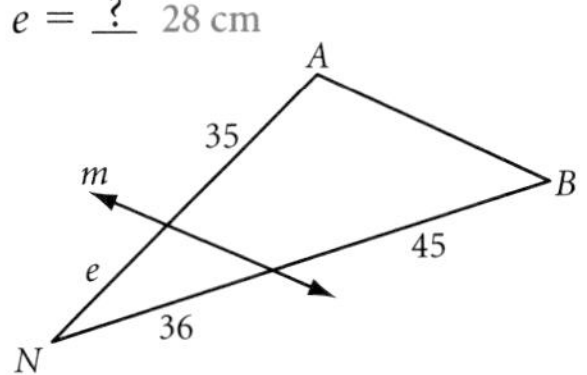

6. Is $r \parallel \overline{AN}$? ⓗ no

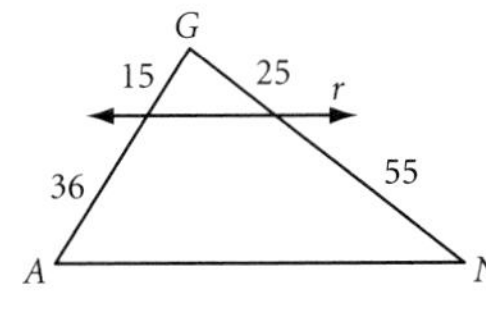

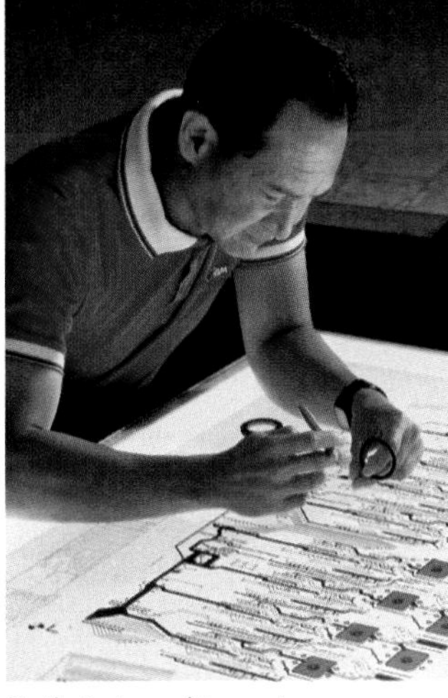

Similarity is used to create integrated circuits. Electrical engineers use large-scale maps of extremely small silicon chips. This engineer is making a scale drawing of a computer chip.

BUILDING UNDERSTANDING

If you think students are not yet comfortable with the Parallel/Proportionality Conjecture, you might have them work a few exercises and share results before students begin work on their own.

ASSIGNING HOMEWORK

Essential	1–21 odds
Performance assessment	21
Portfolio	15
Journal	16
Group	2–20 evens
Review	22–28

Helping with the Exercises

Exercises 1–3 [Alert] Students may neglect to use the entire side lengths in the proportions.

Exercises 8, 9 Students may need help in seeing that they have to set up a separate proportion for each variable. Several different proportions are legitimate.

Exercise 12 Several approaches are possible here. One that uses the Parallel/Proportionality Conjecture is to note that $\frac{a}{b} = \frac{4}{8} = \frac{1}{2}$, so you can find a and b after calculating the total length of the third side by the distance formula. A more complicated method is to determine the coordinates of the intersection point by finding the equations of the lines and then use the distance formula to find a and b. A hybrid approach involves using the conjecture to note that a point moving from (3, 9) to (12, 0) has moved $\frac{2}{3}$ of the way when it reaches the intersection point, so its coordinates are (9, 3). The distance formula will then give the actual lengths.

13.

Exercise 14 As needed, remind students how to construct a regular hexagon inside a circle.

14.

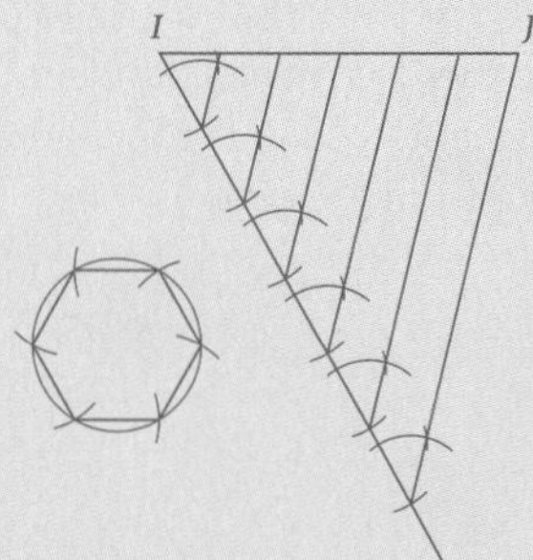

Exercise 15 If students are having difficulty, you might suggest that they visualize the segment as the hypotenuse of a right triangle.

15. Extended Parallel/Proportionality Conjecture

7. Is $m \parallel \overline{FL}$? yes

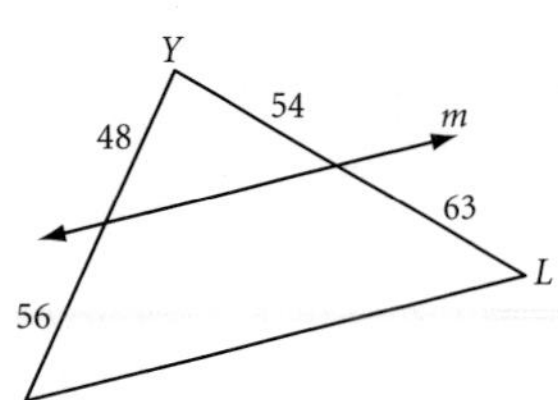

8. $r \parallel s \parallel \overline{OU}$

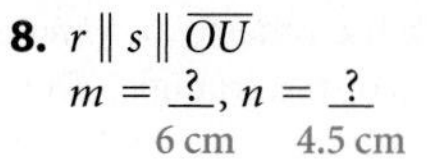

$m = \underline{?}$, $n = \underline{?}$
6 cm 4.5 cm

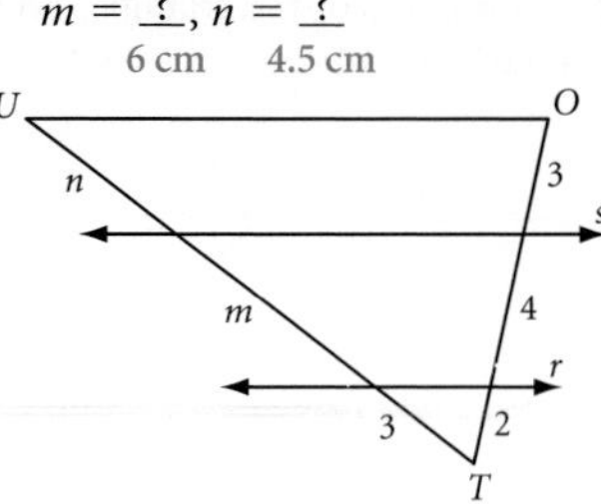

9. $\overline{MR} \parallel p \parallel q$
$w = \underline{?}$, $x = \underline{?}$
$13.\overline{3}$ cm 21.6 cm

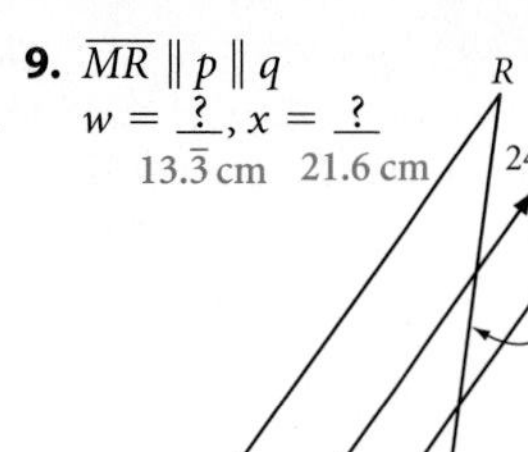

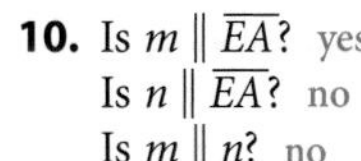

10. Is $m \parallel \overline{EA}$? yes
Is $n \parallel \overline{EA}$? no
Is $m \parallel n$? no

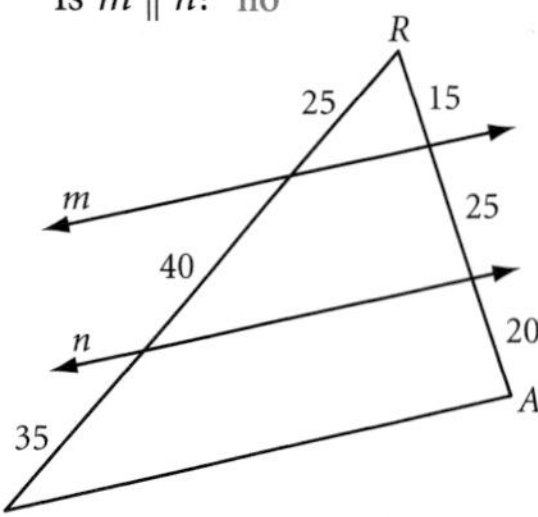

11. Is $\overline{XY} \parallel \overline{GO}$? yes
Is $\overline{XY} \parallel \overline{FR}$? yes
Is $FROG$ a trapezoid? yes

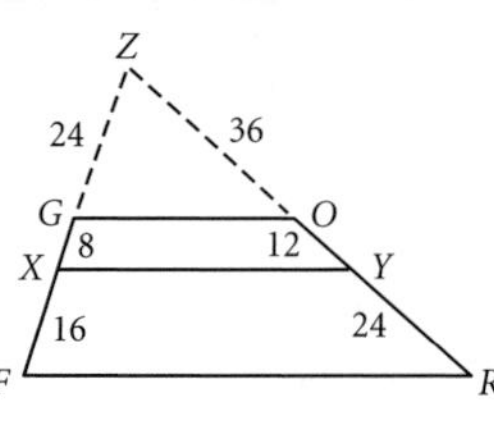

12. $a = \underline{?}$, $b = \underline{?}$ ⓗ
$3\sqrt{2}$ cm $6\sqrt{2}$ cm

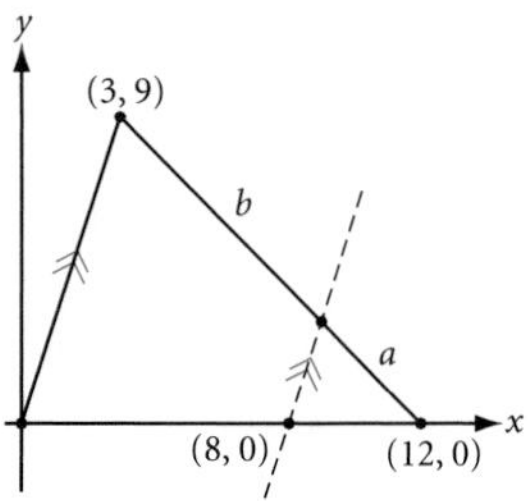

13. ***Construction*** Draw segment EF. Use compass and straightedge to divide it into five equal parts.

14. ***Construction*** Draw segment IJ. Construct a regular hexagon with IJ as the perimeter.

15. You can use a sheet of lined paper to divide a segment into equal parts. Draw a segment on a piece of patty paper, and divide it into five equal parts by placing it over lined paper. What conjecture explains why this works?

16. The drafting tool shown at right is called a sector compass. You position a given segment between the 100-marks. What points on the compass should you connect to construct a segment that is three-fourths (or 75%) of BC? Explain why this works.

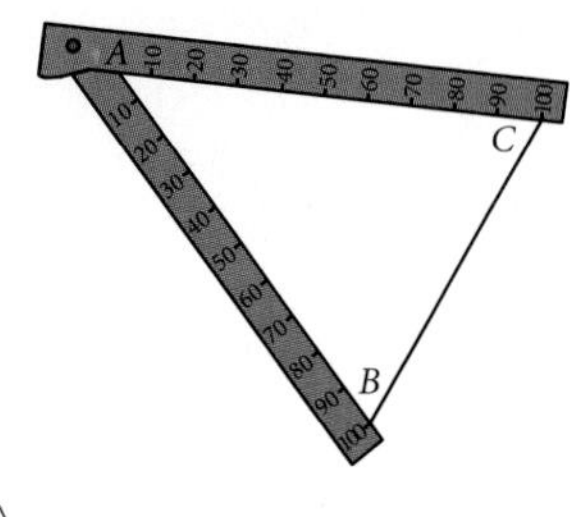

17. This truncated cone was formed by cutting off the top of a cone with a slice parallel to the base of the cone. What is the volume of the truncated cone? ⓗ $2064\pi\text{ cm}^3 \approx 6484\text{ cm}^3$

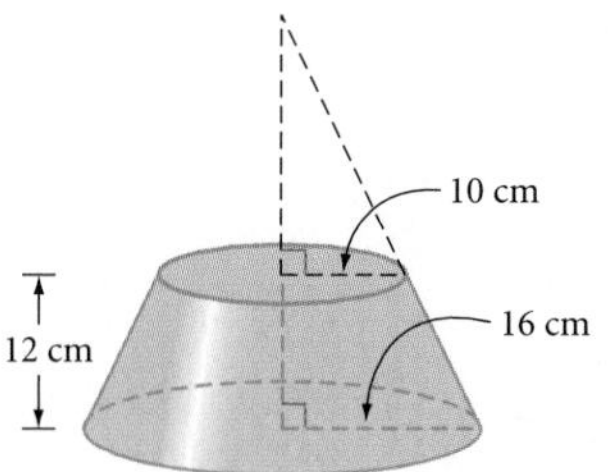

16. You should connect the two 75-marks. By the Extended Parallel/Proportionality Conjecture, drawing a segment between the 75-marks will form a similar segment that has length $\frac{75}{100}$, or 75%, of the original.

18. Assume that the SAS Similarity Conjecture and the Converse of the Parallel Lines Conjecture are true. Write a proof to show that if a line cuts two sides of a triangle proportionally, then it is parallel to the third side.

Given: $\frac{a}{c} = \frac{b}{d}$ (Assume $c \neq 0$ and $d \neq 0$.)

Show: $\overleftrightarrow{AB} \parallel \overline{YZ}$

19. Another drafting tool used to construct segments is a pair of proportional dividers, shown at right. Two styluses of equal length are connected by a screw. The tool is adjusted for different proportions by moving the screw. Where should the screw be positioned so that AB is three-fourths of CD?

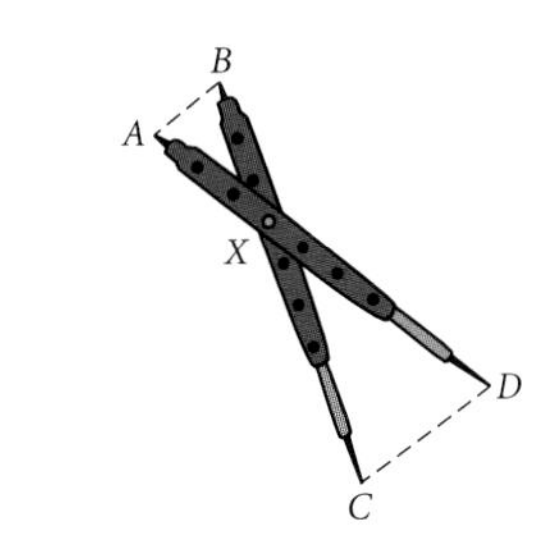

The Extended Parallel/Proportionality Conjecture can be extended even further. That is, you don't necessarily need a triangle. If three or more parallel lines intercept two other lines (transversals) in the same plane, they do so proportionally. For Exercises 20 and 21 use this extension.

20. Find x and y. $x \approx 4.6$ cm, $y \approx 3.4$ cm

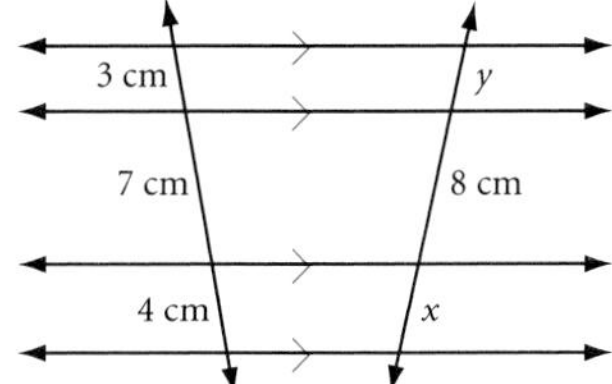

21. A real estate developer has parceled land between a river and River Road as shown. The land has been divided by segments perpendicular to the road. What is the "river frontage" (lengths x, y, and z) for each of the three lots?
$x \approx 9.8$ yd, $y \approx 8.7$ yd, $z \approx 6.5$ yd

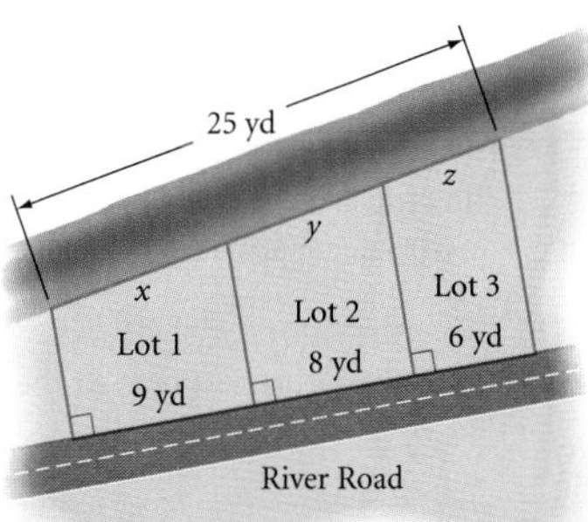

Review

11.5 **22.** The ratio of the surface areas of two cubes is $\frac{49}{81}$. What is the ratio of their volumes? $\frac{343}{729}$

11.5 **23.** Romunda's original recipe for her special "cannonball" cookies makes 36 spheres with 4 cm diameters. She reasons that she can make 36 cannonballs with 8 cm diameters by doubling the amount of dough. Is she correct? If not, how many 8 cm diameter cannonballs can she make by doubling the recipe? She is incorrect. She can make only nine 8 cm diameter spheres.

8.7 **24.** Find the surface area of a cube with edge x. Find the surface area of a cube with edge $2x$. Find the surface area of a cube with edge $3x$. $6x^2$; $24x^2$; $54x^2$

18. possible proof:

$$\frac{a}{c} = \frac{b}{d}$$
$$ad = cb$$
$$ad + ab = cb + ab$$
$$\frac{a(d+b)}{ab} = \frac{b(c+a)}{ab}$$
$$\frac{d+b}{b} = \frac{c+a}{a}$$

So two pairs of corresponding sides of $\triangle XYZ$ and $\triangle XAB$ are proportional. $\angle X \cong \angle X$, so $\triangle XYZ \sim \triangle XAB$ by the SAS Similarity Conjecture. Because $\triangle XYZ \sim \triangle XAB$, $\angle XAB \cong \angle XYZ$. Hence, $\overleftrightarrow{AB} \parallel \overline{YZ}$ by the Converse of the Parallel Lines Conjecture.

Exercise 19 The two isosceles triangles will always be similar because their vertex angles are congruent vertical angles.

19. Set the screw so that the shorter lengths of the styluses are three-fourths as long as the longer lengths.

EXTENSIONS

A. Use Take Another Look activities 6 and 7 on page 618.

B. Have students complete this algebraic argument showing that if a line parallel to one side of a triangle passes through the other two sides, then it divides the other two sides proportionally. That is, complete the reasoning for this argument:

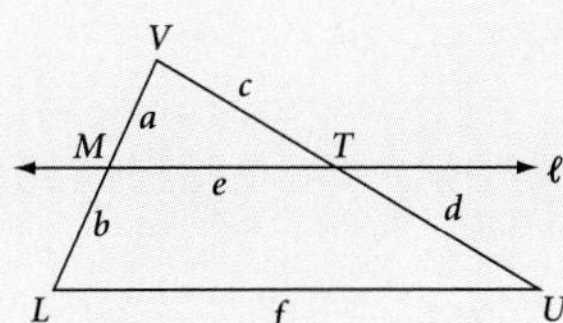

If $\ell \parallel \overline{LU}$, then $\triangle LUV \sim \triangle MTV$.

If $\triangle LUV \sim \triangle MTV$, then $\frac{a+b}{a} = \frac{c+d}{c}$.

If $\frac{a+b}{a} = \frac{c+d}{c}$, then $\frac{a}{b} = \frac{c}{d}$.

[One solution: $\frac{a+b}{a} = \frac{c+d}{c} \Rightarrow \frac{a}{a} + \frac{b}{a} = \frac{c}{c} + \frac{d}{c} \Rightarrow 1 + \frac{b}{a} = 1 + \frac{d}{c} \Rightarrow \frac{b}{a} = \frac{d}{c} \Rightarrow \frac{a}{b} = \frac{c}{d}$]

Exercise 26 Students who are interested in the golden rectangle might complete the project on page 598.

26a. Possible construction method: Use the triangle-and-circle construction from Lesson 11.3, Exercise 17, to locate the golden cut, X, of $\overline{AB}$. Then use perpendicular lines and circles to create a rectangle with length AB and width AX.

26b. Possible construction method: Construct golden rectangle $ABCD$ following the method from 26a. For square $AEFD$, locate $\overline{EF}$ by constructing circle A and circle D each with radius AD. Repeat the process of cutting off squares as often as desired. For the golden spiral from point D to point E, construct circle F with radius EF; select point D, point E, and circle F and choose **Arc On Circle** from the **Construct** menu.

Exercise 28 Students might prefer to work backward, putting together four copies of this figure to create a larger similar figure rather than dividing up the shape. Realizing that each of the four smaller figures has half the linear dimensions of the larger piece will also be helpful. Puzzles like this are sometimes called *rep-tiles*. *Rep* stands for "replica."

28.

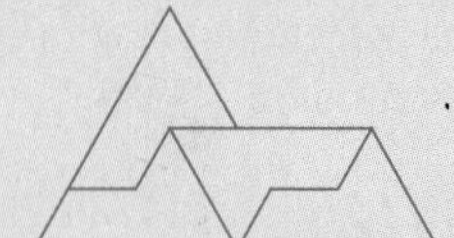

See page 775 for the answer to Exercise 27.

6.7 **25.** A circle of radius r has a chord of length r. Find the length of the minor arc. $\frac{1}{3}\pi r$

11.3 **26.** ***Technology*** In Lesson 11.3, Exercise 17, you learned about the golden cut and the golden ratio. A **golden rectangle** is a rectangle in which the ratio of the length to the width is the golden ratio. That is, a golden rectangle's length, l, and width, w, satisfy the proportion

$$\frac{w}{l} = \frac{l}{w + l}$$

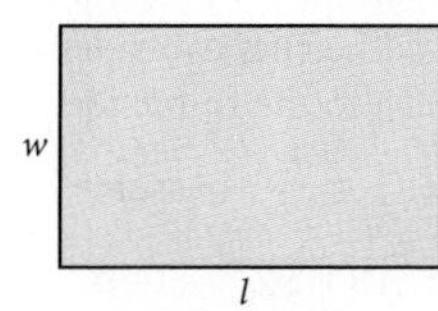

A golden rectangle

a. Use geometry software to construct a golden rectangle. Your construction for Exercise 17 in Lesson 11.3 will help.

b. When a square is cut off one end of a golden rectangle, the remaining rectangle is a smaller, similar golden rectangle. If you continue this process over and over again, and then connect opposite vertices of the squares with quarter-circles, you create a curve called the golden spiral. Use geometry software to construct a **golden spiral.** The first three quarter-circles are shown below.

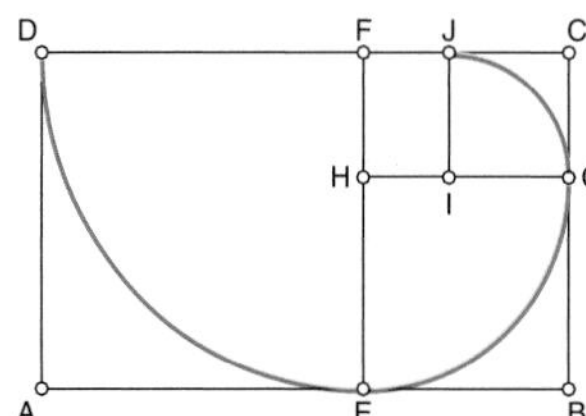

ABCD is a golden rectangle.

EBCF is a golden rectangle.

HGCF is a golden rectangle.

IJFH is a golden rectangle.

The curve from *D* to *E* to *G* to *J* is the beginning of a golden spiral.

Some researchers believe Greek architects used golden rectangles to design the Parthenon. You can learn more about the historical importance of golden rectangles using the links at www.keymath.com/DG .

6.3 **27.** A circle is inscribed in a quadrilateral. Write a proof showing that the two sums of the opposite sides of the quadrilateral are equal.

11.1 **28.** Copy the figure at right onto your own paper. Divide it into four figures similar to the original figure.

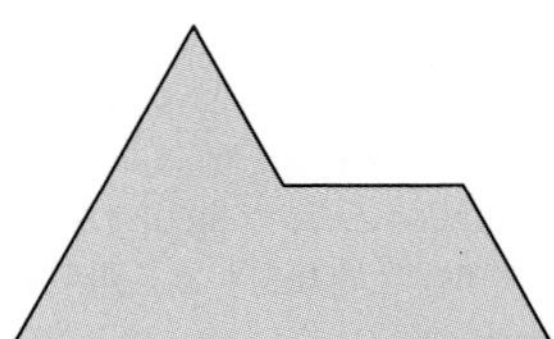

IMPROVING YOUR VISUAL THINKING SKILLS

Connecting Cubes

The two objects shown at right can be placed together to form each of the shapes below except one. Which one?

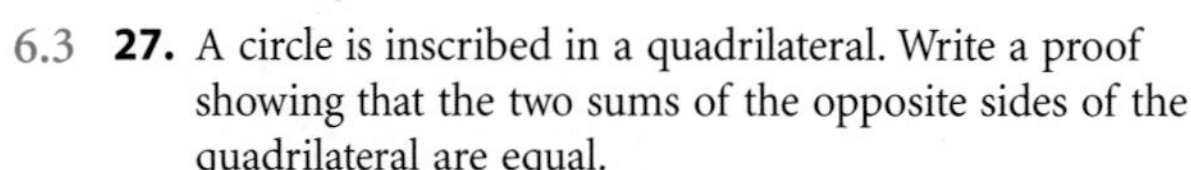

A.

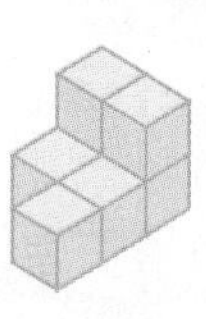

B.

C.

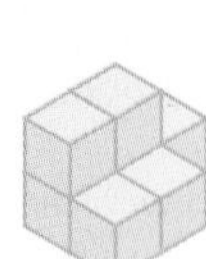

D.

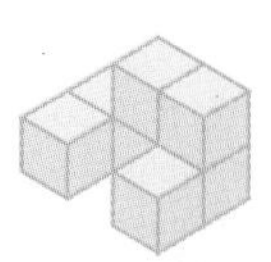

IMPROVING VISUAL THINKING SKILLS

A.

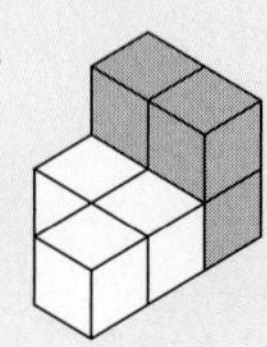

B.

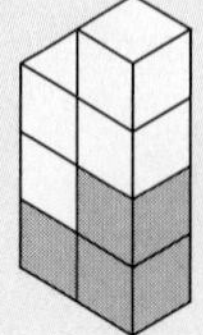

C.

D. This shape cannot be made.

Exploration

Two More Forms of Valid Reasoning

In the Chapter 10 Exploration Sherlock Holmes and Valid Forms of Reasoning, you learned about *Modus Ponens* and *Modus Tollens.* A third valid form of reasoning is called the Law of Syllogism.

According to the **Law of Syllogism** (LS), if you accept "If P then Q" as true and if you accept "If Q then R" as true, then you must logically accept "If P then R" as true.

Here is an example of the Law of Syllogism.

English statement	Symbolic translation
If I eat pizza after midnight, then I will have nightmares. If I have nightmares, then I will get very little sleep. Therefore, if I eat pizza after midnight, then I will get very little sleep.	P: I eat pizza after midnight. Q: I will have nightmares R: I will get very little sleep. $P \rightarrow Q$ $Q \rightarrow R$ $\therefore P \rightarrow R$

To work on the next law, you need some new statement forms. Every conditional statement has three other conditionals associated with it. To get the converse of a statement, you switch the "if" and "then" parts. To get the **inverse,** you negate both parts. To get the **contrapositive,** you reverse and negate the two parts. These new forms may be true or false.

Statement	If two angles are vertical angles, then they are congruent.	$P \rightarrow Q$	true
Converse	If two angles are congruent, then they are vertical angles.	$Q \rightarrow P$	false
Inverse	If two angles are not vertical angles, then they are not congruent.	$\sim P \rightarrow \sim Q$	false
Contrapositive	If two angles are not congruent, then they are not vertical angles.	$\sim Q \rightarrow \sim P$	true

NCTM STANDARDS

CONTENT		PROCESS	
	Number		Problem Solving
	Algebra	✓	Reasoning
✓	Geometry	✓	Communication
	Measurement	✓	Connections
	Data/Probability	✓	Representation

LESSON OBJECTIVES

- Learn to apply the Law of Syllogism
- Learn to apply the Law of Contrapositive

EXPLORATION

PLANNING

LESSON OUTLINE

One day:

35 min Activity

5 min Sharing

5 min Closing

MATERIALS

none

TEACHING

Two more structures for logical reasoning are the Law of Syllogism (LS) and the Law of Contrapositive (LC). The negation symbol is the same as the symbol for similarity.

One step Ask students to decide the validity of this argument: "If Jeannine comes over to study, then I won't miss my late-night talk show. But if I study all night, then I will miss my show. Jeannine is coming over to study. Therefore I won't study all night." Either while groups discuss the argument or during Sharing, bring up the ideas of syllogism and contrapositive and the idea that statements and their contrapositives, unlike converses, are either both true or both false. Things that are only sometimes true are considered false.

INTRODUCTION

Students might be aware of the transitive property of equality, which says that if $a = b$ and $b = c$ then $a = c$. The Law of Syllogism is analogous, but it connects statements with implications rather than connecting expressions with equal signs.

Introduction (continued)

If you want students to practice writing statement forms or wish them to discover LC for themselves, have them write the converse, the inverse, and the contrapositive of conditional statements such as those given here. Then they should say whether they think each of the original and new statements is true or false.

a. If it is a rose, then it is a flower.

b. If you're out of chocolate cake, then you're out of dessert.

c. If the triangle is isosceles, then the triangle's base angles are congruent.

d. If $\triangle ABC$ is congruent to $\triangle DEF$, then $AB = DE$.

MAKING THE CONNECTION

The conclusion for the puzzle from *Symbolic Logic* is "Babies cannot manage a crocodile." The argument can be represented symbolically as:

$B \rightarrow I$

$I \rightarrow D$

$\therefore B \rightarrow D$ by LS

$C \rightarrow \sim D$

$\therefore D \rightarrow \sim C$ by LC

$\therefore B \rightarrow \sim C$ by LS

No, Tweedledee is not really using logic or valid reasoning.

[Language] A *pseudonym* ['sü-dᵊn-im] is a fictitious name.

Notice that the original conditional statement and its contrapositive have the same truth value. This leads to a fourth form of valid reasoning. The **Law of Contrapositive** (LC) says that if a conditional statement is true, then its contrapositive is also true. Conversely, if the contrapositive is true, then the original conditional statement must also be true. This also means that if a conditional statement is false, so is its contrapositive.

Often, a logical argument contains multiple steps, applying the same rule more than once, or applying more than one rule. Here is an example.

English statement	Symbolic translation
If the consecutive sides of a parallelogram are congruent, then it is a rhombus. If a parallelogram is a rhombus, then its diagonals are perpendicular bisectors of each other. The diagonals are not perpendicular bisectors of each other. Therefore the consecutive sides of the parallelogram are not congruent.	P: The consecutive sides of a parallelogram are congruent. Q: The parallelogram is a rhombus. R: The diagonals are perpendicular bisectors of each other. $P \rightarrow Q$ $Q \rightarrow R$ $\sim R$ $\therefore \sim P$

You can show that this argument is valid in three logical steps.

Step 1
$P \rightarrow Q$
$Q \rightarrow R$
$\therefore P \rightarrow R$ by the Law of Syllogism

Step 2
$P \rightarrow R$
$\therefore \sim R \rightarrow \sim P$ by the Law of Contrapositive

Step 3
$\sim R \rightarrow \sim P$
$\sim R$
$\therefore \sim P$ by *Modus Ponens*

Literature CONNECTION

Lewis Carroll was the pseudonym of the English novelist and mathematician Charles Lutwidge Dodgson (1832–1898). He is often associated with his famous children's book *Alice's Adventures in Wonderland.*

In 1886 he published *The Game of Logic,* which used a game board and counters to solve logic problems. In 1896 he published *Symbolic Logic, Part I,* which was an elementary book intended to teach symbolic logic. Here is one of the silly problems from *Symbolic Logic.* What conclusion follows from these premises?

> Babies are illogical.
> Nobody is despised who can manage a crocodile.
> Illogical persons are despised.

Lewis Carroll enjoyed incorporating mathematics and logic into all of his books. Here is a quote from *Through the Looking Glass.* Is Tweedledee using valid reasoning?

> "Contrariwise," said Tweedledee, "if it was so, it might be; and if it were so, it would be, but as it isn't, it ain't. That's logic."

So far, you have learned four basic forms of valid reasoning.

Now let's apply them in symbolic proofs.

Four Forms of Valid Reasoning

$P \to Q$	$P \to Q$	$P \to Q$	$P \to Q$
P	$\sim Q$	$Q \to R$	$\therefore \sim Q \to \sim P$
$\therefore Q$	$\therefore \sim P$	$\therefore P \to R$	
by MP	by MT	by LS	by LC

Activity
Symbolic Proofs

Step 1 Determine whether or not each logical argument is valid. If it is valid, state what reasoning form or forms it follows. If it is not valid, write "no valid conclusion."

a. $P \to \sim Q$ MT
Q
$\therefore \sim P$

b. $\sim S \to P$ LS
$R \to \sim S$
$\therefore R \to P$

c. $\sim Q \to \sim R$ MP
$\sim Q$
$\therefore \sim R$

d. $R \to P$ no valid conclusion
$T \to \sim P$
$\therefore R \to T$

e. $\sim P \to \sim R$ MT
R
$\therefore P$

f. $P \to Q$ LC, LS
$\sim R \to \sim Q$
$\therefore P \to R$

Step 2 Translate parts a–c into symbols, and give the reasoning form(s) or state that the conclusion is not valid.

a. If I study all night, then I will miss my late-night talk show. If Jeannine comes over to study, then I study all night. Jeannine comes over to study. Therefore I will miss my late-night talk show.

b. If I don't earn money, then I can't buy a computer. If I don't get a job, then I don't earn money. I have a job. Therefore I can buy a computer.

c. If $\overline{EF}$ is not parallel to side $\overline{AB}$ in trapezoid $ABCD$, then $\overline{EF}$ is not a midsegment of trapezoid $ABCD$. If $\overline{EF}$ is parallel to side $\overline{AB}$, then $ABFE$ is a trapezoid. $\overline{EF}$ is a midsegment of trapezoid $ABCD$. Therefore $ABFE$ is a trapezoid.

Step 3 Show how you can use *Modus Ponens* and the Law of Contrapositive to make the same logical conclusions as *Modus Tollens.*

Guiding the Activity

Step 1 In part a, you might need to remind some students that $\sim(\sim Q)$ is Q. In part b, the statements are given in a different order from that of the example. In part e, some students may have forgotten that the contrapositive of $\sim R \to \sim Q$ is $Q \to R$.

Step 3 What's given and what they are to prove might not be clear to some students. Given are $P \to Q$ and $\sim Q$ (the beginning of *Modus Tollens*) and LC, which says that from $P \to Q$ you can get $\sim Q \to \sim P$. To be shown is $\sim P$ (the conclusion of *Modus Tollens*).

SHARING IDEAS

If time is limited, you might pick out just a few parts of the three steps of the activity for the class critique. You might ask students to write real-life arguments that fit the forms of Step 1. One of the most commonly cited examples of *Modus Ponens* is from Aristotle: "All men are mortal; Socrates was a man; therefore Socrates was mortal." Ask how this might be put into the $P \to Q$ form considered in this book. [The first statement could be something like "If x is a man, then x is mortal" or "If a person is a man, then the person is mortal."] Similarly, a syllogism is often taken to have the "all" format. **[Ask]** "What are some geometric examples?" [One example of LS: All squares are rectangles; all rectangles are parallelograms; therefore, all squares are parallelograms.]

Assessing Progress

You can assess students' understanding of *Modus Ponens* and *Modus Tollens* and their intuition about what's logical and what isn't.

See page 776 for answers to Steps 2a–c.

Closing the Lesson

The main points of this lesson concern two new logical structures: the **Law of Syllogism (LS)** (if $P \to Q$ and $Q \to R$, then $P \to R$) and the **Law of Contrapositive (LC)** (if $P \to Q$, then $\sim Q \to \sim P$).

EXTENSION

Students might enjoy investigating logically impossible statements such as "This statement is false."

PLANNING

LESSON OUTLINE

First day:

15 min Reviewing

30 min Exercises

Second day:

30 min Exercises

15 min Student self-assessment

REVIEWING

Direct students' attention to Investigation 2 of Lesson 11.1. There they drew a pentagon on graph paper and dilated it, multiplying the coordinates of its vertices by some constant. They then measured angles and sides to check for similarity. Ask how they might determine similarity without measuring. One way to see that lengths of corresponding sides have the same ratios is to draw lines from the origin through the vertices and apply the Extended Parallel/Proportionality Conjecture (or find various similar triangles). To show that the angles are congruent, they might divide the polygon into triangles and apply the SSS shortcut. As they work through this exercise, remind students of other shortcuts and ask them how the areas compare.

ASSIGNING HOMEWORK

Because of their variety, it's best if you can assign all the exercises. Be sure not to skip Exercise 19; it's historically interesting, and the relationship it describes is thought provoking.

CHAPTER 11 REVIEW

Similarity, like area, volume, and the Pythagorean Theorem, has many applications. Any scale drawing or model, anything that is reduced or enlarged, is governed by the properties of similar figures. So engineers, visual artists, and film-makers all use similarity. It is also useful in indirect measurement. Do you recall the two indirect measurement methods you learned in this chapter? The ratios of area and volume in similar figures are also related to the ratios of their dimensions. But recall that as the dimensions increase, the area increases by a squared factor and volume increases by a cubed factor.

EXERCISES

You will need

Construction tools for Exercise 9

For Exercises 1–4, solve each proportion.

1. $\frac{x}{15} = \frac{8}{5}$ $x = 24$

2. $\frac{4}{11} = \frac{24}{x}$ $x = 66$

3. $\frac{4}{x} = \frac{x}{9}$ $x = \pm 6$

4. $\frac{x}{x+3} = \frac{34}{40}$ $x = 17$

In Exercises 5 and 6, measurements are in centimeters.

5. $ABCDE \sim FGHIJ$
$w = \underline{?}$, $x = \underline{?}$, $y = \underline{?}$, $z = \underline{?}$
6 cm 4.5 cm 7.5 cm 3 cm

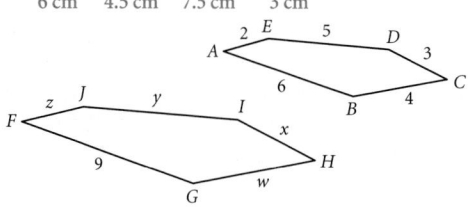

6. $\triangle ABC \sim \triangle DBA$
$x = \underline{?}$, $y = \underline{?}$
$4\frac{1}{6}$ cm $7\frac{1}{2}$ cm

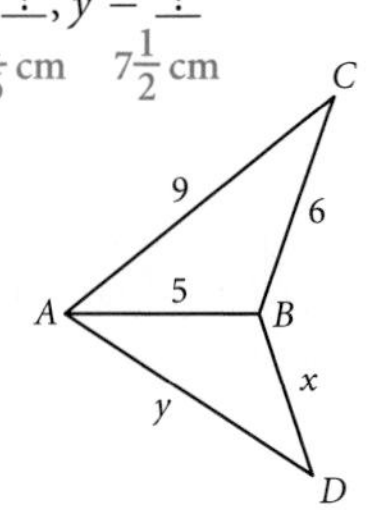

7. APPLICATION David is 5 ft 8 in. tall and wants to find the height of an oak tree in his front yard. He walks along the shadow of the tree until his head is in a position where the end of his shadow exactly overlaps the end of the tree's shadow. He is now 11 ft 3 in. from the foot of the tree and 8 ft 6 in. from the end of the shadows. How tall is the oak tree? 13 ft 2 in.

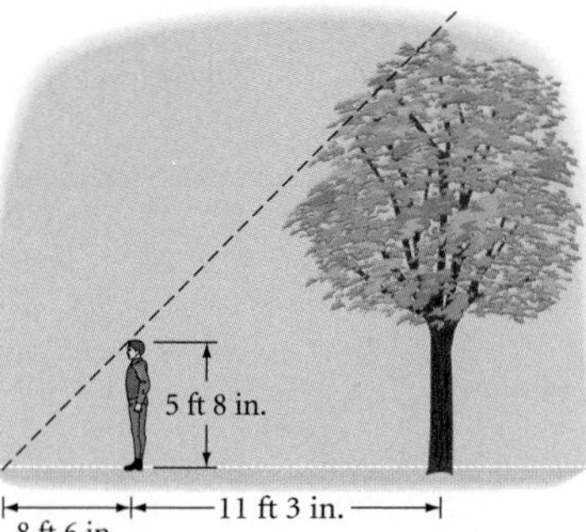

▶ Helping with the Exercises

Exercise 2 If any students are tempted to cross multiply, point out how easy it is to invert both fractions.

Exercise 4 Be open to a variety of approaches. Perhaps the simplest is to reduce the right side to $\frac{17}{20}$ and then wonder what value x might have.

Exercise 6 Students might benefit from redrawing the two triangles as separate so that the corresponding angles are in the same position.

8. A certain magnifying glass when held 6 in. from an object creates an image that is 10 times the size of the object being viewed. What is the measure of a 20° angle under this magnifying glass? It would still be a 20° angle.

9. ***Construction*** Construct $\overline{KL}$. Then find a point P that divides $\overline{KL}$ into two segments that have a ratio $\frac{3}{4}$. ⓗ

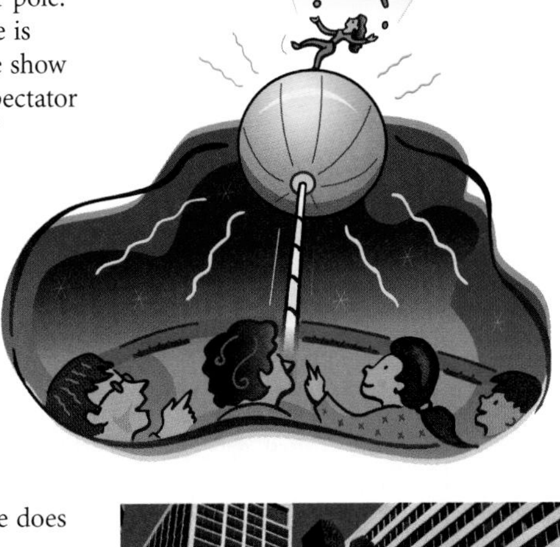

10. Patsy does a juggling act. She sits on a stool that sits on top of a rotating ball that spins at the top of a 20-meter pole. The diameter of the ball is 4 meters, and Patsy's eye is approximately 2 meters above the ball. Seats for the show are arranged on the floor in a circle so that each spectator can see Patsy's eyes. Find the radius of the circle of seats to the nearest meter. ⓗ 15 m

11. Charlie builds a rectangular box home for his pet python and uses 1 gallon of paint to cover its surface. Lucy also builds a box for Charlie's pet, but with dimensions twice as great. How many gallons of paint will Lucy need to paint her box? How many times as much volume does her box have? 4 gal; 8 times

12. Suppose you had a real clothespin similar to the sculpture at right and made of the same material. What measurements would you make to calculate the weight of the sculpture? Explain your reasoning.

13. The ratio of the perimeters of two similar parallelograms is $\frac{3}{7}$. What is the ratio of their areas? $\frac{9}{49}$

14. The ratio of the areas of two circles is $\frac{25}{16}$. What is the ratio of their radii? $\frac{5}{4}$

15. **APPLICATION** The Jones family paid \$150 to a painting contractor to stain their 12-by-15-foot deck. The Smiths have a similar deck that measures 16 ft by 20 ft. What price should the Smith family expect to pay to have their deck stained? \$266.67

This sculpture, called *Clothespin* (1976), was created by Swedish-American sculptor Claes Oldenburg (b 1929). His art reflects how everyday objects can be intriguing.

9.

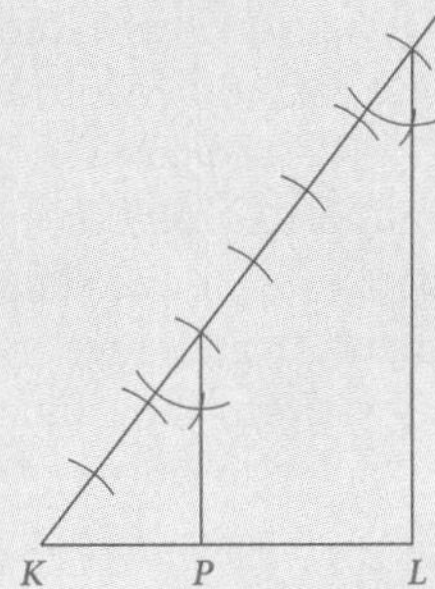

Exercise 10 Drawing an accurate picture might challenge some students.

Exercise 11 [Language] A *python* is a kind of snake.

Exercise 12 Students could actually do these calculations using a plastic or wooden clothespin. The sculpture in the photo is in Philadelphia.

12. Possible answer: You would measure the height and weight of the real clothespin and the height of the sculpture.

$$\frac{W_{\text{sculpture}}}{W_{\text{clothespin}}} = \left(\frac{H_{\text{sculpture}}}{H_{\text{clothespin}}}\right)^3$$

If you don't know the height of the sculpture, you could estimate it from this photo by setting up a ratio, for example

$$\frac{H_{\text{person}}}{H_{\text{person's photo}}} = \frac{H_{\text{sculpture}}}{H_{\text{sculpture's photo}}}$$

Exercise 13 As needed, remind students that perimeters, like sides and diagonals, are linear relationships.

Exercise 15 Students might set up a proportion using the actual areas of the rectangles: $\frac{\$150}{12(15)} = \frac{\$x}{16(20)}$. Lead them to realize that, because the scale factor is $\frac{4}{3}$, the area—and therefore the cost—will be $\frac{16}{9}$ as much.

Exercise 18 [Context] The statue of Bahubali was carved between 978 and 993 C.E. The ceremony is called *Maha Masthakabhisheka* and includes covering the statue in milk, yogurt, fruit, butter, seeds, coins, saffron, and sandalwood. Bahubali, also called *Gommateshwara,* was a Jain ruler who gave up his kingdom for a life of religious meditation.

Exercise 19 Students may have already seen a related problem if you did the one-step investigation in Lesson 10.7. If not, challenge them to find the ratios of surface area of the cylinder, sphere, and cone. Archimedes was most impressed that the cylinder and the sphere have the same ratios in both surface area and volume. The ratio of the three volumes, $2\pi : \frac{4}{3}\pi : \frac{2}{3}\pi$, reduces nicely.

16. The dimensions of the smaller cylinder are two-thirds of the dimensions of the larger cylinder. The volume of the larger cylinder is 2160π cm³. Find the volume of the smaller cylinder. 640π cm³

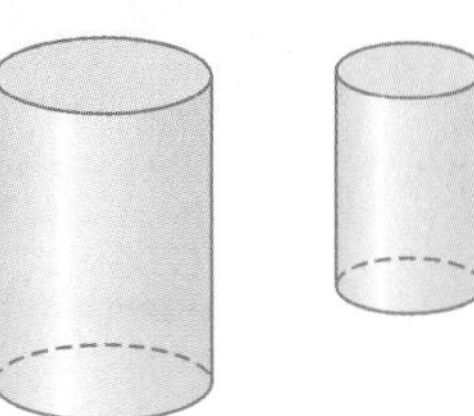

17. $\mathfrak{z} \parallel \ell \parallel \mathfrak{g} \parallel \mathfrak{h}$
$w = \underline{?}$, $x = \underline{?}$, $y = \underline{?}$, $z = \underline{?}$
32, 24, 40, 126

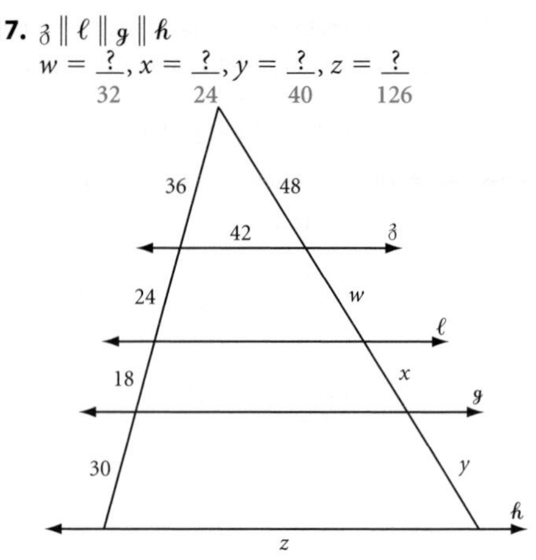

18. Below is a 58-foot statue of Bahubali, in Sravanabelagola, India. Every 12 years, worshipers of the Jain religion bathe the statue with coconut milk. Suppose the milk of one coconut is just enough to cover the surface of the similar 2-foot statuette shown at right. How many coconuts would be required to cover the surface of the full-size statue? 841 coconuts

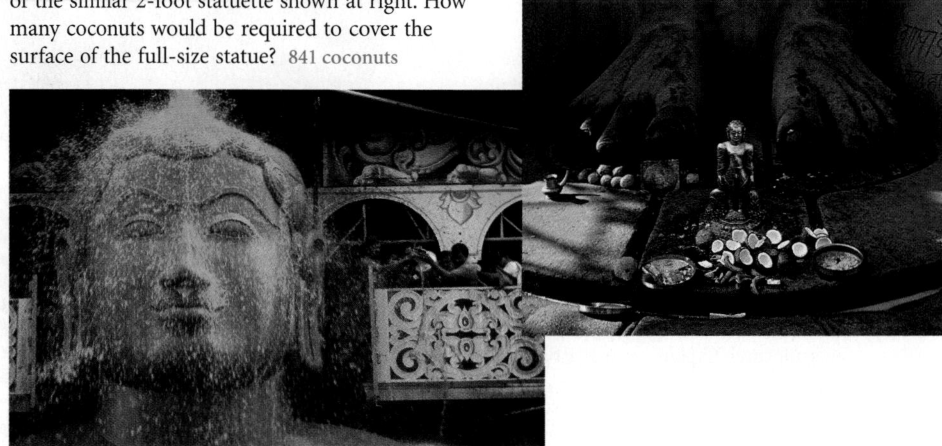

This 58-foot statue is carved from a single stone.

19. Greek mathematician Archimedes liked the design at right so much that he wanted it on his tombstone. ⓗ

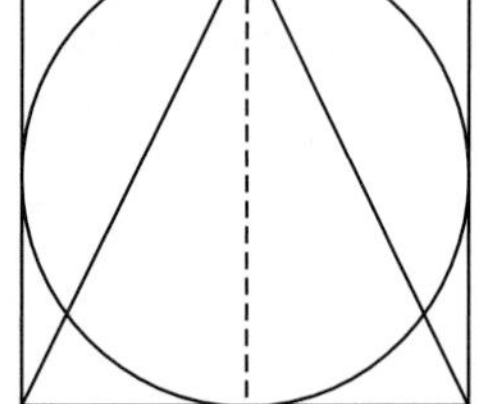

a. Calculate the ratio of the area of the square, the area of the circle, and the area of the isosceles triangle. Copy and complete this statement of proportionality.

Area of square to Area of circle to Area of triangle is $\underline{?}$ to $\underline{?}$ to $\underline{?}$.

1 to $\frac{\pi}{4}$ to $\frac{1}{2}$, or 4 to π to 2

b. When each of the figures is revolved about the vertical line of symmetry, it generates a solid of revolution—a cylinder, a sphere, and a cone. Calculate their volumes. Copy and complete this statement of proportionality.
Volume of cylinder to Volume of sphere to Volume of cone is _?_ to _?_ to _?_.
3 to 2 to 1

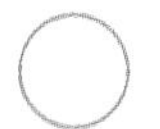   

c. What is so special about this design?

20. Many fanciful stories are about people who accidentally shrink to a fraction of their original height. If a person shrank to one-twentieth his original height, how would that change the amount of food he'd require, or the amount of material needed to clothe him, or the time he'd need to get to different places? Explain.

This scene is from the 1957 science fiction movie *The Incredible Shrinking Man.*

21. Would 15 pounds of 1-inch ice cubes melt faster than a 15-pound block of ice? Explain. The ice cubes would melt faster because they have greater surface area.

TAKE ANOTHER LOOK

1. You've learned that an ordered pair rule such as $(x, y) \rightarrow (x + b, y + c)$ is a translation. You discovered in this chapter that an ordered pair rule such as $(x, y) \rightarrow (kx, ky)$ is a dilation in the coordinate plane, centered at the origin. What transformation is described by the rule $(x, y) \rightarrow (kx + b, ky + c)$? Investigate.

2. In Lesson 11.1, you dilated figures in the coordinate plane, using the origin as the center of dilation. What happens if a different point in the plane is the center of dilation? Copy the polygon at right onto graph paper. Draw the polygon's image under a dilation with a scale factor of 2 and with point A as the center of dilation. Draw another image using a scale factor of $\frac{2}{3}$. Explain how you found the image points. How does dilating about point A differ from dilating about the origin?

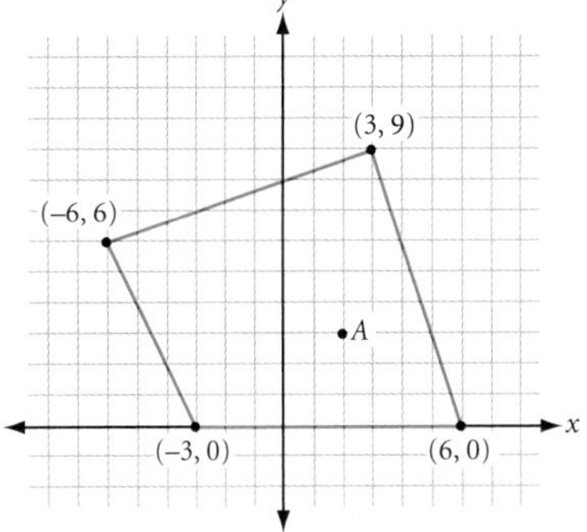

3. True or false? The angle bisector of one of the nonvertex angles of a kite will divide the diagonal connecting the vertex angles into two segments whose lengths are in the same ratio as two unequal sides of the kite. If true, explain why. If false, show a counterexample that proves it false.

19c. Answers will vary.

20. Possible answer: If food is proportional to body volume, then $\frac{1}{8000}$ of the usual amount of food is required. If clothing is proportional to surface area, then $\frac{1}{400}$ of the usual amount of clothing is required. It would take 20 times longer to walk a given distance.

Take Another Look

1. This rule describes a dilation by a factor of k followed by a translation by (b, c).

3. This is true by the Angle Bisector/Opposite Side Conjecture.

2. For each vertex, draw a ray from point A through the vertex. Mark off a point on the ray whose distance from point A is the scale factor times the distance of the vertex from point A. The coordinates of the vertices are not multiplied by the scale factor, but the lengths of the sides are.

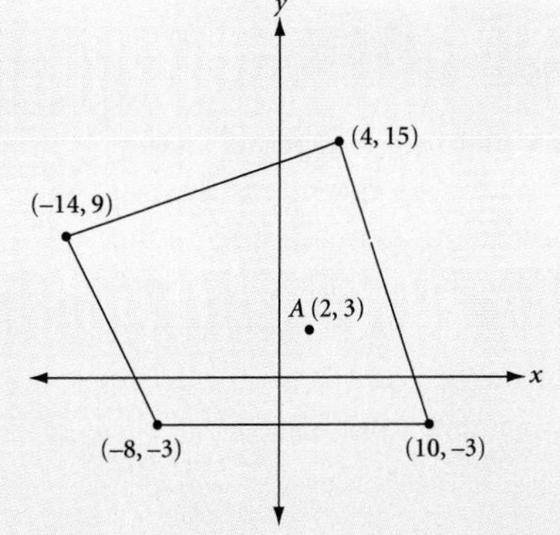

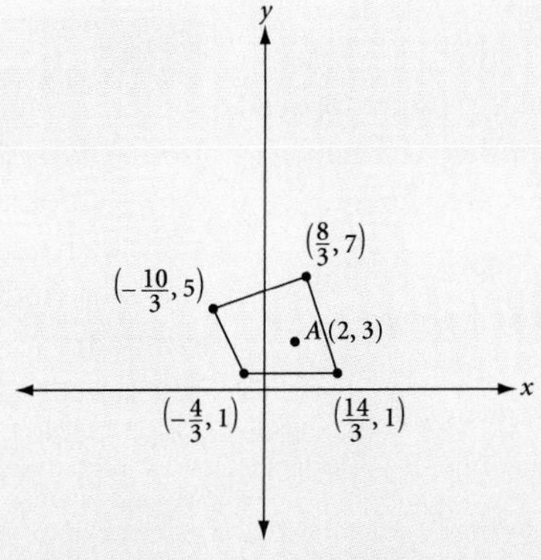

4. Figure A shows the positions of the Moon and the Sun during a total eclipse, relative to an observer at point A. The Moon blocks all of the Sun except the Sun's corona. $\triangle ABC \sim \triangle ADE$ by the AA Similarity Conjecture. AB is the approximate distance from Earth to the Moon. BC is the approximate diameter of the Moon. AD is the approximate distance from Earth to the Sun. DE is the approximate diameter of the Sun. For further explanation see page 776.

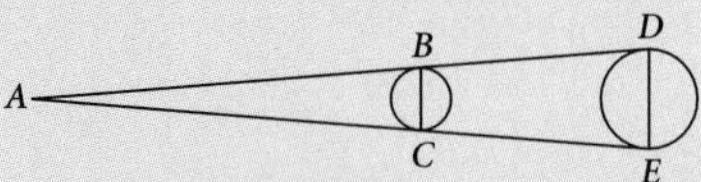

Figure A

[Context] Total solar eclipses occur about every six months. The Moon's ecliptic is tilted about 5° to that of the Sun, so the two paths meet in only two places. Have students research the actual diameters and distances.

5. Possible answers include any two triangles one of whose sides have lengths a, b, and c with the sides of the other having lengths b, c, and $\frac{c^2}{b}$. If one similar triangle has sides a, b, c, then the other triangle has sides ar, br, cr where r is the scale factor. Since two sides must be equal without the triangles being congruent, let $ra = b$, $rb = c$. This means $c = ar^2$. See page 776 for restrictions.

6. The converse is not true. One counterexample:

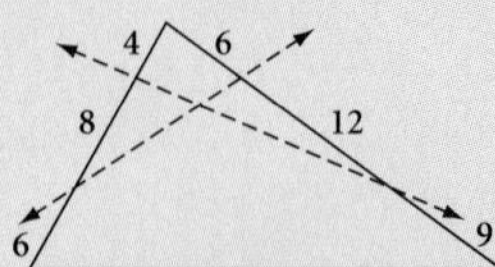

7. Conjecture: If the three sides of one triangle are parallel to the three sides of another triangle, then the triangles are similar.

Proof: Extend all sides so that they intersect. Then, for each angle, apply the Corresponding Angles Conjecture twice.

4. A total eclipse of the Sun can occur because the ratio of the Moon's diameter to its distance from Earth is about the same as the ratio of the Sun's diameter to its distance to Earth. Draw a diagram and use similar triangles to explain why it works.

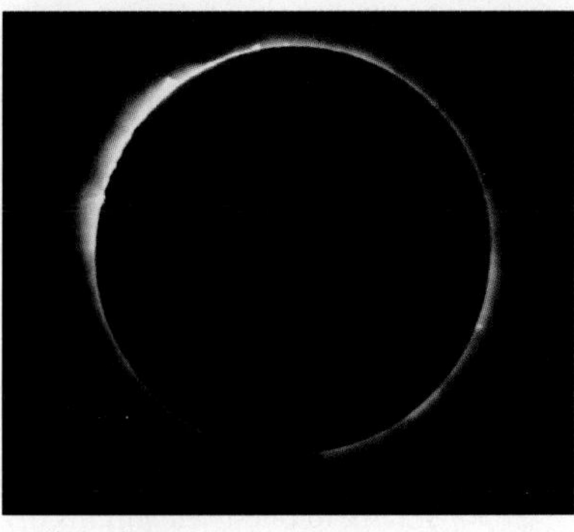

A solar eclipse

5. It is possible for the three angles and two of the sides of one triangle to be congruent to the three angles and two of the sides of another triangle, and yet the two triangles won't be congruent. Two such triangles are shown below. Use geometry software or patty paper to find another pair of similar (but not congruent) triangles in which five parts of one are congruent to five parts of the other.

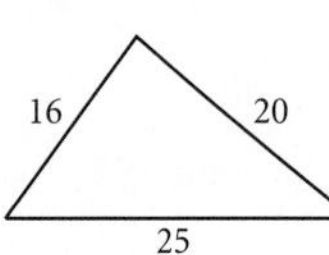

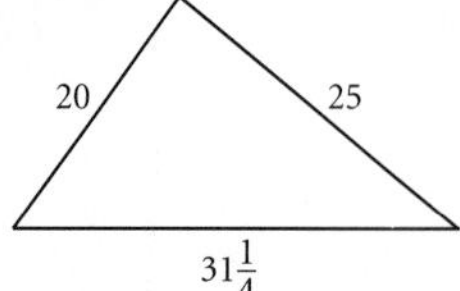

Explain why these sets of side lengths work. Use algebra to explain your reasoning.

6. Is the converse of the Extended Parallel Proportionality Conjecture true? That is, if two lines intersect two sides of a triangle, dividing the two sides proportionally, must the two lines be parallel to the third side? Prove that it is true or find a counterexample showing that it is not true.

7. If the three sides of one triangle are each parallel to one of the three sides of another triangle, what might be true about the two triangles? Use geometry software to investigate. Make a conjecture and explain why you think your conjecture is true.

Assessing What You've Learned

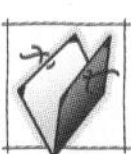

UPDATE YOUR PORTFOLIO If you did the Project Making a Mural, add your mural to your portfolio.

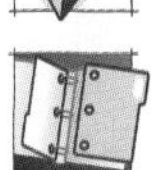

ORGANIZE YOUR NOTEBOOK Review your notebook to be sure it's complete and well organized. Be sure you have each definition and the conjecture. Write a one-page summary of Chapter 11.

GIVE A PRESENTATION Give a presentation about one or more of the similarity conjectures. You could even explain how an overhead projector produces similar figures!

ASSESSING

Similarity is an idea that brings together many things students have learned and opens them up to a broader understanding of geometry. You might consider student presentations of applications of symmetry as part of students' chapter test grade. You can also use or create a test from the *Discovering Geometry* assessment resources.

FACILITATING SELF-ASSESSMENT

For their portfolios, students might consider including their work on these exercises: Lesson 11.1, Exercise 16; Lesson 11.2, Exercise 5; Lesson 11.3, Exercise 7; Lesson 11.4, Exercise 19; Lesson 11.5, Exercises 8, 19; and Lesson 11.6, Exercise 15.

CHAPTER

12

Trigonometry

Overview

In **Lesson 12.1,** students learn the definitions of three trigonometric ratios in a right triangle: sine, cosine, and tangent. The first **exploration**—on using a clinometer to measure heights indirectly—can be done before or after **Lesson 12.2,** in which students use trigonometric ratios to solve simple problems. In **Lessons 12.3** and **12.4,** students learn about the Law of Sines and the Law of Cosines (restricted to acute angles, for which the cosine is positive). These two laws enable students to solve problems involving triangles other than right triangles. **Lesson 12.5** puts all that students have learned about trigonometry to use in solving more problems. The Geometer's Sketchpad **exploration**—on the unit circle—leads naturally into the graphing calculator project Trigonometric Functions, although both of these can stand alone. The chapter concludes with an **exploration** of three types of proof, including conditional and indirect proofs.

The Mathematics

Right Triangle Trigonometry

In measuring large distances, ancient astronomers needed to *solve* (measure all sides and angles of) immense triangles whose vertices might be the center of the earth or the moon.

In this course students have determined the measures of parts of triangles by using corresponding parts of congruent or similar triangles, using known angles, or using the fact that the triangle is isosceles or right. But the techniques discussed so far don't allow us to solve all triangles. For example, the congruence shortcut SSS determines a triangle, but it doesn't help us know the measures of the angles.

The Alexandrian Greeks, led by the mathematician Hipparchus (fl. 146–127 B.C.E.) and the astronomer Ptolemy (fl. 2nd century), realized that any two right triangles are similar if one nonright angle in one of the triangles is congruent to one nonright angle in the other. For those triangles, we can write an equation such as $\frac{a}{a'} = \frac{b}{b'}$ to show that corresponding sides are proportional. But if $\frac{a}{a'} = \frac{b}{b'}$, then $\frac{a}{b} = \frac{a'}{b'}$. That is, ratios of corresponding sides of each triangle are also equal. Therefore associated with every angle are some ratios independent of the size of the triangle.

How does this help us solve immense triangles? Imagine that you're 3 miles high in an airplane. There's a huge right triangle with vertices at your eye, a point you're looking at on the horizon, and the center of the earth. If you find that the angle between the vertical and your line of sight to the horizon measures 87.77°, then you could draw a small right triangle with an 87.77° angle and find the ratio of, say, the opposite side to the hypotenuse. You'll know, then, that the ratio of the opposite side to the hypotenuse of your huge triangle is the same, and from that you can find the radius of the earth. (See the extension for Lesson 12.2.)

Hipparchus developed tables of all six ratios of sides (sine, cosine, tangent, cotangent, secant, cosecant) so that mathematicians and scientists wouldn't have to draw and measure smaller triangles. Moreover, if a ratio was known, the related acute angle could be found by going backward in the table.

How can these ratios help solve nonright triangles? If you construct an altitude from an unknown angle (not splitting a known angle), then you get two right triangles in which both the known and the unknown parts of the original triangle appear. The Law of Sines and the Law of Cosines give shortcuts that actually remove the need to draw any altitudes. The former allows you to solve triangles determined by ASA or SAA. The latter allows you to solve triangles determined by SSS or SAS.

Calculators have replaced tables for finding trigonometric ratios. To deepen students' understanding beyond what they need in order to enter numbers into a calculator, emphasize ratios and similar triangles rather than formulas.

Trigonometric Functions

The right triangle trigonometry in the student book is done with acute angles only. In an exploration and a project following Lesson 12.5, students can see how to extend trigonometric ratios to angles that aren't acute. They see functions that are *periodic,* that is, functions that begin repeating as the angle measures become larger than 360° (or smaller than −360°).

To make the derivatives of these periodic functions easier to handle in calculus, the angles are traditionally measured not in degrees but in radians. One radian is the measure of an angle that intercepts one radius of a circle laid out along its circumference. The entire circumference consists of 2π radii, so 360° corresponds to 2π radians. In the Sketchpad exploration, students graph some periodic functions using radians and see that their period is 2π.

Using This Chapter

Unless your curriculum requires trigonometry or you want to focus on problem solving, Chapter 12 is an optional chapter. If you want to make trigonometry a strong component of your course, you might choose to extend the definitions of the trigonometric ratios to functions of angles with measures greater than 90°. Graphing calculators and The Geometer's Sketchpad are technology tools well suited to exploring this extension.

This chapter assumes your students are using scientific or graphing calculators with which they can find values of trigonometric ratios.

Resources

Discovering Geometry Resources

Teaching and Worksheet Masters
- Lessons 12.1, 12.5, and Chapter 12 Review
- Exploration: Indirect Measurement
- Exploration: Trigonometric Ratios and the Unit Circle

Sketchpad Demonstrations
- Lesson 12.4
- Exploration: Trigonometric Ratios and the Unit Circle

Discovering Geometry with The Geometer's Sketchpad
- Lessons 12.1 and 12.3

Assessment Resources A and B
- Quiz 1 (Lessons 12.1 and 12.2)
- Quiz 2 (Lessons 12.3–12.5)
- Chapter 12 Test
- Chapter 12 Constructive Assessment Options

Practice Your Skills for Chapter 12

Condensed Lessons for Chapter 12

Other Resources

www.keypress.com/DG

Materials

- construction tools
- protractors
- rulers
- calculators
- self-made clinometers (protractors, drinking straws, weights, string, and tape)
- measuring tape or metersticks

Pacing Guide

	day 1	day 2	day 3	day 4	day 5	day 6	day 7	day 8	day 9	day 10
standard	12.1	12.2	quiz, Exploration	12.3	12.4	12.5	quiz, project	Exploration	Exploration	review
enriched	12.1	12.2, project	quiz, Exploration	12.3	12.4	12.5	quiz, Exploration	Exploration	project	Exploration
block	12.1, 12.2	quiz, Exploration	12.3, 12.4	12.5, Exploration	Exploration, quiz, project	Exploration	review, TAL	assessment, TAL		

	day 11	day 12	day 13	day 14	day 15	day 16	day 17	day 18	day 19	day 20
standard	review	assessment								
enriched	review	review, TAL	assessment, TAL							

CHAPTER

12

Trigonometry

I wish I'd learn to draw a little better! What exertion and determination it takes to try and do it well. . . . It is really just a question of carrying on doggedly, with continuous and, if possible, pitiless self-criticism.

M. C. ESCHER

Belvedere, M. C. Escher, 1958

OBJECTIVES

In this chapter you will

- learn about the branch of mathematics called trigonometry
- define three important ratios between the sides of a right triangle
- use trigonometry to solve problems involving right triangles
- discover how trigonometry extends beyond right triangles

CHAPTER 12 OBJECTIVES

- Discover the sine, cosine, and tangent ratios
- Discover and apply the Law of Sines
- Investigate the Pythagorean identity
- Learn and apply the Law of Cosines
- Use trigonometry to solve applied problems
- Develop reading comprehension, visual thinking, cooperative behavior, and problem-solving skills

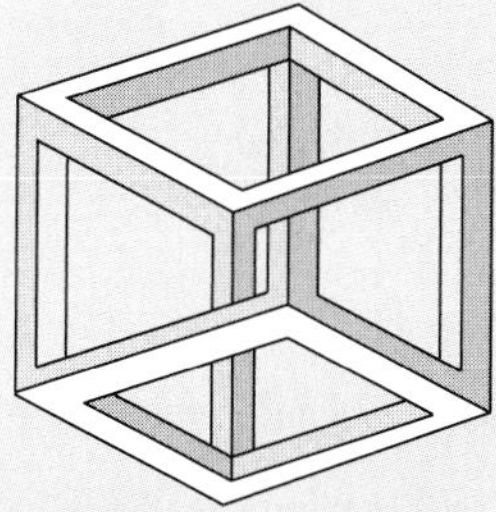

Escher's *Belvedere* is a lithograph of impossibilities. **[Ask]** "What do you see that is impossible?" [ladder from outside to inside, cube the boy is holding, pillars on the building] "How is the cube the boy is holding like the building he is sitting next to?" [Diagonally opposite sides that shouldn't be connected in a cube are connected with an edge. In the building a ladder or pillars go from the inside to the outside, from the back to the front.]

"What does the drawing on the paper at the boy's feet show?" [Circled parts show where one edge is behind the other when looked at one way and in front of the other when looked at another way. When one is in front and the other is in back, it becomes an impossible figure.] "Where do you see right angles?"

LESSON

12.1

PLANNING

LESSON OUTLINE

One day:

20 min	Investigation and Examples
10 min	Sharing
5 min	Closing
10 min	Exercises

MATERIALS

- calculators
- protractors
- rulers
- Trigonometry Calculator Note (W), *optional*

TEACHING

For every acute angle there are numbers that give the ratios of the sides of any right triangle that has the given angle as one of its angles; all such triangles are similar.

One step Pose this problem, from Exercise 7 of Lesson 12.5: "During a strong wind, a tree cracks and bends over, touching the ground as if the trunk were hinged. The tip of the tree touches the ground 20 feet 6 inches from the base of the tree. It's too difficult to measure the other lengths, but you can determine that the former treetop forms a 38° angle with the ground. Is this enough information to determine the length of the tree?" As you circulate, some students may claim that they don't have enough information. Ask them what more they'd need to know, and suggest that they discuss their ideas with each other. Encourage students to draw several right triangles with a 38° angle and to measure the sides and the ratios of the sides.

LESSON 12.1

Trigonometric Ratios

Research is what I am doing when I don't know what I'm doing.

WERNHER VON BRAUN

Trigonometry is the study of the relationships between the sides and the angles of triangles. In this lesson you will discover some of these relationships for right triangles.

Science CONNECTION

Trigonometry has origins in astronomy. The Greek astronomer Claudius Ptolemy (100–170 C.E.) used tables of chord ratios in his book known as *Almagest.* These chord ratios and their related angles were used to describe the motion of planets in what were thought to be circular orbits. This woodcut shows Ptolemy using astronomy tools.

When studying right triangles, early mathematicians discovered that whenever the ratio of the shorter leg's length to the longer leg's length was close to a specific fraction, the angle opposite the shorter leg was close to a specific measure. They found this (and its converse) to be true for all similar right triangles. For example, in every right triangle in which the ratio of the shorter leg's length to the longer leg's length is $\frac{3}{5}$, the angle opposite the shorter leg is approximately 31°.

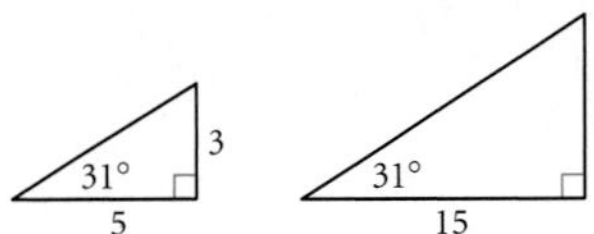

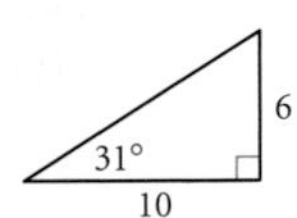

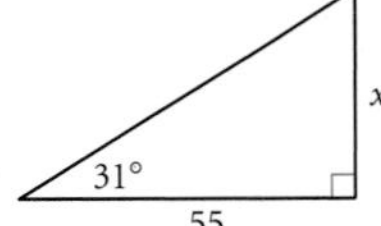

What is a good approximation for *x*?

What early mathematicians discovered is supported by what you know about similar triangles. If two right triangles each have an acute angle of the same measure, then the triangles are similar by the AA Similarity Conjecture. And if the triangles are similar, then corresponding sides are proportional. For example, in the similar right triangles shown below, these proportions are true:

$$\frac{BC}{AB} = \frac{EF}{DE} = \frac{HI}{GH} = \frac{KL}{JK}$$

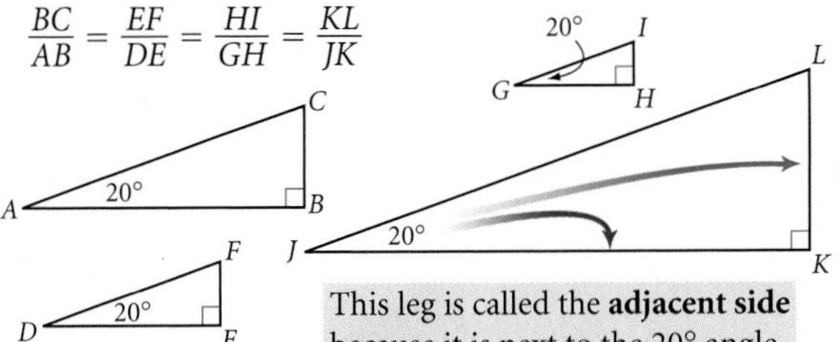

This leg is called the **opposite side** because it is across from the 20° angle.

This leg is called the **adjacent side** because it is next to the 20° angle.

The ratio of the length of the opposite side to the length of the adjacent side in a right triangle came to be called the **tangent** of the angle.

LESSON OBJECTIVES

- Encounter trigonometry and discover the sine, cosine, and tangent ratios
- Understand the usefulness of trigonometry
- Learn new vocabulary
- Develop cooperative behavior

NCTM STANDARDS

CONTENT		PROCESS	
	Number		Problem Solving
✓	Algebra		Reasoning
✓	Geometry	✓	Communication
✓	Measurement	✓	Connections
	Data/Probability	✓	Representation

In Chapter 11, you used mirrors and shadows to measure heights indirectly. Trigonometry gives you another indirect measuring method.

EXAMPLE A

At a distance of 36 meters from a tree, the angle from the ground to the top of the tree is 31°. Find the height of the tree.

▶ Solution

As you saw in the right triangles on page 620, the ratio of the length of the side opposite a 31° angle divided by the length of the side adjacent to a 31° angle is approximately $\frac{3}{5}$, or 0.6. You can set up a proportion using this tangent ratio.

$\frac{HT}{HA} \approx \tan 31°$ — The definition of tangent.

$\frac{HT}{HA} \approx 0.6$ — The tangent of 31° is approximately 0.6.

$\frac{HT}{36} \approx 0.6$ — Substitute 36 for HA.

$HT \approx (36)(0.6)$ — Multiply both sides by 36 and reduce the left side.

$HT \approx 22$ — Multiply.

The height of the tree is approximately 22 meters.

Deg.	Sin	Cos	Tan
12.0	0.2079	0.9781	0.2126
.1	.2096	.9778	.2144
.2	.2113	.9774	.2162
.3	.2130	.9770	.2180
.4	.2147	.9767	.2199
.5	.2164	.9763	.2217
.6	.2181	.9759	.2235
.7	.2198	.9755	.2254
.8	.2215	.9751	.2272
.9	.2233	.9748	.2290
13.0	0.2250	0.9744	0.2309
.1	.2267	.9740	.2327
.2	.2284	.9736	.2345
.3	.2300	.9732	.2364
.4	.2317	.9728	.2382
.5	.2334	.9724	.2401
.6	.2351	.9720	.2419
.7	.2368	.9715	.2438
.8	.2385	.9711	.2456
.9	.2402	.9707	.2475
14.0	0.2419	0.9703	0.2493
.1	.2436	.9699	.2512
.2	.2453	.9694	.2530

This excerpt from a trigonometric table shows sine, cosine, and tangent ratios for angles measuring from 12.0° to 14.2°.

In order to solve problems like Example A, early mathematicians made tables that related ratios of side lengths to angle measures. They named six possible ratios. You will work with these three: **sine, cosine,** and **tangent,** abbreviated sin, cos, and tan. **Sine** is the ratio of the length of the opposite side to the length of the hypotenuse. **Cosine** is the ratio of the length of the adjacent side to the length of the hypotenuse.

After they find the length of one side, they might use the Pythagorean Theorem to find the other. Don't disagree with the method, but try to be sure that at least one group uses ratios to find the hypotenuse and that another finds the other leg. During Sharing, attach the labels *sine* and *tangent* to the ratios that are useful for this problem, and define *cosine* as well. Then ask students how they might go backward, for example, finding the measure of an acute angle that has a known cosine.

INTRODUCTION

[Language] *Trigonometry* is made up of *trigon,* meaning "triangle," and *metry,* meaning "measurement." *Sine,* from the Latin for "fold," is derived from Arabic and Hindu. The Hindu word *jya* for the sine was adopted by the Arabs, who called the sine *jiba,* an otherwise meaningless word with the same sound as *jya.* In later Arabic writings *jiba* became *jaib,* meaning "fold." When European authors translated the Arabic into Latin, they translated *jaib* into the word *sinus. Cosine* is short for *complement's sine,* because $\cos A = \sin(90° - A)$.

A common mnemonic for remembering how these trigonometric ratios are defined is SOH CAH TOA.

MAKING THE CONNECTION

[Ask] "How are things seen differently in the Ptolemaic universe and in the Copernican universe?" [Ptolemaic: Earth-centered; Copernican: Sun-centered]

▶ EXAMPLE A

[Ask] "How do you decide which ratio to use?" [The ratio you use depends on which measures you have.]

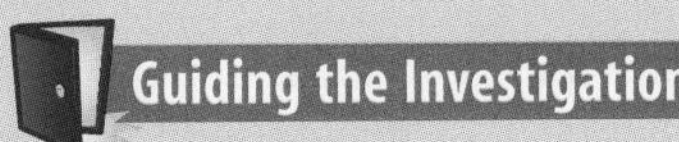

Guiding the Investigation

The hands-on experience with the trigonometric ratios leads students to connect the ratios with measures of parts of triangles instead of seeing them simply as numbers that their calculators magically produce. Students should understand that sin 20° is a pure number without degrees or any other unit.

As an alternative, you might assign each group a different angle measure from which they create a right triangle containing the given angle and its complement.

Step 5 **[Ask]** "What do you notice about the ratios?" [They don't depend on the size of the triangle.]

Step 5 $\sin A = \cos C$ because the side opposite $\angle A$ is the side adjacent to $\angle C$.

$\cos A = \sin C$ because the side adjacent to $\angle A$ is the side opposite $\angle C$.

$\tan 20 = \frac{1}{\tan 70°}$ because by definition tan 20° is the reciprocal of tan 70°.

Trigonometric Ratios

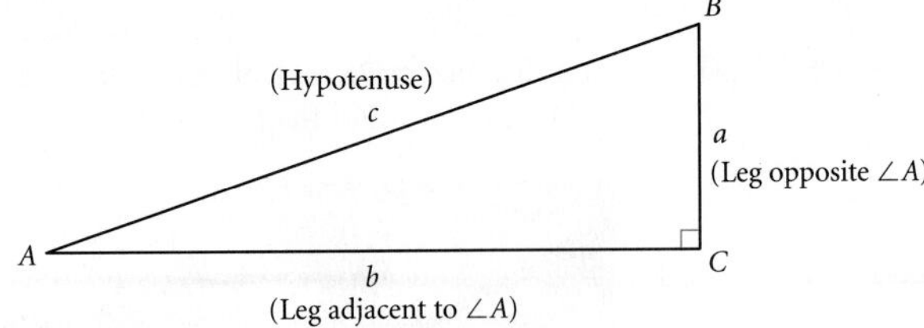

For an acute angle A in any right triangle ABC:

$$\text{sine of } \angle A = \frac{\text{length of leg opposite } \angle A}{\text{length of hypotenuse}} \quad \text{or} \quad \sin A = \frac{a}{c}$$

$$\text{cosine of } \angle A = \frac{\text{length of leg adjacent to } \angle A}{\text{length of hypotenuse}} \quad \text{or} \quad \cos A = \frac{b}{c}$$

$$\text{tangent of } \angle A = \frac{\text{length of leg opposite } \angle A}{\text{length of leg adjacent to } \angle A} \quad \text{or} \quad \tan A = \frac{a}{b}$$

Investigation
Trigonometric Tables

You will need
- a protractor
- a ruler

In this investigation you will make a small table of trigonometric ratios for angles measuring 20° and 70°.

Step 1 Use your protractor to make a large right triangle ABC with $m\angle A = 20°$, $m\angle B = 90°$, and $m\angle C = 70°$.

Step 2 Measure AB, AC, and BC to the nearest millimeter.

Step 3 Use your side lengths and the definitions of sine, cosine, and tangent to complete a table like this. Round your calculations to the nearest thousandth.

$m\angle A$	$\sin A$	$\cos A$	$\tan A$
20°	0.342	0.940	0.364

$m\angle C$	$\sin C$	$\cos C$	$\tan C$
70°	0.940	0.342	2.747

Step 4 Share your results with your group. Calculate the average of each ratio within your group. Create a new table with your group's average values.

Step 5 Discuss your results. What observations can you make about the trigonometric ratios you found? What is the relationship between the values for 20° and the values for 70°? Explain why you think these relationships exist.

Go to **www.keymath.com/DG** to find complete tables of trigonometric ratios.

Step 6 Students can experiment with their calculators on their own or use the Trigonometry Calculator Note worksheet to determine what works for their calculator.

Step 7 **[Alert]** Many calculators default to radian mode and need to be changed to degree mode. Some students might enjoy seeing how to use a trigonometry table; for a historical connection, you could show an old book of mathematical tables or show the table available at www.keymath.com/DG.

Today, trigonometric tables have been replaced by calculators that have sin, cos, and tan keys.

Step 6 Experiment with your calculator to determine how to find the sine, cosine, and tangent values of angles.

Step 7 Use your calculator to find sin 20°, cos 20°, tan 20°, sin 70°, cos 70°, and tan 70°. Check your group's table. How do the trigonometric ratios found by measuring sides compare with the trigonometric ratios you found on the calculator?

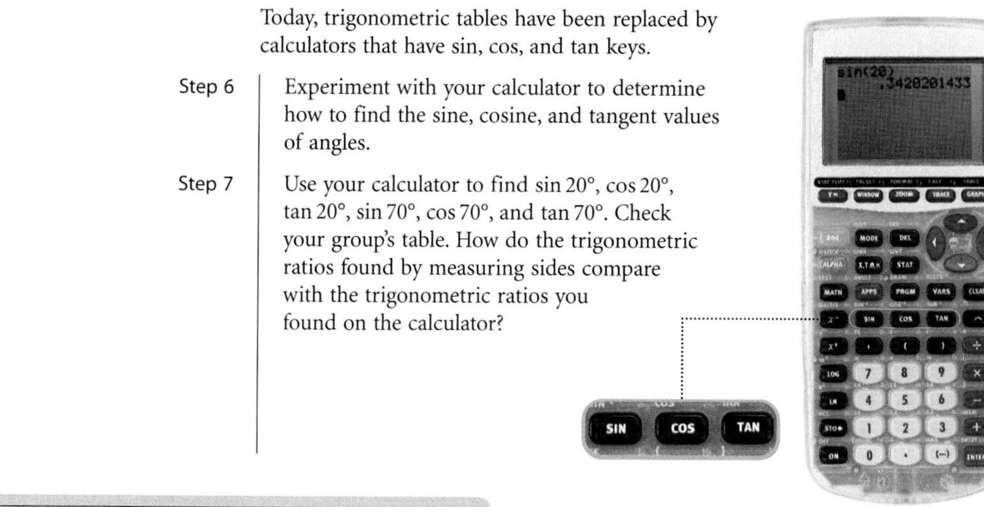

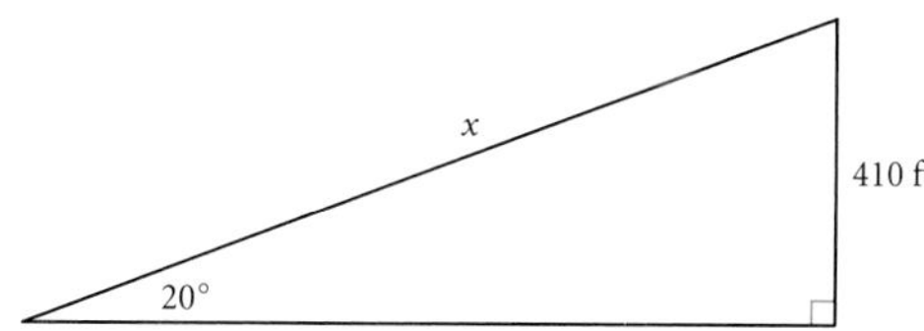

Using a table of trigonometric ratios, or using a calculator, you can find the approximate lengths of the sides of a right triangle given the measures of any acute angle and any side.

EXAMPLE B

Find the length of the hypotenuse of a right triangle if an acute angle measures 20° and the side opposite the angle measures 410 feet.

▶ Solution

x

410 ft

20°

Sketch a diagram. The trigonometric ratio that relates the lengths of the opposite side and the hypotenuse is the sine ratio.

$\sin 20° = \frac{410}{x}$ — Substitute 20° for the measure of $\angle A$ and substitute 410 for the length of the opposite side. The length of the hypotenuse is unknown, so use x.

$x(\sin 20°) = 410$ — Multiply both sides by x and reduce the right side.

$x = \frac{410}{\sin 20°}$ — Divide both sides by sin 20° and reduce the left side.

From your table in the investigation, or from a calculator, you know that sin 20° is approximately 0.342.

$x \approx \frac{410}{0.342}$ — Sin 20° is approximately 0.342.

$x \approx 1199$ — Divide.

The length of the hypotenuse is approximately 1199 feet.

Sharing Ideas (continued)

numerator. The definition of *tangent* relies on opposite and adjacent sides, *not* shorter and longer.

[Ask] "How does using trigonometric ratios compare with using the Pythagorean Theorem or similar triangles to find lengths and distances?" [To use the Pythagorean Theorem, you need to know the lengths of two sides of a right triangle. To use similar triangles, you need two triangles. To use trigonometric ratios, you need only one triangle, but it needs to be a right triangle and you need to know the length of one side and the measure of one nonright angle.]

[Ask] "Why doesn't the scale factor depend on the angle?" [By AA, all right triangles with a given nonright angle are similar, so they all have the same ratios of corresponding sides.]

For an exercise in systematic reasoning, ask what other ratios of sides of a right triangle are possible. The other three ratios won't appear in the student book. They are the reciprocals (not the inverses) of the sine, cosine, and tangent and include the complement's tangent, or *cotangent.*

▶ EXAMPLE B

[Ask] "Why is the variable in the denominator?" [The unknown is length of the hypotenuse.] You might encourage students to rework the problem using the other nonright angle.

Note that the approximation of sin 20° does not occur until the end. As with fractions, π, and radicals, using a decimal approximation of a trigonometric ratio too early can lead to compounded round-off errors. You might illustrate this by finding sin 20°, rounding it off to 0.32, and comparing the result to the result obtained when you put off approximating sin 20° until the end of the calculation.

[Ask] "How does Example B compare to Example A?" [In both examples an angle measure is given and two sides are described, but the trigonometric ratios differ according to which sides are given.]

SHARING IDEAS

As students present their ideas, **[Ask]** "How do the ratios here compare with those in similar triangles?" [For similar triangles, most ratios involved sides from two triangles; here they involve sides from one triangle.] Elicit the idea that if $\frac{a}{a'} = \frac{b}{b'}$, then $\frac{a}{b} = \frac{a'}{b'}$. It's a subtle point that some students are unable to articulate.

If some students are confusing the leg opposite an angle with the leg adjacent to the angle, **[Ask]** "How are the opposite and adjacent sides related for the 20° angle and the 70° angle? *Cosine* stands for *complement's sine.* Does that make sense?" [The side adjacent to an angle is opposite its complement, the other nonright angle in the triangle.] "What is sin 90°?" [1] "Cos 90°?" [0]

[Alert] The example that uses 31° may lead students to think that the shorter leg must be in the

Sharing Ideas (continued)
Ask students what sense they have made of the inverse process. Bring out the idea that it gives the acute angle that has the given ratio. In Example C, $\tan^{-1}(0.5333)$ is the acute angle whose tangent is 0.5333. Students might benefit more from seeing how to "go backward" on a table than from pushing buttons on a calculator. You can help students think about the statement "The inverse tangent of x is the angle whose tangent is x" by asking them to translate into words the claims that $\tan(\tan^{-1} x) = x$ and $\tan^{-1}(\tan A) = A$.

[Ask] "Does calculating the sine of an angle on a calculator and then pressing the x^{-1} button get the angle measure back?" [The x^{-1} button gives the reciprocal of the ratio, not the angle measure.] Because the notation has the potential to confuse students, $\sin^{-1}$ is sometimes called *arcsine,* $\tan^{-1}$ *arctangent,* and so on. Students' understanding might be deepened if you have them draw triangles appropriate for Exercises 10–13.

▸ EXAMPLE C

To build students' understanding, you might mention that the missing step after $\tan A = \frac{8}{15}$ is $\tan^{-1}(\tan A) = \tan^{-1}\frac{8}{15}$. If students are using a table rather than a calculator, they will find the value of the tangent closest to 0.5333 and look at the row and column headings to find the angle measure associated with that tangent.

You might ask students how else they might solve this problem. They might use the Pythagorean Theorem to find the length of the hypotenuse and then use either the sine or the cosine.

With the help of a calculator, it is also possible to determine the size of either acute angle in a right triangle if you know the length of any two sides of that triangle. For instance, if you know the ratio of the legs in a right triangle, you can find the measure of one acute angle by using the **inverse tangent,** or $\tan^{-1}$, function. Let's look at an example.

The inverse tangent of x is defined as the measure of the acute angle whose tangent is x. The tangent function and inverse tangent function undo each other. That is, $\tan^{-1}(\tan A) = A$ and $\tan(\tan^{-1} x) = x$.

EXAMPLE C

A right triangle has legs of length 8 inches and 15 inches. Find the measure of the angle opposite the 8-inch leg.

▸ Solution

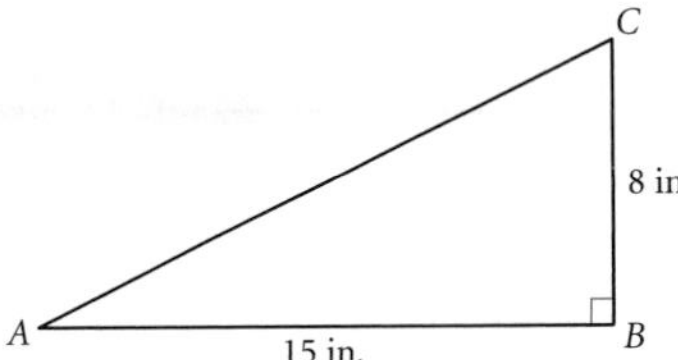

Sketch a diagram. In this sketch the angle opposite the 8-inch side is $\angle A$. The trigonometric ratio that relates the lengths of the opposite side and the adjacent side is the tangent ratio.

$\tan A = \frac{8}{15}$ — Substitute 8 for the length of the opposite side and substitute 15 for the length of the adjacent side.

To find the angle that has an approximate tangent value of $\frac{8}{15}$, you can use a calculator to find the inverse tangent of $\frac{8}{15}$, or $\tan^{-1}\left(\frac{8}{15}\right)$.

$A \approx \tan^{-1}\left(\frac{8}{15}\right)$ — Take the inverse tangent of both sides.

$A \approx 28$ — Use your calculator to evaluate $\tan^{-1}\left(\frac{8}{15}\right)$.

The measure of the angle opposite the 8-inch side is approximately 28°.

You can also use inverse sine, or $\sin^{-1}$, and inverse cosine, or $\cos^{-1}$, to find angle measures.

EXERCISES

You will need

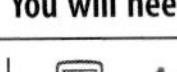
A calculator for Exercises **1–6** and **10–22**

For Exercises 1–3, use a calculator to find each trigonometric ratio accurate to four decimal places.

1. $\sin 37°$ 0.6018 **2.** $\cos 29°$ 0.8746 **3.** $\tan 8°$ 0.1405

For Exercises 4–6, solve for x. Express each answer accurate to two decimal places.

4. $\sin 40° = \frac{x}{18}$ 11.57 **5.** $\cos 52° = \frac{19}{x}$ 30.86 **6.** $\tan 29° = \frac{x}{112}$ 62.08

Assessing Progress
You can see how well students understand that congruent corresponding angles imply similarity and how well they measure angles and work with ratios and with triangles oriented differently in the plane.

Closing the Lesson

Trigonometry is very useful in finding distances in situations where constructing similar triangles is difficult. The similarity of all right triangles with a congruent nonright angle means that they all have the same ratios of corresponding sides. These **trigonometric ratios** (**sine** for opposite over hypotenuse, **cosine** for adjacent over hypotenuse, and **tangent** for opposite over adjacent) allow you to find any unknown length of a side of a right triangle if you know the length of one side and the measure of one nonright angle. You can work backward to find angles that have given ratios.

For Exercises 7–9, find each trigonometric ratio.

7. $\sin A = \underline{?}$ $\frac{s}{t}$
$\cos A = \underline{?}$ $\frac{r}{t}$
$\tan A = \underline{?}$ ⓗ $\frac{s}{r}$

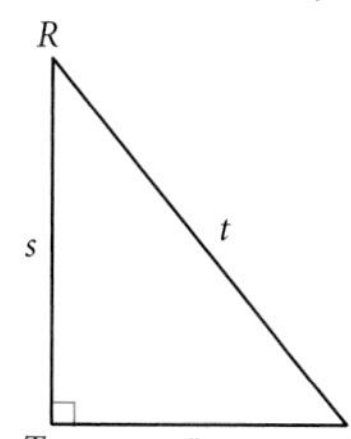

8. $\sin \theta = \underline{?}$ $\frac{4}{5}$
$\cos \theta = \underline{?}$ $\frac{3}{5}$
$\tan \theta = \underline{?}$ $\frac{4}{3}$

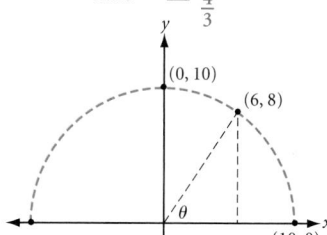

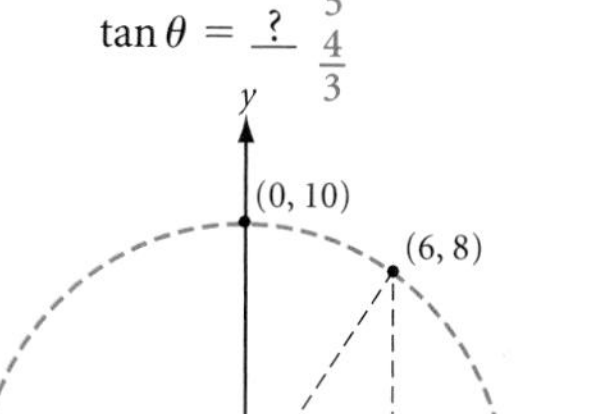

9. $\sin A = \underline{?}$ $\frac{7}{25}$ $\sin B = \underline{?}$ $\frac{24}{25}$
$\cos A = \underline{?}$ $\frac{24}{25}$ $\cos B = \underline{?}$ $\frac{7}{25}$
$\tan A = \underline{?}$ $\frac{7}{24}$ $\tan B = \underline{?}$ $\frac{24}{7}$

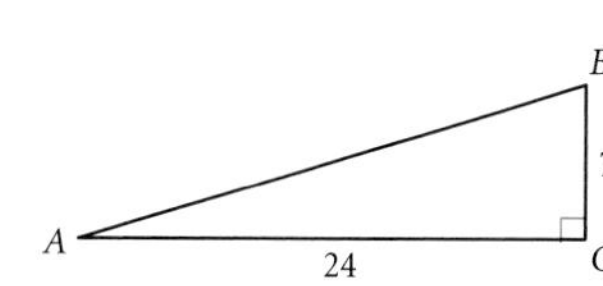

For Exercises 10–13, find the measure of each angle accurate to the nearest degree.

10. $\sin A = 0.5$ ⓗ 30°

11. $\cos B = 0.6$ 53°

12. $\tan C = 0.5773$ 30°

13. $\tan x = \frac{48}{106}$ 24°

For Exercises 14–20, find the values of a–g accurate to the nearest whole unit.

14. ⓗ $a \approx 35$ cm

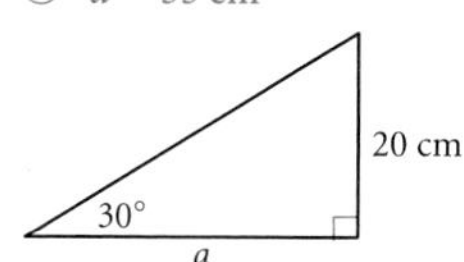

15. $b \approx 15$ cm

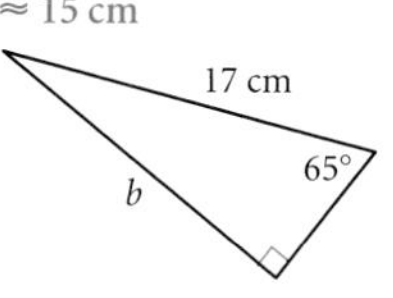

16. $c \approx 105$ yd

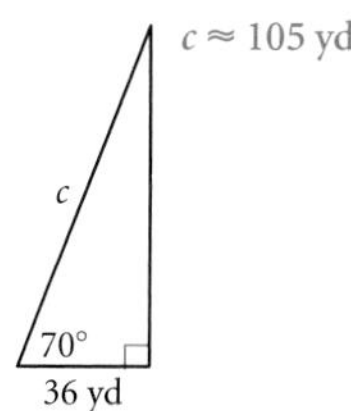

17. $d \approx 40°$

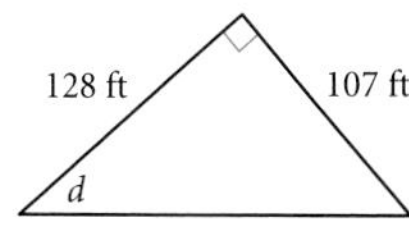

18. $e \approx 50$ cm

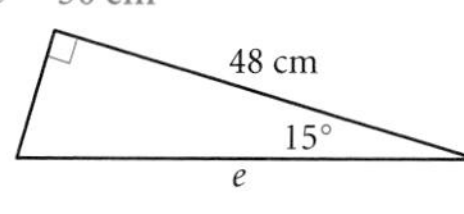

19. $f \approx 33°$

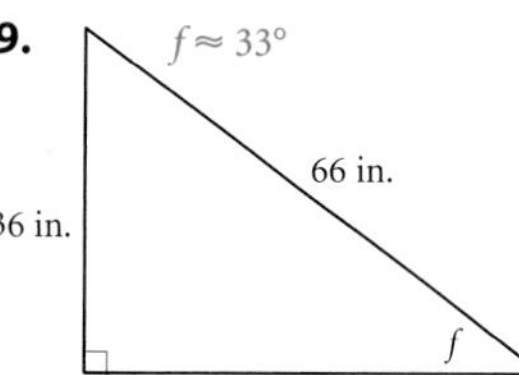

20. $g \approx 18$ in.

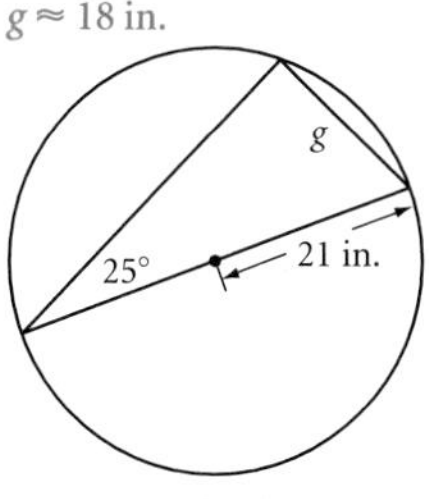

21. Find the perimeter of this quadrilateral. ⓗ approximately 237 m

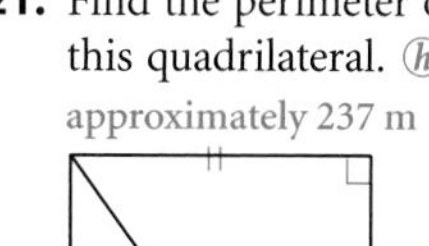
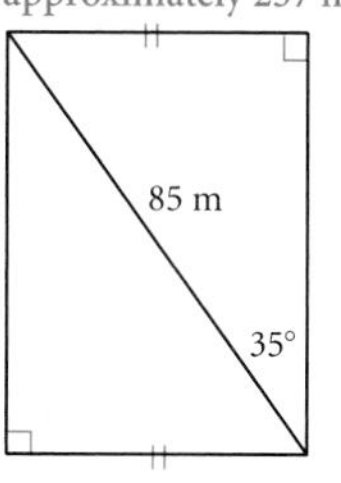

22. Find x. $x \approx 121$ ft

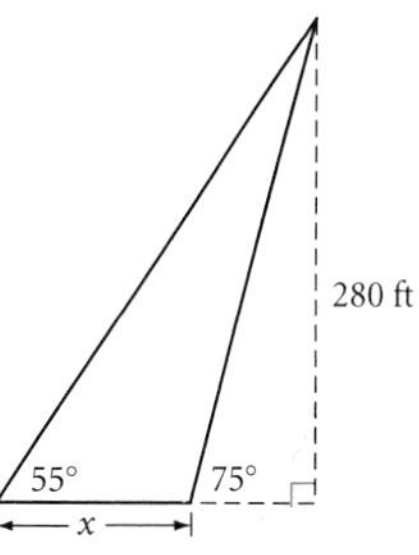

BUILDING UNDERSTANDING

Students who do not have a scientific or graphing calculator can complete these exercises using a table of trigonometric ratios. One can be found using the links at www.keymath.com/DG. It will help students to write an equation representing each situation.

ASSIGNING HOMEWORK

Essential	1–20
Performance assessment	21
Portfolio	9
Group	14–22
Review	23–28

▶ Helping with the Exercises

Exercises 1–6 You might review rounding again. The number of decimal places requested is arbitrary. The degree of accuracy needed in real-world applications is determined from the context.

Exercise 8 The Greek letters θ (theta), α (alpha), and β (beta) are common variables used to represent angle measures.

Exercise 20 As needed, point out that the dot along one chord indicates that the chord goes through the circle's center and thus is a diameter. Therefore the triangle is inscribed in a semicircle.

Exercise 21 [Ask] "The quadrilateral looks like a rectangle. Is it?" [Because two sides of the right triangles are congruent, the third sides are also, by the Pythagorean Theorem. Therefore the quadrilateral is a parallelogram. Every parallelogram with a right angle is a rectangle.]

Exercise 22 If students are having difficulty, see if they're working with right triangles to find lengths of horizontal segments, for subtraction.

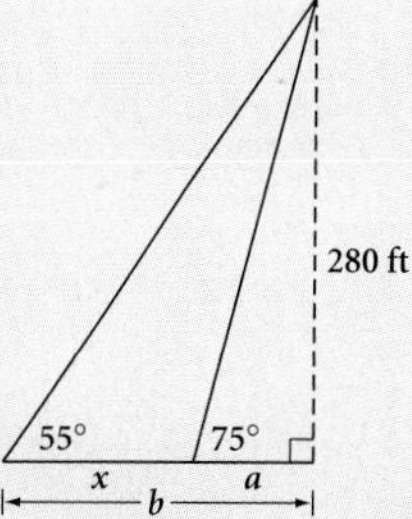

Exercise 25 Students should understand that area is the criterion of comparison, but they need not calculate the areas of the pizzas. The square of the ratio of the diameters allows the comparison.

Exercise 26 Students should immediately realize that volume is the quantity they are comparing.

Exercise 27 As needed, remind students that when working with circles it's often useful to draw radii to points important to the problem.

EXTENSIONS

A. Have students develop the cotangent, secant, and cosecant ratios.

B. Have students complete a trigonometry table for angles measuring from 5° to 85° (in 5° increments), using the process of carefully drawing right triangles and measuring sides.

Review

For Exercises 23 and 24, solve for x.

UYAS 9 **23.** $\frac{x}{3} = \frac{17}{8}$ 6.375

UYAS 9 **24.** $\frac{5}{x} = \frac{25}{11}$ 2.2

11.5 **25.** APPLICATION Which is the better buy? A pizza with a 16-inch diameter for $12.50, or a pizza with a 20-inch diameter for $20.00? 16-inch pizza

10.2 **26.** APPLICATION Which is the better buy? Ice cream in a cylindrical container with a base diameter of 6 inches and a height of 8 inches for $3.98, or ice cream in a box (square prism) with a base edge of 6 inches and a height of 8 inches for $4.98? box of ice cream

9.6 **27.** A diameter of a circle is cut at right angles by a chord into a 12 cm segment and a 4 cm segment. How long is the chord? ⓗ $8\sqrt{3}$ cm

10.7 **28.** Find the volume and surface area of this sphere. $V = 288\pi\ \text{ft}^3, S = 144\pi\ \text{ft}^2$

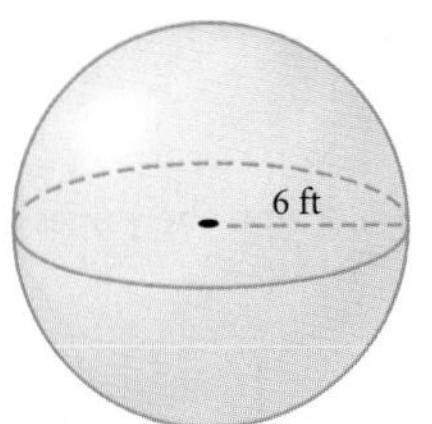

IMPROVING YOUR VISUAL THINKING SKILLS

3-by-3 Inductive Reasoning Puzzle II

Sketch the figure missing in the lower right corner of this pattern.

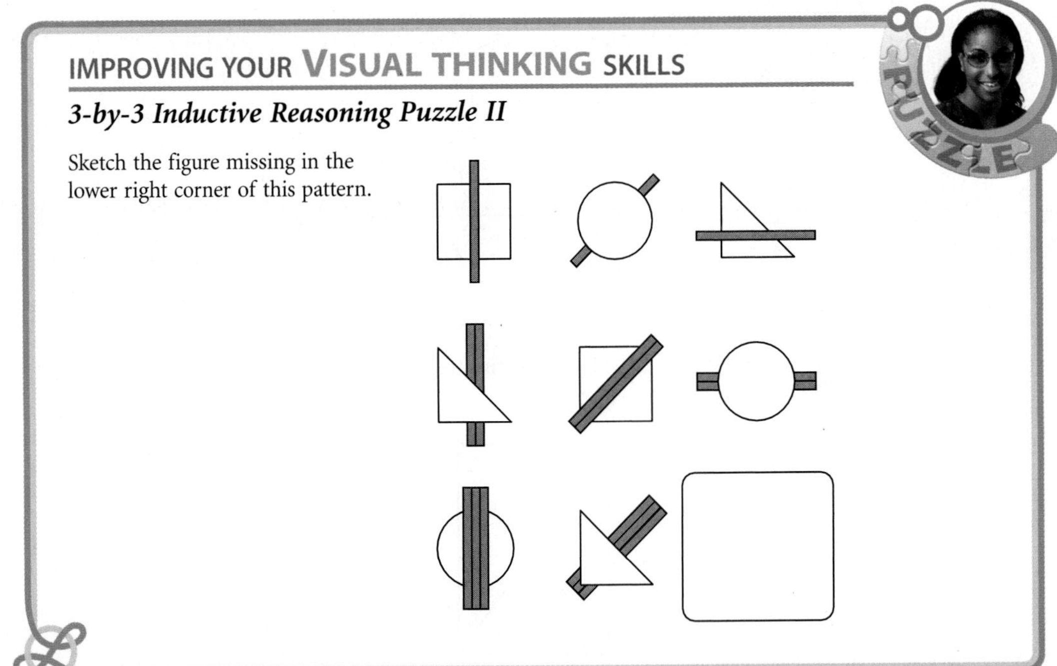

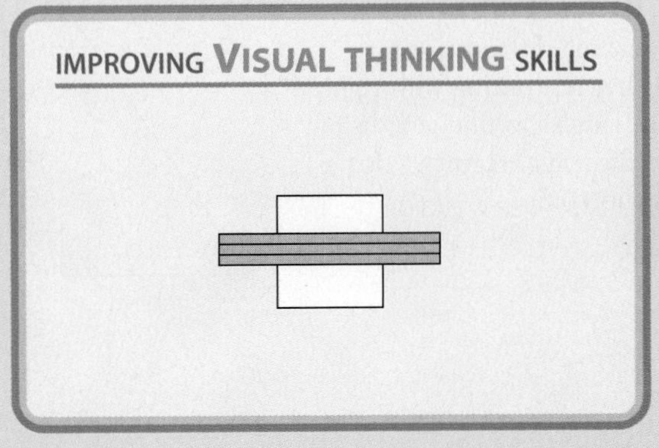

LESSON

12.2 Problem Solving with Right Triangles

What science can there be more noble, more excellent, more useful . . . than mathematics?

BENJAMIN FRANKLIN

Right triangle trigonometry is often used indirectly to find the height of a tall object. To solve a problem of this type, measure the angle from the horizontal to your line of sight when you look at the top or bottom of the object.

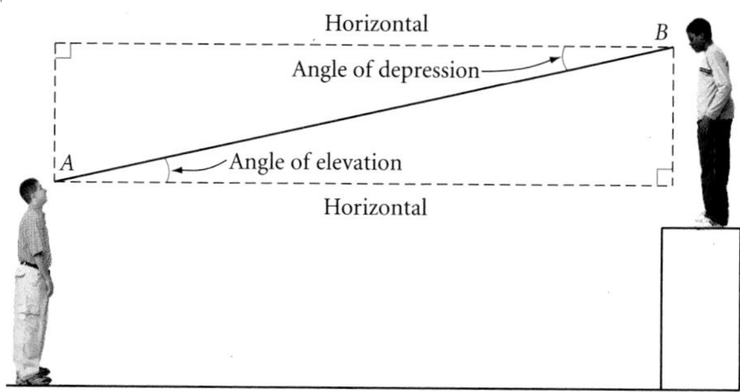

If you look up, you measure the **angle of elevation.** If you look down, you measure the **angle of depression.**

Here's an example.

EXAMPLE

The angle of elevation from a sailboat to the top of a 121-foot lighthouse on the shore measures 16°. To the nearest foot, how far is the sailboat from shore?

▸ Solution

The height of the lighthouse is opposite the 16° angle. The unknown distance is the adjacent side. Set up a tangent ratio.

$$\tan 16^\circ = \frac{121}{d}$$

$$d(\tan 16^\circ) = 121$$

$$d = \frac{121}{\tan 16^\circ}$$

$$d \approx 422$$

The sailboat is approximately 422 feet from shore.

NCTM STANDARDS

CONTENT		PROCESS	
	Number	✓	Problem Solving
✓	Algebra		Reasoning
✓	Geometry	✓	Communication
✓	Measurement	✓	Connections
	Data/Probability	✓	Representation

LESSON OBJECTIVES

- Use trigonometry to solve applied problems
- Learn new vocabulary
- Develop reading comprehension, problem-solving skills, and cooperative behavior

LESSON 12.2

PLANNING

LESSON OUTLINE

One day:

5 min Example

40 min Exercises and Sharing

MATERIALS

- calculators

TEACHING

In this lesson, students see a variety of trigonometric applications, mostly involving angles of elevation or depression.

[ESL] In a nonmathematical context, *elevation* might be a "lifting up" from the horizontal and *depression* might be a "pushing down." Students might have heard the latter word only in the psychological sense.

One step Pose this problem: "The string on your kite has an angle of elevation of 20°. You know that you've let out 800 feet of string. How high is your kite?" Define "angle of elevation" as students ask about it. Encourage them to draw and mark right triangles to represent the situation.

▸ EXAMPLE

This example assumes that the lighthouse is vertical, thus creating a right triangle. You could also solve the equation by inverting both sides first and then multiplying by 121. Note that the decimal approximation of tan 16° is not found until the last step. Many trigonometric ratios are irrational values. Answers need to be rounded to the appropriate number of significant digits.

SHARING IDEAS

[Ask] "Is the angle of elevation defined with respect to the horizontal or the vertical?" [the horizontal] Refer students to the diagram at the beginning of this lesson and note that the angle of elevation from viewer *A* looking up to point *B* is marked to have the same measure as the angle of depression from viewer *B* looking down to point *A*.

[Ask] "Are the angle measures really equal? Why?" [yes; by the Parallel Lines Conjecture, assuming horizontal lines are parallel] You might ask students to bring in photographs from magazines and newspapers that illustrate angles of elevation and depression.

In the example, the horizontal line of sight conveniently goes to the bottom of the lighthouse. **[Ask]** "How would you solve this problem if the horizontal line of sight went to the rocks?"

Assessing Progress

Through students' work on the exercises and their presentations, you can assess their skills at drawing representation diagrams and using trigonometry to find missing parts of those diagrams.

Closing the Lesson

Go through the steps students followed in solving applied trigonometric problems so far: They drew right triangles; they labeled the known sides and angles and what they wanted to find; they decided on a trigonometric ratio that related those items; they used that ratio to write an equation and then solved it.

Because the focus of this lesson is on applications, you might have students work on and share several exercises before you close the lesson.

EXERCISES

You will need

 *A calculator* for Exercises **1–19**

1. According to a Chinese legend from the Han dynasty (206 B.C.E.–220 C.E.), General Han Xin flew a kite over the palace of his enemy to determine the distance between his troops and the palace. If the general let out 800 meters of string and the kite was flying at a 35° angle of elevation, how far away was the palace from General Han Xin's position? approximately 655 m

2. Benny is flying a kite directly over his friend, Frank, who is 125 meters away. When he holds the kite string down to the ground, the string makes a 39° angle with the level ground. How high is Benny's kite? approximately 101 m

3. **APPLICATION** The angle of elevation from a ship to the top of a 42-meter lighthouse on the shore measures 33°. How far is the ship from the shore? (Assume the horizontal line of sight meets the bottom of the lighthouse.) approximately 65 m

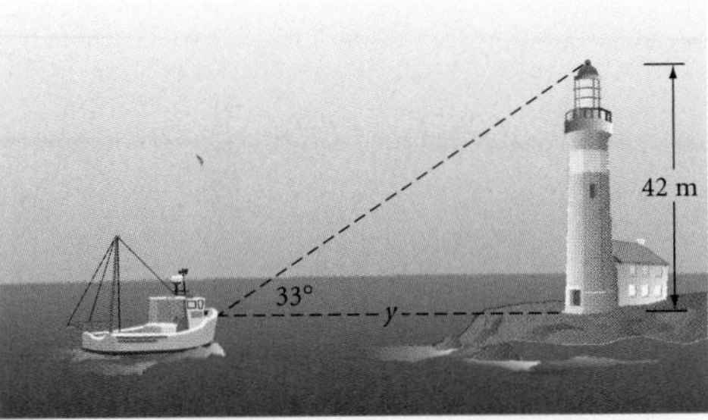

4. **APPLICATION** A salvage ship's sonar locates wreckage at a 12° angle of depression. A diver is lowered 40 meters to the ocean floor. How far does the diver need to walk along the ocean floor to the wreckage? approximately 188 m

5. **APPLICATION** A meteorologist shines a spotlight vertically onto the bottom of a cloud formation. He then places an angle-measuring device 65 meters from the spotlight and measures a 74° angle of elevation from the ground to the spot of light on the clouds. How high are the clouds? approximately 227 m

The distance from the ground to a cloud formation is called the cloud *ceiling*.

6. **APPLICATION** Meteorologist Wendy Stevens uses a theodolite (an angle-measuring device) on a 1-meter-tall tripod to find the height of a weather balloon. She views the balloon at a 44° angle of elevation. A radio signal from the balloon tells her that it is 1400 meters from her theodolite.
   a. How high is the balloon? ⓗ approximately 974 m
   b. How far is she from the point directly below the balloon? approximately 1007 m
   c. If Wendy's theodolite were on the ground rather than on a tripod, would your answers change? Explain your reasoning. Yes, the height of the balloon would be 1 meter less because you don't have to account for the tripod. The distance to a point under the balloon would not change.

Science CONNECTION

Weather balloons carry into the atmosphere what is called a *radiosonde*, an instrument with sensors that detect information about wind direction, temperature, air pressure, and humidity. Twice a day across the world, this upper-air data is transmitted by radio waves to a receiving station. Meteorologists use the information to forecast the weather.

BUILDING UNDERSTANDING

These exercises help prepare students for the exploration that follows, in which they will find the height of very tall objects. As needed, encourage students to draw a diagram for each problem. **[Alert]** Students might label the angle of elevation or depression as the angle made with a vertical line instead of a horizontal line, even if they can recite the definitions.

ASSIGNING HOMEWORK

Essential	2, 4, 6, 8–16
Performance assessment	1–7
Portfolio	1–7
Journal	6
Group	8–16
Review	17–25

7. **APPLICATION** A ship's officer sees a lighthouse at a 42° angle to the path of the ship. After the ship travels 1800 m, the lighthouse is at a 90° angle to the ship's path. What is the distance between the ship and the lighthouse at this second sighting? ⓗ

approximately 1621 m

When there are no visible landmarks, sailors at sea depend on the location of stars or the Sun for navigation. For example, in the Northern Hemisphere, Polaris (the North Star), stays approximately at the same angle above the horizon for a given latitude. If Polaris appears higher overhead or closer to the horizon, sailors can tell whether their course is taking them north or south.

This painting by Winslow Homer (1836–1910) is titled *Breezing Up* (1876).

For Exercises 8–16, find each length or angle measure accurate to the nearest whole unit.

8. $a \approx$? 9 cm

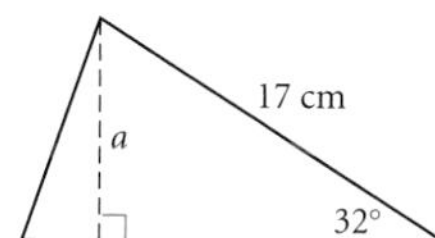

9. $x \approx$? 64°

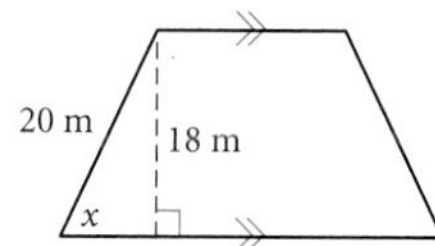

10. $r \approx$? 7 cm

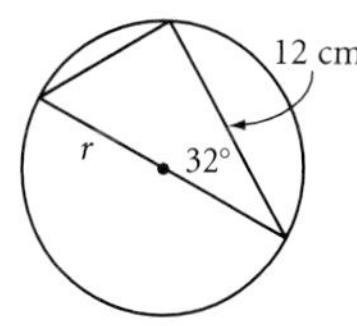

11. $e \approx$? 2 m

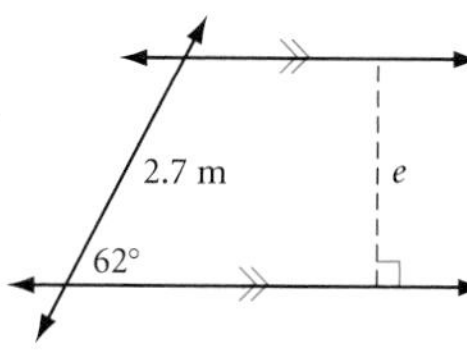

12. $d_1 \approx$? ⓗ 22 in.

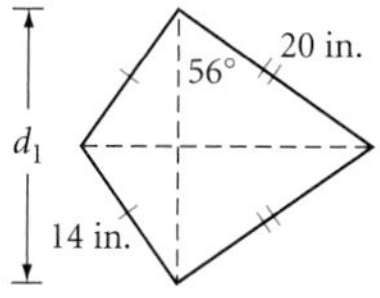

13. $f \approx$? 49°

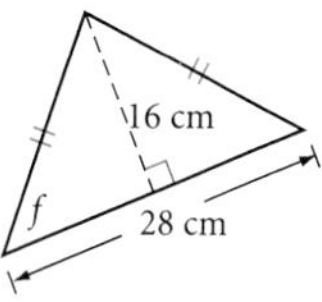

14. $\theta \approx$? 127°

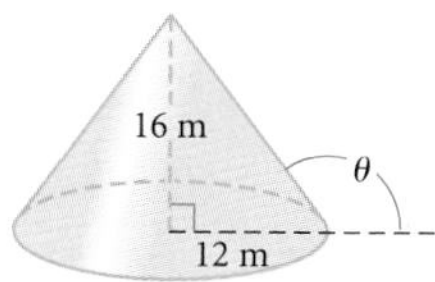

15. $\beta \approx$? ⓗ 30°

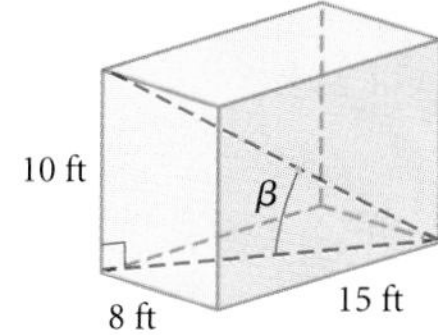

16. $h \approx$? 64 cm

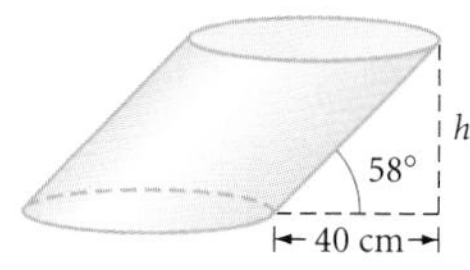

▶ Helping with the Exercises

Exercise 1 The problem assumes that the troops and the palace are on the same horizontal plane.

Exercise 4 **[ESL]** *Salvage* means "save what is still of value." *Sonar* is an acronym for "sound navigation and ranging"; it is a method of locating an object by timing sound waves that bounce off the object.

Exercise 6 This exercise offers a good opportunity to talk about appropriate accuracy in different situations. For example, if the weather balloon were only 3 meters above Wendy's sextant, the 1-meter height of the sextant would be crucially important. However, in this situation its height may be irrelevant compared with the distance of nearly 1000 meters.

Exercise 7 Even though this problem does not use angles of elevation, it does use right triangle trigonometry.

Exercises 8–16 You might suggest students complete these problems before they do the applications.

Exercise 10 As needed, **[Ask]** "Is there anything you can say about angles inscribed in a semicircle?" [They are right angles.]

Exercise 13 If students are having difficulty, ask if anything they know about the altitude to the base of an isosceles triangle might be useful. [It bisects the base.]

Exercise 14 Students might find the measure of the top angle of the triangle and then write the measure θ (theta) as the sum of the measures of the top angle and the right angle; or they might see angle θ as the supplement of the third angle of the triangle.

Exercise 15 The symbol β is beta, the second letter of the Greek alphabet. The Pythagorean Theorem will be helpful in finding the diagonal of the bottom face.

MAKING THE CONNECTION

The Polynesian method used two legs of a right triangle (the length of the navigator's arm and the length of the hook) to measure the angle of elevation of Polaris. Because the length of the navigator's arm was constant, the angle of elevation was dependent upon the hook used. Thus, each hook represented a different latitude location from Polaris.

Exercise 21 [Alert] Students might have difficulty realizing that the Inscribed Angles Intercepting Arcs Conjecture implies that the triangles are similar.

Exercise 22 In the past, students have seen that if the wood sinks, then the amount of water displaced equals the volume of the wood. In this exercise, they use the contrapositive, which is logically equivalent: If the volume of water displaced does not equal the volume of the wood, then the wood floats.

22. The block has a volume of 90 cm^3 but it only displaces 62.8 cm^3 of water. So none of the block is under water, which means it floats.

Exercise 24 If students have difficulty imagining this, you might suggest that they think of point P as being so far out that $\overrightarrow{PT}$ and $\overrightarrow{PS}$ are virtually parallel to $\overline{PA}$.

24a. decreases, approaching 0

24b. decreases, approaching 0

24c. remains 90°

24d. increases, approaching $(AO)^2$

24e. decreases, approaching 1

24f. decreases, approaching 1

Review

12.1 For Exercises 17–19, find the measure of each angle to the nearest degree.

17. $\sin D = 0.7071$ 45°

18. $\tan E = 1.7321$ 60°

19. $\cos F = 0.5$ 60°

Technology CONNECTION

The earliest known navigation tool was used by the Polynesians, yet it didn't measure angles. Early Polynesians carried several different-length hooks made from split bamboo and shells. A navigator held a hook at arm's length, positioned the bottom of the hook on the horizon, and sighted the North Star through the top of the hook. The length of the hook indicated the navigator's approximate latitude. Can you use trigonometry to explain how this method works?

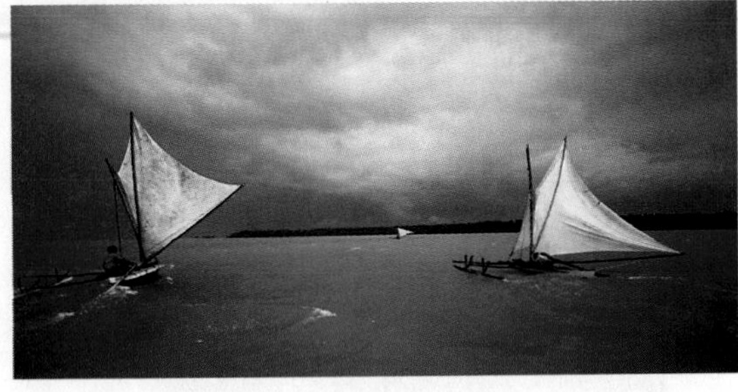

12.1 **20.** Solve for x.

a. $4.7 = \dfrac{x}{3.2}$ 15.04

b. $8 = \dfrac{16.4}{x}$ 2.05

c. $0.3736 = \dfrac{x}{14}$ 5.2304

d. $0.9455 = \dfrac{2.5}{x}$ 2.644

11.2 **21.** Find x and y. $x = 3.5, y = 9\frac{1}{7} \approx 9.14$

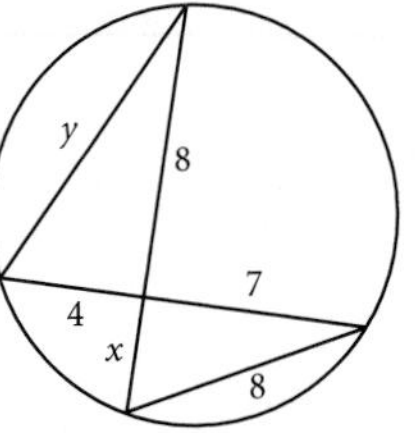

10.5 **22.** A 3-by-5-by-6 cm block of wood is dropped into a cylindrical container of water with radius 5 cm. The level of the water rises 0.8 cm. Does the block sink or float? Explain how you know.

9.5 **23.** Scalene triangle ABC has altitudes $\overline{AX}$, $\overline{BY}$, and $\overline{CZ}$. If $AB > BC > AC$, write an inequality that relates the heights. $CZ < AX < BY$

6.2 **24.** In the diagram at right, $\overrightarrow{PT}$ and $\overrightarrow{PS}$ are tangent to circle O at points T and S, respectively. As point P moves to the right along $\overrightarrow{AB}$, describe what happens to each of these measures or ratios.

a. $m\angle TPS$

b. OD

c. $m\angle ATB$

d. Area of $\triangle ATB$

e. $\dfrac{AP}{BP}$

f. $\dfrac{AD}{BD}$

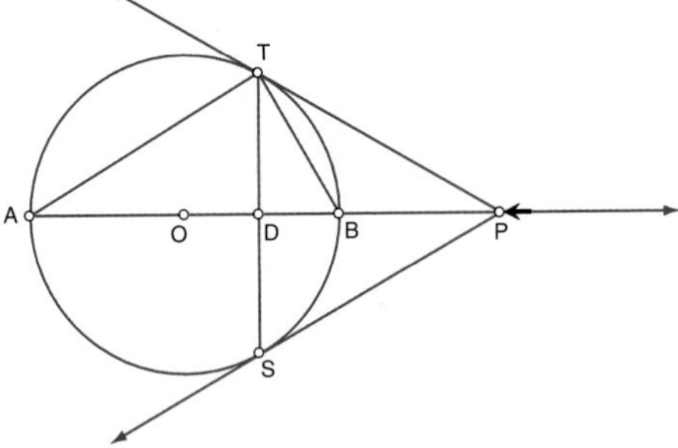

5.6 **25.** Points S and Q, shown at right, are consecutive vertices of square $SQRE$. Find coordinates for the other two vertices, R and E. There are two possible answers. Try to find both.
$R(8, 7)$ and $E(3, 9)$, or $R(4, -3)$ and $E(-1, -1)$

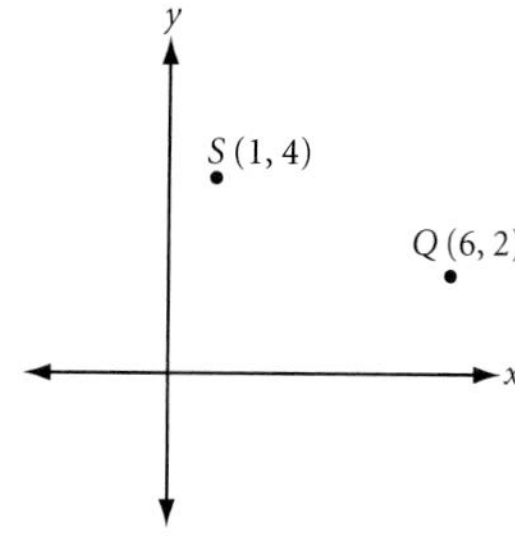

project

LIGHT FOR ALL SEASONS

You have seen that roof design is a practical application of slope—steep roofs shed snow and rain. But have you thought about the overhang of a roof?

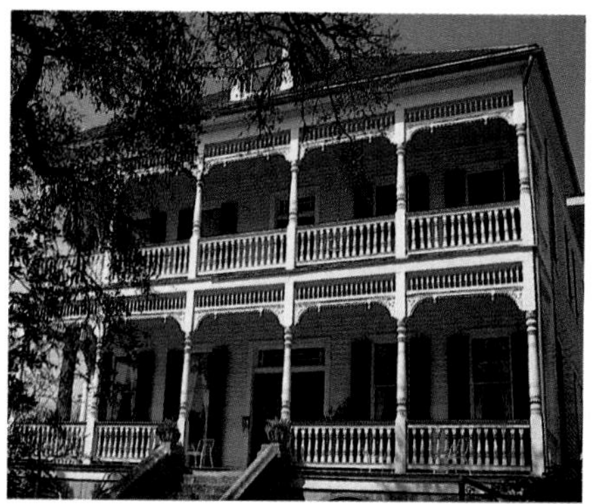

In a hot climate, a deep overhang shelters windows from the sun.

In a cold climate, a narrow overhang lets in more light and warmth.

What roof design is common for homes in your area? What factors would an architect consider in the design of a roof relative to the position, size, and orientation of the windows? Do some research and build a shoebox model of the roof design you select.

What design is best for your area will depend on your latitude, because that determines the angle of the sun's light in different seasons. Research the astronomy of solar angles, then use trigonometry and a movable light source to illustrate the effects on your model.

Your project should include

- Research notes on seasonal solar angles.
- A narrative explanation, with mathematical support, for your choice of roof design, roof overhang, and window placement.
- Detailed, labeled drawings showing the range of light admitted from season to season, at a given time of day.
- A model with a movable light source.

EXTENSION

Ask students to investigate a problem of the sort that motivated the development of trigonometry: Measure the radius of the earth. [Possible solution: Climb or fly to a point that's, say, 3 miles high and measure the angle between the horizon and the vertical. Because your line of sight to the horizon is a tangent line perpendicular to a radius, the sine of that angle is $\frac{r}{r+3}$.]

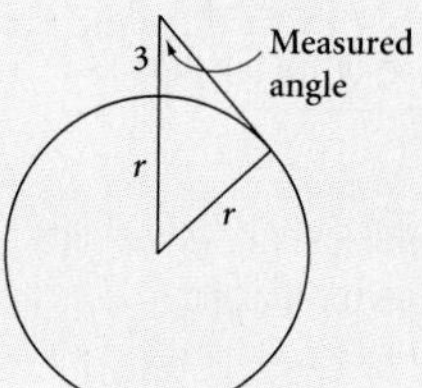

Supporting the project

The farther away from the equator you are, the lower the sun will be in the winter.

OUTCOMES

- Project includes research, narrative, drawings, and a model appropriate for the latitude.
- In climates with greater temperature extremes: The overhang should keep sunshine off the windows in the summer but allow it to hit the windows in the winter.
- In a tropical climate: Windows on the south and west sides of the model should be smaller and higher, or a covered patio could be attached to the house so the sun's rays never hit the windows.

EXPLORATION

PLANNING

LESSON OUTLINE

One day:

35 min Activity

10 min Sharing

MATERIALS

- measuring tape or metersticks
- calculators
- protractors, drinking straws, weights, string, and tape for making clinometers
- Making a Clinometer (W)

TEACHING

You might want to have students make their clinometers in advance. Students will need the Making a Clinometer worksheet and a paper protractor (pages 4 and 5 of Teaching and Worksheet Masters). Before the activity, identify some objects to measure around the school or grounds.

One step Assign this problem: "Use a clinometer and trigonometry to determine the heights of several tall objects." As students work, have them check their results with shadows or mirrors and also against the results of other groups.

Guiding the Activity

Groups of four or five can divide up the responsibilities of taking measurements, recording the measurements, performing the calculations, keeping track of the equipment, and (for shadows or mirrors) being the person measured.

You might also want to devote some class time to working with clinometers. Students might try using them to find the height of

Exploration

Indirect Measurement

In Chapter 11, you used shadows, mirrors, and similar triangles to measure the height of tall objects that you couldn't measure directly. Right triangle trigonometry gives you yet another method of indirect measurement.

In this exploration, you will use two or three different methods of indirect measurement. Then you will compare your results from each method.

Activity
Using a Clinometer

You will need

- a measuring tape or metersticks
- a clinometer (use the Making a Clinometer worksheet or make one of your own design)
- a mirror

In this activity, you will use a **clinometer**—a protractor-like tool used to measure angles. You probably will want to make your clinometer in advance, based on one of the designs below. Practice using it before starting the activity.

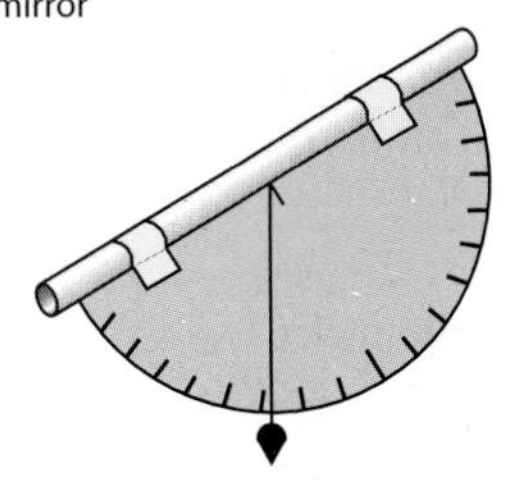

Clinometer 1

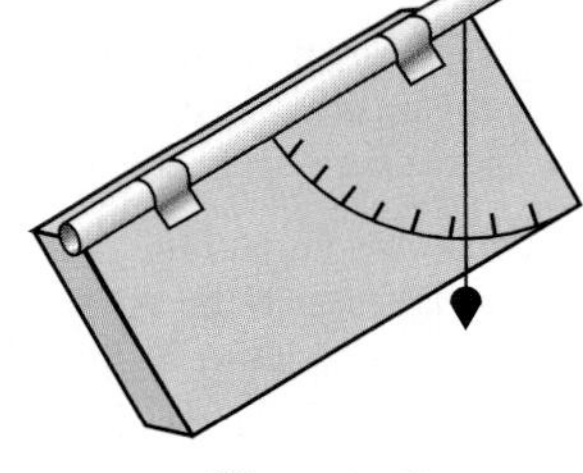

Clinometer 2

Step 1 Locate a tall object that would be difficult to measure directly. Start a table like this one.

Name of object	Viewing angle	Height of observer's eye	Distance from observer to object	Calculated height of object

LESSON OBJECTIVES

- Learn how a clinometer works
- Measure a height using trigonometry

NCTM STANDARDS

CONTENT		PROCESS	
	Number	✓	Problem Solving
✓	Algebra	✓	Reasoning
✓	Geometry	✓	Communication
✓	Measurement		Connections
	Data/Probability	✓	Representation

Step 2 Use your clinometer to measure the viewing angle from the horizontal to the top of the object.

Step 3 Measure the observer's eye height. Measure the distance from the observer to the base of the object.

Step 4 Calculate the approximate height of the object.

U.S. Forest Service Ranger Al Sousi uses a clinometer to measure the angle of a mountain slope. In snowy conditions, a slope steeper than 35° can be a high avalanche hazard.

Step 5 Different methods should produce the same answer. Possible sources of error: a poorly constructed clinometer, wind blowing the string around, person leaning over to look in the mirror, or other measurement errors.

Step 5 Use either the shadow method or the mirror method or both to measure the height of the same object. How do your results compare? If you got different results, explain what part of each process could contribute to the differences.

Step 6 Repeat Steps 1–5 for another tall object. If you measure the height of the same object as another group, compare your results when you finish.

IMPROVING YOUR VISUAL THINKING SKILLS

Puzzle Shapes

Make five of these shapes and assemble them to form a square. Does it take three, four, or five of the shapes to make a square?

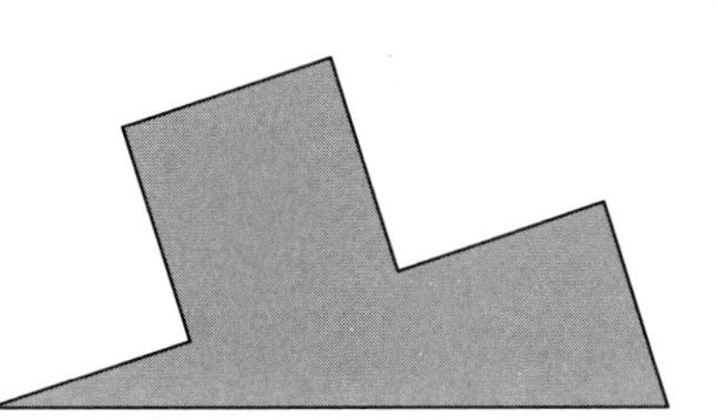

Guiding the Activity (continued)
an object they can measure directly.

To practice estimation skills, students should estimate the height of their object before using the clinometer. They can use their estimate to check the reasonableness of their result.

Step 1 As necessary, encourage students to select a tall object that sits on level ground. Possible objects include a school building, a football goalpost, a flagpole, or a tall tree.

Step 3 Indirect measurement with trigonometry often involves adding the height from the ground to the viewer's eye level. That is, the horizontal is not always at ground level. **[Ask]** "How does the height of the observer's eye affect the calculations?"

Step 5 Students could also check their estimation of the height of an object by using their clinometers from a different spot either farther from the object or closer to it. **[Ask]** "Is the calculated height the same? Why?" [If measurements are accurate, calculated heights will be approximately equal because as the angle of elevation changes so does the distance from the object.]

Step 6 This step is optional.

SHARING IDEAS

Have groups share their measurements. If students' results appear to be too large or too small, discuss where they may have made errors in measuring or calculating. If they're skeptical about results, suggest that they draw triangles to scale to assist them in estimating. Help students realize that they are working with similar triangles whose sides are proportional. You might want to calculate the percent errors and recognize those groups that determined the height most accurately.

IMPROVING VISUAL THINKING SKILLS

It takes four of the shapes to make a square.

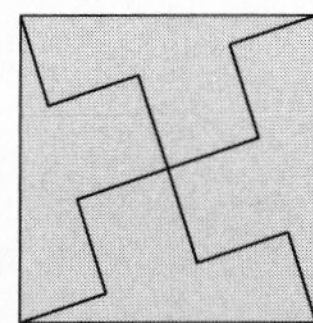

Assessing Progress
You can assess students' ability to apply trigonometric ratios, measure directly, and measure using shadows or mirrors.

Closing the Lesson

The point of this exploration is that, with careful measurement and calculation (using a clinometer for measuring angles), you can use trigonometry to determine the heights of inaccessible objects.

LESSON 12.3

PLANNING

LESSON OUTLINE

One day:

30 min Investigation and Examples

10 min Sharing

5 min Closing

MATERIALS

- calculators

TEACHING

Properties of sines allow us to find the measures of missing parts and areas of triangles when we know only ASA or SAA. Begin with the one-step investigation, or go over the example before starting groups on the guided investigations.

▶ *EXAMPLE A*

Note that approximating sin 40° is saved until the last step and that the answer is rounded to the nearest square meter.

Guiding Investigation 1

This investigation will help students set up the ratios in Investigation 2. Students might benefit from covering up part of the larger triangle so they can concentrate on just one of the two smaller triangles.

One step Pose this problem, from Exercise 12: "Archaeologists have recently started uncovering remains of Jamestown Fort in Virginia. The fort was in the shape of an isosceles triangle. Unfortunately, one corner has disappeared into the James River. If the remaining complete wall measures 300 feet and the remaining corners measure 46.5° and 87°, what was the

LESSON 12.3

The Law of Sines

To think and to be fully alive are the same.

HANNAH ARENDT

So far you have used trigonometry only to solve problems with right triangles. But you can use trigonometry with any triangle. For example, if you know the measures of two angles and one side of a triangle, you can find the other two sides with a trigonometric property called the **Law of Sines.** The Law of Sines is related to the area of a triangle. Let's first see how trigonometry can help you find area.

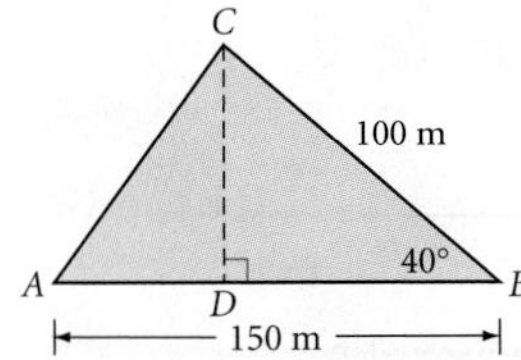

EXAMPLE A Find the area of $\triangle ABC$.

▶ *Solution* Consider $\overline{AB}$ as the base and use trigonometry to find the height, CD.

$$\sin 40° = \frac{CD}{100}$$ In $\triangle BCD$, CD is the length of the opposite side and 100 is the length of the hypotenuse.

$$(100)(\sin 40°) = CD$$ Multiply both sides by 100 and reduce the right side.

Now find the area.

$$A = 0.5bh$$ Area formula for a triangle.

$$A = (0.5)(AB)(CD)$$ Substitute AB for the length of the base and CD for the height.

$$A = (0.5)(150)[(100)(\sin 40°)]$$ Substitute 150 for AB and substitute the expression $(100)(\sin 40°)$ for CD.

$$A \approx 4821$$ Evaluate.

The area is approximately 4821 m^2.

In the next investigation, you will find a general formula for the area of a triangle given the lengths of two sides and the measure of the included angle.

Investigation 1
Area of a Triangle

Step 1 Find the area of each triangle. Use Example A as a guide.

a.

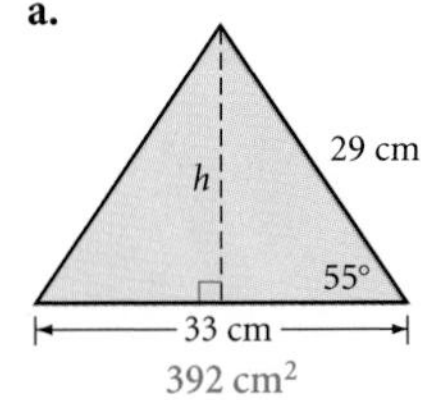

392 cm^2

b.

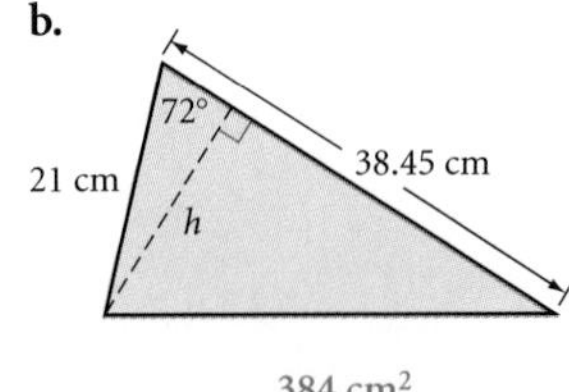

384 cm^2

c.

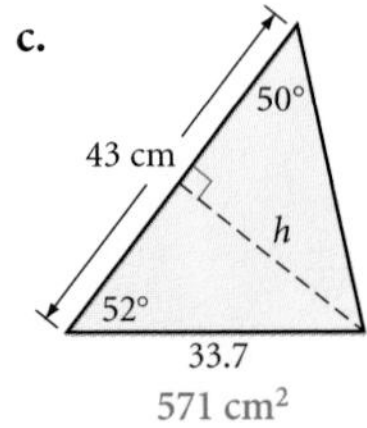

571 cm^2

LESSON OBJECTIVES

- Discover and apply the Law of Sines
- Develop problem-solving skills and cooperative behavior

NCTM STANDARDS

CONTENT		PROCESS	
	Number	✓	Problem Solving
✓	Algebra	✓	Reasoning
✓	Geometry	✓	Communication
✓	Measurement	✓	Connections
	Data/Probability	✓	Representation

Step 2 Generalize Step 1 to find the area of this triangle in terms of a, b, and $\angle C$. State your general formula as your next conjecture.

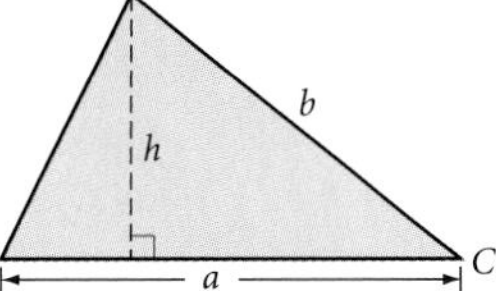

SAS Triangle Area Conjecture C-102

The area of a triangle is given by the formula $A = \underline{?}$ [$\frac{1}{2}ab\sin C$], where a and b are the lengths of two sides and C is the angle between them.

Now use what you've learned about finding the area of a triangle to derive the property called the Law of Sines.

Investigation 2
The Law of Sines

Consider $\triangle ABC$ with height h.

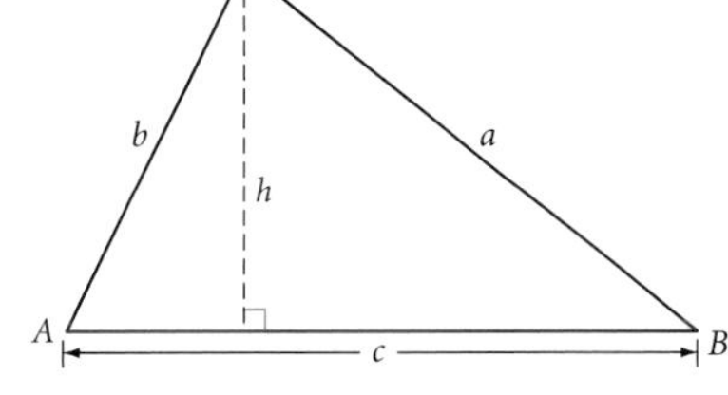

Step 1 Find h in terms of a and the sine of an angle.

[Step 1 $h = a\sin B$]

Step 2 Find h in terms of b and the sine of an angle.

[Step 2 $h = b\sin A$]

Step 3 Use algebra to show $\frac{\sin A}{a} = \frac{\sin B}{b}$

[Step 3 $b\sin A = a\sin B$; $\frac{b\sin A}{ab} = \frac{a\sin B}{ab}$; $\frac{\sin A}{a} = \frac{\sin B}{b}$]

Now consider the same $\triangle ABC$ using a different height, k.

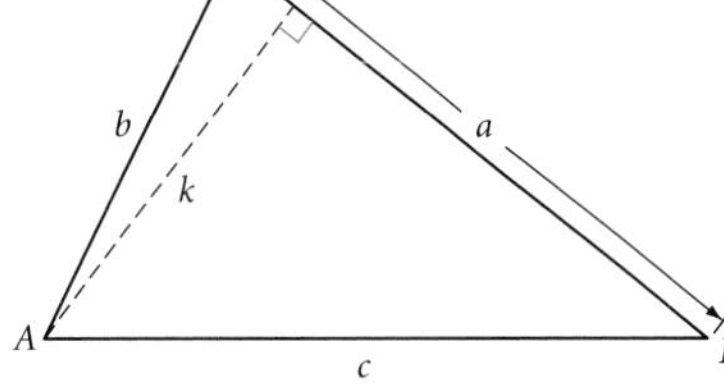

Step 4 Find k in terms of c and the sine of an angle.

[Step 4 $k = c\sin B$]

Step 5 Find k in terms of b and the sine of an angle.

[Step 5 $k = b\sin C$]

Step 6 Use algebra to show $\frac{\sin B}{b} = \frac{\sin C}{c}$

[Step 6 $c\sin B = b\sin C$; $\frac{c\sin B}{bc} = \frac{b\sin C}{bc}$; $\frac{\sin B}{b} = \frac{\sin C}{c}$]

Step 7 Combine Steps 3 and 6. Complete this conjecture.

Law of Sines C-103

For a triangle with angles A, B, and C and sides of lengths a, b, and c (a opposite A, b opposite B, and c opposite C),

$$\frac{\sin A}{?} = \frac{?}{b} = \frac{?}{?}$$

[$\frac{\sin A}{a} = \frac{\sin B}{b} = \frac{\sin C}{c}$]

Sharing Ideas (continued)

Ask what other properties of triangles students have studied. Wait at least until they mention the Triangle Inequality Conjecture. **[Ask]** "Is the Side-Angle Inequality Conjecture consistent with the Law of Sines?" [The bigger an angle, the larger its sine, but also the larger the opposite side. It might not be surprising, then, that all three ratios of sine of an angle to the length of the opposite turn out to be the same.] Other properties of triangles students might mention include the congruence shortcuts. Remind them that these shortcuts tell us what determines a triangle, and ask if we can find the missing parts of any determined triangle. We can use the Law of Sines (perhaps coupled with the Triangle Sum Conjecture) to measure all missing parts of triangles determined by ASA or SAA. But what about triangles determined by SAS or SSS? You need not answer this question now; it motivates the Law of Cosines in the next lesson.

One step (continued)

approximate area of the original fort? How long were the two incomplete walls?" As needed, ask students if they can make right triangles in their pictures of the original triangle, because right triangles are easier to work with. Students can draw an altitude and express its length in terms of the known side length and trigonometric ratios. Without seeing the general Law of Sines, students can answer the questions. Ask advanced groups to apply the same procedure to finding ratios of sides in arbitrary triangles, to culminate Sharing.

Guiding Investigation 2

Steps 1, 2 You might want to help students set up the algebraic equations for $\sin A$ and $\sin B$. Because both ratios involve the same height, each can be used to write an expression for h.

Step 3 Set the two expressions for h equal to each other and divide.

Steps 4, 5 Using the same idea with height k as for height h will generate the ratio in Step 6.

SHARING IDEAS

After students reach consensus about the SAS Triangle Area Conjecture, **[Ask]** "What happens if the included angle is a right angle?" [The sine is 1, so the formula becomes $\frac{1}{2}$(base · height).]

[Ask] "What do you need to know to use the Law of Sines?" [The measure of one angle and the length of the opposite side. If they're trying to find the length of another side, they must also know the measure of the angle opposite that side. If they're trying to find the measure of an angle, they must know the length of the side opposite that angle. If one of the needed angle measures isn't given, they may be able to find it using the Triangle Sum Conjecture.]

Sharing Ideas (continued)

Point out the question following the Law of Sines about discovery through deductive reasoning. The Law of Sines came not from considering lots of cases inductively, but from rewriting h and k and seeing what developed. Whatever leads to a good conjecture is a valid method of discovery.

If students need more experience using the Law of Sines, direct their attention to Examples B and C. After they've worked through them, discuss what they've noticed. **[Ask]** "Why does the method of Example C produce only the acute angle? [Because the longer of the two given sides is opposite the given angle, there is only one triangle; in this case SSA does determine a triangle. If the shorter side were opposite the given angle, there would be two possible triangles, one of them obtuse. In that case, $\sin^{-1}$ would give only the acute angle of the acute triangle.]

▶ EXAMPLE B

[Ask] "How would you find the length of segment AB?" [Use the Triangle Sum Conjecture to find $m\angle C$. Then solve $\frac{\sin A}{a} = \frac{\sin C}{c}$ for c.]

▶ EXAMPLE C

[Ask] "Can we use $\frac{a}{\sin A} = \frac{b}{\sin B}$?" [Yes; if two fractions are equivalent, then so are their reciprocals.]

[Ask] "If you know $\sin B$, how do you find angle B?" [Take the inverse sine: $\sin^{-1}(\sin B) = B$.] More mechanically, students might think of taking the inverse sine of both sides and realizing that the left side, $\sin^{-1}(\sin B)$, is B.

Did you notice that you used deductive reasoning rather than inductive reasoning to discover the Law of Sines?

You can use the Law of Sines to find the lengths of a triangle's sides when you know one side's length and two angles' measures.

EXAMPLE B Find the length of side $\overline{AC}$ in $\triangle ABC$.

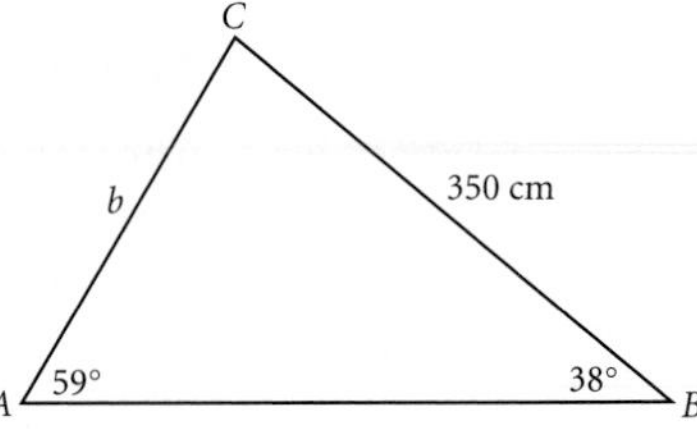

▶ Solution Start with the Law of Sines, and solve for b.

$\frac{\sin A}{a} = \frac{\sin B}{b}$ — The Law of Sines.

$b \sin A = a \sin B$ — Multiply both sides by ab and reduce.

$b = \frac{a \sin B}{\sin A}$ — Divide both sides by $\sin A$ and reduce the left side.

$b = \frac{(350)(\sin 38°)}{\sin 59°}$ — Substitute 350 for a, 38° for B, and 59° for A.

$b \approx 251$ — Multiply and divide.

The length of side $\overline{AC}$ is approximately 251 cm.

You can also use the Law of Sines to find the measure of a missing angle, but only if you know whether the angle is acute or obtuse. Recall from Chapter 4 that SSA failed as a congruence shortcut. For example, if you know in $\triangle ABC$ that $BC = 160$ cm, $AC = 260$ cm, and $m\angle A = 36°$, you would not be able to find $m\angle B$. There are two possible measures for $\angle B$, one acute and one obtuse.

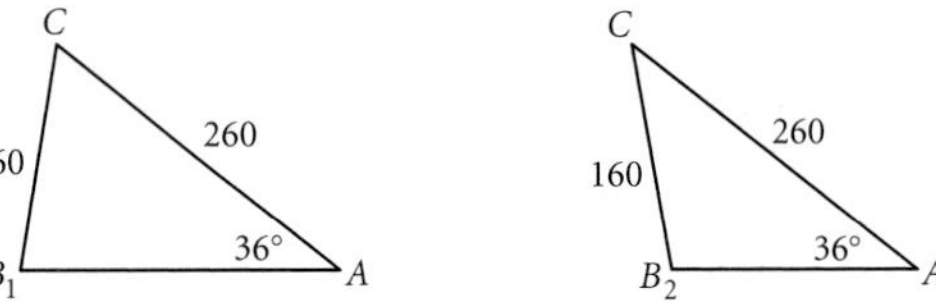

Because you've defined trigonometric ratios only for acute angles, you'll be asked to find only acute angle measures.

EXAMPLE C Find the measure of acute angle B in $\triangle ABC$.

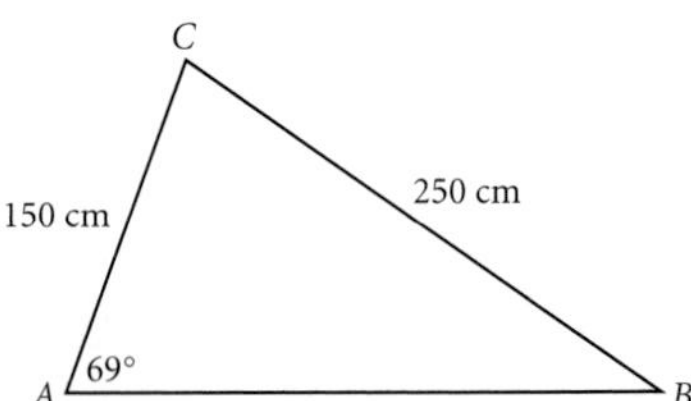

▶ ***Solution***

Start with the Law of Sines, and solve for B.

$$\frac{\sin A}{a} = \frac{\sin B}{b}$$ The Law of Sines.

$$\sin B = \frac{b \sin A}{a}$$ Solve for sin B.

$$\sin B = \frac{(150)(\sin 69°)}{250}$$ Substitute known values.

$$B = \sin^{-1}\left[\frac{(150)(\sin 69°)}{250}\right]$$ Take the inverse sine of both sides.

$$B \approx 34$$ Use your calculator to evaluate.

The measure of $\angle B$ is approximately 34°.

EXERCISES

You will need

A calculator for Exercises **1–16**

Construction tools for Exercise **18**

In Exercises 1–4, find the area of each polygon to the nearest square centimeter.

1.

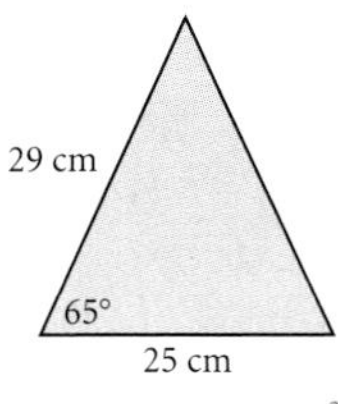

329 cm²

2.

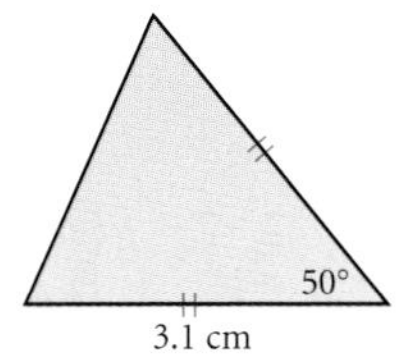

4 cm²

3. ⓗ

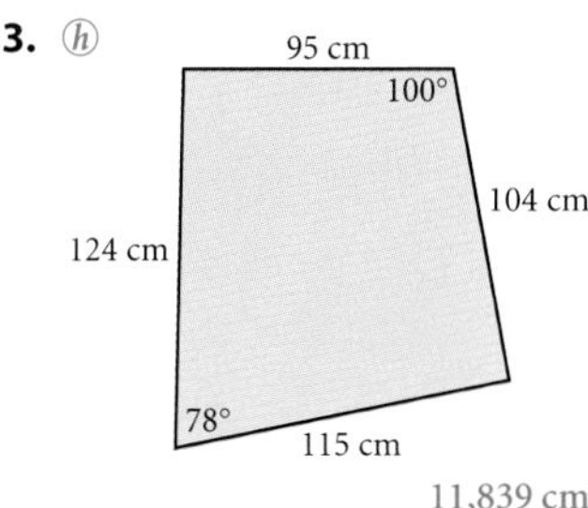

11,839 cm²

4. ⓗ

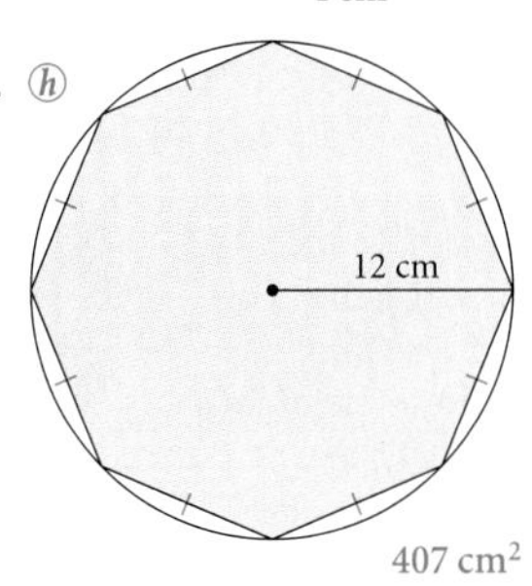

407 cm²

In Exercises 5–7, find each length to the nearest centimeter.

5. $w \approx$? ⓗ 35 cm

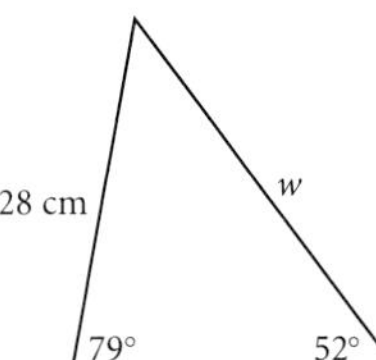

6. $x \approx$? 17 cm

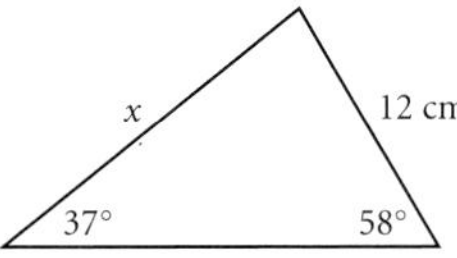

7. $y \approx$? 30 cm

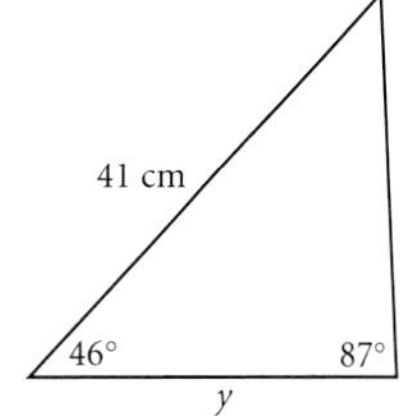

Assessing Progress

You can assess how well students know how to find the sine ratio of a given angle and how proficient they are at finding the areas of triangles.

Closing the Lesson

Reiterate the two mathematical points of this lesson: The area of a triangle can be found from lengths of two sides a and b and the measure of the included angle C $\left(\text{it's } \frac{1}{2}ab\sin C\right)$. If we know two angle measures and one side length of a triangle we can find the measures of the missing parts by using the **Law of Sines:** $\frac{\sin A}{a} = \frac{\sin B}{b} = \frac{\sin C}{c}$.

BUILDING UNDERSTANDING

The exercises give students practice in using the Law of Sines and in finding areas of triangles when they know two side lengths and the measure of the included angle.

ASSIGNING HOMEWORK

Essential	1–10
Performance assessment	11
Portfolio	4
Group	12, 13
Review	14–20

▶ Helping with the Exercises

Exercise 4 As needed, encourage students to consider the area of $\frac{1}{8}$ of the octagon.

Exercise 11 [Alert] Students might not think to find the measure of the third angle by the Triangle Sum Conjecture.

Exercise 12 This exercise was the one-step investigation.

12. The other two walls were 300 ft and approximately 413 ft. The area was approximately 45,000 ft².

For Exercises 8–10, each triangle is an acute triangle. Find each angle measure to the nearest degree.

8. $m\angle A \approx$? 56°

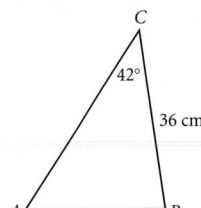

C 42° 36 cm A 29 cm B

9. $m\angle B \approx$? 45°

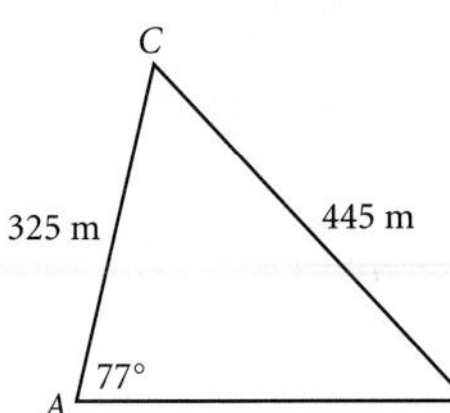

10. $m\angle C \approx$? 66°

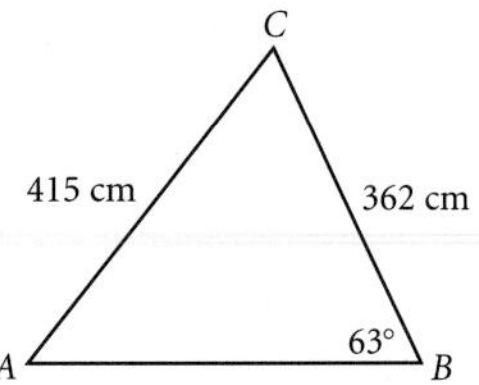

11. Alphonse (point A) is over a 2500-meter landing strip in a hot-air balloon. At one end of the strip, Beatrice (point B) sees Alphonse with an angle of elevation measuring 39°. At the other end of the strip, Collette (point C) sees Alphonse with an angle of elevation measuring 62°.

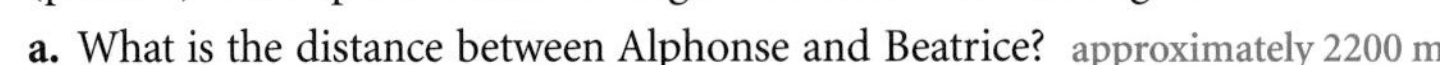

a. What is the distance between Alphonse and Beatrice? approximately 2200 m

b. What is the distance between Alphonse and Collette? approximately 1600 m

c. How high up is Alphonse? approximately 1400 m

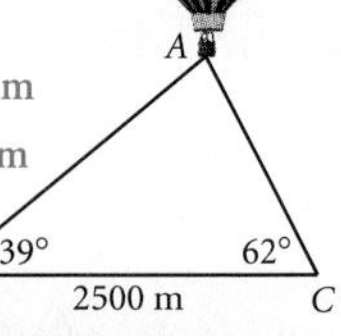

History CONNECTION

For over 200 years, people believed that the entire site of James Fort was washed into the James River. Archaeologists have recently uncovered over 250 feet of the fort's wall, as well as hundreds of thousands of artifacts dating to the early 1600s.

12. APPLICATION Archaeologists have recently started uncovering remains of James Fort (also known as Jamestown Fort) in Virginia. The fort was in the shape of an isosceles triangle. Unfortunately, one corner has disappeared into the James River. If the remaining complete wall measures 300 feet and the remaining corners measure 46.5° and 87°, how long were the two incomplete walls? What was the approximate area of the original fort?

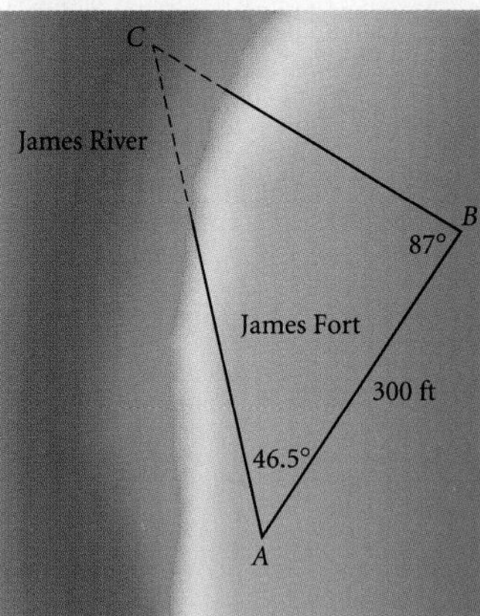

13. A tree grows vertically on a hillside. The hill is at a 16° angle to the horizontal. The tree casts an 18-meter shadow up the hill when the angle of elevation of the sun measures 68°. How tall is the tree? ⓗ approximately 48 m

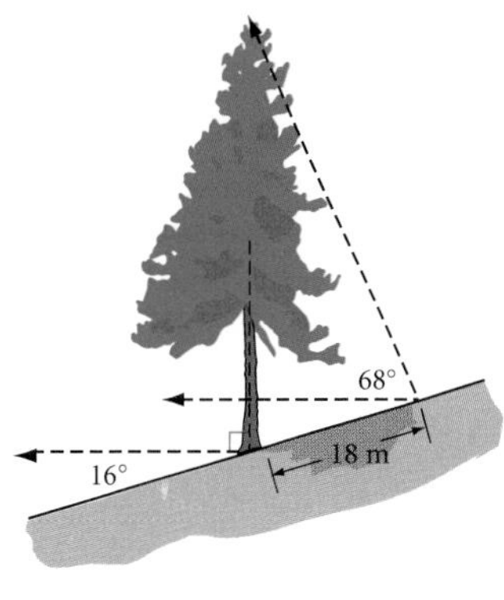

Exercise 13 [Alert] Students might have difficulty making this sketch. After they have done so, you might want to **[Ask]** "What angles can you find?"

Review

12.2 **14.** Read the History Connection below. Each step of El Castillo is 30 cm deep by 26 cm high. How tall is the pyramid, not counting the platform at the top? What is the angle of ascent? 2366 cm; approximately 41°

Exercise 14 [Language] *Angle of ascent* means "angle of elevation." The pyramid is about 23.7 meters high.

History CONNECTION

One of the most impressive Mayan pyramids is El Castillo in Chichén Itzá, Mexico. Built in approximately 800 C.E., it has 91 steps on each of its four sides, or 364 steps in all. The top platform adds a level, so the pyramid has 365 levels to represent the number of days in the Mayan year.

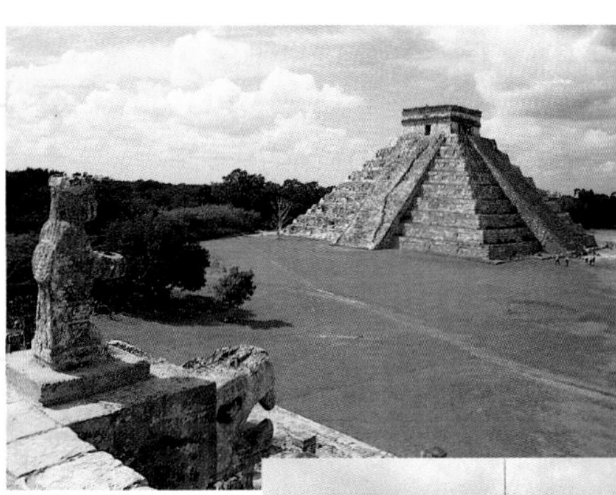

12.1 **15.** According to legend, Galileo (1564–1642, Italy) used the Leaning Tower of Pisa to conduct his experiments in gravity. Assume that when he dropped objects from the top of the 55-meter tower (this is the measured length, not the height, of the tower), they landed 4.8 meters from the tower's base. What was the angle that the tower was leaning from the vertical?

Exercise 15 [Link] The tangent ratio is closely related to slope. On a coordinate grid, the tangent of an angle (with the horizontal) is the slope of the line.

10.3 **16.** Find the volume of this cone.

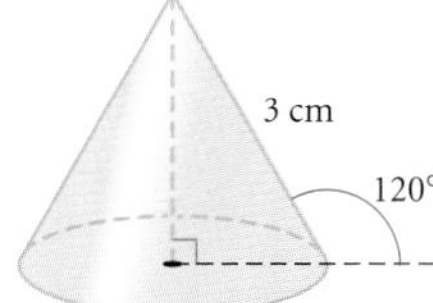

16. $\frac{9\pi\sqrt{3}}{8}$ cm^3 or approximately 6 cm^3

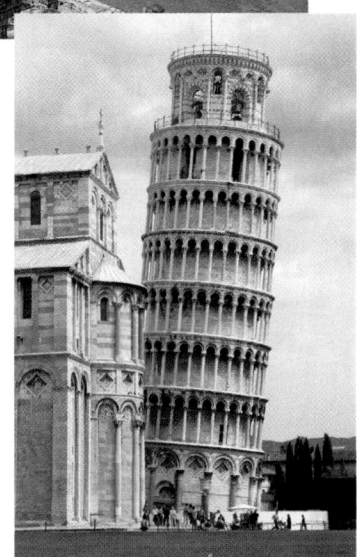

17. Because $\overline{AB} \parallel \overline{CD}$, $\angle A \cong \angle D$ by the AIA Conjecture. Because $\angle D$ and $\angle B$ intercept the same arc, $\angle D \cong \angle B$. Therefore $\angle A \cong \angle B$ by the transitive property. So $\triangle ABE$ is isosceles by the Converse of the Isosceles Triangle Conjecture.

EXTENSION

Use Take Another Look activities 1 and 2 on page 665.

6.3 **17.** Use the circle diagram at right and write a paragraph proof to show that $\triangle ABE$ is isosceles.

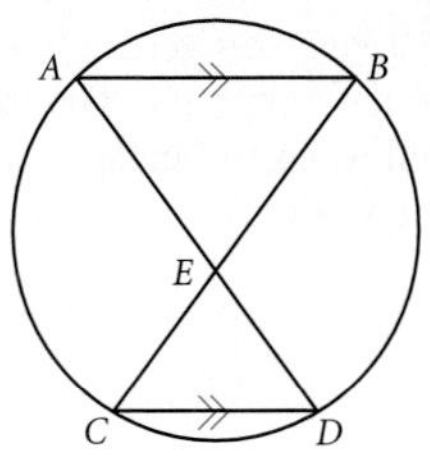

5.6 **18.** ***Construction*** Put two points on patty paper. Assume these points are opposite vertices of a square. Find the two missing vertices. Fold the paper so that the two points coincide. Draw a line along the fold. Draw another line through the two points. These two lines continue the diagonals of the square. Now fold the paper so that the two lines coincide. Mark the vertices on the other line.

11.6 **19.** Find AC, AE, and AF. All measurements are in centimeters.

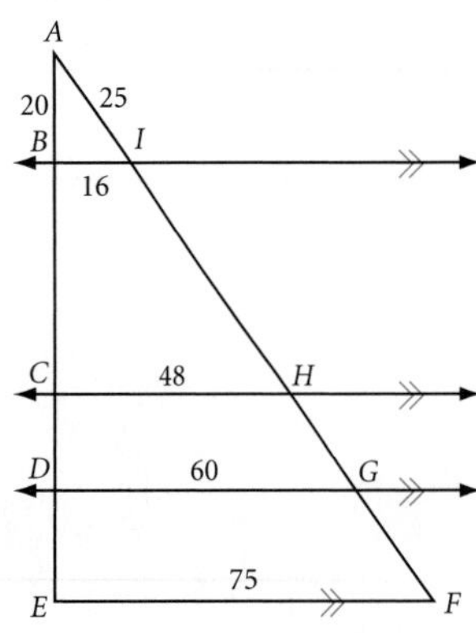

$AC = 60$ cm, $AE = 93.75$ cm, $AF \approx 117$ cm

9.1 **20.** Both boxes are right rectangular prisms. In which is the diagonal rod longer? Box 1

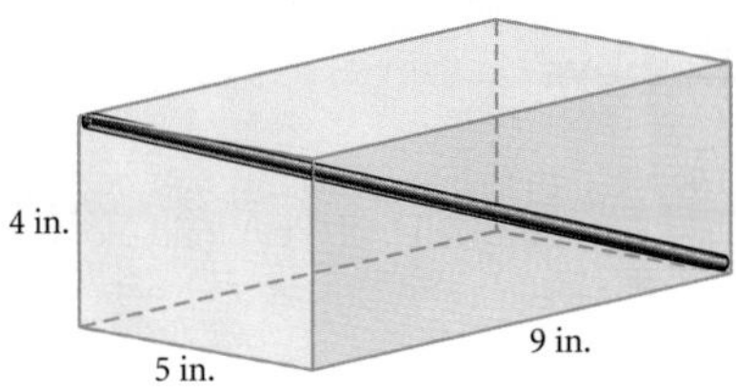

Box 1

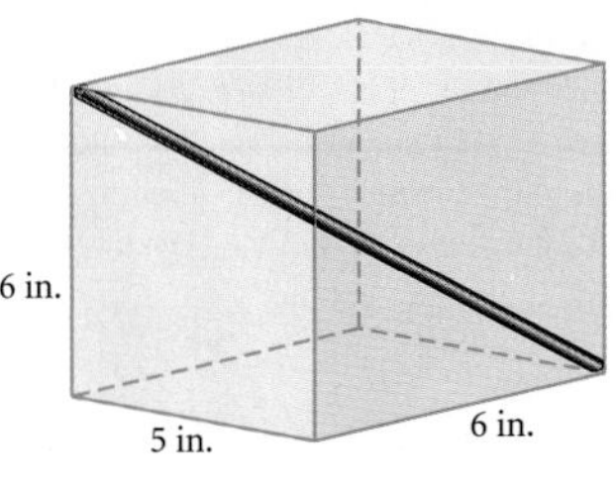

Box 2

IMPROVING YOUR VISUAL THINKING SKILLS

Rope Tricks

Each rope will be cut 50 times as shown. For each rope, how many pieces will result?

1.

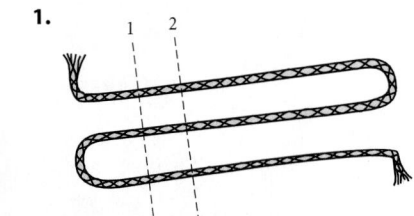

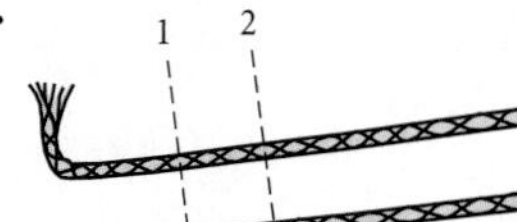

2.

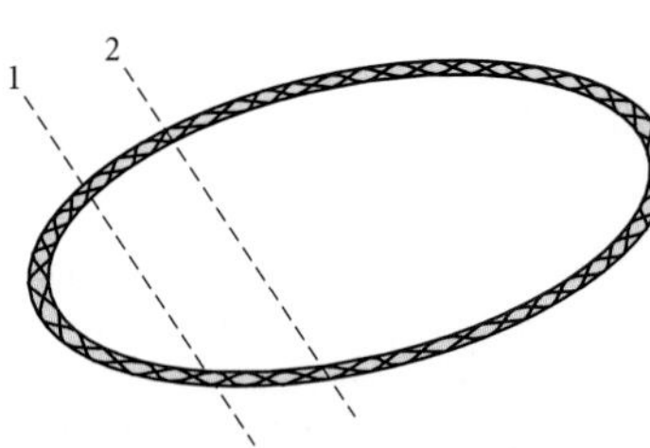

PUZZLE

IMPROVING VISUAL THINKING SKILLS

Students might make a table or see recursively how many pieces are added by each cut (and what the number is after the first cut).

1. 151

2. 100

LESSON

12.4

The Law of Cosines

A ship in a port is safe, but that is not what ships are built for.

JOHN A. SHEDD

You've solved a variety of problems with the Pythagorean Theorem. It is perhaps your most important geometry conjecture. In Chapter 9, you found that the distance formula was really just the Pythagorean Theorem. You even used the Pythagorean Theorem to derive the equation of a circle.

You can also derive trigonometry relationships from the Pythagorean Theorem. These are called Pythagorean identities. Complete the steps below to derive one of the Pythagorean identities.

Investigation
A Pythagorean Identity

Step 1 $(\sin A)^2 + (\cos A)^2 = 1$

Step 1 Pick any measure for $\angle A$ and find

$$(\sin A)^2 + (\cos A)^2 = \underline{?}$$

Step 2 Repeat Step 1 for several different measures for $\angle A$. When you are ready, make a tentative conjecture.

Let's see if you can derive your conjecture. Use this triangle for Steps 3–6.

Step 3 $\sin A = \frac{a}{c}$ $\cos A = \frac{b}{c}$

Step 4 $\left(\frac{a}{c}\right)^2 + \left(\frac{b}{c}\right)^2$

Step 5 $\frac{a^2 + b^2}{c^2}$

Step 6 $\frac{c^2}{c^2} = 1$

Step 7 yes

Step 3 Find ratios for $\sin A$ and $\cos A$.

Step 4 Substitute your results from Step 3 into this equation.

$$(\sin A)^2 + (\cos A)^2 = \left(\frac{?}{?}\right)^2 + \left(\frac{?}{?}\right)^2$$

Step 5 Add the two fractions on the right side of your equation.

Step 6 Triangle ABC is a right triangle. How can you use the Pythagorean Theorem to further simplify your equation?

Step 7 Does your result in Step 6 support your conjecture in Step 2? You should now be ready to state the Pythagorean identity.

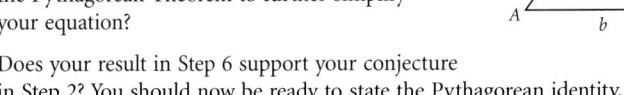

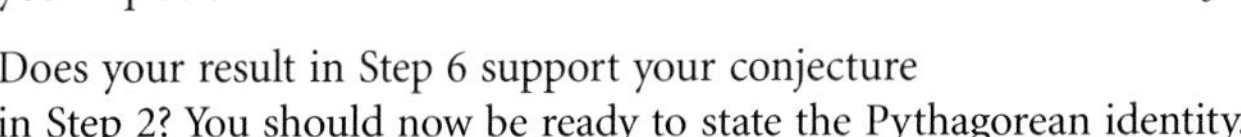

Pythagorean Identity C-104

For any angle A, $\underline{?}$. $(\sin A)^2 + (\cos A)^2 = 1$

The Pythagorean Theorem is very powerful, but its use is still limited to right triangles. Recall from Chapter 9 that the Pythagorean Theorem does not work for acute triangles or obtuse triangles. You might ask, "What happens to the Pythagorean equation for acute triangles or obtuse triangles?"

NCTM STANDARDS

CONTENT		PROCESS	
	Number	✓	Problem Solving
✓	Algebra	✓	Reasoning
✓	Geometry	✓	Communication
✓	Measurement	✓	Connections
	Data/Probability	✓	Representation

LESSON OBJECTIVES

- Investigate the Pythagorean identity
- Learn and apply the Law of Cosines
- Practice solving problems

LESSON 12.4

PLANNING

LESSON OUTLINE

One day:

25 min Investigation and Examples

15 min Sharing

5 min Closing

MATERIALS

- calculators
- Sketchpad demonstration Deriving the Law of Cosines, *optional*

TEACHING

The Pythagorean Theorem allows the derivation of two identities. One of them, the Law of Cosines, allows us to find the measures of missing parts of triangles when we know only SAS or SSS.

You might want to demonstrate the inequality that leads to the Law of Cosines using the Sketchpad demonstration or have students investigate for themselves. Students can easily recall these inequalities if they think of an acute angle as "smaller than" (less than) a right angle and an obtuse angle as "bigger than" (greater than) a right angle, but make sure c^2 is on the left side. A similar demonstration appears in Lesson 9.1. **[Language]** *Derive* means to trace the source of something or to draw a conclusion.

Guiding the Investigation

You might do the investigation as a follow-along activity or use the one-step investigation on page 642. An alternate derivation might be to rewrite a as $c \sin A$ and to rewrite b as $c \cos A$. Then $c^2 = a^2 + b^2 = c^2(\sin^2 A + \cos^2 A)$, so the last factor must be 1.

$\sin^2 A$ is another way of writing $(\sin A)^2$. Thus the Pythagorean identity can be written two ways: $(\sin A)^2 + (\cos A)^2 = 1$ or $\sin^2 A + \cos^2 A = 1$.

One step Pose this problem, adapted from Exercise 10 of Lesson 12.5: "A water pipe for a farm's irrigation system must go through a small hill. Farmer Gold attaches a 14.5-meter rope to the pipe's entry point and an 11.2-meter rope to the exit point. When he pulls the ropes taut, their ends meet at a 58° angle. Does he have enough information to determine the length of pipe needed to go through the hill?" Students may disagree about whether or not the triangle is determined from the given data; someone will probably mention SAS. Students may try to use the Law of Sines but find that they don't know any side and its opposite angle. They might think to use the Pythagorean Theorem, but they can't use it because the angle measure isn't 90°. Ask students if they can draw an altitude to make right triangles, which are easier to work with. If they split the known angle, they lose information. If they draw an altitude from one end of the pipe, they can use the Pythagorean Theorem, algebra, and trigonometric ratios to express the unknown side in terms of the given information.

Law of Cosines

The book delays the derivation of the Law of Cosines until Take Another Look activity 4 at the end of the chapter. The result is given here, without derivation, so that students have the tools for solving any triangle. **[Ask]** "What happens to the Law of Cosines when the included angle measure is 90°?" [The cosine is 0, so the equation becomes the Pythagorean Theorem.]

For an interactive version of this sketch, visit www.keymath.com/DG .

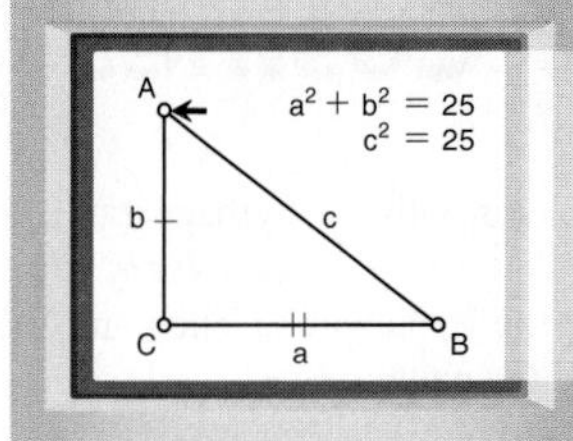

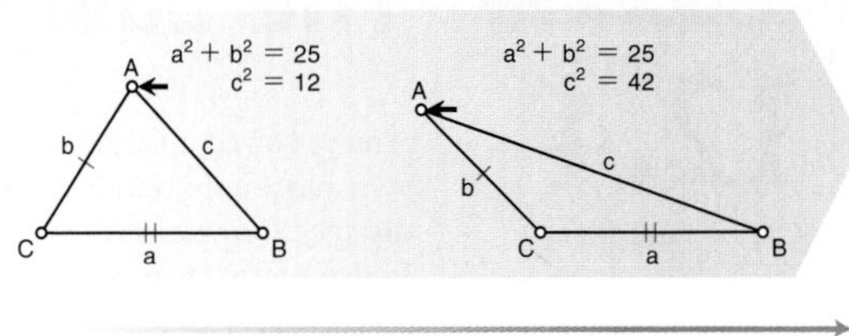

In this right triangle $c^2 = a^2 + b^2$

In this acute triangle $c^2 < a^2 + b^2$

In this obtuse triangle $c^2 > a^2 + b^2$

If the legs of a right triangle are brought closer together so that the right angle becomes an acute angle, you'll find that $c^2 < a^2 + b^2$. In order to make this inequality into an equality, you would have to subtract something from $a^2 + b^2$.

$$c^2 = a^2 + b^2 - \textit{something}$$

If the legs are widened to form an obtuse angle, you'll find that $c^2 > a^2 + b^2$. Here, you'd have to add something to make an equality.

$$c^2 = a^2 + b^2 + \textit{something}$$

Mathematicians found that the "something" was $2ab\cos C$. The Pythagorean Theorem generalizes to all triangles with a trigonometric property called the **Law of Cosines.** The steps used to derive the Law of Cosines are left for you as a Take Another Look activity.

Law of Cosines C-105

For any triangle with sides of lengths a, b, and c, and with C the angle opposite the side with length c,

$$c^2 = a^2 + b^2 - 2ab\cos C$$

You can use the Law of Cosines when you are given three side lengths or two side lengths and the angle measure between them (SSS or SAS). Again, you'll be asked to work only with acute angles.

EXAMPLE A Find the length of side $\overline{CT}$ in acute triangle CRT.

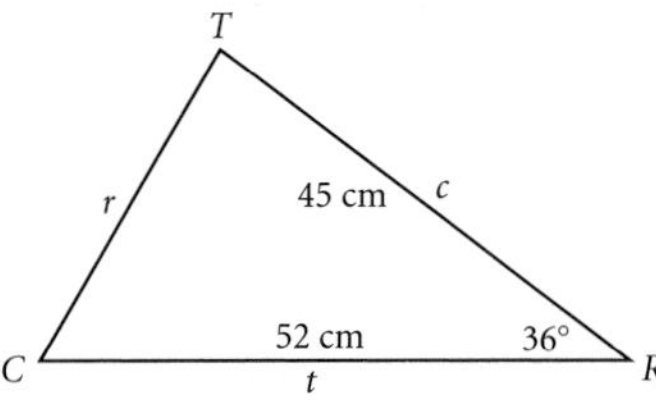

▶ Solution To find r, use the Law of Cosines:

$c^2 = a^2 + b^2 - 2ab\cos C$ The Law of Cosines.

[Ask] "What information do you need about a triangle in order to use the Law of Cosines?" [You need three sides, or two sides and an angle. If you know SSS, you can use the Law of Cosines to solve for one angle and find the other parts of the triangle using the Law of Sines.] The Law of Sines and the Law of Cosines give us tools for finding the measures of missing parts in any determined triangle. To find the measure of the obtuse angle in an obtuse triangle, we need to expand the definition of cosine beyond acute angles. The cosine of obtuse angles is negative.

Students can explore and verify the Law of Cosines using the dynamic geometry exploration at www.keymath.com/DG.

▶ EXAMPLE A

If students are using a graphing calculator that uses algebraic syntax, then they can simply enter and evaluate the radical expression in the second-to-last step. By taking r to be a nonnegative square root, this equation makes the reasonable assumption that length r is not negative.

Using the variables in this problem, the Law of Cosines becomes

$r^2 = c^2 + t^2 - 2ct\cos R$	Substitute r for c, c for a, t for b, and R for C.
$r^2 = 45^2 + 52^2 - 2(45)(52)(\cos 36°)$	Substitute 45 for c, 52 for t, and 36° for R.
$r = \sqrt{45^2 + 52^2 - 2(45)(52)(\cos 36°)}$	Take the positive square root of both sides.
$r \approx 31$	Evaluate.

The length of side $\overline{CT}$ is about 31 cm.

EXAMPLE B Find the measure of $\angle Q$ in acute triangle QED.

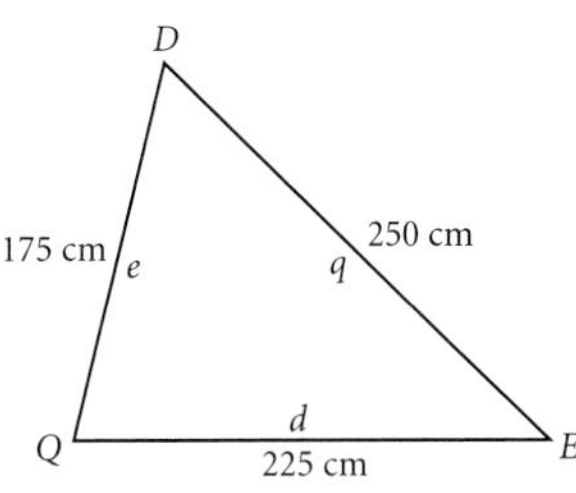

▶ ***Solution*** Use the Law of Cosines and solve for Q.

$q^2 = e^2 + d^2 - 2ed\cos Q$	The Law of Cosines with respect to $\angle Q$.
$\cos Q = \dfrac{q^2 - e^2 - d^2}{-2ed}$	Solve for $\cos Q$.
$\cos Q = \dfrac{250^2 - 175^2 - 225^2}{-2(175)(225)}$	Substitute known values.
$Q = \cos^{-1}\left(\dfrac{250^2 - 175^2 - 225^2}{-2(175)(225)}\right)$	Take the inverse cosine of both sides.
$Q \approx 76$	Evaluate.

The measure of $\angle Q$ is about 76°.

EXERCISES

You will need

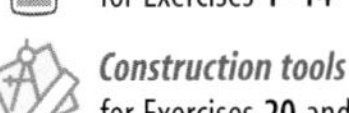

A calculator for Exercises **1–14**

Construction tools for Exercises **20** and **21**

Geometry software for Exercise **22**

In Exercises 1–3, find each length to the nearest centimeter.

1. $w \approx$? ⓗ 32 cm

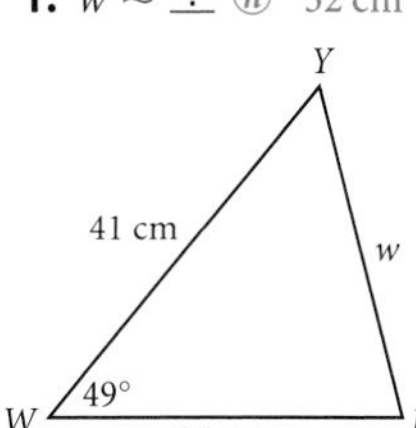

2. $y \approx$? 47 cm

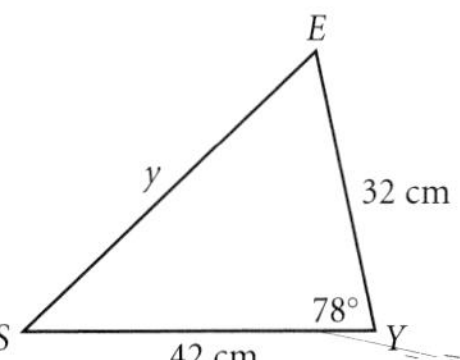

3. $x \approx$? 341 cm

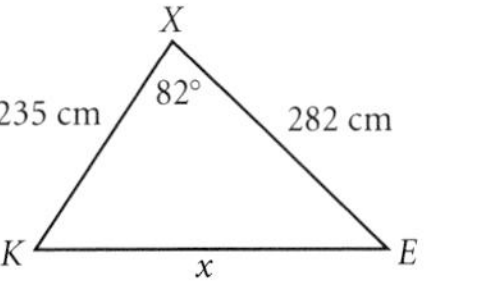

Closing the Lesson

One **Pythagorean identity,** derived from the Pythagorean Theorem, says that for any angle A, $\sin^2 A + \cos^2 A = 1$. Another identity derived from the Pythagorean Theorem is the **Law of Cosines**: For any triangle with sides of lengths a and b and included angle C (opposite side c), $c^2 = a^2 + b^2 - 2ab\cos C$. This law, a generalization of the Pythagorean Theorem, allows us to find the measures of missing parts of triangles when we know only SAS or SSS.

[Alert] Students are tempted to subtract the product of 2 and the included side lengths before multiplying this product by the cosine of the included angle.

SHARING IDEAS

If you did the one-step investigation, it is possible that no students will have completely solved the problem by the time you must bring them together. A derivation that arises from the suggestion to draw an altitude is to let e be the altitude and d be the distance from the foot of the altitude to the point where the ropes meet.

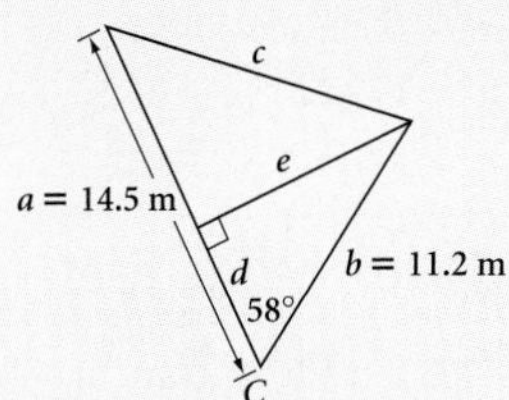

Then the Pythagorean Theorem gives $c^2 = (14.5 - d)^2 + e^2$, which algebra and another use of the theorem turn into $c^2 = 14.5^2 + 11.2^2 - 2(14.5)d$. A trigonometric ratio gives $d = 11.2\cos 58°$ to complete the calculation. Now ask students to generalize for any lengths of sides a and b and any measure of angle C to get the Law of Cosines.

▶ *EXAMPLE B*

[Alert] Students might have difficulty using the Law of Cosines if the angles and sides are not labeled A, B, C and a, b, c, respectively.

[Context] Although the Greek mathematician Euclid lived before trigonometry was developed, in his *Elements* he established two propositions that generalize the Pythagorean Theorem and are equivalent to the Law of Cosines.

Assessing Progress

You can check students' ability to find trigonometric ratios and to apply the Pythagorean Theorem.

BUILDING UNDERSTANDING

The exercises in this lesson are restricted to acute angles. Trigonometric ratios for other angles are defined using coordinate geometry in the Exploration Trigonometric Ratios and the Unit Circle.

ASSIGNING HOMEWORK

Essential	1–9
Performance assessment	9
Portfolio	7
Group	10
Review	11–22

Helping with the Exercises

Exercise 9 The parallelogram has two diagonals. Finding the acute angle using $\cos^{-1}$ assumes accurately that the diagonal of length 19 cm is the shorter of the two.

Exercise 10 The Law of Cosines leads to a quadratic equation: $960^2 = x^2 + 720^2 - (2)(x)(720)(\cos 20°)$. If students don't know how to solve this equation, suggest that they try an alternative approach.

They can use the Law of Sines several times. As needed, caution students about approximating too early; ideally, they should enter into their calculators the equivalent of 960/sin(20)*sin(160 − $\sin^{-1}$ (720*sin(20)/960))/720.

In Exercises 4–6, each triangle is an acute triangle. Find each angle measure to the nearest degree.

4. $m\angle A \approx$ _?_ ⓗ 74°

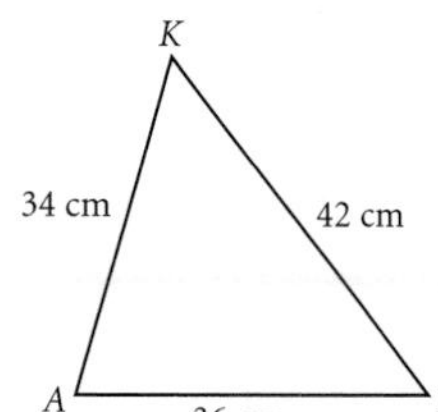

5. $m\angle B \approx$ _?_ 64°

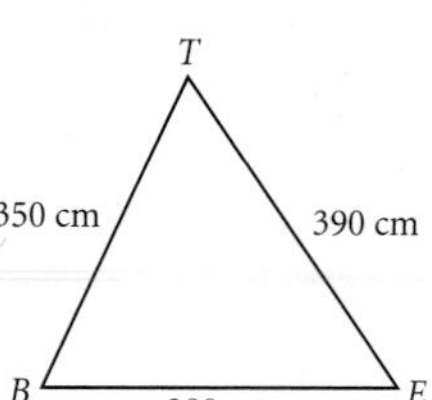

6. $m\angle C \approx$ _?_ 85°

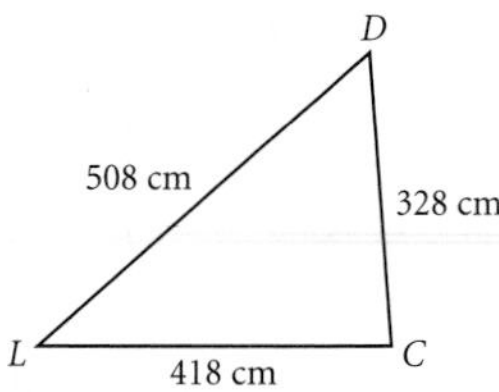

7. Two 24-centimeter radii of a circle form a central angle measuring 126°. What is the length of the chord connecting the two radii? approximately 43 cm

8. Find the measure of the smallest angle in an acute triangle whose side lengths are 4 m, 7 m, and 8 m. ⓗ approximately 30°

9. Two sides of a parallelogram measure 15 cm and 20 cm, and one of the diagonals measures 19 cm. What are the measures of the angles of the parallelogram to the nearest degree? approximately 116° and 64°

10. **APPLICATION** Captain Malloy is flying a passenger jet. He is heading east at 720 km/hr when he sees an electrical storm straight ahead. He turns the jet 20° to the north to avoid the storm and continues in this direction for 1 hr. Then he makes a second turn, back toward his original flight path. Eighty minutes after his second turn, he makes a third turn and is back on course. By avoiding the storm, how much time did Captain Malloy lose from his original flight plan? ⓗ approximately 6 min

Review

12.1 **11.** **APPLICATION** A cargo company loads truck trailers into ship cargo containers. The trucks drive up a ramp to a horizontal loading platform 30 ft off the ground, but they have difficulty driving up a ramp at an angle steeper than 20°. What is the minimum length that the ramp needs to be? 87.8 ft

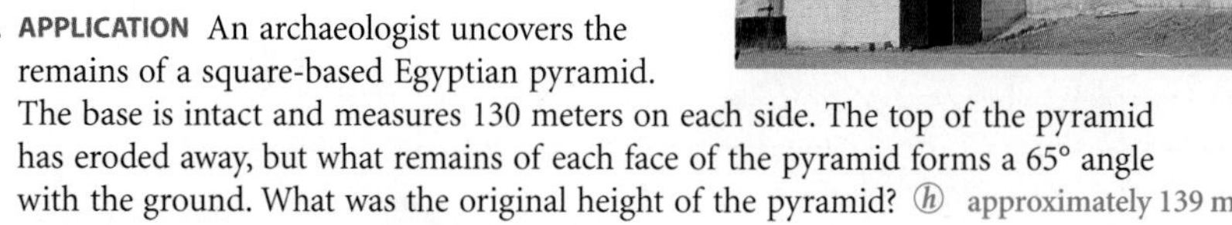

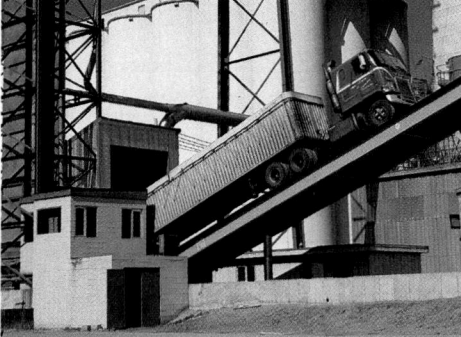

12.1 **12.** **APPLICATION** An archaeologist uncovers the remains of a square-based Egyptian pyramid. The base is intact and measures 130 meters on each side. The top of the pyramid has eroded away, but what remains of each face of the pyramid forms a 65° angle with the ground. What was the original height of the pyramid? ⓗ approximately 139 m

12.2 **13.** **APPLICATION** A lighthouse 55 meters above sea level spots a distress signal from a sailboat. The angle of depression to the sailboat measures 21°. How far away is the sailboat from the base of the lighthouse? approximately 143 m

14. A painting company has a general safety rule to place ladders at an angle measuring between 55° and 75° from the level ground. Regina places the foot of her 25 ft ladder 6 ft from the base of a wall. What is the angle of the ladder? Is the ladder placed safely? If not, how far from the base of the wall should she place the ladder?

12.1 **15.** Show that $\frac{\sin A}{\cos A} = \tan A$.

9.2 **16.** *TRAP* is an isosceles trapezoid. ⓗ

a. Find *PR* in terms of *x*. $PR = x\sqrt{3}$

b. Write a paragraph proof to show that $m\angle TPR = 90°$.

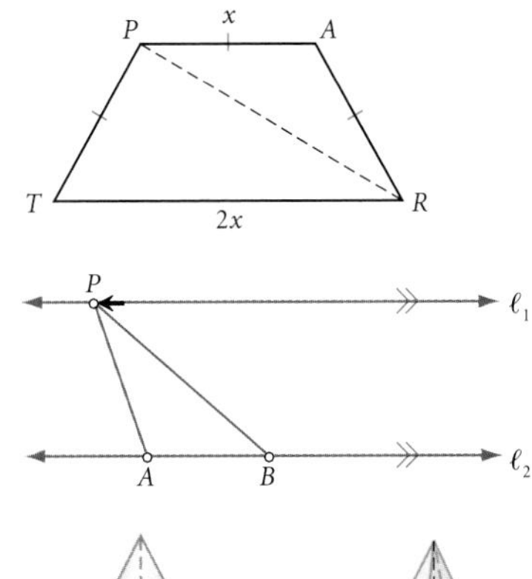

17. As *P* moves to the right on line ℓ_1, describe what happens to

a. $m\angle PAB$ decreases

b. $m\angle APB$ increases then decreases

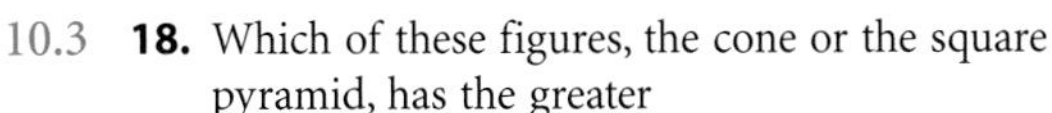

10.3 **18.** Which of these figures, the cone or the square pyramid, has the greater

a. Base perimeter? The base perimeters are equal.

b. Volume? The cone has the greater volume.

c. Surface area? The cone has the greater surface area.

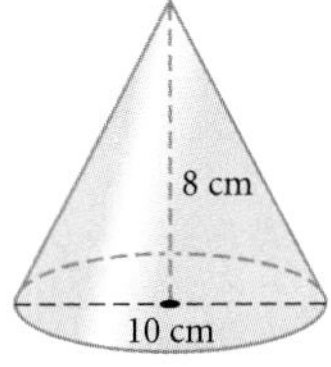

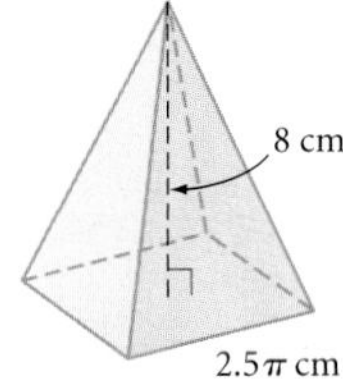

7.3 **19.** What single transformation is equivalent to the composition of each pair of functions? Write a rule for each.

a. A reflection over the line $x = -2$ followed by a reflection over the line $x = 3$

b. A reflection over the *x*-axis followed by a reflection over the *y*-axis

11.1 **20.** ***Construction*** Construct two rectangles that are not similar.

11.1 **21.** ***Construction*** Construct two isosceles trapezoids that are similar.

22. ***Technology*** Use geometry software to construct two circles. Connect the circles with a segment and construct the midpoint of the segment. Animate the endpoints of the segment around the circles and trace the midpoint of the segment. What shape does the midpoint of the segment trace? Try adjusting the relative size of the radii of the circles; try changing the distance between the centers of the circles; try starting the endpoints of the segment in different positions; or try animating the endpoints of the segment in different directions. Explain how these changes affect the shape traced by the midpoint of the segment.

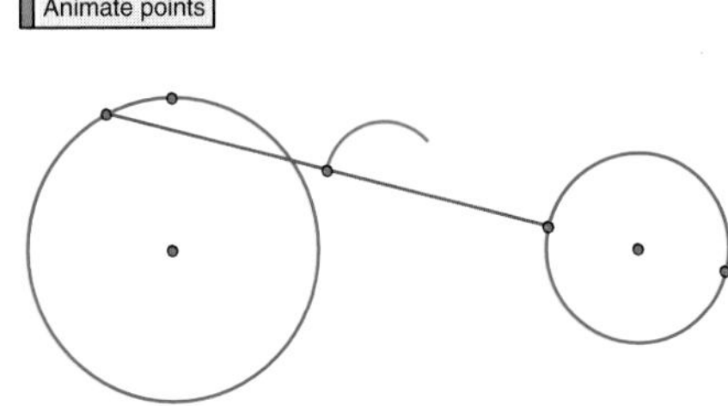

22. Answers will vary from simple (circles and straight lines) to complex (an array of polar curves, including cardioids, roses, epicycloids, and spirals). See page 777 for a more detailed answer.

EXTENSION

Use Take Another Look activities 3 and 4 on page 665.

Exercise 14 [Ask] "Why should she worry about what angle the ladder makes with the ground?" [If the angle is too small, the ladder might slip down; if it's too large, the ladder might tip backward away from the wall.]

14. The ladder at approximately a 76° angle is not safe. The ladder should be at least 6.5 ft and no more than 14.3 ft from the base of the wall.

Exercise 16 An altitude from point *A* or point *P* gives a right triangle with one leg $\frac{x}{2}$ and hypotenuse *x*.

16b. Since $x^2 + (x\sqrt{3})^2 = (2x)^2$, $\triangle TPR$ is a right triangle by the Converse of the Pythagorean Theorem. Therefore $m\angle TPR = 90°$.

19a. a translation to the right 10 units; $(x, y) \rightarrow (x + 10, y)$

19b. a rotation 180° about the origin; $(x, y) \rightarrow (-x, -y)$

Exercise 21 To construct one trapezoid, students could start with any isosceles triangle and mark off equal lengths on two sides and connect those marks. Ask students to explain why the shorter bases are proportional to any other pair of corresponding sides.

Exercise 22 When students construct the circles, they will probably get points on the circles that control the radii. For proper animation, they should not use these points as the endpoints of the segment or the animation will make the radii change size. There are at least five factors that students can adjust in different combinations: relative radius length, distance between centers, direction of animation, relative speed of animation, and starting position of the segment's endpoints on the circles. Hence, there are at least 32 possible answers.

See pages 776–777 for answers to Exercises 15 and 20–22.

Sangaku Problem Solution

You might mention that in problems involving tangent circles it's often convenient to draw segments between centers of tangent circles. Students may not realize that such segments pass through the point of tangency. The length of such a segment is the sum of the two radii. You might ask if it's possible to make any right triangles.

Indeed, students can draw three right triangles, each with its hypotenuse connecting the centers of two circles and equal to the sum of the radii and with the length of one leg equal to the difference of the radii. Then they can use the Pythagorean Theorem to find the length of the other leg of each triangle. They might have more difficulty seeing the top triangle than seeing the others.

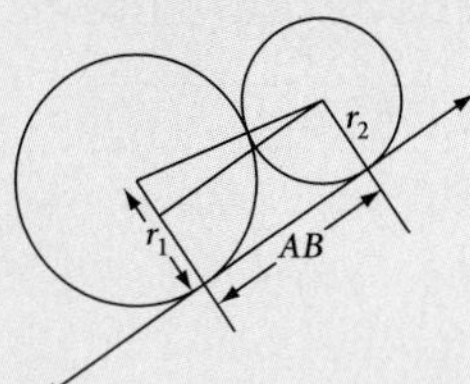

$hyp = r_1 + r_2$; $leg = r_1 - r_2$

$AB = 2\sqrt{r_1r_2}$

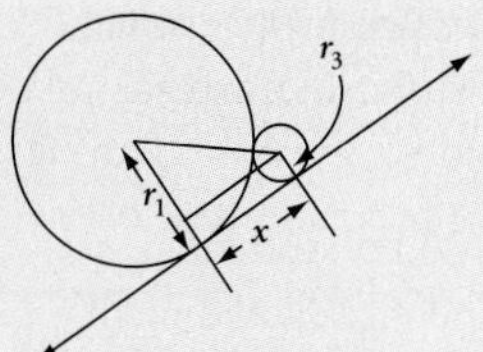

$hyp = r_1 + r_3$; $leg = r_1 - r_3$

$x = 2\sqrt{r_1r_3}$

See page 777 for the rest of the solution.

JAPANESE TEMPLE TABLETS

For centuries it has been customary in Japan to hang colorful wooden tablets in Shinto shrines to honor the gods of this native religion. During Japan's historical period of isolation (1639–1854), this tradition continued with a mathematical twist. Merchants, farmers, and others who were dedicated to mathematical learning made tablets containing mathematical problems, called *sangaku,* to inspire and challenge visitors. See if you can answer this *sangaku* problem.

These circles are tangent to each other and to the line. How are the radii of the three circles related?

Research other *sangaku* problems, then design your own tablet. Your project should include

- Your solution to the problem above.
- Some problems you found during your research and your sources.
- Your own decorated *sangaku* tablet with its solution on the back.

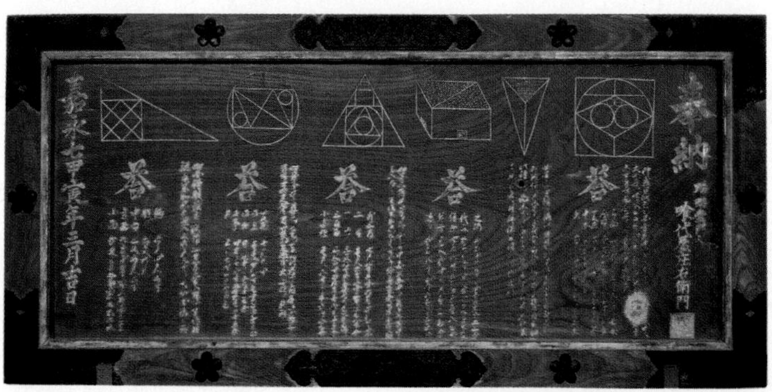

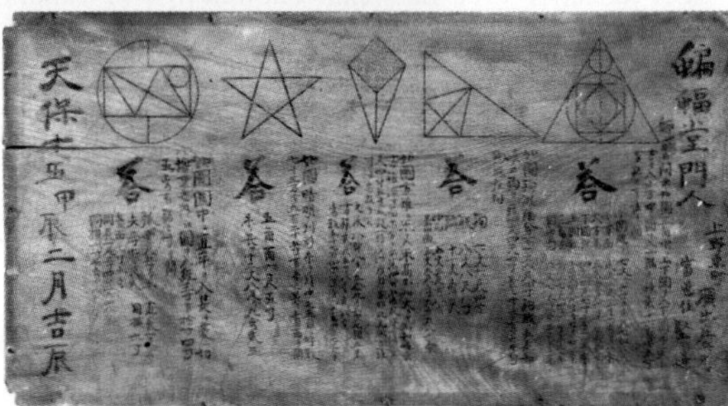

These colorful tablets, some with gold engraving, usually contain geometry problems.
Photographs by Hiroshi Umeoka.

Supporting the project

Sangaku often contain circles and ellipses, more than one problem, and equations requiring integer solutions, but they never require proofs.

OUTCOMES

- The project problem is solved.
- A *sangaku* tablet is replicated.
- At least two other *sangaku* are given, and their solutions are attempted.
- Additional cultural information is included (for example, that *sangaku* were hung in both Shinto shrines and Buddhist temples).
- The project includes some history of Japanese mathematics (*wasan*) or the origins of *sangaku.*
- The relationship $2\sqrt{r_1r_2} = 2\sqrt{r_1r_3} + 2\sqrt{r_2r_3}$ is rewritten as $\frac{1}{\sqrt{r_3}} = \frac{1}{\sqrt{r_1}} + \frac{1}{\sqrt{r_2}}$ and related to the Pythagorean Theorem.

LESSON

12.5 Problem Solving with Trigonometry

One ship drives east and another drives west
With the self-same winds that blow,
'Tis the set of the sails and not the gales
Which tells us the way to go.

ELLA WHEELER WILCOX

There are many practical applications of trigonometry. Some of them involve vectors. In earlier vector activities, you used a ruler or a protractor to measure the size of the resulting vector or the angle between vectors. Now you will be able to calculate the resulting vectors with the Law of Sines or the Law of Cosines.

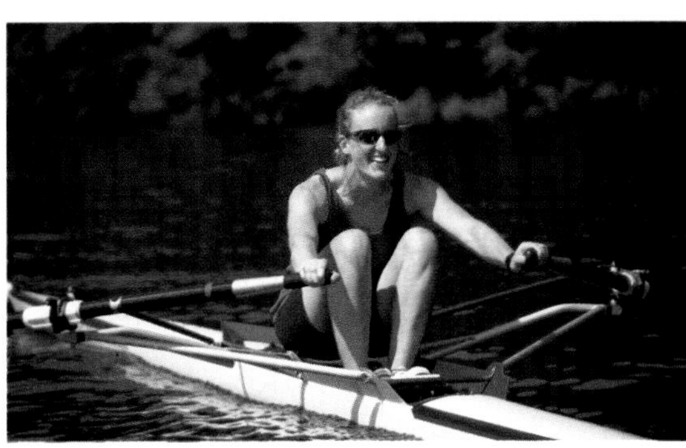

EXAMPLE

Rowing instructor Calista Thomas is in a stream flowing north to south at 3 km/hr. She is rowing northeast at a rate of 4.5 km/hr. At what speed is she moving? What direction (bearing) is she actually moving?

▶ ***Solution***

First, sketch and label the vector parallelogram. The resultant vector, r, divides the parallelogram into two congruent triangles. In each triangle you know the lengths of two sides and the measure of the included angle. Use the Law of Cosines to find the length of the resultant vector or the speed that it represents.

$$r^2 = 4.5^2 + 3^2 - 2(4.5)(3)(\cos 45°)$$

$$r^2 = 4.5^2 + 3^2 - 2(4.5)(3)(\cos 45°)$$

$$r \approx 3.2$$

Calista is moving at a speed of approximately 3.2 km/hr.

To find Calista's bearing (an angle measured clockwise from north), you need to find θ, and add its measure to 45°. Use the Law of Sines.

$$\frac{\sin\theta}{3} = \frac{\sin 45°}{3.2}$$

$$\sin\theta = \frac{3(\sin 45°)}{3.2}$$

$$\theta = \sin^{-1}\left[\frac{3(\sin 45°)}{3.2}\right] \approx 42°$$

Add 42° and 45° to find that Calista is moving at a bearing of 87°.

LESSON

12.5

PLANNING

LESSON OUTLINE

One day:

10 min Example

35 min Exercises

MATERIALS

- calculators
- Moon Distance (T) for One step

TEACHING

In Lesson 12.2, students saw applications of trigonometric ratios, primarily related to angles of elevation and depression. In this lesson they see a mixture of applications that use not only the ratios themselves but also the Law of Sines and the Law of Cosines.

▶ ***EXAMPLE***

Remind students of the vector diagrams in Lesson 5.5. A vector giving speed and direction is called *velocity.* Students may not see how they know the lengths of two sides and the measure of the included angle until they realize that the figure is a parallelogram, so opposite sides are congruent. In the equation $\frac{\sin\theta}{3} = \frac{\sin 45°}{3.2}$ for finding the bearing, 3.2 is an approximation. Though it is best not to round until the last step, students who don't have graphing calculators might need to. A more accurate equation would be $\frac{\sin\theta}{3} = \frac{\sin 45°}{\sqrt{4.5^2 + 3^2 - 2(4.5)(3)(\cos 45°)}}$. The Law of Cosines might also be used to find the angle measure.

NCTM STANDARDS

CONTENT		PROCESS	
	Number	✔	Problem Solving
✔	Algebra	✔	Reasoning
✔	Geometry		Communication
✔	Measurement	✔	Connections
	Data/Probability	✔	Representation

LESSON OBJECTIVES

- Use trigonometry to solve applied problems
- Reinforce visual thinking
- Develop reading comprehension, cooperative behavior, and problem-solving skills

One step Show the Moon Distance transparency and pose this problem. "Use trigonometry to find the distance from Earth to the Moon, assuming that at a time when the Moon is directly overhead point P it's barely visible from point Q, which is 89.07° around Earth from point P." As you circulate, you may need to remind students of the Tangent Conjecture and that the radius of Earth is about 4000 miles. (Average radius is 3959 miles.) You might ask groups that finish early to find how far a spaceship from Earth to the Moon must travel.

SHARING IDEAS

After students work on some exercises, they can share their approaches.

Assessing Progress
You can check students' ability to draw diagrams to represent situations and their understanding of trigonometric ratios and the Law of Sines and the Law of Cosines.

Closing the Lesson

Knowing how to use the tools of trigonometry can give you a lot of power to solve problems.

BUILDING UNDERSTANDING

Exercises 2 and 5 require vectors. The rest of the exercises offer an array of applications of trigonometry. Urge students to sketch a diagram for each problem.

ASSIGNING HOMEWORK

Essential	2–4, 6–8, 10
Performance assessment	5
Portfolio	4
Journal	12
Group	1, 9
Review	11–18

EXERCISES

You will need

A calculator for Exercises **1–11**

Geometry software for Exercise **18**

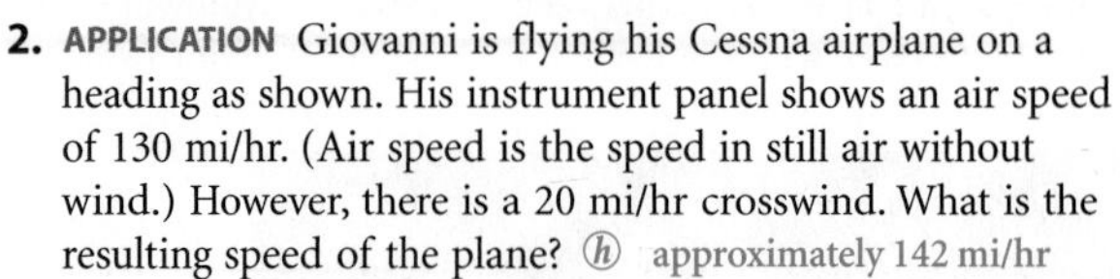

1. **APPLICATION** The steps to the front entrance of a public building rise a total of 1 m. A portion of the steps will be replaced by a wheelchair ramp. By a city ordinance, the angle of inclination for a ramp cannot measure greater than 4.5°. What is the minimum distance from the entrance that the ramp must begin? approximately 12.7 m

2. **APPLICATION** Giovanni is flying his Cessna airplane on a heading as shown. His instrument panel shows an air speed of 130 mi/hr. (Air speed is the speed in still air without wind.) However, there is a 20 mi/hr crosswind. What is the resulting speed of the plane? ⓗ approximately 142 mi/hr

3. **APPLICATION** A lighthouse is east of a Coast Guard patrol boat. The Coast Guard station is 20 km north of the lighthouse. The radar officer aboard the boat measures the angle between the lighthouse and the station to be 23°. How far is the boat from the station? approximately 51 km

4. **APPLICATION** The Archimedean screw is a water-raising device that consists of a wooden screw enclosed within a cylinder. When the cylinder is turned, the screw raises water. The screw is very efficient at an angle measuring 25°. If a screw needs to raise water 2.5 meters, how long should its cylinder be? approximately 5.9 m

Technology CONNECTION

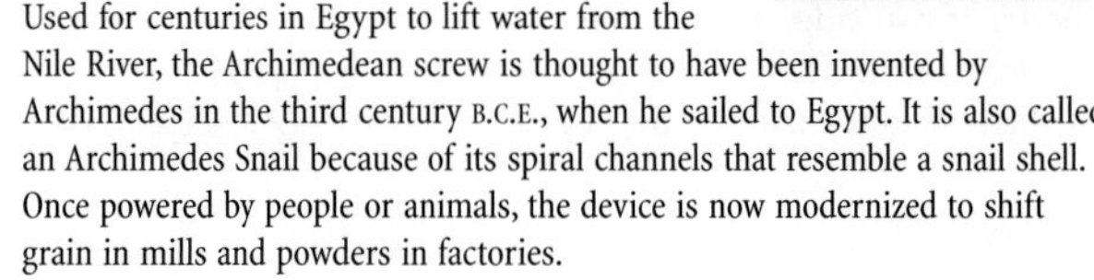

Used for centuries in Egypt to lift water from the Nile River, the Archimedean screw is thought to have been invented by Archimedes in the third century B.C.E., when he sailed to Egypt. It is also called an Archimedes Snail because of its spiral channels that resemble a snail shell. Once powered by people or animals, the device is now modernized to shift grain in mills and powders in factories.

5. **APPLICATION** Annie and Sashi are backpacking in the Sierra Nevada. They walk 8 km from their base camp at a bearing of 42°. After lunch, they change direction to a bearing of 137° and walk another 5 km. ⓗ
   a. How far are Annie and Sashi from their base camp?
   b. At what bearing must Sashi and Annie travel to return to their base camp?

▶Helping with the Exercises

Exercise 1 [Language] An *ordinance* is a law.

Exercise 2 [Language] "The resulting speed of the plane" is called *ground speed.*

Exercise 3 [Language] *Radar* is an acronym for "radio detection and ranging."

Exercise 4 [Context] Archimedes (ca. 287–212 B.C.E.) was a Greek mathematician born in Sicily.

Exercise 5 As needed, remind students that a bearing is measured clockwise from due north.

5a. approximately 9.1 km

5b. approximately 255°

6. A surveyor at point A needs to calculate the distance to an island's dock, point C. He walks 150 meters up the shoreline to point B such that $\overline{AB} \perp \overline{AC}$. Angle ABC measures 58°. What is the distance between A and C? approximately 240 m

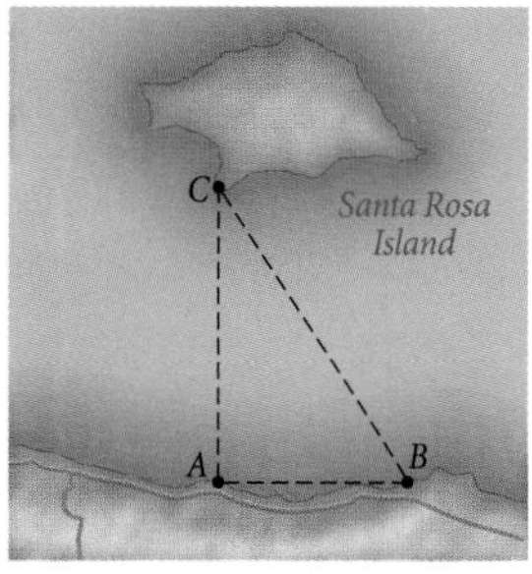

7. During a strong wind, the top of a tree cracks and bends over, touching the ground as if the trunk were hinged. The tip of the tree touches the ground 20 feet 6 inches from the base of the tree and forms a 38° angle with the ground. What was the tree's original height? approximately 42 ft

8. **APPLICATION** A pocket of matrix opal is known to be 24 meters beneath point A on Alan Ranch. A mining company has acquired rights to mine beneath Alan Ranch, but not the right to bring equipment onto the property. So the mining company cannot dig straight down. Brian Ranch has given permission to dig on its property at point B, 8 meters from point A. At what angle to the level ground must the mining crew dig to reach the opal? What distance must they dig?

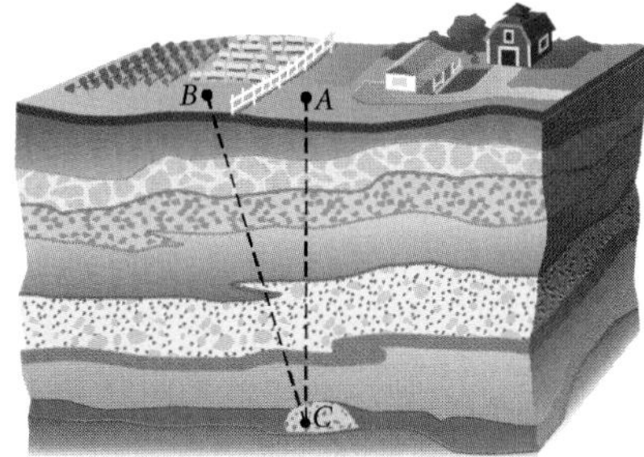

9. Todd's friend Olivia is flying her stunt plane at an elevation of 6.3 km. From the ground, Todd sees the plane moving directly toward him from the west at a 49° angle of elevation. Three minutes later he turns and sees the plane moving away from him to the east at a 65° angle of elevation. How fast is Olivia flying in kilometers per hour? ⓗ approximately 168 km/hr

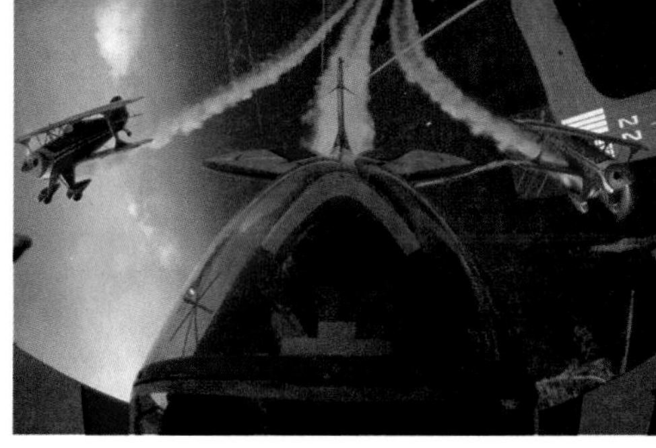

10. A water pipe for a farm's irrigation system must go through a small hill. Farmer Golden attaches a 14.5-meter rope to the pipe's entry point and an 11.2-meter rope to the exit point. When he pulls the ropes taut, their ends meet at a 58° angle. What is the length of pipe needed to go through the hill? At what angle with respect to the first rope should the pipe be laid so that it comes out of the hill at the correct exit point? ⓗ approximately 12.8 m at an angle of approximately 48°

Review

10.2 11. Find the volume of this right regular pentagonal prism. ⓗ approximately 108 cm^3

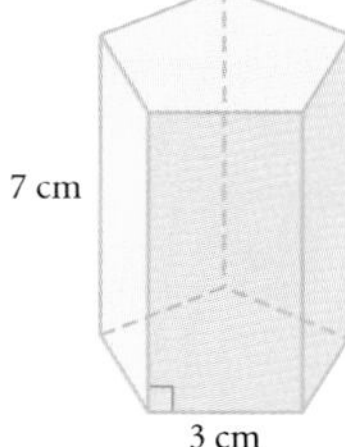

8.4 12. A formula for the area of a regular polygon is $A = \frac{ns^2}{4\tan\theta}$, where n is the number of sides, s is the length of a side, and $\theta = \frac{360}{2n}$. Explain why this formula is correct.

Exercise 7 This is the one-step investigation for Lesson 12.1; it involves both sine and cosine ratios. **[Alert]** Students might forget to add the two pieces of the tree together.

Exercise 8 **[Language]** Opals are a kind of iridescent gemstone softer than quartz.

8. They must dig at an angle of between 71° and 72° and dig for at least 25 m.

Exercise 11 If students are confused, **[Ask]** "Can you find the apothem of the base?" $\left[\text{Use } \tan\left(\frac{1}{2} \cdot \frac{3 \cdot 180°}{5}\right) = \frac{a}{1.5}.\right]$

12. Sample answer: Any regular polygon can be divided into n congruent isosceles triangles, each with a vertex angle of $\frac{360°}{n}$.

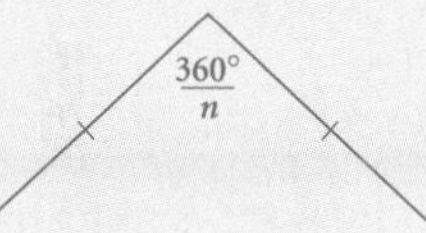

The altitude from the vertex angle of an isosceles triangle bisects the angle and the opposite side. This altitude is also an apothem of the regular polygon.

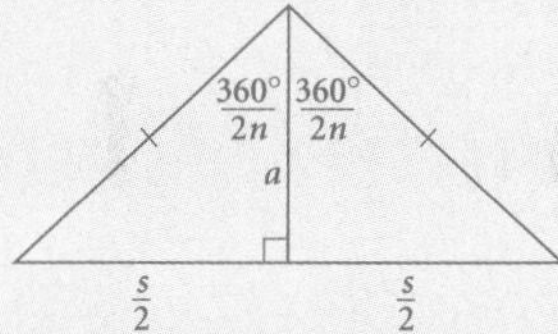

For simplicity, let $\theta = \frac{360}{2n}$. Now use the tangent ratio to find the length of the apothem.

$$\tan\theta = \frac{\frac{s}{2}}{a}$$

$$a = \frac{s}{2\tan\theta}$$

Now use the area formula for a regular polygon.

$$A = \frac{1}{2}aP$$

$$A = \frac{1}{2} \cdot \frac{s}{2\tan\theta} \cdot ns$$

$$A = \frac{ns^2}{4\tan\theta} \text{ where } \theta = \frac{360}{2n}$$

Exercise 13 Students might think that the side of the cube is the same as the side of a square inscribed in a circle of diameter 24. Help them see that no face of the cube goes through the sphere's center. **[Ask]** "What part of the cube is a diameter of the sphere?" [a diagonal] "How do you find the diagonal of a cube?" [Apply the Pythagorean Theorem to the right triangle whose legs are an edge of the cube and a diagonal of one face.] If x represents the length of a cube's edge, we get:

$$x^2 + \left(x\sqrt{2}\right)^2 = 24^2$$

$$x^2 + 2x^2 = 576$$

$$3x^2 = 576$$

$$x^2 = 192$$

$$x = \sqrt{64}\sqrt{3} = 8\sqrt{3}$$

From this we can find the volume of the cube.

14. The area increases by a factor of 9.

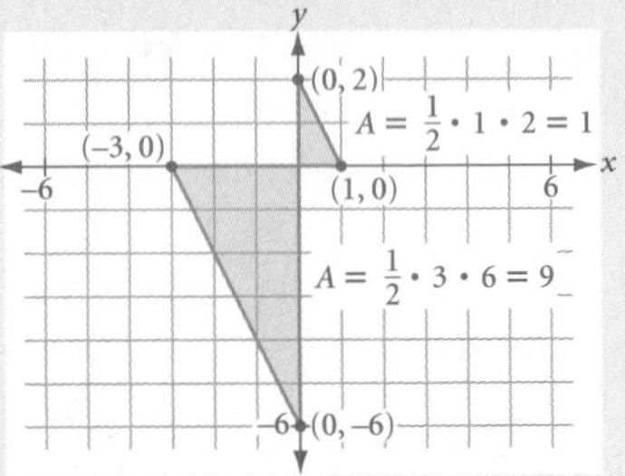

Exercise 15 **[Alert]** Students might miss the fact that 15 cm is the length of just part of the base.

17a. a reflection over the x-axis; $(x, y) \rightarrow (x, -y)$

17b. a reflection over the y-axis; $(x, y) \rightarrow (-x, y)$

Exercise 18 This tiling is monohedral, though it appears to be more complex.

EXTENSIONS

A. Pose this problem: The distance from Earth to the Moon is about 233,900 miles. The angle intercepted by the center of the moon and one edge, as viewed from Earth, measures 0.26°. Find the radius of the Moon. [1070 miles]

9.1 **13.** Find the volume of the largest cube that can fit into a sphere with a radius of 12 cm. $1536\sqrt{3}$ cm³ ≈ 2660 cm³

11.5 **14.** How does the area of a triangle change if its vertices are transformed by the rule $(x, y) \rightarrow (-3x, -3y)$? Give an example to support your answer.

11.2 **15.** What's wrong with this picture? $\frac{5}{4} \neq \frac{5 + 15}{12}$

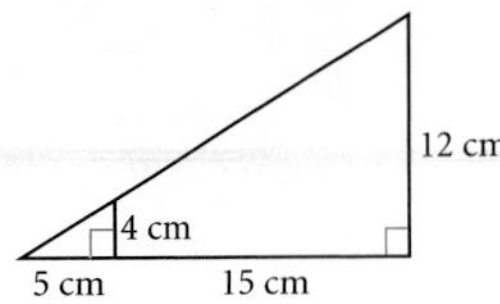

16. As P moves to the right on line ℓ_1, describe what happens to

a. PA decreases then increases

b. Area of $\triangle APB$ does not change

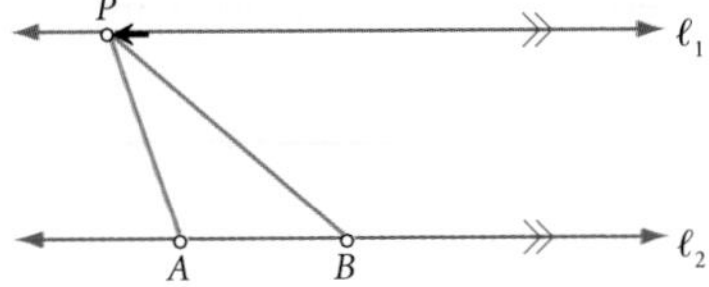

7.3 **17.** What single transformation is equivalent to the composition of each pair of functions? Write a rule for each.

a. A reflection over the line $y = x$ followed by a counterclockwise 270° rotation about the origin

b. A rotation 180° about the origin followed by a reflection over the x-axis

7.4 **18.** ***Technology*** Tile floors are often designed by creating simple, symmetric patterns on squares. When the squares are lined up, the patterns combine, often leaving the original squares hardly visible. Use geometry software to create your own tile-floor pattern. Answers will vary.

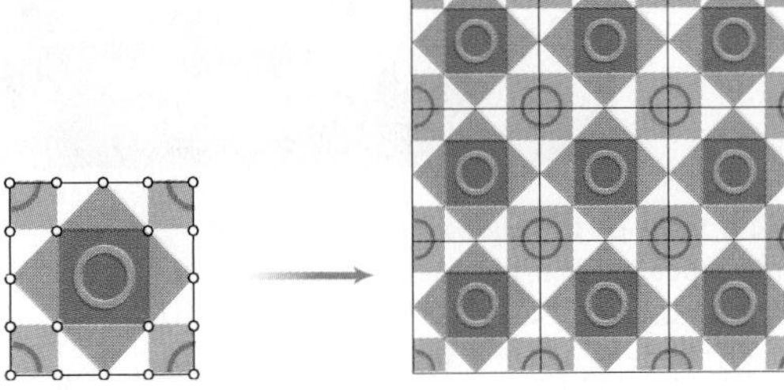

IMPROVING YOUR ALGEBRA SKILLS

Substitute and Solve

1. If $2x = 3y$, $y = 5w$, and $w = \frac{20}{3z}$, find x in terms of z.

2. If $7x = 13y$, $y = 28w$, and $w = \frac{9}{26z}$, find x in terms of z.

B. Revisit the Project Random Triangles on page 218 and challenge students to explore the probability that a random triangle is acute, obtuse, right, isosceles, or equilateral. [The probability of an exact isosceles or equilateral triangle is theoretically 0 since there are infinitely many points along the straw, the probability of choosing the same point more than once is $\frac{1}{\text{infinity}}$. The probability that one angle will measure exactly 90° is similarly 0. But, because measurements are rounded, students will occasionally get a special triangle. To sort the data for acute and obtuse triangles students can use the inequality based on the Pythagorean Theorem.]

IMPROVING ALGEBRA SKILLS

1. $x = \frac{50}{z}$

2. $x = \frac{18}{z}$

Trigonometric Ratios and the Unit Circle

In Lesson 12.1, you defined trigonometric ratios in terms of the sides of a right triangle. That limited you to talking about acute angles. But in the coordinate plane, it's possible to define trigonometric ratios for angles with measures less than 0° and greater than 90°. These definitions use a **unit circle**—a circle with center (0, 0) and radius 1 unit.

The height of a seat on a Ferris wheel can be modeled by unit-circle trigonometry. This Ferris wheel, called the *London Eye,* was built for London's year 2000 celebration.

Activity
The Unit Circle

You will need

- The Unit Circle worksheet

In this activity, you will use a Sketchpad construction to explore the unit circle. The first part of this activity will give you some understanding of how a unit circle simplifies the trigonometric ratios for acute angles. Then you will use the unit circle to explore the ratios for all angles, from 0° to 360°, and even negative angle measures.

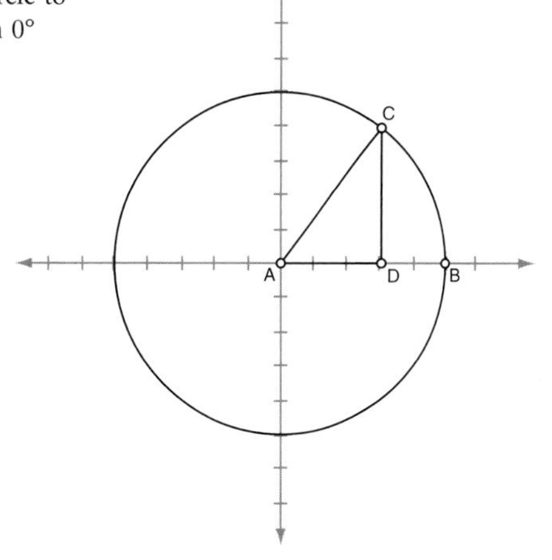

Step 1 Follow the steps on the worksheet to construct a unit circle with right triangle *ADC*.

Step 2 In right triangle *ADC*, write ratios for the sine, cosine, and tangent of $\angle DAC$.

Step 2
$\sin \angle DAC = \frac{DC}{AC}$
$\cos \angle DAC = \frac{AD}{AC}$
$\tan \angle DAC = \frac{DC}{AD}$

Step 3 The length of *AC* in this unit circle should be 1 in. If it is not, adjust your axes. Use this length to simplify your trigonometric definitions in Step 2.

NCTM STANDARDS

CONTENT		PROCESS	
	Number		Problem Solving
✓	Algebra		Reasoning
✓	Geometry	✓	Communication
✓	Measurement	✓	Connections
	Data/Probability	✓	Representation

LESSON OBJECTIVES

- Explore the unit circle
- See definitions of the trigonometric functions for angles with measures greater than 90° and less than 0°

EXPLORATION

PLANNING

LESSON OUTLINE

First day:

30 min Activity
10 min Sharing
5 min Closing

Second day:

25 min Activity
15 min Sharing
5 min Closing

MATERIALS

- The Geometer's Sketchpad
- The Unit Circle (W)
- Sketchpad demonstration The Unit Circle, *optional*

TEACHING

The definition of *angle* in Lesson 1.2 limited it to measures between 0° and 180°, and our applications of triangle trigonometry have limited angles to acute angles. But the definition of *angle* can be extended. **[Ask]** "What are some uses for having trigonometric functions for all the angles of a circle?" [sum of two angles; bearings of up to 360° and negative bearings] "What are other, equivalent ways of naming a 90° angle?" [450°, −270°, and so on] The amount or direction of rotation differs, but the net result is the same.

Step 3 The length of the hypotenuse is 1.
$\sin \angle DAC = DC$
$\cos \angle DAC = AD$

[Language] You might want to clarify that *less than 0°* means "negative." Negative angle measures result from directed measurements, in which positive angle measures are measured counterclockwise and negative angle measures are measured clockwise. This may result in some confusion with bearings, in which positive angle measures are measured clockwise from north. You might also want to mention that *greater than 90°* includes obtuse angles (to 180°) and angles that measure 180° or more. (You can have an angle of, say, 190°, 360°, or 525°.)

Guiding the Activity

The goal of the activity is *not* to construct the unit circle but to see how it behaves. If students use the premade sketch in the Unit Circle Sketchpad demonstration instead of making their own, they won't need to press the Show buttons until Steps 6 and 13.

Steps 1–7 Advise students to keep $\triangle ADC$ in the first quadrant.

Step 2 This step asks for ratios, not values.

Step 3 If needed, **[Ask]** "What is the radius of the circle?"

Step 4 **[Ask]** "Why do the legs represent cosine and sine?" [The length of the side adjacent to $\angle DAC$, AD, determines how far point C is from point A in the x-direction.] If students have trouble making the connection between physical lengths, the coordinates of point C, and trigonometric ratios, this may be an appropriate time to have students actually measure the lengths AD, DC, and AC.

Step 6 If you are using the premade sketch, have students press the *Show Tangent* button.

Step 7 **[Ask]** "Why are triangles ADC and ABE similar?"

Step 4 The y-coordinate corresponds to the sine of $\angle DAC$. The x-coordinate corresponds to the cosine of $\angle DAC$. The vertical leg of $\triangle ADC$, $\overline{CD}$, represents the sine of $\angle DAC$, and the horizontal leg of $\triangle ADC$, $\overline{AD}$, represents the cosine of $\angle DAC$.

Step 5 To calculate the tangent of $\angle DAC$, divide the y-coordinate of point C by the x-coordinate of point C, or $\frac{y}{x}$.

Step 7 The y-coordinate corresponds to the tangent of $\angle DAC$, and $\overline{BE}$ represents the tangent of $\angle DAC$. Explanations will vary; here's a sample answer: By the definition of tangent in Step 2, $\tan\angle DAC = \frac{CD}{AD}$; but by similar triangles, $\frac{CD}{AD} = \frac{BE}{AB}$; because $\overline{AB}$ is a radius of the unit circle, $AB = 1$, and $\frac{CD}{AD} = BE$, or $\tan\angle DAC = BE$; in a coordinate plane, the numeric value of BE is the same as the y-coordinate of E.

Step 9 Positive angle measures are measured in a counterclockwise direction from $\overline{AB}$, up to 180°. Negative angle measures are measured in a clockwise direction from $\overline{AB}$, up to $-180°$.

Step 10 When point C is in the first quadrant, $m\angle DAC = m\angle BAC$. In the second quadrant, $m\angle DAC = m\angle BAC - 180°$. In the third quadrant, $m\angle DAC = 180° + m\angle BAC$. In the fourth quadrant, $m\angle DAC = m\angle BAC$.

Step 11 The trigonometric values should confirm students' answers about the x- and y-coordinates of point C and point E.

Step 4 Measure the coordinates of point C. Which coordinate corresponds to the sine of $\angle DAC$? Which coordinate corresponds to the cosine of $\angle DAC$? What parts of your sketch physically represent the sine of $\angle DAC$ and the cosine of $\angle DAC$?

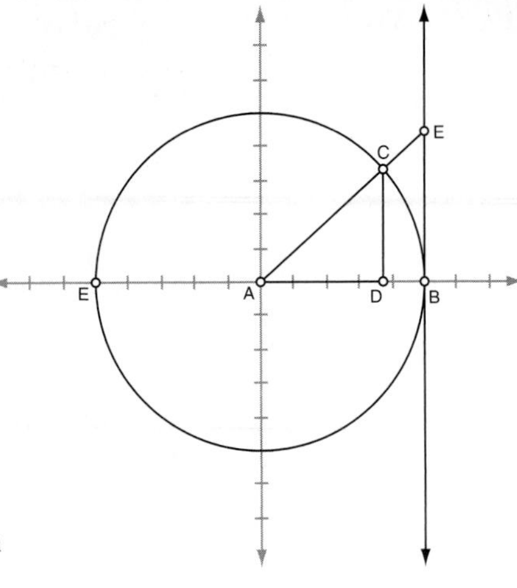

Step 5 How can you use the coordinates of point C to calculate the tangent of $\angle DAC$?

Step 6 Follow the steps on the worksheet to add a physical representation of tangent to your unit circle.

Step 7 Measure the coordinates of point E. Which coordinate corresponds to the tangent of $\angle DAC$? What part of your sketch physically represents the tangent of $\angle DAC$? Use similar triangles ADC and ABE to explain your answers.

So far, you have looked only at right triangle ADC with acute angle DAC. It may seem that you have not gotten any closer to defining trigonometric ratios for angles with measures less than 0° or greater than 90°. That is, even if you move point C into another quadrant, $\angle DAC$ would still be an acute angle.

You may recall from Chapter 6 that a point on a rolling tire traces a curve called a cycloid. Cycloids are defined by trigonometry.

In order to modify the definition of trigonometric ratios in a unit circle, you need to measure $\angle BAC$ instead. That is, measure the amount of rotation from $\overline{AB}$ to $\overline{AC}$.

Step 8 Select point B, point A, and point C, in that order. Measure $\angle BAC$.

Step 9 Move point C around the circle and watch how the measure of $\angle BAC$ changes. Summarize your observations.

Step 10 When point C is in the first quadrant, how is the measure of $\angle DAC$ related to the measure of $\angle BAC$? How about when point C is in the second quadrant? The third quadrant? The fourth quadrant?

Step 11 Use Sketchpad's calculator to calculate the value of the sine, cosine, and tangent functions for $\angle BAC$. Compare these values to the coordinates of point C and point E. Do the values support your answers to Steps 4 and 7?

Step 8 Because angle measures are set to directed degrees in Preferences, selection order is important.

Step 9 Theoretically you can find measures of angles greater than 180° and less than $-180°$. **[Ask]** "What would $m\angle BAC = 270°$ mean?" [that $m\angle DAC = 90°$ and point C is between the third and fourth quadrants] "What would $m\angle BAC = -360°$ mean?" [$m\angle DAC = 0°$] "What would $m\angle BAC = -550°$ mean?" [the same as $m\angle BAC = 170°$]

Step 10 If students are having difficulty, suggest that they think about supplementary angles.

Step 11 To use the calculator, students need to select the measure of $\angle BAC$, choose **Calculate** from the Measure menu, and then select the appropriate function from the **Functions** menu. Sketchpad will show the resulting measures in the form "$\sin(m\angle BAC) = X$."

Step 12 — See below.

Move point C around the circle and watch how the trigonometric ratios change for angle measures between $-180°$ and $180°$. Answer these questions.

a. How does the sine of $\angle BAC$ change as the measure of the angle goes from $0°$ to $90°$ to $180°$? From $-180°$ to $-90°$ to $0°$?

b. How does the cosine of $\angle BAC$ change?

c. If the sine of one angle is equal to the cosine of another angle, how are the angles related to each other?

d. How does the tangent of $\angle BAC$ change? What happens to the tangent of $\angle BAC$ as its measure approaches $90°$ or $-90°$? Based on the definition of tangent and the side lengths in $\triangle ADC$, what value do you think the tangent of $90°$ equals?

You can add an interesting animation that will graph the changing sine and tangent values in your sketch. You can construct points that will trace curves that algebraically represent the functions $y = \sin(x)$ and $y = \tan(x)$.

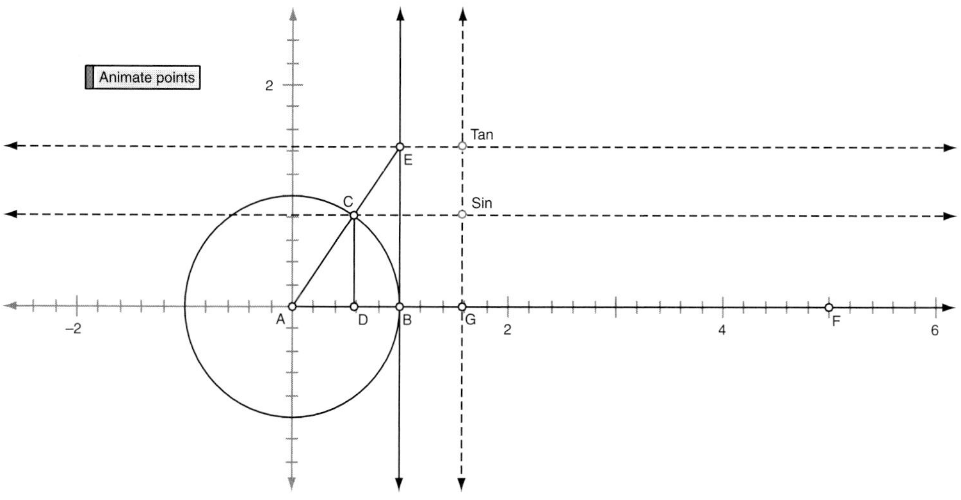

Step 13 — Follow the steps on the worksheet to add an animation that will trace curves representing the sine and tangent functions.

Step 14 — Measure the coordinates of point F, then locate it as close to (6.28, 0) as possible. Move point G to the origin and move point C to (1, 0). Press the Animation button to trace the sine and tangent functions.

The high and low points of tides can be modeled with trigonometry. This tide table from the Savannah River in Fort Jackson, Georgia, shows a familiar pattern in its data.

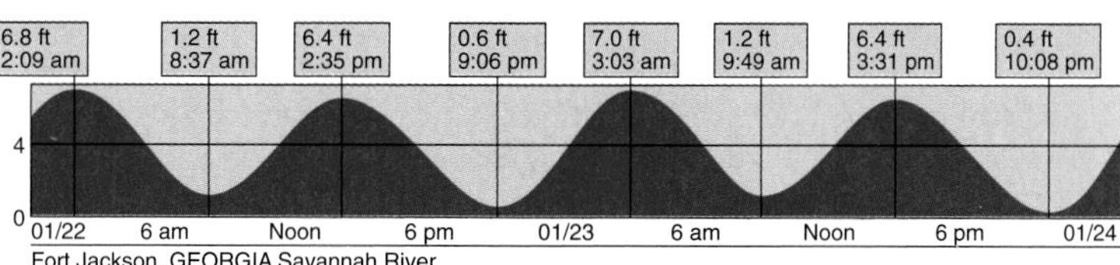

Step 12a The sine of $\angle BAC$ increases from 0 to 1 as the measure of the angle increases from $0°$ to $90°$, then decreases from 1 to 0 as the measure increases from $90°$ to $180°$. The sine of $\angle BAC$ decreases from 0 to -1 as the measure increases from $-180°$ to $-90°$, then increases from -1 to 0 as the measure increases from $-90°$ to $0°$.

Step 12b The cosine of $\angle BAC$ decreases from 1 to 0 as the measure of the angle increases from $0°$ to $90°$, then decreases from 0 to -1 as the measure increases from $90°$ to $180°$. The cosine of $\angle BAC$ increases from -1 to 0 as the measure increases from $-180°$ to $-90°$, then increases from 0 to 1 as the angle increases from $-90°$ to $0°$.

Step 12c The angles are complementary.

Step 12d The tangent of $\angle BAC$ approaches $(\pm)$ infinity as its measure approaches $90°$ or $-90°$. The tangent of $90°$ is undefined because $\tan\angle DAC = \frac{CD}{AD} = \frac{1}{0}$, but division by zero is undefined.

Step 12 In Sketchpad, students might be able to make sensitive adjustments to their sketch to get an increasingly larger y-coordinate for point E and for the value of the tangent, but they will still not get the theoretical value of infinity.

Technically, the animation shows that $y = \sin(x)$ and $y = \tan(x)$ only for the domain defined by point F. If students do not start the animation with points C, F, and G in the appropriate locations, the resulting curves will be some transformation of $y = \sin(x)$ and $y = \tan(x)$.

Adding an animation of $y = \cos(x)$ is more challenging because it requires translating a horizontal length into a vertical motion. You might want to challenge students to use rotations to animate this curve.

Step 13 If students are using the premade sketch, have them press the *Show Sine and Tangent Curves* button.

Step 14 If point F is offscreen and students cannot locate (6.28, 0), they can scale the axes by dragging point B closer to point A.

Using a different color for point *Sin* or point *Tan* might make distinguishing the curves easier.

In the premade sketch, the button is called *Animate Sine and Tangent Curves.* To stop the animation, students can press the Animation button again. Students can choose **Erase Traces** from the Display menu to clear the previous animation's traces. If point G is moving from right to left, students can press the *Animate Points* button, choose **Properties** from the Edit menu, and adjust the direction in the Animation panel.

[Language] The word *tide* comes from old English meaning "period" or "season." It is often used for the rise and fall of waters, but it can also be used for anything that periodically rises and falls or comes and goes.

Step 15 Some students may enjoy fully experimenting with the positions of points *C*, *F*, and *G* to create geometric designs.

Sketchpad evaluates trigonometric functions for angles measured in *radians* rather than degrees. You may want to introduce the radian measure of arcs and angles. One radian is the length of the arc (or the measure of the central angle intercepting that arc) that is one radius of a circle laid out along its circumference, so there are 2π radians in 360°. A central angle with measure 60° would measure $\frac{\pi}{3}$ radians. In general, radian measure is defined by the relationship $radians = \frac{2\pi\theta}{360°}$, where θ is the measure of the central angle in degrees. Although Sketchpad and some books treat radians as measurement units, they're often considered as unitless to emphasize that the trigonometric functions are defined for all real numbers.

SHARING IDEAS

Some students may understand this concept better if you describe it as extending the trigonometric definitions from angles in right triangles to central angles in a circle measured from a common radius.

[Ask] "The graphs can be described as *periodic*. Why?" **[Language]** You might mention the English word *periodical*, which refers to newspapers and magazines whose publication dates are a fixed time interval apart.

Assessing Progress
You can assess students' understanding of trigonometric ratios and of coordinates as distances.

Closing the Lesson

The unit circle helps us understand definitions of trigonometric functions for angles greater than 90° or less than 0°.

Step 15 What's special about 6.28 as the *x*-coordinate of point *F*? Try other locations for point *F* to see what happens. Use what you know about circles to explain why 6.28 is a special value for the unit circle.

Step 15 The value 6.28 makes the animation cycle repeat at exactly the same place each time. Other values for the *x*-coordinate of point *F* will create several overlapping, translated versions of the curves. The value 6.28 is special because it is approximately the circumference of the circle; that is $C = 2\pi r = 2\pi(1) \approx 6.28$.

You will probably learn much more about unit-circle trigonometry in a future mathematics course.

project

TRIGONOMETRIC FUNCTIONS

You've seen many applications where you can use trigonometry to find distances or angle measures. Another important application of trigonometry is to model **periodic** phenomena, which repeat over time.

In this project you'll discover characteristics of the graphs of trigonometric functions, including their periodic nature. The three functions you'll look at are

$y = \sin(x)$
$y = \cos(x)$
$y = \tan(x)$

These functions are defined not only for acute angles but also for angles with measures less than 0° and greater than 90°.

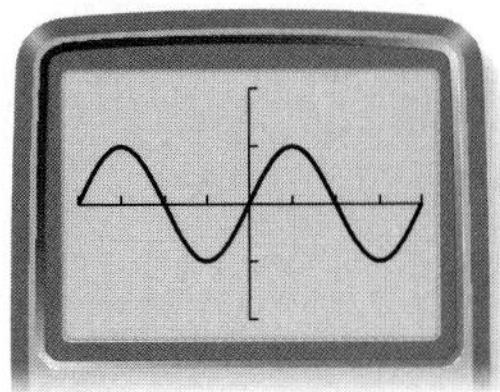

The swinging motion of a pendulum is an example of periodic motion that can be modeled by trigonometry.

Set your calculator in *degree* mode and set a window with an *x*-range of −360 to 360 and a *y*-range of −2 to 2. One at a time, graph each trigonometric function. Describe the characteristics of each graph, including maximum and minimum values for *y* and the **period**—the horizontal distance after which the graph starts repeating itself. Use what you know about the definitions of sine, cosine, and tangent to explain any unusual occurrences.

Try graphing pairs of trigonometric functions. Describe any relationships you see between the graphs. Are there any values in common?

Prepare an organized presentation of your results.

Supporting the project

[Language] A *period* is the length of one complete cycle. The period of $y = \sin(x)$ is 360°, and the period of $y = \tan(x)$ is 180°. In this project, allow students to define and explore the period of each function. See page 777 for samples of the outcomes.

OUTCOMES

- ▸ Sketches and descriptions show important characteristics of each function.
- ▸ Descriptions show relationships.
- Symmetry in the graphs is recognized.
- Observations are generalized.
- Characteristics are explained in terms of the trigonometric definitions.

Exploration

Three Types of Proofs

In previous explorations, you learned four forms of valid reasoning: *Modus Ponens* (MP), *Modus Tollens* (MT), the Law of Syllogism (LS), and the Law of Contrapositive (LC). You can use these forms of reasoning to make logical arguments, or proofs. In this exploration you will learn the three basic types of proofs: direct proofs, conditional proofs, and indirect proofs.

In a **direct proof,** the given information or premises are stated, then valid forms of reasoning are used to arrive directly at a conclusion. Here is a direct proof given in two-column form. In a **two-column proof,** each statement in the argument is written in the left column, and the reason for each statement is written directly across in the right column.

Direct Proof

Premises: $P \rightarrow Q$
$R \rightarrow P$
$\sim Q$

Conclusion: $\sim R$

Statement	Reason
1. $P \rightarrow Q$	**1.** Premise
2. $\sim Q$	**2.** Premise
3. $\sim P$	**3.** From lines 1 and 2, using MT
4. $R \rightarrow P$	**4.** Premise
5. $\therefore \sim R$	**5.** From lines 3 and 4, using MT

A **conditional proof** is used to prove that a $P \rightarrow Q$ statement follows from a set of premises. In a conditional proof, the first part of the conditional statement, called the **antecedent,** is assumed to be true. Then logical reasoning is used to demonstrate that the second part, called the **consequent,** must also be true. If this process is successful, it's demonstrated that *if* P *is true, then* Q *must be true.*

EXPLORATION

PLANNING

LESSON OUTLINE

One day:

30 min	Activity
10 min	Sharing
5 min	Closing

MATERIALS

none

TEACHING

Review the four forms of valid reasoning, which can be used as reasons in proofs: *Modus Ponens, Modus Tollens,* the Law of Syllogism, and the Law of Contrapositives. In this lesson students see descriptions of three different proof forms: direct, conditional, and indirect.

The difference between direct proof and conditional proof is subtle. A conditional proof proves a conditional (if-then) statement; a direct proof might prove any kind of statement. So far all proofs in this book have been direct; many of them have also been conditional.

NCTM STANDARDS

CONTENT		PROCESS	
	Number		Problem Solving
	Algebra	✓	Reasoning
	Geometry	✓	Communication
	Measurement	✓	Connections
	Data/Probability		Representation

LESSON OBJECTIVES

- Examine conditional proof
- Explore indirect proof
- Deepen understanding of direct proof
- Broaden understanding of reasoning and proof

[Language] *Antecedent* means "that which precedes" in Latin. *Ante-* is a prefix used to mean "before" in many words, for example, *anteroom. Ante meridian,* referring to before the time when the sun reaches the meridian (directly overhead), gives us the abbreviation A.M. for "before noon." Students may not be familiar with *consequent* meaning "that which follows along."

In other words, a conditional proof shows that the antecedent implies the consequent. Here is an example.

Conditional Proof

Premises: $P \to R$

$S \to \sim R$

Conclusion: $P \to \sim S$

1. P	**1.** Assume the antecedent
2. $P \to R$	**2.** Premise
3. R	**3.** From lines 1 and 2, using MP
4. $S \to \sim R$	**4.** Premise
5. $\sim S$	**5.** From lines 3 and 4, using MT

Assuming P is true, the truth of $\sim S$ is established.

$\therefore P \to \sim S$

An **indirect proof** is a clever approach to proving something. To prove indirectly that a statement is true, you begin by assuming it is *not* true. Then you show that this assumption leads to a contradiction. For example, if you are given a set of premises and are asked to show that some conclusion P is true, begin by assuming that the opposite of P, namely $\sim P$, is true. Then show that this assumption leads to a contradiction of an earlier statement. If $\sim P$ leads to a contradiction, it must be false and P must be true. Here is an example.

Indirect Proof

Premises: $R \to S$

$\sim R \to \sim P$

P

Conclusion: S

1. $\sim S$	**1.** Assume the opposite of the conclusion
2. $R \to S$	**2.** Premise
3. $\sim R$	**3.** From lines 1 and 2, using MT
4. $\sim R \to \sim P$	**4.** Premise
5. $\sim P$	**5.** From lines 3 and 4, using MP
6. P	**6.** Premise

But lines 5 and 6 contradict each other. It's impossible for both P and $\sim P$ to be true.

Therefore, $\sim S$, the original assumption, is false. If $\sim S$ is false, then S is true.

$\therefore S$

Many logical arguments can be proved using more than one type of proof. For instance, you can prove the argument in the example above by using a direct proof. (Try it!) With practice you will be able to tell which method will work best for a particular argument.

Activity
Prove It!

Step 1 Copy the direct proof below, including the list of premises and the conclusion. Provide each missing reason.

Premises: $P \to Q$
$Q \to \sim R$
R

Conclusion: $\sim P$

1. $Q \to \sim R$	**1.** ? Premise
2. R	**2.** ? Premise
3. $\sim Q$	**3.** ? From lines 1 and 2, using MT
4. $P \to Q$	**4.** ? Premise
5. $\therefore \sim P$	**5.** ? From lines 3 and 4, using MT

Step 2 Copy the conditional proof below, including the list of premises and the conclusion. Provide each missing statement or reason.

Premises: $\sim R \to \sim Q$
$T \to \sim R$
$S \to T$

Conclusion: $S \to \sim Q$

1. S	**1.** ? Assume the antecedent
2. $S \to T$	**2.** ? Premise
3. T	**3.** From lines 1 and 2, using ? MP
4. $T \to \sim R$	**4.** ? Premise
5. $\sim R$	**5.** ? From lines 3 and 4, using MP
6. ? $\sim R \to \sim Q$	**6.** ? Premise
7. ? $\sim Q$	**7.** ? From lines 5 and 6, using MP

Assuming S is true, the truth of $\sim Q$ is established.
$\therefore$? $S \to \sim Q$

Step 3 Copy the indirect proof below and at the top of page 658, including the list of premises and the conclusion. Provide each missing statement or reason.

Premises: $P \to Q \to R$
$Q \to \sim R$
Q

Conclusion: $\sim P$

1. P	**1.** Assume the ? of the ? opposite; conclusion
2. $P \to (Q \to R)$	**2.** ? Premise
3. $Q \to R$	**3.** ? From lines 1 and 2, using MP
4. Q	**4.** ? Premise

Guiding the Activity

Students might find these logical proofs challenging. Encourage them to think of these as puzzles. They're putting pieces together in various ways.

Step 5 Your class might discuss the truth of the premises and how it affects the truth of the conclusions. In simple Boolean logic, a statement must be either true or false; it can't be both or neither. If valid reasoning is followed starting from true statements, the conclusion is logically true. In assessing arguments in the real world, you need to examine both the validity of the logical argument and the truth of the premises. Indeed, you must examine the premises to see whether they are logical statements that must be either true or false, or statements that could be both true and false, or neither.

SHARING IDEAS

The form of indirect proof described here is also called *proof by contradiction.* Symbolically, $(\sim P \to Q \text{ and } \sim P \to \sim Q) \to P$. In words, if the negation of P leads to both some statement Q and its negation, then $\sim P$ is false; so P is true. Another form of indirect proof will appear in examples and exercises in Lesson 13.5. Both forms of indirect proof require assuming the negation of a statement and finding a contradiction.

Assessing Progress

You can assess students' understanding of the logical rules from earlier in the course and their ability to use these rules to solve puzzles.

Step 3 (continued)

5. R	**5.** ? From lines 3 and 4, using MP
6. ? $Q \to \sim R$	**6.** ? Premise
7. ? $\sim R$	**7.** From lines ? and ?, using ? 4; 6; MP

But lines ? and ? contradict each other. 5; 7

Therefore, P, the assumption, is false.

$\therefore \sim P$

Step 4

Provide the steps and reasons to prove each logical argument. You will need to decide whether to use a direct, conditional, or indirect proof.

a. Premises: $P \to Q$
$Q \to \sim R$
$T \to R$
Conclusion: $T \to \sim P$

b. Premises: $(R \to S) \to P$
$T \to Q$
$\sim T \to \sim P$
$\sim Q$
Conclusion: $\sim(R \to S)$

c. Premises: $S \to Q$
$P \to S$
$\sim R \to P$
$\sim Q$
Conclusion: R

d. Premises: $P \to Q$
$\sim P \to S$
$R \to \sim S$
$\sim Q$
Conclusion: $\sim R$

Step 5

Translate each argument into symbolic terms, then prove it is valid.

a. If all wealthy people are happy, then money can buy happiness. If money can buy happiness, then true love doesn't exist. But true love exists. Therefore, not all wealthy people are happy.

b. If Clark is performing at the theater today, then everyone at the theater has a good time. If everyone at the theater has a good time, then Lois is not sad. Lois is sad. Therefore, Clark is not performing at the theater today.

c. If Evette is innocent, then Alfa is telling the truth. If Romeo is telling the truth, then Alfa is not telling the truth. If Romeo is not telling the truth, then he has something to gain. Romeo has nothing to gain. Therefore, if Romeo has nothing to gain, then Evette is not innocent.

Closing the Lesson

A **conditional proof** is used to prove a relationship between an antecedent and a consequent. Many proofs in geometry can be stated as conditional statements: If a triangle is isosceles, then its median is the same segment as its altitude. **Indirect proof** involves showing that the opposite of what you are trying to prove leads to a contradiction. Therefore what you are trying to prove is true.

Step 4a

1. $P \to Q$	1. Premise
2. $Q \to \sim R$	2. Premise
3. $P \to \sim R$	3. From lines 1 and 2, using LS
4. $T \to R$	4. Premise
5. $\sim R \to \sim T$	5. From line 4, using LC
6. $P \to \sim T$	6. From lines 3 and 5, using LS
7. $T \to \sim P$	7. From line 6, using LC

Step 4b

1. $T \to Q$	1. Premise
2. $\sim Q$	2. Premise
3. $\sim T$	3. From lines 1 and 2, using MT
4. $\sim T \to \sim P$	4. Premise
5. $\sim P$	5. From lines 3 and 4, using MP
6. $(R \to S) \to P$	6. Premise
7. $\sim(R \to S)$	7. From lines 5 and 6, using MT

Step 4c

1. $P \to S$	1. Premise
2. $S \to Q$	2. Premise
3. $P \to Q$	3. From lines 1 and 2, using LS
4. $\sim Q$	4. Premise
5. $\sim P$	5. From lines 3 and 4, using MT
6. $\sim R \to P$	6. Premise
7. R	7. From lines 5 and 6, using MT

Step 4d

1. $P \to Q$	1. Premise
2. $\sim Q$	2. Premise
3. $\sim P$	3. From lines 1 and 2, using MT
4. $\sim P \to S$	4. Premise
5. S	5. From lines 3 and 4, using MP
6. $R \to \sim S$	6. Premise
7. $\sim R$	7. From lines 5 and 6, using MT

See pages 777–778 for answers to Steps 5a–c.

CHAPTER 12 REVIEW

Trigonometry was first developed by astronomers who wanted to map the stars. Obviously, it is hard to directly measure the distances between stars and planets. That created a need for new methods of indirect measurement. As you've seen, you can solve many indirect measurement problems by using triangles. Using sine, cosine, and tangent ratios, you can find unknown lengths and angle measures if you know just a few measures in a right triangle. You can extend these methods to any triangle using the Law of Sines or the Law of Cosines.

What's the least you need to know about a right triangle in order to find all its measures? What parts of a nonright triangle do you need to know in order to find the other parts? Describe a situation in which an angle of elevation or depression can help you find an unknown height.

EXERCISES

You will need

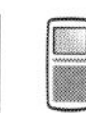

A calculator for Exercises 1–3, 7–28, 51, and 53

For Exercises 1–3, use a calculator to find each trigonometric ratio accurate to four decimal places.

1. $\sin 57°$ 0.8387

2. $\cos 9°$ 0.9877

3. $\tan 88°$ 28.6363

For Exercises 4–6, find each trigonometric ratio.

4. $\sin A = \underline{?}$ $\frac{a}{b}$
$\cos A = \underline{?}$ $\frac{c}{b}$
$\tan A = \underline{?}$ $\frac{a}{c}$

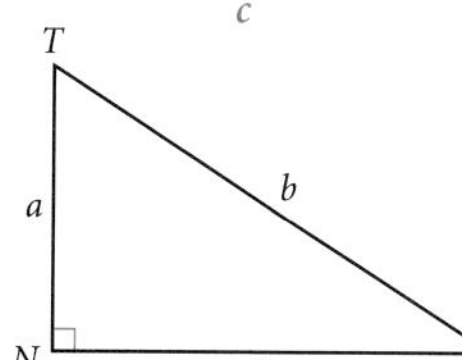

5. $\sin B = \underline{?}$ $\frac{8}{17}$
$\cos B = \underline{?}$ $\frac{15}{17}$
$\tan B = \underline{?}$ $\frac{8}{15}$

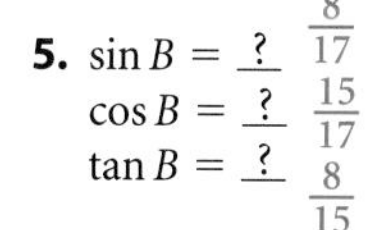

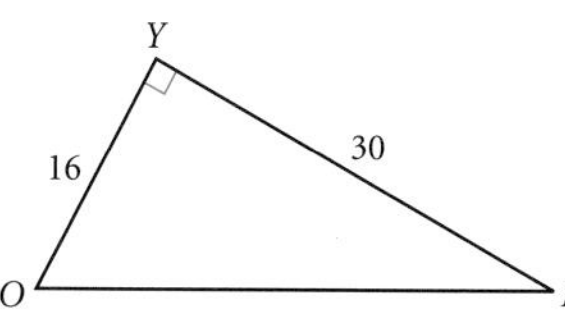

6. $\sin \phi = \underline{?}$ s
$\cos \phi = \underline{?}$ t
$\tan \phi = \underline{?}$ $\frac{s}{t}$

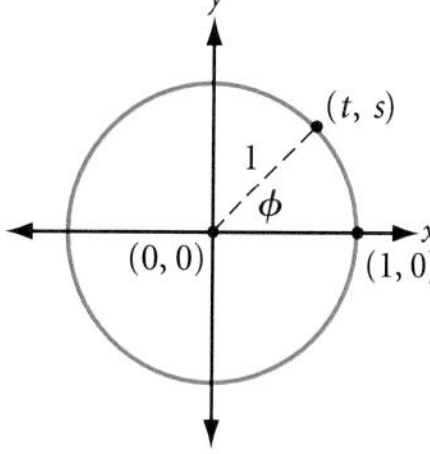

For Exercises 7–9, find the measure of each angle to the nearest degree.

7. $\sin A = 0.5447$ 33°

8. $\cos B = 0.0696$ 86°

9. $\tan C = 2.9043$ 71°

10. Shaded area ≈ $\underline{?}$ 1823 cm²

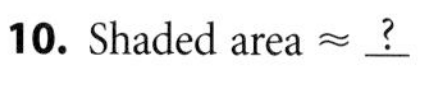

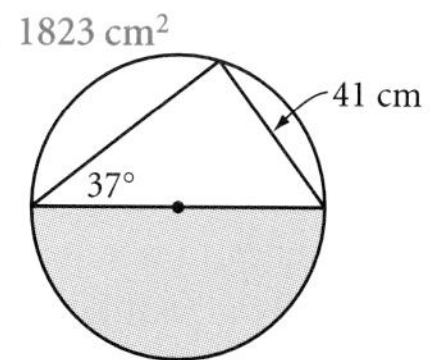

11. Volume ≈ $\underline{?}$
15,116 cm³

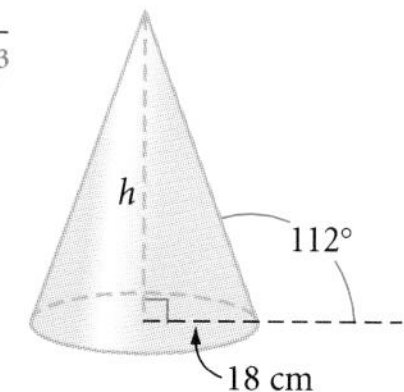

Helping with the Exercises

Exercise 6 The symbol ϕ is the Greek letter *phi.*

CHAPTER REVIEW 12

PLANNING

LESSON OUTLINE

First day:

15 min Reviewing

30 min Exercises

Second day:

30 min Exercises

15 min Student self-assessment

MATERIALS

- Exercise 12 (T), *optional*

REVIEWING

Ask students how many ways they can find the area of a triangular plot of land whose sides have lengths 5 km, 8 km, and 9 km. Some may remember Hero's formula. Be sure that at least one method involves the Law of Sines and another the Law of Cosines and that definitions of all three trigonometric ratios and at least one inverse trigonometric function are reviewed. For example, the Law of Cosines gives the measure of the angle between the sides of lengths 5 and 8 as $\cos^{-1}(0.1)$, so the SAS Triangle Area Conjecture gives the area of the triangle as $20 \sin(\cos^{-1}(0.1))$, which is about 19.9 km². (Hero's formula gives exactly $6\sqrt{11}$, which is also about 19.9.)

ASSIGNING HOMEWORK

The exercise set is a comprehensive review, so you might want to assign it over several days. If you want a review of Chapter 12 only, assign Exercises 1–28.

12. APPLICATION According to the Americans with Disabilities Act, enacted in 1990, the slope of a wheelchair ramp must be less than $\frac{1}{12}$ and there must be a minimum 5-by-5 ft landing for every 2.5 ft of rise. These dimensions were chosen to accommodate handicapped people who face physical barriers in public buildings and at work. An architect has submitted the orthographic plan shown below. Does the plan meet the requirements of the act? What will be the ramp's angle of ascent? Yes, the plan meets the act's requirements. The angle of ascent is approximately 4.3°.

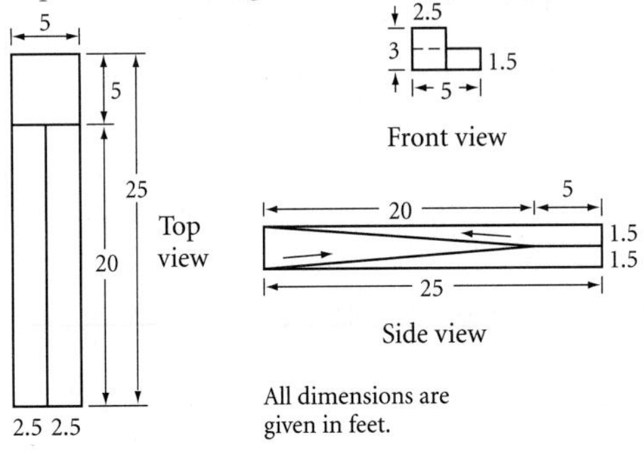

The Axis Dance Company includes performers in wheelchairs. Increased tolerance and accessibility laws have broadened the opportunities available to people with disabilities.

13. APPLICATION A lighthouse is east of a sailboat. The sailboat's dock is 30 km north of the lighthouse. The captain measures the angle between the lighthouse and the dock and finds it to be 35°. How far is the sailboat from the dock? approximately 52 km

Exercise 14 **[Language]** *Land distance* refers to distance measured on the land from directly beneath the jet. **[Alert]** Students might try to measure the angle of descent (depression) with respect to the vertical rather than the horizontal.

14. APPLICATION An air traffic controller must calculate the angle of descent (the angle of depression) for an incoming jet. The jet's crew reports that their land distance is 44 km from the base of the control tower and that the plane is flying at an altitude of 5.6 km. Find the measure of the angle of descent. approximately 7.3°

15. APPLICATION A new house is 32 feet wide. The rafters will rise at a 36° angle and meet above the center line of the house. Each rafter also needs to overhang the side of the house by 2 feet. How long should the carpenter make each rafter? approximately 22 ft

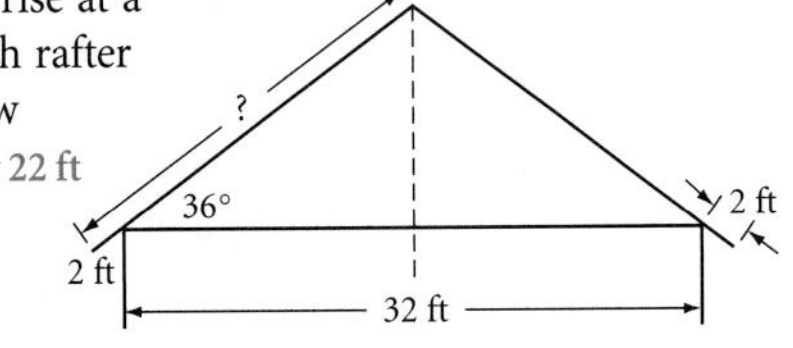

16. APPLICATION During a flood relief effort, a Coast Guard patrol boat spots a helicopter dropping a package near the Florida shoreline. Officer Duncan measures the angle of elevation to the helicopter to be 15° and the distance to the helicopter to be 6800 m. How far is the patrol boat from the point where the package will land? approximately 6568 m

Exercise 17 Students may need to make several attempts before they are successful. Encourage persistence.

17. At an air show, Amelia sees a jet heading south away from her at a 42° angle of elevation. Twenty seconds later the jet is still moving away from her, heading south at a 15° angle of elevation. If the jet's elevation is constantly 6.3 km, how fast is it flying in kilometers per hour? approximately 2973 km/hr

For Exercises 18–23, find each measure to the nearest unit or to the nearest square unit.

18. Area = ? 393 cm²

19. w = ? 30 cm

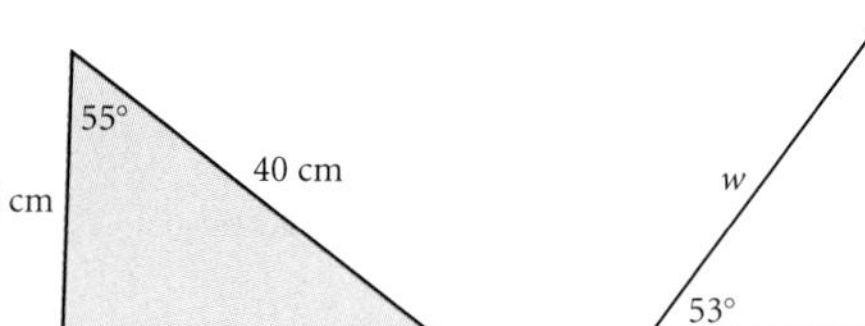

20. $\triangle ABC$ is acute. $m\angle A$ = ? 78°

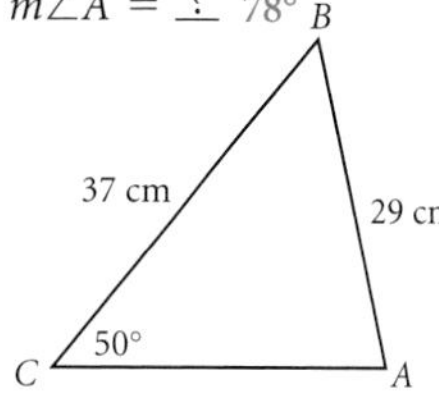

21. x = ? 105 cm

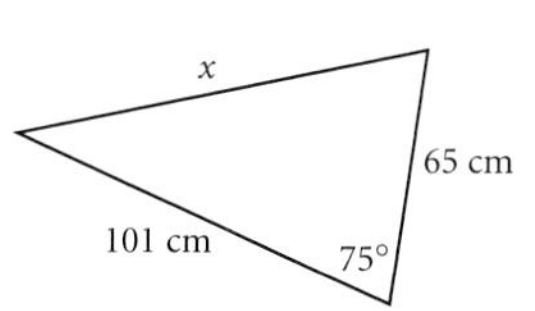

22. $m\angle B$ = ? 51°

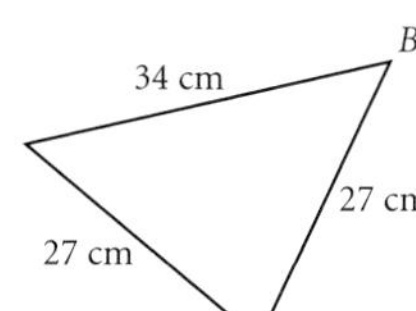

23. Area = ? 759 cm²

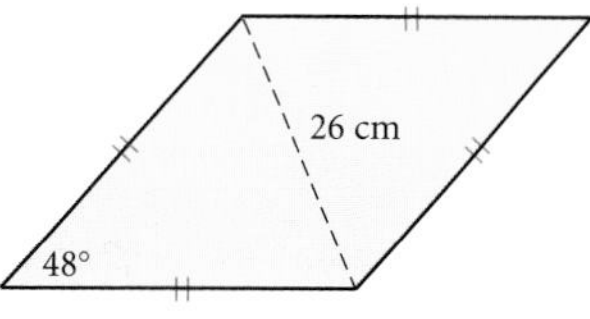

24. Find the length of the apothem of a regular pentagon with a side measuring 36 cm. approximately 25 cm

25. Find the area of a triangle formed by two 12 cm radii and a 16 cm chord in a circle. 72 cm²

26. A circle is circumscribed about a regular octagon with a perimeter of 48 cm. Find the diameter of the circle. approximately 15.7 cm

27. A 16 cm chord is drawn in a circle of diameter 24 cm. Find the area of the segment of the circle. ⓗ approximately 33.5 cm²

28. Leslie is paddling his kayak at a bearing of 45°. In still water his speed would be 13 km/hr but there is a 5 km/hr current moving west. What is the resulting speed and direction of Leslie's kayak? ⓗ approximately 10.1 km/hr at an approximate bearing of 24.5°

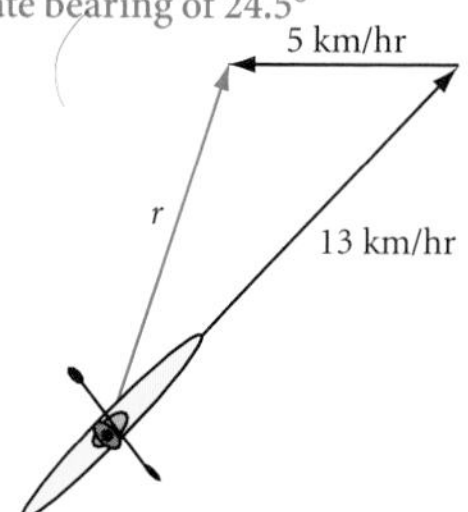

Exercise 25 Though this problem can be solved using trigonometry, easier solutions use the Pythagorean Theorem or Hero's formula.

Exercise 26 This exercise can be solved using either the Law of Sines or a sine ratio.

Exercise 27 Students might find the measure of the central angle either by the Law of Cosines or by realizing that an angle with half its measure has sine $\frac{8}{12}$. Because $A_{segment} = A_{sector} - A_{triangle}$, the former approach gives

$$A = \pi(12)^2 \frac{\cos^{-1}\left(\frac{1}{9}\right)}{360} - 0.5(12)^2 \sin\left(\cos^{-1}\left(\frac{1}{9}\right)\right)$$

The latter approach leads to

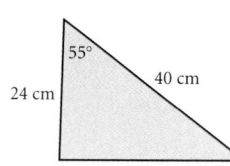

$$A = \frac{\pi(12)^2\left(2\sin^{-1}\left(\frac{8}{12}\right)\right)}{360} - \frac{16 \cdot 4\sqrt{5}}{2}$$

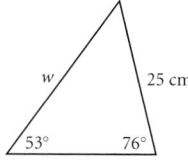

MIXED REVIEW

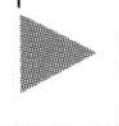

For Exercises 29–41, identify each statement as true or false. For each false statement, explain why it is false or sketch a counterexample.

10.1 **29.** An octahedron is a prism that has an octagonal base. False; an octahedron is a polyhedron with eight faces.

11.1 **30.** If the four angles of one quadrilateral are congruent to the four corresponding angles of another quadrilateral, then the two quadrilaterals are similar.

30. false

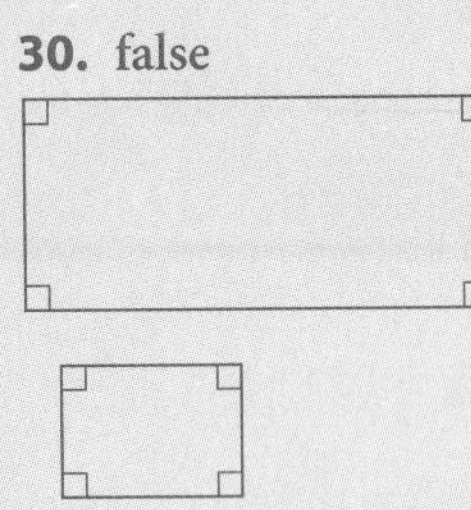

3.8 **31.** The three medians of a triangle meet at the centroid. true

12.4 **32.** To use the Law of Cosines, you must know three side lengths or two side lengths and the measure of the included angle. true

11.5 **33.** If the ratio of corresponding sides of two similar polygons is $\frac{m}{n}$, then the ratio of their areas is $\frac{m}{n}$. False; the ratio of their areas is $\frac{m^2}{n^2}$.

6.3 **34.** The measure of an angle inscribed in a semicircle is always 90°. true

12.1 **35.** If $\angle T$ is an acute angle in a right triangle, then

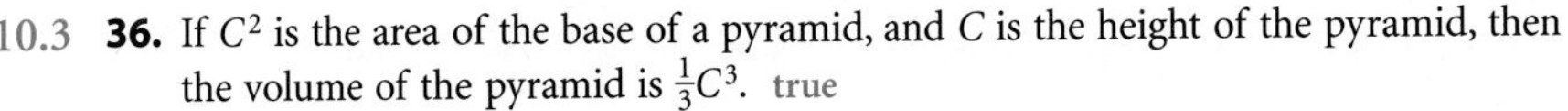

$$\text{tangent of } \angle T = \frac{\text{length of side adjacent to } \angle T}{\text{length of side opposite } \angle T}$$

False; tangent of $\angle T = \frac{\text{length of side opposite } \angle T}{\text{length of side adjacent to } \angle T}$

10.3 **36.** If C^2 is the area of the base of a pyramid, and C is the height of the pyramid, then the volume of the pyramid is $\frac{1}{3}C^3$. true

2.5 **37.** If two different lines intersect at a point, then the sum of the measures of at least one pair of vertical angles will be equal to or greater than 180°. true

11.6 **38.** If a line cuts two sides of a triangle proportionally, then it is parallel to the third side. true

12.3 **39.** If two sides of a triangle measure 6 cm and 8 cm and the angle between the two sides measures 60°, then the area of the triangle is $12\sqrt{3}$ cm². true

Exercise 39 In Lesson 12.3, the SAS Triangle Area Conjecture usually led to an *approximation* of the area of a triangle. Here the triangle has a 60° angle, so the area is *exactly* $12\sqrt{3}$ cm².

UYAS 3 **40.** A nonvertical line ℓ_1 has slope m and is perpendicular to line ℓ_2. The slope of ℓ_2 is also m. False; the slope of line ℓ_2 is $-\frac{1}{m}$.

11.2 **41.** If two sides of one triangle are proportional to two sides of another triangle, then the two triangles are similar.

41. false

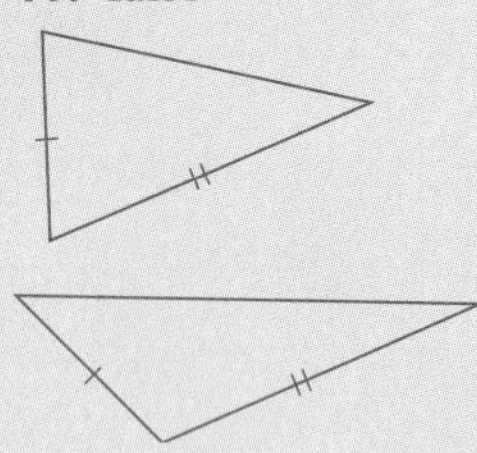

For Exercises 42–53, select the correct answer.

5.5 **42.** The diagonals of a parallelogram B

i. Are perpendicular to each other.

ii. Bisect each other.

iii. Form four congruent triangles.

A. i only **B.** ii only **C.** iii only **D.** i and ii

10.6 **43.** What is the formula for the volume of a sphere? C

A. $V = 4\pi r^2$ B. $V = \pi r^2 h$ C. $V = \frac{4}{3}\pi r^3$ D. $V = \frac{1}{3}\pi r^2 h$

12.4 **44.** For the triangle at right, what is the value of $(\cos L)^2 + (\sin L)^2$? C

A. About 0.22 B. About 1.41

C. 1 D. Cannot be determined

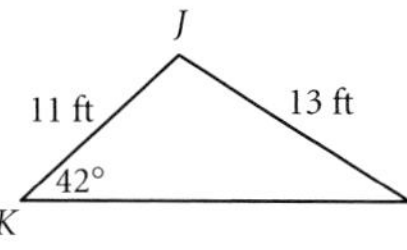

Exercise 44 This exercise relies on the Pythagorean identity that students learned in 12.4. Students don't need the diagram or the measure of angle L.

5.6 **45.** The diagonals of a rhombus D

i. Are perpendicular to each other.

ii. Bisect each other.

iii. Form four congruent triangles.

A. i only B. iii only C. i and ii D. All of the above

11.5 **46.** The ratio of the surface areas of two similar solids is $\frac{4}{9}$. What is the ratio of the volumes of the solids? B

A. $\frac{2}{3}$ B. $\frac{8}{27}$ C. $\frac{64}{729}$ D. $\frac{16}{81}$

10.2 **47.** A cylinder has height T and base area K. What is the volume of the cylinder? B

A. $V = \pi K^2 T$ B. $V = KT$ C. $V = 2\pi KT$ D. $V = \frac{1}{3}KT$

11.2 **48.** Which of the following is *not* a similarity shortcut? A

A. SSA B. SSS C. AA D. SAS

12.4 **49.** If a triangle has sides of lengths a, b, and c, and C is the angle opposite the side of length c, which of these statements must be true? B

A. $a^2 = b^2 + c^2 - 2ab\cos C$ B. $c^2 = a^2 + b^2 - 2ab\cos C$

C. $c^2 = a^2 + b^2 + 2ab\cos C$ D. $a^2 = b^2 + c^2$

11.6 **50.** In the drawing at right, $\overline{WX} \parallel \overline{YZ} \parallel \overline{BC}$. What is the value of m? C

A. 6 ft B. 8 ft

C. 12 ft D. 16 ft

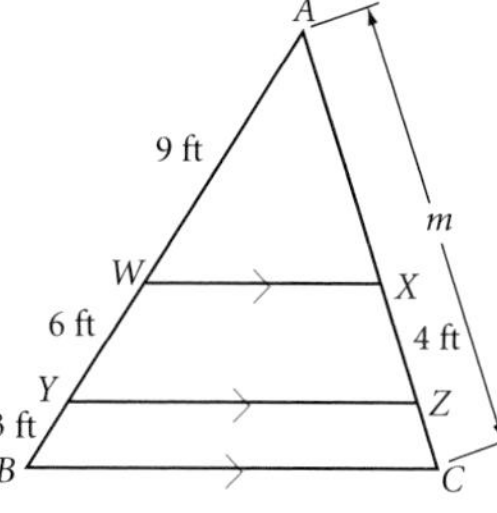

10.5 **51.** When a rock is added to a container of water, it raises the water level by 4 cm. If the container is a rectangular prism with a base that measures 8 cm by 9 cm, what is the volume of the rock? D

A. 4 cm^3 B. 32 cm^3

C. 36 cm^3 D. 288 cm^3

12.4 **52.** Which law could you use to find the value of v? C

A. Law of Supply and Demand

B. Law of Syllogism

C. Law of Cosines

D. Law of Sines

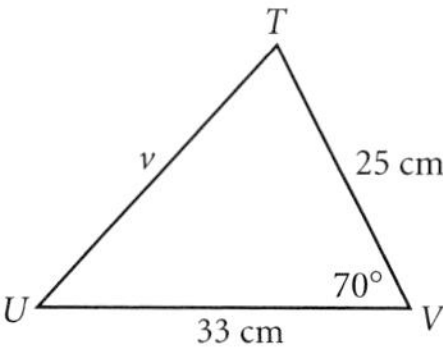

Exercises 54–56 If students give approximate answers not containing π, the answers are:
54. 105 cm^3
55. 88 cm^3
56. 96 cm^3

11.3 **53.** A 32-foot telephone pole casts a 12-foot shadow at the same time a boy nearby casts a 1.75-foot shadow. How tall is the boy? A

A. 4 ft 8 in. **B.** 4 ft 6 in. **C.** 5 ft 8 in. **D.** 6 ft

10.3 Exercises 54–56 are portions of cones. Find the volume of each solid.

54.

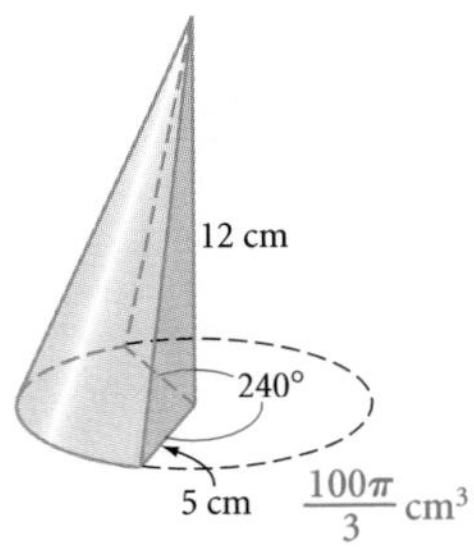

$\frac{100\pi}{3}$ cm^3

55.

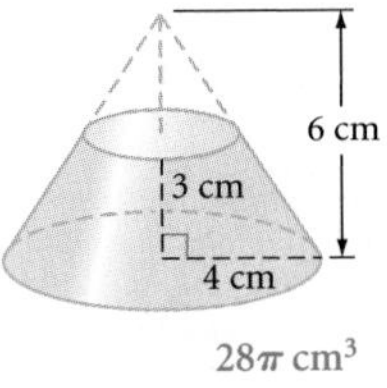

28π cm^3

56.

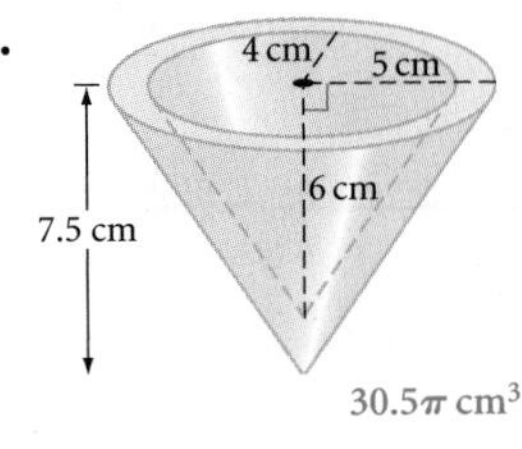

30.5π cm^3

2.4 **57.** Each person at a family reunion hugs everyone else exactly once. There were 528 hugs. How many people were at the reunion? 33

7.3 **58.** Triangle *TRI* with vertices $T(-7, 0)$, $R(-5, 3)$, and $I(-1, 0)$ is translated by the rule $(x, y) \rightarrow (x + 2, y - 1)$. Then its image is translated by the rule $(x, y) \rightarrow (x - 1, y - 2)$. What single translation is equivalent to the composition of these two translations? $(x, y) \rightarrow (x + 1, y - 3)$

12.1 **59.** $\triangle LMN \sim \triangle PQR$. Find *w*, *x*, and *y*.
$w = 48$ cm, $x = 24$ cm, $y = 28.5$ cm

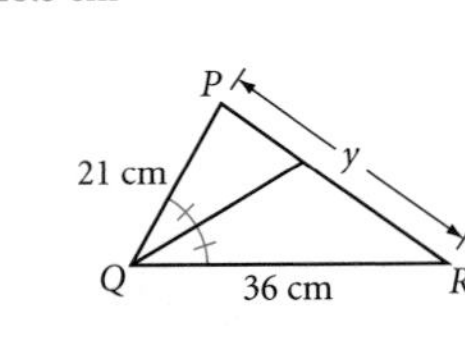

12.1 **60.** Find *x*. approximately 18 cm

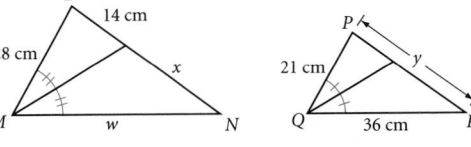

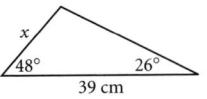

9.5 **61.** The diameter of a circle has endpoints $(5, -2)$ and $(5, 4)$. Find the equation of the circle. $(x - 5)^2 + (y - 1)^2 = 9$

7.4 **62.** Explain why a regular pentagon cannot create a monohedral tessellation.

12.2 **63.** Archaeologist Ertha Diggs uses a clinometer to find the height of an ancient temple. She views the top of the temple with a 37° angle of elevation. She is standing 130 meters from the center of the temple's base, and her eye is 1.5 meters above the ground. How tall is the temple? approximately 99.5 m

62. Sample answer: Each interior angle in a regular pentagon is 108 degrees. Three angles would have a sum of 324 degrees, 36 degrees short of 360, which would leave a gap. Four angles would have a sum exceeding 360 degrees and hence create an overlap.

6.7 **64.** In the diagram below, the length of $\overset{\frown}{HK}$ is 20π ft. Find the radius of the circle. 30 ft

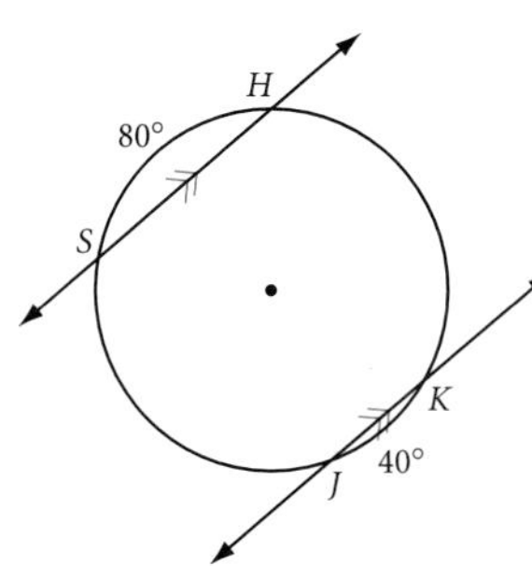

8.6 **65.** The shaded area is 10π cm². Find r. 4 cm

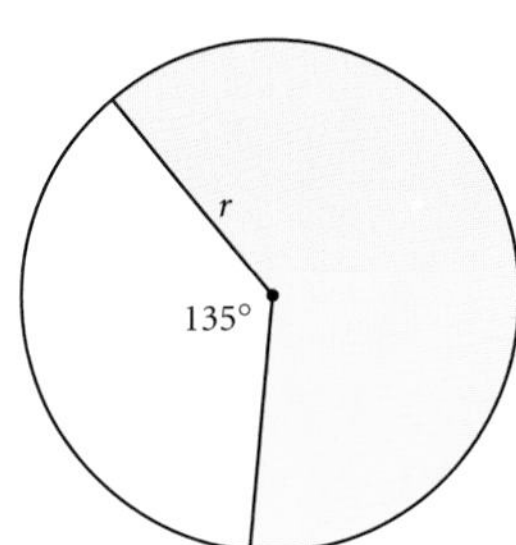

4.2 **66.** Triangle ABC is isosceles with $\overline{AB}$ congruent to $\overline{BC}$. Point D is on $\overline{AC}$ such that $\overline{BD}$ is perpendicular to $\overline{AC}$. Make a sketch and answer these questions.

a. $m\angle ABC = \underline{\ ?\ }\ m\angle ABD$ $m\angle ABC = 2 \cdot m\angle ABD$

b. What can you conclude about $\overline{BD}$?

TAKE ANOTHER LOOK

1. You learned the Law of Sines as

$$\frac{\sin A}{a} = \frac{\sin B}{b} = \frac{\sin C}{c}$$

Use algebra to show that

$$\frac{a}{\sin A} = \frac{b}{\sin B} = \frac{c}{\sin C}$$

2. Recall that SSA does not determine a triangle. For that reason, you've been asked to find only acute angles using the Law of Sines. Take another look at a pair of triangles, $\triangle AB_1C$ and $\triangle AB_2C$, determined by SSA. How is $\angle CB_1A$ related to $\angle CB_2A$? Find $m\angle CB_1A$ and $m\angle CB_2A$. Find the sine of each angle. Find the sines of another pair of angles that are related in the same way, then complete this conjecture: for any angle θ, $\sin\theta = \sin(\underline{\ ?\ })$.

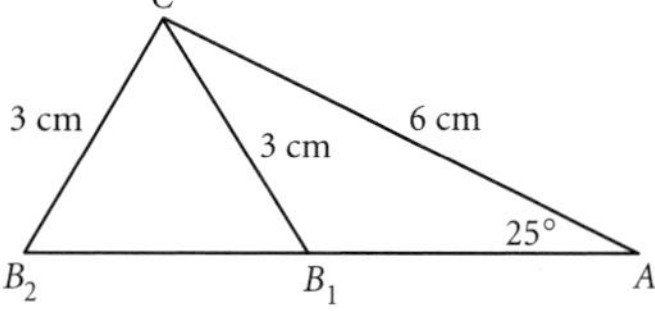

3. The Law of Cosines is generally stated using $\angle C$.

$$c^2 = a^2 + b^2 - 2ab\cos C$$

State the Law of Cosines in two different ways, using $\angle A$ and $\angle B$.

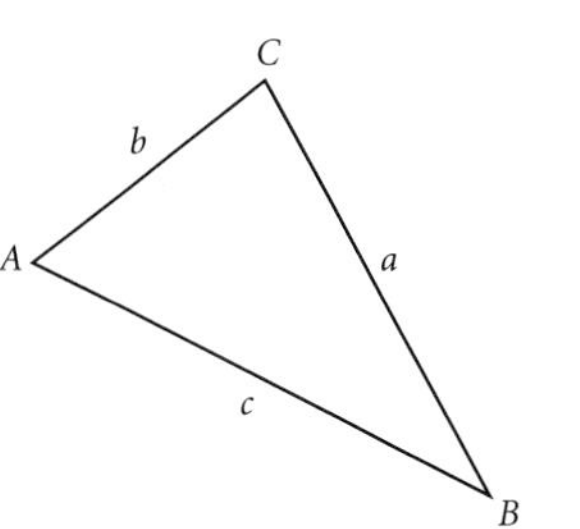

4. Derive the Law of Cosines.

Take Another Look

1. Several approaches are possible. One of the simplest:

$$\frac{a}{\sin A} = \frac{1}{\frac{\sin A}{a}} = \frac{1}{\frac{\sin B}{b}} = \frac{b}{\sin B}.$$

A similar argument can be used for $\frac{c}{\sin C}$.

2. Students might want to use geometry software to help them see patterns. Measurements indicate that $\angle CB_2A$ and $\angle CB_1A$ are supplementary; for example, $m\angle CB_2A = 57.7°$ and $m\angle CB_1A = 122.3°$. The Law of Sines, then, says that $\sin\theta = \sin(180° - \theta)$. You might ask if the result is consistent with the graphs in the Exploration Trigonometric Ratios and the Unit Circle or in the Project Trigonometric Functions.

3. $a^2 = b^2 + c^2 - 2bc\cos A$; $b^2 = a^2 + c^2 - 2ac\cos B$

4. Students might have done this derivation in the one-step investigation of Lesson 12.4. Several approaches are possible. If students are stuck, you might ask if they can make a right triangle (by drawing an altitude) and then apply the Pythagorean Theorem to the two triangles formed. For example, let $\overline{AD}$ be the altitude to $\overline{BC}$, let $x = DC$, and let $h = AD$. Then $c^2 = (a - x)^2 + h^2 = a^2 - 2ax + x^2 + h^2$. Because $b^2 = x^2 + h^2$, we have $c^2 = a^2 - 2ax + b^2 = a^2 + b^2 - 2ax$. But $\frac{x}{b} = \cos C$, so $x = b\cos C$. Therefore $c^2 = a^2 + b^2 - 2ab\cos C$.

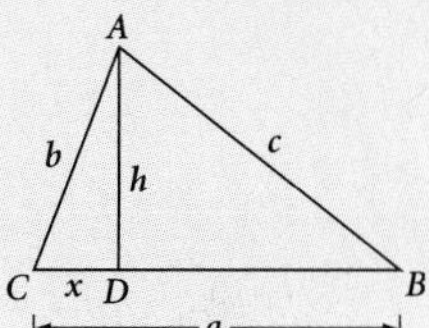

66.

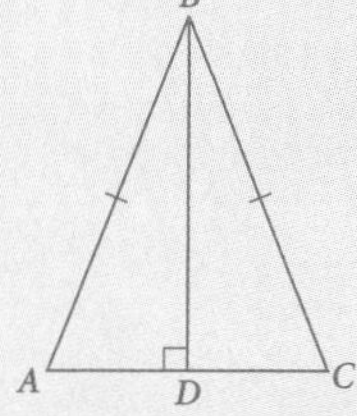

66b. Possible answers: $\overline{BD}$ is the perpendicular bisector of $\overline{AC}$. It is the angle bisector of $\angle ABC$; a median, and divides $\triangle ABC$ insto two congruent right triangles.

5. Both x and y can be related to the circumference of the cone's base, which is the length of the sector's arc. The radius of the arc is L, the slant height of the cone, so the arc's length is $\frac{x}{360°} \cdot 2\pi L = \pi L \frac{x}{180°}$. The radius of the cone, then, is this circumference divided by 2π, or $L\frac{x}{360°}$. The sine of $\frac{y}{2}$ is this radius over L, or $\frac{x}{360°}$, so $y = 2\sin^{-1}\left(\frac{x}{360°}\right)$. Or use the Law of Cosines with $c = \frac{x}{180°}$, $a = L$, and $b = L$ to arrive at the equivalent answer: $y = \cos^{-1}\left(1 - \frac{x^2}{64{,}800\,L}\right)$.

ASSESSING

You might use the chapter test from Assessment Resource A or B, or you might choose to use one or more of the Constructive Assessments Options. Use the test generator if you want to combine forms of assessment or limit the test to only part of the chapter content.

FACILITATING SELF-ASSESSMENT

As students select problems for their portfolios, suggest that they use one of these:
Lesson 12.1, Exercise 9;
Lesson 12.2, Exercises 1–7;
Lesson 12.3, Exercise 4;
Lesson 12.4, Exercise 7;
Lesson 12.5, Exercise 4.

5. Is there a relationship between the measure of the central angle of a sector of a circle and the angle at the vertex of the right cone formed when rolled up?

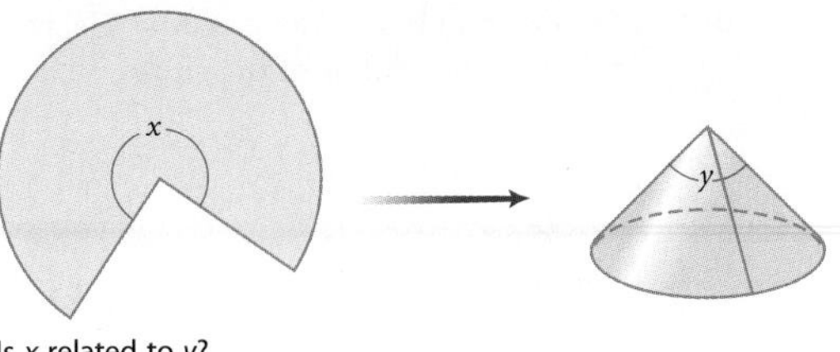

Is x related to y?

Assessing What You've Learned

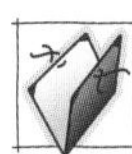

UPDATE YOUR PORTFOLIO Choose a real-world indirect measurement problem that uses trigonometry, and add it to your portfolio. Describe the problem, explain how you solved it, and explain why you chose it for your portfolio.

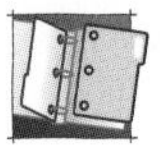

ORGANIZE YOUR NOTEBOOK Make sure your notebook is complete and well organized. Write a one-page chapter summary. Reviewing your notes and solving sample test items are good ways to prepare for chapter tests.

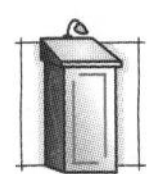

GIVE A PRESENTATION Demonstrate how to use an angle-measuring device to make indirect measurements of actual objects. Use appropriate visual aids.

WRITE IN YOUR JOURNAL The last five chapters have had a strong problem-solving focus. What do you see as your strengths and weaknesses as a problem solver? In what ways have you improved? In what areas could you improve or use more help? Has your attitude toward problem solving changed since you began this course?

CHAPTER

13

Geometry as a Mathematical System

Overview

The focus of this chapter is on understanding and developing geometry as a mathematical system. **Lesson 13.1** begins with a brief history of geometry as a deductive system and then presents properties of equality and arithmetic, as well as postulates. Students learn to plan a proof in **Lesson 13.2.** They turn some of their conjectures into theorems with triangle proofs in **Lesson 13.3** and with quadrilateral proofs in **Lesson 13.4.** In The Geometer's Sketchpad **exploration,** students experience the relationship between observing properties and proving conjectures about those properties. Indirect proof is presented in **Lesson 13.5.** In **Lesson 13.6,** students prove circle theorems. Properties of similarity and theorems that follow from them are investigated in **Lesson 13.7. Using Your Algebra Skills 10** explores proofs using coordinates. The **exploration** that ends the chapter presents non-Euclidean geometries.

The Mathematics

In this chapter, the conjectures of the previous chapters become theorems as they are proved in the context of a deductive system. Only students who have achieved van Hiele level 3 will fully appreciate this chapter, but other students can have success with the nonproof exercises.

Proving theorems within a deductive system ensures that we avoid circular reasoning. Within a deductive system, we can develop the logical family tree of each theorem, tracing it back to the postulates and seeing how it relates logically to other theorems.

To develop a deductive system, we lay out the definitions and theorems so that all technical terms in the theorem statements have been defined earlier and all reasons in the proofs are previously proved theorems. But lists of definitions and theorems must begin somewhere. The definitions begin with terms taken explicitly as undefined: *point, line, plane,* and *space.* The theorems begin with assumptions called *postulates, properties,* or *axioms.*

Beyond Mechanics

Proving theorems is an art, not an algorithm. If writing a proof were algorithmic, there wouldn't be much to mathematical research, which consists of making conjectures and trying to prove them. This chapter gives a five-task outline for proof writing, but the planning step is not mechanical.

Proofs are not unique. Most theorems can be proved in a variety of ways. An ideal proof is brief and elegant but also gives insight into the ideas. Such proofs are rare. At this level, it is more important that proofs be insightful than brief.

Indirect proofs rarely show insight. In these, the negation of the statement to be proved leads to a contradiction. Lesson 13.5 concentrates on the form of indirect proof, $(\sim Q \rightarrow \sim P) \rightarrow (P \rightarrow Q)$, in which you assume the negation of what you want to prove ($\sim Q$), show that it leads to a contradiction ($\sim P$) of something you know (the antecedent), and conclude that "P implies Q" must be true. The proofs in the project on page 717, use indirect proofs by contradiction, symbolically written as $(\sim P \rightarrow Q \text{ and } \sim P \rightarrow \sim Q) \rightarrow P$, the form first discussed on page 656.

The logic involved in indirect proof depends rather subtly on the assumption that every statement is either true or false—there's no middle possibility. Some mathematicians and logicians object to this "Law of the Excluded Middle" and reject any statement proved using it.

Truth

Until the middle of the 1800s, the common perception was "A proof is valid if you've used valid forms of logical reasoning from true statements." Because Euclid's postulates were self-evidently true, all of the theorems of Euclidean geometry were therefore true. But Euclid's fifth postulate led to complications. It was so complex that for centuries mathematicians attempted to prove it from the other postulates. Attempts were so unsuccessful that in the late 1800s some mathematicians asked, "What could we prove if we negated this postulate?" What at first appeared to be a game actually led to applications, and the nature of mathematics changed. The concept of absolute truth was replaced by the idea of truth relative to a deductive system.

How can we be sure that we at least have truth relative to a given system? A deductive system should be *consistent*; that is, the postulates should not contradict one another. How can we know that we will never be able to prove a theorem that contradicts another theorem in the system? Work in the early 1900s showed that we can't ever know that most deductive systems are consistent. Today's students can find their conceptual frameworks shaken when they realize that mathematics lacks not only absolute truth but even the certainty of relative truth.

Using This Chapter

Because proofs are a means of communicating mathematics (and because students can find proofs challenging), it's very helpful to have students work together on proofs. The dialogue that takes place among students is essential in developing logical reasoning as a tool to convince others. You can jigsaw proofs among groups. You might warn a group that one of its members will present a proof without specifying which member, so that all in the group will be prepared.

Resources

Discovering Geometry Resources

Teaching and Worksheet Masters
Lessons 13.1, 13.2, and 13.7
Using Your Algebra Skills 10

Assessment Resources A and B
Quiz 1 (Lessons 13.1–13.3)
Quiz 2 (Lessons 13.4–13.7)
Chapter 13 Test
Chapter 13 Constructive Assessment Options
Final Exam

Practice Your Skills for Chapter 13

Condensed Lessons for Chapter 13

Other Resources

Rethinking Proof with The Geometer's Sketchpad by Michael de Villiers.

For complete references on this and other sources see www.keypress.com/DG.

Materials

- construction tools
- geometry software, *optional*
- dynamic statistics software, *optional*
- spheres that can be drawn on, *optional*
- large rubber bands to go around the spheres, *optional*
- circles of latex with the edges stretched out, *optional*

Pacing Guide

	day 1	day 2	day 3	day 4	day 5	day 6	day 7	day 8	day 9	day 10
standard	13.1	13.2	13.3	quiz, 13.4	13.5	13.6	13.7	Exploration	quiz, review	review
enriched	13.1	13.2	13.3	quiz, 13.4	Exploration	13.5	13.6	13.7, project	quiz, Exploration	review
block	13.1, 13.2	13.3, 13.4	quiz, 13.5, Exploration	13.6, 13.7	project, quiz, Exploration	review	assessment	review	assessment	

	day 11	day 12	day 13	day 14	day 15	day 16	day 17	day 18	day 19	day 20
standard	assessment	review	review	assessment						
enriched	assessment	review	review	assessment						

CHAPTER

13

Geometry as a Mathematical System

This search for new possibilities, this discovery of new jigsaw puzzle pieces, which in the first place surprises and astonishes the designer himself, is a game that through the years has always fascinated and enthralled me anew.

M. C. ESCHER

Another World (Other World), M. C. Escher, 1947

OBJECTIVES

In this chapter you will

- look at geometry as a mathematical system
- see how some conjectures are logically related to each other
- review a number of proof strategies, such as working backward and analyzing diagrams

CHAPTER 13 OBJECTIVES

- Encounter the concept of a deductive system
- See the postulates of geometry
- Learn to prove conjectures using definitions, properties of algebra and equality, and postulates
- Prove theorems about triangles, quadrilaterals, circles, and similar figures
- Practice using triangle theorems to prove quadrilateral theorems
- Learn how to write indirect proofs
- Explore non-Euclidean geometries
- Learn new vocabulary
- Develop visual thinking, deductive reasoning, and cooperative behavior

Escher's *Another World* shows a non-Euclidean world in which each bird has a unique orientation. The perspective of one bird is not shared by the others. Because they do not have a common horizon, a deductive system about the geometry of one bird's world would not be valid for another's. **[Ask]** "How are the birds' worlds the same? How are they different?"

LESSON 13.1

PLANNING

LESSON OUTLINE

One day:

15 min Introduction and Example

15 min Exercises

10 min Sharing

5 min Closing

MATERIALS

- Two Proofs (W) for One step
- Properties of Arithmetic (T), *optional*
- Properties of Equality (T), *optional*
- Postulates of Geometry (T), *optional*

TEACHING

Students begin to see how to arrange definitions and conjectures into a deductive system, concentrating first on building algebraic arguments.

One step Hand out the Two Proofs worksheet and ask students to write down what they observe as they work through it. Students will protest that the statements aren't true; ask what's wrong with them. As you circulate, suggest that students write a flowchart for each proof. Keep asking "Why?" so that during Sharing you can ask what rules about numbers they would like to use as reasons. Then **[Ask]** "How can the reasoning be valid if both conclusions are false?" Bring out the idea of circular reasoning, and lead students to the idea of making a deductive system—that is, a linear list of premises (statements of accepted facts). Discuss the criteria such a list should meet. [Every definition and theorem statement uses only previously defined terms; every reason in every proof is already proved or accepted as a postulate.]

LESSON 13.1

The Premises of Geometry

Geometry is the art of correct reasoning on incorrect figures.

GEORGE POLYA

As you learned in previous chapters, for thousands of years Babylonian, Egyptian, Chinese, and other mathematicians discovered many geometry principles and developed procedures for doing practical geometry.

By 600 B.C.E., a prosperous new civilization had begun to grow in the trading towns along the coast of Asia Minor (present-day Turkey) and later in Greece, Sicily, and Italy. People had free time to discuss and debate issues of government and law. They began to insist on reasons to support statements made in debate. Mathematicians began to use logical reasoning to deduce mathematical ideas.

This map detail shows Sicily, Italy, Greece, and Asia Minor along the north coast of the Mediterranean Sea. The map was drawn by Italian painter and architect Pietro da Cortona (1596–1669).

History CONNECTION

Greek mathematician Thales of Miletus (ca. 625–547 B.C.E.) made his geometry ideas convincing by supporting his discoveries with logical reasoning. Over the next 300 years, the process of supporting mathematical conjectures with logical arguments became more and more refined. Other Greek mathematicians, including Thales' most famous student, Pythagoras, began linking chains of logical reasoning. The tradition continued with Plato and his students. Euclid, in his famous work about geometry and number theory, *Elements,* established a single chain of deductive arguments for most of the geometry known then.

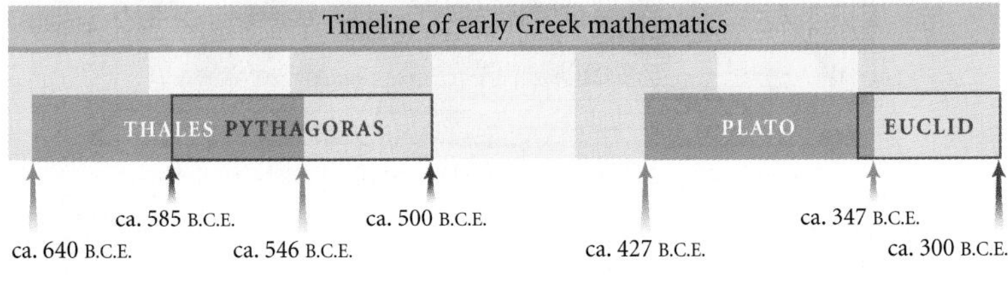

You have learned that Euclid used geometric constructions to study properties of lines and shapes. Euclid also created a **deductive system**—a set of **premises,** or accepted facts, and a set of logical rules—to organize geometry properties. He started from a collection of simple and useful statements he called **postulates.** He then systematically demonstrated how each geometry discovery followed logically from his postulates and his previously proved conjectures, or **theorems.**

LESSON OBJECTIVES

- Encounter the concept of a deductive system
- Learn new vocabulary
- See the postulates of geometry
- Learn to support statements with definitions, properties of algebra and equality, and postulates
- Develop deductive reasoning and cooperative behavior

NCTM STANDARDS

CONTENT		PROCESS	
✓	Number		Problem Solving
✓	Algebra	✓	Reasoning
✓	Geometry	✓	Communication
	Measurement	✓	Connections
	Data/Probability		Representation

Up to now, you have been discovering geometry properties inductively, the way many mathematicians have over the centuries. You have studied geometric figures and have made conjectures about them. Then, to explain your conjectures, you turned to deductive reasoning. You used informal proofs to explain why a conjecture was true. However, you did not prove every conjecture. In fact, you sometimes made critical assumptions or relied on unproved conjectures in your proofs. A conclusion in a proof is true if and only if your premises are true and all your arguments are valid. Faulty assumptions can lead to the wrong conclusion. Have all your assumptions been reliable?

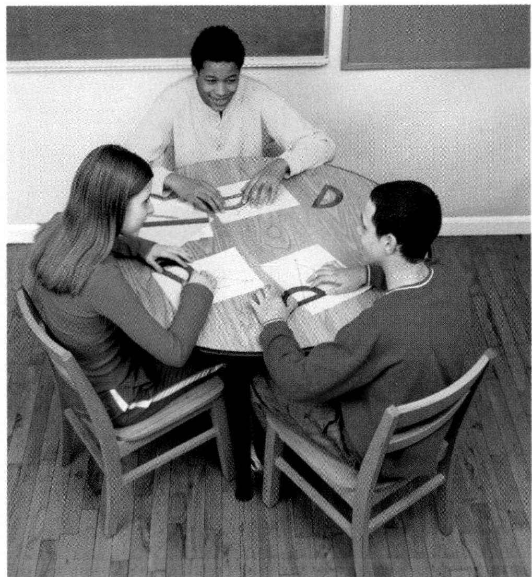
Inductive reasoning process

Deductive reasoning process

In this chapter you will look at geometry as Euclid did. You will start with premises: definitions, properties, and postulates. From these premises you will systematically prove your earlier conjectures. Proved conjectures will become theorems, which you can use to prove other conjectures, turning them into theorems, as well. You will build a logical framework using your most important ideas and conjectures from geometry.

Premises for Logical Arguments in Geometry

1. Definitions and undefined terms
2. Properties of arithmetic, equality, and congruence
3. Postulates of geometry
4. Previously proved geometry conjectures (theorems)

You are already familiar with the first type of premise on the list: the undefined terms—point, line, and plane. In addition, you have a list of basic definitions in your notebook.

You used the second set of premises, properties of arithmetic and equality, in your algebra course.

INTRODUCTION

Introduce the new vocabulary: *postulate, theorem,* and *deductive system.* Review the difference between inductive and deductive reasoning. You might use the timeline in the book and talk about the history of geometry.

HISTORY OF GEOMETRY

Students might appreciate hearing a story that elaborates on the history connections in the book and also shows how geometry has both reflected and influenced civilization. You might introduce the story by writing six numbers on the board and having students speculate on their meaning: −600, −300, 400, 1200, 1700, 1850. The more anecdotes you can tell about individual characters, the more interesting the story will be. Stories about the characters can be found in history of mathematics books such as those by Eves, Burton, and Katz.

Early Geometers

Although examples of geometric principles can be found in cave drawings, the earliest-known uses of geometry tools were by the Egyptians and Babylonians before 600 B.C.E. Because the Nile River flooded every year, Egyptians had to use geometry to resurvey land; the word *geometry* means "earth measure." They also used measurement techniques to construct maps and the pyramids. Toward the end of this period, the Greek philosopher Thales visited Egypt and returned to Greece with a great deal of geometric knowledge.

600 B.C.E.: Classical Greeks

Thales trusted reasoning more than inexact measurements and proposed that mathematical relationships not be accepted unless they were proved deductively. This view was promulgated by Pythagoras, who believed that all creation was based on number. He or one of his followers proved the Pythagorean Theorem, a relationship known earlier by the Egyptians.

600 B.C.E.: Classical Greeks (continued)

Another Pythagorean proved that a common length—that of a square's diagonal—was not a number (a ratio of integers). This disturbing finding helped divorce Greek geometry from measurement. Greek mathematicians began to eschew length and area formulas; instead, where we would say that two objects had the same size, they would simply say that they were equal.

The philosopher Plato even defined existence: A geometric object exists if it can be constructed with straightedge and compass. Such philosopher/mathematicians were not interested in applications of mathematics.

Meanwhile, the mathematician Eudoxus realized that proving theorems wasn't enough; to avoid circular reasoning, a deductive system was needed. Plato's student Aristotle studied logical arguments, seeing patterns such as those we now call *Modus Ponens* and *Modus Tollens.*

300 B.C.E.: Alexandrian Greeks
One of Aristotle's students, Alexander the Great, conquered most of the known world and set up the city Alexandria in northern Egypt. Alexandria became the intellectual capital of the world, attracting scholars from Greece and Asia to a large library and the world's first university (called the Museum).

The first director of the Museum was Euclid, best known for his *Elements,* which summarized in a deductive system most of the mathematics known at the time.

The Alexandrians studied cones and conic sections (ellipses, parabolas, and hyperbolas). Unlike the Classical Greeks, these mathematicians were also interested in applications. The mathematician Archimedes, for example, is known not only for finding the area of a circle but also for his principle of buoyancy and displacement. Hipparchus developed trigonometry to aid astronomy. The Roman Empire, gradually incorporating Alexander's conquests, contributed more to engineering (for example, the arch) than to mathematics (other than Roman numerals). In fact, a battle with the Romans burned the library at Alexandria, and Archimedes was killed by a conquering Roman soldier. What the Romans left intact was eventually destoyed by zealous Christians (and later Muslims), who believed that any learning not found in their scriptures was in error.

These Mayan stone carvings, found in Tikal, Guatemala, show the glyphs, or symbols, used in the Mayan number system. Learn more about Mayan numerals at www.keymath.com/DG .

Properties of Arithmetic

For any numbers a, b, and c:

Commutative property of addition

$a + b = b + a$

Commutative property of multiplication

$ab = ba$

Associative property of addition

$(a + b) + c = a + (b + c)$

Associative property of multiplication

$(ab)c = a(bc)$

Distributive property

$a(b + c) = ab + ac$

Properties of Equality

For any numbers a, b, c, and d:

Reflexive property (also called the identity property)

$a = a$

Any number is equal to itself.

Transitive property

If $a = b$ and $b = c$, then $a = c$. (This property often takes the form of the **substitution property,** which says that if $b = c$, you can substitute c for b.)

Symmetric property

If $a = b$, then $b = a$.

Addition property

If $a = b$, then $a + c = b + c$. (Also, if $a = b$ and $c = d$, then $a + c = b + d$.)

Subtraction property

If $a = b$, then $a - c = b - c$. (Also, if $a = b$ and $c = d$, then $a - c = b - d$.)

Multiplication property

If $a = b$, then $ac = bc$. (Also, if $a = b$ and $c = d$, then $ac = bd$.)

Division property

If $a = b$, then $\frac{a}{c} = \frac{b}{c}$ provided $c \neq 0$. (Also, if $a = b$ and $c = d$, then $\frac{a}{c} = \frac{b}{d}$ provided that $c \neq 0$ and $d \neq 0$.)

Square root property

If $a^2 = b$, then $a = \pm\sqrt{b}$.

Zero product property

If $ab = 0$, then $a = 0$ or $b = 0$ or both a and $b = 0$.

400 C.E.: Arabic Influence
With the decline of Alexandrian culture, the intellectual center moved back to Mesopotamia. Ideas from Greece and Alexandria were merged with ideas from India and China, resulting in the translation of Greek works into Arabic, the Hindu-Arabic number system, and algebra. Prominent Arab mathematicians (such as al-Khwārizmī) and mathematicians in India (such as Bhaskara and Bramagupta) did not concentrate on geometry, though the strengthening of Islam led to sophisticated geometric designs in art.

1200: European Exploration
The rise of universities in medieval Europe slowly resulted in a revival of interest in learning beyond that taught by Christian doctrine. Increasing connections with the Arab world gave European scholars access to classical Greek works, which they translated into Latin. A few mathematicians tried to prove Euclid's fifth postulate from his other postulates.

Renewed interest in the physical world produced maps and coordinate geometry (René Descartes and Blaise Pascal). Artists such as Leonardo da Vinci developed a system of perspective that made paintings look more realistic and resulted in projective geometry. Toward the end of the period, aided by coordinate geometry, Isaac Newton devised a deductive system in which he developed calculus and proved physical laws that could make dramatic predictions about the earth and the heavens.

Whether or not you remember their names, you've used these properties to solve algebraic equations. The process of solving an equation is really an algebraic proof that your solution is valid. To arrive at a correct solution, you must support each step by a property. The addition property of equality, for example, permits you to add the same number to both sides of an equation to get an equivalent equation.

EXAMPLE | Solve for x: $5x - 12 = 3(x + 2)$

▶ ***Solution***

$5x - 12 = 3(x + 2)$	Given.
$5x - 12 = 3x + 6$	Distributive property.
$5x = 3x + 18$	Addition property of equality.
$2x = 18$	Subtraction property of equality.
$x = 9$	Division property of equality.

Why are the properties of arithmetic and equality important in geometry? The lengths of segments and the measures of angles involve numbers, so you will often need to use these properties in geometry proofs. And just as you use equality to express a relationship between numbers, you use congruence to express a relationship between geometric figures.

Definition of Congruence

If $AB = CD$, then $\overline{AB} \cong \overline{CD}$, and conversely, if $\overline{AB} \cong \overline{CD}$, then $AB = CD$.

If $m\angle A = m\angle B$, then $\angle A \cong \angle B$, and conversely, if $\angle A \cong \angle B$, then $m\angle A = m\angle B$.

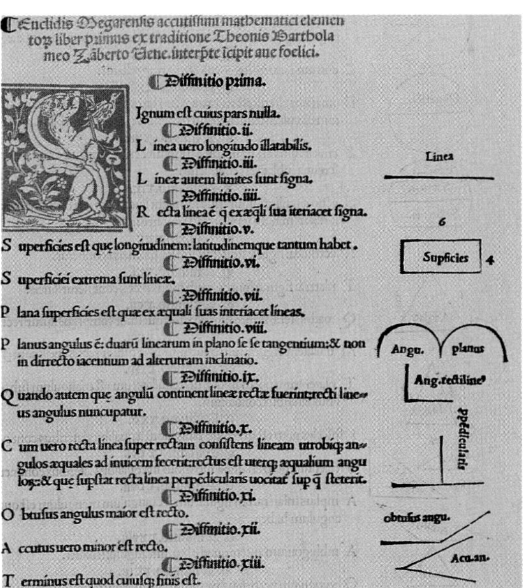
Euclidis Megarensis accutissimi mathematici elementorum liber primus ex traditione Theonis Bartholameo Zaberto Uenetiano interprete incipit aue foelici.

Diffinitio prima.

Signum est cuius pars nulla.

Diffinitio. ii.

Linea uero longitudo illatabilis.

Diffinitio. iii.

Lineæ autem limites sunt signa.

Diffinitio. iiii.

Recta linea ē q ex æqli sua iteriacet signa.

Diffinitio. v.

Superficies est quę longitudinem: latitudinemque tantum habet.

Diffinitio. vi.

Superficiei extrema sunt lineæ.

Diffinitio. vii.

Plana superficies est quæ ex æquali suas interiacet lineas.

Diffinitio. viii.

Planus angulus ē: duarū linearum in plano se se tangentium: & non in directo iacentium ad alterutram inclinatio.

Diffinitio. ix.

Quando autem quę angulū continent lineæ rectæ fuerint: recti lineus angulus nuncupatur.

Diffinitio. x.

Cum uero recta linea super rectam consistens lineam utrobiq; angulos æquales ad inuicem fecerit: rectus est uterq; æqualium angulorum: & quę supstat recta linea perpēdicularis uocitat sup q̄ steterit.

Diffinitio. xi.

Obtusus angulus maior est recto.

Diffinitio. xii.

Accutus uero minor est recto.

Diffinitio. xiii.

Terminus est quod cuiusq; finis est.

A page from a Latin translation of Euclid's *Elements*. Which of these definitions do you recognize?

Congruence is defined by equality, so you can extend the properties of equality to a **reflexive property of congruence,** a **transitive property of congruence,** and a **symmetric property of congruence.** This is left for you to do in the exercises.

The third set of premises is specific to geometry. These premises are traditionally called postulates. Postulates should be very basic. Like undefined terms, they should be useful and easy for everyone to agree on, with little debate.

As you've performed basic geometric constructions in this class, you've observed some of these "obvious truths." Whenever you draw a figure or use an auxiliary line, you are using these postulates.

▶ ***EXAMPLE***

[Alert] The example demonstrates the use of properties to support why the *given* statement leads to the *show* statement. Just as students support why they are applying a particular operation to an equation, students will support why they take each step in a geometry proof.

Definitions

These definitions of congruence, repeated from Chapter 1, will help students make the transition from two line segments (or angles) being equal in measure to their being congruent.

1700: Certainty

Newton's success in using a deductive system spawned a belief that basic postulates could be found for all knowledge. In some areas, such as economics, the efforts were successful. They were less successful in music and literature. "Self-evident truths" in political science contributed to the U.S. Declaration of Independence. An interest in statistics developed, but, except for a few more attempts to prove Euclid's fifth postulate, geometry was neglected until the end of the period. At that point several mathematicians, notably Carl Friedrich Gauss, Nikolay Lobachevsky, János Bolyai, and Georg Friedrich Bernhard Riemann, entertained the idea that geometries other than Euclidean geometry might be possible.

1850: Uncertainty

Mathematician Felix Kline made a strong effort to unify the various geometries by considering transformations. He found that they could all be considered subgeometries of the long-ignored projective geometry. But finite geometries and topology led to a change in the nature of mathematics from a pursuit of absolute truth to an investigation of what theorems could be proved within various deductive systems. And attempts to prove that those deductive systems were consistent resulted in a realization that their lack of contradiction must always remain uncertain.

Properties

Properties are common to arithmetic, a basis of mathematics. In this respect they are like Euclid's "common notions," often called *axioms* or *postulates.* You might use the Properties transparencies as you talk about the properties.

Postulates

[Ask] "Sometimes mathematicians want to set up a deductive system with only the postulates that are absolutely necessary to prove everything within the system. Does it look as if any of these postulates are unnecessary, that is, they could be proved from the others?" [Historically, many mathematicians have tried to prove the Parallel Postulate. Students may also suspect that the Perpendicular Postulate can be proved from the others. Only one of the congruence shortcuts must be taken as a postulate; the others can be proved from it.] You might use the Postulates of Geometry transparency as you discuss the postulates.

SHARING IDEAS

Ask what's new here. Students have been using many of the properties and postulates all along or have written them as conjectures. What's new are some of the names of the properties and the attempt to build a deductive system so that we can be sure we're avoiding circular reasoning.

[Ask] "What is the difference between a postulate and a definition?" [Generally, a definition of a mathematical object tells what category the object is in and what distinguishes it from other objects in that category. A postulate usually relates objects in some way.]

[Ask] "What definitions are needed to make these postulates legitimate in a deductive system?" [The terms *angle, line segment, midpoint of segment, angle bisector, parallel lines, perpendicular lines, length of segment, measure of angle, supplementary angles,* and *triangle* should be defined before the postulates referring to them are stated.] You might mention that all the definitions that students have written in their notebooks,

There are certain rules that everyone needs to agree on so we can drive safely! What are the "road rules" of geometry?

Postulates of Geometry

Line Postulate You can construct exactly one line through any two points.

Line Intersection Postulate The intersection of two distinct lines is exactly one point.

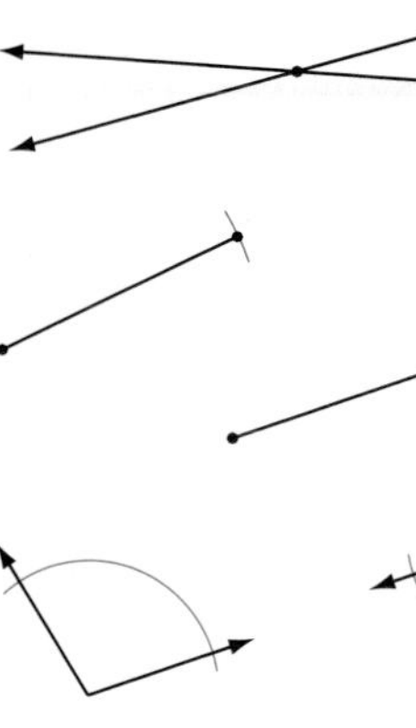

Segment Duplication Postulate You can construct a segment congruent to another segment.

Angle Duplication Postulate You can construct an angle congruent to another angle.

Midpoint Postulate You can construct exactly one midpoint on any line segment.

Angle Bisector Postulate You can construct exactly one angle bisector in any angle.

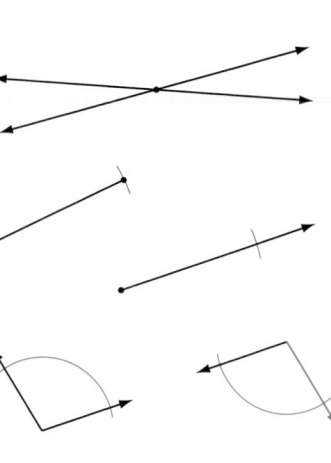

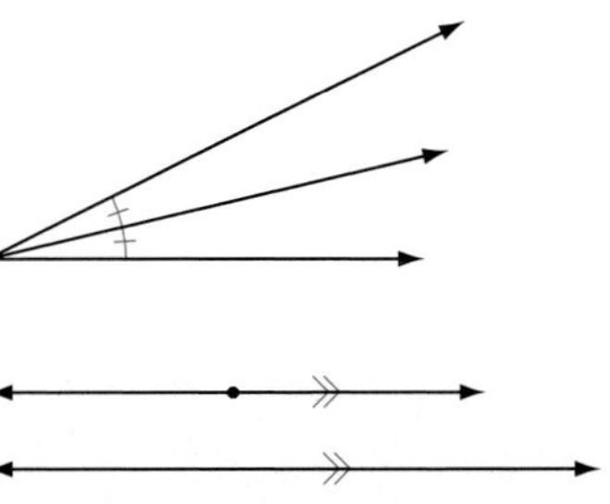

Parallel Postulate Through a point not on a given line, you can construct exactly one line parallel to the given line.

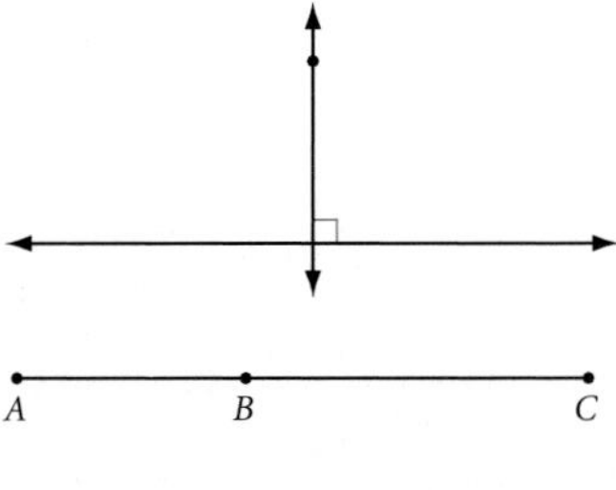

Perpendicular Postulate Through a point not on a given line, you can construct exactly one line perpendicular to the given line.

Segment Addition Postulate If point B is on $\overline{AC}$ and between points A and C, then $AB + BC = AC$.

A B C

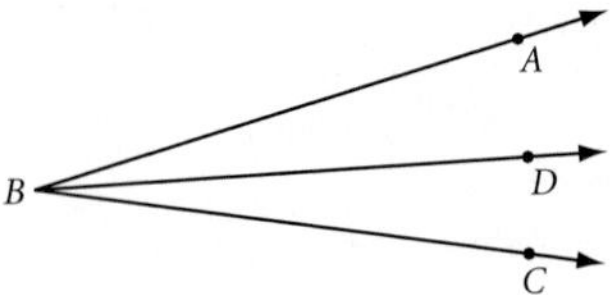

Angle Addition Postulate If point D lies in the interior of $\angle ABC$, then $m\angle ABD + m\angle DBC = m\angle ABC$.

Linear Pair Postulate If two angles are a linear pair, then they are supplementary. (Previously called the Linear Pair Conjecture.)

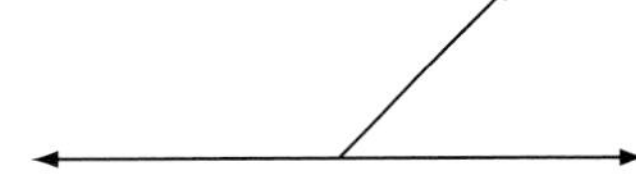

Corresponding Angles Postulate (CA Postulate) If two parallel lines are cut by a transversal, then the corresponding angles are congruent. Conversely, if two lines are cut by a transversal forming congruent corresponding angles, then the lines are parallel. (Previously called the CA Conjecture.)

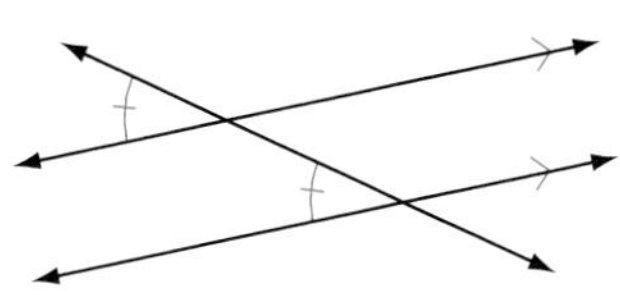

SSS Congruence Postulate If the three sides of one triangle are congruent to three sides of another triangle, then the two triangles are congruent. (Previously called the SSS Congruence Conjecture.)

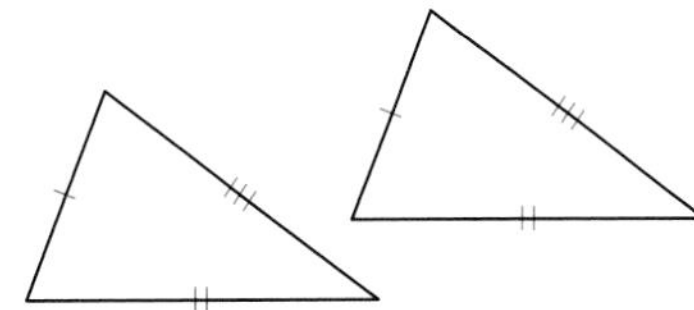

SAS Congruence Postulate If two sides and the included angle in one triangle are congruent to two sides and the included angle in another triangle, then the two triangles are congruent.

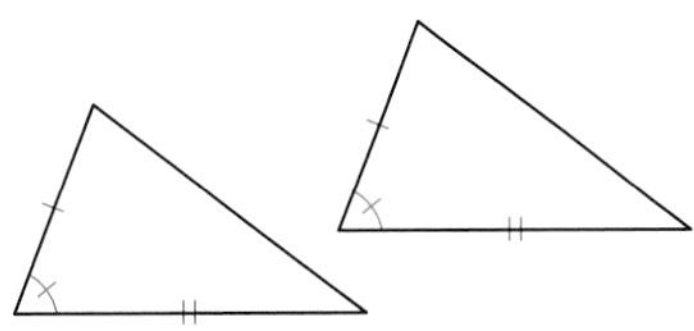

ASA Congruence Postulate If two angles and the included side in one triangle are congruent to two angles and the included side in another triangle, then the two triangles are congruent.

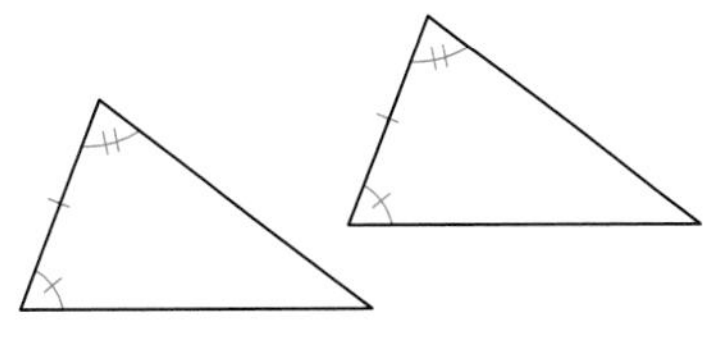

DO NOT ENTER

Mathematics CONNECTION

Euclid wrote 13 books covering, among other topics, plane geometry and solid geometry. He started with definitions, postulates, and "common notions" about the properties of equality. He then wrote hundreds of propositions, which we would call conjectures, and used constructions based on the definitions and postulates to show that they were valid. The statements that we call postulates were actually Euclid's postulates, plus a few of his propositions.

Sharing Ideas (continued)

not just the congruence definitions given in this lesson, are part of the deductive system being developed in this chapter. Because definitions can involve only previously defined terms, arranging them can be quite a challenging task. And some terms need to work as descriptors in the first definitions. *Point, line, plane,* and *space* are usually taken to be explicitly undefined terms. If you have several days for this lesson, you might have students review the definitions and conjectures in their notebooks and try to arrange them in an order they think would be valid.

[Ask] "Are the postulates and properties true?" We will accept them as true, for the sake of seeing what we can prove using them. In effect, though, we're saying "If all these postulates and properties are true, then these theorems are true." However, if we decide to drop one of these assumptions, then we have to say that any theorem whose proof depends on that assumption, even indirectly, is no longer part of our system.

Ask what happens after we have stated assumptions and a few definitions. The next step is to begin proving conjectures in order to make them theorems. As a warm-up to proving the geometric conjectures we've proposed throughout the course, we begin with some algebraic conjectures. Refer students to the example and perhaps go through one of the proofs in the exercises.

MAKING THE CONNECTION

Euclid's work also included a good bit of number theory—in fact, virtually all the mathematics known at the time. Trigonometry was developed by later Greek mathematicians; algebra was developed even later, first in the Arab world and then in western Europe.

Closing the Lesson

Mention that deductive systems organize mathematical ideas so we can be sure to avoid circular deductive reasoning. Go over the assumptions on which the mathematical system of geometry will be based: the properties of arithmetic and algebra, and the postulates of geometry.

Assessing Progress

As your students revisit statements about algebra and geometry in the form of properties and postulates, you can assess how well they understand the statements themselves.

BUILDING UNDERSTANDING

You may want to have the class work on the exercises in groups. As students encounter statements and proofs in geometry, ask them to write down the definitions that would need to precede these theorems in a deductive system.

ASSIGNING HOMEWORK

Essential	1–22
Portfolio	9, 22
Journal	1
Group	23–25
Review	26–31

Helping with the Exercises

1. A postulate is a statement accepted as true without proof. A theorem is deduced from other theorems or postulates.

Exercise 2 You might honor diverse cultures by asking for translations in other languages.

2. Subtraction: Equals minus equals are equal. Multiplication: Equals times equals are equal. Division: Equals divided by nonzero equals are equal.

Exercise 3 These statements about congruence are being taken as properties in this exercise, but they can be proved from the analogous properties about equality.

3. See below.

Exercise 6 Either the subtraction property or the addition property (adding a negative) is a legitimate answer here. In fact, in a deductive system for numbers, the definition of subtraction might be adding the negative of a number.

To build a logical framework for the geometry you have learned, you will start with the premises of geometry. In the exercises, you will see how these premises are the foundations for some of your previous assumptions and conjectures. You will also use these postulates and properties to see how some geometry statements are logical consequences of others.

EXERCISES

1. What is the difference between a postulate and a theorem?

2. Euclid might have stated the addition property of equality (translated from the Greek) in this way: "If equals are added to equals, the results are equal." State the subtraction, multiplication, and division properties of equality as Euclid might have stated them. (You may write them in English—extra credit for the original Greek!)

3. Write the reflexive property of congruence, the transitive property of congruence, and the symmetric property of congruence. Add these properties to your notebook. Include a diagram for each property. Illustrate one property with congruent triangles, another property with congruent segments, and another property with congruent angles. (These properties may seem ridiculously obvious. This is exactly why they are accepted as premises, which require no proof!)

4. When you state $AC = AC$, what property are you using? When you state $\overline{AC} \cong \overline{AC}$, what property are you using? ⓗ reflexive property of equality; reflexive property of congruence

5. Name the property that supports this statement: If $\angle ACE \cong \angle BDF$ and $\angle BDF \cong \angle HKM$, then $\angle ACE \cong \angle HKM$. transitive property of congruence

6. Name the property that supports this statement: If $x + 120 = 180$, then $x = 60$. subtraction property of equality

7. Name the property that supports this statement: If $2(x + 14) = 36$, then $x + 14 = 18$. division property of equality

In Exercises 8 and 9, provide the missing property of equality or arithmetic as a reason for each step to solve the algebraic equation or to prove the algebraic argument.

8. Solve for x: $7x - 22 = 4(x + 2)$ ⓗ

Solution:	
$7x - 22 = 4(x + 2)$	Given.
$7x - 22 = 4x + 8$	? property. Distributive
$3x - 22 = 8$	? property of equality. Subtraction
$3x = 30$	? property of equality. Addition
$x = 10$	? property of equality. Division

9. Conjecture: If $\frac{x}{m} - c = d$, then $x = m(c + d)$, provided that $m \neq 0$. ⓗ

Proof:	
$\frac{x}{m} - c = d$	? Given.
$\frac{x}{m} = d + c$	? Addition property of equality.
$x = m(d + c)$	? Multiplication property of equality.
$x = m(c + d)$	? Commutative property of addition.

3. Reflexive: Any figure is congruent to itself.

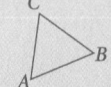

$\triangle ABC \cong \triangle ABC$

Transitive: If Figure A is congruent to Figure B and Figure B is congruent to Figure C, then Figure A is congruent to Figure C.

If $\overline{PQ} \cong \overline{RS} \cong \overline{XY}$, then $\overline{PQ} \cong \overline{XY}$

If $\overline{PQ} \cong \overline{RS}$ and $\overline{RS} \cong \overline{XY}$, then $\overline{PQ} \cong \overline{XY}$.

Symmetric: If Figure A is congruent to Figure B, then Figure B is congruent to Figure A.

If $\angle XYZ \cong \angle LMN$, then $\angle LMN \cong \angle XYZ$

If $\angle XYZ \cong \angle LMN$, then $\angle LMN \cong \angle XYZ$.

In Exercises 10–17, identify each statement as true or false. Then state which definition, property of algebra, property of congruence, or postulate supports your answer.

10. If M is the midpoint of $\overline{AB}$, then $AM = BM$. true, definition of midpoint

11. If M is the midpoint of $\overline{CD}$ and N is the midpoint of $\overline{CD}$, then M and N are the same point. ⓗ true, Midpoint Postulate

12. If $\overrightarrow{AB}$ bisects $\angle CAD$, then $\angle CAB \cong \angle DAB$. true, definition of angle bisector

13. If $\overrightarrow{AB}$ bisects $\angle CAD$ and $\overrightarrow{AF}$ bisects $\angle CAD$, then $\overrightarrow{AB}$ and $\overrightarrow{AF}$ are the same ray. true, Angle Bisector Postulate

14. Lines ℓ and m can intersect at different points A and B. false, Line Intersection Postulate

15. If line ℓ passes through points A and B and line m passes through points A and B, lines ℓ and m do not have to be the same line. false, Line Postulate

16. If point P is in the interior of $\angle RAT$, then $m\angle RAP + m\angle PAT = m\angle RAT$. true, Angle Addition Postulate

17. If point M is on $\overline{AC}$ and between points A and C, then $AM + MC = AC$. true, Segment Addition Postulate

18. The Declaration of Independence states "We hold these truths to be self-evident . . . ," then goes on to list four postulates of good government. Look up the Declaration of Independence and list the four self-evident truths that were the original premises of the United States government. You can find links to this topic at **www.keymath.com/DG** .

Arthur Szyk (1894–1951), a Polish American whose propaganda art helped aid the Allied war effort during World War II, created this patriotic illustrated version of the Declaration of Independence.

19. Copy and complete this flowchart proof. For each reason, state the definition, the property of algebra, or the property of congruence that supports the statement.

Given: $\overline{AO}$ and $\overline{BO}$ are radii

Show: $\triangle AOB$ is isosceles

1	→	2	→	3
? ($\overline{AO}$ and $\overline{BO}$ are radii)	→	$\overline{AO} \cong \overline{BO}$	→	? ($\triangle AOB$ is isosceles)
Given		Definition of circle		Definition of ? (isosceles)

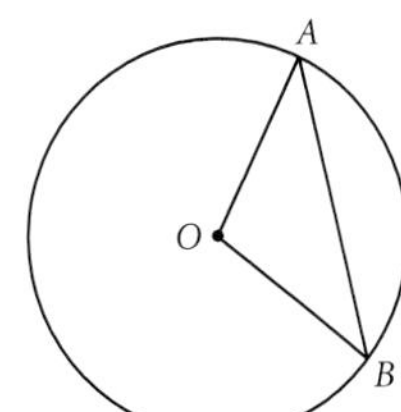

Exercise 17 Some deductive systems might elaborate on the notion that one point is between two others, either calling *between* an undefined term or defining it through lengths as in this exercise.

Exercise 18 [Context] Isaac Newton's deductive system for physics was so successful that, in the 1700s, a movement arose to find deductive systems for all areas of life. Wolfgang Amadeus Mozart (1756–1791), for example, experimented with postulates for great music. The belief in a deductive system for political organizations led to the postulates in this exercise.

18.

- That all men are created equal.
- That they are endowed by their creator with certain inalienable rights, that among these are life, liberty, and the pursuit of happiness.
- That to secure these rights, governments are instituted among men, deriving their just powers from the consent of the governed.
- That whenever any form of government becomes destructive to these ends, it is the right of the people to alter or to abolish it, and to institute new government, laying its foundation on such principles and organizing its powers in such form as to them shall seem most likely to effect their safety and happiness.

Exercises 19–22 These partially completed proofs will help students learn how to write more complete proofs. You might ask students what definitions are being used.

Exercise 21 If students object that CPCTC is not given as a postulate to be cited in statement 5, you might point out that it's really part of the definition of congruent triangles, which says that all six pairs of corresponding parts are congruent. (See the introduction to Lesson 4.6.)

Exercise 22 This exercise proves the Isosceles Triangle Theorem. With it, students can begin a list of theorems, that is, conjectures that have been proved. This theorem will be used as a reason in later proofs.

For Exercises 20–22, copy and complete each flowchart proof.

20. Given: $\angle 1 \cong \angle 2$

Show: $\angle 3 \cong \angle 4$

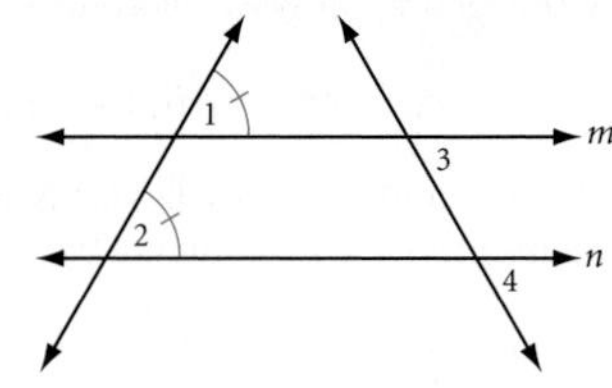

1 $\angle 1 \cong$? $\angle 2$ →	2 ? $m \parallel n$ →	3 $\angle 3 \cong$? $\angle 4$
? Given	Corresponding Angles Postulate	? Corresponding Angles Postulate

21. Given: $\overline{AC} \cong \overline{BD}$, $\overline{AD} \cong \overline{BC}$

Show: $\angle D \cong \angle C$

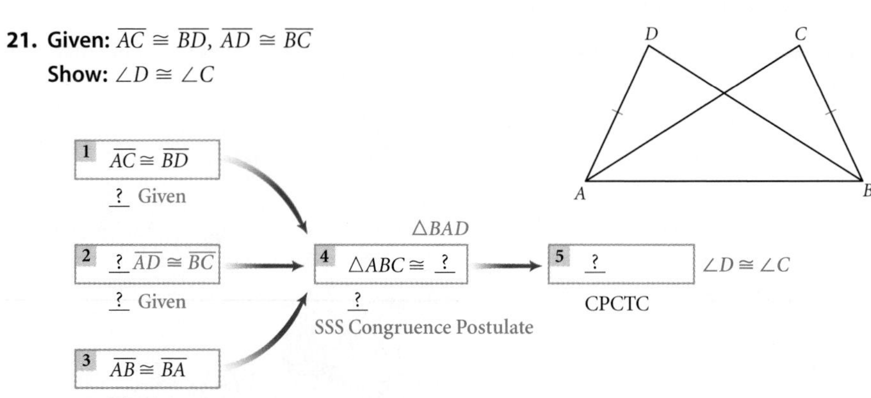

22. Given: Isosceles triangle ABC with $\overline{AB} \cong \overline{BC}$

Show: $\angle A \cong \angle C$ ⓗ

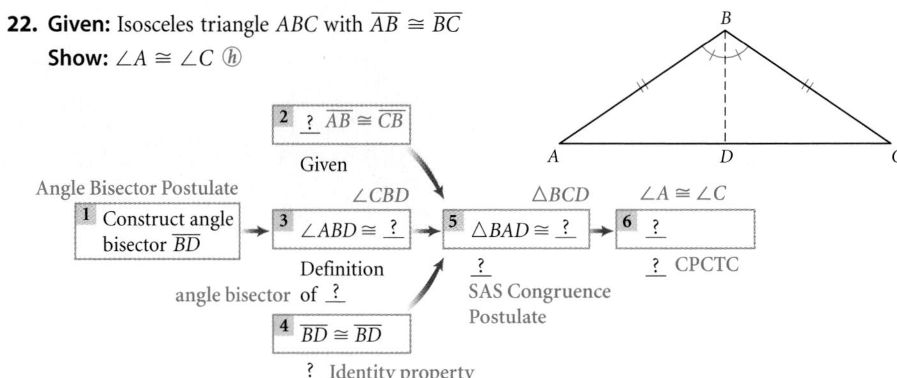

23. You have probably noticed that the sum of two odd integers is always an even integer. The rule $2n$ generates even integers and the rule $2n - 1$ generates odd integers. Let $2n - 1$ and $2m - 1$ represent any two odd integers and prove that the sum of two odd integers is always an even integer.

$(2n - 1) + (2m - 1) = 2n + 2m - 2 = 2(n + m - 1)$

24. Let $2n - 1$ and $2m - 1$ represent any two odd integers and prove that the product of any two odd integers is always an odd integer.

25. Show that the sum of any three consecutive integers is always divisible by 3. ⓗ

Review

12.2 **26.** Shannon and Erin are hiking up a mountain. Of course, they are packing the clinometer they made in geometry class. At point A along a flat portion of the trail, Erin sights the mountain peak straight ahead at an angle of elevation of 22°. The level trail continues 220 m straight to the base of the mountain at point B. At that point, Shannon measures the angle of elevation to be 38°. From B the trail follows a ridge straight up the mountain to the peak. At point B, how far are they from the mountain peak? 299 m

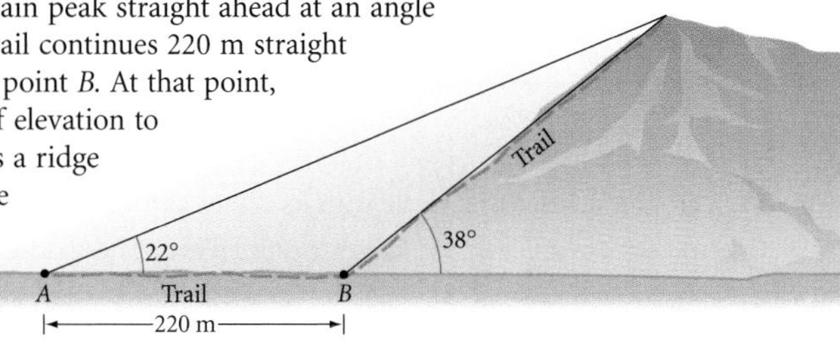

Chapter 10 **27.**

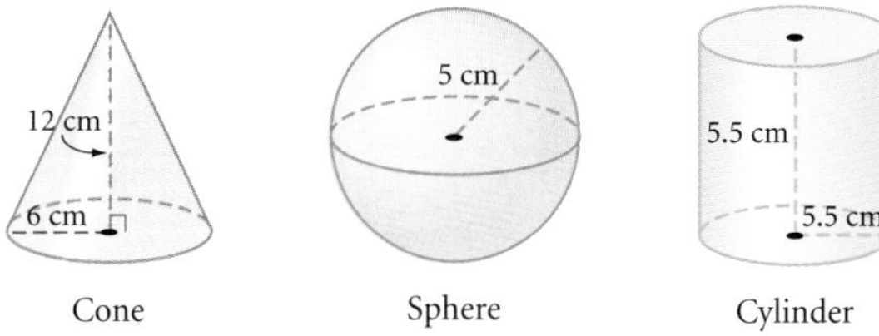

Cone Sphere Cylinder

Arrange the names of the solids in order, greatest to least.

Volume:	?	?	? sphere, cylinder, cone
Surface area:	?	?	? cylinder, cone, sphere
Length of the longest rod that will fit inside:	?	?	? cone, cylinder, sphere

11.2 **28.** Two communication towers stand 64 ft apart. One is 80 ft high and the other is 48 ft high. Each has a guy wire from its top anchored to the base of the other tower. At what height do the two guy wires cross? 30 ft

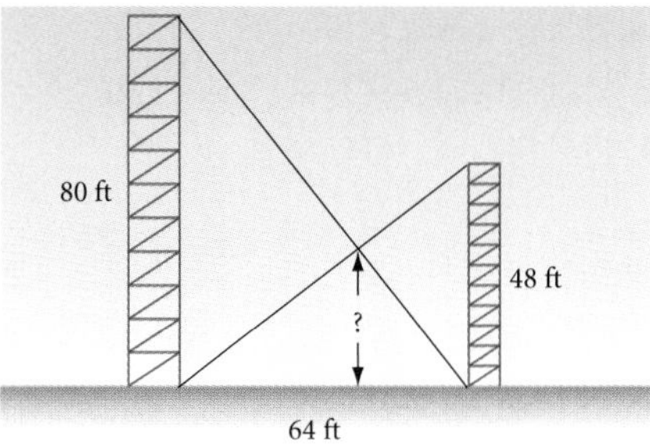

24. $(2n - 1)(2m - 1) =$
$4nm - 2n - 2m + 1 =$
$4nm - 2n - 2m + 2 - 1 =$
$2(2nm - n - m + 1) - 1$

25. Let n be any integer. Then the next two consecutive integers are $n + 1$ and $n + 2$. The sum of these three integers is $(n) + (n + 1) + (n + 2) =$ $n + n + 1 + n + 2$. Combining like terms: $3n + 3 = 3(n + 1)$, which is divisible by 3.

Exercise 26 If students are having difficulty, wonder aloud whether a right triangle might be useful given that they need to relate angles to distances. If they draw a perpendicular from the top of the mountain to the horizontal line, they can express its length and the distance from its base to point B using trigonometric functions of both 38° and 22°.

Exercise 28 [ESL] If you haven't previously explained the term *guy wire*, you might state now that the guy wires are used to stabilize the towers.

29. $FG = 2\sqrt{6}$ and $DG = 2\sqrt{3}$ because *ABGF* and *BCDG* are parallelograms. Triangle *FGD* is right ($m\angle FGD = 90°$) by the Converse of the Pythagorean Theorem because $(2\sqrt{6})^2 + (2\sqrt{3})^2 = 6^2$. But $m\angle FGB = 128°$ and $m\angle DGB = 140°$ by conjectures regarding angles in a parallelogram. So, $m\angle FGD = 92°$ because the sum of the angles around *G* is 360°. So, $\angle FGD$ is both 90° and 92°.

Exercise 31 These puzzles begin a sequence that builds through four lessons spread throughout this chapter, so saving the results will be helpful; perhaps you can post them in the room. Although students might legitimately express the area as a portion of the area of the square, the puzzle specifies that each square has side lengths 1, so they should also give their answers as numbers. Tell students to leave their answers in terms of π.

In Exercises 29 and 30, all length measurements are given in meters.

29. What's wrong with this picture?

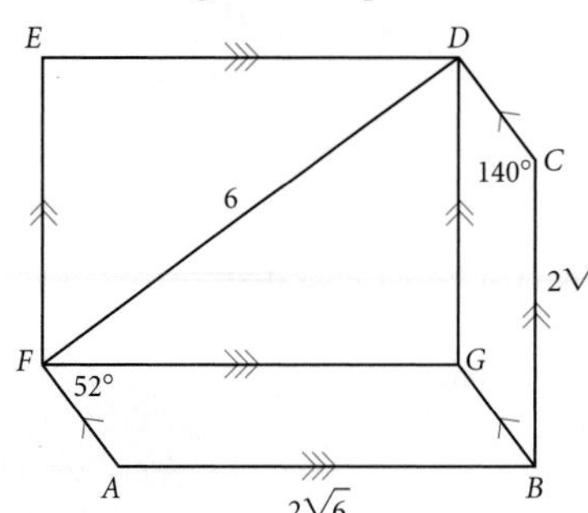

30. Find angle measures *x* and *y*, and length *a*. $x = 54°, y = 126°, a = 7.3$

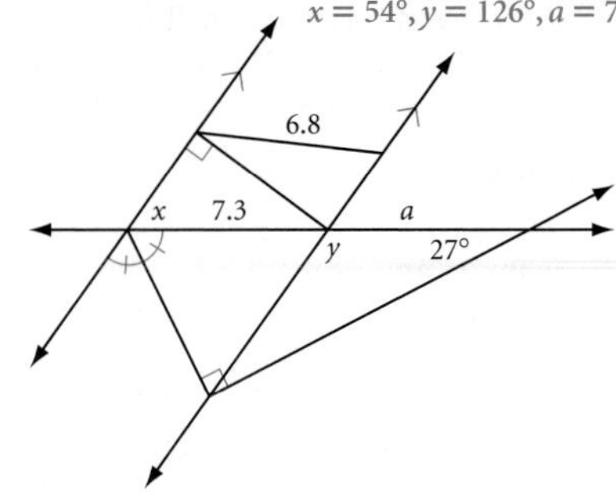

Chapter 8 **31.** Each arc is a quarter of a circle with its center at a vertex of the square.

Given: Each square has side length 1 unit **Find:** The shaded area

a.

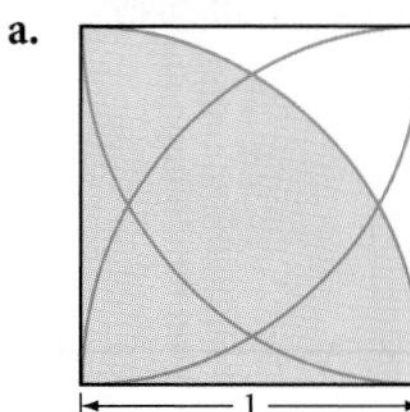

$\frac{\pi}{4}$

b.

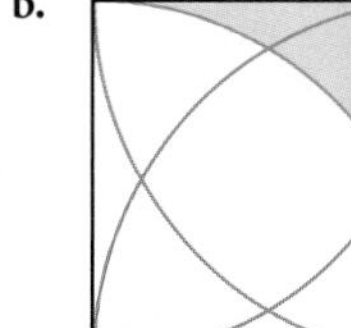

$1 - \frac{\pi}{4}$

c.

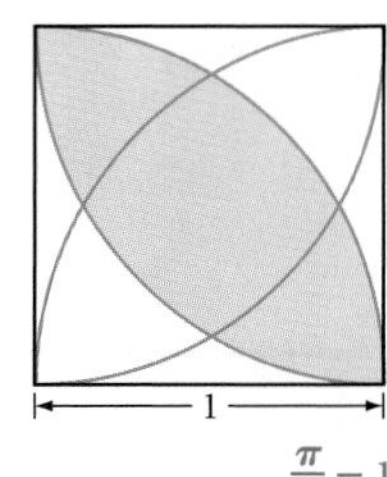

$\frac{\pi}{2} - 1$

IMPROVING YOUR REASONING SKILLS

Logical Vocabulary

Here is a logical vocabulary challenge. It is sometimes possible to change one word to another of equal length by changing one letter at a time. Each change, or move, you make gives you a new word. For example, DOG can be changed to CAT in exactly three moves.

DOG ⇒ DOT ⇒ COT ⇒ CAT

Change MATH to each of the following words in exactly four moves.

1. MATH ⇒ ? ⇒ ? ⇒ ? ⇒ ROSE

2. MATH ⇒ ? ⇒ ? ⇒ ? ⇒ CORE

3. MATH ⇒ ? ⇒ ? ⇒ ? ⇒ HOST

4. MATH ⇒ ? ⇒ ? ⇒ ? ⇒ LESS

5. MATH ⇒ ? ⇒ ? ⇒ ? ⇒ LIVE

Now create one of your own. Change MATH to another word in four moves.

IMPROVING REASONING SKILLS

Because only four moves are allowed and the letter in each place changes, each letter must change only once. There are several possibilities for each string and for original creations. Here's one of many possible sets:

1. MATH ⇒ MATE ⇒ RATE ⇒ ROTE ⇒ ROSE

2. MATH ⇒ MATE ⇒ MARE ⇒ MORE ⇒ CORE

3. MATH ⇒ MASH ⇒ MAST ⇒ MOST ⇒ HOST

4. MATH ⇒ MASH ⇒ MASS ⇒ MESS ⇒ LESS

5. MATH ⇒ LATH ⇒ LATE ⇒ LAVE ⇒ LIVE

Sample originals: MATH ⇒ BATH ⇒ BASH ⇒ BASS ⇒ BOSS

MATH ⇒ PATH ⇒ PITH ⇒ PITA ⇒ PICA

LESSON

13.2

Planning a Geometry Proof

What is now proved was once only imagined.

WILLIAM BLAKE

A proof in geometry consists of a sequence of statements, starting with a given set of premises and leading to a valid conclusion. Each statement follows from one or more of the previous statements and is supported by a reason. A reason for a statement must come from the set of premises that you learned about in Lesson 13.1.

In earlier chapters you informally proved many conjectures. Now you can formally prove them, using the premises of geometry. In this lesson you will identify for yourself what is given and what you must show, in order to prove a conjecture. You will also create your own labeled diagrams.

"I THINK YOU SHOULD BE MORE EXPLICIT HERE IN STEP TWO."

As you have seen, you can state many geometry conjectures as conditional statements. For example, you can write the conjecture "Vertical angles are congruent" as a conditional statement: "If two angles are vertical angles, then they are congruent." To prove that a conditional statement is true, you assume that the first part of the conditional is true, then logically demonstrate the truth of the conditional's second part. In other words, you demonstrate that the first part implies the second part. The first part is what you assume to be true in the proof; it is the *given* information. The second part is the part you logically demonstrate in the proof; it is what you want to *show.*

Given	Show
Two angles are vertical angles	They are congruent

Next, draw and label a diagram that illustrates the given information. Then, use the labels in the diagram to restate graphically what is given and what you must show.

Once you've created a diagram to illustrate your conjecture and you know where to start and where to go, make a plan. Use your plan to write the proof. Here's the complete process.

Writing a Proof

Task 1 From the conditional statement, identify what is given and what you must show.

Task 2 Draw and label a diagram to illustrate the given information.

Task 3 Restate what is given and what you must show in terms of your diagram.

Task 4 Plan a proof. Organize your reasoning mentally or on paper.

Task 5 From your plan, write a proof.

LESSON

13.2

PLANNING

LESSON OUTLINE

One day:

15 min Examples

10 min Sharing

5 min Closing

15 min Exercises

MATERIALS

- Writing a Proof (T), *optional*

TEACHING

In this lesson students see five steps for planning a (flowchart) proof and see how to develop a family tree for a theorem, tracing its logical ancestry back to properties, postulates, and definitions.

Although students saw a paragraph proof of the Vertical Angles Conjecture in the example in Lesson 2.5, the conjecture could not be called a theorem until it fit into a deductive system. Now they can add the Vertical Angles Theorem to their list of theorems.

From this point on, students' proofs may differ slightly from those in the book or in the solutions to the exercises, because the definitions and conjectures your students have agreed on may differ somewhat from those on which the proofs in the book are based.

NCTM STANDARDS

CONTENT		PROCESS	
	Number		Problem Solving
	Algebra	✓	Reasoning
✓	Geometry	✓	Communication
	Measurement		Connections
	Data/Probability	✓	Representation

LESSON OBJECTIVES

- Understand the outline for planning and writing a proof
- Learn to state conjectures as conditional statements
- Develop deductive reasoning and cooperative behavior

One step Ask students to write a flowchart proof of the Alternate Interior Angles Conjecture (AIA): If two parallel lines are cut by a transversal, then the alternate interior angles are congruent. Let them work for a while in groups. If a group is successful, ask group members to share how they came up with their proof. Let the five tasks for writing a proof grow out of their experience. Then ask the groups to use those tasks to write a flowchart proof of the Triangle Sum Conjecture. Next ask how they can be sure they've avoided circular reasoning, and let them draw a family tree of the Third Angle Theorem. Finally, have groups compare their ideas with those in the examples.

▶ *EXAMPLE A*

Emphasize the tasks rather than the final proof. To help with Task 4, students can look through their lists of postulates and theorems and decide which premises would be helpful. Encourage students to keep their lists handy. They might also benefit from creating a list of statements by starting at the bottom of a sheet of paper and physically working up and down the paper.

In Chapter 2, you proved the Vertical Angles Conjecture using conjectures that have now become postulates.

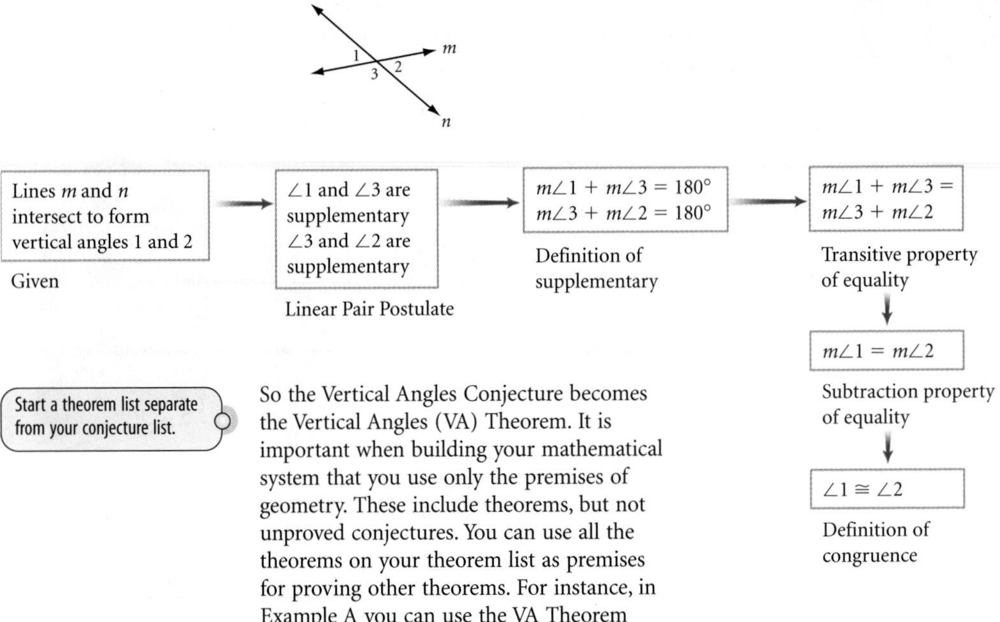

So the Vertical Angles Conjecture becomes the Vertical Angles (VA) Theorem. It is important when building your mathematical system that you use only the premises of geometry. These include theorems, but not unproved conjectures. You can use all the theorems on your theorem list as premises for proving other theorems. For instance, in Example A you can use the VA Theorem to prove another theorem.

You may have noticed that in the previous lesson we stated the CA Conjecture as a postulate, but not the AIA Conjecture or the AEA Conjecture. In this first example you will see how to use the five tasks of the proof process to prove the AIA Conjecture.

EXAMPLE A Prove the Alternate Interior Angles Conjecture: If two parallel lines are cut by a transversal, then the alternate interior angles are congruent.

▶ *Solution* For Task 1 identify what is given and what you must show.

Given: Two parallel lines are cut by a transversal

Show: Alternate interior angles formed by the lines are congruent

For Task 2 draw and label a diagram.

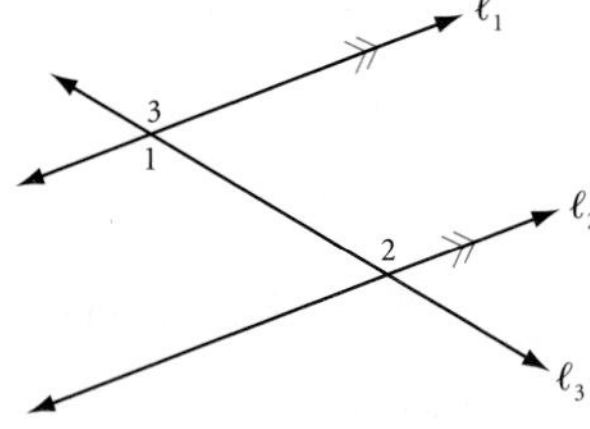

For Task 3 restate what is given and what you must show in terms of the diagram.

Given: Parallel lines ℓ_1 and ℓ_2 cut by transversal ℓ_3 to form alternate interior angles $\angle 1$ and $\angle 2$

Show: $\angle 1 \cong \angle 2$

For Task 4 plan a proof. Organize your reasoning mentally or on paper.

Plan:
I need to show that $\angle 1 \cong \angle 2$.
Looking over the postulates and theorems, the ones that look useful are the CA Postulate and the VA Theorem.
From the CA Postulate, I know that $\angle 2 \cong \angle 3$ and from the VA Theorem, $\angle 1 \cong \angle 3$.
If $\angle 2 \cong \angle 3$ and $\angle 1 \cong \angle 3$, then by substitution $\angle 1 \cong \angle 2$.

For Task 5 create a proof from your plan.

Flowchart Proof

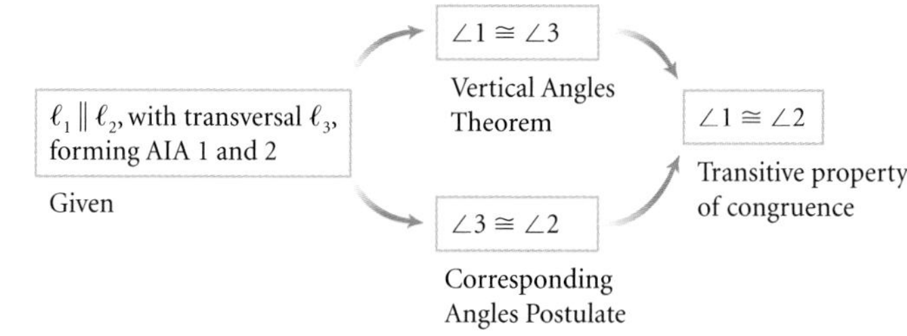
$\ell_1 \parallel \ell_2$, with transversal ℓ_3, forming AIA 1 and 2
Given
$\angle 1 \cong \angle 3$
Vertical Angles Theorem
$\angle 3 \cong \angle 2$
Corresponding Angles Postulate
$\angle 1 \cong \angle 2$
Transitive property of congruence

So the AIA Conjecture becomes the AIA Theorem. Add this theorem to your theorem list.

In Chapter 4, you informally proved the Triangle Sum Conjecture. The proof is short, but clever, too, because it required the construction of an auxiliary line. All the steps in the proof use properties that we now designate as postulates. Example B shows the flowchart proof. For example, the Parallel Postulate guarantees that it will always be possible to construct an auxiliary line through a vertex, parallel to the opposite side.

▶ EXAMPLE B

Students can check their understanding by reading the proof, then closing the book and reproducing it. The two theorems proved in Examples A and B are used as reasons in several later proofs.

[Alert] Students may not see that the Triangle Sum Theorem is the crucial step in proving the Third Angle Theorem. **[Ask]** "Why is a logical family tree important?" [It can help you check that no circular reasoning has taken place.]

EXAMPLE B

Prove the Triangle Sum Conjecture: The sum of the measures of the angles of a triangle is 180°.

▶ Solution

Given: $\angle 1$, $\angle 2$, and $\angle 3$ are the three angles of $\triangle ABC$

Show: $m\angle 1 + m\angle 2 + m\angle 3 = 180°$

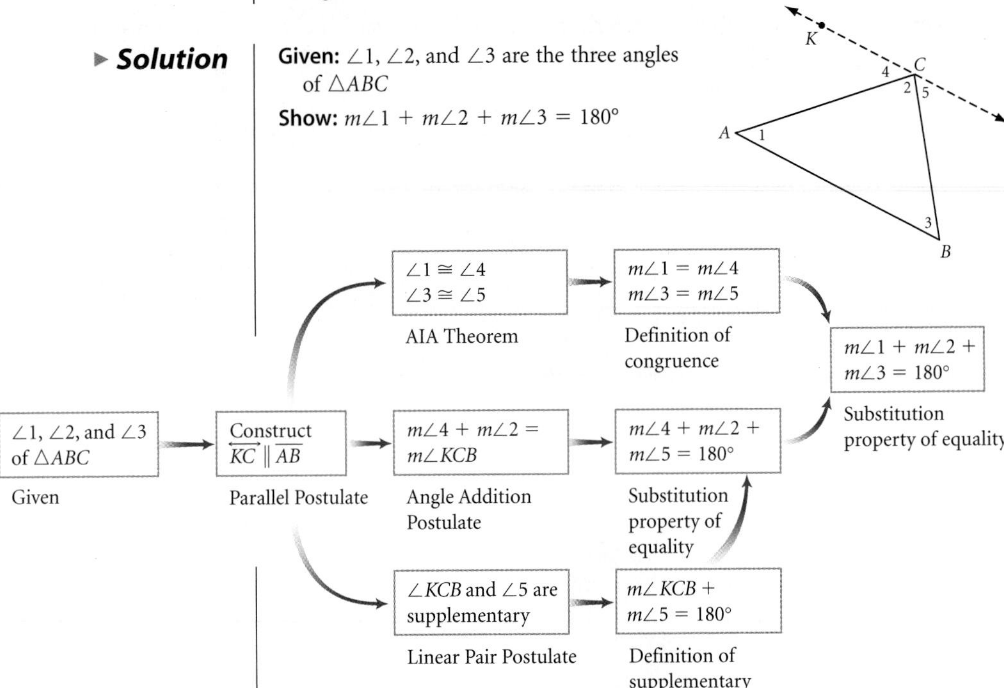

So the Triangle Sum Conjecture becomes the Triangle Sum Theorem. Add it to your theorem list. Notice that each reason we now use in a proof is a postulate, theorem, definition, or property.

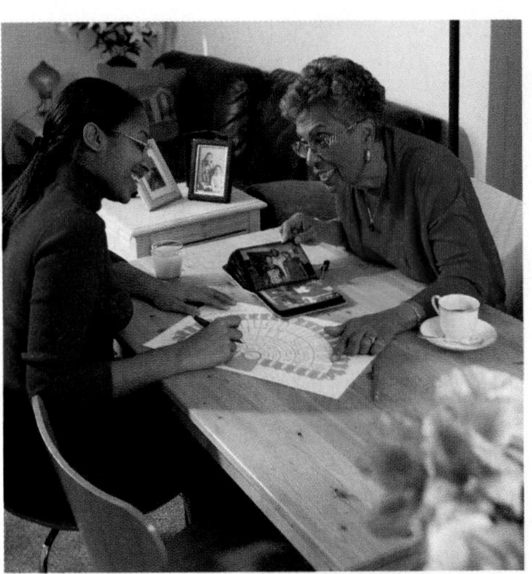

When you trace back your family tree, you include the names of your parents, the names of their parents, and so on.

To make sure a particular theorem has been properly proved, you can also check the "logical family tree" of the theorem. When you create a family tree for a theorem, you trace it back to all the postulates that the theorem relied on. You don't need to list all the definitions and properties of equality and congruence: list only the theorems and postulates used in the proof. For the theorems that were used in the proof, what postulates and theorems were used in *their* proofs, and so on. In Chapter 4, you informally proved the Third Angle Conjecture. Let's look again at the proof.

Third Angle Conjecture: If two angles of one triangle are congruent to two angles of a second triangle, then the third pair of angles are congruent.

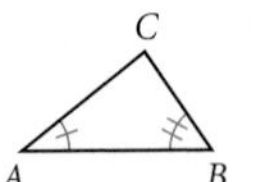

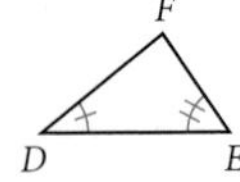

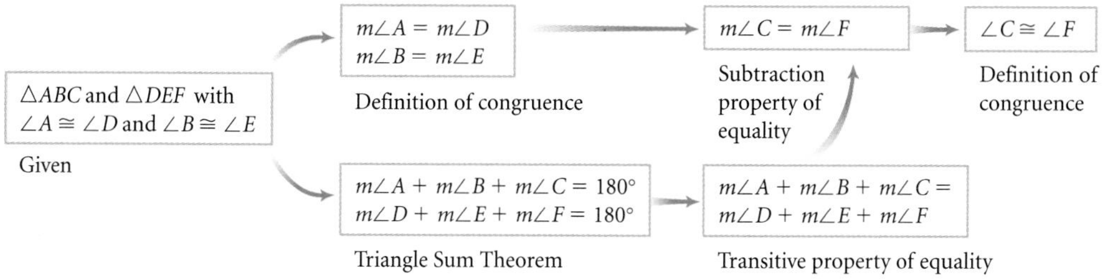

$m\angle A = m\angle D$
$m\angle B = m\angle E$
$m\angle C = m\angle F$
$\angle C \cong \angle F$
$\triangle ABC$ and $\triangle DEF$ with
$\angle A \cong \angle D$ and $\angle B \cong \angle E$
Definition of congruence
Subtraction property of equality
Definition of congruence
Given
$m\angle A + m\angle B + m\angle C = 180°$
$m\angle D + m\angle E + m\angle F = 180°$
$m\angle A + m\angle B + m\angle C =$
$m\angle D + m\angle E + m\angle F$
Triangle Sum Theorem
Transitive property of equality

What does the logical family tree of the Third Angle Theorem look like?

You start by putting the Third Angle Theorem in a box. Find all the postulates and theorems used in the proof. The only postulate or theorem used was the Triangle Sum Theorem. Put that box above it.

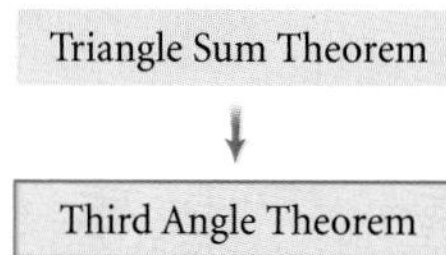

Next, locate all the theorems and postulates used to prove the Triangle Sum Theorem. That proof used the Parallel Postulate, the Linear Pair Postulate, the Angle Addition Postulate, and the AIA Theorem. You place these postulates in boxes above the Triangle Sum Theorem. Connect the boxes with arrows showing the logical connection. Now the family tree looks like this:

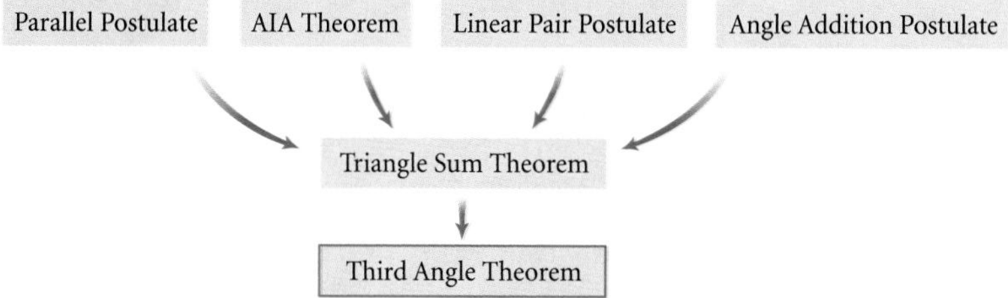

To prove the AIA Theorem, we used the CA Postulate and the VA Theorem, and we used the Linear Pair Postulate to prove the VA Theorem. Notice that the Linear Pair Postulate is already in the family tree, but we move it up so it's above both the Triangle Sum Theorem and the VA Theorem. The completed family tree looks like this:

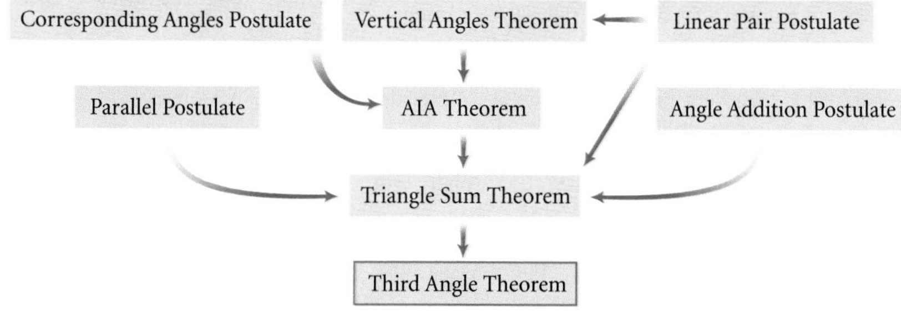

Assessing Progress

You can assess students' knowledge of postulates, properties, and definitions and their appreciation of the need for a deductive system.

Closing the Lesson

Go over the five tasks for writing a proof and the notion of a logical family tree as assurance that a theorem is not the result of circular reasoning.

SHARING IDEAS

If students are having difficulty seeing what is given and what they are to prove, point out that the conjecture can be rewritten as a conditional, as in Example A. The "if" part is given, and the "then" part is to be proved.

[Ask] "How did you come up with these conjectures originally?" [They came from inductive reasoning.] Now that they have been proved within the deductive system, they are no longer conjectures but theorems.

Ask what theorems we now have, in order. Point out that the Vertical Angles Theorem was used in proving the Alternate Interior Angles Theorem, which appeared as a reason in the proof of the Triangle Sum Theorem, which in turn was cited in proving the Third Angle Theorem. After a conjecture has become a theorem, it can be used as a reason in the proof of another theorem. **[Ask]** "Do the tasks for writing a proof seem familiar?" Students might recognize them as steps in solving applied problems. Remind students that they might actually plan their proof in reverse order, as they did in Lesson 5.7. Reassure them that making a plan is an art that they can master, but there's no foolproof method for doing it.

If you did the one-step investigation of Lesson 13.1, ask whether students think they could prove either of the propositions in that investigation. They contradict the Triangle Sum Theorem and the Third Angle Theorem. The given proofs were valid, but the reasoning would not be valid in a deductive system because it was circular.

BUILDING UNDERSTANDING

Encourage students to follow the five tasks for writing a proof.

You might jigsaw Exercises 5–14 among groups. When presented proofs are accepted by the class, students can add the theorems to their lists.

ASSIGNING HOMEWORK

Essential	1–4, any two of 5–14, 15
Performance assessment	5–14 (any)
Portfolio	5–14 (any)
Group	5–14
Review	16–19

▶Helping with the Exercises

Exercises 5, 7, 8, 11, 12 These theorems are used in later proofs. If you jigsaw them among groups, be sure all students record the theorems when the proofs are shared.

5.

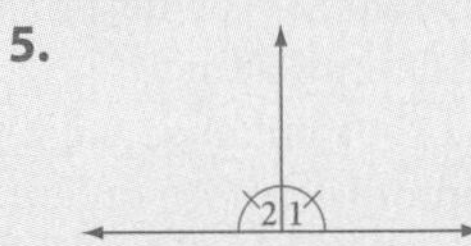

Use the definition of supplementary angles and the substitution property to get $m\angle 1 + m\angle 1 = 180°$. Then use the division property and the definition of a right angle.

6.

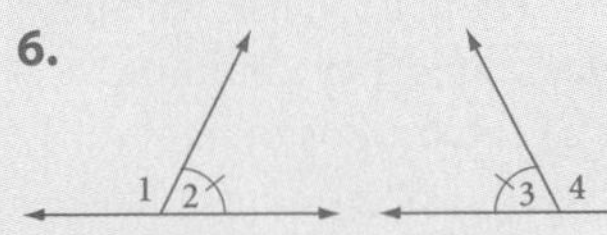

Use the definition of supplementary angles and the transitive property to get $m\angle 1 + m\angle 2 = m\angle 3 + m\angle 4$. Then use the substitution property and the subtraction property to get $m\angle 1 = m\angle 4$.

See page 778 for answers to Exercises 9–13.

The family tree shows that, ultimately, the Third Angle Theorem relies on the Parallel Postulate, the CA Postulate, the Linear Pair Postulate, and the Angle Addition Postulate. You might notice that the family tree of a theorem looks similar to a flowchart proof. The difference is that the family tree focuses on the premises and traces them back to the postulates.

EXERCISES

1. What postulate(s) does the VA Theorem rely on? Linear Pair Postulate

2. What postulate(s) does the Triangle Sum Theorem rely on?
Parallel Postulate, Angle Addition Postulate, Linear Pair Postulate, Corresponding Angles Postulate

3. If you need a parallel line in a proof, what postulate allows you to construct it? Parallel Postulate

4. If you need a perpendicular line in a proof, what postulate allows you to construct it? Perpendicular Postulate

In Exercises 5–14, write a paragraph proof or a flowchart proof of the conjecture. Once you have completed their proofs, add the statements to your theorem list.

5. If two angles are both congruent and supplementary, then each is a right angle. (Congruent and Supplementary Theorem)

6. Supplements of congruent angles are congruent. (Supplements of Congruent Angles Theorem)

7. All right angles are congruent. (Right Angles Are Congruent Theorem)

8. If two lines are cut by a transversal forming congruent alternate interior angles, then the lines are parallel. (Converse of the AIA Theorem)

9. If two parallel lines are cut by a transversal, then the alternate exterior angles are congruent. (AEA Theorem)

10. If two lines are cut by a transversal forming congruent alternate exterior angles, then the lines are parallel. (Converse of the AEA Theorem)

11. If two parallel lines are cut by a transversal, then the interior angles on the same side of the transversal are supplementary. (Interior Supplements Theorem)

12. If two lines are cut by a transversal forming interior angles on the same side of the transversal that are supplementary, then the lines are parallel. (Converse of the Interior Supplements Theorem)

13. If two lines in the same plane are parallel to a third line, then they are parallel to each other. (Parallel Transitivity Theorem)

7.

Use the definition of a right angle and the transitive property to get $m\angle 1 = m\angle 2$. Then use the definition of congruence to get $\angle 1 \cong \angle 2$.

8.

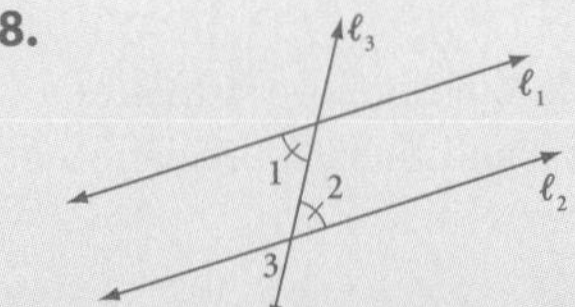

Use the VA Theorem and the transitive property to get $\angle 1 \cong \angle 3$. Therefore the lines are parallel by the CA Postulate.

14. If two lines in the same plane are perpendicular to a third line, then they are parallel to each other. (Perpendicular to Parallel Theorem)

15. Draw a family tree of the Converse of the Alternate Exterior Angles Theorem.

Review

10.3 **16.** Suppose the top of a pyramid with volume 1107 cm^3 is sliced off and discarded. The remaining portion is called a **truncated pyramid.** If the cut was parallel to the base and two-thirds of the distance to the vertex, what is the volume of the truncated pyramid? 1066 cm^3

8.3 **17.** Abraham is building a dog house for his terrier. His plan is shown at right.

He will cut a door and a window later. After he builds the frame for the structure, can he complete it using one piece of 4-by-8-foot plywood? If the answer is yes, show how he should cut the plywood. If no, explain why not.

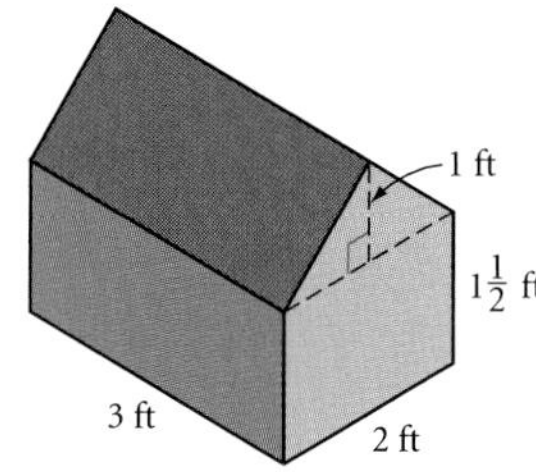

4.1 **18.** Find x. $x = 92°$

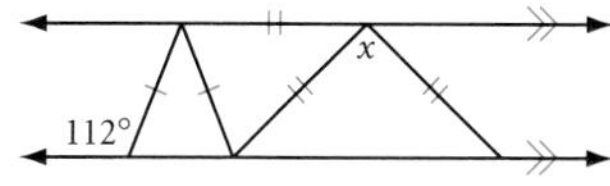

5.5 **19.** M is the midpoint of $\overline{AC}$ and $\overline{BD}$. For each statement, select always (A), sometimes (S), or never (N).

a. $\angle BAD$ and $\angle ADC$ are supplementary. A

b. $\angle ADM$ and $\angle MAD$ are complementary. S

c. $AD + BC < AC$ S

d. $AD + CD < AC$ N

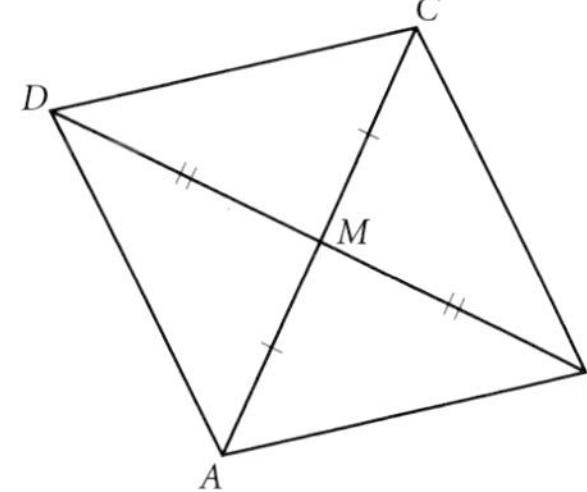

IMPROVING YOUR REASONING SKILLS

Calculator Cunning

Using the calculator shown at right, what is the largest number you can form by pressing the keys labeled 1, 2, and 3 exactly once each and the key labeled y^x at most once? You cannot press any other keys.

14.

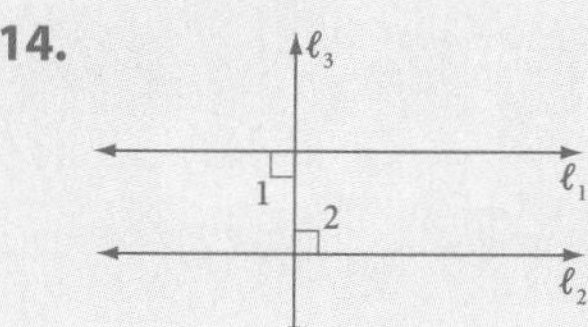

Use the definition of perpendicular lines and the transitive property to get $m\angle 1 = m\angle 2$. Therefore lines ℓ_1 and ℓ_2 are parallel by the Converse of the AIA Theorem.

15.

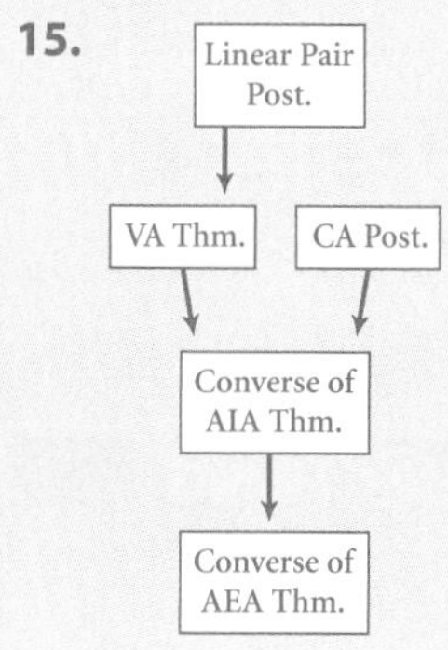

Exercise 16 A truncated pyramid (seen in the Chapter 10 project on page 527) is analogous to a truncated cone, which students saw in Lesson 11.6, Exercise 17.

17.

	Area (ft^2)
Bottom	6
2 sides	9
Back and front	6
2 rooftops	$\approx 8\frac{1}{2}$
2 gable ends	2
Total	$31\frac{1}{2}$
Plywood (4-by-8)	32

The area is less than that of one sheet of plywood. However, it is impossible to cut the correct size pieces from one piece. Two sheets would be enough.

IMPROVING REASONING SKILLS

3^{21}

EXTENSION

Pose this problem: "Suppose AEA is taken as a postulate in place of CA. How can CA be proved as a theorem?" [To show that $\angle 2 \cong \angle 6$, for example, we can start by noting that $\angle 4 \cong \angle 6$ by AEA. But $\angle 2 \cong \angle 4$ by the VA Theorem, so $\angle 2 \cong \angle 6$ by the Transitive Property of Congruence.]

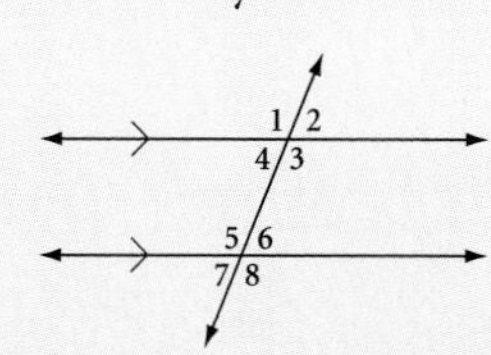

LESSON

13.3

PLANNING

LESSON OUTLINE

One day:

15 min Example

25 min Exercises and Sharing

5 min Closing

MATERIALS

none

TEACHING

This lesson concentrates on proving geometry relationships using congruent triangles. If you think it's necessary, you might have students review the three postulates concerning triangle congruence.

▶ *EXAMPLE*

This example follows the five-task outline for constructing a proof. You might want to refer students to those tasks, listed in the previous lesson.

A two-column proof with arrows, as used in this book, is sometimes called a *directed proof.* The arrows preserve some of the benefits of the flowchart proof, showing the flow of the logic in places where consecutive steps are not necessarily related.

[Alert] As needed, remind students that the distance from a point to a line is always measured along a perpendicular to the line from the point.

[Alert] You might want to help students see that the same steps are used in both the flowchart proof and the two-column proof. As proofs get longer, the flowchart method can be very awkward. The two-column proof then becomes easier to use.

LESSON 13.3

Triangle Proofs

The most violent element in our society is ignorance.

EMMA GOLDMAN

Now that the theorems from the previous lesson have been proved, you should add them to your theorem list. They will be useful to you in proving future theorems.

Triangle congruence is so useful in proving other theorems that we will focus next on triangle proofs. You may have noticed that in Lesson 13.1, three of the four triangle congruence conjectures were stated as postulates (the SSS Congruence Postulate, the SAS Congruence Postulate, and the ASA Congruence Postulate). The SAA Conjecture was not stated as a postulate. In Lesson 4.5, you used the ASA Conjecture (now the ASA Postulate) to explain the SAA Conjecture. The family tree for SAA congruence looks like this:

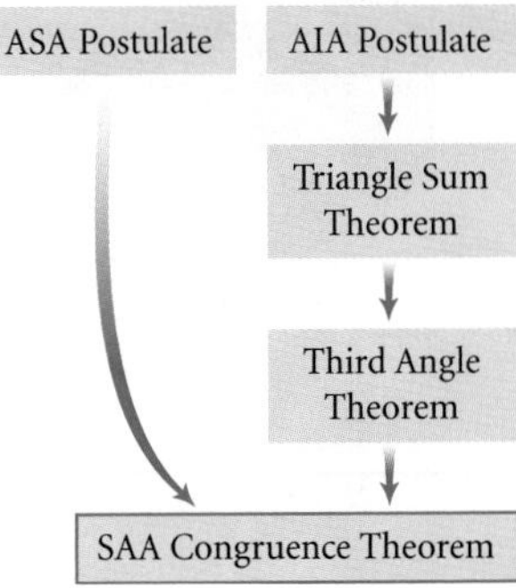

So the SAA Conjecture becomes the SAA Theorem. Add this theorem to your theorem list. This theorem will be useful in some of the proofs in this lesson.

Let's use the five-task proof process and triangle congruence to prove the Angle Bisector Conjecture.

EXAMPLE Prove the Angle Bisector Conjecture: Any point on the bisector of an angle is equidistant from the sides of the angle.

▶ *Solution*

Given: Any point on the bisector of an angle

Show: The point is equidistant from the sides of the angle

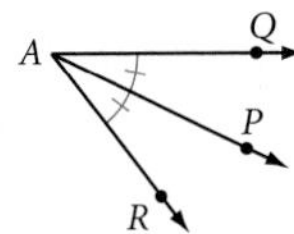

Given: $\overrightarrow{AP}$ bisecting $\angle QAR$

Show: P is equally distant from sides $\overrightarrow{AQ}$ and $\overrightarrow{AR}$

LESSON OBJECTIVES

- Prove the Angle Bisector Conjecture using triangle congruence
- Practice using triangle congruence to prove conjectures

NCTM STANDARDS

CONTENT		PROCESS	
	Number		Problem Solving
	Algebra	✓	Reasoning
✓	Geometry	✓	Communication
	Measurement		Connections
	Data/Probability		Representation

Plan: The distance from a point to a line is measured along the perpendicular from the point to the line. So I begin by constructing $\overline{PB} \perp \overrightarrow{AQ}$ and $\overline{PC} \perp \overrightarrow{AR}$ (the Perpendicular Postulate permits me to do this). I can show that $\overline{PB} \cong \overline{PC}$ if they are corresponding parts of congruent triangles. $\overline{AP} \cong \overline{AP}$ by the identity property of congruence, and $\angle QAP \cong \angle RAP$ by the definition of an angle bisector. $\angle ABP$ and $\angle ACP$ are right angles and thus they are congruent.

So $\triangle ABP \cong \triangle ACP$ by the SAA Theorem. If the triangles are congruent, then $\overline{PB} \cong \overline{PC}$ by CPCTC.

Based on this plan, I can write a flowchart proof.

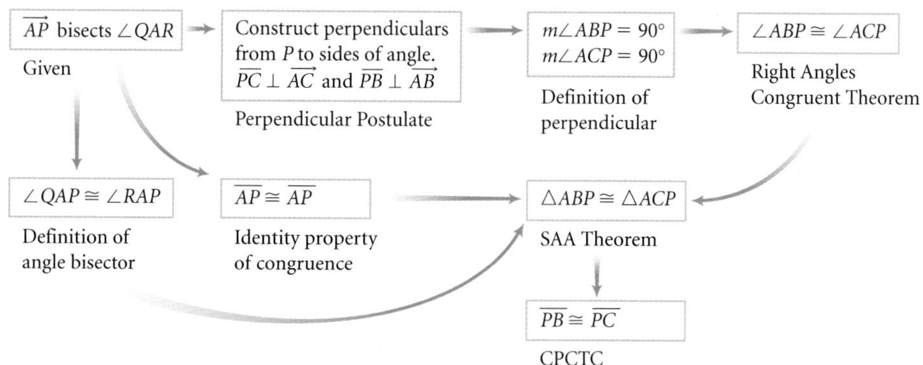

Thus the Angle Bisector Conjecture becomes the Angle Bisector Theorem.

As our own proofs build on each other, flowcharts can become too large and awkward. You can also use a two-column format for writing proofs. A **two-column proof** is identical to a flowchart or paragraph proof, except that the statements are listed in the first column, each supported by a reason (a postulate, definition, property, or theorem) in the second column.

Here is the same proof from the example above, following the same plan, presented as a two-column proof. Arrows link the steps.

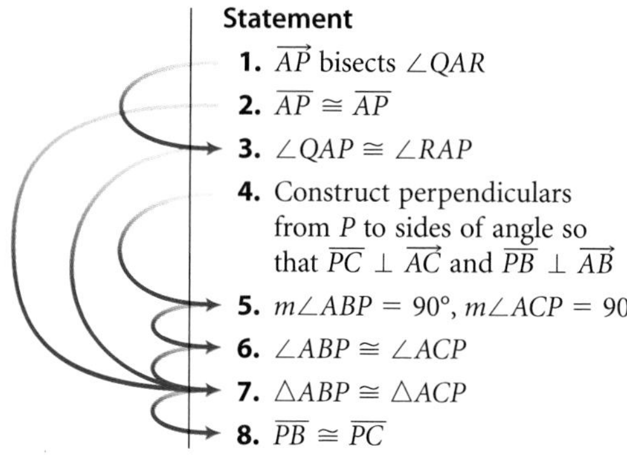

Statement	Reason
1. $\overrightarrow{AP}$ bisects $\angle QAR$	**1.** Given
2. $\overline{AP} \cong \overline{AP}$	**2.** Identity property of congruence
3. $\angle QAP \cong \angle RAP$	**3.** Definition of angle bisector
4. Construct perpendiculars from P to sides of angle so that $\overline{PC} \perp \overrightarrow{AC}$ and $\overline{PB} \perp \overrightarrow{AB}$	**4.** Perpendicular Postulate
5. $m\angle ABP = 90°$, $m\angle ACP = 90°$	**5.** Definition of perpendicular
6. $\angle ABP \cong \angle ACP$	**6.** Right Angles Congruent Theorem
7. $\triangle ABP \cong \triangle ACP$	**7.** SAA Theorem
8. $\overline{PB} \cong \overline{PC}$	**8.** CPCTC

One step Ask students to prove the Angle Bisector Conjecture. They might have to look it up. As you circulate, be sure students remind each other of how to measure the distance from a point to a line. If needed, suggest that they work backward as they plan the proof. Encourage a variety of proofs, even if they vary only in the order in which statements are presented.

SHARING IDEAS

[Ask] "What was involved in creating this proof?" Encourage students to discuss the planning process.

[Ask] "How would you prove the Angle Bisector Theorem if your definition of angle bisector were 'a reflection line for the angle'?" [The reflection that takes each side of the angle to the other also takes each perpendicular to the other, so they have the same length.] Ask which proof students think is more elegant. You need not reach consensus on this question; its purpose is to help students realize that the words *elegance* and *mathematics* can be compatible. You might also make the point that more than one proof of a theorem might be possible even given the same set of definitions and postulates and that definitions and postulates can be chosen so as to lead to more elegant proofs.

[Ask] "What are some advantages and disadvantages of each kind of proof: paragraph, flowchart, two-column?" [Paragraph proofs are compact and may seem more comfortable to people who like to write, but they require making sense of sentences; flowchart proofs show how different statements follow from each other, but they take space; two-column proofs are more compact than flowchart proofs, but sometimes the logical sequence of reasoning may be hidden because of their linear nature.]

Sharing Ideas (continued)

You might break up Sharing by giving students a chance to work in pairs on some exercises and report back to the class.

[Ask] "How do you feel at this point about writing proofs?" Many students may feel uncomfortable and awkward. Assure them that it's okay. Unlike arithmetic calculations and solving equations, there are no steps to follow that will guarantee coming up with a proof. The planning of Task 4, like solving puzzles, is an art and takes practice. Because most of what research mathematicians do is make conjectures and try to prove them, there would be no work involved if the proving part were mechanical.

Assessing Progress

You can assess how well students are following the five tasks for writing a proof and their understanding of the premises on their lists.

Closing the Lesson

The three postulates that determine triangle congruence (SSS, SAS, and ASA) are useful in proving other theorems as well. Students now have the Angle Bisector Theorem to add to their notebooks.

BUILDING UNDERSTANDING

Discuss with students what format(s) you would like them to use, or whether they have a choice of formats. Again, you might jigsaw your assignment of the proofs so that students can use theorems they did not themselves prove. Many of the theorems proved will be used in subsequent proofs (such as Exercises 1–4 and Exercises 7–9).

ASSIGNING HOMEWORK

Essential	2–12 (evens)
Performance assessment	1–13 (any)
Portfolio	1–13 (any)
Group	1–13 (odds)
Review	14–22

▶ Helping with the Exercises

Exercise 3 You may or may not choose to remind students that they saw a proof of this theorem in an exercise in Lesson 13.1. Encourage a variety of proofs. For example, students might construct a median instead of an angle bisector and use SSS to prove congruence. You might refer more ambitious students to Euclid's proof (*Elements,* Book I, Proposition 5).

Exercise 5 If students are stuck, you might suggest that they draw an auxiliary line.

See pages 778–779 for answers to Exercises 1–7.

Compare the two-column proof you just saw with the flowchart proof in Example A. What similarities do you see? What are the advantages of each format?

No matter what format you choose, your proof should be clear and easy for someone to follow.

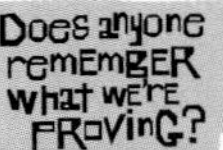

EXERCISES

You will need

Geometry software for Exercise **22**

In Exercises 1–13, write a proof of the conjecture. Once you have completed the proofs, add the theorems to your list.

1. If a point is on the perpendicular bisector of a segment, then it is equally distant from the endpoints of the segment. (Perpendicular Bisector Theorem)

2. If a point is equally distant from the endpoints of a segment, then it is on the perpendicular bisector of the segment. (Converse of the Perpendicular Bisector Theorem) ⓗ

3. If a triangle is isosceles, then the base angles are congruent. (Isosceles Triangle Theorem)

4. If two angles of a triangle are congruent, then the triangle is isosceles. (Converse of the Isosceles Triangle Theorem)

5. If a point is equally distant from the sides of an angle, then it is on the bisector of the angle. (Converse of the Angle Bisector Theorem) ⓗ

6. The three perpendicular bisectors of the sides of a triangle are concurrent. (Perpendicular Bisector Concurrency Theorem)

7. The three angle bisectors of the sides of a triangle are concurrent. (Angle Bisector Concurrency Theorem)

8. The measure of an exterior angle of a triangle is equal to the sum of the measures of the two remote interior angles. (Triangle Exterior Angle Theorem)

9. The sum of the measures of the four angles of a quadrilateral is 360°. (Quadrilateral Sum Theorem)

8.

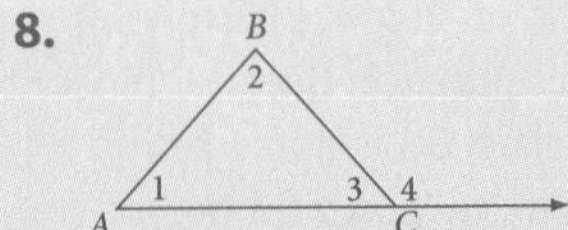

Use the Linear Pair Postulate and the definition of supplementary angles to get $m\angle 3 + m\angle 4 = 180°$. Then use the Triangle Sum Theorem and the transitive property to get $m\angle 1 + m\angle 2 + m\angle 3 = m\angle 3 + m\angle 4$. Therefore $m\angle 1 + m\angle 2 = m\angle 4$ by the subtraction property.

9.

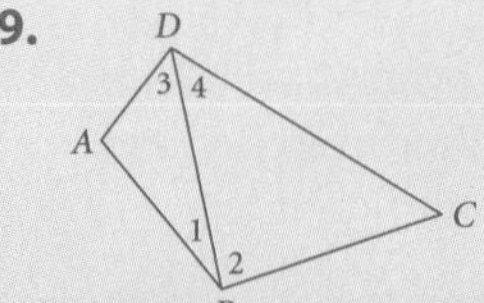

Use the Triangle Sum Theorem and the addition property to get $m\angle A + m\angle 1 + m\angle 3 + m\angle C + m\angle 4 + m\angle 2 = 360°$. Then use the Angle Addition Postulate and the substitution property to get $m\angle A + m\angle ABC + m\angle C + m\angle CDA = 360°$.

10. In an isosceles triangle, the medians to the congruent sides are congruent. (Medians to the Congruent Sides Theorem)

11. In an isosceles triangle, the angle bisectors to the congruent sides are congruent. (Angle Bisectors to the Congruent Sides Theorem)

12. In an isosceles triangle, the altitudes to the congruent sides are congruent. (Altitudes to the Congruent Sides Theorem)

13. In Lesson 4.8, you were asked to complete informal proofs of these two conjectures:

The bisector of the vertex angle of an isosceles triangle is also the median to the base.

The bisector of the vertex angle of an isosceles triangle is also the altitude to the base.

To demonstrate that the altitude to the base, the median to the base, and the bisector of the vertex angle are all the same segment in an isosceles triangle, you really need to prove three theorems. One possible sequence is diagrammed at right.

Prove the three theorems that confirm the conjecture, then add it as a theorem to your theorem list. (Isosceles Triangle Vertex Angle Theorem)

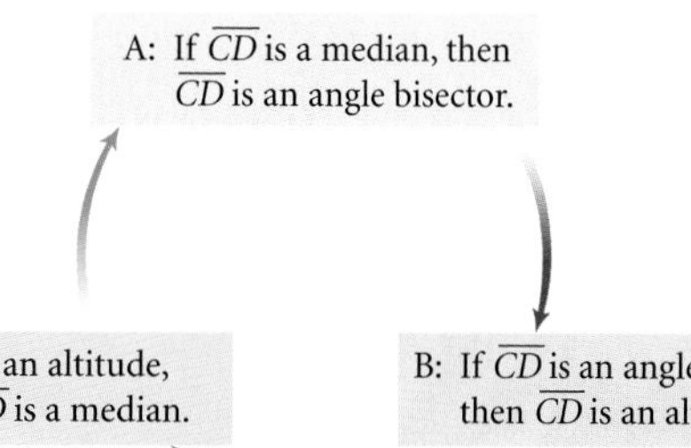
A: If $\overline{CD}$ is a median, then $\overline{CD}$ is an angle bisector.
B: If $\overline{CD}$ is an angle bisector, then $\overline{CD}$ is an altitude.
C: If $\overline{CD}$ is an altitude, then $\overline{CD}$ is a median.

Review

9.1 **14.** Find x and y. ⓗ $x = 6, y = 3$

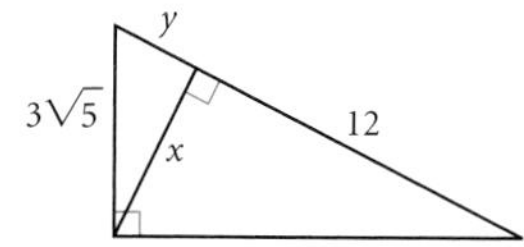
y
$3\sqrt{5}$
12
x

12.2 **15.** Two bird nests, 3.6 m and 6.1 m high, are on trees across a pond from each other, at points P and Q. The distance between the nests is too wide to measure directly (and there is a pond between the trees). A birdwatcher at point R can sight each nest along a dry path. $RP = 16.7$ m and $RQ = 27.4$ m. $\angle QPR$ is a right angle. What is the distance d between the nests? 21.9 m

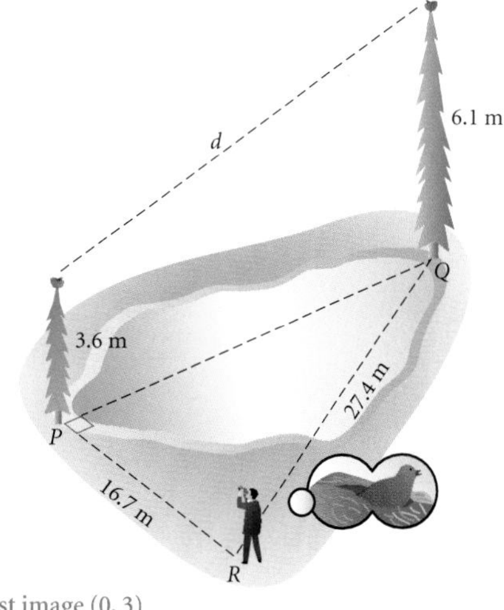
d
6.1 m
Q
3.6 m
P
27.4 m
16.7 m
R

7.3 **16.** Apply the glide reflection rule twice to find the first and second images of the point $A(-2, 9)$. ⓗ

Glide reflection rule: A reflection across the line $x + y = 5$ and a translation $(x, y) \rightarrow (x + 4, y - 4)$.

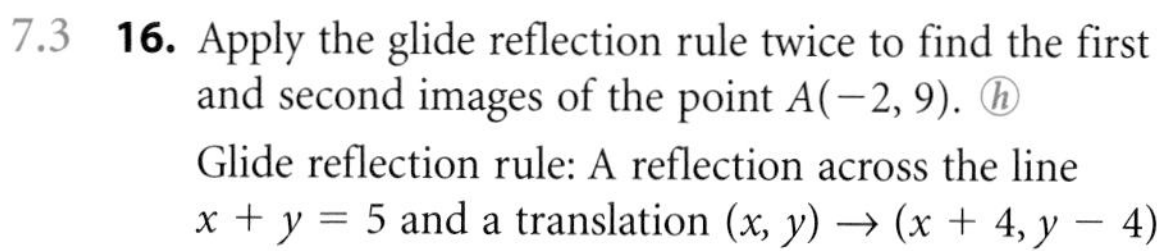

First image $(0, 3)$
Second image $(6, 1)$

13.

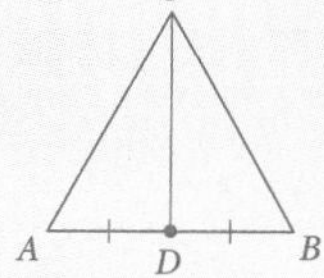
C
A
D
B

median → angle bisector
Use the definitions of median, midpoint, and isosceles triangle, the identity property, and the SSS Congruence Postulate to prove that $\triangle ADC \cong \triangle BDC$. Then use CPCTC and the definition of angle bisector.

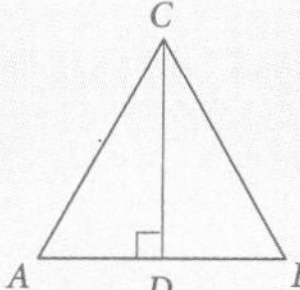
C
A
D
B

altitude → median
Use the Right Angles Are Congruent Theorem, the Isosceles Triangle Theorem, and the SAA Theorem to get $\triangle ADC \cong \triangle BDC$. Therefore $\overline{CD}$ is the median by CPCTC and the definitions of midpoint and median.

10.

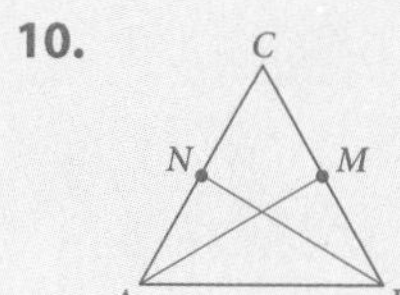
C
N
M
A
B

Use the definitions of median and midpoint to get $BM = \frac{1}{2}BC$ and $AN = \frac{1}{2}AC$. Then use the multiplication property and the substitution property to get $\overline{AN} \cong \overline{BM}$. By the identity property, the Isosceles Triangle Theorem, and the SAS Congruence Postulate, $\triangle ABN \cong \triangle BAM$. Therefore, $\overline{BN} \cong \overline{AM}$ by CPCTC.

11.

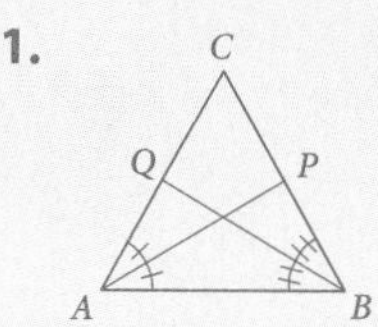
C
Q
P
A
B

Use the Angle Addition Postulate and the definition of angle bisector to get $m\angle PAB = \frac{1}{2}m\angle CAB$ and $m\angle QBA = \frac{1}{2}m\angle CBA$. Then use the Isosceles Triangle Theorem, the multiplication property, and the substitution property to get $\angle PAB \cong \angle QBA$. By the identity property and the ASA Congruence Postulate, $\triangle ABP \cong \triangle BAQ$. Therefore, $\overline{AP} \cong \overline{BQ}$ by CPCTC.

12.

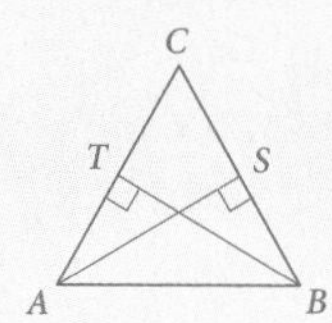
C
T
S
A
B

Use the Isosceles Triangle Theorem, the Right Angles Are Congruent Theorem, and the SAA Theorem to get $\triangle ABT \cong \triangle BAS$. Therefore $\overline{AS} \cong \overline{BT}$ by CPCTC.

Exercise 13 Students might wonder whether this is circular reasoning. It is not. The order of the theorems is represented as a circle, but each theorem can be proved independently.

See page 779 for additional answers to Exercise 13.

17. $BC = FC$ makes $ABCF$ a rhombus, so its diagonals are perpendicular. $m\angle FGC = 90°$, so $m\angle CFG + m\angle FCG = 90°$. $\overline{FD} \perp \overline{GE}$, so by substitution $m\angle 2 = m\angle FCG$. $\angle 1 \cong \angle FCG$ by AIA, so $\angle 1 \cong \angle 2$.

Exercise 18 These are three more in the sequence of puzzles that builds throughout the chapter. If students are having difficulty with the first one here, ask them what it looks like and whether they can justify the conjecture. [The radii of all the arcs are the same.] The second is just a sector. If needed, **[Ask]** "What's added to the second to get the third? How might you find that portion?" [the second minus the first]

19. One possible sequence:

1. Fold A onto B and crease. Label as ℓ_1. Label the midpoint of the arc M.

2. Fold line ℓ_1 onto itself so that M is on the crease. Label as ℓ_2.

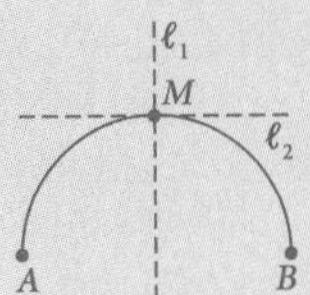

M is the midpoint of $\widehat{AB}$, and ℓ_2 is the desired tangent.

Exercise 21 **[Ask]** "How does the area of sector XOW compare in the two figures?" [They are equal.]

5.6 **17.** Explain why $\angle 1 \cong \angle 2$.

Given:

B, G, F, E are collinear

$m\angle DFE = 90°$

$BC = FC$

$\overline{AF} \parallel \overline{BC}$

$\overline{BE} \parallel \overline{CD}$

$\overline{AB} \parallel \overline{FC} \parallel \overline{ED}$

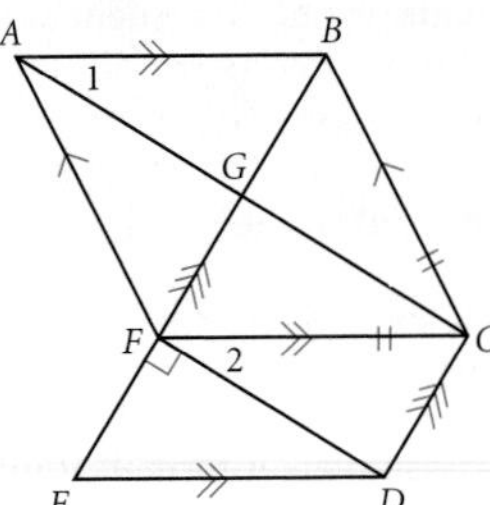

Chapter 8 **18.** Each arc is a quarter of a circle with its center at a vertex of the square.

Given: The square has side length 1 unit **Find:** The shaded area

a. Shaded area = $\underline{?}$ $\frac{\sqrt{3}}{4}$

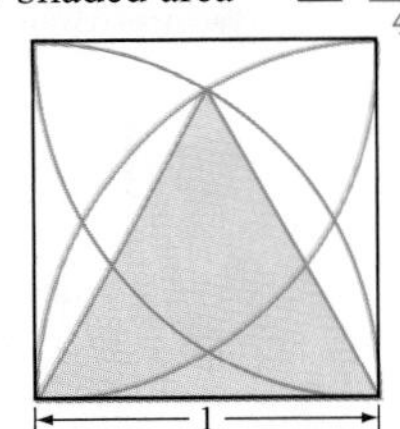

b. Shaded area = $\underline{?}$ $\frac{\pi}{6}$

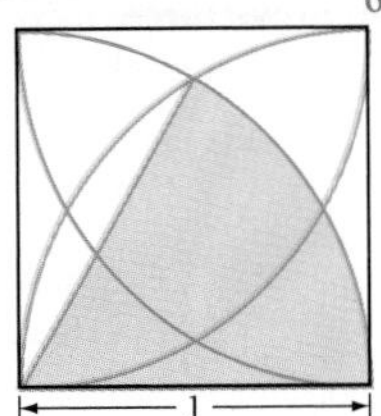

c. Shaded area = $\underline{?}$ $\frac{\pi}{3} - \frac{\sqrt{3}}{4}$

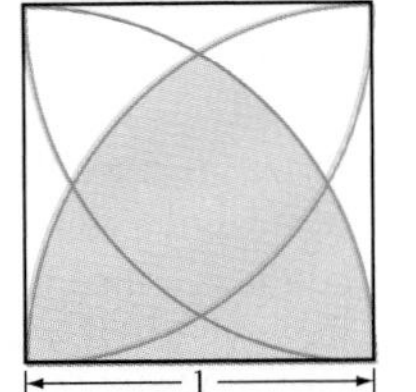

6.2 **19.** Given an arc of a circle on patty paper but not the whole circle or the center, fold the paper to construct a tangent at the midpoint of the arc.

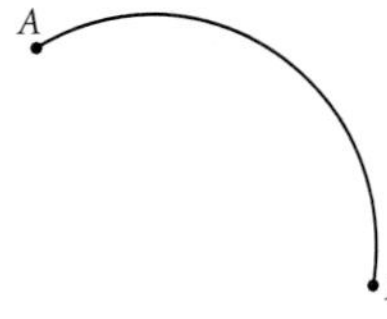

9.1 **20.** Find $m\angle BAC$ in this right rectangular prism. $m\angle BAC \approx 13°$

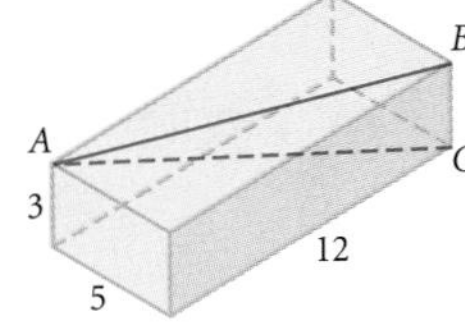

12.4 **21.** Choose **A** if the value of the expression is greater in Figure A.

Choose **B** if the value of the expression is greater in Figure B.

Choose **C** if the values are equal for both figures.

Choose **D** if it cannot be determined which value is greater.

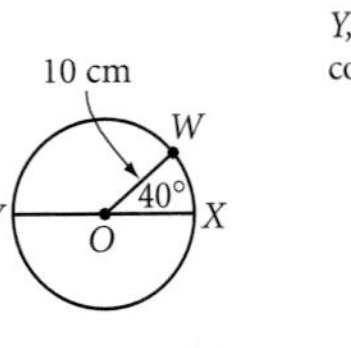

Figure A

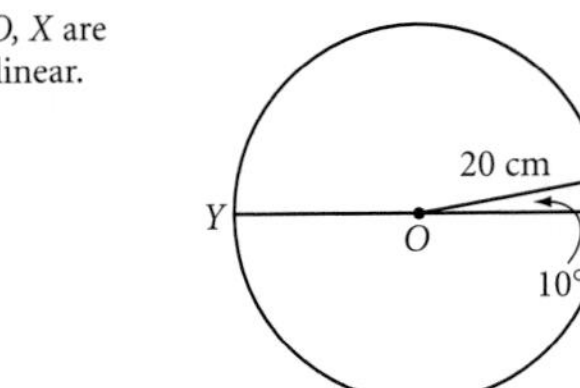

Figure B

a. Perimeter of $\triangle WXY$ B

b. Area of $\triangle XOW$ B

Chapter 6 **22.** ***Technology*** Use geometry software to construct a circle and label any three points on the circle. Construct tangents at those three points to form a circumscribed triangle and connect the points of tangency to form an inscribed triangle.

a. Drag the points and observe the angle measures of each triangle. What relationship do you notice between x, a, and c? Is the same true for y and z?

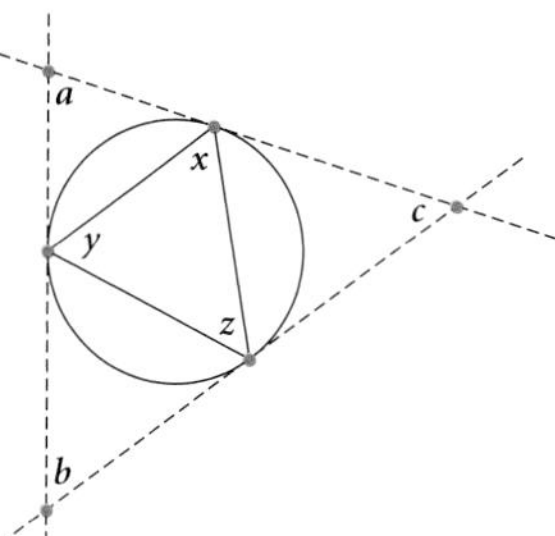

b. What is the relationship between the angle measures of a circumscribed quadrilateral and the inscribed quadrilateral formed by connecting the points of tangency?

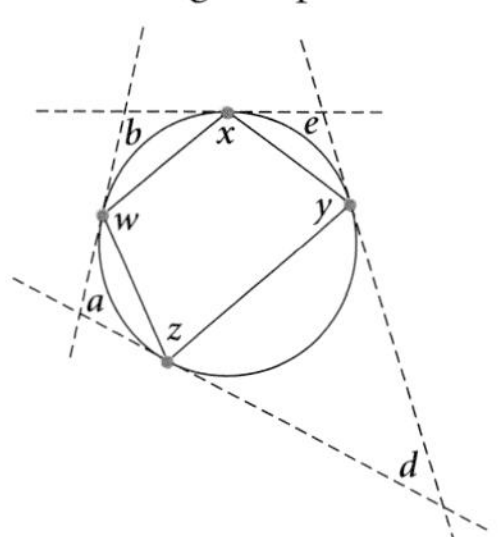

Exercise 22 Students might be curious enough to attempt to explain why this relationship occurs.

22a.

$x = \frac{1}{2}(a + c)$

$y = \frac{1}{2}(a + b)$

$z = \frac{1}{2}(b + c)$

22b.

$w = \frac{1}{2}(a + b)$

$x = \frac{1}{2}(b + c)$

$y = \frac{1}{2}(c + d)$

$z = \frac{1}{2}(d + a)$

IMPROVING YOUR VISUAL THINKING SKILLS

Picture Patterns III

Sketch the figure that goes in box 12 below.

PUZZLE

IMPROVING VISUAL THINKING SKILLS

If students are struggling, you might suggest that they concentrate on the columns within the boxes one at a time.

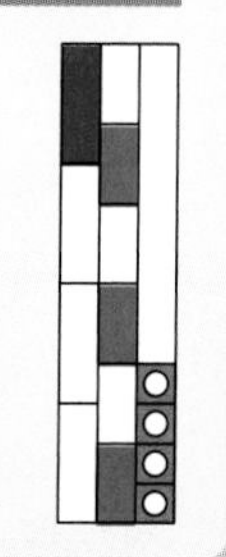

LESSON

13.4

Quadrilateral Proofs

All geometric reasoning is, in the last result, circular.

BERTRAND RUSSELL

In Chapter 5, you discovered and informally proved several quadrilateral properties. As reasons for the statements in some of these proofs, you used conjectures that are now postulates or that you have proved as theorems. So those steps in the proofs are valid. Occasionally, however, you may have used unproven conjectures as reasons. In this lesson you will write formal proofs of some of these quadrilateral conjectures, using only definitions, postulates, and theorems. After you have proved the theorems, you'll create a family tree tracing them back to postulates and properties.

You can prove many quadrilateral theorems by using triangle theorems. For example, you can prove some parallelogram properties by using the fact that a diagonal divides a parallelogram into two congruent triangles. In the example below, we'll prove this fact as a **lemma.** A lemma is an auxiliary theorem used specifically to prove other theorems.

EXAMPLE **Prove:** A diagonal of a parallelogram divides the parallelogram into two congruent triangles.

▶ **Solution**

Given: Parallelogram $ABCD$ with diagonal $\overline{AC}$

Show: $\triangle ABC \cong \triangle CDA$

Two-column Proof

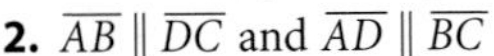

Statement	Reason
1. $ABCD$ is a parallelogram	**1.** Given
2. $\overline{AB} \parallel \overline{DC}$ and $\overline{AD} \parallel \overline{BC}$	**2.** Definition of parallelogram
3. $\angle CAB \cong \angle ACD$ and $\angle BCA \cong \angle DAC$	**3.** AIA Theorem
4. $\overline{AC} \cong \overline{AC}$	**4.** Identity property of congruence
5. $\triangle ABC \cong \triangle CDA$	**5.** ASA Congruence Postulate

We'll call the lemma proved in the example the Parallelogram Diagonal Lemma. You can now use it to prove other parallelogram conjectures in the investigation.

Investigation
Proving Parallelogram Conjectures

This investigation is really a proof activity. You will work with your group to prove three of your previous conjectures about parallelograms. Before you try to prove each conjecture, remember to draw a diagram, restate what is given and what you must show in terms of your diagram, and then make a plan.

Step 1 The Opposite Sides Conjecture states that the opposite sides of a parallelogram are congruent. Write a two-column proof of this conjecture.

LESSON OBJECTIVES

- Write proofs of parallelogram conjectures
- Practice using triangle theorems to prove quadrilateral theorems
- Learn new vocabulary
- Develop cooperative behavior

NCTM STANDARDS

	CONTENT		PROCESS
	Number	✓	Problem Solving
	Algebra	✓	Reasoning
✓	Geometry	✓	Communication
	Measurement		Connections
	Data/Probability	✓	Representation

LESSON

13.4

PLANNING

LESSON OUTLINE

One day:

5 min Example

20 min Investigation

15 min Sharing and Exercises

5 min Closing

MATERIALS

none

TEACHING

We can now prove earlier conjectures about quadrilaterals within our deductive system. Begin with the example if you are not using the one-step investigation (page 693).

▶ ***EXAMPLE***

[Language] In biology, *lemma* means "the intermediate part between the stalk and the flower." The two meanings of *lemma* can be traced back to different Greek roots, but the botanical definition makes a nice analogy.

Ask whether "a diagonal" means "either diagonal" or "one of the diagonals." In other words, does the lemma hold true no matter which diagonal is drawn?

Students might recognize that they completed a flowchart proof of this statement in an exercise in Lesson 5.7.

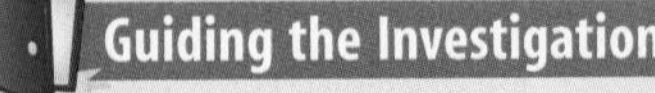

Guiding the Investigation

You can point out that the investigations in this chapter do not involve a series of steps and observations toward making

See page 779 for the answer to Step 1.

Step 2 The Opposite Angles Conjecture states that the opposite angles of a parallelogram are congruent. Write a two-column proof of this conjecture.

Step 3 State the converse of the Opposite Sides Conjecture. Then write a two-column proof of this conjecture.

After you have successfully proved the parallelogram conjectures above, you can call them theorems and add them to your theorem list.

Step 4 Create a family tree that shows the relationship among these theorems in Steps 1–3 and that traces each theorem back to the postulates of geometry.

EXERCISES

In Exercises 1–12, write a two-column proof or a flowchart proof of the conjecture. Once you have completed the proofs, add the theorems to your list.

1. If the opposite angles of a quadrilateral are congruent, then the quadrilateral is a parallelogram. (Converse of the Opposite Angles Theorem) ⓗ
2. If one pair of opposite sides of a quadrilateral are parallel and congruent, then the quadrilateral is a parallelogram. (Opposite Sides Parallel and Congruent Theorem)
3. Each diagonal of a rhombus bisects two opposite angles. (Rhombus Angles Theorem)
4. The consecutive angles of a parallelogram are supplementary. (Parallelogram Consecutive Angles Theorem)
5. If a quadrilateral has four congruent sides, then it is a rhombus. (Four Congruent Sides Rhombus Theorem)
6. If a quadrilateral has four congruent angles, then it is a rectangle. (Four Congruent Angles Rectangle Theorem)
7. The diagonals of a rectangle are congruent. (Rectangle Diagonals Theorem)
8. If the diagonals of a parallelogram are congruent, then the parallelogram is a rectangle. (Converse of the Rectangle Diagonals Theorem)
9. The base angles of an isosceles trapezoid are congruent. (Isosceles Trapezoid Theorem)
10. The diagonals of an isosceles trapezoid are congruent. (Isosceles Trapezoid Diagonals Theorem)
11. If a diagonal of a parallelogram bisects two opposite angles, then the parallelogram is a rhombus. (Converse of the Rhombus Angles Theorem)

Guiding the Investigation (continued) conjectures, but rather they offer an opportunity to work together in creating a proof.

Steps 1–3 Jigsaw these first three steps among groups so that two groups are working on proving each of the three theorems. The Parallelogram Opposite Sides Theorem is used extensively in later proofs. It is referred to as the Opposite Sides Theorem in the student book, but you might want to also use the word *Parallelogram.*

If students have a difficult time getting started with a proof, suggest that they start backward or in the middle. If they start in the middle, they will work backward to the "given" and forward to the "prove."

Step 4 All groups will benefit from doing this step.

One step Ask students what conjectures they have seen that concern parallelograms. After collecting ideas, ask students to prove the Parallelogram Opposite Sides Conjecture and its converse, as well as the Parallelogram Opposite Angles Conjecture. (You might want to jigsaw these tasks.) Be sure that among the proofs presented are several that use the fact that a diagonal of a parallelogram divides the parallelogram into two congruent triangles. During Sharing, elicit the idea that you might have saved time by first proving that a diagonal of a parallelogram divides it into congruent triangles, introduce the term *lemma,* and prove the Parallelogram Diagonal Lemma.

SHARING IDEAS

After students present their ideas, **[Ask]** "Is the Parallelogram Diagonal Lemma related to the Parallelogram Diagonals Conjecture of Lesson 5.5?" As needed, have students look up the latter. [The conjecture says that the diagonals bisect each other; the lemma says that either one divides the parallelogram into congruent triangles.]

If you have time, wonder aloud whether they can prove the earlier conjecture. [They can show that two of the four smaller triangles formed by the two diagonals are congruent by AIA, the Opposite Sides Theorem, and ASA.]

To help prepare students for the exercises, **[Ask]** "What premises in the deductive system so far allow you to prove that a quadrilateral is a parallelogram?" [definition of *parallelogram,* Converse of the Parallelogram Opposite Sides Theorem] "How can you prove that the opposite sides are parallel?" [Converse of the AIA Theorem, Converse of the AEA Theorem, or Converse of the Interior Supplements Theorem]

You might break up Sharing by giving students a chance to work on some exercises in pairs or larger groups and report back to the class. As they work, encourage creative thinking, and, if possible, choose a variety of proofs for presentation.

See pages 779–781 for answers to Steps 2–4 and Exercises 1–11.

Assessing Progress

You can continue to assess students' use of the five-task outline for writing proofs. You can also see how well students understand the ideas they first developed as conjectures and are now proving or using as reasons in proofs.

Closing the Lesson

A **lemma** is a theorem whose primary importance is helping to prove other theorems. The **Parallelogram Opposite Sides Conjecture** and its converse are now theorems, as are the **Parallelogram Opposite Angles Conjecture** and any theorems students have proved in the exercises.

BUILDING UNDERSTANDING

The exercises include proving 12 earlier conjectures about quadrilaterals; many theorems proved will be used to prove further theorems.

ASSIGNING HOMEWORK

Essential	1–14
Performance assessment	1–14 (any one)
Portfolio	1–14 (any one)
Group	1–14
Review	15–20

Helping with the Exercises

Exercise 7 This theorem is half of the Rectangle Diagonals Conjecture.

Exercise 9 As needed, ask whether an auxiliary line would be helpful.

Exercise 17 Having some rope or string available might help some students see that they need to calculate the areas of sectors centered at corners of the barn.

12. If two parallel lines are intersected by a second pair of parallel lines that are the same distance apart as the first pair, then the parallelogram formed is a rhombus. (Double-Edged Straightedge Theorem)

13. Create a family tree for the Parallelogram Consecutive Angles Theorem.

14. Create a family tree for the Double-Edged Straightedge Theorem.

Review

5.5 **15.** Find the length and the bearing of the resultant vector $\vec{V}_1 + \vec{V}_2$. $\overline{V_1 + V_2}$ has length 12.8 and bearing 72.6°.

$\vec{V}_1$ has length 5 and a bearing of 40°.
$\vec{V}_2$ has length 9 and a bearing of 90°.

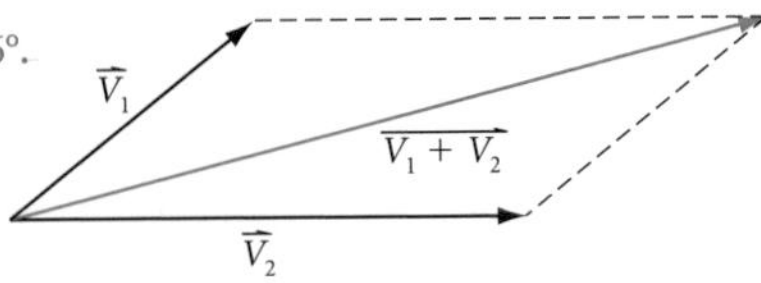

11.1 **16.** A triangle has vertices $A(7, -4)$, $B(3, -2)$, and $C(4, 1)$. Find the coordinates of the vertices after a dilation with center (8, 2) and scale factor 2. Complete the mapping rule for the above dilation: $(x, y) \rightarrow (\underline{?}, \underline{?})$. ⓗ $A'(6, -10), B'(-2, -6), C'(0, 0)$, mapping rule: $(x, y) \rightarrow (2x - 8, 2y - 2)$

8.6 **17.** Yan uses a 40 ft rope to tie his horse to the corner of the barn to which a fence is attached. How many square feet of grazing, to the nearest square foot, does the horse have? 2386 ft²

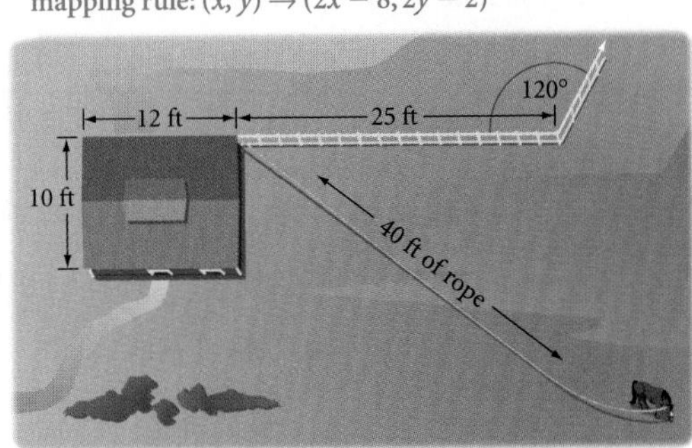

7.1 **18.** Complete the following chart with the symmetries and names of each type of special quadrilateral: parallelogram, rhombus, rectangle, square, kite, trapezoid, and isosceles trapezoid.

Name	Lines of symmetry	Rotational symmetry
parallelogram	none	2-fold
trapezoid	none	none
kite	1 diagonal	none
square	2 diagonals 2 ⊥ bisectors of sides	4-fold
rectangle	2 ⊥ bisectors of sides	2-fold
rhombus	2 diagonals	2-fold
isosceles trapezoid	1 ⊥ bisector of sides	none

13.

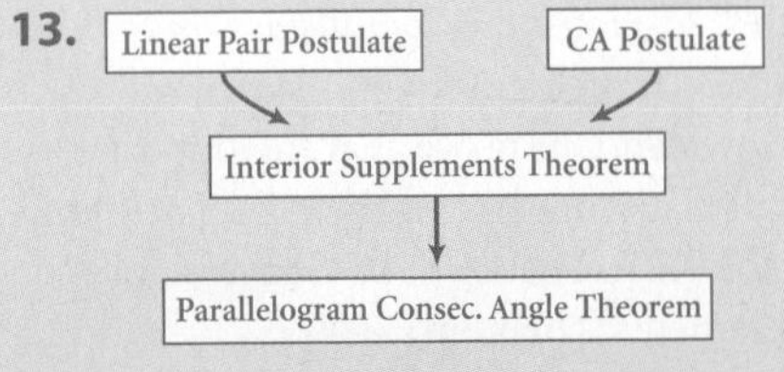

14.

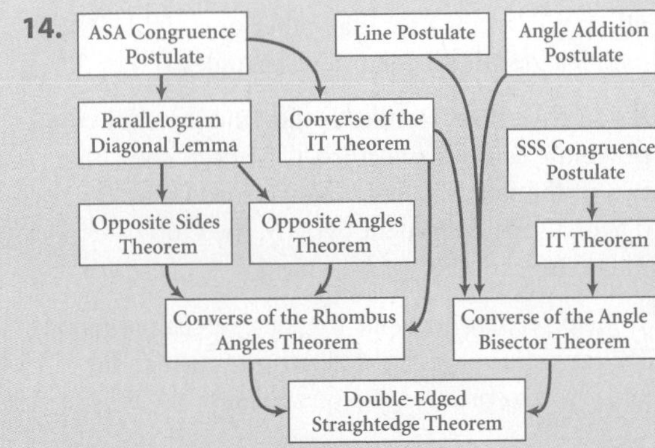

Chapter 12 **19.** Consider the rectangular prisms in Figure A and Figure B.
Choose **A** if the value of the expression is greater in Figure A.
Choose **B** if the value of the expression is greater in Figure B.
Choose **C** if the values are equal in both rectangular prisms.
Choose **D** if it cannot be determined which value is greater.

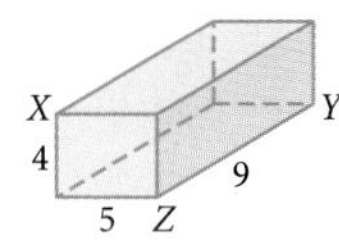

Figure A

X
6
Y
6
5 Z

Figure B

a. Measure of $\angle XYZ$ B

b. Shortest path from X to Y along the surface of the prism B

Chapter 6 **20. Given:**

A, O, D are collinear

$\overleftrightarrow{GF}$ is tangent to circle O at point D

$m\angle EOD = 38°$

$\overline{OB} \parallel \overline{EC} \parallel \overline{GF}$

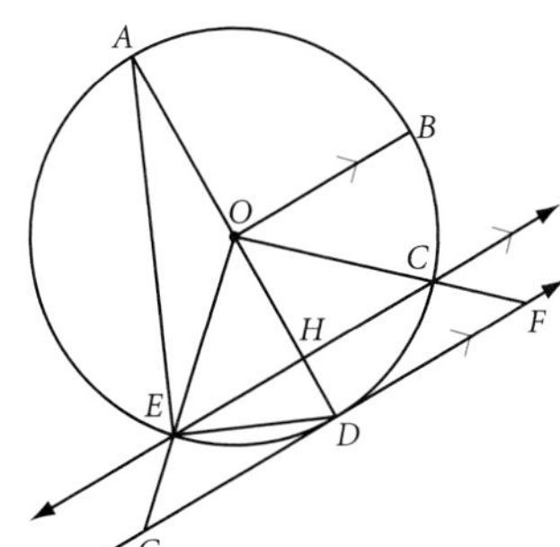

Find:

a. $m\angle AEO$ 19°

b. $m\angle DGO$ 52°

c. $m\angle BOC$ 52°

d. $m\overset{\frown}{EAB}$ 232°

e. $m\angle HED$ 19°

IMPROVING YOUR VISUAL THINKING SKILLS

Mental Blocks

In the top figure at right, every cube is lettered exactly alike. Copy and complete the two-dimensional representation of one of the cubes to show how the letters are arranged on the six faces.

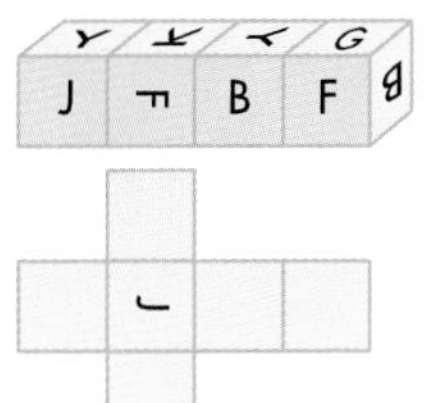

12.

X P Y W Z Q

Use the Converse of the Angle Bisector Theorem to prove that $\overline{WY}$ is the angle bisector of $\angle Y$. In like manner, $\overline{WY}$ is the angle bisector of $\angle Y$ and of $\angle W$ and $\overline{XZ}$ is the angle bisector of $\angle X$ and $\angle Z$. Therefore, $WXYZ$ is a rhombus by the Converse of the Rhombus Angles Theorem.

EXTENSION

Ask students what they think of the quote by Bertrand Russell that opens the lesson.

IMPROVING VISUAL THINKING SKILLS

Many students will benefit from actually making at least one block and net.

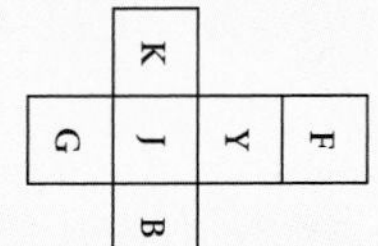

EXPLORATION

PLANNING

LESSON OUTLINE

One day:
30 min Activity
10 min Sharing
5 min Closing

MATERIALS

- The Geometer's Sketchpad

TEACHING

Students use geometry software to make conjectures that they then try to prove.

Guiding the Activity

Step 4 To help students get started with the proof of the conjecture in Step 1, **[Ask]** "Can you prove something about other angles to prove that these are right angles? Are they part of triangles? Is there something about the sum of the nonright angles of a right triangle that you might show?" Good questions to help students prove the conjecture in Step 2 include: "Are these segments related to segments you can prove something about? How might you prove that segments are congruent?" For the conjecture in Step 3, you might **[Ask]** "Do the diagonals of a rhombus have special properties?"

Step 4 Plan for proving Step 1: Consecutive angles in a parallelogram are supplementary, so the bisected halves are complementary. Therefore, when the bisecting rays intersect to complete a triangle, the third angle must measure 90°, by the Triangle Sum Theorem.

Proof as Challenge and Discovery

So far, you have proved many theorems that are useful in geometry. You can also use proof to explore and possibly discover interesting properties. You might make a conjecture, and then use proof to decide whether or not it is always true.

These activities have been adapted from the book *Rethinking Proof with The Geometer's Sketchpad,* 1999, by Michael deVilliers.

Activity

Exploring Properties of Special Constructions

Use Sketchpad to construct these figures. Drag them and notice their properties. Then prove your conjectures.

Parallelogram Angle Bisectors

Construct a parallelogram and its angle bisectors. Label your sketch as shown.

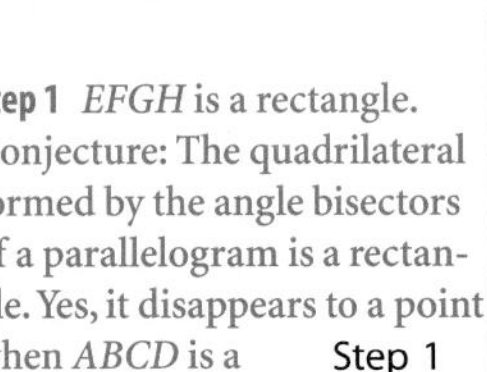
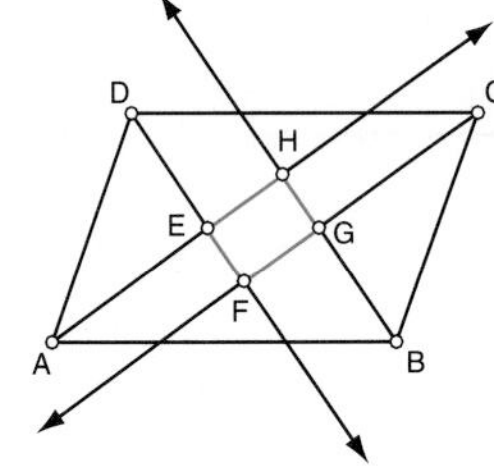

Step 1 *EFGH* is a rectangle. Conjecture: The quadrilateral formed by the angle bisectors of a parallelogram is a rectangle. Yes, it disappears to a point when *ABCD* is a square or rhombus.

Step 2 *EFGH* becomes a square.

Step 3 *EFGH* disappears to a point.

Step 1 Is *EFGH* a special quadrilateral? Make a conjecture. Drag the vertices around. Are there cases when *EFGH* does not satisfy your conjecture?

Step 2 Drag so that *ABCD* is a rectangle. What happens?

Step 3 Drag so that *ABCD* is a rhombus. What happens?

Step 4 Prove your conjectures for Steps 1–3.

Step 5 Construct the angle bisectors of another polygon. Investigate and write your observations. Make a conjecture and prove it.

LESSON OBJECTIVES

- Understand the link between observing a property and proving it
- Enhance understanding of parallelograms

NCTM STANDARDS

	CONTENT		PROCESS
	Number		Problem Solving
	Algebra	✓	Reasoning
✓	Geometry	✓	Communication
	Measurement		Connections
	Data/Probability		Representation

Parallelogram Squares

Construct parallelogram $ABCD$ and a square on each side. Construct the center of each square, and label your sketch as shown.

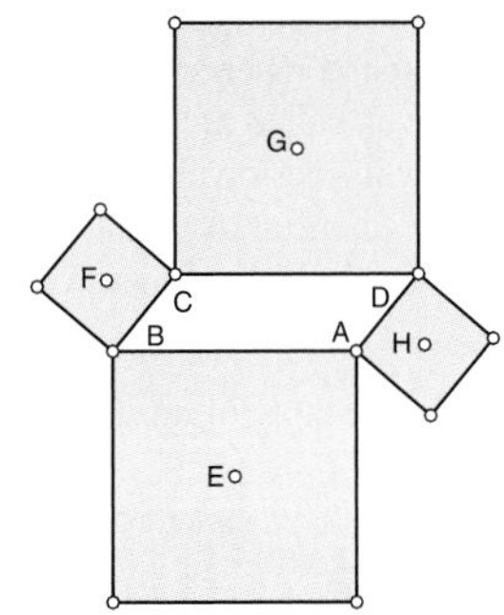

Step 6 $EFGH$ is a square. Conjecture: The quadrilateral with vertices at the centers of squares built on the sides of a parallelogram is a square. No.

Step 7 $EFGH$ remains a square.

Step 6 Connect E, F, G, and H with line segments. (Try using a different color.) Drag the vertices of $ABCD$. What do you observe? Make a conjecture. Drag your sketch around. Are there cases when $EFGH$ does not satisfy your conjecture?

Step 7 Drag so that A, B, C, and D are collinear. What happens to $EFGH$?

Step 8 Prove your conjectures for Steps 6 and 7.

Step 9 Investigate other special quadrilaterals and the shapes formed by connecting the centers of the squares on their sides. Write your observations. Make a conjecture and prove it.

IMPROVING YOUR ALGEBRA SKILLS

A Precarious Proof

You have all the money you need.

Let h = the money you have.
Let n = the money you need.

Most people think that the money they have is some amount less than the money they need. Stated mathematically, $h = n - p$ for some positive p.

If $h = n - p$, then

$h(h - n) = (n - p)(h - n)$

$h^2 - hn = hn - n^2 - hp + np$

$h^2 - hn + hp = hn - n^2 + np$

$h(h - n + p) = n(h - n + p)$

Therefore $h = n$.

So the money you have is equal to the money you need!

Is there a flaw in this proof?

Step 4 Plan for proving Step 2: When $ABCD$ is a rectangle, the proof of Step 1 is still valid; additionally, each bisected half measures 45°, making the four triangles formed isosceles. The side lengths of the quadrilateral can be shown to be equal, by subtracting the lengths of the legs of the isosceles triangles.

Plan for proving Step 3: In a rhombus, the angle bisectors are the diagonals. The diagonals intersect in a point. Therefore, there is no quadrilateral.

Step 8 As needed, **[Ask]** "What are good ways to prove that two sides of the figure are congruent?" [Use congruent triangles; $\triangle HAE$ and $\triangle HDG$ are congruent by SAS.] "Do you know enough to prove that angle GHE is a right angle?" [yes, from the same congruent triangles and, in effect, the overlapping angle property]

SHARING IDEAS

As students share their ideas, ask what they tried that didn't work. Point out that the work of professional mathematicians calls for making and testing conjectures and that the interplay between intuition (making conjectures) and proof can lead to emotional highs and lows.

Assessing Progress

You can assess how well students are using the five-task scheme for writing a proof and how willing they are to experiment using Sketchpad.

Closing the Lesson

The process of doing mathematics calls for making conjectures based on inductive reasoning and trying to prove them deductively. Often a failed attempt to prove something gives insight into how the conjecture can be modified to become provable.

IMPROVING ALGEBRA SKILLS

There is a flaw in the proof. If $h = n - p$, then $h - n + p = 0$. The step from $h(h - n + p) = n(h - n + p)$ to $h = n$ is not valid because when you divide both sides by $h - n + p$ you are dividing by zero. **[Ask]** "Why is it not legal to divide by zero?" [$\frac{0}{0}$ could be anything, say the nonzero number b, because $0 = (0)(b)$. An indirect proof can show that dividing by zero leads to a contradiction: If $a \neq 0$ and $\frac{a}{0} = b$, then $a = (b)(0) = 0$, a contradiction.]

See page 781 for answers to Step 8.

LESSON

13.5

PLANNING

LESSON OUTLINE

One day:

5 min	Examples
20 min	Investigation
15 min	Sharing and Exercises
5 min	Closing

MATERIALS

none

TEACHING

An indirect proof is often easier to develop than a direct proof. Students who did the Exploration Three Types of Proofs in Chapter 12 will have some familiarity with indirect proofs. In general, direct proofs are preferred over indirect proofs, because they're clearer. Often, though, the most successful first thinking can come through trying to construct an indirect proof. Begin with the examples or use the one-step investigation (page 699).

▶ ***EXAMPLE A***

This indirect proof starts by assuming the truth of the opposite of what we want to prove ($NT = OT$) and finding that this leads to a contradiction of our assumption that the angles are not equal; therefore $NT \neq OT$. It is equivalent to proving "If $NT = OT$, then $m\angle N = m\angle O$." If students did the Exploration Three Types of Proofs, they might recognize this statement as the contrapositive of the conjecture. A contrapositive is logically equivalent to the original statement.

LESSON 13.5

Indirect Proof

How often have I said to you that when you have eliminated the impossible, whatever remains, however improbable, must be the truth?

SHERLOCK HOLMES IN *THE SIGN OF THE FOUR* BY SIR ARTHUR CONAN DOYLE

In the proofs you have written so far, you have shown *directly,* through a sequence of statements and reasons, that a given conjecture is true. In this lesson you will write a different type of proof, called an indirect proof. In an **indirect proof,** you show something is true by eliminating all the other possibilities. You have probably used this type of reasoning when taking multiple-choice tests. If you are unsure of an answer, you can try to eliminate choices until you are left with only one possibility.

This mystery story gives an example of an indirect proof.

Detective Sheerluck Holmes and three other people are alone on a tropical island. One morning, Sheerluck entertains the others by playing show tunes on his ukulele. Later that day, he discovers that his precious ukulele has been smashed to bits. Who could have committed such an antimusical act? Sheerluck eliminates himself as a suspect because he knows he didn't do it. He eliminates his girlfriend as a suspect because she has been with him all day. Colonel Moran recently injured both arms and therefore could not have smashed the ukulele with such force. There is only one other person on the island who could have committed the crime. So Sheerluck concludes that the fourth person, Sir Charles Mortimer, is the guilty one.

For a given mathematical statement, there are two possibilities: either the statement is true or it is not true. To prove indirectly that a statement is true, you start by assuming it is not true. You then use logical reasoning to show that this assumption leads to a contradiction. If an assumption leads to a contradiction, it must be false. Therefore, you can eliminate the possibility that the statement is not true. This leaves only one possibility—namely, that the statement is true!

EXAMPLE A

Conjecture: If $m\angle N \neq m\angle O$ in $\triangle NOT$, then $NT \neq OT$.

Given: $\triangle NOT$ with $m\angle N \neq m\angle O$

Show: $NT \neq OT$

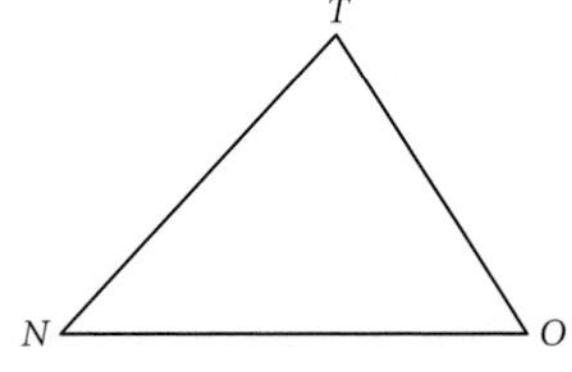

LESSON OBJECTIVES

- Learn how to write indirect proofs in paragraph form
- Develop visual thinking and deductive reasoning

NCTM STANDARDS

	CONTENT		PROCESS
	Number		Problem Solving
	Algebra	✓	Reasoning
✓	Geometry	✓	Communication
	Measurement		Connections
	Data/Probability		Representation

▸ Solution

To prove indirectly that the statement $NT \neq OT$ is true, start by assuming that it is *not* true. That is, assume $NT = OT$. Then show that this assumption leads to a contradiction.

Paragraph Proof

Assume $NT = OT$. If $NT = OT$, then $m\angle N = m\angle O$ by the Isosceles Triangle Theorem. But this contradicts the given fact that $m\angle N \neq m\angle O$. Therefore, the assumption $NT = OT$ is false and so $NT \neq OT$ is true. ■

Here is another example of an indirect proof.

EXAMPLE B

Conjecture: The diagonals of a trapezoid do not bisect each other.

Given: Trapezoid *ZOID* with parallel bases $\overline{ZO}$ and $\overline{ID}$ and diagonals $\overline{DO}$ and $\overline{IZ}$ intersecting at point *Y*

Show: The diagonals of trapezoid *ZOID* do not bisect each other; that is, $DY \neq OY$ and $ZY \neq IY$

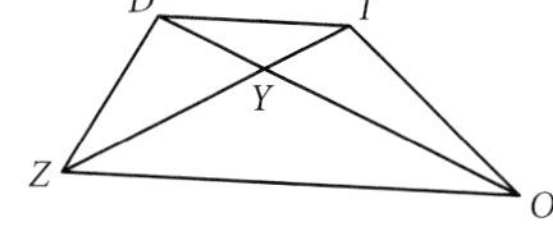

▸ Solution

Paragraph Proof

Assume that at least one of the diagonals of trapezoid *ZOID* *does* bisect the other. Then $\overline{DY} \cong \overline{OY}$. Also, by the AIA Theorem, $\angle DIY \cong \angle OZY$, and $\angle IDY \cong \angle YOZ$. Therefore, $\triangle DYI \cong \triangle OYZ$ by the SAA Theorem. By CPCTC, $\overline{ZO} \cong \overline{ID}$. It is given that $\overline{ZO} \parallel \overline{ID}$. In Lesson 13.4, you proved that if one pair of opposite sides of a quadrilateral are parallel and congruent, then the quadrilateral is a parallelogram. So, *ZOID* is a parallelogram. Thus, *ZOID* has two pairs of opposite sides parallel. But because it is a trapezoid, it has exactly one pair of parallel sides. This is contradictory. So the assumption that its diagonals bisect each other is false and the conjecture is true. ■

In the investigation you'll write an indirect proof of the Tangent Conjecture from Chapter 6.

Investigation
Proving the Tangent Conjecture

This investigation is really a group proof activity. Copy the information and diagram below, then work with your group to complete an indirect proof of the Tangent Conjecture.

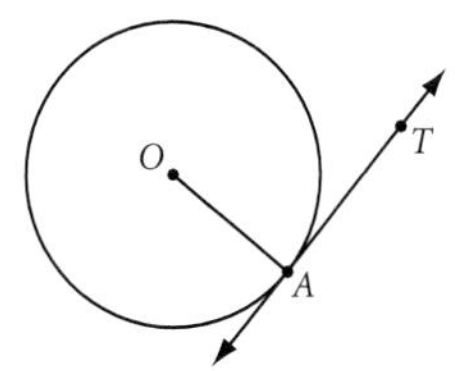

Conjecture: A tangent is perpendicular to the radius drawn to the point of tangency.

Given: Circle *O* with tangent $\overleftrightarrow{AT}$ and radius $\overline{AO}$

Show: $\overline{AO} \perp \overleftrightarrow{AT}$

One step Ask students to prove the Tangent Conjecture. They could prove the logically equivalent statement "If a line through the endpoint of a circle's radius is *not* perpendicular to that radius, then the line is *not* a tangent line." As needed, ask students how they can produce the other point at which the line intersects the circle. They can draw a perpendicular from center *O* to the line at point *Q* and then construct a segment on the other side of that intersection point to get to point *R*. They might have difficulty not assuming that *R* is a point of intersection, but that must be proved, probably by showing that $\triangle OQP \cong \triangle OQR$. During Sharing, refer students to the examples and the investigation to see if they can articulate what an indirect proof method is.

▸ EXAMPLE B

This indirect proof uses the logical relationship between an implication and its contrapositive. We start by assuming the negation of a statement (one of the diagonals *does* bisect the other) and show that this makes the quadrilateral a parallelogram. The contrapositive to be proved is "If at least one of the diagonals of a quadrilateral bisects the other, then the quadrilateral is not a trapezoid."

If students are having difficulty remembering the quadrilateral properties they have proved, they might be ready for a reminder to keep their list of theorems up-to-date.

SHARING IDEAS

Suggest that students write out one of the proofs from the examples or the investigation as a two-column proof. They might not be sure what to put as reasons for the statements at the end. Refer them to Exercise 5, where a paragraph at the end notes the contradiction. Alternatively, you might want them to include "This leads to a contradiction" as a statement, accompanied by a reason such as "contradicts the assumption that . . ." or just the premise that's the negation of the previous step. Some teachers like to have students write one last step that restates the theorem. In this case, the corresponding reason can be "Any assumption that leads to a contradiction is false" or "contrapositive."

Some students might doubt that indirect proofs are logically valid. They'll be in the company of quite a few mathematicians and logicians who don't like to assume that every statement is either true or false.

Guiding the Investigation

Many students will find that constructing this indirect proof is not easy. Groups might need to take some time to see that the negation of what they're to prove is that a line through an endpoint of the circle's radius is not perpendicular to the radius.

Step 4 $\angle ABO$ and $\angle CBO$ are right angles because of the definition of perpendicular. $\angle ABO \cong \angle CBO$ because of the Right Angles Congruent Theorem.

Step 9 If $\overline{AO} \cong \overline{CO}$, then $\overline{CO}$ must be a radius of circle *O*. Therefore, $\overleftrightarrow{AT}$ intersects the circle in *two* points (*A* and *C*) and thus $\overleftrightarrow{AT}$ is not a tangent.

Step 10 So the assumption that $\overline{AO}$ is not perpendicular to $\overleftrightarrow{AT}$ is false, and $\overline{AO} \perp \overleftrightarrow{AT}$. Proof will include the steps of the investigation.

Assessing Progress
You can assess how well students find negations of mathematical statements and how well they understand the mathematical ideas that arise in these proofs.

Closing the Lesson

We've used indirect proof to prove the Tangent Theorem. Students can add it to the theorem lists in their notebooks, along with any theorems proved in the exercises.

BUILDING UNDERSTANDING

The exercises provide practice in developing indirect proofs.

ASSIGNING HOMEWORK

Essential	1–5
Performance assessment	6–8
Portfolio	6–8
Journal	3, 4
Group	6–9
Review	10–13

Helping with the Exercises

Exercise 1 [Alert] For students who are uncertain, read the alternatives aloud. They might not realize that Tucson, Arizona, is the U.S. city.

Paragraph Proof

Step 1 Assume $\overline{AO}$ is *not* perpendicular to $\overleftrightarrow{AT}$. Construct a perpendicular from point *O* to $\overleftrightarrow{AT}$ and label the intersection point *B* ($\overline{OB} \perp \overleftrightarrow{AT}$). Which postulate allows you to do this? Perpendicular Postulate

Step 2 Select a point *C* on $\overleftrightarrow{AT}$ so that *B* is the midpoint of $\overline{AC}$. Which postulate allows you to do this?

Step 2 Midpoint Postulate

Step 3 Next, construct $\overline{OC}$. Which postulate allows you to do this? Line Postulate

Step 4 $\angle ABO \cong \angle CBO$. Why?

Step 5 $\overline{AB} \cong \overline{BC}$. What definition tells you this?

Step 6 $\overline{OB} \cong \overline{OB}$. What property of congruence tells you this?

Step 5 Two definitions: Definition of midpoint and definition of congruence.

Step 6 reflexive property of congruence

Step 7 Therefore, $\triangle ABO \cong \triangle CBO$. Which congruence shortcut tells you the triangles are congruent? SAS Congruence Postulate

Step 8 If $\triangle ABO \cong \triangle CBO$, then $\overline{AO} \cong \overline{CO}$. Why? CPCTC

Step 9 *C* must be a point on the circle (because a circle is the set of *all* points in the plane at a given distance from the center and points *A* and *C* are both the same distance from the center). Therefore, $\overleftrightarrow{AT}$ intersects the circle in *two* points (*A* and *C*) and thus $\overleftrightarrow{AT}$ is not a tangent. But this leads to a contradiction. Why?

Step 10 Discuss the steps with your group. What was the contradiction? What does it prove? Use the steps above to write a two-column indirect proof of the Tangent Conjecture.

Rename the Tangent Conjecture as the Tangent Theorem and add it to your list of theorems.

EXERCISES

For Exercises 1 and 2, the correct answer is one of the choices listed. Determine the correct answer by indirect reasoning, explaining how you eliminated each incorrect choice.

1. Which is the capital of Mali? D: Paris is in France; Tucson is in the U.S.; London is in England. Bamako must be the capital of Mali.

A. Paris **B.** Tucson **C.** London **D.** Bamako

2. Which Italian scientist used a new invention called the telescope to discover the moons of Jupiter?

A. Sir Edmund Halley **B.** Julius Caesar **C.** Galileo Galilei **D.** Madonna

Exercise 2 If students are having trouble, ask what "Sir" in the first choice means [that Halley was English] and whether they can rule out any of the other choices because of their occupations.

2. C: The "Sir" in part A shows that Halley is English; Julius Caesar was an emperor, not a scientist; Madonna is a singer. Galileo Galilei must be the answer.

3. Is the proof in Example A claiming that if two angles of a triangle are not congruent, then the triangle is not isosceles? Explain.

4. Is the proof in Example B claiming that if one diagonal of a quadrilateral bisects the other, then the quadrilateral is not a trapezoid? Explain.

5. Fill in the blanks in the indirect proof below.

Conjecture: No triangle has two right angles.

Given: $\angle ABC$

Show: No two angles are right angles

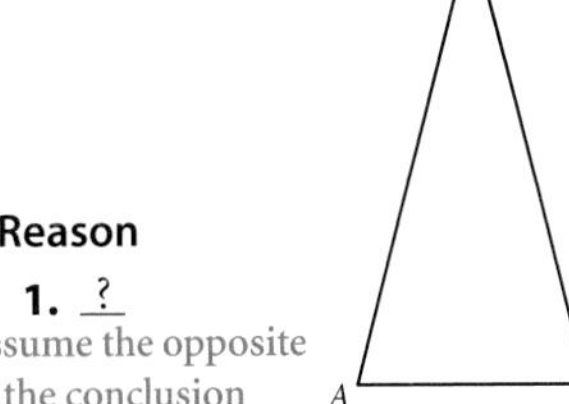

Two-column proof

Statement	Reason
1. Assume $\angle ABC$ has two right angles (Assume $m\angle A = 90°$ and $m\angle B = 90°$ and $0° < m\angle C < 180°$.)	1. ? Assume the opposite of the conclusion
2. $m\angle A + m\angle B + m\angle C = 180°$	2. ? Triangle Sum Theorem
3. $90° + 90° + m\angle C = 180°$	3. ? Substitution property of equality
4. $m\angle C =$? 0	4. ? Subtraction property of equality

But if $m\angle C = 0$, then the two sides $\overline{AC}$ and $\overline{BC}$ coincide, and thus there is no angle at C. This contradicts the given information. So the assumption is false. Therefore, no triangle has two right angles.

6. Write an indirect proof of the conjecture below.

Conjecture: No trapezoid is equiangular.

Given: Trapezoid $ZOID$ with bases $\overline{ZO}$ and $\overline{ID}$

Show: $ZOID$ is not equiangular

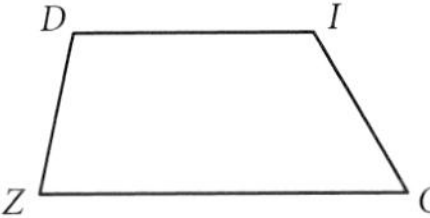

7. Write an indirect proof of the conjecture below.

Conjecture: In a scalene triangle, the median cannot be the altitude.

Given: Scalene triangle ABC with median $\overline{CD}$

Show: $\overline{CD}$ is not the altitude to $\overline{AB}$

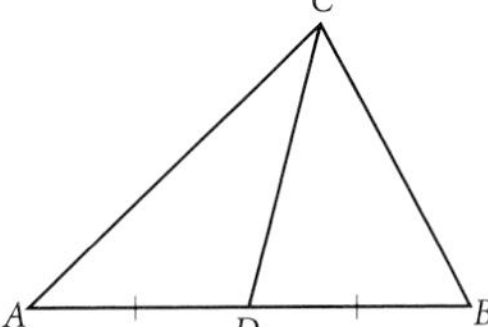

8. Write an indirect proof of the conjecture below.

Conjecture: The bases of a trapezoid have unequal lengths.

Given: Trapezoid $ZOID$ with parallel bases and $\overline{ZO}$ and $\overline{ID}$

Show: $ZO \neq ID$

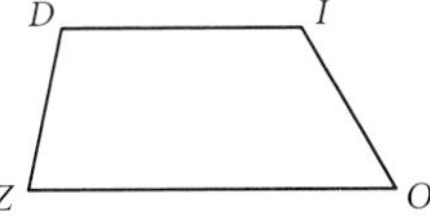

9. Write the "given" and the "show," and then plan and write the proof of the Perpendicular Bisector of a Chord Conjecture: The perpendicular bisector of a chord passes through the center of the circle.

Exercise 3 A few students might not yet have come to realize that the measure of the vertex angle of an isosceles triangle will be different from the base angle measures unless the triangle is also equilateral.

3. No, the proof is claiming only that if two particular angles are not congruent, then the two particular sides opposite them are not congruent. It still might be the case that a different pair of angles are congruent and that therefore a different pair of sides are congruent.

4. Yes, this statement is the contrapositive of Example B and they are logically equivalent.

6. Assume $ZOID$ is equiangular. Use the definition of equiangular and the Four Congruent Angles Rectangle Theorem to prove that $ZOID$ is a rectangle. Therefore $ZOID$ is a parallelogram, which creates a contradiction.

7. Assume $\overline{CD}$ is the altitude to $\overline{AB}$. Use the definitions of median and midpoint, the Right Angles Are Congruent Theorem, and the SAS Congruence Postulate to get $\triangle ADC \cong \triangle BDC$. Therefore $\overline{AC} \cong \overline{BC}$, which creates a contradiction.

8. Assume $ZO = ID$. Use the Opposite Sides Parallel and Congruent Theorem to prove that $ZOID$ is a parallelogram, which creates a contradiction.

Exercise 9 Students might need a suggestion to help them get started. You might **[Ask]** "What three points do you need to include in your drawing?" [the circle's center and the chord's endpoints] "What do three points suggest?" [a triangle] "What kind of triangle do you get?" [isosceles triangle] Ask whether they can do anything now. They might draw an altitude or a median to get two congruent triangles. Students can write a direct proof or an indirect proof.

9. Given: Circle O with chord $\overline{AB}$ and perpendicular bisector $\overleftrightarrow{CD}$

Show: $\overleftrightarrow{CD}$ passes through O

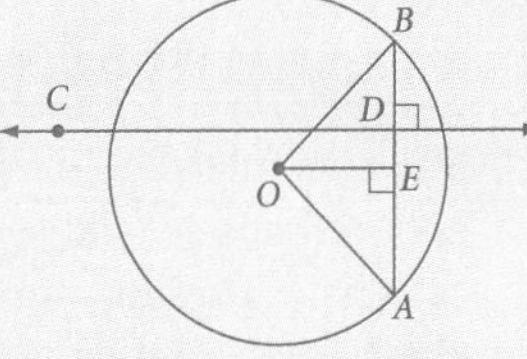

Assume $\overleftrightarrow{CD}$ does not pass through O. Use the Line Postulate to construct $\overline{OB}$ and $\overline{OA}$ and the Perpendicular Postulate to construct $\overline{OE}$. Then use the Isosceles Triangle Theorem, the Right Angles Are Congruent Theorem, and the SAA Theorem to get $\triangle OEA \cong \triangle OEB$. From CPCTC and the definition of midpoint, prove that E is the midpoint of $\overline{AB}$, which creates a contradiction.

Exercise 12 As needed, remind students to look back at results from earlier puzzles of this type. The shaded figure in part a is the shaded portion of Exercise 31a in Lesson 13.1 minus the shaded part of Exercise 18c in Lesson 13.3. Part b can follow from part a.

Exercise 13b Some students might not recall that a major arc is larger than a semicircle; others might forget the difference between *inscribed in* and *intercepts.* An angle that intercepts a major arc is obtuse.

EXTENSIONS

A. Have students prove that the largest angle of a triangle must have a measure of at least 60°. [Students might find that the most natural indirect proof leads to the negation of the Triangle Sum Theorem.]

B. Have students use the theorem from Extension A to prove that the largest side in a triangle must be opposite an angle with a measure greater than or equal to 60°.

Review

2.6 **10.** Find a, b, and c. $a = 75°, b = 47°, c = 58°$

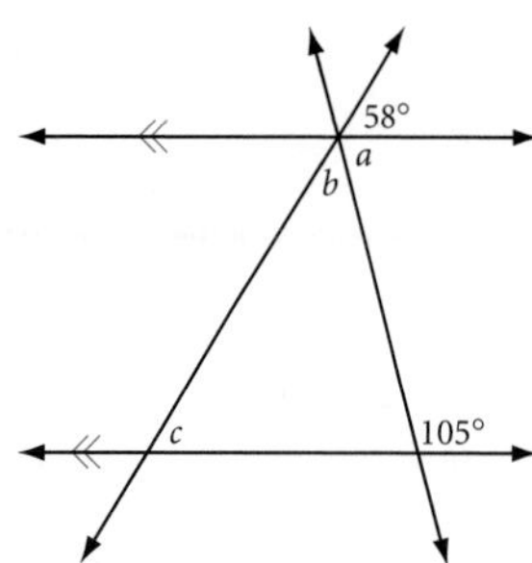

10.3 **11.** A clear plastic container is in the shape of a right cone atop a right cylinder, and their bases coincide. Find the volume of the container. 42π ft³

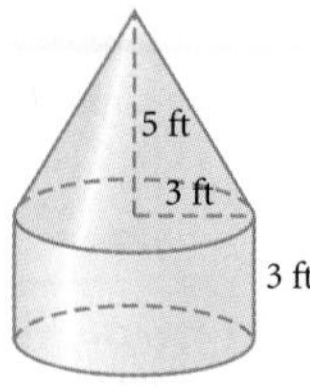

Chapter 8 **12.** Each arc is a quarter of a circle with its center at a vertex of the square.

Given: The square has side length 1 unit **Find:** The shaded area

a. Shaded area = _?_ $\frac{\sqrt{3}}{4} - \frac{\pi}{12}$

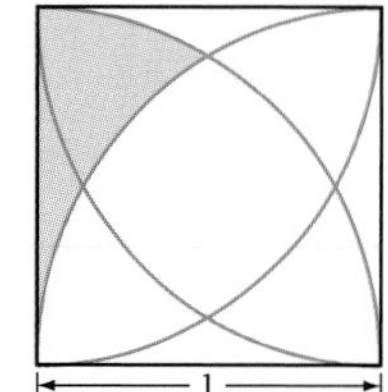

b. Shaded area = _?_ $1 - \sqrt{3} + \frac{\pi}{3}$

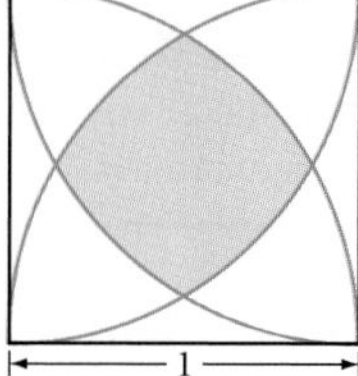

Chapter 6 **13.** For each statement, select always (A), sometimes (S), or never (N).

a. An angle inscribed in a semicircle is a right angle. A

b. An angle inscribed in a major arc is obtuse. N

c. An arc measure equals the measure of its central angle. S

d. The measure of an angle formed by two intersecting chords equals the measure of its intercepted arc. S

e. The measure of the angle formed by two tangents to a circle equals the supplement of the central angle of the minor intercepted arc. A

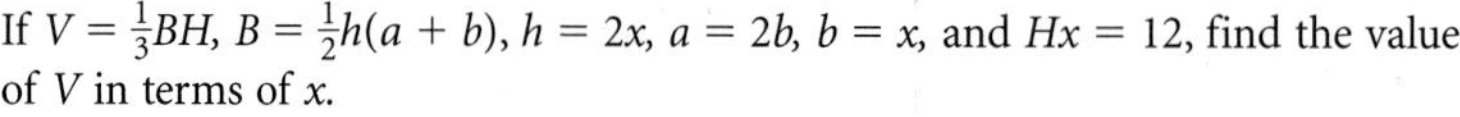

IMPROVING YOUR REASONING SKILLS

Symbol Juggling

If $V = \frac{1}{3}BH$, $B = \frac{1}{2}h(a + b)$, $h = 2x$, $a = 2b$, $b = x$, and $Hx = 12$, find the value of V in terms of x.

IMPROVING REASONING SKILLS

Students might be inclined to use lots of steps and perhaps several sets of parentheses. After they have a result, you might suggest that they check it by carefully working backward. A few students might be able to simply write down an expression in terms of x, from left to right. Don't discourage them, but again ask that they check their result by using a different method.

$V = 12x$

LESSON

13.6

Circle Proofs

When people say, "It can't be done," or "You don't have what it takes," it makes the task all the more interesting.

LYNN HILL

In Chapter 6, you completed the proof of the three cases of the Inscribed Angle Conjecture: The measure of an inscribed angle in a circle equals half the measure of its intercepted arc. There was a lot of algebra in the proof. You may not have noticed that the Angle Addition Postulate was used, as well as a property that we called *arc addition.* Arc Addition is a postulate that you need to add to your list.

Arc Addition Postulate

If point B is on $\overset{\frown}{AC}$ and between points A and C, then $m\overset{\frown}{AB} + m\overset{\frown}{BC} = m\overset{\frown}{AC}$.

Is the proof of the Inscribed Angle Conjecture now completely supported by the premises of geometry? Can you call it a theorem? To answer these questions, trace the family tree.

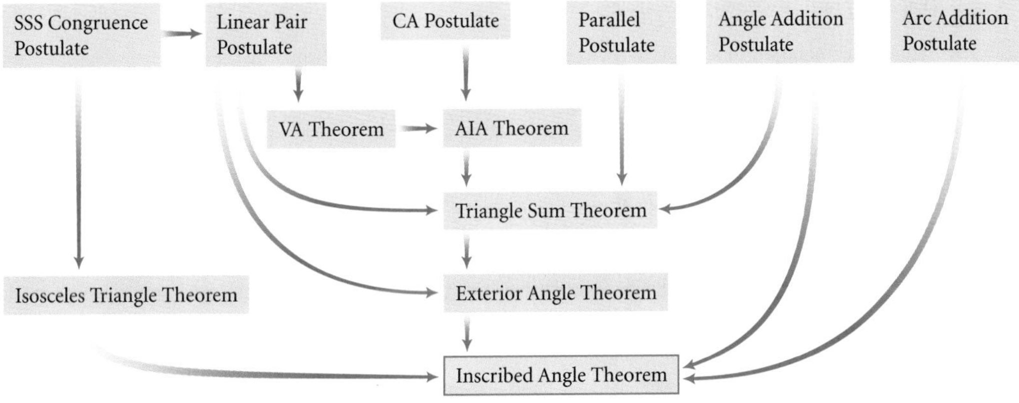

So the Inscribed Angle Conjecture is completely supported by premises of geometry; therefore you can call it a theorem and add it to your theorem list.

A double rainbow creates arcs in the sky over Stonehenge near Wiltshire, England. Built from bluestone and sandstone from 3000 to 1500 B.C.E., Stonehenge itself is laid out in the shape of a major arc.

NCTM STANDARDS

CONTENT		PROCESS	
	Number		Problem Solving
	Algebra	✓	Reasoning
✓	Geometry	✓	Communication
	Measurement		Connections
	Data/Probability		Representation

LESSON OBJECTIVES

- Review circle relationships
- Prove circle conjectures

LESSON 13.6

PLANNING

LESSON OUTLINE

One day:

10 min Introduction

30 min Exercises and Sharing

5 min Closing

MATERIALS

none

TEACHING

Many circle conjectures can now be proved within our deductive system.

One step Ask students to write a two-column proof of the Inscribed Angle Conjecture within the deductive system. They can look back at the proofs of Lesson 6.4 as needed. When they find they need reasons for conclusions they want to draw about arc measures, suggest that they introduce one or more postulates. Ask groups that finish early to make a family tree for the new theorem. During Sharing, have students compare their family tree to the one in the book.

SHARING IDEAS

Try to be sure students are clear on why a postulate about arc addition is needed. **[Ask]** "Do we need a similar postulate for arc subtraction?" Elicit the realization that arc subtraction, at least for this proof, can be covered by the Arc Addition Postulate and the subtraction property of equality. Remind students that we often want as few postulates as possible.

Most of this lesson involves students working on exercises. You can jigsaw the proofs in Exercises 1–7 and finish Sharing with group reports.

Sharing Ideas (continued)
Ask students how they feel at this point about creating proofs. Remind them that they're learning the art of planning a proof.

Assessing Progress
You can assess students' ability to construct proofs, including any tendencies to begin writing indirect proofs. You can also continue to assess their understanding of the premises needed for proofs in this lesson.

Closing the Lesson

Several circle conjectures have now become theorems that students can add to their lists.

BUILDING UNDERSTANDING

You might require a specific proof format or give students a choice of two-column, flowchart, or paragraph proof. You can also specify how detailed a set-up and plan you want them to write out. In several of the exercises, auxiliary lines will be useful.

ASSIGNING HOMEWORK

Essential	1–9
Performance assessment	1–7
Portfolio	1–9
Group	1–3
Review	10–16

Helping with the Exercises

Exercises 1–3 Students may have seen proofs of these conjectures in Lesson 6.4.

Exercise 5 Students might construct triangles by drawing an auxiliary line from the intersection of the tangents to the center of the circle and by drawing radii to the points of tangency yet still be unsuccessful in proving the triangles congruent. (They seem to have only SSA.) They might find the third sides of the right triangles using the Pythagorean Theorem but realize that that theorem isn't yet part of our deductive system. As needed, ask students how far the center is from the tangent segments and if they know anything about points equidistant from two sides of an angle. (See Exercise 5 in Lesson 13.3.)

Exercise 6 If students are having difficulty, remind them that there was a $\frac{1}{2}$ in the Inscribed Angle Theorem and wonder aloud whether the approach of using the Exterior Angle Theorem might work here, too.

Exercise 7 Let students try adding various auxiliary lines until they find one that makes angles that intercept both arcs.

See pages 781–782 for answers to Exercises 1–9.

In the exercises, you will create proofs or family trees for many of your earlier discoveries about circles.

EXERCISES

You will need

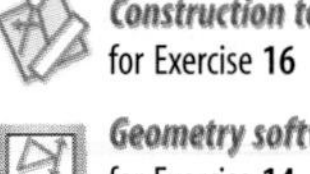

Construction tools for Exercise **16**

Geometry software for Exercise **14**

In Exercises 1–7, set up and write a proof of each conjecture. Once you have completed the proofs, add the theorems to your list.

1. Inscribed angles that intercept the same or congruent arcs are congruent. (Inscribed Angles Intercepting Arcs Theorem)

2. The opposite angles of an inscribed quadrilateral are supplementary. (Cyclic Quadrilateral Theorem)

3. Parallel lines intercept congruent arcs on a circle. (Parallel Secants Congruent Arcs Theorem)

4. If a parallelogram is inscribed within a circle, then the parallelogram is a rectangle. (Parallelogram Inscribed in a Circle Theorem)

5. Tangent segments from a point to a circle are congruent. (Tangent Segments Theorem)

6. The measure of an angle formed by two intersecting chords is half the sum of the measures of the two intercepted arcs. (Intersecting Chords Theorem)

7. Write and prove a theorem about the arcs intercepted by secants intersecting outside a circle, and the angle formed by the secants. (Intersecting Secants Theorem)

8. Create a family tree for the Tangent Segments Theorem.

9. Create a family tree for the Parallelogram Inscribed in a Circle Theorem.

Review

12.4 **10.** Find the coordinates of A and P to the nearest tenth. $A(4.0, 2.9), P(-1.1, -2.8)$

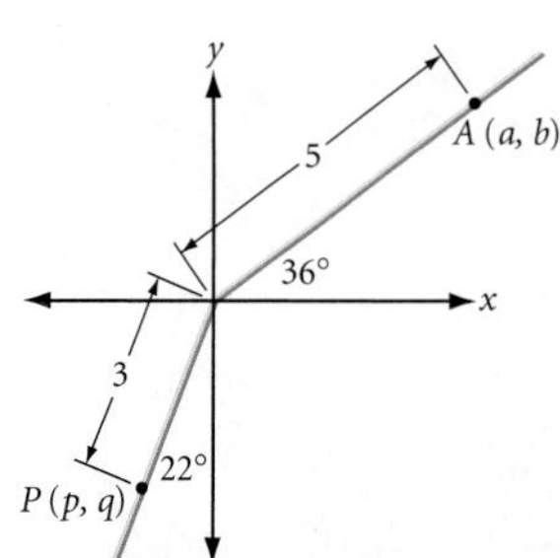

11.6 **11.** **Given:** $AX = 6$, $XB = 2$, $BC = 4$, $ZC = 3$
Find: $BY = \underline{?}$, $YC = \underline{?}$, $AZ = \underline{?}$ (3, 1, 9)

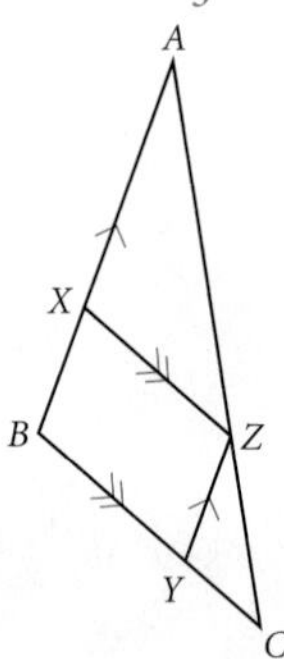

4.3 **12.** List the five segments in order from shortest to longest. $\overline{BC}, \overline{AB}, \overline{AC}, \overline{CD}, \overline{AD}$

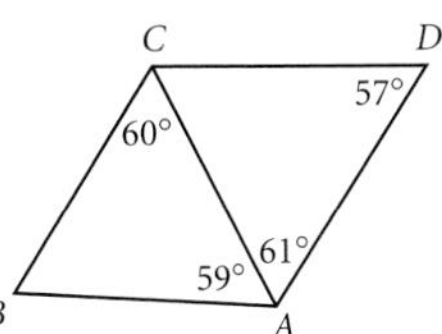

9.1 **13.** $\overline{AB}$ is a common external tangent. Find the length of $\overline{AB}$ (to a tenth of a unit). 32.5

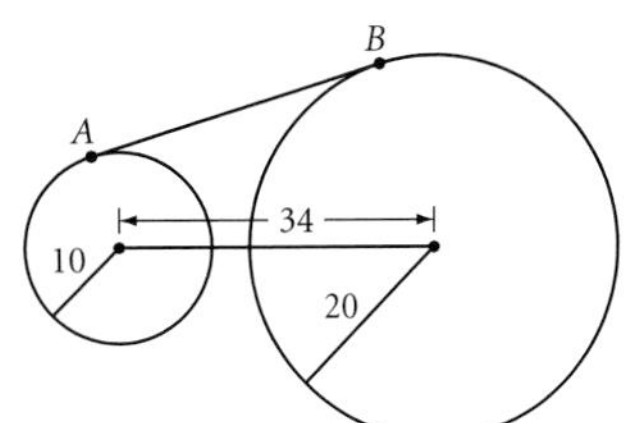

8.2 **14.** ***Technology*** P is any point inside an equilateral triangle. Is there a relationship between the height h and the sum $a + b + c$? Use geometry software to explore the relationship and make a conjecture. Then write a proof of your conjecture. ⓗ

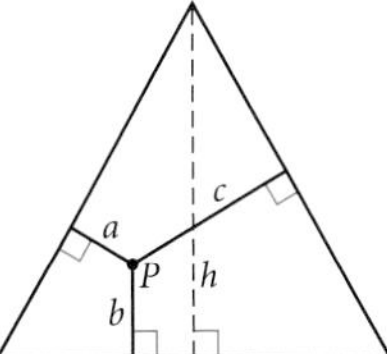

14. As long as point P is inside the triangle, $a + b + c = h$. Proof: Let x be the length of a side. The areas of the three small triangles are $\frac{1}{2}xa$, $\frac{1}{2}xb$, and $\frac{1}{2}xc$. The area of the large triangle is $\frac{1}{2}xh$. So, $\frac{1}{2}xa + \frac{1}{2}xb + \frac{1}{2}xc = \frac{1}{2}xh$. Divide both sides by $\frac{1}{2}x$. So, $a + b + c = h$.

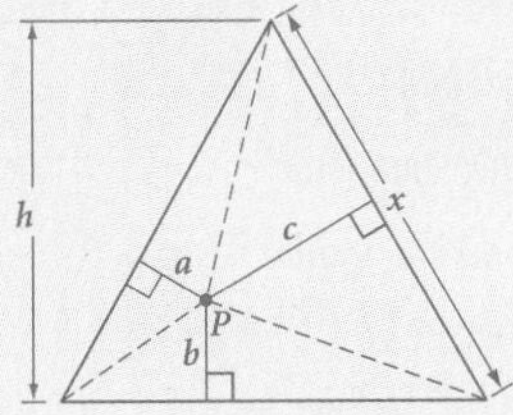

Chapter 6 **15.** Find each measure or conclude that it "cannot be determined."

a. $m\angle P$ 27° **b.** $m\angle QON$ 47°

c. $m\angle QRN$ 67° **d.** $m\angle QMP$ 133°

e. $m\angle ONF$ cannot be determined **f.** $m\widehat{MN}$ cannot be determined

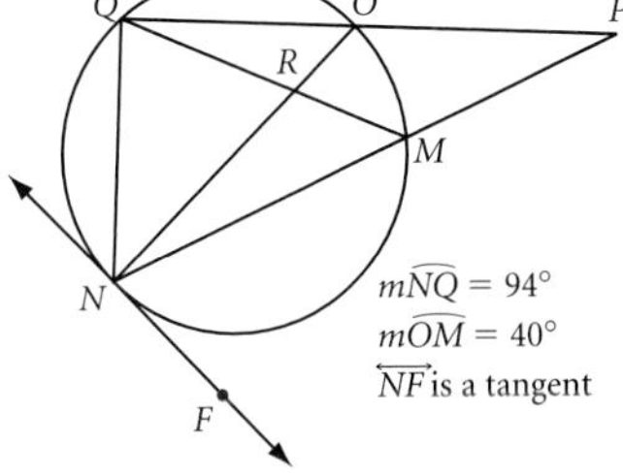

6.2 **16.** ***Construction*** Use a compass and straightedge to construct the two tangents to a circle from a point outside the circle. ⓗ

IMPROVING YOUR REASONING SKILLS

Seeing Spots

The arrangement of green and yellow spots at right may appear to be random, but there is a pattern. Each row is generated by the row immediately above it. Find the pattern and add several rows to the arrangement. Do you think a row could ever consist of all yellow spots? All green spots? Could there ever be a row with one green spot? Does a row ever repeat itself?

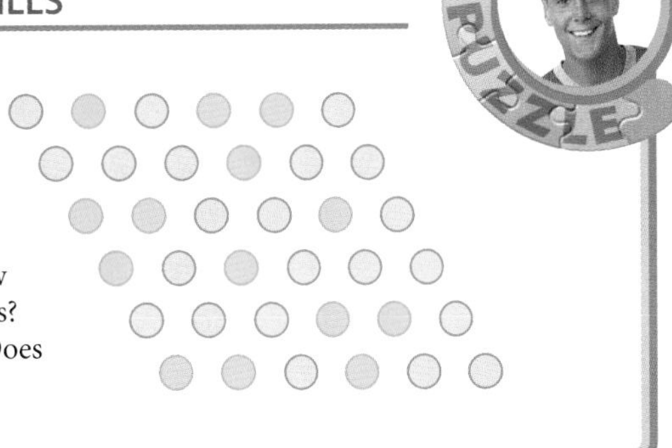

Seeing Spots

Here are rows 7 through 11:

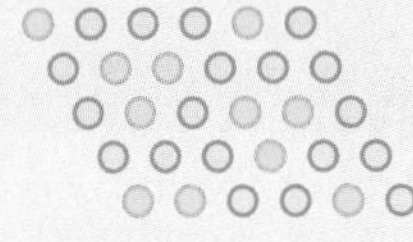

See page 783 for the answer to Exercise 16.

IMPROVING REASONING SKILLS

The color of a spot is determined by the colors of the two spots above it. If they are the same, the spot is yellow; otherwise, the spot is green. (The last spot in a row is always green because there can't be two same-colored spots above it.) A row could never be all yellow because the last spot is always green.

Because there are only $2^5 = 32$ possible ways to color a row (two choices for each of the first five spots), some row must be repeated after at most 32 rows. Thus there will be a repeated cycle. For example, in the pattern shown here, the first row is repeated as the ninth row, so the cycle is eight rows long.

The cycle based on this starting pattern does not include an all-green row. However, some other starting pattern can lead to an all-green row. In fact, starting with an all-green row gives an eight-row cycle, after which the ninth row is all green and any row in that cycle would lead to all green.

LESSON

13.7

PLANNING

LESSON OUTLINE

One day:

10 min Example

15 min Investigation

15 min Sharing and Exercises

5 min Closing

MATERIALS

- Properties of Similarity (T), *optional*
- SAS Similarity Theorem (T), *optional*

TEACHING

Moving on from the most basic Euclidean geometry of congruence, we find that theorems in similarity geometry can be proved with the addition of three properties and a postulate. Begin with the example, or use the one-step investigation.

▶ ***EXAMPLE***

Focus students' attention on the plan, even though it's long. Have them read and think about it one sentence at a time. Point out how it begins at the end and works back and forth. Students might follow it by listing statements and reasons at various places.

One step Ask students to prove the similarity shortcuts, introducing properties and postulates as needed. (They can't just introduce them all as postulates and be done, though!) As you circulate, you might need to encourage the construction of *congruent* triangles.

LESSON 13.7

Similarity Proofs

Mistakes are part of the dues one pays for a full life.

SOPHIA LOREN

To prove conjectures involving similarity, we need to extend the properties of equality and congruence to similarity.

Properties of Similarity

Reflexive property of similarity

Any figure is similar to itself.

Symmetric property of similarity

If Figure A is similar to Figure B, then Figure B is similar to Figure A.

Transitive property of similarity

If Figure A is similar to Figure B and Figure B is similar to Figure C, then Figure A is similar to Figure C.

The AA Similarity Conjecture is actually a similarity postulate.

AA Similarity Postulate

If two angles of one triangle are congruent to two angles of another triangle, then the two triangles are similar.

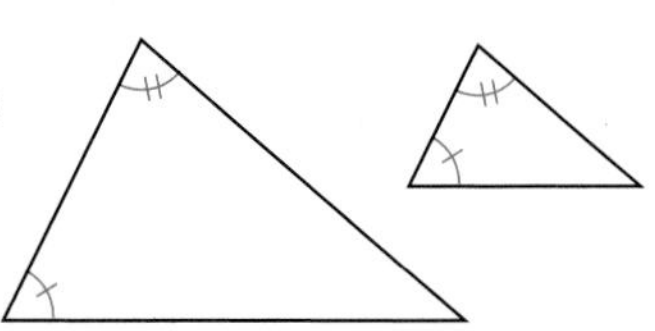

In Chapter 11, you also discovered the SAS and SSS shortcuts for showing that two triangles are similar. In the example that follows, you will see how to use the AA Similarity Postulate to prove the SAS Similarity Conjecture, making it the SAS Similarity Theorem.

EXAMPLE Prove the SAS Similarity Conjecture: If two sides of one triangle are proportional to two sides of another triangle and the included angles are congruent, then the two triangles are similar.

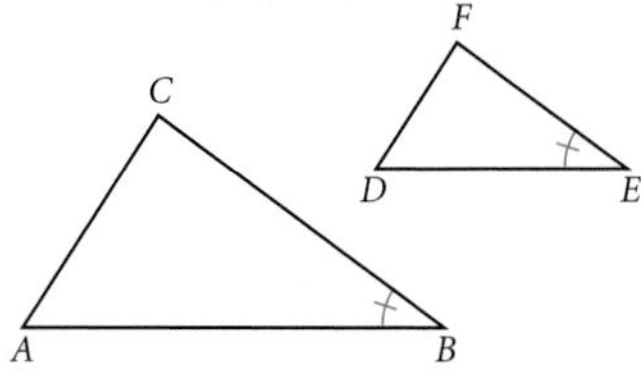

▶ ***Solution***

Given: $\triangle ABC$ and $\triangle DEF$ so that $\frac{AB}{DE} = \frac{BC}{EF}$ and $\angle B \cong \angle E$

Show: $\triangle ABC \sim \triangle DEF$

Plan: The only shortcut for showing that two triangles are similar is the AA Postulate, so you need to find another pair of congruent angles. One way of getting two congruent angles is to find two congruent triangles. You can draw a triangle within $\triangle ABC$ that is congruent to $\triangle DEF$. The Segment Duplication Postulate allows you to locate a point P on $\overline{AB}$ so that $PB = DE$. The Parallel Postulate allows you to construct a line $\overleftrightarrow{PQ}$ parallel to $\overline{AC}$. Then $\angle A \cong \angle QPB$ by the CA Postulate.

LESSON OBJECTIVES

- Prove conjectures using properties of similarity
- Review similar triangles

NCTM STANDARDS

	CONTENT		PROCESS
	Number		Problem Solving
✔	Algebra	✔	Reasoning
✔	Geometry	✔	Communication
	Measurement		Connections
	Data/Probability	✔	Representation

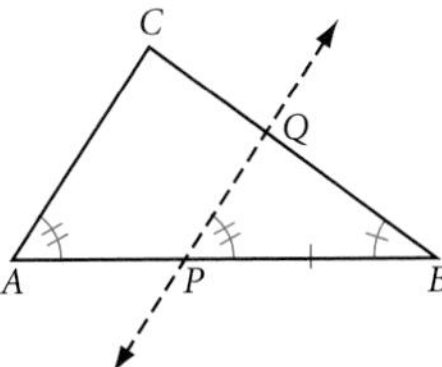

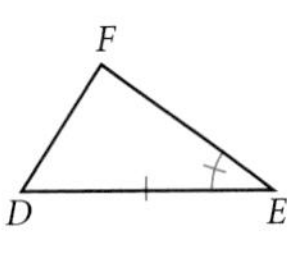

Now, if you can show that $\triangle PBQ \cong \triangle DEF$, then you will have two congruent pairs of angles to prove $\triangle ABC \sim \triangle DEF$. So, how do you show that $\triangle PBQ \cong \triangle DEF$? If you can get $\triangle ABC \sim \triangle PBQ$, then $\frac{AB}{PB} = \frac{BC}{BQ}$. It is given that $\frac{AB}{DE} = \frac{BC}{EF}$, and you constructed $PB = DE$. With some algebra and substitution, you can get $EF = BQ$. Then the two triangles will be congruent by the SAS Congruence Postulate.

Here is the two-column proof.

Statement	Reason
1. Locate P so that $PB = DE$	**1.** Segment Duplication Postulate
2. Construct $\overline{PQ} \parallel \overline{AC}$	**2.** Parallel Postulate
3. $\angle A \cong \angle QPB$	**3.** CA Postulate
4. $\angle B \cong \angle B$	**4.** Identity property of congruence
5. $\triangle ABC \sim \triangle PBQ$	**5.** AA Similarity Postulate
6. $\frac{AB}{PB} = \frac{BC}{BQ}$	**6.** Corresponding sides of similar triangles are proportional (CSSTP)
7. $\frac{AB}{DE} = \frac{BC}{BQ}$	**7.** Substitution
8. $\frac{AB}{DE} = \frac{BC}{EF}$	**8.** Given
9. $\frac{BC}{BQ} = \frac{BC}{EF}$	**9.** Transitive property of equality
10. $BQ = EF$	**10.** Algebra operations
11. $\angle B \cong \angle E$	**11.** Given
12. $\triangle PBQ \cong \triangle DEF$	**12.** SAS Congruence Postulate
13. $\angle QPB \cong \angle D$	**13.** CPCTC
14. $\angle A \cong \angle D$	**14.** Substitution
15. $\triangle ABC \sim \triangle DEF$	**15.** AA Similarity Postulate

This proves the SAS Similarity Conjecture.

The proof in the example above may seem complicated, but it relies on triangle congruence and triangle similarity postulates. Reading the plan again can help you follow the steps in the proof.

You can now call the SAS Similarity Conjecture the SAS Similarity Theorem and add it to your theorem list.

In this investigation you will use the SAS Similarity Theorem to prove the SSS Similarity Conjecture.

Guiding the Investigation

Step 3 Use the clever approach used in the proof of the SAS Theorem. Locate a point R on $\overline{KL}$ so that $RL = NP$. Then, through R, construct a line $\overleftrightarrow{RS}$ parallel to $\overline{KM}$. From the CA Postulate, $\angle SRL \cong \angle K$ and $\angle RSL \cong \angle M$. This means that $\triangle KLM \sim \triangle RLS$ by the AA Similarity Postulate. Now, if we can show that $\triangle RLS \cong \triangle NPQ$, then $\angle L \cong \angle P$ by CPCTC. Because $\triangle KLM \sim \triangle RLS$, then $\frac{KL}{RL} = \frac{LM}{LS} = \frac{MK}{SR}$ by the definition of similar triangles (CSSTP). Then, with some algebra on the proportions $\frac{KL}{NP} = \frac{LM}{LS}$ and $\frac{KL}{NP} = \frac{MK}{SR}$ and the fact that $RL = NP$, we can get $LS = PQ$ and $SR = QN$. Then the two triangles will be congruent by the SSS Congruence Postulate.

Step 4 As needed, remind students that part of the investigation is to complete the proof. Have groups discuss how the given statements and reasons relate to their Task 4 plan in Step 3.

SHARING IDEAS

After one or more groups have presented any variety of ideas, **[Ask]** "Why might the book have taken AA as a postulate rather than, say, SSS?" [One reason might be that the AA Similarity Postulate depends on a basic property of similar polygons: congruent angles. Because of the Third Angle Theorem, AA is sufficient to guarantee that two triangles are similar.]

As time allows, break up Sharing with group work on the exercises and finish with progress reports.

Assessing Progress

You can assess how well students can read and understand a plan for a proof and the depth of their understanding of ideas about similar triangles and congruence.

See page 783 for answers to Step 4.

Investigation
Can You Prove the SSS Similarity Conjecture?

Similarity proofs can be challenging. Follow the steps and work with your group to prove the SSS Similarity Conjecture: If the three sides of one triangle are proportional to the three sides of another triangle, then the two triangles are similar.

Step 1 Given: Two triangles with corresponding sides proportional

Show: The two triangles are similar

Step 2 Given: $\triangle KLM$ and $\triangle NPQ$ so that $\frac{KL}{NP} = \frac{LM}{PQ} = \frac{MK}{QN}$

Show: $\triangle KLM \sim \triangle NPQ$

Step 1 Identify the given and show.

Step 2 Restate what is given and what you must show in terms of this diagram.

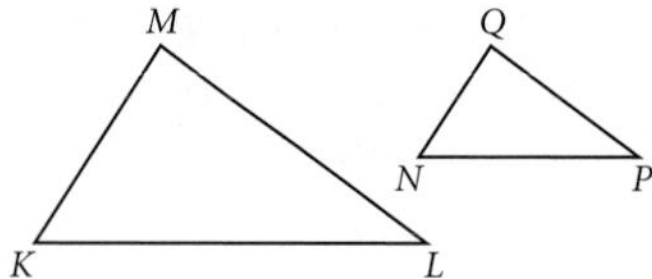

Step 3 Plan your proof. (Hint: Use an auxiliary line like the one in the example.)

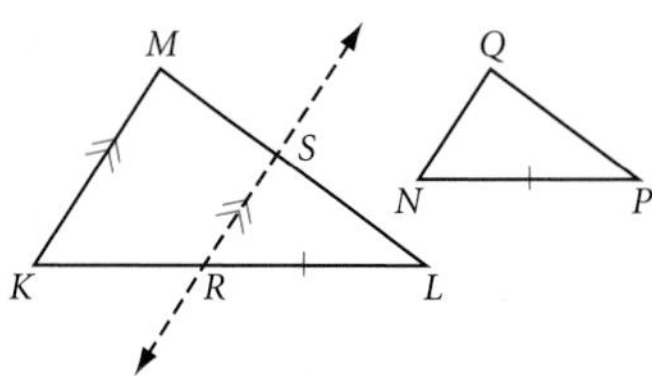

Step 4 Copy the first ten statements and provide the reasons. Then write the remaining steps and reasons necessary to complete the proof.

Statement	Reason
1. Locate R so that $RL = NP$	1. ? Postulate Segment Duplication
2. Construct $\overleftrightarrow{RS} \parallel \overline{KM}$	2. ? Postulate Parallel
3. $\angle SRL \cong \angle K$	3. ? Postulate CA
4. $\angle RSL \cong \angle M$	4. ? Postulate CA
5. $\triangle KLM \sim \triangle RLS$	5. ? AA Similarity Postulate
6. $\frac{KL}{RL} = \frac{LM}{LS} = \frac{MK}{SR}$	6. ? CSSTP
7. $\frac{KL}{NP} = \frac{LM}{LS}$	7. ? Substitution property of equality
8. $\frac{KL}{NP} = \frac{LM}{PQ}$	8. ? Given
9. $\frac{KL}{NP} = \frac{MK}{SR}$	9. ? Substitution property of equality
10. $\frac{KL}{NP} = \frac{MK}{QN}$	10. ? Given
⋮	⋮

Step 5 Draw arrows to show the flow of logic in your two-column proof.

Closing the Lesson

Review the similarity properties and the AA Similarity Postulate, and note that the SAS and SSS Similarity Theorems can now be added to the theorem lists in students' notebooks.

When you have completed the proof, you can call the SSS Similarity Conjecture the SSS Similarity Theorem and add it to your theorem list.

EXERCISES

You will need

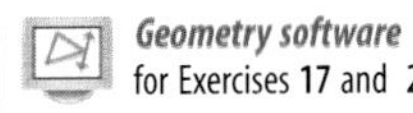
Geometry software for Exercises 17 and 21

In Exercises 1 and 2, write a proof and draw the family tree of each theorem. If the family tree is completely supported by theorems and postulates, add the theorem to your list.

1. If two triangles are similar, then corresponding altitudes are proportional to the corresponding sides. (Corresponding Altitudes Theorem)

2. If two triangles are similar, then corresponding medians are proportional to the corresponding sides. (Corresponding Medians Theorem)

In Exercises 3–10, write a proof of the conjecture. Once you have completed the proofs, add the theorems to your list. As always, you may use theorems that have been proved in previous exercises in your proofs.

3. If two triangles are similar, then corresponding angle bisectors are proportional to the corresponding sides. (Corresponding Angle Bisectors Theorem)

4. If a line passes through two sides of a triangle parallel to the third side, then it divides the two sides proportionally. (Parallel/Proportionality Theorem) ⓗ

5. If a line passes through two sides of a triangle dividing them proportionally, then it is parallel to the third side. (Converse of the Parallel/Proportionality Theorem) ⓗ

6. If you drop an altitude from the vertex of a right angle to its hypotenuse, then it divides the right triangle into two right triangles that are similar to each other and to the original right triangle. (Three Similar Right Triangles Theorem) ⓗ

7. The length of the altitude to the hypotenuse of a right triangle is the geometric mean of the lengths of the two segments on the hypotenuse. (Altitude to the Hypotenuse Theorem) ⓗ

8. The Pythagorean Theorem ⓗ

9. Converse of the Pythagorean Theorem ⓗ

10. If the hypotenuse and one leg of a right triangle are congruent to the hypotenuse and one leg of another right triangle, then the two right triangles are congruent. (Hypotenuse Leg Theorem) ⓗ

11. Create a family tree for the Parallel/Proportionality Theorem.

12. Create a family tree for the SSS Similarity Theorem.

13. Create a family tree for the Pythagorean Theorem.

This monument in Wellington, New Zealand, was designed by Maori architect Rewi Thompson. How would you describe the shape of the monument? How might the artist have used geometry in planning the construction?

BUILDING UNDERSTANDING

The exercises extend students' knowledge of proof to ideas about similarity. As needed, encourage students to draw and mark diagrams and plan their proofs, perhaps writing statements from the bottom of a sheet of paper toward the top.

ASSIGNING HOMEWORK

Essential	3–9 (any two)
Performance assessment	3–9
Portfolio	1–13
Group	1, 2, 11–13
Review	14–21

Helping with the Exercises

Exercise 7 The teacher note for Exercise 19 of Lesson 11.4 defines *geometric mean* as the result of multiplying two numbers and taking the square root. You might need to remind students of this definition.

7.

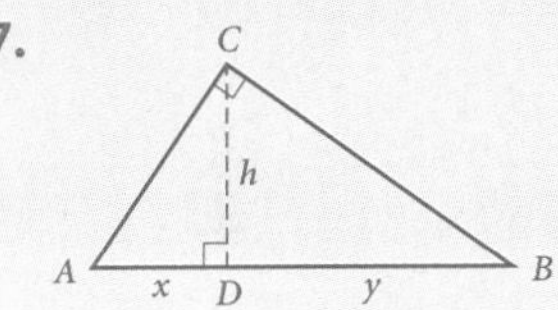

Use the Three Similar Right Triangles Theorem to get $\triangle ADC \sim \triangle CDB$. Then use CSSTP to get $\frac{x}{h} = \frac{h}{y}$.

Wellington Monument
The monument is made up of a truncated pyramid and the tetrahedron that was cut off the pyramid. The artist may have used parallel proportionality to plan the number of blocks in each layer or used similarity to work from a scale model.

Exercise 8 If students are having difficulty getting started, ask if they've done anything recently with right triangles. From Exercise 6 they might get the idea to construct an altitude to the hypotenuse. Tinkering with the ratios of corresponding sides of the three similar triangles can give equations that can be combined into the Pythagorean Theorem. For example, if the altitude cuts the hypotenuse into lengths d (closer to side b) and $c - d$, then from one pair of triangles students can get $a^2 = c^2 - cd$, which is close to the desired equation, so they might look at another pair to get $b^2 = cd$.

Exercise 9 You might need to remind students that the Pythagorean Theorem is one of the few theorems that is used in proving its own converse. They might refer back to Lesson 9.2 for ideas.

Exercise 10 The Hypotenuse Leg Theorem was examined informally in Lesson 9.1, Exercise 18. It is used in Exercise 18.

See pages 783–784 for answers to Exercises 1–6 and 8–13.

Review

9.1 **14.** A circle with diameter 9.6 cm has two parallel chords with lengths 5.2 cm and 8.2 cm. How far apart are the chords? Find two possible answers. 1.5 cm and 6.5 cm

15. Choose **A** if the value is greater in the regular hexagon.
Choose **B** if the value is greater in the regular pentagon.
Choose **C** if the values are equal in both figures.
Choose **D** if it cannot be determined which value is greater.

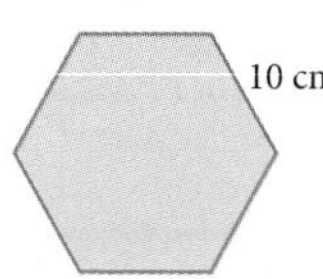

12 cm

Regular hexagon Regular pentagon

a. Perimeter C **b.** Apothem A **c.** Area A
d. Sum of interior angles A **e.** Sum of exterior angles C

7.5 **16.** ***Mini-Investigation*** Cut out a small nonsymmetric concave quadrilateral. Label the vertices *A, B, C, D.* Use your cut-out as a template to create a tessellation. Trace about 10 images that fit together to cover part of the plane. Number the vertices of each image to match the numbers on your cut-out.

a. Draw two different translation vectors that map your tessellation onto itself. How do these two vectors relate to your original quadrilateral?

b. Pick a quadrilateral in your tessellation. What transformation will map the quadrilateral you picked onto an adjacent quadrilateral? With that transformation, what happens to the rest of the tessellation?

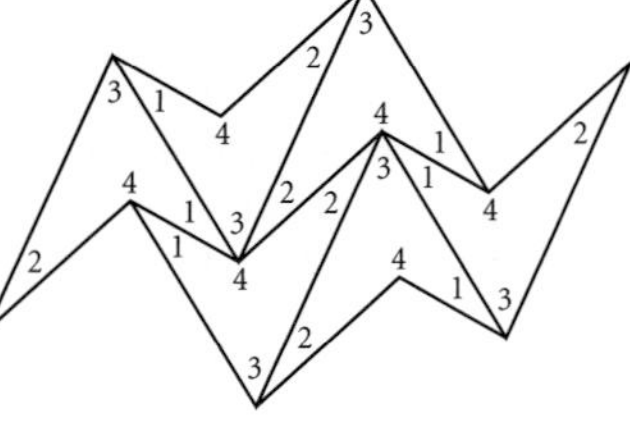

7.5 **17.** ***Technology*** Use geometry software to draw a small nonsymmetric concave quadrilateral.

a. Describe the transformations that will make the figure tessellate.

b. Describe two different translation vectors that map your tessellation onto itself.

Chapter 6 **18. Given:**

Circles *P* and *Q*
$\overline{PS}$ and $\overline{PT}$ are tangent to circle *Q*
$m\angle SPQ = 57°$
$m\overset{\frown}{GS} = 118°$

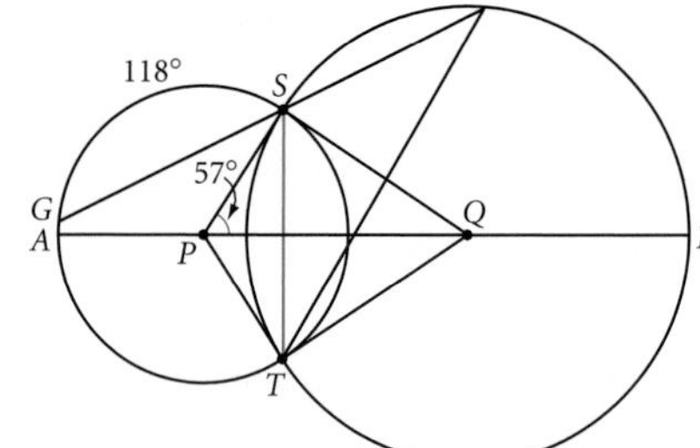

Find:

a. $m\angle GLT$ 33° **b.** $m\angle SQT$ 66°
c. $m\angle TSQ$ 57° **d.** $m\overset{\frown}{SL}$ 62°
e. Explain why *PSQT* is cyclic.
f. Explain why $\overline{SQ}$ is tangent.

16a. The vectors are diagonals of your quadrilateral.

16b. A 180° rotation about the midpoint of the common side; the entire tessellation maps onto itself.

Exercise 17 This exercise is a technology alternative to Exercise 16.

17a. a 180° rotation about the midpoint of any side

17b. possible answer: a vector running from each vertex of the quadrilateral to the opposite vertex (or any multiple of it)

18e. $\angle PSQ$ and $\angle PTQ$ are 90° by the Tangent Theorem and so are supplementary. So, $\angle SPT$ and $\angle SQT$ must also be supplementary by the Quadrilateral Sum Theorem. Therefore, opposite angles are supplementary, so it's cyclic.

18f. Because $\overline{PS}$ is a tangent, $m\angle PSQ = 90°$ (Tangent Theorem). Because $m\angle PSQ = 90°$, $\overline{SQ}$ must be a tangent (Converse of the Tangent Theorem).

Chapter 8 In the figures for Exercises 19 and 20, each arc is a quarter of a circle with its center at a vertex of the square.

Given: The square has side length 1 unit **Find:** The shaded area

19. Shaded area = ? ⓗ $\frac{\pi}{12} + \frac{\sqrt{3}}{2} - 1$

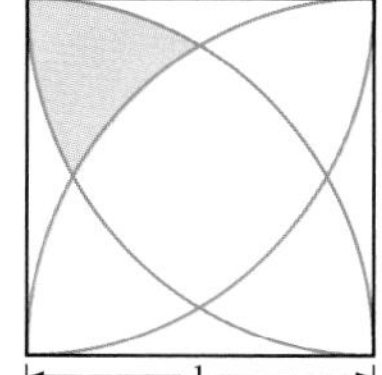

20. Shaded area = ? ⓗ $-\frac{\pi}{6} - \frac{\sqrt{3}}{4} + 1$

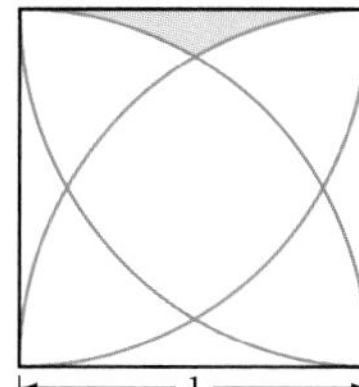

4.2 **21.** ***Technology*** The diagram below shows a scalene triangle with angle bisector $\overline{CG}$, and perpendicular bisector $\overline{GE}$ of side $\overline{AB}$. Study the diagram.

a. Which triangles are congruent?

b. You can use congruent triangles to prove that $\triangle ABC$ is isosceles. How?

c. Given a scalene triangle, you proved that it is isosceles. What's wrong with this proof?

d. Use geometry software to re-create the construction. What does the sketch tell you about what's wrong?

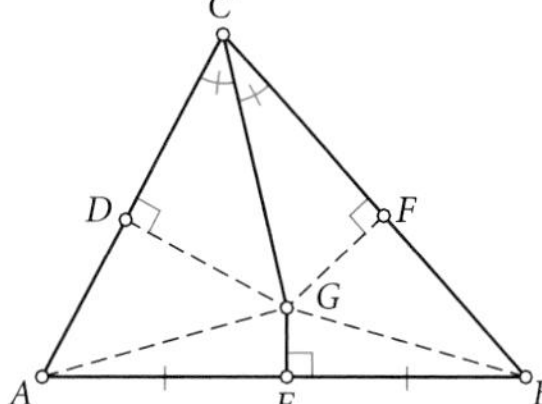

5.3 **22.** Dakota Davis is at an archaeological dig where he has uncovered a stone voussoir that resembles an isosceles trapezoidal prism. Each trapezoidal face has bases that measure 27 cm and 32 cm, and congruent legs that measure 32 cm each. Help Dakota determine the rise and span of the arch when it was standing, and the total number of voussoirs. Explain your method.

IMPROVING YOUR ALGEBRA SKILLS

The Eye Should Be Quicker Than the Hand

How fast can you answer these questions?

1. If $2x + y = 12$ and $3x - 2y = 17$, what is $5x - y$?

2. If $4x - 5y = 19$ and $6x + 7y = 31$, what is $10x + 2y$?

3. If $3x + 2y = 11$ and $2x + y = 7$, what is $x + y$?

Exercises 19, 20 These exercises rely on areas found in earlier lessons; the solution to Exercise 20 can be found from Exercise 19 and either Exercise 31b in Lesson 13.1 or Exercise 12a in Lesson 13.5.

21a. $\triangle CDG \cong \triangle CFG$ by SAA; $\triangle GEA \cong \triangle GEB$ by SAS; $\triangle DGA \cong \triangle FGB$ by the HL Theorem.

21b. $\overline{CD} \cong \overline{CF}$ and $\overline{DA} \cong \overline{FB}$ by CPCTC; $CD + DA = CF + FB$ (addition property of equality). Therefore, $\overline{CA} \cong \overline{CB}$, and $\triangle ABC$ is isosceles.

21c. The figure is inaccurate.

21d. The angle bisector does not intersect the perpendicular bisector inside the triangle as shown, except in the special case of an isosceles triangle, when they coincide.

EXTENSIONS

A. Ask students to prove that if one triangle is similar to another with scale factor s, then the area of the first is s^2 times the area of the second. [Plan: If the shorter base and height have lengths b and h, then the larger triangle has area $\frac{1}{2}(sb)(sh) = s^2\left(\frac{1}{2}bh\right)$.]

B. Have students prove that the relationship stated about two triangles in Extension A holds true for two polygons. [Outline: Divide the polygons into n (or $n - 2$) pairs of similar triangles and use the previous result.]

IMPROVING ALGEBRA SKILLS

1. Add; $5x - y = 29$

2. Add; $10x + 2y = 50$

3. Subtract; $x + y = 4$

22. 173 cm, 346 cm, 20 stones. Draw the trapezoid and extend the legs until they meet to form a triangle. Use parallel proportionality to find the rise. The span is twice the rise. Use inverse tangent to find the central angle measure. Divide into 180° to find the number of voussoirs.

PLANNING

LESSON OUTLINE

One day:

15 min Introduction and Examples

25 min Sharing and Exercises

5 min Closing

MATERIALS

- Coordinate Proof Properties (T), *optional*

TEACHING

Coordinate geometry can be used for geometry proofs, some of which are simpler than non-coordinate proofs. Students can add these properties to their postulates, properties, and theorems list.

One step Ask students to look over the properties given at the beginning of the lesson (including the distance formula) and to use them to prove the Pythagorean Theorem. As needed, refer students to the examples. During Sharing, ask why this proof was so much easier than the proof(s) they developed in Lesson 13.7. [The distance formula was derived from the Pythagorean Theorem; if it is taken as a property, it implies the Pythagorean Theorem.]

Coordinate Proof

You can prove conjectures involving midpoints, slope, and distance using analytic geometry. When you do this, you create a **coordinate proof.** Coordinate proofs rely on the premises of geometry, and these three properties from algebra.

Coordinate Midpoint Property

If (x_1, y_1) and (x_2, y_2) are the coordinates of the endpoints of a segment, then the coordinates of the midpoint are $\left(\frac{x_1 + x_2}{2}, \frac{y_1 + y_2}{2}\right)$.

Parallel Slope Property

In a coordinate plane, two distinct lines are parallel if and only if their slopes are equal.

Perpendicular Slope Property

In a coordinate plane, two nonvertical lines are perpendicular if and only if their slopes are negative reciprocals of each other.

For coordinate proofs, you also use the coordinate version of the Pythagorean Theorem, the distance formula.

Distance Formula

The distance between points $A(x_1, y_1)$ and $B(x_2, y_2)$ is given by $AB^2 = (x_2 - x_1)^2 + (y_2 - y_1)^2$ or $AB = \sqrt{(x_2 - x_1)^2 + (y_2 - y_1)^2}$.

The process you use in a coordinate proof contains the same five tasks that you learned in Lesson 13.2. However, in Task 2, you draw and label a diagram on a coordinate plane. Locate the vertices and other points of your diagram such that they reflect the given information, yet their coordinates should not restrict the generality of your diagram. In other words, do not assume any extra properties for your figure, besides the ones given in its definition.

EXAMPLE A Write a coordinate proof of the Square Diagonals Conjecture: The diagonals of a square are congruent and are perpendicular bisectors of each other.

▶ ***Solution***

Task 1

Given: A square with both diagonals

Show: The diagonals are congruent and are perpendicular bisectors of each other

LESSON OBJECTIVES

- Review parallel and perpendicular slope properties
- Review the distance formula
- Use the coordinate proof properties
- Learn to plan and write coordinate proofs

NCTM STANDARDS

CONTENT		PROCESS	
	Number		Problem Solving
✓	Algebra	✓	Reasoning
✓	Geometry	✓	Communication
✓	Measurement	✓	Connections
	Data/Probability	✓	Representation

Task 2

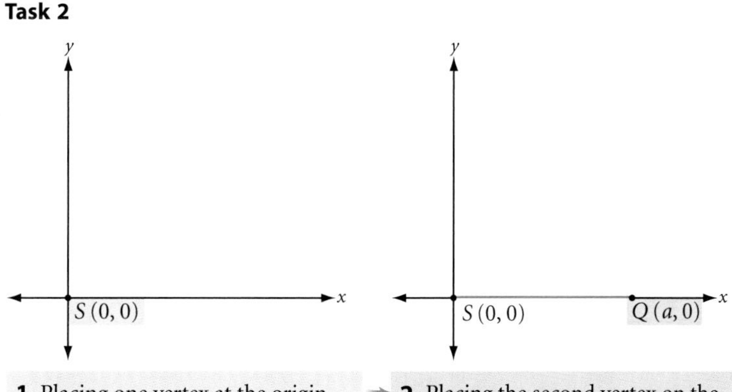

1. Placing one vertex at the origin will simplify later calculations because it is easy to work with zeros.

2. Placing the second vertex on the x-axis also simplifies calculations because the y-coordinate is zero. To remain general, call the x-coordinate a.

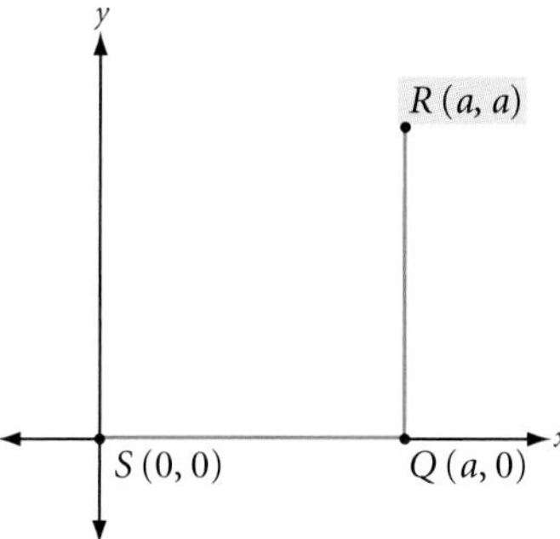

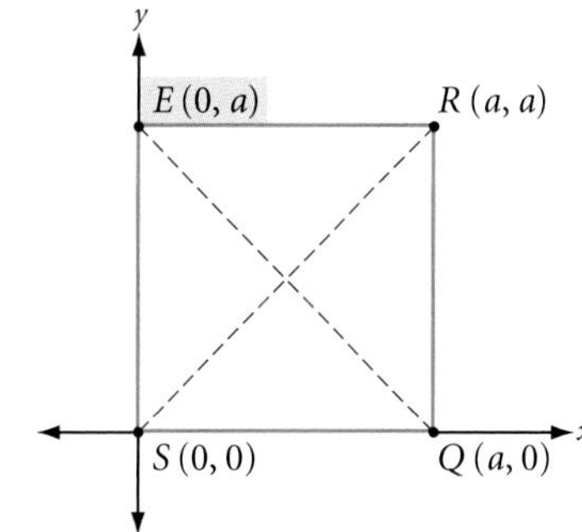

3. $\overline{RQ}$ needs to be vertical to form a right angle with $\overline{SQ}$, which is horizontal. $\overline{RQ}$ also needs to be the same length. So R is placed a units vertically above Q.

4. The last vertex is placed a units above S.

You can check that $SQRE$ fits the definition of a square—an equiangular, equilateral parallelogram.

$$\text{Slope of } \overline{SQ} = \frac{0-0}{a-0} = \frac{0}{a} = 0$$

$$SQ = \sqrt{(a-0)^2 + (0-0)^2} = \sqrt{a^2} = a$$

$$\text{Slope of } \overline{QR} = \frac{a-0}{a-a} = \frac{a}{0} \text{ (undefined)}$$

$$QR = \sqrt{(a-a)^2 + (a-0)^2} = \sqrt{a^2} = a$$

▶ *EXAMPLE A*

Task 2 Students may ask if we're considering only a special case by placing one vertex at the origin and the other on the x-axis. Any square can be moved to this position by an isometry, which also preserves congruence and perpendicularity, so if this particular theorem can be proved for this square it will hold for any other.

Tasks 2, 5 If students have difficulty handling the general ordered pair $(a, 0)$, you might want to simplify the problem by giving specific points, such as $(2, 0)$, for the students to use, at least at first. They will still use the distance formula and the slope to prove their ideas. In a general proof the numbers will be replaced by variables.

You might need to remind students that a coordinate gives a distance from an axis, so to find the distance between two points on a horizontal line they subtract the smaller x-coordinate from the larger. To find the distance between points on a vertical line, they do the same with the y-coordinates.

Slope of $\overline{RE} = \frac{a - a}{0 - a} = \frac{0}{-a} = 0$

$RE = \sqrt{(0 - a)^2 + (a - a)^2} = \sqrt{a^2} = a$

Slope of $\overline{ES} = \frac{0 - a}{0 - 0} = \frac{-a}{0}$ (undefined)

$ES = \sqrt{(0 - 0)^2 + (0 - a)^2} = \sqrt{a^2} = a$

Opposite sides have the same slope and are therefore parallel, so *SQRE* is a parallelogram. Also, from the slopes, $\overline{SQ}$ and $\overline{RE}$ are horizontal and $\overline{QR}$ and $\overline{ES}$ are vertical, so all angles are right angles and the parallelogram is equiangular. Lastly, all the sides have the same length, so the parallelogram is equilateral. *SQRE* is an equiangular, equilateral parallelogram and is a square by definition.

Task 3

Given: Square *SQRE* with diagonals $\overline{SR}$ and $\overline{QE}$

Show: $\overline{SR} \cong \overline{QE}$, $\overline{SR}$ and $\overline{QE}$ bisect each other, and $\overline{SR} \perp \overline{QE}$

Task 4

To show that $\overline{SR} \cong \overline{QE}$, you must show that both segments have the same length. To show that $\overline{SR}$ and $\overline{QE}$ bisect each other, you must show that the segments share the same midpoint. To show that $\overline{SR} \perp \overline{QE}$, you must show that the segments have negative reciprocal slopes. Because you know the coordinates of the endpoints of both $\overline{SR}$ and $\overline{QE}$, you can do the necessary calculations to use the distance formula, the coordinate midpoint property, and the perpendicular slope property.

Task 5

Use the distance formula to find *SR* and *QE*.

$SR = \sqrt{(a - 0)^2 + (a - 0)^2} = \sqrt{2a^2} = a\sqrt{2}$

$QE = \sqrt{(a - 0)^2 + (0 - a)^2} = \sqrt{2a^2} = a\sqrt{2}$

So, by the definition of congruence, $\overline{SR} \cong \overline{QE}$ because both segments have the same length.

Use the coordinate midpoint property to find the midpoints of $\overline{SR}$ and $\overline{QE}$.

Midpoint of $\overline{SR} = \left(\frac{0 + a}{2}, \frac{0 + a}{2}\right) = (0.5a, 0.5a)$

Midpoint of $\overline{QE} = \left(\frac{0 + a}{2}, \frac{a + 0}{2}\right) = (0.5a, 0.5a)$

So, $\overline{SR}$ and $\overline{QE}$ bisect each other because both segments have the same midpoint.

Finally, compare the slopes of $\overline{SR}$ and $\overline{QE}$.

$$\text{Slope of } \overline{SR} = \frac{a-0}{a-0} = 1$$

$$\text{Slope of } \overline{QE} = \frac{a-0}{0-a} = -1$$

So, $\overline{SR} \perp \overline{QE}$ by the perpendicular slope property because the segments have negative reciprocal slopes.

Therefore, the diagonals of a square are congruent and are perpendicular bisectors of each other.

Add the Square Diagonals Theorem to your list.

Here's another example. See if you can recognize how the five tasks result in this proof.

EXAMPLE B

Write a coordinate proof of this conditional statement: If the diagonals of a quadrilateral bisect each other, then the quadrilateral is a parallelogram.

▶ Solution

Given: Quadrilateral $ABCD$ with diagonals $\overline{AC}$ and $\overline{BD}$ that bisect each other (common midpoint M)

Show: $ABCD$ is a parallelogram

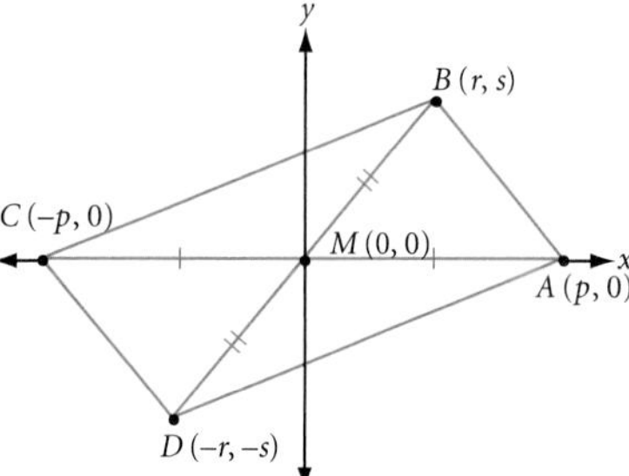

Proof

$$\text{Slope of } \overline{AB} = \frac{s-0}{r-p} = \frac{s}{r-p}$$

$$\text{Slope of } \overline{BC} = \frac{0-s}{-p-r} = \frac{-(s)}{-(p+r)} = \frac{s}{p+r}$$

$$\text{Slope of } \overline{CD} = \frac{-s-0}{-r-(-p)} = \frac{-(s)}{-(r-p)} = \frac{s}{r-p}$$

$$\text{Slope of } \overline{DA} = \frac{0-(-s)}{p-(-r)} = \frac{s}{p+r}$$

Opposite sides $\overline{AB}$ and $\overline{CD}$ have equal slopes of $\frac{s}{r-p}$. Opposite sides $\overline{BC}$ and $\overline{DA}$ have equal slopes of $\frac{s}{p+r}$. So each pair is parallel by the parallel slope property. Therefore, quadrilateral $ABCD$ is a parallelogram by definition. Add this theorem to your list.

It is clear from these examples that creating a diagram on a coordinate plane is a significant challenge in a coordinate proof. The first seven exercises will give you some more practice creating these diagrams.

▶ *EXAMPLE B*

Challenge students to make their own coordinate diagram before reading Example B. Compare different strategies. **[Ask]** "Why might the book have placed the common midpoint at the origin?" [The coordinates of opposite vertices are then related nicely.] Again, if students need to work first with particular numbers, let them.

SHARING IDEAS

Focus on how parts of figures are placed on a coordinate plane. Placing them so for simple calculations while maintaining generality can require some experimentation. In general, it is helpful to locate parts of the given figure at the origin and along the axes. To ensure that you maintain generality, you must consider the situation. A general rectangle can have sides located on the x-axis and the y-axis. A general quadrilateral can have one side on an axis, but it cannot have two sides on axes without losing generality.

[Ask] "How does analytic, or coordinate, geometry relate to the other geometry we've been studying?" [Analytic geometry is based on algebra; its postulates are those of arithmetic and algebra, and it can include definitions of terms that are undefined in "regular" geometry, which is called *synthetic geometry.* A proof in analytic geometry requires placing the figure on a coordinate plane. The reasons used in the proof are mostly algebraic.]

[Ask] "Are all parallel lines included in the Parallel Slope Property?" [yes, if we take "equal slopes" to include the undefined slopes of vertical lines] "Are all perpendicular lines included in the Perpendicular Slope Property? [yes, if 0 and undefined are considered to be negative reciprocals]

Assessing Progress

Assess students' understanding of the slope properties and the distance formula.

Closing the Lesson

Coordinate geometry can be used in writing proofs, some of which are simpler than proofs that don't use algebra. A coordinate proof often doesn't give insight into why the property is true. A further disadvantage is that the algebraic manipulations can be messy.

BUILDING UNDERSTANDING

The exercises give students experience with coordinate proofs, some of which prove theorems they've already proved synthetically (without algebra). Exercises 1–3 concern figures located on a coordinate plane.

ASSIGNING HOMEWORK

Essential	1–7
Performance assessment	8–13
Portfolio	8–13
Group	8–13

▶Helping with the Exercises

[Alert] Students might accidentally interchange x- and y-coordinates.

Exercise 1 Because all isosceles triangles have a line of symmetry, positioning that line on the y-axis is sufficiently general to represent all isosceles triangles.

Exercise 2 If students are having difficulty, ask how they might move from point A to point D. [They could go right b units and up c units.] They can do the same thing to get from point B to point C.

Exercise 3 Students might have difficulty finding the second coordinate of point D. **[Ask]** "What distance does that coordinate represent geometrically?" [the length of a perpendicular from point D to $\overline{AB}$, which can be determined by the Pythagorean Theorem] Because the figure is a rhombus, the y-coordinate is $\sqrt{a^2 - b^2}$.

Exercise 7 You might need to help students by asking them whether half an equilateral triangle is a special right triangle.

See pages 785–788 for answers to Exercises 4–13.

EXERCISES

In Exercises 1–3, each diagram shows a convenient general position of a polygon on a coordinate plane. Find the missing coordinates.

1. Triangle ABC is isosceles. $B(a, 0)$

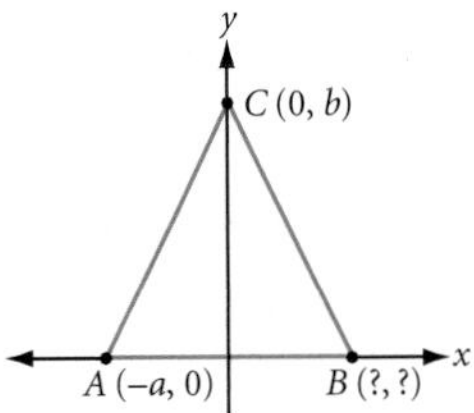

2. Quadrilateral $ABCD$ is a parallelogram. $C(a + b, c)$

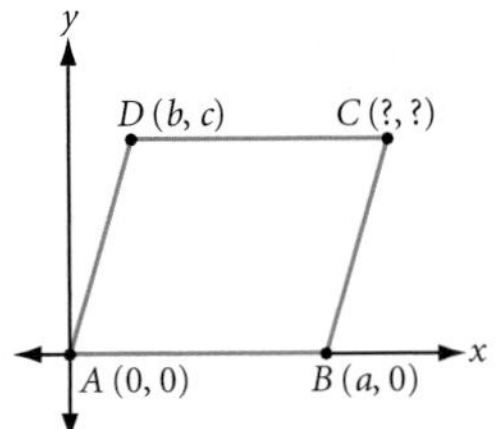

3. Quadrilateral $ABCD$ is a rhombus. $C(a + b, \sqrt{a^2 - b^2})$, $D(b, \sqrt{a^2 - b^2})$

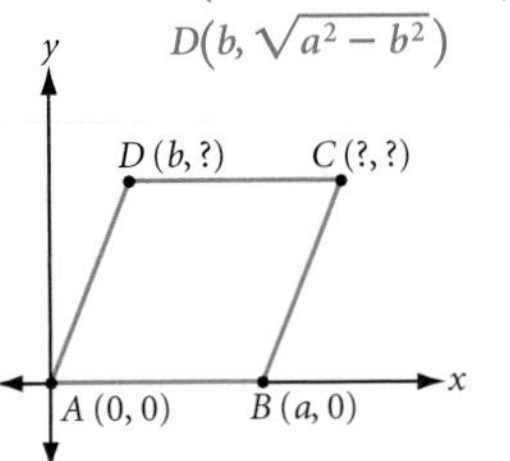

In Exercises 4–7, draw each figure on a coordinate plane. Assign general coordinates to each point of the figure. Then use the coordinate midpoint property, parallel slope property, perpendicular slope property, and/or the distance formula to check that the coordinates you have assigned meet the definition of the figure.

4. Rectangle $RECT$

5. Triangle TRI with its three midsegments

6. Isosceles trapezoid $TRAP$

7. Equilateral triangle EQU

In Exercises 8–13, write a coordinate proof of each conjecture. If it cannot be proven, write "cannot be proven."

8. The diagonals of a rectangle are congruent.

9. The midsegment of a triangle is parallel to the third side and half the length of the third side.

10. The midsegment of a trapezoid is parallel to the bases.

11. If only one diagonal of a quadrilateral is the perpendicular bisector of the other diagonal, then the quadrilateral is a kite.

12. The figure formed by connecting the midpoints of the sides of a quadrilateral is a parallelogram.

13. The quadrilateral formed by connecting the midpoint of the base to the midpoint of each leg in an isosceles triangle is a rhombus.

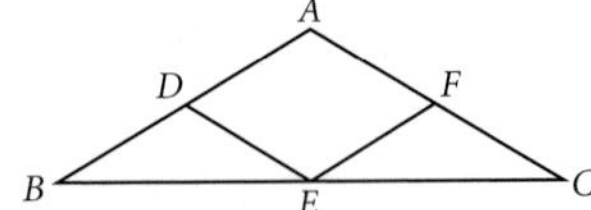

E is the midpoint of base $\overline{BC}$.
D and F are the midpoints of the legs.

Exercise 8 An exercise in Lesson 13.4 asked for a synthetic proof of this Rectangle Diagonals Theorem.

Exercise 9 This exercise is the Triangle Midsegment Conjecture.

Exercise 10 This exercise is half of the Trapezoid Midsegment Conjecture. **[Ask]** "How would you prove the other half of the Trapezoid Midsegment Conjecture—that the midsegment's length is the average of the bases' lengths?"

Exercise 11 This exercise explores the converse of the Kite Diagonal Bisector Conjecture.

Exercise 12 Students might struggle with making a diagram that is not a special quadrilateral. This exercise uses more variable coordinates than any other and therefore is algebraically challenging.

project

SPECIAL PROOFS OF SPECIAL CONJECTURES

In this project your task is to research and present logical arguments in support of one or more of these special properties.

1. Prove that there are only five regular polyhedra.

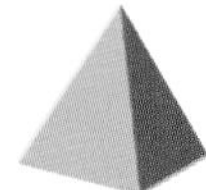

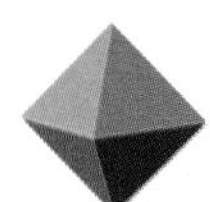
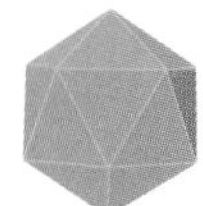
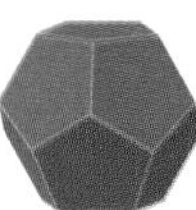

2. You discovered Euler's rule for determining whether a planar network can or cannot be traveled. Write a proof defending Euler's formula for networks.

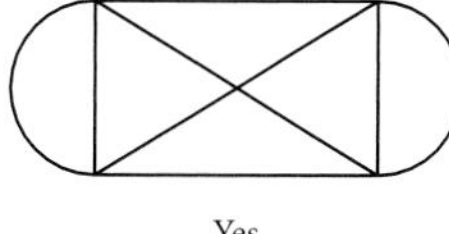
Yes

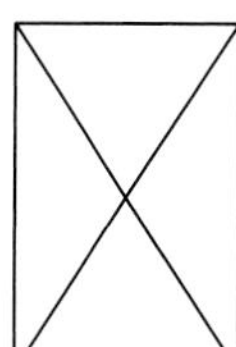
No

3. You discovered that the formula for the sum of the measures of the interior angles of an n-gon is $(n - 2)180°$. Prove that this formula is correct.

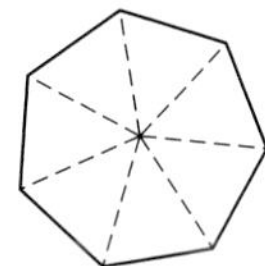
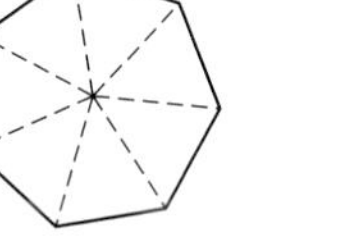

4. You discovered that the composition of two reflections over intersecting lines is equivalent to one rotation. Prove that this always works.

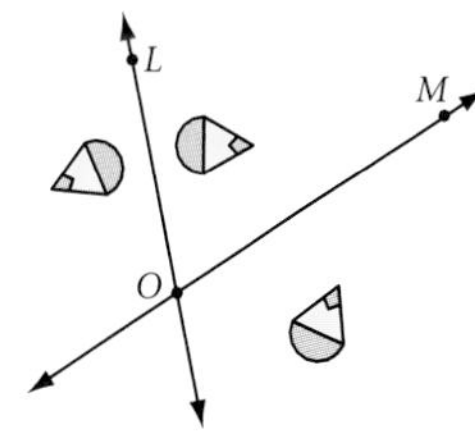

5. The coordinates of the centroid of a triangle are equal to the average of the coordinates of the triangle's three vertices. Prove that this is always true.

6. Prove that $\sqrt{2}$ is irrational.

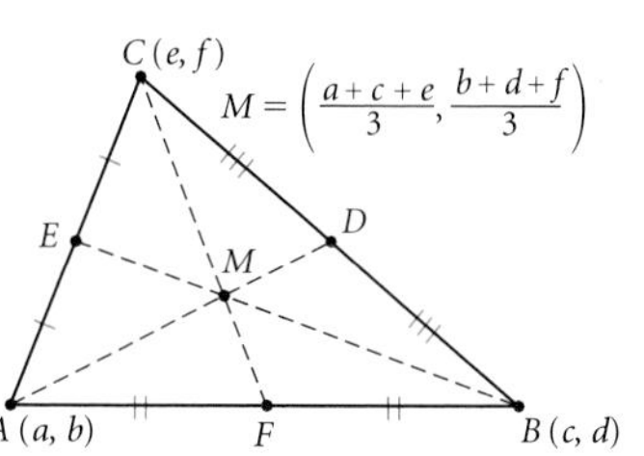

7. When you explored all the 1-uniform tilings (Archimedean tilings), you discovered that there are exactly 11 Archimedean tilings of the plane. Prove that there are exactly 11.

Sample Project Proofs

1. Three, four, or five triangles fitted about a point leave a gap that can be closed by folding the triangles to start a tetrahedron, an octahedron, and an icosahedron, respectively. Likewise three squares or three pentagons leave a gap and can be folded to start a cube or a dodecahedron. Three hexagons leave no gap, and three of any polygon with more than six sides overlap. (See the *Platonic Solids* video.)

2. If each vertex is an endpoint of an even number of edges, then whenever a traveler enters that vertex on one edge at least one unused edge is available for departure. (The vertex at which the traveler begins will have one edge left for ending there.)

For the rest of this proof and samples of other project proofs see pages 788–789.

EXTENSION

Ask students to prove Hero's formula. (Geometry textbooks tend to have algebraic proofs of the formula, like the one in the Solutions Manual. Hero's original proof was geometric but quite complicated. Students can find a copy of it in *Journey Through Genius* by William Dunham.)

Supporting the project

Students are not expected to be able to create these proofs themselves. Rather, they are to research them and then write them up in a way that shows their understanding.

OUTCOMES

- Proofs, which might not match the sample proofs, are logically valid and clearly written.
- Students use the Triangle Sum Theorem for proof 3. To prove it formally for any n-gon requires mathematical induction.
- To illustrate proof 4, students draw rays that start at the point of intersection of the two lines and that pass through corresponding points on the original figure and draw its first and second images.
- In proof 5, students find the ordered pairs of the three midpoints and the equations of the three medians. Then they solve the equations simultaneously.

EXPLORATION

PLANNING

LESSON OUTLINE

One day:

5 min	Introduction
30 min	Activity
10 min	Sharing

MATERIALS

- compasses
- spheres that can be drawn on such as the Lénárt Sphere
- large rubber bands to go around the spheres, *optional*
- circles of latex with the edges stretched out, *optional*

TEACHING

Different deductive systems produce different geometries. To point to an application of other geometries, **[Ask]** "What is the shortest flight path from Los Angeles to London? Will you fly over Pennsylvania or Greenland?" [Greenland, because you will be flying along a great circle] A straight line on most maps will represent a longer path on the globe. A globe makes it clear why the shortest route takes you over Greenland. In spherical geometry, the shortest path between two points is along a great circle.

[Context] Euclid's statement of his fifth postulate (translated from the Greek) was: "If two straight lines lying in a plane are met by another line and if the sum of the interior angles on one side is less than two right angles, then the straight lines, if extended sufficiently, will meet on the side on which the sum of the angles is less than two right angles." You will notice that it never mentions parallel lines! The version given in the book is known as the

Exploration

Non-Euclidean Geometries

Have you ever changed the rules of a game? Sometimes, changing just one simple rule creates a completely different game. You can compare geometry to a game whose rules are postulates. If you change even one postulate, you may create an entirely new geometry.

Hungarian mathematician János Bolyai, one of the discoverers of hyperbolic geometry, said, "I have discovered such wonderful things that I was amazed . . . out of nothing I have created a strange new Universe."

Euclidean geometry—the geometry you learned in this course—is based on several postulates. A postulate, according to the contemporaries of Euclid, is an obvious truth that cannot be derived from other postulates.

The list below contains the first five of Euclid's postulates.

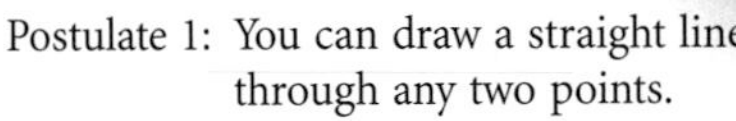

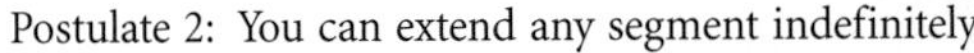

Postulate 1: You can draw a straight line through any two points.

Postulate 2: You can extend any segment indefinitely.

Postulate 3: You can draw a circle with any given point as center and any given radius.

Postulate 4: All right angles are equal.

Postulate 5: Through a given point not on a given line, you can draw exactly one line that is parallel to the given line.

The fifth postulate, known as the Parallel Postulate, does not seem as obvious as the others. In fact, for centuries, many mathematicians did not believe it was a postulate at all and tried to show that it could be proved using the other postulates. Attempting to use indirect proof, mathematicians began by assuming that the fifth postulate was false and then tried to reach a logical contradiction.

If the Parallel Postulate is false, then one of these assumptions must be true.

Assumption 1: Through a given point not on a given line, you can draw *more than one line* parallel to the given line.

Assumption 2: Through a given point not on a given line, you can draw *no line* parallel to the given line.

LESSON OBJECTIVES

- See that different postulates lead to different geometries
- Explore plane geometry on the surface of a sphere
- Learn new vocabulary

NCTM STANDARDS

	CONTENT		PROCESS
	Number		Problem Solving
	Algebra	✓	Reasoning
✓	Geometry	✓	Communication
	Measurement	✓	Connections
	Data/Probability	✓	Representation

Interestingly, neither of these assumptions contradict any of Euclid's other postulates. Assumption 1 leads to a new deductive system of non-Euclidean geometry, called **hyperbolic geometry.** Assumption 2 leads to another non-Euclidean system, called **elliptic geometry.**

One model of elliptic geometry applies to lines and angles on a sphere. On Earth, if you walk in a "straight line" indefinitely, what shape will your path take? Theoretically, if you walk long enough, you will end up back at the same point, after walking a complete circle around Earth! (Find a globe and check it!) So, on a sphere, a "straight line" is not a line at all, but a circle.

Hyperbolic geometry is confined to a circular disk. The edges of the disk represent infinity so lines curve and come to an end at the edge of the circle. This may sound like a strange model, but it fits physicists' theory that we live in a closed universe.

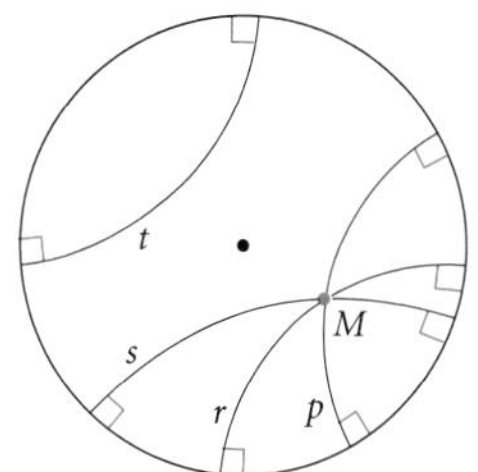

In hyperbolic geometry, many lines can be drawn through a point parallel to another line. Lines *p*, *r*, and *s* all pass through point *M*, and are parallel to line *t*.

In this activity, you will explore elliptic geometry.

Activity
Elliptic Geometry

You will need

- a sphere that you can draw on
- a compass

You can use the surface of a sphere as a model to explore elliptic geometry. Of course, you can't draw a straight line on a sphere. On a plane, the shortest distance between two points is measured along a line. On a sphere, the shortest distance between two points is measured along a great circle. Recall that a **great circle** is a circle on the surface of a sphere whose diameter passes through the center of the sphere. So, in this elliptic-geometry model, a "segment" is an arc of a great circle.

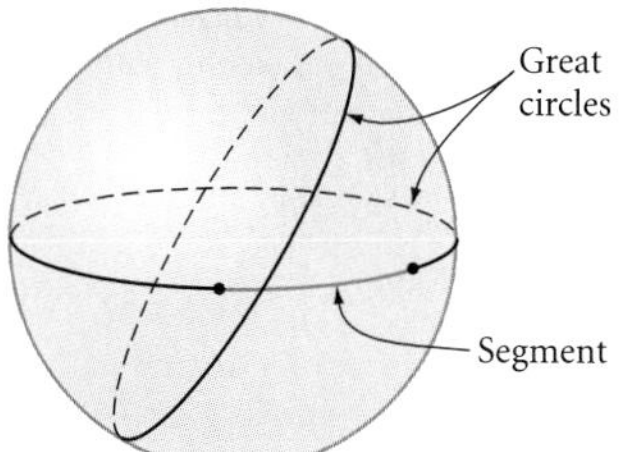

Playfair Postulate, named after Scottish physicist and mathematician John Playfair (1748–1819). On the plane, the two statements are logically equivalent. The Playfair Postulate is traditionally used because it is a simpler statement to understand and work with. Euclid's version still holds on a sphere (with "great circle" replacing "line"), while Playfair's does not.

[Context] German mathematician Carl Friedrich Gauss (1777–1855), Russian mathematician Nikolay Lobachevsky (1792–1856), and Hungarian mathematician János Bolyai (1802–1860) independently investigated the possibility of more than one parallel line and came up with hyperbolic geometry. German mathematician Georg Riemann (1826–1866) chose to investigate Assumption 2 and developed elliptic geometry. One model of hyperbolic geometry is a disk, in which the role of lines is played by arcs (or diameters) that form right angles to the circle at their endpoints. The terms *elliptic geometry* and *hyperbolic geometry* came not from the use of these shapes in the geometries but from deep analogies between properties of these geometries and the corresponding shapes.

[Context] French mathematician Henri Poincaré (1854–1912) devised the model for hyperbolic geometry, called the Poincaré disk. It consists of all the points in the interior of a circle. The model is like a circle made of latex with the edges stretched out (like the edges of lasagna noodles). Pull the edges tight, draw a line with a straightedge, and then let go of the edges. The line will appear curved.

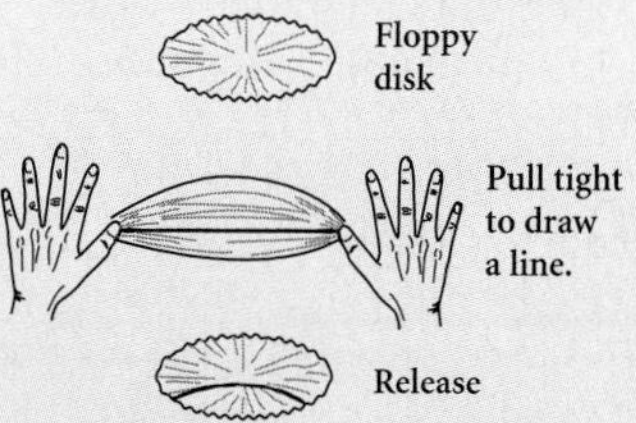

Guiding the Activity

Step 1 In Postulate 1, students might wonder whether "a straight line" means "one and only one." Euclid meant a unique line segment, but in elliptic geometry there are two line segments between most pairs of points (going along the minor arc or the major arc of a great circle) and infinitely many lines between points that are diametrically opposite. So for elliptic geometry "a" means "at least one." Students are asked to show this in Step 3.

Students might argue about what *indefinitely* means in Postulate 2. If it means "without end," then lines in elliptic geometry satisfy the postulate; if it means "unbounded," they don't.

In elliptic geometry, circles still exist (satisfying the third postulate). For example, all lines of latitude are considered circles except the equator, which is a great circle and thus is considered to be a line.

Steps 2, 4–6 Angles between curved lines are measured between the tangent lines through the point of intersection.

SHARING IDEAS

As students present their ideas, keep focusing on how elliptic and Euclidean geometry are alike and different.

[Ask] "Are there really no parallel lines on the sphere?" Students might think that there are; for example, two "lines" of latitude are parallel. Actually, no latitude lines (except the equator) are lines (great circles) on a sphere because the plane containing them does not pass through the center of the sphere.

[Ask] "Does the Segment Addition Postulate hold for elliptic geometry?" [No; in fact, the notion of "betweenness" is unusable, because you could always go from one point to another "around the other way."] The existence of non-Euclidean geometries gives us some insight into why we needed various postulates for our Euclidean proofs.

This exploration may disturb students. If they have thought that theorems in the deductive system they've been developing are absolute truths, then they can be shaken by seeing other deductive systems that are just as valid as Euclidean geometry but contradict it. The geometries introduced in this lesson were the first to challenge the 2000-year-old claim of Euclidean geometry to be the epitome of mathematical truth. As acceptance of their legitimacy grew, mathematicians were free to think broadly about all kinds of creative ideas. Try to get your students to experience some of that same change in their conception of mathematics, but be prepared for some students to be disturbed by the implications for their understanding of the world in general.

Ask whether students know of any other non-Euclidean geometries. Some might wonder about coordinate geometry; the theorems of standard coordinate geometry are those of Euclidean geometry. Fractal geometry, with fractional dimensions, is non-Euclidean. Students have also had a glimpse of projective geometry, in which all lines parallel to each other "intersect" at a "vanishing point." They may have heard of taxicab geometry, in which the distance between points is the sum of the horizontal and vertical distances. In addition, there are geometries that have only a finite number of points.

See page 789 for answers to Steps 2–6.

In elliptic geometry, "lines" (that is, great circles) never end; however, their length is finite! Because all great circles have the same diameter, all "lines" have the same length.

A model for elliptic geometry must satisfy the assumption that, through a given point not on a given line, there are *no* lines parallel to the given line. Simply put, there are no parallel lines in elliptic geometry. All great circles intersect, so the spherical model of elliptic geometry supports this assumption.

Step 1 Write a set of postulates for elliptic geometry by rewriting Euclid's first five postulates. Replace the word *line* with the words *great circle.*

Step 2 In Euclidean geometry, two lines that are perpendicular to the same line are parallel to each other. This is not true in elliptic geometry. On your sphere, draw an example of two "lines" that are perpendicular to the same "line" but that are not parallel to each other.

Step 3 On your sphere, show that two points do not always determine a unique "line."

Step 4 Draw an isosceles triangle on your sphere. (Remember, the "segments" that form the sides of a triangle must be arcs of great circles.) Does the Isosceles Triangle Theorem appear to hold in elliptic geometry?

Step 5 In elliptic geometry, the sum of the measures of the three angles of a triangle is always *greater than* 180°. Draw a triangle on your model and use it to help you explain why this makes sense.

Step 6 In Euclidean geometry, no triangle can have two right angles. But in elliptic geometry, a triangle can have three right angles. Find such a triangle and sketch it.

Japanese *temari* balls, colorful balls made of thread or scrap material, are embroidered with geometric designs derived from nature, like flowers or trees. Also called "princess balls," they originated in 700 C.E., when young nobility made them from silk and gave them as gifts. Notice that each "line segment" in the design of a *temari* ball is actually an arc of a great circle.

Assessing Progress

You can assess students' understanding of the role of postulates in a deductive system and their visualization skills.

Closing the Lesson

Two **non-Euclidean geometries** are **elliptic,** which can be modeled on a sphere, and **hyperbolic,** which can be modeled on a disk. The "lines" in each model appear curved when viewed from outside the system.

CHAPTER 13 REVIEW

In this course you have discovered geometry properties and made conjectures based on inductive reasoning. You have also used deductive reasoning to explain why some of your conjectures were true. In this chapter you have focused on geometry as a deductive system. You learned about the premises of geometry. Starting fresh with these premises, you built a system of theorems.

By discovering geometry, and then examining it as a mathematical system, you have been following in the footsteps of mathematicians throughout history. Your discoveries gave you an understanding of how geometry works. Proofs gave you the tools for taking apart your discoveries and understanding why they work.

EXERCISES

In Exercises 1–7, identify each statement as true or false. For each false statement, sketch a counterexample or explain why it is false.

1. If one pair of sides of a quadrilateral are parallel and the other pair of sides are congruent, then the quadrilateral is a parallelogram.
2. If consecutive angles of a quadrilateral are supplementary, then the quadrilateral is a parallelogram. true
3. If the diagonals of a quadrilateral are congruent, then the quadrilateral is a rectangle.
4. Two exterior angles of an obtuse triangle are obtuse. true
5. The opposite angles of a quadrilateral inscribed within a circle are congruent.
6. The diagonals of a trapezoid bisect each other.
7. The midpoint of the hypotenuse of a right triangle is equidistant from all three vertices. true

In Exercises 8–12, complete each statement.

8. A tangent is _?_ to the radius drawn to the point of tangency. perpendicular
9. Tangent segments from a point to a circle are _?_. congruent
10. The perpendicular bisector of a chord passes through _?_. the center of the circle
11. The three midsegments of a triangle divide the triangle into _?_.
12. A lemma is _?_.
13. Restate this conjecture as a conditional: The segment joining the midpoints of the diagonals of a trapezoid is parallel to the bases.

12. an auxiliary theorem proven specifically to help prove other theorems

13. If a segment joins the midpoints of the diagonals of a trapezoid, then it is parallel to the bases.

CHAPTER REVIEW 13

PLANNING

LESSON OUTLINE

First day:

15 min Reviewing

30 min Exercises

Second day:

20 min Proofs in groups

15 min Sharing

10 min Student self-assessment

REVIEWING

In this chapter students have reviewed many of the definitions and about half the conjectures from earlier chapters.

Have students make a concept map of all 50 or so postulates and theorems that have appeared so far in this chapter. An arrow connecting one to another can mean that the first is required in proving the second.

ASSIGNING HOMEWORK

Students will benefit from completing the first 23 exercises independently. The proofs and mini-investigations can be done in groups and shared with the class.

Helping with the Exercises

1. False. The quadrilateral could be an isosceles trapezoid.

3. False. The figure could be an isosceles trapezoid or a kite.

5. False. The angles are supplementary, but not necessarily congruent.

6. False. See Lesson 13.5, Example B.

11. four congruent triangles that are similar to the original triangle

14. Sometimes a proof requires a construction. If you need an angle bisector in a proof, what postulate allows you to construct one? Angle Bisector Postulate

15. If an altitude is needed in a proof, what postulate allows you to construct one? Perpendicular Postulate

16. Describe the procedure for an indirect proof.

17. **a.** What point is this anti-smoking poster trying to make?

b. Write an indirect argument to support your answer to part a.

In Exercises 18–23, identify each statement as true or false. If true, prove it. If false, give a counterexample or explain why it is false.

18. If the diagonals of a parallelogram bisect the angles, then the parallelogram is a square.

19. The angle bisectors of one pair of base angles of an isosceles trapezoid are perpendicular.

20. The perpendicular bisectors to the congruent sides of an isosceles trapezoid are perpendicular.

21. The segment joining the feet of the altitudes on the two congruent sides of an isosceles triangle is parallel to the third side. true

22. The diagonals of a rhombus are perpendicular. true

23. The bisectors of a pair of opposite angles of a parallelogram are parallel. true

In Exercises 24–27, devise a plan and write a proof of each conjecture.

24. Refer to the figure at right.

Given: Circle O with chords $\overline{PN}$, $\overline{ET}$, $\overline{NA}$, $\overline{TP}$, $\overline{AE}$

Show: $m\angle P + m\angle E + m\angle N + m\angle T + m\angle A = 180°$

T A N O P E

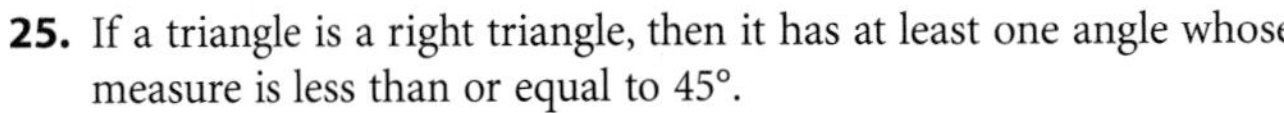

25. If a triangle is a right triangle, then it has at least one angle whose measure is less than or equal to 45°.

26. Prove the Triangle Midsegment Conjecture. ⓗ

27. Prove the Trapezoid Midsegment Conjecture.

In Exercises 28–30, use construction tools or geometry software to perform each mini-investigation. Then make a conjecture and prove it.

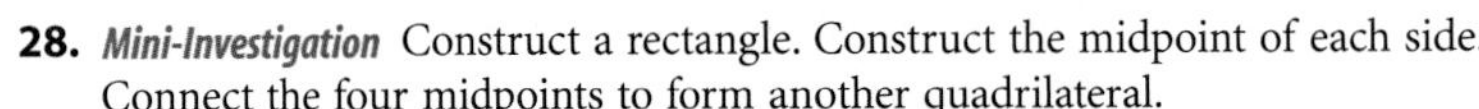

28. ***Mini-Investigation*** Construct a rectangle. Construct the midpoint of each side. Connect the four midpoints to form another quadrilateral.

a. What do you observe about the quadrilateral formed? From a previous theorem, you already know that the quadrilateral is a parallelogram. State a conjecture about the type of parallelogram formed.

b. Prove your conjecture.

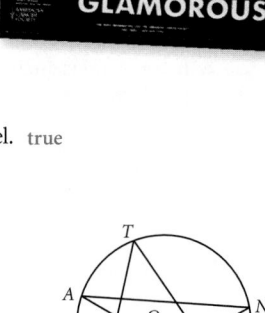

16. Assume the opposite of what you want to prove, then use valid reasoning to derive a contradiction or an absurdity.

17a. Smoking is *not* glamorous.

17b. If smoking were glamorous, then this smoker would look glamorous. This smoker does not look glamorous, therefore smoking is not glamorous.

18. False. The parallelogram is a rhombus.

19. False. In fact, the measure of the angle between them equals the measure of one of the other base angles. If the angle bisectors were perpendicular, then the base angles would be right angles. Then the shape would be a rectangle. Therefore, it could not be a trapezoid.

20. False; $x = 360° - 2b$ so $x = 90°$ only if $b = 135°$.

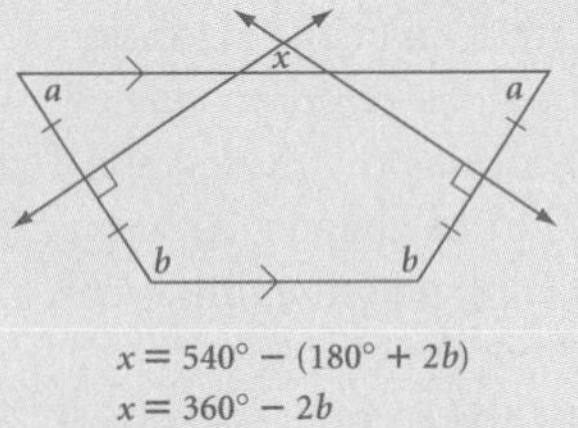

$x = 540° - (180° + 2b)$
$x = 360° - 2b$

Exercise 22 Students might be confused by the logic here. The diagonals of a rhombus bisect the angles and are perpendicular. Because an angle can have only one bisector, the bisectors are, in fact, the diagonals.

24. Use the Inscribed Angle Theorem, the addition property, and the distributive property to get $m\angle P + m\angle E + m\angle N + m\angle T + m\angle A = \frac{1}{2}(m\widehat{TN} + m\widehat{AT} + m\widehat{PA} + m\widehat{EP} + m\widehat{NE})$. Because there are 360° in a circle, $m\angle P + m\angle E + m\angle N + m\angle T + m\angle A = 180°$.

25.

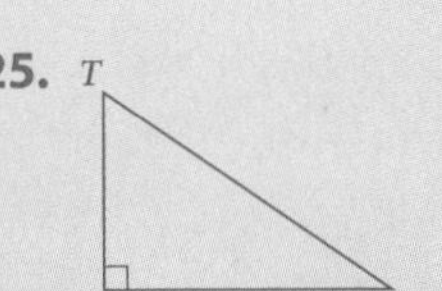

Assume $m\angle H > 45°$ and $m\angle T > 45°$. Use the Triangle Sum Theorem, the substitution property, and the subtraction property to get $m\angle H + m\angle T > 90°$, which creates a contradiction. Therefore $m\angle H \leq 45°$ or $m\angle T \leq 45°$.

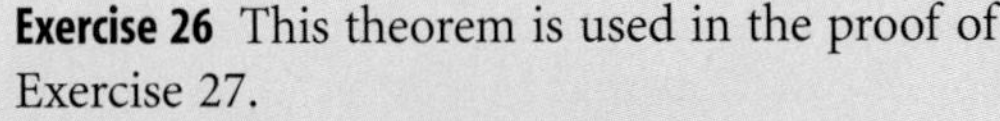

Exercise 26 This theorem is used in the proof of Exercise 27.

Exercises 28–30 These exercises are mini-investigations.

28a. The quadrilateral formed when the midpoints of the sides of a rectangle are connected is a rhombus.

See pages 789–790 for answers to Exercises 21–23 and 26–28b.

29. ***Mini-Investigation*** Construct a rhombus. Construct the midpoint of each side. Connect the four midpoints to form another quadrilateral.

a. You know that the quadrilateral is a parallelogram, but what type of parallelogram is it? State a conjecture about the parallelogram formed by connecting the midpoints of a rhombus. The quadrilateral formed when the midpoints of the sides of a rhombus are connected is a rectangle.

b. Prove your conjecture.

30. ***Mini-Investigation*** Construct a kite. Construct the midpoint of each side. Connect the four midpoints to form another quadrilateral.

a. State a conjecture about the parallelogram formed by connecting the midpoints of a kite.

b. Prove your conjecture.

31. Prove this theorem: If two chords intersect in a circle, the product of the segment lengths on one chord is equal to the product of the segment lengths on the other chord.

Assessing What You've Learned

WRITE IN YOUR JOURNAL How does the deductive system in geometry compare to the underlying organization in your study of science, history, and language?

UPDATE YOUR PORTFOLIO Choose a project or a challenging proof you did in this chapter to add to your portfolio.

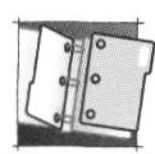

ORGANIZE YOUR NOTEBOOK Review your notebook to be sure it's complete and well organized. Be sure you have all the theorems on your theorem list. Write a one-page summary of Chapter 13.

PERFORMANCE ASSESSMENT While a classmate, friend, family member, or teacher observes, demonstrate how to prove one or more of the theorems proved in this chapter. Explain what you're doing at each step.

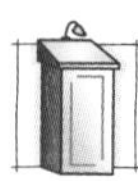

GIVE A PRESENTATION Give a presentation on a puzzle, exercise, or project from this chapter. Work with your group, or try presenting on your own.

29b.

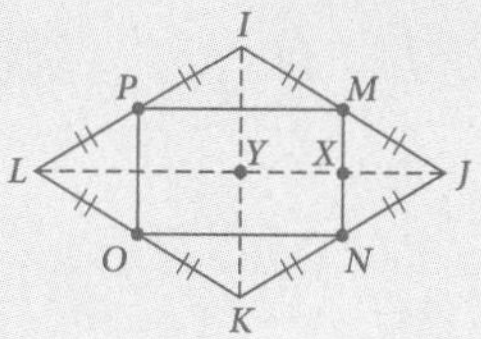

By the Triangle Midsegment Theorem both $\overline{PM}$ and $\overline{ON}$ are parallel to $\overline{LJ}$, and both $\overline{PO}$ and $\overline{MN}$ are parallel to $\overline{IK}$. Because $\overline{LJ}$ and $\overline{IK}$ are perpendicular, we can use corresponding angles on parallel lines to prove that the lines that are adjacent sides of the quadrilateral are also perpendicular.

30a. The quadrilateral formed when the midpoints of the sides of a kite are connected is a rectangle.

30b.

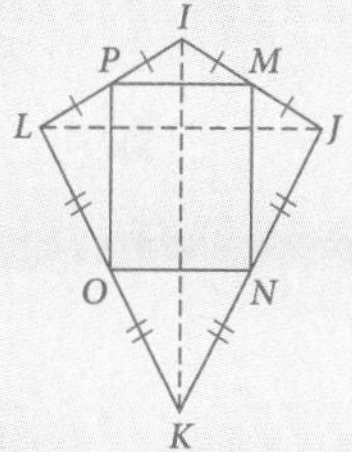

By the Triangle Midsegment Theorem both $\overline{PM}$ and $\overline{ON}$ are parallel to $\overline{LJ}$, and both $\overline{PO}$ and $\overline{MN}$ are parallel to $\overline{IK}$. Because $\overline{LJ}$ and $\overline{IK}$ are perpendicular, we can use the CA Postulate to prove that the lines that are adjacent sides of the quadrilateral are also perpendicular.

31.

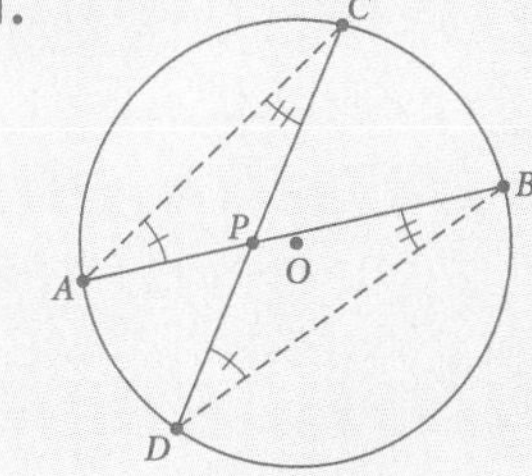

Use the Line Postulate to construct chords $\overline{DB}$ and $\overline{AC}$. Then use the Inscribed Angles Intercepting Arcs Theorem and the AA Similarity Postulate to get $\triangle APC \sim \triangle DPB$. Therefore, by CSSTP and the multiplication property, $AP \cdot PB = DP \cdot PC$.

ASSESSING

For the chapter test you can use items from any of the assessment resources. Be sure to include enough items like the first 23 review exercises so that students who are not yet at van Hiele level 3 will have some success. You might also include in the chapter grade a partner presentation of a proof.

For a final exam you can use form A or form B from the Assessment Resources or create your own test using the Test Generator.

FACILITATING SELF-ASSESSMENT

Any of the proofs make good portfolio selections. As students organize their notebooks, they will be preparing for the final exam.

Hints for Selected Exercises

... there are no answers to the problems of life in the back of the book.

SØREN KIERKEGAARD

You will find hints below for exercises that are marked with an ⓗ in the text. Instead of turning to a hint before you've tried to solve a problem on your own, make a serious effort to solve the problem without help. But if you need additional help to solve a problem, this is the place to look.

CHAPTER 0

LESSON 0.1

7. Here's the title of the sculpture.

Early morning calm
knotweed stalks
pushed into lake bottom
made complete by their own reflection

Derwent Water, Cumbria, 20 February & 8–9 March, 1988

LESSON 0.2

3. Design 1 Do one-half of the Astrid four times.

Design 2 Connect the midpoints of the sides of an equilateral triangle with line segments and leave the middle triangle empty. Repeat the process on the three other triangles. Then, repeat the rule again.

Design 3 On each side of an equilateral hexagon, mark the point that is one-third of the length of the side. Connect the points and repeat the process.

LESSON 0.3

2. Use isometric dot paper, or draw an equilateral equiangular hexagon with sides of length 2. Each vertex of the hexagon will be the center of a circle with radius 1. Fit the seventh small circle inside the other six. The large circle has the same center as the seventh small circle and has radius 3.

LESSON 0.6

5. Draw two identical squares, one rotated $\frac{1}{8}$ turn, or 45°, from the other. Where is the center of each arc located?

CHAPTER 1

LESSON 1.1

3. Because a line is infinitely long in two directions, it doesn't matter where the point used to name the line lies on the line. There are three possible ways to name the line if you don't count switching the letters as two different ways.

21. Because a ray is infinitely long in one direction, it doesn't matter which point you use for the second letter as long as it's not the endpoint.

LESSON 1.2

13. Find $m\angle CQA$ and $m\angle BQA$ and subtract.

26. Don't forget that at half past the hour, the hour hand will be halfway between the 3 and the 4.

36. A $\frac{1}{4}$ rotation $= \frac{1}{4} \cdot 360°$. Subtract the sum of 15° and 21° from that result.

LESSON 1.3

15. Do not limit your thinking to just two dimensions.

24. The measure of the incoming angle equals the measure of the outgoing angle (just as in pool).

25. Use trial and error.

LESSON 1.4

18. The order of the letters matters.

31. Draw your diagram on patty paper or tracing paper. Test your diagram by folding your paper along the line of reflection to see if the two halves coincide. Your diagram should have only one pair of parallel sides.

34. Label the width of each small rectangle as w and its length as l. Therefore the perimeter of the large rectangle is $5w + 4l = 198$ cm.

38. Only one of these is impossible.

LESSON 1.5

24. There are four possible locations for R. The slope of $\overline{CL} = \frac{1}{5}$. Therefore the slope of the perpendicular segment $= \frac{-5}{1}$ or $\frac{5}{-1}$.

31. Locate the midpoint of each rod. Draw the segment that contains all the midpoints. This segment is called the median of the triangle.

LESSON 1.6

19. This ordered pair rule tells you to double the abscissa and double the ordinate. (abscissa, ordinate)

LESSON 1.7

3. Make a large graph (Quadrant I only). Label the vertical axis "feet" and the horizontal axis "days." Or try a number line.

6. The vertical distance from the top of the pole to the lowest point of the cable is 15 feet. Compare that distance with the length of the cable.

7. Draw a diagram. Draw two points, A and B, on your paper. Locate a point that appears to be equally spaced from points A and B. The midpoint of $\overline{AB}$ is only one such point; find others. Connect the points into a line. For points in space, picture a plane between the two points.

11. Copy trapezoid $ABCD$ onto patty paper or tracing paper. Rotate the tracing paper 90°, or $\frac{1}{4}$ turn, counterclockwise. Point A on the tracing paper should coincide with point A on the diagram in the book.

15. The number of hexagons is increasing by one each time, but the perimeter is increasing by four.

34. Because $\overline{PA}$, $\overline{PB}$, $\overline{QA}$, and $\overline{QB}$ are all radii, quadrilateral $PAQB$ is a rhombus. $\overline{AB}$ and $\overline{PQ}$ are the diagonals of rhombus $PAQB$.

LESSON 1.8

8. The biggest face is 3 m by 4 m. Your diagram will look similar to the diagram for Step 4 on page 80, except that the shortest segment will be vertical.

9. The number of boxes that will fit in the solid equals the volume, which is found by $l \times w \times h$.

18. Cut out a rectangle like the one shown and tape it to your pencil. Rotate your pencil to see what shape the rotating rectangle forms.

20. Imagine slicing an orange in half. What shape is revealed?

24. Do not limit your thinking to two dimensions. This situation can be modeled by using three pencils to represent the three lines.

CHAPTER 1 REVIEW

37. Here is one possible method. Draw a circle and one diameter. Draw another diameter perpendicular to the first. Draw two more diameters so that eight 45° angles are formed. Draw the regular octagon formed by the endpoints of the diameters.

45. A clock forms 12 central angles that each measure $30° \left(\frac{360°}{12}\right)$. The angle formed by the hands is $3\frac{1}{2}$ of those central angles.

54. Cut out a semicircle and tape it to your pencil. Rotate your pencil to see what shape the rotating semicircle forms.

57. Rotate your book so that the red line is vertical.

CHAPTER 2 • CHAPTER 2 CHAPTER 2 • CHAPTER

LESSON 2.1

1. Conjectures are statements that generalize from a number of instances to "all." Therefore, Stony is saying "All __?__."

4. Change all fractions to the same denominator.

7. $1 + 1 = 2, 1 + 2 = 3, 2 + 3 = 5,$
$3 + 5 = 8, \ldots$

8. $1^2, 2^2, 3^2, 4^2, \ldots$

13. Add another row with one more rectangle.

14. Each segment branches off into two segments.

15. Connect the midpoints of the sides of the triangle. Make the triangle formed in the middle white. Connect the midpoints of the sides of the shaded triangles. Make the triangles formed in the middle white.

17. Substitute 1 for n and evaluate the expression to find the first term. Substitute 2 for n to find the second term, and so on.

21. For example, "I learned by trial and error that you turn wood screws clockwise to screw them into wood and counterclockwise to remove them."

26. Imagine folding the square up and "wrapping" the two rectangles and the other triangle around the square.

27. Turn your book so that the red line is vertical. Imagine rotating the figure so that the part jutting out is facing back to the right.

28. Cut out a quarter-circle and tape it to your pencil. Rotate your pencil to see the figure formed.

42. Remember that a kite is a quadrilateral with two pairs of consecutive, congruent sides. One of the diagonals does bisect the angles of the kite, the other does not.

LESSON 2.2

8. What is the smallest possible size for an obtuse angle?

9. Compare how many 1's there are in the numbers that are multiplied with the middle digit of the answer; then compare both quantities with the row number.

12. Look for a constant difference among terms.

16. The number of rows increases by one, and the number of columns increases by one.

17. The number of rows increases by two, and the number of columns increases by one.

LESSON 2.3

1. Look for a constant difference, then adjust the rule for the first term.

4. See below.

7. Draw the polygons and all possible diagonals from one vertex. Fill in the table and look for a pattern. You should be able to see the pattern by the time you get to a hexagon.

LESSON 2.4

4. Compare this exercise with the Investigation Party Handshakes, and with Exercise 3. What change can you make to each of those functions to fit this pattern?

5. This is like Exercise 4 except that you add the number of sides to the number of diagonals.

6. In other words, each time a new line is drawn, it passes through all the others. This also gives the maximum number of intersections.

7. Exercises 5 and 6 have the same rule. Every term in the sequence for Exercise 4 is n less than the corresponding term in the sequences for Exercises 5 and 6. This is because in Exercise 5 you count the sides of the polygons.

9. Let a point represent each team, and let the segments connecting the points represent *one* game played between them. What do you then have to multiply this answer by?

10. Use the model from Exercise 5.

14. The tricky part to this problem is that points A and B could be on the same side of point E.

---

4. (*Lesson 2.3*)

Figure number	1	2	3	4	5	6	n
Number of tiles	$1 \cdot 8$	$2 \cdot 8$	$3 \cdot 8$	$4 \cdot 8$	$? \cdot ?$	$? \cdot ?$	$? \cdot ?$

LESSON 2.5

4. Here is how to begin:

$a = 60°$ because of the Vertical Angles Conjecture. $c = 120°$ because of the Linear Pair Conjecture.

23. Refer to Lesson 2.4, Exercise 5.

24. Refer to Lesson 2.4, Exercise 6.

25. Refer to Lesson 2.4, Exercise 5, but subtract the number of couples from each term because the couples don't shake hands.

27. Refer to Lesson 2.4, Exercise 4. Then use "guess and check."

LESSON 2.6

4. Because quadrilateral *TUNA* is a parallelogram, $\overline{TU} \parallel \overline{AN}$ and $\overline{TA} \parallel \overline{UN}$. Form $\overrightarrow{NA}$ by extending side $\overline{NA}$. Place a point Q on $\overrightarrow{NA}$, to the left of A. $\angle T \cong \angle QAT$ by the Alternate Interior Angles Conjecture. $\angle N \cong \angle QAT$ by the Corresponding Angles Conjecture. Because $\angle T$ and $\angle N$ are both congruent to $\angle QAT$, $\angle N \cong \angle T$.

6.

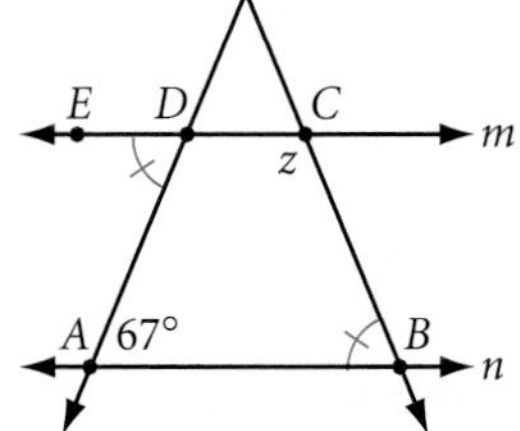

$\angle DAB$ and $\angle EDA$ are congruent by the Alternate Interior Angles Conjecture. $\angle EDA$ and $\angle CDA$ are a linear pair. Now every angle in quadrilateral *ABCD* is known except the one labeled z. The sum of the angles of a quadrilateral is 360°.

7. Measures a, b, c, and d are all related by parallel lines. Measures e, f, g, h, i, j, k, and s are also all related by parallel lines.

13. Squares, rectangles, rhombuses, and kites are eliminated because they have reflectional symmetry.

16. Graph the original triangle and the new triangle on separate graphs. Cut one out and lay it on top of the other to see if they are congruent.

20. Proceed in an organized way.

Number of 1-by-1 squares = ?
Number of 2-by-2 squares = ?
Number of 3-by-3 squares = ?
Number of 4-by-4 squares = ?
Then add.

21. You can add the first two function rules to find the third function rule.

CHAPTER 2 REVIEW

5. Try the alphabet backward and the powers of 2 forward.

7. For the pattern of the letters, number each letter of the alphabet and find the pattern of their differences.

9. Here is how to begin:

$f(1) = 2^{1-1} = 2^0 = 1$

$f(2) = 2^{2-1} = 2^1 = 2$

11. The diagrams are alternating net and solid. The number of sides of the base increases by one.

14. Refer to Lesson 2.4, the Investigation Party Handshakes, discussion of triangular numbers.

15. Exercises 14 and 15 are closely related. Let's examine the rule for Exercise 14.

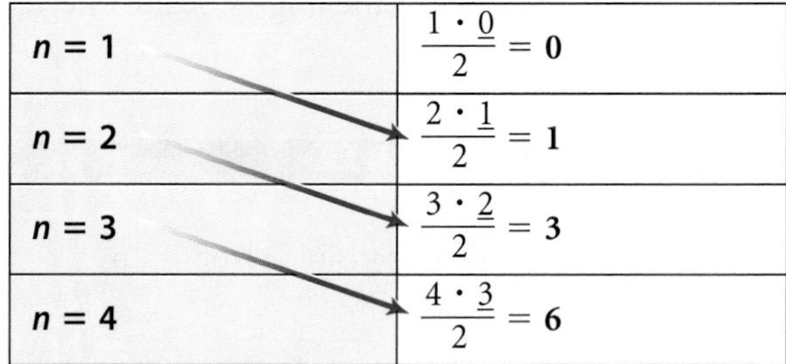

$n = 1$	$\frac{1 \cdot \underline{0}}{2} = 0$
$n = 2$	$\frac{2 \cdot \underline{1}}{2} = 1$
$n = 3$	$\frac{3 \cdot \underline{2}}{2} = 3$
$n = 4$	$\frac{4 \cdot \underline{3}}{2} = 6$

We want 1 to be the first term, not 0. Now look at the pattern for the rest of the terms. The underlined numbers are the n, and the numbers in front of the n are one higher.

17. See below.

18.

$1 = 1 = 1^2$

$1 + 3 = 4 = 2^2$

$1 + 3 + 5 = 9 = 3^2$

$1 + 3 + 5 + 7 = 16 = 4^2$

And so on . . .

20. How many vertical interior segments are there? How many horizontal?

23. Refer to Lesson 2.4, Exercise 6. Then use "guess and check."

CHAPTER 3 • CHAPTER 3 CHAPTER 3 • CHAPTER

LESSON 3.1

2. Copy the first segment onto a ray. Copy the second segment immediately after the first.

10. You duplicated a triangle in Exercise 7. You can think of the quadrilateral as two triangles stuck together (they meet at the diagonal).

14. Fold the paper so that the two congruent sides of the triangle coincide.

LESSON 3.2

2. Bisect, then bisect again.

3. Construct one pair of intersecting arcs, then change your compass setting to construct a second pair of intersecting arcs on the same side of the line segment as the first pair.

4. Bisect $\overline{CD}$ to get the length $\frac{1}{2}CD$. Subtract this length from $2AB$.

5. The average is the sum of the two lengths divided by the number of segments (two). Construct a segment of length $AB + CD$. Bisect the segment to get the average length. Or take half of each, then add them.

8. Construct the median from the vertex to the midpoint.

LESSON 3.3

3. Construct the perpendicular through point B to $\overrightarrow{TO}$.

4. Does your method from Investigation 1 still work? Can you modify it?

5. Construct right angles at Q and R.

13. Look at two columns as a "group."

1st rectangle is 2 groups of 1

2nd rectangle is 3 groups of 3

3rd rectangle is 4 groups of 5

4th rectangle is 5 groups of 7

. . .

nth rectangle is $n + 1$ groups of $2n - 1$

---

17. (*Chapter 2 Review*)

2	2 + 4	2 + 4 + 6	2 + 4 + 6 + 8	2 + 4 + 6 + 8 + 10
2	6	12	20	30

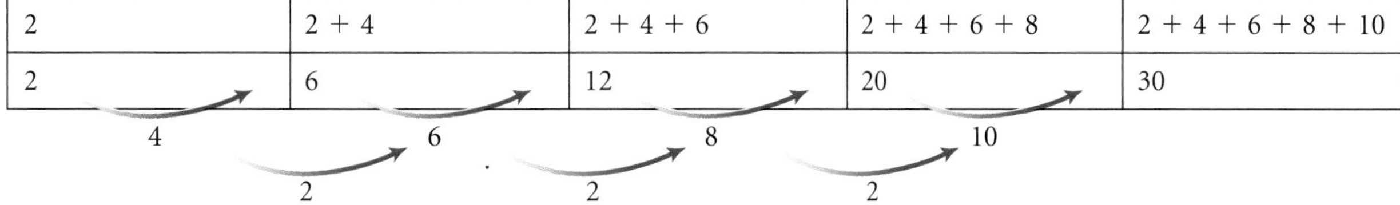

The differences between terms aren't constant, so it's not a linear pattern, but the second set of differences is a constant. Sequences of this type have two linear factors, as the table below shows, and are called *quadratic sequences.*

n	1	2	3	4	5
Term	2	6	12	20	30
Factors	1 × 2	2 × 3	3 × 4	4 × 5	5 × 6

17. Each angle of a regular pentagon is 108°.

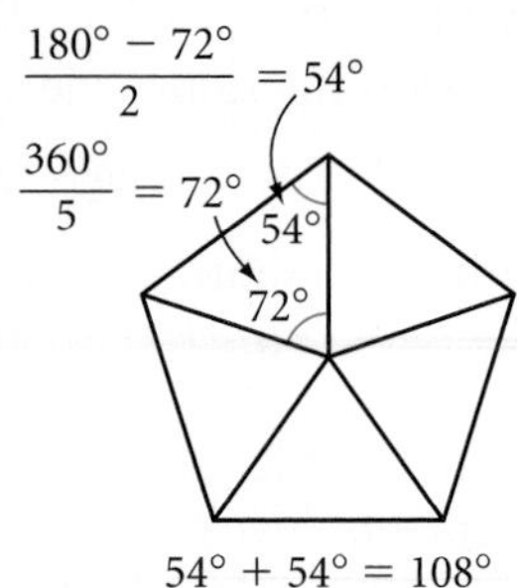

(Or, divide a circle into five congruent arcs, and join the endpoints.)

LESSON 3.4

14. Use your protractor and measure off eight rays 45° apart about a point. Use your compass and swing a circle at the point of intersection.

15. Construct two lines perpendicular to each other, and then bisect the right angles.

16. Because the angles of a triangle add to 180°, the problem could be restated as "Draw a second triangle with a 40° angle, an 80° angle, and a side between the given angles measuring 8 cm."

LESSON 3.5

3. If the perimeter is z, then each side has length $\frac{1}{4}z$. Construct the perpendicular bisector of z to get $\frac{1}{2}z$. Construct the perpendicular bisector of $\frac{1}{2}z$ to get $\frac{1}{4}z$.

10. According to the Perpendicular Bisector Conjecture, if a point is on the perpendicular bisector, then it is equidistant from the endpoints of the segment (which in this case represent fire stations). Therefore, if a point is on one side of the perpendicular bisector, it is closer to the fire station on that side of the perpendicular bisector.

LESSON 3.6

1. Construct a segment, $\overline{MS}$. Draw an arc with radius AS from point S and an arc with radius MA from point M. Connect the point at which the arcs intersect to points M and S to form your triangle.

5. Duplicate $\angle A$ and $\overline{AB}$ on one side of $\angle A$. Open the compass to length BC. If you put the compass point at point B, you'll find two possible locations to mark arcs for point C.

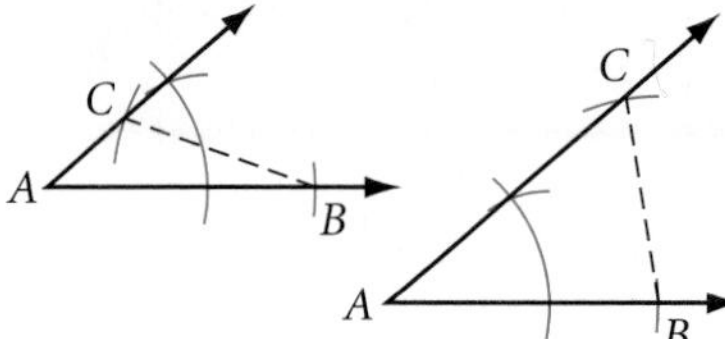

6. $y - x$ is the sum of the two equal sides. Find this length and bisect it to get the length of the other two legs of your triangle.

LESSON 3.7

6. Find the incenter.

7. Find the circumcenter.

8. Draw a slightly larger circle on patty paper and try to fit it inside the triangle.

9. Draw a slightly smaller circle on patty paper and try to fit it outside the triangle.

16. Start by finding points whose coordinates add to 9, such as (3, 6) and (7, 2). Try writing an equation and graphing it.

17. One way is to construct the incenter by bisecting the two given angles. Then find two points on the unfinished sides, equidistant from the incenter and in the same direction (both closer to the missing point.) Now find a point equidistant from those two points. Draw the missing angle bisector through that point and the incenter.

LESSON 3.8

2. If $CM = 16$, then $UM = \frac{1}{2}(16) = 8$. If $TS = 21$, then $SM = \frac{1}{3}(21) = 7$.

8. A quadrilateral can be divided into two triangles in two different ways. How can you use the centroids of these triangles to find *the* centroid?

15. Construct the altitudes for the two other vertices. From the point where the two altitudes meet, construct a line perpendicular to the southern boundary of the triangle.

16. How many people does each person greet? Don't count any greeting twice. There are 60 people. If everyone greets each other, the number of greetings would be $\frac{60 \cdot 59}{2}$. But dorm members aren't greeting their guests, so the number of greetings would be $\frac{60 \cdot 59}{2} - 40$.

CHAPTER 3 REVIEW

28. Draw a long segment and use your compass to add y plus y plus x, bisect z, then subtract it from the sum.

CHAPTER 4 • CHAPTER  CHAPTER 4 • CHAPTER

LESSON 4.1

4. Ignore the 100° angle and the line that intersects the larger triangle. Find the three interior angles of the triangle. Then find z.

6. The total measure of the three angles is 3 times 360° minus the sum of the interior angles of the triangle.

7. The sum of a linear pair of angles is 180°. So the total measure of the three angles is 3 times 180° minus the sum of the interior angles of the triangle.

8. You can find a by looking at the large triangle that has 40° and 71° as its other measures. You can find b because it forms a linear pair with the 133° angle. Continue on your own.

15. $m\angle A + m\angle B + x = 180°$ and $m\angle D + m\angle E + y = 180°$. Then use substitution to prove $x = y$.

LESSON 4.2

1. $m\angle H + m\angle O = 180° - 22°$ and $m\angle H = m\angle O$.

7. Notice that $d = e$ and $d + e + e + 66° = 180°$. Next, find the alternate interior angle to c.

8. Notice that all the triangles are isosceles!

12. The sides do not have to be congruent.

13. Make $GK < MP$.

15. Find the slopes.

21. Move each point right 5 units and down 3 units.

LESSON 4.3

5. Find the value of the unmarked angle and use the Side-Angle Inequality Conjecture.

9. Use the Side-Angle Inequality Conjecture to find an inequality of sides for each triangle, then combine the inequalities.

11. Any side must be smaller than the sum of the other two sides. What must it be larger than?

13. Try using the Triangle Sum Conjecture.

14. Use the Triangle Exterior Angle Conjecture.

17. You need to show that $x = a + b$. From the Triangle Sum Conjecture, you know that $a + b + c = 180°$. Also, $\angle BCA$ and $\angle BCD$ are a linear pair, so $x + c = 180°$.

21. All corresponding sides and angles are congruent. Can you see why? (And remember that the ordering of the points is important in correctly stating the answer.)

LESSON 4.4

1. Rotate one triangle 180°.

2. The shared side is congruent to itself.

9. Match congruent sides.

12. Take a closer look. Are congruent parts corresponding?

15. $UN = YA = 4$, $RA = US = 3$, $m\angle A = m\angle U = 90°$

LESSON 4.5

3. Flip one triangle over.

19. The sides do not have to be congruent.

LESSON 4.6

1. Don't forget to mark the shared segment as congruent to itself.

2. Use $\triangle CRN$ and $\triangle WON$.

4. Use $\triangle ATI$ and $\triangle GTS$.

5. Draw $\overline{UF}$.

7. Draw $\overline{UT}$.

10. Count the lengths of the horizontal and vertical segments, and label the right angles congruent.

17. Make the included angles different.

LESSON 4.7

7. Use $\triangle ABD$ and $\triangle CBD$.

8. Don't forget about the shared side and the Side-Angle Inequality Conjecture.

10. When you look at the larger triangles, ignore the marks for $\overline{OS} \cong \overline{RS}$. When you look at the smaller triangles, ignore the right-angle mark and the given statement $\overline{PO} \cong \overline{PR}$.

11. First, mark the vertical angles. In $\triangle ADM$, the side is included between the two angles. In $\triangle CRM$, the side is not included between the two angles.

14. Review incenter, circumcenter, orthocenter, and centroid.

17. See if your teacher has 14 cubes. Build the figure shown, take away the indicated blocks, and draw what is left.

LESSON 4.8

1. $AB + BC + AC = 48$

$AD = \frac{1}{2}AB$

8. Use the vertex angle bisector as your auxiliary line segment.

12. At 3:15 the hands have not yet crossed each other. At 3:20 the hands have already crossed each other, because the minute hand is on the 4 but the hour hand is only one-third of its way from the 3 toward the 4. So the hands overlap sometime between 3:15 and 3:20.

14. Make a table and look for a pattern.

17. How many H's branch off each C?

CHAPTER 4 REVIEW

19. Look for alternate interior angles.

21. Not enough information is given. The two angles at point H may look the same, but you just don't know.

23. There are actually two isosceles triangles in the figure, and there are three possible answers. It may help to redraw the triangles so that they don't overlap.

25. Calculate the missing angle measure.

32. Look for congruent triangles. Then look for congruent angles to show that lines are parallel.

35. Vertical angles are congruent.

CHAPTER 5 • CHAPTER 5 CHAPTER 5 • CHAPTER

LESSON 5.1

2. All angles are equal in measure.

6. $d + 44° + 30° = 180°$

7. $3g + 117° + 108° = 540°$

13. $(n - 2) \cdot 180° = 2700°$

14. $\frac{(n-2) \cdot 180°}{n} = 156°$

17. Use the Triangle Sum Conjecture and angle addition.

LESSON 5.2

6. First, find the measure of an angle of the equiangular heptagon. Then, find c by the Linear Pair Conjecture.

10. $24° = \frac{360°}{n}$

12. An obtuse angle measures greater than 90°, and the sum of exterior angles of a polygon is always 360°.

15. Look at $\triangle RAC$ and $\triangle DCA$.

16. Draw $\overline{AT}$.

LESSON 5.3

11. Construct $\angle I$ and $\angle W$ at the ends of $\overline{WI}$. Construct $\overline{IS}$. Construct a line through point S parallel to $\overline{WI}$.

13. The nonshared endpoints of the consecutive congruent segments are equidistant from the shared endpoint. So the shared endpoint is on the perpendicular bisector of one diagonal.

16. Look at $\triangle AFG$ and $\triangle BEH$.

LESSON 5.4

2. $PO = \frac{1}{2}RA$

4. Use the Three Midsegments Conjecture.

9. Draw a diagonal of the original quadrilateral. Note that it's parallel to two other segments.

LESSON 5.5

4. $VN = \frac{1}{2}VF$ and $NI = \frac{1}{2}EI$

8. With the midpoint of the longer diagonal as center and using the length of half the shorter diagonal as radius, construct a circle.

10. Complete the parallelogram with the given vectors as sides. The resultant vector is the diagonal of the parallelogram. Refer to the diagram right before the Exercises.

11. $PR = a$. Therefore $MA = a$. $\underline{?} + a = b$. Solve for $\underline{?}$. The height of A is c. Therefore the height of M is c.

LESSON 5.6

1. Consider the parallelogram below.

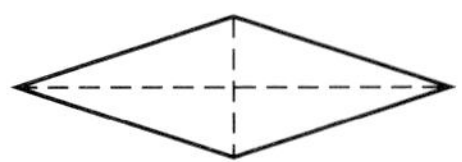

12. $\angle P$ and $\angle PEA$ are supplementary.

17. The diagonals of a square are equal in length and are perpendicular bisectors of each other.

18. Construct $\angle B$, then bisect it. Mark off the length of diagonal $\overline{BK}$ on the angle bisector. Then construct the perpendicular bisector of $\overline{BK}$.

23. The diagonal of a rhombus bisects the angle.

24. Construct a rhombus with your segment as the diagonal. The other diagonal will be the perpendicular bisector.

31. Use the Quadrilateral Sum Conjecture to prove the measure of each angle is 90°. If the consecutive interior angles are supplementary, then the lines are parallel.

LESSON 5.7

1. If you start from square 100 and work backward, the problem becomes much easier.

7. Look at $\triangle YIO$ and $\triangle OGY$.

8. Break up the rectangle into four triangles ($\triangle EAR$, etc.), and show that they are congruent triangles.

12. Imagine what happens to the rectangles when you pull them at their vertices.

13. Calculate the measures of the angles of the regular polygons. Remember that there are 360° around any point.

14. Look at the alternate interior angles.

15. You miss 5 minutes out of 15 minutes.

16. The container is $\frac{8}{12} = \frac{2}{3}$ full. It will be $\frac{2}{3}$ full no matter which face it rests on.

CHAPTER 5 REVIEW

20. Refer to the figure at the end of the Investigation Four Parallelogram Properties for a similar example. Let 1 cm = 100 km be your scale.

23. Construct $\overline{LP}$ and copy $\angle L$. Mark off $\overline{LN}$. At point N, construct a line parallel to $\overline{LP}$.

LESSON 6.1

4. $y + y + y + 72° = 360°$

18. Calculate the slope and midpoint of $\overline{AB}$. Recall that slopes of perpendicular lines are negative reciprocals.

20.

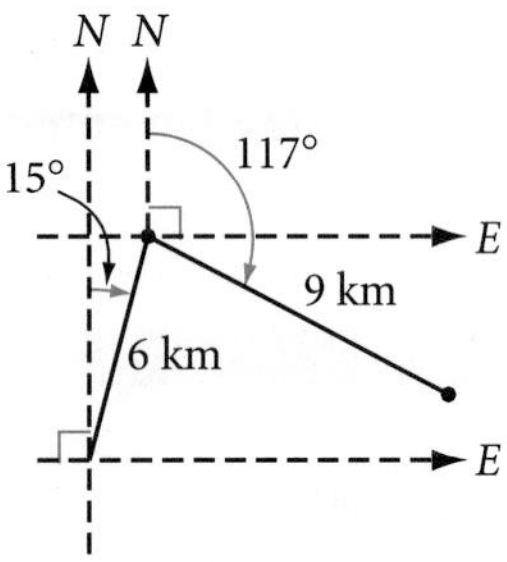

LESSON 6.2

1. $130° + 90° + w + 90° = 360°$

2. $x + x + 70° = 180°$

5. $CP = PA = AO = OR, CT = TD = DS = SR$

8. From the Tangent Conjecture, you know that the tangent is perpendicular to the radius at the point of tangency.

15. Draw a diameter. Then bisect it repeatedly to find the centers of the circles.

16. Look at the angles in the quadrilateral formed.

23. Draw the triangle formed by the three light switches. The center of the circumscribed circle would be equidistant from the three points.

24. Make a list of the powers of 3, beginning with $3^0 = 1$. Look for a pattern in the units digit.

25. Use a protractor and a centimeter ruler to make a careful drawing. Let 1 cm represent 1 mile.

LESSON 6.3

3. $c + 120° = 2(95°)$

4. Draw in the radius to the tangent to form a right triangle.

14. The measure of each of the five angles is half the measure of its intercepted arc. But the five arcs add up to the complete circle (360°).

15. $a = \frac{1}{2}(70°), b = \frac{1}{2}(80°), y = a + b$

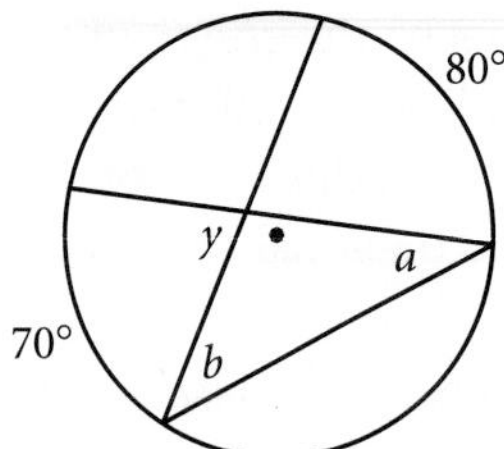

19. Draw the altitude to the point where the side of the triangle (extended if necessary) intersects the circle.

20.

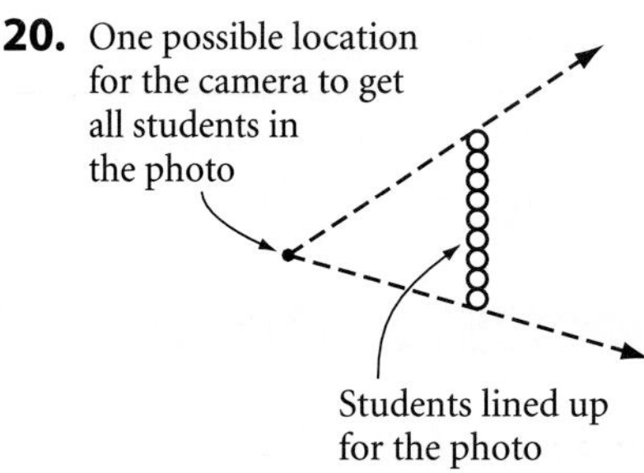

23. Show congruent right triangles inside congruent isosceles triangles.

24. Start with an equilateral triangle whose vertices are the centers of the three congruent circles. Then locate the incenter/circumcenter/orthocenter/centroid to find the center of the larger circle.

LESSON 6.4

1. Use angle addition, arc addition, and Case 1.

4. Note that $m\overparen{YLI} + m\overparen{YCI} = 360°$.

5. $\angle 1 \cong \angle 2$ by AIA, and $\angle 1$ and $\angle 2$ are inscribed angles.

6. Apply the Cyclic Quadrilateral Conjecture.

7. Draw one diagonal and use the Inscribed Angle Conjecture.

9. Think about the pair of angles that form a linear pair and the isosceles triangle.

10. Number the points in the grid 1–9. Make a list of all the possible combinations of three numbers. Do this in a logical manner.

Order doesn't matter, so the list beginning with 2 will be shorter than the list beginning with 1. The 3 list will be shorter than the 2 list, and so on. See how many of the possibilities are collinear, and divide that by the total number of possibilities.

11. Make an orderly list. Here is a beginning:

$\overline{RA}$ to $\overline{AL}$ to $\overline{LG}$

$\overline{RA}$ to $\overline{AN}$ to $\overline{NG}$

LESSON 6.5

9. $C = 2\pi r$, $44 \approx 2(3.14)r$

12. The diameter of the circle is 6 cm.

17. Use the Inscribed Angle Conjecture and the Triangle Exterior Angle Conjecture.

LESSON 6.6

1. $\text{speed} = \dfrac{\text{distance}}{\text{time}} = \dfrac{\text{circumference}}{12 \text{ hours}}$

$= \dfrac{2\pi(2000 + 6400) \text{ km}}{12 \text{ hours}}$

8. Calculate the distance traveled in one revolution, or the circumference, at each radius. Multiply this by the rpm to get the distance traveled in 1 minute. Remember, your answer is in inches. You may want to divide your answer by 12 and then by 60 to change its units into feet per second.

10. Use the Inscribed Angle Conjecture and the Triangle Exterior Angle Conjecture.

LESSON 6.7

3. $\dfrac{210}{360}\pi(24)$

8. $m\widehat{AR} + 70° + m\widehat{AR} + 146° = 360°$,

$\dfrac{m\widehat{AR}}{360°}(2\pi r) = 40\pi$

9. The length of one lap is equal to $(2 \cdot 100) + (2 \cdot 20\pi)$. The total distance covered in 6 minutes is 4 laps.

11. $\frac{1}{9}(2\pi r) = 12$ meters

15. The midsegment of a trapezoid is parallel to the bases, and the median to the base of an isosceles triangle is also the altitude.

16. The overlaid figure consists of two pairs of congruent equilateral triangles. The length of the side of the smaller pair is half the length of the side of the larger pair. All of the arcs use the lengths of the sides of the triangles as radii.

17. It is not 180°. What fraction of a complete cycle has the minute hand moved since 10:00? Hasn't the little hand moved that same fraction of the way from 10:00 to 11:00?

CHAPTER 6 REVIEW

5. Draw in the radius to the tangent to form a right triangle.

8. See Lesson 6.5, Exercises 16 and 17.

10. The supplement of 88° is 92°. $\frac{1}{2}(118° + f) = 92°$.

12. $C = \pi d$, $132 = \pi d$, $d = \dfrac{132}{\pi}$

13. Arc length of $\widehat{AB}$ is $\left(\frac{100°}{360°}\right)\pi(54)$.

14. To find the length of $\widehat{DC}$, first find the degree measure of $\widehat{DL}$. $\frac{m\widehat{DL} - 60°}{2} = 50°$.

29. Here is how to calculate 1 nautical mile near a pole: $\frac{2\pi \cdot 6357}{360 \cdot 60}$.

30. The locus of possible locations for Dmitri is a circle with radius $5 \cdot 1100$ ft $= 5500$ ft, and the locus for Tara is a circle with radius $7 \cdot 1100$ ft $= 7700$ ft. How many times can the two circles intersect?

31. The circumference of the table is 2×100. Calculate the diameter.

LESSON 7.2

2. All positive y's become negative y's; therefore, the figure is reflected over the x-axis.

7. Compare the ordered pairs for V and V', R and R', and Y and Y'.

LESSON 7.3

7. Connect a pair of corresponding points with a segment. Construct two perpendiculars to the segment with half the distance between the two given figures between them.

16. Find the midpoint of the segment connecting the two points. Connect the midpoint to one of the endpoints with a curve. Copy the curve onto patty paper and rotate it about the midpoint.

LESSON 7.4

13.

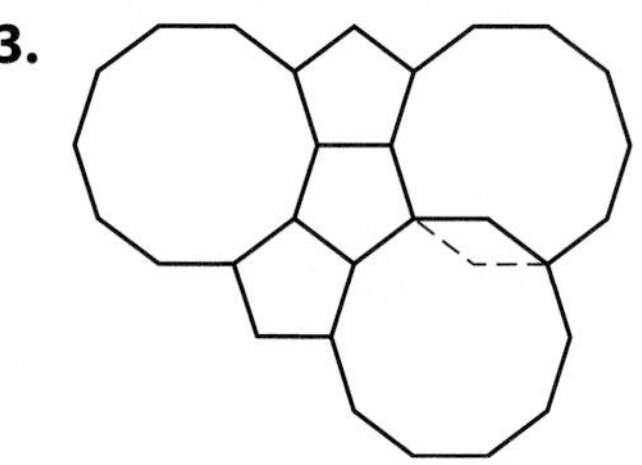

18. Work backward. Reflect a point of the 8-ball over the S cushion. Then reflect this image over the N cushion. Aim at this second image.

LESSON 7.5

2. Connect centers across the common side.

LESSON 7.6

9. If you are still unsure, use patty paper to trace the steps in the examples ("Pegasus" and *Monster Mix*).

LESSON 7.8

5. If you are still unsure, use patty paper to trace the four steps in the Escher *Horseman* example and the Escher *Symmetry Drawing E108* example.

LESSON 8.1

10. Factor 48 in two different ways.

19. Convert inches to fractions of a foot.

LESSON 8.2

8. $50 = \frac{1}{2}h(7 + 13)$

12. The area of the triangle can be calculated in three different ways, but each should give the same area: $\frac{1}{2}(5)y = \frac{1}{2}(15)x = \frac{1}{2}(6)(9)$.

22. Refer to the diagram below.

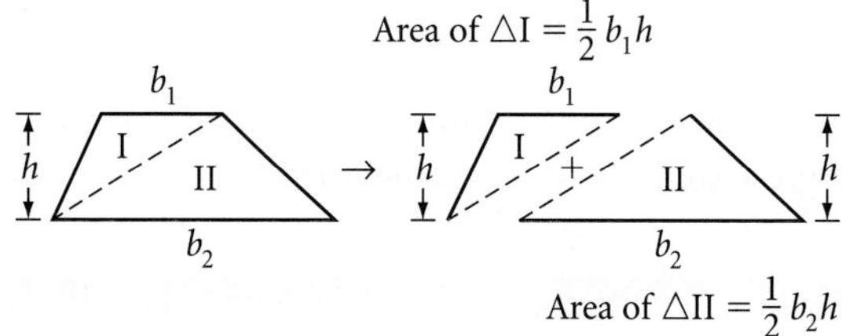

29. Draw the prism unfolded.

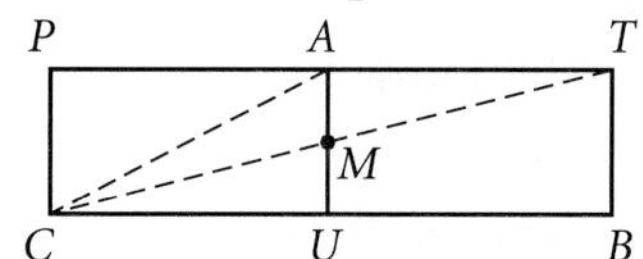

LESSON 8.3

4. Total cost is $\$20/\text{yd}^2 = \$20/9\ \text{ft}^2$; $A_{\text{carpet}} = 17 \cdot 27 - (6 \cdot 10 + 7 \cdot 9)$; 1 yd = 3 ft

8. First, find the area of all the vertical rectangles (walls). Notice that the area of the front and back triangles are the same.

LESSON 8.4

9. Construct a circle with radius 4 cm. Mark off six 4 cm chords around the circle.

10. Draw a regular pentagon circumscribed about a circle with radius 4 cm. Use your protractor to create five 72° angles from the center. Use your protractor to draw five tangent segments.

13. Find the area of the large hexagon and subtract from it the area of the small hexagon. Because they are regular hexagons, the distance from the center to each vertex equals the length of each side.

15. Divide the quadrilateral into two triangles (A and B). Find the areas of the two triangles and add them.

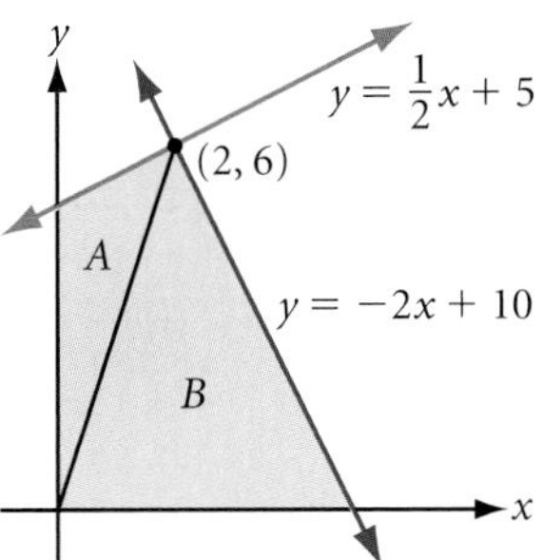

LESSON 8.5

15. Calculate the area of two circles, one with radius 3 cm and one with radius 6 cm. Compare the two areas.

16.

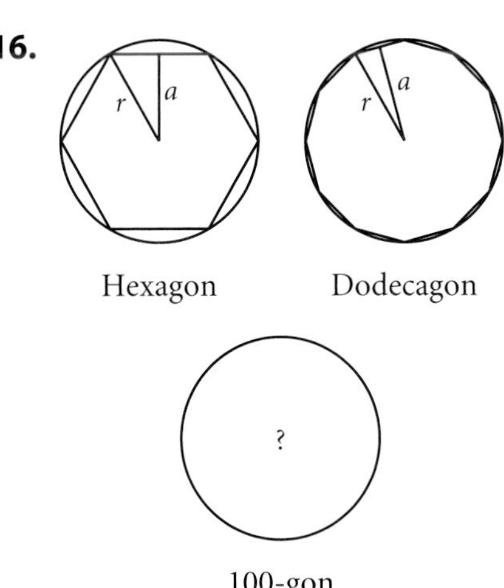

LESSON 8.6

6. The shaded area is equal to the area of the whole circle less the area of the smaller circle.

12. $10\pi = \frac{x}{360} \cdot \pi(10^2 - 8^2)$

18. $A = \frac{1}{2} \cdot h(b_1 + b_2)$. Because the length of the midsegment is $\frac{1}{2}(b_1 + b_2)$, the formula can be rewritten $A = \textit{midsegment} \cdot \textit{height}$.

LESSON 8.7

7. Use the formula for finding the area of a regular hexagon to find the area of each base.

To find the area of the six lateral faces, imagine unwrapping the six rectangles into one rectangle. The lateral area of this "unwrapped" rectangle is the height times the perimeter.

9.

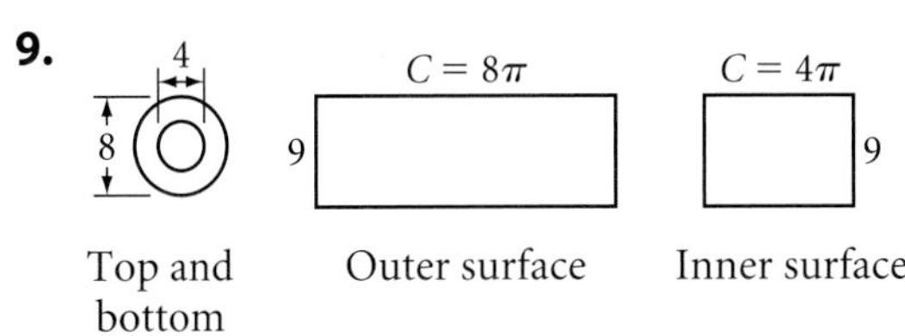

CHAPTER 8 REVIEW

37. Refer to Lesson 8.2 Project Maximizing Area.

39.

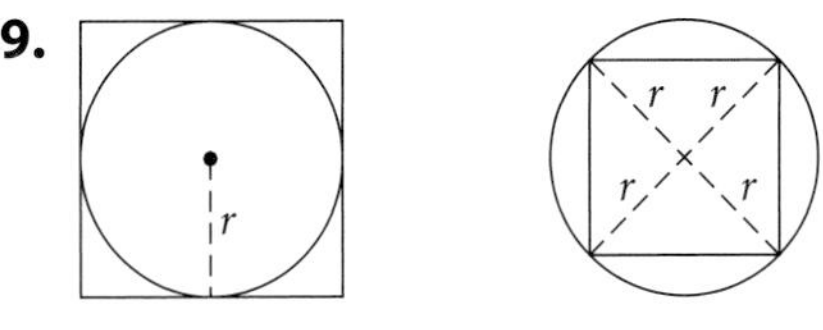

43a.

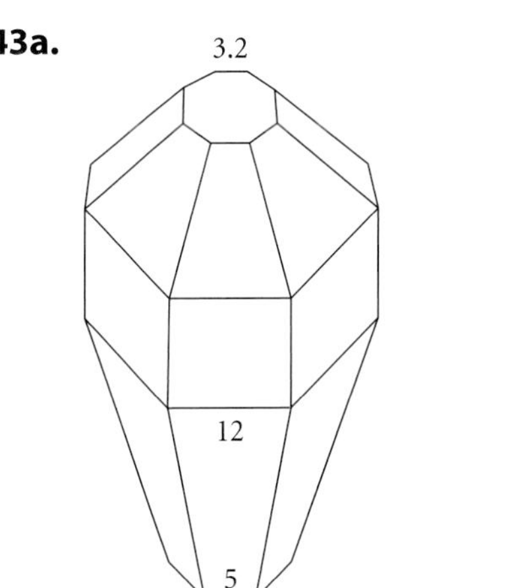

43b. Total surface area = area of octagon + 8 · area of small trapezoid + 8 · area of large trapezoid + 8 · area of square.

LESSON 9.1

6. $6^2 + 6^2 = c^2$

11. The radius of the circle is the hypotenuse of the right triangle.

13. Let s represent the length of the side of the square. Then $s^2 + s^2 = 32^2$.

15. Three consecutive integers can be written algebraically as n, $n + 1$, and $n + 2$.

17. Show that the area of the entire square (c^2) is equal to the sum of the areas of the four right triangles and the area of the smaller square.

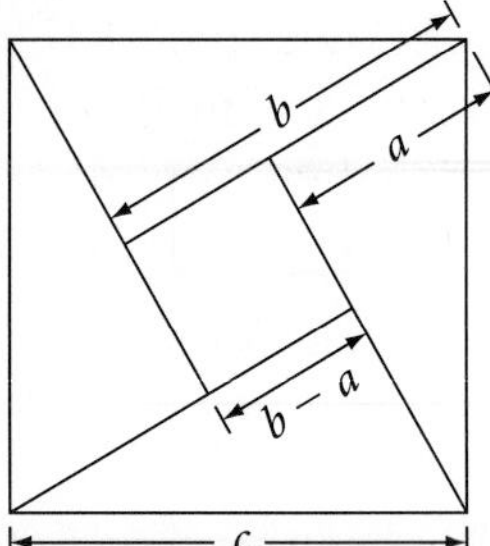

LESSON 9.2

6. $a^2 + b^2$ must exactly equal c^2.

10. Drop a perpendicular from the ordered pair to the x-axis to form a right triangle.

12. Check the list of Pythagorean triples in the beginning of this lesson for a right triangle that has three consecutive even integers.

22. Because a radius is perpendicular to a tangent, $m\angle DCF = 90°$. Because all radii in a circle are congruent, $\triangle DCE$ is isosceles.

LESSON 9.3

2. $b = \text{hypotenuse} \div \sqrt{2}$

4. $d = \frac{1}{2} \cdot 20$, $c = d \cdot \sqrt{3}$

7. Draw diagonal $\overline{DB}$ to form a right triangle on the base of the cube and another right triangle in the interior of the cube.

9. Divide by $\sqrt{2}$ for the length of the leg.

12. This is one way to show the relationship. Draw three 30°-60°-90° triangles with sides of lengths 1, $\sqrt{3}$, and 2. $6^2 - 3^2 = 27$, so $3\sqrt{3} = \sqrt{27}$.

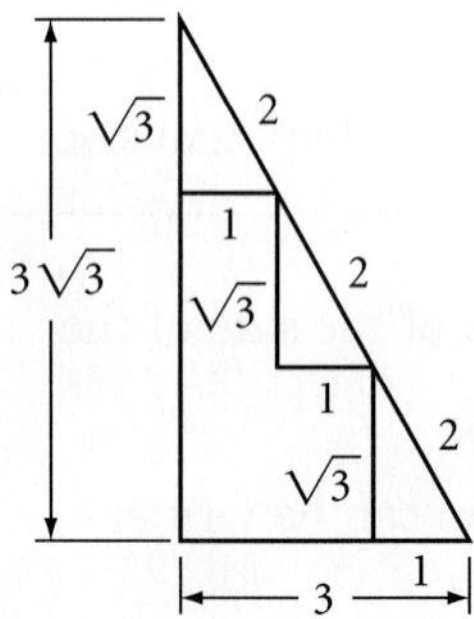

16. Draw an altitude of the equilateral triangle to form two 30°-60°-90° triangles.

19. Construct an isosceles right triangle with legs of length a; construct an equilateral triangle with sides of length $2a$ and construct an altitude; and construct a right triangle with legs of length $a\sqrt{2}$ and $a\sqrt{3}$.

22. Make the rays that form the right angle into lines. OR: Draw an auxiliary line parallel to the other parallel lines through the vertex of the right angle.

LESSON 9.4

1. The length of the hypotenuse is $(36 - x)$. Solve for x.

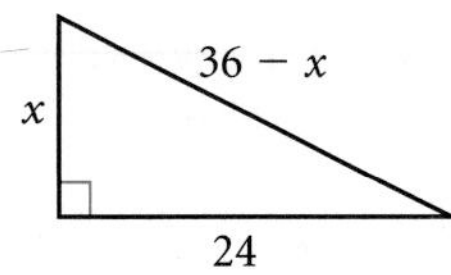

3. Average speed $= \dfrac{d}{4 \text{ hours}}$

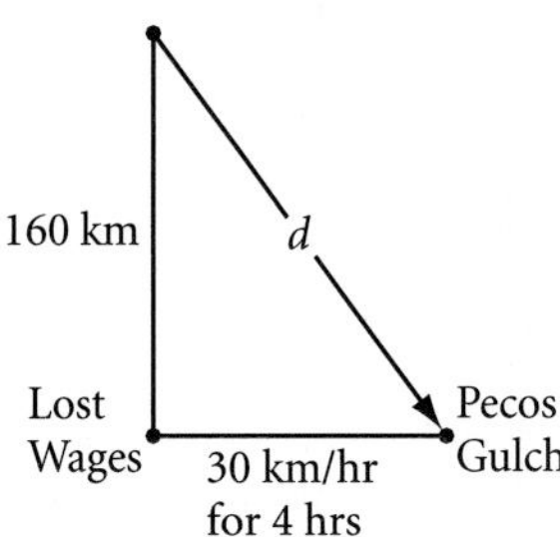

4. This is a two-step problem, so draw two right triangles. Find h, the height of the first triangle. The height of the second is 4 ft less than the height of the first. Then find x.

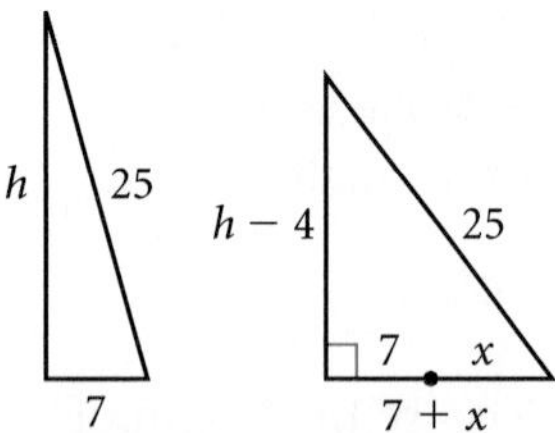

5.

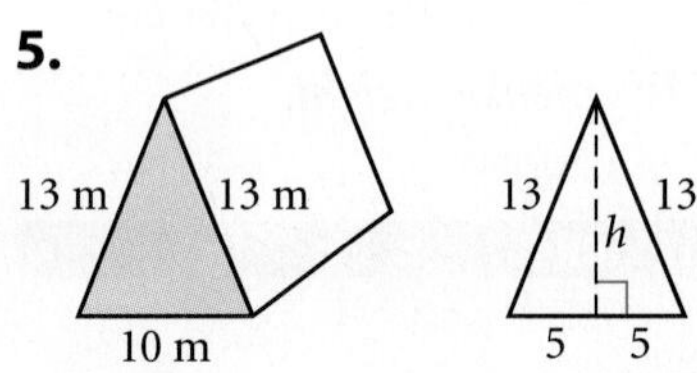

6. Find the apothem of the hexagon.

16. Use the Reflection Line Conjecture and special right triangles.

LESSON 9.5

11. Use the distance formula to find the length of the radius.

12. This is the same as finding the length of the space diagonal of the rectangular prism.

14. In the 45°-45°-90° triangle, $m = \sqrt{3} \cdot \sqrt{2}$; in the 30°-60°-90° triangle, $m = k\sqrt{3}$.

16. $(x + 8)^2 = 40^2 + x^2$

LESSON 9.6

1. Find $m\angle DOB$ using the Quadrilateral Sum Conjecture.

3. See below.

5. When $\overline{OT}$ and $\overline{OA}$ are drawn, they form a right triangle, with $OA = 15$ (length of hypotenuse) and $OT = 12$ (length of leg).

8.

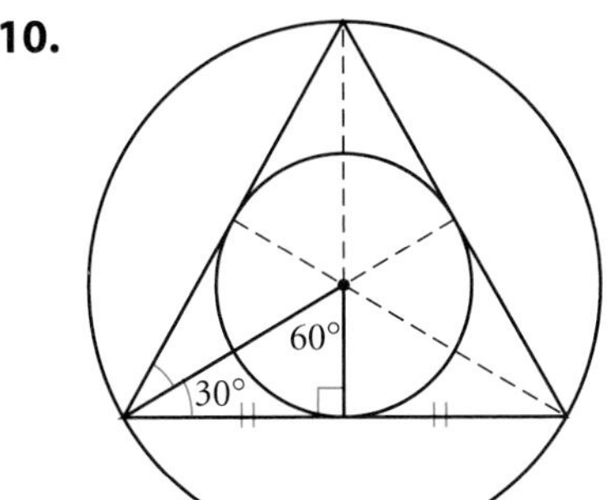

10.

60°
30°

14. The arc length of $\widehat{AC}$ is $\frac{80}{360}[2\pi(9)] = 4\pi$. Therefore, the circumference of the base of the cone is 4π. From this you can determine the radius of the base. The radius of the sector (9) becomes the slant height (the distance from the tip of the cone to the circumference of the base). The radius of the base, the slant height, and the height of the cone form a right triangle.

19. Rearrange the equation:

$$x^2 - 2x + 1 + y^2 = 100$$
$$(\underline{?})^2 + y^2 = 100$$

CHAPTER 9 REVIEW

10. The diameter of the semicircle is the longer leg of a 7-$\underline{?}$-25 right triangle.

12. Each half of the shaded area is equal to a quarter of a circle less the area of the isosceles right triangle.

15. $(45 \cdot 2)^2 + (60 \cdot 2)^2 = d^2$

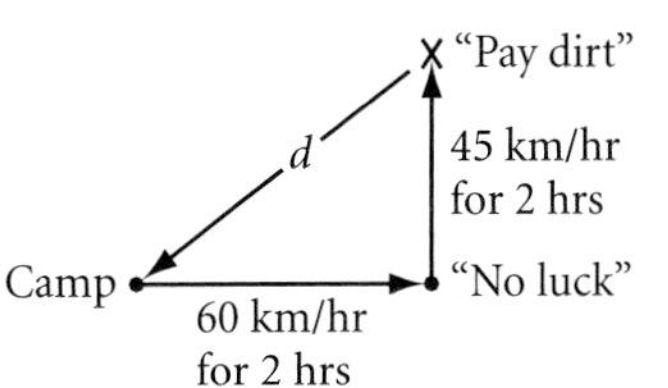

16. What will be the length of the diagonal if the shape is a rectangle?

LESSON 10.1

29. Think of a prism as a stack of thin copies of the bases.

31.

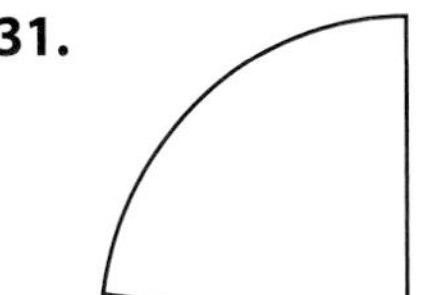

3.

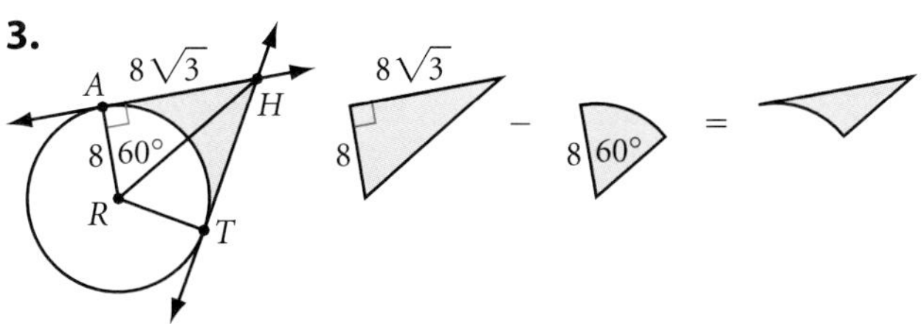

Hints for Selected Exercises

LESSON 10.2

2. $V = BH = \left(\frac{1}{2}bh\right)H$

5. You have only $\frac{1}{2}$ of a cylinder.
$V = BH = \left(\frac{1}{2}\pi r^2\right)H$

6. $\frac{90}{360}$, or $\frac{1}{4}$, of the cylinder is removed. Therefore, you need to find $\frac{3}{4}$ of the volume of the whole cylinder.

7a. What is the difference between this prism and the one in Exercise 2? Does it make a difference in the formula for the volume?

9. Cutie pie!

26. *SOTA* is a square, so the diagonals, $\overline{ST}$ and $\overline{OA}$, are congruent and are perpendicular bisectors of each other and $SM = OM = 6$. Use right triangle *SMO* to find *OS*, which also equals *OP*. Find *PA* with the equation $PA = OA - OP$.

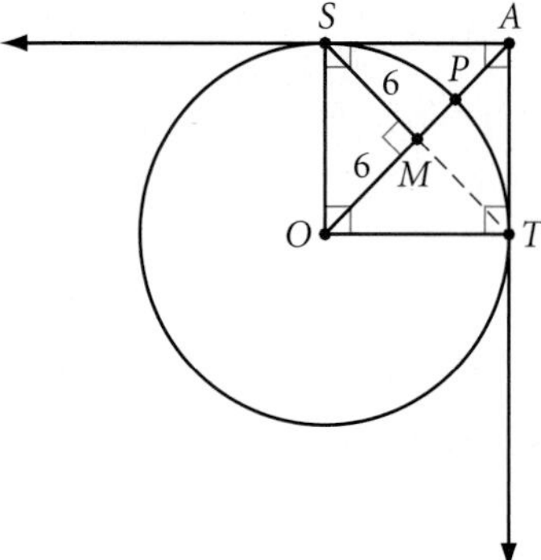

LESSON 10.3

3. $V = \frac{1}{3}BH = \frac{1}{3}\left(\frac{b_1 + b_2}{2} \cdot h\right)H$

6. $V = V_{cylinder} - V_{cone}$
$= BH - \frac{1}{3}BH$

10a. What is *B*, the area of the triangular base?

15.

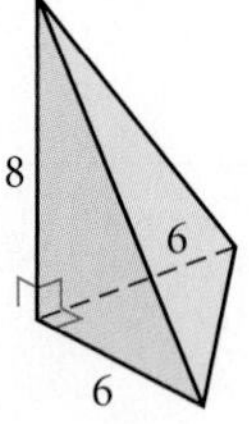

18. The swimming pool is a pentagonal prism resting on one of its lateral faces. The area of the pentagonal base can be found by dividing it into a rectangular region and a trapezoidal region.

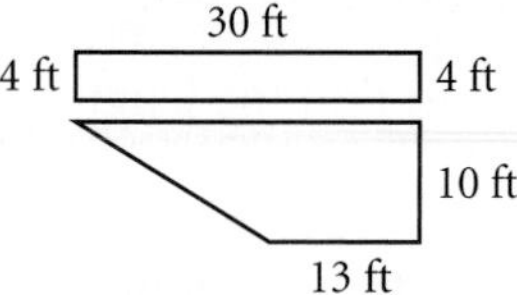

LESSON 10.4

4. $V = \frac{1}{3}BH$; $3168 = \frac{1}{3}\left[\frac{1}{2}(20 + 28)h\right](36)$

9. $V_{ring} = V_{larger\ prism} - V_{missing\ prism} =$
$\left[\left(\frac{1}{2}\right)(3\sqrt{3})(36)\right](2) - \left[\left(\frac{1}{2}\right)(2\sqrt{3})(24)\right](2)$
Then compare V_{ring} to $V_{missing\ prism}$.

10. First, change 8 inches to $\frac{2}{3}$ foot.

LESSON 10.5

6. $0.97 = \frac{145.5}{V_{displacement}}$ and $V_{displacement} = (10)(10)H$

8. $V_{displacement} = \frac{7}{8}\left(V_{block\ of\ ice}\right)$ or
$\frac{8}{7}V_{displacement} = V_{block\ of\ ice}$

LESSON 10.6

4. $V_{capsule} = 2 \cdot V_{hemisphere} + V_{cylinder} =$
$2\left[\left(\frac{2}{3}\right)\pi(6)^3\right] + [\pi(6)^2(12)]$

6. $\frac{40}{360}$, or $\frac{1}{9}$, of the hemisphere is missing. What fraction is still there?

12. $972\pi = \frac{4}{3}\pi r^3$

LESSON 10.7

1. $V = \frac{4}{3}\pi r^3$, $S = 4\pi r^2$

3. The surface area is technically the curved hemisphere *and* the circular bottom.

4. The surface area of a sphere is how many times the area of a circle with the same radius?

CHAPTER 10 REVIEW

5. $B = (12)(12) - (4)(6)$

12. One-fourth of the hemisphere is missing.

19. $V_{\text{one pipe}} = V_{\text{outer cylinder}} - V_{\text{inner cylinder}} = \pi(3)^2(160) - \pi(2.5)^2(160)$. Remember, a truck cannot carry a fraction of a pipe.

26. The volume of the hollow ball is its weight divided by its density.

27. You'll need to find the area of a segment. Also, look for a familiar triangle.

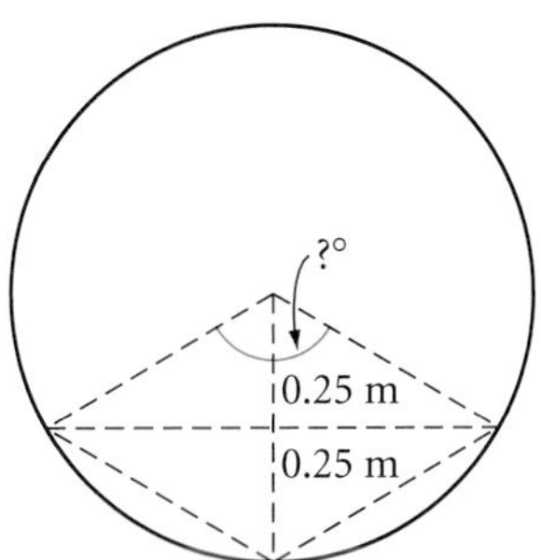

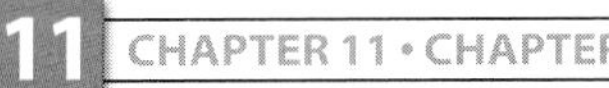

CHAPTER 11

LESSON 11.1

8. All the corresponding angles are congruent. (Why?) Are all these ratios equal? $\frac{150}{165} = \underline{?}$, $\frac{120}{128} = \underline{?}$, $\frac{140}{154} = \underline{?}$, $\frac{180}{192} = \underline{?}$

13. Because the segments are parallel, $\angle B \cong \angle AED$ and $\angle C \cong \angle ADE$.

25. During a rotation, each vertex of the triangle will trace the path of a circle. So, if you connect any vertex of the original figure to its corresponding vertex in the image, you will get a chord. Now, recall that the perpendicular bisector of a chord passes through the center of a circle.

LESSON 11.2

3. It helps to rotate $\triangle ARK$ so that you can see which sides correspond.

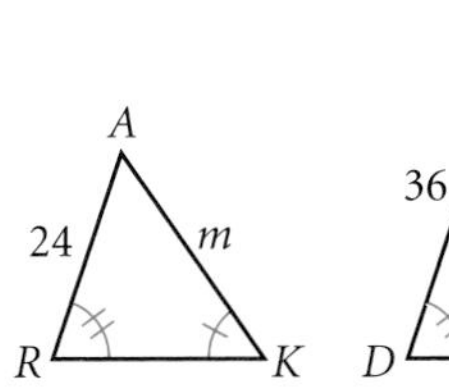

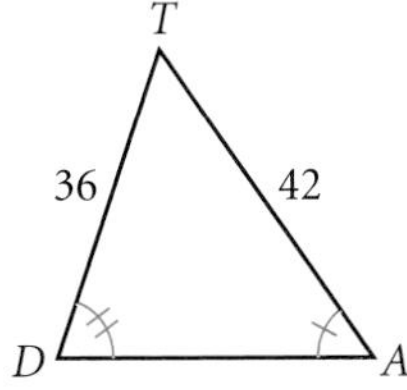

8.

11. Because $\angle H$ and $\angle D$ are two angles inscribed in the same arc, they are congruent. $\angle T$ and $\angle G$ are congruent for the same reason.

15. Draw a perpendicular segment from each point to the x-axis. Then use similar triangles.

16.

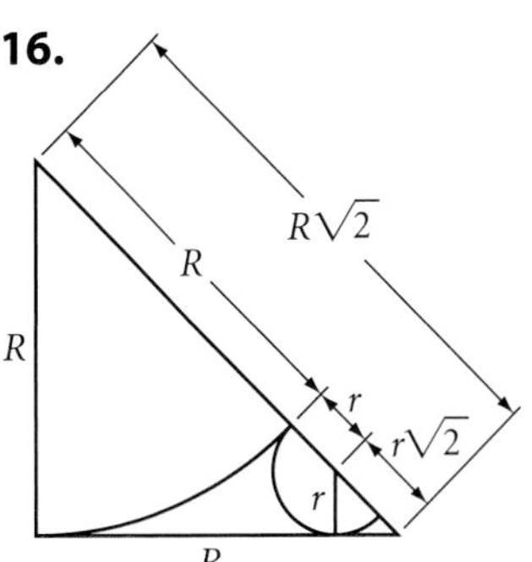

LESSON 11.3

3. Find the height of the flagpole first.

7. Because $\triangle PRE \sim \triangle POC$, then $\frac{PR}{RE} = \frac{PO}{OC}$. Let $x = PR$. Then $\frac{x}{60} = \frac{x + 45}{90}$.

8.

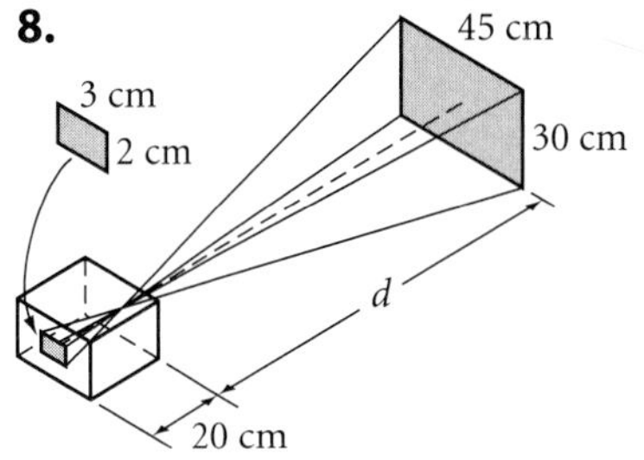

9. Think about what Juanita did in Exercise 5.

11. Draw the large and small triangles separately to label and see them more clearly.

13.

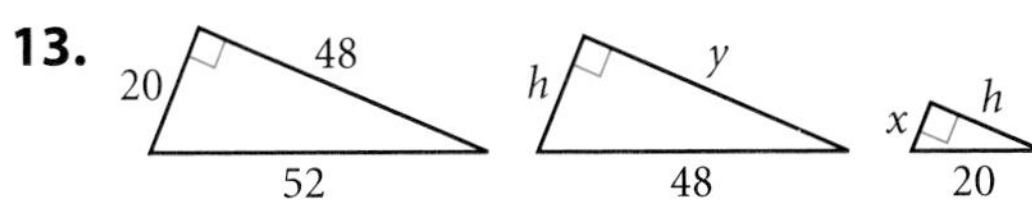

17. The golden ratio is $\frac{2}{\sqrt{5} - 1}$. Let $AB = 2$ units. How would you construct the length $\sqrt{5}$? How would you construct the length $\sqrt{5} - 1$?

LESSON 11.4

3. $\frac{IC}{IE} = \frac{CS}{PE}, \frac{IC}{IE} = \frac{CL}{SE}$

9. $\frac{12}{15} = \frac{x}{10 - x}$

12. You don't know the length of the third side, but you do know the ratio of its two parts is $\frac{2}{3}$.

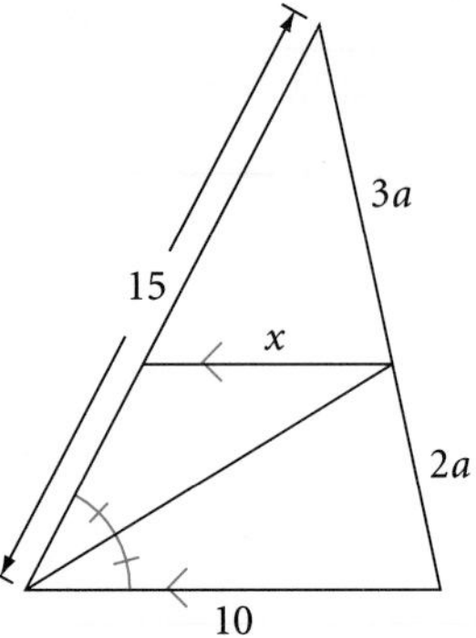

16. Bisect the angle between the sides of lengths $2x$ and $3x$.

17. Use the AA Similarity Conjecture for this proof. One pair of corresponding angles will be a nonbisected pair. The other pair of corresponding angles will consist of one-half of each bisected angle.

20. $\frac{a}{b} = \frac{c}{d}$, then $\frac{a}{b} + 1 = \frac{c}{d} + 1$, then $\frac{a}{b} + \frac{b}{b} = \frac{c}{d} + \frac{d}{d}$.

26. Copy the diagram on your own paper, and connect the centers of two large circles and the center of the small circle to form a 45°-45°-90° triangle. Each radius of the larger circles will be $\frac{s}{4}$. Use the properties of special right triangles and algebra to find the radius of the smaller circle.

LESSON 11.5

1. $\left(\frac{1}{2}\right)^2 = \frac{\text{Area of } \triangle MSE}{72}$

3. If $\frac{\text{Area of } ZOID}{\text{Area of } TRAP} = \frac{16}{25}$, then the ratio of the lengths of corresponding sides is $\frac{4}{5}$.

7.

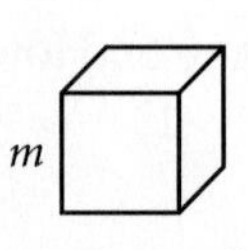

Area = $6m^2$

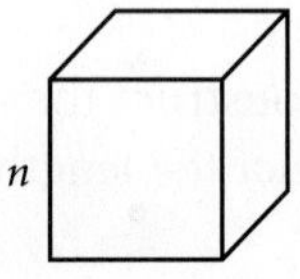

Area = $6n^2$

12. $\left(\frac{h}{H}\right)^2 = \frac{9}{25}; \frac{\text{Volume of large prism}}{\text{Volume of small prism}} = \left(\frac{h}{H}\right)^3$

17. Volume of large warehouse = $2.5^3 \cdot$ (Volume of small warehouse)

26. What kind of triangle is this?

27. A cross section is a section that is perpendicular to the axis.

LESSON 11.6

1. $\frac{4}{4 + 12} = \frac{a}{20}$

3. $\frac{60}{40} = \frac{c + 60}{70}$

4. If $\frac{24}{14} = \frac{36}{d}$, then $\frac{12}{7} = \frac{36}{d}$.

6. $\frac{15}{36} \stackrel{?}{=} \frac{25}{55}$

12. $a + b = \sqrt{(12 - 3)^2 + (0 - 9)^2}$. Once you have solved for $a + b$, then $\frac{4}{12} = \frac{a}{a + b}$.

17. $\frac{x}{10} = \frac{x + 12}{16}$; x is the height of the small missing cone.

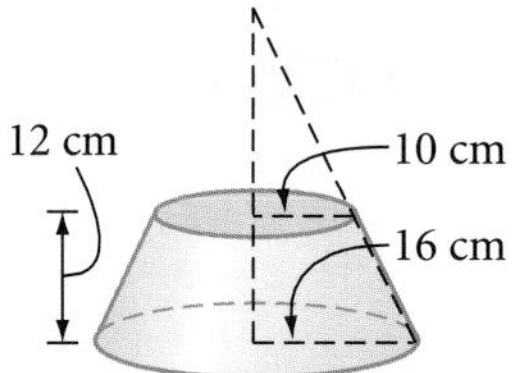

CHAPTER 11 REVIEW

9. Divide $\overline{KL}$ into seven equal lengths.

10. $\triangle ABE \sim \triangle ADC$, $\frac{AB}{BE} = \frac{AD}{CD}$

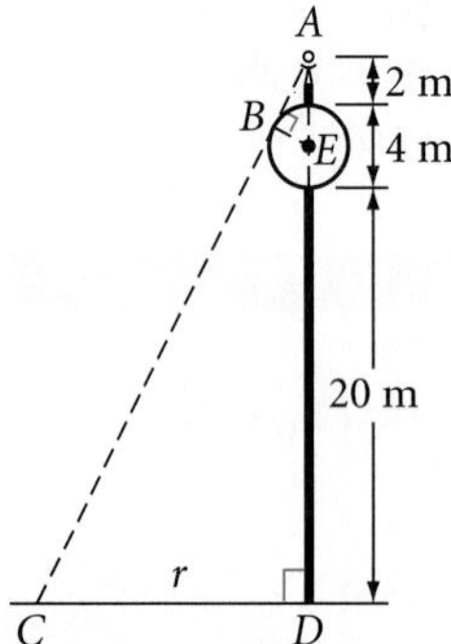

Hints for Selected Exercises

19. Because you are concerned with ratios, it doesn't make any difference what lengths you choose. So, for convenience, assign the square a side of length 2 before calculating the areas and volumes.

LESSON 12.1

7. The length of the side opposite $\angle A$ is s; the length of the side adjacent to $\angle A$ is r; the length of the hypotenuse is t.

10. Use your calculator to find $\sin^{-1}(0.5)$.

14. $\tan 30° = \frac{20}{a}$

21. Use $\sin 35° = \frac{b}{85}$ to find the length of the base, and then use $\cos 35° = \frac{h}{85}$ to find the height.

27. First, find the length of the radius of the circle and the length of the segment between the chord and the center of the circle. Use the Pythagorean Theorem to find the length of half of the chord.

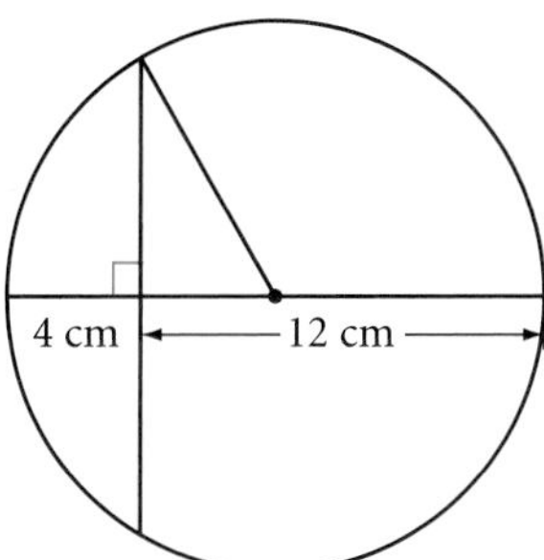

LESSON 12.2

6a. $\sin 44° = \frac{h}{1400}$, where h is the height of the balloon *above* Wendy's sextant.

7.

First sighting
42°
Second sighting
90°
1800 m

12. $\frac{\left(\frac{1}{2}\right)d_1}{20} = \cos 56°$

15. $\tan \beta = \frac{10}{17}$

LESSON 12.3

3. Sketch a diagonal connecting the vertices of the unmeasured angles. Then find the area of the two triangles.

4. Divide the octagon into eight isosceles triangles. Then use trigonometry to find the area of each triangle.

5. $\frac{\sin 52°}{28°} = \frac{\sin 79°}{w}$

13. $\sin 16° = \frac{a}{18}$

$\cos 16° = \frac{b}{18}$

$\tan 68° = \frac{c}{b}$

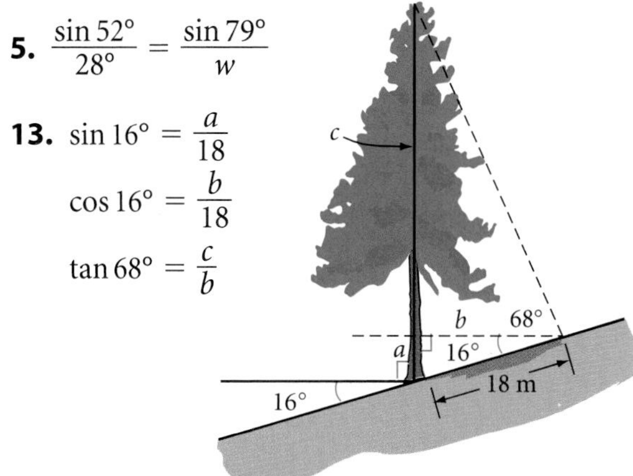

LESSON 12.4

1. $w^2 = 36^2 + 41^2 - 2(36)(41)\cos 49°$

4. $42^2 = 34^2 + 36^2 - 2(34)(36)\cos A$

8. The smallest angle is opposite the shortest side.

10. One approach divides the triangle into two right triangles, where $x = a + b$. When you have the straight-line distance, compare that time against the detour.

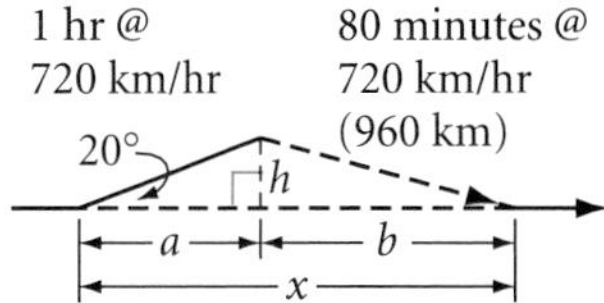

12.

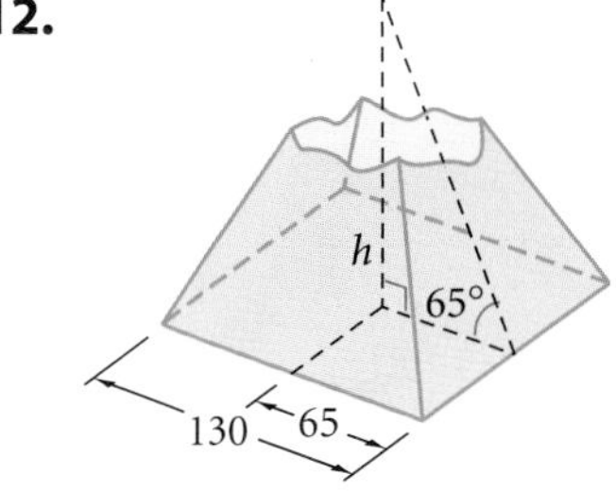

Hints for Selected Exercises

16. The midpoint of the base can be used to create three equilateral triangles.

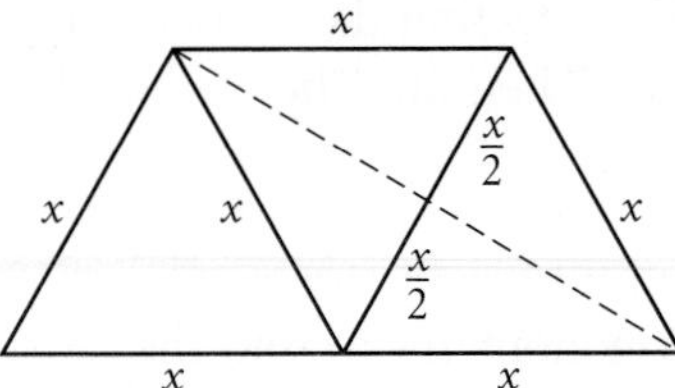

LESSON 12.5

2.

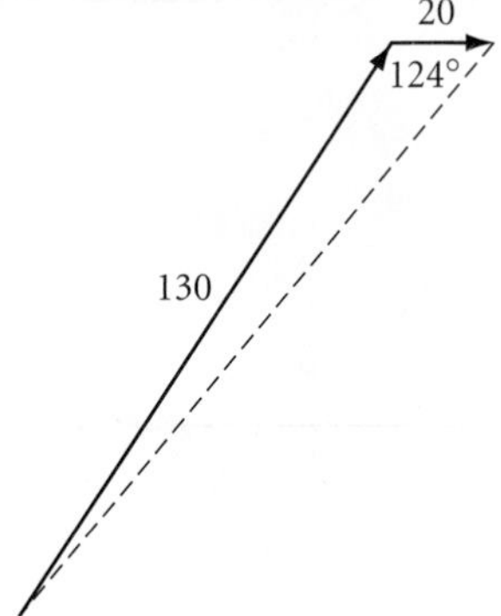

5. First find θ.

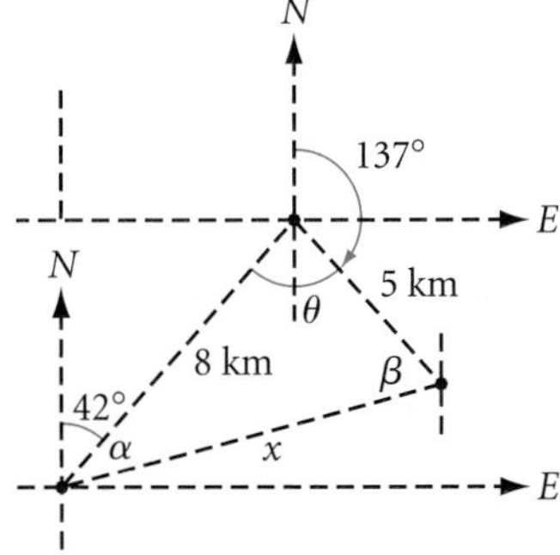

9.

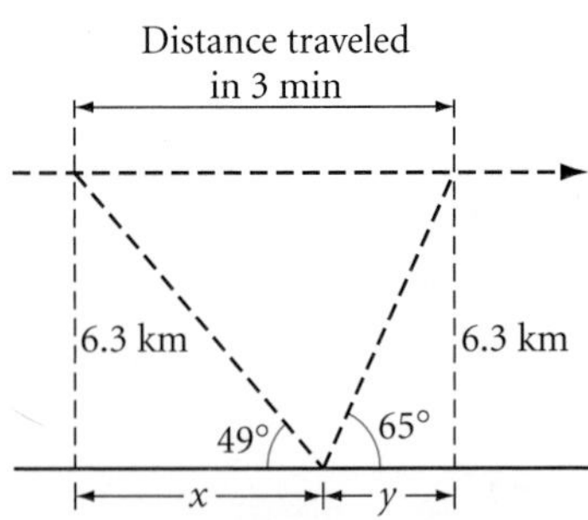

10.

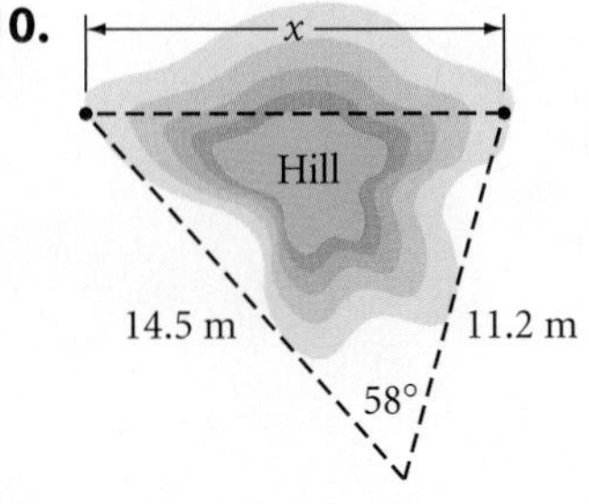

11. Divide the pentagon into five congruent triangles. What is the measure of the interior angle of each triangle at the vertex in the center?

CHAPTER 12 REVIEW

27. $A_{\text{segment}} = A_{\text{sector}} - A_{\text{triangle}}$. You found part of the solution in Exercise 25.

28.

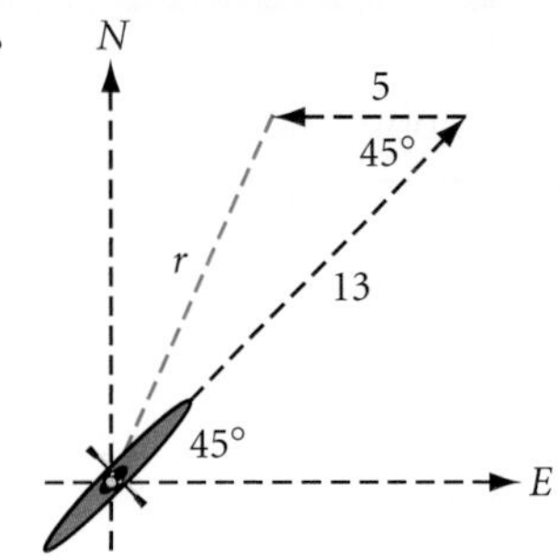

CHAPTER 13 • CHAPTER 13 CHAPTER 13 • CHAPTER

LESSON 13.1

4. It's also called the identity property.

8. Distributive property, subtraction property of equality, _?_, _?_

9. _?_, _?_, multiplication property of equality, _?_

11. The Midpoint Postulate says that a segment has exactly one midpoint.

22. Reason for Box 1: Angle Bisector Postulate

25. Two consecutive integers can be written as n and $n + 1$.

LESSON 13.3

2. Draw an auxiliary line from the point to the midpoint of the segment.

5. Draw an auxiliary line that creates two isosceles triangles. Use isosceles triangle properties and angle subtraction.

14. Use similarity of triangles to set up two proportions.

16. Graph point A and the line. Fold the graph paper along the line to see where point A reflects.

LESSON 13.4

1. Use the Quadrilateral Sum Theorem.

16.

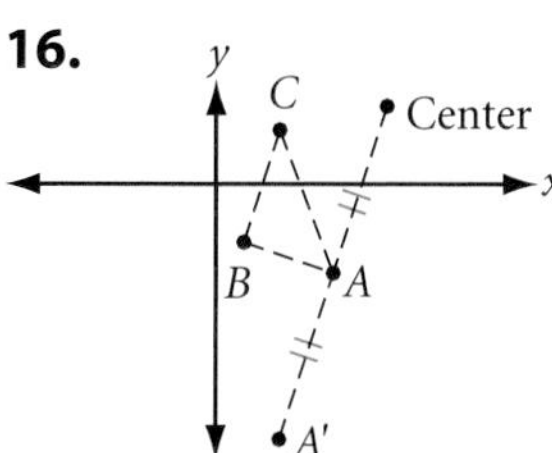

LESSON 13.6

14. Divide the triangle into three triangles with common vertex *P*.

16. Draw a segment from the point to the center of the circle. Using this segment as a diameter, draw a circle. How does this help you find the points of tangency?

LESSON 13.7

4.

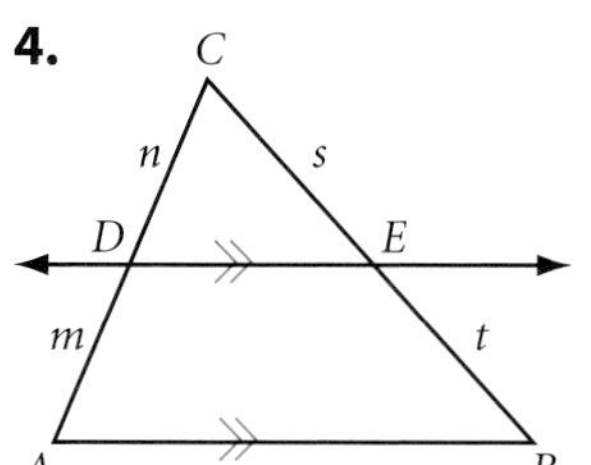

$$\frac{m+n}{n} = \frac{t+s}{s}$$

$$\frac{m}{n} + \frac{n}{n} = \frac{t}{s} + \frac{s}{s}$$

$$\frac{m}{n} + 1 = \frac{t}{s} + 1$$

$$\therefore \frac{m}{n} = \frac{t}{s}$$

5. Try revising the steps of the proof for the Parallel Proportionality Theorem.

6. In $\triangle ATH$, let $m\angle A = a$, $m\angle T = t$, then $a + t = 90$. In $\triangle LTH$, $m\angle T = t$, $m\angle H = h$, then $h + t = 90$. Therefore, $h + t = a + t$ and so $h = a$. Therefore, $\triangle ATH \sim \triangle HTL$ by AA. In like manner you can demonstrate that $\triangle ATH \sim \triangle AHL$, and thus by the transitive property of similarity all three are similar.

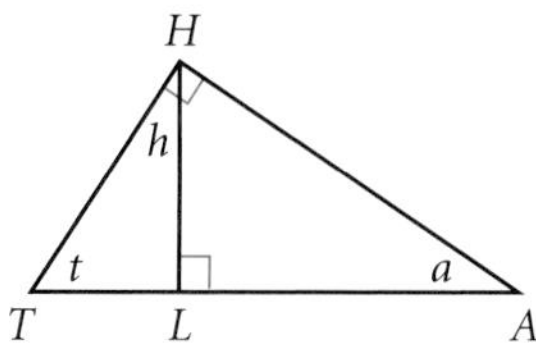

7. If a is the geometric mean of b and c, then $\frac{b}{a} = \frac{a}{c}$, or $a^2 = bc$.

8. Construct $\overline{AD}$ so that it's perpendicular to $\overline{AB}$ and intersects $\overleftrightarrow{BC}$ at point D.

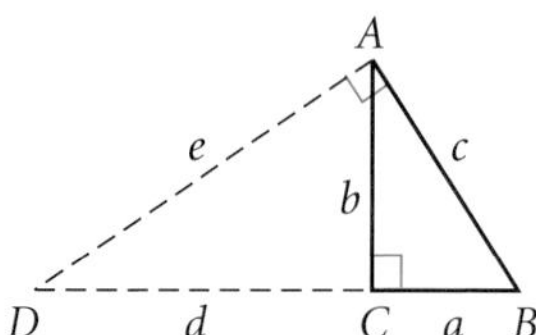

Use the Three Similar Right Triangles Theorem to write proportions and solve.

9.

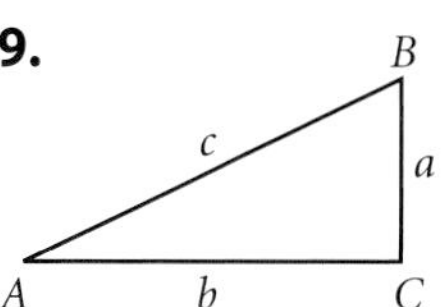

Plan: Construct a right triangle DEF with legs of lengths a and b and hypotenuse of length x.

Then, $x^2 = a^2 + b^2$ by the Pythagorean Theorem.

It is given that $c^2 = a^2 + b^2$. Therefore, $x^2 = c^2$, or $x = c$.

If $x = c$, then $\triangle DEF \cong \triangle ABC$.

10. See Exercise 18 in Lesson 9.1.

19.

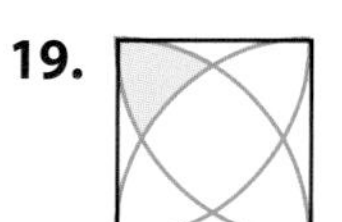 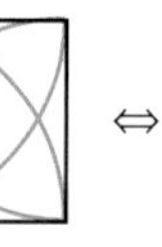 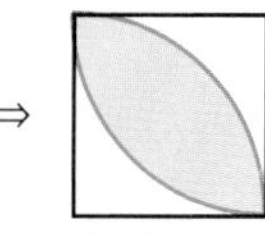 – 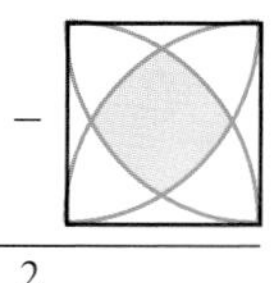

2

20.

 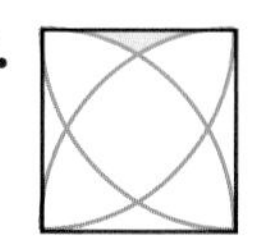 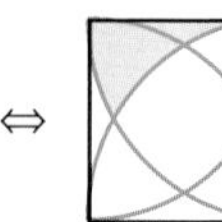 – 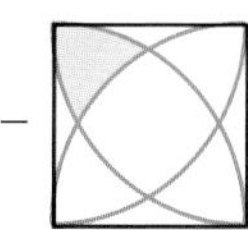

CHAPTER 13 REVIEW

26.

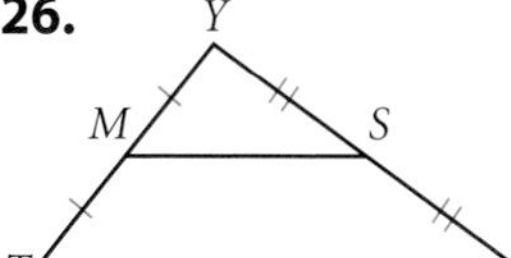

Given: $\triangle TRY$ with midsegment $\overline{MS}$

Show: $\overline{MS} \parallel \overline{TR}$ and $MS = \left(\frac{1}{2}\right)TR$

Index

A

B

C

F

G

H

I

Index

M

N

O

P

Q

R

Index

S

T

Photo Credits

Abbreviations: top (T), center (C), bottom (B), left (L), right (R).

Cover

Background image: Doug Wilson/Corbis; Construction image: Sonda Dawes/The Image Works; All other images: Ken Karp Photography.

Front Matter

v : Ken Karp Photography; **xv:** Cheryl Fenton; **xxix (T):** Ken Karp Photography; **xxix (B):** Ken Karp Photography; **xxx:** Ken Karp Photography; **xxxi:** Ken Karp Photography; **xxxiii:** Ken Karp Photography; **xxxv:** Ken Karp Photography; **xxxvi (T):** Ken Karp Photography; **xxxvi (B):** Ken Karp Photography.

Chapter 0

1: *Print Gallery,* M. C. Escher, 1956/©2002 Cordon Art B. V.–Baarn–Holland. All rights reserved.; **2 (B):** ©1993 Metropolitan Museum of Art, Bequest of Edward C. Moore, 1891 (91.1.)2064 **2 (C):** Cheryl Fenton; **2 (TL):** NASA; **3 (BL):** Christie's Images; **3 (T):** *Tsiga I,II,III* (1991), Victor Vasarely, Courtesy of the artist.; **4 (CR):** Hillary Turner; **4 (TL):** Cheryl Fenton; **4 (TR):** Cheryl Fenton; **5 (B):** ©Andy Goldsworthy, Courtesy of the artist and Galerie Lelong; **5 (C):** Cheryl Fenton; **5 (CL):** Cheryl Fenton; **5 (TC):** Cheryl Fenton; **5 (TL):** Cheryl Fenton; **6:** Corbis; **7 (BL):** Dave Bartruff/Stock Boston; **7 (BR):** Robert Frerck/Woodfin Camp & Associates; **7 (CL):** Rex Butcher/Bruce Coleman Inc.; **7 (CR):** Randy Juster; **9:** Schumacher & Co./Frank Lloyd Wright Foundation; **10 (R):** Sean Sprague/Stock Boston; **10 (TC):** Christie's Images/Corbis; **12:** W. Metzen/Bruce Coleman Inc.; **13 (L):** *Hesitate,* Bridget Riley/Tate Gallery, London/Art Resource, NY; **13 (R):** *Harlequin* by Victor Vasarely, Courtesy of the artist.; **15 (C):** National Tourist Office of Spain; **15 (T):** Tim Davis/Photo Researchers; **16:** Cheryl Fenton; **17:** *Snakes,* M. C. Escher, 1969/©2002 Cordon Art B. V.–Baarn–Holland. All rights reserved.; **18:** Will & Deni McIntyre/Photo Researchers Inc.; **19:** *SEKI/PY XVIII* (1978), Kunito Nagaoka/Courtesy of the artist.; **19 (L):** Cheryl Fenton; **19 (R):** Cheryl Fenton; **20 (B):** Corbis; **20 (T):** Nathan Benn/Corbis; **22 (B):** Ken Karp Photography; **22 (C):** Peter Sanders Photography; **22 (TL):** Peter Sanders Photography; **22 (TR):** Peter Sanders Photography; **23:** Photo Researchers Inc.; **24:** *Hot Blocks* (1966–67) ©Edna Andrade, Philadelphia Museum of Art, Purchased by Philadelphia Foundation Fund; **25 (L):** Comstock; **25 (R):** Scala/Art Resource; **29 (T):** George Lepp/Photo Researchers Inc.

Chapter 1

27: *Three Worlds,* M. C. Escher, 1955/©2002 Cordon Art B. V.–Baarn–Holland. All rights reserved.; **28 (B):** Spencer Grant/Photo Researchers Inc.; **28 (C):** Cheryl Fenton; **28 (T):** Hillary Turner; **29:** By permission of Johnny Hart and Creators Syndicate, Inc.; **30:** Bachman/Photo Researchers Inc.; **32:** S. Craig/Bruce Coleman Inc.; **33 (R):** Grafton Smith/Corbis Stock Market; **33 (L):** Michael Daly/Corbis Stock Market; **34:** Addison Geary/Stock Boston; **35:** Bob Stovall/Bruce Coleman Inc.; **36:** Archivo Iconografico, S. A./Corbis; **38 (TL):** Bruce Coleman Inc.; **38 (TR):** David Leah/Getty Images; **39 (B):** Hillary Turner; **39 (BR):** Cheryl Fenton; **39 (BR):** Comstock; **39 (T):** Ken Karp Photography; **41:** Pool & Billiard Magazine; **47:** Illustration by John Tenniel; **48:** Osentoski & Zoda/Envision; **49:** Christie's Images; **50:** Corbis; **51:** Hillary Turner; **54:** Cheryl Fenton; **55:** Ira Lipsky/International Stock Photography; **56:** Quilt by Diane Venters/*More Mathematical Quilts*; **56 (C):** Cheryl Fenton; **56 (TCL):** Hillary Turner; **56 (TCR):** Hillary Turner; **56 (TL):** Hillary Turner; **56 (TR):** Hillary Turner; **59:** Spencer Swanger/Tom Stack & Associates; **60:** Gerard Degeorge/Corbis; **61:** Sol LeWitt—Wall Drawing #652—On three walls, continuous forms with color ink washes superimposed, Color in wash. Collection: Indianapolis Museum of Art, Indianapolis, IN. September, 1990. Courtesy of the Artist.; **62 (C):** Michael Moxter/Photo Researchers Inc.; **62 (L):** Larry Brownstein/Rainbow; **62 (R):** Stefano Amantini/Bruce Coleman Inc.; **63 (B):** Cheryl Fenton; **63 (T):** Cheryl Fenton; **65:** Friedensreich ©Erich Lessing/Art Resource, NY; **66:** From WALTER WICK'S OPTICAL TRICKS. Published by Cartwheel books, a division of Scholastic Inc. ©1998 by Walter Wick. Reprinted by permission.; **67 (BL):** Joel Tribhout/Agence Vandystadt/Getty Images; **67 (BR):** Terry Eggers/Corbis Stock Market; **67 (T):** By permission of Johnny Hart and Creators Syndicate Inc.; **68 (L):** Cheryl Fenton; **68 (R):** Getty Images; **70 (CL):** Corbis; **70 (CR):** Alfred Pasieka/Photo Researchers Inc.; **70 (T):** Corbis; **73:** *Bookplate for Albert Ernst Bosman,* M. C. Escher, 1946/©2002 Cordon Art B. V.–Baarn–Holland. All rights reserved.; **74 (BC):** Stock Montage, Inc.; **74 (BL):** Stock Montage, Inc.; **74 (BR):** AP/Wide World; **79:** William Thomas Williams, *"DO YOU THINK A IS B,"* Acrylic on Canvas, 1975–77, Fisk University Galleries, Nashville, Tennessee; **80 (C):** Cheryl Fenton; **80 (L):** Cheryl Fenton; **80 (R):** Cheryl Fenton; **81:** Cheryl Fenton; **82:** Cheryl Fenton; **83:** Courtesy of Kazumata Yamashita, Architect; **84 (B):** Ken Karp Photography; **84 (C):** Mike Yamashita/Woodfin Camp & Associates; **85:** T. Kitchin/Tom Stack & Associates; **86 (C):** Cheryl Fenton; **86 (T):** Ken Karp Photography; **88:** Paul Steel/Corbis-Stock Market; **90:** Cheryl Fenton.

Chapter 2

93: *Hand with Reflecting Sphere (Self-Portrait in Spherical Mirror),* M. C. Escher/©2002 Cordon Art B. V.–Baarn–Holland. All rights reserved.; **94 (B):** Barry Rosenthal/FPG; **94 (T):** Ken Karp Photography; **95:** Andrew McClenaghan/Photo Researchers Inc.; **100:** Bob Daemmrich/Stock Boston; **101:** California Institute of Technology and Carnegie Institution of Washington; **104:** NASA; **106:** Drabble reprinted by permission of United Feature Syndicate, Inc.; **112 (L):** National Science Foundation Network; **112 (R):** Hank Morgan/Photo Researchers Inc.; **113:** Hillary Turner; **115:** Cheryl Fenton; **118 (B):** Ken Karp Photography; **118 (T):** Culver Pictures; **121:** Ken Karp Photography; **126 (B):** Ken Karp Photography; **126 (T):** Alex MacLean/Landslides; **128:** Hillary Turner; **130:** James Blank/Bruce Coleman Inc.; **134 (L):** Photo Researchers; **134 (R):** Mark Gibson/Index Stock; **135 (B):** Ted Scott/Fotofile, Ltd.; **135 (C):** Ken Karp Photography; **137:** Art Matrix.

Chapter 3

141: *Drawing Hand,* M. C. Escher, 1948/©2002 Cordon Art B. V.–Baarn–Holland. All rights reserved.; **142 (L):** Hillary Turner; **142 (R):** Hillary Turner; **142 (T):** Bettmann/Corbis; **143 (L):** Hillary Turner; **143 (R):** Hillary Turner; **144:** Travel Ink/Corbis; **154:** *Overseas Highway* by Crawford Ralston, 1939 by Crawford Ralston/Art Resource, NY; **156:** Rick Strange/Picture Cube; **159:** Corbis; **172 (BL):** Ken Karp Photography; **172 (BR):** Dover Publications; **172 (T):** Greg Vaughn/Tom Stack & Associates; **174:** Art Resource; **175:** Timothy Eagan/Woodfin Camp & Associates; **176:** Ken Karp Photography; **177:** *Rounds and Triangles* by Rudolf Bauer /Christie's Images; **180:** Corbis; **185 (B):** Corbis; **185 (T):** Ken Karp Photography; **186:** Keith Gunnar/Bruce Coleman Inc.; **189:** Ken Karp Photography; **191:** Victoria & Albert Museum, London/Art Resource, NY.

Chapter 4

197: *Symmetry Drawing E103,* M. C. Escher,1959/©2002 Cordon Art B. V.–Baarn–Holland. All rights reserved.; **198 (B):** Courtesy, St. John's Presbyterian Church; **198 (C):** Jim Corwin/Stock Boston; **198 (TL):** Cheryl Fenton; **198 (TR):** Cheryl Fenton; **199:** Ken Karp Photography; **202:** The Far Side® by Gary Larson ©1987 FarWorks, Inc. All rights reserved. Used with permission.; **203:** Hillary Turner; **204 (L):** David L. Brown/Picture Cube; **204 (R):** Joe Sohm/The Image Works; **207:** Art Stein/Photo Researchers Inc.; **213:** Robert Frerck/Woodfin Camp & Associates; **217:** Judy March/Photo

Photo Credits

Researchers Inc.; **220:** Adamsmith Productions/Corbis; **222:** Carolyn Schaefer/Gamma Liaison; **227:** Cheryl Fenton; **234 (B):** Ken Karp Photography; **234 (T):** AP/Wide World; **240:** Ken Karp Photography; **241:** Eric Schweikardt/The Image Bank; **247:** Archivo Iconografico, SA/Corbis; **249 (T):** Ken Karp Photography; **251:** Ken Karp Photography; **252 (L):** Cheryl Fenton; **252 (R):** Cheryl Fenton; **253:** Cheryl Fenton.

Chapter 5

255: *Still Life and Street,* M. C. Escher, 1967–68/©2002 Cordon Art B. V.–Baarn–Holland. All rights reserved.; **256:** Ken Karp Photography; **256 (T):** Cheryl Fenton; **260:** *Emerging Order* by Hannah Hoch/Christie's Images/Corbis; **263:** Richard Megna/Fundamental Photographs; **265:** Courtesy of the artist, Teresa Archuleta-Sagel; **266:** Steve Dunwell/The Image Bank; **268 (C):** Lindsay Hebberd/Woodfin Camp & Associates; **268 (T):** Photo Researchers Inc.; **271:** Cheryl Fenton; **278:** Malcolm S. Kirk/Peter Arnold Inc.; **284:** ©Paula Nadelstern/Photo by Bobby Hansson; **286:** Corbis; **289:** Ken Karp Photography; **290:** Cheryl Fenton; **291:** Bill Varie/The Image Bank; **292:** Bill Varie/The Image Bank; **292:** Alex MacLean/Landslides; **298:** Cheryl Fenton; **299:** *Red and Blue Puzzle* (1994) Mabry Benson/Photo by Carlberg Jones; **302:** Ken Karp Photography; **303:** *Boy With Birds* by David C. Driskell/Collection of Mr. and Mrs. David C. Driskell.

Chapter 6

305: *Curl-Up,* M. C. Escher,1951/©2002 Cordon Art B. V.–Baarn–Holland. All rights reserved.; **306 (B):** Stephen Saks/Photo Researchers, Inc.; **306 (C):** Corbis; **308:** Tom Sanders/Corbis Stock Market; **311:** NASA; **312:** Tony Freeman/PhotoEdit; **313 (L):** Stephen A. Smith; **313 (R):** Mark Burnett/Stock Boston; **314:** NASA; **315:** Gray Mortimore/Getty Images; **316 (L):** Corbis; **316 (L):** Jim Zuckerman/Corbis; **319:** Xinhua/Gamma Liaison; **328 (L):** Cheryl Fenton; **328 (R):** Cheryl Fenton; **331 (B):** Cheryl Fenton; **331 (C):** Ken Karp Photography; **332:** Hillary Turner; **334 (B):** Don Mason/Corbis Stock Market; **334 (C):** David R. Frazier/Photo Researchers Inc.; **334 (T):** Ken Karp Photography; **337:** Photofest; **339:** Calvin and Hobbes ©Watterson. Reprinted with permission of UNIVERSAL PRESS SYNDICATE. All rights reserved.; **340:** Guido Cozzi/Bruce Coleman Inc.; **341:** Grant Heilman Photography; **344 (B):** Nick Gunderson/Corbis; **344 (T):** Charles Feil/Stock Boston; **345 (B):** Bob Daemmrich/Stock Boston; **345 (T):** Cathedrale de Reims; **346:** Gamma Liaison; **349 (B):** Ken Karp Photography; **349 (T):** Cheryl Fenton; **351:** Ken Karp Photography; **352:** The Far Side® by Gary Larson ©1990 FarWorks, Inc. All rights reserved. Used with permission.; **353:** David Malin/Anglo-Australian Telescope Board; **355:** Private collection, Berkeley, California/Ceramist, Diana Hall.

Chapter 7

357: *Magic Mirror,* M. C. Escher,1946/©2002 Cordon Art B. V.–Baarn–Holland. All rights reserved.; **358:** Giraudon/Art Resource; **358 (B):** Ken Karp Photography; **360:** Corbis; **361:** Grant Heilman Photography; **363 (BC):** Denver Museum of Natural History; **363 (BL):** Michael Lustbader/Photo Researchers; **363 (BR):** Richard Cummins/Corbis; **363 (TL):** Phil Cole/Getty Images; **363 (TR):** Corbis; **364:** Oxfam; **369:** Corbis; **372:** By Holland ©1976 Punch Cartoon Library; **373:** Gina Minielli/Corbis; **378:** Ken Karp Photography; **379 (L):** W. Treat Davison/Photo Researchers; **379 (R):** Ancient Art and Architecture Collection; **381:** Springer-Verlag; **385:** Courtesy Doris Schattschneider; **386:** Lucy Birmingham/Photo Researchers Inc.; **388 (B):** Carleton College/photo by Hilary N. Bullock; **388 (T):** Ashton, Ragget, McDougall Architects; **389 (C):** *Symmetry Drawing E105,* M. C. Escher 1960/©2002 Cordon Art B. V.–Baarn–Holland. All rights reserved.; **389 (T):** *Brickwork,* Alhambra, M. C. Escher/©2002 Cordon Art B. V.–Baarn–Holland. All rights reserved.; **393:** *Symmetry Drawing E25,* M. C. Escher, 1939/©2002 Cordon Art B. V.–Baarn–Holland. All rights reserved.; **394:** *Reptiles,* M. C. Escher, 1943/©2002 Cordon Art B. V.–Baarn–Holland. All rights reserved.; **395 (T):** *Symmetry Drawing E99,* M. C. Escher, 1954/©2002 Cordon Art B. V.–Baarn–Holland. All rights reserved.; **396 (L):** *Interwoven patterns–V–structure 17* by Rinus Roelofs/Courtesy of the artist & ©2002 Artist Rights Society (ARS), New York/Beeldrecht, Amsterdam; **396 (R):** *Impossible structures–III–structure 24* by Rinus Roelofs/Courtesy of the artist & ©2002 Artist Rights Society (ARS), New York/Beeldrecht, Amsterdam; **398 (B):** *Horseman sketch,* M. C. Escher/©2002 Cordon Art B. V.–Baarn–Holland. All rights reserved.; **398 (T):** *Horseman,* M. C. Escher, 1946/©2002 Cordon Art B. V.–Baarn–Holland. All rights reserved.; **399:** *Symmetry Drawing E108,* M. C. Escher, 1967/©2002 Cordon Art B. V.–Baarn–Holland. All rights reserved.; **404:** *King* by Minne Evans/Corbis & Luise Ross Gallery; **405 (C):** Paul Schermeister/Corbis; **405 (TR):** Comstock; **406:** Ken Karp Photography; **407 (B):** Starbuck Goldner; **407 (C):** *Day and Night,* M. C. Escher, 1938/©2002 Cordon Art B. V.–Baarn–Holland. All rights reserved.

Chapter 8

409: *Square Limit,* M. C. Escher, 1964/©2002 Cordon Art B. V.–Baarn–Holland. All rights reserved.; **410:** Spencer Grant/Stock Boston; **414 (B):** Karl Weatherly/Corbis; **414 (T):** Courtesy Naoko Hirakura Associates; **421:** Ken Karp Photography; **422:** Joseph Nettis/Photo Researchers Inc.; **423 (B):** NASA; **423 (C):** Ken Karp Photography; **424:** Phil Schermeister/Corbis; **428:** Cheryl Fenton; **434:** Cheryl Fenton; **435 (B):** Reuters NewMedia Inc./Corbis; **435 (C):** Georg Gerster/Photo Researchers Inc.; **437:** Shahn Kermani/Gamma Liaison; **440:** Eye Ubiquitous/Corbis; **442:** Ken Karp Photography; **444:** Cheryl Fenton; **445 (BL):** Stefano Amantini/Bruce Coleman Inc.; **445 (BR):** Alain Benainous/Gamma Liaison; **445 (CB):** Joan Iaconetti/Bruce Coleman Inc.; **445 (CT):** Bill Bachmann/The Image Works; **446:** Greg Pease/Corbis; **447 (L):** Sonda Dawes/The Image Works; **447 (R):** John Mead/Photo Researchers Inc.; **449:** Library of Congress; **451:** Bryn Campbell/Getty Images; **452:** Douglas Peebles; **458:** Ken Karp Photography.

Chapter 9

461: *Waterfall,* M. C. Escher, 1961/©2002 Cordon Art B. V.–Baarn–Holland. All rights reserved.; **462:** FUNKY WINKERBEAN by Batiuk. Reprinted with special permission of North American Syndicate; **463:** Corbis; **463 (L):** Corbis; **464:** Will & Deni McIntyre/Photo Researchers Inc.; **467 (C):** Corbis; **467 (T):** Ken Karp Photography; **468:** Ken Karp Photography; **469:** Rare Book and Manuscript Library/Columbia University; **470:** John Colett/Stock Boston; **472:** Christie's Images/©2002 Sol LeWitt/Artists Rights Society (ARS), New York; **475:** Turner Entertainment ©1939. All rights reserved.; **482:** FUNKY WINKERBEAN by Batiuk. Reprinted with special permission of North American Syndicate; **483:** Bob Daemmrich/The Image Works; **484 (B):** Private collection, Berkeley, California/Photo by Cheryl Fenton; **484 (T):** Ken Karp Photography; **490:** David Muench/Corbis; **494:** Bruno Joachim/Gamma Liaison; **495:** Ken Karp Photography; **498:** Ken Karp Photography.

Chapter 10

503: *Verblifa tin,* M. C. Escher, 1963/©2002 Cordon Art B. V.–Baarn–Holland. All rights reserved.; **504 (BL):** J. Bernholc, etal./North Carolina State/Photo Researchers Inc.; **504 (CB):** Ken Eward/Photo Researchers Inc.; **504 (CT):** Runk-Schoenberger/Grant Heilman Photography; **504 (CT):** Ken Eward/Photo Researchers; **504 (L):** Archivo Iconografico, S. A. /Corbis; **504 (T):** Cheryl Fenton; **505:** Esaias Baitel/Gamma Liaison; **506:** Cheryl Fenton; **507:** Burstein Collection/Corbis/© Andy Warhol/Artists Rights Society (ARS), New York; **510:** ©1996 C. Herscovici, Brussels, Artists Rights Society (ARS) NY/Photo courtesy Minneapolis Institute of Art; **512:** Ken Karp Photography; **514:** Ken Karp Photography; **514:** Christie's Images/Corbis; **516:** Hillary Turner; **519 (B):** Jeff Tinsly/Names Project; **519 (C):** Larry Lee Photography/

Corbis; **520 (B):** Thomas Kitchin/Tom Stack & Associates; **520 (C):** Eye Ubiquitous/Corbis; **521 (B):** Cheryl Fenton; **521 (C):** Cheryl Fenton; **522:** Ken Karp Photography; **525:** Masao Hayashi/Photo Researchers Inc.; **527:** Charles Lenars/Corbis; **528 (B):** Ken Karp Photography; **528 (T):** Fitzwilliam Museum, Cambridge; **532 (T):** David Sutherland/Stone/Getty Images; **533:** Parson's School of Design; **537:** David Morris/Gamma Liaison; **539 (B):** C. J. Allen/Stock Boston; **539 (T):** Ken Karp Photography; **540:** David Hockney, *Sunday Morning Mayflower Hotel, N.Y.,* Nov. 28, 1982/Photographic collage, ED: 20/50″ × 77″ ©David Hockney; **541:** Ken Karp Photography; **542 (B):** Ken Karp Photography; **544 (B):** The Far Side® by Gary Larson ©1986 FarWorks, Inc. All rights reserved. Used with permission.; **544 (T):** Culver Pictures/ Picture Quest; **546 (C):** John Cooke/Comstock; **546 (T):** NASA; **548:** Larry Lefevre/Grant Heilman Photography; **549:** Arte & Immagini/Corbis; **551 (L):** Ken Karp Photography; **551 (T):** Illustration by Sidney Paget from The Strand Magazine, 1892; **555:** Piranha Club by B. Grace. Reprinted with special permission of King Features Syndicate; **558:** Douglas Peebles/Corbis.

Chapter 11

559: *Path of Life I,* M. C. Escher, 1958/©2002 Cordon Art B. V.–Baarn–Holland. All rights reserved.; **564 (R):** J. Greenberg/The Image Works; **564 (R):** Chromosohn/Photo Researchers Inc.; **567 (B):** National Geographic Society; **567 (C):** Giaudon/Art Resource, NY; **567 (T):** Erich Lessing/Art Resource, NY; **569:** John Elk III/Stock Boston; **570:** Daniel Sheehan/Black Star Publishing/PictureQuest; **571 (C):** Ken Karp Photography; **571 (T):** Michael S. Yamashita/Corbis; **575:** Patricia Lanza/Bruce Coleman Inc.; **576 (B):** Thomas Dove/Douglas Peebles; **576 (L):** Rossi & Rossi; **576 (R):** Rossi & Rossi; **577:** Dave Bartruff/Corbis; **583:** Ken Karp Photography; **586:** Ken Karp Photography; **592:** Alon Reininger/Contact Press Images/PictureQuest; **594:** Ken Karp Photography; **595:** David Fraser/Photo Researchers Inc.; **597 (B):** Dr. Paul A. Zahl/Photo Researchers Inc.; **597 (T):** *La Petite Chatelaine, Version a La Natte Courbe* by Camille Claudel/Christie's Images/© 2002 Artists Rights Society (ARS), New York/ADAGP, Paris; **599:** Ken Karp Photography; **600 (B):** ©1996 Demart Pro Arte Geneva/© Salvador Dali, Gala-Salvador Dali Foundation/ARS NY; **600 (T):** Corbis; **601 (C):** Kurt Krieger/Corbis; **601 (T):** Bettmann/ Corbis; **607:** Charles Feil/Stock Boston; **611 (B):** Ken Karp Photography; **612:** *Alice in Wonderland*; **615 (B):** Robert Holmes/ Corbis; **615 (T):** Dan McCoy/Rainbow; **616 (L):** Chris Lisle/Corbis; **616 (R):** Alex Webb/Magnum; **617:** Underwood & Underwood/ Corbis; **618:** NASA.

Chapter 12

619: *Belvedere*, M. C. Escher, 1958/©2002 Cordon Art B. V.–Baarn–Holland. All rights reserved.; **620:** Bettmann/Corbis; **621 (B):** Perry Collection; **621 (T):** Gary Braasch/Woodfin Camp & Associates; **623:** Cheryl Fenton; **627:** Ken Karp Photography; **628 (B):** Ecoscene/ Corbis; **628 (C):** H. Reinhard/Photo Researchers; **629:** *Breezing Up* by Winslow Homer/Photo by Francis G. Mayer/Corbis; **630:** Dennis Marsico/Corbis; **631 (L):** Wendell Metzen/Bruce Coleman Inc.; **631 (R):** Corbis; **632 (C):** Ken Karp Photography; **633:** Greg Rynders; **638 (C):** Courtesy of Association for the Preservation of Virginia Antiquities; **639 (B):** Stevan Stefanovic/Photo Researchers Inc.; **639 (T):** Steve Owlett/Bruce Coleman Inc.; **644 (B):** Grant Heilman Photography; **646:** Photograph by Hiroshi Umeoka; **647:** Sonda Dawes/The Image Works; **649:** James A. Sugar/Black Star Publishing/Picture Quest; **651:** Angelo Hornak/Corbis; **652:** Walter Hodges/Corbis; **654:** Courtesy California Academy of Sciences; **655:** Ken Karp Photography; **660:** © Marty Sohl; **661:** B. Christensen/Stock Boston.

Chapter 13

667: *Another World (Other World),* M. C. Escher/©2002 Cordon Art B. V.–Baarn–Holland. All rights reserved.; **668:** Springer-Verlag; **668:** Araldo de Luca/CORBIS; **669 (C):** Ken Karp Photography; **669 (R):** Ken Karp Photography; **670:** Charles & Josette Lenars/ Corbis; **671:** Art Resource; **675:** Library of Congress; **679:** ©1977 by Sidney Harris, *American Scientist Magazine*; **682:** Ken Karp Photography; **684:** Ken Karp Photography; **703:** M. Dillon/Corbis; **709:** Paul A. Souders/Corbis; **718 (L):** Springer-Verlag; **718 (R):** Ken Karp Photography; **720:** Collection of Suzanne Summer/Cheryl Fenton Photography.

Additional Answers

LESSON 0.2, PAGE 9

5. possible answer:

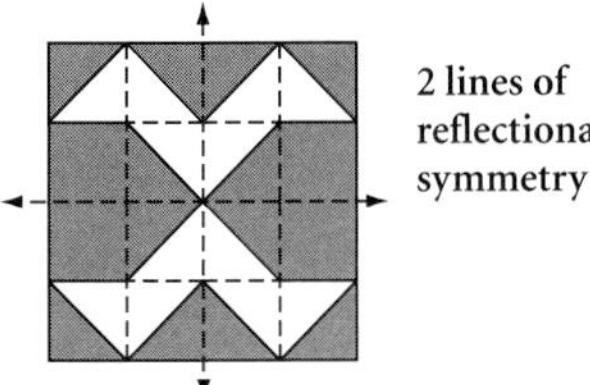

6. possible answer:

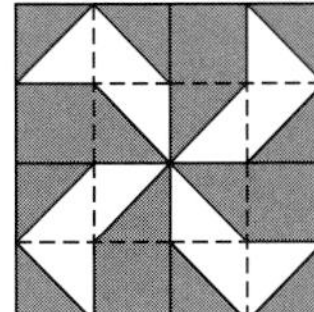

7.

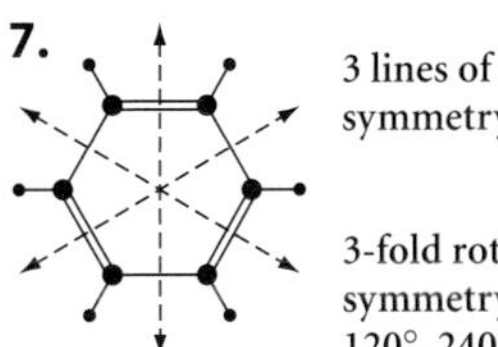

3 lines of reflectional
symmetry
3-fold rotational
symmetry: rotated
120°, 240°, 360°

LESSON 0.3, PAGE 12

4. possible answer:

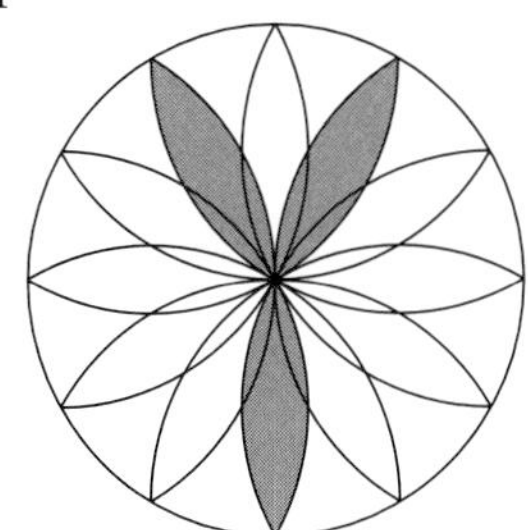

LESSON 0.4, PAGE 15

1. Possible answer: The designs appear to go in and out of the page (they appear 3-D). The squares appear to spiral (although there are no curves in the drawing). The spiral appears to go down as if into a hole. Lines where curves meet look wavy. Bigger squares appear to bulge out.

2. Possible answer: When zebras group together, their stripes make it hard for predators to see individual zebras.

LESSON 1.3, PAGE 51

4.

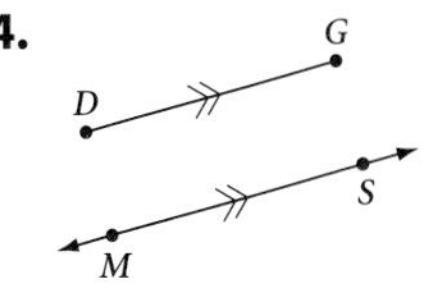

5.

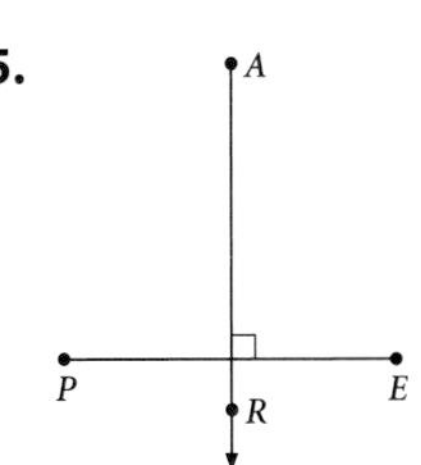

6.

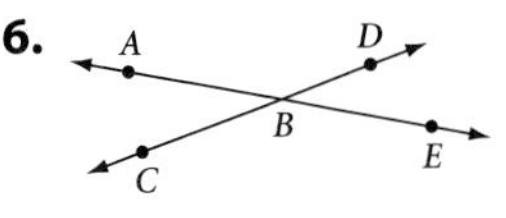

7.

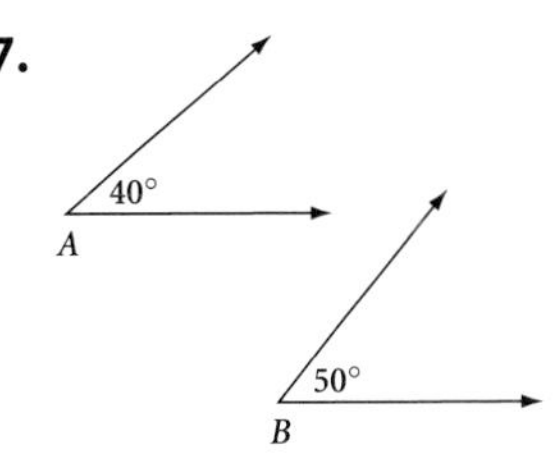

8.

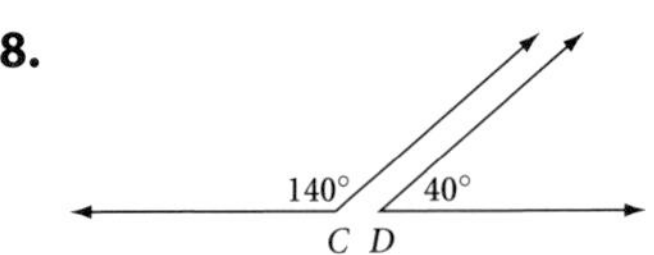

9. B is a Zoid. A Zoid is a creature that has in its interior a small triangle with a large black dot taking up most of its center.

LESSON 1.4, PAGE 58

29.

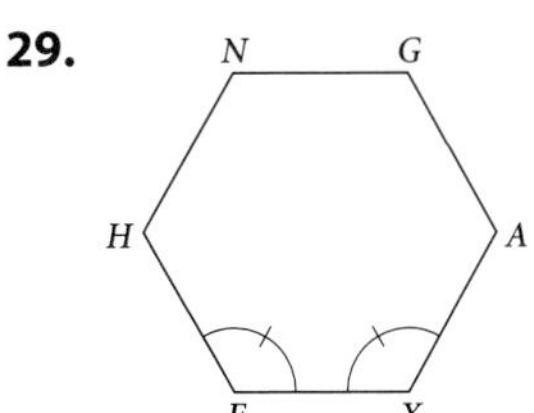

33.

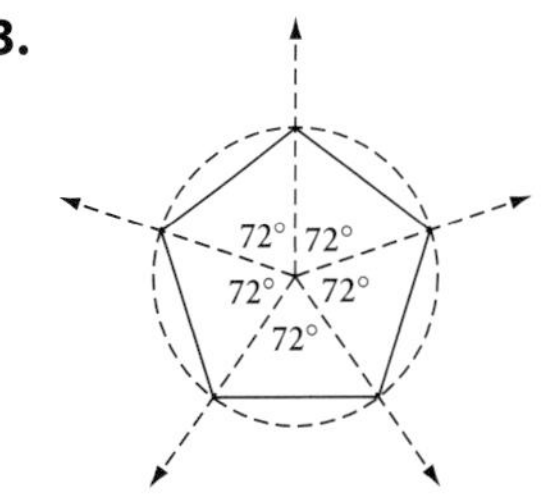

Additional Answers

36. 

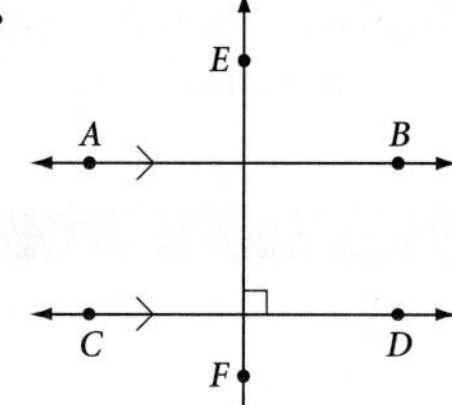

38. See below.

LESSON 1.6, PAGE 71

20. 

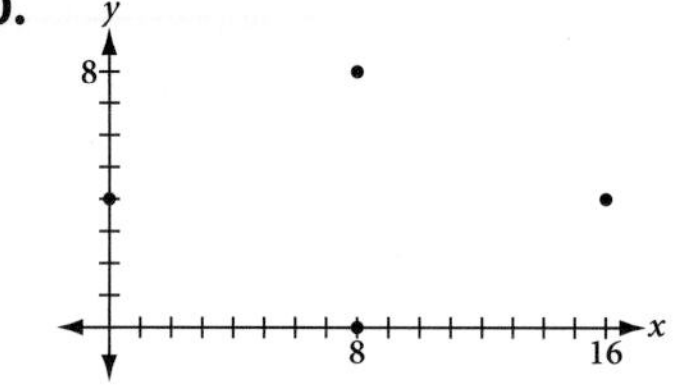

EXPLORATION, PAGE 119

Step 5 A network can be traveled no matter how many even points there are, as long as there are no odd points. If a network has two odd points, it can be traveled as long as you start at one of the odd points and end at the other (so it is impossible to end at your starting point).

LESSON 3.1, PAGE 145

3.

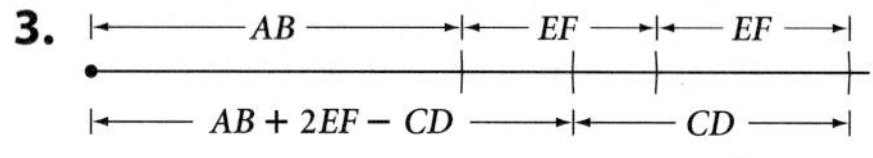

4. 

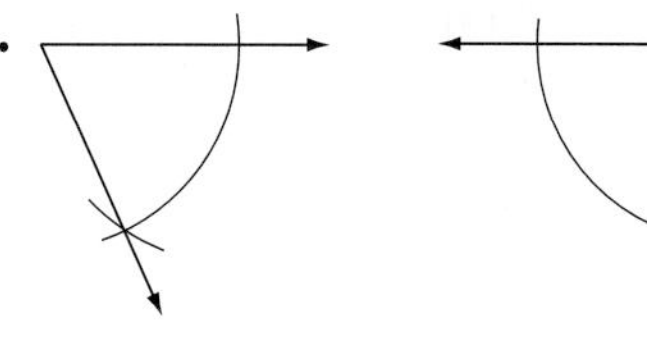

5. possible answer:

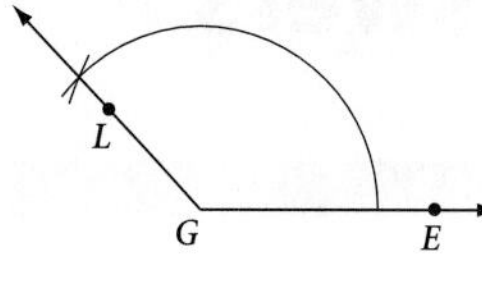

6. $m\angle 3 = m\angle 1 + m\angle 2$. Possible answer:

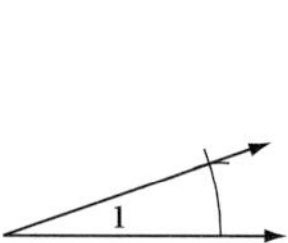

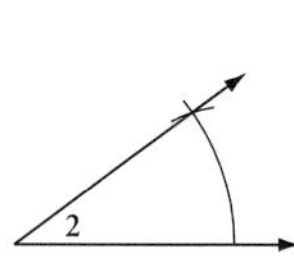

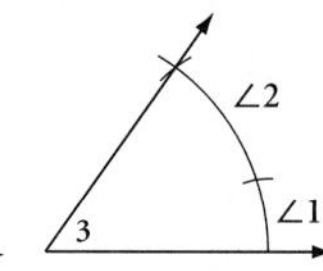

7. possible answer:

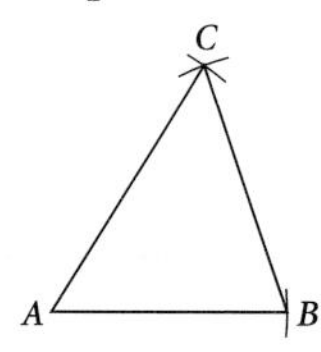

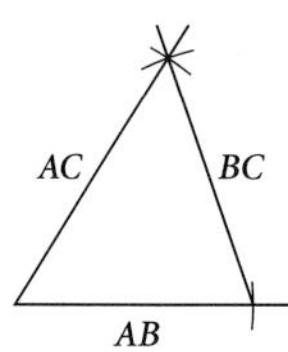

8.

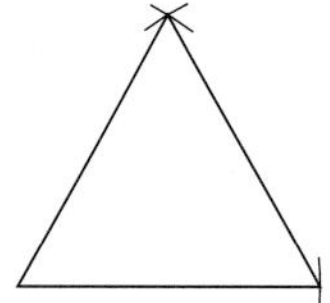

11. One construction method is to create congruent circles that pass through each other's center. One side of the triangle is between the centers of the circles; the other sides meet where the circles intersect.

LESSON 3.2, PAGES 149–150

1.

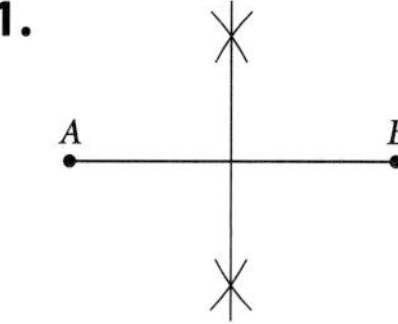

---

38. (*Lesson 1.4*)

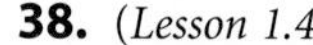

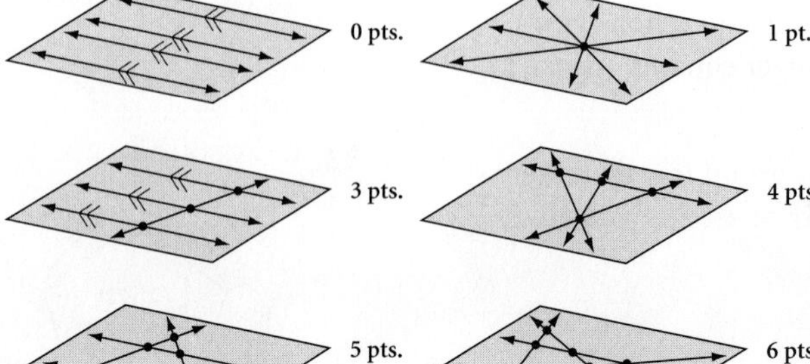

2.

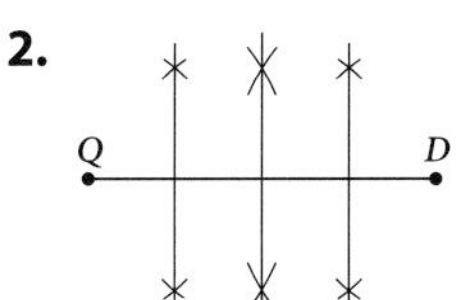

3.

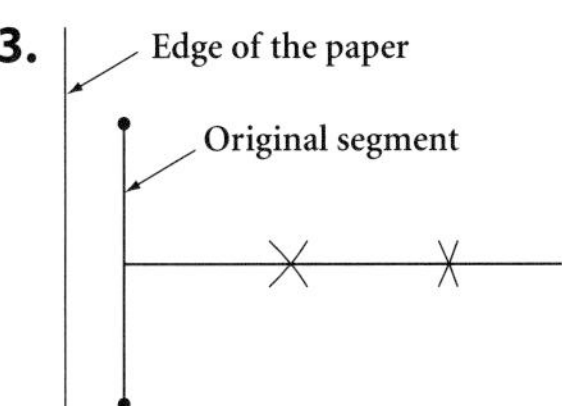

4.

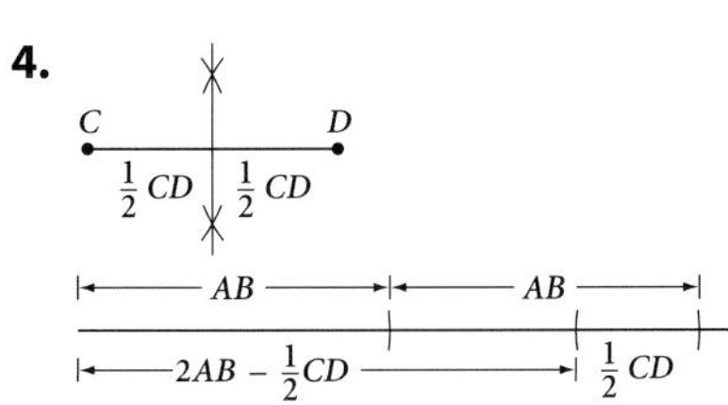

5.

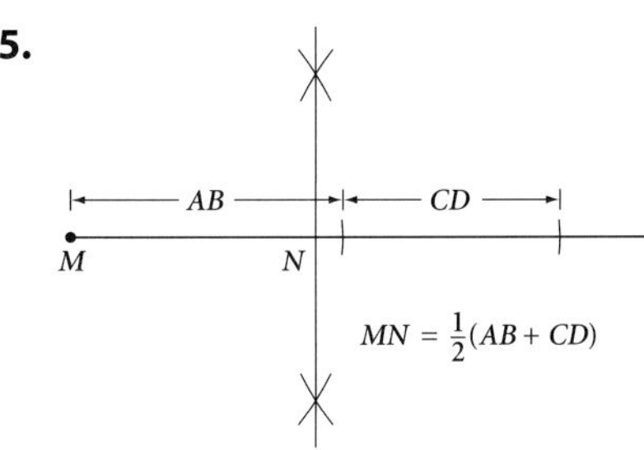

6. Exercises 1–5 with patty paper:

Exercise 1 This is the same as Investigation 1.

Exercise 2

Step 1 Draw a segment on patty paper. Label it $\overline{QD}$.

Step 2 Fold your patty paper so that endpoints *Q* and *D* coincide. Crease along the fold.

Step 3 Unfold and draw a line in the crease.

Step 4 Label the point of intersection *A*.

Step 5 Fold your patty paper so that endpoints *Q* and *A* coincide. Crease along the fold.

Step 6 Unfold and draw a line in the crease.

Step 7 Label the point of intersection *B*.

Step 8 Fold your patty paper so that endpoints *A* and *D* coincide. Crease along the fold.

Step 9 Unfold and draw a line in the crease.

Step 10 Label the point of intersection *C*.

Exercise 3 This is the same as Investigation 1.

Exercise 4

Step 1 Do Investigation 1 to get $\frac{1}{2}CD$.

Step 2 On a second piece of patty paper, trace $\overline{AB}$ two times so that the two segments form a segment of length $2AB$.

Step 3 Lay the first piece of patty paper on top of the second so that the endpoints coincide and the shorter segment is on top of the longer segment.

Step 4 Trace the rest of the longer segment with a different colored writing utensil. That will be the answer.

Exercise 5

Step 1 Trace segments *AB* and *CD* so that the two segments form a segment of length $AB + CD$.

Step 2 Fold your patty paper so that points *A* and *D* coincide. Crease along the fold.

Step 3 Unfold and draw a line in the crease.

LESSON 3.3, PAGE 154

1.

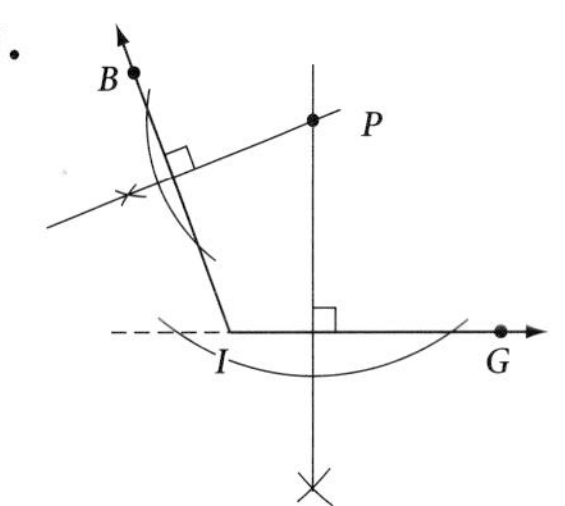

The answer depends on the angle drawn and where *P* is placed.

2.

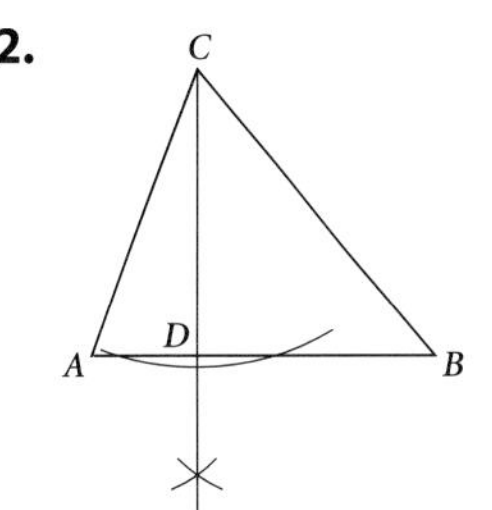

3.

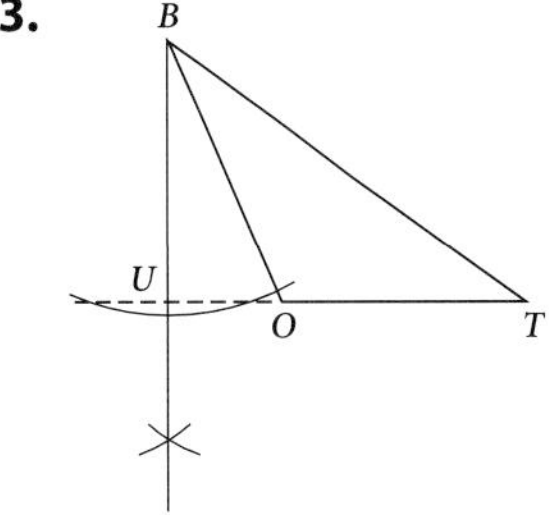

Two altitudes fall outside the triangle, and one falls inside.

4. From the point, swing arcs on the line to construct a segment whose midpoint is that point. Then construct the perpendicular bisector of the segment.

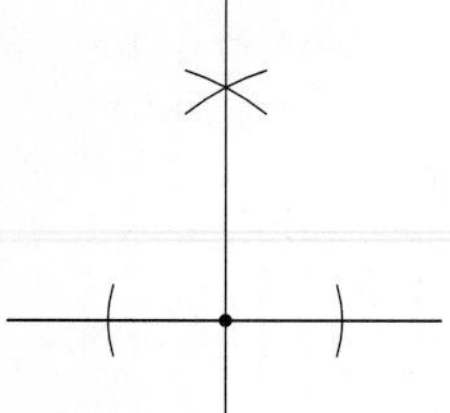

5. Construct perpendiculars from point Q and point R. Mark off $\overline{QS}$ and $\overline{RE}$ congruent to $\overline{QR}$. Connect points S and E.

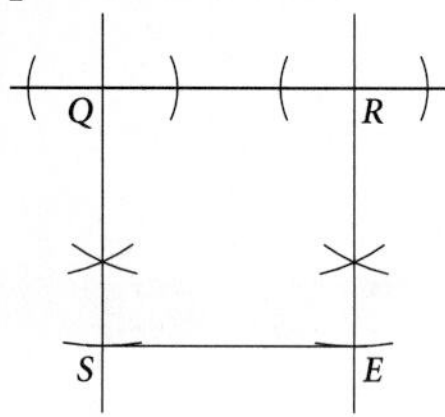

LESSON 3.4, PAGE 159

6.

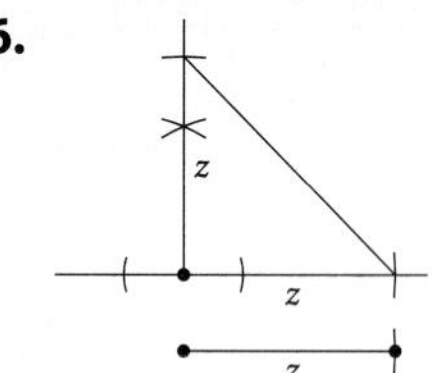

7.

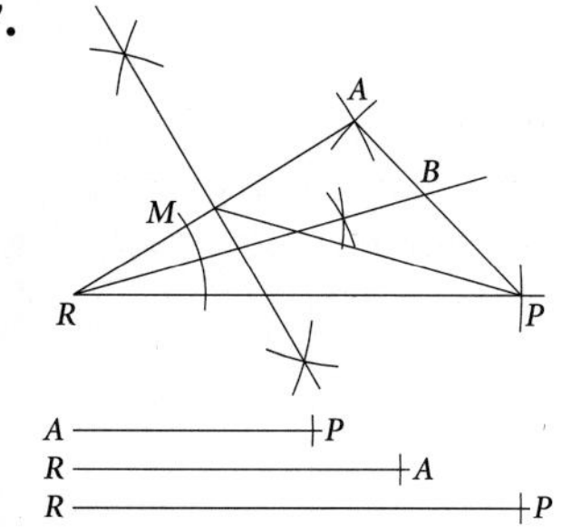

8.

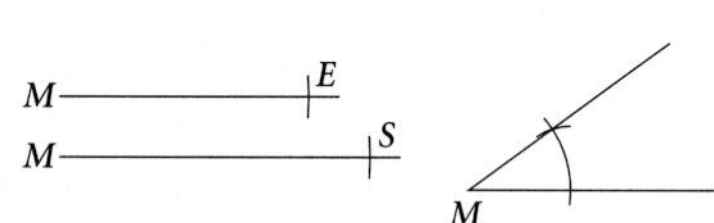

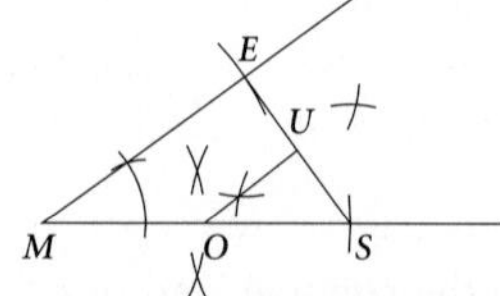

9a, b.

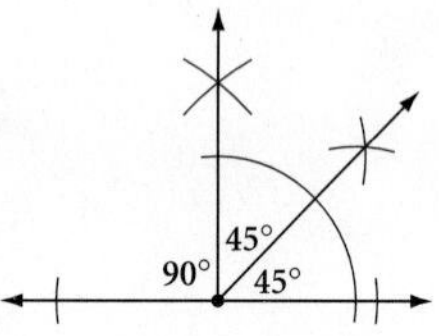

9c.

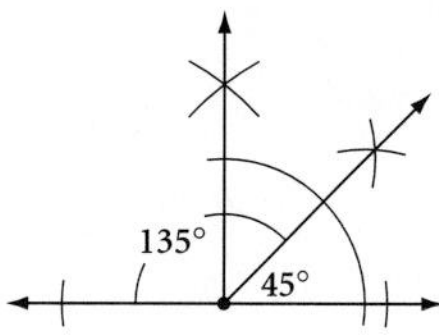

10.

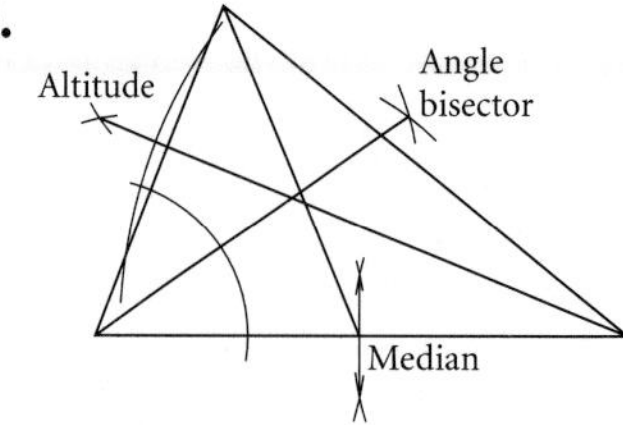

11.

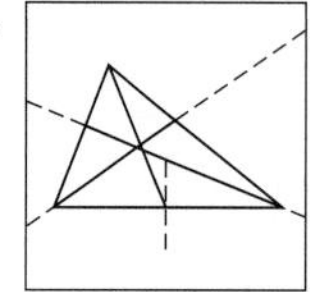

12. The angle bisectors are perpendicular. The sum of the measures of the linear pair is 180°. The sum of half of each must be 90°.

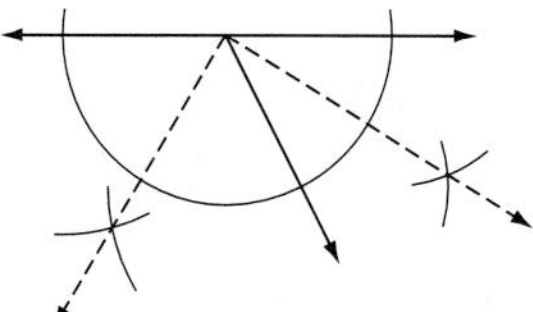

LESSON 3.5, PAGE 162

1.

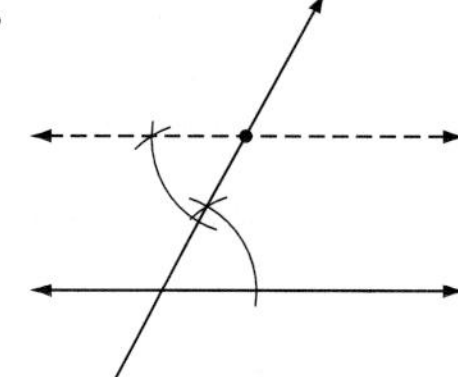

2.

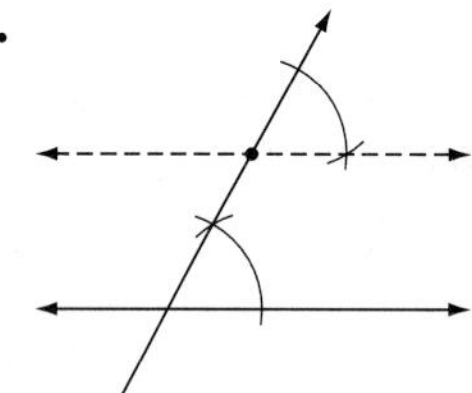

4.

5. sample construction:

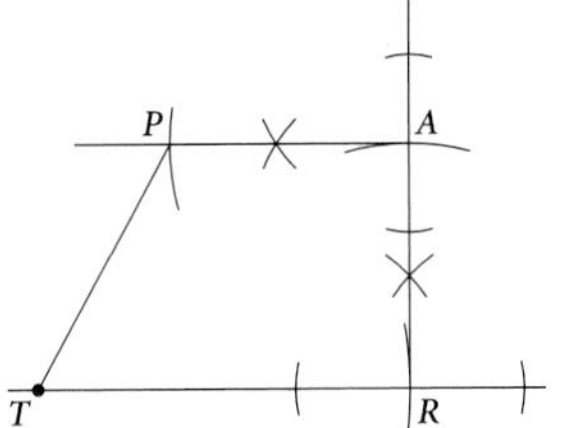

6.

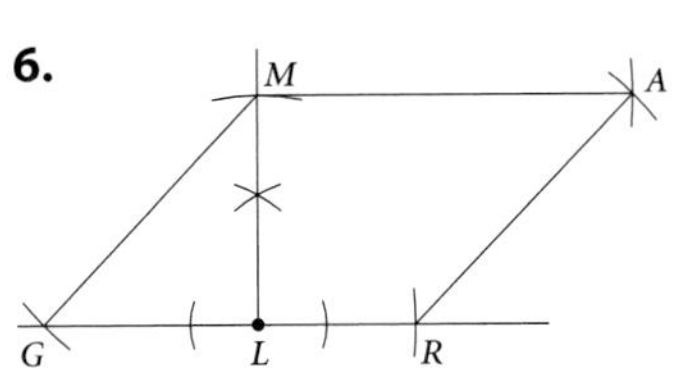

LESSON 3.6, PAGE 170

1. Construct one of the segments, and mark arcs of the correct length from the endpoints. Draw sides to where those arcs meet.

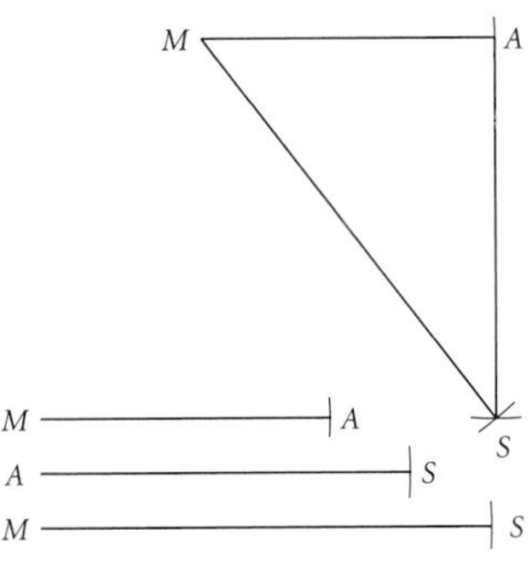

2.

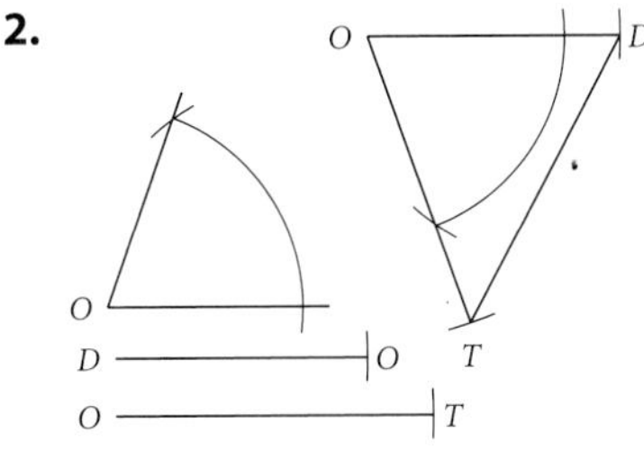

Sample description: Construct $\angle O$. Mark off distances OD and OT on the sides of the angle. Connect D and T.

3.

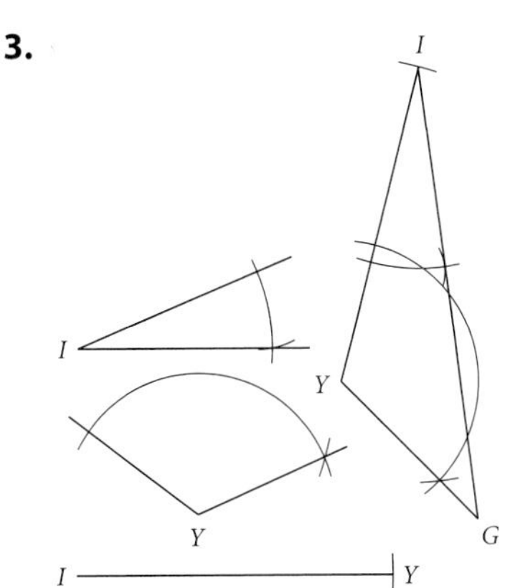

Sample description: Construct $\overline{IY}$. Construct $\angle I$ at I and $\angle Y$ at Y.

4.

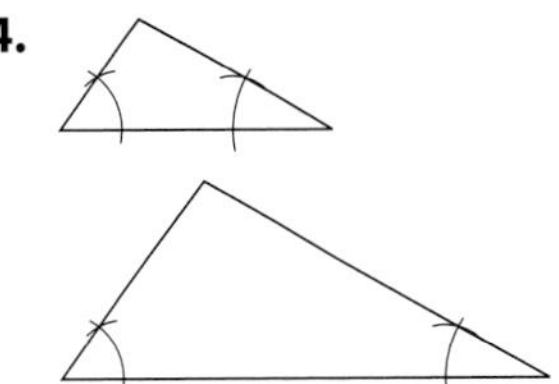

Sample description: Draw one side with a different length than the lengths in the book. Copy an angle at each end of that segment congruent to one of the angles in the book. Where they meet is the third vertex of the triangle.

5.

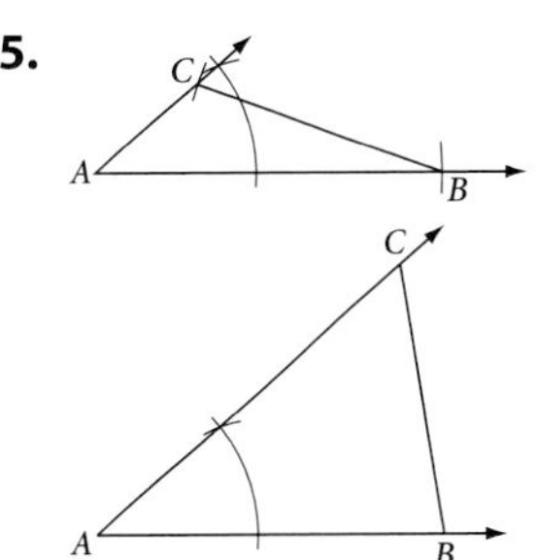

Sample description: Construct $\angle A$ and mark off the distance AB. From B swing an arc of length BC to intersect the other side of $\angle A$ at two points. Each gives a different triangle.

6.

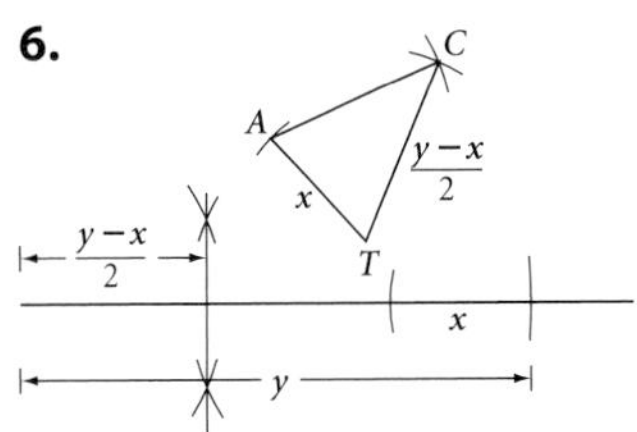

Sample description: Mark the distance y, mark back the distance x, and bisect the remaining length of y. Using an arc of that length, mark arcs on the ends of segment x. The point where they intersect is the vertex angle of the triangle.

7.

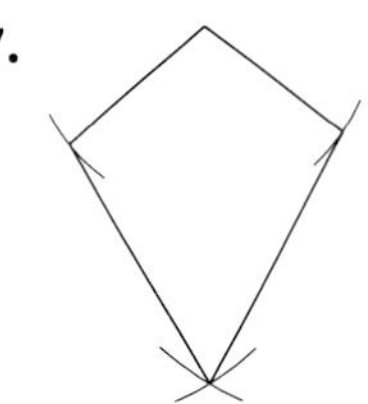

Sample description: Draw an angle. Mark off equal segments on the sides of the angle. Use a different compass setting to draw intersecting arcs from the ends of those segments.

LESSON 4.6, PAGE 231

1. Yes. $\overline{BD} \cong \overline{BD}$ (same segment), $\angle A \cong \angle C$ (given), and $\angle ABD \cong \angle CBD$ (given), so $\triangle DBA \cong \triangle DBC$ by SAA. $\therefore \overline{AB} \cong \overline{CB}$ by CPCTC.

2. Yes. $\overline{CN} \cong \overline{WN}$ and $\angle C \cong \angle W$ (given), and $\angle RNC \cong \angle ONW$ (vertical angles), $\triangle CNR \cong \triangle WON$ by ASA. $\therefore \overline{RN} \cong \overline{ON}$ by CPCTC.

3. Cannot be determined. The congruent parts lead to the ambiguous case SSA.

4. Yes. $\angle S \cong \angle I$, $\angle G \cong \angle A$ (given), and $\overline{TS} \cong \overline{IT}$ (definition of midpoint), so $\triangle TIA \cong \triangle TSG$ by SAA. $\therefore \overline{SG} \cong \overline{IA}$ by CPCTC.

5. Yes. $\overline{FO} \cong \overline{FR}$ and $\overline{UO} \cong \overline{UR}$ (given), and $\overline{UF} \cong \overline{UF}$ (same segment), so $\triangle FOU \cong \triangle FRU$ by SSS. $\therefore \angle O \cong \angle R$ by CPCTC.

6. Yes. $\overline{MN} \cong \overline{MA}$ and $\overline{ME} \cong \overline{MR}$ (given), and $\angle M \cong \angle M$ (same angle), so $\triangle EMA \cong \triangle RMN$ by SAS. $\therefore \angle E \cong \angle R$ by CPCTC.

7. Yes. $\overline{BT} \cong \overline{EU}$ and $\overline{BU} \cong \overline{ET}$ (given), and $\overline{UT} \cong \overline{UT}$ (same segment), so $\triangle TUB \cong \triangle UTE$ by SSS. $\therefore \angle B \cong \angle E$ by CPCTC.

8. Cannot be determined. $\triangle HLF \cong \triangle LHA$ by ASA, but $\overline{HA}$ and $\overline{HF}$ are not corresponding sides.

9. Cannot be determined. AAA does not guarantee congruence.

USING YOUR ALGEBRA SKILLS 5, PAGE 286

6. All the variables cancel out and you're left with a false statement.

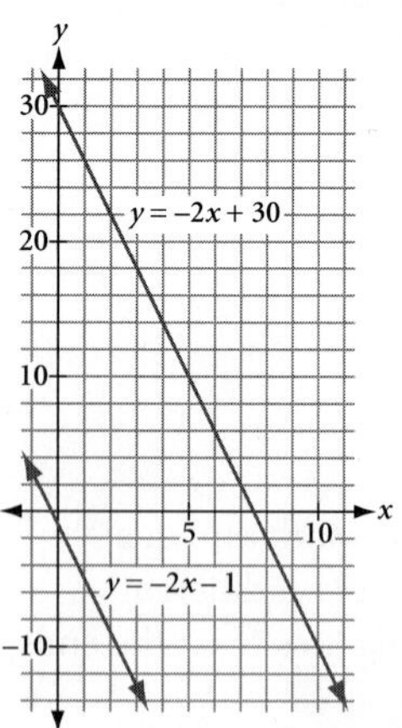

The lines are parallel (the slopes are the same, but the y-intercepts are different). There is no solution.

7a. $y = 4x + 20$; $y = 7x$; (6 hr 40 min, \$46.67)

7b.

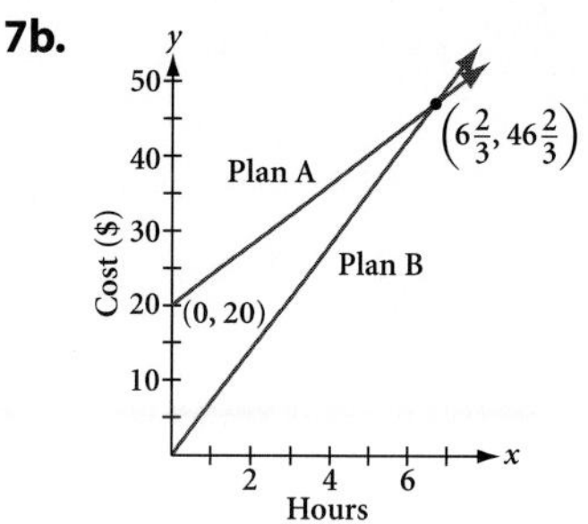

The point of intersection is where both plans are the same, the answer for 7a.

LESSON 5.7, PAGE 297

8.

1. *BEAR* is a parallelogram — Given
2. $\overline{RE} \cong \overline{AB}$ — Given
3. $\overline{BR} \cong \overline{EA}$ — Parallelogram Opposite Sides Conjecture
4. $\overline{AR} \cong \overline{EB}$ — Parallelogram Opposite Sides Conjecture
5. $\triangle EBR \cong \triangle ARB \cong \triangle RAE \cong \triangle BEA$ — SSS
6. $\angle EBR \cong \angle ARB \cong \angle RAE \cong \angle BEA$ — CPCTC
7. *BEAR* is a rectangle — Definition of rectangle

CHAPTER 6 REVIEW, PAGE 350

23. Sample answer: Construct a right angle and label the vertex R. Mark off $\overline{RE}$ and $\overline{RT}$ with any lengths. From point E, swing an arc with radius RT. From point T, swing an arc with radius RE. Label the intersection of the arcs as C. Construct the diagonals $\overline{ET}$ and $\overline{RC}$. Their intersection is the center of the circumscribed circle. The circle's radius is the distance from the center to a vertex. It is not possible to construct an inscribed circle in a rectangle unless it is a square.

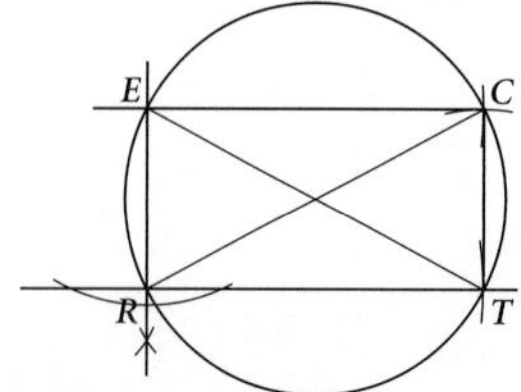

LESSON 7.1, PAGE 365

Extension B

96	11	89	68
88	69	**91**	16
61	**86**	18	99
19	98	66	**81**

LESSON 7.4, PAGE 381

Step 3 two regular polygons:

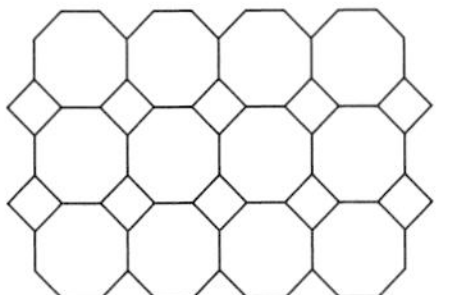

4.8.8

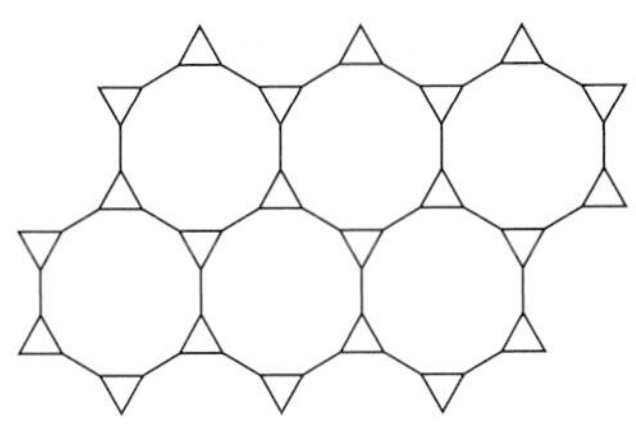

3.12.12

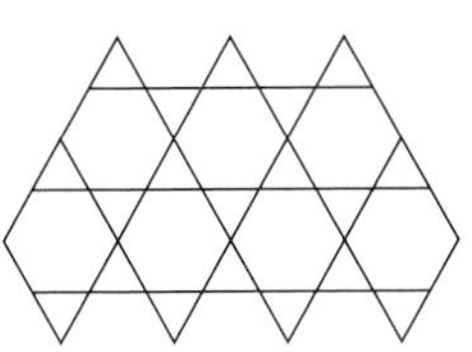

3.6.3.6

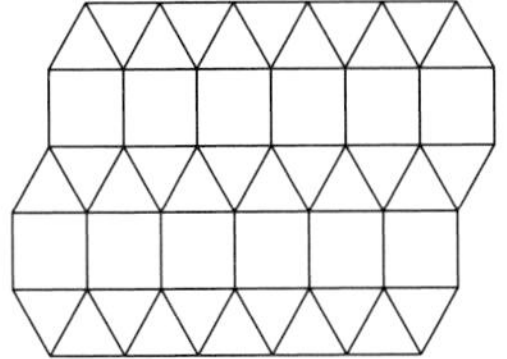

3.3.3.4.4

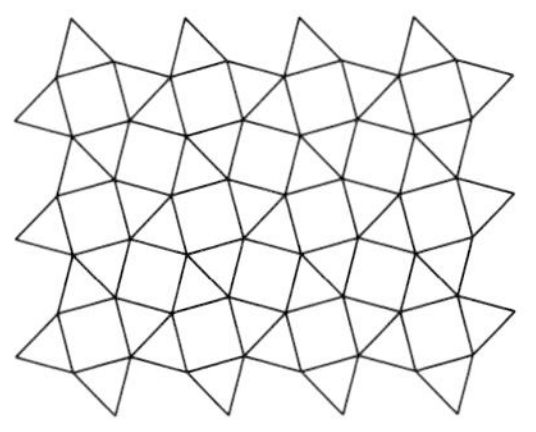

3.3.4.3.4

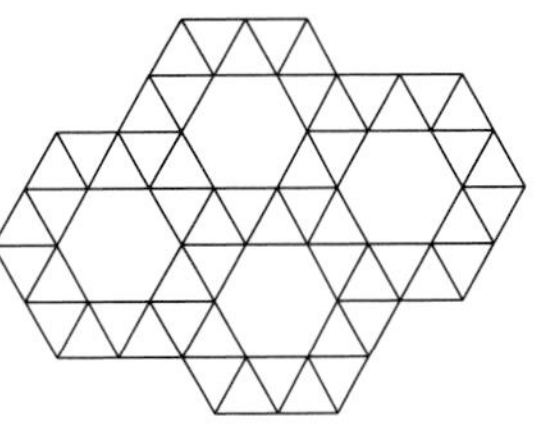

3.3.3.3.6

three regular polygons:

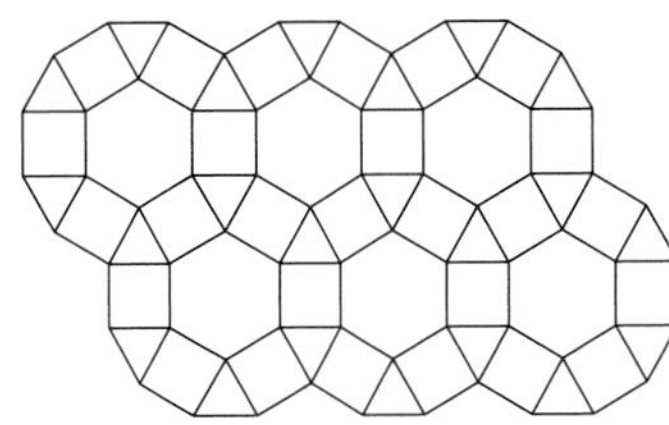

3.4.6.4

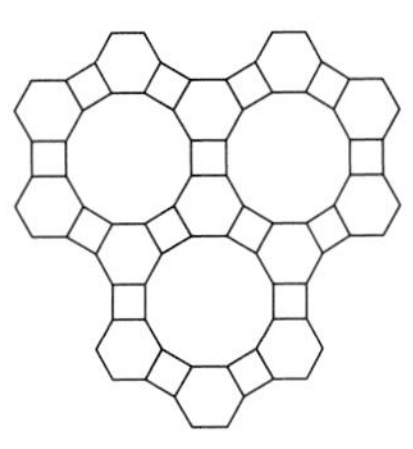

4.6.12

LESSON 8.1, PAGE 416

28b.

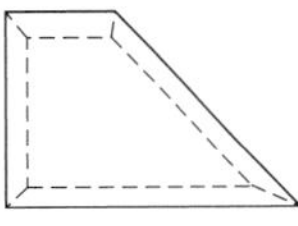

28c.

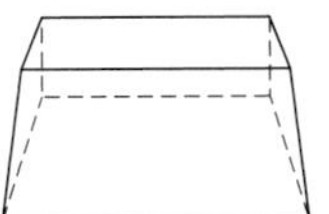

Graphs for the Project

rectan Rerandomize

3x4 6x1 0x2 1x4

rectangles

	length	width	Perimeter	Area
=	random(0, max)	random(0, max)	2length + 2w	length·width
1	3.24629	3.92518	14.343	12.7423
2	3.32037	0.106836	6.85441	0.354735
3	2.75019	5.1598	15.82	14.1905
4	0.36319	4.05468	8.83573	1.47262
5	0.975262	1.69671	5.34395	1.65474
6	5.5357	1.12208	13.3156	6.21151
7	0.904393	2.97746	7.7637	2.69279
8	4.08555	3.39797	14.967	13.8826
9	4.58701	3.11885	15.4117	14.3062

max = 6.00

0 2 4 6 8 10 12

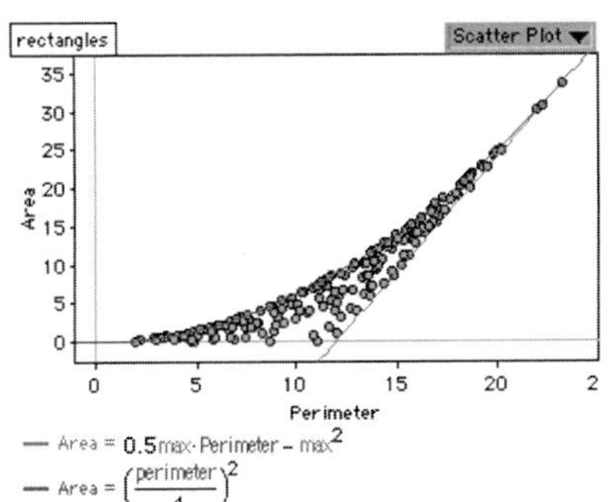

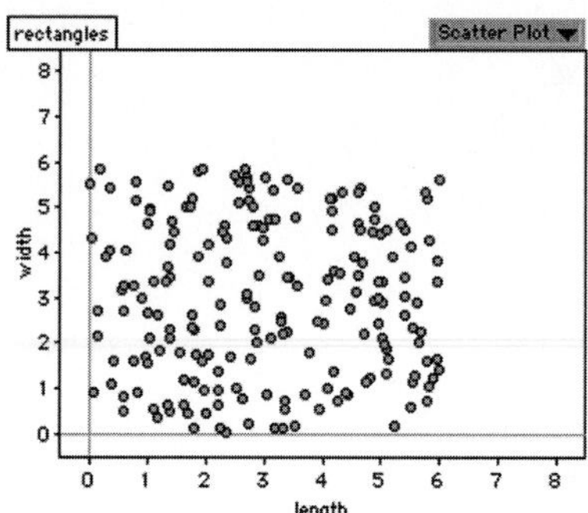

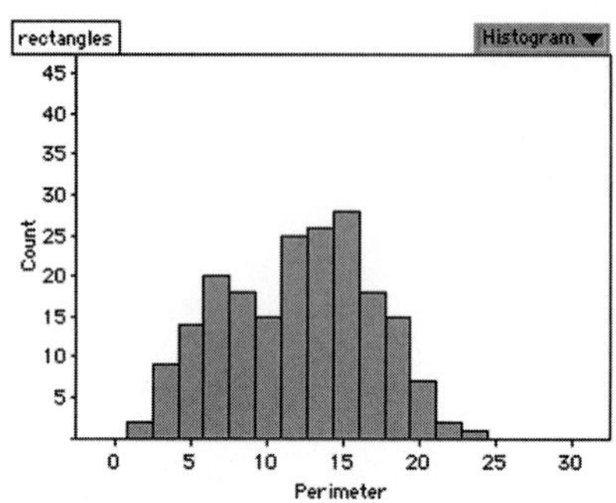

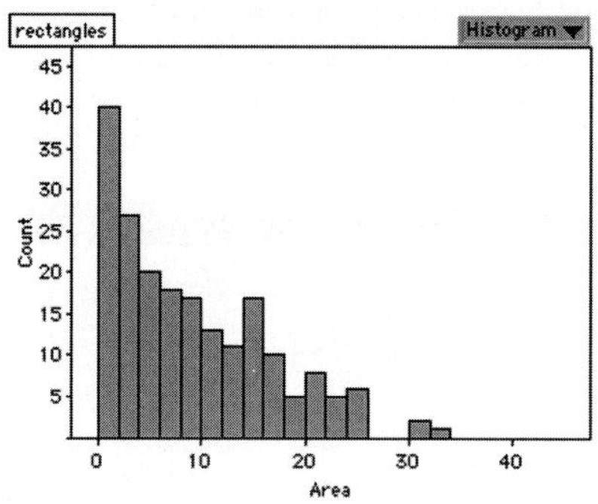

LESSON 8.2, PAGE 420

13. sample answer:

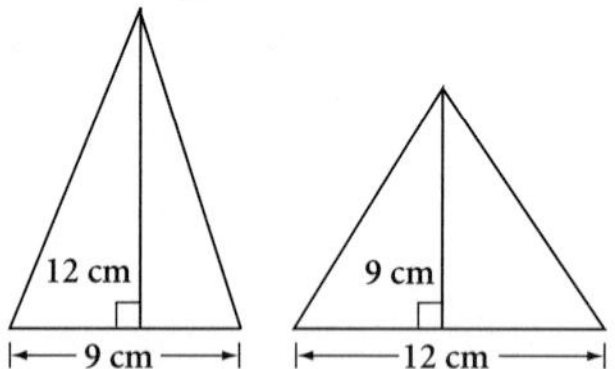

14. sample answer:

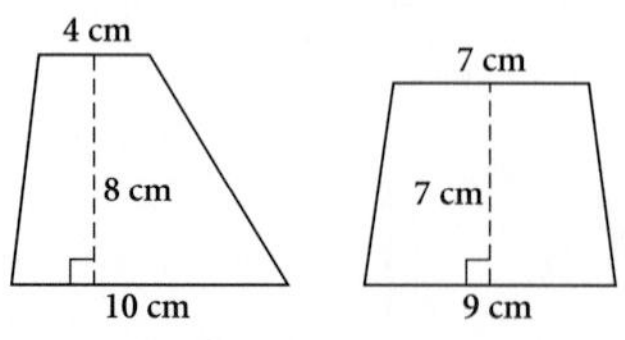

15. sample answer:

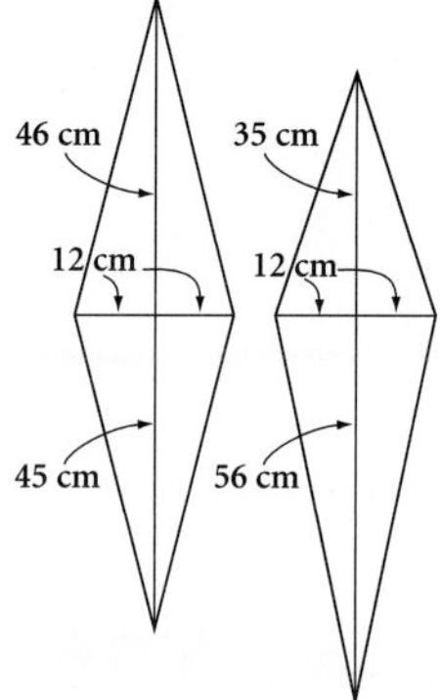

16. The length of the base of the triangle equals the sum of the lengths of both bases of the trapezoid.

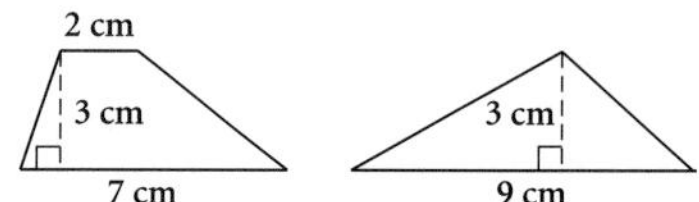

19a. 86 in. of balsa wood and 960 in.^{2} of Mylar

19b. 56 in. (or less, if he tilts the kite)

LESSON 8.6, PAGE 440

15a.

15b.

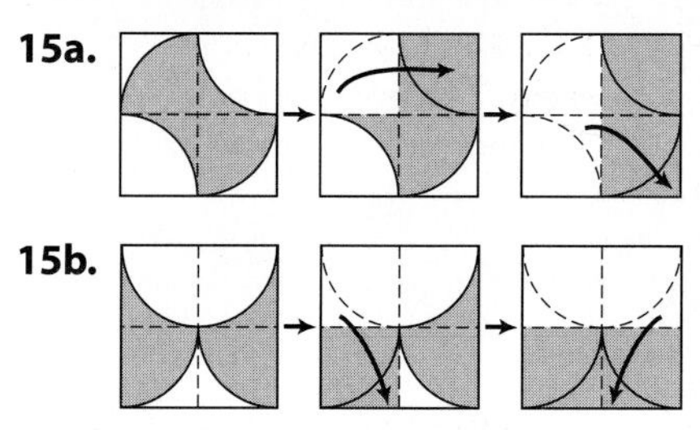

15c.

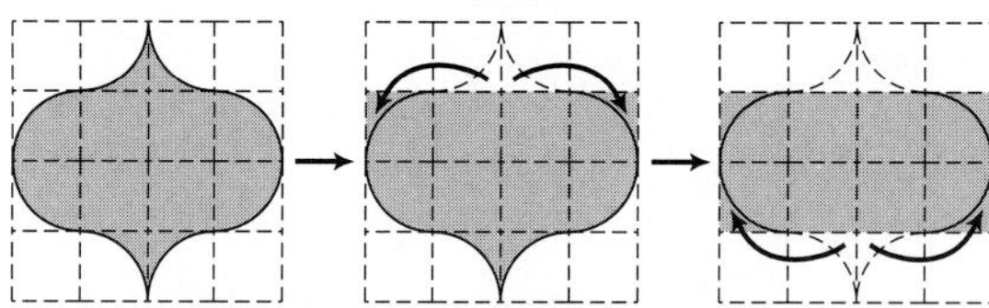

15d.

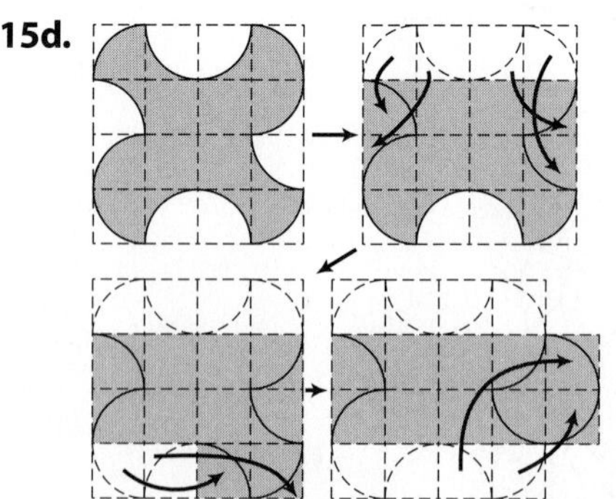

16. sample answer:

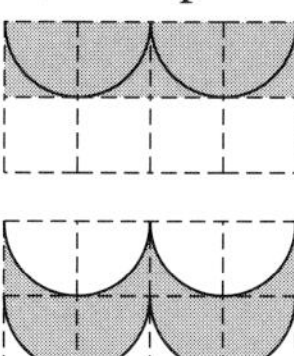

LESSON 9.2, PAGE 472

22. Because $m\angle DCF = 90°$, $m\angle DCE = (90 - x)°$. Because $\triangle DCE$ is isosceles, $m\angle DEC = (90 - x)°$. $m\angle D = 180° - 2 \cdot ((90 - x)°) = 2x$. Because $\angle D$ is a central angle, $2x = a$. Therefore, $x = \left(\frac{1}{2}\right)a$.

25.

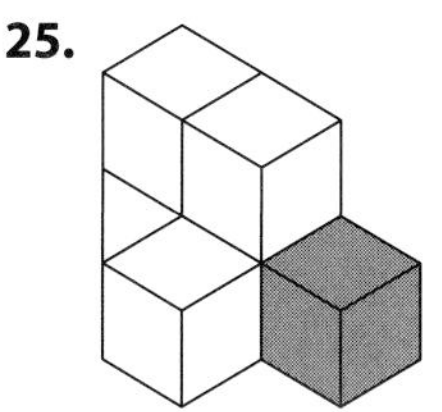

EXPLORATION, PAGE 491

Step 6 If the ladder is pulled out too far from the wall, it might slip too easily. The graph shows that for values of x greater than y, the curve drops off steeply.

LESSON 11.5, PAGE 598

Graphs for the Project

In the graph (shorter side, ratio of longer side to shorter side), the slope may be nearly zero.

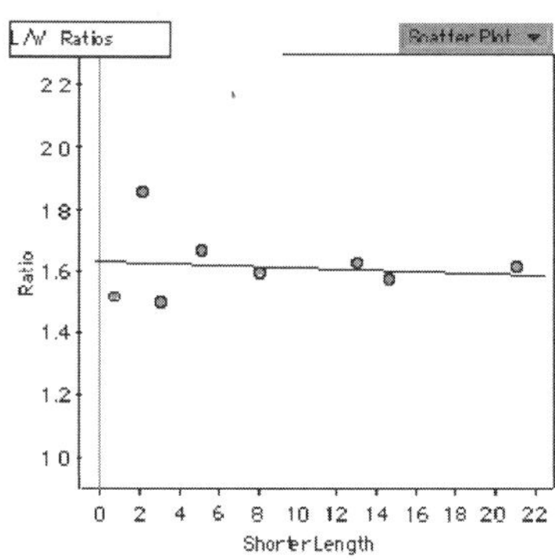

Other representations of the data might include a distribution of the ratios along with the plotted mean value.

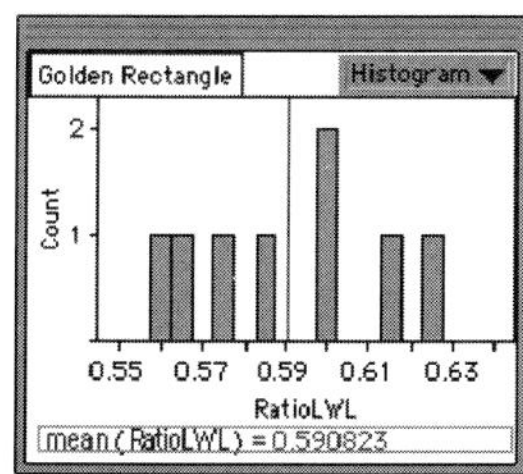

LESSON 11.6, PAGE 610

27. possible answer:

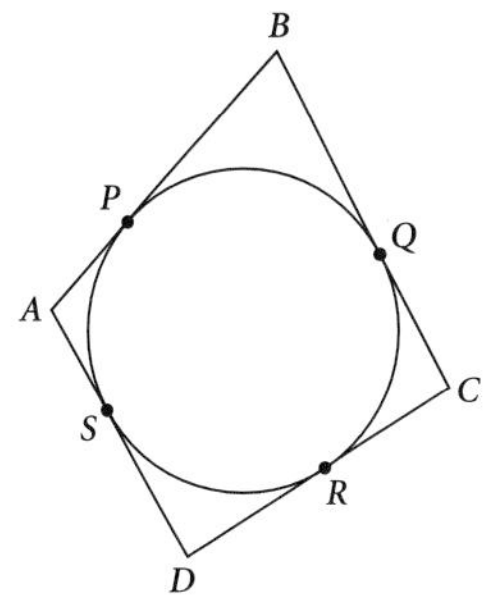

Given: Circumscribed quadrilateral *ABCD,* with points of tangency *P, Q, R,* and *S*

Show: $AB + DC = AD + BC$

If you use segment addition, you can show that each sum of lengths of opposite sides is composed of four lengths, $AB + CD = (AP + BP) + (DR + CR)$ and $AD + BC = (AS + DS) + (BQ + CQ)$. If you accept the Tangent Segments Conjecture as true, you know that $AP = AS$, $BP = BQ$, $CR = CQ$, and $DR = DS$, and the four lengths in each sum are equivalent. Here are the algebraic steps to show that the whole sums are equivalent.

$AB + DC = (AP + BP) + (DR + CR)$	Segment addition.
$= (AS + BQ) + (DS + CQ)$	Substitute *AS* for *AP, BQ* for *BP, CQ* for *CR,* and *DS* for *DR.*
$= (AS + DS) + (BQ + CQ)$	Regroup the measurements by common points of tangency.
$AB + DC = AD + BC$	Use segment addition to rewrite the right side as the other sum of opposite sides.

EXPLORATION, PAGE 613

Steps 2a–c and 3 See below.

CHAPTER 11 REVIEW, PAGE 618

Take Another Look

4. (Note: The figures below are not drawn to scale. Because the actual distances are so great relative to the diameters, we won't worry that $\overline{AB}$ and $\overline{AD}$ are not precisely tangent to the spheres of the Moon and the Sun; nor will we worry about what points on the Moon and the Sun we use in measuring the distance from Earth.)

By similar triangles, $\frac{AB}{BC} = \frac{AD}{DE}$. If the Moon were smaller (or farther away), these ratios wouldn't be equal—the Moon wouldn't block all of the Sun's light (Figure B). If the Moon were larger (or closer), it would block an area larger than that of the Sun—we wouldn't be able to see the Sun's corona during an eclipse (Figure C).

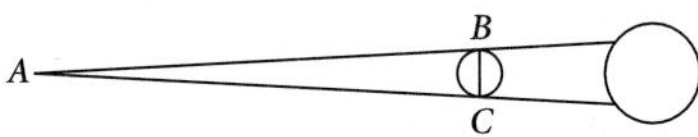

Figure B

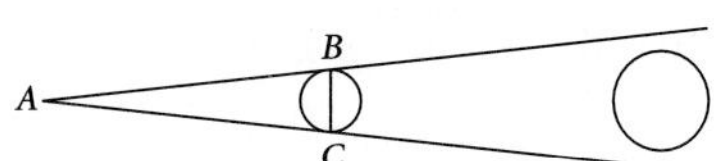

Figure C

5. $ra = b$ and $rb = c \Rightarrow c = ar^2$ is not true for only some values of r. The sum of the lengths of any two sides of a triangle must be greater than the length of the third side: $a + ar > ar^2$. (Similar equations that reduce to this occur for other pairs of sides.) Solve the inequality $r < \frac{1 + \sqrt{5}}{2}$. In other words, r must be less than the golden ratio.

LESSON 12.4, PAGES 645–646

15.

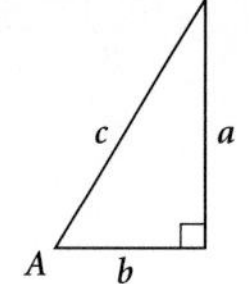

$\sin A = \frac{a}{c}$

$\cos A = \frac{b}{c}$

$\tan A = \frac{a}{b}$

$$\frac{\sin A}{\cos A} = \frac{\frac{a}{c}}{\frac{b}{c}} = \frac{a}{c} \cdot \frac{c}{b} = \frac{a}{b} = \tan A$$

20. possible answer:

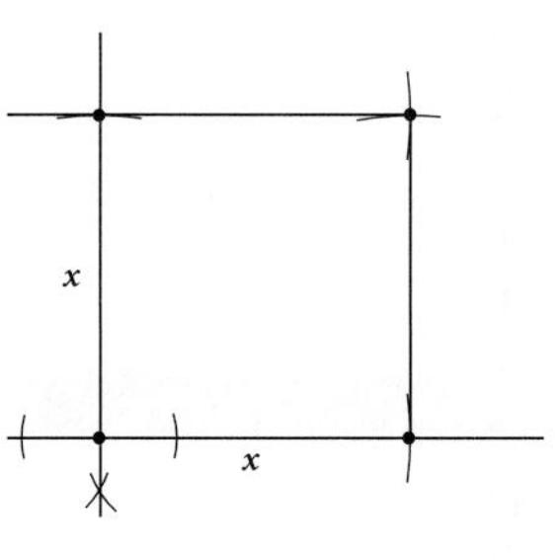

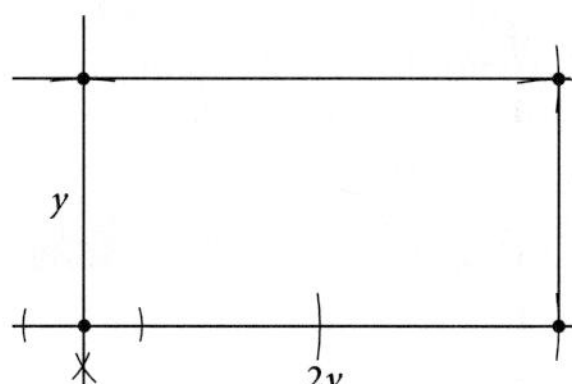

Step 2a	**Step 2b**	**Step 2c**
	not valid	
P: study	P: don't earn money	P: $\overline{EF} \parallel \overline{AB}$
Q: miss show	Q: can't buy computer	Q: EF is a midsegment.
R: Jeannine comes	R: don't get job	R: $ABFE$ is a trapezoid.
$P \rightarrow Q$	$P \rightarrow Q$	$\sim P \rightarrow \sim Q$
$R \rightarrow P$	$R \rightarrow P$	$Q \rightarrow P$ by LC
$\therefore R \rightarrow Q$ by LS	$\therefore R \rightarrow Q$ by LS	$P \rightarrow R$
R	$\sim R$	$\therefore Q \rightarrow R$ by LS
$\therefore Q$ by MP	(R does not imply $\sim Q$)	Q
		$\therefore R$ by MP

Step 3

$P \rightarrow Q$		$P \rightarrow Q$
$\sim Q$	is equivalent to	$\sim Q \rightarrow \sim P$ by LC
$\therefore \sim P$ by MT		$\sim Q$
		$\therefore \sim P$ by MP

Additional Answers

21. possible answer:

22. Students might begin with the simplest case where all factors are equal. With circles of the same radius and with endpoints of the segment traveling in the same direction, at the same rotational speed, and starting from the same relative position, the midpoint will trace a circle equal in size to those constructed. Changing the size of both circles will change the size of the circle traced, as will changing the starting positions of the endpoints. The maximum radius of the traced circle is limited by the radius of the constructed circles; the smallest observable trace is a single point.

With all other factors equal and the endpoints of the segment traveling in opposite directions around the circles, the midpoint will trace an ellipse. The major axis of the ellipse is equal to the sum of the radii of the two constructed circles. The minor axis is equal to their difference. Varying the starting positions of the endpoints changes the orientation of the ellipse. Changing the rotational speed of the endpoints will produce more complex polar curves, which students might describe as flowers, roses, or "spirograph-like."

Changing the distance between the centers has no effect on the shape of the trace, only its position. No matter how they vary the factors, students should find the midpoint trace will always trace over itself.

Sangaku Problem Solution

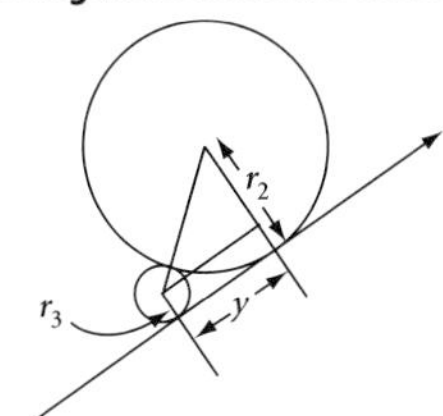

$hyp = r_2 + r_3$; $leg = r_2 - r_3$

$y = 2\sqrt{r_2 r_3}$

The three legs AB, x, and y are related. $AB = x + y$, or $2\sqrt{r_1 r_2} = 2\sqrt{r_1 r_3} + 2\sqrt{r_2 r_3}$. Divide by $2\sqrt{r_1 r_2 r_3}$ to get

$$\frac{1}{\sqrt{r_3}} = \frac{1}{\sqrt{r_1}} + \frac{1}{\sqrt{r_2}}$$

EXPLORATION, PAGE 654

Project Outcome Samples

- The graph of $y = \sin x$ has a minimum y-value of -1 and a maximum y-value of $+1$. The period is 360°.
- Sine and cosine have the same shape, but the cosine curve is translated 90° left. Both graphs have points in common when x equals $-315°$, $-135°$, 45°, and 225°, or every 180° from 45°.
- $\cos x = \sin(x + 90)$ or $\sin x = \cos x$ for $x = 45 + 180n$, where n is any integer value.
- As x approaches 90°, the tangent function approaches infinity, because as the measure of one of the acute angles in a right triangle approaches 90°, the opposite side gets longer and longer and the adjacent side gets shorter and shorter; hence the ratio $\frac{\text{length of opposite side}}{\text{length of adjacent side}}$ gets infinitely large.

EXPLORATION, PAGE 658

Step 5a

Let P = All wealthy people are happy.

Let Q = Money can buy happiness.

Let R = True love exists.

$P \rightarrow Q$

$Q \rightarrow \sim R$

R

$\therefore \sim P$

1. $P \rightarrow Q$	1. Premise
2. $Q \rightarrow \sim R$	2. Premise
3. $P \rightarrow \sim R$	3. From lines 1 and 2, using LS
4. R	4. Premise
5. $\sim P$	5. From lines 3 and 4, using MT

Step 5b

Let P = Clark is performing at the theater today.

Let Q = Everyone at the theater has a good time.

Let R = Lois is sad.

$P \rightarrow Q$

$Q \rightarrow \sim R$

R

$\therefore \sim P$

1. $P \rightarrow Q$	1. Premise
2. $Q \rightarrow \sim R$	2. Premise
3. $P \rightarrow \sim R$	3. From lines 1 and 2, using LS
4. R	4. Premise
5. $\sim P$	5. From lines 3 and 4, using MT

Step 5c

Let P = Evette is innocent.

Let Q = Alfa is telling the truth.

Let R = Romeo is telling the truth.

Let S = Romeo has something to gain.

$P \rightarrow Q$

$R \rightarrow \sim Q$

$\sim R \rightarrow S$

$\sim S$

$\therefore \sim S \rightarrow \sim P$

1. $\sim S$	1. Assume the antecedent
2. $\sim R \rightarrow S$	2. Premise
3. R	3. From lines 1 and 2, using MT
4. $R \rightarrow \sim Q$	4. Premise
5. $\sim Q$	5. From lines 3 and 4, using MP
6. $P \rightarrow Q$	6. Premise
7. $\sim P$	7. From lines 5 and 6, using MT

Assuming $\sim S$ is true, the truth of $\sim P$ is established.
$\therefore \sim S \rightarrow \sim P$

LESSON 13.2, PAGE 684

9.

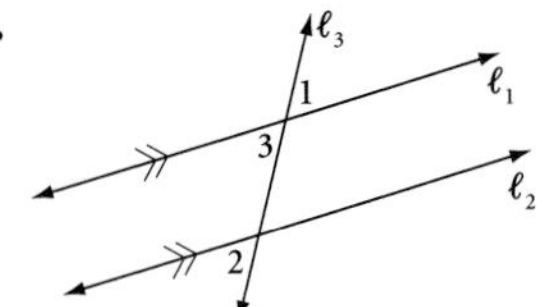

Use the VA Theorem and the CA Postulate to get $\angle 1 \cong \angle 3$ and $\angle 2 \cong \angle 3$. Then use the transitive property to get $\angle 1 \cong \angle 2$.

10.

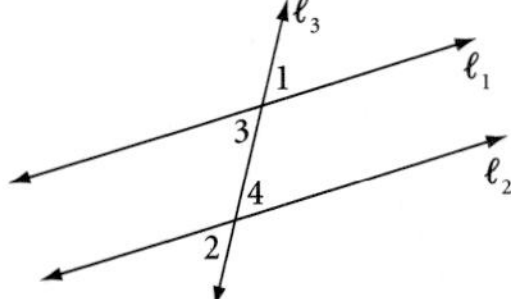

Use the VA Theorem and the substitution property to get $\angle 3 \cong \angle 4$. Therefore the lines are parallel by the Converse of the AIA Theorem.

11.

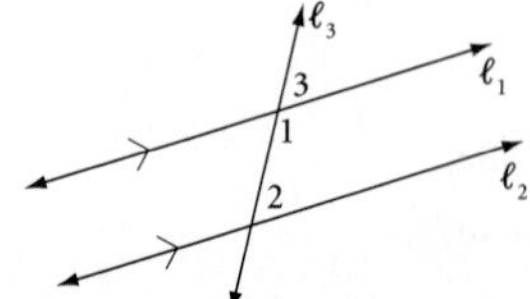

Use the Linear Pair Postulate and the definition of supplementary angles to get $m\angle 1 + m\angle 3 = 180°$. Then use the CA Postulate and the substitution property to get $m\angle 1 + m\angle 2 = 180°$.

12.

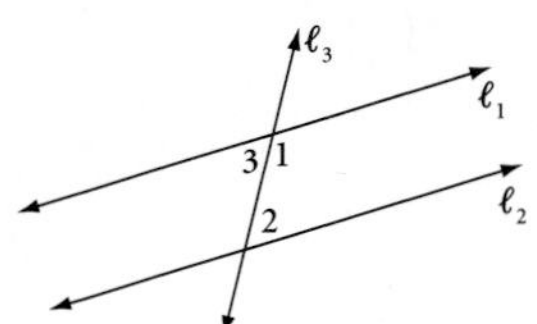

Use the Linear Pair Postulate and the definition of supplementary angles to get $m\angle 1 + m\angle 3 = m\angle 1 + m\angle 2$. Then use the subtraction property and the Converse of the AIA Theorem to get $\ell_1 \parallel \ell_2$.

13.

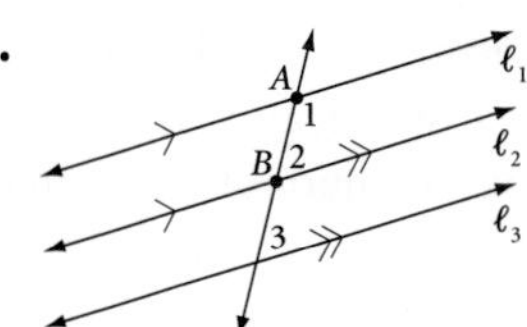

Construct a transversal across lines ℓ_1 and ℓ_2; it will intersect line ℓ_3 by the Parallel Postulate. Use the Interior Supplements Theorem and the definition of supplementary angles to get $m\angle 1 + m\angle 2 = 180°$. Use the CA Postulate and the substitution property to get $m\angle 1 + m\angle 3 = 180°$. Therefore $\ell_1 \parallel \ell_3$ by the Converse of the Interior Supplements Theorem.

LESSON 13.3, PAGES 688–689

1.

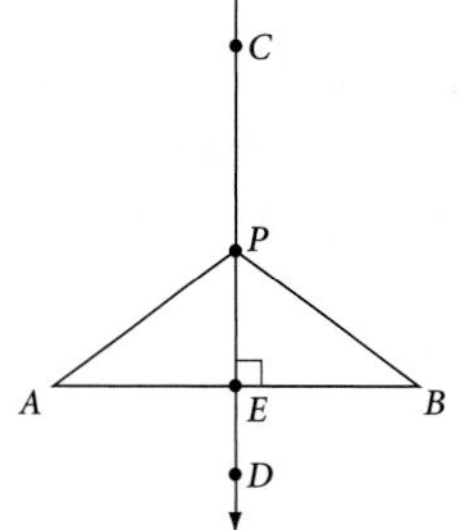

Use the SAS Congruence Postulate to get $\triangle AEP \cong \triangle BEP$. Then use CPCTC to get $\overline{AP} \cong \overline{BP}$.

2.

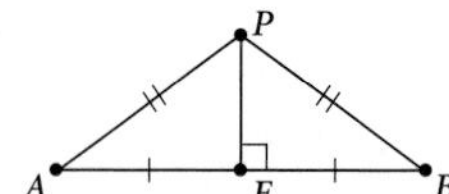

Draw midpoint E and $\overline{PE}$. Use the SSS Congruence Postulate to get $\triangle AEP \cong \triangle BEP$. Then use CPCTC and the Congruent and Supplementary Theorem to prove that $\angle AEP$ and $\angle BEP$ are both right angles. Therefore $\overline{PE}$ is the perpendicular bisector of $\overline{AB}$ by the definitions of midpoint and perpendicular.

3.

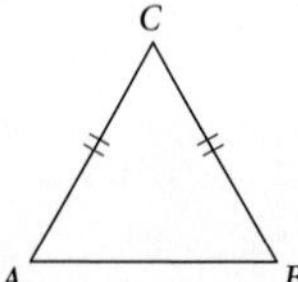

Use the identity property and the SSS Congruence Postulate to get $\triangle ABC \cong \triangle BAC$. Therefore $\angle A \cong \angle B$ by CPCTC.

4.

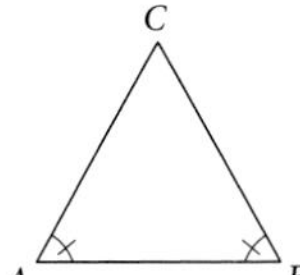

Use the identity property and the ASA Congruence Postulate to get $\triangle ABC \cong \triangle BAC$. Then use CPCTC and the definition of isosceles triangle.

5.

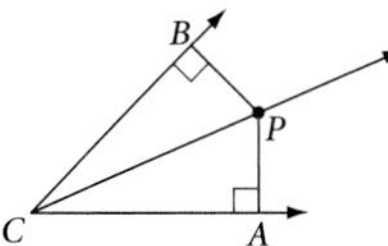

Draw line *BA*.

Use the Isosceles Triangle Theorem to get $\angle PAB \cong \angle PBA$. Use the Angle Addition Postulate and the subtraction property to get $\angle BAC \cong \angle ABC$. Then use the Converse of the Isosceles Triangle Theorem ($CB = CA$), the identity property, and the SSS Congruence Postulate to get $\triangle ACP \cong \triangle BCP$. Therefore, $\angle ACP \cong \angle BCP$ by CPCTC.

6.

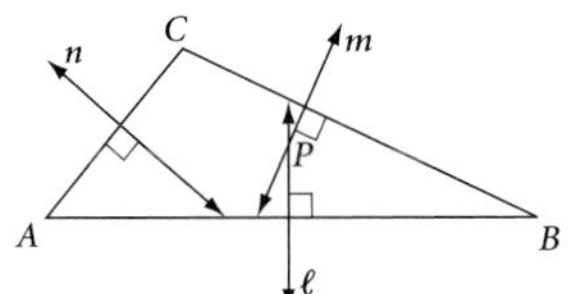

Use the Line Intersection Postulate and the Perpendicular Bisector Theorem to get $AP = BP$ and $BP = CP$. Then use the transitive property and the Converse of the Perpendicular Bisector Theorem to prove that point *P* is on line *n*.

7.

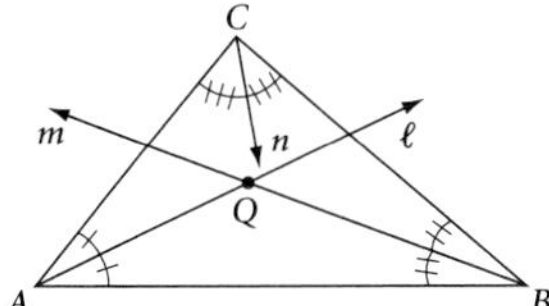

Use the Line Intersection Postulate and the Angle Bisector Theorem to prove that *Q* is equally distant from $\overline{AB}$ and $\overline{AC}$ and from $\overline{AB}$ and $\overline{BC}$. Then use the transitive property and the Converse of the Angle Bisector Theorem to prove that point *Q* is on line *n*.

13.

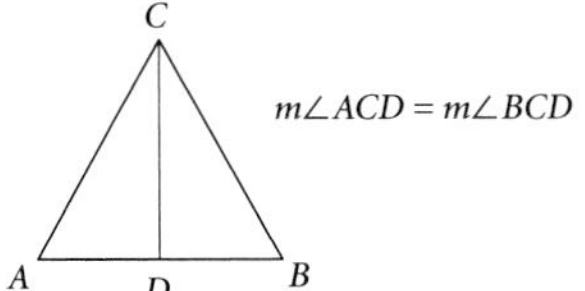

angle bisector → altitude
Use the definitions of angle bisector and isosceles triangle, the identity property, and the SAS Congruence Postulate to get $\triangle ADC \cong \triangle BDC$. Then use CPCTC, the Linear Pair Postulate, and the Congruent and Supplementary Theorem to prove that $\angle ADC$ and $\angle BDC$ are both right angles. Therefore $\overline{CD}$ is the altitude by the definitions of perpendicular and altitude.

LESSON 13.4, PAGES 692–393

Step 1

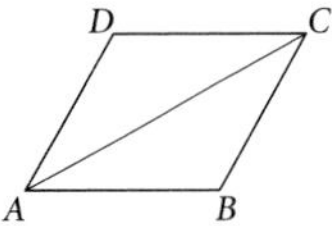

Given: Parallelogram *ABCD*
Show: $\overline{AB} \cong \overline{DC}$; $\overline{AD} \cong \overline{BC}$

Statement	Reason
1. Parallelogram *ABCD*	1. Given
2. $\triangle ABC \cong \triangle CDA$	2. Parallelogram Diagonal Lemma
3. $\overline{AB} \cong \overline{DC}$; $\overline{AD} \cong \overline{BC}$	3. CPCTC

Step 2 Given: Parallelogram *ABCD*
Show: $\angle ADC \cong \angle CBA$; $\angle DAB \cong \angle BCD$

Statement	Reason
1. Parallelogram *ABCD*	1. Given
2. $\triangle ADC \cong \triangle CBA$; $\triangle DAB \cong \triangle BCD$	2. Parallelogram Diagonal Lemma
3. $\angle ADC \cong \angle CBA$; $\angle DAB \cong \angle BCD$	3. CPCTC

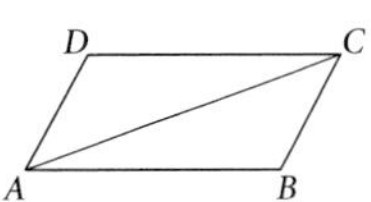

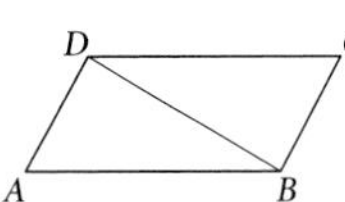

Step 3 If the opposite sides of a quadrilateral are congruent, then the quadrilateral is a parallelogram.
Given: Quadrilateral *ABCD* with $\overline{AB} \cong \overline{DC}$ and $\overline{AD} \cong \overline{BC}$
Show: *ABCD* is a parallelogram

Statement	Reason
1. Quadrilateral *ABCD*; $\overline{AB} \cong \overline{DC}$; $\overline{AD} \cong \overline{BC}$	1. Given
2. $\overline{AC} \cong \overline{AC}$; $\overline{DB} \cong \overline{DB}$	2. Identity property of congruence
3. $\triangle ADC \cong \triangle CBA$; $\triangle DAB \cong \triangle BCD$	3. SSS Congruence Postulate
4. $\angle DAC \cong \angle BCA$; $\angle ADB \cong \angle CBD$	4. CPCTC
5. $\overline{AD} \parallel \overline{BC}$; $\overline{DC} \parallel \overline{AB}$	5. Converse of the AIA Theorem
6. *ABCD* is a parallelogram	6. Definition of parallelogram

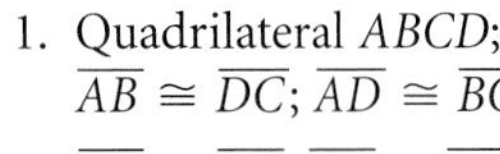

Additional Answers

Step 4

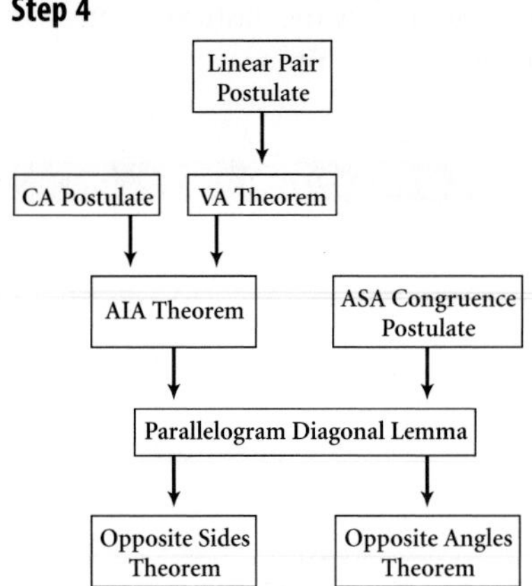

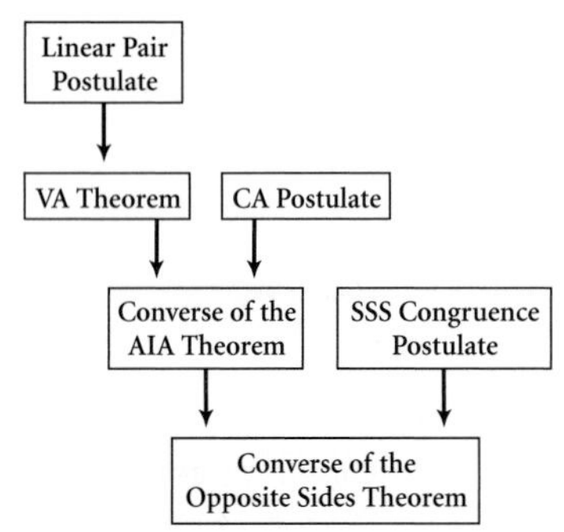

1.

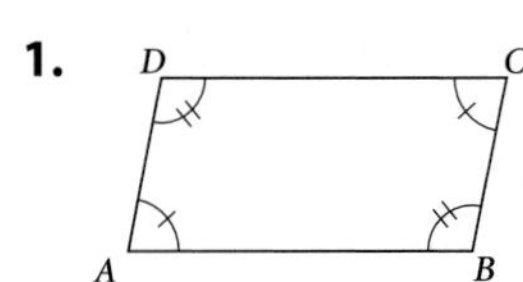

Use x to represent the measures of one pair of congruent angles and y for the other pair. Use the Quadrilateral Sum Theorem and the division property to get $x + y = 180°$. Therefore, the opposite sides are parallel by the Converse of the Interior Supplements Theorem.

2.

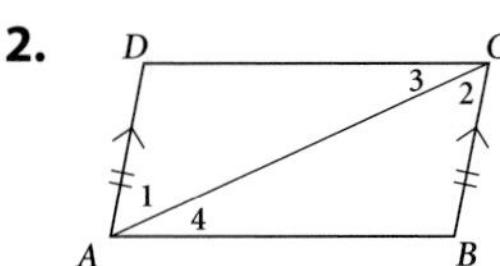

Use the AIA Theorem, the identity property, and the SAS Congruence Postulate to get $\triangle ADC \cong \triangle CBA$. Then use CPCTC and the Converse of the AIA Theorem to get $\overline{AB} \parallel \overline{DC}$.

3.

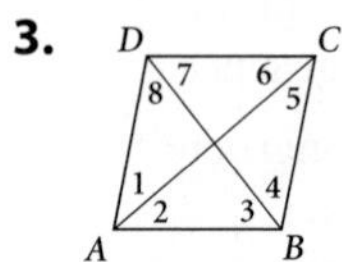

Use the definition of rhombus, the identity property, and the SSS Congruence Postulate to get $\triangle ABC \cong \triangle ADC$. Then use CPCTC and the definition of angle bisector to prove that $\overline{AC}$ bisects $\angle DAB$ and $\angle BCD$. Repeat the steps above using diagonal $\overline{DB}$.

4.

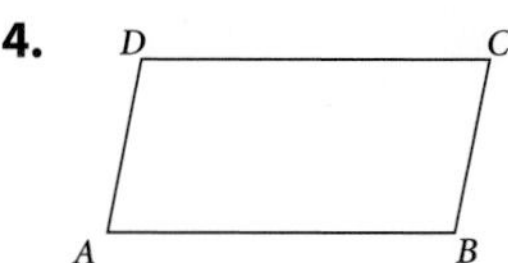

Use the definition of parallelogram to get $\overline{AD} \parallel \overline{BC}$ and $\overline{AB} \parallel \overline{DC}$. Then use the Interior Supplements Theorem.

5.

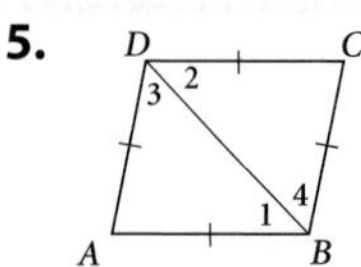

Use the identity property and the SSS Congruence Postulate to get $\triangle ABD \cong \triangle CDB$. Then use CPCTC and the Converse of the AIA Theorem to get $\overline{AB} \parallel \overline{CD}$ and $\overline{AD} \parallel \overline{CB}$. Therefore, $ABCD$ is a rhombus by the definitions of parallelogram and rhombus.

6.

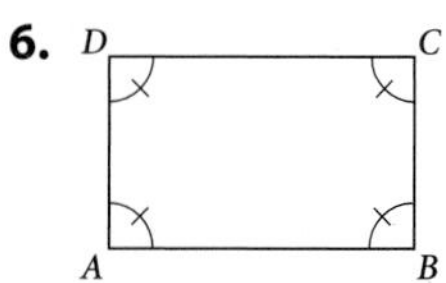

Use the Converse of the Opposite Angles Theorem to prove that $ABCD$ is a parallelogram. Then use the definition of rectangle.

7.

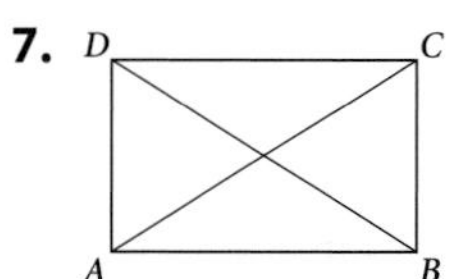

Use the definition of rectangle to prove that $ABCD$ is a parallelogram and $\angle DAB \cong \angle ABC$. Then use the Parallelogram Opposite Sides Theorem, the identity property, and the SAS Congruence Postulate to get $\triangle DAB \cong \triangle CBA$. Finish with CPCTC.

8.

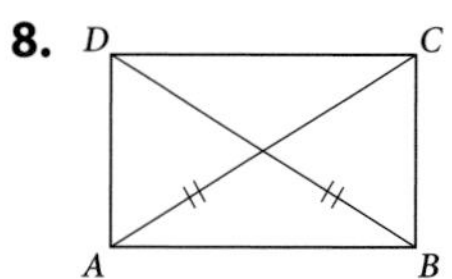

Use the Parallelogram Opposite Sides Theorem, the identity property, and the SSS Congruence Postulate to get $\triangle DAB \cong \triangle CBA$. Repeat the above steps to get $\triangle ADC \cong \triangle CBA$ and $\triangle DAB \cong \triangle BCD$. Then use CPCTC and the transitive property to get $\angle DAB \cong \angle ABC \cong \angle BCD \cong \angle ADC$. Finish with the Four Congruent Angles Rectangle Theorem.

9.

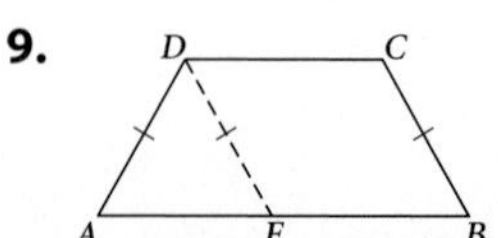

Use the Parallel Postulate to construct $\overline{DE} \parallel \overline{CB}$. Then use the Parallelogram Opposite Sides Theorem and the transitive property to prove that $\triangle AED$ is isosceles. Therefore $\angle A \cong \angle B$ by the Isosceles Triangle Theorem, the CA Postulate, and substitution.

10. 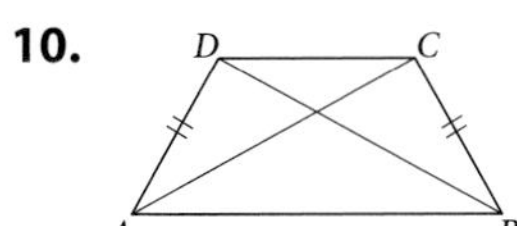

Use the Isosceles Trapezoid Theorem, the identity property, and the SAS Congruence Postulate to get $\triangle DAB \cong \triangle CBA$. Then $\overline{AC} \cong \overline{BD}$ by CPCTC.

11. 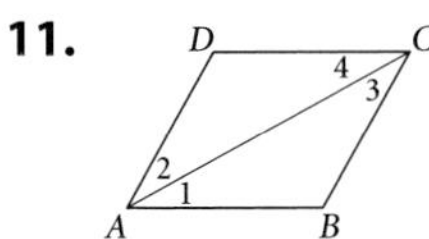

Use the Parallelogram Opposite Angles Theorem, the multiplication property, and the definition of angle bisector to get $\angle 1 \cong \angle 3$. Then use the Converse of the Isosceles Triangle Theorem, the definition of isosceles triangle, and the Parallelogram Opposite Sides Theorem to get $\overline{AB} \cong \overline{BC} \cong \overline{DC} \cong \overline{AD}$.

EXPLORATION, PAGE 697

Step 8 It is easiest to prove Step 7 first. Plan for proving Step 7: Connect each of the points *A, B, C, D* with the centers of two squares, as shown. Using the properties of the square diagonals, prove that the four triangles are right triangles, then show that they are congruent by SAS. Their hypotenuses are therefore congruent.

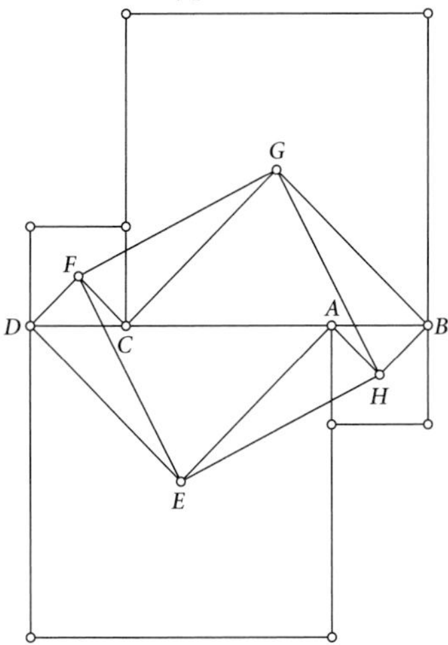

Next, show that *EFGH* is equiangular.
$\angle DFE + \angle EFC = 90°$, because square diagonals are perpendicular. Because $\angle DFE \cong \angle CFG$ by CPCTC, $\angle EFC + \angle CFG = 90°$ by substitution. Therefore, $\angle EFG = 90°$. Similar arguments can be made for the other three angles of *EFGH*.

Plan for proving Step 6:

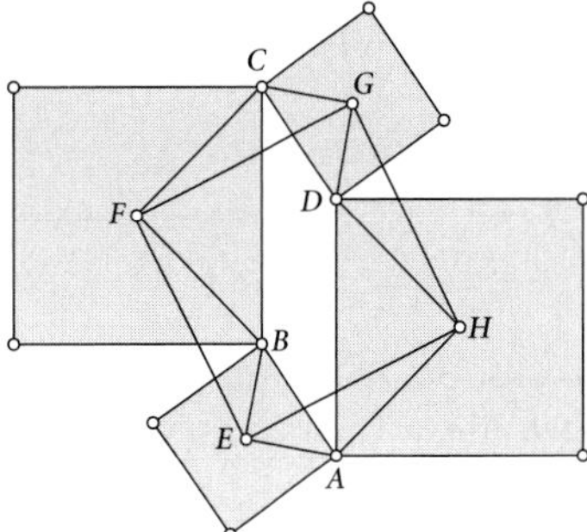

$\triangle FCG$, $\triangle HDG$, $\triangle HAE$, and $\triangle FBE$ are not right triangles, but it can be shown (and it can be seen by dragging the sketch) that their obtuse angles are all greater than 90° by the same amount. Therefore, you can use angle subtraction to show that *EFGH* is still equiangular.

LESSON 13.6, PAGES 704–705

1. 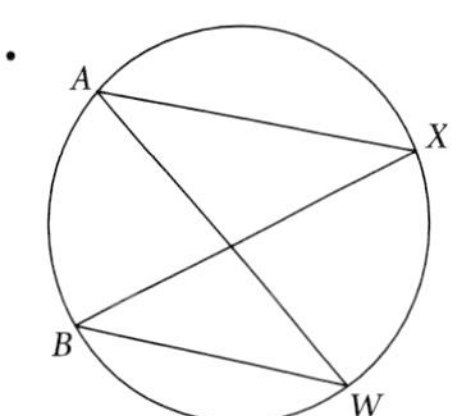

Case 1 The Same: Use the Inscribed Angle Theorem and the transitive property to get $\angle A \cong \angle B$.

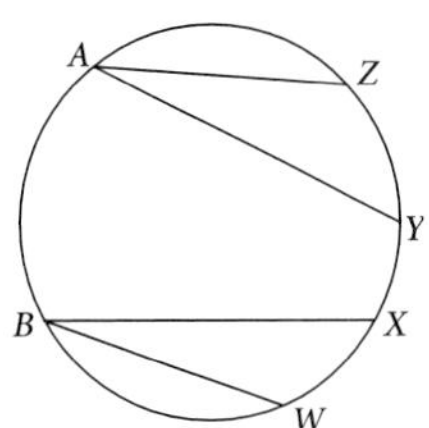

Case 2 Congruent: Use the multiplication property to get $\frac{1}{2}m\overset{\frown}{YZ} = \frac{1}{2}m\overset{\frown}{WX}$. Then follow the steps in Case 1.

2. 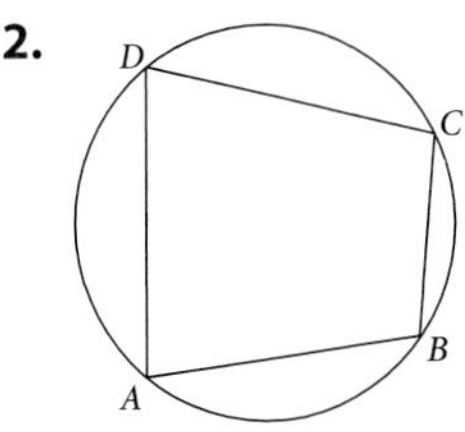

Use the Inscribed Angle Theorem, the addition property, and the distributive property to get $m\angle A + \angle C = \frac{1}{2}(m\overset{\frown}{BCD} + m\overset{\frown}{DAB})$. Then use the definition of degrees in a circle, the substitution property, and the definition of supplementary angles to get $\angle A$ and $\angle C$ are supplementary. Follow the above steps to get $\angle B$ and $\angle D$ are supplementary.

3.

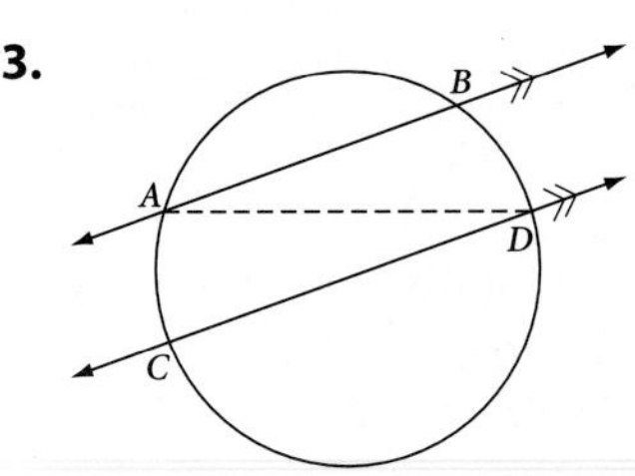

Use the Line Postulate to construct $\overline{AD}$. Then use the AIA Theorem, the Inscribed Angle Theorem, and substitution to get $\overparen{AC} \cong \overparen{BD}$.

4.

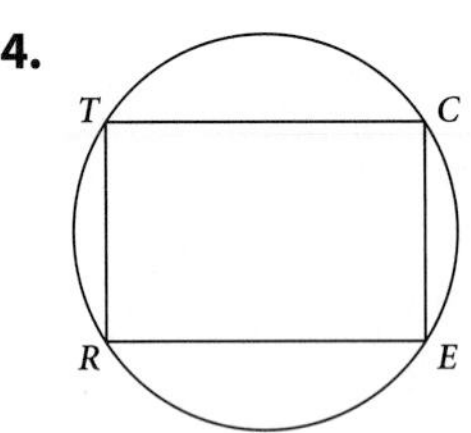

Use the Cyclic Quadrilateral Theorem, the Opposite Angles Theorem, and the Congruent and Supplementary Theorem to get $\angle R \cong \angle C \cong \angle E \cong \angle T$.

5.

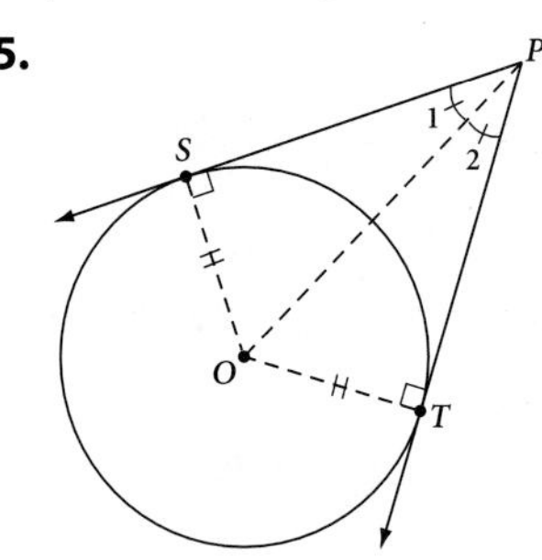

Use the Line Postulate to construct $\overline{OS}$, $\overline{OT}$, and $\overline{OP}$. Then use the Tangent Theorem, the Converse of the Angle Bisector Theorem, and the SAA Theorem to get $\triangle OSP \cong \triangle OTP$.

6.

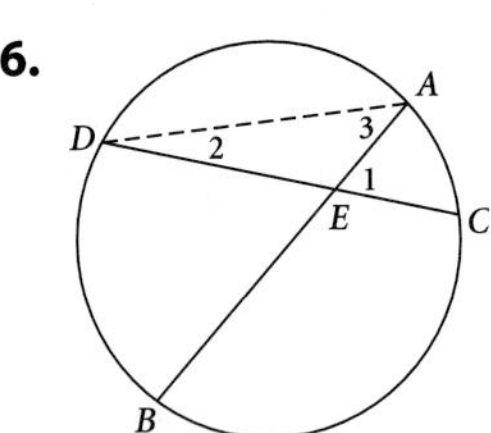

Use the Line Postulate to construct $\overline{AD}$. Then use the Inscribed Angle Theorem, the addition property, and the distributive property to get $m\angle 2 + m\angle 3 = \frac{1}{2}(m\overparen{AC} + m\overparen{BD})$. Therefore $m\angle 1 = \frac{1}{2}(m\overparen{AC} + m\overparen{BD})$ by the Triangle Exterior Angle Theorem and the transitive property.

7.

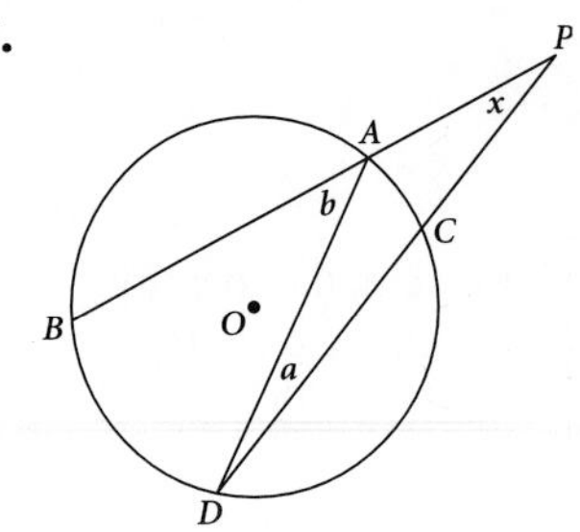

Intersecting Secants Theorem: The measure of an angle formed by two secants intersecting outside a circle is half the difference of the measure of the larger intercepted arc and the measure of the smaller intercepted arc. Use the Triangle Exterior Angle Theorem and the subtraction property to get $x = b - a$. Then use the Inscribed Angle Theorem, the substitution property, and the distributive property to get $x = \frac{1}{2}(m\overparen{BD} - m\overparen{AC})$.

8.

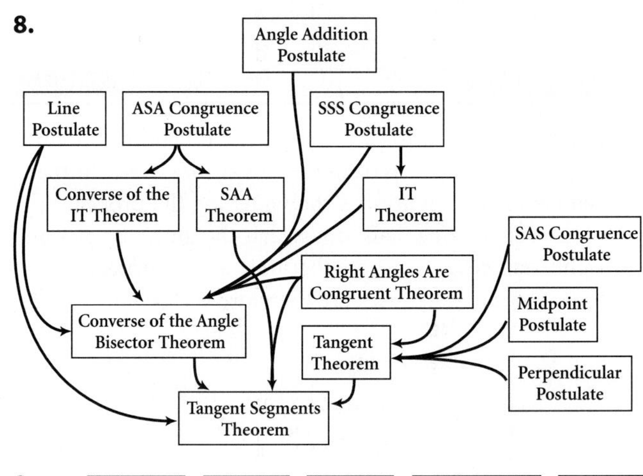

9.

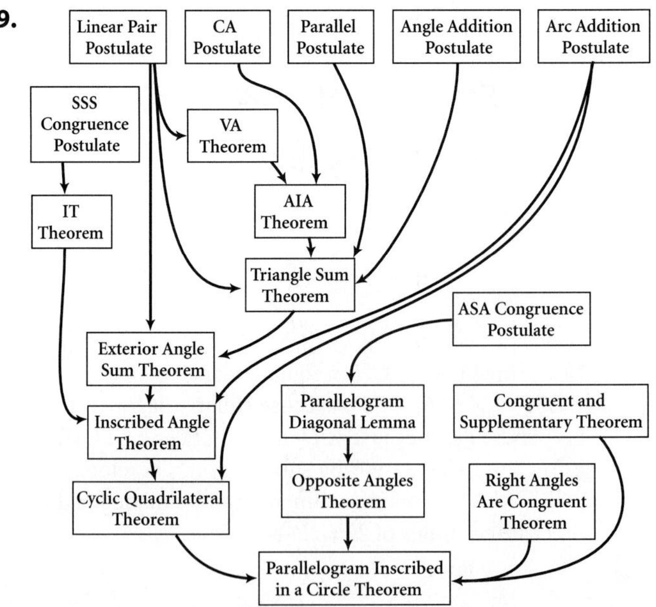

16.

Steps:

1. Construct $\overline{OP}$.
2. Bisect $\overline{OP}$. Label midpoint M.
3. Construct circle with center M and radius PM.
4. Label the intersection of the two circles A and B.
5. Construct $\overline{PA}$ and $\overline{PB}$. $\overline{PA}$ and $\overline{PB}$ are the required tangents.

LESSON 13.7, PAGES 708–709

Step 4 See below.

1. Use the Right Angles Are Congruent Theorem, CASTC, and the AA Similarity Postulate to get $\triangle BHT \sim \triangle GEV$. Therefore, $\frac{BT}{GV} = \frac{TH}{VE}$ by CSSTP. See the Solutions Manual for the family tree.

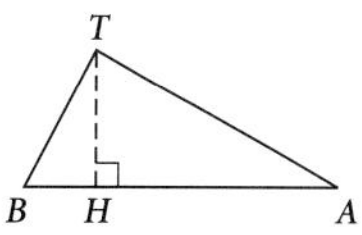

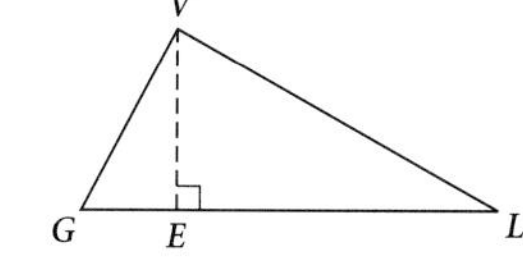

2. Use the definitions of median and midpoint, the Segment Addition Postulate, and the substitution property to get $BI = 2BY$ and $SM = 2SL$. Then use CASTC, CSSTP, and the SAS Similarity Theorem to get $\triangle BYG \sim \triangle SLA$. Therefore, $\frac{BG}{SA} = \frac{GY}{AL}$ by CSSTP. See the Solutions Manual for the family tree.

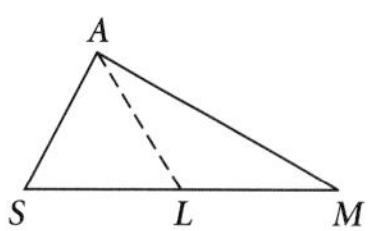

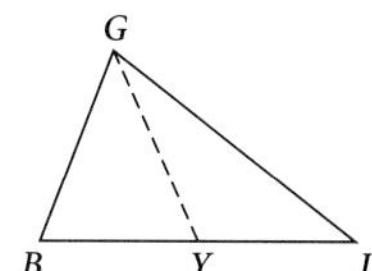

Step 4

Statement	Reason
1. Locate R so that $RL = NP$	1. Segment Duplication Postulate
2. Construct $\overleftrightarrow{RS} \parallel \overleftrightarrow{KM}$	2. Parallel Postulate
3. $\angle SRL \cong \angle K$	3. CA Postulate
4. $\angle RSL \cong \angle M$	4. CA Postulate
5. $\triangle KLM \sim \triangle RLS$	5. AA Similarity Postulate
6. $\frac{KL}{RL} = \frac{LM}{LS} = \frac{MK}{SR}$	6. CSSTP
7. $\frac{KL}{NP} = \frac{LM}{LS}$	7. Substitution property of equality
8. $\frac{KL}{NP} = \frac{LM}{PQ}$	8. Given
9. $\frac{KL}{NP} = \frac{MK}{SR}$	9. Substitution property of equality
10. $\frac{KL}{NP} = \frac{MK}{QN}$	10. Given
11. $\frac{LM}{LS} = \frac{LM}{PQ}$	11. Transitive property of equality
12. $\frac{MK}{SR} = \frac{MK}{QN}$	12. Transitive property of equality
13. $LS = PQ$	13. Multiplication and division properties of equality
14. $SR = QN$	14. Multiplication and division properties of equality
15. $\triangle RLS \cong \triangle NPQ$	15. SSS Congruence Postulate
16. $\angle L \cong \angle P$	16. Corresponding angles of similar triangles are congruent (CASTC)
17. $\triangle KLM \sim \triangle NPQ$	17. SAS Similarity Postulate

3. 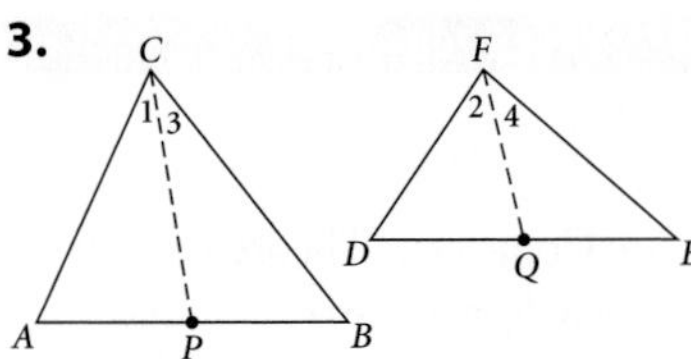

Use the definition of angle bisector, the Angle Addition Postulate, and the substitution property to get $m\angle ACB = 2m\angle 1$ and $m\angle DFE = 2m\angle 2$. Then use CASTC and the AA Similarity Postulate to get $\triangle APC \sim \triangle DQF$. Therefore, $\frac{AC}{DF} = \frac{CP}{FQ}$ by CSSTP.

4. 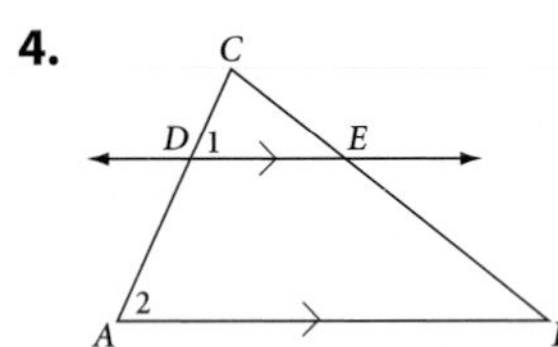

Use the CA Postulate and the AA Similarity Postulate to get $\triangle CDE \sim \triangle CAB$. Then use CSSTP and the Segment Addition Postulate to get $\frac{CD + DA}{CD} = \frac{CE + EB}{CE}$. Therefore, $\frac{DA}{CD} = \frac{EB}{CE}$ by algebra.

5. 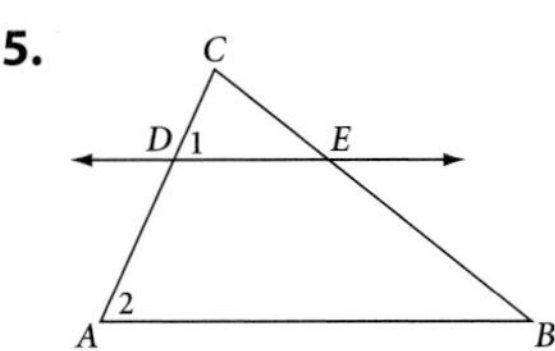

Use the addition property to get $\frac{DA}{CD} + 1 = \frac{EB}{CE} + 1$. Then use algebra and the Segment Addition Postulate to get $\frac{CA}{CD} = \frac{CB}{CE}$. Therefore $\triangle ABC \sim \triangle DEC$ by the SAS Similarity Theorem, $\angle 1 \cong \angle 2$ by CASTC, and $\overleftrightarrow{DE} \parallel \overline{AB}$ by the CA Postulate.

6. 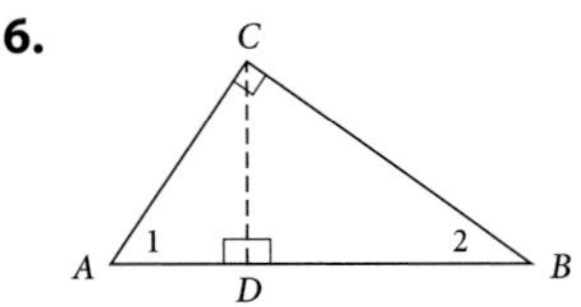

Use the Right Angles Are Congruent Theorem, the identity property, and the AA Similarity Postulate to get $\triangle ADC \sim \triangle ACB$ and $\triangle ACB \sim \triangle CDB$. Therefore, $\triangle ADC \sim \triangle ACB \sim \triangle CDB$ by the transitive property of similarity.

8. 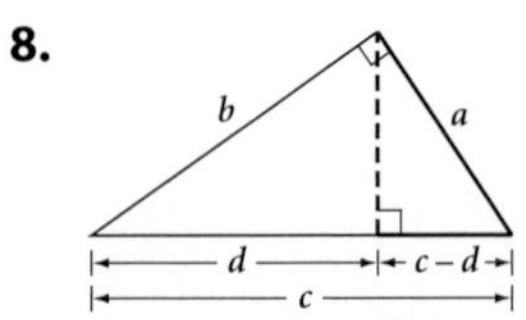

Draw the altitude to the hypotenuse, then use the ratios given by the Three Similar Right Triangles Theorem. In particular, $\frac{a}{c-d} = \frac{c}{a}$ yields $a^2 = c^2 - cd$. Now look at the other small triangle and use $\frac{b}{d} = \frac{c}{b}$ to get $b^2 = cd$.

9. 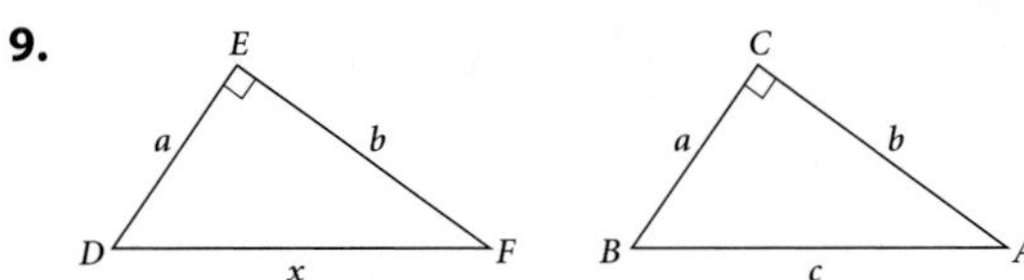

Begin by constructing a second triangle, right triangle DEF (with $\angle E$ a right angle), with legs of lengths a and b and hypotenuse of length x. The plan is to show that $x = c$, so that the triangles are congruent. Then show that $\angle C$ and $\angle E$ are congruent. Once you show that $\angle C$ is a right angle, then $\triangle ABC$ is a right triangle.

10. Use the Pythagorean Theorem to write expressions for the lengths of the unknown legs. Show that the expressions are equivalent. The triangles are congruent by SSS or SAS.

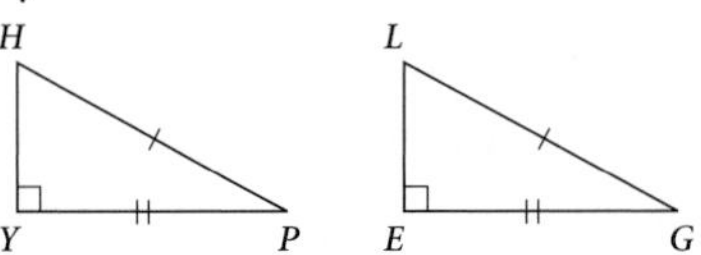

11. 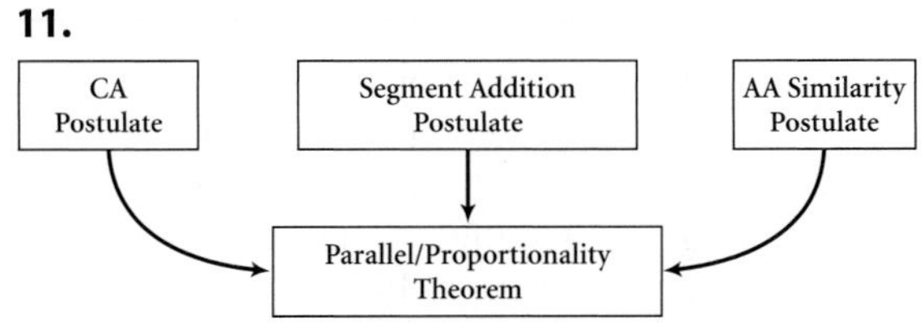

12. 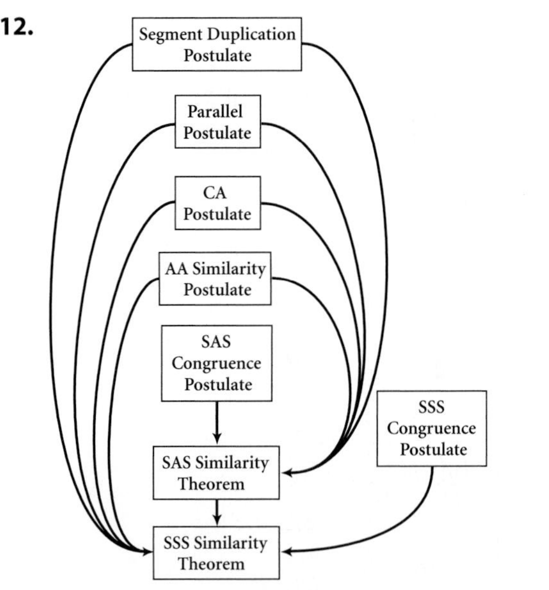

13. 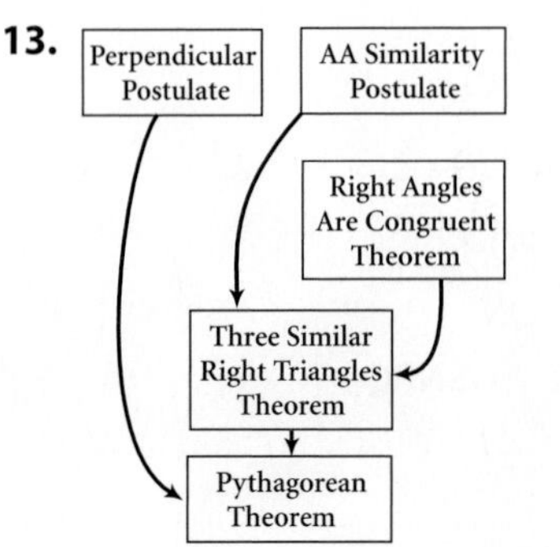

USING YOUR ALGEBRA SKILLS 10, PAGES 716–717

4. possible answer:

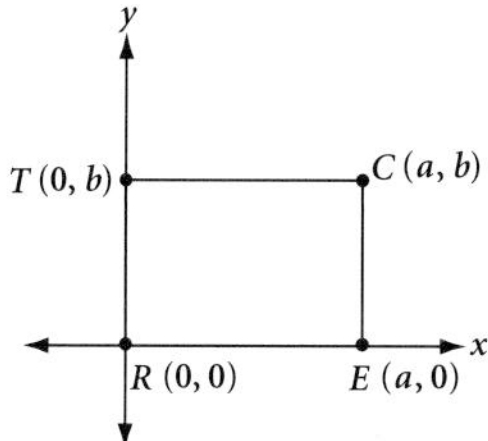

slope of $\overline{RE} = \frac{0-0}{a-0} = \frac{0}{a} = 0$

slope of $\overline{CE} = \frac{b-0}{a-a} = \frac{b}{0}$ (undefined)

slope of $\overline{TC} = \frac{b-b}{a-0} = \frac{0}{a} = 0$

slope of $\overline{TR} = \frac{b-0}{0-0} = \frac{b}{0}$ (undefined)

Opposite sides have the same slope and are therefore parallel by the parallel slope property. Two sides are horizontal and two sides are vertical, so the angles are all congruent right angles. *RECT* is an equiangular parallelogram and is a rectangle by definition.

5. possible answer:

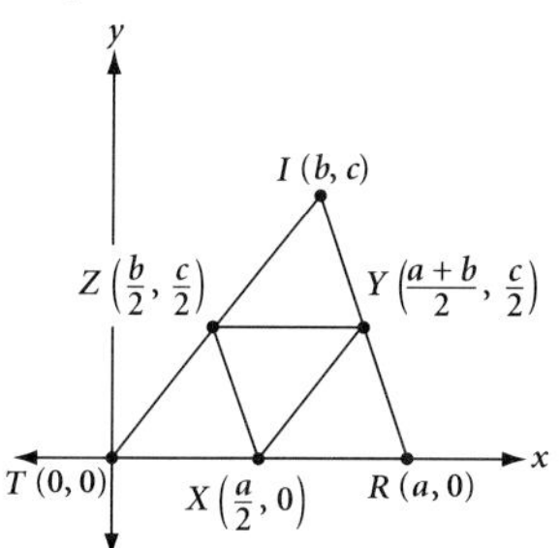

Let *X* be the midpoint of $\overline{TR}$.

$$X = \left(\frac{a+0}{2}, \frac{0+0}{2}\right) = \left(\frac{a}{2}, 0\right)$$

Let *Y* be the midpoint of $\overline{RI}$.

$$Y = \left(\frac{a+b}{2}, \frac{0+c}{2}\right) = \left(\frac{a+b}{2}, \frac{c}{2}\right)$$

Let *Z* be the midpoint of $\overline{TI}$.

$$Z = \left(\frac{b+0}{2}, \frac{c+0}{2}\right) = \left(\frac{b}{2}, \frac{c}{2}\right)$$

X, *Y*, and *Z* are the midpoints of $\overline{TR}$, $\overline{RI}$, and $\overline{TI}$, respectively, by the coordinate midpoint property. So $\overline{XY}$, $\overline{YZ}$, and $\overline{ZX}$ are midsegments by definition.

6. possible answer:

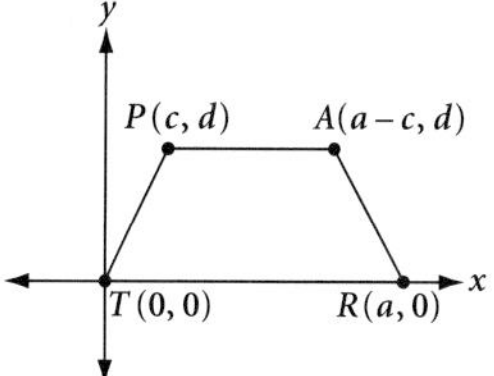

slope of $\overline{TR} = \frac{0-0}{a-0} = \frac{0}{a} = 0$

slope of $\overline{RA} = \frac{d-0}{a-c-a} = \frac{d}{-c}$

slope of $\overline{AP} = \frac{d-d}{a-2c} = \frac{0}{a-2c} = 0$

slope of $\overline{PT} = \frac{d-0}{c-0} = \frac{d}{c}$

$\overline{TR}$ and $\overline{AP}$ have the same slope and are parallel by the parallel slope property. So *TRAP* has only one pair of parallel sides and is a trapezoid by definition.

$PT = \sqrt{(c-0)^2 + (d-0)^2} = \sqrt{c^2 + d^2}$

$RA = \sqrt{(a-c-a)^2 + (d-0)^2} = \sqrt{(-c)^2 + d^2}$

$= \sqrt{c^2 + d^2}$

The nonparallel sides of the trapezoid have the same length. So trapezoid *TRAP* is isosceles by definition.

7.

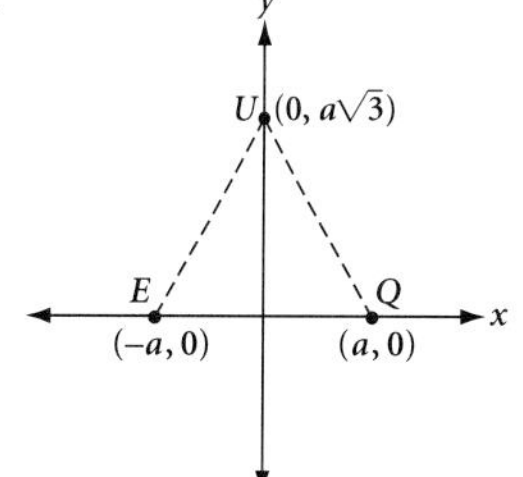

Show: $\triangle EQU$ is equilateral

$EQ = 2a$

$EU = \sqrt{(-a-0)^2 + (0-a\sqrt{3})^2}$

$= \sqrt{a^2 + 3a^2}$

$= \sqrt{4a^2}$

$= 2a$

$UQ = \sqrt{(a-0)^2 + (0-a\sqrt{3})^2}$

$= \sqrt{a^2 + 3a^2}$

$= \sqrt{4a^2}$

$= 2a$

$\therefore EQ = EU = UQ$

$\therefore \triangle EQU$ is equilateral

8. Task 1: Given: A rectangle with both diagonals

Show: The diagonals are congruent

Task 2:

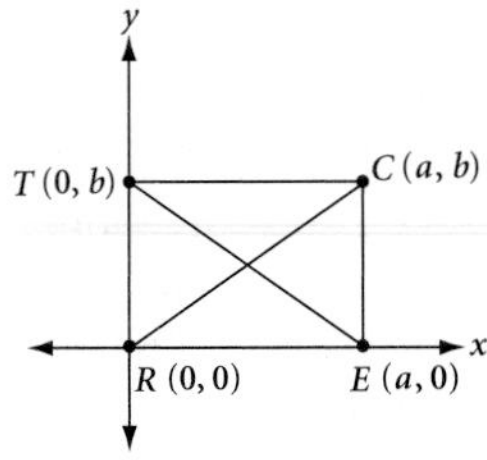

Task 3: Given: Rectangle *RECT* with diagonals $\overline{RC}$ and $\overline{TE}$

Show: $\overline{RC} \cong \overline{TE}$

Task 4: To show that two segments are congruent, you use the distance formula to show that they have the same length.

Task 5: $RC = \sqrt{(a-0)^2 + (b-0)^2} = \sqrt{a^2 + b^2}$

$TE = \sqrt{(a-0)^2 + (0-b)^2} = \sqrt{a^2 + b^2}$

So $\overline{RC} \cong \overline{TE}$ because both segments have the same length. Therefore the diagonals of a rectangle are congruent.

9. Task 1: Given: A triangle with one midsegment

Show: The midsegment is parallel to and half the length of the third side

Task 2:

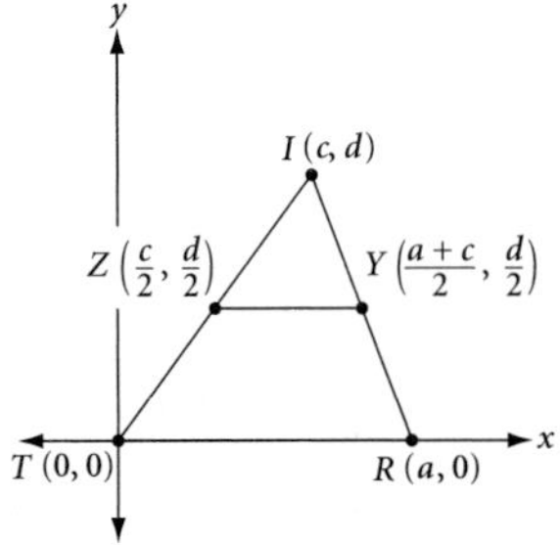

Task 3: Given: $\triangle TRI$ and midsegment $\overline{YZ}$

Show: $\overline{YZ} \parallel \overline{TR}$ and $YZ = \frac{1}{2}TR$

Task 4: To show that two segments are parallel, use the parallel slope property. To compare lengths, use the distance formula.

Task 5:

Slope of $\overline{TR} = \frac{0-0}{a-0} = \frac{0}{a} = 0$

Slope of $\overline{YZ} = \dfrac{\frac{d}{2} - \frac{d}{2}}{\frac{a+c}{2} - \frac{c}{2}} = \dfrac{0}{\frac{a}{2}} = 0$

The slopes are the same, so the segments are parallel by the parallel slope property.

$TR = \sqrt{(a-0)^2 + (0-0)^2} = \sqrt{a^2} = a$

$$YZ = \sqrt{\left(\frac{a+c}{2} - \frac{c}{2}\right)^2 + \left(\frac{d}{2} - \frac{d}{2}\right)^2}$$

$$= \sqrt{\left(\frac{a}{2}\right)^2 + 0^2} = \frac{a}{2} = \frac{1}{2}a = \frac{1}{2}TR$$

So the midsegment is half the length of the third side. Therefore the midsegment of a triangle is parallel to the third side and half the length of the third side.

10. Task 1: Given: A trapezoid

Show: The midsegment is parallel to the bases

Task 2:

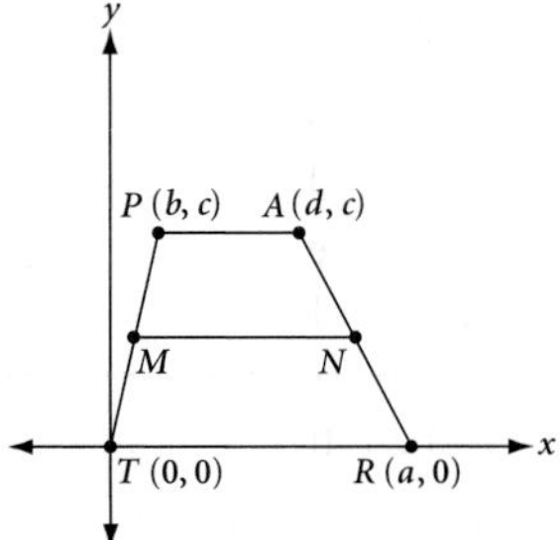

One possible set of the coordinates for *TRAP* is shown in the figure. By the coordinate midpoint property, the coordinates of *M* are $\left(\frac{b}{2}, \frac{c}{2}\right)$ and of *N* are $\left(\frac{a+d}{2}, \frac{c}{2}\right)$.

Task 3: Given: Trapezoid *TRAP* with midsegment $\overline{MN}$

Show: $\overline{MN} \parallel \overline{TR}$

Task 4: To show that the midsegment and bases are parallel, you need to find their slopes.

Task 5: Slope of $\overline{MN}$ is

$$\dfrac{\frac{c}{2} - \frac{c}{2}}{\frac{a+d}{2} - \frac{b}{2}} = \dfrac{0}{\frac{a+d-b}{2}} = 0$$

Slope of $\overline{TR} = \frac{0-0}{a-0} = \frac{0}{a} = 0$

The slope of $\overline{PA}$ is $\frac{c-c}{d-b} = \frac{0}{d-b} = 0$. The slopes are equal, therefore the lines are parallel.

11. Task 1: Given: A quadrilateral in which only one diagonal is the perpendicular bisector of the other

Show: The quadrilateral is a kite

Task 2:

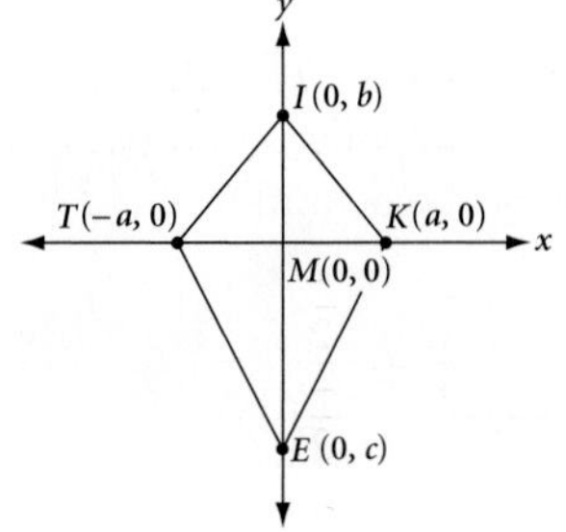

Task 3: Given: Quadrilateral *KITE* with diagonal $\overline{IE}$, which is the perpendicular bisector of diagonal $\overline{TK}$

Show: *KITE* is a kite

Task 4: To show that a quadrilateral is a kite, you use the distance formula to show that only two pairs of adjacent sides have the same length.

Task 5:

$$KI = \sqrt{(0 - a)^2 + (b - 0)^2} = \sqrt{a^2 + b^2}$$

$$IT = \sqrt{(0 - (-a))^2 + (b - 0)^2} = \sqrt{a^2 + b^2}$$

$$TE = \sqrt{(0 - (-a))^2 + (c - 0)^2} = \sqrt{a^2 + c^2}$$

$$EK = \sqrt{(a - 0)^2 + (0 - c)^2} = \sqrt{a^2 + c^2}$$

Adjacent sides $\overline{KI}$ and $\overline{IT}$ have the same length and adjacent sides $\overline{TE}$ and $\overline{EK}$ have the same length, and because $|b| \neq |c|$ the pairs are not equal in length to each other. Therefore, *KITE* is a kite by definition. Therefore, if only one diagonal of a quadrilateral is the perpendicular bisector of the other diagonal, then the quadrilateral is a kite.

12. Task 1: Given: A quadrilateral with midpoints connected to form a second quadrilateral

Show: The second quadrilateral is a parallelogram

Task 2:

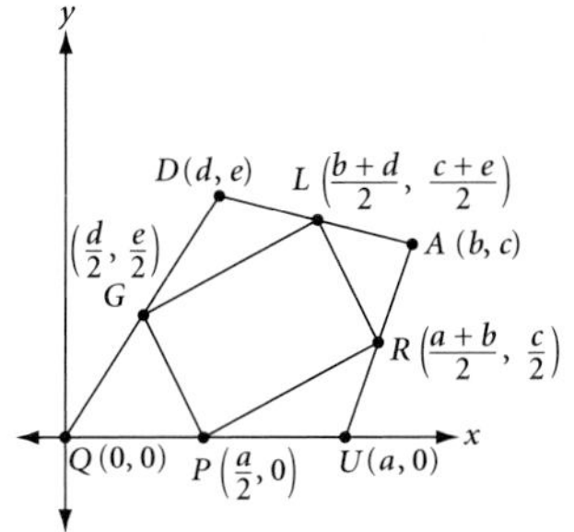

Task 3: Given: Quadrilateral *QUAD* with midpoints *P*, *R*, *L*, and *G*

Show: *PRLG* is a parallelogram

Task 4: To show that a quadrilateral is a parallelogram, we need to show that opposite sides have the same slope.

Task 5: Slope of $\overline{PR} = \dfrac{\frac{c}{2} - 0}{\frac{a+b}{2} - \frac{a}{2}} = \dfrac{\frac{c}{2}}{\frac{b}{2}} = \dfrac{c}{b}$

Slope of $\overline{RL} = \dfrac{\frac{c+e}{2} - \frac{c}{2}}{\frac{b+d}{2} - \frac{a+b}{2}} = \dfrac{\frac{e}{2}}{\frac{d-a}{2}} = \dfrac{e}{d-a}$

Slope of $\overline{LG} = \dfrac{\frac{e}{2} - \frac{c+e}{2}}{\frac{d}{2} - \frac{b+d}{2}} = \dfrac{\frac{-c}{2}}{\frac{-b}{2}} = \dfrac{c}{b}$

Slope of $\overline{GP} = \dfrac{\frac{e}{2} - 0}{\frac{d}{2} - \frac{a}{2}} = \dfrac{\frac{e}{2}}{\frac{d-a}{2}} = \dfrac{e}{d-a}$

Opposite sides $\overline{PR}$ and $\overline{LG}$ have the same slope, and opposite sides $\overline{RL}$ and $\overline{GP}$ have the same slope. So they are parallel by the parallel slope property, and *PRLG* is a parallelogram by definition. Therefore the figure formed by connecting the midpoints of the sides of a quadrilateral is a parallelogram.

13. Task 1: Given: An isosceles triangle with the midpoint of the base connected to the midpoint of each leg, to form a quadrilateral

Show: The quadrilateral is a rhombus

Task 2:

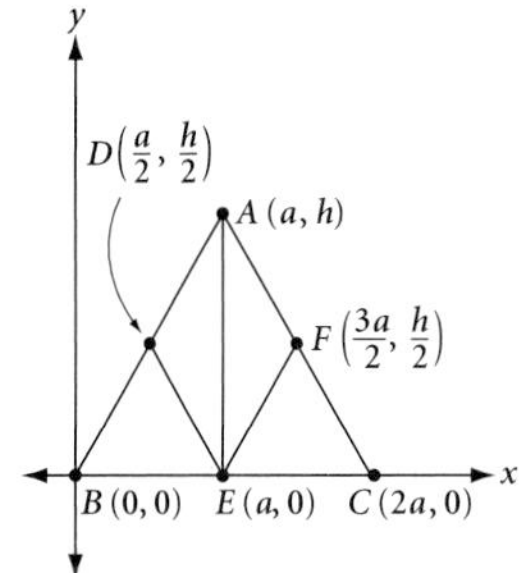

Task 3: Given: isosceles triangle *ABC* with midpoint of base, *E*, and midpoints of legs, *D* and *F*, connected to form quadrilateral *ADEF*.

Show: *ADEF* is a rhombus

Task 4: You need to show that all the sides of *ADEF* have the same length.

Task 5: By the distance formula,

$$AD = \sqrt{\left(a - \frac{a}{2}\right)^2 + \left(h - \frac{h}{2}\right)^2} = \sqrt{\left(\frac{a}{2}\right)^2 + \left(\frac{h}{2}\right)^2}$$

$$= \frac{\sqrt{a^2 + h^2}}{2}$$

$$AF = \sqrt{\left(\frac{3a}{2} - a\right)^2 + \left(h - \frac{h}{2}\right)^2} = \sqrt{\left(\frac{a}{2}\right)^2 + \left(\frac{h}{2}\right)^2}$$

$$= \frac{\sqrt{a^2 + h^2}}{2}$$

$$DE = \sqrt{\left(a - \frac{a}{2}\right)^2 + \left(\frac{h}{2} - 0\right)^2} = \sqrt{\left(\frac{a}{2}\right)^2 + \left(\frac{h}{2}\right)^2}$$

$$= \frac{\sqrt{a^2 + h^2}}{2}$$

$$EF = \sqrt{\left(\frac{3a}{2} - a\right)^2 + \left(\frac{h}{2} - 0\right)^2} = \sqrt{\left(\frac{a}{2}\right)^2 + \left(\frac{h}{2}\right)^2}$$

$$= \frac{\sqrt{a^2 + h^2}}{2}$$

$AD = AF = DE = EF$ by the transitive property of equality.

Therefore, $ADEF$ is a rhombus by the definition of a rhombus.

Sample Project Proofs

2. (continued) If all but two vertices have an even number of edges, then the same argument applies to the nonspecial vertices; moreover, one of those special vertices can be used as a beginning and the other as an ending, so the network can be traveled. If more than two vertices have an odd number of edges, the network cannot be traveled.

3. The n-gon can be divided into n triangles with a common vertex by drawing a segment from an interior point to each of the n vertices. (Each segment drawn to one of the n vertices is the side of two triangles, and each side of the n-gon is the side of one triangle; this gives $2n + n = 3n$ sides and therefore n triangles.) Each triangle has interior angles whose measures sum to 180°. Because the sum of the measures of the interior angles of the n-gon is the sum of the measures of the triangles minus the 360° around the central point, it equals $n \cdot 180° - 360° = (n - 2)180°$.

4. To consider $\overline{PQ}$ reflected over two intersecting lines, $\overleftrightarrow{OM}$ and $\overleftrightarrow{OL}$, you must consider at least three cases: $\overline{PQ}$ is outside the angle and is reflected over the nearer line first; $\overline{PQ}$ is inside $\angle MOL$; and $\overline{PQ}$ is outside the angle and is reflected over the farther line first. Let's consider the second case:

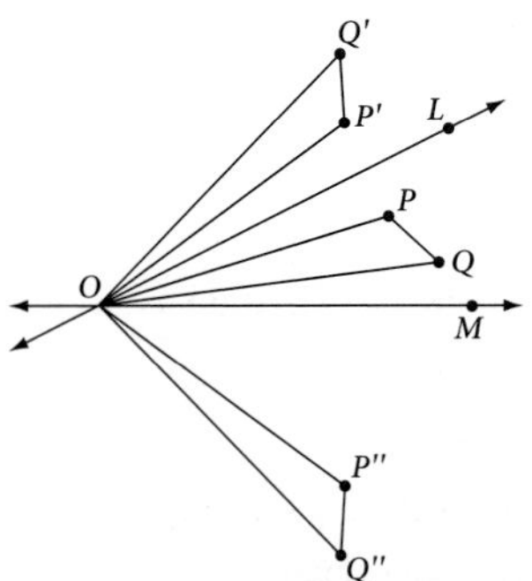

Because reflection is an isometry, $\overline{PO} \cong \overline{P'O}$ and $\overline{P'O} \cong \overline{P''O}$, so $\overline{PO} \cong \overline{P''O}$. Likewise $\overline{QO} \cong \overline{Q'O}$ and $\overline{Q'O} \cong \overline{Q''O}$, so $\overline{Q'O} \cong \overline{Q''O}$. By angle addition $m\angle POP'' = (m\angle P''OM + m\angle MOP') - (m\angle P'OL + m\angle LOP)$. Also because reflection is an isometry, $\angle P''OM \cong \angle MOP'$ and $\angle P'OL \cong \angle LOP$. So by substitution, $m\angle POP'' = 2(m\angle MOP' - m\angle P'OL)$. But $m\angle MOP' - m\angle P'OL = m\angle MOL$. Therefore, $m\angle POP'' = 2m\angle MOL$. The same procedure applies for $\angle QOQ''$. Because $\overline{PQ}$ is the same distance from point O as is $\overline{P''Q''}$ and because both images move the same number of degrees, by the definition of *rotation* the image $\overline{P''Q''}$ is a rotation of $\overline{PQ}$ about point O by an angle of $2m\angle MOL$. Similar proofs can be given for the other cases.

5. Call vertex A (a, b), vertex B (c, d) and vertex C (e, f). Then the midpoints are $D, \left(\frac{c+e}{2}, \frac{d+f}{2}\right)$; $E, \left(\frac{a+e}{2}, \frac{b+f}{2}\right)$; and $F, \left(\frac{a+c}{2}, \frac{b+d}{2}\right)$. The equations of the medians are:

$$\overleftrightarrow{AD}: \ y = \frac{d + f - 2b}{c + e - 2a}x + \frac{b(c + e) - a(d + f)}{c + e - 2a}$$

$$\overleftrightarrow{BE}: \ y = \frac{b + f - 2d}{a + e - 2c}x + \frac{d(a + e) - c(b + f)}{a + e - 2c}$$

$$\overleftrightarrow{CF}: \ y = \frac{b + d - 2f}{a + c - 2e}x + \frac{f(a + c) - e(b + d)}{a + c - 2e}$$

Solving any two of these equations simultaneously yields the coordinates of the centroid,

$$(x, y) = \left(\frac{a + c + e}{3}, \frac{b + d + f}{3}\right)$$

6. Here's one of many proofs that $\sqrt{2}$ is irrational:

We will assume $\sqrt{2}$ is rational and then arrive at a contradiction.

If $\sqrt{2}$ is rational, then it can be written as a fraction $\frac{a}{b}$ in reduced form. Because $\frac{a}{b} = \sqrt{2}$, $\frac{a^2}{b^2} = 2$. Because a and b have no common factors, $\frac{a^2}{b^2}$ cannot reduce to an integer, so $\frac{a^2}{b^2} \neq 2$. This is a contradiction, so $\sqrt{2}$ is irrational.

7. An Archimedean tiling is a distinct edge-to-edge tiling by regular polygons with all vertices of the same type. For these shapes to fill the plane from edge to edge without gaps or overlaps, their angles, when arranged around a point, must have measures that add to exactly 360°. An Archimedean tiling can be constructed using only equilateral triangles, squares, or regular hexagons. Any other regular polygon would create either a gap or an overlap in the single shape tiling. Hence there are three *monohedral* tessellations, which are Archimedean tilings. To find other possible edge-to-edge tilings of regular polygons, use the fact that the measure of an interior angle of a regular n-gon is $\frac{180(n-2)}{n}$ degrees. If the n_1-gon (n_1), n_2-gon (n_2), . . . , and n_k-gon (n_k) meet at a vertex, we know that:

$$\frac{180(n_1 - 2)}{n_1} + \frac{180(n_2 - 2)}{n_2} + \ldots + \frac{180(n_k - 2)}{n_k} = 360$$

$$\frac{n_1 - 2}{n_1} + \frac{n_2 - 2}{n_2} + \ldots + \frac{n_k - 2}{n_k} = 2$$

There are 17 groups of positive integers that satisfy this equation. Therefore, there are 17 choices of polygons that can be fitted around a vertex without gaps or overlaps. In four cases, these polygons can be arranged in two ways (such as $3^2.4.12$ and $3.4.3.12$). Thus there are 21 possible types of vertices: $\mathbf{3^6}$, $\mathbf{3^4.6}$, $\mathbf{3^3.4^2}$, $\mathbf{3^2.4.3.4}$, $3^2.4.12$, $3.4.3.12$, $\mathbf{3.6.3.6}$, $3^2.6^2$, $3.4^2.6$, $\mathbf{3.4.6.4}$, $3.7.42$, $3.8.24$, $3.9.18$, $3.10.15$, $\mathbf{3.12^2}$, $\mathbf{4^4}$, $4.5.20$, $\mathbf{4.6.12}$, $\mathbf{4.8^2}$, $5^2.10$, and $\mathbf{6^3}$.

After checking each of these types, we find 11 that are edge-to-edge tilings by regular polygons with all vertices of the same type: 3^6, $3^4.6$, $3^3.4^2$, $3^2.4.3.4$, $3.6.3.6$, $3.4.6.4$, 3.12^2, 4^4, $4.6.12$, 4.8^2, and 6^3.

(See *Tilings and Patterns* by Gruenbaum and Shephard.)

EXPLORATION, PAGE 720

Step 2

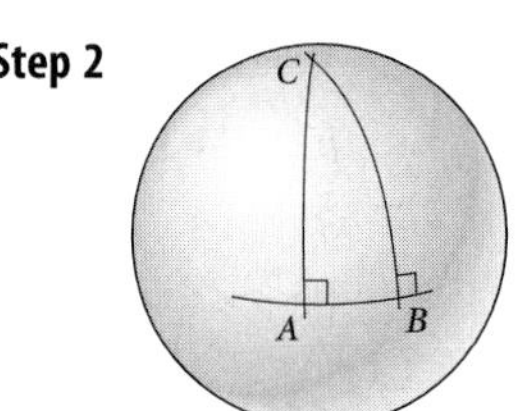

Step 3

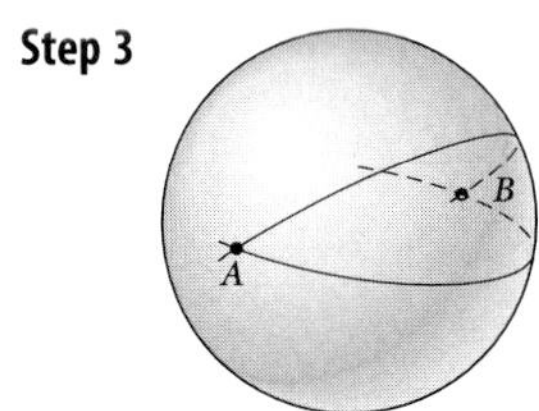

Step 4

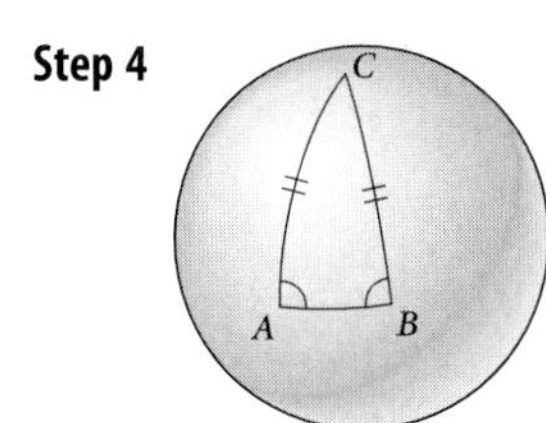

yes

Step 5

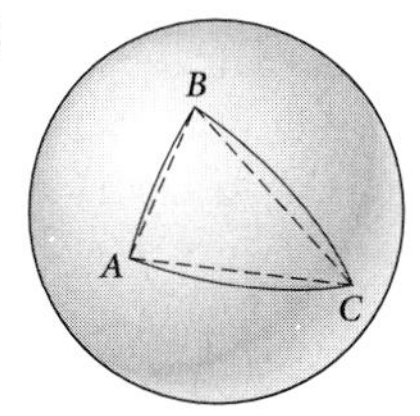

Step 6

CHAPTER 13 REVIEW, PAGE 722

21. True (except in the special case of an isosceles right triangle, in which the segment is not defined because the feet coincide). Given: Isosceles $\triangle ABC$ with altitudes $\overline{AD}$ and $\overline{BE}$. Draw $\overline{ED}$ by the Line Postulate. $\angle EAB \cong \angle DBA$ by the definition of isosceles triangle. $\angle AEB \cong \angle BDA$ by the definition of altitude and because right angles are congruent. $\overline{AB} \cong \overline{AB}$ by the reflexive property of congruence. $\triangle AEB \cong \triangle BDA$ by SAA. $\therefore \overline{AE} \cong \overline{BD}$. $\angle AXE \cong \angle BXD$ because vertical angles are congruent. $\therefore \triangle AXE \cong \triangle BXD$ by SAA. $\therefore \overline{EX} \cong \overline{DX}$ and $\overline{AX} \cong \overline{BX}$ by CPCTC. $\therefore \triangle AXB$ and $\triangle EXD$ are isosceles.

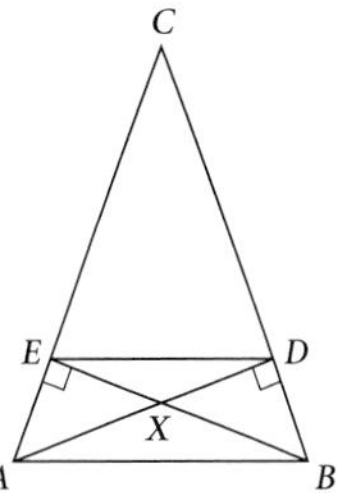

$\angle XAB \cong \angle XBA$ and $\angle XED \cong \angle XDE$ by the definition of isosceles triangle. $\angle EXD \cong \angle AXB$ because vertical angles are congruent. $\therefore$ By the Triangle Sum Theorem, $m\angle XAB + m\angle XBA + m\angle AXB = 180° = m\angle XED + m\angle XDE + m\angle EXD$. $\therefore m\angle XAB + m\angle XBA = m\angle XED + m\angle XDE$. $\therefore m\angle XBA + m\angle XBA = m\angle XED + m\angle XED$. $\therefore 2m\angle XBA = 2m\angle XED$. $\therefore \angle XBA \cong \angle XED$. $\therefore \overline{ED} \parallel \overline{AB}$ by AIA.

22. true

Given: Rhombus *ROME* with diagonals $\overline{RM}$ and $\overline{EO}$ intersecting at *B*

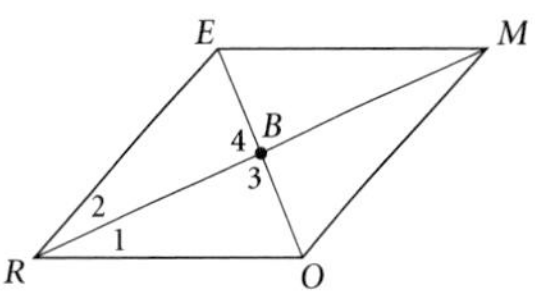

Show: $\overline{RM} \perp \overline{EO}$

Because diagonals bisect the angles in a rhombus, the diagonals are angle bisectors.

Statement	Reason
1. $\angle 1 \cong \angle 2$	1. Rhombus Angles Theorem
2. $RO = RE$	2. Definition of rhombus
3. $\overline{RO} \cong \overline{RE}$	3. Definition of congruence
4. $\overline{RB} \cong \overline{RB}$	4. Identity property of congruence
5. $\triangle ROB \cong \triangle REB$	5. SAS Congruence Postulate

6. $\angle 3 \cong \angle 4$	6. CPCTC
7. $\angle 3$ and $\angle 4$ are a linear pair	7. Definition of linear pair
8. $\angle 3$ and $\angle 4$ are supplementary	8. Linear Pair Postulate
9. $\angle 3$ and $\angle 4$ are right angles	9. Congruent and Supplementary Theorem
10. $\overline{RM} \perp \overline{EO}$	10. Definition of perpendicular

23. true

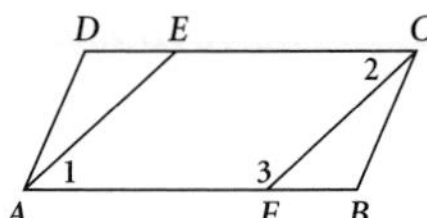

$\angle BAD \cong \angle DCB$ by the Opposite Angles Theorem. $\therefore m\angle 1 = \frac{1}{2}m\angle BAD = \frac{1}{2}m\angle DCB = m\angle 2$ by the definition of angle bisector. $\overline{AB} \parallel \overline{DC}$ by the definition of parallelogram. $\therefore$ $\angle 2$ and $\angle 3$ are supplementary by the Interior Supplements Theorem.

$\therefore$ $\angle 1$ and $\angle 3$ are supplementary by the substitution property.

$\therefore$ $\overline{AE} \parallel \overline{FC}$ by the Converse of the Interior Supplements Theorem.

26.

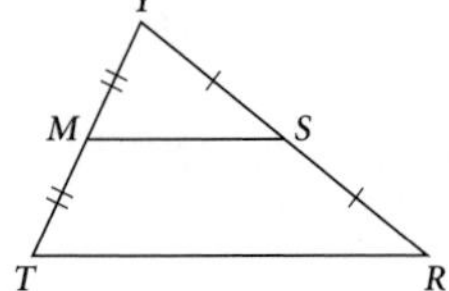

Use the definition of midpoint, the Segment Addition Postulate, the substitution property, and the division property to get $\frac{MY}{TY} = \frac{1}{2}$ and $\frac{YS}{YR} = \frac{1}{2}$. Then use the identity property and the SAS Similarity Theorem to get $\triangle MSY \sim \triangle TRY$. Therefore, $MS = \frac{1}{2}TR$ by CSSTP and the multiplication property and $\overline{MS} \parallel \overline{TR}$ by CASTC and the CA Postulate.

27.

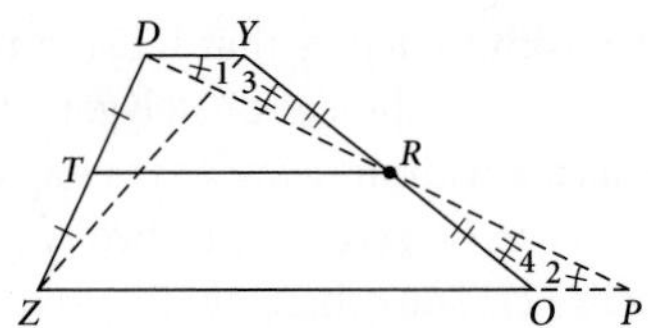

Use the Line Postulate to extend $\overline{ZO}$ and $\overline{DR}$. Then use the Line Intersection Postulate to label P as the intersection of $\overline{ZO}$ and $\overline{DR}$. $\triangle DYR \cong \triangle POR$ by the SAA Theorem; thus $\overline{DY} \cong \overline{OP}$ by CPCTC. Use the Triangle Midsegment Theorem and the substitution property to get $TR = \frac{1}{2}(ZO + DY)$.

28b.

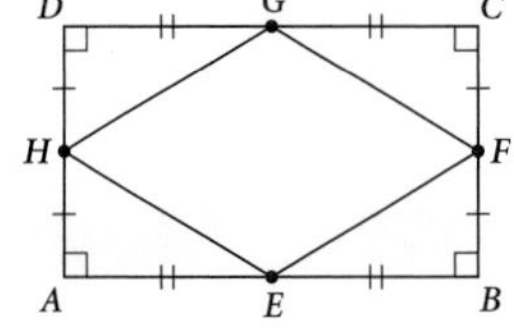

Use the Right Angles Are Congruent Theorem and the SAS Congruence Postulate to get $\triangle AEH \cong \triangle BEF \cong \triangle DGH \cong \triangle CGF$. Then use CPCTC to prove that $EFGH$ is a rhombus.